2025 Directory of Chain Restaurant Operators®

Chain Store Guide
3710 Corporex Park Dr. Suite 310
Tampa, FL 33619
Phone: (800) 927-9292
chainstoreguide.com

2025 Directory of Chain Restaurant Operators®
Published by Chain Store Guides, LLC
Copyright 2025. All Rights Reserved.
ISBN 0-86730-194-6
Published in U.S.A., April, 2025

Sales/Marketing
Carmen Vasquez-Perez……………………………………………………………………………Executive VP
Shawn Tommelleo…………………………………………………………………… Director of Marketing
Tamara Fisher……………………………………………………… Sr. Digital Marketing Coordinator

Editorial
Natasha Perry………………………………………………………………………Senior Research Editor

Production
Jonathan Adhikari………………………………………………Data Analytics Research Manager
Calvin Liang…………………………………………………………………………………………Data Analyst

Chain Store Guide Editorial Office
3710 Corporex Park Dr. Suite 310
Tampa, FL 33619
For Product and Sales Information Please Call:
(813) 627-6800
Call Toll Free (800) 927-9292

Visit our Web Site at chainstoreguide.com

CSG has been providing
Sales and Marketing Solutions
for the Retail and Foodservice Industries
since 1933

All Rights Reserved. No part of this directory can be reproduced in any manner, stored in any retrieval system, or transmitted, in any form or by any means, electronic, mechanical, photocopying, or otherwise, without the prior written permission of the publisher. The information published by Chain Store Guides, LLC is provided by the companies listed, gathered through other research sources, or estimated by CSG editors. Although every effort has been made to validate the information, Chain Store Guides, LLC cannot accept any responsibility or guarantee its accuracy or completeness.

2025 Directory of Chain Restaurant Operators®

INTRODUCTION

2025 Revisions	a1
Executive Summary and Overview	a2
Criteria for Inclusion	a4
Explanation of Data Elements	a5
Statistical Analysis	a8

MAIN SECTIONS

Chain Restaurant Operators	1
Alpha Index	1207

WARNING:

It has come to the attention of Chain Store Guides, LLC that subscribers to some of its publications have, on occasion, used these publications to compile mailing lists, marketing aids, and/or other types of data, which are sold or otherwise provided to third parties. Such use may be illegal and a violation of the federal copyright laws. Chain Store Guides, LLC intends to exercise its right to prohibit and punish such misuse.

YOU QUALIFY

Since you purchased this CSG Directory, you have access to a free 30-day subscription to CSG LITE.

You Have Unlimited Access for 30 Days
Got Questions? Contact Your Account Manager

 800-927-9292

Target the Right Businesses

Explore Key Market Data

Get Data Anytime and Anyplace

Save Time & Resources

Scan Code for Access

Offer Ends 12/31/2025

Why Choose Us ?

For over 90 years, Chain Store Guide (CSG) has provided reliable retail and foodservice industry data, helping businesses identify decision-makers, discover opportunities, and enhance sales growth with accurate location and contact information.

2025 Total Companies

Listings	6,663
Corporate Office	35
Distribution Center	43
Divisional Office	34
Headquarters	6,453
Regional Office	31
Subsidiary	44
Total Units	670,925

2025 Revisions

Total Company Listings	6,663
Total Personnel	30,932
Changes in Information	44,620
Changes/Additions in Personnel	24,758
Total Revisions	69,378

Executive Summary

The U.S. restaurant industry this year has been a tale of adaptation and experimentation, as businesses navigated a post-inflation landscape with uneven success. Customer traffic remained a persistent challenge, though the sting of rising costs began to ease for some operators. After years of battling inflation, this year saw stabilization in supply chain expenses, yet menu prices stayed elevated—a reality diners have grudgingly accepted. Restaurants doubled down on their divergent strategies from prior years: some chased value-conscious patrons with streamlined offerings, while others solidified their premium positioning, banking on customers willing to splurge for quality or experience. Neither approach proved a silver bullet, but both underscored an industry still searching for its footing in a transformed market.

Technology took center stage, with AI and automation no longer just buzzwords but tangible fixtures in many operations. Automated drive-thrus and AI-driven ordering systems expanded, particularly among fast-food giants, while some casual dining chains tested robotic kitchen assistants to offset labor pressures. For example, Taco Bell rolled out more of its high-tech "Defy" locations with multiple drive-thru lanes and minimal staff, aiming to boost speed and efficiency. Meanwhile, Olive Garden experimented with AI-powered prep tools in select kitchens, cutting labor costs but sparking mixed reviews from diners who noticed a shift in consistency. The results were promising yet inconsistent—automated stores drew curiosity and efficiency gains, but glitches and high upfront costs tempered enthusiasm. Mobile-only locations gained traction, catering to a convenience-obsessed consumer base, though traditionalists pushed back, arguing that dining is as much about human connection as it is about food. This tech tug-of-war defined much of the year, with 2025 poised to reveal which innovations stick and which fade.

Profitability has been a mixed bag. Many restaurants maintained the record highs of previous years, buoyed by higher check averages and strategic surcharges, but the cost was often fewer guests walking through the door. Thin margins remained a tightrope act, with operators leaning heavily on loyalty apps and data-driven personalization to keep diners engaged. Labor challenges persisted, though less acutely than in prior years—automation eased some staffing woes, but the industry still grappled with recruitment and retention.

Looking to 2025, the restaurant industry stands at a crossroads. The proliferation of tech-heavy concepts will accelerate, with more brands testing hybrid models that blend automation and human touch. Price sensitivity isn't going away, forcing operators to refine their value propositions—whether through budget-friendly deals or elevated experiences that justify the cost. Customer traffic will remain the elusive prize, and success will hinge on who can crack the code of bringing diners back without sacrificing the bottom line. The industry's cutting-edge vibe is undeniable, but its future will depend on balancing innovation with the timeless appeal of a good meal out.

Executive Summary

Chain Store Guide has been researching companies and providing accurate, accessible and actionable data for more than 85 years. As a result, CSG has a clear understanding of what's important to our clients and customers.

The Digital Advantage

Today more than ever, access to timely and reliable industry information is crucial in achieving measurable, substantial results and a clear competitive advantage. In response to this need, Chain Store Guide also offers online access to the **Chain Restaurant Premier** database. The Premier version of the online database provides a number of great features not included in the print directory:

- ✓ **Verified Email Addresses:** Today, subscribers have access to more than 20,000 email addresses for the personnel listed in this directory, including 9,000+ **executive emails.**

- ✓ **Social Media Handles:** Enhance your multi-channel marketing with company and personnel social handles, including Facebook, LinkedIn, and Twitter.

- ✓ **Daily Updates:** The online databases refresh each day so that our customers have real-time access to the most current industry news, data and contact information. Each month, CSG makes thousands of additions, deletions and adjustments to our data, changes that have a major impact on our customers' activities.

- ✓ **Dynamic Search:** Database users can filter and search companies by dozens of attributes including menu type, geography, sales, and number of locations. They can also filter and search personnel and contact information by attributes like job title and functional area.

If you've purchased this edition of the Chain Restaurant Operators Directory, contact your CSG representative about upgrading to the online database at a reduced price.

No other data company provides the same breadth and depth of industry-specific information as Chain Store Guide.

Criteria for Inclusion

To be included in this directory, companies must generate at least $1,000,000 in annual foodservice sales, either system wide or corporate. Below are the types of business included in this directory:

Chain Restaurant Operators: Chain restaurant companies in this directory must operate two (2) or more units. (Example: McDonald's Corporation)

Foodservice Management Operators: Companies that are indicated with a (†) are those whose primary business is to provide on-site foodservice management and which have at least two (2) foodservice management accounts. (Example: ARAMARK Inc.)

Foodservice Operations - Bowling Alley: Companies whose primary business is the operation of bowling alleys but which provide foodservice (in-house snack bars and restaurants) as a secondary operation. (Example: Bowl America Inc.)

Foodservice Operations - Casinos: Companies whose primary business is the operation of casinos but which provide on-site foodservice as part of its operations. (Example: Caesars Entertainment Corporation)

Foodservice Operations - Hotel/Motels: Hotel/motel companies that are indicated with a (‡) must control two (2) or more foodservice operations. The company may own and operate its hotels; own but not manage the hotels; or manage but not own the hotels. A company which only franchises out, i.e., sells the rights to use a name (Shoney's Inn), is not qualified. A company which acts only as a referral service (Best Western, Budget Host) is not qualified. (Example: Hilton Worldwide Holdings Inc.)

Foodservice Operations - Movie Theatre: Companies whose primary business is the operation of movie theatres but which provide foodservice (concessions) as a secondary operation. (Example: AMC Entertainment)

Foodservice Operations - Theme Parks: Companies whose primary business is the operation of theme parks and family amusement centers but which provide foodservice as a secondary operation. (Example: Walt Disney World Co.)

Nontraditional Foodservice Operators: Companies which provide foodservice as a secondary operation, e.g., discount stores, department stores; revenues from foodservice are less than 50% of total sales. (Example: Target Corporation)

Explanation of Data Elements

Alcohol Sales: The percentage of revenue derived from beer, wine and/or liquor sales.

Alcohol Served: The types of alcoholic beverages served.

Areas of Operation: The US states and territories and Canadian provinces in which the company operates.

Average Check: The average amount spent for each meal for one person (breakfast, lunch, and/or dinner).

Branch Office: The name and location of the company's branch offices.

Catering Services: This indicates the company provides off-premises catering at the place of customer's request (e.g., banquet hall). Most restaurants will provide on-premises catering upon request.

Company Email: The address at which the company receives electronic mail. Personal email addresses are not included.

Company-Owned Units: The number of units owned and operated by the company and excludes franchised units.

Distribution Centers: The locations in which the company operates distribution centers.

Divisional Offices: The name and location of the company's divisional offices.

Fax Number: The company's primary fax number.

Foodservice Management Operator - The (†) indicator denotes a company which has on-site or contract feeding operations.

Foodservice Management Venues: The types of institutions for which the company provides foodservice.

Foodservice Sales: This is the revenue derived from prepared food sales and includes revenue from institutional foodservice and restaurant foodservice. For chains that franchise, sales include franchise and/or license fees in addition to revenues from company-owned units.

Foreign Countries: The foreign countries in which the company operates.

Franchise Affiliation: Name and location of the company's franchise headquarters. Includes all individual franchisees of a particular trade name/company (i.e., all franchisees of KFC).

Franchisee: The (●) indicator denotes a company that franchises its retail concept from another company.

Franchise Headquarters: The (▲) indicator denotes a company that acts as a Franchise Headquarters for other companies.

Headquarters: The name and location of the company's headquarter office to which this subordinate office reports.

Headquarter Offices: The name and location of subordinate headquarters offices for corporate listings.

Hotel/Motel Operator: The (‡) indicator denotes a company that operates a Hotel/Motel retail location.

Internet Homepage: The company's Internet homepage address.

Internet Order Processing: This indicates the company sells products and collects payment via an Internet homepage.

Internet Sales: This indicates the percentage of revenue derived from selling products via an Internet homepage.

Key Personnel: This lists executive, administrative and buying personnel with their titles as reported by the company.

Explanation of Data Elements

Listing Type: The company's position within the corporate hierarchy (e.g., corporate, subsidiary, regional, division). No listing type will appear for Headquarters companies.

Mailing Address: The mailing address, city, state or province, and ZIP or postal code of the company, if it differs from the primary address.

New Listing: The (♦) indicates a company that was not included in the previous year's edition of this publication.

Notes: This is any pertinent company information that does not appear in other data elements collected.

Number of Employees: The total number of employees of this company.

Number of Locations Served: This indicates the number of separate locations served by the foodservice management accounts.

On-site Distribution Center: This indicates that the company operates a distribution center at the same address.

Parent Company: The name and location of the parent company.

Preferred Location Types: The real-estate types in which the company operates units.

Preferred Square Footage: The standard or projected size of new or remodeled units for the company.

Primary Distributors: The name and location of the wholesale distributors supplying the company with food, equipment and/or supplies.

Primary Menu: The primary type of food served.

Projected Openings: The number of units the company plans to open during the next 12 months.

Projected Remodelings: The number of units the company plans to remodel during the next 12 months.

Publicly Held: This indicates that company issues shares of unrestricted stock to the general public.

Regional Offices: The name and location of the company's regional offices.

Restaurants in Hotels: The total number of foodservice operations in hotels/motels.

Subsidiaries: The name and location of the company's subsidiaries.

Systemwide Sales: The estimated foodservice revenue generated by units which are company-owned and/or franchised to others. Companies which only "franchise from" another company have no systemwide sales.

Total Foodservice Mgmt Accounts: The number of foodservice management accounts the company currently serves.

Total Sales: The most current sales figure available for the company and typically represents the company's most recent fiscal year end. Sources for sales figures are: 1) an estimated sales figure provided by the company; 2) an exact sales figure taken from the annual report of a public company; 3) an estimate derived by CSG through industry research. CSG estimates are noted with an (e).

Explanation of Data Elements

Total Units: The total number of units the company currently operates and/or franchises to others.

Trade Names: This indicates the trade names the company uses to do business, and the number of units operating under each name.

Type of Business: The type of business in which the company engages.

Type of Foodservice: This indicates the type of restaurants operated by the company, or the type of foodservice provided by foodservice management operators:

- **Cafeteria:** self-service, varied menu, cafeteria-type line at counter.
- **Casual Dining:** limited menu, full-service, menu identity (seafood, steaks, Italian, etc.), may serve beer, wine, liquor.
- **Family Restaurant:** full-service, sit-down, table service, wider range menu, typically does not serve beer, wine, liquor.
- **Fast Casual:** limited menu, food prepared to order, limited table service often provided, may serve beer or wine.
- **Fine Dining:** gourmet meals, tablecloth, full service.
- **Full-Service Sit-Down Dining:** table service, menu selection (in foodservice management venues).
- **In-Store Feeder:** restaurants/snack bars within existing retail units (e.g., department stores, drug stores, supermarkets, etc.).
- **Mobile Units/Kiosks:** typically small foodservice units with limited menu, capable of being moved to meet demand (in foodservice management venues).
- **Quick Serve:** quick-service/self-service, limited menu (hamburger, chicken, pizza, etc.).
- **Vending Machines:** automated units with limited selections to provide snacks, sandwiches, beverages, etc. (in foodservice management venues).

Units Franchised From: This indicates the number of units franchised from a franchise headquarters.

Units Franchised To: This indicates the number of units franchised to other companies.

Year Founded: This is the year in which the company was established.

Statistical Analysis

Chain Restaurant Operators – United States

Total Listings

Corporate Offices	31
Headquarters	6,395
Subsidiaries	35
Regional Offices	19
Divisional Offices	22
Distribution Centers	61
Total Listings	**6,563**

Total Foodservice Revenue

Total	$474,456,089,000

Personnel

Total Personnel Listed	26,540

Breakdown by Type of Foodservice

Type of Foodservice	Companies	Units
Cafeteria	21	176
Casual Dining	1,934	36,898
Family Restaurant	319	14,163
Fast Casual	922	36,674
Fine Dining	443	2,492
In-Store Feeder	75	10,399
Quick Serve	3,369	369,220

Breakdown by Type of Menu

Menu	Companies	Units	Menu	Companies	Units
American	1,319	40,586	Italian	355	3,944
Asian	135	2,779	Japanese	78	776
Bagels	23	370	Latin American/Cuban	30	154
Bar-B-Q	172	2,357	Mexican	344	8,974
Cajun/Creole	30	256	Middle Eastern	28	305
Californian	38	247	Miscellaneous	128	2,818
Caribbean	18	218	Pizza	1,120	82,930
Chicken	398	56,070	Sandwiches/Deli	684	62,533
Chinese	50	3,050	Seafood	320	3,843
Coffee	126	36,681	Snacks	631	49,052
Eastern European	7	69	Southern	38	164
French/Continental	83	375	Southwest/Tex-Mex	94	3,010
German	6	9	Spanish	28	86
Greek/Mediterranean	93	1,979	Steak	217	3,997
Hamburger	1,256	106,079	Steak/Seafood	139	589
Health Foods	94	4,611	Taco	216	15,554
Hot Dogs	45	1,009	Thai	8	237
Indian	19	77			

Statistical Analysis

Chain Restaurant Operators – Canada

Total Listings

Corporate Office	3
Headquarters	167
Subsidiaries	5
Regional Offices	5
Divisional Offices	1
Distribution Centers	11
Total Listings	**192**

Total Foodservice Revenue

Total	$18,124,303,000

Personnel

Total Personnel Listed	1,037

Breakdown by Type of Foodservice

Type of Foodservice	Companies	Units
Cafeteria	3	37
Casual Dining	75	3,121
Family Restaurant	9	576
Fast Casual	27	990
Fine Dining	17	69
In-Store Feeder	5	227
Quick Serve	74	16,492

Breakdown by Type of Menu

Menu	Companies	Units	Menu	Companies	Units
American	42	1,685	Italian	21	237
Asian	7	80	Japanese	8	758
Bagels	3	39	Mexican	3	11
Bar-B-Q	2	204	Miscellaneous	11	272
Cajun/Creole	3	22	Pizza	21	2,477
Caribbean	2	3	Sandwiches/Deli	17	277
Chicken	14	1,149	Seafood	8	63
Chinese	5	166	Snacks	21	8,502
Coffee	9	125	Southern	1	1
Eastern European	2	2	Southwest/Tex-Mex	1	23
French/Continental	10	112	Steak	13	173
Greek/Mediterranean	8	839	Steak/Seafood	9	84
Hamburger	19	3,152	Taco	2	171
Health Foods	5	419	Thai	2	5

Statistical Analysis

Hotel/Motel Companies – United States and Canada

Total Listings

Headquarters	155
Subsidiaries	4
Total Listings	**159**

Total Foodservice Revenue

Total	$32,345,538,000

Personnel

Total Personnel Listed	2,882

Breakdown by Type of Foodservice

Type of Food Service	Companies
Cafeteria	3
Casual Dining	136
Family Restaurant	18
Fast Casual	14
Fine Dining	71
Quick Serve	29

Statistical Analysis

Foodservice Management Operators – United States and Canada

Total Listings

Corporate Offices	1
Headquarters	79
Subsidiaries	3
Regional Offices	16
Divisional Offices	14
Branch Offices	33
Total Listings	**146**

Total Foodservice Revenues

Total	$79,477,000,000

Personnel

Total Personnel Listed	1,098

Breakdown by Type of Foodservice

Type of Foodservice	Companies
Cafeteria	50
Fast Casual	3
Full-service sit-down dining	18
Mobile units/kiosks	6
Quick Serve	26
Vending machines	20

LOCUS™

CSG's Retail & Foodservice Locational Data is driven by our unique Locus™ sync & multi-step update service that blends spatial geocoding and revolutionary technology with a human touch.

97.6%
CSG Data Accuracy Rating

Develop Data-Driven Business Decisions
Use our data for predictive forecasting with 10 years of historical data, competitive mapping, site selection, void analysis, data blending, spatial modeling, and more.

Blend Data to Fit Your Needs
Select the data that works for you with our scalable services.

Competitive Edge
- 97.6% Chain Store Guide Accuracy Rating: A
- 65% Competitor 1 Accuracy Rating: C
- 15% Competitor 2 Accuracy Rating: D

720,221 GEO-CODED STORE LOCATIONS

30-60-90 DAY REFRESH CYCLE

Cannabis Store Locations
CSG has tracked and compiled a list of over **18,000** store locations that sell or distribute cannabis & CBD products at retail.

EACH STORE LOCATION FILE INCLUDES:
- Monthly Updated Data
- Parent Company HQ Linkages
- Regional / Divisional Linkages
- 10 Digit Unique Company ID
- Industry Classifications
- Complete Addresses
- GEO-Coding (Latitude & Longitude)
- 90% Street Level GEO-Coding
- Phone Numbers
- Store Numbers
- Average Weekly Sales Volume
- Square Footage
- Primary Wholesaler Linkages**

ChainStoreGuide.com | 1.800.927.9292

*Database counts are approximate and subject to change.
**Databases may not contain all listed data points. Speak to an Account Manager for more details.

INDUSTRY	# OF LOCATIONS*
Apparel Stores	50,000+
Bank Retail Locations**	29,000+
Category Killers	71,000+
Convenience Stores	130,000+
Department Stores	4,000+
Discount Stores, Club Stores & Supercenters	8,000+
Drug Store Chains	31,000+
General Merchandise & Dollar Stores	39,000+
Grocery Store Chains	31,000+
Gyms & Health Clubs**	10,000+
HBC/Cosmetics Stores	12,000+
Home Centers & Hardware Chains	26,000+
Home Furnishing Stores	10,000+
Independent Drug Stores	3,000+
Independent Restaurants	2,000+
Independent Supermarkets	3,000+
Liquor Stores**	21,000+
Locations: Cannabis	18,000+
Restaurant Chains	214,000+

ALASKA

D of Alaska Inc
1345 Rudakof Cir Ste 203
Anchorage, AK 99508-6105

Telephone: (907) 333-6776
Fax Number: (907) 338-2690
Type of Business: Chain Restaurant Operator
Total Sales: $9,145,000 (e)
Total Units: 3
Trade Names: Denny's (3)
Units Franchised From: 3
Primary Menu: American (3)
Areas of Operation: AK
Type of Foodservice: Family Restaurant (3)
Franchise Affiliation: Denny's Corporation, SPARTANBURG, SC

Key Personnel
DAVID FICKES - President; General Buyer
NIKKI CROMBIE - Manager Human Resources

Denali Foods Inc.
3301 Denali St Ste 200
Anchorage, AK 99503-4051

Telephone: (907) 334-3100
Fax Number: (907) 334-3180
Type of Business: Chain Restaurant Operator
Year Founded: 1983
Total Sales: $35,980,000 (e)
Number of Employees: 465
Average Check: Lunch(6); Dinner(6)
Total Units: 13
Trade Names: Taco Bell (13)
Units Franchised From: 13
Preferred Square Footage: 2,200
Preferred Location Types: Freestanding; Strip Mall
Primary Menu: Taco (13)
Areas of Operation: AK
Type of Foodservice: Quick Serve (13)
Franchise Affiliation: Taco Bell Corp., IRVINE, CA
Primary Distributors: (Full Line) US Foods, ANCHORAGE, AK

Key Personnel
DALE MARTENS - President; VP Purchasing; General Manager; Director Facility/Maintenance, Information Systems, Real Estate, Human Resources
MELANIE VEEH - CFO
JOHN MAYFIELD - VP Operations
BRIAN AIKENS - District Manager

Domino's Franchisee
601 W 36th Ave Ste 80
Anchorage, AK 99503-5848

Telephone: (907) 561-8166
Type of Business: Chain Restaurant Operator
Total Sales: $16,092,000 (e)
Total Units: 8
Trade Names: Domino's (8)
Units Franchised From: 8
Primary Menu: Pizza (8)
Areas of Operation: AK
Type of Foodservice: Quick Serve (8)
Franchise Affiliation: Domino's Pizza Inc, ANN ARBOR, MI

Key Personnel
BRYAN DOBB - Partner; General Buyer
IAN HURD - Partner; General Buyer

Fresh Ale Pubs
3300 Old Seward Hwy
Anchorage, AK 99503-4129

Telephone: (907) 222-1560
Fax Number: (907) 258-7361
Internet Homepage: beartooththeatre.net; moosestooth.net
Type of Business: Chain Restaurant Operator
Year Founded: 1996
Total Sales: $6,503,000 (e)
Alcohol Sales: 20%
Number of Employees: 275
Average Check: Lunch(12); Dinner(18)
Total Units: 3
Trade Names: Bear Tooth Grill (1); Bear Tooth Theatre Pub (1); Moose's Tooth Pub & Pizzeria (1)
Company-Owned Units: 3
Preferred Location Types: Freestanding; Other
Alcohol Served: Beer, Wine, Liquor
Primary Menu: American (2); Pizza (1)
Areas of Operation: AK
Type of Foodservice: Casual Dining (3)
Primary Distributors: (Full Line) SYSCO Food Services of Alaska Inc., ANCHORAGE, AK

Key Personnel
ROD HANCOCK - Partner; Director Purchasing
MATT JONES - Partner; General Buyer
WARREN HANCOCK - CFO
DAN FIACCO - General Manager

J & D Restaurants Inc.
8777 Toloff St Ste A
Anchorage, AK 99507-3530

Telephone: (907) 336-9900
Fax Number: (907) 336-9901
Company Email: carlsjr3@ak.net
Type of Business: Chain Restaurant Operator
Year Founded: 2002
Total Sales: $10,850,000 (e)
Number of Employees: 37
Average Check: Breakfast(8); Lunch(8); Dinner(8)
Total Units: 5
Trade Names: Carl's Jr. (5)
Units Franchised From: 5
Preferred Square Footage: 2,500; 3,000; 4,000
Preferred Location Types: Freestanding
Primary Menu: Hamburger (5)
Areas of Operation: AK
Type of Foodservice: Quick Serve (5)
Franchise Affiliation: Carl's Jr., FRANKLIN, TN
Primary Distributors: (Full Line) McLane/Rocky Mount, ROCKY MOUNT, NC

Key Personnel
DEBRA KINN - Partner; General Buyer
JERRY KINN - Partner; General Buyer

KH2 Corporation
7731 E Northern Lights Blvd Ste 200
Anchorage, AK 99504-3572

Telephone: (907) 337-2044
Type of Business: Chain Restaurant Operator
Total Sales: $1,207,000 (e)
Total Units: 2
Trade Names: Cold Stone Creamery (2)
Units Franchised From: 2
Primary Menu: Snacks (2)
Areas of Operation: AK
Type of Foodservice: Quick Serve (2)
Franchise Affiliation: Kahala Brands, SCOTTSDALE, AZ

Key Personnel
KEVIN HWANG - Partner
KIM HWANG - Partner

Kurani Inc.
210 Center Ct
Anchorage, AK 99518-1621

Telephone: (907) 562-2205
Type of Business: Chain Restaurant Operator
Year Founded: 1984
Total Sales: $8,787,000 (e)
Alcohol Sales: 1%
Average Check: Dinner(14)
Total Units: 7
Trade Names: Pizza Hut (7)
Units Franchised From: 7
Preferred Square Footage: 1,400; 4,500
Preferred Location Types: Freestanding
Alcohol Served: Beer

Primary Menu: Pizza (7)
Areas of Operation: AK
Type of Foodservice: Quick Serve (7)
Franchise Affiliation: Pizza Hut Inc., PLANO, TX

Key Personnel
KURBAN KURANI - CEO; General Buyer

Midnight Moon Co. Inc.
6921 Brayton Dr Ste 201
Anchorage, AK 99507-5601

Telephone: (907) 344-4480
Fax Number: (866) 893-4708
Internet Homepage: blackcupak.com; kaladi.com
Company Email: info@kaladi.com
Type of Business: Nontraditional Foodservice Operator
Year Founded: 1986
Systemwide Sales: $25,123,000 (e)
Total Sales: $20,120,000 (e)
Number of Employees: 175
Average Check: Breakfast(5); Lunch(5); Dinner(5)
Internet Order Processing: Yes
Internet Sales: 4.00%
Total Units: 17
Trade Names: Black Cup (1); Kaladi Bros. Coffee (16)
Company-Owned Units: 8
Units Franchised To: 9
Preferred Square Footage: 1,500
Preferred Location Types: Freestanding; Strip Mall
Primary Menu: Coffee (17)
Areas of Operation: AK, WA
Type of Foodservice: Quick Serve (17)
Foodservice Management Venues: Health Care
On-site Distribution Center: Yes
Primary Distributors: (Full Line) SYSCO Food Services of Alaska Inc., ANCHORAGE, AK
Notes: The company derives approximately 60% of its revenue from wholesale operations.

Key Personnel
TIM GRAVEL - President; Partner; Exec VP Information Systems, Real Estate; Director Finance; Manager Design
BRAD BIGELOW - Partner; Director Facility/Maintenance, Menu Development; General Buyer
MICHELLE PARKER - COO; Manager Operations, Human Resources

MRD INC
800 W Northern Lights Blvd
Anchorage, AK 99503-3713

Telephone: (907) 561-6036
Fax Number: (907) 561-6075
Type of Business: Chain Restaurant Operator
Total Sales: $91,000,000 (e)
Total Units: 19
Trade Names: McDonald's (19)
Units Franchised From: 19
Preferred Square Footage: 2,500
Preferred Location Types: Discount Dept. Stores; Freestanding
Primary Menu: Hamburger (19)
Areas of Operation: AK
Type of Foodservice: Quick Serve (19)
Franchise Affiliation: McDonald's Corporation, CHICAGO, IL

Key Personnel
MICHAEL DAVIDSON - President; General Buyer

North-Wend Foods Inc.
2601 Blueberry Rd
Anchorage, AK 99503-2623

Telephone: (907) 562-7275
Fax Number: (907) 562-1251
Type of Business: Chain Restaurant Operator
Total Sales: $22,670,000 (e)
Number of Employees: 240
Average Check: Lunch(8); Dinner(8)
Total Units: 8
Trade Names: Wendy's Old Fashioned Hamburgers (8)
Units Franchised From: 8
Preferred Square Footage: 2,100; 2,900
Preferred Location Types: Freestanding; Regional Mall
Primary Menu: Hamburger (8)
Areas of Operation: AK
Type of Foodservice: Quick Serve (8)
Franchise Affiliation: The Wendy's Company, DUBLIN, OH

Key Personnel
JAY SUTHERLAND - President; Director Finance, Operations, Purchasing, Facility/Maintenance, Information Systems, Real Estate, Human Resources; General Buyer
JASON SARATE - Controller

Subway of Alaska Inc
1118 E 70th Ave Ste 200
Anchorage, AK 99518-2352

Telephone: (907) 563-4228
Fax Number: (907) 563-4288
Internet Homepage: subwayak.com
Type of Business: Chain Restaurant Operator
Total Sales: $18,450,000 (e)
Total Units: 30
Trade Names: Subway (30)
Units Franchised From: 30
Primary Menu: Sandwiches/Deli (30)
Areas of Operation: AK
Type of Foodservice: Quick Serve (30)
Franchise Affiliation: Doctor's Associates Inc., MILFORD, CT

Key Personnel
STEVE ADAMS - Owner; General Buyer
CHRIS WILSON - VP

Taco King
8615 Old Seward Hwy
Anchorage, AK 99515-2017

Telephone: (907) 771-6060
Internet Homepage: gallosak.com; tacokingak.com
Type of Business: Chain Restaurant Operator
Year Founded: 1992
Total Sales: $6,804,000 (e)
Alcohol Sales: 5%
Number of Employees: 28
Average Check: Lunch(8); Dinner(14)
Total Units: 11
Trade Names: Burrito King (1); Gallos (2); Taco King (8)
Company-Owned Units: 11
Preferred Location Types: Freestanding
Alcohol Served: Beer, Wine, Liquor
Primary Menu: Mexican (11)
Areas of Operation: AK
Type of Foodservice: Casual Dining (2); Family Restaurant (1); Quick Serve (8)
Catering Services: Yes
Primary Distributors: (Full Line) US Foods, ANCHORAGE, AK

Key Personnel
ABRAHAM GALLO - President; General Manager; Director Operations, Purchasing

Wit-Rey Inc.
1120 Huffman Rd Ste 232
Anchorage, AK 99515-3516

Telephone: (907) 349-9142
Fax Number: (907) 344-1619

Type of Business: Chain Restaurant Operator
Year Founded: 1962
Total Sales: $7,632,000 (e)
Number of Employees: 180
Total Units: 4
Trade Names: KFC (4)
Units Franchised From: 4
Preferred Square Footage: 2,900
Preferred Location Types: Freestanding; Strip Mall
Primary Menu: Chicken (4)
Areas of Operation: AK
Type of Foodservice: Quick Serve (4)
Catering Services: Yes
Franchise Affiliation: KFC Corporation, LOUISVILLE, KY

Key Personnel
BOB CARLE - President; General Buyer

Chugach Creamery, Inc.
11432 Business Blvd Ste 8
Eagle River, AK 99577-7740

Telephone: (907) 696-3441
Type of Business: Chain Restaurant Operator
Total Sales: $1,777,000 (e)
Total Units: 3
Trade Names: Cold Stone Creamery (3)
Units Franchised From: 3
Primary Menu: Snacks (3)
Areas of Operation: AK
Type of Foodservice: Quick Serve (3)
Franchise Affiliation: Kahala Brands, SCOTTSDALE, AZ

Key Personnel
GREGORY PERSINGER - Partner
CATHARINE PERSINGER - Partner

Bullwinkle's Pizza Parlor
318 Willoughby Ave
Juneau, AK 99801-1723

Telephone: (907) 463-5252
Fax Number: (907) 463-5254
Internet Homepage: bullwinklespizza.com
Type of Business: Chain Restaurant Operator
Year Founded: 1973
Total Sales: $3,618,000 (e)
Alcohol Sales: 20%
Number of Employees: 52
Average Check: Lunch(8); Dinner(12)
Total Units: 2
Trade Names: Bullwinkle's Pizza Parlor (2)
Company-Owned Units: 2
Preferred Location Types: Community Mall; Freestanding
Alcohol Served: Beer, Wine
Primary Menu: Pizza (2)
Areas of Operation: AK
Type of Foodservice: Casual Dining (2)
Primary Distributors: (Food) Food Services of America, KENT, WA

Key Personnel
MITCH FALK - Owner; Executive Chef; Manager Food Safety; General Buyer

The Sand Piper Cafe
429 W Willoughby Ave
Juneau, AK 99801-1727

Telephone: (907) 586-3150
Internet Homepage: sandpiper.cafe
Company Email: sandpipercafe@gmail.com
Type of Business: Chain Restaurant Operator
Total Sales: $1,826,000 (e)
Total Units: 2
Trade Names: The Sand Piper Cafe (2)
Company-Owned Units: 2
Primary Menu: Coffee (2)
Type of Foodservice: Casual Dining (2)

Key Personnel
DOUGLAS ARENDS - Owner; General Manager; Executive Chef; General Buyer

Zan Inc.
10733 Kenai Spur Hwy
Kenai, AK 99611

Mailing Address: PO Box 2009, KENAI, AK, 99611-2009
Telephone: (907) 283-5636
Fax Number: (907) 283-3062
Company Email: alaskaarbys@zaninc.net
Type of Business: Chain Restaurant Operator
Year Founded: 1983
Total Sales: $11,070,000 (e)
Number of Employees: 131
Average Check: Lunch(10); Dinner(10)
Total Units: 6
Trade Names: Arby's (6)
Units Franchised From: 6
Preferred Square Footage: 2,500; 3,000
Preferred Location Types: Freestanding; Regional Mall
Primary Menu: Sandwiches/Deli (6)
Areas of Operation: AK
Type of Foodservice: Quick Serve (6)
Franchise Affiliation: Arby's Restaurant Group, ATLANTA, GA
Primary Distributors: (Full Line) Systems Services of America, SCOTTSDALE, AZ

Key Personnel
MICHAEL S. NAVARRE - President; Director Finance, Purchasing, Facility/Maintenance, Design, Store Fixtures
TED NAVARRE - Director Operations, Real Estate
STEVE GRAVELLE - Director Supply Chain

The Alaska Culinary Academy
809 2nd Ave
Seward, AK 99664

Mailing Address: P.O. Box 889, Seward, AK, 99664
Telephone: (907) 224-3322
Fax Number: (907) 224-4400
Internet Homepage: avtec.edu
Company Email: admisions@avtec.edu
Type of Business: Culinary Schools
Areas of Operation: AK

Key Personnel
ELIZABETH KENNEDY-JOHNSTON - Executive Chef; Director Culinary Development; General Buyer

ALABAMA

Chicken Salad Chick
724 N Dean Rd Ste 100
Auburn, AL 36830-4306

Telephone: (334) 275-4578
Fax Number: (334) 209-0251
Internet Homepage: chickensaladchick.com
Company Email: info@simplysouthernrg.com
Listing Type: Subsidiary
Type of Business: Chain Restaurant Operator
Year Founded: 2008
Systemwide Sales: $190,172,000 (e)
Total Sales: $135,740,000 (e)
Average Check: Lunch(16);
Internet Order Processing: Yes
Total Units: 225
Trade Names: Chicken Salad Chick (225)
Company-Owned Units: 53
Units Franchised To: 172
Preferred Location Types: Lifestyle Center; Regional Mall; Strip Mall
Primary Menu: Sandwiches/Deli (225)
Projected Openings: 40
Areas of Operation: AL, AR, FL, GA, IL, KY, LA, MO, MS, NC, OH, OK, SC, TN, TX, VA
Type of Foodservice: Fast Casual (225)
Catering Services: Yes
Parent Company: Brentwood Associates, LOS ANGELES, CA

Key Personnel
STACY BROWN - Co-Founder; VP Branding
SCOTT DEVINEY - CEO
DAVID OSTRANDER - CFO
JIM THOMPSON - COO
TOM CARR - Chief Marketing Officer

TERRY MCKEE - Chief Development Officer
RYLES DODD - VP Information Technology
STEVE CALE - VP Operations
SARAH THOMASON - Controller
PATTI EVANOSKY - Director Training
PAUL GRILLI - Director Operations
JON MUSSER - Director Supply Chain
ERIN MCVICKER - Director Store Systems
MILES COGGINS - Manager Construction
ANGELA HAND - Manager Human Resources
ALLISON BRADFORD - Manager Marketing
LAUREN LONG - Specialist Store Systems

Guthrie Franchise Corp
2320 Moores Mill Rd Ste 600
Auburn, AL 36830

Telephone: (334) 887-6555
Fax Number: (205) 977-5694
Internet Homepage: guthrieschicken.com
Type of Business: Chain Restaurant Operator
Year Founded: 1965
Total Sales: $29,530,000 (e)
Number of Employees: 126
Average Check: Lunch(8); Dinner(10)
Total Units: 29
Trade Names: Guthrie's Chicken (29)
Company-Owned Units: 4
Units Franchised To: 25
Preferred Square Footage: 1,800; 2,000
Preferred Location Types: Downtown; Freestanding; Strip Mall
Primary Menu: Chicken (29)
Areas of Operation: AL, FL, GA, OH, TN
Type of Foodservice: Family Restaurant (29)
Catering Services: Yes

Key Personnel
JOE K. GUTHRIE - President
MATTHEW MYERS - Director Operations

McDonald's Franchise
PO Box 1210
Auburn, AL 36831-1210

Telephone: (334) 826-8633
Type of Business: Chain Restaurant Operator
Total Sales: $23,690,000 (e)
Average Check: Dinner(12)
Total Units: 5
Trade Names: McDonald's (5)
Units Franchised From: 5
Preferred Square Footage: 2,500
Preferred Location Types: Freestanding
Primary Menu: Hamburger (5)
Areas of Operation: AL
Type of Foodservice: Quick Serve (5)
Franchise Affiliation: McDonald's Corporation, CHICAGO, IL

Key Personnel
PAUL MARSHALL - President; General Buyer

Tenda Chick
232 N Dean Rd
Auburn, AL 36830-5019

Telephone: (334) 821-8543
Fax Number: (334) 821-3129
Type of Business: Chain Restaurant Operator
Year Founded: 1989
Total Sales: $1,502,000 (e)
Number of Employees: 60
Average Check: Dinner(10)
Total Units: 2
Trade Names: Tenda Chick (2)
Company-Owned Units: 2
Preferred Location Types: Freestanding
Primary Menu: Chicken (2)
Areas of Operation: AL
Type of Foodservice: Family Restaurant (2)
Primary Distributors: (Food) US Foods, MONTGOMERY, AL

Key Personnel
BRIAN P. MOORE - President; VP; General Manager; Executive Chef; General Buyer
TERESA MOORE - Owner

Domino's Franchisee
5031 Ford Pkwy
Bessemer, AL 35022-5283

Telephone: (205) 428-6262
Type of Business: Chain Restaurant Operator
Total Sales: $5,967,000 (e)
Total Units: 3
Trade Names: Domino's (3)
Units Franchised From: 3
Primary Menu: Pizza (3)
Areas of Operation: AL
Type of Foodservice: Quick Serve (3)
Franchise Affiliation: Domino's Pizza Inc, ANN ARBOR, MI

Key Personnel
DEREK M. PARRIS - Owner; General Buyer
ERICK CROSS - General Manager

Chicken Scratch Holdings Inc.
110 Doug Baker Blvd
Birmingham, AL 35242-2674

Telephone: (205) 981-4536
Type of Business: Chain Restaurant Operator
Total Sales: $32,020,000 (e)
Total Units: 9
Trade Names: Zaxby's (9)
Units Franchised From: 9
Primary Menu: Chicken (9)
Areas of Operation: AL
Type of Foodservice: Fast Casual (9)
Franchise Affiliation: Zaxby's Franchising Inc., ATHENS, GA

Key Personnel
COURTNEY H. MASON - President
RUSSELL PATE - VP

CMX Cinemas
2000B Southbridge Pkwy Ste 100
Birmingham, AL 35209-7723

Telephone: (205) 802-7766
Fax Number: (205) 802-7771
Internet Homepage: cinebistro.com; cmxcinemas.com
Company Email: comments@cobbtheatres.com
Type of Business: Foodservice Operations - Movie Theatre
Total Sales: $134,740,000 (e)
Number of Employees: 700
Average Check: Lunch(14); Dinner(14)
Total Units: 31
Trade Names: CineBistro (10); CMX Cinema (21)
Company-Owned Units: 31
Preferred Square Footage: 2,500
Preferred Location Types: Community Mall; Freestanding; Regional Mall
Alcohol Served: Beer, Wine, Liquor
Primary Menu: American (12); Snacks (31)
Areas of Operation: AL, CO, FL, GA, OH
Type of Foodservice: In-Store Feeder (31)
Primary Distributors: (Full Line) US Foods, MONTGOMERY, AL
Notes: The company derives approximately 72% of its revenue from movie theatre operations.

Key Personnel
PATRICK RYAN - CEO
ROBERT M. COBB - President
JENNIFER HERRING GOSSETT - VP Human Resources
STEPHANIE MASON - VP Marketing
LORETTA THOMAS - VP Operations, Purchasing, Foodservice
GUY AUSTIN - VP Operations
PILAR PETERSON - VP Finance
VIVIAN NOVO - Director Talent
PETER HURWITZ - Director
ISAI OLIVERA - Regional Director Operations

2025 Chain Restaurant Operators

Costa's Famous BBQ
613 Springville Rd
Birmingham, AL 35215-7401

Telephone: (205) 853-9933
Fax Number: (205) 854-1411
Internet Homepage: costasfamous.com
Type of Business: Chain Restaurant Operator
Total Sales: $3,103,000 (e)
Number of Employees: 30
Average Check: Lunch(8); Dinner(12)
Total Units: 2
Trade Names: Costa's Famous BBQ (2)
Company-Owned Units: 2
Primary Menu: Bar-B-Q (2)
Areas of Operation: AL
Type of Foodservice: Casual Dining (2)
Catering Services: Yes
Primary Distributors: (Full Line) US Foods, MONTGOMERY, AL

Key Personnel
PEGGY PATE - Partner; General Manager; Director Operations
RICK PATE - Partner; General Manager; General Buyer

Dreamland Holding LLC
19 W Oxmoor Rd
Birmingham, AL 35209-6409

Telephone: (205) 822-9800
Fax Number: (205) 943-0824
Internet Homepage: dreamlandbbq.com
Company Email: contactus@dreamlandbbq.com
Type of Business: Chain Restaurant Operator
Year Founded: 1958
Systemwide Sales: $12,060,000 (e)
Total Sales: $8,950,000 (e)
Alcohol Sales: 12%
Number of Employees: 150
Average Check: Lunch(18); Dinner(18)
Internet Order Processing: Yes
Internet Sales: 5.00%
Total Units: 10
Trade Names: Dreamland Bar-B-Q (10)
Company-Owned Units: 9
Units Franchised To: 1
Preferred Square Footage: 5,500; 6,000
Preferred Location Types: Freestanding
Alcohol Served: Beer
Primary Menu: Bar-B-Q (10)
Areas of Operation: AL, FL, GA
Type of Foodservice: Casual Dining (10)
Catering Services: Yes
Primary Distributors: (Full Line) SYSCO Food Services of Central Alabama Inc., CALERA, AL

Key Personnel
BETSY MCATEE - CEO; President; Director Real Estate, Design, Franchise Development, Menu Development, Catering

Highlands Bar & Grill
2011 11th Ave S
Birmingham, AL 35205-2801

Telephone: (205) 939-1400
Fax Number: (205) 939-1405
Internet Homepage: bottegarestaurant.com; fonfonbham.com; highlandsbarandgrill.com
Company Email: info@highlandsbarandgrill.com
Type of Business: Chain Restaurant Operator
Year Founded: 1982
Total Sales: $7,336,000 (e)
Alcohol Sales: 15%
Number of Employees: 170
Average Check: Lunch(24); Dinner(48)
Total Units: 4
Trade Names: Bottega Restaurant (1); Cafe Bottega (1); Chez Fonfon (1); Highlands Bar & Grill (1)
Company-Owned Units: 4
Preferred Location Types: Freestanding
Alcohol Served: Beer, Wine, Liquor
Primary Menu: French/Continental (1); Greek/Mediterranean (2); Southern (1)
Areas of Operation: AL
Type of Foodservice: Casual Dining (2); Fine Dining (2)
Primary Distributors: (Full Line) SYSCO Atlanta LLC, COLLEGE PARK, GA

Key Personnel
FRANK STITT - Partner; Executive Chef; General Buyer
PARDIS STITT - Partner; General Manager; General Buyer
JULIE KELLY - Business Manager

Jack's Family Restaurants Inc.
124 W Oxmoor Road
Birmingham, AL 35209-6303

Telephone: (205) 945-8167
Fax Number: (205) 945-9820
Internet Homepage: eatatjacks.com
Type of Business: Chain Restaurant Operator
Year Founded: 1960
Systemwide Sales: $144,434,000 (e)
Total Sales: $153,980,000 (e)
Number of Employees: 3,580
Average Check: Breakfast(12); Lunch(14); Dinner(14)
Total Units: 202
Trade Names: Jack's (202)
Company-Owned Units: 202
Preferred Square Footage: 3,200
Preferred Location Types: Downtown; Freestanding
Primary Menu: American (202)
Areas of Operation: AL, GA, MS, TN
Type of Foodservice: Quick Serve (202)
Foodservice Management Venues: Business & Industry; Prison Feeding; Schools
On-site Distribution Center: Yes
Primary Distributors: (Food) Southeastern Food Merchandisers, PELHAM, AL
Parent Company: Onex Corporation, TORONTO, ON CANADA
Notes: Set to be sold by its parent company Onex Corporation at the end of Q3.

Key Personnel
TODD BARTMESS - CEO
MATT LALLATINE - CFO
BILLIE JO WAARA - Chief Marketing Officer
BRANDON WEAVER - Executive Director
TAYLOR KITCHENS - Director Region
MICHAEL GRECO - Director Development, Training
JACE GORDON - Director Finance
CHERISE THOMAS - Director Human Resources
EMILY ZEIGLER - Director Accounting, Tax
VERONICA DE CAMPOS - Director Digital Marketing
JESSIE AUSTERMANN - Director Recruitment, Talent
DAVID RIDDELL - Regional Director
BRANDY WEATHERMAN - Regional Director
PETE MORANDO - Regional Director
KIM HAWKINS - Regional Director
RONDA REEVES - Regional Director Operations
TREY HUETT - Manager POS/Scanning
CHRISTY MALONE - Manager
RYAN LOVE - Manager Construction
KEVIN COOPER - Supervisor Area
DANA BOZEMAN - Supervisor Area
TERRI SIMPSON - Supervisor Area
MICHAELLE LEATH - Supervisor Area
LOREN KUNZE - Specialist Digital Marketing
KEISA YEARWOOD - Coordinator Human Resources

PJ United Inc.
2300 Resource Dr
Birmingham, AL 35242-2996

Mailing Address: PO Box 380366, BIRMINGHAM, AL, 35238-0366
Telephone: (205) 981-2800
Fax Number: (205) 981-2882
Internet Homepage: mypapajohns.com
Type of Business: Chain Restaurant Operator
Year Founded: 1991
Total Sales: $136,910,000 (e)
Number of Employees: 6,525
Average Check: Lunch(10); Dinner(10)

Internet Order Processing: Yes
Total Units: 101
Trade Names: Papa John's Pizza (101)
Units Franchised From: 101
Preferred Square Footage: 1,200
Preferred Location Types: Freestanding; Stadiums; Strip Mall
Primary Menu: Pizza (101)
Projected Openings: 3
Areas of Operation: AL, IL, LA, MO, MS, OH, TN, TX, UT, VA
Type of Foodservice: Quick Serve (101)
Foodservice Management Venues: College & University; Recreational; Schools
Franchise Affiliation: Papa Johns International Inc., LOUISVILLE, KY
Primary Distributors: (Full Line) US Foods, MONTGOMERY, AL
Parent Company: The Halifax Group, WASHINGTON, DC

Key Personnel
MICHAEL FLEISHMAN - Vice Chairman; Corporate Secretary
DOUGLAS S. STEPHENS - CEO; President; General Buyer
BRAD LEONARD - CFO; Treasurer; Controller; Director Facility/Maintenance
LOUIS ROMANUS - COO; VP
BILL GREEN - VP
JIM ENSIGN - VP Communications
MICHELE EZELL - Director Marketing
BECKY GWARJANSKI - Director Human Resources
REBECCA LAIR - Senior Manager Information Technology
PAULA GREENWELL - Manager Marketing

Revelator Coffee Company
730 1st Ave N
Birmingham, AL 35203-3006

Telephone: (205) 224-5900
Internet Homepage: revelatorcoffee.com
Company Email: info@revelatorcoffee.com
Type of Business: Chain Restaurant Operator
Year Founded: 2014
Total Units: 14
Trade Names: Octane Coffee (6); Revelator (8)
Company-Owned Units: 14
Primary Menu: Coffee (14)
Projected Openings: 3
Areas of Operation: AL, GA, LA, SC, TN
Type of Foodservice: Quick Serve (14)

Key Personnel
MARGARET BARRY - CFO

Subway Franchisee
1321 10th Ave S
Birmingham, AL 35205-7800

Telephone: (205) 939-3100
Type of Business: Chain Restaurant Operator
Total Sales: $721,000 (e)
Total Units: 2
Trade Names: Subway (2)
Units Franchised From: 2
Areas of Operation: AL
Franchise Affiliation: Doctor's Associates Inc., MILFORD, CT

Key Personnel
ANDREW MCMEANS - Owner; General Buyer

T & C Foods Inc.
3270 Morrow Rd
Birmingham, AL 35235-3124

Telephone: (205) 661-0673
Type of Business: Chain Restaurant Operator
Total Sales: $15,109,000 (e)
Total Units: 4
Trade Names: Zaxby's (4)
Units Franchised From: 4
Primary Menu: Chicken (4)
Areas of Operation: AL
Type of Foodservice: Fast Casual (4)
Franchise Affiliation: Zaxby's Franchising Inc., ATHENS, GA

Key Personnel
TIMOTHY P. LEBLANC - President

Yarbrough Companies Inc.
2809 5th Ave S
Birmingham, AL 35233-2819

Telephone: (205) 252-9431
Fax Number: (205) 252-0136
Type of Business: Foodservice Management Operator
Year Founded: 1971
Total Sales: $11,567,000 (e)
Number of Employees: 300
Number of Locations Served: 12
Total Foodservice Mgmt Accounts: 12
Areas of Operation: AL
Type of Foodservice: Quick Serve (12)
Foodservice Management Venues: Business & Industry; College & University; Other; Parks & Recreation
Primary Distributors: (Full Line) Wood-Fruitticher Grocery Co. Inc., BIRMINGHAM, AL

Key Personnel
ROBERT YARBROUGH - CEO; President; Manager Information Systems, Marketing

Yogurt Mountain LLC
402 Industrial Ln
Birmingham, AL 35211-4465

Telephone: (205) 909-1321
Fax Number: (205) 909-1327
Internet Homepage: yogurtmountain.com
Type of Business: Chain Restaurant Operator
Total Sales: $18,196,000 (e)
Total Units: 29
Trade Names: Yogurt Mountain (29)
Company-Owned Units: 20
Units Franchised To: 9
Primary Menu: Snacks (37)
Areas of Operation: AL, AR, FL, GA, LA, MD, MS, NC, OH, SC, TN, TX, WV
Type of Foodservice: Quick Serve (37)
Parent Company: Books-A-Million Inc., BIRMINGHAM, AL

Key Personnel
BEN OLIVER - Division Manager

Ashley Mac's
3147 Green Valley Rd
Cahaba Heights, AL 35243

Telephone: (205) 968-4126
Internet Homepage: ashleymacs.com
Company Email: info@ashleymacs.com
Type of Business: Chain Restaurant Operator
Internet Order Processing: Yes
Total Units: 4
Trade Names: Ashley Mac's (4)
Company-Owned Units: 4
Primary Menu: Sandwiches/Deli (4)
Projected Openings: 1
Areas of Operation: AL
Type of Foodservice: Fast Casual (4)
Catering Services: Yes

Key Personnel
ASHLEY MCMAKIN - Partner; General Buyer
MOLLY MORROW - VP Customer Service

Domino's Franchisee
6845 US Highway 90 Ste 9
Daphne, AL 36526-9545

Telephone: (251) 626-8333
Type of Business: Chain Restaurant Operator
Total Sales: $26,146,000 (e)
Total Units: 13
Trade Names: Domino's (13)
Units Franchised From: 13

Primary Menu: Pizza (13)
Areas of Operation: AL, FL
Type of Foodservice: Quick Serve (13)
Franchise Affiliation: Domino's Pizza Inc, ANN ARBOR, MI

Key Personnel
ROY J. MAY - Owner; General Buyer

S & J Allday Foods, Inc.
6890 US Highway 90
Daphne, AL 36526-9529

Telephone: (251) 625-8723
Fax Number: (251) 625-8703
Type of Business: Chain Restaurant Operator
Total Sales: $5,084,000 (e)
Total Units: 4
Trade Names: Firehouse Subs (4)
Units Franchised From: 4
Primary Menu: Sandwiches/Deli (4)
Areas of Operation: AL
Type of Foodservice: Fast Casual (4)
Franchise Affiliation: Firehouse Restaurant Group Inc., JACKSONVILLE, FL

Key Personnel
SCOTT ALLDAY - President; Partner; General Buyer
JENNIFER ALLDAY - Partner

McCatur Inc.
2014 Central Pkwy SW
Decatur, AL 35601-6837

Telephone: (256) 355-8533
Type of Business: Chain Restaurant Operator
Year Founded: 1980
Total Sales: $42,260,000 (e)
Number of Employees: 600
Average Check: Breakfast(8); Lunch(8); Dinner(10)
Total Units: 9
Trade Names: McDonald's (9)
Units Franchised From: 9
Preferred Square Footage: 2,500; 3,000
Preferred Location Types: Convenience Store/Gas Station; Freestanding
Primary Menu: Hamburger (9)
Areas of Operation: AL
Type of Foodservice: Quick Serve (9)
Franchise Affiliation: McDonald's Corporation, CHICAGO, IL
Primary Distributors: (Full Line) The Martin-Brower Co. LLC, ROSEMONT, IL

Key Personnel
LINDA WALTER - Partner; Director Finance
MAX DAVIS - Director Operations, Facility/Maintenance, Information Systems

Villarreal Pizza Inc
1402 Stratford Rd SE
Decatur, AL 35601-6019

Telephone: (256) 351-1221
Fax Number: (256) 340-3407
Company Email: dominospizzadecatur@hotmail.com
Type of Business: Chain Restaurant Operator
Total Sales: $19,780,000 (e)
Total Units: 10
Trade Names: Domino's (10)
Units Franchised From: 10
Primary Menu: Pizza (10)
Areas of Operation: AL
Type of Foodservice: Quick Serve (10)
Franchise Affiliation: Domino's Pizza Inc, ANN ARBOR, MI

Key Personnel
ANDREW J. VILLARREAL - President; General Buyer

Auntie Anne's Franchise
900 Commons Dr Ste 821
Dothan, AL 36303-2271

Telephone: (334) 671-2771
Type of Business: Chain Restaurant Operator
Total Sales: $1,569,000 (e)
Total Units: 2
Trade Names: Auntie Anne's Hand-Rolled Soft Pretzels (2)
Units Franchised From: 2
Primary Menu: Snacks (2)
Areas of Operation: AL
Type of Foodservice: Quick Serve (2)
Franchise Affiliation: Auntie Anne's Inc., LANCASTER, PA

Key Personnel
MARC TAYLOR - Owner; General Buyer

BBG Specialty Foods Inc.
1676 Whatley Dr
Dothan, AL 36303-1986

Telephone: (334) 793-0083
Fax Number: (334) 702-0302
Type of Business: Chain Restaurant Operator
Year Founded: 1986
Total Sales: $11,964,000 (e)
Number of Employees: 800
Average Check: Lunch(10); Dinner(12)
Total Units: 4
Trade Names: Taco Bell (4)
Units Franchised From: 4
Preferred Square Footage: 800; 2,500
Preferred Location Types: Freestanding; Regional Mall
Primary Menu: Taco (4)
Areas of Operation: AL
Type of Foodservice: Quick Serve (4)
Franchise Affiliation: Taco Bell Corp., IRVINE, CA
Primary Distributors: (Food) McLane/Memphis, MEMPHIS, TN

Key Personnel
CHARLES NAILEN JR - President; General Manager; General Buyer
KAY NAILEN - VP; Director Operations, Facility/Maintenance, Real Estate, Design, Store Fixtures
TONYA MUGLER - Controller

Domino's Franchisee
2115 E Main St Ste 1
Dothan, AL 36301-3050

Telephone: (334) 793-4010
Type of Business: Chain Restaurant Operator
Total Sales: $6,113,000 (e)
Total Units: 3
Trade Names: Domino's (3)
Units Franchised From: 3
Primary Menu: Pizza (3)
Areas of Operation: AL
Type of Foodservice: Quick Serve (3)
Franchise Affiliation: Domino's Pizza Inc, ANN ARBOR, MI

Key Personnel
JERRY LOGAN - Owner

Harrison Foods, LLC
4521 Montgomery Hwy
Dothan, AL 36303

Telephone: (334) 671-2808
Company Email: welcome2moesdothan@yahoo.com
Type of Business: Chain Restaurant Operator
Total Sales: $3,476,000 (e)
Total Units: 2
Trade Names: Moe's Southwest Grill (2)
Units Franchised From: 2
Primary Menu: Southwest/Tex-Mex (2)
Areas of Operation: AL
Type of Foodservice: Fast Casual (2)
Franchise Affiliation: Moe's Southwest Grill LLC, ATLANTA, GA

Key Personnel
STACEY HARRISON - Owner; General Buyer

Larry Blumberg and Associates Inc.
2733 Ross Clark Cir
Dothan, AL 36301-3214

Mailing Address: PO Box 5566, DOTHAN, AL, 36302-5566
Telephone: (334) 793-6855
Fax Number: (334) 793-1707
Internet Homepage: lbaproperties.com
Company Email: info@lbaproperties.com
Type of Business: Foodservice Operations - Hotel/Motels
Year Founded: 1972
Total Sales: $180,980,000 (e)
Alcohol Sales: 25%
Number of Employees: 2,028
Foodservice Sales: $27,147,000 (e)
Total Units: 78
Restaurants in Hotels: 70
Trade Names: Courtyard by Marriott (16); Delta Hotel (1); Fairfield Inn (5); Hampton Inn (12); Hilton Garden Inn (10); Holiday Inn (1); Home 2 Suites (10); Homewood Suites (5); Hyatt Place (1); Residence Inn by Marriott (10); Springhill Suites (3); Staybridge Suites (1); Townplace Suites (3)
Company-Owned Units: 70
Alcohol Served: Beer, Wine, Liquor
Projected Openings: 1
Projected Remodelings: 2
Areas of Operation: AL, FL, GA, LA, MS, NC, SC, TN, TX, VA
Type of Foodservice: Casual Dining (70)
Primary Distributors: (Food) SYSCO Food Services of South Florida Inc., MEDLEY, FL
Notes: The company derives approximately 85% of its revenue from hotel operations.

Key Personnel
LARRY BLUMBERG - Chairman; CEO
BEAU BENTON - President
STEPHEN SMITH - CFO; VP Accounting
FARRAH ADAMS - COO
JUDY CLUCK - VP Marketing, Sales
TERRELL HODNETT - VP Finance

Seven Restaurants
117 Hidden Glen Way
Dothan, AL 36303-2951

Telephone: (954) 909-8141
Internet Homepage: goldcollc.com
Type of Business: Chain Restaurant Operator
Year Founded: 1980
Total Sales: $104,680,000 (e)
Number of Employees: 1,960
Average Check: Breakfast(8); Lunch(8); Dinner(10)
Total Units: 46
Trade Names: Burger King (46)
Units Franchised From: 46
Preferred Square Footage: 3,000
Preferred Location Types: Freestanding
Primary Menu: Hamburger (46)
Areas of Operation: FL
Type of Foodservice: Quick Serve (46)
Franchise Affiliation: Burger King Worldwide Inc., MIAMI, FL
Primary Distributors: (Equipment) QualServ Corporation, FORT SMITH, AR; (Food) Reinhart FoodService, AUSTELL, GA; (Supplies) QualServ Corporation, FORT SMITH, AR
Parent Company: PNC Riverarch Capital, PITTSBURGH, PA

Key Personnel
LEO LEON - CEO; President
BOB FARGO - Chief Development Officer
ANGELA FOX - VP Operations

Domino's Franchisee
705 Glover Ave
Enterprise, AL 36330-2015

Telephone: (334) 393-5505
Type of Business: Chain Restaurant Operator
Total Sales: $6,111,000 (e)
Total Units: 3
Trade Names: Domino's (3)
Units Franchised From: 3
Primary Menu: Pizza (3)
Areas of Operation: AL
Type of Foodservice: Quick Serve (3)
Franchise Affiliation: Domino's Pizza Inc, ANN ARBOR, MI

Key Personnel
WALID J. SAFADI - Owner; General Buyer

LA Cluckers Inc.
623 Boll Weevil Cir
Enterprise, AL 36330-2733

Telephone: (334) 475-4149
Type of Business: Chain Restaurant Operator
Total Sales: $15,197,000 (e)
Total Units: 4
Trade Names: Zaxby's (4)
Units Franchised From: 4
Primary Menu: Chicken (4)
Areas of Operation: AL
Type of Foodservice: Fast Casual (4)
Franchise Affiliation: Zaxby's Franchising Inc., ATHENS, GA

Key Personnel
NICK CARTER - Partner; General Buyer
SCOTT ROLAND - Partner

Joy Enterprises, Inc.
1074 N Eufaula Ave
Eufaula, AL 36027-5538

Mailing Address: PO Box 1116, EUFAULA, AL, 36072-1116
Telephone: (334) 616-6213
Fax Number: (334) 687-7732
Type of Business: Chain Restaurant Operator
Total Sales: $9,280,000 (e)
Average Check: Dinner(14)
Total Units: 16
Trade Names: Subway (16)
Units Franchised From: 16
Primary Menu: Sandwiches/Deli (16)
Areas of Operation: AL
Type of Foodservice: Quick Serve (16)
Franchise Affiliation: Doctor's Associates Inc., MILFORD, CT

Key Personnel
MARK JOY - President; General Buyer
BRENT PETERSON - President
MELVA JOY - VP; General Buyer

Domino's Franchisee
7201 Aaron Aronov Dr Ste 300
Fairfield, AL 35064-1831

Telephone: (205) 923-2626
Type of Business: Chain Restaurant Operator
Total Sales: $10,400,000 (e)
Total Units: 5
Trade Names: Domino's (5)
Units Franchised From: 5
Primary Menu: Pizza (5)
Areas of Operation: AL
Type of Foodservice: Quick Serve (5)
Franchise Affiliation: Domino's Pizza Inc, ANN ARBOR, MI

Key Personnel
MOHAMMED DAWOUD - Owner; General Buyer

Panini Pete's
42 1/2 S Section St
Fairhope, AL 36532-2226

Telephone: (251) 929-0122
Internet Homepage: paninipetes.com
Type of Business: Chain Restaurant Operator
Internet Order Processing: Yes
Total Units: 3
Trade Names: Panini Pete's (3)
Company-Owned Units: 2
Units Franchised To: 1
Primary Menu: Sandwiches/Deli (3)
Areas of Operation: AL, WV

Type of Foodservice: Fast Casual (3)

Key Personnel
PETE BLOHME - Founder; Executive Chef; General Buyer

RPH Management, Inc
204 Temple Ave S
Fayette, AL 35555-2714

Mailing Address: Po Box 967, FAYETTE, AL, 35555
Telephone: (205) 932-8691
Fax Number: (877) 847-9686
Type of Business: Chain Restaurant Operator
Total Sales: $19,717,000 (e)
Number of Employees: 300
Total Units: 4
Trade Names: McDonald's (4)
Units Franchised From: 4
Preferred Square Footage: 2,500
Preferred Location Types: Freestanding
Primary Menu: Hamburger (4)
Projected Remodelings: 1
Areas of Operation: AL
Type of Foodservice: Quick Serve (4)
Franchise Affiliation: McDonald's Corporation, CHICAGO, IL

Key Personnel
RICHARD HANNA - President; General Buyer

Markor Enterprises
1126 Bradshaw Dr
Florence, AL 35630-1438

Telephone: (256) 764-3335
Fax Number: (256) 764-3487
Company Email: flmarkor@aol.com
Type of Business: Chain Restaurant Operator
Total Sales: $27,790,000 (e)
Number of Employees: 257
Average Check: Dinner(12)
Total Units: 6
Trade Names: McDonald's (6)
Units Franchised From: 6
Preferred Square Footage: 2,500
Preferred Location Types: Downtown; Freestanding
Primary Menu: Hamburger (6)
Areas of Operation: AL
Type of Foodservice: Quick Serve (6)
Franchise Affiliation: McDonald's Corporation, CHICAGO, IL

Key Personnel
DAVID FIELDS - President; General Buyer
DAVID CRUZ - Director Operations

I F Bledsoe
1715 Dogtown Rd SE
Fort Payne, AL 35967-7287

Mailing Address: PO Box 680553, FORT PAYNE, AL, 35968
Telephone: (256) 845-6244
Type of Business: Chain Restaurant Operator
Total Sales: $15,113,000 (e)
Average Check: Dinner(12)
Total Units: 3
Trade Names: McDonald's (3)
Units Franchised From: 3
Preferred Location Types: Freestanding
Primary Menu: Hamburger (3)
Areas of Operation: AL
Type of Foodservice: Quick Serve (3)
Franchise Affiliation: McDonald's Corporation, CHICAGO, IL

Key Personnel
DAVID BLEDSOE - President; Partner
PEGGY BLEDSOE - Partner; Director Human Resources

King Kohl's Food Services Inc
1616 Gunter Ave
Guntersville, AL 35976-1820

Telephone: (256) 582-8438
Fax Number: (256) 582-3213
Type of Business: Chain Restaurant Operator
Total Sales: $5,810,000 (e)
Total Units: 3
Trade Names: KFC (3)
Units Franchised From: 3
Primary Menu: Chicken (3)
Areas of Operation: AL
Type of Foodservice: Quick Serve (3)
Franchise Affiliation: KFC Corporation, LOUISVILLE, KY

Key Personnel
MAURICE L. KOHL - President; Owner; General Buyer
DOUG GALASZEWSKI - Manager Media, Production

CLP Corp.
121 Summit Pkwy
Homewood, AL 35209-4707

Telephone: (256) 236-5224
Fax Number: (205) 942-1218
Type of Business: Chain Restaurant Operator
Year Founded: 1962
Total Sales: $77,410,000 (e)
Number of Employees: 220

Average Check: Breakfast(8); Lunch(8); Dinner(8)
Total Units: 16
Trade Names: McDonald's (16)
Units Franchised From: 16
Preferred Square Footage: 3,500
Preferred Location Types: Discount Dept. Stores; Freestanding
Primary Menu: Hamburger (16)
Areas of Operation: AL
Type of Foodservice: Quick Serve (16)
Franchise Affiliation: McDonald's Corporation, CHICAGO, IL

Key Personnel
JIM BLACK - President
RICHARD WOOD - CFO; Treasurer; Director Information Systems, Loss Prevention, Risk Management
BYRON FRENCH - VP Operations, Purchasing; Manager Facility/Maintenance
DEB MCCULLEY - Manager Purchasing

Milos Hamburgers
828 Columbiana Rd Ste 130
Homewood, AL 35209-6112

Telephone: (205) 871-2000
Fax Number: (205) 871-2120
Internet Homepage: miloshamburgers.com
Company Email: notices@miloshamburgers.com
Type of Business: Chain Restaurant Operator
Year Founded: 1985
Total Sales: $59,530,000 (e)
Number of Employees: 645
Average Check: Lunch(12); Dinner(14)
Internet Order Processing: Yes
Internet Sales: 2.00%
Total Units: 20
Trade Names: Milo's Hamburgers (20)
Company-Owned Units: 20
Preferred Square Footage: 2,500
Preferred Location Types: Freestanding; Strip Mall
Primary Menu: Hamburger (20)
Areas of Operation: AL
Type of Foodservice: Quick Serve (20)
Primary Distributors: (Food) US Foods, MONTGOMERY, AL

Key Personnel
TOM DEKLE - CEO; President; General Buyer
DONALD WOOD - CFO
BOBBY LONG - General Manager
MARY PROCTOR - Director Marketing

SAW's BBQ, LLC
1008 Oxmoor Rd
Homewood, AL 35209-5318

Telephone: (205) 879-1937
Internet Homepage: sawsbbq.com
Company Email: catering@sawsbbq.com
Type of Business: Chain Restaurant Operator
Year Founded: 2009
Total Units: 5
Trade Names: Saw's BBQ (2); SAW's Juke Joint (1); SAW's Soul Kitchen (1); Saw's Street Kitchen (1)
Company-Owned Units: 5
Primary Menu: Bar-B-Q (4); Southern (1)
Projected Openings: 1
Areas of Operation: AL
Type of Foodservice: Casual Dining (5)

Key Personnel
MIKE WILSON - Founder; Partner
BRANDON CAIN - Partner; Executive Chef
DOUG SMITH - Partner

Full Moon BBQ
3228 Lorna Rd
Hoover, AL 35216-5487

Telephone: (205) 822-0300
Fax Number: (205) 822-0800
Internet Homepage: fullmoonbbq.com
Company Email: comments@fullmoonbbq.com
Type of Business: Chain Restaurant Operator
Year Founded: 1950
Total Sales: $14,390,000 (e)
Number of Employees: 150
Average Check: Lunch(10); Dinner(10)
Total Units: 15
Trade Names: Full Moon Bar-B-Que (15)
Company-Owned Units: 15
Alcohol Served: Beer
Primary Menu: Bar-B-Q (15)
Areas of Operation: AL
Type of Foodservice: Casual Dining (15)

Key Personnel
DAVID MALUFF - Partner
JOE MALUFF - Partner; General Manager; Executive Chef; General Buyer

Gulf States Restaurant Management LLC
1851 Montgomery Hwy Ste 113
Hoover, AL 35244-2505

Telephone: (205) 987-7115
Type of Business: Chain Restaurant Operator
Total Sales: $5,818,000 (e)
Total Units: 4
Trade Names: Jersey Mike's Subs (4)
Units Franchised From: 4
Primary Menu: Sandwiches/Deli (4)
Areas of Operation: AL
Type of Foodservice: Quick Serve (4)
Franchise Affiliation: Jersey Mike's Franchise Systems, MANASQUAN, NJ

Key Personnel
CHRISTOPHER M. DECKER - Partner; General Buyer
PATRICK DECKER - Partner

JFC Development LLC
5984 S Fork Dr
Hoover, AL 35244

Telephone: (334) 695-1271
Type of Business: Chain Restaurant Operator
Total Sales: $13,080,000 (e)
Total Units: 11
Trade Names: Firehouse Subs (11)
Company-Owned Units: 11
Primary Menu: Sandwiches/Deli (11)
Type of Foodservice: Fast Casual (11)
Franchise Affiliation: Firehouse Restaurant Group Inc., JACKSONVILLE, FL

Key Personnel
JAMES CAIN - President; General Buyer

Right Way Restaurants Inc
2105 Drake Ave SW
Huntsville, AL 35805-5107

Mailing Address: PO Box 466, HUNTSVILLE, AL, 35804-0466
Telephone: (256) 880-7723
Fax Number: (256) 880-0404
Type of Business: Chain Restaurant Operator
Number of Employees: 250
Total Units: 5
Trade Names: Steak-Out Char-Broiled Delivery (5)
Units Franchised From: 5
Primary Menu: Steak (5)
Areas of Operation: AL
Type of Foodservice: Quick Serve (5)
Franchise Affiliation: Steak-Out Franchising Inc., ROSWELL, GA

Key Personnel
DAVID MARTIN - President; General Buyer
DEE DEE LYLES - Director Marketing
DANNY MARTIN - Director Training
DEBRA NORTON - Specialist Accounting

Schlotzsky's Franchisee
11120 Memorial Pkwy SW
Huntsville, AL 35803-2122

Telephone: (256) 650-6300
Type of Business: Chain Restaurant Operator
Total Sales: $1,519,000 (e)
Total Units: 2
Trade Names: Schlotzsky's (2)
Units Franchised From: 2
Primary Menu: Sandwiches/Deli (2)
Areas of Operation: AL
Type of Foodservice: Quick Serve (2)
Franchise Affiliation: Schlotzsky's Deli, HUNTSVILLE, AL

Key Personnel
KUMAR PATEL - Owner; General Buyer
ALEX BROWN - Senior Director Brand Marketing
EVAN HOGAN - Senior Director Franchise Operations
TEE MORGAN - Director Marketing
SCOTT BLACK - Director Operations
CHUCK WOOD - Director Operations

Valley Pizza Inc.
3224 Bob Wallace Ave SW
Huntsville, AL 35805-4006

Telephone: (256) 534-7300
Fax Number: (256) 534-7388
Internet Homepage: dominos.com
Type of Business: Chain Restaurant Operator
Year Founded: 1982
Total Sales: $30,000,000 (e)
Number of Employees: 425
Average Check: Lunch(14); Dinner(22)
Total Units: 15
Trade Names: Domino's (15)
Units Franchised From: 15
Preferred Square Footage: 1,500
Preferred Location Types: Freestanding; Strip Mall
Primary Menu: Pizza (15)
Areas of Operation: AL, TN
Type of Foodservice: Quick Serve (15)
Franchise Affiliation: Domino's Pizza Inc, ANN ARBOR, MI
Primary Distributors: (Food) Domino's Distribution Center, KENNESAW, GA; (Supplies) Domino's Distribution Center, KENNESAW, GA

Key Personnel
CYNTHIA STREAMS - CFO; VP Finance; Controller
MICHAEL DOHERTY - VP Operations; Director Human Resources
TOMMIE SCOTT - Manager Administration

CRISSY HUNT - Supervisor Franchising

Golden Rule Franchising Inc.
2504 Crestwood Blvd
Irondale, AL 35210

Telephone: (205) 965-2678
Internet Homepage: goldenrulebbq.com
Company Email:
 FEEDBACK@GoldenRuleBBQ.com
Type of Business: Chain Restaurant Operator
Year Founded: 2009
Systemwide Sales: $6,125,000 (e)
Total Sales: $9,310,000 (e)
Alcohol Sales: 5%
Number of Employees: 90
Average Check: Breakfast(12); Lunch(12); Dinner(12)
Internet Order Processing: Yes
Total Units: 9
Trade Names: Golden Rule Bar-B-Q and Grill (9)
Units Franchised To: 9
Preferred Square Footage: 5,500; 6,000
Preferred Location Types: Community Mall; Freestanding; Regional Mall
Alcohol Served: Beer, Wine, Liquor
Primary Menu: Bar-B-Q (9)
Areas of Operation: AL
Type of Foodservice: Casual Dining (9)
Catering Services: Yes
Primary Distributors: (Food) Red Diamond Inc., MOODY, AL

Key Personnel
JEFF MILLER - Owner

Aloha Hospitality International
26801 Railroad Ave
Loxley, AL 36551-7519

Telephone: (251) 424-1240
Fax Number: (251) 424-1241
Internet Homepage: alohahospitality.com
Type of Business: Chain Restaurant Operator
Year Founded: 1981
Systemwide Sales: $7,882,000 (e)
Total Sales: $2,914,000 (e)
Alcohol Sales: 10%
Number of Employees: 825
Average Check: Lunch(14); Dinner(24)
Internet Order Processing: Yes
Total Units: 11
Trade Names: Bob's Victory Grill (10); Dauphin's (1)
Company-Owned Units: 10
Units Franchised To: 4
Preferred Square Footage: 6,000
Preferred Location Types: Freestanding
Alcohol Served: Beer, Wine, Liquor
Primary Menu: American (4); Pizza (7)
Areas of Operation: AL
Type of Foodservice: Casual Dining (11)
Catering Services: Yes
Primary Distributors: (Food) US Foods, MONTGOMERY, AL

Key Personnel
ROBERT BAUMHOWER - CEO; President; General Buyer
BOB BAUMHOWER - President
DON PARKER - General Manager
CHRIS KOENIG - General Manager
SONYA CHAPPELL - General Manager
RICHARD AMBROSE - General Manager
ALEX CONNER - General Manager
XAVIER CRAWLEY - General Manager
DONYA DRAKEFORD - General Manager
REMY HELU - General Manager
CHARLIE VATELLA - General Manager
HAROLD JACKSON - Executive Chef
GEORGE BAILEY - Executive Chef
GALEN COLEMAN - Executive Chef
WILLIE LOWE - Executive Chef
LORENZO MILLER - Executive Chef
DARREN MITCHELL - Executive Chef
KIM ROGERS - Executive Chef
IAN NICHOLSON - Executive Chef
ANGEL MERRY - Director
CINDY MYLES - Manager Accounting

Jubilee Restaurant Group LLC
30181 State Highway 59
Loxley, AL 36551-3154

Telephone: (251) 964-4041
Internet Homepage: jubileerestaurants.com
Type of Business: Chain Restaurant Operator
Total Sales: $40,530,000 (e)
Total Units: 26
Trade Names: Five Guys Burgers & Fries (13); Uncle Maddio's Pizza (13)
Units Franchised From: 26
Primary Menu: Hamburger (13); Pizza (13)
Areas of Operation: AL, FL, LA, MS, TN
Type of Foodservice: Fast Casual (26)
Franchise Affiliation: Five Guys Holdings Inc., LORTON, VA

Key Personnel
ROD BISH - Director Operations

H&R Restaurants LLC
8572 Madison Blvd
Madison, AL 35758-2621

Telephone: (850) 261-5344
Type of Business: Chain Restaurant Operator
Total Sales: $10,460,000 (e)
Number of Employees: 60
Total Units: 9
Trade Names: Firehouse Subs (9)
Units Franchised From: 9
Preferred Square Footage: 1,500
Preferred Location Types: Strip Mall
Primary Menu: Sandwiches/Deli (9)
Areas of Operation: AL
Type of Foodservice: Fast Casual (9)
Franchise Affiliation: Firehouse Restaurant Group Inc., JACKSONVILLE, FL

Key Personnel
LARRY RICHARD - President; General Buyer

Logos Pizza Inc.
8000 Madison Blvd STE D106
Madison, AL 35758

Telephone: (256) 772-6789
Type of Business: Chain Restaurant Operator
Total Sales: $4,635,000 (e)
Number of Employees: 90
Average Check: Lunch(8); Dinner(20)
Total Units: 1
Trade Names: Donatos Pizza (1)
Units Franchised From: 1
Preferred Location Types: Freestanding; Strip Mall
Primary Menu: Pizza (1)
Areas of Operation: AL
Type of Foodservice: Family Restaurant (1)
Catering Services: Yes
Franchise Affiliation: Donatos Pizzeria LLC, COLUMBUS, OH

Key Personnel
NEIL JENSEN - President; Partner
JIM WEINBERGER - Partner; General Buyer

Mamie Raines Inc.
55 Kelley Blvd
Millbrook, AL 36054-2224

Mailing Address: P.O. Box 230788, Montgomery, AL, 36123
Telephone: (334) 285-6933
Type of Business: Chain Restaurant Operator
Total Sales: $27,960,000 (e)
Total Units: 8
Trade Names: Zaxby's (8)
Units Franchised From: 8
Primary Menu: Chicken (8)
Areas of Operation: AL
Type of Foodservice: Fast Casual (8)
Franchise Affiliation: Zaxby's Franchising Inc., ATHENS, GA

Key Personnel
DAVID R. CONNOR - President; Partner;

General Buyer
BRANDON MILLER - Partner

Belote Foods LLC
950 Schillinger Rd S
Mobile, AL 36695-8913

Telephone: (251) 607-7645
Fax Number: (251) 776-6279
Type of Business: Chain Restaurant Operator
Total Sales: $17,570,000 (e)
Number of Employees: 50
Average Check: Lunch(10); Dinner(16)
Total Units: 5
Trade Names: Zaxby's (5)
Units Franchised From: 5
Preferred Location Types: Freestanding
Primary Menu: Chicken (5)
Areas of Operation: AL
Type of Foodservice: Fast Casual (5)
Franchise Affiliation: Zaxby's Franchising Inc., ATHENS, GA

Key Personnel
REGGIE BELOTE - President; General Buyer
JOHANNE BELOTE - Owner; General Manager; General Buyer
JEREMY GILL - General Manager
JOANNIE BELOTE - Director Marketing-Training
CHARLES R. BELOTE - Manager Operations

Foosackly's
324 S University Blvd
Mobile, AL 36609-2909

Telephone: (251) 380-2001
Fax Number: (866) 674-0139
Internet Homepage: foosacklys.net
Company Email: info@foosacklys.net
Type of Business: Chain Restaurant Operator
Total Sales: $2,924,000 (e)
Number of Employees: 172
Average Check: Dinner(12)
Internet Order Processing: Yes
Total Units: 12
Trade Names: Foosackly's (12)
Company-Owned Units: 12
Preferred Location Types: Freestanding; Strip Mall
Primary Menu: Chicken (12)
Areas of Operation: AL
Type of Foodservice: Quick Serve (12)

Key Personnel
WILL M. FUSAIOTTI - President; General Manager; General Buyer
J D BAXTER - CFO
NICK BETTNER - General Manager
AMBER BOURGEOIS - General Manager
ERIC BRECHTEL - General Manager
JOHN BUNKLEY II - General Manager

KEITH NOBLE - General Manager

GPF, Inc.
PO Box 180399
Mobile, AL 36618-0399

Mailing Address: PO Box 180399, MOBILE, 36618
Telephone: (251) 402-5951
Type of Business: Chain Restaurant Operator
Total Sales: $1,741,000 (e)
Total Units: 3
Trade Names: Godfather's Pizza (3)
Units Franchised From: 3
Primary Menu: Pizza (3)
Areas of Operation: AL
Type of Foodservice: Casual Dining (3)
Franchise Affiliation: Godfather's Pizza, Inc., OMAHA, NE

Key Personnel
SANDRA FUQUA - President; General Buyer

Jim Barnes Enterprises Inc.
6110 Grelot Rd
Mobile, AL 36609-3640

Telephone: (251) 478-3223
Fax Number: (251) 479-0735
Type of Business: Chain Restaurant Operator
Year Founded: 1993
Total Sales: $20,205,000 (e)
Number of Employees: 200
Average Check: Breakfast(8); Lunch(10); Dinner(10)
Total Units: 4
Trade Names: McDonald's (4)
Units Franchised From: 4
Preferred Square Footage: 3,000
Preferred Location Types: Convenience Store/Gas Station; Freestanding; Regional Mall
Primary Menu: Hamburger (4)
Projected Remodelings: 1
Areas of Operation: AL
Type of Foodservice: Quick Serve (4)
Franchise Affiliation: McDonald's Corporation, CHICAGO, IL
Primary Distributors: (Full Line) The Martin-Brower Co., PORT ALLEN, LA

Key Personnel
JAMES E. BARNES - President; Partner; Director Real Estate, Design; General Buyer
WILLIAM BARNES - Partner; Director Operations, Facility/Maintenance

John (Eddie) Webster
390 Schillinger Rd S Unit A
Mobile, AL 36695-8960

Telephone: (251) 633-0303
Type of Business: Chain Restaurant Operator
Total Sales: $3,518,000 (e)
Total Units: 2
Trade Names: Moe's Southwest Grill (2)
Units Franchised From: 2
Primary Menu: Southwest/Tex-Mex (2)
Areas of Operation: AL
Type of Foodservice: Fast Casual
Franchise Affiliation: Moe's Southwest Grill LLC, ATLANTA, GA

Key Personnel
JOHN WEBSTER - Owner; General Buyer

Pollman's Bake Shop Inc.
750 S Broad St
Mobile, AL 36603-1116

Telephone: (251) 438-1511
Fax Number: (251) 438-9461
Type of Business: Chain Restaurant Operator
Year Founded: 1941
Total Sales: $2,158,000 (e)
Number of Employees: 40
Average Check: Breakfast(8); Lunch(8);
Total Units: 3
Trade Names: Pollman's Bake Shop (3)
Company-Owned Units: 3
Preferred Square Footage: 800; 1,000
Preferred Location Types: Freestanding; Strip Mall
Primary Menu: Snacks (3)
Areas of Operation: AL
Type of Foodservice: Quick Serve (3)
On-site Distribution Center: Yes
Primary Distributors: (Full Line) SYSCO Corporation, HOUSTON, TX

Key Personnel
FRED POLLMAN - President; Executive Chef; General Buyer

Rock N Roll Sushi
273 S McGregor Ave
Mobile, AL 36608

Telephone: (251) 287-0445
Internet Homepage: rnrsushi.com
Type of Business: Chain Restaurant Operator
Year Founded: 2010
Total Sales: $15,440,000 (e)
Total Units: 55
Trade Names: Rock N Roll Sushi (55)
Company-Owned Units: 5

Units Franchised To: 50
Primary Menu: Asian (55)
Projected Openings: 25
Type of Foodservice: Casual Dining (55)

Key Personnel
LANCE HALLMARK - Founder; President; Owner
GERRY A. MACH - Founder; Owner
CRAIG LEMIEUX - CEO
JOSEPH C. RAGSDALE - Owner; Senior VP Business Development
RYAN HALLMARK - Owner; VP Development
IKA NASA - Corporate Chef Training; Director Training

Wayne's Fast Food Corporation
830 Dauphin Island Pkwy
Mobile, AL 36606-4230

Telephone: (251) 471-2491
Fax Number: (251) 471-1954
Internet Homepage: hartsfriedchicken.com
Type of Business: Chain Restaurant Operator
Year Founded: 1965
Total Sales: $6,472,000 (e)
Number of Employees: 80
Average Check: Lunch(8); Dinner(8)
Total Units: 5
Trade Names: Hart's Fried Chicken (5)
Company-Owned Units: 5
Preferred Location Types: Freestanding
Primary Menu: Chicken (5)
Areas of Operation: AL
Type of Foodservice: Quick Serve (5)
On-site Distribution Center: Yes
Primary Distributors: (Supplies) Bay Paper Co, MOBILE, AL

Key Personnel
MATTHEW JOHNSON - President; General Manager; Executive Chef; General Buyer
KEVIN HEPLER - VP

Chappy's Deli
3815 Interstate Ct Ste 102B
Montgomery, AL 36109-5224

Telephone: (334) 277-6590
Fax Number: (334) 277-6593
Internet Homepage: chappysdeli.com
Type of Business: Chain Restaurant Operator
Year Founded: 1986
Total Sales: $26,630,000 (e)
Alcohol Sales: 2%
Number of Employees: 300
Average Check: Lunch(10); Dinner(10)
Internet Order Processing: Yes
Internet Sales: 1.00%
Total Units: 5
Trade Names: Chappy's Deli (5)
Company-Owned Units: 5
Preferred Square Footage: 5,500; 6,000
Preferred Location Types: Institution (college/hospital)
Alcohol Served: Beer
Primary Menu: Sandwiches/Deli (5)
Areas of Operation: AL, MO
Type of Foodservice: Casual Dining (5)
Catering Services: Yes
Primary Distributors: (Full Line) Wood-Fruitticher Grocery Co. Inc., BIRMINGHAM, AL

Key Personnel
DAVID BARRANCO - President; Director Finance, Purchasing, Facility/Maintenance, Real Estate, Design, Human Resources
GALEN RUMP - General Manager
MICHAEL CASTANZA - Executive Chef; Director Operations; Manager Operations; General Buyer
LAURA FEELY - Manager Human Resources
BEN BARRANCO - Manager; Designer

Montgomery Catering
770 Washington Ave Ste 117
Montgomery, AL 36104-3816

Telephone: (334) 269-6090
Fax Number: (334) 832-7383
Internet Homepage: montgomery-catering.com
Type of Business: Chain Restaurant Operator
Year Founded: 1992
Total Sales: $2,457,000 (e)
Alcohol Sales: 10%
Number of Employees: 45
Average Check: Dinner(10)
Total Units: 2
Trade Names: Commerce Cafe (1); RSA Plaza Terrace & Grill (1)
Company-Owned Units: 2
Preferred Square Footage: 7,000
Preferred Location Types: Freestanding, Office Complex
Alcohol Served: Beer, Wine, Liquor
Primary Menu: American (2)
Areas of Operation: AL
Type of Foodservice: Cafeteria (1); In-Store Feeder (1)
Catering Services: Yes
Primary Distributors: (Full Line) US Foods, MONTGOMERY, AL

Key Personnel
RANDY GAINEY - Partner; General Manager; General Buyer
JOHNNY SULLIVAN - Partner; General Manager; General Buyer

▲
Chester's International LLC
2020 Cahaba Rd
Mountain Brk, AL 35223-1179

Telephone: (205) 949-4690
Fax Number: (205) 298-0332
Internet Homepage: chestersinternational.com
Company Email: info@chestersinternational.com
Type of Business: Chain Restaurant Operator
Year Founded: 2002
Systemwide Sales: $190,000,000 (e)
Total Sales: $42,540,000 (e)
Average Check: Lunch(8); Dinner(8)
Internet Order Processing: Yes
Internet Sales: 1.00%
Total Units: 505
Trade Names: Chester's (505)
Units Franchised To: 505
Preferred Square Footage: 400; 1,200
Preferred Location Types: Airports; Convenience Store/Gas Station; Grocery Stores; Strip Mall; Travel Plazas
Primary Menu: Chicken (505)
Projected Openings: 10
Areas of Operation: AK, AL, CA, CO, FL, GA, IA, IL, IN, KY, LA, MA, MD, MI, NJ, NM, NV, NY, OH, PA, PR, SC, SD, TN, TX, VA, WY
Type of Foodservice: Quick Serve (505)
Catering Services: Yes
Primary Distributors: (Full Line) McFarling Foods, INDIANAPOLIS, IN; (Full Line) Reinhart FoodService, BOWLING GREEN, KY; (Full Line) Brown Foodservice Inc., LOUISA, KY; (Full Line) H.T. Hackney Co., NEWTON, NC
Notes: Total sales includes revenue derived from the distribution of breading and packaging products. The franchising business operates as Chester's and Chester's On The Fly; the latter is a grab-and-go concept that operates from a modular kiosk inside an existing business. The store count shown is for franchised locations only and does not include licensed locations operating as Chester Fried or the Chester's Chicken on the Fly units.

Key Personnel
TED GILES - CEO; President; General Buyer
WILLIAM CULPEPPER - VP Marketing
MARYBETH EASON - Coordinator Operations

†
Southern Foodservice Management Inc.
431 Office Park Dr 1st Floor
Mountain Brk, AL 35223-2441

Telephone: (205) 871-8000
Fax Number: (205) 871-8020
Internet Homepage: southernfoodservice.com
Company Email:

info@southernfoodservice.com
Type of Business: Foodservice Management Operator
Year Founded: 1951
Total Sales: $110,927,000 (e)
Number of Employees: 1,050
Number of Locations Served: 70
Total Foodservice Mgmt Accounts: 70
Areas of Operation: AL
Type of Foodservice: Cafeteria (50); Vending machines (20)
Foodservice Management Venues: Business & Industry; College & University; Health Care; Transportation
Primary Distributors: (Full Line) SYSCO Food Services of Houston Inc., HOUSTON, TX

Key Personnel
MICHAEL BARCLAY - President
WALTER E. BERRY - Exec VP
FRED HOEFER III - Senior VP Operations; Director Purchasing, Menu Development
TOMMY PARSONS - Controller; Director Risk Management
RANDY WILSON - Director Purchasing
LAURA LAIRD - Manager Human Resources

Kentucky Fried Chicken of Colbert County Inc.
1910 Woodward Ave
Muscle Shoals, AL 35661-2846

Telephone: (256) 381-5755
Fax Number: (256) 381-9326
Type of Business: Chain Restaurant Operator
Year Founded: 1966
Total Sales: $5,784,000 (e)
Number of Employees: 55
Average Check: Lunch(12); Dinner(12)
Total Units: 3
Trade Names: KFC (3)
Units Franchised From: 3
Preferred Square Footage: 1,800
Preferred Location Types: Freestanding
Primary Menu: Chicken (3)
Areas of Operation: AL
Type of Foodservice: Quick Serve (3)
Franchise Affiliation: KFC Corporation, LOUISVILLE, KY
Primary Distributors: (Food) Ben E Keith, ELBA, AL; (Supplies) Ben E Keith, ELBA, AL

Key Personnel
JEFF CLARK - President; General Buyer
CHARLES CLARK - Owner; Controller; Manager Advertising
TIM CLARK - VP
DON TIDWELL - General Manager; General Buyer

Brick & Spoon
24705 Canal Road
Orange Beach, AL 36561

Telephone: (251) 981-7772
Internet Homepage: brickandspoon.com
Type of Business: Chain Restaurant Operator
Year Founded: 2020
Total Sales: $4,200,000 (e)
Total Units: 11
Trade Names: Brick & Spoon (11)
Company-Owned Units: 11
Primary Menu: American (11)
Type of Foodservice: Casual Dining (11)

Key Personnel
KENTRAIL DAVIS - Founder

Tacky Jacks Seafood Restaurant and Tavern
27206 Safe Harbor Dr
Orange Beach, AL 36561

Telephone: (251) 981-4144
Internet Homepage: tackyjacks.com
Type of Business: Chain Restaurant Operator
Year Founded: 1979
Total Units: 3
Trade Names: Tacky Jacks (3)
Company-Owned Units: 2
Units Franchised To: 1
Preferred Square Footage: 7,000
Preferred Location Types: Freestanding
Primary Menu: Seafood (3)
Areas of Operation: AL
Type of Foodservice: Casual Dining (3)

Key Personnel
GEORGE SKIPPER III - Owner
KEN KICHLER - CFO
SUSAN SIZEMORE - Manager Marketing, Event Planning

Domino's Franchisee
2681 Pelham Pkwy
Pelham, AL 35124-1354

Telephone: (205) 663-9425
Type of Business: Chain Restaurant Operator
Total Sales: $12,408,000 (e)
Total Units: 6
Trade Names: Domino's (6)
Units Franchised From: 6
Primary Menu: Pizza (6)
Areas of Operation: AL
Type of Foodservice: Quick Serve (6)
Franchise Affiliation: Domino's Pizza Inc, ANN ARBOR, MI

Key Personnel
JAMES MIDGETTE - Owner; General Buyer

DBR Inc
508 Fiveash Oak
Prattville, AL 36066-3609

Telephone: (334) 361-0041
Type of Business: Chain Restaurant Operator
Total Sales: $43,210,000 (e)
Average Check: Dinner(12)
Total Units: 9
Trade Names: McDonald's (9)
Units Franchised From: 9
Preferred Square Footage: 2,500
Preferred Location Types: Downtown; Freestanding
Primary Menu: Hamburger (9)
Areas of Operation: AL
Type of Foodservice: Quick Serve (9)
Franchise Affiliation: McDonald's Corporation, CHICAGO, IL

Key Personnel
AUSTIN ROGERS II - President; General Buyer
AUSTIN ROGERS III - Exec VP
DANIEL LYNCH - Manager Business Development
KAT PHELPS - Manager Marketing
JORGE RAMOS - Project Manager
SCOTT KALEY - Project Manager; Assistant
CARSON KOENIGS - Project Manager; Assistant
BRYAN SOTO SALINAS - Project Manager; Assistant

Drain Enterprises Inc.
825 S Broad St Ste 100
Scottsboro, AL 35768-2559

Telephone: (256) 259-4530
Fax Number: (256) 259-3124
Type of Business: Chain Restaurant Operator
Year Founded: 1972
Total Sales: $23,260,000 (e)
Number of Employees: 455
Average Check: Breakfast(8); Lunch(10); Dinner(12)
Total Units: 13
Trade Names: Hardee's (13)
Units Franchised From: 13
Preferred Square Footage: 3,000
Preferred Location Types: Freestanding
Primary Menu: Hamburger (13)
Areas of Operation: AL, TN
Type of Foodservice: Quick Serve (13)
Franchise Affiliation: Hardee's Food Systems Inc., FRANKLIN, TN
Primary Distributors: (Food) McLane/Rocky Mount, ROCKY MOUNT, NC

Key Personnel
JOHN DRAIN - Partner; VP
DENISE DRAIN - Partner; Administrator Business Development
JAMES DRAIN SR - General Manager

Domino Pizza Franchise
383 James Payton Blvd
Sylacauga, AL 35150-8064

Mailing Address: PO Box 458, TALLADEGA, AL, 35161-0458
Telephone: (256) 249-4333
Fax Number: (256) 249-4337
Type of Business: Chain Restaurant Operator
Total Sales: $6,239,000 (e)
Average Check: Dinner(28)
Total Units: 3
Trade Names: Domino's (3)
Units Franchised From: 3
Primary Menu: Pizza (3)
Areas of Operation: AL
Type of Foodservice: Quick Serve (3)
Franchise Affiliation: Domino's Pizza Inc, ANN ARBOR, MI

Key Personnel
BRAD TWILLEY - President

Cypress Inn
501 Rice Mine Rd N
Tuscaloosa, AL 35406-2308

Telephone: (205) 345-6963
Fax Number: (205) 345-6997
Internet Homepage: cypressinnrestaurant.com
Type of Business: Chain Restaurant Operator
Year Founded: 1984
Total Sales: $4,369,000 (e)
Alcohol Sales: 1%
Number of Employees: 300
Average Check: Breakfast(12); Lunch(14); Dinner(14)
Total Units: 2
Trade Names: Cypress Inn (1); The Loft (1)
Company-Owned Units: 2
Preferred Location Types: Downtown
Alcohol Served: Beer, Wine, Liquor
Primary Menu: American (2)
Areas of Operation: AL
Type of Foodservice: Casual Dining (2)
Catering Services: Yes
Primary Distributors: (Full Line) Sysco Food Services of Nashville, NASHVILLE, TN

Key Personnel
DANA COLLINS - General Manager

Domino's Franchisee
417 15th St
Tuscaloosa, AL 35401-3552

Telephone: (205) 366-0663
Type of Business: Chain Restaurant Operator
Total Sales: $27,059,000 (e)
Total Units: 13
Trade Names: Domino's (13)
Units Franchised From: 13
Primary Menu: Pizza (13)
Areas of Operation: AL
Type of Foodservice: Quick Serve (13)
Franchise Affiliation: Domino's Pizza Inc, ANN ARBOR, MI

Key Personnel
ZAN R. HALL - Owner; General Buyer
CHRIS DARWIN - Director Operations

Jack Marshall Foods Inc.
113 25th Ave E
Tuscaloosa, AL 35404-2526

Telephone: (205) 553-8621
Fax Number: (205) 556-0851
Internet Homepage: jmfkfc.com
Company Email: phillip@jmfkfc.com
Type of Business: Chain Restaurant Operator
Year Founded: 1962
Total Sales: $30,800,000 (e)
Number of Employees: 315
Average Check: Lunch(10); Dinner(10)
Total Units: 17
Trade Names: KFC (17)
Units Franchised From: 17
Preferred Square Footage: 3,000
Preferred Location Types: Freestanding
Primary Menu: Chicken (17)
Areas of Operation: AL, KY, MS, TN
Type of Foodservice: Quick Serve (17)
Franchise Affiliation: KFC Corporation, LOUISVILLE, KY
Primary Distributors: (Food) Ben E Keith, ELBA, AL; (Supplies) Sysco Food Services of Nashville, NASHVILLE, TN

Key Personnel
PHILLIP MARSHALL - President; VP; General Manager; Director Marketing

LAD Foods Inc.
521 15th St
Tuscaloosa, AL 35401-4707

Telephone: (205) 345-4608
Type of Business: Chain Restaurant Operator
Year Founded: 1996
Total Sales: $6,385,000 (e)

Number of Employees: 60
Average Check: Lunch(8); Dinner(8)
Total Units: 4
Trade Names: Checkers (4)
Units Franchised From: 4
Preferred Square Footage: 760; 980
Preferred Location Types: Freestanding
Primary Menu: Hamburger (4)
Areas of Operation: AL
Type of Foodservice: Quick Serve (4)
Franchise Affiliation: Checkers Drive-In Restaurants Inc., TAMPA, FL

Key Personnel
LARRY ROCKWELL - President; Director Operations, Facility/Maintenance, Real Estate; General Buyer

McDonald's Franchise
4720 Jug Factory Rd
Tuscaloosa, AL 35405-4201

Telephone: (205) 758-4495
Fax Number: (205) 758-3878
Type of Business: Chain Restaurant Operator
Total Sales: $20,257,000 (e)
Average Check: Dinner(12)
Total Units: 4
Trade Names: McDonald's (4)
Units Franchised From: 4
Preferred Square Footage: 2,500
Preferred Location Types: Downtown; Freestanding
Primary Menu: Hamburger (4)
Areas of Operation: AL
Type of Foodservice: Quick Serve (4)
Franchise Affiliation: McDonald's Corporation, CHICAGO, IL

Key Personnel
KENNETH BAIRD - President; General Buyer

Terry & Karen White Enterprises
2501 University Blvd E
Tuscaloosa, AL 35404-3230

Telephone: (205) 752-9351
Type of Business: Chain Restaurant Operator
Year Founded: 1980
Total Sales: $13,690,000 (e)
Number of Employees: 25
Average Check: Lunch(8); Dinner(14)
Total Units: 11
Trade Names: Church's Chicken (11)
Units Franchised From: 11
Preferred Square Footage: 1,500; 2,000
Preferred Location Types: Freestanding
Primary Menu: Chicken (11)
Areas of Operation: AL

Type of Foodservice: Quick Serve (11)
Franchise Affiliation: Church's Chicken, ATLANTA, GA

Key Personnel
TERRY WHITE - President; Partner; Controller; Manager Operations, Facility/Maintenance, Information Systems, Marketing
KAREN WHITE - Partner; Manager Real Estate, Human Resources; General Buyer

Jim 'N Nick's Bar-B-Q
3755 Corporate Woods Dr
Vestavia, AL 35242-2244

Telephone: (205) 451-1868
Fax Number: (205) 871-8831
Internet Homepage: jimnnicks.com
Company Email: feedback@jimnnicks.com
Type of Business: Chain Restaurant Operator
Year Founded: 1984
Total Sales: $139,090,000 (e)
Alcohol Sales: 10%
Number of Employees: 2,402
Average Check: Lunch(10); Dinner(12)
Internet Order Processing: Yes
Total Units: 40
Trade Names: Jim 'N Nick's Bar-B-Q (40)
Company-Owned Units: 40
Preferred Square Footage: 5,500
Preferred Location Types: Freestanding; Strip Mall
Alcohol Served: Beer, Wine, Liquor
Primary Menu: Bar-B-Q (40)
Areas of Operation: AL, CO, FL, GA, NC, SC, TN
Type of Foodservice: Casual Dining (40)
Catering Services: Yes
Primary Distributors: (Full Line) US Foods, MONTGOMERY, AL
Parent Company: Roark Capital Group, ATLANTA, GA

Key Personnel
NICK PIHAKIS - CEO; Owner
LARRY RYBACK - CEO
BRIAN LYMAN - President
CHARITY ANDERSON - VP Purchasing, Distribution
CHARITY A. BUSH - VP Purchasing, Distribution

Quality Restaurant Concepts
601 Vestavia Pkwy Ste 1000
Vestavia, AL 35216-3772

Telephone: (205) 824-5060
Fax Number: (205) 824-5070
Internet Homepage: qrcllc.net
Type of Business: Chain Restaurant Operator
Year Founded: 1998
Total Sales: $208,840,000 (e)
Alcohol Sales: 25%
Number of Employees: 933
Average Check: Lunch(12); Dinner(20)
Total Units: 62
Trade Names: Applebee's Neighborhood Grill & Bar (57); Pie Five Pizza Co (5)
Company-Owned Units: 5
Units Franchised From: 57
Preferred Square Footage: 5,500; 6,500
Preferred Location Types: Freestanding; Regional Mall
Alcohol Served: Beer, Wine, Liquor
Primary Menu: American (57); Pizza (5)
Areas of Operation: AL, MS, TN
Type of Foodservice: Casual Dining (57); Fast Casual (5)
Franchise Affiliation: Applebee's Services Inc., KANSAS CITY, MO

Key Personnel
KURT GUTTSHALL - CEO
FRED GUSTIN - President; Director Real Estate; General Buyer
CHARLES GALLOWAY - CFO
STEPHEN PACK - Area Director
RICK HOUSER - VP Operations
MICHAEL MCMANUS - Director Operations
MIKE MCMANUS - Director Operations
STEPHEN BEASLEY - Director Information Technology
EDDIE COOK - Director Operations
BLAKE SLY - Director Operations
TRACY VOTEL - Director Training
TOM WINSTON - Director Operations
WENDY PHILLIPS - Coordinator Loss Prevention

S.P. Food Services, Inc.
100 Centerview Dr Ste 191
Vestavia, AL 35216-3774

Telephone: (205) 824-0855
Fax Number: (205) 824-0852
Internet Homepage: sneakypetes.com
Company Email: generalinfo@sneakypeteshotdogs.com
Type of Business: Chain Restaurant Operator
Year Founded: 1966
Systemwide Sales: $12,278,000 (e)
Total Sales: $2,689,000 (e)
Number of Employees: 5
Average Check: Breakfast(8); Lunch(8); Dinner(8)
Total Units: 40
Trade Names: Sneaky Pete's Hot Dogs (40)
Units Franchised To: 40
Preferred Square Footage: 3,500
Preferred Location Types: Community Mall; Convenience Store/Gas Station; Downtown; Freestanding; Regional Mall; Strip Mall
Primary Menu: Hot Dogs (40)
Areas of Operation: AL

Type of Foodservice: Quick Serve (40)
Primary Distributors: (Food) US Foods, MONTGOMERY, AL

Key Personnel
FRANK D'AMICO - Partner; CFO; VP; Treasurer; Manager Information Systems, Risk Management, Human Resources, Research & Development, Menu Development
MARK LOVELL - Director Operations, Purchasing, Supply Chain

Tacala LLC
3750 Corporate Woods Dr
Vestavia, AL 35242-2207

Telephone: (205) 443-9600
Fax Number: (205) 443-9700
Internet Homepage: tacala.com
Company Email: info@tacala.com
Type of Business: Chain Restaurant Operator
Year Founded: 1989
Total Sales: $774,360,000 (e)
Number of Employees: 3,860
Average Check: Breakfast(6); Lunch(8); Dinner(10)
Total Units: 285
Trade Names: KFC (1); Taco Bell (284)
Units Franchised From: 285
Preferred Square Footage: 2,500
Preferred Location Types: Freestanding; Strip Mall
Primary Menu: Chicken (1); Taco (284)
Areas of Operation: AL, GA, KY, NC, TN, TX, VA
Type of Foodservice: Quick Serve (285)
Franchise Affiliation: KFC Corporation, LOUISVILLE, KY; Taco Bell Corp., IRVINE, CA
Primary Distributors: (Full Line) McLane/Midwest, DANVILLE, IL
Parent Company: Altamont Capital Partners, PALO ALTO, CA

Key Personnel
DONALD GHAREEB - Chairman Emeritus; Founder
JOEY PIERSON - Co-CEO
TIM MORRISON - Co-CEO; President
DAVID MORRISON - COO
RAGAN CAIN - Chief Administrative Officer; Treasurer
MARJORIE PERLMAN - Chief Marketing Officer
MICHAEL BORDER - Chief Development Officer
ANGELIQUE GISIN DEFRANCO - Chief Compliance Officer
ANTHONY SMITH - Area Director
CARRIE BROWN - Area Director
JAVIER MARAVI - VP Training
LAURA MARAVI - VP Region
RICHARD MCCRACKEN - Regional VP
KRISTY EZELL - Controller
PENNY AMARAL - Controller

MIKE GRAY - Director Construction
BLAINE SALEM - Director Development
DENA SMITH - Director Training
APRIL HURST - Area Manager
JENCY NAKA - Manager Information
  Technology
CARRIE SELF - Manager Financial Planning
CHERYL MCDANIEL - Manager Marketing-
  Training
ERIC FRENCH - Manager Customer Analytics
TABITHA KING - Manager Training
ELIZABETH HARKINS - Manager Business
  Development
SUSAN JERNIGAN - Product Manager
  Development
CARRIE RIGGS - Administrator Benefits

Taziki's Cafe
3755 Corporate Woods Dr Ste 100
Vestavia, AL 35242

Telephone: (205) 451-1860
Internet Homepage: tazikiscafe.com
Company Email: careers@tazikiscafe.com
Type of Business: Chain Restaurant Operator
Year Founded: 1998
Systemwide Sales: $67,084,000 (e)
Total Sales: $33,560,000 (e)
Total Units: 94
Trade Names: Taziki's Mediterranean Cafe (92)
Company-Owned Units: 24
Units Franchised To: 70
Preferred Location Types: Institution
  (college/hospital); Strip Mall
Primary Menu: Greek/Mediterranean (92)
Projected Openings: 10
Areas of Operation: AL, AR, CO, FL, GA, KY,
  MS, NC, OK, SC, TN, TX, VA, WV
Type of Foodservice: Fast Casual (92)
Parent Company: Fresh Hospitality LLC,
  NASHVILLE, TN

Key Personnel
KEITH RICHARDS - Founder; Partner
AMY RICHARDS - Founder; Partner
DAN SIMPSON - CEO
TONY TOMSIC - Partner; Director Operations
BILLY MAGRUDER - CFO
ROBERT BROWN - VP Operations
LYNN EDWARDS - VP Human Resources
JULIE WADE - Senior Director Marketing
TOMMY TERRELL - Director Branding
JOSEPH BAILEY - Director Catering
OLIVIA BANE - Director Marketing
TRAVIS LAHA - Director Marketing
PENNY MCCALL - Director Marketing, Catering
MICHAEL TAYLOR - Director Training
ALEX GARMEZY - Director Franchise
  Development
MCKENNA JONES - Director Marketing, Sales
TOMMY TRAYNHAM - Director Technology
FRANK EGAN - Manager Franchise Operations
PATRICK GADILHE - Manager Franchise
  Operations
MEAGAN CAMPBELL - Specialist Development,
  Training
NATALIE TOKAR - Specialist Marketing,
  Catering
ANNA DUFFY - Engineer Recruitment
EMILIE HOLCOMB - Executive Assistant

Bush Investments Inc
7495 US Highway 231
Wetumpka, AL 36092-2048

Telephone: (334) 567-6444
Type of Business: Chain Restaurant Operator
Total Sales: $930,000 (e)
Total Units: 1
Trade Names: Huddle House (1)
Units Franchised From: 1
Primary Menu: American (1)
Areas of Operation: AL
Type of Foodservice: Family Restaurant (1)
Franchise Affiliation: Huddle House Inc.,
  ATLANTA, GA

Key Personnel
CHARLES BUSH - President; General Buyer

ARKANSAS

Andy's Restaurants Inc.
2749 Pine St
Arkadelphia, AR 71923

Telephone: (870) 245-2292
Fax Number: (870) 574-0052
Internet Homepage: andys-restaurant.com
Type of Business: Chain Restaurant Operator
Year Founded: 1978
Total Sales: $6,685,000 (e)
Number of Employees: 200
Average Check: Breakfast(8); Lunch(8);
  Dinner(8)
Total Units: 8
Trade Names: Andy's Restaurant (8)
Company-Owned Units: 8
Preferred Square Footage: 3,000
Preferred Location Types: Downtown;
  Freestanding
Primary Menu: Hamburger (8)
Areas of Operation: AR
Type of Foodservice: Quick Serve (8)
Primary Distributors: (Equipment) Aimco
  Equipment, LITTLE ROCK, AR; (Food)
  Henley's Wholesale Meats, NORTH LITTLE
  ROCK, AR

Key Personnel
JEFF HENDERSON - Director Operations;
  Manager Operations

Domino's Franchisee
1436 Harrison St
Batesville, AR 72501-7219

Telephone: (870) 698-9099
Type of Business: Chain Restaurant Operator
Total Sales: $6,098,000 (e)
Total Units: 3
Trade Names: Domino's (3)
Units Franchised From: 3
Primary Menu: Pizza (3)
Areas of Operation: AR
Type of Foodservice: Quick Serve (3)
Franchise Affiliation: Domino's Pizza Inc, ANN
  ARBOR, MI

Key Personnel
JOHN M. POWELL - Owner; General Buyer

KFC of Benton
522 N East St
Benton, AR 72015-3703

Telephone: (501) 778-4343
Type of Business: Chain Restaurant Operator
Year Founded: 1966
Total Sales: $3,881,000 (e)
Number of Employees: 75
Average Check: Dinner(14)
Total Units: 2
Trade Names: KFC (2)
Units Franchised From: 2
Preferred Square Footage: 2,500
Preferred Location Types: Freestanding
Primary Menu: Chicken (2)
Areas of Operation: AR
Type of Foodservice: Quick Serve (2)
Catering Services: Yes
Franchise Affiliation: KFC Corporation,
  LOUISVILLE, KY
Primary Distributors: (Full Line) SYSCO Food
  Services of Arkansas LLC, LITTLE ROCK, AR

Key Personnel
MARK FIKES - President; Manager Operations,
  Purchasing; General Buyer

Walmart Stores Inc.
702 SW 8th St
Bentonville, AR 72712-6209

Telephone: (479) 273-4000
Fax Number: (479) 273-6738
Internet Homepage: walmartstores.com
Type of Business: Nontraditional Foodservice
  Operator
Year Founded: 1962
Publicly Held: Yes
Total Sales: $441,817,000,000 (e)

Number of Employees: 2,200,000
Total Units: 4,615
Trade Names: Auntie Anne's Hand-Rolled Soft Pretzels; BLIMPIE; Checkers; Dunkin' Donuts; McDonald's; Subway
Company-Owned Units: 4,615
Preferred Square Footage: 300; 1,200; 2,000; 2,500; 3,000
Preferred Location Types: Community Mall; Freestanding; Regional Mall; Strip Mall
Areas of Operation: AK, AL, AR, AZ, CA, CO, CT, DE, FL, GA, HI, IA, ID, IL, IN, KS, KY, LA, MA, MD, ME, MI, MN, MO, MS, MT, NC, ND, NE, NH, NJ, NM, NV, NY, OH, OK, OR, PA, PR, RI, SC, SD, TN, TX, UT, VA, VT, WA, WI, WV, WY, AB, BC, MB, NB, NL, NS, NT, ON, PE, QC, SK
Foreign Countries: CANADA
Type of Foodservice: In-Store Feeder (4,769)
Franchise Affiliation: Auntie Anne's Inc., LANCASTER, PA; Checkers Drive-In Restaurants Inc., TAMPA, FL; DD IP Holder, CANTON, MA; Doctor's Associates Inc., MILFORD, CT; Kahala Brands, SCOTTSDALE, AZ; McDonald's Corporation, CHICAGO, IL
Primary Distributors: (Full Line) McLane Company, Inc., TEMPLE, TX
Notes: Total store count and total sales reflects Walmart's U.S. segment (excluding Sam's Club), although not all stores have in-store foodservice. The company derives more than 99% of its revenue from retail operations.

Key Personnel
ENRIQUE OSTALE - CEO International Division; President International Division; Exec VP
DOUG MCMILLON - CEO; President
GREG FORAN - CEO Division; President Division
JUDITH MCKENNA - CEO Division; President Division; Exec VP
CHRIS NICHOLAS - CEO; President
KATHLEEN MCLAUGHLIN - President Division; Chief Sustainability Officer
MICHAEL DASTUGUE - CFO United States; Exec VP
JOHN RAINEY - CFO
DAVID CHOJNOWSKI - Chief Accounting Officer; Senior VP; Controller
JUDY WERTHAUSER - Chief People Officer
A. DENISE MALLOY-DEADERICK - Chief People Officer
WILLIAM WHITE - Chief Marketing Officer
LATRIECE WATKINS - Chief Merchandising Officer; Exec VP
ALLYSON PARK - Chief Communications Officer Corporate Affairs
BEN-SABA HASAN - Chief Diversity Officer; Chief Culture Officer; Chief Inclusion Officer; Senior VP
RACHEL BRAND - Chief Legal Officer; Exec VP Government Affairs; Corporate Secretary
MATT MINER - Chief Compliance Officer; Chief Ethics Officer; Exec VP
JEAN BATTHANY - Chief Creative Officer
SETH DALLAIRE - Chief Growth Officer
JANEY WHITESIDE - Chief Customer Officer; Exec VP
JERRY GEISLER III - Chief Information Security Officer; Senior VP
KAREN ROBERTS - Exec VP; General Counsel
ANDY BARRON - Exec VP Merchandising
DAN BARTLETT - Exec VP Corporate Affairs
JULIE MURPHY - Exec VP People
GREG SMITH - Exec VP Supply Chain
TOM WARD - Exec VP; Chief E-Commerce Officer
KAREN STUCKEY - Senior VP Sourcing, Softlines Division, Private Label
JANE EWING - Senior VP People
COURTNEY CARLSON - Senior VP Marketing
JENNIFER MCKEEHAN - Senior VP Logistics
JUAN GALARRAGA - Senior VP Business Development
VENESSA YATES - Senior VP; General Manager
JOSEPH GODSEY - Senior VP Transformation
VALERIE CASEY - Senior VP Design
JEFF RICE - VP Sustainability, Sourcing
MARTY ESARTE - VP Private Label
MARK VANDERHELM - VP Sustainability
CREIGHTON KIPER - VP Merchandising
LAURA HIMES - VP Sourcing, International
JASON O'DELL - VP Security
RINA HURST - VP Transportation
TASHA TANDY - VP Merchandising
HALEY MCSHANE - General Manager
KIM BRANDNER - Senior Director Sourcing-Food
BRONWEN HUTCHINS - Director Private Brands
REGAN LANCE - Senior Manager Sourcing, Quality Assurance, Private Label-Food
PAOLA DE VILLIERS - Senior Manager Product Development
JUBAL HAUSAM - Senior Manager Sourcing, Quality Assurance
LIBBY MCELROY - Senior Manager Communications
MEGHAN KLOSTERMAN - Senior Program Manager
TAMMY HUFF - Senior Buyer

McDonald's Franchise
112 S 4th St
Cabot, AR 72023-2910

Telephone: (501) 843-0069
Fax Number: (501) 843-0269
Type of Business: Chain Restaurant Operator
Total Sales: $42,400,000 (e)
Number of Employees: 285
Total Units: 9
Trade Names: McDonald's (9)
Units Franchised From: 9
Preferred Square Footage: 2,500
Primary Menu: Hamburger (9)
Areas of Operation: AR
Type of Foodservice: Quick Serve (9)
Franchise Affiliation: McDonald's Corporation, CHICAGO, IL

Key Personnel
WILLIAM LLOYD STOKES - President; General Buyer

Pizza Pro Inc.
2107 N 2nd St
Cabot, AR 72023-2228

Mailing Address: PO Box 1285, CABOT, AR, 72023-1285
Telephone: (501) 605-1175
Fax Number: (501) 605-1204
Internet Homepage: pizzapro.com
Company Email: franchiseservice@pizzapro.com
Type of Business: Chain Restaurant Operator
Year Founded: 1985
Systemwide Sales: $79,956,000 (e)
Total Sales: $5,491,000 (e)
Alcohol Sales: 0.50%
Number of Employees: 282
Average Check: Lunch(20); Dinner(26)
Internet Order Processing: Yes
Internet Sales: 5.00%
Total Units: 167
Trade Names: Brick Oven Pizza Company (14); Pizza Pro (151); Sub City (2)
Company-Owned Units: 16
Units Franchised To: 151
Preferred Square Footage: 800
Preferred Location Types: Convenience Store/Gas Station; Freestanding; Grocery Stores; Other; Regional Mall; Strip Mall
Alcohol Served: Beer, Wine
Primary Menu: Pizza (165); Sandwiches/Deli (2)
Areas of Operation: AL, AR, GA, KS, KY, LA, MO, MS, NC, SC, TN, TX
Type of Foodservice: Family Restaurant (151); Quick Serve (16)
Foodservice Management Venues: Parks & Recreation; Schools
Catering Services: Yes
Primary Distributors: (Full Line) Performance Foodservice, SPRINGFIELD, MO

Key Personnel
SCOTT STEVENS - President; CFO; Director Purchasing, Real Estate, Design, Menu Development
COBY DODD - VP Information Systems

Tacos 4 Life Grill
2235 Dave Ward Dr
Conway, AR 72034

Telephone: (501) 205-1380
Internet Homepage: tacos4life.com
Type of Business: Chain Restaurant Operator
Year Founded: 2014
Systemwide Sales: $32,021,000 (e)
Total Sales: $29,300,000 (e)
Total Units: 16
Trade Names: Tacos 4 Life Grill (16)
Units Franchised To: 16
Primary Menu: Taco (16)
Projected Openings: 2
Areas of Operation: AR, NC, TN, TX
Type of Foodservice: Fast Casual (16)

Key Personnel
AUSTIN SAMUELSON - Co-Founder
ASHTON SAMUELSON - Co-Founder
NOAH MORRISON - General Manager

Diamond Hospitality
5 Mystic Isle Rd
Edgemont, AR 72044-9547

Telephone: (501) 723-5150
Fax Number: (501) 723-5154
Type of Business: Chain Restaurant Operator
Year Founded: 1997
Total Sales: $59,290,000 (e)
Number of Employees: 2,628
Average Check: Breakfast(6); Lunch(8); Dinner(8)
Total Units: 32
Trade Names: Hardee's (32)
Units Franchised From: 32
Preferred Square Footage: 3,000; 3,500
Preferred Location Types: Freestanding
Primary Menu: Hamburger (32)
Areas of Operation: AL, AR, MS, OK
Type of Foodservice: Quick Serve (32)
Franchise Affiliation: Hardee's Food Systems Inc., FRANKLIN, TN

Key Personnel
ROB SCHMIDT - Owner; Director Finance, Operations, Purchasing, Facility/Maintenance, Information Systems, Real Estate; General Buyer
DOLLY SCHMIDT - VP Human Resources

7 Brew Drive-Thru Coffee
LLC 313 N Rollston Ave.
Fayetteville, AR 72701

Telephone: (479) 358-9274
Company Email: info@7brew.com
Type of Business: Chain Restaurant Operator
Year Founded: 2017
Total Units: 341
Trade Names: 7 Brew Drive-Thru Coffee (341)
Company-Owned Units: 341
Primary Menu: Coffee (341)
Areas of Operation: AL, AR, CO, CT, FL, GA, IA, IL, IN, KS, KY, LA, MI, MN, MO, MS, NC, NE, NM, NY, OH, OK, PA, SC, SD, TN, TX, UT, VA, WI, WV, WY
Type of Foodservice: Quick Serve (341)

Key Personnel
DANIEL COLLINS - Founder; President

AJW Holdings, LLC
1364 E Augustine Ln
Fayetteville, AR 72703-4942

Telephone: (479) 251-0044
Type of Business: Chain Restaurant Operator
Total Sales: $2,487,000 (e)
Total Units: 2
Trade Names: Firehouse Subs (2)
Units Franchised From: 2
Preferred Location Types: Strip Mall
Primary Menu: Sandwiches/Deli (2)
Projected Openings: 1
Projected Remodelings: 1
Areas of Operation: AR
Type of Foodservice: Fast Casual (2)
Franchise Affiliation: Firehouse Restaurant Group Inc., JACKSONVILLE, FL

Key Personnel
JIM WHITE - President; Partner; General Buyer
AUDIE WHITE - Partner; General Buyer

Brew Culture LLC
313 N Rollston Ave.
Fayetteville, AR 72701

Telephone: (479) 358-9274
Internet Homepage: 7brew.com
Company Email: info@7brew.com
Type of Business: Chain Restaurant Operator
Total Sales: $195,790,000 (e)
Total Units: 233
Trade Names: 7 Brew (233)
Company-Owned Units: 233
Primary Menu: Coffee (233)
Areas of Operation: AL, AR, CO, FL, GA, IA, IL, IN, KS, KY, LA, MI, MO, MS, NC, NE, NY, OH, OK, PA, SC, SD, TN, TX, VA, WI
Type of Foodservice: Quick Serve (233)

Key Personnel
JOHN DAVIDSON - CEO
DREW RITGER - COO; Director Franchising
JORDAN SMITH - Director Information Technology
JOHNNY JONES - Director Real Estate

Eureka System Corp.
1905 E Mission Blvd Ste 1
Fayetteville, AR 72703-3129

Mailing Address: PO Box 1913, FAYETTEVILLE, AR, 72702-1913
Telephone: (479) 444-8282
Fax Number: (479) 444-7877
Internet Homepage: eurekapizza.com
Company Email: mail@eurekapizza.com
Type of Business: Chain Restaurant Operator
Year Founded: 1992
Total Sales: $5,704,000 (e)
Number of Employees: 300
Average Check: Lunch(8); Dinner(12)
Internet Order Processing: Yes
Internet Sales: 1.00%
Total Units: 10
Trade Names: Eureka Pizza (10)
Company-Owned Units: 10
Preferred Square Footage: 1,500
Preferred Location Types: Freestanding; Strip Mall
Primary Menu: Pizza (10)
Areas of Operation: AR
Type of Foodservice: Quick Serve (10)
Foodservice Management Venues: Schools
Catering Services: Yes
Primary Distributors: (Full Line) Performance Foodservice, SPRINGFIELD, MO

Key Personnel
ROLF WILKIN - President; Executive Chef; Director Purchasing, Facility/Maintenance, Real Estate, Design, Store Fixtures; General Buyer
BONNIE TURNER - Controller; Director Finance, Accounting, Information Systems, Human Resources

KVS Sonic Group
2786 E Millennium Dr Ste 1
Fayetteville, AR 72703-4941

Mailing Address: PO Box 8099, FAYETTEVILLE, AR, 72703
Telephone: (479) 582-0444
Fax Number: (479) 582-0446
Internet Homepage: kvsgroup.net
Type of Business: Chain Restaurant Operator
Total Sales: $45,940,000 (e)
Total Units: 22
Trade Names: Sonic America's Drive-In (22)
Units Franchised From: 22
Preferred Location Types: Freestanding
Primary Menu: Hamburger (22)
Areas of Operation: AR, OK
Type of Foodservice: Quick Serve (22)

Franchise Affiliation: Sonic Corp., OKLAHOMA CITY, OK

Key Personnel
JOHN R. FRIEND - Partner
BRANDON DRAKE - Partner
MATT MASON - Partner; Supervisor Marketing
KENNETH SMITH - Director Operations

Loafin Joe's Inc.
201 W Mountain St
Fayetteville, AR 72701-5968

Telephone: (479) 443-9944
Internet Homepage: loafinjoes.com
Company Email: info@loafinjoes.com
Type of Business: Chain Restaurant Operator
Year Founded: 1991
Systemwide Sales: $1,518,000 (e)
Total Sales: $1,001,000 (e)
Alcohol Sales: 1%
Number of Employees: 28
Average Check: Lunch(10); Dinner(10)
Internet Order Processing: Yes
Total Units: 3
Trade Names: Loafin Joe's (3)
Company-Owned Units: 3
Preferred Square Footage: 1,900
Preferred Location Types: Freestanding
Primary Menu: Sandwiches/Deli (3)
Areas of Operation: AR
Type of Foodservice: Casual Dining (3)
Catering Services: Yes
Primary Distributors: (Full Line) US Foods, NORTH LITTLE ROCK, AR

Key Personnel
JOE WEBER - President; General Manager; Director Menu Development; General Buyer
EDWARD FITZPATRICK - Manager

Mamaka Bowls
495 W. Prairie St.
Fayetteville, AR 72701

Telephone: (479) 935-3411
Internet Homepage: mamakabowls.com
Type of Business: Chain Restaurant Operator
Year Founded: 2018
Total Sales: $5,007,000 (e)
Total Units: 6
Trade Names: Mamaka Bowls (6)
Company-Owned Units: 6
Primary Menu: Californian (6)
Areas of Operation: AR, OK, TX
Type of Foodservice: Fast Casual (6)

Key Personnel
KK GOODWIN - Co-Founder; CEO
CARRIE HUDSON - Co-Founder
CODY GOODWIN - COO

SF Group, Inc
160 E Joyce Blvd Ste 109
Fayetteville, AR 72703-6080

Telephone: (479) 582-9050
Type of Business: Chain Restaurant Operator
Total Sales: $2,384,000 (e)
Total Units: 4
Trade Names: Cold Stone Creamery (4)
Units Franchised From: 4
Primary Menu: Snacks (4)
Areas of Operation: AR, MO
Type of Foodservice: Quick Serve (4)
Franchise Affiliation: Kahala Brands, SCOTTSDALE, AZ

Key Personnel
MARK STILL - Partner
ANGELA STILL - Partner
JAMES FUNDERBURK - Partner
DAWN FUNDERBURK - Partner

Shakes Frozen Custard Inc.
PO Box 8700
Fayetteville, AR 72703-0011

Mailing Address: PO Box 8700, FAYETTEVILLE, AR, 72703-0011
Telephone: (479) 587-9115
Fax Number: (479) 587-0780
Internet Homepage: shakesfrozencustard.com
Company Email: info@shakesfrozencustard.com
Type of Business: Chain Restaurant Operator
Year Founded: 1991
Systemwide Sales: $12,523,000 (e)
Total Sales: $1,416,000 (e)
Number of Employees: 19
Average Check: Lunch(10); Dinner(10)
Internet Order Processing: Yes
Total Units: 7
Trade Names: Shake's Frozen Custard (7)
Company-Owned Units: 5
Units Franchised To: 2
Preferred Square Footage: 2,000
Preferred Location Types: Freestanding; Strip Mall
Primary Menu: Snacks (7)
Areas of Operation: AR, FL, MO, TX
Type of Foodservice: Quick Serve (7)
Primary Distributors: (Food) Pacific Valley Dairy, PACIFIC, MO

Key Personnel
COREY OSBORNE - CEO; President; General Buyer
AARON OSBORNE - CFO

Slim Chickens
1088 E Millsap Rd
Fayetteville, AR 72703-5148

Telephone: (479) 935-4444
Fax Number: (479) 695-1673
Internet Homepage: slimchickens.com
Company Email: info@slim-chickens.com
Type of Business: Chain Restaurant Operator
Year Founded: 2003
Total Sales: $341,110,000 (e)
Average Check: Lunch(10); Dinner(10)
Total Units: 118
Trade Names: Slim Chickens (118)
Company-Owned Units: 20
Units Franchised To: 98
Preferred Square Footage: 3,000
Primary Menu: Chicken (118)
Projected Openings: 31
Areas of Operation: AR, IL, KS, KY, LA, MO, MS, NE, OH, OK, SD, TN, TX, FC
Foreign Countries: ENGLAND; KUWAIT
Type of Foodservice: Fast Casual (118)

Key Personnel
TOM GORDON - CEO; Partner
GREG SMART - Partner; Chief Brand Officer
SETH JENSEN - CFO
CHRISTINA VAUGHAN - COO
STEPHEN CARDINAL - Area Director
ERIN KIEFFER - Area Director Franchising
BRIAN SIMOWITZ - VP Franchise Operations
GREG MARKEL - VP Finance
BARRY BEAM - VP Operations
ROB GERSTENFELD - VP Real Estate, Construction
CHRIS PATTERSON - Executive Director Training
JACKIE LOBDELL - Executive Director Franchise Development
TRIP JONES - Controller
DARRELL LINDABURY - Director Construction
VERONICA TORRES - Director Construction
KRISTEN GAGE - Director Technology, Marketing
PETER BINDER - Director Operations
DAVID NANCE - Director Franchise Operations
RHONDA WHITE - Director Human Resources
ROBERT ANDERSON - Director Operations
JERRY LITTLE - Director Franchising
MARY CRAWLEY - Associate Director Procurement
TERESA ERTRACHTER - Coordinator Payroll
SARAH CHAPMAN - Coordinator Accounting

SmitCo Eateries Inc.
31 E Center St Ste 211
Fayetteville, AR 72701-5391

Telephone: (479) 527-0326
Fax Number: (479) 527-6657

Company Email: popeyesmitty@aol.com
Type of Business: Chain Restaurant Operator
Total Sales: $17,860,000 (e)
Number of Employees: 100
Average Check: Breakfast(5); Lunch(6); Dinner(8)
Total Units: 7
Trade Names: Popeyes Louisiana Kitchen (7)
Units Franchised From: 7
Preferred Square Footage: 2,000
Preferred Location Types: Freestanding
Primary Menu: Chicken (7)
Areas of Operation: AR
Type of Foodservice: Quick Serve (7)
Franchise Affiliation: Popeyes Louisiana Kitchen Inc., ATLANTA, GA; The Krystal Co., DUNWOODY, GA

Key Personnel
BRIAN SMITH - CEO; General Buyer
WILLIAM COATS - CFO
LAURIE HILL - Director Operations

Circle N Investment Corp.
2900 Grand Ave
Fort Smith, AR 72901-3110

Telephone: (479) 783-8880
Fax Number: (479) 783-8885
Type of Business: Chain Restaurant Operator
Year Founded: 1986
Total Sales: $29,000,000 (e)
Number of Employees: 390
Average Check: Breakfast(10); Lunch(10); Dinner(10)
Total Units: 13
Trade Names: Burger King (13)
Units Franchised From: 13
Preferred Square Footage: 3,500
Preferred Location Types: Freestanding
Primary Menu: Hamburger (13)
Areas of Operation: AR, OK
Type of Foodservice: Quick Serve (13)
Franchise Affiliation: Burger King Worldwide Inc., MIAMI, FL
Primary Distributors: (Food) McLane/Fort Worth, FORT WORTH, TX

Key Personnel
JOHN NEUBAUER - President; Controller; Director Finance, Purchasing, Real Estate
JOSEPH NEUBAUER - VP Operations, Facility/Maintenance, Marketing, Design, Human Resources, Store Fixtures
KATHY THOMAS - Director Operations
LORETTA DOTSON - Manager Administration, Purchasing, Information Systems, Risk Management

Fort Smith 3 Inc.
3001 McKinley Ave
Fort Smith, AR 72908-7545

Telephone: (479) 646-7006
Fax Number: (479) 646-3430
Type of Business: Chain Restaurant Operator
Year Founded: 1974
Total Sales: $41,470,000 (e)
Number of Employees: 325
Average Check: Breakfast(8); Lunch(8); Dinner(8)
Total Units: 9
Trade Names: McDonald's (9)
Units Franchised From: 9
Preferred Square Footage: 2,500
Preferred Location Types: Freestanding
Primary Menu: Hamburger (9)
Areas of Operation: AR, OK
Type of Foodservice: Quick Serve (9)
Franchise Affiliation: McDonald's Corporation, CHICAGO, IL
Primary Distributors: (Full Line) The Martin-Brower Co., NORTH LITTLE ROCK, AR

Key Personnel
JAMES HADLEY - President; Director Finance, Purchasing, Information Systems, Real Estate; General Buyer
DONNA RODDY - Manager District
PATTY BORUM - Manager Branch

JRAN Inc.
2317 S 57th St
Fort Smith, AR 72903-3812

Telephone: (479) 452-8483
Fax Number: (479) 452-8479
Company Email: westersiz@coxinternet.com
Type of Business: Chain Restaurant Operator
Year Founded: 1976
Total Sales: $14,061,000 (e)
Number of Employees: 250
Average Check: Lunch(14); Dinner(20)
Total Units: 4
Trade Names: WesterN SizzliN Steak & More (4)
Units Franchised From: 4
Preferred Location Types: Freestanding
Primary Menu: Steak (4)
Areas of Operation: AR
Type of Foodservice: Family Restaurant (4)
Catering Services: Yes
Franchise Affiliation: The Western Sizzlin Corp., ROANOKE, VA

Key Personnel
WYATT KAUNDART - President; General Manager
GARY STOVALL - Owner; Manager Operations; General Buyer

K-Mac Enterprises Inc.
1820 S Zero St
Fort Smith, AR 72901-8414

Mailing Address: PO Box 6538, FORT SMITH, AR, 72906-6538
Telephone: (479) 646-2053
Fax Number: (479) 646-8748
Internet Homepage: kmaccorp.com
Company Email: terry@kmaccorp.com
Type of Business: Chain Restaurant Operator
Year Founded: 1964
Total Sales: $840,410,000 (e)
Number of Employees: 4,700
Average Check: Lunch(10); Dinner(12)
Internet Order Processing: Yes
Total Units: 311
Trade Names: KFC (10); Taco Bell (301)
Units Franchised From: 311
Preferred Square Footage: 2,500; 3,000
Preferred Location Types: Community Mall; Convenience Store/Gas Station; Discount Dept. Stores; Freestanding; Institution (college/hospital); Strip Mall
Primary Menu: Chicken (10); Taco (301)
Areas of Operation: AR, IL, IN, KY, MO, MS, OK, TN, TX
Type of Foodservice: Quick Serve (311)
Catering Services: Yes
Franchise Affiliation: Golden Corral Corp., RALEIGH, NC; KFC Corporation, LOUISVILLE, KY; Taco Bell Corp., IRVINE, CA
Primary Distributors: (Full Line) McLane Company, Inc., TEMPLE, TX

Key Personnel
SAM FIORI - CEO
TINA REAGAN - President; COO
JOHN DYER - CFO
JASON MILLER - VP Finance, Administration, Development
PHILIP HINDMAN - Director Risk Management, Human Resources
ROGER MORRIS - Director Information Systems
JOE WHITE - Director Operations
DENNIS CASEY - Director Operations
MATTHEW PARRY - Director People
SHANE CRUM - Director Development
THERESA ESTEP - Director Purchasing, Development
JOSEPH MARTIN - Director Operations
JASON MOORE - District Manager
SARAH STOECKER - Manager Food
BECKY LAWSON - Manager Information Technology
KEILEN RICHARDSON - Analyst Real Estate

Domino's Franchisee
1002 S Main St
Hope, AR 71801-7235

Telephone: (870) 777-3400
Type of Business: Chain Restaurant Operator
Total Sales: $4,003,000 (e)
Total Units: 2
Trade Names: Domino's (2)
Units Franchised From: 2
Primary Menu: Pizza (2)
Areas of Operation: AR
Type of Foodservice: Quick Serve (2)
Franchise Affiliation: Domino's Pizza Inc, ANN ARBOR, MI

Key Personnel
MAC MCKINNON - Owner; General Buyer

Balke Trucking, Inc
3545 Central Ave
Hot Springs, AR 71913-6202

Mailing Address: PO Box 21818, HOT SPRINGS, AR, 71903-1818
Telephone: (501) 624-5890
Fax Number: (501) 623-6842
Type of Business: Chain Restaurant Operator
Total Sales: $13,460,000 (e)
Average Check: Dinner(12)
Total Units: 6
Trade Names: Burger King (6)
Units Franchised From: 6
Primary Menu: Hamburger (6)
Areas of Operation: AR
Type of Foodservice: Quick Serve (6)
Franchise Affiliation: Burger King Worldwide Inc., MIAMI, FL

Key Personnel
MAX BALKE - President; General Buyer

Domino's Franchisee
4656 N Highway 7
Hot Springs Village, AR 71909-9483

Telephone: (501) 915-9595
Type of Business: Chain Restaurant Operator
Total Sales: $4,044,000 (e)
Total Units: 2
Trade Names: Domino's (2)
Units Franchised From: 2
Primary Menu: Pizza (2)
Areas of Operation: AR
Type of Foodservice: Quick Serve (2)
Franchise Affiliation: Domino's Pizza Inc, ANN ARBOR, MI

Key Personnel
PHILLIP E. SCHIRMER - Owner; General Buyer

Clairday Foodservice Enterprises
2005 E Highland Dr
Jonesboro, AR 72401-6123

Mailing Address: P O Box 1677, JONESBORO, AR, 72403
Telephone: (870) 932-3300
Fax Number: (870) 931-0508
Type of Business: Chain Restaurant Operator
Year Founded: 1974
Total Sales: $4,621,000 (e)
Number of Employees: 195
Average Check: Lunch(10); Dinner(10)
Total Units: 3
Trade Names: Pizza Inn (3)
Units Franchised From: 3
Preferred Square Footage: 1,000; 4,400; 5,000
Preferred Location Types: Freestanding
Primary Menu: Pizza (3)
Areas of Operation: AR
Type of Foodservice: Family Restaurant (3)
Catering Services: Yes
Franchise Affiliation: RAVE Restaurant Group Inc., THE COLONY, TX
Primary Distributors: (Full Line) Norco Manufacturing & Distribution Co., THE COLONY, TX

Key Personnel
BOB CLAIRDAY - President; Director Facility/Maintenance, Real Estate, Design
IVA CLAIRDAY - VP Risk Management; Controller; Director Finance, Information Systems
GREG CLAIRDAY - Manager Operations, Purchasing, Marketing, Store Fixtures

T.R.M. Enterprises
2227 S Caraway Rd
Jonesboro, AR 72401-6204

Telephone: (870) 932-2227
Type of Business: Chain Restaurant Operator
Total Sales: $3,663,000 (e)
Total Units: 2
Trade Names: Little Caesars Pizza (2)
Units Franchised From: 2
Preferred Location Types: Strip Mall
Primary Menu: Pizza (2)
Areas of Operation: AR
Type of Foodservice: Quick Serve (2)
Franchise Affiliation: Little Caesar Enterprises Inc., DETROIT, MI

Key Personnel
RICK BIANCO - Partner; General Buyer
TONI BIANCO - Partner

Burge's Hickory Smoked Turkeys
526 Spruce St
Lewisville, AR 71845-8711

Mailing Address: PO Box 759, LEWISVILLE, AR, 71845-0759
Telephone: (870) 921-4292
Fax Number: (870) 921-4500
Internet Homepage: smokedturkeys.com
Company Email: burges@smokedturkeys.com
Type of Business: Chain Restaurant Operator
Year Founded: 1962
Total Sales: $1,835,000 (e)
Number of Employees: 20
Average Check: Lunch(10); Dinner(14)
Internet Order Processing: Yes
Internet Sales: 55.00%
Total Units: 2
Trade Names: Burge's Hickory Smoked Turkeys (2)
Company-Owned Units: 2
Preferred Square Footage: 1,500
Preferred Location Types: Freestanding
Primary Menu: American (2)
Areas of Operation: AR
Type of Foodservice: Family Restaurant (2)
Catering Services: Yes
Primary Distributors: (Food) SYSCO Food Services of Arkansas LLC, LITTLE ROCK, AR

Key Personnel
JEFF VOYLES - Owner; General Manager; Executive Chef; General Buyer

Arkansas Culinary School Pulaski Technical College
13000 Interstate 30
Little Rock, AR 72210-7016

Telephone: (501) 812-2200
Fax Number: (501) 812-2316
Internet Homepage: uaptc.edu/culinary
Type of Business: Culinary Schools
Areas of Operation: AR

Key Personnel
TODD R. GOLD - Director Operations; General Buyer

Canteen Vending Services
4001 Pratt Remmel Rd
Little Rock, AR 72206-3887

Telephone: (501) 562-0111
Fax Number: (501) 490-0953
Listing Type: Branch Office
Type of Business: Foodservice Management Operator
Year Founded: 1948
Number of Employees: 30
Number of Locations Served: 110
Total Foodservice Mgmt Accounts: 110
Areas of Operation: AR
Type of Foodservice: Vending machines (110)
Foodservice Management Venues: Business & Industry; College & University; Health Care; Prison Feeding; Transportation
Parent Company: Compass Group The Americas, CHARLOTTE, NC
Headquarters: Canteen Vending Services, CHARLOTTE, NC

Key Personnel
BYRON HURST - General Manager; Director Operations

Chi's Fine Chinese cuisine
17200 Chenal Pkwy
Little Rock, AR 72223

Telephone: (501) 821-8000
Type of Business: Chain Restaurant Operator
Total Sales: $21,242,000 (e)
Alcohol Sales: 30%
Number of Employees: 40
Average Check: Lunch(8); Dinner(14)
Total Units: 2
Trade Names: Chi's Asian Cafe (1); Chi's Chinese Cuisine (1)
Company-Owned Units: 2
Preferred Square Footage: 3,500; 7,000
Preferred Location Types: Freestanding; Strip Mall
Alcohol Served: Beer, Wine, Liquor
Primary Menu: Chinese (2)
Areas of Operation: AR
Type of Foodservice: Casual Dining (2)
Catering Services: Yes
Primary Distributors: (Food) SYSCO Food Services of Arkansas LLC, LITTLE ROCK, AR

Key Personnel
I-KANG CHI - Owner; Executive Chef; Director Menu Development; General Buyer

Colton's Restaurant Group Inc.
5 Shackleford Plz Ste 200
Little Rock, AR 72211-1872

Telephone: (501) 225-6021
Fax Number: (501) 225-3946
Internet Homepage: coltonssteakhouse.com
Type of Business: Chain Restaurant Operator
Total Sales: $48,260,000 (e)
Alcohol Sales: 5%
Number of Employees: 287
Internet Order Processing: Yes
Total Units: 37
Trade Names: Colton's Steak House & Grill (37)
Company-Owned Units: 37
Alcohol Served: Beer, Wine, Liquor
Primary Menu: Steak (37)
Areas of Operation: AR, KS, KY, MO, MS, TN
Type of Foodservice: Casual Dining (37)

Key Personnel
ROBERT C. FAIN - President; General Buyer
THOMAS ORR - General Manager
DIXIE IVEY - Director Marketing

Razors Edge Pizza Inc
11600 N Rodney Parham Rd Ste B
Little Rock, AR 72212-4128

Telephone: (501) 228-8111
Type of Business: Chain Restaurant Operator
Total Sales: $9,990,000 (e)
Total Units: 5
Trade Names: Domino's (5)
Units Franchised From: 5
Primary Menu: Pizza (5)
Areas of Operation: AR
Type of Foodservice: Quick Serve (5)
Franchise Affiliation: Domino's Pizza Inc, ANN ARBOR, MI

Key Personnel
LANCE L. DENNER - Owner; General Buyer

TCBY The Country's Best Yogurt
11418 W Markham St
Little Rock, AR 72211-2806

Telephone: (501) 221-9020
Fax Number: (501) 221-9020
Internet Homepage: tcby.com
Type of Business: Chain Restaurant Operator
Total Units: 3
Trade Names: TCBY (3)
Units Franchised From: 3
Primary Menu: Snacks (3)
Areas of Operation: AR
Type of Foodservice: Quick Serve (3)
Franchise Affiliation: TCBY Systems LLC, BROOMFIELD, CO

Key Personnel
DON WEIR - President; General Buyer

US Pizza Co. Inc.
2710 Kavanaugh Blvd
Little Rock, AR 72205-3862

Mailing Address: PO Box 251710, LITTLE ROCK, AR, 72225-1710
Telephone: (501) 280-0399
Fax Number: (501) 280-0420
Internet Homepage: uspizzaco.net
Company Email: corporate@uspizzaco.net
Type of Business: Chain Restaurant Operator
Year Founded: 1972
Systemwide Sales: $15,730,000 (e)
Total Sales: $20,660,000 (e)
Alcohol Sales: 30%
Number of Employees: 387
Average Check: Lunch(18); Dinner(18)
Internet Order Processing: Yes
Total Units: 17
Trade Names: US Pizza Co. (17)
Company-Owned Units: 10
Units Franchised To: 7
Preferred Square Footage: 3,500
Preferred Location Types: Freestanding
Alcohol Served: Beer, Wine, Liquor
Primary Menu: Pizza (17)
Projected Openings: 1
Areas of Operation: AR
Type of Foodservice: Casual Dining (17)
Primary Distributors: (Equipment) Aimco Equipment, LITTLE ROCK, AR; (Food) SYSCO Food Services of Arkansas LLC, LITTLE ROCK, AR

Key Personnel
DREW WEBER - COO; Manager Finance, Human Resources

Whole Hog Cafe LLC
2516 Cantrell Rd
Little Rock, AR 72202-2116

Telephone: (501) 664-5025
Fax Number: (501) 664-6596
Internet Homepage: wholehogcafe.com
Company Email: wholehawg@alltel.net
Type of Business: Chain Restaurant Operator
Year Founded: 2000
Internet Order Processing: Yes
Total Units: 18
Trade Names: Whole Hog Cafe (18)
Company-Owned Units: 10

Units Franchised To: 8
Primary Menu: Bar-B-Q (18)
Areas of Operation: AR, MO, NJ, NM
Type of Foodservice: Fast Casual (18)
Catering Services: Yes

Key Personnel
MIKE DAVIS - Founder; Partner
STEVE LUCCHI - Founder; Partner
BLAIRE BLASINGAME - Partner

West Foods Inc.
810 Spring Creek Rd
Lowell, AR 72745-9008

Mailing Address: PO Box 1520, Lowell, AR, 72745
Telephone: (479) 927-3005
Fax Number: (479) 927-2998
Internet Homepage: westfoods.org
Company Email: Info@WestFoods.org
Type of Business: Chain Restaurant Operator
Year Founded: 1972
Total Sales: $22,790,000 (e)
Number of Employees: 180
Total Units: 40
Trade Names: Subway (40)
Units Franchised From: 40
Preferred Square Footage: 2,500
Preferred Location Types: Freestanding; Strip Mall
Primary Menu: Sandwiches/Deli (40)
Areas of Operation: AR, OK
Type of Foodservice: Quick Serve (40)
Franchise Affiliation: Doctor's Associates Inc., MILFORD, CT
Primary Distributors: (Full Line) Springfield Grocer Co. Inc., SPRINGFIELD, MO

Key Personnel
RANDY WEST - President; Executive Chef; Director Finance, Operations, Purchasing, Facility/Maintenance, Information Systems, Supply Chain, Ethnic Marketing, Real Estate, Design, Store Fixtures; General Buyer
SUSAN WEST - Treasurer

M & G Pizza Enterprises
8410 Counts Massie Rd
Maumelle, AR 72113-6691

Telephone: (501) 753-4111
Type of Business: Chain Restaurant Operator
Total Sales: $44,236,000 (e)
Total Units: 22
Trade Names: Domino's (22)
Units Franchised From: 22
Primary Menu: Pizza (22)
Areas of Operation: AR
Type of Foodservice: Quick Serve (22)
Franchise Affiliation: Domino's Pizza Inc, ANN ARBOR, MI

Key Personnel
BRENT J. MEDDERS - Owner; General Buyer

Leesco Inc
120 Commerce Dr
Monticello, AR 71655-9161

Telephone: (870) 460-0540
Fax Number: (870) 460-0541
Type of Business: Chain Restaurant Operator
Year Founded: 1983
Total Sales: $20,210,000 (e)
Number of Employees: 265
Average Check: Lunch(8); Dinner(8)
Total Units: 8
Trade Names: Popeyes Louisiana Kitchen (8)
Units Franchised From: 8
Preferred Square Footage: 2,500
Preferred Location Types: Freestanding
Primary Menu: Chicken (8)
Areas of Operation: AR, MS
Type of Foodservice: Quick Serve (8)
Franchise Affiliation: Popeyes Louisiana Kitchen Inc., ATLANTA, GA
Primary Distributors: (Full Line) McLane/Memphis, MEMPHIS, TN

Key Personnel
BOB LEE JR - CEO; President; Manager District; General Buyer

AR Fresh Mex, Inc.
4834 N Hills Blvd
North Little Rock, AR 72116-7621

Telephone: (501) 812-5577
Type of Business: Chain Restaurant Operator
Total Sales: $8,274,000 (e)
Total Units: 5
Trade Names: Moe's Southwest Grill (5)
Units Franchised From: 5
Primary Menu: Southwest/Tex-Mex (5)
Areas of Operation: AR
Type of Foodservice: Fast Casual (5)
Franchise Affiliation: Moe's Southwest Grill LLC, ATLANTA, GA

Key Personnel
MELANIE HOGGARD - Owner; General Buyer

Fourjay L.L.C.
42 Parkstone Cir
North Little Rock, AR 72116-7086

Telephone: (501) 372-2000
Fax Number: (501) 372-3055
Internet Homepage: fourjayllc.com
Type of Business: Chain Restaurant Operator
Year Founded: 1975
Total Sales: $131,520,000 (e)
Number of Employees: 2,100
Average Check: Lunch(6); Dinner(8)
Total Units: 48
Trade Names: Wendy's Old Fashioned Hamburgers (48)
Units Franchised From: 48
Preferred Square Footage: 3,000
Preferred Location Types: Freestanding
Primary Menu: Hamburger (48)
Areas of Operation: AR
Type of Foodservice: Quick Serve (48)
Franchise Affiliation: The Wendy's Company, DUBLIN, OH
Primary Distributors: (Food) The SYGMA Network Inc. - Oklahoma, PRYOR, OK

Key Personnel
HOWARD MARTINDALE - CEO

Hamner Enterprises
3210 E Race Ave
Searcy, AR 72143-4810

Telephone: (501) 268-2464
Fax Number: (501) 268-2465
Internet Homepage: westernsizzlin.com
Type of Business: Chain Restaurant Operator
Year Founded: 1988
Total Sales: $9,236,000 (e)
Alcohol Sales: 20%
Number of Employees: 250
Average Check: Breakfast(14); Lunch(16); Dinner(16)
Total Units: 3
Trade Names: WesterN SizzliN Steak & More (3)
Units Franchised From: 3
Preferred Location Types: Freestanding
Primary Menu: Steak (3)
Areas of Operation: AR
Type of Foodservice: Casual Dining (3)
Franchise Affiliation: The Western Sizzlin Corp., ROANOKE, VA

Key Personnel
ELGIN HAMNER III - President; General Manager; General Buyer
BOBBY HAMNER - General Manager

Alpha Subway
3920 E Kiehl Ave
Sherwood, AR 72120-3513

Telephone: (501) 835-6068
Fax Number: (501) 791-3399
Type of Business: Chain Restaurant Operator
Year Founded: 1985
Total Sales: $5,665,000 (e)

Number of Employees: 70
Average Check: Lunch(10); Dinner(16)
Total Units: 10
Trade Names: Subway (10)
Units Franchised From: 10
Preferred Square Footage: 300; 1,200; 2,000
Preferred Location Types: Freestanding
Primary Menu: Sandwiches/Deli (10)
Areas of Operation: AR
Type of Foodservice: Quick Serve (10)
Franchise Affiliation: Doctor's Associates Inc., MILFORD, CT

Key Personnel
TED THOMAS - President; General Buyer
LYNN THOMAS - Owner; VP; Controller; Manager Operations, Purchasing, Information Systems, Marketing, Advertising
JESS RENARD - General Manager

Sweet P Enterprises Inc.
1037 Lantrip Rd
Sherwood, AR 72120-4161

Telephone: (501) 834-0286
Fax Number: (501) 834-9197
Type of Business: Chain Restaurant Operator
Year Founded: 1988
Total Sales: $20,300,000 (e)
Number of Employees: 256
Average Check: Lunch(8); Dinner(8)
Total Units: 8
Trade Names: Popeyes Louisiana Kitchen (8)
Units Franchised From: 8
Preferred Square Footage: 2,000
Preferred Location Types: Freestanding
Primary Menu: Chicken (8)
Areas of Operation: AR
Type of Foodservice: Quick Serve (8)
Franchise Affiliation: Popeyes Louisiana Kitchen Inc., ATLANTA, GA
Primary Distributors: (Food) Performance Foodservice - Little Rock, LITTLE ROCK, AR

Key Personnel
DANNY GILILLAND - President; Director Finance, Operations, Purchasing, Information Systems, Marketing, Human Resources; General Buyer

Best Burgers LLC
1509 Wesley Ave
Springdale, AR 72764-0901

Telephone: (870) 741-2232
Fax Number: (479) 756-1850
Type of Business: Chain Restaurant Operator
Year Founded: 1937
Total Sales: $17,730,000 (e)
Number of Employees: 175
Average Check: Breakfast(5); Lunch(8); Dinner(8)
Total Units: 8
Trade Names: Burger King (8)
Units Franchised From: 8
Preferred Square Footage: 3,000; 4,000
Preferred Location Types: Freestanding; Travel Plazas
Primary Menu: Hamburger (8)
Areas of Operation: AR
Type of Foodservice: Quick Serve (8)
Franchise Affiliation: Burger King Worldwide Inc., MIAMI, FL

Key Personnel
TERRY CLARK - President; General Manager; Director Real Estate; Manager Purchasing, Facility/Maintenance, Information Systems, Store Planning
ANDY REA - VP Operations

ESCH Inc
4100 Corporate Center Dr Ste 220
Springdale, AR 72762-5768

Telephone: (479) 443-5881
Fax Number: (479) 443-5895
Type of Business: Chain Restaurant Operator
Year Founded: 1970
Total Sales: $140,840,000 (e)
Number of Employees: 1,348
Average Check: Breakfast(8); Lunch(8); Dinner(10)
Total Units: 66
Trade Names: Sonic America's Drive-In (66)
Units Franchised From: 66
Preferred Square Footage: 1,200
Preferred Location Types: Freestanding
Primary Menu: Hamburger (66)
Areas of Operation: AR, GA, IL, KS, MO, TN
Type of Foodservice: Quick Serve (66)
Franchise Affiliation: Sonic Corp., OKLAHOMA CITY, OK
Primary Distributors: (Food) US Foods, LUBBOCK, TX

Key Personnel
A.J. MOSES - CFO
TONY SHERMAN - COO; General Manager; Director Facility/Maintenance, Supply Chain; General Buyer
MEGAN WILLIAMS - Director Human Resources
GINA GRANT - Coordinator Accounting

McDonald's of Northwest Arkansas
1468 E Mountain Rd Ste A
Springdale, AR 72764-3753

Mailing Address: PO Box 1366, SPRINGDALE, AR, 72765-1366
Telephone: (479) 751-9617
Fax Number: (479) 751-4089
Type of Business: Chain Restaurant Operator
Year Founded: 1983
Total Sales: $46,220,000 (e)
Number of Employees: 1,850
Average Check: Breakfast(8); Lunch(8); Dinner(8)
Total Units: 35
Trade Names: McDonald's (35)
Units Franchised From: 35
Preferred Square Footage: 3,000
Preferred Location Types: Discount Dept. Stores; Freestanding
Primary Menu: Hamburger (35)
Projected Openings: 10
Areas of Operation: AR, MO, OK
Type of Foodservice: Quick Serve (35)
Franchise Affiliation: McDonald's Corporation, CHICAGO, IL
Primary Distributors: (Full Line) The Martin-Brower Co., NORTH LITTLE ROCK, AR

Key Personnel
BILL MATHEWS - President; Partner; Controller; General Manager; Director Supply Chain, Real Estate; General Buyer
WALTER MATHEWS - Partner; Manager Facility/Maintenance, Information Systems, Design, Human Resources
MARK MOTLEY - Director Operations

Sonic Drive-In of Stuttgart
1121 S Main St
Stuttgart, AR 72160-5305

Telephone: (870) 673-8700
Fax Number: (870) 673-6571
Type of Business: Chain Restaurant Operator
Year Founded: 1974
Total Sales: $38,170,000 (e)
Number of Employees: 515
Average Check: Breakfast(8); Lunch(10); Dinner(10)
Total Units: 18
Trade Names: Sonic America's Drive-In (18)
Units Franchised From: 18
Preferred Square Footage: 1,320
Preferred Location Types: Freestanding
Primary Menu: Hamburger (18)
Areas of Operation: AR, GA
Type of Foodservice: Quick Serve (18)
Franchise Affiliation: Sonic Corp., OKLAHOMA CITY, OK
Primary Distributors: (Food) US Foods, OKLAHOMA CITY, OK

Key Personnel
MARC MACKENZIE - Owner; General Manager; Director Finance, Operations, Facility/Maintenance, Information Systems, Marketing, Real Estate, Human Resources;

General Buyer

ARIZONA

Barnett Management
650 N 99th Ave Ste 108
Avondale, AZ 85323-5328

Telephone: (602) 864-9874
Fax Number: (602) 864-9791
Internet Homepage: barnettburgerkings.com
Company Email: info@barnettmgt.com
Type of Business: Chain Restaurant Operator
Year Founded: 1980
Total Sales: $81,070,000 (e)
Number of Employees: 1,285
Average Check: Breakfast(6); Lunch(8); Dinner(8)
Total Units: 36
Trade Names: Burger King (36)
Units Franchised From: 36
Preferred Square Footage: 2,500
Preferred Location Types: Airports; Freestanding; Regional Mall
Alcohol Served: Beer, Wine, Liquor
Primary Menu: Hamburger (36)
Projected Openings: 3
Areas of Operation: AZ
Type of Foodservice: Quick Serve (36)
Franchise Affiliation: Burger King Worldwide Inc., MIAMI, FL
Primary Distributors: (Full Line) Shamrock Foods Co., PHOENIX, AZ

Key Personnel
TOM BARNETT - CEO; Director Supply Chain, Real Estate; Manager Purchasing
SHELLEY KRISPIN - President; Director Operations, Facility/Maintenance, Information Systems, Risk Management, Design, Store Fixtures
STEPHANIE STOUT - Controller
TONYA SCOTT - Director Human Resources
BRAD FLAHIFF - Director Development
EZEQUIEL FERNANDEZ - Director Operations
SHANE JACOBS - Manager Operations

Yogurtland Franchisee
10220 W McDowell Rd Ste 140
Avondale, AZ 85392-4848

Telephone: (623) 478-5455
Type of Business: Chain Restaurant Operator
Total Sales: $4,170,000 (e)
Total Units: 4
Trade Names: Yogurtland (4)
Units Franchised From: 4
Primary Menu: Snacks (4)
Areas of Operation: AZ
Type of Foodservice: Quick Serve (4)
Franchise Affiliation: Yogurtland Franchising Inc., FARMERS BRANCH, TX

Key Personnel
JERRY COLANGELO - Owner; General Buyer
GARY HUNTER - Director Franchise Operations
MICHAEL WALLACE - Director Operations
JIN LEE - Project Manager

B & D Restaurants
2250 N Pinal Ave Ste 2
Casa Grande, AZ 85122-6218

Mailing Address: PO Box 10550, CASA GRANDE, AZ, 85130-0079
Telephone: (520) 836-4850
Company Email: mcdonalds.customer.comment@gmail.com
Type of Business: Chain Restaurant Operator
Total Sales: $47,340,000 (e)
Number of Employees: 444
Total Units: 10
Trade Names: McDonald's (10)
Units Franchised From: 10
Preferred Square Footage: 2,500
Preferred Location Types: Convenience Store/Gas Station; Discount Dept. Stores; Freestanding
Primary Menu: Hamburger (10)
Projected Remodelings: 2
Areas of Operation: AZ
Type of Foodservice: Quick Serve (10)
Franchise Affiliation: McDonald's Corporation, CHICAGO, IL

Key Personnel
ROBERT SOUZA - President; General Buyer

Superior Fast Foods, LLC
1194 E Florence Blvd
Casa Grande, AZ 85122-4216

Telephone: (520) 836-0304
Type of Business: Chain Restaurant Operator
Total Sales: $55,430,000 (e)
Total Units: 22
Trade Names: Jack in the Box (22)
Units Franchised From: 22
Primary Menu: Hamburger (22)
Projected Openings: 1
Areas of Operation: AZ
Type of Foodservice: Quick Serve (22)
Franchise Affiliation: Jack in the Box Restaurants, SAN DIEGO, CA

Key Personnel
ADEL FARAG - President; General Buyer
SAUNDRA ANDERSON - Manager Human Resources
MICHELLE FARAG - Manager Administration

HODA ELIA - Office Manager

El Encanto Restaurants
6248 E Cave Creek Rd
Cave Creek, AZ 85331

Telephone: (480) 488-1752
Fax Number: (480) 488-2485
Internet Homepage: elencantorestaurants.com
Type of Business: Chain Restaurant Operator
Year Founded: 1989
Total Units: 3
Trade Names: El Encanto (3)
Company-Owned Units: 3
Preferred Location Types: Freestanding
Primary Menu: Mexican (3)
Areas of Operation: AZ
Type of Foodservice: Casual Dining (3)

Key Personnel
CHRISTINE NELSON - Owner
BJ LAMIS - General Manager
DAVID LAUFER - General Manager

Stingley Management
28706 N 56th St
Cave Creek, AZ 85331

Telephone: (480) 585-4142
Type of Business: Chain Restaurant Operator
Total Sales: $60,620,000 (e)
Number of Employees: 221
Total Units: 13
Trade Names: McDonald's (13)
Units Franchised From: 13
Preferred Square Footage: 2,500
Preferred Location Types: Airports; Discount Dept. Stores; Freestanding
Primary Menu: Hamburger (13)
Areas of Operation: AZ
Type of Foodservice: Quick Serve (13)
Franchise Affiliation: McDonald's Corporation, CHICAGO, IL

Key Personnel
WAYNE STINGLEY - President; General Buyer
ANGELA BOWDEN - Director Human Resources

AMD Pizza LLC
3125 S Alma School Rd Ste 1
Chandler, AZ 85248-3759

Telephone: (480) 786-3338
Type of Business: Chain Restaurant Operator
Total Sales: $62,546,000 (e)
Total Units: 31
Trade Names: Domino's (31)
Units Franchised From: 31

Primary Menu: Pizza (31)
Areas of Operation: AZ, ID, NV, UT
Type of Foodservice: Quick Serve (31)
Franchise Affiliation: Domino's Pizza Inc, ANN ARBOR, MI

Key Personnel
CHARLES M. RIDDLE - Owner; General Buyer

BARZZA LLC
3330 N Dobson Rd Ste 1
Chandler, AZ 85224-1249

Telephone: (480) 897-0521
Fax Number: (480) 897-1551
Internet Homepage: barrospizza.com
Company Email: social@barrospizza.com
Type of Business: Chain Restaurant Operator
Year Founded: 1980
Total Units: 43
Trade Names: Barro's Pizza (43)
Company-Owned Units: 43
Alcohol Served: Beer, Wine
Primary Menu: Pizza (43)
Areas of Operation: AZ
Type of Foodservice: Casual Dining (43)

Key Personnel
BRUCE BARRO - Partner; General Buyer

Chompie's
3481 W Frye Rd Ste 324
Chandler, AZ 85226

Telephone: (480) 398-3008
Fax Number: (602) 765-9128
Internet Homepage: chompies.com
Type of Business: Chain Restaurant Operator
Year Founded: 1978
Total Sales: $36,590,000 (e)
Alcohol Sales: 2%
Number of Employees: 350
Average Check: Breakfast(12); Lunch(12); Dinner(12)
Internet Order Processing: Yes
Total Units: 9
Trade Names: Chompie's (9)
Company-Owned Units: 9
Preferred Location Types: Freestanding
Alcohol Served: Beer, Wine, Liquor
Primary Menu: Sandwiches/Deli (9)
Areas of Operation: AZ
Type of Foodservice: Fast Casual (9)
Catering Services: Yes
Primary Distributors: (Food) SYSCO Food Services of Arizona Inc., TOLLESON, AZ

Key Personnel
LOU BORENSTEIN - President; Partner; General Manager Menu Development;
General Buyer
MARK BORENSTEIN - Partner; General Manager; General Buyer
NEAL BORENSTEIN - Partner; General Manager; General Buyer
WENDY BORENSTEIN - Partner; Exec VP; General Manager; General Buyer

Desert Subway Inc.
100 S McClintock Dr Ste 100
Chandler, AZ 85226-4816

Telephone: (480) 705-8500
Fax Number: (480) 705-8505
Internet Homepage: desertsubway.net
Company Email: desertsubway@gmail.com
Type of Business: Chain Restaurant Operator
Year Founded: 1987
Total Sales: $62,730,000 (e)
Number of Employees: 684
Average Check: Lunch(8); Dinner(8)
Total Units: 46
Trade Names: Subway (46)
Units Franchised From: 46
Preferred Square Footage: 800; 1,200; 1,600
Preferred Location Types: Freestanding; Regional Mall; Strip Mall
Primary Menu: Sandwiches/Deli (46)
Areas of Operation: AZ, HI
Type of Foodservice: Quick Serve (46)
Franchise Affiliation: Doctor's Associates Inc., MILFORD, CT
Primary Distributors: (Full Line) Shamrock Foods Co., PHOENIX, AZ

Key Personnel
MARK RODEN - President; General Buyer
CHERRYL WICKWIRE - VP Human Resources
CHERRYL WORK - VP Human Resources
PATRICK PATTERSON - Controller

GB Restaurants Inc./Top Line Restaurants
3170 S Gilbert Rd
Chandler, AZ 85286

Telephone: (480) 722-9196
Fax Number: (480) 722-9197
Type of Business: Chain Restaurant Operator
Total Sales: $89,290,000 (e)
Total Units: 31
Trade Names: Denny's (31)
Units Franchised From: 31
Preferred Location Types: Freestanding
Primary Menu: American (31)
Areas of Operation: AZ, NY
Type of Foodservice: Family Restaurant (31)
Franchise Affiliation: Denny's Corporation, SPARTANBURG, SC
Notes: The Denny's restaurants in NY operate as Top Line Restaurants.

Key Personnel
GLENN BEATTIE - President; Partner
TINA BEATTIE - Partner
ALLEN STINER - Director Human Resources

JNH / BBH / CNH Food LLC
1919 W Chandler Blvd
Chandler, AZ 85224

Telephone: (480) 899-2172
Type of Business: Chain Restaurant Operator
Total Sales: $50,990,000 (e)
Total Units: 52
Trade Names: Pizza Hut (52)
Units Franchised From: 52
Primary Menu: Pizza (52)
Areas of Operation: AZ, TX
Type of Foodservice: Quick Serve (52)

Key Personnel
NICOLE N. HOUSEHOLDER - President; Partner; General Buyer
BRIAN HOUSEHOLDER - Partner

S & M Desert Pizza, Inc.
3800 S Alma School Rd
Chandler, AZ 85248

Telephone: (480) 242-6096
Type of Business: Chain Restaurant Operator
Total Sales: $7,382,000 (e)
Total Units: 6
Trade Names: Little Caesars Pizza (6)
Units Franchised From: 6
Primary Menu: Pizza (6)
Projected Openings: 1
Areas of Operation: AZ
Type of Foodservice: Quick Serve (6)
Franchise Affiliation: Little Caesar Enterprises Inc., DETROIT, MI

Key Personnel
TIM MOUSER - Partner; General Buyer
BRUCE SAPIRO - Partner; General Buyer

Someburros, Inc.
2727 W Frye Rd Ste 205
Chandler, AZ 85224-4941

Telephone: (480) 240-9399
Internet Homepage: isabelsamor.com; someburros.com
Company Email: info@IsabelsAmor.com
Type of Business: Chain Restaurant Operator
Year Founded: 1986
Total Units: 10
Trade Names: Isabel's Amor (1); Someburros

(9)
Company-Owned Units: 10
Preferred Location Types: Freestanding; Stadiums
Primary Menu: Mexican (10)
Projected Openings: 2
Areas of Operation: AZ
Type of Foodservice: Casual Dining (1); Fast Casual (9)

Key Personnel
TIM VASQUEZ - CEO; President
JOHNNY BEERLING - COO
DORA BARNES - General Manager
ALMA VELASQUEZ - General Manager
CESAR MARQUEZ - General Manager
RENEE PRADO - General Manager
ABI ARROYO - General Manager
BRIAN GERLACH - General Manager
ALLYSON DELL AMICO - Director Human Resources
DANIELLE DRESSOR - Director Marketing, Sales
ISABEL HUDSON - Manager Operations

Tom's BBQ Systems, Inc.
2820 S Alma School Rd Ste 6
Chandler, AZ 85286

Telephone: (480) 812-2733
Internet Homepage: tomsbbq.com
Company Email: info@tomsbbq.com
Type of Business: Chain Restaurant Operator
Year Founded: 1988
Total Units: 4
Trade Names: Tom's BBQ (4)
Company-Owned Units: 4
Primary Menu: Bar-B-Q (4)
Areas of Operation: AZ
Type of Foodservice: Casual Dining (4)

Key Personnel
RICK PAWLAK - Partner
BRENDA RYAN - Partner

Valley Subs of Arizona, L.L.C.
1085 W Queen Creek Rd Ste 6-7
Chandler, AZ 85248-8128

Telephone: (480) 857-8184
Internet Homepage: rlrestaurants.com/jerseymikes/index.htm
Type of Business: Chain Restaurant Operator
Total Sales: $29,830,000 (e)
Total Units: 22
Trade Names: Jersey Mike's Subs (22)
Units Franchised From: 22
Primary Menu: Sandwiches/Deli (22)
Areas of Operation: AZ

Type of Foodservice: Quick Serve (22)
Franchise Affiliation: Jersey Mike's Franchise Systems, MANASQUAN, NJ

Key Personnel
STEVE ROSENFIELD - Partner; General Buyer
ALICIA ROSENFIELD - Partner
DUANE LAYTON - Partner

Yogurtland Franchisee
3355 W Chandler Blvd
Chandler, AZ 85226-5096

Telephone: (480) 857-2515
Type of Business: Chain Restaurant Operator
Total Sales: $8,370,000 (e)
Total Units: 9
Trade Names: Yogurtland (9)
Units Franchised From: 9
Primary Menu: Snacks (9)
Projected Openings: 8
Areas of Operation: AZ, CA, TX
Type of Foodservice: Quick Serve (9)
Franchise Affiliation: Yogurtland Franchising Inc., FARMERS BRANCH, TX

Key Personnel
CHARLIE YANG - Chairman; Owner; General Buyer
ALLAN YANG - CEO

Domino's Franchisee
1529 S Milton Rd
Flagstaff, AZ 86001-6309

Telephone: (928) 779-3686
Type of Business: Chain Restaurant Operator
Total Sales: $3,991,000 (e)
Total Units: 2
Trade Names: Domino's (2)
Units Franchised From: 2
Primary Menu: Pizza (2)
Areas of Operation: AZ
Type of Foodservice: Quick Serve (2)
Franchise Affiliation: Domino's Pizza Inc, ANN ARBOR, MI

Key Personnel
RICHARD S. HULEATT - Owner; General Buyer

Northern Arizona Fast Foods, Inc.
619 N Humphreys St
Flagstaff, AZ 86001-3023

Telephone: (928) 213-8996
Type of Business: Chain Restaurant Operator
Total Sales: $15,290,000 (e)

Total Units: 6
Trade Names: Jack in the Box (6)
Units Franchised From: 6
Primary Menu: Hamburger (6)
Areas of Operation: AZ
Type of Foodservice: Quick Serve (6)
Franchise Affiliation: Jack in the Box Restaurants, SAN DIEGO, CA

Key Personnel
ADAM SCHMITZ - Owner; General Buyer

SACO Management
1024 N San Francisco St Ste 103
Flagstaff, AZ 86001-3266

Telephone: (928) 779-4523
Fax Number: (928) 779-3118
Type of Business: Chain Restaurant Operator
Year Founded: 1991
Total Sales: $9,374,000 (e)
Number of Employees: 300
Average Check: Lunch(6); Dinner(14)
Total Units: 9
Trade Names: Del Taco (7); Sizzler (2)
Units Franchised From: 9
Preferred Square Footage: 2,100; 2,800
Preferred Location Types: Freestanding
Primary Menu: Steak (2); Taco (7)
Areas of Operation: AZ
Type of Foodservice: Family Restaurant (2); Quick Serve (7)
Franchise Affiliation: Del Taco Restaurants Inc., LAKE FOREST, CA; Sizzler USA Inc., MISSION VIEJO, CA
Primary Distributors: (Food) Shamrock Foods Co., PHOENIX, AZ

Key Personnel
FERREL FREER - Partner; General Buyer
MARY FREER - Partner; General Buyer
BOB BOYLE - CFO; Controller
JOHN FREER - General Manager

Adcorp Inc
15430 E Crested Butte Trl
Fountain Hills, AZ 85268-5984

Telephone: (480) 661-0261
Type of Business: Chain Restaurant Operator
Total Sales: $47,570,000 (e)
Total Units: 10
Trade Names: McDonald's (10)
Units Franchised From: 10
Primary Menu: Hamburger (10)
Areas of Operation: AZ
Type of Foodservice: Quick Serve (10)
Franchise Affiliation: McDonald's Corporation, CHICAGO, IL

Key Personnel
EARNEST ADAIR - President; Partner; General Buyer
MARY L. ADAIR - Partner; General Buyer

FX4 LLC
225 E Germann Rd Ste 150
Gilbert, AZ 85297-2909

Telephone: (480) 990-7144
Fax Number: (480) 990-1839
Internet Homepage: azarbys.com
Company Email: info@azarbys.com
Type of Business: Chain Restaurant Operator
Year Founded: 2000
Total Sales: $80,190,000 (e)
Number of Employees: 114
Average Check: Lunch(8); Dinner(8)
Total Units: 42
Trade Names: Arby's (42)
Units Franchised From: 42
Preferred Square Footage: 2,500; 3,000
Preferred Location Types: Freestanding
Primary Menu: Sandwiches/Deli (42)
Areas of Operation: AZ, NM
Type of Foodservice: Quick Serve (42)
Franchise Affiliation: Arby's Restaurant Group, ATLANTA, GA

Key Personnel
CHARLES R. HARMON - President; Partner; General Manager; General Buyer
LINDA L. HARMON - Partner
CHRIS HARMON - Manager Information Systems

Gecko Grill Enterprises LLC
4341 E Baseline Rd
Gilbert, AZ 85234-2959

Telephone: (480) 539-2988
Internet Homepage: geckogrillaz.com
Type of Business: Chain Restaurant Operator
Year Founded: 2001
Total Units: 8
Trade Names: Moreno's Gecko Grill (1); Moreno's Mexican Grill (7)
Company-Owned Units: 8
Primary Menu: Mexican (8)
Projected Openings: 1
Areas of Operation: AZ
Type of Foodservice: Casual Dining (8)
Catering Services: Yes

Key Personnel
FRANCISCO MORENO - Partner; General Manager; Executive Chef
JOSE A. MORENO - Partner
MARTINA MORENO - Partner

Papa John's Distribution Center
2075 W Obispo Ave
Gilbert, AZ 85233-3411

Telephone: (480) 497-8800
Listing Type: Distribution Center
Type of Business: Chain Restaurant Operator
Areas of Operation: AZ, CA, NM, NV, TX
Parent Company: Papa Johns International Inc., LOUISVILLE, KY

Key Personnel
ALEX CORRALES - Manager Distribution

Protein House
3097 E Pecos Rd Suite 106
Gilbert, AZ 85295

Telephone: (702) 487-7890
Internet Homepage: www-protein-house.com
Type of Business: Chain Restaurant Operator
Year Founded: 2012
Total Units: 9
Trade Names: ProteinHouse (9)
Company-Owned Units: 9
Primary Menu: Health Foods (9)
Type of Foodservice: Quick Serve (9)

Key Personnel
TOM GAUPEL - Owner
HEIDI GAUPEL - Owner
KAREY NORTHINGTON - Owner

Salad and Go
743 N Gilbert Rd
Gilbert, AZ 85234-4532

Telephone: (480) 304-5662
Internet Homepage: saladandgo.com
Company Email: info@saladandgo.com
Type of Business: Chain Restaurant Operator
Year Founded: 2013
Systemwide Sales: $13,028,000 (e)
Total Sales: $14,750,000 (e)
Total Units: 20
Trade Names: Salad and Go (20)
Company-Owned Units: 20
Preferred Square Footage: 656
Primary Menu: American (20)
Areas of Operation: AZ
Type of Foodservice: Quick Serve (20)

Key Personnel
DANIEL PATINO - Co-Founder; Executive Chef
CHARLIE MORRISON - CEO
DIJA FRASER - Chief People Officer
TYLER STRAKER - Chief of Staff; VP Strategy

BRIAN STEELE - Director Information Technology, Infrastructure, Security

Cupbop
9410 W Hanna Ln Suite A101
Glendale, AZ 85305

Telephone: (160) 286-02713
Internet Homepage: cupbop.com
Type of Business: Chain Restaurant Operator
Year Founded: 2013
Total Sales: $22,450,000 (e)
Total Units: 52
Trade Names: Cupbop (52)
Company-Owned Units: 1
Units Franchised To: 51
Primary Menu: Bar-B-Q (52)
Areas of Operation: AZ, CO, ID, NV, OK, TX, UT
Type of Foodservice: Quick Serve (52)

Key Personnel
JUNGHUN SONG - Founder; Owner

JMJ LLC
5535 W Glenn Dr
Glendale, AZ 85301-2544

Telephone: (623) 463-2885
Fax Number: (623) 463-2886
Internet Homepage: jmj-llc.com
Type of Business: Chain Restaurant Operator
Total Sales: $35,550,000 (e)
Total Units: 13
Trade Names: Wendy's Old Fashioned Hamburgers (13)
Units Franchised From: 13
Primary Menu: Hamburger (13)
Areas of Operation: AZ
Type of Foodservice: Quick Serve (13)
Franchise Affiliation: The Wendy's Company, DUBLIN, OH

Key Personnel
JASON PASTORE - Partner; General Buyer
JOHN MOORE - CFO
VANNESSA BROWN - Director Operations

Lanini Corp
5842 W Olive Ave
Glendale, AZ 85302-3100

Telephone: (623) 931-2153
Listing Type: Subsidiary
Type of Business: Chain Restaurant Operator
Total Sales: $38,220,000 (e)
Total Units: 8
Trade Names: McDonald's (8)
Units Franchised From: 8

Primary Menu: Hamburger (8)
Areas of Operation: AZ
Type of Foodservice: Quick Serve (8)
Franchise Affiliation: McDonald's Corporation, CHICAGO, IL

Key Personnel
STEPHEN K. LANINI - President; General Buyer

Stine Enterprises, Inc
4305 W Bethany Home Rd
Glendale, AZ 85301-5401

Telephone: (623) 931-0026
Type of Business: Chain Restaurant Operator
Total Sales: $181,350,000 (e)
Total Units: 86
Trade Names: Jack in the Box (86)
Units Franchised From: 86
Primary Menu: Hamburger (86)
Areas of Operation: AZ
Type of Foodservice: Quick Serve (86)
Franchise Affiliation: Jack in the Box Restaurants, SAN DIEGO, CA

Key Personnel
ADAM STINE - President; Partner
STEPHEN STINE - Partner
TIM FLYNN - CFO
CLIFFORD COLMONE - VP Operations
AUTUMN LACISTE - Controller
CLIFF COLMONE - Director Operations
CATHERINE MONROE - Director Administration, Risk Management, Legal

Tailgaters Sports Grill & II Primo
6070 W Bell Rd
Glendale, AZ 85308

Telephone: (602) 547-9366
Internet Homepage: tgpizza.com
Type of Business: Chain Restaurant Operator
Total Sales: $6,600,000 (e)
Total Units: 6
Trade Names: Tailgaters (6)
Company-Owned Units: 6
Primary Menu: American (6)
Areas of Operation: AZ
Type of Foodservice: Casual Dining (6)

Key Personnel
TODD LOHR - Owner

Mellon & Son Inc.
1616 N Litchfield Rd Ste 270
Goodyear, AZ 85395-1289

Telephone: (623) 932-7992
Fax Number: (623) 932-4895
Type of Business: Chain Restaurant Operator
Year Founded: 1980
Total Sales: $81,660,000 (e)
Number of Employees: 745
Average Check: Breakfast(8); Lunch(8); Dinner(8)
Total Units: 17
Trade Names: McDonald's (17)
Units Franchised From: 17
Preferred Square Footage: 3,000
Preferred Location Types: Freestanding
Primary Menu: Hamburger (17)
Areas of Operation: AZ
Type of Foodservice: Quick Serve (17)
Franchise Affiliation: McDonald's Corporation, CHICAGO, IL
Primary Distributors: (Food) The Martin-Brower Co., PHOENIX, AZ

Key Personnel
DON MELLON SR - President; Director Real Estate

Hot Tacos, Inc.
2255 Airway Ave
Kingman, AZ 86409-3644

Mailing Address: PO Box 4179, KINGMAN, AZ, 86402-6279
Telephone: (602) 268-9266
Type of Business: Chain Restaurant Operator
Total Sales: $203,760,000 (e)
Total Units: 73
Trade Names: Taco Bell (73)
Units Franchised From: 73
Primary Menu: Taco (73)
Areas of Operation: AZ
Type of Foodservice: Quick Serve (73)
Franchise Affiliation: Taco Bell Corp., IRVINE, CA

Key Personnel
LESLIE PIERSON - President

Peterson-Burge Enterprises/Desert De Oro Foods
3845 N Stockton Hill Rd
Kingman, AZ 86409-3059

Mailing Address: PO Box 4179, KINGMAN, AZ, 86402-3839

Telephone: (928) 681-3344
Fax Number: (928) 681-3338
Internet Homepage: ddofoods.com; desertbbq.com
Company Email: info@tacos.com
Type of Business: Chain Restaurant Operator
Year Founded: 1982
Total Sales: $480,530,000 (e)
Alcohol Sales: 1%
Number of Employees: 4,364
Average Check: Breakfast(6); Lunch(6); Dinner(14)
Total Units: 195
Trade Names: Dickey's Barbecue Pit (9); KFC (16); Long John Silver's (11); Pizza Hut (63); Taco Bell (96)
Units Franchised From: 195
Preferred Square Footage: 3,000
Preferred Location Types: Freestanding; Regional Mall; Strip Mall
Primary Menu: Bar-B-Q (9); Chicken (16); Pizza (63); Seafood (11); Taco (96)
Areas of Operation: AZ, CA, NV, TX, UT, WY
Type of Foodservice: Fast Casual (9); Quick Serve (186)
Franchise Affiliation: Dickey's Barbecue Restaurants Inc., DALLAS, TX; KFC Corporation, LOUISVILLE, KY; Long John Silver's Inc., LOUISVILLE, KY; Pizza Hut Inc., PLANO, TX; Taco Bell Corp., IRVINE, CA
Primary Distributors: (Full Line) McLane/Phoenix, PHOENIX, AZ

Key Personnel
MARK PETERSON - President; Partner
KRYSTAL BURGE - Partner; General Buyer
MICHAEL DOBBERPUHL - CFO
DAVID PEAR - VP
CHRISTOPHER BRADY - Director Marketing, Communications, Public Relations
JO ADAMS - Director Human Resources
KORD CARTRETTE - Director Facility/Maintenance
KIM CARTRETTE - Director Operations
DEBBIE CARVER - Director Operations
MICKEY GRANT - Director Training
RICHARD GALLAGHER - Regional Director
TERESA ELY - Manager Accounting
RENEE GRIGG - Manager Risk Management
MATT SIMPSON - Manager Marketing
PAM PLEW - Coordinator Development
LUPO JASO - Coach

Shugrue's Restaurant & Lounge
1425 McCulloch Blvd N
Lake Havasu City, AZ 86403-6597

Telephone: (928) 453-1400
Internet Homepage: flyingxsaloon.com; makaicafe.com; barleybrothers.com; javelinacantina.com; legendzbarandfrill.com; shugrues.com; shugrueslakehavasu.com

Company Email: lakehavasu@shugrues.com
Type of Business: Chain Restaurant Operator
Year Founded: 1988
Total Sales: $12,270,000 (e)
Alcohol Sales: 30%
Number of Employees: 385
Average Check: Lunch(14); Dinner(30)
Total Units: 7
Trade Names: Barley Brothers Brewery & Grill (1); Flying X Saloon (1); Javelina Cantina (1); Legendz Sports Bar and Grill (1); Makai Cafe (1); Shugrue's Restaurant & Bar (1); Taver 95 (1)
Company-Owned Units: 7
Preferred Square Footage: 5,500; 6,000
Preferred Location Types: Freestanding
Alcohol Served: Beer, Wine, Liquor
Primary Menu: American (6); Mexican (1)
Areas of Operation: AZ
Type of Foodservice: Casual Dining (6); Fine Dining (1)
Catering Services: Yes
Primary Distributors: (Food) Shamrock Foods Co., PHOENIX, AZ; (Supplies) Shamrock Foods Colorado Division, COMMERCE CITY, CO

Key Personnel
THOM FELKE - Partner; General Manager; Director Facility/Maintenance, Information Systems, Design
MARK SHUGRUE - Partner; Director Finance, Real Estate, Design
TIM SHUGRUE - Partner; Director Supply Chain; General Buyer
DANI WEBB - Partner; General Manager
GREG GUGLIOTTA - Executive Chef; Director Menu Development; General Buyer

P R H Foods Inc
RR 1 Box 402-B5
Lakeside, AZ 85929

Telephone: (928) 367-2224
Type of Business: Chain Restaurant Operator
Total Sales: $4,543,000 (e)
Total Units: 8
Trade Names: Subway (8)
Units Franchised From: 8
Primary Menu: Sandwiches/Deli (8)
Areas of Operation: AZ
Type of Foodservice: Quick Serve (8)
Franchise Affiliation: Doctor's Associates Inc., MILFORD, CT

Key Personnel
PHIL HAGAERON - President

Wigwam Golf Resort and Spa
300 E Wigwam Blvd
Litchfield Park, AZ 85340-4410

Telephone: (623) 935-3811
Fax Number: (623) 935-3737
Internet Homepage: wigwamarizona.com
Company Email: wigwaminfo@wigwamarizona.com
Type of Business: Chain Restaurant Operator
Year Founded: 1929
Total Sales: $8,700,000 (e)
Alcohol Sales: 30%
Number of Employees: 150
Average Check: Breakfast(20); Lunch(40); Dinner(66)
Total Units: 4
Trade Names: Litchfield's (1); Red's Bar & Grille (1); The Tower Bar & Grill (1); The Wigwam Bar (1)
Company-Owned Units: 4
Preferred Square Footage: 1,500; 1,950; 2,250
Preferred Location Types: Hotel/Motel
Alcohol Served: Beer, Wine, Liquor
Primary Menu: American (3); Steak/Seafood (1)
Areas of Operation: AZ
Type of Foodservice: Casual Dining (2); Fine Dining (1); Quick Serve (1)
Catering Services: Yes
Primary Distributors: (Full Line) Shamrock Foods Co., PHOENIX, AZ

Key Personnel
MARIE SIMPSON - Manager Sales, National
JENNA SULLIVAN - Manager Event Planning
MARK HUTCHINS - Corporate Manager Sales

Angry Crab Shack
2740 S Alma School Rd
Mesa, AZ 85210-4025

Telephone: (480) 730-2722
Internet Homepage: angrycrabshack.com
Company Email: info@angrycrabshack.com
Type of Business: Chain Restaurant Operator
Year Founded: 2013
Total Sales: $32,860,000 (e)
Total Units: 19
Trade Names: Angry Crab Shack (19)
Company-Owned Units: 8
Units Franchised To: 11
Primary Menu: Seafood (19)
Projected Openings: 1
Areas of Operation: AZ
Type of Foodservice: Casual Dining (19)

Key Personnel
RON LOU - Partner

DAVID ENG - Partner
BRIAN HERSKOVETS - Director Franchise Operations
STEVEN ROGERS - Director Information Technology
JASON BECK - Regional Manager

Comida Corporation
1264 S Gilbert Rd
Mesa, AZ 85204-6002

Telephone: (480) 892-7955
Internet Homepage: miamigos.com
Type of Business: Chain Restaurant Operator
Year Founded: 1977
Total Sales: $5,469,000 (e)
Alcohol Sales: 25%
Number of Employees: 250
Average Check: Lunch(8); Dinner(12)
Total Units: 2
Trade Names: Mi Amigos (2)
Company-Owned Units: 2
Preferred Location Types: Freestanding; Strip Mall
Alcohol Served: Beer, Wine, Liquor
Primary Menu: Mexican (2)
Areas of Operation: AZ
Type of Foodservice: Casual Dining (2)
Primary Distributors: (Full Line) Shamrock Foods Co., PHOENIX, AZ

Key Personnel
OSCAR CORONADO - General Manager

DWG Enterprises, LLC
408 W Juanita Ave
Mesa, AZ 85210-6010

Telephone: (480) 833-6540
Type of Business: Chain Restaurant Operator
Total Sales: $1,574,000 (e)
Total Units: 4
Trade Names: Schlotsky's (4)
Units Franchised From: 4
Primary Menu: Sandwiches/Deli (4)
Areas of Operation: AZ
Type of Foodservice: Quick Serve (4)
Franchise Affiliation: Cinnabon Inc., ATLANTA, GA

Key Personnel
GENE DENISON - Owner; General Buyer
DAVID GONNERMAN - Owner
DOUG WINTER - Director Sales

Mc Donald's Restaurants Inc
1212 W Main St
Mesa, AZ 85201-7016

Telephone: (480) 834-9585
Fax Number: (480) 834-9585
Type of Business: Chain Restaurant Operator
Total Sales: $32,210,000 (e)
Total Units: 7
Trade Names: McDonald's (7)
Units Franchised From: 7
Primary Menu: Hamburger (7)
Areas of Operation: AZ
Type of Foodservice: Quick Serve (7)
Franchise Affiliation: McDonald's Corporation, CHICAGO, IL

Key Personnel
BRAD TEUFEL - President

Pete's Fish & Chips Inc.
203 N MacDonald
Mesa, AZ 85201-6622

Telephone: (480) 962-7992
Fax Number: (480) 464-7885
Internet Homepage: petesfishandchips.com
Type of Business: Chain Restaurant Operator
Year Founded: 1947
Total Sales: $6,056,000 (e)
Number of Employees: 65
Average Check: Lunch(8); Dinner(22)
Total Units: 8
Trade Names: Pete's Fish & Chips (8)
Company-Owned Units: 8
Preferred Square Footage: 1,000
Preferred Location Types: Freestanding
Primary Menu: Seafood (8)
Areas of Operation: AZ
Type of Foodservice: Quick Serve (8)
Primary Distributors: (Full Line) US Foods, PHOENIX, AZ

Key Personnel
KATHY ADAMS - CEO; President; Director Finance, Facility/Maintenance, Information Systems, Risk Management, Real Estate, Design, Human Resources, Menu Development, Food Safety; General Buyer
PAT FOSTER - VP; Treasurer; General Manager; Director Risk Management, Menu Development, Food Safety

Restaurant Management Co.
3514 N Power Rd Ste 121
Mesa, AZ 85215-2909

Telephone: (480) 830-7380
Fax Number: (480) 830-7381
Company Email: cindyq@rionkk.com
Type of Business: Chain Restaurant Operator
Year Founded: 1983
Total Sales: $66,610,000 (e)
Number of Employees: 800
Average Check: Breakfast(8); Lunch(14); Dinner(14)
Total Units: 23
Trade Names: Arby's (13); Famous Dave's (7); Krispy Kreme Doughnuts (3)
Units Franchised From: 23
Preferred Square Footage: 2,300; 2,500
Preferred Location Types: Community Mall; Freestanding
Primary Menu: Bar-B-Q (7); Sandwiches/Deli (13); Snacks (3)
Projected Openings: 1
Areas of Operation: AZ, IA, NE, NV, WI
Type of Foodservice: Quick Serve (23)
Franchise Affiliation: Arby's Restaurant Group, ATLANTA, GA; BBQ Holdings, Inc., MINNETONKA, MN; Krispy Kreme Doughnut Corporation, CHARLOTTE, NC
Primary Distributors: (Food) US Foods, PHOENIX, AZ; (Food) McLane/Mason City, MASON CITY, IA

Key Personnel
BILL DWORAK - President
ED DWORAK - Treasurer; Director Finance, Operations, Real Estate; Manager Information Systems, Risk Management, Supply Chain, Marketing, Advertising, Design, Food Safety, Region
JODEE ROLLAND - Controller; Manager Human Resources
SUE SCHELL - Director Operations
MIKE BREITFELDER - Director Operations
LON CHANEY - Director Operations
CAROLYN DONNELLY - Manager District
JIM HOSKINSON - Manager District
MIKE TURGASEN - Manager District

Rucker Restaurant Holdings, LLC
1945 W Main St
Mesa, AZ 85201-6919

Telephone: (480) 962-9919
Type of Business: Chain Restaurant Operator
Total Sales: $176,810,000 (e)
Total Units: 77
Trade Names: Denny's (19); Jack in the Box (58)
Units Franchised From: 77
Primary Menu: Hamburger (77)
Areas of Operation: AZ, TX
Type of Foodservice: Quick Serve (77)
Franchise Affiliation: Jack in the Box Restaurants, SAN DIEGO, CA

Key Personnel
JAKE WESNER - CFO
LINDA HOUSE - VP Operations
SHANA BLACK - Director Operations
CHRISTIAN TORRES - Manager
JUDY GLASSER - Manager
JAIME OGUS - Manager Media
MICHAEL LEHMAN - Manager Systems
SAMUEL FAYZAKOV - Manager

Osborne Ventures LLC
9918 W Happy Valley Pkwy Ste 203
Peoria, AZ 85383-1218

Telephone: (623) 566-1400
Type of Business: Chain Restaurant Operator
Total Sales: $1,207,000 (e)
Total Units: 2
Trade Names: Cold Stone Creamery (2)
Units Franchised From: 2
Primary Menu: Snacks (2)
Areas of Operation: AZ
Type of Foodservice: Quick Serve (2)
Franchise Affiliation: Kahala Brands, SCOTTSDALE, AZ

Key Personnel
JEFF OSBORNE - Partner
PAMELA OSBORNE - Partner

Bhatti, Inc.
5901 W Camelback Rd
Phoenix, AZ 85033-1735

Telephone: (623) 846-6001
Type of Business: Chain Restaurant Operator
Total Sales: $10,000,000 (e)
Average Check: Dinner(10)
Total Units: 8
Trade Names: Church's Chicken (8)
Units Franchised From: 8
Preferred Square Footage: 1,850
Preferred Location Types: Freestanding
Primary Menu: Chicken (8)
Areas of Operation: AZ
Type of Foodservice: Quick Serve (8)
Franchise Affiliation: Church's Chicken, ATLANTA, GA

Key Personnel
INDERJIT BHATTI - Owner; General Buyer
HARDEEP BHATTI - Director Operations

Cinnabon Franchisee
9617 N Metro Pkwy W
Phoenix, AZ 85051-1400

Telephone: (602) 331-4400
Internet Homepage: cinnabon.com

Type of Business: Chain Restaurant Operator
Total Sales: $1,142,000 (e)
Total Units: 3
Trade Names: Cinnabon (3)
Units Franchised From: 3
Primary Menu: Snacks (3)
Areas of Operation: AZ
Type of Foodservice: Quick Serve (3)
Franchise Affiliation: Cinnabon Inc., ATLANTA, GA

Key Personnel
PARDEEP MEHRA - Owner; General Buyer

David and Sun Kim
2815 W Peoria Ave Ste 104
Phoenix, AZ 85029-5219

Telephone: (602) 371-0144
Type of Business: Chain Restaurant Operator
Total Sales: $1,245,000 (e)
Total Units: 2
Trade Names: Cold Stone Creamery (2)
Units Franchised From: 2
Primary Menu: Snacks (2)
Areas of Operation: AZ
Type of Foodservice: Quick Serve (2)
Franchise Affiliation: Kahala Brands, SCOTTSDALE, AZ

Key Personnel
DAVID KIM - Partner
SUN KIM - Partner

Filimex L.L.C.
2700 N 3rd St Ste 2000
Phoenix, AZ 85004-4602

Telephone: (602) 954-8121
Fax Number: (602) 954-8652
Internet Homepage: filibertos.com
Company Email: filbertoscorp@filbertos.com
Type of Business: Chain Restaurant Operator
Year Founded: 1993
Total Sales: $72,070,000 (e)
Number of Employees: 2,331
Total Units: 79
Trade Names: Filiberto's (79)
Units Franchised To: 79
Primary Menu: Mexican (79)
Areas of Operation: AZ, CA, NM
Type of Foodservice: Fast Casual (79)

Key Personnel
JUAN TENORIO - President; Director Purchasing, Menu Development

Fired Pie, Inc.
3049 W Agua Fria Fwy
Phoenix, AZ 85027-3965

Telephone: (623) 879-6500
Internet Homepage: firedpie.com
Company Email: info@firedpie.com
Type of Business: Chain Restaurant Operator
Year Founded: 2013
Total Units: 21
Trade Names: Fired Pie (21)
Company-Owned Units: 21
Preferred Location Types: Regional Mall; Strip Mall
Alcohol Served: Beer, Wine
Primary Menu: Pizza (21)
Projected Openings: 2
Areas of Operation: AZ
Type of Foodservice: Fast Casual (21)

Key Personnel
DOUG DOYLE - Co-Founder; Partner; General Buyer

Fox Restaurant Concepts
4455 E Camelback Rd Ste B100
Phoenix, AZ 85018-2874

Telephone: (480) 905-6920
Fax Number: (480) 905-6921
Internet Homepage: foxrc.com
Company Email: info@foxrc.net
Listing Type: Subsidiary
Type of Business: Chain Restaurant Operator
Year Founded: 2001
Total Sales: $190,270,000 (e)
Alcohol Sales: 10%
Number of Employees: 496
Average Check: Lunch(12); Dinner(24)
Total Units: 76
Trade Names: Blanco (10); Culinary Dropout (11); Dough Bird Pizza & Rotisserie (5); Flower Child (32); Fly Bye (2); Olive & Ivy Restaurant & Marketplace (2); Pushing Daisies (1); The Arrogant Butcher (1); The Greene House (1); The Henry (4); Wildflower (1); Zinburger (6)
Company-Owned Units: 76
Preferred Square Footage: 3,000; 4,000; 5,500; 6,000
Preferred Location Types: Freestanding
Alcohol Served: Beer, Wine, Liquor
Primary Menu: American (22); Californian (1); Greek/Mediterranean (6); Hamburger (6); Health Foods (32); Mexican (10); Pizza (2); Seafood (1); Snacks (1)
Projected Openings: 10
Areas of Operation: AZ, CA, CO, GA, KS, NV, TX, VA
Type of Foodservice: Casual Dining (68); Fast Casual (8)
Primary Distributors: (Food) US Foods, PHOENIX, AZ
Parent Company: The Cheesecake Factory Incorporated, CALABASAS HILLS, CA

Key Personnel
SAM FOX - Founder; CEO; Partner
ANGELA HANING - President Human Resources
CHRISTOPHER CRISTIANO - Partner; General Buyer
MARJI ARON - Senior VP Facility/Maintenance, Development, Construction, Design
LANCE HOIBY - VP Information Technology
ADAM IZZETT - VP Accounting
MARK MCINTOSH - VP
ANITA C. WALKER - VP Marketing
CLINT WOODS - VP Culinary Operations
DANIEL YENTER - General Manager
VICTORIA ROMERO - General Manager
SEAN FUNDILLER - General Manager
ZACK BILLINGS - Executive Chef
ANTONIO CARDADEIRO - Executive Chef
KENNETH WOODS - Executive Chef
DAVID LUZ - Senior Director Operations
KERI MAHONEY - Director Sales, Group
HEATHER LANIER - Director Training
STEPHANIE RYDER - Director Development, Design
JENNIFER SHAW - Director Training
SHANG SKIPPER - Director Culinary Operations
KRISTI MEDLAND - Director Human Resources
MONICA COPELAND - Director Store Operations
TAYLOR DOMET - Director Culinary Operations
ERIKA EIDSON - Director Operations
PEDER BONDHUS - Director Culinary Operations
JALEN GARRISON JONES - Director Culinary Operations
CHRISTINA GEROME - Director People
JASON FRANDSEN - Director Culinary Development
ADAM YEAGER - Director International; Senior Manager Finance
HAYDEN WOLVEN - Director Marketing
JOHN STEEN - Director Facility/Maintenance
MIKE WILCOX - Regional Director Operations
CRYSTAL BOYMISTRUK - Senior Manager Development, Design
ZACHARY BURNS - Manager Restaurant Operations
KATELYN HANSON - Manager Marketing
JAY HARTWIG - Manager Development- Training
TREVOR MEDLAND - Manager Operations
KIM MEZZETTA - Manager Procurement
KATHY KOCHIS - Manager Email Marketing
TRISHA HOUFEK - Manager Talent
LAURA SPENCER - Manager Recruitment
CHELSEY SCHMIT - Manager Finance
LEXI VALLERY - Manager Event Planning
HAYDEN RASSAS - Brand Manager Marketing
BRIANNA VANNELLI ROSS - Project Manager
MARLO WHITE - Project Manager

Communications
TYLER NYPEN - Specialist Training
CAITLIN HILBRANDS - Coordinator Human Resources

Honey Bear's BBQ
5012 E Van Buren St
Phoenix, AZ 85008-7007

Telephone: (602) 273-9148
Internet Homepage: honeybearsbbq.com
Company Email: intouch@honeybearsbbq.com
Type of Business: Chain Restaurant Operator
Year Founded: 1986
Total Sales: $4,030,000 (e)
Alcohol Sales: 5%
Number of Employees: 60
Average Check: Lunch(10); Dinner(18)
Internet Order Processing: Yes
Internet Sales: 20.00%
Total Units: 2
Trade Names: Honey Bears BBQ (2)
Company-Owned Units: 2
Preferred Location Types: Freestanding
Alcohol Served: Beer, Wine
Primary Menu: Bar-B-Q (2)
Areas of Operation: AZ
Type of Foodservice: Casual Dining (2)
Catering Services: Yes
Primary Distributors: (Food) Shamrock Foods Co., PHOENIX, AZ

Key Personnel
GARY CLARK - President; Partner; Director Menu Development
MARK SMITH - Partner; VP; General Manager; Executive Chef; General Buyer
ANNA SMITH - Director Operations

InnSuites Hospitality Trust
1625 E Northern Ave Ste 105
Phoenix, AZ 85020-3921

Telephone: (602) 944-1500
Fax Number: (602) 678-0281
Internet Homepage: innsuites.com
Type of Business: Foodservice Operations - Hotel/Motels
Year Founded: 1979
Total Sales: $28,650,000 (e)
Alcohol Sales: 15%
Number of Employees: 200
Total Units: 5
Restaurants in Hotels: 6
Trade Names: InnSuites Hotel and Suites (5)
Company-Owned Units: 5
Alcohol Served: Beer, Wine, Liquor
Areas of Operation: AZ, CA, NM, TX
Type of Foodservice: Casual Dining (5)
Primary Distributors: (Food) SYSCO Food Services of Arizona Inc., TOLLESON, AZ

Notes: The company derives approximately 80% of its revenue from hotel operations.

Key Personnel
JAMES F. WIRTH - Chairman; CEO
MARK E. BERG - Exec VP Operations; Manager Real Estate

Keegan's Grill & Taproom
3114 E Camelback Rd
Phoenix, AZ 85016-4502

Telephone: (602) 955-6616
Internet Homepage: keegansgrill.com
Type of Business: Chain Restaurant Operator
Year Founded: 1989
Total Sales: $3,951,000 (e)
Alcohol Sales: 20%
Number of Employees: 75
Average Check: Breakfast(10); Lunch(14); Dinner(18)
Total Units: 3
Trade Names: Keegan's Grill & Taproom (3)
Company-Owned Units: 3
Preferred Location Types: Freestanding
Alcohol Served: Beer, Wine, Liquor
Primary Menu: American (3)
Areas of Operation: AZ
Type of Foodservice: Casual Dining (3)
Catering Services: Yes
Primary Distributors: (Food) Shamrock Foods Co., PHOENIX, AZ

Key Personnel
STEVE JOHNSON - President; Owner; Executive Chef; Director Catering; General Buyer

Kraf Inc.
5070 N 40th St Ste 100
Phoenix, AZ 85018-2141

Telephone: (602) 273-7997
Fax Number: (602) 273-9170
Type of Business: Chain Restaurant Operator
Year Founded: 1983
Total Sales: $62,990,000 (e)
Number of Employees: 1,200
Average Check: Breakfast(8); Lunch(12); Dinner(14)
Total Units: 28
Trade Names: Burger King (28)
Units Franchised From: 28
Preferred Square Footage: 1,400
Preferred Location Types: Freestanding; Strip Mall
Primary Menu: Hamburger (28)
Areas of Operation: AZ
Type of Foodservice: Quick Serve (28)
Franchise Affiliation: Burger King Worldwide Inc., MIAMI, FL

Primary Distributors: (Full Line) Shamrock Foods Co., PHOENIX, AZ
Parent Company: Broatch Management Inc., SCOTTSDALE, AZ

Key Personnel
RONALD T. BROATCH - Partner; Director Finance
ERIC DREIER - Partner; Director Operations, Facility/Maintenance
NICOLE DREIER - Partner; VP

Leigh Enterprises
3521 W Van Buren St
Phoenix, AZ 85009-4106

Telephone: (602) 484-7707
Fax Number: (602) 233-2705
Type of Business: Chain Restaurant Operator
Total Sales: $13,810,000 (e)
Total Units: 6
Trade Names: Burger King (6)
Units Franchised From: 6
Primary Menu: Hamburger (6)
Areas of Operation: AZ
Type of Foodservice: Quick Serve (6)
Franchise Affiliation: Burger King Worldwide Inc., MIAMI, FL

Key Personnel
KIM WALKER - Owner; Director
ADAM GODDARD - Director Marketing, Sales

Lo Lo's Inc
740 N 52nd St
Phoenix, AZ 85008-7980

Telephone: (480) 444-8285
Internet Homepage: loloschickenandwaffles.com
Company Email: info@loloschickenandwaffles.com
Type of Business: Chain Restaurant Operator
Year Founded: 1997
Total Units: 6
Trade Names: Lo-Lo's Chicken & Waffles (6)
Company-Owned Units: 6
Preferred Location Types: Airports; Freestanding
Alcohol Served: Beer, Wine, Liquor
Primary Menu: Southern (6)
Areas of Operation: AZ, NE, NV, OK
Type of Foodservice: Casual Dining (6)
Catering Services: Yes

Key Personnel
LARRY WHITE - Co-Founder; President; Partner
RASHEEDAH WHITE - Co-Founder; Exec VP Operations

MIKE ANDERSON - Co-CEO
GREG CUTCHALL - Co-CEO; Partner
BRET ANDERSON - Exec VP Administration
DAVID SELLERS - Executive Director Real Estate, Construction

Los Dos Molinos
8646 S Central Ave
Phoenix, AZ 85042-7605

Mailing Address: PO Box 90663, PHOENIX, AZ, 85066-0663
Telephone: (602) 243-9113
Internet Homepage: losdosmolinosphoenix.com; losdosmolinosphoenix.com
Type of Business: Chain Restaurant Operator
Total Sales: $1,915,000 (e)
Alcohol Sales: 15%
Number of Employees: 32
Average Check: Lunch(16); Dinner(28)
Total Units: 3
Trade Names: Los Dos Molinas (3)
Company-Owned Units: 3
Preferred Location Types: Freestanding; Strip Mall
Alcohol Served: Beer, Wine, Liquor
Primary Menu: Mexican (3)
Areas of Operation: AZ
Type of Foodservice: Casual Dining (3)
Primary Distributors: (Food) Restaurant Depot, MESA, AZ; (Full Line) SYSCO Food Services of Arizona Inc., TOLLESON, AZ

Key Personnel
VICTORIA CHAVEZ - President; Executive Chef; General Buyer
DOMINIQUE DELAPAZ - General Manager

Macayo Restaurants LLC
1480 E Bethany Home Rd Ste 215
Phoenix, AZ 85014-2022

Telephone: (602) 264-1831
Fax Number: (602) 277-1795
Internet Homepage: macayo.com
Company Email: wecare@macayo.com
Type of Business: Chain Restaurant Operator
Year Founded: 1945
Total Sales: $50,383,000 (e)
Alcohol Sales: 25%
Number of Employees: 1,070
Average Check: Lunch(8); Dinner(14)
Internet Order Processing: Yes
Internet Sales: 2.00%
Total Units: 10
Trade Names: Macayo Mexican Restaurant (10)
Company-Owned Units: 10
Preferred Square Footage: 7,500
Preferred Location Types: Freestanding
Alcohol Served: Beer, Wine, Liquor
Primary Menu: Mexican (10)
Areas of Operation: AZ, NV
Type of Foodservice: Casual Dining (10)
Catering Services: Yes
Primary Distributors: (Full Line) Shamrock Foods Co., PHOENIX, AZ

Key Personnel
MILES JOSLIN - VP

Manuel's Mexican Food
2980 E Northern Ave Ste B1
Phoenix, AZ 85028-4842

Telephone: (602) 266-9111
Fax Number: (602) 266-9188
Internet Homepage: manuelsaz.com; manuelscatering.com
Company Email: alexr@manuelsaz.com
Type of Business: Chain Restaurant Operator
Year Founded: 1964
Total Sales: $12,010,000 (e)
Alcohol Sales: 15%
Number of Employees: 225
Average Check: Breakfast(8); Lunch(10); Dinner(14)
Internet Order Processing: Yes
Internet Sales: 1.00%
Total Units: 7
Trade Names: Manuel's Mexican Food (7)
Company-Owned Units: 7
Preferred Square Footage: 10,000; 15,000
Preferred Location Types: Freestanding; Strip Mall
Alcohol Served: Beer, Wine, Liquor
Primary Menu: Mexican (7)
Areas of Operation: AZ
Type of Foodservice: Casual Dining (7)
Catering Services: Yes
On-site Distribution Center: Yes

Key Personnel
ALEX ROMERO - CEO; Controller
MICHAEL SALAZAR - Partner
PATTY ROMERO - VP; Director Purchasing, Research & Development, Product Development, Menu Development
ANDREA MARTIN - General Manager

Mapes Food Service, Inc.
4550 E Bell Rd Ste 194
Phoenix, AZ 85032-9383

Telephone: (602) 569-6453
Type of Business: Chain Restaurant Operator
Total Sales: $22,490,000 (e)
Total Units: 16
Trade Names: Jersey Mike's Subs (16)
Units Franchised From: 16
Primary Menu: Sandwiches/Deli (16)
Areas of Operation: AZ
Type of Foodservice: Quick Serve (16)
Franchise Affiliation: Jersey Mike's Franchise Systems, MANASQUAN, NJ

Key Personnel
WILLIAM MAPES - Partner; General Buyer
LESLIE MAPES - Partner

Pizzarose, LLC
2601 W Dunlap Ave Ste 10
Phoenix, AZ 85021-2711

Telephone: (602) 395-2600
Fax Number: (602) 395-2677
Type of Business: Chain Restaurant Operator
Total Sales: $8,558,000 (e)
Total Units: 7
Trade Names: Little Caesars Pizza (7)
Units Franchised From: 7
Primary Menu: Pizza (7)
Areas of Operation: AZ
Type of Foodservice: Quick Serve (7)
Franchise Affiliation: Little Caesar Enterprises Inc., DETROIT, MI

Key Personnel
MARVIN ROSE - President; General Buyer
TODD PIERSON - Director Purchasing, Marketing

Pizzeria Bianco
623 E Adams St
Phoenix, AZ 85004-2334

Telephone: (602) 258-8300
Internet Homepage: pizzeriabianco.com
Company Email: events@chrisbiancogroup.com
Type of Business: Chain Restaurant Operator
Year Founded: 1998
Total Sales: $2,450,000 (e)
Alcohol Sales: 5%
Number of Employees: 7
Average Check: Lunch(12); Dinner(26)
Total Units: 4
Trade Names: Bar Bianco (1); Pane Bianco (1); Pizzeria Bianco (2)
Company-Owned Units: 4
Preferred Location Types: Freestanding
Alcohol Served: Beer, Wine
Primary Menu: Italian (4)
Areas of Operation: AZ
Type of Foodservice: Casual Dining (4)
Primary Distributors: (Full Line) US Foods, PHOENIX, AZ

Key Personnel
CHRIS BIANCO - President; General Manager;

Executive Chef; General Buyer

Pride Restaurant Group
11020 N Tatum Blvd Ste 103
Phoenix, AZ 85028-6072

Telephone: (602) 569-6100
Fax Number: (602) 493-4784
Type of Business: Chain Restaurant Operator
Year Founded: 1980
Total Sales: $22,500,000 (e)
Number of Employees: 230
Average Check: Breakfast(8); Lunch(8); Dinner(8)
Total Units: 10
Trade Names: Burger King (10)
Units Franchised From: 10
Preferred Square Footage: 2,500
Preferred Location Types: Freestanding
Primary Menu: Hamburger (10)
Areas of Operation: AZ, NV, TX
Type of Foodservice: Quick Serve (10)
Franchise Affiliation: Burger King Worldwide Inc., MIAMI, FL
Primary Distributors: (Food) Shamrock Foods Co., PHOENIX, AZ; (Supplies) Shamrock Foods Co., PHOENIX, AZ

Key Personnel
SHANE HITZEMAN - President; Partner; General Buyer
DENNIS HITZEMAN - Partner; Director Finance, Purchasing, Facility/Maintenance, Design, Store Planning
RICK MUTERSPAUGH - Exec VP
BRENDA BLANCHARD - Controller
LISA BECK - Supervisor District
KAREN HITZEMAN - Office Manager

Romulus Inc.
1048 N 44th St Ste 210
Phoenix, AZ 85008-5754

Telephone: (602) 852-0555
Fax Number: (602) 443-3465
Internet Homepage: romulusinc.com
Type of Business: Chain Restaurant Operator
Year Founded: 1990
Total Sales: $273,630,000 (e)
Number of Employees: 6,000
Average Check: Breakfast(6); Lunch(8); Dinner(12)
Total Units: 105
Trade Names: IHOP Restaurant (105)
Units Franchised From: 105
Preferred Square Footage: 4,400; 5,000
Preferred Location Types: Freestanding
Primary Menu: American (105)
Projected Openings: 2
Areas of Operation: AZ, ID, IN, KS, NM, OH, OK, PA, TX
Type of Foodservice: Family Restaurant (105)
Franchise Affiliation: IHOP Restaurant System, GLENDALE, CA

Key Personnel
CHRISTOPHER R. MILISCI - Founder; CEO
MARK STEINMETZ - CFO; Director Real Estate
BUD MORGAN - CIO
NICHOLAS PERRY - VP Operations
MIKE ENGSBERG - VP Human Resources
CHRIS TRESSLER - Controller
JAMES MOORE - General Manager
HAVEN FITTS - General Manager
CATIE BELL - Director Development
NOELLE DIAZ - Director Operations
LOWELL HORNER - Director Operations
TRACY LUJAN - Director Development
SHAUNA MULLINS - Director Operations
MICHAEL ROUEN - Director Information Technology
KIM TRUJILLO - District Manager
KELLEY LUTTRELL - Manager Purchasing
KRISTINA GERTH - Manager Marketing
CASSY HIGHFILL - Manager Operations
JORDAN PACE - Assistant

Streets of New York Inc.
11811 N Tatum Blvd Ste P180
Phoenix, AZ 85028-1697

Telephone: (602) 953-8777
Fax Number: (602) 953-8778
Internet Homepage: streetsofnewyork.com
Company Email: info@streetsofnewyork.com
Type of Business: Chain Restaurant Operator
Year Founded: 1976
Total Sales: $20,240,000 (e)
Alcohol Sales: 10%
Number of Employees: 486
Average Check: Lunch(12); Dinner(18)
Internet Order Processing: Yes
Total Units: 23
Trade Names: Streets of New York (23)
Company-Owned Units: 18
Units Franchised To: 8
Preferred Square Footage: 2,200; 3,000
Preferred Location Types: Freestanding; Strip Mall
Alcohol Served: Beer, Wine
Primary Menu: Italian (23)
Areas of Operation: AZ, NV
Type of Foodservice: Casual Dining (23)
Catering Services: Yes
On-site Distribution Center: Yes

Key Personnel
RICK PETERSON - COO; Manager Food Safety

The Buffalo Spot
2080 West Northern Ave Suite 100
Phoenix, AZ 85021

Telephone: (602) 973-1515
Internet Homepage: thebuffalospot.com
Type of Business: Chain Restaurant Operator
Total Sales: $36,680,000 (e)
Total Units: 30
Trade Names: The Buffalo Spot (30)
Units Franchised To: 30
Primary Menu: American (30)
Type of Foodservice: Fast Casual (30)

Key Personnel
MELINA RAYGOZA - General Manager
JESSICA ALEXANDER - Manager

Tokyo Express Inc.
3120 W Carefree Hwy Ste 1-226
Phoenix, AZ 85086-3264

Telephone: (602) 234-0555
Fax Number: (602) 277-1666
Internet Homepage: tokyoexpressaz.com
Type of Business: Chain Restaurant Operator
Year Founded: 1982
Total Sales: $1,582,000 (e)
Number of Employees: 125
Average Check: Lunch(16); Dinner(16)
Total Units: 2
Trade Names: Tokyo Express (2)
Company-Owned Units: 2
Preferred Square Footage: 2,500
Preferred Location Types: Freestanding; Strip Mall
Primary Menu: Japanese (2)
Areas of Operation: AZ
Type of Foodservice: Quick Serve (2)
Primary Distributors: (Equipment) Mutual Trading Co. Inc., LOS ANGELES, CA; (Food) Shamrock Foods Co., PHOENIX, AZ

Key Personnel
CHARLIE ISHIDA - President; CFO; Director Menu Development; General Buyer
KAKO IWAOKA - VP Operations, Facility/Maintenance, Information Systems, Loss Prevention, Real Estate, Product Development; General Manager

Top Shelf
3301 W Greenway Rd
Phoenix, AZ 85053-3806

Telephone: (602) 993-5463
Fax Number: (602) 993-6024
Internet Homepage: topshelfmexicanfood.com
Company Email:

customerservice@topshelfaz.com
Type of Business: Chain Restaurant Operator
Year Founded: 1976
Total Sales: $6,109,000 (e)
Alcohol Sales: 13%
Number of Employees: 130
Average Check: Lunch(12); Dinner(18)
Total Units: 2
Trade Names: Top Shelf Mexican Food (2)
Company-Owned Units: 2
Preferred Location Types: Freestanding
Alcohol Served: Beer, Wine, Liquor
Primary Menu: Mexican (2)
Areas of Operation: AZ
Type of Foodservice: Casual Dining (2)
Catering Services: Yes
Primary Distributors: (Full Line) Shamrock Foods Co., PHOENIX, AZ

Key Personnel
CHARLES MCCRACKEN - CEO; VP Operations, Purchasing, Marketing, Real Estate, Human Resources
K. SLESARIK - General Manager
J. RAVEN - General Manager

True Food Kitchen
4455 E Camelback Rd Ste A115
Phoenix, AZ 85018

Telephone: (480) 212-0175
Internet Homepage: truefoodkitchen.com
Type of Business: Chain Restaurant Operator
Year Founded: 2008
Total Sales: $340,350,000 (e)
Number of Employees: 1,000
Internet Sales: 15.00%
Total Units: 43
Trade Names: True Food Kitchen (44)
Company-Owned Units: 44
Primary Menu: Health Foods (44)
Projected Openings: 11
Areas of Operation: AZ, CA, CO, FL, GA, IL, LA, MD, MO, NV, OH, PA, TN, TX, VA
Type of Foodservice: Casual Dining (44)

Key Personnel
JAMES LIAKAKOS - COO
DANIELLA VOYSEY OLSON - Chief Growth Officer
VAL KING - VP Information Technology
CHUCK CHAVEZ - VP Development, Real Estate
GARRETT RAYBURN - VP Accounting
MATTHEW PADILLA - VP
JONATHAN PEREZ - General Counsel
REY CRUZ - Senior Director Facility/Maintenance
MATTHEW WANSTEN - Senior Director Information Systems
LINDA PRATT - Senior Director Talent
MARK MILLER - Director
AMY LEGERE - Director Recruitment

JOSHUA SEGUIN - Director People
ZACHARY HELLMANN - Director Culinary Operations
JANELLE ROSS - Director Product Development
TRENT DAVIS - Regional Director Operations
CHRISTINA FOX - Regional Director
JAIME MANSOUR - Regional Director Operations
ANNE DAVIS - Regional Director
JOANNA LAWLER - Senior Manager Employee Compensation, Employee Benefits
SIERRA THRESHER - Manager Licensing; Administrator
BRITTANY PIERCE - Manager Finance
TYLER SCHRAMECK - Manager Information Technology
STEPHAN MANNING - Manager Purchasing
KATE GLENDE - Manager Accounting
SAIRA NOORANI - Specialist Payroll
JANE YOUNG - Coordinator Construction
STEPHANIE KOHLMEIER - Coordinator Operations

Upward Projects
5210 N Central Ave Ste 101
Phoenix, AZ 85012

Telephone: (602) 246-7555
Fax Number: (602) 277-5991
Internet Homepage: postinowinecafe.com; upwardprojects.com
Company Email: info@upwardprojects.com
Type of Business: Chain Restaurant Operator
Total Sales: $18,310,000 (e)
Total Units: 21
Trade Names: Churn (1); Federal Pizza (1); Joyride (2); Postino Wine Cafe (16); Windsor (1)
Company-Owned Units: 21
Primary Menu: American (17); Pizza (1); Snacks (1); Taco (2)
Areas of Operation: AZ, CO, TX
Type of Foodservice: Casual Dining (18); Fast Casual (2); Quick Serve (1)

Key Personnel
LAUREN BAILEY - CEO; Partner
CRAIG DEMARCO - Partner
WYATT BAILEY - Partner
ANOOP MATHEW - CFO
BRENT RENNER - Chief Development Officer
AMY HWANG - Controller
BRIANNA JACOBSON - General Manager
MATT SMITH - Executive Chef
SAMUEL FOOS - Senior Director Human Resources
BRITTANY BALDWIN - Director Marketing
BRENT KARLICEK - Director Beverages
ERIC HERDERSON - Director Operations

Valle Luna
3346 W Bell Rd
Phoenix, AZ 85053

Telephone: (602) 548-2692
Fax Number: (602) 548-2694
Internet Homepage: valleluna.com
Company Email: vluna1@aol.com
Type of Business: Chain Restaurant Operator
Year Founded: 1982
Total Sales: $23,209,000 (e)
Alcohol Sales: 15%
Number of Employees: 380
Average Check: Lunch(12); Dinner(18)
Total Units: 3
Trade Names: Valle Luna (3)
Company-Owned Units: 3
Preferred Location Types: Freestanding
Alcohol Served: Beer, Wine, Liquor
Primary Menu: Mexican (3)
Areas of Operation: AZ
Type of Foodservice: Casual Dining (3)
Catering Services: Yes
Primary Distributors: (Full Line) Shamrock Foods Co., PHOENIX, AZ

Key Personnel
JANIE RIDDLE - CEO; Partner; Treasurer; General Manager
WILLIAM RIDDLE III - President; Partner; General Manager; Director Real Estate; General Buyer
CHRIS ESPINOZA - General Manager Region; Manager Human Resources

Willis & Willis Investments, Inc
21001 N Tatum Blvd
Phoenix, AZ 85050-4206

Telephone: (480) 585-7952
Type of Business: Chain Restaurant Operator
Total Sales: $1,232,000 (e)
Total Units: 2
Trade Names: Cold Stone Creamery (2)
Units Franchised From: 2
Primary Menu: Snacks (2)
Areas of Operation: AZ
Type of Foodservice: Quick Serve (2)
Franchise Affiliation: Kahala Brands, SCOTTSDALE, AZ

Key Personnel
FRED WILLIS - Partner
DONNA WILLIS - Partner

Canteen Vending Services
1510 E Riverview Dr
Phoenx, AZ 85034-6613

Telephone: (602) 269-5879
Fax Number: (602) 288-1833
Listing Type: Branch Office
Type of Business: Foodservice Management Operator
Year Founded: 1929
Number of Employees: 100
Number of Locations Served: 300
Total Foodservice Mgmt Accounts: 300
Areas of Operation: AZ
Type of Foodservice: Vending machines (300)
Foodservice Management Venues: Business & Industry; College & University; Health Care; Military Feeding; Prison Feeding; Schools; Travel Plazas
Parent Company: Compass Group The Americas, CHARLOTTE, NC
Headquarters: Canteen Vending Services, CHARLOTTE, NC

Key Personnel
RENEE PERRY - Manager Finance, Accounting

Martinez Management Inc.
625 E White Mountain Blvd
Pinetop, AZ 85935

Mailing Address: PO Box 3130, PINETOP, AZ, 85935-3130
Telephone: (928) 367-5902
Fax Number: (928) 367-3817
Type of Business: Chain Restaurant Operator
Year Founded: 1978
Total Sales: $159,120,000 (e)
Number of Employees: 490
Average Check: Breakfast(5); Lunch(8); Dinner(8)
Total Units: 34
Trade Names: McDonald's (34)
Units Franchised From: 34
Preferred Square Footage: 3,000
Preferred Location Types: Discount Dept. Stores; Freestanding
Primary Menu: Hamburger (34)
Areas of Operation: AZ, NM
Type of Foodservice: Quick Serve (34)
Franchise Affiliation: McDonald's Corporation, CHICAGO, IL
Primary Distributors: (Full Line) The Martin-Brower Co., PHOENIX, AZ

Key Personnel
ABE MARTINEZ JR - Partner; Director Information Systems, Real Estate, Design; General Buyer
SHARON MARTINEZ - Partner

CHRIS TACKETT - Director Operations

Arcadia Farms
7025 E 1st Ave
Scottsdale, AZ 85251-4303

Telephone: (480) 947-2596
Fax Number: (480) 941-0895
Internet Homepage: arcadiafarmscafe.com
Type of Business: Chain Restaurant Operator
Year Founded: 1990
Total Sales: $4,584,000 (e)
Alcohol Sales: 5%
Number of Employees: 10
Average Check: Breakfast(8); Lunch(10);
Total Units: 2
Trade Names: Arcadia Farms (2)
Company-Owned Units: 2
Preferred Location Types: Other; Strip Mall
Alcohol Served: Beer, Wine
Primary Menu: American (2)
Areas of Operation: AZ
Type of Foodservice: Family Restaurant (2)
Catering Services: Yes

Key Personnel
CAROLYN ELLIS - President; Executive Chef; General Buyer
HELEN KIM - VP Marketing
TAMMIE ALCIATORE - Director Marketing
RANDY ALLEN - Director Sales, Business Development
HANS DOMINGO - Director Manufacturing
ZACH MCNALLY - Regional Director Sales
JULINDA SENTMAN - Manager Credit, Payroll
ASHLEY JONES - Manager Accounting, Catering

Barrio Culinary Concepts, LLC
7114 E Stetson Dr
Scottsdale, AZ 85251

Telephone: (480) 656-4197
Internet Homepage: barrioqueen.com
Company Email: info@barrioqueen.com
Type of Business: Chain Restaurant Operator
Total Units: 4
Trade Names: Barrio Queen (4)
Company-Owned Units: 4
Primary Menu: Mexican (4)
Areas of Operation: AZ
Type of Foodservice: Casual Dining (4)

Key Personnel
LINDA NASH - Owner; General Buyer
JONATHAN MYRES - CFO; Controller
JUAN BOSIO - Executive Chef

Black Rock Coffee Bar
9170 E Bahia Dr Suite 101
Scottsdale, AZ 85260

Internet Homepage: br.coffee
Company Email: hello@br.coffee
Type of Business: Chain Restaurant Operator
Year Founded: 2008
Number of Employees: 800
Total Units: 116
Trade Names: Black Rock Coffee Bar (116)
Company-Owned Units: 116
Primary Menu: Coffee (116)
Projected Openings: 10
Areas of Operation: AR, CA, CO, ID, OR, TX, WA
Type of Foodservice: Quick Serve (116)

Key Personnel
MARK DAVIS - CEO
RODD BOOTH - CFO
BOBBY KAUFMANN - VP Development
REBECCA MYROM - Director Human Resources
AUBREY CARUTH - Director Marketing

Cold Stone Creamery Inc.
9311 E Via De Ventura
Scottsdale, AZ 85258-3599

Telephone: (480) 362-4800
Fax Number: (480) 362-4812
Internet Homepage: coldstonecreamery.com; kahalamgmt.com
Company Email: info@coldstonecreamery.com
Listing Type: Subsidiary
Type of Business: Chain Restaurant Operator
Year Founded: 1988
Systemwide Sales: $690,033,000 (e)
Total Sales: $79,400,000 (e)
Number of Employees: 550
Average Check: Lunch(8); Dinner(8)
Internet Order Processing: Yes
Internet Sales: 1.00%
Total Units: 1,450
Trade Names: Cold Stone Creamery (1,450)
Company-Owned Units: 10
Units Franchised To: 1,440
Preferred Square Footage: 800; 1,600
Preferred Location Types: Airports; Downtown; Freestanding; Institution (college/hospital); Lifestyle Center; Outlet Mall; Regional Mall; Stadiums; Strip Mall
Primary Menu: Snacks (1,450)
Projected Openings: 50
Areas of Operation: AK, AL, AR, AZ, CA, CO, CT, DC, DE, FL, GA, GU, HI, IA, ID, IL, IN, KS, KY, LA, MA, MD, ME, MI, MN, MO, MS, MT, NC, ND, NE, NH, NJ, NM, NV, NY, OH, OK, OR, PA, PR, RI, SC, SD, TN, TX, UT, VA, WA, WI, WV, WY

Foreign Countries: BAHRAIN; CANADA; CHINA; CYPRUS; DENMARK; EL SALVADOR; INDIA; INDONESIA; JAPAN; KUWAIT; MEXICO; OMAN; PAKISTAN; QATAR; SAUDI ARABIA; SINGAPORE; SOUTH AFRICA; SOUTH KOREA; SRI LANKA; TAIWAN; THAILAND; TRINIDAD & TOBAGO; UNITEDARAB EMIRATES
Type of Foodservice: Quick Serve (1,450)
Foodservice Management Venues: Recreational; Transportation
Catering Services: Yes
Primary Distributors: (Food) SYSCO Food Services of Arizona Inc., TOLLESON, AZ
Parent Company: Kahala Brands, SCOTTSDALE, AZ

Key Personnel
FRED WILLIS - Owner
JOANI BIANCA - VP Operations
JIM BURKARD - Senior Director Purchasing, Distribution
CHERRI SCOGGIN - Regional Director Operations
LAURA DONOVAN - Manager Marketing

Desert Island Restaurants
6263 N Scottsdale Rd Ste 374
Scottsdale, AZ 85250-5437

Telephone: (480) 945-0088
Fax Number: (480) 945-4747
Internet Homepage: desertislandrestaurants.com; lingandlouies.com; thaifoon.com
Company Email: contactus@direstaurants.com
Type of Business: Chain Restaurant Operator
Year Founded: 1998
Systemwide Sales: $33,497,000 (e)
Total Sales: $57,370,000 (e)
Alcohol Sales: 15%
Number of Employees: 545
Average Check: Lunch(30); Dinner(48)
Total Units: 13
Trade Names: Blaze Pizza (1); Ling & Louie's (4); Romano's Macaroni Grill (2); Ruth's Chris Steak House (6)
Company-Owned Units: 4
Units Franchised From: 9
Preferred Square Footage: 7,000
Preferred Location Types: Freestanding; Regional Mall
Alcohol Served: Beer, Wine, Liquor
Primary Menu: Asian (4); Italian (2); Pizza (1); Steak (6)
Areas of Operation: AZ, HI, ID, TX
Type of Foodservice: Casual Dining (7); Fine Dining (6)
Franchise Affiliation: Dividend Restaurant Group, DENVER, CO; Ruth's Hospitality Group Inc., WINTER PARK, FL
Primary Distributors: (Full Line) US Foods,

PHOENIX, AZ

Key Personnel
RANDY SCHOCH - Chairman; CEO; General Buyer
BOB SNYDER - President
BOB WARD - VP Finance, Accounting
LISA MUZACHI - Controller
GREG SMITH - Corporate Chef; Executive Chef; Director Operations
PAUL SCHOSHODY - Director Marketing
KATE KUCHARSKI - Director Human Resources
DEB HARGRAVE - Manager Accounting

DLite Healthy On The Go
2613 N Scottsdale Rd
Scottsdale, AZ 85257

Telephone: (480) 247-8537
Internet Homepage: dlishdrivethru.com
Type of Business: Chain Restaurant Operator
Total Units: 3
Trade Names: D'Lite Healthy On The Go (3)
Company-Owned Units: 3
Areas of Operation: AZ

Key Personnel
CHAD KNUDSEN - Founder; CEO; Partner
BROOKE KNUDSON - Partner; COO

Grimaldi's Pizza
15005 N Northsight Blvd
Scottsdale, AZ 85260-2617

Telephone: (480) 947-7100
Fax Number: (480) 947-7105
Internet Homepage: grimaldispizzeria.com
Type of Business: Chain Restaurant Operator
Total Sales: $26,830,000 (e)
Alcohol Sales: 5%
Number of Employees: 92
Average Check: Dinner(14)
Internet Order Processing: Yes
Total Units: 42
Trade Names: Grimaldi's Pizza (42)
Company-Owned Units: 42
Preferred Square Footage: 3,000; 4,000
Preferred Location Types: Downtown; Lifestyle Center
Alcohol Served: Beer, Wine, Liquor
Primary Menu: Pizza (42)
Projected Openings: 5
Areas of Operation: AZ, CA, CO, FL, ID, LA, NJ, NV, NY, SC, TX
Type of Foodservice: Casual Dining (42)
Catering Services: Yes

Key Personnel
JOE CIOLLI - CEO; President; General Buyer

JERRY BERTHOLDI - Manager Real Estate

Guy and Larry Restaurants
7377 E Doubletree Ranch Rd Ste 180
Scottsdale, AZ 85258

Telephone: (480) 425-4610
Fax Number: (480) 425-4611
Internet Homepage: roaringfork.com
Company Email: info@roaringfork.com
Type of Business: Chain Restaurant Operator
Total Sales: $46,938,000 (e)
Alcohol Sales: 30%
Average Check: Dinner(60)
Total Units: 3
Trade Names: Roaring Fork An American Western Bistro & Saloon (3)
Company-Owned Units: 3
Preferred Location Types: Freestanding
Alcohol Served: Beer, Wine, Liquor
Primary Menu: Steak (3)
Areas of Operation: AZ, TX
Type of Foodservice: Fine Dining (3)

Key Personnel
LARRY FOLES - Chairman; Partner
GUY VILLAVASO - Founder; Partner
JIM VANDERCOOK - President
EDITH METZGER - CFO

Harkins Amusement Enterprises
7511 E McDonald Dr
Scottsdale, AZ 85250-6085

Telephone: (480) 627-7777
Fax Number: (480) 443-0950
Internet Homepage: harkinstheatres.com
Company Email: guestservices@harkins.com
Type of Business: Foodservice Operations - Movie Theatre
Total Sales: $32,660,000 (e)
Number of Employees: 571
Average Check: Dinner(6)
Internet Order Processing: Yes
Total Units: 34
Trade Names: Harkins Theatres (34)
Company-Owned Units: 34
Preferred Square Footage: 2,500
Preferred Location Types: Community Mall; Freestanding; Regional Mall
Primary Menu: Snacks (34)
Areas of Operation: AZ, CA, CO, OK, TX
Type of Foodservice: In-Store Feeder (34)
Primary Distributors: (Food) US Foods, PHOENIX, AZ
Notes: The company derives approximately 72% of its revenue from movie theater operations.

Key Personnel
DAN HARKINS - CEO; Owner
MIKE BOWERS - President; COO
WHITNEY MURREY - Director Marketing
ANGELIQUE SCHMIDTZ - Manager Food and Beverage

Jest Enterprises
15025 N 74th St
Scottsdale, AZ 85260-2498

Telephone: (480) 948-9969
Fax Number: (480) 948-9970
Internet Homepage: arribamexicangrill.com; jestenterprises.com
Company Email: reception@jestenterprises.com
Type of Business: Chain Restaurant Operator
Total Sales: $21,000,000 (e)
Number of Employees: 275
Internet Order Processing: Yes
Total Units: 13
Trade Names: Arriba Mexican Grill (6); Burger King (7)
Company-Owned Units: 6
Units Franchised From: 7
Preferred Square Footage: 2,500
Alcohol Served: Beer, Wine, Liquor
Primary Menu: Hamburger (7); Mexican (6)
Areas of Operation: AZ
Type of Foodservice: Casual Dining (6); Quick Serve (7)
Franchise Affiliation: Burger King Worldwide Inc., MIAMI, FL

Key Personnel
STEVE MORALES - President
NICOLE PERRY - CFO; VP
GLEN MORALES - Director Marketing
TRACY COLEMAN - Manager Accounting

JNK Concepts
7299 N Scottsdale Rd
Scottsdale, AZ 85253-3617

Telephone: (480) 582-4552
Internet Homepage: enolowinecafe.com; marigoldmaison.com; nobuofukuda.com; rokaakor.com
Company Email: Scottsdale@RokaAkor.com
Type of Business: Chain Restaurant Operator
Year Founded: 2008
Total Units: 10
Trade Names: Enolo Wine Cafe (1); Marigold Maison (2); Nubuo at Teeter House (1); Roka Akor (6)
Company-Owned Units: 10
Primary Menu: American (1); Indian (2); Japanese (7)
Areas of Operation: AZ, CA, IL, TX

Type of Foodservice: Casual Dining (10)

Key Personnel
JOHN N. KAPOOR - Founder; Owner
JOHN DUFFIELD - CFO; Controller
NOBUO FUKUDA - Executive Chef
MIRNES MEHIC - Director Marketing
STEVE TINDLE - Regional Manager
ERIN KOSS - Manager Marketing, Sales

Jungle Concepts LLC
7318 E Shea Blvd Ste 106
Scottsdale, AZ 85260-6428

Telephone: (480) 969-2427
Fax Number: (480) 656-1411
Internet Homepage: pitajungle.com
Company Email: service@pitajungle.com
Type of Business: Chain Restaurant Operator
Year Founded: 1994
Total Sales: $12,910,000 (e)
Number of Employees: 553
Internet Order Processing: Yes
Total Units: 23
Trade Names: Pita Jungle (23)
Company-Owned Units: 10
Units Franchised To: 13
Alcohol Served: Beer, Wine
Primary Menu: Greek/Mediterranean (23)
Projected Openings: 1
Areas of Operation: AZ, CA
Type of Foodservice: Fast Casual (23)
Catering Services: Yes

Key Personnel
BASSEL OSMANI - Co-Founder; Partner
NELLY KOHSOK - Co-Founder; CEO; Partner
FOUAD EL KHODR - Co-Founder; Partner
RICK HOWARD - VP Operations, Development
KENNY HOLMES - Director Information Systems, Human Resources
MICHAEL DARWISH - Director Franchise Operations, Region
BETTINA LOISON - Manager Communications

Kahala Brands
9311 E Via De Ventura
Scottsdale, AZ 85258-3599

Telephone: (480) 362-4800
Fax Number: (480) 362-4812
Internet Homepage: blimpie.com; coldstonecreamery.com; frullati.com; johnniesnypizza.com; kahalacorp.com; kisstheconegoodbye.com; mauiwowi.com; nrgizejuice.com; pinkberry.com; rollerz.com; samuraisams.net; surfcitysqueeze.com; tacotime.com; thegreatsteak.com
Company Email: info@kahalamgmt.com
Type of Business: Chain Restaurant Operator
Year Founded: 1997

Systemwide Sales: $1,478,181,000 (e)
Total Sales: $214,620,000 (e)
Number of Employees: 600
Average Check: Breakfast(8); Lunch(12); Dinner(12)
Total Units: 3,292
Trade Names: America's Taco Shop (2); Baja Fresh Express (8); Baja Fresh Mexican Grill (72); Ben & Florentine (64); BLIMPIE (111); Built Custom Burgers(5); Cold Stone Creamery (1,365); Extreme Pita (24); Frullati Cafe and Bakery (10); Grabba Green (4); Great Steak (33); Johnnie's New York Pizzeria (2); Kahala Coffee Traders (5); La Salsa Fresh Mexican Grill (6); Maui Wowi (268); Mucho Burrito (146); NRgize Lifestyle Cafe (57); Pinkberry (93); Planet Smoothie (163); Ranch One (2); Samurai Sam's Teriyaki Grill (13); Surf City Squeeze (66); sweetFrog (226); Taco Time (222); Tasti D-Lite (2); Thai Express/Pad Thai(306); the Counter Custom Burger (17)
Company-Owned Units: 3,292
Preferred Location Types: Airports; Community Mall; Convenience Store/Gas Station; Discount Dept. Stores; Downtown; Freestanding; Grocery Stores; Institution (college/hospital); Kiosk; Lifestyle Center; Office Complex; Other; Outlet Mall; Regional Mall; Stadiums; Strip Mall; Travel Plazas
Primary Menu: American (97); Chicken (2); Hamburger (22); Health Foods (133); Japanese (13); Mexican (232); Pizza (2); Sandwiches/Deli (135); Snacks(2,126); Taco (224); Thai (306)
Areas of Operation: AK, AL, AR, AZ, CA, CO, CT, DC, FL, GA, GU, HI, IA, ID, IL, IN, KS, KY, LA, MA, MD, ME, MI, MN, MO, MS, MT, NC, ND, NE, NH, NJ, NM, NV, NY, OH, OK, OR, PA, PR, RI, SC, SD, TN, TX, UT, VA, WA, WI, WV, WY, ON, QC
Foreign Countries: CAMBODIA; CANADA; CHINA; DENMARK; EGYPT; EL SALVADOR; INDONESIA; JAPAN; KUWAIT; MEXICO; OMAN; QATAR; SAUDI ARABIA; SOUTH KOREA; TAIWAN; TRINIDAD & TOBAGO; UNITED ARAB EMIRATES
Type of Foodservice: Casual Dining (64); Fast Casual (313); Quick Serve (2,915)
Foodservice Management Venues: Business & Industry; College & University; Health Care; Military Feeding; Recreational; Schools; Transportation
Catering Services: Yes
Subsidiaries: Cold Stone Creamery Inc., SCOTTSDALE, AZ; Tasti D-Lite LLC, SCOTTSDALE, AZ
Primary Distributors: (Full Line) SYSCO Food Services of Arizona Inc., TOLLESON, AZ
Parent Company: MTY Food Group Inc., SAINT-LAURENT, QC CANADA

Key Personnel
JEFF SMIT - COO
STEVE EVANS - Senior VP Marketing
JOHN WUYCHECK - Senior VP Franchise

Development
JAY GOLDSTEIN - VP Franchise Development
ANDREA JOKSIMOVIC - VP Payroll, Human Resources
JOANI BIANCA - VP Restaurant Operations
RACHEL DAVIDSON - VP Operations, Licensing
LOGAN REVES - VP Restaurant Operations
KERRI KUDLA - VP Training
COURTNEY MAXEDON - VP Marketing
MICHAEL RANA - VP Operations
JILL SILBERBERG - Senior Director Real Estate
JON SILVA - Senior Director Purchasing, Supply Chain
JILL ANAYA - Senior Director Operations
JESSICA BENEDICK - Senior Director Public Affairs
SARAH CURTIS - Senior Director
MELISSA HUBBELL - Senior Director Marketing
LAURA VANDEVIER - Senior Director Marketing
ERIC WEIGEL - Senior Director Operations
BRANDON HODGINS - Director Loyalty Program
NICOLE HOFFMAN - Director Operations
RAQUEL GARCIA - Director Operations
NICOLE BUTCHER - Director Marketing
TODD CABLE - Director Operations
SAMANTHA CARITY - Director Marketing
KIRANNE REBER - Director Franchise Operations
LAURA LOOMIS - Director Operations
MICHAEL LUDWIG - Regional Director Operations
DANIEL LYNAM - Regional Director Operations
TIMOTHY THOMPSON - Regional Director Operations
AMIT TIKYANI - Regional Director Operations
JAMES DYER - Regional Director Operations
ALISON BRANCH - Regional Director Operations
BASHAR KATAT - Regional Director Operations
JAN MESSIANT - Art Director Digital
BRANDON SIEVERT - Manager Purchasing
LAUREN MCDONALD - Manager Digital Marketing
MICHAEL ROGOFF - Designer

Koi Franchise LLC
18221 N Pima Rd Suite 100 & 105
Scottsdale, AZ 85255

Telephone: (480) 209-1137
Internet Homepage: koipoke.com
Type of Business: Chain Restaurant Operator
Year Founded: 2017
Total Units: 5
Trade Names: Koibito Poke (5)
Company-Owned Units: 5
Preferred Location Types: Downtown; Institution (college/hospital); Strip Mall
Primary Menu: Asian (5)
Projected Openings: 7
Areas of Operation: AZ
Type of Foodservice: Casual Dining (5)

Key Personnel
STEPHEN DEAN - Partner
ANTHONY MCMAHON - Partner
TODD STOTTLEMYRE - Partner; Director New Store Development
OSCAR JIMENEZ - Executive Chef

Kona Grill Inc.
15059 N Scottsdale Rd Ste 300
Scottsdale, AZ 85254

Telephone: (480) 922-8100
Fax Number: (480) 922-6811
Internet Homepage: konagrill.com
Company Email: information@konagrill.com
Type of Business: Chain Restaurant Operator
Year Founded: 1998
Publicly Held: Yes
Total Sales: $181,742,000 (e)
Alcohol Sales: 30%
Number of Employees: 3,364
Average Check: Lunch(20); Dinner(30)
Internet Order Processing: Yes
Internet Sales: 2.00%
Total Units: 27
Trade Names: Kona Grill (27)
Company-Owned Units: 27
Preferred Square Footage: 6,500; 7,000
Preferred Location Types: Freestanding; Lifestyle Center; Mixed-use Center; Power Center; Regional Mall
Alcohol Served: Beer, Wine, Liquor
Primary Menu: American (27)
Areas of Operation: AL, AZ, CO, FL, GA, ID, IL, IN, MD, MI, MN, MO, NE, NJ, NV, OH, PR, TX, ON
Foreign Countries: CANADA
Type of Foodservice: Casual Dining (27)
Primary Distributors: (Food) US Foods, PHOENIX, AZ
Parent Company: The ONE Group LLC, NEW YORK, NY

Key Personnel
SEAN DOWNEY - Director Facility/Maintenance

McDonald's of Scottsdale
16097 N 82nd St Ste 300
Scottsdale, AZ 85260-1852

Telephone: (480) 367-9500
Fax Number: (480) 367-9501
Type of Business: Chain Restaurant Operator
Total Sales: $51,090,000 (e)
Number of Employees: 190
Total Units: 11
Trade Names: McDonald's (11)
Units Franchised From: 11
Preferred Square Footage: 2,500
Preferred Location Types: Convenience Store/Gas Station; Discount Dept. Stores; Freestanding
Primary Menu: Hamburger (11)
Projected Openings: 1
Areas of Operation: AZ
Type of Foodservice: Quick Serve (11)
Franchise Affiliation: McDonald's Corporation, CHICAGO, IL

Key Personnel
MARK KRAMER - President; Partner; General Buyer
JERRY WERNAU - Partner
NANCY SCHULTZ - Manager Marketing

Old Town Tortilla Factory
6910 E Main St
Scottsdale, AZ 85251-4312

Telephone: (480) 945-4567
Fax Number: (480) 945-0815
Internet Homepage: ckgrill.com; oldtowntortillafactory.com
Company Email: tortillafactory@aol.com
Type of Business: Chain Restaurant Operator
Total Sales: $3,098,000 (e)
Alcohol Sales: 5%
Number of Employees: 27
Average Check: Lunch(24); Dinner(54)
Total Units: 2
Trade Names: CK's Grill & Tavern (1); Old Town Tortilla Factory (1)
Company-Owned Units: 2
Preferred Location Types: Freestanding
Alcohol Served: Beer, Wine, Liquor
Primary Menu: American (1); Southwest/Tex-Mex (1)
Areas of Operation: AZ
Type of Foodservice: Casual Dining (1); Fine Dining (1)
Primary Distributors: (Food) Shamrock Foods Co., PHOENIX, AZ

Key Personnel
CHAD FLAUM - Owner; Executive Chef
DARRY BALDWIN - General Manager; General Buyer

Oregano Inc.
8300 N Hayden Rd Suite A207
Scottsdale, AZ 85258

Telephone: (480) 829-0898
Internet Homepage: oreganos.com
Company Email: guestservices@oreganos.com
Type of Business: Chain Restaurant Operator
Year Founded: 1993
Total Sales: $67,900,000 (e)
Alcohol Sales: 15%

Average Check: Lunch(12); Dinner(14)
Total Units: 25
Trade Names: Oregano's Pizza Bistro (25)
Company-Owned Units: 25
Alcohol Served: Beer, Wine, Liquor
Primary Menu: Pizza (25)
Projected Openings: 1
Areas of Operation: AZ
Type of Foodservice: Casual Dining (25)
Catering Services: Yes

Key Personnel
DOMINIC GAMARANO - Partner
STEVE DUNSIRE - COO
KYLE BYRNE - Director Talent Acquisitions
ALI ABAS - Manager Information Technology

Original ChopShop
7158 E 5th Ave
Scottsdale, AZ 85251-3236

Telephone: (480) 794-1536
Internet Homepage: originalchopshop.com
Company Email: info@chopshopco.com
Type of Business: Chain Restaurant Operator
Year Founded: 2013
Total Units: 13
Trade Names: Original ChopShop (13)
Company-Owned Units: 13
Preferred Square Footage: 2,800
Primary Menu: Health Foods (13)
Projected Openings: 1
Areas of Operation: AZ, TX
Type of Foodservice: Fast Casual (13)
Parent Company: Hargett Hunter Capital Partners, RALEIGH, NC

Key Personnel
CAITLIN JOCQUE - Co-Founder
JASON MORGAN - CEO; Partner
JEFF BROCK - Partner
KYLE FREDERICK - COO
CHAD HOHENSEE - Director Employee Development

P.F. Chang's China Bistro Restaurants
7676 E Pinnacle Peak Rd
Scottsdale, AZ 85255-3404

Telephone: (480) 888-3000
Fax Number: (480) 888-3001
Internet Homepage: pfchangs.com
Company Email: comments@pfchangs.com
Type of Business: Chain Restaurant Operator
Year Founded: 1993
Systemwide Sales: $2,354,890,000 (e)
Total Sales: $1,288,384,000 (e)
Alcohol Sales: 12%
Number of Employees: 27,530
Average Check: Lunch(24); Dinner(26)
Internet Order Processing: Yes
Total Units: 216
Trade Names: P.F. Chang's China Bistro (218)
Company-Owned Units: 138
Units Franchised To: 80
Preferred Square Footage: 6,900
Preferred Location Types: Community Mall; Downtown; Freestanding; Lifestyle Center; Regional Mall; Strip Mall
Alcohol Served: Beer, Wine, Liquor
Primary Menu: Chinese (218)
Projected Openings: 9
Areas of Operation: AL, AR, AZ, CA, CO, CT, FL, GA, HI, IA, ID, IL, IN, KS, KY, LA, MA, MD, MI, MN, MO, MS, NC, NE, NJ, NM, NV, NY, OH, OK, OR, PA, PR, RI, SC, TN, TX, UT, VA, WA, WI, ON, QC
Foreign Countries: ARGENTINA; BAHRAIN; BRAZIL; CANADA; CHILE; CHINA; COLOMBIA; COSTA RICA; DOMINICAN REPUBLIC; ENGLAND; GERMANY; GUATEMALA; KUWAIT; LEBANON; MEXICO; PAKISTAN; PANAMA; QATAR; SAUDI ARABIA; SOUTH KOREA; UNITED ARAB EMIRATES
Type of Foodservice: Casual Dining (218)
Primary Distributors: (Full Line) US Foods-Los Angeles, LA MIRADA, CA
Parent Company: TriArtisan Capital Advisors LLC/Paulson & Co. Inc., NEW YORK, NY

Key Personnel
EDUARDO LUZ - CEO; President
SWINT SMALLEY - CIO
TAYLOR VIERSEN - Area Director Division
BRAD HILL - Senior VP Finance
BRETT MANGOLD - Regional VP
CANDICE BARNETT - Senior Director Operations
CARRIE BELL - Director Recruitment, Global
HEATHER BEUTEL - Director Operations
KRISTEN BRIEDE - Director International
ANDI CRAMER - Director Distribution
MARY ERIKSSON-GROOMS - Director
CRYSTAL MARTIN - Director Training, International
SANDI JAPP - Director Talent
AFTON FRIEND - Director Real Estate
JENNIFER GRIDLEY - Director Internal Audit
ERIC HALL - Director Marketing
JULIE SNELL - Director Tax
COREY ROCKWELL - Director Internal Audit
KELLY SCHMITTEL - Director Business Development
CHRISTINA SERINO - Director Quality Assurance, Food Safety
WENDY SKARIN - Director Development, Vendor Relations
CALEIGH MOONEY - Senior Manager
SHELLEY NARDUCCI - Senior Manager Talent Acquisitions
ANTHONY KONECHNIK - Manager
ERICA FLORA - Manager Training
ASHLEY DIEHL - Manager Catering
MARY COOPER - Manager Training

Prime Steak Concepts
8355 E Hartford Dr Ste 100
Scottsdale, AZ 85255-2533

Telephone: (480) 889-1188
Fax Number: (480) 889-1189
Internet Homepage: dominickssteakhouse.com; steak44.com; steak48.com
Type of Business: Chain Restaurant Operator
Year Founded: 1990
Total Sales: $20,150,000 (e)
Alcohol Sales: 15%
Number of Employees: 270
Average Check: Lunch(22); Dinner(30)
Total Units: 5
Trade Names: Dominick's Steakhouse (1); Steak 44 (2); Steak 48 (2)
Company-Owned Units: 4
Preferred Square Footage: 5,500; 6,000
Preferred Location Types: Freestanding
Alcohol Served: Beer, Wine, Liquor
Primary Menu: Steak (1); Steak/Seafood (4)
Areas of Operation: AZ, IL, NM, TX
Type of Foodservice: Fine Dining (5)
Primary Distributors: (Food) Shamrock Foods Co., PHOENIX, AZ

Key Personnel
JEFF MASTRO - CEO; President
MICHAEL MASTRO - Partner; Executive Chef; Director Real Estate; General Buyer
SCOTT TROILO - Partner
KEITH KINARD - Controller
OLIVER BADGIO - Director Business Development

Sauce Holdings LLC
7144 E Stetson Dr Ste 420
Scottsdale, AZ 85251-3260

Telephone: (602) 954-4005
Internet Homepage: saucepizzaandwine.com
Company Email: SaucePizzaAndWine@gmail.com
Type of Business: Chain Restaurant Operator
Year Founded: 2014
Internet Order Processing: Yes
Total Units: 16
Trade Names: Sauce Pizza & Wine (16)
Company-Owned Units: 16
Alcohol Served: Liquor
Primary Menu: Italian (16)
Projected Openings: 1
Areas of Operation: AZ
Type of Foodservice: Casual Dining (16)

Key Personnel
LEAH AITKEN - Director Human Resources

Square One Concepts
7600 E Camelback Rd Ste 1
Scottsdale, AZ 85251

Telephone: (480) 941-0101
Fax Number: (480) 941-4617
Internet Homepage: squareoneconceptsinc.com
Type of Business: Chain Restaurant Operator
Total Sales: $14,130,000 (e)
Total Units: 18
Trade Names: Bootlegger (1); Bourbon & Bones (1); Cold Beers & Cheeseburgers (12); Famous 48 (1); High Dive (1); Pacific Beach Shore Club (1); Park 101(1)
Company-Owned Units: 18
Primary Menu: American (16); Bar-B-Q (1); Steak (1)
Projected Openings: 3
Areas of Operation: AZ, CA
Type of Foodservice: Casual Dining (18)

Key Personnel
BARRETT RINZLER - Founder; CEO; President
HOWARD GINSBERG - Chief Marketing Officer
ROBERT WAGNER - Corporate Chef
TRACY FRAZIER - Director Operations
WILLIAM PRICHARD - Director Purchasing
ZACH BRASH - Director Marketing
TONY ISHAK - Specialist Training

Star Buffet Inc.
2501 N Hayden Rd Ste 103
Scottsdale, AZ 85257-2326

Telephone: (480) 425-0487
Fax Number: (480) 425-0999
Internet Homepage: starbuffet.com
Company Email: starbuffet@msn.com
Type of Business: Chain Restaurant Operator
Year Founded: 1997
Total Sales: $37,276,000 (e)
Alcohol Sales: 6%
Number of Employees: 1,476
Average Check: Breakfast(8); Lunch(8); Dinner(8)
Total Units: 26
Trade Names: 4 Aces (1); 4 B's Restaurant (11); Bar H Steakhouse (1); Barnhill's Buffet (1); BuddyFreddys (1); Casa Bonita (1); JB's Family Restaurant (5); Pecos Diamond Steakhouse (2); Ranchers Grill (1); Western Sizzlin (1); Whistle Junction (1)
Company-Owned Units: 25
Units Franchised From: 3
Preferred Square Footage: 5,000; 7,000; 10,200
Preferred Location Types: Freestanding; Strip Mall
Alcohol Served: Beer, Wine, Liquor
Primary Menu: American (24); Mexican (1); Steak (1)
Areas of Operation: AL, AR, AZ, CO, FL, ID, LA, MS, MT, NM, OK, OR, TN, TX, UT, WY
Type of Foodservice: Casual Dining (2); Family Restaurant (24)
Franchise Affiliation: JB's Family Restaurants Inc., TEMPE, AZ
Primary Distributors: (Full Line) SYSCO Intermountain Food Services Inc., WEST JORDAN, UT

Key Personnel
ROBERT E. WHEATON - Chairman; CEO; President; Director Facility/Maintenance, Real Estate, Site Selection, Design
RONALD E. DOWDY - CFO; Corporate Secretary; Controller; General Buyer
CALVIN TOLMAN - Director Information Systems

Tasti D-Lite LLC
9311 E Via De Ventura Ste 100
Scottsdale, AZ 85258-3599

Telephone: (480) 362-4800
Internet Homepage: planetsmoothie.com; planetsmoothiefranchise.com; tastidlite.com; kahalamgmt.com
Company Email: info@kahalamgmt.com
Listing Type: Subsidiary
Type of Business: Chain Restaurant Operator
Year Founded: 1987
Total Sales: $13,880,000 (e)
Number of Employees: 50
Total Units: 149
Trade Names: Planet Smoothie (141); Tasti D-Lite (20)
Units Franchised To: 161
Preferred Square Footage: 600; 900; 1,200
Primary Menu: Snacks (161)
Projected Openings: 15
Areas of Operation: AL, AR, AZ, CA, FL, GA, HI, MA, MD, MO, NC, NJ, NV, NY, OH, PA, SC, TN, TX
Foreign Countries: AUSTRALIA; SAUDI ARABIA; UNITED ARAB EMIRATES
Type of Foodservice: Quick Serve (161)
Parent Company: Kahala Brands, SCOTTSDALE, AZ
Headquarters: MTY Food Group Inc., SAINT-LAURENT, QC CANADA
Notes: The company derives approximately 33% of total revenue from the sale of product to franchisees.

Key Personnel
PAT FOX - CFO
KEVIN BURNETT - Senior VP Operations
MARK LIEBEL - Director Operations

The Scottsdale Plaza Resort
7200 N Scottsdale Rd
Scottsdale, AZ 85253-3633

Telephone: (480) 948-5000
Fax Number: (480) 951-5108
Internet Homepage: scottsdaleplaza.com
Company Email: info@scottsdaleplaza.com
Type of Business: Foodservice Operations - Hotel/Motels
Year Founded: 1975
Total Sales: $6,303,000 (e)
Alcohol Sales: 20%
Number of Employees: 50
Average Check: Breakfast(16); Lunch(20); Dinner(52)
Total Units: 4
Trade Names: Cafe Cabana (1); Garden Court Restaurant (1); J.D.'s Lounge (1); The Market (1)
Company-Owned Units: 4
Preferred Location Types: Freestanding; Hotel/Motel
Alcohol Served: Beer, Wine, Liquor
Primary Menu: American (3); Sandwiches/Deli (1)
Areas of Operation: AZ
Type of Foodservice: Casual Dining (3); Quick Serve (1)
Catering Services: Yes
Primary Distributors: (Food) Shamrock Foods Co., PHOENIX, AZ

Key Personnel
SEAN SACHS - Senior VP
TRAVIS GILES - VP Operations
BRUCE JOHNSON - Director Information Systems
KATIE MODAHL - Manager Sales
LAUREN SACHS - Manager Sales, National
KATE GALLAGHER - Manager Special Projects

Westaco Inc.
7155 E Thomas Rd Ste 105
Scottsdale, AZ 85251-6330

Telephone: (480) 429-6999
Fax Number: (480) 424-7160
Internet Homepage: aztacos.com
Company Email: info@aztacos.com
Type of Business: Chain Restaurant Operator
Year Founded: 1980
Total Sales: $67,242,000 (e)
Number of Employees: 615
Total Units: 42
Trade Names: Long John Silver's (3); Taco Bell (39)
Units Franchised From: 42
Preferred Square Footage: 2,400; 2,600;

2,800
Preferred Location Types: Freestanding
Primary Menu: Seafood (3); Taco (39)
Areas of Operation: AZ
Type of Foodservice: Quick Serve (42)
Franchise Affiliation: Long John Silver's Inc., LOUISVILLE, KY; Taco Bell Corp., IRVINE, CA

Key Personnel
ARLEN KORE - VP

Wildflower Bread Company
8130 E Cactus Rd Ste 500
Scottsdale, AZ 85260

Telephone: (480) 951-9453
Fax Number: (480) 951-9464
Internet Homepage: wildflowerbread.com
Company Email: customerservice@wildflowerbread.com
Type of Business: Chain Restaurant Operator
Year Founded: 1996
Total Sales: $15,210,000 (e)
Number of Employees: 468
Average Check: Breakfast(8); Lunch(8); Dinner(12)
Total Units: 16
Trade Names: Wildflower Bakery (16)
Company-Owned Units: 16
Preferred Square Footage: 3,000; 4,200; 4,600
Preferred Location Types: Strip Mall
Primary Menu: Sandwiches/Deli (16)
Projected Remodelings: 2
Areas of Operation: AZ
Type of Foodservice: Fast Casual (16)
Catering Services: Yes
Primary Distributors: (Food) SYSCO Food Services of Arizona Inc., TOLLESON, AZ
Notes: The company derives approximately 8% of its revenue from wholesale operations.

Key Personnel
LOUIS J. BASILE JR - President; Partner; Director Operations, Menu Development, Catering
TRACY BASILE - Partner
BRENDON FRANKO - Manager Purchasing, Supply Chain
KYLE SMITH - Advisor Finance

Zipps Sports Grill
9319 N 94th Way Suite 100
Scottsdale, AZ 85258-5564

Telephone: (480) 948-5544
Internet Homepage: zippssportsgrills.com
Type of Business: Chain Restaurant Operator
Year Founded: 1993
Total Sales: $18,000,000 (e)
Total Units: 15
Trade Names: Zipps Sports Grill (15)
Company-Owned Units: 15
Primary Menu: American (15)
Areas of Operation: AZ
Type of Foodservice: Casual Dining (15)

Key Personnel
TODD GOLDMAN - Founder; Owner
TIFFANY DOBY - Director Marketing

Picazzos Pizza
1855 W State Route 89A
Sedona, AZ 86336-5557

Telephone: (928) 282-4140
Fax Number: (928) 282-5758
Internet Homepage: picazzos.com
Type of Business: Chain Restaurant Operator
Year Founded: 2002
Total Sales: $13,180,000 (e)
Alcohol Sales: 10%
Number of Employees: 80
Average Check: Lunch(14); Dinner(14)
Total Units: 5
Trade Names: Picazzo's Gourmet Pizza and Salads and Pasta (5)
Company-Owned Units: 5
Preferred Location Types: Freestanding; Strip Mall
Alcohol Served: Beer, Wine, Liquor
Primary Menu: Pizza (5)
Areas of Operation: AZ
Type of Foodservice: Casual Dining (5)
Primary Distributors: (Full Line) SYSCO Food Services of Arizona Inc., TOLLESON, AZ

Key Personnel
RICK FREEDMAN - Owner; Executive Chef; General Buyer
CHRIS DISNEY - Director Operations

Canyon Fast Foods, Inc.
4435 S White Mountain Rd
Show Low, AZ 85901-7701

Telephone: (928) 537-0696
Type of Business: Chain Restaurant Operator
Total Sales: $5,421,000 (e)
Total Units: 2
Trade Names: Jack in the Box (2)
Units Franchised From: 2
Primary Menu: Hamburger (2)
Areas of Operation: AZ
Type of Foodservice: Quick Serve (2)
Franchise Affiliation: Jack in the Box Restaurants, SAN DIEGO, CA

Key Personnel
GARY BEHMER - Owner; General Buyer

Patann, Inc
1802 E Fry Blvd
Sierra Vista, AZ 85635-2703

Telephone: (520) 459-2524
Fax Number: (520) 459-2802
Type of Business: Chain Restaurant Operator
Total Sales: $20,074,000 (e)
Total Units: 4
Trade Names: McDonald's (4)
Units Franchised From: 4
Primary Menu: Hamburger (4)
Areas of Operation: AZ
Type of Foodservice: Quick Serve (4)
Franchise Affiliation: McDonald's Corporation, CHICAGO, IL

Key Personnel
PAT RICHARDS - President; Partner; General Buyer
LEANN RICHARDS - Partner

Calzona Foods, Inc.
3102 S Mill Ave
Tempe, AZ 85282-3654

Telephone: (480) 966-1201
Type of Business: Chain Restaurant Operator
Total Sales: $28,520,000 (e)
Total Units: 11
Trade Names: Jack in the Box (11)
Units Franchised From: 11
Primary Menu: Hamburger (11)
Areas of Operation: AZ
Type of Foodservice: Quick Serve (11)
Franchise Affiliation: Jack in the Box Restaurants, SAN DIEGO, CA

Key Personnel
JOSEPH ESPINOSA - Owner; General Buyer

Dirty Dough
1537 W Broadway Rd
Tempe, AZ 85282

Telephone: (623) 404-6471
Internet Homepage: dirtydoughcookies.com
Type of Business: Chain Restaurant Operator
Total Units: 31
Trade Names: Dirty Dough (31)
Company-Owned Units: 31
Primary Menu: Snacks (31)
Projected Openings: 30
Areas of Operation: AZ, FL, IN, KY, ND, OH, OK, TX, UT
Type of Foodservice: Quick Serve (31)

Key Personnel
BENNETT MAXWELL - Founder

JILL SUMMERHAYS - CEO
MIKE NORTON - CTO
JOSHUA STEELE - VP Production
CHALLIS HOBBS - VP Franchise Sales
MELISSA BOTH - Director Operations

Kyoto Bowl
3101 S Mill Ave
Tempe, AZ 85282-3653

Telephone: (480) 731-9888
Fax Number: (480) 629-4995
Internet Homepage: thekyotobowl.com
Type of Business: Chain Restaurant Operator
Year Founded: 1987
Total Sales: $6,370,000 (e)
Number of Employees: 72
Average Check: Lunch(12); Dinner(18)
Total Units: 4
Trade Names: Kyoto Bowl (4)
Company-Owned Units: 4
Preferred Square Footage: 2,500; 3,000
Preferred Location Types: Freestanding; Strip Mall
Primary Menu: Asian (4)
Areas of Operation: AZ
Type of Foodservice: Family Restaurant (4)
Catering Services: Yes
Distribution Centers: TEMPE, AZ
Primary Distributors: (Full Line) Shamrock Foods Co., PHOENIX, AZ

Key Personnel
CHARLES CHIU - CEO; President; Director Real Estate, Menu Development, Catering
RONALD ROSTAS - CFO; Controller; Director Information Systems, E-Commerce, Internet Development
CHRISTIANA CHIU - Exec VP Advertising; Treasurer; General Buyer
GUSTAVO SANTIAGO - Director Foodservice

LeVecke and Company
5210 S Priest Dr
Tempe, AZ 85283-1431

Telephone: (480) 736-2461
Type of Business: Chain Restaurant Operator
Year Founded: 2001
Total Sales: $16,830,000 (e)
Number of Employees: 4,000
Average Check: Breakfast(8); Lunch(10); Dinner(10)
Total Units: 8
Trade Names: Carl's Jr. (8)
Units Franchised From: 8
Preferred Square Footage: 2,500; 3,000; 4,000
Preferred Location Types: Freestanding
Primary Menu: Hamburger (8)
Areas of Operation: AZ, CA, IL, KY, MO
Type of Foodservice: Quick Serve (8)
Franchise Affiliation: Carl's Jr., FRANKLIN, TN; Hardee's Food Systems Inc., FRANKLIN, TN; Pizza Patron Inc., DALLAS, TX
Notes: The Hardee's/Carl's Jr. operate as MJKL Enterprises and Frontier Star LLC. The Pizza Patron restaurants operate as Pizza Revolucion LLC.

Key Personnel
JASON LEVECKE - CEO; Partner; Director Facility/Maintenance, Design, Human Resources, Store Fixtures
MARGARET LEVECKE - President; Partner; Director Finance, Operations, Supply Chain, Real Estate; General Buyer
CARL LEVECKE - Partner
JUAN ACON - Director Information Systems

Mountain Range Restaurants LLC
825 S 48th St
Tempe, AZ 85281-5101

Telephone: (480) 829-5090
Fax Number: (480) 446-9661
Internet Homepage: mountainrangerestaurants.net
Type of Business: Chain Restaurant Operator
Year Founded: 2001
Total Sales: $17,330,000 (e)
Number of Employees: 935
Average Check: Breakfast(6); Lunch(10); Dinner(12)
Total Units: 6
Trade Names: Denny's (6)
Units Franchised From: 6
Preferred Square Footage: 3,000; 5,000
Preferred Location Types: Freestanding
Primary Menu: American (6)
Areas of Operation: AZ, ID, OR, UT
Type of Foodservice: Family Restaurant (6)
Franchise Affiliation: Denny's Corporation, SPARTANBURG, SC
Primary Distributors: (Full Line) McLane/Rocky Mount, ROCKY MOUNT, NC

Key Personnel
ROBERT GENTZ - Partner; General Manager; Director Supply Chain, Real Estate, Design
STEVE HALL - Director Human Resources, Training

Arizona Ice Cream Company, Inc
475 W Wetmore Rd Ste 125
Tucson, AZ 85705-1512

Telephone: (520) 887-3131
Type of Business: Chain Restaurant Operator
Total Sales: $1,182,000 (e)
Total Units: 2
Trade Names: Cold Stone Creamery (2)
Units Franchised From: 2
Primary Menu: Snacks (2)
Areas of Operation: AZ
Type of Foodservice: Quick Serve (2)
Franchise Affiliation: Kahala Brands, SCOTTSDALE, AZ

Key Personnel
RODNEY LANDS - Owner

Baggin's, Inc.
4645 S Contractors Way
Tucson, AZ 85714-2150

Telephone: (520) 325-1860
Internet Homepage: bagginsgourmet.com
Company Email: contact@bagginsgourmet.com
Type of Business: Chain Restaurant Operator
Year Founded: 1984
Internet Order Processing: Yes
Total Units: 11
Trade Names: Baggin's Gourmet Sandwiches (11)
Company-Owned Units: 11
Primary Menu: Sandwiches/Deli (11)
Areas of Operation: AZ
Type of Foodservice: Fast Casual (11)

Key Personnel
CHEREE GARRETT-JEFFRIES - Founder; CEO; General Buyer
MELONIE PRUETT - General Manager
NANCY MURPHY - Director Operations

Bjf Financial Limited Partnership
5762 E 22nd St
Tucson, AZ 85711-5527

Telephone: (520) 790-0769
Internet Homepage: dairyqueen.com
Type of Business: Chain Restaurant Operator
Total Sales: $4,546,000 (e)
Total Units: 3
Trade Names: Dairy Queen Store (3)
Units Franchised From: 3
Primary Menu: Snacks (3)
Areas of Operation: AZ
Type of Foodservice: Quick Serve (3)
Franchise Affiliation: International Dairy Queen Inc., BLOOMINGTON, MN

Key Personnel
ERIC HOFFMAN - President; General Buyer

Canteen Vending Services
1101 E Palmdale St
Tucson, AZ 85714-1660

Telephone: (520) 327-6888
Fax Number: (520) 326-3175
Listing Type: Branch Office
Type of Business: Foodservice Management Operator
Year Founded: 1929
Number of Employees: 12
Number of Locations Served: 135
Total Foodservice Mgmt Accounts: 135
Areas of Operation: AZ
Type of Foodservice: Vending machines (135)
Foodservice Management Venues: Business & Industry; College & University; Health Care; Lodging; Military Feeding; Schools; Travel Plazas
Parent Company: Compass Group The Americas, CHARLOTTE, NC
Headquarters: Canteen Vending Services, CHARLOTTE, NC

Key Personnel
MICHAEL LOUNSBURY - General Manager; General Buyer

D & J Holdings LLC
PO Box 40245
Tucson, AZ 85717-0245

Telephone: (913) 707-3504
Type of Business: Chain Restaurant Operator
Total Sales: $11,920,000 (e)
Total Units: 6
Trade Names: Five Guys Burgers and Fries (6)
Units Franchised From: 6
Preferred Location Types: Strip Mall
Primary Menu: Hamburger (6)
Projected Openings: 1
Areas of Operation: AZ
Type of Foodservice: Fast Casual (6)
Franchise Affiliation: Five Guys Holdings Inc., LORTON, VA

Key Personnel
DOUGLAS VAUGHAN - Partner; General Buyer
JEFF NOYCE - Partner

eegee's Inc.
3360 E Ajo Way
Tucson, AZ 85713-5228

Telephone: (520) 294-3333
Fax Number: (520) 889-4340
Internet Homepage: eegees.com
Company Email: info@eegees.com
Type of Business: Chain Restaurant Operator
Year Founded: 1971
Total Sales: $29,850,000 (e)
Number of Employees: 550
Average Check: Lunch(8); Dinner(8)
Total Units: 32
Trade Names: eegee's (32)
Company-Owned Units: 32
Preferred Square Footage: 2,400
Preferred Location Types: Freestanding; Strip Mall
Primary Menu: Sandwiches/Deli (32)
Areas of Operation: AZ
Type of Foodservice: Fast Casual (32)
Foodservice Management Venues: College & University
Catering Services: Yes
On-site Distribution Center: Yes
Primary Distributors: (Full Line) Shamrock Foods Co., PHOENIX, AZ
Parent Company: CEO Foods, VICTORVILLE, CA
Notes: The company derives approximately 10% of its revenue from wholesale operations.

Key Personnel
JASON VAUGHN - CEO

El Charro Enterprises
311 N Court Ave
Tucson, AZ 85701-1016

Mailing Address: P.O. Box 1203, TUCSON, AZ, 85702
Telephone: (520) 622-1922
Internet Homepage: elcharrocafe.com
Type of Business: Chain Restaurant Operator
Year Founded: 1922
Total Sales: $13,258,000 (e)
Alcohol Sales: 2%
Number of Employees: 300
Average Check: Lunch(10); Dinner(14)
Internet Order Processing: Yes
Internet Sales: 0.50%
Total Units: 3
Trade Names: El Charro Cafe (3)
Company-Owned Units: 3
Preferred Location Types: Freestanding
Alcohol Served: Beer, Wine, Liquor
Primary Menu: Mexican (3)
Areas of Operation: AZ
Type of Foodservice: Casual Dining (3)
Foodservice Management Venues: College & University
Catering Services: Yes
Primary Distributors: (Food) Shamrock Foods Co., PHOENIX, AZ
Notes: The company derives approximately 20% of its revenue from wholesale operations.

Key Personnel
RAYMON FLORES - CEO; Partner; General Manager
CARLOTTA FLORES - Partner; Executive Chef; General Buyer
RAY FLORES - Partner; General Manager
MARQUES FLORES - General Manager
GARRET BOOS - Manager Information Systems

I Chief, LLC
6079 E Grant Rd
Tucson, AZ 85712-2319

Telephone: (520) 398-7610
Type of Business: Chain Restaurant Operator
Total Sales: $51,200,000 (e)
Total Units: 20
Trade Names: Jack in the Box (20)
Units Franchised From: 20
Primary Menu: Hamburger (20)
Areas of Operation: AZ
Type of Foodservice: Quick Serve (20)
Franchise Affiliation: Jack in the Box Restaurants, SAN DIEGO, CA

Key Personnel
MUSTAHIL SHAH - Partner; General Buyer
JACQUE AKE - Partner; COO
JACQUELYN AKE - COO
VANESSA MARTINEZ - General Manager

International Restaurants
2720 N Oracle Rd
Tucson, AZ 85705-4316

Telephone: (520) 624-9855
Fax Number: (520) 624-4014
Internet Homepage: laparrillasuiza.com
Company Email: contact@laparrillasuiza.com
Type of Business: Chain Restaurant Operator
Year Founded: 1980
Total Sales: $8,181,000 (e)
Alcohol Sales: 20%
Number of Employees: 144
Average Check: Lunch(10); Dinner(14)
Total Units: 4
Trade Names: La Parrilla Suiza (4)
Company-Owned Units: 4
Preferred Square Footage: 5,500; 6,000
Preferred Location Types: Freestanding; Strip Mall
Alcohol Served: Beer, Wine, Liquor
Primary Menu: Mexican (4)
Areas of Operation: AZ
Type of Foodservice: Casual Dining (4)
Primary Distributors: (Equipment) Standard Restaurant Equipment Inc., TUCSON, AZ; (Food) Shamrock Foods Co., PHOENIX, AZ; (Supplies) Standard Restaurant Equipment Inc., TUCSON, AZ

Key Personnel
AGUSTIN GONGORA - President; Controller; Executive Chef; Director Loss Prevention

J. Herndon Inc.
4500 E Speedway Blvd Ste 64
Tucson, AZ 85712-5322

Telephone: (520) 325-4504
Type of Business: Chain Restaurant Operator
Total Sales: $22,790,000 (e)
Total Units: 10
Trade Names: Burger King (10)
Units Franchised From: 10
Primary Menu: Hamburger (10)
Areas of Operation: AZ
Type of Foodservice: Quick Serve (10)
Franchise Affiliation: Burger King Worldwide Inc., MIAMI, FL

Key Personnel
JAMES HERNDON - President; General Buyer

Lucky Wishbone
4701 E Broadway Blvd
Tucson, AZ 85711-3607

Telephone: (520) 327-5679
Fax Number: (520) 326-8830
Internet Homepage: luckywishbone.com
Company Email: info@luckywishbone.com
Type of Business: Chain Restaurant Operator
Year Founded: 1953
Total Sales: $8,895,000 (e)
Number of Employees: 165
Average Check: Lunch(8); Dinner(14)
Internet Order Processing: Yes
Total Units: 7
Trade Names: Lucky Wishbone (7)
Company-Owned Units: 2
Units Franchised To: 5
Preferred Square Footage: 2,500
Preferred Location Types: Freestanding
Primary Menu: American (7)
Areas of Operation: AZ
Type of Foodservice: Casual Dining (7)
Catering Services: Yes
Primary Distributors: (Full Line) US Foods, PHOENIX, AZ

Key Personnel
CLYDE BUZZARD - President; Partner; Executive Chef; Director Finance, Facility/Maintenance, Real Estate; General Buyer
JAN BOYD - Partner

MCL Enterprises, Inc.
2040 E Irvington Rd
Tucson, AZ 85714-1825

Telephone: (520) 889-8389
Fax Number: (520) 889-8389
Type of Business: Chain Restaurant Operator
Total Sales: $67,250,000 (e)
Total Units: 30
Trade Names: Burger King (30)
Units Franchised From: 30
Primary Menu: Hamburger (30)
Areas of Operation: AZ
Type of Foodservice: Quick Serve (30)
Franchise Affiliation: Burger King Worldwide Inc., MIAMI, FL

Key Personnel
MICHAEL LAIRD - CEO
MITCH LAIRD - President
HARRY LOVELESS - Director Operations
LAURA FONTENOT - District Manager

Pizza Hut of Arizona Inc.
5902 E Pima St
Tucson, AZ 85712-4322

Telephone: (520) 886-5271
Fax Number: (520) 886-9180
Type of Business: Chain Restaurant Operator
Year Founded: 1965
Total Sales: $36,220,000 (e)
Alcohol Sales: 5%
Number of Employees: 965
Average Check: Lunch(14); Dinner(14)
Total Units: 30
Trade Names: Pizza Hut (30)
Units Franchised From: 30
Preferred Square Footage: 2,500
Preferred Location Types: Downtown; Freestanding; Regional Mall; Strip Mall
Alcohol Served: Beer, Wine
Primary Menu: Pizza (30)
Areas of Operation: AZ
Type of Foodservice: Quick Serve (30)
Franchise Affiliation: Pizza Hut Inc., PLANO, TX
Primary Distributors: (Full Line) McLane/Sunwest, GOODYEAR, AZ

Key Personnel
BRENT KYTE - Chairman

Tucson Golden Corral
4380 E 22nd St
Tucson, AZ 85711-5706

Telephone: (520) 512-0088
Fax Number: (520) 512-0087
Internet Homepage: tucsongoldencorral.com
Type of Business: Chain Restaurant Operator
Total Sales: $4,115,000 (e)
Number of Employees: 160
Average Check: Breakfast(8); Lunch(8); Dinner(14)
Total Units: 1
Trade Names: Golden Corral Buffet & Grill (1)
Units Franchised From: 1
Preferred Square Footage: 7,800; 10,300; 11,500
Preferred Location Types: Freestanding
Primary Menu: American (1)
Areas of Operation: AZ
Type of Foodservice: Family Restaurant (1)
Franchise Affiliation: Golden Corral Corp., RALEIGH, NC
Primary Distributors: (Full Line) McLane/Fort Worth, FORT WORTH, TX

Key Personnel
DALE P. SCHAUFEL - President; General Manager; General Buyer
PETER SALCIDO - Manager Catering

Viva Burrito Development Corp.
860 E 16th St
Tucson, AZ 85719-6603

Telephone: (303) 227-0399
Fax Number: (520) 620-6468
Type of Business: Chain Restaurant Operator
Year Founded: 1997
Total Sales: $13,140,000 (e)
Number of Employees: 120
Average Check: Breakfast(8); Lunch(8); Dinner(8)
Total Units: 10
Trade Names: Viva Burrito (10)
Company-Owned Units: 10
Preferred Square Footage: 1,600
Preferred Location Types: Freestanding
Primary Menu: Mexican (10)
Areas of Operation: AZ, CO
Type of Foodservice: Quick Serve (10)
On-site Distribution Center: Yes
Primary Distributors: (Food) SYSCO Food Services of Arizona Inc., TOLLESON, AZ

Key Personnel
ARACELY BELTRAN - Partner; Manager Finance, Operations, Human Resources
EDGAR BELTRAN - Partner; Executive Chef; Director Purchasing, Supply Chain, Real Estate, Design; General Buyer
JUAN BELTRAN - Partner; Director Facility/Maintenance, Design

El Guero Canelo
2480 N Oracle Rd
Tucson, AZ 85705

Telephone: (520) 807-9620
Fax Number: (520) 807-6321
Internet Homepage: elguerocanelo.com
Company Email: elliet@elguerocanelo.com
Type of Business: Chain Restaurant Operator

Year Founded: 1993
Total Units: 5
Trade Names: El Guero Canelo (5)
Company-Owned Units: 5
Primary Menu: Mexican (5)
Areas of Operation: AZ
Type of Foodservice: Quick Serve (5)

Key Personnel
DANIEL CONTRERAS - Owner; General Buyer

Neek Inc
680 W Catalina Dr
Yuma, AZ 85364-8011

Telephone: (928) 341-0200
Fax Number: (928) 314-4584
Type of Business: Chain Restaurant Operator
Total Sales: $4,774,000 (e)
Total Units: 7
Trade Names: Little Caesars Pizza (7)
Units Franchised From: 7
Primary Menu: Pizza (7)
Areas of Operation: AZ
Type of Foodservice: Quick Serve (7)
Franchise Affiliation: Little Caesar Enterprises Inc., DETROIT, MI

Key Personnel
JOHNNY BAKLINI - Owner; General Buyer

Oasis Pizza Inc
11361 S Foothills Blvd Ste 5
Yuma, AZ 85367-7743

Telephone: (928) 342-9798
Type of Business: Chain Restaurant Operator
Total Sales: $10,408,000 (e)
Total Units: 5
Trade Names: Domino's (5)
Units Franchised From: 5
Primary Menu: Pizza (5)
Areas of Operation: AZ
Type of Foodservice: Quick Serve
Franchise Affiliation: Domino's Pizza Inc, ANN ARBOR, MI

Key Personnel
VIRGIL TODD - Owner; General Buyer

CALIFORNIA

Herrick Foods, LLC
5033 Kanan Rd
Agoura, CA 91301-2515

Telephone: (818) 889-1653
Type of Business: Chain Restaurant Operator
Total Sales: $5,279,000 (e)
Total Units: 2
Trade Names: Jack in the Box (2)
Units Franchised From: 2
Primary Menu: Hamburger (2)
Areas of Operation: CA
Type of Foodservice: Quick Serve (2)
Franchise Affiliation: Jack in the Box Restaurants, SAN DIEGO, CA

Key Personnel
MIKE HERRICK - Owner; General Buyer

Gul Food Management, Inc.
1257 Park St
Alameda, CA 94501-5247

Telephone: (510) 522-8865
Type of Business: Chain Restaurant Operator
Total Sales: $22,890,000 (e)
Total Units: 9
Trade Names: Jack in the Box (9)
Units Franchised From: 9
Primary Menu: Hamburger (9)
Areas of Operation: CA
Type of Foodservice: Quick Serve (9)
Franchise Affiliation: Jack in the Box Restaurants, SAN DIEGO, CA

Key Personnel
SAEED KHAN - Owner; General Buyer
MUSTAQEEM HUMAYOUN - Assistant Manager; Administrative Assistant

Island Pizza Inc
1215 Lincoln Ave
Alameda, CA 94501-2325

Telephone: (510) 865-8000
Type of Business: Chain Restaurant Operator
Total Sales: $14,587,000 (e)
Total Units: 7
Trade Names: Domino's (7)
Units Franchised From: 7
Primary Menu: Pizza (7)
Areas of Operation: CA
Type of Foodservice: Quick Serve (7)
Franchise Affiliation: Domino's Pizza Inc, ANN ARBOR, MI

Key Personnel
DAN T. BRUMLEVE - Owner; General Buyer

Shakey's USA
2200 W Valley Blvd
Alhambra, CA 91803-1928

Telephone: (626) 576-0616
Fax Number: (626) 284-6870
Internet Homepage: shakeys.com
Company Email: contact@shakeys.com
Type of Business: Chain Restaurant Operator
Year Founded: 2004
Systemwide Sales: $69,407,000 (e)
Total Sales: $15,360,000 (e)
Alcohol Sales: 7%
Number of Employees: 40
Internet Order Processing: Yes
Total Units: 50
Trade Names: Shakey's Pizza (50)
Company-Owned Units: 22
Units Franchised To: 28
Preferred Square Footage: 1,200
Preferred Location Types: Downtown; Freestanding; Strip Mall
Alcohol Served: Beer, Wine
Primary Menu: Pizza (50)
Areas of Operation: AL, CA, HI, WA
Foreign Countries: MEXICO
Type of Foodservice: Casual Dining (50)
Catering Services: Yes
Primary Distributors: (Food) US Foods, CORONA, CA
Parent Company: Jacmar Companies, ALHAMBRA, CA
Notes: Formerly known as Shakey's Inc.

Key Personnel
DAVID REID - CFO
SONIA BARAJAS-NAJERA - VP Franchise Development
CINDY G. STAATS - VP Marketing
WILLIAM GRAHAM - VP Human Resources
THOMAS TOGIA - Director Information Technology
LEO LOPEZ - Regional Manager
COREY SHUM - Manager Information Technology

Chronic Tacos Enterprises
31 Journey Ste 230
Aliso Viejo, CA 92656-5311

Telephone: (949) 366-9936
Fax Number: (949) 366-9937
Internet Homepage: eatchronictacos.com
Company Email: mkovacs@blazepr.com
Type of Business: Chain Restaurant Operator
Year Founded: 2001
Systemwide Sales: $17,881,000 (e)
Total Sales: $2,044,000 (e)
Alcohol Sales: 5%
Number of Employees: 139
Average Check: Lunch(14); Dinner(14)
Total Units: 59
Trade Names: Chronic Tacos (59)
Company-Owned Units: 1
Units Franchised To: 58
Preferred Location Types: Downtown; Strip Mall
Alcohol Served: Beer, Wine, Liquor
Primary Menu: Taco (59)

Projected Openings: 10
Areas of Operation: AL, AZ, CA, CO, FL, NC, NV, UT, WA, AB, BC
Foreign Countries: CANADA
Type of Foodservice: Fast Casual (59)
Primary Distributors: (Full Line) SYSCO Food Services of Los Angeles Inc., WALNUT, CA
Notes: Chronic Taco locations in Canada provide full liquor service.

Key Personnel
RANDY WYNER - Founder; President
MICHAEL MOHAMMED - CEO
DAVID MOHAMMED - Director Marketing

●▲
Bromley Food
2305 Lake Ave
Altadena, CA 91001-2416

Telephone: (626) 791-5402
Fax Number: (626) 222-1184
Type of Business: Chain Restaurant Operator
Total Sales: $8,087,000 (e)
Total Units: 3
Trade Names: Jack In The Box (3)
Units Franchised From: 3
Primary Menu: Hamburger (3)
Areas of Operation: CA
Type of Foodservice: Quick Serve (3)
Franchise Affiliation: Jack in the Box Restaurants, SAN DIEGO, CA

Key Personnel
TERENCE F. JONES - President; General Buyer

●▲
Disneyland Resort
1313 S Harbor Blvd
Anaheim, CA 92802-2309

Mailing Address: PO Box 3232, ANAHEIM, CA, 92803-3232
Telephone: (714) 781-4000
Fax Number: (714) 781-1145
Internet Homepage: disneyland.disney.go.com; disneyland.com
Type of Business: Foodservice Operations - Theme Parks
Year Founded: 1955
Publicly Held: Yes
Total Sales: $11,430,700,000 (e)
Alcohol Sales: 25%
Number of Employees: 11,500
Foodservice Sales: $2,286,140,000 (e)
Internet Order Processing: Yes
Total Units: 130
Trade Names: Disney Springs (68); Disney's California Adventure Park (49); Disneyland Park (46); Disneyland Resort Hotels (14)
Company-Owned Units: 130
Preferred Square Footage: 2,500; 3,000; 5,500; 6,000
Preferred Location Types: Parks
Alcohol Served: Beer, Wine, Liquor
Primary Menu: Miscellaneous (177)
Areas of Operation: CA
Type of Foodservice: Cafeteria; Casual Dining; Family Restaurant; Fast Casual; Fine Dining; Quick Serve
Foodservice Management Venues: Recreational
Primary Distributors: (Food) US Foods-Los Angeles, LA MIRADA, CA
Parent Company: The Walt Disney Company, BURBANK, CA
Notes: The company derives approximately 80% of its revenue from theme park attractions, hotel/resort operations & sales of merchandise in these locations. All purchasing is now handled in the Florida offices (407 367-6000).

Key Personnel
ROBERT A. IGER - Executive Chairman
ROBERT CHAPEK - CEO
PATRICK FINNEGAN - Senior VP Operations
SUZI BROWN - VP Communications
JANET VOGELGESANG - VP Optimization
BRENT DAVIES - VP
CHRISTOPHER MAGGETTI - Executive Chef
MICHELE GENDREAU - Director Product Development
LARRY LABRADO - Director
CARRIE NOCELLA - Director
MIKE LOLLI - Director Operations
JASON SMITH - Director Engineering
ROBERT DONAHUE - Director Sales
KIMBERLY SUDEN - Director Safety
NICOLETTA VAN DER LOO - Director Communications, Event Planning
RUSS GEE - Director Marketing
VINCENT CACHOT - Director Food
PAT DOYLE - Director Engineering, Design
JESSICA GOOD - Director Communications
CHRIS MISTERLY - Director Finance
ERIC WILLHITE - Director Food
ROBYN VOSSEN - Director Operations
COLLEEN CRAIG - Director Engineering
NICK ROSS - Director Operations
DAVID MAGGARD - Director Security
NATE PONTIUS - Director Technology
MARK SHAFRAN - Assistant Director Catering
ROBERT CLUNIE - Senior Manager Food and Beverage
MICHAEL KEETON - Senior Manager Finance
KARLOS SIQUEIROS - Manager Food and Beverage
TONY RYNEARSON - Manager Engineering
MARJORIE CALZADA - Manager Customer Service
JENNY SWEETMAN - Manager Operations
RICHARD STONER - Manager Operations
CASEY BROWN - Manager Strategy, Marketing
VICKI SOFFE - Project Manager Food and Beverage
JOEY WARREN - Consultant Special Projects
MATT GRAY - Senior Analyst Business Development

●▲
Polly's Inc.
173 E Freedom Ave
Anaheim, CA 92801-1006

Telephone: (714) 459-0041
Fax Number: (714) 459-0078
Internet Homepage: pollyspies.com
Company Email: comments@pollyspies.com
Type of Business: Chain Restaurant Operator
Year Founded: 1965
Total Sales: $44,760,000 (e)
Alcohol Sales: 1%
Number of Employees: 875
Average Check: Breakfast(6); Lunch(14); Dinner(14)
Internet Order Processing: Yes
Total Units: 25
Trade Names: KFC (7); KFC/A&W All American Food (1); KFC/Long John Silver's (1); KFC/Taco Bell (1); Polly's Bakery Cafe (15)
Company-Owned Units: 15
Units Franchised From: 10
Preferred Square Footage: 3,000; 5,000
Preferred Location Types: Freestanding; Strip Mall
Alcohol Served: Beer, Wine
Primary Menu: American (15); Chicken (8)
Projected Openings: 1
Areas of Operation: CA
Type of Foodservice: Casual Dining (15); Quick Serve (8)
Distribution Centers: FULLERTON, CA
Franchise Affiliation: A&W Restaurants Inc., LEXINGTON, KY; KFC Corporation, LOUISVILLE, KY; Long John Silver's Inc., LOUISVILLE, KY; Taco Bell Corp., IRVINE, CA
Primary Distributors: (Full Line) SYSCO Food Services of Los Angeles Inc., WALNUT, CA; (Full Line) The SYGMA Network Inc. - Northern California, STOCKTON, CA

Key Personnel
KATHY CAVANAUGH - CEO
DONALD SHELDRAKE - Partner; VP; Director Finance
JAMES KAA - CFO
JESSICA HELLWIG - Controller
XUAN NGUYEN - General Manager
DAVE HOLT - Director Operations
KYLE HUNT - Director Information Technology
JACK WILLIAMS - Manager Purchasing, Inventory, Quality Assurance, Menu Development, Food Safety; General Buyer
CHUCK ELISON - Manager Store Systems
MICHELLE JONES - Supervisor Accounting
JOHANNA RIVERA - Specialist Human Resources

Specialty Restaurants Corp.
8191 E Kaiser Blvd
Anaheim, CA 92808-2214

Telephone: (714) 279-6100
Fax Number: (714) 998-7574
Internet Homepage: specialtyrestaurants.com
Company Email: Info@SRCMail.com
Type of Business: Chain Restaurant Operator
Year Founded: 1968
Total Sales: $110,820,000 (e)
Alcohol Sales: 30%
Number of Employees: 2,147
Average Check: Lunch(8); Dinner(14)
Total Units: 15
Trade Names: 94th Aero Squadron (1); Boat House (1); Castaway (1); Luminarias (1); Monterey Hill Steak & Seafood Restaurant (1); Orange Hill (1); Rusty Pelican (2); Templeton Landing (1); The Odyssey (1); The Proud Bird (1); Whiskey Joe's (4)
Company-Owned Units: 15
Preferred Square Footage: 5,000; 7,000; 8,000; 10,000; 11,000; 18,000; 20,000
Preferred Location Types: Airports; Freestanding; Other; Parks
Alcohol Served: Beer, Wine, Liquor
Primary Menu: American (2); Mexican (1); Seafood (4); Steak/Seafood (7)
Areas of Operation: CA, CO, FL, NY, OH, TX
Type of Foodservice: Casual Dining (5); Fine Dining (9)
Primary Distributors: (Food) SYSCO Corporation, HOUSTON, TX
Notes: The company derives approximately 7% of its revenue from sub-leased properties & shopping centers.

Key Personnel
JOHN TALLICHET - Chairman; CEO
JOHN G. GHUZZI - CFO; VP
JIM MCKENNON - COO
ANDREA DE LAO - VP Purchasing, Supply Chain
RYAN SMITH - VP Food and Beverage
MICHAEL BRENNAN - VP Operations
RON DEUTSCH - Director Human Resources
DENNIS YEE - Director Financial Planning
JHONY ACOSTA - Director Compliance
AALIYAH DE LA TORRE - Director Catering
OSCAR AMAYA - Director Beverages
KAREN CRUZ - Senior Manager Sales, Catering
DERRICK BADENHORST - District Manager
SAMANTHA HERNANDEZ ALVARADO - Manager Digital Marketing
ANGIE HUFF - Corporate Director Human Resources

The Marwaha Group
2551 W Woodland Dr
Anaheim, CA 92801-2608

Telephone: (714) 232-8122
Fax Number: (714) 994-3942
Internet Homepage: marwahagroup.com
Type of Business: Chain Restaurant Operator
Year Founded: 1992
Total Sales: $61,650,000 (e)
Number of Employees: 130
Average Check: Lunch(8); Dinner(10)
Total Units: 98
Trade Names: Subway (98)
Units Franchised From: 98
Preferred Square Footage: 300; 1,200; 2,000
Preferred Location Types: Strip Mall
Primary Menu: Sandwiches/Deli (98)
Areas of Operation: CA
Type of Foodservice: Quick Serve (98)
Franchise Affiliation: Doctor's Associates Inc., MILFORD, CT
Primary Distributors: (Full Line) Saladino's Inc., FRESNO, CA

Key Personnel
RAVINDER MARWAHA - Chairman; President
RAGHU MARWAHA - CEO
RAVI MARWAHA - President
ROHIT MARWAHA - COO; General Buyer
ELAN SALEH - Manager Business Development

The Pizza Press
2390 E Orangewood Ave Ste 550
Anaheim, CA 92806-6174

Telephone: (714) 408-9487
Fax Number: (714) 991-5600
Internet Homepage: rms-inds.com; thepizzapress.com
Company Email: info@thepizzapress.com
Type of Business: Chain Restaurant Operator
Year Founded: 2012
Systemwide Sales: $29,140,000 (e)
Total Sales: $2,445,000 (e)
Internet Order Processing: Yes
Total Units: 26
Trade Names: Pizza Press (26)
Company-Owned Units: 2
Units Franchised To: 24
Primary Menu: Pizza (26)
Projected Openings: 10
Areas of Operation: CA, FL, HI, TX, WA
Type of Foodservice: Casual Dining (26)

Key Personnel
DARA MALEKI - Founder; CEO
JACOB CLEMONS - Director Operations; General Buyer
GILBERT PEREZ - Manager Beverages, Food

Widdicombe Enterprises
10900 Katella Ave
Anaheim, CA 92804-6134

Telephone: (714) 956-9393
Fax Number: (714) 956-9395
Type of Business: Chain Restaurant Operator
Year Founded: 1957
Total Sales: $24,220,000 (e)
Number of Employees: 100
Average Check: Breakfast(5); Lunch(8); Dinner(8)
Total Units: 5
Trade Names: McDonald's (5)
Units Franchised From: 5
Preferred Square Footage: 3,000
Preferred Location Types: Freestanding
Primary Menu: Hamburger (5)
Areas of Operation: CA
Type of Foodservice: Quick Serve (5)
Franchise Affiliation: McDonald's Corporation, CHICAGO, IL
Primary Distributors: (Full Line) The Martin-Brower Co., CITY OF INDUSTRY, CA

Key Personnel
PATTI WIDDICOMBE - CFO; General Manager; Director Operations, Purchasing, Human Resources

Yogurtland Franchisee
683 N Euclid St
Anaheim, CA 92801-4622

Telephone: (714) 956-0400
Type of Business: Chain Restaurant Operator
Total Sales: $2,100,000 (e)
Total Units: 2
Trade Names: Yogurtland (2)
Units Franchised From: 2
Primary Menu: Snacks (2)
Areas of Operation: CA
Type of Foodservice: Quick Serve (2)
Franchise Affiliation: Yogurtland Franchising Inc., FARMERS BRANCH, TX

Key Personnel
MAGED MOTAWEH - Partner; General Buyer
EMAN MOTAWEH - Partner; General Buyer

Gotta Luv Pizza Inc
27 N Main St
Angels Camp, CA 95222

Telephone: (209) 754-5900
Fax Number: (209) 920-4588
Type of Business: Chain Restaurant Operator
Total Sales: $4,954,000 (e)
Total Units: 4

Trade Names: Round Table Pizza (4)
Units Franchised From: 4
Primary Menu: Pizza (4)
Areas of Operation: CA
Type of Foodservice: Casual Dining (4)
Franchise Affiliation: Round Table Franchise Corp., CONCORD, CA

Key Personnel
SHEILA HOWARD - Partner; General Buyer
DAVID HOWARD - Partner; General Buyer

T.G.G. Inc.
18447 US Highway 18
Apple Valley, CA 92307-2305

Telephone: (760) 242-2351
Type of Business: Chain Restaurant Operator
Total Sales: $7,583,000 (e)
Total Units: 4
Trade Names: KFC (4)
Units Franchised From: 4
Areas of Operation: CA
Franchise Affiliation: KFC Corporation, LOUISVILLE, KY

Key Personnel
PATTY MCCRAYER - President; General Buyer

Lyon Et Al
13480 Luther Rd
Auburn, CA 95603-3117

Telephone: (530) 889-9191
Fax Number: (530) 889-2816
Type of Business: Chain Restaurant Operator
Year Founded: 1967
Total Sales: $25,100,000 (e)
Number of Employees: 285
Average Check: Lunch(12); Dinner(12)
Total Units: 9
Trade Names: Taco Bell (9)
Units Franchised From: 9
Preferred Square Footage: 2,500
Preferred Location Types: Community Mall; Freestanding
Primary Menu: Taco (9)
Projected Openings: 1
Areas of Operation: CA
Type of Foodservice: Quick Serve (9)
Franchise Affiliation: Taco Bell Corp., IRVINE, CA
Primary Distributors: (Full Line) McLane/Pacific, MERCED, CA

Key Personnel
GARY LYON - Owner; General Manager; Director Purchasing, Facility/Maintenance, Information Systems, Real Estate, Design
BRENDA RITCHEY - Controller; Manager Administration

Taco Bill Inc.
11879 Kemper Rd Ste 11
Auburn, CA 95603-9021

Telephone: (530) 885-2455
Fax Number: (530) 885-8267
Internet Homepage: tacobill.net
Type of Business: Chain Restaurant Operator
Year Founded: 1979
Total Sales: $78,770,000 (e)
Number of Employees: 1,560
Average Check: Lunch(8); Dinner(8)
Total Units: 41
Trade Names: Long John Silver (13); Long John Silver/A & W (6); Taco Bell (22)
Units Franchised From: 41
Preferred Square Footage: 2,500; 3,200
Preferred Location Types: Freestanding; Regional Mall; Strip Mall
Primary Menu: Seafood (19); Taco (22)
Areas of Operation: CA, MD, PA
Type of Foodservice: Quick Serve (41)
Franchise Affiliation: Long John Silver's Inc., LOUISVILLE, KY; Taco Bell Corp., IRVINE, CA
Primary Distributors: (Full Line) McLane/Pacific, MERCED, CA

Key Personnel
WILLIAM MULLIN - Chairman
CHRIS WALSH - CEO; President; General Manager; General Buyer
SUSAN WOZNIAK - Manager Human Resources

California Sunrise, Incorporated
126 N Azusa Ave
Azusa, CA 91702-3521

Telephone: (626) 334-7504
Type of Business: Chain Restaurant Operator
Total Sales: $8,211,000 (e)
Total Units: 3
Trade Names: Jack in the Box (3)
Units Franchised From: 3
Primary Menu: Hamburger (3)
Areas of Operation: CA
Type of Foodservice: Quick Serve (3)
Franchise Affiliation: Jack in the Box Restaurants, SAN DIEGO, CA

Key Personnel
GARREN GRIEVE - Owner; General Buyer

Marie Callender's Inc.
1175 E Alosta Ave
Azusa, CA 91702

Telephone: (626) 963-9475
Fax Number: (901) 766-6482
Internet Homepage: mariecallenders.com; mariecallendersgrill.com
Company Email: mccustomerservice@prkmc.com
Listing Type: Subsidiary
Type of Business: Chain Restaurant Operator
Year Founded: 1948
Total Sales: $1,035,300,000 (e)
Alcohol Sales: 1%
Number of Employees: 14,600
Average Check: Breakfast(8); Lunch(14); Dinner(18)
Internet Order Processing: Yes
Total Units: 328
Trade Names: Marie Callender's Restaurant & Bakery (28)
Company-Owned Units: 7
Units Franchised To: 21
Preferred Location Types: Community Mall; Downtown; Freestanding; Strip Mall
Alcohol Served: Beer, Wine
Primary Menu: American (28)
Areas of Operation: CA, NV
Type of Foodservice: Casual Dining (28)
Franchise Affiliation: East Side Mario's Restaurants Inc., VAUGHAN, ON
Primary Distributors: (Food) US Foods, MEMPHIS, TN
Parent Company: Elite Restaurant Group, LA CANADA FLINTRIDGE, CA
Notes: In 2019, Perkins and Marie Callender's split. This file illustrates only Marie Callendar's locations. Perkins was acquired by Huddle House.

Key Personnel
DAVE BLOUIN - VP Franchise Operations
JOHN BOWLER - VP Operations
KEVIN GREENE - VP Sales

Asbury Knight Investments
5120 Stockdale Hwy Ste B
Bakersfield, CA 93309-2673

Telephone: (661) 716-2711
Type of Business: Chain Restaurant Operator
Total Sales: $4,476,000 (e)
Total Units: 3
Trade Names: Jersey Mike's Subs (3)
Units Franchised From: 3
Primary Menu: Sandwiches/Deli (3)
Areas of Operation: CA
Type of Foodservice: Quick Serve (3)
Franchise Affiliation: Jersey Mike's Franchise

Systems, MANASQUAN, NJ

Key Personnel
STACY KNIGHT - Partner
CARRIE ASBURY - Partner

Joint Heirs Food Corp
PO Box 10839
Bakersfield, CA 93389-0839

Telephone: (661) 835-8022
Fax Number: (661) 836-3125
Company Email: kfc@jhfc-corp.com
Type of Business: Chain Restaurant Operator
Total Sales: $10,810,000 (e)
Total Units: 6
Trade Names: KFC (6)
Units Franchised From: 6
Primary Menu: Chicken (6)
Areas of Operation: CA
Type of Foodservice: Quick Serve (6)
Franchise Affiliation: KFC Corporation, LOUISVILLE, KY

Key Personnel
CHARLES BUCKNER - President; General Buyer

Mexicali Restaurant Inc.
419 Baker St
Bakersfield, CA 93305-5807

Telephone: (661) 327-4218
Fax Number: (661) 327-4245
Internet Homepage: mexicalirestaurants.com
Type of Business: Chain Restaurant Operator
Year Founded: 1957
Total Sales: $7,458,000 (e)
Alcohol Sales: 15%
Number of Employees: 115
Average Check: Lunch(16); Dinner(26)
Total Units: 2
Trade Names: Mexicali (2)
Company-Owned Units: 2
Preferred Location Types: Freestanding
Alcohol Served: Beer, Wine, Liquor
Primary Menu: Mexican (2)
Areas of Operation: CA
Type of Foodservice: Casual Dining (2)
Primary Distributors: (Equipment) SYSCO Food Services of Los Angeles Inc., WALNUT, CA; (Supplies) SYSCO Food Services of Los Angeles Inc., WALNUT, CA

Key Personnel
REUBEN CREWS - President; General Manager; General Buyer
MICHAEL GUERRA - Controller; General Buyer
KENNETH GAMEZ - General Manager; General Buyer

GLORIA GRIEGO - General Manager; General Buyer

Scoop This!, LLC
9000 Ming Ave Ste H2
Bakersfield, CA 93311-1321

Telephone: (661) 664-4950
Type of Business: Chain Restaurant Operator
Total Sales: $1,278,000 (e)
Total Units: 2
Trade Names: Cold Stone Creamery (2)
Units Franchised From: 2
Primary Menu: Snacks (2)
Areas of Operation: CA
Type of Foodservice: Quick Serve (2)
Franchise Affiliation: Kahala Brands, SCOTTSDALE, AZ

Key Personnel
JERRY STUEVE JR - Partner; General Buyer
CHARLENE STUEVE - Partner; General Buyer

SKBH Bobs
5153 Ming Ave
Bakersfield, CA 93309-4691

Telephone: (661) 398-0770
Type of Business: Chain Restaurant Operator
Total Sales: $5,168,000 (e)
Total Units: 8
Trade Names: Subway (8)
Units Franchised From: 8
Primary Menu: Sandwiches/Deli (8)
Areas of Operation: CA
Type of Foodservice: Quick Serve (8)
Franchise Affiliation: Doctor's Associates Inc., MILFORD, CT

Key Personnel
JONATHAN STEWART - Partner; General Buyer
ROBERT STEWART - Partner

Sonic Drive-in Restaurant
13015 Stockdale Hwy
Bakersfield, CA 93314-9005

Telephone: (661) 587-9400
Type of Business: Chain Restaurant Operator
Total Sales: $60,700,000 (e)
Total Units: 28
Trade Names: Sonic America's Drive-In (28)
Units Franchised From: 28
Primary Menu: Hamburger (28)
Areas of Operation: CA
Type of Foodservice: Quick Serve (28)
Franchise Affiliation: Sonic Corp.,

OKLAHOMA CITY, OK

Key Personnel
SCOTT MCMILLAN - Owner

Subway Sandwiches & Salads of Kern County
1215 Olive Dr Ste F
Bakersfield, CA 93308-4173

Telephone: (661) 393-2776
Fax Number: (661) 393-2613
Type of Business: Chain Restaurant Operator
Total Sales: $2,910,000 (e)
Total Units: 5
Trade Names: Subway (5)
Units Franchised From: 5
Primary Menu: Sandwiches/Deli (5)
Areas of Operation: CA
Type of Foodservice: Quick Serve (5)
Franchise Affiliation: Doctor's Associates Inc., MILFORD, CT

Key Personnel
NICK KHULLUR - Partner; General Buyer
RAINY KHULLUR - Partner

In-N-Out Burgers Distribution Center
13502 Hamburger Ln
Baldwin Park, CA 91706-5823

Telephone: (626) 813-8200
Fax Number: (626) 813-8235
Listing Type: Distribution Center
Type of Business: Chain Restaurant Operator
Areas of Operation: AZ, CA, NV, OR, TX, UT
Parent Company: In-N-Out Burger, IRVINE, CA

Key Personnel
LUIS AMAYA - General Manager
BRANT STURGEON - Manager Distribution, Transportation

Domino's Franchisee
3559 W Ramsey St Ste B
Banning, CA 92220-3505

Telephone: (951) 849-7770
Type of Business: Chain Restaurant Operator
Total Sales: $4,146,000 (e)
Total Units: 2
Trade Names: Domino's (2)
Units Franchised From: 2
Primary Menu: Pizza (2)
Areas of Operation: CA
Type of Foodservice: Quick Serve (2)
Franchise Affiliation: Domino's Pizza Inc, ANN

ARBOR, MI

Key Personnel
JONEY E. TAYLOR - Owner; General Buyer

Highland Food Express, Inc.
89 Beaumont Ave
Beaumont, CA 92223-2904

Telephone: (951) 769-2888
Type of Business: Chain Restaurant Operator
Total Sales: $67,870,000 (e)
Total Units: 26
Trade Names: Jack in the Box (26)
Units Franchised From: 26
Primary Menu: Hamburger (26)
Areas of Operation: CA
Type of Foodservice: Quick Serve (26)
Franchise Affiliation: Jack in the Box Restaurants, SAN DIEGO, CA

Key Personnel
HAI ZAIDUL - Owner; General Buyer

Norm's Restaurant Inc.
17904 Lakewood Blvd
Bellflower, CA 90706-6416

Telephone: (562) 804-4485
Internet Homepage: normsrestaurants.com
Company Email: info@normsrestaurants.com
Type of Business: Chain Restaurant Operator
Year Founded: 1949
Total Sales: $109,680,000 (e)
Alcohol Sales: 10%
Number of Employees: 1,000
Average Check: Breakfast(12); Lunch(14); Dinner(16)
Internet Order Processing: Yes
Total Units: 22
Trade Names: Norm's Restaurant (22)
Company-Owned Units: 22
Preferred Square Footage: 4,000
Preferred Location Types: Freestanding
Alcohol Served: Beer, Wine
Primary Menu: American (18)
Projected Openings: 1
Areas of Operation: CA
Type of Foodservice: Casual Dining (22)
Primary Distributors: (Full Line) SYSCO Food Services of Los Angeles Inc., WALNUT, CA
Parent Company: RMG, NEW YORK CITY, NY

Key Personnel
JUDY LEWIS - CFO
MICHAEL L. COLONNA - COO
AMIR DURRANI - VP Human Resources; Director Training
INGRID MARTINEZ - VP Marketing
KRISTA HOSKINS - VP Employee Development
LEO THOMAS - VP Operations
BRANDON TYERMAN - General Manager
DAVID COX - Executive Chef; Director Purchasing; General Buyer
JEFFREY NAUMANN - Director Foodservice

Barney's Gourmet Hamburgers
1591 Solano Ave
Berkeley, CA 94707-2116

Telephone: (510) 526-8185
Fax Number: (510) 558-8538
Internet Homepage: barneyshamburgers.com
Type of Business: Chain Restaurant Operator
Year Founded: 1978
Total Sales: $11,570,000 (e)
Alcohol Sales: 5%
Number of Employees: 175
Average Check: Lunch(14); Dinner(18)
Internet Order Processing: Yes
Total Units: 7
Trade Names: Barney's Gourmet Hamburgers (7)
Company-Owned Units: 7
Preferred Square Footage: 1,200; 2,500
Preferred Location Types: Freestanding; Office Complex; Strip Mall
Alcohol Served: Beer, Wine
Primary Menu: American (7)
Areas of Operation: CA
Type of Foodservice: Casual Dining (7)
Primary Distributors: (Full Line) SYSCO Food Services of San Francisco Inc., FREMONT, CA

Key Personnel
ALBERT SARSHAR - President; General Manager; Director Facility/Maintenance, Design
PERRY JOORABCHI - Controller; General Manager; Director Finance, Supply Chain
KAMRAN NASIRE - Executive Chef; Director Menu Development

Drago Enterprises Corp.
415 N Beverly Dr Ste 208
Beverly Hills, CA 90210-4642

Telephone: (310) 828-1585
Fax Number: (310) 585-2294
Internet Homepage: celestinodrago.com
Company Email: info@celestinodrago.com
Type of Business: Chain Restaurant Operator
Year Founded: 1991
Total Sales: $10,657,000 (e)
Alcohol Sales: 24%
Number of Employees: 100
Average Check: Lunch(24); Dinner(46)
Total Units: 4
Trade Names: Drago Bakery (1); Drago Centro (1); Drago Ristorante (1); il Pastaio (1)
Company-Owned Units: 4
Preferred Location Types: Downtown; Freestanding
Alcohol Served: Beer, Wine, Liquor
Primary Menu: Italian (3); Snacks (1)
Areas of Operation: CA
Type of Foodservice: Casual Dining (1); Fine Dining (2); Quick Serve (1)
Catering Services: Yes
Primary Distributors: (Full Line) SYSCO Food Services of Los Angeles Inc., WALNUT, CA

Key Personnel
CELESTINO DRAGO - Owner; Executive Chef; General Buyer
FRANCISCO OJEDA - VP Operations, Business Development
IAN GRESIK - General Buyer

Fat Brands, Inc.
9720 Wilshire Blvd Ste 500
Beverly Hills, CA 90212-2014

Telephone: (310) 319-1850
Fax Number: (310) 319-1863
Internet Homepage: buffalos.com; fatbrands.com; fatburger.com; yallamedi.com; fatbrands.com; hurricanewings.com
Company Email: info@fatburger.com
Listing Type: Corporate Office
Type of Business: Chain Restaurant Operator
Year Founded: 1952
Systemwide Sales: $2,332,935,000 (e)
Publicly Held: Yes
Total Sales: $487,337,000 (e)
Number of Employees: 5,200
Average Check: Lunch(8); Dinner(10)
Internet Sales: 1.00%
Total Units: 2,342
Trade Names: Bonanza Steakhouse (13); Buffalo's Cafe (14); Elevation Burger (38); Fatburger (201); Fatburger/Buffalo's Express (113); Fazoli's (211); Great American Cookies (371); Hot Dog On A Stick (51); Hurricane Grill & Wings (42); Johnny Rockets (276); Marble Slab Creamery (255); Nativo Grill & Wings (24); Ponderosa/ Bonanza Steakhouse (23); Pretzelmaker (188); Round Table Pizza (412); Twin Peaks Restaurant (107); Yalla Mediterranean (3)
Company-Owned Units: 189
Units Franchised To: 2,153
Preferred Square Footage: 1,200; 2,000
Preferred Location Types: Downtown; Freestanding; Lifestyle Center; Other; Strip Mall
Alcohol Served: Beer, Wine, Liquor
Primary Menu: American (262); Chicken (38); Greek/Mediterranean (3); Hamburger (515); Hot Dogs (51); Italian (211); Pizza (412); Seafood (0); Snacks(814); Steak (36)
Projected Openings: 110

Areas of Operation: AZ, CA, FL, GA, HI, IL, MD, NE, NJ, NM, NV, TX, WA, AB, BC
Foreign Countries: BAHRAIN; CANADA; CHINA; EGYPT; ENGLAND; INDONESIA; IRAQ; JAPAN; KUWAIT; MALAYSIA; PAKISTAN; PANAMA; QATAR; SAUDI ARABIA; SINGAPORE; THE PHILIPPINES; TUNISIA; UNITED ARAB EMIRATES
Type of Foodservice: Casual Dining (543); Family Restaurant (312); Fast Casual (411); Quick Serve (1,076)
Catering Services: Yes
Subsidiaries: Elevation Franchise Ventures LLC, FALLS CHURCH, VA; Hurricane AMT LLC, WEST PALM BEACH, FL; The Johnny Rockets Group Inc., LAKE FOREST, CA; Twin Restaurant Holding LLC, DALLAS, TX
Primary Distributors: (Full Line) SYSCO Corporation, HOUSTON, TX
Parent Company: Fog Cutter Capital Group Inc., PORTLAND, OR
Headquarter Offices: Great American Cookies, NORCROSS, GA; HDOS Enterprises, BEVERLY HILLS, CA; Pretzelmaker Inc., NORCROSS, GA; Round Table Franchise Corp., CONCORD, CA

Key Personnel
ED RENSI - Chairman
KEN KUICK - Co-CEO; CFO
ROB ROSEN - Co-CEO; Exec VP Finance
GREGG NETTLETON - President Division; COO Division
ALLISON LAUENSTEIN - President Division, Division, Division
DAVID PEAR - President Division
MICHAEL CHACHULA - CIO
JENN JOHNSTON - Chief Marketing Officer
JUSTIN NEDELMAN - Chief Real Estate Officer
JORDAN CHIRICO - Exec VP
AMMY HARRISON - Senior VP Development
BENTLEY HETRICK - VP Facility/Maintenance, Construction
JAMES NEWELL - VP Operations
MAIYO HOOD - VP Development
CAMERON STOLZ - Senior Director Information Systems
KATIE THOMS - Senior Director Marketing
BRENDA SERRANO - Senior Director Supply Chain
MASON WIEDERHORN - Director Marketing
MADISON WIEDERHORN - Director Training
SCOT HOBERT - Director Franchise Sales
JENNIFER BONILLA - Director Training
TAYLOR FISCHER - Director Marketing, Division
ERIN MANDZIK - Director Communications
JENNIFER RYAN - Director Marketing
GEORGINA SOTO - Manager Human Resources

HDOS Enterprises
9720 Wilshire Blvd Ste 500
Beverly Hills, CA 90212-2014

Telephone: (310) 319-1850
Fax Number: (760) 930-0420
Internet Homepage: hotdogonastick.com
Type of Business: Chain Restaurant Operator
Year Founded: 1946
Total Sales: $28,680,000 (e)
Number of Employees: 1,200
Average Check: Lunch(10); Dinner(12)
Internet Order Processing: Yes
Internet Sales: 1.00%
Total Units: 51
Trade Names: Hot Dog On A Stick (51)
Company-Owned Units: 29
Units Franchised To: 15
Preferred Square Footage: 500
Preferred Location Types: Community Mall; Lifestyle Center; Regional Mall; Strip Mall
Primary Menu: Hot Dogs (51)
Areas of Operation: AK, CA, HI, NM, NV, OR, TX, UT
Foreign Countries: BRAZIL; SOUTH KOREA; THE PHILIPPINES
Type of Foodservice: Quick Serve (51)
Parent Company: Fat Brands, Inc., BEVERLY HILLS, CA

Key Personnel
CHRIS DULL - CEO; President
LEWIS LOEB - CFO; Treasurer; Corporate Secretary
DANIEL BYLUND - CFO
JEAN JOHNSTON - COO; Chief Marketing Officer
RAPHAEL TOMLIN - Exec VP Manufacturing
BETHANY MARSHALL - VP Human Resources; General Counsel Human Resources
JENNIFER JONES - Regional Director Marketing
ERIKA BOER - Regional Manager

Hillstone Restaurant Group Inc.
147 S Beverly Dr
Beverly Hills, CA 90212-3002

Telephone: (310) 385-7343
Fax Number: (310) 385-7119
Internet Homepage: hillstone.com
Type of Business: Chain Restaurant Operator
Year Founded: 1977
Total Sales: $679,090,000 (e)
Alcohol Sales: 26.50%
Number of Employees: 3,689
Total Units: 44
Trade Names: Bandera (4); Cherry Creek Grill (1); East Hampton Grill (1); Gulfstream (1); Hillstone (11); Honor Bar (4); Houston's (12); Los Altos Grill (1); Palm Beach Grill (1); R+D Kitchen (4); Rutherford Grill (1); South Beverly Grill (1); White House Tavern (1); Woodmont Grill (1)
Company-Owned Units: 44
Preferred Square Footage: 5,500; 6,000
Preferred Location Types: Downtown; Freestanding; Office Complex
Alcohol Served: Beer, Wine, Liquor
Primary Menu: American (44)
Areas of Operation: AZ, CA, CO, FL, GA, IL, LA, MD, NJ, NY, TN, TX
Type of Foodservice: Casual Dining (44)
Notes: Unit count and total sales exclude results from the operation of convenience store and shop, Kelly's Fuel and Provisions and Honor Wine and Spirits, in CA.

Key Personnel
GEORGE W. BIEL - Chairman; CEO; President
ROBERT WILKINSON - Exec VP
JEFF BELL - Exec VP
BRIAN BIEL - VP Design
GREER ILLINGWORTH - General Counsel
DAVE WADE - Director Facility/Maintenance
PUTNAM GIBSON - Manager
BRIAN WHELAN - Manager Systems
MARK PRICE - Manager Information/Data Security
KEITH CLANCY - Manager Human Resources
KAREN DONALDSON - Manager Training
LAURIE HERL - Manager Accounting
JOHN LYLE - Manager Training
TAMBI YU - Manager Human Resources

LemonShark Franchising, LLC
439 N Bedford Dr
Beverly Hills, CA 90210

Telephone: (310) 556-5646
Internet Homepage: lemonsharkpoke.com
Type of Business: Chain Restaurant Operator
Systemwide Sales: $71,847,000 (e)
Total Sales: $10,990,000 (e)
Average Check: Dinner(22)
Total Units: 13
Trade Names: LemonShark Poke (13)
Company-Owned Units: 4
Units Franchised To: 9
Preferred Square Footage: 1,850
Primary Menu: Caribbean (13)
Projected Openings: 30
Areas of Operation: AZ, CA, FL, LA, TX
Type of Foodservice: Family Restaurant (13); Fast Casual (15)
Catering Services: Yes

Key Personnel
TOBIAS MILLER - Co-Founder; President
RICHARD GOTTLIEB - Co-Founder; CEO
KALIDOU BA - Director Operations

MARIA WINN - Director Communications, Franchise Sales

Mr. Chow Inc.
344 N Camden Dr
Beverly Hills, CA 90210-5112

Telephone: (310) 278-9911
Fax Number: (310) 278-4671
Internet Homepage: mrchow.com
Type of Business: Chain Restaurant Operator
Year Founded: 1968
Total Sales: $19,850,000 (e)
Alcohol Sales: 25%
Number of Employees: 132
Average Check: Lunch(48); Dinner(84)
Total Units: 7
Trade Names: Mr. Chow (7)
Company-Owned Units: 7
Preferred Square Footage: 5,500; 6,000
Preferred Location Types: Freestanding
Alcohol Served: Beer, Wine, Liquor
Primary Menu: Chinese (7)
Areas of Operation: CA, FL, NY, FC
Foreign Countries: ENGLAND
Type of Foodservice: Fine Dining (7)
Primary Distributors: (Full Line) SYSCO Food Services of Central California Inc., MODESTO, CA

Key Personnel
MICHAEL CHOW - CEO; President
EDDY WONG - General Manager; Executive Chef; General Buyer
CHRIS DENTON - General Manager; Manager Menu Development

The Edward Thomas Collection
9950 Santa Monica Blvd
Beverly Hills, CA 90212-1607

Telephone: (310) 859-0366
Fax Number: (310) 859-0823
Internet Homepage: edwardthomasco.com; hotelcasadelmar.com; shuttersonthebeach.com
Company Email: fkuebler@edwardthomasco.com
Type of Business: Foodservice Operations - Hotel/Motels
Year Founded: 1983
Total Sales: $46,020,000 (e)
Alcohol Sales: 20%
Number of Employees: 600
Average Check: Lunch(8); Dinner(14)
Total Units: 2
Restaurants in Hotels: 6
Trade Names: Casa Del Mar (1); Shutters On The Beach (1)
Company-Owned Units: 6
Alcohol Served: Beer, Wine, Liquor
Areas of Operation: CA
Type of Foodservice: Casual Dining (6)
Primary Distributors: (Food) SYSCO Food Services of Los Angeles Inc., WALNUT, CA
Notes: The company derives approximately 80% of its revenue from hotel operations.

Key Personnel
EDWARD SLATKIN - Partner
THOMAS SLATKIN - Partner
JON ANDERA - VP Finance; Controller
KLAUS MENNEKES - VP Operations

The Peninsula Hotels
9882 Santa Monica Blvd
Beverly Hills, CA 90212-1605

Telephone: (310) 551-2888
Fax Number: (310) 788-2319
Internet Homepage: peninsula.com
Company Email: pbh@peninsula.com
Type of Business: Foodservice Operations - Hotel/Motels
Total Sales: $67,677,000 (e)
Alcohol Sales: 10%
Number of Employees: 500
Total Units: 3
Restaurants in Hotels: 10
Trade Names: The Peninsula Beverly Hills (1); The Peninsula Chicago (1); The Peninsula New York (1)
Company-Owned Units: 10
Alcohol Served: Beer, Wine, Liquor
Areas of Operation: CA, IL, NY
Type of Foodservice: Casual Dining (10)
Primary Distributors: (Food) SYSCO Food Services of Central California Inc., MODESTO, CA
Notes: Restaurants within the hotel include: The Lobby, Shanghai Terrace, Pierrot Gourmet, Clement, Salon de Ning, The Living Room and The Roof Garden

Key Personnel
ELIZABETH LOUIE - Controller
OFFER NISSENBAUM - General Manager
NANCY KUPKA - Director Human Resources
SAMUEL LINDER - Director Food and Beverage
DINA NILI - Manager Sales
DAVID RETUMALTA - Manager Payroll

Dennys Franchise
1014 N Main St
Bishop, CA 93514-2431

Telephone: (760) 873-5656
Fax Number: (760) 873-8801
Internet Homepage: dennys.com
Type of Business: Chain Restaurant Operator
Total Sales: $6,085,000 (e)
Total Units: 2
Trade Names: Denny's (2)
Units Franchised From: 2
Primary Menu: American (2)
Areas of Operation: CA
Type of Foodservice: Family Restaurant (2)
Franchise Affiliation: Denny's Corporation, SPARTANBURG, SC

Key Personnel
MOHAMED ALSAMAR - Partner; General Manager
RASHID AWWAD - Partner; General Buyer

McDonalds of Bishop
562 N Main St
Bishop, CA 93514-2745

Telephone: (760) 873-4501
Type of Business: Chain Restaurant Operator
Total Sales: $9,913,000 (e)
Total Units: 2
Trade Names: McDonald's (2)
Units Franchised From: 2
Primary Menu: Hamburger (2)
Areas of Operation: CA
Type of Foodservice: Quick Serve (2)
Franchise Affiliation: McDonald's Corporation, CHICAGO, IL

Key Personnel
LIS MAZZU - President; Partner; General Buyer
KEVIN MAZZU - Partner; General Buyer

The Tides Wharf
835 Highway One
Bodega Bay, CA 94923

Mailing Address: PO Box 518, BODEGA BAY, CA, 94923-0518
Telephone: (707) 875-2777
Fax Number: (707) 875-3285
Internet Homepage: innatthetides.com
Company Email: Christian@innatthetides.com
Type of Business: Chain Restaurant Operator
Total Sales: $3,345,000 (e)
Alcohol Sales: 15%
Number of Employees: 30
Average Check: Breakfast(12); Lunch(18); Dinner(36)
Total Units: 2
Trade Names: The Bay View (1); The Tides Wharf (1)
Company-Owned Units: 2
Preferred Location Types: Freestanding
Alcohol Served: Beer, Wine, Liquor
Primary Menu: Seafood (2)
Areas of Operation: CA
Type of Foodservice: Fine Dining (2)
Primary Distributors: (Food) SYSCO Food Services of San Francisco Inc., FREMONT,

CA

Key Personnel
GENE BUGATTO - President; Executive Chef; General Buyer
CHRIS WEDEL - Assistant

85C Bakery Cafe
1415 Moonstone
Brea, CA 92821

Telephone: (714) 525-8585
Internet Homepage: 85cbakerycafe.com
Company Email: customerservice@85cbakerycafe.com
Type of Business: Chain Restaurant Operator
Year Founded: 2008
Total Sales: $52,700,000 (e)
Number of Employees: 3,000
Total Units: 60
Trade Names: 85C Bakery Cafe (60)
Company-Owned Units: 60
Primary Menu: Snacks (60)
Areas of Operation: CA, TX, WA
Type of Foodservice: Fast Casual (60)

Key Personnel
HERMANSYAH LIM - General Manager
HENRY CHENG - Executive Chef
LI CHE CHEN - Executive Chef
CHILI YIN - Executive Chef
DAVE LAZARO - Director Marketing
GLORIA GORDEN - Director Operations
RICKEY VUONG - Area Manager Operations
CECILIA MA - Manager Real Estate, Business Development
TRACY WELBURN - Manager
STEPHANIE HERNANDEZ - Manager Human Resources
NEIL MOODY - Project Manager Construction
DERICK RIVERA - Project Manager Construction

JPOC Corp.
955 E Birch St Ste J
Brea, CA 92821-5826

Telephone: (714) 674-4999
Type of Business: Chain Restaurant Operator
Total Sales: $4,401,000 (e)
Total Units: 3
Trade Names: Jersey Mike's Subs (3)
Units Franchised From: 3
Primary Menu: Sandwiches/Deli (3)
Areas of Operation: CA
Type of Foodservice: Quick Serve (3)
Franchise Affiliation: Jersey Mike's Franchise Systems, MANASQUAN, NJ

Key Personnel
CLARISSA PALOMARIA - Owner; General Buyer
SHORENA ZAZUNISHVILI - Specialist Administration, Human Resources

Domino's Franchisee
8300 Brentwood Blvd Ste D
Brentwood, CA 94513-1172

Telephone: (925) 240-8555
Type of Business: Chain Restaurant Operator
Total Sales: $14,580,000 (e)
Total Units: 7
Trade Names: Domino's (7)
Units Franchised From: 7
Primary Menu: Pizza (7)
Areas of Operation: CA
Type of Foodservice: Quick Serve (7)
Franchise Affiliation: Domino's Pizza Inc, ANN ARBOR, MI

Key Personnel
SAMMY M. SHARIFI - Owner; General Buyer

Yogurtland Franchisee
5972 Orangethorpe Ave
Buena Park, CA 90620-1262

Telephone: (714) 739-9700
Type of Business: Chain Restaurant Operator
Total Sales: $2,059,000 (e)
Total Units: 2
Trade Names: Yogurtland (2)
Units Franchised From: 2
Primary Menu: Snacks (2)
Areas of Operation: CA
Type of Foodservice: Quick Serve (2)
Franchise Affiliation: Yogurtland Franchising Inc., FARMERS BRANCH, TX

Key Personnel
MUYLY SITEA - Partner; General Buyer
JOSH SITEA - Partner; General Buyer

Black Angus Steakhouse LLC
111 N. First Street Ste 204
Burbank, CA 91502

Telephone: (818) 208-9903
Fax Number: (650) 949-6442
Internet Homepage: blackangus.com
Company Email: guestrelations@blackangus.com
Type of Business: Chain Restaurant Operator
Year Founded: 1964
Systemwide Sales: $253,877,000 (e)
Total Sales: $213,091,000 (e)
Alcohol Sales: 15%
Number of Employees: 4,945
Average Check: Lunch(14); Dinner(30)
Internet Order Processing: Yes
Internet Sales: 2.00%
Total Units: 32
Trade Names: Black Angus Steak House (32)
Company-Owned Units: 32
Preferred Square Footage: 6,700; 7,800; 12,000
Preferred Location Types: Community Mall; Downtown; Freestanding; Regional Mall
Alcohol Served: Beer, Wine, Liquor
Primary Menu: Steak (32)
Areas of Operation: AK, AZ, CA, HI, NM, WA
Type of Foodservice: Casual Dining (32)
Primary Distributors: (Food) Systems Services of America, FONTANA, CA; (Supplies) Systems Services of America, FONTANA, CA
Parent Company: Versa Capital Management Inc., PHILADELPHIA, PA

Key Personnel
DEBORAH SHAPIRO - VP Business Development
JOHNNY LINDH - VP Operations
DAVID BOLOSAN - Senior Director Procurement, Product Development
CHASTITY CLARIDY - Director Marketing
JAMES LITTLE - Director Culinary Development
JENNI SALAZAR - Director Training
STEPHANIE GOOSBY - Director Human Resources
TIM PANATONE - District Manager

JINYA Holdings, Inc.
3334 Burton Ave
Burbank, CA 91504-3105

Telephone: (323) 930-2477
Fax Number: (818) 565-5528
Internet Homepage: jinya-ramenbar.com
Company Email: franchise@jinya-ramenbar.com
Type of Business: Chain Restaurant Operator
Year Founded: 2010
Systemwide Sales: $124,126,000 (e)
Total Sales: $49,450,000 (e)
Total Units: 47
Trade Names: Bushi by JINYA (1); JINYA Ramen Bar (42); JINYA Ramen Express (2); Robata JINYA (2)
Company-Owned Units: 3
Units Franchised To: 44
Primary Menu: Asian (47)
Projected Openings: 9
Areas of Operation: CA, DC, GA, IL, NE, NV, OK, TX, UT, WA, AB, BC, ON
Foreign Countries: CANADA; JAPAN
Type of Foodservice: Casual Dining (45); Fast

Casual (2)

Key Personnel
TOMONORI TAKAHASHI - Founder; CEO; President

Ocean View Foods, Inc.
23801 Calabasas Rd Ste 2002
Calabasas, CA 91302-1569

Telephone: (818) 222-1141
Type of Business: Chain Restaurant Operator
Total Sales: $12,520,000 (e)
Total Units: 5
Trade Names: Jack in the Box (5)
Units Franchised From: 5
Primary Menu: Hamburger (5)
Projected Openings: 2
Areas of Operation: CA
Type of Foodservice: Quick Serve (5)
Franchise Affiliation: Jack in the Box Restaurants, SAN DIEGO, CA

Key Personnel
TERENCE JONES - Owner; General Buyer

Pizza Studio Holding Company
4766 Park Granada Ste 209
Calabasas, CA 91302-3338

Telephone: (818) 224-5250
Internet Homepage: pizzastudio.com
Company Email: info@pizzastudio.com
Type of Business: Chain Restaurant Operator
Year Founded: 2012
Average Check: Lunch(10); Dinner(10)
Internet Order Processing: Yes
Total Units: 36
Trade Names: Pizza Studio (36)
Company-Owned Units: 32
Units Franchised To: 4
Preferred Square Footage: 1,500; 2,000; 2,500
Preferred Location Types: Institution (college/hospital); Regional Mall; Strip Mall
Primary Menu: Pizza (36)
Projected Openings: 2
Areas of Operation: AK, AZ, CA, IL, KS, MA, MD, MN, NY, UT
Type of Foodservice: Fast Casual (36)

Key Personnel
SAMIT VARMA - Co-Founder; Co-CEO

The Cheesecake Factory Incorporated
26901 Malibu Hills Rd
Calabasas Hills, CA 91301-5354

Telephone: (818) 871-3000
Fax Number: (818) 871-3100
Internet Homepage: grandluxcafe.com; rocksugarpanasiankitchen.com; thecheesecakefactory.com
Type of Business: Chain Restaurant Operator
Year Founded: 1978
Systemwide Sales: $2,831,669,000 (e)
Publicly Held: Yes
Total Sales: $3,638,475,000 (e)
Alcohol Sales: 13%
Number of Employees: 38,700
Average Check: Lunch(24); Dinner(26)
Internet Order Processing: Yes
Internet Sales: 5.00%
Total Units: 330
Trade Names: Blanco Tacos (10); Culinary Dropout (11); Dough Bird Pizza & Rotisserie (5); Flower Child (32); Fly Bye (2); North Italia (37); Olive & Ivy Restaruant & Marketplace (2); Pushing Daisies (1); The Arrogant Butcher (1); The Cheesecake Factory (216); The Greene House (1); The Henry (5); Wildflower(1); Zinburger (6)
Company-Owned Units: 297
Units Franchised To: 33
Preferred Square Footage: 5,400; 9,800; 11,000; 21,000
Preferred Location Types: Community Mall; Downtown; Freestanding; Hotel/Motel; Lifestyle Center; Office Complex; Outlet Mall; Regional Mall; Strip Mall
Alcohol Served: Beer, Wine, Liquor
Primary Menu: American (239); Asian (0); Californian (1); Greek/Mediterranean (2); Hamburger (6); Health Foods (32); Italian (37); Mexican (10); Pizza (2); Snacks (1)
Projected Openings: 20
Areas of Operation: AL, AZ, CA, CO, CT, DC, DE, FL, GA, HI, IA, ID, IL, IN, KS, KY, MA, MD, MN, MO, NC, NE, NJ, NV, NY, OH, OK, OR, PA, RI, TN, TX, UT, VA, WA, WI, ON
Foreign Countries: CANADA; CHINA; KUWAIT; MEXICO; SAUDI ARABIA; UNITED ARAB EMIRATES
Type of Foodservice: Casual Dining (322); Fast Casual (8); Quick Serve (0)
Distribution Centers: CALABASAS HILLS, CA; ROCKY MOUNT, NC
On-site Distribution Center: Yes
Subsidiaries: Fox Restaurant Concepts, PHOENIX, AZ
Primary Distributors: (Full Line) SYSCO Food Services of Los Angeles Inc., WALNUT, CA
Notes: The company derives approximately 4% of its revenue from third-party bakery sales; systemwide sales are based on foodservice revenues only. Total store count does not include 12 international licensed restaurants.

Key Personnel
DAVID OVERTON - Chairman; CEO
KEITH CARANGO - President Manufacturing, Division
DAVID M. GORDON - President
MATTHEW CLARK - CFO; Exec VP
MARINA LUBINSKY - CIO; Senior VP
DONALD EVANS - Chief Marketing Officer
JIM ZAZZARO - Area Director Operations
CHRIS BEAVERS - Area Director Operations
JAMES FRASER - Area Director Operations
SCARLETT MAY - Exec VP; Corporate Secretary; General Counsel
JACK K. BELK - Senior VP Operations, East Region; Regional VP Operations
CHERYL SLOMANN - Senior VP Finance; Controller
DINA BARMASSE-GRAY - Senior VP Human Resources
SPERO ALEX - Senior VP Operations
LISA MCDOWELL - Senior VP Global Development
ROBERT OKURA - VP Culinary Development
CHRIS RADOVAN - VP Research & Development
CHUCK WENSING - VP
RICHARD REINACH - VP Facility/Maintenance
HEATHER BERRY - VP Food and Beverage
ASHLEY HANSCOM - VP Finance; Controller
ATA BAROUDI - VP Quality Assurance, Food Safety
JENNIFER BISPO - VP Human Resources
RUSSELL GREENE - VP Operations, Sustainability
DEBBY R ZURZOLO - VP; General Counsel
SIDNEY GREATHOUSE - VP Legal
SANDY SAKAIDA - VP Benefits
JOEL SHAFER - VP
TOM PETERSON - VP Infrastructure
MERV DEGUZMAN - VP Information Technology
ADON CULLINS - VP Operations
JEFF STEPLER - VP Talent
PUNEET SALANIWAL - VP Finance, Accounting
JOSEPH PHILLIPS - Regional VP Operations
JEFF NEMET - Regional VP Operations
ALETHEA ROWE - Senior Director Public Relations
JASON HICKS - Senior Director Financial Planning
VINAY SOITKAR - Senior Director Data Warehouse
TONI KELLY - Senior Director Accounting
TAMAR TRUSHINSKI - Director Information Technology
TIM BELCHER - Director Operations
TOM DAVIS - Director Operations
MARK HARTWIG - Director Operations
DAVID LARSON - Director Operations
DONNIE WATSON - Director Operations
DURRE HASAN - Director Accounting
REBECCA HURST - Director Distribution, Logistics

TINA RUIZ - Director
WENDY WIMMER - Director Talent Acquisitions
ROBERT BRANNEN - Director Technology
BRANDON COOK - Director Culinary Operations, Research & Development
EMILY CHISHOLM - Director Food Safety
TODD COHEN - Associate Director
MICHAEL LEE - Associate Director Operations
ANGELLA LUZ - Associate Director Tax
DANIEL MYERS - Senior Manager Development-Training
JEREMY HUGHES - Senior Manager
BRENDAN MAYHEW - Senior Manager
RAJA THANISLAS - Manager
RUBEN FLORES - Senior Category Manager
RICK BORCHERT - Senior Category Manager
BENJAMIN YU - Category Manager
MAUREEN SHAMPINE - Category Manager Procurement
REBECCA STOBIE - Senior Buyer
ALVA AMADOR - Buyer

SB Food Express, Inc.
1199 7th St
Calimesa, CA 92320-1013

Telephone: (909) 795-8112
Type of Business: Chain Restaurant Operator
Total Sales: $66,820,000 (e)
Total Units: 26
Trade Names: Jack in the Box (26)
Units Franchised From: 26
Primary Menu: Hamburger (26)
Areas of Operation: CA
Type of Foodservice: Quick Serve (26)
Franchise Affiliation: Jack in the Box Restaurants, SAN DIEGO, CA

Key Personnel
HAI ZAIDUL - Owner; General Buyer

DTR Subs, Inc.
5800 Santa Rosa Rd Ste 143
Camarillo, CA 93012-7061

Telephone: (805) 484-5525
Type of Business: Chain Restaurant Operator
Total Sales: $5,852,000 (e)
Total Units: 4
Trade Names: Jersey Mike's Subs (4)
Units Franchised From: 4
Primary Menu: Sandwiches/Deli (4)
Areas of Operation: CA
Type of Foodservice: Quick Serve (4)
Franchise Affiliation: Jersey Mike's Franchise Systems, MANASQUAN, NJ

Key Personnel
DAWN ROBINSON - Partner
TROY ROBINSON - Partner

Lure Fish House
259 W. Ventura Blvd
Camarillo, CA 93010

Telephone: (805) 388-5556
Internet Homepage: lurefishhouse.com
Type of Business: Chain Restaurant Operator
Year Founded: 2010
Total Sales: $8,925,000 (e)
Total Units: 7
Trade Names: Lure Fish House (7)
Company-Owned Units: 7
Primary Menu: Seafood (7)
Areas of Operation: AZ, CA
Type of Foodservice: Casual Dining (7)

Key Personnel
DAVID CORTINA - Founder; Owner

Paschen Management Corp. Inc.
484 Mobil Ave Ste 23
Camarillo, CA 93010-6362

Telephone: (805) 484-0459
Fax Number: (805) 484-7898
Company Email: mcdpmc@aol.com
Type of Business: Chain Restaurant Operator
Year Founded: 1967
Total Sales: $74,590,000 (e)
Number of Employees: 750
Average Check: Breakfast(5); Lunch(8); Dinner(8)
Total Units: 16
Trade Names: McDonald's (16)
Units Franchised From: 16
Preferred Square Footage: 2,500
Preferred Location Types: Community Mall; Freestanding
Primary Menu: Hamburger (16)
Areas of Operation: CA
Type of Foodservice: Quick Serve (16)
Franchise Affiliation: McDonald's Corporation, CHICAGO, IL
Primary Distributors: (Full Line) The Martin-Brower Co., CITY OF INDUSTRY, CA

Key Personnel
CLAY PASCHEN - President; Director Purchasing, Real Estate
GREG PASCHEN - Controller; Director Finance
KEANE MURKAMI - Director Information Systems
KELLY REEVE - Manager Human Resources

Yogurtland Franchisee
1790 S Bascom Ave Ste 100
Campbell, CA 95008-0637

Telephone: (408) 377-9868
Type of Business: Chain Restaurant Operator
Total Sales: $4,271,000 (e)
Total Units: 4
Trade Names: Yogurtland (4)
Units Franchised From: 4
Primary Menu: Snacks (4)
Areas of Operation: CA
Type of Foodservice: Quick Serve (4)
Franchise Affiliation: Yogurtland Franchising Inc., FARMERS BRANCH, TX

Key Personnel
NATHAN NG - Partner; General Buyer
DEE DEE NG - Partner; General Buyer

Ameci Pizza & Pasta
6603 Independence Ave Ste B
Canoga Park, CA 91303-3845

Telephone: (818) 712-0110
Fax Number: (818) 712-0792
Internet Homepage: amecipizzaandpasta.com
Company Email: nandrisano@aol.com
Type of Business: Chain Restaurant Operator
Year Founded: 1984
Systemwide Sales: $30,947,000 (e)
Total Sales: $4,036,000 (e)
Alcohol Sales: 1%
Number of Employees: 85
Average Check: Lunch(14); Dinner(28)
Total Units: 35
Trade Names: Ameci Pizza & Pasta (35)
Company-Owned Units: 4
Units Franchised To: 31
Preferred Square Footage: 1,200
Preferred Location Types: Regional Mall; Strip Mall
Alcohol Served: Beer, Wine
Primary Menu: Italian (35)
Areas of Operation: CA
Type of Foodservice: Quick Serve (35)
Foodservice Management Venues: College & University; Schools
Catering Services: Yes

Key Personnel
NICK ANDRISANO - President; CFO; Manager Finance, Purchasing, Facility/Maintenance, Marketing, Real Estate, Design, Human Resources, Franchise Development, Store Fixtures; General Buyer
MAURICE RASSON - Owner
TIMOTHY EKBLAD - Owner
MARIA SPACCARELLI - Supervisor Operations

Marmalade LLC
6800 Owensmouth Ave Ste 350
Canoga Park, CA 91303-4251

Mailing Address: PO Box 1979, Santa Monica, CA, 90404
Telephone: (310) 829-0093
Fax Number: (888) 828-3056
Internet Homepage: marmaladecafe.com
Company Email: info@marmaladecafe.com
Type of Business: Chain Restaurant Operator
Year Founded: 1990
Total Sales: $10,660,000 (e)
Alcohol Sales: 10%
Number of Employees: 390
Average Check: Breakfast(12); Lunch(18); Dinner(30)
Internet Order Processing: Yes
Total Units: 7
Trade Names: Marmalade Cafe (7)
Company-Owned Units: 7
Preferred Square Footage: 3,000
Preferred Location Types: Freestanding; Strip Mall
Alcohol Served: Beer, Wine, Liquor
Primary Menu: American (7)
Areas of Operation: CA
Type of Foodservice: Casual Dining (7)
Catering Services: Yes
Primary Distributors: (Full Line) SYSCO Food Services of Los Angeles Inc., WALNUT, CA

Key Personnel
SELWYN YOSSLOWITZ - CFO; General Buyer

MEL-Z ENTERPRISE, INC.
18955 Soledad Canyon Rd
Canyon Country, CA 91351-3300

Telephone: (661) 252-4321
Type of Business: Chain Restaurant Operator
Total Sales: $24,830,000 (e)
Total Units: 10
Trade Names: Jack in the Box (10)
Units Franchised From: 10
Primary Menu: Hamburger (10)
Areas of Operation: CA
Type of Foodservice: Quick Serve (10)
Franchise Affiliation: Jack in the Box Restaurants, SAN DIEGO, CA

Key Personnel
MELVIN THOMPSON SR - Owner; General Buyer
MOHAMMED AHMED - Senior Director Operations
DANIEL MACDONALD - Manager Communications, Media

Raja Enterprises Inc
31546 Railroad Canyon Rd
Canyon Lake, CA 92587-9433

Telephone: (951) 244-5111
Type of Business: Chain Restaurant Operator
Total Sales: $26,691,000 (e)
Total Units: 13
Trade Names: Domino's (13)
Units Franchised From: 13
Primary Menu: Pizza (13)
Areas of Operation: CA
Type of Foodservice: Quick Serve (13)
Franchise Affiliation: Domino's Pizza Inc, ANN ARBOR, MI

Key Personnel
RAJA SYRIANI - Owner; General Buyer

L K Foods
1955 41st Ave Ste A3
Capitola, CA 95010-2514

Telephone: (831) 476-7330
Fax Number: (831) 476-7256
Type of Business: Chain Restaurant Operator
Total Sales: $9,660,000 (e)
Total Units: 14
Trade Names: Togo's (14)
Units Franchised From: 14
Primary Menu: Sandwiches/Deli (14)
Areas of Operation: CA
Type of Foodservice: Quick Serve (14)
Franchise Affiliation: Togo's Eateries LLC, SAN JOSE, CA

Key Personnel
JEFF STIKES - President; General Buyer

Yogurtland Franchisee
1955 41st Ave Ste A4
Capitola, CA 95010-2514

Telephone: (831) 462-3100
Type of Business: Chain Restaurant Operator
Total Sales: $4,218,000 (e)
Total Units: 4
Trade Names: Yogurtland (4)
Units Franchised From: 4
Primary Menu: Snacks (4)
Areas of Operation: CA
Type of Foodservice: Quick Serve (4)
Franchise Affiliation: Yogurtland Franchising Inc., FARMERS BRANCH, TX

Key Personnel
KEVIN DUECK - Partner; General Buyer
BRIAN DUECK - Partner; General Buyer

Urban Plates LLC
2053 San Elijo Ave
Cardiff, CA 92007-1726

Telephone: (760) 230-1700
Internet Homepage: urbanplates.com
Type of Business: Chain Restaurant Operator
Year Founded: 2011
Total Units: 18
Trade Names: Urban Plates (18)
Company-Owned Units: 18
Primary Menu: American (16)
Projected Openings: 3
Areas of Operation: CA
Type of Foodservice: Cafeteria (16)

Key Personnel
JOHN R. ZAGARA - Co-Founder
SAAD NADHIR - Co-Founder; CEO
JOE O'DONNELL - COO
JAMES CANNON - VP Culinary Operations

Islands Restaurants LP
5750 Fleet St Ste 120
Carlsbad, CA 92008-4709

Telephone: (760) 268-1800
Fax Number: (760) 918-1500
Internet Homepage: islandsrestaurants.com
Company Email: info@islandsrestaurants.com
Type of Business: Chain Restaurant Operator
Year Founded: 1982
Systemwide Sales: $260,421,000 (e)
Total Sales: $238,820,000 (e)
Alcohol Sales: 10%
Number of Employees: 4,275
Average Check: Lunch(12); Dinner(18)
Internet Order Processing: Yes
Internet Sales: 0.50%
Total Units: 47
Trade Names: Islands Fine Burgers & Drinks (47)
Company-Owned Units: 47
Preferred Square Footage: 5,000
Preferred Location Types: Freestanding; Lifestyle Center
Alcohol Served: Beer, Wine, Liquor
Primary Menu: Hamburger (47)
Areas of Operation: AZ, CA, HI, NV
Type of Foodservice: Casual Dining (47)
Catering Services: Yes
Primary Distributors: (Food) SYSCO Food Services of Los Angeles Inc., WALNUT, CA

Key Personnel
TONY DEGRAZIER - CEO; COO; Director Purchasing, Facility/Maintenance, Real Estate, Design
MIKE SMITH - President; Director Purchasing, Information Systems, Supply Chain, Human Resources

MIKE WONG - CFO
MELISSA WILLIAMSON - Area Director Operations
GREG SAMBRANO - VP Operations
LEWIS JACKSON - VP Real Estate
REIKO MATSUMOTO - VP Training
JERRY KOLBLY - General Manager
LISA ERICKSON - Senior Director Marketing
RICH LONG - Director Finance, Accounting
IAN REISCHL - Director Operations-Food
STEVE SILVEY - Director
RACHEL NELSON - Regional Manager
SANDY RIEHMAN - Regional Manager
DAN MCCAUSLAND - Regional Manager
ALAN MOLINA - Manager

Rubio's Restaurants Inc.
2200 Faraday Ave Ste 250
Carlsbad, CA 92008

Telephone: (760) 929-8226
Internet Homepage: rubios.com
Type of Business: Chain Restaurant Operator
Year Founded: 1983
Systemwide Sales: $300,152,000 (e)
Total Sales: $319,310,000 (e)
Alcohol Sales: 3%
Number of Employees: 4,400
Average Check: Lunch(12); Dinner(16)
Internet Order Processing: Yes
Total Units: 167
Trade Names: Rubio's Coastal Grill (167)
Company-Owned Units: 162
Units Franchised To: 5
Preferred Square Footage: 2,000; 2,200; 2,400; 2,800
Preferred Location Types: Community Mall; Freestanding; Lifestyle Center; Strip Mall
Alcohol Served: Beer
Primary Menu: Mexican (167)
Areas of Operation: AZ, CA, CO, FL, NV, UT
Type of Foodservice: Fast Casual (167)
Primary Distributors: (Food) US Foods, CORONA, CA
Parent Company: Mill Road Capital, GREENWICH, CT

Key Personnel
FRANK HENIGMAN - CFO; Senior VP
KATHLEEN JOHNSTON - Chief People Officer
STACEY SULTAR - Senior VP Marketing
JOSE N. RODRIGUEZ - VP Supply Chain, Quality Control
MICHAEL AGUILAR - VP Information Technology
CHRISTOPHER CHARLTON - Regional VP
AVRA S. HARROLD - Director; Assistant Controller
JUSTIN MOSEL - Director Culinary Operations
DENNIS KRETA - Director Internal Audit
MELINDA BUSTOS - Director Food and Beverage
AARON BAKER - Director Operations-Training
SARAH CATO - Director Risk Management
ADAM FOX - Director Loyalty Program
CHRISTOPH HILSCHER - Director People
VENIECA YU THORSON - Director Safety, Quality Assurance-Food
DAWN DECREMER - Director Real Estate
BRIAN STRAYER - Director Sales, Catering
DAVID BOSSHART - Regional Director
CLYDE LEWIS - Regional Director
JEN SCHEER - Senior Manager Marketing
RON WOOD - Senior Manager Training
JAIME G - Senior Manager Security, Safety
ALISON PAPPAS - Manager Quality Assurance, Food Safety
BRAD BEARDSLEY - Manager Operations
LUIS VISCARRA - Manager

Vigilucci's
3878 Carlsbad Blvd
Carlsbad, CA 92008-4008

Telephone: (760) 434-2580
Internet Homepage: vigiluccis.com
Company Email: info@vigiluccis.com
Type of Business: Chain Restaurant Operator
Year Founded: 1994
Total Sales: $53,672,000 (e)
Alcohol Sales: 5%
Average Check: Dinner(60)
Total Units: 4
Trade Names: Vigilucci's Cucina Italiana (1); Vigilucci's Market (1); Vigilucci's Seafood & Steakhouse (1); Vigilucci's Trattoria Italiana (1)
Company-Owned Units: 4
Preferred Location Types: Freestanding
Alcohol Served: Beer, Wine, Liquor
Primary Menu: Italian (3); Steak/Seafood (1)
Projected Remodelings: 1
Areas of Operation: CA
Type of Foodservice: Casual Dining (3); Fine Dining (1)
Catering Services: Yes

Key Personnel
ROBERTO VIGILUCCI - CEO; President; Executive Chef
ANDREA BALZARINI - General Manager
MATT MOORE - General Manager Catering

Baja Cantina
7166 Carmel Valley Rd
Carmel, CA 93923-9525

Telephone: (831) 625-2252
Fax Number: (831) 625-2279
Internet Homepage: carmelcantina.com
Company Email: bajacantina@redshift.com
Type of Business: Chain Restaurant Operator
Year Founded: 1970
Total Sales: $4,705,000 (e)
Alcohol Sales: 40%
Number of Employees: 100
Average Check: Breakfast(10); Lunch(14); Dinner(22)
Total Units: 2
Trade Names: Baja Cantina (2)
Company-Owned Units: 2
Preferred Location Types: Freestanding; Strip Mall
Alcohol Served: Beer, Wine, Liquor
Primary Menu: Southwest/Tex-Mex (2)
Areas of Operation: CA
Type of Foodservice: Casual Dining (2)
Catering Services: Yes
Primary Distributors: (Full Line) SYSCO Food Services of Sacramento Inc., PLEASANT GROVE, CA

Key Personnel
GINA PHINNY - Partner; General Manager; Director Catering
PATRICK PHINNY - Partner; Executive Chef; General Buyer

Gar Woods Grill & Pier
5000 N Lake Blvd
Carnelian Bay, CA 96140

Mailing Address: PO Box 1133, CARNELIAN BAY, CA, 96140
Telephone: (530) 546-3366
Fax Number: (530) 546-2184
Internet Homepage: barofamerica.com; calientetahoe.com; garwoods.com; rivagrill.com
Company Email: onthewater@garwoods.com
Type of Business: Chain Restaurant Operator
Total Sales: $9,426,000 (e)
Alcohol Sales: 25%
Number of Employees: 140
Average Check: Lunch(22); Dinner(30)
Internet Order Processing: Yes
Internet Sales: 0.50%
Total Units: 4
Trade Names: Bar of America (1); Caliente (1); Gar Woods Grill and Pier (1); Riva Grill (1)
Company-Owned Units: 4
Preferred Location Types: Downtown; Freestanding; Other
Alcohol Served: Beer, Wine, Liquor
Primary Menu: American (3); Southwest/Tex-Mex (1)
Areas of Operation: CA
Type of Foodservice: Casual Dining (4)
Catering Services: Yes
Primary Distributors: (Food) SYSCO Food Services of Sacramento Inc., PLEASANT GROVE, CA

Key Personnel
TOM TURNER - President; General Manager
AMY GRIGSBY - Manager Sales; General

Buyer

Dob-Sab Inc
21836 Avalon Blvd
Carson, CA 90745-3303

Telephone: (310) 549-2950
Fax Number: (310) 549-0143
Type of Business: Chain Restaurant Operator
Total Sales: $23,860,000 (e)
Total Units: 5
Trade Names: McDonald's (5)
Units Franchised From: 5
Primary Menu: Hamburger (5)
Areas of Operation: CA
Type of Foodservice: Quick Serve (5)
Franchise Affiliation: McDonald's Corporation, CHICAGO, IL

Key Personnel
KIM DOBBINS - CEO; President; General Buyer

The Burrito Shop Inc.
3843 Castro Valley Blvd
Castro Valley, CA 94546-4501

Telephone: (510) 538-1189
Fax Number: (510) 538-1480
Internet Homepage: burritoshops.com
Company Email: info@burritoshops.com
Type of Business: Chain Restaurant Operator
Year Founded: 1978
Total Sales: $4,248,000 (e)
Alcohol Sales: 1%
Number of Employees: 55
Average Check: Lunch(6); Dinner(12)
Total Units: 2
Trade Names: The Burrito Shop (2)
Company-Owned Units: 2
Preferred Square Footage: 1,200; 1,800
Preferred Location Types: Freestanding; Strip Mall
Primary Menu: Mexican (2)
Areas of Operation: CA
Type of Foodservice: Quick Serve (2)

Key Personnel
DAVID SPOTT - President; CFO; General Manager; General Buyer
JOSE ORTIZ - VP Operations; General Manager; Executive Chef

Graspointner Management, Inc.
2250 Rockefeller Dr Ste 7
Ceres, CA 95307-7243

Telephone: (209) 538-9500
Fax Number: (209) 538-8097
Internet Homepage: new.mcdgmi.com
Type of Business: Chain Restaurant Operator
Year Founded: 1978
Total Sales: $90,060,000 (e)
Number of Employees: 800
Average Check: Breakfast(8); Lunch(12); Dinner(12)
Total Units: 19
Trade Names: McDonald's (19)
Units Franchised From: 19
Preferred Square Footage: 3,000
Preferred Location Types: Discount Dept. Stores; Freestanding
Primary Menu: Hamburger (19)
Areas of Operation: CA
Type of Foodservice: Quick Serve (19)
Franchise Affiliation: McDonald's Corporation, CHICAGO, IL
Primary Distributors: (Food) The Martin-Brower Co., STOCKTON, CA

Key Personnel
DENNIS GRASPOINTNER - President; Director Finance, Operations, Real Estate; Manager Information Systems; General Buyer
DEBBIE HEDRICK - Manager Human Resources
MARTHA HILGEN - Manager Customer Service
HARGIT DALIWAL - Manager Accounting

DanBarb Inc.
10758 Arabella Pl
Cerritos, CA 90703-8019

Telephone: (562) 867-8783
Type of Business: Chain Restaurant Operator
Year Founded: 1980
Total Sales: $11,986,000 (e)
Number of Employees: 60
Average Check: Lunch(8); Dinner(12)
Total Units: 4
Trade Names: Taco Bell (4)
Units Franchised From: 4
Preferred Square Footage: 2,500; 3,200
Preferred Location Types: Freestanding
Primary Menu: Taco (4)
Areas of Operation: CA
Type of Foodservice: Quick Serve (4)
Franchise Affiliation: Taco Bell Corp., IRVINE, CA
Primary Distributors: (Food) McLane/Arlington, ARLINGTON, TX

Key Personnel
DAN JONES - President; Partner; General Manager Finance; General Buyer
BARBARA JONES - Partner; Director Purchasing
ROBIN MARZ - Controller; Manager Operations, Marketing, Human Resources, Franchising, Food Safety

Dhillon Foods, Inc.
17315 Studebaker Rd
Cerritos, CA 90703-2563

Telephone: (562) 402-4110
Type of Business: Chain Restaurant Operator
Total Sales: $66,260,000 (e)
Total Units: 26
Trade Names: Jack in the Box (26)
Units Franchised From: 26
Primary Menu: Hamburger (26)
Areas of Operation: CA
Type of Foodservice: Quick Serve (26)
Franchise Affiliation: Jack in the Box Restaurants, SAN DIEGO, CA

Key Personnel
DARIN HARRIS - CEO
PRIYA DHILLON - Owner; General Buyer
TIM MULLANY - CFO; VP

GEN Restaurant Group, Inc.
11480 South St. Suite 205
Cerritos, CA 90703

Telephone: (562) 356-9929
Internet Homepage: genkoreanbbq.com
Type of Business: Chain Restaurant Operator
Year Founded: 2011
Number of Employees: 400
Total Units: 33
Trade Names: Gen Korean BBQ House (33)
Company-Owned Units: 33
Primary Menu: Korean (33)
Areas of Operation: AZ, CA, FL, HI, NV, NY, TX
Type of Foodservice: Casual Dining (33)

Key Personnel
DAVID KIM - Co-CEO
JAE CHANG - Co-CEO
THOMAS V. CROAL - CFO

Chi-Chi's Pizza Inc.
9205 Alabama Ave Ste A
Chatsworth, CA 91311-5859

Telephone: (818) 700-9029
Fax Number: (818) 700-1332
Internet Homepage: chichispizza.com
Company Email: info@chichispizza.com
Type of Business: Chain Restaurant Operator
Year Founded: 1958
Total Sales: $7,815,000 (e)
Alcohol Sales: 5%
Number of Employees: 291
Average Check: Lunch(30); Dinner(42)
Total Units: 5
Trade Names: Chi-Chi's Pizza (4); Lido Pizza

(1)
Company-Owned Units: 5
Preferred Square Footage: 8,000
Preferred Location Types: Freestanding; Strip Mall
Alcohol Served: Beer, Wine, Liquor
Primary Menu: Italian (5)
Areas of Operation: CA
Type of Foodservice: Casual Dining (5)
On-site Distribution Center: Yes

Key Personnel
IDA MAE MICCOLIS - Treasurer
TONY CASTILLO - Manager Purchasing, Supply Chain, Food Safety

Majestic Retail Group, Inc.
1950 E 20th St Ste E-503
Chico, CA 95928-6369

Telephone: (530) 342-8733
Type of Business: Chain Restaurant Operator
Total Sales: $3,163,000 (e)
Total Units: 4
Trade Names: Auntie Anne's Hand-Rolled Soft Pretzels (4)
Units Franchised From: 4
Primary Menu: Snacks (4)
Areas of Operation: CA
Type of Foodservice: Quick Serve (4)
Franchise Affiliation: Auntie Anne's Inc., LANCASTER, PA

Key Personnel
STEVEN WILLIAMSON - Owner; General Buyer

Lollicup USA Inc.
6185 Kimball Ave
Chino, CA 91708-9126

Telephone: (626) 965-8882
Fax Number: (626) 965-8729
Internet Homepage: lollicup.com
Company Email: info@lollicup.com
Type of Business: Chain Restaurant Operator
Systemwide Sales: $9,905,000 (e)
Total Units: 19
Trade Names: Lollicup Coffee & Tea (19)
Units Franchised To: 19
Primary Menu: Coffee (19)
Areas of Operation: AZ, CA, CO, FL, MA, MO, NV, UT
Type of Foodservice: Quick Serve (19)

Key Personnel
ALAN YU - CEO; President; Partner; General Buyer
MARVIN CHENG - Partner; VP
JOANNE WANG - COO; VP Operations, Sales
DANIEL QUIRE - Director Sales

JASON LEE - Manager Plant

Lolita's Restaurants
2060 Otay Lakes Rd Ste 340
Chula Vista, CA 91913

Telephone: (619) 946-5025
Internet Homepage: lolitasmexicanfood.com
Company Email: contact@lolitasmexicanfood.com
Type of Business: Chain Restaurant Operator
Total Units: 6
Trade Names: Lolita's (6)
Company-Owned Units: 6
Primary Menu: Mexican (6)
Areas of Operation: CA
Type of Foodservice: Casual Dining (6)

Key Personnel
DOLORES JACKSON - President

Reyes International Enterprises, Inc.
374 E H St Ste 1711
Chula Vista, CA 91910-7492

Telephone: (619) 420-2064
Type of Business: Chain Restaurant Operator
Total Sales: $1,249,000 (e)
Total Units: 2
Trade Names: Cold Stone Creamery (2)
Units Franchised From: 2
Primary Menu: Snacks (2)
Areas of Operation: CA
Type of Foodservice: Quick Serve (2)
Franchise Affiliation: Kahala Brands, SCOTTSDALE, AZ

Key Personnel
ALBERTO REYES HERNANDEZ - Owner; General Buyer

Honeybee Foods Corporation
16125 E Valley Blvd
City Of Industry, CA 91744-5432

Telephone: (626) 369-7118
Fax Number: (626) 626-4245
Internet Homepage: chowkingusa.com; jollibeeusa.com; redribbonbakeshop.us
Type of Business: Chain Restaurant Operator
Year Founded: 2003
Total Sales: $55,360,000 (e)
Number of Employees: 717
Average Check: Breakfast(6); Lunch(8); Dinner(14)
Total Units: 92

Trade Names: Chowking (15); Jollibee (42); Red Ribbon Bakeshop (35)
Company-Owned Units: 92
Preferred Square Footage: 2,500
Preferred Location Types: Freestanding; Strip Mall
Primary Menu: Asian (92)
Areas of Operation: CA, HI, IL, NJ, NV, NY, TX, VA, WA
Foreign Countries: CHINA
Type of Foodservice: Quick Serve (92)
Primary Distributors: (Full Line) SYSCO Food Services of San Francisco Inc., FREMONT, CA; (Full Line) Reinhart FoodService, OMAHA, NE
Parent Company: Jollibee Foods Corporation, WEST COVINA, CA

Key Personnel
JOSE MANILA - President
MARIBETH DELA CRUZ - VP; General Manager
TESS CHUA - Controller; Director Finance
MACKEY DIMACULANGAN - Director Operations
CRISTINA LACSAMANA - Director Operations
MARIA LUISA JAVIER - Manager Recruitment
THERESA ROMERA - Manager Quality Assurance

WaBa Grill Franchise Corp
13191 Crossroads Pkwy N Ste 525
City Of Industry, CA 91746

Telephone: (562) 908-9222
Fax Number: (562) 699-1575
Internet Homepage: wabagrill.com
Company Email: feedback@wabagrill.com
Type of Business: Chain Restaurant Operator
Year Founded: 2004
Total Sales: $66,000,000 (e)
Alcohol Sales: 5%
Average Check: Dinner(50)
Total Units: 198
Trade Names: WaBa Grill (198)
Company-Owned Units: 29
Units Franchised To: 169
Preferred Square Footage: 1,500; 2,000
Preferred Location Types: Freestanding; Regional Mall; Strip Mall
Primary Menu: Asian (198)
Projected Openings: 10
Areas of Operation: CA
Type of Foodservice: Quick Serve (198)
Catering Services: Yes

Key Personnel
ANDREW KIM - CEO; President
ERIC S. LEE - Partner
KYLE H. LEE - Partner; Treasurer; Corporate Secretary; General Buyer
BRIAN S. HAM - CFO
ERIK HECKMAN - Director Supply Chain,

Product Development
AMY LY - Senior Manager Accounting, Administration
ERIN CARTAYA - Regional Manager Marketing
STEVEN WAYNE - Manager Real Estate
YOUNGMIN LEE - Senior Designer

Yum Yum Donut Shops Inc.
18830 San Jose Ave
City Of Industry, CA 91748-1325

Telephone: (626) 964-1478
Fax Number: (626) 912-2779
Internet Homepage: winchells.com; yumyumdonuts.com
Company Email: customerservice@yumyumdonuts.com
Type of Business: Chain Restaurant Operator
Year Founded: 1971
Systemwide Sales: $104,665,000 (e)
Total Sales: $49,342,000 (e)
Number of Employees: 500
Average Check: Breakfast(6); Lunch(6); Dinner(8)
Total Units: 193
Trade Names: Winchell's Donut House (100); Yum Yum Donut Shop (93)
Company-Owned Units: 69
Units Franchised To: 124
Preferred Square Footage: 1,250
Preferred Location Types: Freestanding; Strip Mall
Primary Menu: Snacks (193)
Projected Openings: 3
Areas of Operation: AR, CA, CO, KS, NE, NV, OK, TX
Type of Foodservice: Quick Serve (193)

Key Personnel
MEL ALLISON - Director Quality Assurance

Auntie Anne's Franchise
15960 Dam Rd
Clearlake, CA 95422-7906

Telephone: (707) 995-1196
Internet Homepage: auntieannesfranchising.com
Type of Business: Chain Restaurant Operator
Total Sales: $1,594,000 (e)
Total Units: 2
Trade Names: Auntie Anne's Hand-Rolled Soft Pretzels (2)
Units Franchised From: 2
Primary Menu: Snacks (2)
Areas of Operation: CA
Type of Foodservice: Quick Serve (2)
Franchise Affiliation: Auntie Anne's Inc., LANCASTER, PA

Key Personnel
CHIRAYU PATEL - Owner; General Buyer

BPB Foods Inc.
2151 Shaw Ave
Clovis, CA 93611

Telephone: (559) 297-3450
Internet Homepage: fostersfreeze.com
Type of Business: Chain Restaurant Operator
Year Founded: 1985
Total Sales: $3,594,000 (e)
Number of Employees: 68
Average Check: Lunch(10); Dinner(12)
Total Units: 4
Trade Names: Fosters Freeze (4)
Units Franchised From: 4
Preferred Square Footage: 2,200
Preferred Location Types: Freestanding
Primary Menu: Snacks (4)
Areas of Operation: CA
Type of Foodservice: Quick Serve (4)
Franchise Affiliation: Foster's Freeze LLC, RANCHO CUCAMONGA, CA
Primary Distributors: (Full Line) SYSCO Food Services of Central California Inc., MODESTO, CA

Key Personnel
DAVID BELDEN - President; Manager Operations, Purchasing
DON BEIDERWELL - President; Partner
JEAN PRATER - Partner

OC Food Express, Inc.
756 W Valley Blvd
Colton, CA 92324-2252

Telephone: (909) 783-0640
Type of Business: Chain Restaurant Operator
Total Sales: $23,190,000 (e)
Total Units: 9
Trade Names: Jack in the Box (9)
Units Franchised From: 9
Primary Menu: Hamburger (9)
Areas of Operation: CA
Type of Foodservice: Quick Serve (9)
Franchise Affiliation: Jack in the Box Restaurants, SAN DIEGO, CA

Key Personnel
HUGH ONEILL - President
HAI ZAIDUL - Owner; General Buyer
CHRISTIE STRUPE - Director; Customer Care

King Taco Restaurants Inc.
6055 E Washington Blvd Ste 700
Commerce, CA 90040-2428

Telephone: (323) 724-0270
Fax Number: (323) 266-6565
Internet Homepage: kingtaco.com
Company Email: customerservice@kingtaco.net
Type of Business: Chain Restaurant Operator
Year Founded: 1974
Total Sales: $33,030,000 (e)
Number of Employees: 970
Average Check: Lunch(8); Dinner(8)
Total Units: 22
Trade Names: King Taco (22)
Company-Owned Units: 22
Preferred Square Footage: 1,500
Preferred Location Types: Freestanding; Stadiums; Travel Plazas
Primary Menu: Taco (22)
Areas of Operation: CA
Type of Foodservice: Quick Serve (22)
Catering Services: Yes
On-site Distribution Center: Yes
Primary Distributors: (Food) SYSCO Food Services of Los Angeles Inc., WALNUT, CA

Key Personnel
LUIS MARTINEZ - VP Operations, Menu Development; Director Finance
SYLVIA MELENDEZ - Manager Catering

Paris Baguette USA Inc.
6100 S Malt Ave
Commerce, CA 90040-3508

Telephone: (562) 946-2010
Internet Homepage: parisbaguetteusa.com
Type of Business: Chain Restaurant Operator
Systemwide Sales: $323,744,000 (e)
Total Sales: $247,160,000 (e)
Total Units: 90
Trade Names: Paris Baguette (90)
Company-Owned Units: 63
Units Franchised To: 27
Primary Menu: French/Continental (90)
Projected Openings: 14
Areas of Operation: CA, GA, MA, NJ, NV, NY, PA
Type of Foodservice: Fast Casual (90)

Key Personnel
DARREN TIPTON - CEO
JACK F. MORAN - CEO Global
YOUNG HUR - President
SAEYONG PARK - CFO
NICK SCACCIO - COO
CATHY CHAVENET - Chief Marketing Officer
ERIC LAVINDER - Chief Development Officer
MICHAEL SPINELLI - VP Operations-Food

MICHELLE JAGROOP - VP Human Resources
ERIC GALKIN - VP Supply Chain
RICHARD KRESS - Director Supply Chain, Sales, International
JOSEPH SHERMAN - Director Loss Prevention
PINAR SIRIN - Director Operations
CHANYOUNG CHUNG - Director Food
ALYSSA MARTIN - Director Marketing
MARKO PETRONIJEVIC - Director Operations
LUIS RODRIGUEZ - Manager Human Resources
ANAND ALLAN - Manager Purchasing, Distribution

Round Table Franchise Corp.
1390 Willow Pass Rd Ste 300
Concord, CA 94520-5250

Telephone: (925) 969-3900
Fax Number: (925) 969-3978
Internet Homepage: roundtablepizza.com
Type of Business: Chain Restaurant Operator
Year Founded: 1959
Systemwide Sales: $707,125,000 (e)
Total Sales: $146,720,000 (e)
Alcohol Sales: 10%
Number of Employees: 10,500
Average Check: Lunch(10); Dinner(36)
Total Units: 412
Trade Names: Round Table Pizza (412)
Company-Owned Units: 75
Units Franchised To: 337
Preferred Square Footage: 400; 1,000; 1,400; 1,500; 2,400; 3,000; 4,000
Preferred Location Types: Airports; Community Mall; Hotel/Motel; Institution (college/hospital); Regional Mall; Stadiums; Strip Mall
Alcohol Served: Beer, Wine
Primary Menu: Pizza (412)
Areas of Operation: AK, AZ, CA, HI, NV, OR, WA
Type of Foodservice: Casual Dining (412)
Catering Services: Yes
Primary Distributors: (Full Line) Saladino's Inc., FRESNO, CA
Parent Company: Fat Brands, Inc., BEVERLY HILLS, CA

Key Personnel
DAVE CHENEY - Director Franchise Operations
SUSAN TONKIN - Director Operations-Training

Trader Vic's Restaurants Inc.
2278 Pike Ct Ste F
Concord, CA 94520-1252

Telephone: (925) 675-6400
Fax Number: (925) 691-9956
Internet Homepage: tradervics.com
Company Email: info@tradervics.com
Type of Business: Chain Restaurant Operator
Year Founded: 1934
Systemwide Sales: $63,410,000 (e)
Total Sales: $17,152,000 (e)
Alcohol Sales: 30%
Number of Employees: 50
Average Check: Lunch(22); Dinner(26)
Internet Order Processing: Yes
Internet Sales: 1.00%
Total Units: 17
Trade Names: Trader Vic's (16); Trader Vic's Mai Tai Lounge (1)
Company-Owned Units: 1
Units Franchised To: 16
Preferred Square Footage: 7,500; 10,000
Preferred Location Types: Freestanding; Hotel/Motel
Alcohol Served: Beer, Wine, Liquor
Primary Menu: Asian (17)
Projected Openings: 1
Areas of Operation: CA, FL, GA, OR
Foreign Countries: BAHRAIN; ENGLAND; GERMANY; INDIA; JAPAN; JORDAN; OMAN; QATAR; SAUDI ARABIA; THAILAND; UNITED ARAB EMIRATES
Type of Foodservice: Fine Dining (17)
Catering Services: Yes
Primary Distributors: (Equipment) BiRite Foodservice Distributors, BRISBANE, CA; (Food) SYSCO Food Services of Los Angeles Inc., WALNUT, CA;(Supplies) BiRite Foodservice Distributors, BRISBANE, CA

Key Personnel
H. JAMES SCHAFER - Chairman
RHETT ROSEN - CEO
LORRAINA HERNANDEZ - Developer Web Design; Assistant Web Design

Burger Boss LLC
4740 Green River Rd Ste 307
Corona, CA 92880

Telephone: (877) 822-0908
Internet Homepage: burgerboss.com
Company Email: info@burgerboss.com
Type of Business: Chain Restaurant Operator
Total Units: 5
Trade Names: Burger Boss (5)
Company-Owned Units: 5
Primary Menu: Hamburger (5)
Projected Openings: 2
Areas of Operation: CA
Type of Foodservice: Fast Casual (5)

Key Personnel
MO FARHA - President

Miguel's Jr
280 Corporate Terrace St
Corona, CA 92879

Telephone: (951) 371-7234
Internet Homepage: miguelsjr.com; miguelsrestaurant.com
Company Email: info@miguelsjr.com
Type of Business: Chain Restaurant Operator
Year Founded: 1975
Total Sales: $17,630,000 (e)
Total Units: 22
Trade Names: Miguel's California Mexican Cocina (2); Miguel's Jr (20)
Company-Owned Units: 22
Primary Menu: Mexican (22)
Areas of Operation: CA
Type of Foodservice: Casual Dining (2); Fast Casual (20)

Key Personnel
MARY VASQUEZ - Co-Founder
JAVIER VASQUEZ - CEO
JANICE BRADY - Controller
CORDELIA PINEDO - Manager Restaurant Operations

Il Fornaio Corporation
770 Tamalpais Dr Ste 400
Corte Madera, CA 94925-1739

Telephone: (415) 945-0500
Fax Number: (415) 924-0906
Internet Homepage: cornerbakerycafe.com; ilfornaio.com
Listing Type: Corporate Office
Type of Business: Chain Restaurant Operator
Year Founded: 1991
Total Sales: $601,310,000 (e)
Alcohol Sales: 5%
Number of Employees: 6,300
Total Units: 195
Trade Names: Canaletto Ristorante Veneto (2); Corner Bakery Cafe (174); Il Fornaio Cucina Italiana e Panetteria (19)
Company-Owned Units: 111
Units Franchised To: 84
Preferred Location Types: Downtown; Freestanding; Hotel/Motel; Lifestyle Center; Office Complex; Regional Mall; Strip Mall
Alcohol Served: Beer, Wine, Liquor
Primary Menu: Italian (21); Sandwiches/Deli (174)
Areas of Operation: AZ, CA, CO, DC, FL, GA, IL, KS, KY, MD, MS, NJ, NM, NV, NY, OK, OR, PA, TN, TX, UT, VA, WA, WI
Type of Foodservice: Fast Casual (174); Fine Dining (21)
Catering Services: Yes
On-site Distribution Center: Yes
Parent Company: Roark Capital Group,

ATLANTA, GA
Headquarter Offices: CBC Restaurant Corp., DALLAS, TX; CBC Restaurant Corp., DALLAS, TX; Il Fornaio Cucina Italiana e Panetteria, CORTE MADERA, CA

Key Personnel
MICHAEL J. HISLOP - Chairman
LAURENCE MINDEL - Founder
ERIN HASSELGREN - President
TED LAYMON - Chief Marketing Officer
MIM MCNULTY - Senior VP Human Resources
FRANK LICATA - VP Operations
MARIO LOMBARDO - VP Operations
JIM BARGER - VP Construction
RYAN ORENDORFF - VP Financial Planning

Il Fornaio Cucina Italiana e Panetteria
770 Tamalpais Dr Ste 400
Corte Madera, CA 94925-1739

Telephone: (415) 945-0500
Fax Number: (415) 924-0906
Internet Homepage: ilfornaio.com
Company Email: info@ilfornaio.com
Type of Business: Chain Restaurant Operator
Year Founded: 1987
Total Sales: $218,060,000 (e)
Alcohol Sales: 20%
Number of Employees: 2,570
Average Check: Breakfast(18); Lunch(30); Dinner(46)
Internet Order Processing: Yes
Internet Sales: 1.00%
Total Units: 20
Trade Names: Canaletto Ristorante Veneto (2); Il Fornaio Cucina Italiana e Panetteria (18)
Company-Owned Units: 20
Preferred Square Footage: 6,200; 8,000
Preferred Location Types: Downtown; Freestanding; Hotel/Motel; Regional Mall
Alcohol Served: Beer, Wine, Liquor
Primary Menu: Italian (20)
Areas of Operation: CA, CO, NV, WA
Type of Foodservice: Fine Dining (20)
On-site Distribution Center: Yes
Primary Distributors: (Food) US Foods-Los Angeles, LA MIRADA, CA
Parent Company: Roark Capital Group, ATLANTA, GA
Headquarters: Il Fornaio Corporation, CORTE MADERA, CA

Key Personnel
MICHAEL HISLOP - Chairman
MICHAEL BEATRICE - President; COO
TED LAYMON - Chief Marketing Officer
MAURIZIO MAZZON - Senior Exec VP Food and Beverage; Executive Chef; General Buyer
FRANK LICATA - VP Operations

JIM BARGER - VP Construction

Pacific Catch
770 Tamalpais Dr
Corte Madera, CA 94925

Telephone: (415) 896-6888
Fax Number: (866) 594-6117
Internet Homepage: pacificcatch.com
Company Email: jobs@pacificcatch.com
Type of Business: Chain Restaurant Operator
Total Units: 8
Trade Names: Pacific Catch (8)
Company-Owned Units: 8
Primary Menu: Seafood (8)
Areas of Operation: CA
Type of Foodservice: Casual Dining (8)
Catering Services: Yes

Key Personnel
MICHAEL HISLOP - Chairman
KEITH COX - Co-Founder; CEO
DEMETRI GILL - CFO
TOM HANSON - COO
JESSICA NAPIER - Director Human Resources

American Restaurant Holdings, Inc.
20060 Santa Ana Ave
Costa Mesa, CA 92626

Telephone: (949) 825-5090
Fax Number: (949) 825-5099
Internet Homepage: americanrestaurantholdings.com; canyonfiresidegrille.com; fronterasgrill.com; jojospizza.com; musclemakergrill.com
Company Email: info@americanrestaurantholdings.com
Listing Type: Corporate Office
Type of Business: Chain Restaurant Operator
Total Sales: $55,043,000 (e)
Number of Employees: 185
Total Units: 63
Trade Names: Canyon Fireside Grille (1); Fresca's Mexican Grill (9); JoJo's Pizza Kitchen (4); Muscle Maker Grill (36); Pokemoto (13)
Company-Owned Units: 32
Units Franchised To: 31
Primary Menu: American (1); Asian (13); Health Foods (36); Mexican (9); Pizza (4)
Areas of Operation: CA, CT, FL, IL, NE, NJ, NV, NY, PA, TX
Type of Foodservice: Casual Dining (5); Fast Casual (58)
Catering Services: Yes
Headquarter Offices: Muscle Maker Inc., IRVINE, CA

Key Personnel
KEVIN MOHAN - Exec VP

Arriba Fresh Baja Grills Inc
901 S Coast Dr Ste C160
Costa Mesa, CA 92626-1774

Telephone: (714) 540-4001
Internet Homepage: arribabajagrill.net
Type of Business: Chain Restaurant Operator
Total Sales: $3,426,000 (e)
Internet Order Processing: Yes
Total Units: 2
Trade Names: Baja Fresh Mexican Grill (2)
Company-Owned Units: 2
Primary Menu: Mexican (2)
Areas of Operation: CA
Type of Foodservice: Fast Casual (2)
Franchise Affiliation: Kahala Brands, SCOTTSDALE, AZ

Key Personnel
RICHARD A. ZAK - President; General Buyer

California Pizza Kitchen Inc.
575 Anton Blvd #100
Costa Mesa, CA 92626

Telephone: (310) 342-5000
Fax Number: (310) 342-4743
Internet Homepage: cpk.com
Type of Business: Chain Restaurant Operator
Year Founded: 1985
Systemwide Sales: $944,778,000 (e)
Total Sales: $802,890,000 (e)
Alcohol Sales: 5%
Number of Employees: 16,500
Average Check: Lunch(16); Dinner(18)
Total Units: 200
Trade Names: California Pizza Kitchen (200)
Company-Owned Units: 148
Units Franchised To: 52
Preferred Square Footage: 600; 3,000; 5,000; 6,000
Preferred Location Types: Airports; Community Mall; Downtown; Freestanding; Hotel/Motel; Kiosk; Lifestyle Center; Office Complex; Regional Mall; Stadiums; Strip Mall; Travel Plazas
Alcohol Served: Beer, Wine, Liquor
Primary Menu: Pizza (200)
Areas of Operation: AL, AZ, CA, CO, CT, DE, FL, GA, GU, HI, IL, KS, KY, LA, MA, MD, MI, MO, NC, NJ, NM, NV, NY, OH, OR, PA, TN, TX, UT, VA, WI
Foreign Countries: HONG KONG; INDIA; JAPAN; MEXICO; SINGAPORE; SOUTH KOREA; THE PHILIPPINES; UNITED ARAB EMIRATES
Type of Foodservice: Casual Dining (200)
Foodservice Management Venues:

Recreational
Catering Services: Yes
Primary Distributors: (Food) McLane/Rocky Mount, ROCKY MOUNT, NC
Parent Company: Golden Gate Capital, SAN FRANCISCO, CA
Notes: California Pizza Kitchen derives approximately 1% of its total revenue from royalties from a licensing agreement with Kraft.

Key Personnel
JEFF WARNE - CEO; President
KIM BOEREMA - COO
CLINT COLEMAN - Chief Development Officer
ASHLEY CERAOLO - Senior VP Marketing
STEVEN RICH - Senior VP Real Estate
SHANNON KIRK - VP People
SCOTT WAGERS - VP Facility/Maintenance, Construction
JT SZCZUKA - VP Procurement
DAVEY JAMES - VP Operations
JIN KIM - VP Finance
JON SILVERTOOTH - VP Information Technology
NATHAN KEELER - VP Operations
KONG CHANG - VP Operations
KAY YAEGER - Controller
CAROL FLYNN - Senior Director Marketing
HARSHVARDHAN CHOWDHARY - Senior Director Finance, Strategy
KIRBY LOTTMAN - Senior Director Training
JAMES LEUNG - Senior Director Supply Chain
KRISTI LEON - Director Information Technology, Systems
LISA PENNINGTON - Director
DANIEL GUTIERREZ - Director Information Technology, Infrastructure
GUILHERME DA CRUZ - Director Operations
JUAN BORRAYO - Director Culinary Development
STEPHANIE MENDOZA - Director Franchising
JULIE CASTRO - Director Operations
LYNN GINSBURG - Director Talent
WADE ADAY - Senior Manager
ART GONZALEZ - Manager Information Technology-Help Desk
JEANETTE PACUN - Manager Compliance, People

El Pollo Loco Inc.
3535 Harbor Blvd Ste 100
Costa Mesa, CA 92626-1494

Telephone: (714) 599-5000
Fax Number: (714) 599-5500
Internet Homepage: elpolloloco.com
Company Email: info@elpolloloco.com
Type of Business: Chain Restaurant Operator
Year Founded: 1975
Systemwide Sales: $1,364,071,000 (e)
Publicly Held: Yes
Total Sales: $482,484,000 (e)
Number of Employees: 5,575
Average Check: Lunch(12); Dinner(12)
Total Units: 498
Trade Names: El Pollo Loco (498)
Company-Owned Units: 172
Units Franchised To: 326
Preferred Square Footage: 1,800; 2,400; 2,800; 3,000
Preferred Location Types: Freestanding; Institution (college/hospital); Other
Primary Menu: Chicken (498)
Projected Openings: 5
Areas of Operation: AZ, CA, LA, NV, TX, UT
Type of Foodservice: Quick Serve (498)
Catering Services: Yes
Primary Distributors: (Full Line) McLane/Rancho Cucamonga, RANCHO CUCAMONGA, CA
Parent Company: Trimaran Capital Partners, NEW YORK, NY
Headquarters: EPL Intermediate Inc., COSTA MESA, CA

Key Personnel
ELIZABETH WILLIAMS - CEO
MARIA HOLLANDSWORTH - President; COO
JILL ADAMS - Chief Marketing Officer
BRIAN CARMICHALL - Chief Development Officer; VP Franchise Operations
ANNE JOLLAY - Chief Legal Officer
CLARK MATTHEWS - VP Information Technology
GABE ALONSO - VP Digital Marketing
KAT GARCIA - VP Marketing
RICK PEPPER - VP Operations-Training
LIZA ANDERSON - Controller
NICK HOSKINS - Senior Director Information Technology
SAM AFANDI - Director Real Estate
JAVIER MARTINEZ - Director Construction, Design
DOLORES SCHWARZ - Director Company Operations
MICHELLE COOMBS - Director Systems, Human Resources
CHAD CANTRELL - Director Franchise Sales
ANNE PORTER - Director Legal
JOSE LUIS FLORES - Director Operations
MICHAEL ANDERSON - Director POS/Scanning
IVAN ABREU - Director Real Estate
ESMERALDA MEJIA - Director Franchising
MELO MARCARIAN - Regional Director Operations
CHERYL FRY - Senior Manager Real Estate
CHRIS MCGILVERY - Manager Product Development
JACK VILLALOBOS - Manager Customer Service

Gala Corporation
3191 Red Hill Ave Ste 200
Costa Mesa, CA 92626-3451

Telephone: (800) 653-3517
Fax Number: (714) 916-5684
Internet Homepage: galacorp.com
Type of Business: Chain Restaurant Operator
Year Founded: 1982
Total Sales: $44,600,000 (e)
Alcohol Sales: 12%
Number of Employees: 960
Average Check: Lunch(10); Dinner(22)
Total Units: 12
Trade Names: Famous Dave's (12)
Units Franchised From: 12
Preferred Square Footage: 1,500; 3,000
Preferred Location Types: Freestanding; Regional Mall; Strip Mall
Alcohol Served: Beer, Wine, Liquor
Primary Menu: Bar-B-Q (12)
Areas of Operation: CA
Type of Foodservice: Casual Dining (12)
Catering Services: Yes
Franchise Affiliation: BBQ Holdings, Inc., MINNETONKA, MN
Primary Distributors: (Full Line) Shamrock Foods Co., PHOENIX, AZ
Notes: Gala Corporation operates as Tacaza (Famous Dave's), Golden West Restaurants Inc. and R&D Restaurant Enterprises Inc. (Applebee's) & Gala AZHoldings (Del Taco).

Key Personnel
ANAND GALA - CEO; President
TIM KOCH - COO
TODD MILLER - Director Operations
SCOTT HOHENSTEIN - Director Marketing, Catering; Manager Operations

Halal or Nothing, LLC
3033 Bristol St STE E
Costa Mesa, CA 92626

Telephone: (714) 850-1080
Internet Homepage: halalornothing.com
Type of Business: Chain Restaurant Operator
Year Founded: 2014
Total Units: 9
Trade Names: The Halal Guys (9)
Units Franchised From: 9
Primary Menu: Middle Eastern (9)
Projected Openings: 2
Areas of Operation: CA
Type of Foodservice: Quick Serve (9)
Franchise Affiliation: The Halal Guys Inc., ASTORIA, NY

Key Personnel
THOMAS PHAM - CEO; Partner
PHILLIP HOANG - Partner; CFO

ALVIN WONG - Partner; Executive Director Human Resources
ATHENA ACOSTA - General Manager; Assistant Manager

King's Seafood Co.
3185 Airway Ave Ste J
Costa Mesa, CA 92626-4601

Telephone: (714) 432-0400
Fax Number: (714) 432-0111
Internet Homepage: kingsseafood.com
Type of Business: Chain Restaurant Operator
Year Founded: 1983
Total Sales: $91,090,000 (e)
Alcohol Sales: 20%
Number of Employees: 1,669
Average Check: Dinner(48)
Total Units: 20
Trade Names: 555 East Prime Steakhouse (1); Fish Camp (1); King's Fish House (10); Lou & Mickeys (1); Pier Burger (1); Water Grill (6)
Company-Owned Units: 20
Preferred Square Footage: 7,500
Preferred Location Types: Freestanding; Lifestyle Center; Office Complex
Alcohol Served: Beer, Wine, Liquor
Primary Menu: Hamburger (1); Seafood (17); Steak (1); Steak (1)
Areas of Operation: AZ, CA, NV
Type of Foodservice: Casual Dining (14); Fine Dining (6)
Catering Services: Yes
Distribution Centers: SANTA ANA, CA
Primary Distributors: (Full Line) US Foods-Los Angeles, LA MIRADA, CA; (Specialty Foods) Santa Monica Seafood Co., RANCHO DOMINGUEZ, CA

Key Personnel
SAM KING - Chairman; CEO; Executive Chef
JEFF KING - Chairman
RJ THOMAS - President; COO
RICHARD FIORE - CFO
KELLY FILFRMAN - Chief People Officer
GARY MAYEDA - Director Facility/Maintenance, Construction
JUAN VARGAS - Director Distribution
DEDE COMMANS - Director Operations
KRISTIN A. ANDERSON - Manager Development, Real Estate
KRISTINA JOHNSON - Manager Customer Analytics
JOYCE J. MOJICA MEJIA - Manager Restaurant Operations
LARISSA CASTILLO - Manager Restaurant Operations

Lazy Dog Restaurant & Bar
3337 Susan St Ste 100
Costa Mesa, CA 92626

Telephone: (714) 596-9960
Fax Number: (714) 596-9970
Internet Homepage: lazydogrestaurants.com
Company Email: info@lazydogrestaurants.com
Type of Business: Chain Restaurant Operator
Year Founded: 2006
Total Sales: $130,920,000 (e)
Alcohol Sales: 20%
Number of Employees: 2,262
Average Check: Lunch(14); Dinner(20)
Total Units: 42
Trade Names: The Lazy Dog Cafe (42)
Company-Owned Units: 42
Preferred Location Types: Freestanding; Strip Mall
Alcohol Served: Beer, Wine, Liquor
Primary Menu: Californian (42)
Projected Openings: 3
Areas of Operation: CA, CO, GA, IL, NV, TX
Type of Foodservice: Casual Dining (42)
Catering Services: Yes

Key Personnel
CHRIS SIMMS - CEO; Partner; Director Facility/Maintenance
THOMAS SIMMS - Partner; Director Information Systems
GABRIEL CALIENDO - Partner; General Manager; Executive Chef; General Buyer
DAN DILLON - Partner
ROBERT LINDER - CFO
KEVIN WHATTOFF - COO
MARIAH MACHNIKOWSKI - Chief People Officer
STEVE PRICE - Chief Development Officer
DAPHNE FELICITAS - VP Employee Development
LAURA LAVIGNE - Senior Director Marketing-Beverages
REBECCA SIMMS - Creative Director
BRIAN PALKO - Director Operations
MICHELE PATTERSON - Director Operations
PATRICK LIGER - Director Finance
LAURA HANSEN - Director Marketing
CHRIS DOTSON - Director Finance
THANH ERWIN - Director Tax
SHELLEY REED - Director People
SCOTT SAGERDAHL - Director Foodservice
MICHAEL SAUCEDO - Director Information Technology
JACOB MILLER - Director Digital
MIKE OGILVIE - Regional Director Operations
NICK HUCKEBA - Regional Director Operations
NICOLE BREIJAK - Regional Director

Panini Kabob Grill
3159A Red Hill Ave
Costa Mesa, CA 92626

Telephone: (949) 788-1620
Internet Homepage: paninikabobgrill.com
Company Email: info@PaniniKabobGrill.com
Type of Business: Chain Restaurant Operator
Year Founded: 1995
Total Sales: $20,470,000 (e)
Total Units: 17
Trade Names: Panini Kabob Grill Healthier Mediterrean Food (17)
Company-Owned Units: 12
Units Franchised To: 5
Primary Menu: Greek/Mediterranean (17)
Projected Openings: 17
Areas of Operation: CA
Type of Foodservice: Casual Dining (17)

Key Personnel
MIKE RAFIPOOR - CEO
HARRY LOPEZ - Director Franchise Operations, Human Resources
JOSE JIMENEZ - District Manager
ANTONIO LOPEZ - District Manager Culinary Operations
ALEX FRIAS - District Manager
MIGUEL VARGAS - Manager Restaurant Operations
FERMIN ALARCON - Manager Information Technology

Ruby Corp.
3198 Airport Loop Dr Ste D1
Costa Mesa, CA 92626-3407

Telephone: (714) 662-5856
Fax Number: (714) 662-2714
Type of Business: Chain Restaurant Operator
Total Sales: $37,160,000 (e)
Number of Employees: 40
Average Check: Breakfast(8), Lunch(8), Dinner(8)
Total Units: 8
Trade Names: McDonald's (8)
Units Franchised From: 8
Preferred Square Footage: 2,500; 3,000
Preferred Location Types: Discount Dept. Stores; Regional Mall; Strip Mall
Primary Menu: Hamburger (8)
Areas of Operation: CA
Type of Foodservice: Quick Serve (8)
Franchise Affiliation: McDonald's Corporation, CHICAGO, IL
Primary Distributors: (Food) The Martin-Brower Co., CITY OF INDUSTRY, CA

Key Personnel
NEIL RUBY - Partner; VP; General Manager Purchasing

KACY BRUCE - Manager Human Resources

Salt Creek Grille Restaurant LLC
3185 Airway Ave Ste C2
Costa Mesa, CA 92626-4601

Telephone: (714) 754-0144
Fax Number: (714) 754-1641
Internet Homepage: saltcreekgrille.com
Company Email: info@saltcreekgrille.com
Type of Business: Chain Restaurant Operator
Year Founded: 1995
Total Sales: $35,460,000 (e)
Alcohol Sales: 20%
Number of Employees: 240
Average Check: Dinner(36)
Internet Order Processing: Yes
Total Units: 5
Trade Names: Salt Creek Grille (5)
Company-Owned Units: 4
Units Franchised To: 1
Preferred Location Types: Freestanding
Alcohol Served: Beer, Wine, Liquor
Primary Menu: Steak/Seafood (5)
Areas of Operation: CA, NJ
Type of Foodservice: Casual Dining (5)
Primary Distributors: (Food) SYSCO Food Services of Los Angeles Inc., WALNUT, CA

Key Personnel
STEVE BIDGOOD - President; Partner
TIM MCCUNE - President; Partner
HUGH PREECE - Partner
NIKI SHUKAR - Controller
JENNIFER CHADWICK - Director Marketing, Sales

The Flame Broiler Inc.
3525 Hyland Ave Ste 270
Costa Mesa, CA 92626-1487

Telephone: (714) 424-0223
Internet Homepage: flamebroilerusa.com
Type of Business: Chain Restaurant Operator
Year Founded: 1995
Systemwide Sales: $139,345,000 (e)
Total Sales: $10,800,000 (e)
Number of Employees: 30
Average Check: Dinner(12)
Total Units: 179
Trade Names: The Flame Broiler (199)
Company-Owned Units: 3
Units Franchised To: 196
Primary Menu: Asian (199)
Areas of Operation: AZ, CA, FL, NV, OK
Type of Foodservice: Fast Casual (199)

Key Personnel
YOUNG R. LEE - CEO; President; Executive Chef; General Buyer
CHRISTIAN LEE - COO
DANIEL LEE - CTO; Chief Marketing Officer
NORMA ROMERO - Manager Franchise Development

WKS Restaurant Corp
5856 Corporate Ave
Cpress, CA 90630

Mailing Address: P O Box 39, LAKEWOOD, CA, 90714
Telephone: (562) 425-1402
Fax Number: (562) 425-2502
Internet Homepage: wksusa.com
Type of Business: Chain Restaurant Operator
Year Founded: 1998
Total Sales: $875,680,000 (e)
Total Units: 293
Trade Names: Blaze Pizza (10); Corner Bakery Cafe (1); Denny's (126); El Pollo Loco (67); Krispy Kreme (35); Wendys Old Fashioned Hamburgers (54)
Units Franchised From: 293
Primary Menu: American (126); Chicken (67); Hamburger (54); Pizza (10); Sandwiches/Deli (1); Snacks (35)
Areas of Operation: AZ, CA, IL, MO, NE, NM, UT, WI
Type of Foodservice: Family Restaurant (127); Fast Casual (4); Quick Serve (144)
Franchise Affiliation: CBC Restaurant Corp., DALLAS, TX; Denny's Corporation, SPARTANBURG, SC; El Pollo Loco Inc., COSTA MESA, CA; Krispy Kreme Doughnut Corporation, CHARLOTTE, NC; The Wendy's Company, DUBLIN, OH

Key Personnel
ROLAND C. SPONGBERG - CEO; President
MATTHEW MCGUINNESS - CFO; Exec VP
JAY SPONGBERG - COO; Senior VP
PAUL E. TANNER - Senior VP Finance, Development
CARLOS ORTIZ - VP Operations
ANDREW FEINOUR - VP Facility/Maintenance, Construction
TREVOR FITZGERALD - VP Information Technology, Innovation
ROSA FUENTES - Director Operations
ADRIANA NUNEZ - Director Training
DANIEL ROONEY - Director Real Estate
LUIS RUANO - Director Operations
RUBEN ARIAS - District Manager
JOE JOHNSON - District Manager
JIMMIE NJOROGE - Manager Accounting
SANDY THIBODEAUX - Manager Employee Benefits

Raize Dough Enterprises
6029 Bristol Pkwy Ste 200
Culver City, CA 90230-6651

Telephone: (310) 473-6575
Fax Number: (310) 215-3367
Type of Business: Chain Restaurant Operator
Total Sales: $195,498,000 (e)
Total Units: 95
Trade Names: Domino's (95)
Units Franchised From: 95
Preferred Square Footage: 1,000
Preferred Location Types: Strip Mall
Primary Menu: Pizza (95)
Areas of Operation: CA
Type of Foodservice: Quick Serve (95)
Franchise Affiliation: Domino's Pizza Inc, ANN ARBOR, MI

Key Personnel
DAN HOSSEINI - Owner; General Manager

Sweetgreen, Inc.
8850 Washington Blvd
Culver City, CA 90232-2356

Mailing Address: CA,
Telephone: (310) 660-7471
Internet Homepage: sweetgreen.com
Company Email: info@sweetgreen.com
Type of Business: Chain Restaurant Operator
Year Founded: 2007
Publicly Held: Yes
Total Sales: $617,080,000 (e)
Number of Employees: 6,186
Average Check: Dinner(20)
Internet Order Processing: Yes
Total Units: 150
Trade Names: sweetgreen (221)
Company-Owned Units: 221
Preferred Square Footage: 3,000
Preferred Location Types: Downtown; Office Complex; Strip Mall
Primary Menu: American (221)
Projected Openings: 25
Areas of Operation: CA, DC, IL, MA, MD, NY, PA, VA
Type of Foodservice: Fast Casual (221)

Key Personnel
NICOLAS JAMMET - Co-Founder; Chief Concept Officer
JONATHAN NEMAN - Co-Founder; CEO
NATHANIEL RU - Co-Founder; Chief Brand Officer
CHRIS CARR - COO
ADRIENNE GEMPERLE - Chief People Officer
WOULETA AYELE - CTO
JIM MCPHAIL - Chief Development Officer
CHRISTOPHER TARRANT - Chief Development Officer; Senior VP

MATT ALEXANDER - Chief Legal Officer
ERIC PAULUCCI - VP Operations
MICHAEL KOTICK - VP; Director Marketing
MICHAEL FARID - VP Technology
ASHLEY VAN - VP; Controller
CARLOS CONDE - VP Engineering
ANTHONY WIGINTON - VP Finance
ADAM MISCHLICH - Executive Director
DENISE ONGE - Executive Chef
SUMMER EDWARDS - Senior Director Facility/Maintenance, Construction
DAVE OSTER - Senior Director Real Estate
JILLIAN WHEELER - Creative Director
JENNIFER GOMEZ - Director
CHAD BRAUZE - Director Culinary Operations
JAMIE MCGLINCHEY SHENKMAN - Director Design
VINCE SU - Director Digital
NICOLE KRAMER - Director Marketing
JENNY SANG - Director Innovation, Menu Development
STEFAN PREMDAS - Director People
LINDA ZHANG - Director Procurement, Store Development
PAMELA HABER - Manager Real Estate, Northeast Region

TYP Restaurant Group Inc.
2633 Fairfax Ave
Culver City, CA 90232-7332

Telephone: (310) 954-1415
Fax Number: (310) 954-1419
Internet Homepage: tendergreens.com
Company Email: info@tendergreens.com
Type of Business: Chain Restaurant Operator
Year Founded: 2006
Total Sales: $21,410,000 (e)
Alcohol Sales: 5%
Number of Employees: 186
Average Check: Dinner(18)
Internet Order Processing: Yes
Internet Sales: 1.00%
Total Units: 31
Trade Names: Tender Greens (31)
Company-Owned Units: 31
Preferred Square Footage: 3,200
Alcohol Served: Beer, Wine
Primary Menu: American (31)
Projected Openings: 3
Areas of Operation: CA, NY
Type of Foodservice: Fast Casual (31)
Catering Services: Yes

Key Personnel
ERIK OBERHOLTZER - Executive Chairman; Partner
MATT LYMAN - Partner; General Buyer
LACY MOODY - General Manager
MATT CANDITO - Assistant Director Development; Manager Training

Cedar Corporation
5554 Market Pl
Cypress, CA 90630-4710

Telephone: (714) 952-3821
Type of Business: Chain Restaurant Operator
Year Founded: 1966
Total Sales: $51,260,000 (e)
Number of Employees: 550
Average Check: Breakfast(5); Lunch(8); Dinner(10)
Total Units: 11
Trade Names: McDonald's (11)
Units Franchised From: 11
Preferred Square Footage: 1,500
Preferred Location Types: Freestanding
Primary Menu: Hamburger (11)
Areas of Operation: CA
Type of Foodservice: Quick Serve (11)
Franchise Affiliation: McDonald's Corporation, CHICAGO, IL
Primary Distributors: (Food) The Martin-Brower Co., PHOENIX, AZ

Key Personnel
ALAN M. RUBY - President; Partner; Director Finance, Facility/Maintenance; General Buyer
RICHARD RUBY - Partner; General Manager; Director Operations, Information Systems, Risk Management, Real Estate, Human Resources
LAUREN BILLINGS - Representative Marketing

Xperience Restaurant Group
11065 Knott Ave Suite A
Cypress, CA 90630

Telephone: (562) 346-1200
Fax Number: (562) 346-1303
Internet Homepage: acapulcorestaurants.com; casagallardo.com; chevys.com; eltorito.com; epcrestaurant.com; etgrill.com; lasbrisaslagunabeach.com; realmexfoods.com; realmexrestaurants.com; sinigualrestaurants.com
Type of Business: Chain Restaurant Operator
Year Founded: 1954
Total Sales: $186,800,000 (e)
Alcohol Sales: 25%
Number of Employees: 5,610
Total Units: 68
Trade Names: Acapulco Restaurant (4); Chevys Fresh Mex (23); El Torito (31); El Torito Grill (2); Las Brisas (1); Sinigual (1); SOL (4); Solita (1); Who Song & Larry's (1)
Company-Owned Units: 55
Units Franchised To: 13
Preferred Square Footage: 7,800; 8,500; 8,800
Preferred Location Types: Community Mall; Freestanding; Office Complex; Regional Mall; Strip Mall
Alcohol Served: Beer, Wine, Liquor
Primary Menu: Mexican (63)
Projected Openings: 2
Areas of Operation: AZ, CA, FL, IL, IN, LA, MD, MN, MO, NJ, NV, NY, OR, SD, VA, WA
Type of Foodservice: Casual Dining (63)
Catering Services: Yes
Distribution Centers: UNION CITY, CA
Parent Company: RM Opco LLC, CYPRESS, CA
Notes: The company derives approximately 7% from outside food sales, admission charges & vending commissions.

Key Personnel
FRANCISCO VELASQUEZ - CEO
MIKE JOHNSON - Senior VP Operations
STACIE MORN - VP Human Resources
JASON PEROVICH - VP Information Technology
GIOVANNI SALVINO - VP Marketing
HOWARD GARDNER - General Manager
MIKE ALASAAD - Senior Director Operations
LESLIE MENDOZA - Director Marketing
ROBERT WINTERS - Director Operations
PATTY SOUTHERN - Director Payroll
ROXANA HERRADA - Director Operations, Systems, Supply Chain
MARICELA DAOUDI - Director Event Planning, Catering
MARIO HERRERA - Director Restaurant Operations
CRYSTAL HUBER - Director Development, Talent
CRISTHIAN SALAZAR - Director Culinary Operations
SHAUN BENESCH - Director Real Estate
JOSE AVILES - Regional Director
ANTONIO SANTANA - Regional Director
PEDRO BAUTISTA - Regional Director Operations
MARTHA GAMBOA - Regional Director
KYLE ELDER - Regional Director
ARTHUR SETLIGHT - Regional Director Operations
CHRIS LANKFORD - Regional Director
MICHELLE ELIZABETH WIDMER - Manager Event Planning
JOY DEVAUGHN - Manager Event Planning

Criselda & Edwin Diaz
1901 Junipero Serra Blvd Ste F
Daly City, CA 94014-3896

Telephone: (650) 992-3889
Type of Business: Chain Restaurant Operator
Total Sales: $1,175,000 (e)
Total Units: 3
Trade Names: Cold Stone Creamery (3)
Units Franchised From: 3
Primary Menu: Snacks (3)
Areas of Operation: CA

Type of Foodservice: Quick Serve (3)
Franchise Affiliation: Kahala Brands, SCOTTSDALE, AZ

Key Personnel
CRISELDA DIAZ - Partner
EDWIN DIAZ - Partner

Koi Palace Restaurants
365 Gellert Blvd
Daly City, CA 94015-2613

Telephone: (650) 239-9068
Fax Number: (650) 992-9046
Internet Homepage: dragonbeaux.com/home; koipalace.com
Company Email: alvinhuomg@gmail.com
Type of Business: Chain Restaurant Operator
Total Sales: $9,686,000 (e)
Alcohol Sales: 10%
Average Check: Lunch(30); Dinner(36)
Total Units: 5
Trade Names: Dragon Beaux (1); Koi Palace (3); Koi Palace Express (1)
Company-Owned Units: 5
Alcohol Served: Beer, Wine, Liquor
Primary Menu: Chinese (5)
Areas of Operation: CA
Type of Foodservice: Casual Dining (1); Fine Dining (4)
Catering Services: Yes
Primary Distributors: (Food) SYSCO Food Services of Los Angeles Inc., WALNUT, CA

Key Personnel
WILLY NG - President; General Manager; General Buyer
RUIXIN MAO - Director Marketing

Wind & Sea Restaurants
34699 Golden Lantern St
Dana Point, CA 92629-2908

Telephone: (949) 496-6500
Fax Number: (949) 496-2605
Internet Homepage: windandsearestaurants.com
Type of Business: Chain Restaurant Operator
Year Founded: 1970
Total Sales: $24,933,000 (e)
Alcohol Sales: 35%
Number of Employees: 200
Total Units: 4
Trade Names: Harpoon Henry's (1); Kona Canoe Club (1); Kona Inn (1); Wind & Sea (1)
Company-Owned Units: 4
Preferred Square Footage: 8,000
Preferred Location Types: Freestanding
Alcohol Served: Beer, Wine, Liquor
Primary Menu: Seafood (4)
Areas of Operation: CA, HI

Type of Foodservice: Casual Dining (4)
Catering Services: Yes
Primary Distributors: (Food) SYSCO Food Services of San Diego Inc., POWAY, CA

Key Personnel
BOB MARDIAN - President; Executive Chef; Director Operations, Catering
ROBERT CONRAD - VP Finance, Purchasing
STEVE FALCINELLA - VP Store Planning; Director Real Estate
PATSY DAMATO - Controller
JAY STYLES - General Manager; Director Facility/Maintenance

High Tech Burrito
383 Diablo Rd Ste 116
Danville, CA 94526

Telephone: (925) 791-5141
Fax Number: (925) 791-5182
Internet Homepage: hightechburrito.com
Company Email: contact@hightechburrito.com
Type of Business: Chain Restaurant Operator
Year Founded: 1986
Total Sales: $6,133,000 (e)
Number of Employees: 100
Average Check: Lunch(8); Dinner(12)
Internet Order Processing: Yes
Total Units: 5
Trade Names: High Tech Burrito (5)
Company-Owned Units: 5
Preferred Square Footage: 1,500
Preferred Location Types: Strip Mall
Primary Menu: Mexican (5)
Areas of Operation: CA
Type of Foodservice: Quick Serve (5)
Foodservice Management Venues: Schools
Catering Services: Yes
Primary Distributors: (Full Line) US Foods, CORONA, CA

Key Personnel
JERRY SCOTT - CFO; Director Information Systems, Human Resources
BRIAN MALONE - VP Marketing, Business Development; Director Facility/Maintenance, Real Estate, Design
GABRIEL LINN - Director Operations, Food Safety
CLARE AGUIRRE - Coordinator Catering

JM Subs North One, L.P.
301 Hartz Ave Ste 100
Danville, CA 94526-3329

Telephone: (925) 406-4978
Type of Business: Chain Restaurant Operator
Total Sales: $4,385,000 (e)
Total Units: 3
Trade Names: Jersey Mike's Subs (3)

Units Franchised From: 3
Primary Menu: Sandwiches/Deli (3)
Areas of Operation: CA
Type of Foodservice: Quick Serve (3)
Franchise Affiliation: Jersey Mike's Franchise Systems, MANASQUAN, NJ

Key Personnel
BENNETT BALL - Partner
CATHY BROWN - Partner
MIKE BROWN - Partner; General Buyer

Coyote Corporation
1784 Picasso Ave Ste B
Davis, CA 95618-0551

Telephone: (530) 753-0202
Fax Number: (530) 753-6247
Internet Homepage: doscoyotes.com
Company Email: contact@doscoyotes.net
Type of Business: Chain Restaurant Operator
Year Founded: 1990
Total Sales: $20,260,000 (e)
Alcohol Sales: 2%
Number of Employees: 310
Average Check: Lunch(8); Dinner(10)
Internet Order Processing: Yes
Total Units: 11
Trade Names: Dos Coyotes Border Cafe (11)
Company-Owned Units: 11
Preferred Square Footage: 3,900
Preferred Location Types: Other; Strip Mall
Alcohol Served: Beer, Wine, Liquor
Primary Menu: Southwest/Tex-Mex (11)
Areas of Operation: CA
Type of Foodservice: Casual Dining (11)
Catering Services: Yes
Primary Distributors: (Full Line) SYSCO Food Services of Sacramento Inc., PLEASANT GROVE, CA

Key Personnel
BOBBY COYOTE - President; Manager Facility/Maintenance, Design, Menu Development; General Buyer

Domino's Franchisee
2038 Lyndell Ter Ste 103
Davis, CA 95616-6220

Telephone: (530) 756-5161
Type of Business: Chain Restaurant Operator
Total Sales: $6,139,000 (e)
Total Units: 3
Trade Names: Domino's (3)
Units Franchised From: 3
Primary Menu: Pizza (3)
Areas of Operation: CA
Type of Foodservice: Quick Serve (3)
Franchise Affiliation: Domino's Pizza Inc, ANN

ARBOR, MI

Key Personnel
DONNA L. DELGADO - Owner; General Buyer

Board & Brew
1212 Camino Del Mar
Del Mar, CA 92014

Telephone: (858) 481-1021
Internet Homepage: boardandbrew.com
Type of Business: Chain Restaurant Operator
Year Founded: 1979
Systemwide Sales: $18,367,000 (e)
Total Sales: $12,290,000 (e)
Total Units: 17
Trade Names: Board & Brew (17)
Company-Owned Units: 10
Units Franchised To: 7
Primary Menu: Sandwiches/Deli (17)
Type of Foodservice: Fast Casual (17)

Key Personnel
TOM POWERS - Founder; CEO
JACOB CLEMONS - Director Operations

Pacifica Del Mar
1555 Camino Del Mar
Del Mar, CA 92014-2467

Telephone: (858) 792-0476
Fax Number: (858) 792-0848
Internet Homepage: pacificadelmar.com
Type of Business: Chain Restaurant Operator
Total Sales: $26,720,000 (e)
Alcohol Sales: 30%
Number of Employees: 150
Average Check: Breakfast(24); Lunch(42); Dinner(66)
Internet Order Processing: Yes
Internet Sales: 3.00%
Total Units: 6
Trade Names: Pacifica Cliff House and Bar (1); Pacifica Del Mar (1); Pacifica in the Dessert (1); Pacifica Ocean Bar (1); Pacifica the Breeze (2)
Company-Owned Units: 6
Preferred Location Types: Freestanding
Alcohol Served: Beer, Wine, Liquor
Primary Menu: Seafood (6)
Areas of Operation: CA
Type of Foodservice: Casual Dining (4); Fine Dining (2)
Catering Services: Yes
Primary Distributors: (Food) SYSCO Food Services of San Diego Inc., POWAY, CA

Key Personnel
SANJIV CHOPRA - Owner; General Buyer

CHRIS IDSO - Executive Chef

Domino's Franchisee
13900 Palm Dr Ste E
Desert Hot Springs, CA 92240-5968

Telephone: (760) 251-1444
Type of Business: Chain Restaurant Operator
Total Sales: $26,703,000 (e)
Total Units: 13
Trade Names: Domino's (13)
Units Franchised From: 13
Primary Menu: Pizza (13)
Areas of Operation: CA
Type of Foodservice: Quick Serve (13)
Franchise Affiliation: Domino's Pizza Inc, ANN ARBOR, MI

Key Personnel
THOMAS E. NOWLAN - Owner; General Buyer

Ahi Mahi Enterprise LLC
1407 Copley Dr
Diamond Bar, CA 91765

Telephone: (909) 861-8868
Internet Homepage: ahipokibowl.com
Company Email: christine@ahipokibowl.com
Type of Business: Chain Restaurant Operator
Year Founded: 2016
Total Sales: $41,910,000 (e)
Total Units: 24
Trade Names: Ahipoki Bowl (24)
Company-Owned Units: 24
Primary Menu: American (24)
Areas of Operation: AZ, CA, WA
Type of Foodservice: Fast Casual (24)

Key Personnel
WING MAR - Owner
HENGKY HUANG - VP
RULLY KUSUMA - Corporate Chef; Executive Chef, Director Development

Ono Hawaiian BBQ
21700 Copley Dr Ste 320
Diamond Bar, CA 91765-5499

Telephone: (909) 895-4998
Fax Number: (909) 594-8388
Internet Homepage: onohawaiianbbq.com
Company Email: info@onobbq.com
Type of Business: Chain Restaurant Operator
Total Sales: $29,800,000 (e)
Average Check: Lunch(10); Dinner(10)
Total Units: 92
Trade Names: Ono Hawaiian BBQ (92)
Units Franchised To: 92
Primary Menu: Bar-B-Q (92)

Projected Openings: 10
Areas of Operation: AZ, CA
Type of Foodservice: Fast Casual (92)
Catering Services: Yes

Key Personnel
JOSHUA LIANG - CEO; General Buyer
JIM NG - Director Administration
ROBERT RAINE - Director Human Resources

C.G.P. Management Inc.
9231 Lakewood Blvd
Downey, CA 90240-2908

Mailing Address: PO Box 1246, DOWNEY, CA, 90240-0246
Telephone: (562) 923-2025
Fax Number: (562) 862-4362
Internet Homepage: chrisandpittsbbqrestaurants.com
Company Email: chrisandpittsbbq@aol.com
Type of Business: Chain Restaurant Operator
Year Founded: 1949
Total Sales: $5,594,000 (e)
Alcohol Sales: 3%
Number of Employees: 250
Average Check: Dinner(14)
Total Units: 3
Trade Names: Chris & Pitts Barbecue (3)
Company-Owned Units: 3
Preferred Square Footage: 2,800; 4,500
Preferred Location Types: Freestanding
Alcohol Served: Beer, Wine
Primary Menu: Bar-B-Q (3)
Areas of Operation: CA
Type of Foodservice: Casual Dining (3)
Catering Services: Yes
On-site Distribution Center: Yes
Primary Distributors: (Full Line) US Foods-Los Angeles, LA MIRADA, CA

Key Personnel
DEBBIE BERRY - President; General Buyer
GEORGE PELONIS - General Manager
PAT RODRIGUEZ - Manager Purchasing, Supply Chain

Domino's Franchisee
1802 Huntington Dr Ste 8
Duarte, CA 91010-2606

Telephone: (626) 359-3030
Type of Business: Chain Restaurant Operator
Total Sales: $4,049,000 (e)
Total Units: 2
Trade Names: Domino's (2)
Units Franchised From: 2
Primary Menu: Pizza (2)
Areas of Operation: CA
Type of Foodservice: Quick Serve (2)
Franchise Affiliation: Domino's Pizza Inc, ANN

ARBOR, MI

Key Personnel
NIKITA BEHM - Owner; General Buyer

SRA Venture Corp.
4920 Dublin Blvd Ste 340
Dublin, CA 94568

Telephone: (925) 875-1333
Type of Business: Chain Restaurant Operator
Total Sales: $1,202,000 (e)
Total Units: 2
Trade Names: Cold Stone Creamery (2)
Units Franchised From: 2
Primary Menu: Snacks (2)
Areas of Operation: CA
Type of Foodservice: Quick Serve (2)
Franchise Affiliation: Kahala Brands, SCOTTSDALE, AZ

Key Personnel
SYED RIZWAN - Partner
SAIRA RIZWAN - Partner

Strizzi's Restaurants
7950 Dublin Blvd Ste 109
Dublin, CA 94568-2966

Telephone: (925) 551-3399
Fax Number: (925) 551-3351
Internet Homepage: rigatonis.com; strizzis.com
Company Email: comments@rigatonis.com
Type of Business: Chain Restaurant Operator
Year Founded: 1986
Total Sales: $8,360,000 (e)
Alcohol Sales: 20%
Number of Employees: 150
Average Check: Lunch(14); Dinner(22)
Internet Order Processing: Yes
Total Units: 6
Trade Names: Rigatoni's Fresh Italian Grill (3); Strizzi's Restaurant (3)
Company-Owned Units: 6
Preferred Square Footage: 5,500; 6,000
Preferred Location Types: Downtown; Freestanding
Alcohol Served: Beer, Wine
Primary Menu: Italian (6)
Areas of Operation: CA
Type of Foodservice: Casual Dining (3); Fine Dining (3)
Primary Distributors: (Food) US Foods-San Francisco, LIVERMORE, CA

Key Personnel
RAY BARTOLOMUCCI - President; CFO; Executive Chef; Director Purchasing, Facility/Maintenance, Real Estate, Design, Research & Development, Product Development, Menu Development; General Buyer
TIM LUDDEN - VP Operations
LIZ PURSELLE - Manager Human Resources

Ground Zero Management
12569 Limonite Ave Ste 320
Eastvale, CA 91752-3674

Telephone: (951) 360-6453
Type of Business: Chain Restaurant Operator
Total Sales: $4,332,000 (e)
Total Units: 3
Trade Names: Jersey Mike's Subs (3)
Units Franchised From: 3
Primary Menu: Sandwiches/Deli (3)
Areas of Operation: CA
Type of Foodservice: Quick Serve (3)
Franchise Affiliation: Jersey Mike's Franchise Systems, MANASQUAN, NJ

Key Personnel
GILBERT RUBALCABA - Owner; General Buyer

Pizza Enterprises, Inc.
936 Broadway
El Cajon, CA 92021-4705

Telephone: (619) 442-1045
Fax Number: (619) 442-9262
Internet Homepage: dominossandiego.com
Company Email: Emiessner@msn.com
Type of Business: Chain Restaurant Operator
Total Sales: $8,323,000 (e)
Internet Order Processing: Yes
Total Units: 4
Trade Names: Domino's (4)
Units Franchised From: 4
Primary Menu: Pizza (4)
Areas of Operation: CA
Type of Foodservice: Quick Serve (4)
Franchise Affiliation: Domino's Pizza Inc, ANN ARBOR, MI

Key Personnel
ERIC MIESSNER - President; General Buyer

R & B Pizza Inc.
111 W Washington Ave
El Cajon, CA 92020-5135

Telephone: (619) 444-0010
Type of Business: Chain Restaurant Operator
Total Sales: $6,100,000 (e)
Total Units: 5
Trade Names: Little Caesars Pizza (5)
Units Franchised From: 5
Primary Menu: Pizza (5)
Areas of Operation: CA
Type of Foodservice: Quick Serve (5)
Franchise Affiliation: Little Caesar Enterprises Inc., DETROIT, MI

Key Personnel
RAY REBAHIM - Owner; General Buyer

Transwest Corral
2018 N Imperial Ave
El Centro, CA 92243-1323

Telephone: (760) 336-0009
Fax Number: (760) 336-2417
Type of Business: Chain Restaurant Operator
Total Sales: $14,368,000 (e)
Number of Employees: 120
Average Check: Breakfast(12); Lunch(14); Dinner(16)
Total Units: 3
Trade Names: Golden Corral Buffet & Grill (3)
Units Franchised From: 3
Primary Menu: American (3)
Areas of Operation: CA
Type of Foodservice: Family Restaurant (3)
Franchise Affiliation: Golden Corral Corp., RALEIGH, NC
Primary Distributors: (Full Line) McLane/Tracy, TRACY, CA

Key Personnel
MICHAEL J. HANSON - Partner; General Buyer
MAYUR PAVAGADHI - Partner
BLANCHA SALDANA - General Manager

Nation's Foodservice Inc.
11090 San Pablo Ave Ste 200
El Cerrito, CA 94530-2365

Telephone: (510) 237-1952
Fax Number: (510) 237-2348
Internet Homepage: nationsrestaurants.com
Type of Business: Chain Restaurant Operator
Year Founded: 1952
Total Sales: $43,680,000 (e)
Number of Employees: 580
Average Check: Breakfast(12); Lunch(12); Dinner(12)
Total Units: 29
Trade Names: Nation's Giant Hamburgers (29)
Company-Owned Units: 29
Preferred Square Footage: 3,000
Preferred Location Types: Freestanding; Strip Mall
Primary Menu: Hamburger (29)
Areas of Operation: CA
Type of Foodservice: Quick Serve (29)

Key Personnel
GRANT POWER - CEO; President
JOANNE WILSON - Director

Facility/Maintenance, Real Estate, Design; Buyer Kitchen Equipment
MONICA SULLIVAN - Director Human Resources, Training
MICHELLE SERRANO - Manager Human Resources

KFC Franchise
3814 Peck Rd
El Monte, CA 91732-2241

Telephone: (626) 443-1367
Fax Number: (626) 443-1368
Type of Business: Chain Restaurant Operator
Total Sales: $7,647,000 (e)
Total Units: 4
Trade Names: KFC (4)
Units Franchised From: 4
Primary Menu: Chicken (4)
Areas of Operation: CA
Type of Foodservice: Quick Serve (4)
Franchise Affiliation: KFC Corporation, LOUISVILLE, KY

Key Personnel
JOSE DIAZ - President; General Buyer

ARGO Hospitality Services, Inc.
4080 San Pablo Dam Rd
El Sobrante, CA 94803-2952

Telephone: (510) 223-3354
Type of Business: Chain Restaurant Operator
Total Sales: $5,542,000 (e)
Total Units: 2
Trade Names: Jack in the Box (2)
Units Franchised From: 2
Primary Menu: Hamburger (2)
Areas of Operation: CA
Type of Foodservice: Quick Serve (2)
Franchise Affiliation: Jack in the Box Restaurants, SAN DIEGO, CA

Key Personnel
AUSTIN TORRES - Owner; General Buyer

Brand Equity Development
9135 W Stockton Blvd
Elk Grove, CA 95758-8052

Telephone: (916) 683-2200
Fax Number: (916) 683-2229
Internet Homepage: stevespizza.com
Company Email: spi@stevespizza.com
Type of Business: Chain Restaurant Operator
Year Founded: 1978
Total Sales: $12,099,000 (e)
Alcohol Sales: 5%
Number of Employees: 115
Average Check: Lunch(14); Dinner(20)
Total Units: 4
Trade Names: Steve's Pizza (4)
Company-Owned Units: 4
Preferred Location Types: Freestanding
Alcohol Served: Beer, Wine
Primary Menu: Italian (4)
Areas of Operation: CA
Type of Foodservice: Casual Dining (4)
Catering Services: Yes
Primary Distributors: (Food) Tony's Fine Foods, WEST SACRAMENTO, CA

Key Personnel
CATHY WILKINSON - Consultant
STEVEN WILKINSON - Consultant

CALJAX, INC.
2368 Maritime Dr Ste 100
Elk Grove, CA 95758-3655

Telephone: (916) 392-3000
Type of Business: Chain Restaurant Operator
Total Sales: $49,710,000 (e)
Total Units: 20
Trade Names: Jack in the Box (20)
Units Franchised From: 20
Primary Menu: Hamburger (20)
Areas of Operation: CA
Type of Foodservice: Quick Serve (20)
Franchise Affiliation: Jack in the Box Restaurants, SAN DIEGO, CA

Key Personnel
METRI LUTFI - President; General Buyer

SMART MANAGEMENT & CO., INC.
2368 Maritime Dr Ste 100
Elk Grove, CA 95758-3655

Telephone: (916) 392-3000
Fax Number: (916) 428-2795
Internet Homepage: marlugroup.com
Type of Business: Chain Restaurant Operator
Total Sales: $248,050,000 (e)
Number of Employees: 4,098
Average Check: Dinner(8)
Total Units: 135
Trade Names: Arby's (47); Church's Chicken (36); Little Caesars Pizza (38); TGI Friday (14)
Units Franchised From: 135
Preferred Square Footage: 1,850
Alcohol Served: Beer, Wine
Primary Menu: American (14); Chicken (36); Pizza (38); Sandwiches/Deli (47)
Projected Remodelings: 22
Areas of Operation: CA, NV, OR, TX, WA
Type of Foodservice: Casual Dining (14); Quick Serve (121)
Franchise Affiliation: Arby's Restaurant Group, ATLANTA, GA; Church's Chicken, ATLANTA, GA; T.G.I. Friday's Inc., DALLAS, TX
Notes: MarLu also operates 8 Sears Appliance Showrooms, 6 Sears Hardware & Appliance.

Key Personnel
TONY LUTFI - CEO; President
STEVE SPACEK - CFO
NADER LUTFI - VP Business Development
SUSAN SCOTT - Controller
JODEE PHILLIPS - Director Operations
CHERYL JONES - Manager Operations, Region

The Munirs Company
9170 E Stockton Blvd
Elk Grove, CA 95624

Telephone: (916) 686-4901
Type of Business: Chain Restaurant Operator
Total Sales: $77,730,000 (e)
Total Units: 25
Trade Names: IHOP (25)
Units Franchised From: 25
Primary Menu: American (25)
Areas of Operation: CA
Type of Foodservice: Family Restaurant (25)
Franchise Affiliation: IHOP Restaurant System, GLENDALE, CA

Key Personnel
TARIQ MUNIR - President; General Buyer

Peet's Coffee & Tea Inc.
1400 Park Ave
Emeryville, CA 94608-3520

Mailing Address: PO Box 12509, BERKELEY, CA, 94712-3509
Telephone: (510) 594-2100
Fax Number: (510) 594-2180
Internet Homepage: peets.com
Type of Business: Chain Restaurant Operator
Year Founded: 1966
Systemwide Sales: $449,967,000 (e)
Total Sales: $802,284,000 (e)
Number of Employees: 4,688
Average Check: Breakfast(6); Lunch(6); Dinner(6)
Internet Order Processing: Yes
Internet Sales: 5.00%
Total Units: 339
Trade Names: Peet's (339)
Company-Owned Units: 339
Preferred Square Footage: 1,500; 2,500
Preferred Location Types: Downtown; Freestanding; Grocery Stores; Hotel/Motel; Kiosk; Lifestyle Center; Office Complex
Primary Menu: Coffee (339)

Areas of Operation: CA, CO, DC, IL, MA, MD, OR, VA, WA
Type of Foodservice: Quick Serve (339)
Foodservice Management Venues: Business & Industry; College & University
On-site Distribution Center: Yes
Primary Distributors: (Full Line) Buy-Rite Wholesale, GLENDALE HEIGHTS, IL
Parent Company: JAB Holding Company, LUDWIGSHAFEN, GER
Headquarter Offices: Intelligentsia Coffee, Inc., CHICAGO, IL; Stumptown Coffee Roasters, PORTLAND, OR
Notes: The company derives approximately 39% of its revenue from wholesale, online & mail order sales; foodservice revenues include retail sales of whole bean coffee & related products as well as prepared beverages in retail locations. Total store count does not include licensed locations.

Key Personnel
ELIOT JORDAN - President
ERIC LAUTERBACH - President Consumer Insights
ALLAN SMITH - CIO
DOUG WELSH - VP Coffee/Tea
ROBYN QUINTAL - Senior Director Operations, Development, Foodservice
DONNIE DIAZ - Senior Director Information Technology
TOM CLARK - Director Development
EVERETT LITTLE - Director Finance, Supply Chain
MIKE MACARTHUR - Director Operations, Sales
PHIL MALONEY - Director Purchasing-Coffee/Tea
JOERG PEDERSEN - Director Quality Assurance, Research & Development
DENNIS ALBRECHT - Regional Director Sales
ERICA HESS - Senior Manager Public Relations
PATRICK MAIN - Senior Manager Research & Development-Beverages
CHRIS LOVERME - Senior Manager Marketing, E-Commerce
STEFANIE M - Senior Manager Human Resources
KELLY NIELSEN - Senior Manager Benefits
KENDRA ROM - Manager
ZOHRE LOWRY - Manager
LISA MITCHELL - Manager
SHANNON JOHNSON - Manager
CHARLES DALE - Manager Safety-Food
ERA BATMANIS - Manager Human Resources
DEBRA CALVAN - Manager
LINDA CHAO - Manager Digital

Burgerim
16861 Ventura Blvd Ste 303
Encino, CA 91436-1765

Telephone: (818) 650-8307
Internet Homepage: burgerim.com
Company Email: office@iburgerim.com
Type of Business: Chain Restaurant Operator
Total Sales: $50,810,000 (e)
Total Units: 97
Trade Names: Burgerim (97)
Company-Owned Units: 1
Units Franchised To: 96
Primary Menu: Hamburger (97)
Projected Openings: 191
Areas of Operation: AL, AZ, CA, CO, CT, DC, FL, GA, IL, IN, KS, KY, LA, MA, MI, MO, NC, NE, NH, NV, NY, OH, OR, PA, SC, TN, TX, VA, WA, WV
Type of Foodservice: Quick Serve (97)

Key Personnel
JANAE GILLIAM - Chief Business Development Officer
JESUS ESTRADA - Director Franchising
MUHAMMAD RIAZ - Director Operations
JOHN BARKER - Project Manager Construction

California Chicken Cafe
17525 Ventura Blvd Ste 304
Encino, CA 91316-5169

Telephone: (818) 530-4880
Fax Number: (818) 530-4890
Internet Homepage: californiachickencafe.com
Type of Business: Chain Restaurant Operator
Year Founded: 1990
Total Sales: $11,570,000 (e)
Number of Employees: 200
Average Check: Breakfast(8); Lunch(8); Dinner(8)
Total Units: 8
Trade Names: California Chicken Cafe (8)
Company-Owned Units: 8
Preferred Square Footage: 2,500
Preferred Location Types: Freestanding
Primary Menu: Chicken (8)
Areas of Operation: CA
Type of Foodservice: Quick Serve (8)
Catering Services: Yes
Primary Distributors: (Full Line) SYSCO Food Services of San Francisco Inc., FREMONT, CA

Key Personnel
ANDRE DEMONTESQUIOU - President; Executive Chef; Manager Finance, Operations, Real Estate, Design, Human Resources; General Buyer
BRIAN STRASBURGER - Director Development, Training, Recruitment

Menchie's Group Inc.
17555 Ventura Blvd Ste 200
Encino, CA 91316-3890

Telephone: (818) 708-0316
Fax Number: (818) 708-0117
Internet Homepage: menchies.com
Company Email: info@menchies.com
Type of Business: Chain Restaurant Operator
Systemwide Sales: $294,779,000 (e)
Total Sales: $22,490,000 (e)
Number of Employees: 125
Total Units: 440
Trade Names: Menchie's (539); MidiCi Neapolitan Pizza (33)
Company-Owned Units: 2
Units Franchised To: 570
Preferred Square Footage: 1,000; 2,000
Preferred Location Types: Airports; Downtown; Strip Mall
Primary Menu: Pizza (33); Snacks (539)
Projected Openings: 2
Areas of Operation: AK, AL, AR, AZ, CA, CO, DC, FL, GA, HI, IA, IL, KY, LA, MD, ME, MN, MS, MT, NC, ND, NE, NH, NM, NV, NY, OH, OK, OR, PA, RI, SC, SD, TN, TX, UT, VA, VT, WA, WV, WY, BC, ON
Foreign Countries: AUSTRALIA; CANADA; JAPAN
Type of Foodservice: Fast Casual (33); Quick Serve (539)

Key Personnel
ELIE BALAS - Chairman; Director Business Development
DANNA CALDWELL - Co-Founder; President
ADAM CALDWELL - Co-Founder; COO
AMIT KLEINBERGER - CEO
YOTAM REGEV - COO
TOM REGEV - VP Operations
LYDIA WARDLE - VP Supply Chain
KRISTIN BELG - VP
ELIZABETH BERRY - Senior Director Marketing
MJ K - Senior Director Business Development, Franchise Sales
LAURA BALDWIN - Director Research & Development
GARY HUNTER - Director Foodservice
LYNN ALIMENT - Director Real Estate
CONNOR JEFFRIES - Director Operations
MAIRA ZAVALA - Manager Development

OLS Hotels and Resorts
16000 Ventura Blvd Ste 1010
Encino, CA 91436-2762

Telephone: (818) 905-8280
Fax Number: (818) 905-7786
Internet Homepage: olshotels.com
Company Email: info@outrigger.net
Type of Business: Foodservice Operations -

Hotel/Motels
Year Founded: 1988
Total Sales: $196,610,000 (e)
Alcohol Sales: 20%
Number of Employees: 1,200
Total Units: 20
Restaurants in Hotels: 8
Trade Names: B.W. Plus Orlando Gateway Hotel (1); Banyan Harbor Resort (1); Chamberlain West Hollywood (1); Grafton on Sunset (1); Harbor Court Hotel(1); Hilton Garden Inn Denver Airport (1); Hotel Amarano (1); Hotel Modera (1); Hotel Triton (1); Jackson Hole Lodge (1); Le Montrose Suite Hotel (1); Le Parc Suite Hotel (1); Marin Suites Hotel (1); Plantation Hale Suites (1); The Carriage House (1); The Gateway (1); The Hideaway (1); Volcano House (1); W Hotel Winters (1); White Sands Hotel (1)
Company-Owned Units: 8
Alcohol Served: Beer, Wine, Liquor
Areas of Operation: CA, CO, FL, HI, NV, OR, WY
Type of Foodservice: Casual Dining (8)
Primary Distributors: (Food) SYSCO Food Services of San Francisco Inc., FREMONT, CA
Notes: The company derives approximately 80% of its revenue from hotel operations.

Key Personnel
MARTTI MANNOJA - COO; Exec VP; Controller; Manager Information Systems
CLAUDIA JACKSON - VP Operations
SARIE MANNOJA - Manager Human Resources

Warner Food Mangement, Inc.
4917 Genesta Ave
Encino, CA 91316-3438

Telephone: (818) 285-2160
Type of Business: Chain Restaurant Operator
Total Sales: $352,620,000 (e)
Total Units: 140
Trade Names: Jack in the Box (140)
Units Franchised From: 140
Primary Menu: Hamburger (140)
Areas of Operation: CA, CO
Type of Foodservice: Quick Serve (140)
Franchise Affiliation: Jack in the Box Restaurants, SAN DIEGO, CA

Key Personnel
SUDESH SOOD - President
PAUL RENYER - Director Finance
JOSE RUIZ - Director Asset Protection

AMUR, LLC
200 E Via Rancho Pkwy Ste 425
Escondido, CA 92025-8010

Telephone: (760) 738-2018
Type of Business: Chain Restaurant Operator
Total Sales: $740,000 (e)
Total Units: 2
Trade Names: Cinnabon (2)
Units Franchised From: 2
Primary Menu: Snacks (2)
Areas of Operation: CA
Type of Foodservice: Quick Serve (2)
Franchise Affiliation: Cinnabon Inc., ATLANTA, GA

Key Personnel
MARTIN LOPEZ - Owner; General Buyer
VIR UPADHYAY - General Manager

HOOTWinc LLC
508 W Mission Ave Ste 101
Escondido, CA 92025-1606

Telephone: (760) 966-3000
Fax Number: (619) 481-3951
Internet Homepage: westcoasthooters.com
Company Email: hr@hootwinc.com
Type of Business: Chain Restaurant Operator
Year Founded: 1993
Total Sales: $38,280,000 (e)
Alcohol Sales: 25%
Number of Employees: 527
Average Check: Lunch(10); Dinner(14)
Total Units: 9
Trade Names: Hooters (9)
Units Franchised From: 9
Preferred Square Footage: 3,800
Preferred Location Types: Freestanding; Other
Alcohol Served: Beer, Wine, Liquor
Primary Menu: American (9)
Areas of Operation: CA
Type of Foodservice: Casual Dining (9)
Catering Services: Yes
Franchise Affiliation: HOA Restaurant Group LLC, ATLANTA, GA

Key Personnel
D J MOSS - CFO
DEBRA GERNES - Director Human Resources
JACKLYN KIM - Bookkeeper

St. Mar Enterprises Inc.
627 N Escondido Blvd
Escondido, CA 92025-1701

Telephone: (760) 743-2479
Fax Number: (760) 743-1590
Company Email: stmarinc@aol.com
Type of Business: Chain Restaurant Operator
Year Founded: 1981
Total Sales: $30,270,000 (e)
Number of Employees: 425
Average Check: Lunch(8); Dinner(8)
Total Units: 11
Trade Names: Taco Bell (11)
Units Franchised From: 11
Preferred Square Footage: 2,500
Preferred Location Types: Community Mall; Freestanding
Primary Menu: Taco (11)
Areas of Operation: CA
Type of Foodservice: Quick Serve (11)
Franchise Affiliation: Taco Bell Corp., IRVINE, CA
Primary Distributors: (Full Line) McLane/High Plains, LUBBOCK, TX

Key Personnel
ROBERT ST JOHN - President; Controller; Director Finance, Facility/Maintenance, Information Systems, Real Estate

AW Malik, Inc.
12340 Highland Ave Ste B
Etiwanda, CA 91739-1578

Telephone: (909) 646-9512
Type of Business: Chain Restaurant Operator
Total Sales: $12,360,000 (e)
Total Units: 5
Trade Names: Jack in the Box (5)
Units Franchised From: 5
Primary Menu: Hamburger (5)
Areas of Operation: CA
Type of Foodservice: Quick Serve (5)
Franchise Affiliation: Jack in the Box Restaurants, SAN DIEGO, CA

Key Personnel
ASLAM MALIK - Owner; General Buyer

Indmex Corporation
1620 Broadway
Eureka, CA 95501-0136

Telephone: (707) 476-0477
Type of Business: Chain Restaurant Operator
Total Sales: $67,160,000 (e)
Total Units: 27
Trade Names: Jack in the Box (27)
Units Franchised From: 27
Primary Menu: Hamburger (27)
Areas of Operation: CA
Type of Foodservice: Quick Serve (27)
Franchise Affiliation: Jack in the Box Restaurants, SAN DIEGO, CA

Key Personnel
SHILPA GOGRI - Owner; General Buyer

Redwood Restaurants
710 E St Ste 136
Eureka, CA 95501-1853

Telephone: (707) 442-8488
Fax Number: (707) 442-0864
Internet Homepage: cafemarina.net; samoacookhouse.net
Type of Business: Chain Restaurant Operator
Year Founded: 1951
Total Sales: $14,924,000 (e)
Alcohol Sales: 8%
Number of Employees: 150
Average Check: Lunch(14); Dinner(32)
Total Units: 3
Trade Names: Cafe Marina (1); Henderson Center Fresh Freeze Drive-In (1); Samoa Cookhouse (1)
Company-Owned Units: 3
Preferred Location Types: Freestanding
Alcohol Served: Beer, Wine, Liquor
Primary Menu: American (3)
Areas of Operation: CA
Type of Foodservice: Fine Dining (2); Quick Serve (1)
Catering Services: Yes
Primary Distributors: (Full Line) SYSCO Food Services of San Francisco Inc., FREMONT, CA

Key Personnel
STEVEN DOLFINI - President; CFO; Executive Chef; Manager Marketing
STEVEN GRAHAM - VP Operations, Purchasing
PAULA HAMILTON - Manager Human Resources

Brian W. Emry
8100 Greenback Ln
Fair Oaks, CA 95628-2503

Telephone: (916) 723-5947
Type of Business: Chain Restaurant Operator
Total Sales: $5,453,000 (e)
Total Units: 2
Trade Names: Jack in the Box (2)
Units Franchised From: 2
Primary Menu: Hamburger (2)
Areas of Operation: CA
Type of Foodservice: Quick Serve (2)
Franchise Affiliation: Jack in the Box Restaurants, SAN DIEGO, CA

Key Personnel
BRIAN EMRY - Owner; General Buyer

PRB Management LLC
4709 Mangels Blvd
Fairfield, CA 94534-4175

Telephone: (707) 864-2919
Fax Number: (707) 864-3301
Type of Business: Chain Restaurant Operator
Year Founded: 1984
Total Sales: $92,160,000 (e)
Number of Employees: 630
Average Check: Lunch(8); Dinner(8)
Total Units: 33
Trade Names: Taco Bell (33)
Units Franchised From: 33
Preferred Square Footage: 2,500
Preferred Location Types: Freestanding
Primary Menu: Chicken (33); Taco (33)
Areas of Operation: CA
Type of Foodservice: Quick Serve (33)
Franchise Affiliation: KFC Corporation, LOUISVILLE, KY; Taco Bell Corp., IRVINE, CA
Primary Distributors: (Food) McLane/Shawnee, SHAWNEE, KS

Key Personnel
RITA BASRA - President; CFO; Manager Purchasing, Real Estate; General Buyer
SHERRI DANIELS - Controller; Manager Accounting, Risk Management, Human Resources
DAVE FULWILER - Director
ANDREW HERNANDEZ - Director Operations

White Family Enterprises, Inc.
1061 S Main Ave
Fallbrook, CA 92028-3338

Telephone: (760) 535-9912
Type of Business: Chain Restaurant Operator
Total Sales: $1,954,000 (e)
Total Units: 3
Trade Names: Little Caesars Pizza (3)
Units Franchised From: 3
Primary Menu: Pizza (3)
Areas of Operation: CA
Type of Foodservice: Quick Serve (3)
Franchise Affiliation: Little Caesar Enterprises Inc., DETROIT, MI

Key Personnel
TIMOTHY WHITE - President; General Buyer

VTP Enterprises
1660 N Farmersville Blvd
Farmersville, CA 93223

Telephone: (559) 625-4887
Fax Number: (559) 651-3225
Type of Business: Chain Restaurant Operator
Total Sales: $67,620,000 (e)
Total Units: 27
Trade Names: Jack in the Box (27)
Units Franchised From: 27
Primary Menu: Hamburger (27)
Areas of Operation: CA
Type of Foodservice: Quick Serve (27)
Franchise Affiliation: Jack in the Box Restaurants, SAN DIEGO, CA

Key Personnel
FREDERICK GIBBY - Partner; General Buyer
PATRICE ROUX - Partner

Jimboy's North America LLC
80 Iron Point Cir Ste 105
Folsom, CA 95630-8592

Telephone: (916) 934-5100
Fax Number: (916) 934-5110
Internet Homepage: jimboystacos.com
Type of Business: Chain Restaurant Operator
Year Founded: 1954
Systemwide Sales: $72,704,000 (e)
Total Sales: $23,744,000 (e)
Alcohol Sales: 1%
Number of Employees: 75
Average Check: Lunch(10); Dinner(12)
Internet Order Processing: Yes
Total Units: 43
Trade Names: Jimboy's Tacos (43)
Company-Owned Units: 3
Units Franchised To: 40
Preferred Square Footage: 2,000
Preferred Location Types: Freestanding; Strip Mall
Alcohol Served: Beer
Primary Menu: Mexican (43)
Areas of Operation: CA, GA, NV
Type of Foodservice: Quick Serve (43)
Primary Distributors: (Full Line) SYSCO Food Services of San Diego Inc., POWAY, CA

Key Personnel
KAREN KNUDSON-FREEMAN - President Group; Director Quality Assurance, Supply Chain
DINA GUILLEN - Director Marketing
JENNY DAVIS - Manager Information Technology

Rishtaa Inc.
2791 E Bidwell St Ste 1000
Folsom, CA 95630-6412

Telephone: (916) 817-2776
Type of Business: Chain Restaurant Operator
Total Sales: $1,230,000 (e)
Total Units: 2
Trade Names: Cold Stone Creamery (2)

Units Franchised From: 2
Primary Menu: Snacks (2)
Areas of Operation: CA
Type of Foodservice: Quick Serve (2)
Franchise Affiliation: Kahala Brands, SCOTTSDALE, AZ

Key Personnel
NIRAJ PATEL - Partner; General Buyer
NEHA PATEL - Partner; General Buyer

Knowlwood Enterprises
17654 Newhope St Ste H
Fountain Valley, CA 92708-4294

Mailing Address: P.O. Box 9448, Fountain Valley, Ca, 927728
Telephone: (714) 429-9356
Fax Number: (714) 429-9214
Internet Homepage: knowlwoodrestaurants.com
Company Email: info@knowlwoodrestaurants.com
Type of Business: Chain Restaurant Operator
Year Founded: 1957
Total Sales: $4,214,000 (e)
Alcohol Sales: 5%
Number of Employees: 100
Average Check: Dinner(8)
Total Units: 4
Trade Names: Knowlwood (4)
Company-Owned Units: 4
Preferred Square Footage: 3,000
Preferred Location Types: Freestanding
Alcohol Served: Beer, Wine
Primary Menu: Hamburger (4)
Areas of Operation: CA
Type of Foodservice: Quick Serve (4)
Catering Services: Yes
Primary Distributors: (Food) Driftwood Dairy, EL MONTE, CA

Key Personnel
THANH D. NGUYEN - President; General Manager; Executive Chef; General Buyer

S & G Foods Inc
9436 Warner Ave
Fountain Valley, CA 92708-2825

Telephone: (714) 968-9846
Type of Business: Chain Restaurant Operator
Total Sales: $3,341,000 (e)
Total Units: 2
Trade Names: Del Taco (2)
Units Franchised From: 2
Primary Menu: Taco (2)
Areas of Operation: CA
Type of Foodservice: Quick Serve (2)
Franchise Affiliation: Del Taco Restaurants Inc., LAKE FOREST, CA

Key Personnel
M. H. SAHMOEDINI - President; General Buyer

Starbucks Western/Pacific Zone
17850 Newhope St Ste 101
Fountain Valley, CA 92708-5410

Telephone: (714) 979-5374
Fax Number: (714) 885-3983
Listing Type: Divisional Office
Type of Business: Chain Restaurant Operator
Number of Employees: 80
Total Units: 1,900
Areas of Operation: AZ, CA, HI, OR, WA
Parent Company: Starbucks Corporation, SEATTLE, WA

Key Personnel
DOUG STEVENS - General Counsel
DEBBIE PETERSEN - Senior Manager Construction
CINDY FREELS - Manager Store Development

The Boiling Crab
16027 Brookhurst St Ste G-168
Fountain Valley, CA 92708-1551

Telephone: (714) 554-6181
Internet Homepage: theboilingcrab.com
Company Email: contact@theboilingcrab.com
Type of Business: Chain Restaurant Operator
Year Founded: 2004
Total Units: 19
Trade Names: The Boiling Crab (19)
Company-Owned Units: 19
Primary Menu: Seafood (19)
Areas of Operation: CA, NV, TX
Type of Foodservice: Casual Dining (19)

Key Personnel
DADA NGO - CEO
DAVID NGUYEN - VP Operations
BILL KILMER - Controller
WINNIE VU - Director Marketing
JULIE TRAN - Regional Director
MELISSA KILL - Manager Human Resources

Bobby Salazar's Mexican Foods Inc.
2810 San Antonio Dr
Fowler, CA 93625-9799

Telephone: (559) 834-4787
Fax Number: (559) 834-2738
Internet Homepage: bobbysalazar.com
Company Email: info@bobbysalazar.com
Type of Business: Chain Restaurant Operator
Year Founded: 1995
Systemwide Sales: $15,768,000 (e)
Total Sales: $9,986,000 (e)
Alcohol Sales: 10%
Number of Employees: 95
Average Check: Breakfast(8); Lunch(12); Dinner(16)
Total Units: 7
Trade Names: Bobby Salazar's Mexican Restaurant & Cantina (3); Bobby Salazar's Taqueria (3); Bobby Salazar's Taqueria Express (1)
Company-Owned Units: 7
Preferred Square Footage: 2,500; 5,500; 6,000
Preferred Location Types: Convenience Store/Gas Station; Discount Dept. Stores; Freestanding; Stadiums
Alcohol Served: Beer, Wine, Liquor
Primary Menu: Mexican (7)
Areas of Operation: CA
Type of Foodservice: Casual Dining (6); Quick Serve (1)
Distribution Centers: FOWLER, CA
On-site Distribution Center: Yes
Primary Distributors: (Full Line) SYSCO Food Services of Central California Inc., MODESTO, CA
Notes: The company derives approximately 30% of its revenue from retail sales of its products through grocery and convenience stores.

Key Personnel
BOBBY SALAZAR - President; Controller; Director Finance, Design, Human Resources, Store Fixtures, Menu Development; General Buyer
CHARLES GAMOIAN - VP Franchise Operations, Supply Chain, Real Estate
WENDY DOUGLAS - Director Franchise Development
ELENA JUAREZ - Manager Manufacturing, Food Safety
LAURA NAVARRO - Manager Distribution, Warehouse, Production-Food

AB Management
42307 Osgood Rd Ste N
Fremont, CA 94539-5062

Telephone: (510) 651-2792
Type of Business: Chain Restaurant Operator
Total Sales: $14,757,000 (e)
Total Units: 3
Trade Names: McDonald's (3)
Units Franchised From: 3
Preferred Location Types: Freestanding
Primary Menu: Hamburger (3)
Areas of Operation: CA
Type of Foodservice: Quick Serve (3)

Franchise Affiliation: McDonald's Corporation, CHICAGO, IL

Key Personnel
MARK BERNARDIN - President; General Buyer

Devika Restaurants Inc.
44816 S Grimmer Blvd
Fremont, CA 94538-6328

Telephone: (510) 490-9717
Fax Number: (510) 490-9718
Type of Business: Chain Restaurant Operator
Total Sales: $36,420,000 (e)
Total Units: 16
Trade Names: Denny's (11); Jack in the Box (5)
Units Franchised From: 16
Primary Menu: American (11); Hamburger (5)
Areas of Operation: CA
Type of Foodservice: Family Restaurant (11); Quick Serve (5)
Franchise Affiliation: Jack in the Box Restaurants, SAN DIEGO, CA

Key Personnel
DEV SAGAR - Owner; General Buyer

Walin Enterprises Inc
4376 Thornton Ave
Fremont, CA 94536-4828

Telephone: (510) 797-0770
Type of Business: Chain Restaurant Operator
Total Sales: $1,576,000 (e)
Total Units: 3
Trade Names: Little Caesars Pizza (3)
Units Franchised From: 3
Primary Menu: Pizza (3)
Areas of Operation: CA
Type of Foodservice: Quick Serve (3)
Franchise Affiliation: Little Caesar Enterprises Inc., DETROIT, MI

Key Personnel
TRINI ROMERO - President; General Buyer

Yadav Enterprises, Inc.
3550 Mowry Ave Ste 301
Fremont, CA 94538-1461

Telephone: (510) 792-3393
Fax Number: (510) 792-3350
Type of Business: Chain Restaurant Operator
Total Sales: $899,380,000 (e)
Alcohol Sales: 5%
Total Units: 491
Trade Names: Denny's (71); Jack in the Box (203); Sizzler (4); T.G.I. Friday's (65); Taco Cabana (148)
Company-Owned Units: 142
Units Franchised To: 6
Units Franchised From: 343
Preferred Square Footage: 2,800; 3,500
Alcohol Served: Beer, Wine
Primary Menu: American (136); Hamburger (203); Mexican (148); Steak (4)
Areas of Operation: CA, TX
Type of Foodservice: Casual Dining (69); Family Restaurant (71); Fast Casual (148); Quick Serve (203)
Franchise Affiliation: CBC Restaurant Corp., DALLAS, TX; Denny's Corporation, SPARTANBURG, SC; El Pollo Loco Inc., COSTA MESA, CA; Jack in the Box Restaurants, SAN DIEGO, CA; Sizzler USA Inc., MISSION VIEJO, CA; T.G.I. Friday's Inc., DALLAS, TX
Headquarter Offices: Taco Cabana Inc., SAN ANTONIO, TX
Notes: Formally operated as JIB Management Group before changing name to Yadav Enterprises, Inc.

Key Personnel
ANIL YADAV - Founder; CEO; President
RICHARD PAWLOWSKI - CFO
ANAMARIE MONTES - COO
DEAN KIMBALL - CIO
MICHAEL FLORES - VP Franchise Operations
ATOUR EYVAZIAN - VP Franchise Operations
BRIAN METEJKA - VP Marketing
TODD NONKEN - VP Marketing
BRIAN MATEJKA - VP Marketing
KEVIN KEVORKIAN - General Counsel
NEAL WILLIAMSON - Director Operations
ERIC O'BRIEN - Director Operations
MARCO RIVERA - Director Operations
SYLVIA SICAIROS - Director Operations
CHAD BAITY - Director Operations
MARY BEAUDRO - Director Safety, Risk Management
BERNARDITA FABRE - Executive Assistant
MARTIN ARAUJO - Technician Information Technology

BJ's Kountry Kitchen Inc.
4539 N Brawley Ave Ste 105
Fresno, CA 93722-3950

Telephone: (559) 275-1981
Fax Number: (559) 275-8786
Internet Homepage: bjskountrykitchen.com
Type of Business: Chain Restaurant Operator
Year Founded: 1981
Systemwide Sales: $6,462,000 (e)
Total Sales: $4,308,000 (e)
Number of Employees: 40
Average Check: Breakfast(10); Lunch(12);
Total Units: 3
Trade Names: BJ's Kountry Kitchen (3)
Company-Owned Units: 3
Preferred Square Footage: 3,000
Preferred Location Types: Freestanding; Strip Mall
Primary Menu: American (3)
Areas of Operation: CA
Type of Foodservice: Family Restaurant (3)
Catering Services: Yes
Primary Distributors: (Full Line) SYSCO Food Services of Central California Inc., MODESTO, CA

Key Personnel
GARY HONEYCUTT - Chairman; General Buyer
JUDY KERR - President; Executive Chef

D. Boyd Enterprises Inc.
466 W Fallbrook Ave Ste 110
Fresno, CA 93711-6267

Telephone: (559) 449-0270
Fax Number: (559) 449-0603
Type of Business: Chain Restaurant Operator
Total Sales: $9,783,000 (e)
Average Check: Dinner(8)
Total Units: 8
Trade Names: Little Caesars Pizza (8)
Units Franchised From: 8
Preferred Square Footage: 1,600; 3,000
Preferred Location Types: Freestanding; Strip Mall
Primary Menu: Pizza (8)
Areas of Operation: CA
Type of Foodservice: Quick Serve (8)
Franchise Affiliation: Little Caesar Enterprises Inc., DETROIT, MI

Key Personnel
DONNA BOYD - President; General Buyer

Deli Delicious Franchising Inc.
2495 W Shaw Ave
Fresno, CA 93711-3302

Telephone: (877) 306-7079
Fax Number: (559) 435-1410
Internet Homepage: deli-delicious.com
Company Email: franchisesupport@deli-d.com
Type of Business: Chain Restaurant Operator
Total Sales: $31,610,000 (e)
Number of Employees: 540
Average Check: Lunch(12); Dinner(12)
Total Units: 54
Trade Names: Deli Delicious (54)
Units Franchised To: 54
Primary Menu: Sandwiches/Deli (54)
Projected Openings: 22
Areas of Operation: CA
Type of Foodservice: Quick Serve (54)

Key Personnel
MOHAMMAD HOBAB - President; General Buyer
ALI NEKUMANESH - Exec VP
FOAD SAFFARZADEH - Regional VP Operations
ELAINA NEWCOMB - Director Training

DiCicco's
2221 W Shaw Ave
Fresno, CA 93711-3408

Telephone: (559) 221-6338
Internet Homepage: diciccos.restaurants.com
Type of Business: Chain Restaurant Operator
Year Founded: 1956
Total Sales: $1,987,000 (e)
Average Check: Dinner(12)
Total Units: 5
Trade Names: DiCicco's (5)
Company-Owned Units: 5
Primary Menu: Italian (5)
Areas of Operation: CA
Type of Foodservice: Family Restaurant (5)

Key Personnel
JOANNA VITUCCI-LOPEZ - Owner; General Buyer

DiCicco's Italian Restaurants
144 N Blackstone Ave
Fresno, CA 93701-1911

Telephone: (559) 237-7054
Fax Number: (559) 497-6122
Internet Homepage: diciccos.com
Type of Business: Chain Restaurant Operator
Year Founded: 1956
Total Sales: $7,755,000 (e)
Alcohol Sales: 5%
Number of Employees: 400
Average Check: Lunch(14); Dinner(20)
Total Units: 6
Trade Names: DiCicco's Italian Restaurant & Pizzeria (6)
Company-Owned Units: 6
Preferred Square Footage: 3,000
Preferred Location Types: Freestanding; Strip Mall
Alcohol Served: Beer, Wine
Primary Menu: Italian (6)
Areas of Operation: CA
Type of Foodservice: Casual Dining (6)
Distribution Centers: FRESNO, CA
On-site Distribution Center: Yes
Primary Distributors: (Food) SYSCO Food Services of Central California Inc., MODESTO, CA

Key Personnel
JOHANA LOPEZ - Owner; General Buyer

JEM Management Corporation
312 W Cromwell Ave
Fresno, CA 93711-6113

Mailing Address: PO Box 25006, FRESNO, CA, 93729-5006
Telephone: (559) 435-9648
Fax Number: (559) 435-9612
Internet Homepage: jemmanagement.com
Type of Business: Chain Restaurant Operator
Year Founded: 1960
Total Sales: $146,030,000 (e)
Number of Employees: 1,770
Average Check: Lunch(8); Dinner(8)
Total Units: 55
Trade Names: KFC (14); Wendy's Old Fashioned Hamburgers (41)
Units Franchised From: 55
Preferred Square Footage: 3,000; 3,300
Preferred Location Types: Freestanding
Primary Menu: Chicken (14); Hamburger (42)
Projected Openings: 1
Areas of Operation: CA
Type of Foodservice: Quick Serve (55)
Franchise Affiliation: KFC Corporation, LOUISVILLE, KY; The Wendy's Company, DUBLIN, OH
Primary Distributors: (Full Line) McLane/Riverside, RIVERSIDE, CA

Key Personnel
KRIS SRUEBNER - Executive Director Administration, Marketing

Landon Investment Co Inc
2415 E Ashlan Ave
Fresno, CA 93726-3109

Telephone: (559) 224-2996
Type of Business: Chain Restaurant Operator
Total Sales: $9,304,000 (e)
Total Units: 3
Trade Names: Denny's (3)
Units Franchised From: 3
Primary Menu: American (3)
Areas of Operation: CA
Type of Foodservice: Family Restaurant (3)
Franchise Affiliation: Denny's Corporation, SPARTANBURG, SC

Key Personnel
MARC MCMAHAN - President; General Buyer

Le Boulanger The Baker, LLC
7080 N Whitney Ave Ste 103
Fresno, CA 93720-0154

Telephone: (559) 324-8535
Fax Number: (408) 523-9810
Internet Homepage: leboulanger.com
Company Email: info@leboulanger.com
Type of Business: Chain Restaurant Operator
Year Founded: 1981
Total Sales: $22,070,000 (e)
Number of Employees: 337
Average Check: Breakfast(8); Lunch(14);
Total Units: 8
Trade Names: Le Boulanger (8)
Company-Owned Units: 8
Preferred Square Footage: 5,500; 6,000
Preferred Location Types: Freestanding; Regional Mall; Strip Mall
Primary Menu: American (0); Sandwiches/Deli (8)
Projected Openings: 1
Areas of Operation: CA
Type of Foodservice: Casual Dining (8); Fast Casual (0)
Catering Services: Yes

Key Personnel
DAN BRUNELLO - CEO; President; Director Menu Development; General Buyer
LARRY CECCATO - VP Purchasing, Facility/Maintenance
JASON KILGORE - Director Product Development
MARIA ALEMAN - Director Retail Operations
ED KUSCH - Area Manager

Milano Restaurants International
6729 N Palm Ave Ste 200
Fresno, CA 93704-1077

Telephone: (559) 432-0399
Fax Number: (559) 432-0398
Internet Homepage: milano-ri.com
Type of Business: Chain Restaurant Operator
Year Founded: 1958
Systemwide Sales: $47,027,000 (e)
Total Sales: $51,810,000 (e)
Alcohol Sales: 5%
Number of Employees: 883
Average Check: Lunch(8); Dinner(8)
Total Units: 56
Trade Names: Blast & Brew (5); Me 'N' Ed's Coney Island Grill (1); Me 'N' Ed's Pizzeria (46); Me 'N' Ed's Victory Grill Cantina (1); Piazza del Pane (2); Vicory Grill (1)
Company-Owned Units: 56
Preferred Square Footage: 2,400
Preferred Location Types: Freestanding; Strip

Mall
Alcohol Served: Beer, Wine, Liquor
Primary Menu: American (1); Italian (2); Pizza (53)
Areas of Operation: CA, TX
Foreign Countries: CANADA
Type of Foodservice: Casual Dining (52); Fast Casual (2); Fine Dining (2)
Catering Services: Yes
Primary Distributors: (Food) Saladino's Inc., FRESNO, CA
Notes: The company derives approximately 1% of its revenue from commissary operations.

Key Personnel
JOHN A. FERDINANDI - Chairman; CEO; President; Executive Chef; Director Information Systems, Real Estate, Design
MARTA GREY - CFO
A. THOMAS FERDINANDI JR - COO; Exec VP; General Buyer
LISA NILMEIER - General Counsel; Manager Risk Management, Human Resources
JOHANAS SETYONO - Director Information Technology
CARL HEDSTROM - Director Facility/Maintenance, Store Fixtures

Subway Franchise
5677 E Kings Canyon Rd Ste 103
Fresno, CA 93727-4657

Telephone: (559) 252-6775
Internet Homepage: subway.com
Type of Business: Chain Restaurant Operator
Total Sales: $2,788,000 (e)
Total Units: 4
Trade Names: Subway (4)
Units Franchised From: 4
Primary Menu: Sandwiches/Deli (4)
Areas of Operation: CA
Type of Foodservice: Quick Serve (4)
Franchise Affiliation: Doctor's Associates Inc., MILFORD, CT

Key Personnel
PETER SINGH - President; General Buyer

Eddie Cheng Corporation
10040 Chapman Ave
Garden Grove, CA 92840-2821

Telephone: (714) 534-6433
Type of Business: Chain Restaurant Operator
Total Sales: $24,250,000 (e)
Total Units: 9
Trade Names: Wendy's Old Fashioned Hamburgers (9)
Units Franchised From: 9
Primary Menu: Hamburger (9)
Areas of Operation: CA
Type of Foodservice: Quick Serve (9)
Franchise Affiliation: The Wendy's Company, DUBLIN, OH

Key Personnel
EDDIE CHENG - President

Mr. Fries Man
14800 S. Western Ave. #108
Gardena, CA 90249

Telephone: (424) 292-3616
Internet Homepage: mrfriesman.com
Company Email: info@mrfriesman.com
Type of Business: Chain Restaurant Operator
Year Founded: 2017
Number of Employees: 150
Total Units: 14
Trade Names: Mr. Fries Man (14)
Company-Owned Units: 1
Units Franchised To: 13
Primary Menu: American (14)
Projected Openings: 4
Areas of Operation: CA, FL, GA, MD, NC, NV, SC, TX, UT
Type of Foodservice: Fast Casual (14)

Key Personnel
CRAIG BATISTE - Co-Founder
DOROTHY BATISTE - Co-Founder

Ramona's Restaurant Group LLC
13633 S Western Ave
Gardena, CA 90249

Telephone: (310) 323-1950
Internet Homepage: ramonas.com
Type of Business: Chain Restaurant Operator
Total Units: 5
Trade Names: Ramona's (5)
Company-Owned Units: 5
Primary Menu: Mexican (5)
Areas of Operation: CA
Type of Foodservice: Casual Dining (5)

Key Personnel
EDWARD MEDINA - CEO

Reins International USA
1225 W 190th St Ste 375
Gardena, CA 90248-4338

Telephone: (310) 532-1137
Fax Number: (310) 532-0236
Internet Homepage: gyu-kaku.com
Company Email: email@gyu-kaku.com
Type of Business: Chain Restaurant Operator
Year Founded: 2000
Total Sales: $23,140,000 (e)
Alcohol Sales: 15%
Number of Employees: 1,256
Average Check: Lunch(16); Dinner(24)
Total Units: 58
Trade Names: Gyu-Kaku (49); Gyu-Kaku Japanese BBQ (7)
Company-Owned Units: 56
Preferred Square Footage: 5,500; 6,000
Preferred Location Types: Freestanding; Regional Mall
Alcohol Served: Beer, Wine, Liquor
Primary Menu: Japanese (56)
Areas of Operation: CA, FL, GA, HI, IL, MA, NV, NY, PA, TX, VA, WA, FC
Foreign Countries: CANADA
Type of Foodservice: Casual Dining (56)
Primary Distributors: (Full Line) SYSCO Food Services of Los Angeles Inc., WALNUT, CA; (Full Line) Mutual Trading Co. Inc., LOS ANGELES, CA
Notes: VR Partners Inc. is a joint venture with Reins International, the Japan-based operator of more than 1,000 Gyu-Kaku restaurants.

Key Personnel
TOSHI HAYAKAWA - President; Owner; Executive Chef; Director Menu Development; General Buyer
AKI YAMAGUCHI - COO; VP; Director Finance, Operations, Purchasing, Supply Chain, Human Resources

RJMG Incorporated
15900 Crenshaw Blvd Ste E
Gardena, CA 90249-4875

Telephone: (310) 523-3390
Type of Business: Chain Restaurant Operator
Total Sales: $1,518,000 (e)
Total Units: 2
Trade Names: Subway (2)
Units Franchised From: 2
Primary Menu: Sandwiches/Deli (2)
Areas of Operation: CA
Type of Foodservice: Quick Serve (2)
Franchise Affiliation: Doctor's Associates Inc., MILFORD, CT

Key Personnel
ROBERT GILEWSKI - President; General Buyer

SushiBoy Inc.
18527 S Broadway
Gardena, CA 90248

Telephone: (310) 515-4800
Fax Number: (310) 515-4700
Internet Homepage: sushiboy.net
Type of Business: Chain Restaurant Operator

Total Sales: $3,608,000 (e)
Total Units: 5
Trade Names: Matsui (1); Mugimaru (1); Sushi Boy (3)
Company-Owned Units: 5
Preferred Location Types: Airports; Freestanding
Alcohol Served: Wine, Liquor
Primary Menu: Japanese (5)
Areas of Operation: CA
Type of Foodservice: Fast Casual (5)
Catering Services: Yes

Key Personnel
HUYEN RITCHEY - President

River Rock Entertainment Authority
3250 Highway 128
Geyserville, CA 95441-8908

Telephone: (877) 883-7777
Fax Number: (707) 473-2189
Internet Homepage: riverrockcasino.com
Type of Business: Foodservice Operations - Casinos
Total Sales: $188,056,000 (e)
Alcohol Sales: 5%
Number of Employees: 660
Average Check: Breakfast(10); Lunch(12); Dinner(18)
Total Units: 3
Trade Names: Center Stage Bar & Grill (1); Fortune Cafe (1); Quail Run Buffet (1)
Company-Owned Units: 3
Preferred Location Types: Other
Alcohol Served: Beer, Wine, Liquor
Primary Menu: American (1); Asian (1); Miscellaneous (1)
Areas of Operation: CA
Type of Foodservice: Casual Dining (3)
Primary Distributors: (Full Line) SYSCO Food Services of Central California Inc., MODESTO, CA
Notes: The company derives approximately 95% of its revenue from casino operations.

Key Personnel
DAVID F. FENDRICK - CEO; General Manager

Straw Hat Pizza
1053 1st St
Gilroy, CA 95020-4817

Telephone: (408) 842-2745
Fax Number: (408) 842-0198
Internet Homepage: strawhatpizzagilroy.com
Type of Business: Chain Restaurant Operator
Total Sales: $2,787,000 (e)
Internet Order Processing: Yes
Total Units: 3
Trade Names: Straw Hat Pizza (3)
Units Franchised From: 3
Primary Menu: Pizza (3)
Areas of Operation: CA
Type of Foodservice: Casual Dining (3)
Franchise Affiliation: Straw Hat Restaurants Inc., SAN RAMON, CA

Key Personnel
RAJ NAYYAR - Owner; General Buyer
JOSE URIBE - Manager Marketing

IHOP Restaurant System
450 N Brand Blvd Fl 7
Glendale, CA 91203-2346

Telephone: (818) 240-6055
Internet Homepage: ihop.com
Company Email: information@ihop.com
Type of Business: Chain Restaurant Operator
Year Founded: 1958
Systemwide Sales: $4,685,299,000 (e)
Publicly Held: Yes
Total Sales: $635,797,000 (e)
Number of Employees: 2,100
Average Check: Breakfast(8); Lunch(10); Dinner(10)
Internet Order Processing: Yes
Internet Sales: 0.50%
Total Units: 1,814
Trade Names: IHOP Restaurant (1,814)
Units Franchised To: 1,814
Preferred Square Footage: 4,000; 4,400; 5,000
Preferred Location Types: Downtown; Freestanding; Hotel/Motel; Strip Mall
Primary Menu: American (1,814)
Projected Openings: 109
Areas of Operation: AK, AL, AR, AZ, CA, CO, CT, DC, DE, FL, GA, IA, ID, IL, IN, KS, KY, LA, MA, MD, ME, MI, MN, MO, MS, MT, NC, ND, NE, NH, NJ, NM, NV, NY, OH, OK, OR, PA, PR, RI, SC, SD, TN, TX, UT, VA, VI, VT, WA, WI, WV, WY, BC, ON
Foreign Countries: BAHRAIN; CANADA; ECUADOR; GUATEMALA; INDIA; KUWAIT; LEBANON; MEXICO; PANAMA; QATAR; SAUDI ARABIA; THAILAND; THE PHILIPPINES; UNITED ARAB EMIRATES
Type of Foodservice: Family Restaurant (1,814)
Primary Distributors: (Food) US Foods Holding Corp., ROSEMONT, IL
Parent Company: Dine Brands Global, Inc., PASADENA, CA

Key Personnel
JAY JOHNS - President
KIERAN DONAHUE - Chief Marketing Officer
GREGG KALVIN - Senior VP; Controller
JOHN B. JAKUBEK - Senior VP Human Resources
MICHAEL KAUFMAN - VP Strategy, Business Development
JACOB BARDEN - VP Development
GREGG BENVENUTO - VP Development
ED BOSZE - Executive Director Field Marketing, National
ASJA COOPER - Director Operations
PAUL JANEWAY - Director Culinary Development
CANDICE JACOBSON - Director Communications
ALEX WILLIS - Director Business Development
DAVID PETERSEN - Regional Director Operations
DAN SMITH - Senior Manager Marketing
SAMANTHA STRONG - Senior Manager Brand Marketing
YVONNE G - Senior Manager Operations
STEVE MILLER - Regional Manager Marketing
AMANDA DWYER - Manager Brand Marketing
JOHN CHATSWORTH - Manager Training
AMANDA TOSTADO - Manager Marketing
STEPHANIE SALES - Manager
ANDREA SLAVIN - Manager Marketing
RICK MCDUFF - Corporate Manager Development; Architect

Porto's Bakery & Cafe
315 N Brand Blvd
Glendale, CA 91203-2303

Telephone: (818) 956-5996
Internet Homepage: portosbakery.com
Type of Business: Chain Restaurant Operator
Total Units: 3
Trade Names: Porto's Bakery & Cafe (3)
Company-Owned Units: 3

Key Personnel
BETTY PORTO - Partner
RAUL PORTO - Partner; VP Finance
MARGARITA PORTO - Partner
TONY SALAZAR - VP Operations, Culinary Operations

Pretzel King, LLC
3030 Edgewick Rd
Glendale, CA 91206-1317

Telephone: (818) 244-7518
Type of Business: Chain Restaurant Operator
Total Sales: $5,180,000 (e)
Total Units: 7
Trade Names: Auntie Anne's Hand-Rolled Soft Pretzels (7)
Units Franchised From: 7
Primary Menu: Snacks (7)
Areas of Operation: CA
Type of Foodservice: Quick Serve (7)
Franchise Affiliation: Auntie Anne's Inc.,

LANCASTER, PA

Key Personnel
LINDA READ - Owner; General Buyer

Timothy L. Behm Inc.
1244 W Glenoaks Blvd
Glendale, CA 91201-2242

Telephone: (818) 247-3340
Type of Business: Chain Restaurant Operator
Total Sales: $13,901,000 (e)
Total Units: 7
Trade Names: Domino's (7)
Units Franchised From: 7
Primary Menu: Pizza (7)
Areas of Operation: CA
Type of Foodservice: Quick Serve (7)
Franchise Affiliation: Domino's Pizza Inc, ANN ARBOR, MI

Key Personnel
TIMOTHY BEHM - Partner; General Buyer
NIKITA BEHM - Partner

Domino's Franchisee
110 W Foothill Blvd
Glendora, CA 91741-3364

Telephone: (626) 914-3881
Type of Business: Chain Restaurant Operator
Total Sales: $3,992,000 (e)
Total Units: 2
Trade Names: Domino's (2)
Units Franchised From: 2
Primary Menu: Pizza (2)
Areas of Operation: CA
Type of Foodservice: Quick Serve (2)
Franchise Affiliation: Domino's Pizza Inc, ANN ARBOR, MI

Key Personnel
DENNIS W. RYAN - Owner; General Buyer

Strings Restaurant Group
11344 Coloma Rd Ste 545
Gold River, CA 95670-4462

Telephone: (916) 635-6465
Fax Number: (916) 631-9775
Internet Homepage: stringscafe.com
Type of Business: Chain Restaurant Operator
Year Founded: 1987
Systemwide Sales: $8,930,000 (e)
Total Sales: $3,245,000 (e)
Alcohol Sales: 10%
Number of Employees: 70
Average Check: Lunch(14); Dinner(20)
Total Units: 14
Trade Names: Strings Bar and Grill (1); Strings Italian Cafe (13)
Company-Owned Units: 2
Units Franchised To: 12
Preferred Square Footage: 2,500
Preferred Location Types: Freestanding; Strip Mall
Alcohol Served: Beer, Wine
Primary Menu: Italian (14)
Areas of Operation: CA
Type of Foodservice: Casual Dining (14)
Catering Services: Yes
Distribution Centers: RANCHO CORDOVA, CA
On-site Distribution Center: Yes
Primary Distributors: (Full Line) SYSCO Food Services of Los Angeles Inc., WALNUT, CA

Key Personnel
ALBERT DECAPRIO - CEO; President; Director Real Estate
ERIC HUNZIKER - Executive Chef; Director Purchasing, Research & Development, Menu Development, Catering

GA Enterprises Inc.
146 S Fairview Ave
Goleta, CA 93117-3322

Telephone: (805) 683-9495
Fax Number: (805) 683-9503
Company Email: sbmcdofc@gmail.com
Type of Business: Chain Restaurant Operator
Year Founded: 1968
Total Sales: $10,031,000 (e)
Number of Employees: 170
Average Check: Breakfast(6); Lunch(8); Dinner(8)
Total Units: 2
Trade Names: McDonald's (2)
Units Franchised From: 2
Preferred Square Footage: 2,500
Preferred Location Types: Freestanding
Primary Menu: Hamburger (2)
Areas of Operation: CA
Type of Foodservice: Quick Serve (2)
Franchise Affiliation: McDonald's Corporation, CHICAGO, IL
Primary Distributors: (Full Line) Golden State Foods Corporation, IRVINE, CA

Key Personnel
DAVID PETERSON - President
MONTE FRAKER - Director Operations, Purchasing; General Buyer
CECILA DOCTOLERO - Manager Human Resources

Yogurtland Franchisee
5880 Calle Real Ste C
Goleta, CA 93117-2343

Telephone: (805) 964-4402
Type of Business: Chain Restaurant Operator
Total Sales: $2,041,000 (e)
Total Units: 2
Trade Names: Yogurtland (2)
Units Franchised From: 2
Primary Menu: Snacks (2)
Areas of Operation: CA
Type of Foodservice: Quick Serve (2)
Franchise Affiliation: Yogurtland Franchising Inc., FARMERS BRANCH, TX

Key Personnel
EUI OH - Owner; General Buyer

Johnson Haller, Inc.
4514 Remuda Ct
Granite Bay, CA 95746-9057

Telephone: (916) 789-7303
Type of Business: Chain Restaurant Operator
Total Sales: $23,520,000 (e)
Total Units: 5
Trade Names: McDonald's (5)
Units Franchised From: 5
Preferred Location Types: Freestanding
Primary Menu: Hamburger (5)
Areas of Operation: CA
Type of Foodservice: Quick Serve (5)
Franchise Affiliation: McDonald's Corporation, CHICAGO, IL

Key Personnel
PERCY JOHNSON - President; General Buyer

Casa Lupe Restaurants
130 Magnolia St
Gridley, CA 95948-2618

Telephone: (530) 846-3218
Fax Number: (530) 846-6812
Internet Homepage: casalupe.com
Company Email: info@casalupe.com
Type of Business: Chain Restaurant Operator
Year Founded: 1956
Total Sales: $6,212,000 (e)
Alcohol Sales: 10%
Number of Employees: 75
Total Units: 2
Trade Names: Casa Lupe Restaurant (2)
Company-Owned Units: 2
Preferred Location Types: Freestanding
Alcohol Served: Beer, Wine, Liquor
Primary Menu: Mexican (2)
Areas of Operation: CA

Type of Foodservice: Casual Dining (2)
Catering Services: Yes
Primary Distributors: (Food) Mexi Foods, WEST SACRAMENTO, CA

Key Personnel
JOSE DE LA TORRE - Owner; General Manager; Executive Chef; General Buyer

Benevedes, Inc.
186 N 12th Ave Ste 111
Hanford, CA 93230-5986

Telephone: (559) 583-9000
Type of Business: Chain Restaurant Operator
Total Sales: $3,494,000 (e)
Total Units: 6
Trade Names: Cold Stone Creamery (6)
Units Franchised From: 6
Primary Menu: Snacks (6)
Areas of Operation: CA
Type of Foodservice: Quick Serve (6)
Franchise Affiliation: Kahala Brands, SCOTTSDALE, AZ

Key Personnel
JEFF BENEVEDES - Partner
ANNETTE BENEVEDES - Partner

BB 2008 Inc.
12150 Carson St
Hawaiian Gardens, CA 90716-1140

Telephone: (562) 496-0540
Type of Business: Chain Restaurant Operator
Total Sales: $10,789,000 (e)
Total Units: 4
Trade Names: Jack in the Box (4)
Units Franchised From: 4
Primary Menu: Hamburger (4)
Areas of Operation: CA
Type of Foodservice: Quick Serve (4)
Franchise Affiliation: Jack in the Box Restaurants, SAN DIEGO, CA

Key Personnel
LEE SU - Owner; General Buyer

Eureka! Restaurant Group
12101 Crenshaw Blvd Ste 400
Hawthorne, CA 90250-3469

Telephone: (310) 331-8233
Internet Homepage: eurekarestaurantgroup.com
Type of Business: Chain Restaurant Operator
Year Founded: 2009
Systemwide Sales: $54,530,000 (e)
Total Sales: $62,360,000 (e)
Alcohol Sales: 35%
Total Units: 24
Trade Names: Eureka! (24)
Company-Owned Units: 24
Primary Menu: American (24)
Projected Openings: 2
Areas of Operation: CA, CO, ID, TX, WA
Type of Foodservice: Casual Dining (24)
Notes: Restaurants focus on small, craft beers - 30 to 40 draft handles.

Key Personnel
PAUL FREDERICK - Co-Founder; Partner; Chief Development Officer
EDUARDO SENDEROS - CEO
JULIO IZAGUIRRE - VP Finance
TREVOR TYLER - Director Food and Beverage
ALEXIA PENNA - Director Marketing; Manager Public Relations

Andersen Bakery Inc.
30703 San Clemente St
Hayward, CA 94544-7134

Telephone: (510) 429-7100
Fax Number: (510) 487-4964
Internet Homepage: andersenbakery.com
Type of Business: Chain Restaurant Operator
Year Founded: 1977
Total Sales: $11,610,000 (e)
Number of Employees: 148
Average Check: Breakfast(10); Lunch(10); Dinner(10)
Internet Order Processing: Yes
Total Units: 12
Trade Names: Andersen Bakery (12)
Company-Owned Units: 12
Preferred Square Footage: 1,500
Preferred Location Types: Freestanding; Regional Mall
Primary Menu: Sandwiches/Deli (12)
Areas of Operation: CA, FC
Foreign Countries: DENMARK; JAPAN
Type of Foodservice: Quick Serve (12)
On-site Distribution Center: Yes

Key Personnel
K YOSHIDA - CEO; President

Auntie Anne's Franchise
267 Southland Mall
Hayward, CA 94545-2129

Telephone: (510) 887-0248
Type of Business: Chain Restaurant Operator
Total Sales: $3,590,000 (e)
Total Units: 5
Trade Names: Auntie Anne's Hand-Rolled Soft Pretzels (5)
Units Franchised From: 5
Primary Menu: Snacks (5)
Areas of Operation: CA
Type of Foodservice: Quick Serve (5)
Franchise Affiliation: Auntie Anne's Inc., LANCASTER, PA

Key Personnel
ALEXANDER JOHNSON - Owner; General Buyer

Domino's Distribution Center
30852 San Antonio St
Hayward, CA 94544-7108

Telephone: (510) 489-0333
Fax Number: (510) 489-8035
Internet Homepage: dominos.com
Listing Type: Distribution Center
Type of Business: Chain Restaurant Operator
Number of Employees: 40
Areas of Operation: CA, NV
Parent Company: Domino's Pizza Inc, ANN ARBOR, MI

Key Personnel
JOSE VILLALOBOS - General Manager; Manager Transportation

Domino's Franchisee
22962 Clawiter Rd Ste 2
Hayward, CA 94545-1335

Telephone: (510) 783-9950
Type of Business: Chain Restaurant Operator
Total Sales: $8,313,000 (e)
Total Units: 4
Trade Names: Domino's (4)
Units Franchised From: 4
Primary Menu: Pizza (4)
Areas of Operation: CA
Type of Foodservice: Quick Serve (4)
Franchise Affiliation: Domino's Pizza Inc, ANN ARBOR, MI

Key Personnel
ABDUL H. RAHIM - Owner; General Buyer

David L. Flohr & Steven J. Flohr, PTRS
1595 E Florida Ave
Hemet, CA 92544-8600

Telephone: (951) 929-2104
Type of Business: Chain Restaurant Operator
Total Sales: $8,190,000 (e)
Total Units: 3
Trade Names: Jack in the Box (3)
Units Franchised From: 3
Primary Menu: Hamburger (3)

Areas of Operation: CA
Type of Foodservice: Quick Serve (3)
Franchise Affiliation: Jack in the Box Restaurants, SAN DIEGO, CA

Key Personnel
STEVEN FLOHR - Owner; General Buyer

Stata, LLC
2433 W Florida Ave
Hemet, CA 92545-3688

Telephone: (951) 652-5400
Type of Business: Chain Restaurant Operator
Total Sales: $1,181,000 (e)
Total Units: 2
Trade Names: Cold Stone Creamery (2)
Units Franchised From: 2
Primary Menu: Snacks (2)
Areas of Operation: CA
Type of Foodservice: Quick Serve (2)
Franchise Affiliation: Kahala Brands, SCOTTSDALE, AZ

Key Personnel
MAHESHKUMAR PATEL - Partner; General Buyer
BHARAT PATEL - Partner; General Buyer

Roscoe's House of Chicken N Waffles
1514 N Gower St Ste 200
Hollywood, CA 90028-6422

Telephone: (323) 466-7453
Fax Number: (323) 962-0279
Internet Homepage: roscoeschickenandwaffles.com
Type of Business: Chain Restaurant Operator
Year Founded: 1978
Total Sales: $8,326,000 (e)
Alcohol Sales: 1%
Number of Employees: 210
Average Check: Lunch(16); Dinner(24)
Internet Order Processing: Yes
Total Units: 7
Trade Names: Roscoe's House of Chicken N Waffles (7)
Company-Owned Units: 7
Preferred Square Footage: 2,500
Preferred Location Types: Community Mall; Freestanding
Alcohol Served: Beer, Wine
Primary Menu: Chicken (7)
Projected Openings: 1
Areas of Operation: CA
Type of Foodservice: Casual Dining (7)
Catering Services: Yes
Primary Distributors: (Full Line) US Foods-Los Angeles, LA MIRADA, CA

Key Personnel
HERB HUDSON - Chairman; CEO; Controller
ALLISON WALKER - VP
HOWARD FOREMAN - Director Food Safety
J.J. KENO - Manager Information Systems

Afters Ice Cream
16130 Gothard St
Huntington Beach, CA 92647

Internet Homepage: aftersicecream.com
Type of Business: Chain Restaurant Operator
Total Sales: $22,030,000 (e)
Number of Employees: 300
Total Units: 27
Trade Names: Afters Ice Cream (27)
Company-Owned Units: 27
Primary Menu: Snacks (27)
Projected Openings: 1
Areas of Operation: CA
Type of Foodservice: Quick Serve (27)

Key Personnel
SCOTT NGHIEM - CEO
JOHN BARBER - CFO
DAVE BARBER - COO
JOSHUA STEVENS - Director Event Planning
MIGUEL CARDENAS - Director Production
EDMOND CARTOJANO - Director Marketing
FAVIOLA RODRIGUEZ - Regional Manager
MONICA RAMIREZ - Manager Operations
ASHLEY LINARES - Manager Store Design

BJ's Restaurants Inc.
7755 Center Ave Ste 300
Huntington Beach, CA 92647-3084

Telephone: (714) 500-2400
Fax Number: (714) 848-8287
Internet Homepage: bjsrestaurants.com
Company Email: corporate@bjsbrewhouse.com
Type of Business: Chain Restaurant Operator
Year Founded: 1978
Publicly Held: Yes
Total Sales: $1,602,870,000 (e)
Alcohol Sales: 22%
Number of Employees: 21,000
Average Check: Lunch(14); Dinner(14)
Internet Order Processing: Yes
Internet Sales: 1.00%
Total Units: 216
Trade Names: BJ's Grill (1); BJ's Pizza & Grill (5); BJ's Restaurant & Brewhouse (210)
Company-Owned Units: 216
Preferred Square Footage: 7,400; 7,500; 8,000; 8,900
Preferred Location Types: Downtown; Freestanding; Regional Mall; Strip Mall
Alcohol Served: Beer, Wine, Liquor
Primary Menu: American (211); Pizza (5)
Areas of Operation: AL, AR, AZ, CA, CO, CT, FL, IN, KS, KY, LA, MD, MI, NC, NJ, NM, NV, NY, OH, OK, OR, PA, RI, SC, TN, TX, VA, WA
Type of Foodservice: Casual Dining (216)
Catering Services: Yes
Primary Distributors: (Full Line) Jacmar Foodservice Distribution, CITY OF INDUSTRY, CA

Key Personnel
GERALD W. DEITCHLE - Chairman
BRADFORD RICHMOND - CEO Interim
ROBERT B. DELIEMA - President Division
LYLE TICK - President; Chief Concept Officer
BRIAN KRAKOWER - CIO
GREGORY S. LYNDS - Chief Development Officer; Exec VP
GREG LYNDS - Chief Development Officer
KENDRA D. MILLER - Exec VP; Corporate Secretary; General Counsel
ALEXANDER M. PUCHNER - Senior VP Operations-Beverages
CHRISTOPHER P. PINSAK - Senior VP Operations, Region
RANA G. SCHIRMER - VP Accounting; Controller
DONALD M. GARDNER JR - VP Facility/Maintenance
STEPHEN J. DEMETOR - VP Construction
JEFFREY R. PRESTON - VP Purchasing
EFREN RAMIREZ - VP Information Technology
JAKE GUILD - VP Accounting; Controller
DEBBIE NICHOLS - VP Risk Management
JAMES DRAKE - VP Operations
DAN GOLDBERG - VP Quality Assurance
STEPHANIE ATENCIO - VP Human Resources
JULIE WEINMAN - Regional VP Operations
CHARLES SEIDENSTUCKER - Area VP Operations
ERIC JOHNSON - Area VP Operations
MIKE LANGFORD - Area VP Operations
MIKE VINIK - Area VP Operations
SCOTT FREDERICK - Area VP Operations
CURT BARNETT - Senior Director Tax
JESSICA SIMMONS - Director Operations
TONY CHEN - Director Operations
BRIAN KUMPF - Director Information Technology
ALANNA BROWN - Director Payroll
CODY SIEGEL - Director Infrastructure, Security
BRYAN LEVINE - Director Loyalty Program
GENA CASTELLON - Manager Safety, Loss Prevention
RYAN GOUIN - Manager Purchasing
SHANT WANES - Manager Systems
AMBER LOYD - Buyer
INDRE JASAITYTE - Buyer Alcoholic Beverages
RAMIN KASHANI - Senior Engineer Network

Ciscel Corporation
6041 Bolsa Ave Ste 5
Huntington Beach, CA 92647

Telephone: (714) 891-1222
Type of Business: Chain Restaurant Operator
Total Sales: $6,809,000 (e)
Total Units: 5
Trade Names: Jersey Mike's Subs (5)
Units Franchised From: 5
Primary Menu: Sandwiches/Deli (5)
Areas of Operation: CA
Type of Foodservice: Quick Serve (5)
Franchise Affiliation: Jersey Mike's Franchise Systems, MANASQUAN, NJ

Key Personnel
DANIEL R. CISCEL - Owner

DPQ Ventures Inc
19750 Beach Blvd
Huntington Beach, CA 92648-2988

Telephone: (714) 963-9877
Fax Number: (714) 965-2385
Type of Business: Chain Restaurant Operator
Total Sales: $3,613,000 (e)
Alcohol Sales: 15%
Total Units: 3
Trade Names: Round Table Pizza (3)
Units Franchised From: 3
Alcohol Served: Beer, Wine
Primary Menu: Pizza (3)
Areas of Operation: CA
Type of Foodservice: Casual Dining (3)
Franchise Affiliation: Round Table Franchise Corp., CONCORD, CA

Key Personnel
DAVID QUATMAN - President; General Buyer
LISA HOPPE - Store Manager

Lardas Systems Inc.
5500 Bolsa Ave Ste 105
Huntington Beach, CA 92649-1198

Mailing Address: P. O. Box 3209, SEAL BEACH, CA, 90740-3209
Telephone: (714) 892-4800
Fax Number: (714) 892-4475
Type of Business: Chain Restaurant Operator
Year Founded: 1993
Total Sales: $20,097,000 (e)
Number of Employees: 110
Average Check: Breakfast(8); Lunch(10); Dinner(12)
Total Units: 4
Trade Names: McDonald's (4)
Units Franchised From: 4
Preferred Square Footage: 3,000
Preferred Location Types: Discount Dept. Stores; Freestanding
Primary Menu: Hamburger (4)
Areas of Operation: CA
Type of Foodservice: Quick Serve (4)
Franchise Affiliation: McDonald's Corporation, CHICAGO, IL
Primary Distributors: (Full Line) The Martin-Brower Co., CITY OF INDUSTRY, CA

Key Personnel
CATHERINE LARDAS - President; Partner
ANGELO LARDAS - Partner
FRAN SCOTT - Manager Finance, Information Systems

North Shore Poke Co. Inc.
214 5th St Ste 101
Huntington Beach, CA 92648-8190

Telephone: (714) 465-9011
Internet Homepage: northshorepokeco.com
Type of Business: Chain Restaurant Operator
Year Founded: 2012
Total Units: 6
Trade Names: North Shore Poke Co (6)
Company-Owned Units: 6
Primary Menu: American (6)
Areas of Operation: CA
Type of Foodservice: Fast Casual (6)

Key Personnel
JACKSON LONG - CEO
SHAWN GOLE - Partner; Executive Chef; General Buyer
MELISSA GOLE-VASQUEZ - Partner
MARK GALE - Partner

SlapFish Restaurant Group
19696 Beach Blvd
Huntington Beach, CA 92648-2992

Telephone: (714) 615-5381
Internet Homepage: slapfishrestaurant.com
Company Email: admin@slapfishrestaurant.com
Type of Business: Chain Restaurant Operator
Systemwide Sales: $31,668,000 (e)
Total Sales: $26,740,000 (e)
Total Units: 25
Trade Names: Butterleaf (1); Raw Bar by Slapfish (1); Slapfish (22); Two Birds (1)
Company-Owned Units: 19
Units Franchised To: 6
Primary Menu: Chicken (1); Seafood (23); Vegetarian (1)
Projected Openings: 25
Areas of Operation: CA, NM, UT
Foreign Countries: ENGLAND
Type of Foodservice: Fast Casual (23); Quick Serve (2)

Key Personnel
ANDREW GRUEL - Founder; CEO; Executive Chef
LAUREN GRUEL - VP Marketing
KAYLA RUNKLE - General Manager
POLLY CAMUNEZ - Executive Assistant

Stacked - Food Well Built
7490 Edinger Ave
Huntington Beach, CA 92647

Telephone: (657) 845-2100
Internet Homepage: stacked.com
Type of Business: Chain Restaurant Operator
Total Units: 5
Trade Names: Stacked - Food Well Built (5)
Company-Owned Units: 5
Primary Menu: American (5)
Areas of Operation: CA
Type of Foodservice: Casual Dining (5)

Key Personnel
PAUL MONTENKO - Co-Founder; Co-CEO
JERRY HENNESSY - Co-Founder; Co-CEO
CRAIG CARLYLE - COO

Wienerschnitzel 358
1253 Palm Ave
Imperial Beach, CA 91932-1727

Telephone: (619) 423-7211
Internet Homepage: wienerschnitzel.com/location/358
Type of Business: Chain Restaurant Operator
Total Sales: $1,956,000 (e)
Total Units: 2
Trade Names: Wienerschnitzel (2)
Units Franchised From: 2
Primary Menu: German (2)
Areas of Operation: CA
Type of Foodservice: Quick Serve (2)
Franchise Affiliation: Galardi Group, IRVINE, CA

Key Personnel
ANNE L. TRELL - President; General Buyer
SYLVIA RANKIN - Manager Sales

Cabazon Indian Enterprises
84245 Indio Springs Dr
Indio, CA 92203-3405

Telephone: (760) 342-5000
Fax Number: (760) 238-5606
Internet Homepage: fantasyspringsresort.com
Company Email: info@fantasysprings.net
Type of Business: Foodservice Operations -

Casinos
Year Founded: 1983
Total Sales: $18,133,000 (e)
Alcohol Sales: 20%
Number of Employees: 565
Average Check: Breakfast(10); Lunch(24); Dinner(42)
Total Units: 9
Trade Names: Bingo Hall Snack Bar (1); Chef Freddys (1); Joy Asian Cuisine (1); Lique Ice Cream (1); POM (1); Starbucks Coffee (1); The Bistro (1); The Fresh Grill Buffet (1); The Pizza Kitchen (1)
Company-Owned Units: 8
Units Franchised From: 1
Preferred Square Footage: 2,500; 5,500; 6,000
Preferred Location Types: Freestanding
Alcohol Served: Beer, Wine, Liquor
Primary Menu: American (2); Asian (1); Californian (1); Coffee (1); Miscellaneous (1); Pizza (1); Snacks (2)
Areas of Operation: CA
Type of Foodservice: Casual Dining (5); Fine Dining (1); Quick Serve (3)
Franchise Affiliation: Starbucks Corporation, SEATTLE, WA
Primary Distributors: (Full Line) SYSCO Corporation, HOUSTON, TX

Key Personnel
DAVID A. ROOSEVELT - Chairman; Director Real Estate, Design; General Buyer
DOUG WELMAS - Vice Chairman; CEO
STEVE OSKIERA - CFO
FREDDY RIEGER - Executive Chef
SELA CURRY - Director Marketing
TONY SANZA - Director Food and Beverage

Randy's Donuts
419 Hindry Ave
Ingelwood, CA 90301

Telephone: (424) 371-6500
Internet Homepage: randysdonuts.com
Company Email: info@randysdonuts.com
Type of Business: Chain Restaurant Operator
Year Founded: 1953
Total Units: 4
Trade Names: Randy's Donuts (4)
Company-Owned Units: 4
Preferred Square Footage: 1,000
Primary Menu: Donut (4)
Projected Openings: 12
Areas of Operation: CA
Type of Foodservice: Quick Serve (4)

Key Personnel
MARK KELEGIAN - CEO
ASHLEY KELEGIAN - Owner
SAMARA FRIEDMAN - VP Operations

Domino's Franchisee
955 N La Brea Ave
Inglewood, CA 90302-2207

Telephone: (310) 673-9090
Type of Business: Chain Restaurant Operator
Total Sales: $8,074,000 (e)
Total Units: 4
Trade Names: Domino's (4)
Units Franchised From: 4
Primary Menu: Pizza (4)
Areas of Operation: CA
Type of Foodservice: Quick Serve (4)
Franchise Affiliation: Domino's Pizza Inc, ANN ARBOR, MI

Key Personnel
ROBERT J. SCHEIPER - Owner; General Buyer

Sugarfina, LLC
3915 W 102nd St
Inglewood, CA 90303-1004

Telephone: (855) 784-2734
Internet Homepage: sugarfina.com
Company Email: hello@sugarfina.com
Type of Business: Chain Restaurant Operator
Year Founded: 2012
Total Sales: $39,290,000 (e)
Internet Order Processing: Yes
Internet Sales: 1.00%
Total Units: 51
Trade Names: Sugarfina (51)
Company-Owned Units: 51
Primary Menu: Snacks (51)
Areas of Operation: CA, FL, GA, HI, IL, MA, MD, MN, NJ, NY, TX, VA, WA
Type of Foodservice: Quick Serve (51)

Key Personnel
SCOTT LAPORTA - CEO
ALISA KILBOURNE - Director Quality Assurance
DARWIN KWONG - Senior Manager Supply Chain
LAUREN AGUIRRE - Senior Manager Procurement
MICHAEL CHEN - Manager Technology, E-Commerce
HELEN CHO - Buyer
KAYLA CHOE - Coordinator Merchandising
JENNIFER BAE - Analyst Allocation

Beyond Franchise Group, LLC
220 Technology Dr Ste 120
Irvine, CA 92618

Telephone: (949) 398-7338
Internet Homepage: pokeworks.com
Type of Business: Chain Restaurant Operator
Year Founded: 2015
Total Sales: $36,320,000 (e)
Total Units: 39
Trade Names: Pokeworks (39)
Company-Owned Units: 39
Primary Menu: American (39)
Projected Openings: 30
Areas of Operation: AZ, CA, CT, FL, IL, LA, MA, NC, NY, OH, RI, TX, VA, WA, WI, BC
Foreign Countries: CANADA
Type of Foodservice: Fast Casual (39)

Key Personnel
MIKE CHEN - Co-Founder
KEVIN HSU - President; Partner; General Buyer
PETER YANG - Partner; Director Operations
MICHAEL WU - Partner; Chief Culinary Officer
WEN WEI - Partner
DIEGO ORTIZ - VP Operations
SHELDON SIMEON - Corporate Chef
ABE VAN BEEK - Director Culinary Operations

California Fish Grill
17310 Red Hill Ave Ste 330
Irvine, CA 92614-5691

Telephone: (714) 525-5809
Internet Homepage: cafishgrill.com
Type of Business: Chain Restaurant Operator
Total Sales: $29,380,000 (e)
Number of Employees: 563
Average Check: Lunch(14); Dinner(14)
Total Units: 28
Trade Names: California Fish Grill (28)
Company-Owned Units: 28
Preferred Location Types: Freestanding; Strip Mall
Alcohol Served: Beer, Wine
Primary Menu: Seafood (28)
Projected Openings: 2
Areas of Operation: AZ, CA
Type of Foodservice: Casual Dining (28)

Key Personnel
BOB HOLDEN - CEO; Partner; General Buyer
VICTOR TOPETE - Partner
PAUL POTVIN - CFO
MARK JOHNSON - COO
PATRICK WAIYAWAYTAR - VP Information Technology
JOSHUA HONG - Director Applications
JAY HASKELL - Director Restaurant Operations
LINDA WALKER - Director Training
LEO CASTILLO - Regional Director
VIET AO - Senior Manager Information Technology

Galardi Group
7700 Irvine Center Dr Ste 550
Irvine, CA 92618-3036

Telephone: (949) 892-2699
Fax Number: (949) 892-2615
Internet Homepage: hamburgerstand.com; tastee-freez.com; wienerschnitzel.com
Type of Business: Chain Restaurant Operator
Year Founded: 1961
Systemwide Sales: $340,560,000 (e)
Total Sales: $2,521,000 (e)
Number of Employees: 50
Average Check: Breakfast(8); Lunch(8); Dinner(8)
Total Units: 345
Trade Names: Hamburger Stand (12); Tastee-Freez (22); Wienerschnitzel (326)
Units Franchised To: 360
Preferred Square Footage: 2,000
Preferred Location Types: Freestanding; Strip Mall
Primary Menu: Hamburger (12); Hot Dogs (326); Snacks (22)
Projected Openings: 10
Areas of Operation: AZ, CA, CO, GU, IL, LA, NM, NV, TX, UT, WA
Type of Foodservice: Quick Serve (360)
Foodservice Management Venues: Schools
Catering Services: Yes
Parent Company: Galardi Group, IRVINE, CA

Key Personnel
CINDY CULPEPPER - Chairman; CEO
J.R. GALARDI - CEO; President
MICHAEL NISHI - CFO
RUSTY BILLS - COO
DOUG KOEGEBOEHN - Chief Marketing Officer
DOUG KOOB - Chief Development Officer
TED BARNETT - Area Director
ROB LONG - Area Director
DON WALENCEY - Area Director
MARIANO COLAO - Area Director
LUJANA WINKLES - Director Operations
TED MILBURN - Director Franchise Development
MOHAMED ELORABY - Director Information Technology
SOPHIA SALDANA CLOVERY - Director Human Resources
JILL ALBANO - Director Purchasing, Supply Chain
LAURIE NEW - Director Real Estate

In-N-Out Burger
4199 Campus Dr Ste 900
Irvine, CA 92612-8604

Telephone: (949) 509-6200
Fax Number: (949) 509-6300
Internet Homepage: in-n-out.com
Type of Business: Chain Restaurant Operator
Year Founded: 1948
Systemwide Sales: $1,647,048,000 (e)
Total Sales: $1,647,048,000 (e)
Number of Employees: 17,272
Average Check: Lunch(8); Dinner(8)
Internet Order Processing: Yes
Internet Sales: 4.00%
Total Units: 394
Trade Names: In-N-Out Burger (394)
Company-Owned Units: 394
Preferred Square Footage: 2,900; 3,500
Preferred Location Types: Freestanding; Lifestyle Center; Mobile Unit
Primary Menu: Hamburger (394)
Projected Openings: 2
Areas of Operation: AZ, CA, NV, OR, TX, UT
Type of Foodservice: Quick Serve (394)
Distribution Centers: BALDWIN PARK, CA; LATHROP, CA

Key Personnel
LYNSI SNYDER - CEO; President
MICHAEL MRAVLE - CFO
ROB HOWARDS - VP Operations, Information Technology
ANDY DAWSON - General Counsel Real Estate
MICHELLE GUZMAN - Director Marketing
MIKE LEAVINS - Director Risk Management
KATHERINE SAULS - Director Human Resources
WALTER DEISSLER - Director Real Estate
JONATHON COHEN - Director
JEFF DREHER - Director Marketing
ALICE CHANG - Director Compensation
DELTA MUNGAI - Director Transportation
MICHAEL LARTER - Senior Manager Internal Audit
VANESSA CANALES - Senior Manager Information Technology
MARICE CARUSO - Manager Customer Service
RANDY EDSON - Manager Benefits
JENNIFER SHEU - Manager Real Estate
SCOTT MERRYMAN - Manager Talent Acquisitions
MICHAEL ENGLISH - Manager Information Technology
HEATHER GARDNER - Manager Development
JEFF HELMRICH - Manager
JASON HORN - Manager Safety-Food
LANA NGUYEN - Manager
BONNIE ULLMANN - Manager Field Marketing
MARIEL COURTWRIGHT - Manager Financial Planning
JUSTIN TRIBE - Manager
LEWIS DARWIN - Manager Software Development
ANNABELLE CATOLICO - Specialist Training

Juice It Up!
17915 Sky Park Cir Ste J
Irvine, CA 92614-6378

Telephone: (949) 475-0146
Fax Number: (949) 475-0137
Internet Homepage: juiceitup.com
Company Email: information@juiceitup.com
Type of Business: Chain Restaurant Operator
Year Founded: 1995
Systemwide Sales: $23,702,000 (e)
Total Sales: $3,335,000 (e)
Number of Employees: 22
Average Check: Lunch(8); Dinner(8)
Total Units: 85
Trade Names: Juice It Up! (85)
Units Franchised To: 85
Preferred Square Footage: 800; 1,000; 1,200
Preferred Location Types: Airports; Freestanding; Institution (college/hospital); Lifestyle Center; Regional Mall
Primary Menu: Health Foods (85)
Areas of Operation: CA, NM, OR, TX
Type of Foodservice: Quick Serve (85)
Catering Services: Yes
Primary Distributors: (Food) Southwest Traders Inc., TEMECULA, CA
Parent Company: Britt Private Capital, NEWPORT BEACH, CA

Key Personnel
SUSAN TAYLOR - CEO; President
ELMER TOLENTINO - Owner
CHRIS BRAUN - Partner
CHRIS BRITT - Partner
ED ST. GEME - Partner
MELISSA AILLS - VP Procurement
NATALIE EAGLIN - Director Marketing
CARLO VERDUGO - Director Operations, Business Development
JON WEDE - Director Construction
NOAH BURGESS - Data Scientist Research & Development

Kura Sushi USA
2700 Alton Pkwy #133
Irvine, CA 92606

Telephone: (949) 553-0747
Internet Homepage: kurausa.com
Company Email: customerservice@kurausa.com
Type of Business: Chain Restaurant Operator
Year Founded: 2008
Total Sales: $65,790,000 (e)
Average Check: Lunch(22); Dinner(26)
Total Units: 21
Trade Names: Kura Sushi (21)
Company-Owned Units: 21
Primary Menu: Japanese (21)
Areas of Operation: CA, GA, IL, TX

Type of Foodservice: Casual Dining (21)
Catering Services: Yes

Key Personnel
KUNIHIKO TANAKA - President
JEFF UTTZ - CFO
SEAN ALLAMEH - COO
ARLENE ESTRADA PETOKAS - Chief People Officer
TOSHIYUKI TAKADA - VP Operations
AMBER MORALES - Senior Director Employee Development-Training
JULIAN FOK - Director Store Operations
HIDEOMI EDA - Manager Public Relations

McNib Corp.
16811 Hale Ave Ste B
Irvine, CA 92606-5066

Telephone: (949) 724-8907
Fax Number: (949) 724-8914
Type of Business: Chain Restaurant Operator
Year Founded: 1970
Total Sales: $70,520,000 (e)
Number of Employees: 800
Average Check: Breakfast(6); Lunch(8); Dinner(8)
Total Units: 15
Trade Names: McDonald's (15)
Units Franchised From: 15
Preferred Square Footage: 3,000
Preferred Location Types: Discount Dept. Stores; Freestanding
Primary Menu: Hamburger (15)
Areas of Operation: CA
Type of Foodservice: Quick Serve (15)
Franchise Affiliation: McDonald's Corporation, CHICAGO, IL
Primary Distributors: (Full Line) The Martin-Brower Co., CITY OF INDUSTRY, CA

Key Personnel
ROBERT NIBEEL - President; General Manager; General Buyer

Muscle Maker Inc.
18818 Teller Ave Ste 115
Irvine, CA 92612-1623

Telephone: (682) 708-8250
Fax Number: (949) 825-5099
Internet Homepage: musclemakergrill.com
Company Email: feedback@musclemakergrill.com
Type of Business: Chain Restaurant Operator
Year Founded: 1995
Systemwide Sales: $37,821,000 (e)
Publicly Held: Yes
Total Sales: $8,005,000 (e)
Number of Employees: 632
Average Check: Dinner(14)
Total Units: 42
Trade Names: Muscle Maker Grill (29); Pokemoto (13)
Company-Owned Units: 22
Units Franchised To: 20
Preferred Square Footage: 1,100; 3,000
Preferred Location Types: Airports; Freestanding; Lifestyle Center; Other; Regional Mall; Strip Mall
Primary Menu: Asian (13); Health Foods (29)
Projected Openings: 10
Areas of Operation: AZ, CA, CT, FL, IL, KS, NE, NJ, NV, NY, PA, TX
Type of Foodservice: Fast Casual (42)
Catering Services: Yes
Parent Company: American Restaurant Holdings, Inc., COSTA MESA, CA

Key Personnel
KEVIN MOHAN - Chairman
RODNEY SILVA - Chairman
MICHAEL ROPER - CEO
FERDINAND GROENEWALD - CFO
KENNETH MILLER - COO
AIMEE INFANTE - Chief Marketing Officer
JAMES GINGER - Director Construction

Pacifica Hotel Company
17300 Red Hill Ave Ste 250
Irvine, CA 92614-5653

Telephone: (805) 957-0095
Fax Number: (949) 486-5970
Internet Homepage: pacificahotels.com
Company Email: info@pacificahotels.com
Type of Business: Foodservice Operations - Hotel/Motels
Year Founded: 1971
Total Sales: $80,600,000 (e)
Alcohol Sales: 8%
Number of Employees: 800
Total Units: 6
Restaurants in Hotels: 6
Trade Names: Beachside Cafe (1); Manhattan's of La Jolla (1); Ristorante Portofino (1); SALT (1); Sam Snead's Oak Grill & Tavern (1); Spyglass Restaurant (1)
Company-Owned Units: 6
Alcohol Served: Beer, Wine, Liquor
Areas of Operation: CA, FL, HI
Type of Foodservice: Casual Dining
Primary Distributors: (Food) SYSCO Food Services of Los Angeles Inc., WALNUT, CA
Parent Company: Invest West Financial Corporation, SANTA BARBARA, CA
Notes: Pacifica also operates a number of limited-service hotels; the company derives approximately 93% of its revenue from hotel operation.

Key Personnel
DALE J. MARQUIS - Chairman
MATHEW D. MARQUIS - CEO
ADAM MARQUIS - President
CHRIS MARQUIS - Exec VP
ALIE GAFFAN - VP Training, People
STEPHEN MEDEL - VP Business Development
JOHN PEDLOW - VP Finance
MAC GREGORY - Director Food and Beverage

Paul Martin's American Grill
100 Spectrum Center Drive #1240
Irvine, CA 92618

Telephone: (949) 336-5237
Fax Number: (949) 336-5238
Internet Homepage: paulmartinsamericangrill.com
Company Email: feedback@paulmartinsamericangrill.com
Type of Business: Chain Restaurant Operator
Year Founded: 2007
Total Sales: $54,330,000 (e)
Total Units: 11
Trade Names: Paul Martin's American Grill (11)
Company-Owned Units: 11
Alcohol Served: Beer, Wine, Liquor
Primary Menu: American (11)
Projected Openings: 1
Areas of Operation: AZ, CA, TX
Type of Foodservice: Casual Dining (11)

Key Personnel
PAUL M. FLEMING - Co-Founder; Partner
MIKE ALOIA - Partner
JOSEPH CORONA - Partner
MANUEL LOPEZ - Partner
JOEY FARIAS - Partner
JUSTIN OTSUKA - CFO
JESSE ALCARAZ - General Manager
JAVIER MARTINEZ - Executive Chef
MIGUEL GARCIA - Executive Chef
MANUEL MUYUC - Executive Chef
LEONARDO GOMEZ - Executive Chef
TERRI HORAN - Director Marketing
SHAWNA STILES - Manager Accounting
KRISTEN IBARRA - Coordinator Risk Management
JILL ZENTI - Coordinator Restaurant Operations

Philly Foods Inc.
13805 Alton Pkwy Ste A
Irvine, CA 92618-1690

Telephone: (949) 206-9724
Fax Number: (949) 206-9723
Internet Homepage: eatphillysbest.com
Company Email: yo@eatphillysbest.com
Type of Business: Chain Restaurant Operator
Year Founded: 1998
Systemwide Sales: $13,300,000 (e)
Total Sales: $35,050,000 (e)
Number of Employees: 76
Total Units: 20

Trade Names: Philly's Best (20)
Company-Owned Units: 5
Units Franchised To: 15
Preferred Square Footage: 1,200; 1,500
Preferred Location Types: Power Center; Strip Mall
Primary Menu: Sandwiches/Deli (20)
Areas of Operation: CA
Type of Foodservice: Quick Serve (20)

Key Personnel
ROBERT D. LEVEY - CEO; President; General Buyer
ANDREA J. LEVEY - CFO; VP; Corporate Secretary
NANCY CLARK - Assistant Administration

Seven Crown Resorts Inc.
9771 Irvine Center Dr Ste 100
Irvine, CA 92618-4344

Telephone: (949) 588-7100
Fax Number: (949) 588-7400
Internet Homepage: sevencrown.com
Company Email: info@sevencrown.com
Type of Business: Foodservice Operations - Hotel/Motels
Year Founded: 1969
Total Sales: $51,373,000 (e)
Alcohol Sales: 5%
Number of Employees: 240
Total Units: 3
Restaurants in Hotels: 3
Trade Names: Bridge Bay at Shasta Lake (1); Lake Mohave Marina (1); Paradise Point Marina (1)
Company-Owned Units: 2
Alcohol Served: Beer, Wine, Liquor
Areas of Operation: AZ, CA
Type of Foodservice: Casual Dining (2)
Primary Distributors: (Food) SYSCO Food Services of Los Angeles Inc., WALNUT, CA; (Specialty Foods) SYSCO Food Services of Los Angeles Inc., WALNUT, CA
Notes: The company derives approximately 88% of its revenue from hotel operations and houseboat rental.

Key Personnel
DAVID A. OHANESIAN - President; Director Real Estate

Sunstone Hotel Investors Inc.
200 Spectrum Center Dr Fl 21
Irvine, CA 92618

Telephone: (949) 330-4000
Internet Homepage: sunstonehotels.com
Company Email: info@sunstonehotels.com
Type of Business: Foodservice Operations - Hotel/Motels
Year Founded: 1997
Publicly Held: Yes
Total Sales: $431,980,000 (e)
Alcohol Sales: 15%
Number of Employees: 8,000
Total Units: 17
Restaurants in Hotels: 17
Trade Names: Boston Park Plaza (1); Embassy Suites (2); Hilton (3); Hyatt Regency (2); JW Marriott (1); Marriott (2); Oceans Edge Resort & Marina (1); Renaissance (4); Wailea Beach Resort (1)
Company-Owned Units: 17
Alcohol Served: Beer, Wine, Liquor
Areas of Operation: CA, DC, FL, IL, LA, MA, MD, NY, OR, PA, TX, UT, VA
Type of Foodservice: Casual Dining; Fine Dining
Primary Distributors: (Food) SYSCO Food Services of San Diego Inc., POWAY, CA
Notes: The company derives approximately 75% of its revenue from hotel operations.

Key Personnel
BRYAN GIGLIA - CFO; Senior VP Finance
MARC A. HOFFMAN - COO; Exec VP
ROBERT C. SPRINGER - Chief Investment Officer; Exec VP
DAVID KLEIN - Senior VP; General Counsel
DENISE HERTLE - VP Accounting
OLIVIER KOLPIN - VP Tax
TODD HERSPERGER - VP Asset Protection
KRISTEN HOOVER - VP Finance
CORMAC O'MODHRAIN - VP Finance, Group
GEORGE HENSEN - VP Construction, Design
MICHAEL TOGGENBURGER - Director Information Systems

Taco Bell Corp.
1 Glen Bell Way
Irvine, CA 92618-3344

Telephone: (949) 863-4500
Fax Number: (949) 863-2246
Internet Homepage: tacobell.com
Type of Business: Chain Restaurant Operator
Year Founded: 1962
Systemwide Sales: $16,687,000 (e)
Publicly Held: Yes
Total Sales: $2,769,246,000 (e)
Number of Employees: 122,000
Average Check: Lunch(8); Dinner(10)
Total Units: 8,564
Trade Names: Taco Bell (8,548); Taco Bell Cantina (16)
Company-Owned Units: 514
Units Franchised To: 8,050
Preferred Square Footage: 2,500; 3,200
Preferred Location Types: Airports; Community Mall; Convenience Store/Gas Station; Discount Dept. Stores; Downtown; Freestanding; Institution (college/hospital); Mobile Unit; Regional Mall; Stadiums; Strip Mall
Primary Menu: Taco (8,564)
Areas of Operation: AK, AL, AR, AZ, CA, CO, CT, DC, DE, FL, GA, GU, HI, IA, ID, IL, IN, KS, KY, LA, MA, MD, ME, MI, MN, MO, MS, MT, NC, ND, NE, NH, NJ, NM, NV, NY, OH, OK, OR, PA, PR, RI, SC, SD, TN, TX, UT, VA, VI, VT, WA, WI, WV, WY, AB, BC, MB, NB, NL, NS, NT, ON, PE, QC, SK, YT
Foreign Countries: ARUBA; CANADA; COSTA RICA; DOMINICAN REPUBLIC; GUATEMALA; ICELAND; INDIA; IRAQ; ITALY; JAPAN; MEXICO; SOUTH KOREA; THE PHILIPPINES
Type of Foodservice: Fast Casual (16); Quick Serve (8,548)
Catering Services: Yes
Primary Distributors: (Full Line) McLane Foodservice, CARROLLTON, TX
Parent Company: YUM! Brands Inc., LOUISVILLE, KY

Key Personnel
MARK KING - CEO
SCOTT MEZVINSKY - President International, United States
MEGHAN FARREN - President
JOHN ARTHUR - Owner Operations; Treasurer; Director
JASON KIDD - COO
KELLY MCCULLOCH - Chief People Officer
STEPHEN PLANK - CIO
NIKKI LAWSON - Chief Brand Officer Global
SEAN TRESVANT - Chief Brand Officer Global; Chief Strategy Officer Global
LIZ MATTHEWS - Chief Innovation Officer Culinary Development
TRACEE LAROCCA - Senior VP Advertising, Branding
MATT SHAW - VP Franchising
FERNANDO CLAUSSEN - VP; General Manager
DARRELL JOHNSON - VP Operations
PAUL TUNG - Senior Director Information Technology
MARK WILSON - Senior Director Employee Development, Business Development
VADIM PARIZHER - Senior Director Engineering
BIRJU AMIN - Senior Director Technology
SERENA SHELDON - Director Consumer Insights
HEATHER JACOBSON - Director Franchise Development
STEVEN GOMEZ - Director Product Development, International
MARK HANKINS - Director Operations, Global
LEANNE TSAI - Director Development, Strategic Planning
TRACEY RUSSELL - Director Human Resources
MICHELLE KELSO-KAY - Director Employee Development
KENNY ANDERSON - Director Operations

BOBBY HAMMAN - Director Franchise Operations
CERA HURTADO - Director Operations
JUDY MARSCHLOWITZ - Director Operations
ALLEN RICHARDSON - Director Operations
DIONSAI RILEY - Director Operations
SARAH SPENGLER - Director Human Resources
MOLLY TROSKO - Director Operations
JESSIE GRABER - Director Marketing
KATIE TAYLOR - Director Marketing
ROBBIE KOHLER - Director Software Engineering, E-Commerce
RISHI GUPTA - Director Technology
RYAN HUO - Senior Manager Franchise Development
STEVE BONSWOR - Senior Manager Restaurant Operations
LORI THOMPSON - Senior Manager Operations
MITCHELL CHEW - District Manager Operations
PETER SCHAAP - Manager Real Estate
LISA LUTHER - Manager Product Development
SUE HARROD - Manager Real Estate
MALIA ALLEY - Manager Information Technology
CARLTON CHAR - Manager Operations
BOBBY GILL - Manager Operations
ANGIE HARVEL - Manager Operations, Area
BILL HSU - Manager
NOLA KRIEG - Manager Product Development
DANIEL SEIF - Manager Information Technology
ARI GARAY - Manager Strategy
TODD EVANS - Manager Engineering, Global
JUSTIN TALLIO - Manager Engineering
KIM DEGEN - Manager Engineering, Quality Assurance
BRITTANY WOLLMERSHAUSER - Associate Manager Consumer Insights

Tacos and Company Holdings LLC
18092 Culver Dr
Irvine, CA 92612

Telephone: (888) 213-7374
Internet Homepage: tacosnco.com
Company Email: info@tacosnco.com
Type of Business: Chain Restaurant Operator
Year Founded: 1991
Total Units: 5
Trade Names: Tacos & Co (5)
Company-Owned Units: 5
Primary Menu: Mexican (5)
Areas of Operation: CA
Type of Foodservice: Fast Casual (5)

Key Personnel
FRANCISCO HERNANDEZ - Owner

The Habit Restaurants Inc
17320 Red Hill Ave Ste 140
Irvine, CA 92614-5695

Telephone: (949) 851-8881
Fax Number: (949) 852-4650
Internet Homepage: habitburger.com
Company Email: info@habitburger.com
Type of Business: Chain Restaurant Operator
Year Founded: 1969
Systemwide Sales: $720,457,000 (e)
Publicly Held: Yes
Total Sales: $606,592,000 (e)
Number of Employees: 1,200
Average Check: Lunch(10); Dinner(12)
Internet Order Processing: Yes
Total Units: 378
Trade Names: The Habit Burger Grill (378)
Company-Owned Units: 306
Units Franchised To: 72
Preferred Square Footage: 2,000; 2,300; 2,500; 2,800
Preferred Location Types: Freestanding; Mobile Unit; Strip Mall
Primary Menu: Hamburger (378)
Projected Openings: 32
Areas of Operation: AZ, CA, FL, ID, MD, NJ, NV, PA, SC, UT, VA, WA
Foreign Countries: CHINA
Type of Foodservice: Fast Casual (378)
Primary Distributors: (Food) Jordano's Inc., SANTA BARBARA, CA
Parent Company: YUM! Brands Inc., LOUISVILLE, KY

Key Personnel
TONY SERRITELLA - COO
MIKE REPETTI - CIO
JACK HINCHLIFFE - Chief Marketing Officer Global
JASON OVIATT - Chief Legal Officer
IWONA ALTER - Chief Brand Officer
PETER WHITWELL - Senior Exec VP Quality Assurance; VP Training
JOHN PHILLIPS - Exec VP Franchising
MADELAINE MORROW - VP Finance
ROB WACH - VP Facility/Maintenance
TONY WARREN - VP Operations
RAY NOPPER - Controller
CRYSTAL CANAVAN - Senior Director Technology, Innovation
BRIAN CHRISTIE - Director Information Technology, Infrastructure
SHANNON COLEMAN - Director Real Estate
TOM BRYAN - Director Operations
JAMESA GONZALEZ - Director Operations
RONALD OBANDO - Director Operations
BRAD JEFFERIES - Director Construction
GEORGE KHOURI - Director New Store Development
SANDEE SALAS - Director
PAULO SALGADO - Director Recruitment
CHARLOTTE LUCICH - Director Marketing
BRAD REYES - Director Information/Data Security
MARK ROSS - Director Restaurant Operations, Information Technology
DIANA SIDI - Director Human Resources
CHERYL THOMPSON - Director Development
JASON TRIAIL - Director Culinary Development
FRANK RUIZ - District Manager
JAY LOPEZ - District Manager
FRANK COSTELLO - District Manager
JORGE GUEVARA - Manager
CRYSTAL WELLS - Manager Administration

Yard House USA Inc.
7700 Irvine Center Dr Ste 300
Irvine, CA 92618-3022

Telephone: (407) 245-4000
Fax Number: (949) 727-0831
Internet Homepage: yardhouse.com
Company Email: yardmaster@yardhouse.com
Type of Business: Chain Restaurant Operator
Year Founded: 1995
Publicly Held: Yes
Total Sales: $569,119,000 (e)
Alcohol Sales: 37%
Number of Employees: 4,400
Average Check: Lunch(20); Dinner(38)
Total Units: 88
Trade Names: Yard House (88)
Company-Owned Units: 88
Preferred Square Footage: 10,000
Preferred Location Types: Freestanding; Lifestyle Center; Strip Mall
Alcohol Served: Beer, Wine, Liquor
Primary Menu: American (88)
Projected Openings: 3
Areas of Operation: AZ, CA, CO, FL, GA, HI, ID, IL, KS, MA, MN, NC, NV, NY, OH, OR, TX, VA, WA
Type of Foodservice: Casual Dining (88)
Primary Distributors: (Food) SYSCO Food Services of Los Angeles Inc., WALNUT, CA
Parent Company: Darden Restaurants Inc., ORLANDO, FL

Key Personnel
RENEE HOLDERBACH - Senior VP Accounting
CARLITO JOCSON - VP; Executive Chef
DREW MINERVINO - Regional VP
MIGUEL MATA - Executive Chef
JOHN YEAMAN - Director Development, Training
AARON DALBERG - Director Operations
MARC HADLEY - Director Operations
RAVEN MAREE - Director Operations
DAVID CAMPO - Director Operations
LORRIE COPPOCK - Manager Accounting
VANCE ARNDT - Manager Facility/Maintenance
RACHELLE JOYCE - Manager Development, Training
LINDA KEITH - Manager Talent Acquisitions
EDWARD LATHROP - Manager Restaurant

Operations
SHANNON DAVIS - Manager Operations
GARY GABEL - Manager New Store Development
YU P. ADALIST - Supervisor Accounting

Sterling Foods
3813 Durbin St
Irwindale, CA 91706-6804

Telephone: (626) 338-5900
Type of Business: Chain Restaurant Operator
Year Founded: 1954
Total Sales: $6,830,000 (e)
Alcohol Sales: 2%
Number of Employees: 122
Average Check: Lunch(8); Dinner(8)
Total Units: 4
Trade Names: Shakey's Pizza (4)
Units Franchised From: 4
Preferred Square Footage: 3,500; 4,000
Preferred Location Types: Freestanding; Strip Mall
Alcohol Served: Beer, Wine
Primary Menu: Pizza (4)
Areas of Operation: CA
Type of Foodservice: Casual Dining (4)
Franchise Affiliation: Shakey's USA, ALHAMBRA, CA

Key Personnel
MICK CLARK - President; Director Finance, Design
RICHARD RITTER - Director Operations, Purchasing, Supply Chain
CHERYL MOWREY - Manager Administration

Gigi's Cupcakes Inc.
466 Foothill Blvd Ste 356
La Canada, CA 91011

Telephone: (310) 279-0673
Internet Homepage: gigiscupcakesusa.com
Company Email: info@gigiscupcakesusa.com
Type of Business: Chain Restaurant Operator
Year Founded: 2008
Total Sales: $2,885,000 (e)
Internet Order Processing: Yes
Total Units: 68
Trade Names: Gigi's Cupcakes (68)
Units Franchised To: 68
Primary Menu: Snacks (68)
Areas of Operation: AL, AR, AZ, CO, FL, GA, IN, KS, KY, MI, MN, MS, NC, ND, NE, NV, OH, OK, PA, SC, TN, TX, WI
Type of Foodservice: Quick Serve (68)
Parent Company: Elite Restaurant Group, LA CANADA FLINTRIDGE, CA

Key Personnel
GIGI BUTLER - Founder

CHRISTINE DEMIRTSHIAN - President; General Buyer
KEVIN WALL - Owner Operations; Director
RAJEEV SAREEN - Director Operations

Chop Stop, Inc.
4515 Ocean View Blvd Ste 315
La Canada Flintridge, CA 91011

Telephone: (818) 369-7350
Internet Homepage: chopstop.com
Company Email: info@chopstop.com
Type of Business: Chain Restaurant Operator
Year Founded: 2010
Total Units: 8
Trade Names: Chop Stop (8)
Company-Owned Units: 8
Primary Menu: Health Foods (8)
Projected Openings: 3
Areas of Operation: CA
Type of Foodservice: Quick Serve (8)

Key Personnel
MARK KULKIS - CEO; President

Elite Restaurant Group
734 Foothill Blvd
La Canada Flintridge, CA 91011

Telephone: (949) 424-3396
Internet Homepage: daphnes.biz; patxispizza.com; slaters5050.com
Type of Business: Chain Restaurant Operator
Total Sales: $101,000,000 (e)
Total Units: 143
Trade Names: Daphne's (21); Gigi's Cupcakes (68); Marie Callender's Restaurant & Bakery (28); Patxi's Pizza (17); Slater's 50/50 (9)
Company-Owned Units: 56
Units Franchised To: 87
Primary Menu: American (37); Greek/Mediterranean (21); Pizza (17); Snacks (68)
Projected Openings: 50
Areas of Operation: AL, AR, CA, CO, FL, GA, HI, IN, KY, MA, MI, MS, NC, ND, NE, NV, OH, OK, PA, SC, TN, TX, UT, VA, WA, WI
Type of Foodservice: Casual Dining (54); Fast Casual (21); Quick Serve (68)
Subsidiaries: Marie Callender's Inc., AZUSA, CA
Headquarter Offices: Gigi's Cupcakes Inc., LA CANADA, CA

Key Personnel
MICHAEL NAKHLEH - President
SCOTT MILLER - VP Finance

JP Management Corp.
1150 Foothill Blvd Ste C
La Canada Flintridge, CA 91011-3282

Telephone: (818) 790-5443
Fax Number: (818) 790-2055
Type of Business: Chain Restaurant Operator
Year Founded: 1999
Total Sales: $29,090,000 (e)
Number of Employees: 240
Average Check: Breakfast(8); Lunch(8); Dinner(10)
Total Units: 6
Trade Names: McDonald's (6)
Units Franchised From: 6
Preferred Square Footage: 2,500; 3,000
Preferred Location Types: Freestanding
Primary Menu: Hamburger (6)
Areas of Operation: CA
Type of Foodservice: Quick Serve (6)
Franchise Affiliation: McDonald's Corporation, CHICAGO, IL
Primary Distributors: (Food) The Martin-Brower Co., CITY OF INDUSTRY, CA

Key Personnel
JULIE PERNECKY - President; Director Purchasing, Real Estate
SHU SHIEH - Manager Finance, Information Systems, Human Resources
SAUL GAITAN - Manager Operations, Facility/Maintenance, Store Fixtures
SANDRA LLAMAS - Supervisor Foodservice

Humphrey & Reanesey Enterprises, Inc
1940 W Whittier Blvd Ste C2
La Habra, CA 90631-3661

Telephone: (562) 690-4922
Type of Business: Chain Restaurant Operator
Total Sales: $1,181,000 (e)
Total Units: 3
Trade Names: Cold Stone Creamery (3)
Units Franchised From: 3
Primary Menu: Snacks (3)
Areas of Operation: CA
Type of Foodservice: Quick Serve (3)
Franchise Affiliation: Kahala Brands, SCOTTSDALE, AZ

Key Personnel
HUMPHREY HOK - Partner
REANGSEY KOK - Partner

Square King Foods, Inc.
1861 W La Habra Blvd
La Habra, CA 90631-5131

Telephone: (714) 606-8828
Type of Business: Chain Restaurant Operator
Total Sales: $25,360,000 (e)
Total Units: 10
Trade Names: Jack in the Box (10)
Units Franchised From: 10
Primary Menu: Hamburger (10)
Areas of Operation: CA
Type of Foodservice: Quick Serve (10)
Franchise Affiliation: Jack in the Box Restaurants, SAN DIEGO, CA

Key Personnel
SAM FONG - Owner; General Buyer

J.C. Resorts LLC
533 Coast Blvd S
La Jolla, CA 92037-4641

Telephone: (858) 454-9793
Fax Number: (858) 459-6758
Internet Homepage: jcresorts.com
Company Email: info@jcresorts.com
Type of Business: Foodservice Operations - Hotel/Motels
Year Founded: 1975
Total Sales: $47,670,000 (e)
Alcohol Sales: 15%
Number of Employees: 550
Total Units: 5
Restaurants in Hotels: 4
Trade Names: JC Golf (1); Rancho Bernardo Inn (1); Scripps Inn (1); Surf & Sand Resort (1); Temecula Creek Inn (1)
Company-Owned Units: 4
Alcohol Served: Beer, Wine, Liquor
Areas of Operation: CA
Type of Foodservice: Casual Dining (4)
Primary Distributors: (Food) SYSCO Food Services of San Diego Inc., POWAY, CA
Notes: The company derives approximately 78% of its revenue from hotel operations.

Key Personnel
PAUL REED - CEO; President; Director Operations, Risk Management, Quality Assurance, Real Estate, Human Resources, Recruitment
RON FOUGERAY - Exec VP
PAUL REID - Director Food and Beverage

Kenny Brothers, Inc.
7836 Herschel Ave Ste 102
La Jolla, CA 92037-4407

Telephone: (858) 200-9888
Type of Business: Chain Restaurant Operator
Total Sales: $8,284,000 (e)
Total Units: 6
Trade Names: Jersey Mike's Subs (6)
Units Franchised From: 6
Primary Menu: Sandwiches/Deli (6)
Areas of Operation: CA
Type of Foodservice: Quick Serve (6)
Franchise Affiliation: Jersey Mike's Franchise Systems, MANASQUAN, NJ

Key Personnel
KEVIN KENNY - Partner; General Buyer
PATRICK KENNY - Partner
DAVID KENNY - Partner
CHRISTOPHER KENNY - General Manager

La Jolla Beach & Tennis Club Inc.
2000 Spindrift Dr
La Jolla, CA 92037-3237

Telephone: (858) 454-7126
Fax Number: (858) 456-3805
Internet Homepage: ljbtc.com; marineroom.com
Company Email: info@ljbtc.com
Type of Business: Chain Restaurant Operator
Year Founded: 1935
Total Sales: $46,573,000 (e)
Alcohol Sales: 20%
Number of Employees: 200
Average Check: Breakfast(14); Lunch(18); Dinner(22)
Internet Order Processing: Yes
Total Units: 3
Trade Names: The LaJolla Club Dining Room (1); The Marine Room (1); The Shores (1)
Company-Owned Units: 3
Preferred Location Types: Freestanding; Other
Alcohol Served: Beer, Wine, Liquor
Primary Menu: French/Continental (3)
Areas of Operation: CA
Type of Foodservice: Casual Dining (2); Fine Dining (1)
Primary Distributors: (Full Line) US Foods-San Francisco, LIVERMORE, CA
Notes: The company derives approximately 70% of its revenue from club operations.

Key Personnel
BERNARD GUILLAS - Executive Chef
LISA ARAIZA - Director Member Services
WU CINDY - Director Finance
MICHAEL O'DONOHUE - Director

DENNIS RUSH - Director Operations
SANDY WHITING - Manager Purchasing
DAN KURTZ - Manager Information Technology

Ladeki Restaurant Group
875 Prospect St Ste 203
La Jolla, CA 92037-4264

Telephone: (858) 456-8018
Fax Number: (858) 456-1368
Internet Homepage: sammyspizza.com
Company Email: info@sammyspizza.com
Type of Business: Chain Restaurant Operator
Year Founded: 1989
Total Sales: $45,240,000 (e)
Alcohol Sales: 10%
Number of Employees: 488
Average Check: Lunch(24); Dinner(30)
Internet Order Processing: Yes
Total Units: 12
Trade Names: Sammy's Woodfired Pizza (12)
Company-Owned Units: 12
Preferred Square Footage: 3,000
Preferred Location Types: Community Mall; Downtown; Freestanding; Regional Mall; Strip Mall
Alcohol Served: Beer, Wine, Liquor
Primary Menu: Pizza (12)
Areas of Operation: CA, NV
Type of Foodservice: Casual Dining (12)
Catering Services: Yes
Primary Distributors: (Food) US Foods-Los Angeles, LA MIRADA, CA

Key Personnel
SAMI LADEKI - CEO; Partner
JEFF MOOGK - Partner; Corporate Chef; General Buyer

D&M Holdings
9001 Grossmont Blvd Ste 714
La Mesa, CA 91941-4095

Telephone: (619) 667-1240
Fax Number: (619) 828-0888
Type of Business: Chain Restaurant Operator
Year Founded: 2000
Total Sales: $15,000,000 (e)
Number of Employees: 128
Average Check: Lunch(8); Dinner(12)
Total Units: 6
Trade Names: Popeyes Louisiana Kitchen (6)
Units Franchised From: 6
Preferred Square Footage: 1,500
Preferred Location Types: Freestanding; Strip Mall
Primary Menu: Chicken (6)
Areas of Operation: CA
Type of Foodservice: Quick Serve (6)
Franchise Affiliation: Popeyes Louisiana Kitchen Inc., ATLANTA, GA

Primary Distributors: (Full Line) McLane/Riverside, RIVERSIDE, CA

Key Personnel
DAVE TAYLOR - Owner; General Buyer
MARLEE TAYLOR - VP Operations

Jaspal Enterprises Inc.
8142 La Mesa Blvd
La Mesa, CA 91942-6437

Telephone: (619) 697-8048
Type of Business: Chain Restaurant Operator
Total Sales: $1,523,000 (e)
Total Units: 2
Trade Names: Subway (2)
Units Franchised From: 2
Primary Menu: Sandwiches/Deli (2)
Areas of Operation: CA
Type of Foodservice: Quick Serve (2)
Franchise Affiliation: Doctor's Associates Inc., MILFORD, CT

Key Personnel
BRIAN DUDA - Owner; General Buyer

Slammed Pizza Inc.
7960 University Ave Ste 200
La Mesa, CA 91942-5544

Telephone: (619) 589-6313
Type of Business: Chain Restaurant Operator
Total Sales: $12,455,000 (e)
Total Units: 6
Trade Names: Domino's (6)
Units Franchised From: 6
Preferred Square Footage: 1,200
Preferred Location Types: Freestanding; Strip Mall
Primary Menu: Pizza (6)
Areas of Operation: CA
Type of Foodservice: Quick Serve (6)
Franchise Affiliation: Domino's Pizza Inc, ANN ARBOR, MI

Key Personnel
PAM TOBIE - Owner; General Manager; General Buyer

Sombrero Mexican Food
5575 Lake Park Way Ste 216
La Mesa, CA 91942

Telephone: (619) 668-1059
Internet Homepage: sombreromex.com
Company Email: ozzie@sombreromex.com
Type of Business: Chain Restaurant Operator
Total Sales: $23,300,000 (e)
Internet Order Processing: Yes
Total Units: 16
Company-Owned Units: 16
Preferred Location Types: Freestanding
Primary Menu: Mexican (16)
Areas of Operation: CA

Key Personnel
JAVIER CORREA - President; Owner; General Manager
OZZIE GARCIA - Director Franchise Development

Domino's Franchisee
14234 Imperial Hwy
La Mirada, CA 90638-1940

Telephone: (562) 229-3070
Type of Business: Chain Restaurant Operator
Total Sales: $49,171,000 (e)
Total Units: 24
Trade Names: Domino's (24)
Units Franchised From: 24
Primary Menu: Pizza (24)
Areas of Operation: CA
Type of Foodservice: Quick Serve (24)
Franchise Affiliation: Domino's Pizza Inc, ANN ARBOR, MI

Key Personnel
FERNANDO TAPIA - Owner; General Buyer

Friendly Franchisees Corp
1 Centerpointe Dr Ste 400
La Palma, CA 90623-2530

Telephone: (714) 736-8900
Fax Number: (714) 736-8909
Internet Homepage: ffcorp.org
Company Email: info@ffcorp.org
Type of Business: Chain Restaurant Operator
Year Founded: 2000
Total Sales: $158,640,000 (e)
Number of Employees: 3,055
Average Check: Breakfast(5); Lunch(8); Dinner(12)
Total Units: 74
Trade Names: Carl's Jr. (74)
Units Franchised From: 74
Preferred Square Footage: 2,500; 3,000; 4,000
Preferred Location Types: Freestanding; Regional Mall; Strip Mall
Primary Menu: Hamburger (74); Mexican (64)
Areas of Operation: CA
Type of Foodservice: Quick Serve (74)
Franchise Affiliation: Carl's Jr., FRANKLIN, TN
Primary Distributors: (Full Line) McLane/Rocky Mount, ROCKY MOUNT, NC

Key Personnel
HARSHAD DHAROD - President; Director Operations, Information Systems; General Buyer
KEVIN WHITTON - CFO
DANIEL BOOSE - COO
WALEED ABDULLAH - COO
ANDREW PIERCE - Senior VP Operations
SHAWN REZAEI - VP Operations
NILESH SHAH - Director Operations
VASILIS KARANTZAVELOS - Director Information Technology
SAI BADARALA - Manager

Boiling Point Group, Inc.
13668 Valley Blvd Unit C2
La Puente, CA 91746-2572

Telephone: (888) 383-8325
Internet Homepage: bpgroupusa.com
Company Email: cs@bpgroupusa.com
Type of Business: Chain Restaurant Operator
Year Founded: 2004
Total Units: 28
Trade Names: Boiling Point (28)
Company-Owned Units: 28
Primary Menu: Asian (28)
Areas of Operation: CA, WA, BC
Foreign Countries: CANADA; CHINA
Type of Foodservice: Casual Dining (28)

Key Personnel
CHEN ANDY - Director Operations
CHIHYAO KO - Director Supply Chain
ANDY HSU - Director Product Development

M Lehmann Enterprises
1073 N Hacienda Blvd
La Puente, CA 91744-2020

Mailing Address: PO Box 938, LA PUENTE, CA, 91747-0938
Telephone: (626) 369-5752
Type of Business: Chain Restaurant Operator
Total Sales: $40,044,000 (e)
Total Units: 20
Trade Names: Domino's (20)
Units Franchised From: 20
Primary Menu: Pizza (20)
Areas of Operation: CA
Type of Foodservice: Quick Serve (20)
Franchise Affiliation: Domino's Pizza Inc, ANN ARBOR, MI

Key Personnel
MARK KRANIGER - President; General Buyer
MONICA GUEVARA - Director Operations

Feist Family Enterprises LLC
78380 Highway 111
La Quinta, CA 92253

Telephone: (760) 771-8242
Type of Business: Chain Restaurant Operator
Total Sales: $1,795,000 (e)
Total Units: 3
Trade Names: Cold Stone Creamery (3)
Units Franchised From: 3
Primary Menu: Snacks (3)
Areas of Operation: CA
Type of Foodservice: Quick Serve (3)
Franchise Affiliation: Kahala Brands, SCOTTSDALE, AZ

Key Personnel
WILLIAM P. FEIST - Partner
JEANNETTE FEIST - Partner

LG's Prime Steak House
78525 Highway 111 Ste 100
La Quinta, CA 92253-2080

Telephone: (760) 771-9911
Fax Number: (760) 779-1979
Internet Homepage: lgsprimesteakhouse.com
Company Email: LQ@lgsprimesteakhouse.com
Type of Business: Chain Restaurant Operator
Year Founded: 1991
Total Sales: $9,327,000 (e)
Alcohol Sales: 10%
Number of Employees: 45
Average Check: Dinner(60)
Internet Order Processing: Yes
Internet Sales: 0.50%
Total Units: 2
Trade Names: LG's Prime Steak House (2)
Company-Owned Units: 2
Preferred Location Types: Freestanding; Strip Mall
Alcohol Served: Beer, Wine, Liquor
Primary Menu: Steak (2)
Areas of Operation: CA
Type of Foodservice: Fine Dining (2)
Primary Distributors: (Food) Crown Meat & Provisions Inc., PALM SPRINGS, CA

Key Personnel
GAIL GREENBERG - President; General Buyer
DANIEL PHELPS - General Manager

J & R Hock Enterprises
555 Corporate Dr Ste 135
Ladera Ranch, CA 92694-2176

Telephone: (949) 276-8276
Fax Number: (949) 276-8280
Type of Business: Chain Restaurant Operator
Total Sales: $19,010,000 (e)
Number of Employees: 836
Total Units: 7
Trade Names: Taco Bell (7)
Units Franchised From: 7
Preferred Location Types: Freestanding
Primary Menu: Taco (7)
Areas of Operation: CA
Type of Foodservice: Quick Serve (7)
Franchise Affiliation: Taco Bell Corp., IRVINE, CA

Key Personnel
RAY HOCK - President; General Buyer
JENNIFER MANCINI - CFO
ANDREW HOCK - VP
CUTBERTO BOLANOS - Director Human Resources
LISA CERVANTES - Director Operations

Janrus & Asbek Inc.
3508 Mt Diablo Blvd Ste J
Lafayette, CA 94549-3888

Telephone: (925) 283-6877
Fax Number: (925) 283-1438
Internet Homepage: caspershotdogs.com
Company Email: paul@caspershotdogs.com
Type of Business: Chain Restaurant Operator
Year Founded: 1934
Total Sales: $7,129,000 (e)
Number of Employees: 50
Average Check: Lunch(8); Dinner(8)
Total Units: 8
Trade Names: Casper's Hot Dogs (8)
Company-Owned Units: 8
Preferred Square Footage: 900; 1,500
Preferred Location Types: Freestanding; Strip Mall
Primary Menu: Hot Dogs (8)
Areas of Operation: CA
Type of Foodservice: Quick Serve (8)

Key Personnel
CAROL RUSTIGAN - Partner; Director Real Estate, Design
MARGIE DORIAN - Partner; Director Facility/Maintenance, Supply Chain
LINDA FORD - Manager Information Systems, Human Resources
JACK DORIAN - General Buyer

zpizza International
30822 Coast Hwy
Laguana Beach, CA 92651

Telephone: (949) 200-7902
Fax Number: (949) 222-0304
Internet Homepage: zpizza.com
Company Email: zpizza@zpizza.com
Type of Business: Chain Restaurant Operator
Year Founded: 1986
Systemwide Sales: $30,406,000 (e)
Total Sales: $5,263,000 (e)
Alcohol Sales: 5%
Number of Employees: 77
Average Check: Lunch(12); Dinner(14)
Internet Order Processing: Yes
Total Units: 24
Trade Names: zpizza (43)
Company-Owned Units: 11
Units Franchised To: 35
Preferred Square Footage: 1,250; 1,500; 3,000
Preferred Location Types: Downtown; Freestanding; Strip Mall
Alcohol Served: Beer, Wine
Primary Menu: Pizza (43)
Areas of Operation: AZ, CA, NC, NV, NY, OR, SC, TX, VA, WA
Foreign Countries: SOUTH KOREA; UNITED ARAB EMIRATES; VIETNAM
Type of Foodservice: Casual Dining (43)
Catering Services: Yes
Primary Distributors: (Full Line) SYSCO Food Services of Los Angeles Inc., WALNUT, CA

Key Personnel
SID FANAROF - Founder
CHRISTOPHER BRIGHT - President; Treasurer
AL ROWE - VP
CATHY TOMBS - VP Administration
JOLLY KAHBRANI - Manager Accounting
MIKE ENSCH - Coordinator Franchise Development

Montage Hotels & Resorts
30801 Coast Hwy
Laguna Beach, CA 92651-4221

Telephone: (949) 715-6000
Fax Number: (949) 715-6100
Internet Homepage: montagebeverlyhills.com; montagehotels.com; montagelagunabeach.com
Type of Business: Foodservice Operations - Hotel/Motels
Year Founded: 2003
Total Sales: $67,760,000 (e)
Alcohol Sales: 10%
Number of Employees: 574
Total Units: 7
Restaurants in Hotels: 8
Trade Names: Montage Beverly Hills (1); Montage Deer Valley (1); Montage Kapalua Bay (1); Montage Laguna Beach (1); Montage Los Cabos (1); Montage Palmetto Bluff (1); Montage Residences Big Sky (1)
Company-Owned Units: 8
Alcohol Served: Beer, Wine, Liquor
Areas of Operation: CA, SC, UT, FC
Type of Foodservice: Casual Dining (7); Family Restaurant (1)

Primary Distributors: (Food) SYSCO Food Services of Central California Inc., MODESTO, CA; (Food) US Foods, CORONA, CA
Notes: The company derives approximately 75% of total revenue from hotel/resort operations.

Key Personnel
ALAN FUERSTMAN - Co-Founder; CEO
MICHAEL FUERSTMAN - Co-Founder; Creative Director
JASON HERTHEL - President; COO
BRIAN KARABA - CFO; Exec VP
ROBIN KENNEDY - Exec VP Acquisitions, Development
CHRISTOPHER HAMAWAY - Exec VP Marketing, Sales
IQBAL BASHIR - Exec VP Finance
BILL CLAYPOOL - Exec VP
MANDY HOLLOWAY - Senior VP Human Resources
TINA NECRASON - Senior VP
OD VINCENT - Senior VP
DAX ACOSTA - VP Acquisitions, Development
ANDREW FLOR - VP Risk Management
BOB FREAR - VP Sales
KACEY BRUNO - VP Communications

Pick Up Stix Inc.
24422 Avenida De La Carlota Ste 360
Laguna Hills, CA 92653-3603

Telephone: (800) 400-7849
Fax Number: (949) 366-0538
Internet Homepage: pickupstix.com
Company Email: stixgeneralinquiries@pickupstix.com
Type of Business: Chain Restaurant Operator
Year Founded: 1989
Systemwide Sales: $101,757,000 (e)
Total Sales: $101,370,000 (e)
Number of Employees: 880
Average Check: Lunch(10); Dinner(16)
Total Units: 55
Trade Names: Pick Up Stix Fresh Asian Kitchen (55)
Company-Owned Units: 55
Preferred Square Footage: 1,800; 2,400; 2,500
Preferred Location Types: Freestanding; Strip Mall
Primary Menu: Asian (55)
Areas of Operation: CA
Type of Foodservice: Fast Casual (55)
Catering Services: Yes
Parent Company: West Coast Capital, SHERMAN OAKS, CA

Key Personnel
LORNE GOLDBERG - CEO; Owner; General Buyer
KELLY KEARNEY - Director Sales, Catering
NEANG KHIT - Regional Director Operations
BREANNE VIRAMONTES - Regional Director Operations
DANA ALEXANDER (ALDRIDGE) - Manager Human Resources

Spikes Fish House
27020 Alicia Pkwy Ste D
Laguna Niguel, CA 92677-3420

Telephone: (949) 448-8488
Internet Homepage: spikesfishhouse.com
Company Email: TimAspel@SpikesFishHouse.com
Type of Business: Chain Restaurant Operator
Year Founded: 1988
Total Sales: $23,736,000 (e)
Alcohol Sales: 15%
Number of Employees: 350
Average Check: Lunch(14); Dinner(20)
Internet Sales: 2.00%
Total Units: 2
Trade Names: Spike's Fish House (2)
Company-Owned Units: 2
Preferred Square Footage: 3,000
Preferred Location Types: Strip Mall
Alcohol Served: Beer, Wine
Primary Menu: Seafood (2)
Areas of Operation: CA
Type of Foodservice: Fast Casual (2)
Catering Services: Yes

Key Personnel
TIM ASPEL - CEO Facility/Maintenance, Supply Chain, Real Estate, Design; President; Director Finance, Operations, Purchasing, Information Systems, Menu Development

Wiles Restaurants Inc
28022 La Paz Rd
Laguna Niguel, CA 92677-7029

Telephone: (949) 389-1970
Fax Number: (949) 931-5181
Internet Homepage: wilescompanies.com
Type of Business: Chain Restaurant Operator
Total Sales: $44,470,000 (e)
Total Units: 21
Trade Names: Carl's Jr. (21)
Units Franchised From: 21
Primary Menu: Hamburger (21)
Areas of Operation: CA, NM
Type of Foodservice: Quick Serve (21)
Franchise Affiliation: Carl's Jr., FRANKLIN, TN

Key Personnel
BRETT WILES - President; General Buyer
BLAINE WILES - VP

Del Taco Restaurants Inc.
25521 Commercentre Dr Ste 200
Lake Forest, CA 92630-8872

Telephone: (949) 462-9300
Fax Number: (949) 462-7444
Internet Homepage: deltaco.com; deltacofranchise.com
Company Email: customercommentline@deltaco.com
Type of Business: Chain Restaurant Operator
Year Founded: 1964
Systemwide Sales: $990,373,000 (e)
Publicly Held: Yes
Total Sales: $439,601,000 (e)
Number of Employees: 14,600
Average Check: Breakfast(8); Lunch(8); Dinner(8)
Internet Order Processing: Yes
Internet Sales: 1.00%
Total Units: 592
Trade Names: Del Taco (592)
Company-Owned Units: 171
Units Franchised To: 421
Preferred Square Footage: 2,260; 2,380; 2,800
Preferred Location Types: Convenience Store/Gas Station; Freestanding; Regional Mall
Primary Menu: Mexican (0); Taco (592)
Projected Openings: 44
Areas of Operation: AZ, CA, CO, FL, GA, GU, ID, NM, NV, OH, OR, TN, TX, UT, WA
Type of Foodservice: Quick Serve (592)
Foodservice Management Venues: Military Feeding
Primary Distributors: (Full Line) McLane/Riverside, RIVERSIDE, CA
Parent Company: Jack in the Box Inc., SAN DIEGO, CA

Key Personnel
LAWRENCE LEVY - Chairman
DAVID A. SNYDER - CIO; VP Information Technology
JACK TANG - Chief Compliance Officer; Senior VP; General Counsel
JASON MCFARLAND - Area Director
KEVIN POPE - VP Operations
JEANNE GRAVES - VP Human Resources
DAVID OCALLAGHAN - VP Operations
KOFI BOAITEY - Senior Director Safety, Quality Assurance-Food
MARCUS MCLAUGHLIN - Director Risk Management
TOM JOHNSON - Director Consumer Insights
AL PACHECO - Director Accounting
JAMES HOWARTH - Director Information Technology
TRUNG HUYNH - Director Accounting
MARK BIXLER - Director Region
ERIK COLLINS - Director Digital Marketing
JEREMIAS AGUAYO - Director Innovation

MICHAEL E. VAZQUEZ - Director Operations
ROB STEVENS - Director Operations
STACEY GOODWIN - Director Media
MUNA AFGHANI - Senior Manager Product Development
PAULA HENKEL - Manager Training
RAPHAEL GROSS - Manager Investor Relations
PEGGY DEMEDIO-LINDSAY - Manager
KAREN RING - Manager Production
AMANDA GARCIA - Manager Restaurant Operations
DANIEL SHAW - Manager Accounting
ANDRES Y. HONG - Manager Financial Planning
MIRYAM HERNANDEZ - Manager Legal
LORENA V - Manager Human Resources
APRIL REINS - Manager Field Marketing
JACQUELINE TERRONES - Manager Field Marketing
ETSY CHANG - Associate Manager Real Estate
CAITLIN ZINN - Coordinator Technology

H&H West, LLC
23572 El Toro Rd Ste B
Lake Forest, CA 92630-4779

Telephone: (949) 770-0270
Type of Business: Chain Restaurant Operator
Total Sales: $4,414,000 (e)
Total Units: 3
Trade Names: Jersey Mike's Subs (3)
Units Franchised From: 3
Primary Menu: Sandwiches/Deli (3)
Areas of Operation: CA
Type of Foodservice: Quick Serve (3)
Franchise Affiliation: Jersey Mike's Franchise Systems, MANASQUAN, NJ

Key Personnel
HECTOR HAGET - Owner; General Buyer

Makar Foods, Inc.
23736 Birtcher Dr
Lake Forest, CA 92630-1771

Telephone: (949) 367-2980
Type of Business: Chain Restaurant Operator
Total Sales: $8,307,000 (e)
Total Units: 3
Trade Names: Jack in the Box (3)
Units Franchised From: 3
Primary Menu: Hamburger (3)
Areas of Operation: CA
Type of Foodservice: Quick Serve (3)
Franchise Affiliation: Jack in the Box Restaurants, SAN DIEGO, CA

Key Personnel
GEORGE CRANKSHAW - Owner; General Buyer

Subway Franchise
22481 El Toro Rd Ste B
Lake Forest, CA 92630-5052

Telephone: (949) 837-3391
Fax Number: (949) 458-8254
Internet Homepage: subway.com
Type of Business: Chain Restaurant Operator
Total Sales: $4,646,000 (e)
Total Units: 8
Trade Names: Subway (8)
Units Franchised From: 8
Primary Menu: Sandwiches/Deli (8)
Areas of Operation: CA
Type of Foodservice: Quick Serve (8)
Franchise Affiliation: Doctor's Associates Inc., MILFORD, CT

Key Personnel
KAM MAKHANI - President

The Johnny Rockets Group Inc.
2 S Pointe Dr Ste 200
Lake Forest, CA 92630-2299

Telephone: (949) 643-6100
Fax Number: (866) 209-9523
Internet Homepage: johnnyrockets.com; thejohnnysburgerfactory.com
Company Email: receptionist@johnnyrockets.com
Listing Type: Subsidiary
Type of Business: Chain Restaurant Operator
Year Founded: 1986
Systemwide Sales: $260,835,000 (e)
Total Sales: $68,250,000 (e)
Number of Employees: 3,310
Internet Order Processing: Yes
Internet Sales: 5.00%
Total Units: 325
Trade Names: Johnny Rockets (325)
Company-Owned Units: 9
Units Franchised To: 316
Preferred Square Footage: 1,100; 1,800; 2,500
Preferred Location Types: Airports; Downtown; Freestanding; Institution (college/hospital); Lifestyle Center; Regional Mall; Strip Mall
Primary Menu: Hamburger (325)
Projected Openings: 20
Projected Remodelings: 20
Areas of Operation: AL, AZ, CA, CO, CT, DC, FL, GA, IL, IN, KY, MA, MD, MI, MN, MO, NC, NJ, NM, NV, NY, OH, PA, PR, RI, SC, TN, TX, UT, VA, WA, ON
Foreign Countries: AUSTRALIA; BAHRAIN; BANGLADESH; BRAZIL; CANADA; CHILE; COSTA RICA; CYPRUS; ECUADOR; GERMANY; HONDURAS; INDONESIA; ITALY; KUWAIT; MALAYSIA; MEXICO; NIGERIA; NORWAY; PANAMA; PERU; POLAND; QATAR; SAUDI ARABIA; SOUTH KOREA; TUNISIA;UNITED ARAB EMIRATES; URUGUAY
Type of Foodservice: Family Restaurant (325)
Primary Distributors: (Full Line) US Foods-Los Angeles, LA MIRADA, CA
Parent Company: Fat Brands, Inc., BEVERLY HILLS, CA
Headquarters: FIC Restaurants, WILBRAHAM, MA

Key Personnel
SUSANNE STOVER - CFO
MARC ABENOJA - VP Operations, International Division
CHAZ DUNHAM - VP Operations
ALAN HINSON - Corporate Secretary; General Counsel
KEVIN MCCARTNEY - General Manager
CHRIS FERGUSON - Senior Director Operations
DAVID ARCHILA - Director Franchise Operations
KYLE ELDRIDGE - Director Operations
MARRIETTE SIMONI - Director Marketing
JORGE RAMOS - Senior Manager Information Technology

DiGiovanni Inc.
13524 Highway 8 Business
Lakeside, CA 92040-5207

Telephone: (619) 561-1651
Fax Number: (619) 561-1616
Internet Homepage: ciao2.com; gaetanoslakeside.com
Company Email: gaetanoslakeside@gmail.com
Type of Business: Chain Restaurant Operator
Year Founded: 1971
Total Sales: $3,884,000 (e)
Alcohol Sales: 10%
Number of Employees: 50
Average Check: Lunch(18); Dinner(30)
Total Units: 2
Trade Names: Ciao 2 (1); Gaetano's Ristorante (1)
Company-Owned Units: 2
Preferred Location Types: Freestanding
Alcohol Served: Beer, Wine
Primary Menu: Italian (2)
Areas of Operation: CA
Type of Foodservice: Casual Dining (2)
Catering Services: Yes
Primary Distributors: (Full Line) SYSCO Food Services of Los Angeles Inc., WALNUT, CA

Key Personnel
ALDO DIGIOVANNI - President; Partner;

Executive Chef; Director Purchasing, Loss Prevention, Product Development, Food Safety; Buyer Beverages
NEIL DIGIOVANNI - Partner; Controller; General Manager; Director Real Estate; General Buyer
MARIA DIGIOVANNI - Director Catering

Dr. Sweet Tooth
5107 Candlewood St
Lakewood, CA 90712-1921

Telephone: (562) 925-1500
Type of Business: Chain Restaurant Operator
Total Sales: $1,257,000 (e)
Total Units: 2
Trade Names: Cold Stone Creamery (2)
Units Franchised From: 2
Primary Menu: Snacks (2)
Areas of Operation: CA
Type of Foodservice: Quick Serve (2)
Franchise Affiliation: Kahala Brands, SCOTTSDALE, AZ

Key Personnel
VINCENT CHAO - Partner
MIN WANG - Partner

Freeman Pizza Companies, Inc.
5924 Edgefield St
Lakewood, CA 90713-1202

Telephone: (562) 773-0432
Type of Business: Chain Restaurant Operator
Total Sales: $1,644,000 (e)
Total Units: 2
Trade Names: Little Caesars Pizza (2)
Units Franchised From: 2
Primary Menu: Pizza (2)
Areas of Operation: CA
Type of Foodservice: Quick Serve (2)
Franchise Affiliation: Little Caesar Enterprises Inc., DETROIT, MI

Key Personnel
MICHAEL FREEMAN - President; General Buyer
LUANNE FREEMAN - CFO

Piazza Family Restaurants Inc.
4128 Paramount Blvd Ste B
Lakewood, CA 90712-3919

Telephone: (562) 497-0055
Fax Number: (562) 497-0060
Type of Business: Chain Restaurant Operator
Year Founded: 1965
Total Sales: $70,320,000 (e)
Number of Employees: 450
Average Check: Breakfast(8); Lunch(10); Dinner(12)
Total Units: 15
Trade Names: McDonald's (15)
Units Franchised From: 15
Preferred Square Footage: 2,500; 3,000
Preferred Location Types: Community Mall; Discount Dept. Stores; Freestanding
Primary Menu: Hamburger (15)
Areas of Operation: CA
Type of Foodservice: Quick Serve (15)
Franchise Affiliation: McDonald's Corporation, CHICAGO, IL
Primary Distributors: (Food) The Martin-Brower Co., CITY OF INDUSTRY, CA

Key Personnel
RONALD PIAZZA - President; Partner; Director Finance, Information Systems, Real Estate, Human Resources; General Buyer
SEAN PIAZZA - Partner; General Manager; General Buyer
LORI MCDOWELL - Controller
CORY THURBER - Director Operations; Supervisor Operations, Facility/Maintenance

Minc
42913 Capital Dr Ste 106
Lancaster, CA 93535-4556

Telephone: (661) 949-8332
Fax Number: (661) 949-8839
Company Email: grimace2@hotmail.com
Type of Business: Chain Restaurant Operator
Total Sales: $125,880,000 (e)
Number of Employees: 850
Total Units: 27
Trade Names: McDonald's (27)
Units Franchised From: 27
Preferred Square Footage: 2,500
Primary Menu: Hamburger (27)
Areas of Operation: CA
Type of Foodservice: Quick Serve (27)
Franchise Affiliation: McDonald's Corporation, CHICAGO, IL

Key Personnel
HERNANDO MARROQUIN - President; General Buyer

Sangha Enterprises
305 Lambeth Ct
Lincoln, CA 95648-7202

Telephone: (530) 624-5999
Fax Number: (916) 209-8604
Type of Business: Chain Restaurant Operator
Total Sales: $6,225,000 (e)
Total Units: 5
Trade Names: Little Caesars Pizza (5)
Units Franchised From: 5
Preferred Location Types: Strip Mall
Primary Menu: Pizza (5)
Areas of Operation: CA
Type of Foodservice: Quick Serve (5)
Franchise Affiliation: Little Caesar Enterprises Inc., DETROIT, MI

Key Personnel
B. J. BAINS - Partner
A. SANGHA - Partner
A. SINGH - Partner
B. J. SINGH - Partner

Hundal Foods Inc.
1813 4th St
Livermore, CA 94550-4453

Telephone: (925) 455-4743
Fax Number: (925) 373-0517
Type of Business: Chain Restaurant Operator
Year Founded: 1991
Total Sales: $54,770,000 (e)
Number of Employees: 688
Average Check: Lunch(8); Dinner(8)
Total Units: 39
Trade Names: Carl's Jr. (13); Jamba Juice (26)
Units Franchised From: 39
Preferred Square Footage: 2,500; 3,000; 4,000
Preferred Location Types: Freestanding
Primary Menu: American (26); Hamburger (13)
Areas of Operation: CA
Type of Foodservice: Quick Serve (39)
Franchise Affiliation: Carl's Jr., FRANKLIN, TN

Key Personnel
DALJIT HUNDAL - President; Partner; General Buyer

McDonald's of Livermore
583 Leisure St
Livermore, CA 94551-5148

Telephone: (925) 454-2964
Type of Business: Chain Restaurant Operator
Total Sales: $32,940,000 (e)
Total Units: 7
Trade Names: McDonald's (7)
Units Franchised From: 7
Preferred Location Types: Freestanding
Primary Menu: Hamburger (7)
Areas of Operation: CA
Type of Foodservice: Quick Serve (7)
Franchise Affiliation: McDonald's Corporation, CHICAGO, IL

Key Personnel
TIMOTHY MORGAN - President; General Buyer

Satgur Enterprises, Inc.
1092 E Stanley Blvd
Livermore, CA 94550-4157

Telephone: (925) 413-9738
Fax Number: (925) 447-4392
Type of Business: Chain Restaurant Operator
Total Sales: $2,075,000 (e)
Total Units: 2
Trade Names: Little Caesars Pizza (2)
Units Franchised From: 2
Primary Menu: Pizza (2)
Areas of Operation: CA
Type of Foodservice: Quick Serve (2)
Franchise Affiliation: Little Caesar Enterprises Inc., DETROIT, MI

Key Personnel
BLUPINDER SINGH - Owner; General Buyer

Rimel's Zenbu Cardiff LLC
1030 Torrey Pines Rd Ste E
Lo Jolla, CA 92037

Telephone: (858) 454-6045
Internet Homepage: rimelsrestaurants.com
Company Email: rimelscardiff@rimelsrestaurants.com
Type of Business: Chain Restaurant Operator
Total Sales: $6,876,000 (e)
Alcohol Sales: 5%
Total Units: 2
Trade Names: Rimel's Rotisserie (2)
Company-Owned Units: 2
Alcohol Served: Beer, Wine, Liquor
Primary Menu: American (2)
Areas of Operation: CA
Type of Foodservice: Casual Dining (2)

Key Personnel
MATT RIMEL - President; General Buyer

Vision F.S., Inc.
701 E Kettleman Ln
Lodi, CA 95240-5916

Telephone: (209) 334-1337
Company Email: dennysrestaurant7189@gmail.com
Type of Business: Chain Restaurant Operator
Total Sales: $5,981,000 (e)
Total Units: 2
Trade Names: Denny's (2)
Units Franchised From: 2
Primary Menu: American (2)
Areas of Operation: CA
Type of Foodservice: Family Restaurant (2)
Franchise Affiliation: Denny's Corporation, SPARTANBURG, SC

Key Personnel
MASHHOUR AZAD - President; General Buyer
GUILLERMO ESTRADA - General Manager

PCH Venture Group, Inc.
25601 Narbonne Ave
Lomita, CA 90717

Telephone: (310) 534-0192
Type of Business: Chain Restaurant Operator
Total Sales: $57,040,000 (e)
Total Units: 22
Trade Names: Jack in the Box (22)
Units Franchised From: 22
Preferred Location Types: Freestanding
Primary Menu: Hamburger (22)
Areas of Operation: CA
Type of Foodservice: Quick Serve (22)
Franchise Affiliation: Jack in the Box Restaurants, SAN DIEGO, CA

Key Personnel
LEE SU - Partner; General Buyer
ERH-MEI SU - Partner; General Buyer

Big Fun Foods
25 Savona Walk
Long Beach, CA 90803-4109

Telephone: (562) 438-1018
Type of Business: Chain Restaurant Operator
Total Sales: $15,190,000 (e)
Total Units: 6
Trade Names: Jack in the Box (6)
Units Franchised From: 6
Primary Menu: Hamburger (6)
Areas of Operation: CA
Type of Foodservice: Quick Serve (6)
Franchise Affiliation: Jack in the Box Restaurants, SAN DIEGO, CA

Key Personnel
WAYNE TOWNSEND - Partner

Charo Chicken Systems Inc.
4752 E Pacific Coast Hwy
Long Beach, CA 90804-3241

Telephone: (562) 498-5600
Internet Homepage: charochicken.com
Company Email: moe@charochicken.com
Type of Business: Chain Restaurant Operator
Year Founded: 1984
Total Sales: $7,506,000 (e)
Number of Employees: 259
Average Check: Lunch(32); Dinner(32)
Total Units: 6
Trade Names: Charo Chicken (6)
Company-Owned Units: 6
Preferred Square Footage: 2,500
Preferred Location Types: Freestanding; Regional Mall; Strip Mall
Primary Menu: Chicken (6)
Areas of Operation: CA
Type of Foodservice: Quick Serve (6)
Catering Services: Yes
Primary Distributors: (Full Line) Jacmar Foodservice Distribution, CITY OF INDUSTRY, CA

Key Personnel
MOE BONAKDAR - Chairman; Owner; CFO; VP Operations, Purchasing, Human Resources, Menu Development, Catering; Corporate Secretary; General Buyer
CARLOS DOS SANTOS - Manager District

Domino's Franchisee
393 Redondo Ave
Long Beach, CA 90814-2656

Telephone: (562) 434-9971
Type of Business: Chain Restaurant Operator
Total Sales: $6,193,000 (e)
Total Units: 3
Trade Names: Domino's (3)
Units Franchised From: 3
Primary Menu: Pizza (3)
Areas of Operation: CA
Type of Foodservice: Quick Serve (3)
Franchise Affiliation: Domino's Pizza Inc, ANN ARBOR, MI

Key Personnel
HOUMAN KHAZAN - Owner; General Buyer

Forty Niner Shops Inc.
6049 E 7th St
Long Beach, CA 90840-0007

Telephone: (562) 985-7700
Fax Number: (562) 985-1593
Internet Homepage: shopthebeach.com
Company Email: fns-communications@csulb.edu
Type of Business: Nontraditional Foodservice Operator
Year Founded: 1949
Total Sales: $70,240,000 (e)
Alcohol Sales: 2%
Number of Employees: 750
Average Check: Breakfast(5); Lunch(10); Dinner(14)
Internet Order Processing: Yes
Internet Sales: 1.00%
Total Units: 8

Trade Names: Beach Walk (1); Chartroom (1); Hibachi San (1); Nugget Grill & Pub (1); Outpost (1); Panda Express (1); Starbucks (2)
Company-Owned Units: 4
Units Franchised From: 4
Preferred Location Types: Freestanding
Alcohol Served: Beer, Wine
Primary Menu: American (4); Chinese (1); Coffee (2); Japanese (1)
Areas of Operation: CA
Type of Foodservice: Cafeteria (1); Casual Dining (4); Quick Serve (3)
Primary Distributors: (Food) SYSCO Food Services of Los Angeles Inc., WALNUT, CA
Notes: The company derives approximately 75% of its revenue from retail operations.

Key Personnel
DON PENROD - CEO; General Manager
KIERSTIN STICKNEY - Director Marketing, Communications
ROSA HERNANDEZ - Director Human Resources
ROSA HERNANDEZ-HENDERSON - Director Human Resources
JASON EISENMANN - Manager Warehouse

Great Circle Family Foods LLC
4760 E Los Coyotes Diagonal
Long Beach, CA 90815-2825

Telephone: (213) 489-2340
Fax Number: (562) 597-5648
Internet Homepage: gcff.com
Type of Business: Chain Restaurant Operator
Year Founded: 1997
Total Sales: $58,670,000 (e)
Number of Employees: 618
Average Check: Breakfast(6); Lunch(6); Dinner(6)
Total Units: 17
Trade Names: Krispy Kreme Doughnuts (17)
Units Franchised From: 17
Preferred Square Footage: 2,000; 4,000
Preferred Location Types: Freestanding; Strip Mall
Primary Menu: Snacks (17)
Areas of Operation: CA
Type of Foodservice: Quick Serve (17)
Franchise Affiliation: Krispy Kreme Doughnut Corporation, CHARLOTTE, NC
Primary Distributors: (Full Line) MBM Corporation, FULLERTON, CA

Key Personnel
WENDY R. GLICKMAN - Exec VP
EDDIE OHAYA - General Manager

K & R Corp./Kashaco Inc.
1084 Redondo Ave
Long Beach, CA 90804-3927

Telephone: (562) 434-8838
Fax Number: (562) 434-8874
Type of Business: Chain Restaurant Operator
Total Sales: $19,813,000 (e)
Average Check: Breakfast(8); Lunch(8); Dinner(8)
Total Units: 4
Trade Names: McDonald's (4)
Units Franchised From: 4
Preferred Square Footage: 2,500; 3,000
Preferred Location Types: Freestanding
Primary Menu: Hamburger (4)
Areas of Operation: CA
Type of Foodservice: Quick Serve (4)
Franchise Affiliation: McDonald's Corporation, CHICAGO, IL
Primary Distributors: (Food) The Martin-Brower Co., CITY OF INDUSTRY, CA

Key Personnel
KEVIN KASHA - President; General Manager; General Buyer

LMS Group, Inc.
5150 Atlantic Ave
Long Beach, CA 90805-6510

Telephone: (562) 423-2164
Type of Business: Chain Restaurant Operator
Total Sales: $8,025,000 (e)
Total Units: 3
Trade Names: Jack in the Box (3)
Units Franchised From: 3
Primary Menu: Hamburger (3)
Areas of Operation: CA
Type of Foodservice: Quick Serve (3)
Franchise Affiliation: Jack in the Box Restaurants, SAN DIEGO, CA

Key Personnel
LEE SU - Owner; General Buyer
DAVID SCHLIEP - Manager Sales, National

Mangione Inc.
3777 Long Beach Blvd Ste 200
Long Beach, CA 90807-3337

Telephone: (562) 988-1600
Fax Number: (562) 988-8037
Company Email: mangioneinc@gmail.com
Type of Business: Chain Restaurant Operator
Year Founded: 1993
Total Sales: $42,820,000 (e)
Number of Employees: 440
Average Check: Breakfast(10); Lunch(10); Dinner(12)
Total Units: 9
Trade Names: McDonald's (9)
Units Franchised From: 9
Preferred Square Footage: 3,000
Preferred Location Types: Discount Dept. Stores; Freestanding
Primary Menu: Hamburger (9)
Areas of Operation: CA
Type of Foodservice: In-Store Feeder (1); Quick Serve (8)
Franchise Affiliation: McDonald's Corporation, CHICAGO, IL
Primary Distributors: (Food) Golden State Foods Corporation, IRVINE, CA

Key Personnel
MICHAEL MANGIONE JR - President; Director Finance, Information Systems, Supply Chain, Real Estate; General Buyer
EVA CARLOS - Manager Accounting
DEANNAH DELFIN - Manager Human Resources

SuperMex Restaurants Inc.
732 E 1st St
Long Beach, CA 90802-5110

Telephone: (562) 436-4728
Fax Number: (562) 684-0839
Internet Homepage: supermex.com
Company Email: info@supermex.com
Type of Business: Chain Restaurant Operator
Year Founded: 1974
Total Sales: $3,687,000 (e)
Average Check: Dinner(12)
Internet Order Processing: Yes
Total Units: 6
Trade Names: Super Mex (6)
Company-Owned Units: 6
Units Franchised To: 7
Primary Menu: Mexican (6)
Areas of Operation: CA
Type of Foodservice: Family Restaurant (6)
Catering Services: Yes

Key Personnel
MANUEL OROZCO JR - CFO; VP Real Estate, Human Resources

The Queen Mary
1126 Queens Hwy
Long Beach, CA 90802-6331

Telephone: (562) 435-3511
Fax Number: (562) 437-4531
Internet Homepage: queenmary.com
Company Email: restaurants@queenmary.com
Type of Business: Foodservice Operations - Hotel/Motels
Total Sales: $4,876,000 (e)

Number of Employees: 40
Average Check: Dinner(58)
Total Units: 3
Trade Names: Midship Marketplace (1); Sir Winston's (1); The Promenade Cafe (1)
Company-Owned Units: 3
Preferred Location Types: Other
Alcohol Served: Beer, Wine, Liquor
Primary Menu: Californian (1); Sandwiches/Deli (1); Seafood (1); Snacks (0)
Areas of Operation: CA
Type of Foodservice: Casual Dining (2); Quick Serve (1)

Key Personnel
CHRISTOPHER WILMOTH - Executive Director Marketing, Communications

Mr. Pickle's Inc.
6207 S Walnut St Ste 100
Loomis, CA 95650

Telephone: (855) 677-4255
Fax Number: (855) 677-4255
Internet Homepage: mrpickles.com
Company Email: info@mrpickles.com
Type of Business: Chain Restaurant Operator
Year Founded: 1996
Total Sales: $27,710,000 (e)
Total Units: 48
Trade Names: Mr. Pickle's (48)
Company-Owned Units: 48
Primary Menu: Sandwiches/Deli (48)
Areas of Operation: CA
Type of Foodservice: Fast Casual (48)

Key Personnel
FRANK FAGUNDES - CEO
HELENA BITTER - Manager

Amber India
4926 El Camino Real
Los Altos, CA 94022-1409

Telephone: (650) 968-7511
Fax Number: (650) 968-1820
Internet Homepage: amber-india.com
Company Email: info.mv@amber-india.com
Type of Business: Chain Restaurant Operator
Total Sales: $5,350,000 (e)
Alcohol Sales: 6%
Number of Employees: 200
Average Check: Lunch(16); Dinner(36)
Total Units: 5
Trade Names: Amber Cafe (1); Amber Dhara (1); Amber India (3)
Company-Owned Units: 5
Preferred Location Types: Community Mall; Freestanding; Hotel/Motel; Strip Mall
Alcohol Served: Beer, Wine, Liquor
Primary Menu: Indian (5)
Areas of Operation: CA
Type of Foodservice: Casual Dining (1); Fine Dining (3)
Catering Services: Yes
Primary Distributors: (Full Line) SYSCO Food Services of Los Angeles Inc., WALNUT, CA

Key Personnel
VIJAY BIST - Partner
VIJAY KUMAR - Partner
A.J. KAHOL - General Manager; General Buyer
APURVA PANCHAL - Executive Chef

Harman Management Corp.
199 1st St Ste 212
Los Altos, CA 94022-2767

Telephone: (650) 941-5681
Fax Number: (650) 948-7532
Type of Business: Chain Restaurant Operator
Year Founded: 1953
Total Sales: $773,840,000 (e)
Number of Employees: 6,400
Average Check: Lunch(8); Dinner(8)
Total Units: 416
Trade Names: KFC; KFC/A&W All American Food; KFC/Long John Silver's; KFC/Pizza Hut; KFC/Pizza Hut/Taco Bell; KFC/Taco Bell; Taco Bell; Taco Bell/Pizza Hut
Units Franchised From: 416
Preferred Square Footage: 3,500
Preferred Location Types: Downtown; Freestanding; Strip Mall
Projected Remodelings: 3
Areas of Operation: CA, CO, UT, WA
Type of Foodservice: Quick Serve (416)
Distribution Centers: UNION CITY, CA
Franchise Affiliation: A&W Restaurants Inc., LEXINGTON, KY; KFC Corporation, LOUISVILLE, KY; Long John Silver's Inc., LOUISVILLE, KY; Pizza Hut Inc., PLANO, TX; Taco Bell Corp., IRVINE, CA
Primary Distributors: (Full Line) SYSCO Food Services of Houston Inc., HOUSTON, TX
Divisional Offices: Harman Management Corp., LAKEWOOD, WA
Regional Offices: Harman Management Corp., MURRAY, UT; Harman Management Corp., UNION CITY, CA; Harman Management Corp., UNION CITY, CA

Key Personnel
JAMES OLSON - Chairman; CEO; President
JIM BEGLIN - President Operations
SHAWN BRADY - Director Human Resources, Training, Recruitment
JON PACKER - Director Information Systems
RON PATTERSON - Director Region
BRUCE GARNER - Director Region
TRAVIS GUTKE - Director Real Estate
JONATHAN PACKER - Director Information Systems
STEVE ORTON - Director Financial Planning
COLLEEN JENSEN - Director Payroll
JOHN MARGO - Regional Director
DAN ROSSER - Regional Director Training
LINDA STRONG-BROWN - Regional Director
DAVID COOMBS - Manager Systems
RENEE PATTERSON - Manager Real Estate
PATRICK JONES - Manager Employee Benefits
MICHELE SHERIDAN - Program Manager Procurement
CHRIS REA - Consultant Area
JESSE POWELL - Senior Analyst Accounting
TAMMIE MEIKLE - Analyst; Programmer
EILEEN MCCABE - Architect Development
ETHAN CAMPBELL - Developer Software
JAY-R SANTOS - Developer Software
CHAD MILLER - Engineer Systems

Texas Turkeys Inc. DBA
994 Acacia Ave
Los Altos, CA 94022-1302

Telephone: (650) 948-4659
Fax Number: (650) 948-1557
Internet Homepage: armadillowillys.com
Type of Business: Chain Restaurant Operator
Year Founded: 1983
Total Sales: $40,180,000 (e)
Alcohol Sales: 10%
Number of Employees: 300
Average Check: Lunch(14); Dinner(14)
Internet Order Processing: Yes
Internet Sales: 1.00%
Total Units: 7
Trade Names: Armadillo Willy's BBQ (7)
Company-Owned Units: 7
Preferred Square Footage: 4,500
Preferred Location Types: Freestanding; Strip Mall
Alcohol Served: Beer, Wine, Liquor
Primary Menu: Bar-B-Q (7)
Areas of Operation: CA
Type of Foodservice: Casual Dining (7)
Catering Services: Yes

Key Personnel
KEVIN ROBERTS - CEO; President
MATT GRANVILLE - CFO; Director Finance
TIM FORD - Director Operations

800 Degrees Woodfired Kitchen
12751 Millennium Ste B135
Los Angeles, CA 90094-2886

Telephone: (323) 538-0275
Internet Homepage: 800degreespizza.com
Company Email: info@800degreespizza.com
Type of Business: Chain Restaurant Operator
Year Founded: 2012
Total Units: 15
Trade Names: 800 Degrees (15)

Company-Owned Units: 7
Units Franchised To: 8
Preferred Location Types: Airports; Downtown; Freestanding; Hotel/Motel
Primary Menu: Pizza (15)
Projected Openings: 3
Areas of Operation: CA, NV, FC
Foreign Countries: JAPAN; UNITED ARAB EMIRATES
Type of Foodservice: Fast Casual (15)

Key Personnel
ANTHONY CARRON - Founder; Executive Chef
TOMMY LEE - CEO
SCOTT BERKOWITZ - Chief Development Officer
ALINA CARRON - Manager Corporate Affairs

American Golf Corp.
6080 Center Dr Ste 500
Los Angeles, CA 90045-9205

Telephone: (310) 664-4000
Fax Number: (310) 664-6164
Internet Homepage: americangolf.com
Type of Business: Nontraditional Foodservice Operator
Year Founded: 1970
Total Sales: $689,780,000 (e)
Alcohol Sales: 24%
Number of Employees: 8,000
Average Check: Breakfast(10); Lunch(16); Dinner(26)
Foodservice Sales: $172,445,000 (e)
Total Units: 102
Trade Names: Dining Room (82); Snack Shop (20)
Company-Owned Units: 102
Preferred Square Footage: 2,500; 5,500; 6,000
Preferred Location Types: Other
Alcohol Served: Beer, Wine, Liquor
Primary Menu: American (102)
Areas of Operation: AZ, CA, CO, CT, FL, GA, HI, ID, IL, KS, LA, MD, MI, MN, MO, NC, NJ, NM, NV, NY, OH, OK, OR, PA, SC, TN, TX, VA, WA
Type of Foodservice: Casual Dining (62); Fine Dining (20); Quick Serve (20)
Foodservice Management Venues: Parks & Recreation
Primary Distributors: (Equipment) Edward Don & Co., WOODRIDGE, IL; (Food) SYSCO Food Services of Los Angeles Inc., WALNUT, CA; (Supplies) Edward Don & Co., WOODRIDGE, IL
Parent Company: Goldman, Sachs & Co. (GS Capital Partners), NEW YORK, NY
Notes: The company derives approximately 75% of its revenue from golf course operations.

Key Personnel
JIM HINCKLEY - CEO; President
GARY PETERSON - President
PAUL BALLAM - Senior VP Business Development
JEFFREY GINTHER - VP Operations
ELIZABETH SPERBER - Regional VP Membership
MATT PALAFOX - General Manager
BRIAN CARRICO - General Manager
CATHERINE CHACON - Director Event Planning
JOHN BRACA - Director Event Planning
KIMBERLY ARRANAGA - Director Sales
JACKIE LOWE - Director Sales
CYNDI MELFI - Director Membership
BONESHIA PERRI - Director Sales
MICHELLE ROMO - Director Food
MELISSA TAPIA - Director Event Planning
GREG VARLEY - Director Event Planning
CHRIS YEE - Director Food
SUE SCHARF - Regional Director Event Planning

B Ventures USA LLC
10250 Santa Monica Blvd Ste 206
Los Angeles, CA 90067-6434

Telephone: (310) 399-9494
Fax Number: (310) 556-2455
Internet Homepage: bventures-usa.com; obikausa.com
Company Email: Info@bventures-usa.com
Type of Business: Chain Restaurant Operator
Total Sales: $15,740,000 (e)
Alcohol Sales: 5%
Average Check: Dinner(26)
Total Units: 5
Trade Names: Obika Mozzarella Bar (5)
Units Franchised From: 5
Alcohol Served: Beer, Wine, Liquor
Primary Menu: Italian (5)
Areas of Operation: CA, NY
Type of Foodservice: Casual Dining (5)
Catering Services: Yes
Notes: B Ventures USA has development rights for California and 18 other Western states for Italy-based F&B S.p.A, the creator and owner of the Obika Mozzarella Bar concept. The U.S. East Coast will be developed by Innovative Hospitality Concepts of New York City. Obika also has locations in England, Turkey, Japan, and Canada.

Key Personnel
RAIMONDO BOGGIA - Founder; Owner; General Buyer

Brentwood Associates
11150 Santa Monica Blvd Ste 1200
Los Angeles, CA 90025-3386

Telephone: (310) 477-6611
Fax Number: (310) 477-1011
Internet Homepage: brentwood.com; jmclaughlin.com; softsurroundings.com; softsurroundingsoutlet.com; bostonproper.com
Company Email: info@brentwood.com
Listing Type: Corporate Office
Type of Business: Chain Restaurant Operator
Total Sales: $2,306,549,000 (e)
Alcohol Sales: 10%
Internet Order Processing: Yes
Internet Sales: 62.00%
Total Units: 318
Trade Names: Chicken Salad Chick (179); Lazy Dog Restaurant & Bar (56); Pacific Catch Westcoast Fish House (10); Snooze (44); Veggie Grill (29)
Company-Owned Units: 198
Units Franchised To: 120
Primary Menu: American (129); Sandwiches/Deli (179); Seafood (10)
Projected Openings: 40
Areas of Operation: CA, CO, NV, OR, TX, WA
Foreign Countries: CANADA
Type of Foodservice: Casual Dining (54); Family Restaurant (56); Fast Casual (208)
Subsidiaries: Chicken Salad Chick, AUBURN, AL
Headquarter Offices: J. McLaughlin, BROOKLYN, NY; The Veggie Grill, SANTA MONICA, CA

Key Personnel
ROGER GODDU - Partner
WILLIAM BARNUM - Partner
STEVE MOORE - Partner
RAHUL AGGARWAL - Partner
ERIC REITER - Partner
JAMES HAYS - CFO
JIM THOMPSON - COO Division
TOM CARR - Chief Marketing Officer
TERRY MCKEE - Chief Development Officer Division
RACHEL PRESSER - VP
MARY LOU ATKINS - VP Human Resources
ALAN CHEN - VP
PATRICK MCGROREY - VP
PETER EDELSON - VP
SHEREE RODGERS - VP Talent
PRISCILLA CHAN - Controller
SUZANNE HOWARD - Director Finance, Accounting
CRAIG MILIUS - Director
CRISTA LEWIS - Director Finance
CHRIS REEKIE - Principal
JONATHAN ANG - Principal
TOROS YEREMYAN - Principal

Camacho's, Inc.
11 Olvera St
Los Angeles, CA 90012

Telephone: (213) 626-1361
Internet Homepage: elpaseoinn.com/home; mariasol.com/home
Company Email: contactus@elpaseoinn.com
Type of Business: Chain Restaurant Operator
Year Founded: 1984
Total Sales: $3,785,000 (e)
Alcohol Sales: 30%
Number of Employees: 265
Average Check: Lunch(10); Dinner(18)
Total Units: 2
Trade Names: El Paseo Inn (1); Mariasol (1)
Company-Owned Units: 2
Preferred Square Footage: 2,700
Preferred Location Types: Downtown; Freestanding; Parks
Alcohol Served: Beer, Wine, Liquor
Primary Menu: Mexican (2)
Areas of Operation: CA
Type of Foodservice: Casual Dining (2)
Catering Services: Yes
Primary Distributors: (Full Line) SYSCO Food Services of Los Angeles Inc., WALNUT, CA

Key Personnel
DON CAMACHO - CEO; President; General Buyer
ANDY CAMACHO - Owner
MARIA ZEPEDA - Director Operations, Purchasing, Store Fixtures

Century Fast Foods Inc.
10350 Santa Monica Blvd Ste 260
Los Angeles, CA 90025-5074

Telephone: (310) 203-8404
Fax Number: (310) 203-8247
Type of Business: Chain Restaurant Operator
Year Founded: 1986
Total Sales: $145,940,000 (e)
Number of Employees: 800
Average Check: Lunch(8); Dinner(8)
Total Units: 52
Trade Names: Taco Bell (52)
Units Franchised From: 52
Preferred Square Footage: 2,000
Preferred Location Types: Freestanding
Primary Menu: Taco (52)
Areas of Operation: CA
Type of Foodservice: Quick Serve (52)
Franchise Affiliation: Taco Bell Corp., IRVINE, CA
Primary Distributors: (Full Line) McLane Company, Inc., TEMPLE, TX

Key Personnel
ROBERT BRUNSON - President
JAMES DEBOARD - Owner; VP Finance, Facility/Maintenance, Real Estate, Design, Store Fixtures
MIKE MONZON - VP Operations; General Buyer
SHEILA COOK - Controller; Manager Risk Management, Human Resources

Cimmarusti Holdings
3061 Riverside Dr
Los Angeles, CA 90039-2060

Telephone: (323) 674-0203
Fax Number: (323) 674-0212
Internet Homepage: originalroadhousegrill.com
Company Email: comments@originalroadhousegrill.com
Type of Business: Chain Restaurant Operator
Year Founded: 1976
Total Sales: $129,280,000 (e)
Alcohol Sales: 10%
Number of Employees: 589
Average Check: Breakfast(8); Lunch(12); Dinner(14)
Internet Order Processing: Yes
Total Units: 8
Trade Names: Original Roadhouse Grill (8)
Company-Owned Units: 8
Preferred Square Footage: 2,500
Preferred Location Types: Freestanding
Alcohol Served: Beer, Wine, Liquor
Primary Menu: American (8)
Projected Openings: 2
Areas of Operation: CA, OR
Type of Foodservice: Casual Dining (8)
Primary Distributors: (Food) McLane/Riverside, RIVERSIDE, CA; (Food) SYSCO Food Services of Sacramento Inc., PLEASANT GROVE, CA

Key Personnel
LAWRENCE CIMMARUSTI - Partner; General Buyer
LINDA BRYANT - VP Operations, Division
STEVE MILLER - Controller

CJ Foods
5700 Wilshire Blvd Ste 550
Los Angeles, CA 90010-2341

Telephone: (213) 427-5566
Fax Number: (213) 427-7878
Internet Homepage: bibigousa.com; cjamerica.com
Type of Business: Chain Restaurant Operator
Total Units: 9
Trade Names: Bibigo (9)
Company-Owned Units: 9
Primary Menu: Japanese (9)
Areas of Operation: CA
Type of Foodservice: Fast Casual (9)

Key Personnel
SUNG SHIN - President
JIEUN LEE - VP Safety-Food
SOO JIN JON - VP Marketing
JOHN SIM - Senior Director Sales
JIM JANZEN - Director Sales
NICOLE KOENIG - Senior Manager Research & Development
JIN S. KIM - Senior Manager
TAE LEE - Senior Manager Strategy, Consumer Insights
CHERYL OLENIK - Manager Customer Service
JENNIFER YOO - Manager Marketing
CACEY CHOI - Manager Design
DENISE KIM - Manager Marketing
WON JUNG - Manager Production
JASON BAIK - Manager Purchasing
JAEWON CHO - Manager Quality Assurance
MICHELLE HWANG - Manager Brand Marketing
SYLVIA SHIN - Manager Brand Marketing
JIM WILKERSON - Manager Sales, West Division
HELEN CHOI - Coordinator
JASON KIM - Coordinator Human Resources

Death & Co.
3756 W. Avenue 40 Suite K #278
Los Angeles, CA 90065

Internet Homepage: deathandcompany.com
Company Email: info@deathandcompanymarket.com
Type of Business: Chain Restaurant Operator
Year Founded: 2007
Total Units: 4
Company-Owned Units: 4
Primary Menu: American (4)
Areas of Operation: CA, CO, DC, NY
Type of Foodservice: Fine Dining (4)

Key Personnel
DAVID KAPLAN - Co-Founder
RAVI DEROSSI - Co-Founder

Disruptive Restaurant Group
5900 Wilshire Blvd Ste 3000
Los Angeles, CA 90036-5030

Telephone: (323) 782-8201
Fax Number: (323) 780-8202
Internet Homepage: umamiburger.com
Company Email: press@umami.com
Type of Business: Chain Restaurant Operator
Total Sales: $33,270,000 (e)
Average Check: Lunch(10); Dinner(14)
Total Units: 57
Trade Names: Cleo Mediterraneo (5); Filia (1); Hyde Sunset Kitchen (1); K.Ramen.Burger.Beer. (1); Katsuya (9); Leynia (1); The Bazaar (4); The Restaurant at the Raleigh (1); Tres by Jose Andres (1); Umami

Burger (33)
Company-Owned Units: 57
Preferred Square Footage: 3,000
Areas of Operation: CA, IL, NV, NY, FC
Foreign Countries: JAPAN; UNITED ARAB EMIRATES
Type of Foodservice: Fast Casual (33); Fine Dining (24)
Parent Company: sbe Entertainment Group LLC, LOS ANGELES, CA

Key Personnel
SAM NAZARIAN - Chairman; CEO
NATE APPLEMAN - COO Division
JOHN POLIZZI - VP Operations
MEI LY - Business Manager Accounting

Domino's Franchisee
1740 S Hoover St
Los Angeles, CA 90006-4912

Telephone: (213) 748-7774
Type of Business: Chain Restaurant Operator
Total Sales: $6,232,000 (e)
Total Units: 3
Trade Names: Domino's (3)
Units Franchised From: 3
Primary Menu: Pizza (3)
Areas of Operation: CA
Type of Foodservice: Quick Serve (3)
Franchise Affiliation: Domino's Pizza Inc, ANN ARBOR, MI

Key Personnel
MAHMOOD SAALABI - Owner; General Buyer

Du-par's Restaurants
6333 W 3rd St Ste 210
Los Angeles, CA 90036-3087

Telephone: (323) 933-8446
Type of Business: Chain Restaurant Operator
Year Founded: 1938
Total Sales: $5,309,000 (e)
Alcohol Sales: 2%
Number of Employees: 240
Average Check: Breakfast(10); Lunch(10); Dinner(12)
Total Units: 2
Trade Names: Du-par Restaurant (2)
Company-Owned Units: 2
Preferred Location Types: Freestanding; Hotel/Motel; Regional Mall
Primary Menu: American (2)
Areas of Operation: CA
Type of Foodservice: Casual Dining (2)
Catering Services: Yes
Primary Distributors: (Food) US Foods-Los Angeles, LA MIRADA, CA

Key Personnel
TARIO FRANCES - Owner; General Buyer

Everytable
1101 W 23rd St
Los Angeles, CA 90007

Telephone: (213) 973-5095
Internet Homepage: everytable.com
Type of Business: Chain Restaurant Operator
Year Founded: 2014
Total Units: 7
Trade Names: Everytable (7)
Company-Owned Units: 7
Preferred Location Types: Downtown; Institution (college/hospital); Office Complex; Strip Mall
Primary Menu: Health Foods (7)
Areas of Operation: CA
Type of Foodservice: Quick Serve (7)

Key Personnel
SAM POLK - CEO
CHRISTINE HASIRCOGLU - VP Store Operations
CHRIS BOURNE - General Manager

Fala Bar
7751 1/2 Melrose Ave
Los Angeles, CA 90046-7328

Telephone: (323) 424-7131
Internet Homepage: falabar.com
Type of Business: Chain Restaurant Operator
Total Units: 3
Trade Names: Fala Bar (3)
Company-Owned Units: 3
Areas of Operation: CA

Key Personnel
MIKE SHAB - Co-Founder; Partner
GINA RAGONE - Partner

Fresh Brothers
11120 Hindry Ave
Los Angeles, CA 90045

Telephone: (310) 642-0533
Internet Homepage: freshbrothers.com
Type of Business: Chain Restaurant Operator
Year Founded: 2008
Systemwide Sales: $34,652,000 (e)
Total Sales: $32,450,000 (e)
Average Check: Dinner(36)
Total Units: 22
Trade Names: Fresh Brothers
Company-Owned Units: 22
Preferred Square Footage: 1,200
Projected Openings: 10
Areas of Operation: CA
Type of Foodservice: Quick Serve
Catering Services: Yes

Key Personnel
ADAM GOLDBERG - Co-Founder; General Buyer
RON COOLBAUGH - CEO
MICHAEL LOEWENBEIN - VP Marketing
ROBERT RIDDLE - Director Operations

Greenleaf Gourmet Chopshop
1888 Century Park E Ste 100
Los Angeles, CA 90067

Telephone: (310) 246-0756
Internet Homepage: greenleafchopshop.com
Company Email: jon@?greenleafchopshop.com
Type of Business: Chain Restaurant Operator
Total Sales: $8,357,000 (e)
Total Units: 7
Trade Names: Greenleaf Gourmet Chopshop (7)
Company-Owned Units: 7
Primary Menu: Health Foods (7)
Areas of Operation: CA
Type of Foodservice: Quick Serve (7)

Key Personnel
JONATHAN ROLLO - Founder; President; Manager Business Development

Hakimianpour Restaurant Group
3532 Overland Ave
Los Angeles, CA 90034

Telephone: (424) 603-4800
Fax Number: (424) 208-3556
Type of Business: Chain Restaurant Operator
Total Sales: $36,070,000 (e)
Number of Employees: 135
Total Units: 16
Trade Names: Burger King (16)
Units Franchised From: 16
Preferred Square Footage: 2,500
Primary Menu: Hamburger (16)
Areas of Operation: CA
Type of Foodservice: Quick Serve (16)
Franchise Affiliation: Burger King Worldwide Inc., MIAMI, FL

Key Personnel
HERBERT HAKIMIANPOUR - President; General Buyer

International Coffee & Tea LLC
5700 Wilshire Blvd
Los Angeles, CA 90036-3659

Telephone: (310) 237-2326
Fax Number: (310) 815-2520
Internet Homepage: coffeebean.com
Company Email: info@coffeebean.com
Type of Business: Chain Restaurant Operator
Year Founded: 1963
Systemwide Sales: $801,609,000 (e)
Total Sales: $196,680,000 (e)
Number of Employees: 3,476
Average Check: Breakfast(10); Lunch(10); Dinner(10)
Internet Order Processing: Yes
Internet Sales: 1.00%
Total Units: 1,080
Trade Names: The Coffee Bean & Tea Leaf (1,080)
Company-Owned Units: 218
Units Franchised To: 862
Preferred Square Footage: 300; 1,200; 1,500
Preferred Location Types: Airports; Downtown; Freestanding; Kiosk; Lifestyle Center; Regional Mall; Stadiums; Strip Mall
Primary Menu: Coffee (1,080)
Areas of Operation: AZ, CA, DC, FL, HI, MI, NV, NY, OK, TX
Foreign Countries: BAHRAIN; BRUNEI; CAMBODIA; CHINA; EGYPT; GERMANY; INDIA; INDONESIA; IRAQ; ISRAEL; JAPAN; JORDAN; KUWAIT; LEBANON; MALAYSIA; MEXICO; MONGOLIA; OMAN; QATAR; SAUDI ARABIA; SINGAPORE; SOUTH KOREA; SRI LANKA; THAILAND; THE PHILIPPINES; UNITED ARAB EMIRATES; VIETNAM
Type of Foodservice: Quick Serve (1,080)
Distribution Centers: CAMARILLO, CA
Primary Distributors: (Full Line) US Foods-Los Angeles, LA MIRADA, CA
Parent Company: Jollibee Foods Corporation, WEST COVINA, CA

Key Personnel
SANJIV RAZDAN - President Area, Area
TERRY MANSKY - Chief Administrative Officer; Chief Legal Officer; Senior VP
J. J. SMITH - VP Franchise Operations, Business Development
BRAD COX - Controller
JOHN ANTHONY ISAIS - Senior Director Manufacturing, Coffee/Tea
DEBBIE SASSOON - Director Product Development
PETER VAVRA - Director Franchise Operations
GARY FELDMAN - Director Sales
BRIAN BAHREMAN - Director Operations
PATRICIA NELSON - Director Real Estate
KECIA ROSS - Senior Manager Payroll

DANIELLE ATWOOD - Manager Marketing

Kabuki Restaurants, Inc.
4465 Wilshire Blvd Ste 100
Los Angeles, CA 90010-3704

Telephone: (323) 648-7460
Fax Number: (323) 648-7461
Internet Homepage: kabukirestaurants.com
Type of Business: Chain Restaurant Operator
Year Founded: 1991
Total Sales: $47,250,000 (e)
Alcohol Sales: 15%
Number of Employees: 1,058
Average Check: Dinner(22)
Total Units: 17
Trade Names: Kabuki (17)
Company-Owned Units: 17
Alcohol Served: Beer, Wine, Liquor
Primary Menu: Japanese (17)
Areas of Operation: AZ, CA, NV, TX
Type of Foodservice: Casual Dining (17)

Key Personnel
DAVID LEE - CEO; Owner
YOUNG KIM - Director Marketing, Real Estate
MICHELLE SHAM - Manager Marketing
FAITH KANG - Manager Human Resources
CHRISTY YOU - Coordinator Marketing

Kogi BBQ
4372 Eagle Rock Blvd
Los Angeles, CA 90041

Telephone: (323) 315-0253
Internet Homepage: eatchego.com; kogibbq.com
Type of Business: Chain Restaurant Operator
Year Founded: 2016
Total Units: 5
Trade Names: Chego (2); Kogi Taqueria (3)
Company-Owned Units: 5
Primary Menu: Asian (2); Taco (3)
Areas of Operation: CA
Type of Foodservice: Fast Casual (5)

Key Personnel
ROY CHOI - Co-Founder; Executive Chef
CAROLINE SHIN - Co-Founder
EDDIE GONZALES - CFO; Director Operations

Laemmle Theaters
11523 Santa Monica Blvd
Los Angeles, CA 90025-3007

Telephone: (310) 478-1041
Fax Number: (310) 478-4452
Internet Homepage: laemmle.com
Type of Business: Foodservice Operations - Movie Theatre
Year Founded: 1938
Total Sales: $32,170,000 (e)
Number of Employees: 228
Average Check: Breakfast(8); Lunch(8); Dinner(8)
Internet Order Processing: Yes
Internet Sales: 0.50%
Total Units: 9
Trade Names: Laemmle Theaters (9)
Company-Owned Units: 9
Preferred Square Footage: 20,000
Preferred Location Types: Freestanding; Strip Mall
Primary Menu: Snacks (9)
Projected Openings: 1
Areas of Operation: CA
Type of Foodservice: In-Store Feeder (9)

Key Personnel
GREGORY LAEMMLE - President
JAY REISBAUM - Senior VP; VP Real Estate

Landmark Theatre Corp.
2222 S Barrington Ave
Los Angeles, CA 90064-1206

Telephone: (888) 724-6362
Fax Number: (310) 477-7509
Internet Homepage: landmarktheatres.com
Company Email: comments@landmarktheatres.com
Type of Business: Foodservice Operations - Movie Theatre
Year Founded: 1974
Total Sales: $95,200,000 (e)
Number of Employees: 1,475
Total Units: 54
Trade Names: Landmark Theatres (54)
Company-Owned Units: 54
Preferred Square Footage: 15,000; 25,000
Preferred Location Types: Freestanding; Regional Mall; Strip Mall
Alcohol Served: Beer, Wine, Liquor
Primary Menu: Snacks (54)
Areas of Operation: CA, CO, DC, GA, IL, IN, MA, MD, MI, MN, MO, NY, PA, TX, WA, WI
Type of Foodservice: In-Store Feeder (54)

Key Personnel
SCHUYLER HANSEN - CFO
CHUCK DELAGRANGE - VP Operations; General Buyer
CHUCK SIMPSON - Assistant Director Sales

Live Nation
7060 Hollywood Blvd Fl 11
Los Angeles, CA 90028-6014

Telephone: (323) 769-4600
Fax Number: (323) 769-4789

Internet Homepage: hob.com; houseofblues.com
Company Email: ir@hob.com
Type of Business: Chain Restaurant Operator
Year Founded: 1992
Publicly Held: Yes
Total Sales: $2,580,266,000 (e)
Alcohol Sales: 30%
Number of Employees: 3,000
Average Check: Lunch(18); Dinner(30)
Foodservice Sales: $851,487,000 (e)
Internet Order Processing: Yes
Internet Sales: 3.00%
Total Units: 17
Trade Names: Brooklyn Bowl (6); House of Blues (11)
Company-Owned Units: 17
Preferred Square Footage: 5,500; 6,000
Preferred Location Types: Freestanding
Alcohol Served: Beer, Wine, Liquor
Primary Menu: American (6); Cajun/Creole (11)
Areas of Operation: CA, FL, IL, LA, MA, NV, OH, SC, TX
Type of Foodservice: Casual Dining (17); Fast Casual (0)
Catering Services: Yes
Primary Distributors: (Full Line) SYSCO Food Services of Los Angeles Inc., WALNUT, CA
Parent Company: Live Nation Inc., BEVERLY HILLS, CA
Notes: Total sales excludes results from concert venue operations. The company derives approximately 38% of its revenue from retail activities.

Key Personnel
MICHAEL RAPINO - CEO; President; Director
BOB ROUX - President
GEOF WILLS - President
JOE BERCHTOLD - President
KELLY FLANIGAN - President
BRITTANY FLORES - President
NEAL JACOBSEN - President
NICK MASTERS - President
LAURIE LAWHORNE - CFO
KATHY WILLARD - CFO
BENJAMIN WEEDEN - COO
WILSON HOWARD - COO
MATTHEW HANSEN - Chief Strategy Officer
JORDAN ZACHARY - Chief Strategy Officer
JACQUELINE (JACKIE) WILGAR - Exec VP Marketing
WILSON ROGERS - Exec VP
RYAN OKUM - Exec VP Digital Marketing
JOHN HOPMANS - Exec VP Acquisitions, Strategic Services
KEITH MYERS - Senior VP Technology
FRANK GUTIERREZ - Senior VP
MIKE GARCIA - Senior VP
JOE FLEISCHER - Senior VP Product Development
LIZ DYER - Senior VP Human Resources
NATHAN SCOTT - Senior VP Finance
BRIAN SIEP - Senior VP Food and Beverage
SHEILA SMALL - Senior VP Legal
BRANDON SQUAR - VP
DAN SCHARTOFF - VP Production
BRAD WAVRA - VP
RINAT RADVINSKY - VP
ROY PIERCE - VP Finance
GEORGE DURAN - VP Finance
BARBARA BOUMAN - VP Sales
DAVID CEA - VP Human Resources
PETER AUBEE - VP Finance
LISA ALULIS - VP Finance
STEVEN BENANAV - VP
PATRICK MOORE - VP Risk Management
CHRIS LAFFOON - VP Legal
KYM FURANO - Executive Director Media
MICHAEL ROWLES - Corporate Secretary; General Counsel
BILL JANNEY - Controller
TINA SUCA - General Manager
PAUL MILLER - Executive Chef
HANNAH NIMAN - Director Finance, Accounting
ERICA PALOMARES-SMITH - Director Operations
FRED SALCE - Director Information Technology
KIRSTEN WATTSON - Director Finance
ANDY YATES - Director Food and Beverage
JOHANNAH JUAREZ - Director Marketing
ANIL GUPTA - Director Sales
HEATHER HUTCHINS - Director Sales, National
DEB HEDGE - Director
MIKE MUELLER - Director Accounting
BEAVIN MEGHAN - Director Event Planning
ANDY MESSERSMITH - Director
AARON LUNA - Director Operations, Information Technology
BOBBY ANDERSON - Director Operations
CARLA AYLESWORTH - Director Sales
LYDIA COLARESI - Director Digital Marketing
MICHAEL MALENITZA - Senior Manager Business Development
EMILY MUNROE - Senior Manager Benefits
NEREYDA GUZMAN - Business Manager Accounting
SCOTT UYECHI - Business Manager Accounting
KIM SUMMER - Manager Accounting
ABBY STROUT - Manager Communications
ALEXA TORRES - Manager Marketing
GEORGE WELLINGER - Manager Business Development
IAN SIFUENTES - Manager Security
CEDRIC REITZELL - Manager Security
JAMES GEE - Manager Accounting
WALTER DE JEAN - Manager Finance
JENNIFER CUDNIK - Manager Finance
BOBBY DANELSKI - Manager Production
SUE BARNABY - Manager Operations
JANETTE BAXA - Manager Marketing
ELAINE NAKAMA - Manager Human Resources
TERRI MIKI - Manager Administration
BABS MILLER - Manager Sales
BRITT MACGREGOR - Manager Inventory
NATHAN LEBLANC - Manager Procurement, Global
ELENA LAM - Manager Operations
DENNIS JARDIEL - Manager Accounting
DEBBIE JOHN - Project Manager
REDD BARUA-NORTON - Project Manager
CELISE YAMASHITA - Project Manager
JENNIFER TAFOLLA - Senior Buyer
ISSY T. - Specialist Information Technology
ANDREW LEVITT - Buyer Talent
PAUL MCGUIGAN - Buyer Talent
JOSH LACEY - Coordinator Marketing
JENNIFER GREENE - Coordinator Facility/Maintenance
DYLAN GREER - Coordinator Special Projects
JESSICA VICTORIAN - Coordinator Human Resources
ANDREW YUEN - Designer
AMY CHEN - Designer
ALAN NATALE - Designer
GARY CHOW - Senior Analyst Business Development
STEVE HALE - Senior Analyst Retail Information Systems
MIKE DOLAN - Analyst Credit
ANDREW DAY - Analyst
SARKIS MAZMANIAN - Analyst
KEVIN HARLOW - Analyst Research & Development
WILLIAM SHEPARD - Analyst HRIS
RODERICK HOLMES - Architect Software
ROBERT EVANSHINE - Developer Software
JOSEPH QUIRING - Developer Database
BRIAN VALDEZ - Senior Engineer Software
NIKHIL DESHPANDE - Engineer Database
FRANK CARULLI - Engineer Construction

Metropolitan Theatres Corporation
8727 W 3rd St Ste 301
Los Angeles, CA 90048-3865

Telephone: (310) 858-2800
Fax Number: (310) 858-2860
Internet Homepage: metrotheatres.com
Company Email: info@metrotheatres.com
Type of Business: Foodservice Operations - Movie Theatre
Year Founded: 1923
Total Sales: $34,380,000 (e)
Number of Employees: 700
Average Check: Lunch(14); Dinner(14)
Internet Order Processing: Yes
Total Units: 18
Trade Names: Metropolitan Theatre (18)
Company-Owned Units: 18
Preferred Square Footage: 25,000
Preferred Location Types: Freestanding; Regional Mall; Strip Mall
Primary Menu: Snacks (18)
Areas of Operation: CA, CO, ID, UT
Foreign Countries: CANADA
Type of Foodservice: In-Store Feeder (18)
Notes: The company derives approximately 75% of its revenue from theater admissions, on-screen advertising, and other sales.

Key Personnel
BRUCE CORWIN - Chairman; CEO
PHILLIP HERMANN - CFO
DALE DAVISON - Senior VP Operations, Development
TIMOTHY SPAIN - VP Operations
ALAN STOKES - VP
VICTORIA UY - VP Finance, Human Resources; Controller; Manager Information Systems, Risk Management

Mundo Management LLC
445 S Figueroa St Ste B115
Los Angeles, CA 90071-1602

Telephone: (213) 542-1100
Fax Number: (213) 542-1101
Internet Homepage: bordergrill.com
Company Email: mail@bordergrill.com
Type of Business: Chain Restaurant Operator
Year Founded: 1990
Total Sales: $16,780,000 (e)
Alcohol Sales: 23%
Number of Employees: 400
Average Check: Lunch(18); Dinner(30)
Total Units: 5
Trade Names: Border Grill (5)
Company-Owned Units: 5
Preferred Location Types: Freestanding
Alcohol Served: Beer, Wine, Liquor
Primary Menu: Mexican (5)
Areas of Operation: CA, NV
Type of Foodservice: Casual Dining (5)
Catering Services: Yes
Primary Distributors: (Full Line) SYSCO Food Services of San Diego Inc., POWAY, CA

Key Personnel
SUSAN FENIGER - Partner; Executive Chef; General Buyer
MARY SUE MILLIKEN - Partner; Executive Chef
NILE PARK - VP Operations; General Buyer
MEGAN PLASKOW - Manager Marketing, Public Relations

Ohana Poké Co.
130 E 6th St
Los Angeles, CA 90014-2006

Telephone: (213) 265-7561
Internet Homepage: ohanapokeco.com
Company Email: catering@ohanapokeco.com
Type of Business: Chain Restaurant Operator
Year Founded: 2015
Total Units: 2
Trade Names: Ohana Poké Co. (2)
Company-Owned Units: 2
Primary Menu: Miscellaneous (2)
Areas of Operation: CA
Type of Foodservice: Fast Casual (2)

Key Personnel
ERIC PARK - Owner; Executive Chef; General Buyer

Pacific Dining Car Inc.
1310 W 6th St
Los Angeles, CA 90017-1204

Telephone: (213) 483-3030
Fax Number: (213) 483-4545
Internet Homepage: pacificdiningcar.com
Company Email: office@pacificdiningcar.com
Type of Business: Chain Restaurant Operator
Year Founded: 1921
Total Sales: $13,048,000 (e)
Alcohol Sales: 25%
Number of Employees: 60
Average Check: Breakfast(16); Lunch(36); Dinner(60)
Total Units: 2
Trade Names: Pacific Dining Car (2)
Company-Owned Units: 2
Preferred Location Types: Freestanding
Alcohol Served: Beer, Wine, Liquor
Primary Menu: Steak (2)
Areas of Operation: CA
Type of Foodservice: Fine Dining (2)
Primary Distributors: (Food) SYSCO Food Services of Los Angeles Inc., WALNUT, CA

Key Personnel
WESLEY IDOL III - President; General Buyer

Pacific Theatres Exhibition Corp.
120 N Robertson Blvd Fl 3
Los Angeles, CA 90048-3115

Telephone: (310) 657-8420
Fax Number: (310) 652-8538
Internet Homepage: pacifictheatres.com
Type of Business: Foodservice Operations - Movie Theatre
Year Founded: 1948
Total Sales: $36,860,000 (e)
Number of Employees: 535
Total Units: 6
Trade Names: Pacific Theatres (6)
Company-Owned Units: 6
Preferred Square Footage: 30,000
Preferred Location Types: Community Mall; Downtown; Freestanding; Regional Mall
Primary Menu: Snacks (6)
Areas of Operation: CA
Type of Foodservice: In-Store Feeder (6)
Primary Distributors: (Full Line) US Foods-Los Angeles, LA MIRADA, CA
Parent Company: Decurion Corp., LOS ANGELES, CA
Notes: The company derives approximately 72% of its revenue from theater admissions, on-screen advertising, & other sales.

Key Personnel
CHRISTOPHER FORMAN - CEO; President; General Buyer

Pasta Mama Inc.
616 N Detroit St
Los Angeles, CA 90036-1946

Telephone: (323) 692-0800
Fax Number: (323) 692-0801
Internet Homepage: hugosrestaurant.com; hugostacos.com
Company Email: hugos@sbcglobal.net
Type of Business: Chain Restaurant Operator
Year Founded: 1999
Total Sales: $16,731,000 (e)
Alcohol Sales: 1%
Number of Employees: 66
Average Check: Breakfast(14); Lunch(16); Dinner(26)
Internet Order Processing: Yes
Total Units: 4
Trade Names: Hugo's Restaurants (2); Hugo's Tacos (2)
Company-Owned Units: 4
Preferred Location Types: Freestanding
Alcohol Served: Beer, Wine, Liquor
Primary Menu: Californian (2); Taco (2)
Areas of Operation: CA
Type of Foodservice: Casual Dining (2); Quick Serve (2)
Catering Services: Yes
Primary Distributors: (Full Line) SYSCO Food Services of Los Angeles Inc., WALNUT, CA

Key Personnel
TOM KAPLAN - President; General Manager; General Buyer
NABOR DIAZ - Executive Chef; Manager Menu Development, Catering; Buyer Food

Potato Corner USA
6380 Wilshire Blvd Ste 1100
Los Angeles, CA 90048-5018

Mailing Address: 8950 W Olympic Blvd, Suite 563, Beverly Hills, CA, 90210
Telephone: (800) 565-1114
Internet Homepage: potatocornerusa.com
Company Email: contactus@PotatoCornerUSA.com
Type of Business: Chain Restaurant Operator
Total Sales: $2,813,000 (e)
Total Units: 35
Company-Owned Units: 35
Primary Menu: Snacks (35)
Areas of Operation: CA, FL, LA, MN, NM, NV, NY, TX, WA

Type of Foodservice: Quick Serve (35)

Key Personnel
GUY KOREN - President
ASHLEY GRUDNOWSKI - Manager Franchise Development
CHRIS MARSHALL - Manager Product Development

Pressed Juicery Inc.
4016 Wilshire Blvd
Los Angeles, CA 90010

Telephone: (310) 477-7171
Internet Homepage: pressedjuicery.com
Type of Business: Chain Restaurant Operator
Total Sales: $102,160,000 (e)
Total Units: 100
Trade Names: Pressed Juicery (100)
Company-Owned Units: 100
Primary Menu: Snacks (100)
Type of Foodservice: Fast Casual (100)

Key Personnel
CARLY BRIEN - Founder
JUSTIN NEDELMAN - CEO
DEBORAH MOROZ - Chief People Officer; General Counsel
ANDREI NAJJAR - Senior VP Branding
KATHLEEN ROGERS - VP Retail Operations
FRANK LOPEZ - Director Human Resources
NICK HERRERA - Director Engineering
ISAI JUAREZ - Director Financial Planning
EMILY GARIBAY - Director Quality Assurance
JOHN KENNEDY - Director Real Estate
STEVE SERRANO - Director Supply Chain, Logistics
DANIELLE WARREN - Manager Operations

Qwench/DRNK
350 S Grand Ave Ste 3070
Los Angeles, CA 90071-3432

Telephone: (323) 825-5373
Fax Number: (323) 825-5365
Internet Homepage: drnkcoffee.com; drnkqwench.com; qwenchjuice.com
Company Email: info@drnkcoffee.com
Type of Business: Chain Restaurant Operator
Total Units: 20
Trade Names: DRNK coffee + tea (10); Qwench (10)
Company-Owned Units: 20
Preferred Location Types: Downtown; Institution (college/hospital); Mixed-use Center
Primary Menu: Health Foods (10); Snacks (10)
Projected Openings: 20
Areas of Operation: CA, VA
Type of Foodservice: Fast Casual (20)

Key Personnel
BORIS HORVAT - VP Operations
AMIR ATIGHEHCHI - VP Strategy

Robeks Corp.
5220 Pacific Concourse Dr Ste 395
Los Angeles, CA 90045-6244

Telephone: (310) 727-0500
Fax Number: (310) 844-1587
Internet Homepage: robeks.com; robeksfranchise.com
Company Email: customercare@robeks.com
Type of Business: Chain Restaurant Operator
Year Founded: 1996
Systemwide Sales: $33,757,000 (e)
Total Sales: $3,112,000 (e)
Number of Employees: 38
Average Check: Breakfast(10); Lunch(10); Dinner(10)
Internet Order Processing: Yes
Total Units: 70
Trade Names: Robeks Fruit Smoothies & Healthy Eats (85)
Units Franchised To: 85
Preferred Square Footage: 2,500
Preferred Location Types: Community Mall; Convenience Store/Gas Station; Downtown; Freestanding; Institution (college/hospital); Kiosk; Lifestyle Center; Office Complex; Regional Mall; Stadiums; Strip Mall
Primary Menu: Health Foods (85)
Areas of Operation: AZ, CA, CT, DC, FL, GA, HI, IL, KS, MA, MD, NC, NM, NY, OH, PA, TX, VA, WA
Foreign Countries: IRELAND
Type of Foodservice: Quick Serve (107)
Foodservice Management Venues: College & University
Catering Services: Yes
Primary Distributors: (Full Line) SYSCO Food Services of Sacramento Inc., PLEASANT GROVE, CA

Key Personnel
DAVID ROBERTSON - Chairman
DAVID RAWNSLEY - President; CFO
TODD PETERSON - Chief Development Officer
MICHAEL PISANI - VP Operations
JIMMER BOLDEN - VP Business Development
DAN RICHMOND - VP
JOHN SCHATTINGER - Director Information Technology
TODD OLDHAM - Administrator Systems Engineering

SLS Hotel Beverly Hills
465 S La Cienega Blvd
Los Angeles, CA 90048-4001

Telephone: (310) 247-0400
Fax Number: (310) 247-0315
Internet Homepage: slshotels.com
Company Email: slsbeverlyhills@luxurycollection.com
Type of Business: Chain Restaurant Operator
Year Founded: 2008
Total Sales: $42,697,000 (e)
Alcohol Sales: 35%
Average Check: Dinner(116)
Total Units: 4
Trade Names: Altitude Pool and Lounge (1); Somni (1); The Bazaar by Jose Andres (1); Tres by Jose Andres (1)
Company-Owned Units: 4
Alcohol Served: Beer, Wine, Liquor
Primary Menu: Miscellaneous (4)
Areas of Operation: CA
Type of Foodservice: Casual Dining (1); Fine Dining (3)
Notes: The restaurant is located in the SLS Hotel.

Key Personnel
HUSSAIN HOUHBI - Executive Chef; General Buyer

Spitz
371 E 2nd St
Los Angeles, CA 90012-4215

Telephone: (213) 613-0101
Internet Homepage: eatatspitz.com
Company Email: talk2us@eatatspitz.com
Type of Business: Chain Restaurant Operator
Total Sales: $43,940,000 (e)
Total Units: 12
Trade Names: Spitz Mediterranean Street Food (12)
Company-Owned Units: 12
Primary Menu: Greek/Mediterranean (12)
Areas of Operation: CA, MN, OR, UT
Type of Foodservice: Fast Casual (12)

Key Personnel
BRYCE RADEMAN - Partner

Sunset Entertainment Group
1666 1/2 N McCadden Pl
Los Angeles, CA 90028-6110

Telephone: (323) 463-1473
Fax Number: (323) 463-0485
Internet Homepage: cabanaclubhollywood.com; sunseteg.com
Type of Business: Chain Restaurant Operator
Total Sales: $9,140,000 (e)
Alcohol Sales: 50%
Number of Employees: 70
Total Units: 3
Trade Names: Le Jardin (1); Lure Nightclub (1); Pig N Whistle (1)

Company-Owned Units: 3
Preferred Location Types: Freestanding
Alcohol Served: Beer, Wine, Liquor
Primary Menu: American (3)
Areas of Operation: CA
Type of Foodservice: Fine Dining (3)
Primary Distributors: (Food) SYSCO Food Services of Central California Inc., MODESTO, CA

Key Personnel
ALAN HAJJAR - President; Partner; Controller; General Buyer
GEORGE NAHAS - Partner; COO
ERIC J. VIRGETS - Partner; Director Security
ERIN ROLF - General Manager
BEN KLAMM - General Manager
GERALDINE DEGUZMAN - Manager Accounting

Tasty Restaurant Group
6701 Center Dr W Floor 14
Los Angeles, CA 90045

Telephone: (310) 943-4990
Internet Homepage: tastyrg.com
Type of Business: Chain Restaurant Operator
Total Sales: $266,480,000 (e)
Total Units: 354
Trade Names: Baskin Robbins (6); Burger King (74); Dunkin' (21); KFC (90); Pizza Hut (163)
Units Franchised From: 354
Primary Menu: Chicken (90); Coffee (21); Hamburger (74); Pizza (163); Snacks (6)
Areas of Operation: AR, GA, IA, IL, KY, MD, NC, SC, TN, VA, WV
Type of Foodservice: Quick Serve (354)

Key Personnel
ROBERT RODRIGUEZ - CEO
NEIL THOMSON - CFO
TASOS DOUGLAS - VP Development
CHRISTOPHER CARROLL - VP Information Technology
ADAM GREENWAY - VP Business Development
BLAKE OVERALL - VP Finance
LINDSAY SELLERS - VP; Controller
UMI HAYATA - Director Finance
CASEY FULD - Director Finance
DANIEL GONZALEZIT - Director Information Technology, Infrastructure
DON HENSLEY - Director Real Estate

Taylor's Steakhouse
3361 W 8th St
Los Angeles, CA 90005-2438

Telephone: (213) 382-8449
Fax Number: (213) 382-2372
Internet Homepage: taylorssteakhouse.com
Company Email: brucetaylor@taylorssteakhouse.com
Type of Business: Chain Restaurant Operator
Year Founded: 1953
Total Sales: $4,560,000 (e)
Alcohol Sales: 30%
Number of Employees: 50
Average Check: Lunch(18); Dinner(24)
Internet Sales: 1.00%
Total Units: 2
Trade Names: Taylor's Steakhouse (2)
Company-Owned Units: 2
Preferred Square Footage: 4,000
Preferred Location Types: Freestanding
Alcohol Served: Beer, Wine, Liquor
Primary Menu: Steak (2)
Areas of Operation: CA
Type of Foodservice: Fine Dining (2)
Primary Distributors: (Food) SYSCO Food Services of Los Angeles Inc., WALNUT, CA

Key Personnel
BRUCE TAYLOR - Owner; General Manager; Executive Chef; General Buyer
FERNANDO MENDEZ - Executive Chef; General Buyer
JONATHAN MENDEZ - Manager Operations

The Dolly Llama
611 S Spring St
Los Angeles, CA 90014

Telephone: (213) 283-8615
Internet Homepage: thedollyllamala.com
Company Email: info@thedollyllamala.com
Type of Business: Chain Restaurant Operator
Total Units: 7
Trade Names: The Dolly Llama Waffle Master (7)
Company-Owned Units: 7
Preferred Location Types: Downtown; Strip Mall
Primary Menu: Snacks (7)
Areas of Operation: CA
Type of Foodservice: Fast Casual (7)

Key Personnel
SAMUEL BAROUX - Founder; Owner

The Ivy
113 N Robertson Blvd
Los Angeles, CA 90048-3101

Telephone: (310) 278-2908
Fax Number: (310) 274-8170
Internet Homepage: theivyrestaurants.com
Company Email: info@theivyrestaurants.com
Type of Business: Chain Restaurant Operator
Year Founded: 1985
Total Sales: $20,340,000 (e)
Alcohol Sales: 20%
Number of Employees: 120
Average Check: Lunch(48); Dinner(90)
Total Units: 3
Trade Names: Dolce Isola (1); Ivy at the Shore (1); The Ivy (1)
Company-Owned Units: 3
Preferred Location Types: Freestanding
Alcohol Served: Beer, Wine, Liquor
Primary Menu: American (3)
Areas of Operation: CA
Type of Foodservice: Cafeteria (1); Fine Dining (2)

Key Personnel
RICHARD IRVING - Partner; Executive Chef; General Buyer
LYNN VON KERSTING - Partner

The Madera Group
8720 W Sunset Blvd Ste A
Los Angeles, CA 90069

Telephone: (323) 645-7800
Internet Homepage: themaderagroup.com
Company Email: info@themaderagroup.com
Type of Business: Chain Restaurant Operator
Year Founded: 2013
Total Sales: $13,300,000 (e)
Total Units: 19
Trade Names: Toca Madera (1); Tocaya Organica (18)
Company-Owned Units: 19
Primary Menu: Mexican (19)
Projected Openings: 2
Areas of Operation: AZ, CA
Type of Foodservice: Casual Dining (1); Fast Casual (18)

Key Personnel
TOSH BERMAN - Co-Founder; Co-CEO
AMROU MANASEER - Co-Founder; Co-CEO
MIKEY TANHA - President

The Pie Hole
714 Traction Ave
Los Angeles, CA 90013-1814

Telephone: (213) 537-0115
Fax Number: (213) 537-0458
Internet Homepage: thepieholefranchise.com; thepieholela.com
Company Email: info@thepieholela.com
Type of Business: Chain Restaurant Operator
Year Founded: 2011
Total Units: 10
Trade Names: The Pie Hole (10)
Company-Owned Units: 10
Primary Menu: Snacks (10)
Areas of Operation: CA, FC
Type of Foodservice: Fast Casual (10)

Key Personnel
MATT HEFFNER - Co-Founder; CEO; Executive Chef; General Buyer

Trejo's Tacos
631 N Larchmont Blvd Ste 2
Los Angeles, CA 90004

Telephone: (323) 466-9559
Internet Homepage: trejostacos.com
Company Email: info@trejostacos.com
Type of Business: Chain Restaurant Operator
Year Founded: 2016
Internet Order Processing: Yes
Total Units: 7
Trade Names: Trejo's Cantina (3); Trejo's Coffee and Donuts (1); Trejo's Tacos (3)
Company-Owned Units: 7
Primary Menu: Mexican (3); Snacks (1); Taco (3)
Areas of Operation: CA
Type of Foodservice: Fast Casual (6); Quick Serve (1)

Key Personnel
DANNY TREJO - Partner
ASH SHAW - Partner
JEFF GEORGINO - Partner
JAY PIERCE - Director Catering
KARLA MORENO - Director Training
MARIE PETUOLA - Director Operations

Tri P's Management Corporation
2220 W Slauson Ave
Los Angeles, CA 90043-3244

Telephone: (323) 298-0653
Type of Business: Chain Restaurant Operator
Total Sales: $5,305,000 (e)
Total Units: 2
Trade Names: Jack in the Box (2)
Units Franchised From: 2
Primary Menu: Hamburger (2)
Areas of Operation: CA
Type of Foodservice: Quick Serve (2)
Franchise Affiliation: Jack in the Box Restaurants, SAN DIEGO, CA

Key Personnel
CEDRIC PRICE - President; General Buyer

Urth Caffe Inc.
451 S Hewitt St
Los Angeles, CA 90013-2215

Telephone: (213) 797-4527
Fax Number: (213) 797-4538
Internet Homepage: urthcaffe.com
Company Email: info@urthcaffe.com
Type of Business: Chain Restaurant Operator
Total Sales: $9,858,000 (e)
Total Units: 10
Trade Names: Urth Caffe (10)
Company-Owned Units: 10
Primary Menu: Coffee (10)
Projected Openings: 1
Areas of Operation: CA
Type of Foodservice: Fast Casual (10)

Key Personnel
SHALLOM BERKMAN - Owner; General Buyer
SANDY TRAN - Director Catering

Wexler's Deli
317 S Broadway
Los Angeles, CA 90013

Telephone: (213) 620-0633
Internet Homepage: wexlersdeli.com
Company Email: info@wexlersdeli.com
Type of Business: Chain Restaurant Operator
Year Founded: 2014
Total Units: 4
Trade Names: Wexler's Deli (4)
Company-Owned Units: 4
Preferred Location Types: Downtown; Hotel/Motel
Primary Menu: Sandwiches/Deli (4)
Areas of Operation: CA
Type of Foodservice: Casual Dining (4)

Key Personnel
MICAH WEXLER - Co-Founder; Partner
MICHAEL KASSAR - Co-Founder; Partner
CHRIS REQUENA - Executive Chef

Wonton Group
12100 W Washington Blvd
Los Angeles, CA 90066-5502

Telephone: (424) 835-3901
Internet Homepage: chinchin.com
Company Email: corporate@chinchin.com
Type of Business: Chain Restaurant Operator
Systemwide Sales: $15,777,000 (e)
Total Sales: $11,044,000 (e)
Alcohol Sales: 10%
Number of Employees: 200
Average Check: Lunch(14); Dinner(26)
Internet Order Processing: Yes
Internet Sales: 1.00%
Total Units: 5
Trade Names: Chin Chin (5)
Company-Owned Units: 5
Preferred Location Types: Freestanding; Regional Mall
Alcohol Served: Beer, Wine
Primary Menu: Chinese (5)
Areas of Operation: CA, NV
Type of Foodservice: Fine Dining (5)

Key Personnel
JASON MOON - Controller

Yang Chow Restaurants
819 N Broadway
Los Angeles, CA 90012-2309

Telephone: (213) 625-0811
Fax Number: (213) 625-7901
Internet Homepage: yangchow.com
Company Email: manager@yangchow.com
Type of Business: Chain Restaurant Operator
Year Founded: 1977
Total Sales: $4,525,000 (e)
Alcohol Sales: 10%
Number of Employees: 50
Average Check: Lunch(12); Dinner(12)
Total Units: 3
Trade Names: Yang Chow (3)
Company-Owned Units: 3
Preferred Location Types: Freestanding
Alcohol Served: Beer, Wine
Primary Menu: Chinese (3)
Areas of Operation: CA
Type of Foodservice: Casual Dining (3)
Primary Distributors: (Food) SYSCO Food Services of Los Angeles Inc., WALNUT, CA

Key Personnel
KIM T. YUN - Owner; General Buyer
BENNY YUN - General Manager
MING TSANG - Executive Chef

Forbes Mill Steakhouse
206 N Santa Cruz Ave
Los Gatos, CA 95030-7207

Telephone: (408) 395-6434
Fax Number: (408) 354-3594
Internet Homepage: forbesmillsteakhouse.com
Company Email: fms@forbesmillsteakhouse.com
Type of Business: Chain Restaurant Operator
Year Founded: 2003
Total Sales: $8,864,000 (e)
Alcohol Sales: 4%
Number of Employees: 20
Average Check: Lunch(30); Dinner(72)
Total Units: 2
Trade Names: Forbes Mill Steakhouse (2)
Company-Owned Units: 2
Preferred Location Types: Freestanding
Alcohol Served: Beer, Wine, Liquor
Primary Menu: Steak/Seafood (2)
Areas of Operation: CA
Type of Foodservice: Casual Dining (2)
Catering Services: Yes
Primary Distributors: (Food) BiRite

Foodservice Distributors, BRISBANE, CA

Key Personnel
DARIN DEVINCENZI - Partner
DEAN DEVINCENZI - Partner
ASHLEY HAYMAN - General Manager
BRIAN WESELBY - Executive Chef; Director Menu Development, Catering; General Buyer

Pizza My Heart, Inc.
16222 Shannon Rd
Los Gatos, CA 95032-4729

Telephone: (408) 502-8099
Internet Homepage: pizzamyheart.com
Company Email: TheBigCheese@PizzaMyHeart.com
Type of Business: Chain Restaurant Operator
Year Founded: 1981
Total Sales: $2,900,000 (e)
Number of Employees: 400
Total Units: 25
Trade Names: Pizza My Heart (25)
Company-Owned Units: 25
Primary Menu: Pizza (25)
Projected Openings: 1
Areas of Operation: CA
Type of Foodservice: Fast Casual (25)
Catering Services: Yes

Key Personnel
CHUCK HAMMERS - CEO; President; Owner

Yogurtland Franchisee
11215 Long Beach Blvd Ste 1007
Lynwood, CA 90262-4293

Telephone: (310) 639-1465
Type of Business: Chain Restaurant Operator
Total Sales: $3,152,000 (e)
Total Units: 3
Trade Names: Yogurtland (3)
Units Franchised From: 3
Primary Menu: Snacks (3)
Areas of Operation: CA
Type of Foodservice: Quick Serve (3)
Franchise Affiliation: Yogurtland Franchising Inc., FARMERS BRANCH, TX

Key Personnel
JAMES LEE - Owner; General Buyer

Bender/Agostini Organization
1500 Howard Rd
Madera, CA 93637-5127

Telephone: (559) 674-8241
Fax Number: (559) 674-8241
Type of Business: Chain Restaurant Operator
Total Sales: $14,901,000 (e)
Total Units: 3
Trade Names: McDonald's (3)
Units Franchised From: 3
Primary Menu: Hamburger (3)
Areas of Operation: CA
Type of Foodservice: Quick Serve (3)
Franchise Affiliation: McDonald's Corporation, CHICAGO, IL

Key Personnel
KENNETH BENDER - President; General Buyer

Sunlife Organics
29169 Heathercliff Rd Ste 110
Malibu, CA 90265

Telephone: (310) 457-6161
Internet Homepage: sunlifeorganics.com
Company Email: info@teamwolverine.com
Type of Business: Chain Restaurant Operator
Year Founded: 2011
Total Units: 10
Trade Names: Sunlife Organics (10)
Company-Owned Units: 10
Primary Menu: Health Foods (10)
Projected Openings: 2
Areas of Operation: CA
Type of Foodservice: Quick Serve (10)

Key Personnel
KHALIL RAFATI - Co-Founder; CEO
HAYLEY GORCEY - Co-Founder

Chicken Dijon Franchise Corp
909 N Aviation Blvd
Manhattan Beach, CA 90266-6241

Telephone: (310) 542-1703
Fax Number: (310) 341-3290
Internet Homepage: chickendijon.com
Company Email: info@chickendijon.com
Type of Business: Chain Restaurant Operator
Total Sales: $2,366,000 (e)
Total Units: 3
Trade Names: Chicken Dijon Rotisserie & Grill (3)
Company-Owned Units: 3
Primary Menu: Chicken (3)
Areas of Operation: CA
Type of Foodservice: Quick Serve (3)

Key Personnel
STEVE NIMEH - President; Partner; General Buyer
MELISSA MERCURIO - Controller

Rock & Brews Franchising LLC
321 12th St Ste 200
Manhattan Beach, CA 90266-5354

Telephone: (310) 545-9977
Internet Homepage: rockandbrews.com
Company Email: Info@rockandbrews.com
Type of Business: Chain Restaurant Operator
Year Founded: 2012
Systemwide Sales: $141,762,000 (e)
Total Sales: $16,750,000 (e)
Total Units: 20
Trade Names: Rock & Brews (20)
Company-Owned Units: 2
Units Franchised To: 18
Preferred Location Types: Airports; Downtown; Stadiums
Alcohol Served: Beer, Wine, Liquor
Primary Menu: American (20)
Areas of Operation: CA, FL, HI, KS, NM
Foreign Countries: MEXICO
Type of Foodservice: Casual Dining (20)
Catering Services: Yes

Key Personnel
ADAM GOLDBERG - CEO
DAVE FURANO - Partner
DELL FURANO - Partner
MICHAEL ZISLIS - Partner
LARRY DRASIN - Director Construction, Design
TERRY WILLS - Manager Marketing, Public Relations

Simms Restaurant Group
1148 Manhattan Ave Ste 1
Manhattan Beach, CA 90266-5323

Telephone: (310) 546-6250
Fax Number: (310) 546-6188
Internet Homepage: eatfwd.com; simmzys.com; tinroofbistro.com; simmsrestaurants.com
Type of Business: Chain Restaurant Operator
Total Units: 10
Trade Names: Arthur J (1); Fishing with Dynamite (1); Manhattan Beach Post (1); Simmzy's (6); Tin Roof Bistro (1)
Company-Owned Units: 10
Primary Menu: American (8); Seafood (1); Steak (1)
Areas of Operation: CA
Type of Foodservice: Casual Dining (8); Fast Casual (1); Fine Dining (1)

Key Personnel
MIKE SIMMS - President; Partner
DAVID LEFEVRE - Partner
CHRIS SIMMS - Partner
JERRY GARBUS - Partner; Director Operations, Alcoholic Beverages

TOM SIMMS - Partner
ADAM BASSUK - VP Operations

Domino's Franchisee
107 W North St Ste 101
Manteca, CA 95336-4592

Telephone: (209) 633-0000
Type of Business: Chain Restaurant Operator
Total Sales: $12,244,000 (e)
Total Units: 6
Trade Names: Domino's (6)
Units Franchised From: 6
Primary Menu: Pizza (6)
Areas of Operation: CA
Type of Foodservice: Quick Serve (6)
Franchise Affiliation: Domino's Pizza Inc, ANN ARBOR, MI

Key Personnel
GREG DEGRANDIS - Owner; General Buyer

T & K LP
236 Reservation Rd
Marina, CA 93933-3083

Telephone: (831) 384-1321
Fax Number: (831) 384-0820
Type of Business: Chain Restaurant Operator
Year Founded: 1979
Total Sales: $27,200,000 (e)
Alcohol Sales: 5%
Number of Employees: 450
Average Check: Lunch(12); Dinner(16)
Total Units: 10
Trade Names: Taco Bell (10)
Units Franchised From: 10
Preferred Square Footage: 3,000
Preferred Location Types: Downtown; Freestanding
Alcohol Served: Beer, Wine, Liquor
Primary Menu: Taco (10)
Areas of Operation: CA
Type of Foodservice: Quick Serve (10)
Franchise Affiliation: Taco Bell Corp., IRVINE, CA
Primary Distributors: (Full Line) McLane Foodservice, CARROLLTON, TX

Key Personnel
TAYLOR LOESCH - President; Director Operations; Manager Marketing
DAVID RICHARDS - Director Operations

Mikuni Restaurant Group, Inc.
5012 Luce Ave Ste 100
Mcclellan, CA 95652-2449

Telephone: (916) 576-2641
Internet Homepage: mikunisushi.com
Company Email: concierge@mikunisushi.com
Type of Business: Chain Restaurant Operator
Year Founded: 1987
Total Units: 9
Trade Names: Mikuni (8); Mikuni Kaizen (1)
Company-Owned Units: 9
Primary Menu: Japanese (9)
Areas of Operation: CA
Type of Foodservice: Casual Dining (9)
Notes: The Arai brothers are sons of company's retired founder (Koki Arai) and CEO Haru Sakata is his son-in-law.

Key Personnel
TARO ARAI - CEO
HARU SAKATA - CEO; Partner
JEANNE MABRY - Executive Director
NAO ARAI - Executive Chef

Eureka Fortune, Inc.
1645 Heartwood Dr
Mckinleyville, CA 95519

Telephone: (707) 839-9299
Type of Business: Chain Restaurant Operator
Total Sales: $9,797,000 (e)
Number of Employees: 2,015
Total Units: 4
Trade Names: Burger King (4)
Units Franchised From: 4
Preferred Square Footage: 2,500
Primary Menu: Hamburger (4)
Projected Remodelings: 1
Areas of Operation: CA
Type of Foodservice: Quick Serve (4)
Franchise Affiliation: Burger King Worldwide Inc., MIAMI, FL

Key Personnel
EDDIE SZETO - Owner; General Buyer

L & K Hodge LLC
1940 Central Ave
Mckinleyville, CA 95519-3606

Telephone: (707) 839-7200
Fax Number: (707) 839-7220
Company Email: hodge@brencam.com
Type of Business: Chain Restaurant Operator
Total Sales: $22,260,000 (e)
Total Units: 25
Trade Names: Papa Murphy's Take 'N' Bake Pizza (25)
Units Franchised From: 25
Primary Menu: Pizza (25)
Areas of Operation: CA, CO, MN, OR, WI
Type of Foodservice: Quick Serve (25)
Franchise Affiliation: Papa Murphy's International Inc., VANCOUVER, WA

Key Personnel
KATHRYN HODGE - Partner; General Buyer
CAMERON HODGE - Partner; Director Marketing
BRENNAN HODGE - Partner

Subway Franchisee
90480 66th Ave
Mecca, CA 92254-6228

Telephone: (760) 396-9616
Type of Business: Chain Restaurant Operator
Total Sales: $714,000 (e)
Total Units: 2
Trade Names: Subway (2)
Units Franchised From: 2
Areas of Operation: CA
Franchise Affiliation: Doctor's Associates Inc., MILFORD, CT

Key Personnel
NACHHATTAR CHANDI - Owner; General Buyer

Flea Street Cafe
3607 Alameda De Las Pulgas
Menlo Park, CA 94025-6213

Telephone: (650) 854-1226
Fax Number: (650) 854-2145
Internet Homepage: cooleatz.com
Company Email: Admin@Cooleatz.com
Type of Business: Chain Restaurant Operator
Year Founded: 1980
Total Sales: $4,172,000 (e)
Alcohol Sales: 10%
Number of Employees: 35
Average Check: Dinner(42)
Total Units: 3
Trade Names: Cool Cafe (2); Flea Street Cafe (1)
Company-Owned Units: 3
Preferred Location Types: Freestanding
Alcohol Served: Beer, Wine, Liquor
Primary Menu: Miscellaneous (3)
Areas of Operation: CA
Type of Foodservice: Casual Dining (2); Fine Dining (1)
Catering Services: Yes

Key Personnel
JESSE COOL - President; Executive Chef;

General Buyer

SAJJ Mediterranean
883 Hamilton Ave
Menlo Park, CA 94025

Telephone: (650) 322-7255
Internet Homepage: sajjstreeteats.com
Company Email: contact@sajjstreeteats.com
Type of Business: Chain Restaurant Operator
Year Founded: 2012
Total Sales: $13,260,000 (e)
Total Units: 15
Trade Names: SAJJ Mediterranean (15)
Company-Owned Units: 15
Primary Menu: Middle Eastern (15)
Projected Openings: 1
Areas of Operation: CA
Type of Foodservice: Fast Casual (15)

Key Personnel
ZAID AYOUB - CEO; Owner
LOAY ALHINDI - Executive Chef; Director Food

Woodside Hotels & Resorts
1100 Alma St Ste 106
Menlo Park, CA 94025-3344

Telephone: (650) 330-8888
Fax Number: (650) 330-0588
Internet Homepage: woodsidehotels.com
Company Email: info@woodsidehotels.com
Type of Business: Foodservice Operations - Hotel/Motels
Year Founded: 1981
Total Sales: $120,354,000 (e)
Alcohol Sales: 10%
Number of Employees: 710
Total Units: 10
Restaurants in Hotels: 10
Trade Names: Bernardus Lodge & Spa (1); Bodega Bay Lodge (1); Dream Inn (1); Harvest Inn (1); Hotel Drisco (1); Indian Springs (1); Lafayette Park Hotel & Spa (1); Monterey Plaza Hotel & Spa (1); Napa Valley Lodge (1); Stanford Park Hotel (1)
Company-Owned Units: 10
Alcohol Served: Beer, Wine, Liquor
Areas of Operation: CA
Type of Foodservice: Casual Dining (6); Fine Dining (4)
Primary Distributors: (Food) SYSCO Food Services of San Francisco Inc., FREMONT, CA
Notes: The company derives approximately 82% of its revenue from hotel operations.

Key Personnel
GREG ALDEN - CEO; President; General Buyer
CAL STAMENOV - Executive Chef

Inmack Foods Inc.
PO Box 2389
Merced, CA 95344-0389

Telephone: (209) 383-7775
Fax Number: (209) 383-0814
Type of Business: Chain Restaurant Operator
Year Founded: 1968
Total Sales: $11,907,000 (e)
Number of Employees: 180
Average Check: Lunch(8); Dinner(10)
Total Units: 4
Trade Names: Taco Bell (4)
Units Franchised From: 4
Preferred Location Types: Freestanding
Primary Menu: Taco (4)
Areas of Operation: CA
Type of Foodservice: Quick Serve (4)
Franchise Affiliation: Taco Bell Corp., IRVINE, CA
Primary Distributors: (Full Line) McLane/Pacific, MERCED, CA

Key Personnel
MARVIN MACKIN - President; Partner; Controller; Manager Purchasing, Information Systems, Loss Prevention, Marketing, Real Estate
LAVERNE MACKIN - Partner; CFO; VP; Treasurer; Manager Human Resources
NATHAN MACKIN - VP
GERALD TERAN - Director Operations; General Buyer

Maria's Taco Shop
1750 R St
Merced, CA 95340-4527

Telephone: (209) 383-4424
Type of Business: Chain Restaurant Operator
Total Sales: $7,712,000 (e)
Number of Employees: 37
Average Check: Breakfast(6); Lunch(8); Dinner(8)
Total Units: 6
Trade Names: Maria's Taco Shop (6)
Company-Owned Units: 6
Preferred Square Footage: 2,500
Preferred Location Types: Freestanding
Primary Menu: Taco (6)
Areas of Operation: CA
Type of Foodservice: Quick Serve (6)
Primary Distributors: (Full Line) SYSCO Food Services of Los Angeles Inc., WALNUT, CA

Key Personnel
ENRIQUE VALENCIA - Owner; General Manager Menu Development; General Buyer

Auberge Resorts Collection
33 Reed Blvd
Mill Valley, CA 94941-6033

Telephone: (415) 380-3460
Fax Number: (415) 380-3461
Internet Homepage: aubergeresorts.com
Company Email: info@aubergeresorts.com
Type of Business: Foodservice Operations - Hotel/Motels
Total Units: 19
Trade Names: Auberge Beach Residences (1); Auberge du Soleil (1); Calistoga Ranch (1); Chileno Bay Resort & Residences (1); Element 52 (1); Esperanza(1); Grace Hotel (1); Hacienda AltaGracia (1); Hotel Jerome (1); Madeline Hotel (1); Malliouhana (1); Mauna Lani (1); Mayflower Inn & Spa (1); Nanuku (1);Sleeping Indian Ranch (1); Solage (1); The Lodge at Blue Sky (1); The Vanderbilt (1); White Barn Inn (1)
Company-Owned Units: 19
Alcohol Served: Beer, Wine, Liquor
Areas of Operation: CA, CO, OR
Foreign Countries: COSTA RICA; MEXICO

Key Personnel
DAN FRIEDKIN - Chairman
CLAUDE ROUAS - Vice Chairman
CRAIG REID - CEO; President
AMY BRANT - CFO
CHRIS GABALDON - COO
MICHAEL MINCHIN - Chief Marketing Officer
RICHARD ARNOLD - Chief Development Officer
URSULA ZOPP - VP Human Resources
WYNN JAMES - Director E-Commerce
DAVE ELCON - Director Operations

Baskin-Robbins Franchise
669 Broadway
Millbrae, CA 94030-1909

Telephone: (650) 697-6968
Type of Business: Chain Restaurant Operator
Total Sales: $829,000 (e)
Total Units: 2
Trade Names: Baskin-Robbins (2)
Company-Owned Units: 2
Primary Menu: Snacks (2)
Areas of Operation: CA
Type of Foodservice: Quick Serve (2)
Franchise Affiliation: BR IP Holder LLC, CANTON, MA

Key Personnel
AGNES SHIN - President; General Buyer

Dean Foods - a Baskin Robbins Distribution Center
3251 De Forest Cir
Mira Loma, CA 91752-3276

Telephone: (951) 361-3131
Fax Number: (951) 361-1530
Internet Homepage: deanfoods.com
Listing Type: Distribution Center
Type of Business: Chain Restaurant Operator
Number of Employees: 3
Areas of Operation: AZ, CA, NV

Key Personnel
JOHN ANDERSON - Manager Distribution

Rockfire Grill
28251 Marguerite Pkwy
Mission Viejo, CA 92692-3721

Telephone: (949) 364-3473
Internet Homepage: rockfiregrill.com
Company Email: info@rockfire-grill.com
Type of Business: Chain Restaurant Operator
Year Founded: 2014
Total Units: 3
Trade Names: Rockfire Grill (3)
Company-Owned Units: 3
Primary Menu: American (3)
Areas of Operation: CA
Type of Foodservice: Casual Dining (3)
Notes: Wood-fire grilled flatbread concept.

Key Personnel
RAJ SYAL - Partner; General Buyer
NEIL SYAL - Partner

Sizzler USA Inc.
25910 Acero Ste 350
Mission Viejo, CA 92691-7908

Telephone: (949) 273-4497
Fax Number: (310) 568-0073
Internet Homepage: sizzler.com
Type of Business: Chain Restaurant Operator
Year Founded: 1958
Systemwide Sales: $381,879,000 (e)
Total Sales: $57,761,000 (e)
Alcohol Sales: 2%
Number of Employees: 1,173
Average Check: Lunch(14); Dinner(14)
Total Units: 111
Trade Names: Sizzler (135)
Company-Owned Units: 14
Units Franchised To: 121
Preferred Square Footage: 5,000; 5,600; 5,800; 6,000
Preferred Location Types: Downtown; Freestanding; Mobile Unit; Regional Mall; Strip Mall
Alcohol Served: Beer, Wine
Primary Menu: Steak (135)
Areas of Operation: AZ, CA, FL, ID, NM, NV, OR, PR, UT, WA
Type of Foodservice: Casual Dining (135)
Catering Services: Yes
Primary Distributors: (Full Line) US Foods-Los Angeles, LA MIRADA, CA

Key Personnel
KEVIN PERKINS - Chairman
DONALD HENRY - VP Purchasing, Distribution
KRISTINA VAN BRUGGEN - VP Marketing
JUDY GOMEZ - Corporate Secretary; General Counsel
MICHAEL TEBO - Senior Director Operations, Development
AL PICKARD - Director Finance

Yogurtland Franchisee
25108 Marguerite Pkwy Ste B
Mission Viejo, CA 92692-2400

Telephone: (949) 768-3000
Type of Business: Chain Restaurant Operator
Total Sales: $2,116,000 (e)
Total Units: 2
Trade Names: Yogurtland (2)
Units Franchised From: 2
Primary Menu: Snacks (2)
Areas of Operation: CA
Type of Foodservice: Quick Serve (2)
Franchise Affiliation: Yogurtland Franchising Inc., FARMERS BRANCH, TX

Key Personnel
SELENA CHWEH - Owner; General Buyer

Andrew Limited Partnerships
400 Lyell Dr Ste 101
Modesto, CA 95356-9291

Telephone: (209) 575-5600
Fax Number: (209) 575-2465
Type of Business: Chain Restaurant Operator
Year Founded: 1986
Total Sales: $7,583,000 (e)
Alcohol Sales: 10%
Number of Employees: 300
Average Check: Breakfast(6); Lunch(8); Dinner(16)
Total Units: 9
Trade Names: Carl's Jr. (5); Hooters (4)
Units Franchised From: 9
Preferred Square Footage: 6,000; 6,500
Preferred Location Types: Freestanding
Alcohol Served: Beer, Wine, Liquor
Primary Menu: American (4); Hamburger (5)
Areas of Operation: CA, WA
Type of Foodservice: Casual Dining (4); Quick Serve (5)
Catering Services: Yes
Franchise Affiliation: Carl's Jr., FRANKLIN, TN; HOA Restaurant Group LLC, ATLANTA, GA
Primary Distributors: (Full Line) McLane/Rocky Mount, ROCKY MOUNT, NC

Key Personnel
NICK J. TRANI - President; Director Catering; General Buyer
SHIRLEY TRANI - VP Finance
DOUG KAPPY - VP Operations, Catering
JOHN TRANI - VP Real Estate, Business Development, Store Fixtures

Auntie Anne's Franchise
3401 Dale Rd Ste 452
Modesto, CA 95356-0593

Telephone: (209) 575-3981
Type of Business: Chain Restaurant Operator
Total Sales: $1,546,000 (e)
Total Units: 2
Trade Names: Auntie Anne's Hand-Rolled Soft Pretzels (2)
Units Franchised From: 2
Primary Menu: Snacks (2)
Areas of Operation: CA
Type of Foodservice: Quick Serve (2)
Franchise Affiliation: Auntie Anne's Inc., LANCASTER, PA

Key Personnel
BETSY POTTRUCK - Owner; General Buyer

B K & R Inc
2900 Standiford Ave Ste 24
Modesto, CA 95350-6576

Telephone: (209) 574-1140
Fax Number: (209) 574-1144
Type of Business: Chain Restaurant Operator
Total Sales: $1,833,000 (e)
Total Units: 2
Trade Names: Togo's (2)
Units Franchised From: 2
Primary Menu: Sandwiches/Deli (2)
Areas of Operation: CA
Type of Foodservice: Quick Serve (2)
Franchise Affiliation: Togo's Eateries LLC, SAN JOSE, CA

Key Personnel
GIVO ISHAYA - Owner

Canteen Vending Services
542 Mariposa Rd
Modesto, CA 95354-4124

Telephone: (209) 529-5350
Fax Number: (209) 529-8652
Listing Type: Branch Office
Type of Business: Foodservice Management Operator
Year Founded: 1929
Number of Employees: 60
Number of Locations Served: 350
Total Foodservice Mgmt Accounts: 350
Areas of Operation: CA
Type of Foodservice: Vending machines (350)
Foodservice Management Venues: Business & Industry; College & University; Health Care; Lodging; Military Feeding; Parks & Recreation; Prison Feeding; Schools; Travel Plazas
Parent Company: Compass Group The Americas, CHARLOTTE, NC
Headquarters: Canteen Vending Services, CHARLOTTE, NC

Key Personnel
LEN VIERIA - General Manager; Director Purchasing

Wendy's of the Pacific Inc.
1308 Kansas Ave Ste 6
Modesto, CA 95351-1530

Telephone: (209) 577-6690
Fax Number: (209) 524-3217
Type of Business: Chain Restaurant Operator
Year Founded: 1976
Total Sales: $70,250,000 (e)
Number of Employees: 843
Average Check: Lunch(6); Dinner(6)
Total Units: 26
Trade Names: Wendy's Old Fashioned Hamburgers (26)
Units Franchised From: 26
Preferred Square Footage: 2,500
Preferred Location Types: Freestanding
Primary Menu: Hamburger (26)
Areas of Operation: CA
Type of Foodservice: Quick Serve (26)
Franchise Affiliation: The Wendy's Company, DUBLIN, OH

Key Personnel
JOE JOHAL - President; Manager Purchasing
MARK SUTEY - Controller; Director Finance, Operations, Facility/Maintenance, Information Systems, Real Estate, Design, Human Resources
JASBIR DHANOTA - General Manager
MICHELLE THOMPSON - General Manager

Tomdan Enterprises Inc.
831 E Huntington Dr Ste 202
Monrovia, CA 91016-6424

Telephone: (626) 357-9201
Fax Number: (626) 359-5216
Internet Homepage: originaltommys.com
Company Email: tommys@originaltommys.com
Type of Business: Chain Restaurant Operator
Year Founded: 1946
Total Sales: $54,310,000 (e)
Number of Employees: 615
Average Check: Breakfast(8); Lunch(12); Dinner(14)
Internet Order Processing: Yes
Internet Sales: 10.00%
Total Units: 33
Trade Names: Original Tommy's World Famous Hamburgers (33)
Company-Owned Units: 33
Preferred Square Footage: 1,800
Preferred Location Types: Freestanding
Primary Menu: Hamburger (33)
Areas of Operation: CA, NV
Type of Foodservice: Quick Serve (33)
Catering Services: Yes
Primary Distributors: (Full Line) SYSCO Food Services of San Francisco Inc., FREMONT, CA

Key Personnel
DAWNA BERNAL - CEO; President; Manager Human Resources

Absolutely Italian Management Group
5549 Arrow Hwy Ste J
Montclair, CA 91763-6601

Telephone: (909) 373-2800
Fax Number: (909) 373-2880
Internet Homepage: aimgroup.org; eddieseatery.com; spaghettieddies.com; tuttimangia.com
Company Email: info@aimgrojup.org
Type of Business: Chain Restaurant Operator
Year Founded: 1985
Total Sales: $6,772,000 (e)
Alcohol Sales: 10%
Number of Employees: 100
Average Check: Lunch(24); Dinner(48)
Total Units: 3
Trade Names: Eddie's Italian Eatery (1); Spaghetti Eddie's Cucina Italiana (1); Tutti Mangia Italian Grill (1)
Company-Owned Units: 3
Preferred Location Types: Downtown; Strip Mall
Alcohol Served: Beer, Wine, Liquor
Primary Menu: Italian (3)
Areas of Operation: CA
Type of Foodservice: Casual Dining (3)
Catering Services: Yes
Primary Distributors: (Full Line) SYSCO Food Services of Central California Inc., MODESTO, CA

Key Personnel
EDDIE INGLESE - President; General Buyer
JAMES HERMANSON - VP

AMSU Financial, Inc.
4565 Holt Blvd
Montclair, CA 91763-4710

Telephone: (909) 447-1214
Type of Business: Chain Restaurant Operator
Total Sales: $15,230,000 (e)
Total Units: 6
Trade Names: Jack in the Box (6)
Units Franchised From: 6
Primary Menu: Hamburger (6)
Areas of Operation: CA
Type of Foodservice: Quick Serve (6)
Franchise Affiliation: Jack in the Box Restaurants, SAN DIEGO, CA

Key Personnel
ASLAM MALIK - Owner; General Buyer

Downtown Dining
2999 Salinas Hwy Ste 1
Monterey, CA 93940-5706

Telephone: (831) 647-1085
Fax Number: (831) 647-8328
Internet Homepage: downtowndining.com; montrio.com; riogrill.com; tarpys.com
Type of Business: Chain Restaurant Operator
Year Founded: 1983
Total Sales: $13,929,000 (e)
Alcohol Sales: 30%
Number of Employees: 110
Average Check: Lunch(22); Dinner(42)
Internet Order Processing: Yes
Total Units: 3
Trade Names: Montrio Bistro (1); Rio Grill (1); Tarpy's Roadhouse (1)
Company-Owned Units: 3
Preferred Location Types: Freestanding; Strip Mall
Alcohol Served: Beer, Wine, Liquor
Primary Menu: American (3)
Areas of Operation: CA
Type of Foodservice: Fine Dining (3)
Catering Services: Yes
Primary Distributors: (Full Line) SYSCO Food Services of San Francisco Inc., FREMONT, CA

Key Personnel
TONY TOLLNER - Partner; Director Operations, Catering
KATHY SOLLEY - General Manager
KELLY FRAISER - Manager Catering

Richard Landon Hoffman, Inc.
1100 Del Monte Ave
Monterey, CA 93940-2426

Telephone: (831) 373-2153
Fax Number: (831) 373-2760
Type of Business: Chain Restaurant Operator
Year Founded: 1990
Total Sales: $33,320,000 (e)
Number of Employees: 330
Average Check: Breakfast(8); Lunch(10); Dinner(12)
Total Units: 7
Trade Names: McDonald's (7)
Units Franchised From: 7
Preferred Square Footage: 2,500; 3,000
Preferred Location Types: Community Mall; Discount Dept. Stores; Freestanding
Primary Menu: Hamburger (7)
Areas of Operation: CA
Type of Foodservice: Quick Serve (7)
Franchise Affiliation: McDonald's Corporation, CHICAGO, IL
Primary Distributors: (Full Line) The Martin-Brower Co., STOCKTON, CA

Key Personnel
RICHARD L. HOFFMAN - Owner; General Buyer
DIANA MCLAUGHLIN - Manager Accounting, Information Systems, Human Resources

Shake Enterprises
700 Cannery Row
Monterey, CA 93940-1063

Mailing Address: PO Box 2289, MONTEREY, CA, 93942-2289
Telephone: (831) 645-9107
Fax Number: (831) 645-9153
Internet Homepage: scalesmonterey.com; fishhopper.com; oldfishermansgrotto.com
Type of Business: Chain Restaurant Operator
Year Founded: 1983
Total Sales: $46,840,000 (e)
Alcohol Sales: 5%
Number of Employees: 75
Average Check: Lunch(14); Dinner(22)
Internet Order Processing: Yes
Total Units: 5
Trade Names: Scales (1); Scales Cafe and Deli (1); The Fish Hopper (2); The Old Fisherman's Grotto (1)
Company-Owned Units: 5
Preferred Location Types: Freestanding
Alcohol Served: Beer, Wine, Liquor
Primary Menu: Seafood (5)
Areas of Operation: CA, HI
Type of Foodservice: Casual Dining (4)
Primary Distributors: (Food) US Foods, CORONA, CA

Key Personnel
CHRIS SHAKE - President; Partner; Executive Chef
SABU SHAKE - Partner; General Manager; General Buyer

H. Salt of Southern California Inc.
1255 Corporate Center Dr Ste 110
Monterey Park, CA 91754-7609

Mailing Address: 300 W Valley Blvd., Alhambra, CA, 91803
Telephone: (323) 264-8766
Fax Number: (323) 264-7262
Internet Homepage: hsalt.com
Type of Business: Chain Restaurant Operator
Year Founded: 1965
Systemwide Sales: $10,724,000 (e)
Total Sales: $1,425,000 (e)
Alcohol Sales: 1%
Number of Employees: 15
Average Check: Lunch(12); Dinner(18)
Total Units: 11
Trade Names: H. Salt Fish and Chips (11)
Units Franchised To: 11
Preferred Square Footage: 5,500; 6,000
Preferred Location Types: Freestanding; Strip Mall
Primary Menu: Seafood (13)
Areas of Operation: CA
Type of Foodservice: Casual Dining (11)
Primary Distributors: (Full Line) SYSCO Food Services of Central California Inc., MODESTO, CA

Key Personnel
TOM CHANG - CEO; President; Director Real Estate, Design, Menu Development; General Buyer
MICHAEL CHANG - VP Operations, Information Systems
MILLIE ESTRADA - Director Operations

Auntie Anne's Franchise
22500 Town Cir Ste 1048
Moreno Valley, CA 92553-7511

Telephone: (951) 656-8122
Type of Business: Chain Restaurant Operator
Total Sales: $1,561,000 (e)
Total Units: 2
Trade Names: Auntie Anne's Hand-Rolled Soft Pretzels (2)
Units Franchised From: 2
Primary Menu: Snacks (2)
Areas of Operation: CA
Type of Foodservice: Quick Serve (2)
Franchise Affiliation: Auntie Anne's Inc., LANCASTER, PA

Key Personnel
AKTHER JAHAN - Owner; General Buyer

Domino's Franchisee
24578 Sunnymead Blvd
Moreno Valley, CA 92553-9353

Telephone: (951) 924-1931
Type of Business: Chain Restaurant Operator
Total Sales: $4,044,000 (e)
Total Units: 2
Trade Names: Domino's (2)
Units Franchised From: 2
Primary Menu: Pizza (2)
Areas of Operation: CA
Type of Foodservice: Quick Serve (2)
Franchise Affiliation: Domino's Pizza Inc, ANN ARBOR, MI

Key Personnel
RYAN P. MILLER - Owner; General Buyer

Freeman Enterprises
1060 N Rengstorff Ave
Mountain View, CA 94043

Telephone: (650) 428-0960
Type of Business: Chain Restaurant Operator
Total Sales: $60,980,000 (e)
Number of Employees: 640
Average Check: Breakfast(8); Lunch(8); Dinner(8)
Total Units: 13
Trade Names: McDonald's (13)
Units Franchised From: 13
Preferred Square Footage: 2,500; 3,000
Preferred Location Types: Freestanding
Primary Menu: Hamburger (13)
Areas of Operation: CA
Type of Foodservice: Quick Serve (13)
Franchise Affiliation: McDonald's Corporation, CHICAGO, IL
Primary Distributors: (Full Line) The Martin-Brower Co., STOCKTON, CA

Key Personnel
CONRAD J. FREEMAN - President; General Manager; General Buyer

FEAST Foods, LLC
41856 Ivy St Ste 201
Murrieta, CA 92562-8805

Telephone: (951) 677-3976
Internet Homepage: feastenterprises.com
Type of Business: Chain Restaurant Operator
Total Sales: $381,360,000 (e)
Total Units: 151
Trade Names: Corner Bakery Cafe (6); Denny's (30); Jack in the Box (115)
Units Franchised From: 151
Primary Menu: American (36); Hamburger (115)
Areas of Operation: CA
Type of Foodservice: Casual Dining (30); Fast Casual (6); Quick Serve (115)
Franchise Affiliation: CBC Restaurant Corp., DALLAS, TX; Denny's Corporation, SPARTANBURG, SC; Jack in the Box Restaurants, SAN DIEGO, CA

Key Personnel
BEN ERAMYA - Partner; General Buyer
DAWOOD BESHAY - Partner
SHAYNE STIMPSON - VP Operations
ANTHONY ERAMYA - Director Social Media
JOSE ALCALA - Manager District
TIFFANY POBLETE - Manager District

SRC Subs, LLC
27614 Clinton Keith Rd Ste 101
Murrieta, CA 92562-8538

Telephone: (951) 301-4433
Type of Business: Chain Restaurant Operator
Total Sales: $11,020,000 (e)
Total Units: 8
Trade Names: Jersey Mike's Subs (8)
Units Franchised From: 8
Primary Menu: Sandwiches/Deli (8)
Areas of Operation: CA
Type of Foodservice: Quick Serve (8)
Franchise Affiliation: Jersey Mike's Franchise Systems, MANASQUAN, NJ

Key Personnel
BORIS ILIC - Owner

Domino's Franchisee
35248 Newark Blvd
Newark, CA 94560-1222

Telephone: (510) 796-4440
Type of Business: Chain Restaurant Operator
Total Sales: $3,974,000 (e)
Total Units: 2
Trade Names: Domino's (2)
Units Franchised From: 2
Primary Menu: Pizza (2)
Areas of Operation: CA
Type of Foodservice: Quick Serve (2)
Franchise Affiliation: Domino's Pizza Inc, ANN ARBOR, MI

Key Personnel
SAUL RAMIREZ - Owner; General Buyer

Sharmac Corp.
35192 Newark Blvd
Newark, CA 94560-1220

Telephone: (510) 791-1389
Type of Business: Chain Restaurant Operator
Total Sales: $15,205,000 (e)
Total Units: 3
Trade Names: McDonald's (3)
Units Franchised From: 3
Preferred Location Types: Freestanding
Primary Menu: Hamburger (3)
Areas of Operation: CA
Type of Foodservice: Quick Serve (3)
Franchise Affiliation: McDonald's Corporation, CHICAGO, IL

Key Personnel
SOHAN SHARMA - President; General Buyer

United Investment Solutions, Inc.
37036 Saint Edwards St
Newark, CA 94560

Telephone: (408) 243-4700
Type of Business: Chain Restaurant Operator
Total Sales: $13,180,000 (e)
Total Units: 6
Trade Names: Carl's Jr. (6)
Units Franchised From: 6
Primary Menu: Hamburger (6)
Areas of Operation: CA
Type of Foodservice: Quick Serve (6)
Franchise Affiliation: Carl's Jr., FRANKLIN, TN

Key Personnel
VIKAS TANDON - President; General Buyer

Domino's Franchisee
23329 Lyons Ave
Newhall, CA 91321

Telephone: (661) 254-0300
Type of Business: Chain Restaurant Operator
Total Sales: $11,930,000 (e)
Total Units: 6
Trade Names: Domino's (6)
Units Franchised From: 6
Primary Menu: Pizza (6)
Areas of Operation: CA
Type of Foodservice: Quick Serve (6)
Franchise Affiliation: Domino's Pizza Inc, ANN ARBOR, MI

Key Personnel
DENNIS E. SCHWESINGER - Owner; General Buyer

Aloha Restaurants Inc.
204 Main St Unit 960
Newport Beach, CA 92661-1822

Telephone: (949) 250-0331
Fax Number: (949) 673-5085
Internet Homepage: aloharestaurants.com
Company Email: alohamain@aol.com
Type of Business: Chain Restaurant Operator
Year Founded: 1997
Total Sales: $13,848,000 (e)
Alcohol Sales: 20%
Number of Employees: 215
Average Check: Lunch(14); Dinner(20)
Total Units: 3
Trade Names: Buster's Beach House & Long Board Bar (1); Jolly Roger Restaurant (1); Monterey Bay Canners Restaurant (1)
Company-Owned Units: 3
Preferred Square Footage: 6,000
Preferred Location Types: Freestanding
Alcohol Served: Beer, Wine, Liquor
Primary Menu: American (2); Seafood (1)
Areas of Operation: CA, HI
Type of Foodservice: Casual Dining (3)
Primary Distributors: (Full Line) SYSCO Food Services of Los Angeles Inc., WALNUT, CA

Key Personnel
STEVEN MOYER - CEO; President

BLD Brands
20377 SW Acacia St Ste 200
Newport Beach, CA 92660-1780

Telephone: (714) 450-7660
Fax Number: (714) 385-1945
Internet Homepage: bldbrands.com
Company Email: info@bldbrands.com
Type of Business: Chain Restaurant Operator
Total Sales: $230,640,000 (e)
Total Units: 133
Trade Names: Hardee's (51); Papa John's Pizza (74); Spaghetti Warehouse (8)
Units Franchised From: 133
Primary Menu: Hamburger (51); Italian (8); Pizza (74)
Areas of Operation: CA, FL, IL, MO, NC, NV, OH, WI
Type of Foodservice: Casual Dining (8); Quick Serve (125)

Subsidiaries: Spaghetti Warehouse Restaurants Inc., DALLAS, TX
Franchise Affiliation: Hardee's Food Systems Inc., FRANKLIN, TN; Papa Johns International Inc., LOUISVILLE, KY

Key Personnel
DOUG PAK - Chairman; Co-CEO
JAY LEE - President; CIO
JOHN THEUER - CFO
MICHELLE ROCKENSTYRE - Chief Administrative Officer
CHRISTOPHER SHEELY - General Manager
ROB LEE - Director Finance
AUSTIN OVERSTREET - Director Operations
TONY GAUTHIER - Director
CHANG KIM - Director Information Technology
KATEY POWELL - District Manager

Bluewater Grill
630 Lido Park Dr
Newport Beach, CA 92663-4442

Telephone: (949) 675-3474
Fax Number: (949) 675-1367
Internet Homepage: bluewatergrill.com
Company Email: Newport@bluewatergrill.com
Type of Business: Chain Restaurant Operator
Total Units: 9
Trade Names: Bluewater Grill (9)
Company-Owned Units: 9
Alcohol Served: Beer, Wine, Liquor
Primary Menu: Seafood (9)
Areas of Operation: AZ, CA
Type of Foodservice: Casual Dining (9)

Key Personnel
CHRIS ROCK - Partner; District Manager
JIM ULCICKAS - Partner
ROBERT HYMAN - VP Operations

Chipotle Mexican Grill Inc.
610 Newport Center Dr Ste 1300
Newport Beach, CA 92660

Telephone: (303) 595-4000
Fax Number: (303) 222-2505
Internet Homepage: chipotle.com; pizzerialocale.com
Company Email: Info@chipotle.com
Type of Business: Chain Restaurant Operator
Year Founded: 1993
Systemwide Sales: $1,118,586,000 (e)
Publicly Held: Yes
Total Sales: $10,186,504,000 (e)
Alcohol Sales: 1%
Number of Employees: 60,000
Average Check: Lunch(10); Dinner(10)
Internet Order Processing: Yes
Internet Sales: 10.20%
Total Units: 3,682
Trade Names: Chipotle Mexican Grill (3,682)
Company-Owned Units: 3,682
Preferred Square Footage: 1,000; 1,800; 2,500; 3,000
Preferred Location Types: Downtown; Freestanding; Regional Mall; Strip Mall
Alcohol Served: Beer, Wine, Liquor
Primary Menu: Mexican (3,682)
Projected Openings: 150
Areas of Operation: AL, AR, AZ, CA, CO, CT, DC, DE, FL, GA, IA, ID, IL, IN, KS, KY, LA, MA, MD, ME, MI, MN, MO, NC, NE, NH, NJ, NM, NV, NY, OH, OK, OR, PA, RI, SC, TN, TX, UT, VA, VT, WA, WI, WV, WY, FC, BC, ON
Foreign Countries: CANADA; ENGLAND; FRANCE; GERMANY
Type of Foodservice: Fast Casual (3,682)
Catering Services: Yes
On-site Distribution Center: Yes

Key Personnel
SCOTT BOATWRIGHT - CEO
JOHN "JACK" R. HARTUNG - President Finance, Strategy, Supply Chain; CFO
ILENE ESKENAZI - Chief Human Resources Officer
LOIS ALEXIS-COLLINS - Chief People Officer
CURT GARNER - CTO
CHRIS BRANDT - Chief Marketing Officer
STEPHEN PIACENTINI - Chief Development Officer
LAURIE SCHALOW - Chief Communications Officer; Director Food Safety
ROGER THEODOREDIS - Chief Legal Officer
DAVE ESTLICK - Chief Information Security Officer
KERRY BRIDGES - VP Food Safety
CARLOS LONDONO - VP Supply Chain
NEVIELLE PANTHAKY - VP Culinary Operations, Menu Development
STEPHANIE PERDUE - VP Brand Marketing
NICOLE WEST - VP Digital, E-Commerce
GRETCHEN C. SELFRIDGE - Executive Director Operations, West Region
NAVEEN VIJAYARAGHAVAN - Senior Director Marketing
JASON SCOGGINS - Senior Director
KEVIN ARNDT - Senior Director Software Development
PANKAJ ARORA - Director Architecture
RICH FIDLER - Director Design
COLIN MCGUIRE - Director Information Technology, Infrastructure
MARK HEATH - Director Real Estate
LOGAN HULL - Director Digital Solutions
JASON WAN - Director Finance
SCOTT SHIPPEY - Director Design
JIM SLATER - Director Group
DAVID PHILLIPS - Director Information Systems
JASON RICCIO - Director Software Development
BRANDON BLOSSER - Senior Manager Innovation
GREGORY DE LA PAZ - Senior Manager People
JESSICA BARNOSKI - Senior Manager Training
HEATHER MALONEY - Regional Manager Construction
TREY REESE - Regional Manager Construction, West Region
ERIC SAILOR - Regional Manager Construction, Central Region
CURTIS WHITE - Regional Manager Construction
LISA WYDLER - Regional Manager Construction
HAL HOBGOOD - Area Manager Real Estate
JULIE DOUGLAS - Manager Asset Management
KATHRYN MCVANE - Manager Real Estate
LORI MADZIN-PELLEGRINO - Manager Real Estate
TODD KEYSER - Manager Real Estate
BRYAN BAUER - Manager Real Estate
JACOB BAXTER - Manager Innovation
RYAN FURLONG - Manager Strategy, Real Estate, Research & Development
JESSICA GARCIA - Manager Real Estate
IFTIKHAR ALI - Manager Software Development
LISA BURBEY - Manager Real Estate, West Region
ANDREW DALY - Manager Construction, Northeast Region
CASEY ZIMMERMAN - Manager Digital
CHRIS RAYMOND - Manager Facility/Maintenance, National
JIM STADELMAN - Manager Real Estate, Midwest Region
KEVIN MCCULLOCH - Brand Manager
CRAIG BUCK - Project Manager Facility/Maintenance
AMANDA BEDNAR - Administrator Leasing
LAURIE KAUFFMAN - Specialist Legal; Analyst Real Estate
BREANNA KHOURIE - Coordinator Leasing
CHRISTINE GRAY - Executive Assistant

Gina's Pizza Inc.
309 Palm St #D
Newport Beach, CA 92661

Mailing Address: PO Box 11269, NEWPORT BEACH, CA, 92658-5024
Telephone: (949) 760-0948
Fax Number: (949) 760-0998
Internet Homepage: ginaspizza.com
Company Email: contact@ginaspizza.com
Type of Business: Chain Restaurant Operator
Year Founded: 1975
Systemwide Sales: $6,891,000 (e)
Total Sales: $4,361,000 (e)
Alcohol Sales: 10%
Number of Employees: 174
Average Check: Lunch(10); Dinner(14)
Internet Order Processing: Yes
Total Units: 6
Trade Names: Gina's Pizza (6)
Company-Owned Units: 4
Units Franchised To: 2

Preferred Square Footage: 2,400
Preferred Location Types: Strip Mall
Alcohol Served: Beer, Wine
Primary Menu: Pizza (6)
Areas of Operation: CA
Type of Foodservice: Casual Dining (6)
Catering Services: Yes
Primary Distributors: (Full Line) Concord Foods Inc., ONTARIO, CA

Key Personnel
ALEX COSTA - Partner; Director Finance, Facility/Maintenance, Information Systems, Supply Chain, Real Estate, Human Resources
KAY BASSETT - Director Menu Development, Catering
KERRY MCMAHAN - Director Operations

Palace Entertainment Holdings LLC
4590 MacArthur Blvd Ste 400
Newport Beach, CA 92660-2027

Telephone: (949) 261-0404
Fax Number: (949) 261-1414
Internet Homepage: miamiseaquarium.com; palaceentertainment.com
Type of Business: Foodservice Operations - Theme Parks
Year Founded: 1998
Total Sales: $188,000,000 (e)
Alcohol Sales: 1%
Number of Employees: 1,474
Average Check: Lunch(8); Dinner(8)
Total Units: 23
Trade Names: Adventureland (1); Boomers! (2); Cartoon Network Hotel (1); Castle Park (1); Dutch Wonderland (1); Idlewild and Soak Zone (1); Kennywood(1); Lake Compounce (1); Malibu Grand Prix (1); Mountasia (1); Noah's Ark (1); Raging Waters (4); Sandcastle (1); Sea Life Park Hawaii (1); Splish Splash (1); StoryLand (1); Water Country (1); Wet n Wild (2)
Company-Owned Units: 23
Preferred Square Footage: 2,500
Preferred Location Types: Parks
Alcohol Served: Beer, Wine
Primary Menu: Snacks (22)
Areas of Operation: CA, CT, FL, GA, HI, NC, NH, NJ, NY, PA, TX
Type of Foodservice: Quick Serve (22)
On-site Distribution Center: Yes
Primary Distributors: (Food) SYSCO Food Services of Los Angeles Inc., WALNUT, CA
Parent Company: Parques Reunidos, MADRID, ES[
Headquarter Offices: Idlewild and SoakZone, LIGONIER, PA
Notes: Palace Entertainment derives approximately 80% of its revenue from park admissions, arcade games & other family amusement operations.

Key Personnel
JOHN REILLY - COO
BRIAN ENGELHARDT - Director Beverages, Food
AMY THOMAS - Director Branding
JERRY BRICK - Director Facility/Maintenance, Construction
DANIELLE TROMBETTA - Director Marketing
HAMED NEFFATI - Director Finance
JESSICA ADAMS - Director Marketing, Division
ANDRE KHOURY - Director Procurement
GENE PETRIELLO - Regional Director Marketing, Sales
KIM MIGLIARA - Manager Beverages, Food

Restaurant Business Inc.
2808 Lafayette Rd
Newport Beach, CA 92663-3716

Telephone: (562) 690-2011
Fax Number: (562) 690-9871
Internet Homepage: cannerynewport.com; catandcustardcup.com; elcholo.com
Type of Business: Chain Restaurant Operator
Year Founded: 1927
Total Sales: $22,109,000 (e)
Alcohol Sales: 20%
Number of Employees: 650
Average Check: Lunch(14); Dinner(20)
Total Units: 8
Trade Names: El Cholo (6); The Cannery (1); The Cat & The Custard Cup (1)
Company-Owned Units: 8
Preferred Square Footage: 5,500; 6,000
Preferred Location Types: Freestanding
Alcohol Served: Beer, Wine, Liquor
Primary Menu: American (1); Mexican (6); Seafood (1)
Areas of Operation: CA
Type of Foodservice: Casual Dining (8)
Catering Services: Yes
Primary Distributors: (Full Line) US Foods-Los Angeles, LA MIRADA, CA

Key Personnel
RON SALISBURY - CEO; President; Director Real Estate, Design
BRENDON SALISBURY - CFO
FELIX SALCEDO - Executive Chef

Solon Management Inc.
1400 Quail St Ste 140
Newport Beach, CA 92660-2713

Telephone: (949) 852-8874
Fax Number: (949) 852-8884
Type of Business: Chain Restaurant Operator
Year Founded: 1998
Total Sales: $24,160,000 (e)
Number of Employees: 170
Average Check: Breakfast(8); Lunch(10); Dinner(12)
Total Units: 5
Trade Names: McDonald's (5)
Units Franchised From: 5
Preferred Square Footage: 2,500
Preferred Location Types: Freestanding
Primary Menu: Hamburger (5)
Areas of Operation: CA
Type of Foodservice: Quick Serve (5)
Franchise Affiliation: McDonald's Corporation, CHICAGO, IL
Primary Distributors: (Food) The Martin-Brower Co., CITY OF INDUSTRY, CA

Key Personnel
TERENCE SOLON - President; Manager Real Estate

Waterfront Enterprises
400 Main St
Newport Beach, CA 92661-1330

Telephone: (949) 673-4633
Fax Number: (949) 673-5085
Internet Homepage: harborside-pavilion.com; newport-landing.com; oceanside-broiler.com
Type of Business: Chain Restaurant Operator
Year Founded: 1987
Total Sales: $13,506,000 (e)
Alcohol Sales: 33%
Number of Employees: 85
Average Check: Lunch(22); Dinner(42)
Total Units: 3
Trade Names: Harbor Side Restaurant and Ballroom (1); Newport Landing (1); Oceanside Broiler (1)
Company-Owned Units: 3
Preferred Location Types: Freestanding
Alcohol Served: Beer, Wine, Liquor
Primary Menu: American (1); Seafood (1); Steak/Seafood (1)
Areas of Operation: CA
Type of Foodservice: Fine Dining (3)
Primary Distributors: (Food) SYSCO Food Services of San Francisco Inc., FREMONT, CA

Key Personnel
DAVID SALISBURY - President; Partner
DOUG SALISBURY - Partner; VP Operations; General Manager
LUIS ZARAGOZA - Manager Purchasing
MARGO HAYES - Manager Operations

Anand, Inc.
4990 Watt Ave
North Highlands, CA 95660-5110

Telephone: (916) 332-4282

Type of Business: Chain Restaurant Operator
Total Sales: $25,300,000 (e)
Total Units: 10
Trade Names: Jack in the Box (10)
Units Franchised From: 10
Primary Menu: Hamburger (10)
Areas of Operation: CA
Type of Foodservice: Quick Serve (10)
Franchise Affiliation: Jack in the Box Restaurants, SAN DIEGO, CA

Key Personnel
DHARMESH PATEL - Owner; General Buyer

AFK Ventures, Inc.
19500 Plummer St Unit F5
Northridge, CA 91324-2146

Telephone: (818) 700-1443
Type of Business: Chain Restaurant Operator
Total Sales: $1,179,000 (e)
Total Units: 2
Trade Names: Cold Stone Creamery (2)
Units Franchised From: 2
Primary Menu: Snacks (2)
Areas of Operation: CA
Type of Foodservice: Quick Serve (2)
Franchise Affiliation: Kahala Brands, SCOTTSDALE, AZ

Key Personnel
MUHAMMAD HAQUE - Owner

Brent's Delicatessen
19565 Parthenia St
Northridge, CA 91324-3406

Telephone: (818) 886-5679
Fax Number: (818) 886-2561
Internet Homepage: brentsdeli.com
Type of Business: Chain Restaurant Operator
Year Founded: 1967
Total Sales: $10,948,000 (e)
Number of Employees: 108
Average Check: Breakfast(8); Lunch(12); Dinner(16)
Total Units: 2
Trade Names: Brent's Delicatessen (2)
Company-Owned Units: 2
Alcohol Served: Beer
Primary Menu: Sandwiches/Deli (2)
Areas of Operation: CA
Type of Foodservice: Casual Dining (2)

Key Personnel
RONALD PESKIN - President
BRENT PESKIN - CFO; VP; General Manager; General Buyer
CRYSTLE COREAS - General Manager

OSCAR COBIAN - Executive Chef

Churchs Chicken of Norwalk
15816 Pioneer Blvd
Norwalk, CA 90650-6535

Telephone: (562) 929-4015
Internet Homepage: churchs.com
Type of Business: Chain Restaurant Operator
Year Founded: 1987
Total Sales: $2,635,000 (e)
Number of Employees: 30
Average Check: Lunch(10); Dinner(12)
Total Units: 2
Trade Names: Church's Chicken (2)
Units Franchised From: 2
Preferred Location Types: Freestanding
Primary Menu: Chicken (2)
Areas of Operation: CA
Type of Foodservice: Quick Serve (2)
Franchise Affiliation: Church's Chicken, ATLANTA, GA
Primary Distributors: (Food) SYSCO Food Services of Central California Inc., MODESTO, CA

Key Personnel
FERAS SABHE - President; Executive Chef
MOHAMMED SHAIKH - Director Operations; General Buyer
VANESSA CARLOS - Manager Operations

Three Powers Foods, Inc.
12603 Norwalk Blvd
Norwalk, CA 90650-3141

Telephone: (562) 868-5677
Type of Business: Chain Restaurant Operator
Total Sales: $27,390,000 (e)
Total Units: 11
Trade Names: Jack in the Box (11)
Units Franchised From: 11
Primary Menu: Hamburger (11)
Areas of Operation: CA
Type of Foodservice: Quick Serve (11)
Franchise Affiliation: Jack in the Box Restaurants, SAN DIEGO, CA

Key Personnel
SAM FONG - Partner; General Buyer
CEDRIC FONG - Partner

Arches of Gold
7340 Redwood Blvd
Novato, CA 94945-3212

Telephone: (707) 253-0767
Fax Number: (415) 492-7182
Type of Business: Chain Restaurant Operator

Total Sales: $14,865,000 (e)
Total Units: 3
Trade Names: McDonald's (3)
Units Franchised From: 3
Primary Menu: Hamburger (3)
Areas of Operation: CA
Type of Foodservice: Quick Serve (3)
Franchise Affiliation: McDonald's Corporation, CHICAGO, IL

Key Personnel
SCOTT LAMSON - Owner; General Buyer

Left Bank Restaurant Group.
7250 Redwood Blvd Ste 113
Novato, CA 94945

Telephone: (415) 927-3308
Fax Number: (415) 891-8131
Internet Homepage: lbsteak.com; leftbank.com
Company Email: info@leftbank.com
Type of Business: Chain Restaurant Operator
Year Founded: 1993
Total Sales: $21,220,000 (e)
Alcohol Sales: 40%
Number of Employees: 375
Average Check: Lunch(30); Dinner(60)
Internet Sales: 1.00%
Total Units: 4
Trade Names: L.B. Steak (1); Left Bank Brasserie (3)
Company-Owned Units: 4
Preferred Square Footage: 5,500; 6,000
Preferred Location Types: Freestanding
Alcohol Served: Beer, Wine, Liquor
Primary Menu: French/Continental (3); Steak (1)
Areas of Operation: CA
Type of Foodservice: Fine Dining (4)
Catering Services: Yes
Primary Distributors: (Food) SYSCO Food Services of Los Angeles Inc., WALNUT, CA

Key Personnel
OBADIAH OSTERGARD - CEO; Partner
ROLAND PASSOT - Partner; Executive Chef

Pizza Factory Inc.
49430 Road 426 Ste D
Oakhurst, CA 93644-8618

Mailing Address: PO Box 989, OAKHURST, CA, 93644-0989
Telephone: (559) 683-3377
Fax Number: (559) 683-6879
Internet Homepage: pizzafactory.com
Company Email: pfinc@pizzafactoryinc.com
Type of Business: Chain Restaurant Operator
Year Founded: 1979
Systemwide Sales: $50,260,000 (e)
Total Sales: $6,036,000 (e)

Alcohol Sales: 3%
Number of Employees: 10
Average Check: Lunch(8); Dinner(10)
Internet Order Processing: Yes
Total Units: 101
Trade Names: Pizza Factory (101)
Company-Owned Units: 1
Units Franchised To: 100
Preferred Square Footage: 1,000; 1,500; 2,400
Preferred Location Types: Downtown; Freestanding; Strip Mall
Alcohol Served: Beer, Wine
Primary Menu: Pizza (101)
Projected Openings: 5
Areas of Operation: AZ, CA, ID, NV, OR, WA
Foreign Countries: CHINA
Type of Foodservice: Casual Dining (101)
Foodservice Management Venues: Schools
Catering Services: Yes
Primary Distributors: (Food) Saladino's Inc., FRESNO, CA

Key Personnel
BOB RIVA - VP
ROB SEARFUS - Specialist Franchise Development

Barney's Gourmet Hamburgers
4162 Piedmont Ave
Oakland, CA 94611-5110

Telephone: (510) 655-7180
Internet Homepage: barneyshamburgers.com
Type of Business: Chain Restaurant Operator
Year Founded: 1978
Total Sales: $7,532,000 (e)
Total Units: 7
Trade Names: Barney's Gourmet Hamburgers (7)
Company-Owned Units: 7
Preferred Location Types: Lifestyle Center; Power Center
Primary Menu: Hamburger (7)
Areas of Operation: CA
Type of Foodservice: Fast Casual (7)

Key Personnel
ALBERT SARSHAR - President; General Buyer

Blue Bottle Coffee
476 9th St
Oakland, CA 94607

Telephone: (510) 653-3394
Internet Homepage: bluebottlecoffee.com
Company Email: support@bluebottlecoffee.com
Type of Business: Chain Restaurant Operator
Year Founded: 2008
Total Sales: $54,070,000 (e)
Total Units: 72
Trade Names: Blue Bottle Coffee (72)
Company-Owned Units: 72
Preferred Location Types: Downtown; Lifestyle Center; Mixed-use Center
Primary Menu: Coffee (72)
Areas of Operation: CA, DC, FL, NY, FC
Foreign Countries: JAPAN; SOUTH KOREA
Type of Foodservice: Quick Serve (72)

Key Personnel
JAMES FREEMAN - Founder; CEO
ELVIRA N. COREY - Chief People Officer
JON ALSTERLIND - VP Finance
ADITI JAIN - Senior Director Global, E-Commerce
BENJAMIN BREWER - Director Quality Assurance
J. NIKOLAUS BAUMAN - Director Digital Media
MICHAEL PHILLIPS - Director Training
SOPHIA BASCO - Director Marketing
RYAN MUNDON - Director Operations
REBECCA MARTINI - Director Sourcing, Supply Chain
DARRELL CHANG - Director Brand Marketing
KATHLEEN NUFFORT - Manager Operations
AUDREY WALDROP - Manager Sustainability

▲ Mountain Mike's Pizza
528 Grand Ave
Oakland, CA 94610-3515

Telephone: (407) 322-1781
Fax Number: (510) 537-0658
Internet Homepage: mountainmikes.com
Company Email: contact@mountainmikes.com
Type of Business: Chain Restaurant Operator
Year Founded: 1978
Systemwide Sales: $126,963,000 (e)
Total Sales: $15,020,000 (e)
Alcohol Sales: 7%
Number of Employees: 5
Average Check: Lunch(10); Dinner(12)
Internet Order Processing: Yes
Total Units: 269
Trade Names: Mountain Mike's Pizza (269)
Units Franchised To: 269
Preferred Square Footage: 2,400
Preferred Location Types: Community Mall; Freestanding
Alcohol Served: Beer, Wine
Primary Menu: Pizza (269)
Projected Openings: 2
Areas of Operation: CA, NV, OR, UT
Type of Foodservice: Casual Dining (269)
Catering Services: Yes
Primary Distributors: (Full Line) Vistar Rocky Mountain, DENVER, CO
Parent Company: Britt Private Capital, NEWPORT BEACH, CA

Key Personnel
JIM METEVIER - CEO; President
STEVEN ADYANI - COO
CAROL DENEMBO - Chief Marketing Officer

Red Boy Pizza Franchising
4308 Arden Pl
Oakland, CA 94602-1909

Mailing Address: PO Box 150785, SAN RAFAEL, CA, 94915-0785
Telephone: (844) 973-3269
Fax Number: (510) 482-2211
Internet Homepage: redboypizza.com
Company Email: info@redboypizza.com
Type of Business: Chain Restaurant Operator
Year Founded: 1969
Systemwide Sales: $10,729,000 (e)
Total Sales: $1,004,000 (e)
Alcohol Sales: 10%
Number of Employees: 4
Average Check: Lunch(12); Dinner(16)
Internet Order Processing: Yes
Internet Sales: 1.00%
Total Units: 7
Trade Names: Red Boy Pizza (7)
Units Franchised To: 7
Preferred Square Footage: 3,000
Preferred Location Types: Downtown; Strip Mall
Alcohol Served: Beer, Wine
Primary Menu: Pizza (7)
Projected Remodelings: 2
Areas of Operation: CA
Type of Foodservice: Quick Serve (7)
Foodservice Management Venues: Schools
Catering Services: Yes
Primary Distributors: (Food) Mike Hudson Distributing, PETALUMA, CA

Key Personnel
ANTOINETTE RADWAN - VP; General Manager; Executive Chef; General Buyer

Scott's Seafood
2 Broadway
Oakland, CA 94607-3748

Telephone: (510) 444-3456
Fax Number: (510) 444-6917
Internet Homepage: scottsjls.com
Company Email: ramiroc@scottsjls.com
Type of Business: Chain Restaurant Operator
Year Founded: 1976
Total Sales: $23,125,000 (e)
Alcohol Sales: 35%
Number of Employees: 100
Average Check: Lunch(36); Dinner(66)
Total Units: 2
Trade Names: Scott's Seafood (2)
Company-Owned Units: 2

Preferred Location Types: Freestanding
Alcohol Served: Beer, Wine, Liquor
Primary Menu: Seafood (2)
Areas of Operation: CA
Type of Foodservice: Fine Dining (2)
Catering Services: Yes
Primary Distributors: (Food) BiRite Foodservice Distributors, BRISBANE, CA

Key Personnel
RAMERO CARABEZ - General Manager; General Buyer
MARI VILLALVAZO - Manager Sales, Catering

Taste Inc.
1111 Broadway 3rd Fl
Oakland, CA 94607

Telephone: (510) 740-4300
Fax Number: (510) 671-0021
Internet Homepage: vinovolo.com
Company Email: contactus@vinovolo.com
Type of Business: Chain Restaurant Operator
Total Sales: $29,451,000 (e)
Alcohol Sales: 40%
Number of Employees: 495
Internet Order Processing: Yes
Total Units: 33
Trade Names: Vino Volo (33)
Company-Owned Units: 33
Preferred Location Types: Airports
Alcohol Served: Beer, Wine
Primary Menu: Miscellaneous (33)
Areas of Operation: CA, DC, LA, MA, MD, MI, MN, NJ, NY, OH, OR, PA, TX, UT, VA, WA, WI, BC
Foreign Countries: CANADA
Type of Foodservice: Casual Dining (33)

Key Personnel
MARK SILL - Senior VP

Domino's Franchisee
650 Douglas Dr Ste 104
Oceanside, CA 92058-6949

Telephone: (760) 439-0500
Type of Business: Chain Restaurant Operator
Total Sales: $4,061,000 (e)
Total Units: 2
Trade Names: Domino's (2)
Units Franchised From: 2
Primary Menu: Pizza (2)
Areas of Operation: CA
Type of Foodservice: Quick Serve (2)
Franchise Affiliation: Domino's Pizza Inc, ANN ARBOR, MI

Key Personnel
SHANE B. CASEY - Owner; General Buyer

In His Grip JM Corp.
4904 N River Rd Ste 400
Oceanside, CA 92057-5975

Telephone: (760) 529-0130
Type of Business: Chain Restaurant Operator
Total Sales: $8,232,000 (e)
Total Units: 6
Trade Names: Jersey Mike's Subs (6)
Units Franchised From: 6
Primary Menu: Sandwiches/Deli (6)
Areas of Operation: CA
Type of Foodservice: Quick Serve (6)
Franchise Affiliation: Jersey Mike's Franchise Systems, MANASQUAN, NJ

Key Personnel
KENNETH NICOLA - Owner; General Buyer

Munch A Licious, LLC
409 Mission Ave Ste C110
Oceanside, CA 92054-2854

Telephone: (760) 722-0880
Type of Business: Chain Restaurant Operator
Total Sales: $2,334,000 (e)
Total Units: 6
Trade Names: Cold Stone Creamery (4); Tapioca Express (2)
Units Franchised From: 6
Primary Menu: Snacks (6)
Areas of Operation: CA
Type of Foodservice: Quick Serve (6)
Franchise Affiliation: Kahala Brands, SCOTTSDALE, AZ

Key Personnel
JOE LIN - Partner
ESTHER WONG - Partner; General Manager

Peg/Lion, LLC
3700 Oceanic Way Ste 101
Oceanside, CA 92056-2654

Telephone: (760) 721-3110
Fax Number: (760) 721-2496
Type of Business: Chain Restaurant Operator
Total Sales: $85,780,000 (e)
Number of Employees: 880
Total Units: 31
Trade Names: El Pollo Loco (31)
Units Franchised From: 31
Primary Menu: Chicken (31)
Areas of Operation: CA
Type of Foodservice: Quick Serve (31)
Franchise Affiliation: El Pollo Loco Inc., COSTA MESA, CA

Key Personnel
AARON PINGEL - CFO; General Buyer
NOEL BUAN - Director Operations
JESSE LARA - Area Manager
CLAUDIA FLORES - District Manager
JENNIFER PINGEL - Coordinator Marketing

Auntie Anne's Franchise
1 Mills Cir Ste 600
Ontario, CA 91764-5211

Telephone: (909) 980-5014
Type of Business: Chain Restaurant Operator
Total Sales: $3,189,000 (e)
Total Units: 4
Trade Names: Auntie Anne's Hand-Rolled Soft Pretzels (4)
Units Franchised From: 4
Primary Menu: Snacks (4)
Areas of Operation: CA
Type of Foodservice: Quick Serve (4)
Franchise Affiliation: Auntie Anne's Inc., LANCASTER, PA

Key Personnel
WIJAYA SULAEMAN - Owner; General Buyer

Domino's Distribution Center
301 S Rockefeller Ave
Ontario, CA 91761-7865

Telephone: (909) 390-1990
Fax Number: (909) 390-1988
Internet Homepage: dominos.com
Listing Type: Distribution Center
Type of Business: Chain Restaurant Operator
Number of Employees: 65
Areas of Operation: CA
Parent Company: Domino's Pizza Inc, ANN ARBOR, MI

Key Personnel
CARLOS JUAREZ - Manager Warehouse

Webb Family Enterprises
3155 Sedona Ct Ste A
Ontario, CA 91764-6559

Telephone: (909) 608-1940
Fax Number: (909) 608-1945
Internet Homepage: webbmcd.com
Company Email: rsvp@webbmcd.com
Type of Business: Chain Restaurant Operator
Year Founded: 1985
Total Sales: $47,180,000 (e)
Number of Employees: 470
Average Check: Breakfast(8); Lunch(8);

Dinner(8)
Total Units: 10
Trade Names: McDonald's (10)
Units Franchised From: 10
Preferred Square Footage: 2,500
Preferred Location Types: Freestanding
Primary Menu: Hamburger (10)
Areas of Operation: CA
Type of Foodservice: Quick Serve (10)
Franchise Affiliation: McDonald's Corporation, CHICAGO, IL
Primary Distributors: (Food) The Martin-Brower Co., PHOENIX, AZ

Key Personnel
KIANA WEBB - President
REGINALD WEBB - President; Director Purchasing, Facility/Maintenance, Information Systems, Real Estate
KYLE WEBB - CFO
ANNA LUEVANO - Director Finance, Risk Management, Human Resources

WHG Restaurant Group, Inc.
1551 E 4th St
Ontario, CA 91764-2635

Telephone: (909) 467-3930
Type of Business: Chain Restaurant Operator
Total Sales: $24,850,000 (e)
Total Units: 10
Trade Names: Jack in the Box (10)
Units Franchised From: 10
Primary Menu: Hamburger (10)
Areas of Operation: CA
Type of Foodservice: Quick Serve (10)
Franchise Affiliation: Jack in the Box Restaurants, SAN DIEGO, CA

Key Personnel
GREGORY GRIBBLE - Owner; General Buyer

Amelia Holdings, Inc.
1545 E Katella Ave
Orange, CA 92867-5025

Telephone: (714) 289-9300
Type of Business: Chain Restaurant Operator
Total Sales: $2,865,000 (e)
Total Units: 2
Trade Names: Jersey Mike's Subs (2)
Units Franchised From: 2
Primary Menu: Sandwiches/Deli (2)
Areas of Operation: CA
Type of Foodservice: Quick Serve (2)
Franchise Affiliation: Jersey Mike's Franchise Systems, MANASQUAN, NJ

Key Personnel
ED CASTANEDA - Owner; General Buyer

American West Restaurant Group
1 City Blvd W Ste 750
Orange, CA 92868-3615

Telephone: (951) 284-7400
Fax Number: (951) 284-7440
Type of Business: Chain Restaurant Operator
Year Founded: 2008
Total Sales: $332,660,000 (e)
Average Check: Dinner(14)
Total Units: 280
Trade Names: Pizza Hut (280)
Units Franchised From: 280
Preferred Square Footage: 1,400; 4,500
Primary Menu: Pizza (280)
Areas of Operation: CA, UT
Type of Foodservice: Quick Serve (280)
Franchise Affiliation: Pizza Hut Inc., PLANO, TX
Parent Company: Sterling Investment Partners, WESTPORT, CT
Notes: This company's Utah Pizza Hut stores (39) are held under the name Wasatch Valley Pizza, LLC.

Key Personnel
JERRY ARDIZZONE - CEO; President; General Buyer
JEFF GEDDES - CFO
JAMIE NELSON - COO
GENE ERDMAN - Chief People Officer
TIM STOCKTON - Senior Director Development, Real Estate
TONY CISNEROS - Director Operations
ALEJANDRO LOPEZ - Manager District
TARAH BARBAR - Specialist Marketing

Bruxie
292 N Glassell St
Orange, CA 92866

Telephone: (714) 633-3900
Internet Homepage: bruxie.com
Company Email: info@bruxie.com
Type of Business: Chain Restaurant Operator
Year Founded: 2010
Total Sales: $24,992,000 (e)
Average Check: Lunch(12); Dinner(14)
Total Units: 8
Trade Names: Bruxie Gourmet Waffle Sandwiches (8)
Company-Owned Units: 8
Primary Menu: Sandwiches/Deli (8)
Projected Openings: 1
Areas of Operation: CA, NV

Type of Foodservice: Fast Casual (8)

Key Personnel
KELLY MULLARNEY - Co-Founder; Corporate Chef

Consolidated Restaurants
172 N Tustin St Ste 206
Orange, CA 92867-7780

Telephone: (714) 532-4200
Fax Number: (714) 532-4201
Internet Homepage: consolidatedrestaurants.com
Company Email: consrest@pacbell.net
Type of Business: Chain Restaurant Operator
Year Founded: 1982
Total Sales: $5,947,000 (e)
Number of Employees: 71
Average Check: Lunch(8); Dinner(10)
Total Units: 2
Trade Names: Wendy's Old Fashioned Hamburgers (2)
Units Franchised From: 2
Preferred Square Footage: 2,100; 2,900
Preferred Location Types: Freestanding
Primary Menu: Hamburger (2)
Areas of Operation: CA
Type of Foodservice: Quick Serve (2)
Franchise Affiliation: The Wendy's Company, DUBLIN, OH

Key Personnel
MICHAEL KOURIE - President; Director Finance, Operations, Facility/Maintenance, Supply Chain, Real Estate, Design, Store Fixtures
KERRY KREITZER - Director Design

Rod Fraser Enterprises
1320 N Manzanita St
Orange, CA 92867-3602

Telephone: (714) 633-7844
Fax Number: (714) 633-0897
Internet Homepage: donjose.net
Type of Business: Chain Restaurant Operator
Year Founded: 1972
Total Sales: $5,276,000 (e)
Alcohol Sales: 20%
Number of Employees: 450
Average Check: Breakfast(10); Lunch(12); Dinner(18)
Total Units: 3
Trade Names: Don Jose's Restaurant (3)
Company-Owned Units: 3
Preferred Square Footage: 8,000
Preferred Location Types: Freestanding
Alcohol Served: Beer, Wine, Liquor
Primary Menu: Mexican (3)
Areas of Operation: CA

Type of Foodservice: Casual Dining (3)

Key Personnel
DAVE QUIMBY - CFO
GENEICE STEPANENKO - Director Human Resources

Spires Restaurants Inc.
1411 N Batavia St Ste 101
Orange, CA 92867-3526

Telephone: (714) 997-9780
Fax Number: (714) 997-3961
Type of Business: Chain Restaurant Operator
Year Founded: 1965
Systemwide Sales: $31,036,000 (e)
Total Sales: $10,740,000 (e)
Number of Employees: 700
Average Check: Breakfast(5); Lunch(10); Dinner(14)
Total Units: 7
Trade Names: Spires Restaurant (7)
Units Franchised To: 7
Preferred Square Footage: 10,000
Preferred Location Types: Community Mall; Freestanding
Primary Menu: American (7)
Areas of Operation: CA
Type of Foodservice: Family Restaurant (7)
Primary Distributors: (Full Line) US Foods, CORONA, CA

Key Personnel
CATHERINE HARETAKIS - President; CFO; Controller; Executive Chef; Manager Facility/Maintenance; General Buyer
JOHN HARETAKIS - VP Operations; Treasurer; Manager Information Systems, Real Estate, Design, Human Resources

Three Brothers III Inc dba Zito's Pizza
2036 N Tustin St
Orange, CA 92865-3902

Telephone: (714) 974-6191
Fax Number: (714) 974-4002
Internet Homepage: zitospizza.com
Type of Business: Chain Restaurant Operator
Total Sales: $6,310,000 (e)
Alcohol Sales: 10%
Number of Employees: 160
Total Units: 4
Trade Names: Zito's New York Style Pizza (4)
Company-Owned Units: 4
Preferred Location Types: Strip Mall
Alcohol Served: Beer, Wine, Liquor
Primary Menu: Italian (4)
Areas of Operation: CA
Type of Foodservice: Casual Dining (4)

Catering Services: Yes

Key Personnel
STEVE SILVERSTEIN - President; Owner; General Buyer

J & S Restaurants Inc.
1851 Lombard St Ste 200
Oxnard, CA 93030-8231

Telephone: (805) 201-1500
Fax Number: (805) 201-1505
Internet Homepage: topperspizzaplace.com
Type of Business: Chain Restaurant Operator
Year Founded: 1981
Total Sales: $11,530,000 (e)
Alcohol Sales: 2%
Number of Employees: 485
Average Check: Lunch(14); Dinner(14)
Total Units: 9
Trade Names: Toppers! Pizza Place (9)
Company-Owned Units: 9
Preferred Square Footage: 5,500; 6,000
Preferred Location Types: Freestanding
Alcohol Served: Beer, Wine
Primary Menu: Pizza (9)
Areas of Operation: CA
Type of Foodservice: Casual Dining (9)
Primary Distributors: (Full Line) Jordano's Inc., SANTA BARBARA, CA

Key Personnel
WILLEM JONKER - President; Controller; Director Operations, Facility/Maintenance, Real Estate, Design
BETH JONKER - VP Marketing
MATT SADOWSKI - General Manager; Director Supply Chain, Menu Development
ANDI CHANEY - Manager Purchasing, Information Systems, Human Resources

Yogurtland Franchisee
1870 E Gonzales Rd
Oxnard, CA 93036-3700

Telephone: (805) 485-6805
Type of Business: Chain Restaurant Operator
Total Sales: $3,092,000 (e)
Total Units: 3
Trade Names: Yogurtland (3)
Units Franchised From: 3
Primary Menu: Snacks (3)
Areas of Operation: CA
Type of Foodservice: Quick Serve (3)
Franchise Affiliation: Yogurtland Franchising Inc., FARMERS BRANCH, TX

Key Personnel
MIRZA ALIKHAN - Partner; General Buyer
YASMEEN ALIKHAN - Partner; General Buyer

Rise & Shine Restaurant Group
5119 Cass St
Pacific Beach, CA 92109

Telephone: (858) 274-2233
Internet Homepage: riseandshinerg.com; breakfastrepublic.com; figtreeeatery.com
Company Email: riseandshineresumes@gmail.com
Type of Business: Chain Restaurant Operator
Year Founded: 2008
Total Sales: $8,297,000 (e)
Total Units: 17
Trade Names: Breakfast Company (1); Breakfast Republic (11); Eggies (1); Feast & Fareway (1); Fig Tree Cafe (3)
Company-Owned Units: 17
Primary Menu: American (17); Mexican (0)
Projected Openings: 3
Areas of Operation: CA
Type of Foodservice: Casual Dining (17)
Notes: Contact note: Phone number is currently for Fig Tree Pacific Beach location

Key Personnel
JOHAN ENGMAN - Founder; Partner
CLAUDETTE ZEPEDA-WILKINS - Partner; Executive Chef
GRANT PRICE - VP Operations, Development
CESAR GARCIA - Corporate Chef; Executive Chef
HEATHER ROSS - Manager Operations
CARMINA KATIGBAK - Manager Operations
COURTENAY DAVIS - Manager Accounting
SEAN STERLING - Project Manager

Chef's Pride Inc.
1996 1/2 Sunset Dr
Pacific Grove, CA 93950-3719

Telephone: (831) 375-7108
Fax Number: (831) 375-4650
Internet Homepage: fishwife.com; turtlebay.tv
Company Email: fishwife@fishwife.com
Type of Business: Chain Restaurant Operator
Year Founded: 1985
Total Sales: $6,829,000 (e)
Alcohol Sales: 18%
Number of Employees: 110
Average Check: Lunch(18); Dinner(28)
Total Units: 3
Trade Names: Fishwife Seafood Cafe (1); The Fishwife Fresh Seafood & Pasta (1); Turtle Bay Tacqueria (1)
Company-Owned Units: 3
Preferred Location Types: Freestanding
Alcohol Served: Beer, Wine, Liquor
Primary Menu: Mexican (1); Seafood (2)

Areas of Operation: CA
Type of Foodservice: Casual Dining (3)
Primary Distributors: (Full Line) US Foods-San Francisco, LIVERMORE, CA

Key Personnel
JEFFERSON SEAY - CEO; Owner; Executive Chef; General Buyer
SCOTT ROBERTS - Manager Distribution

Pala Casino, Resort, Spa
11154 Highway 76
Pala, CA 92059-2904

Mailing Address: 35008 Pala Temecula Rd, PMB 40, PALA, CA, 92059
Telephone: (760) 510-5100
Fax Number: (760) 510-2199
Internet Homepage: palacasino.com
Company Email: guestservices@palacasino.com
Type of Business: Foodservice Operations - Casinos
Total Sales: $170,878,000 (e)
Alcohol Sales: 5%
Number of Employees: 1,500
Total Units: 1
Restaurants in Hotels: 10
Trade Names: Pala Casino, Resort, Spa (1)
Company-Owned Units: 10
Alcohol Served: Beer, Wine, Liquor
Areas of Operation: CA
Type of Foodservice: Casual Dining (5); Fast Casual (1); Fine Dining (1); Quick Serve (3)
Notes: The company derives approximately 75% of its revenue from casino and resort operations.

Key Personnel
BILL BEMBENEK - CEO; Director Finance
SUE WELP - VP Marketing, Business Development

City Wok
73744 Highway 111 Ste 3
Palm Desert, CA 92260-4011

Telephone: (760) 346-7764
Fax Number: (760) 346-6414
Internet Homepage: citywok.com
Type of Business: Chain Restaurant Operator
Total Sales: $3,716,000 (e)
Number of Employees: 60
Internet Order Processing: Yes
Total Units: 4
Trade Names: City Wok (4)
Company-Owned Units: 4
Primary Menu: Chinese (4)
Areas of Operation: CA, CO, DC
Type of Foodservice: Fast Casual (4)

Key Personnel
STUART DAVIS - CEO; Director Operations; General Buyer

Shalhoub Enterprises, Inc.
PO Box 13490
Palm Desert, CA 92255-3490

Telephone: (760) 674-3335
Fax Number: (760) 772-5653
Type of Business: Chain Restaurant Operator
Total Sales: $145,330,000 (e)
Number of Employees: 850
Average Check: Breakfast(8); Lunch(12); Dinner(12)
Total Units: 31
Trade Names: McDonald's (31)
Units Franchised From: 31
Preferred Square Footage: 3,000
Preferred Location Types: Community Mall; Discount Dept. Stores; Freestanding
Primary Menu: Hamburger (31)
Areas of Operation: CA
Type of Foodservice: Quick Serve (31)
Franchise Affiliation: McDonald's Corporation, CHICAGO, IL
Primary Distributors: (Full Line) The Martin-Brower Co., CITY OF INDUSTRY, CA

Key Personnel
RICHARD SHALHOUB - President; Director Finance, Facility/Maintenance, Information Systems, Real Estate, Human Resources; General Buyer
MARK MORRIS - Director Operations

Sherman's Delicatessen & Bakery
401 E Tahquitz Canyon Way
Palm Springs, CA 92262-6630

Telephone: (760) 325-1199
Fax Number: (760) 325-0771
Internet Homepage: shermansdeli.com
Type of Business: Chain Restaurant Operator
Total Sales: $4,511,000 (e)
Alcohol Sales: 5%
Number of Employees: 125
Average Check: Breakfast(12); Lunch(20); Dinner(40)
Total Units: 2
Trade Names: Sherman's Delicatessen & Bakery (2)
Company-Owned Units: 2
Preferred Location Types: Freestanding; Office Complex
Alcohol Served: Beer, Wine
Primary Menu: Sandwiches/Deli (2)
Areas of Operation: CA
Type of Foodservice: Casual Dining (2)
Catering Services: Yes

Primary Distributors: (Full Line) US Foods, CORONA, CA

Key Personnel
SAM HARRIS - Owner
STAN GARMIN - Executive Chef; General Buyer

A.V. Ice Creamery, Inc.
1201 W Rancho Vista Blvd Ste A
Palmdale, CA 93551-3989

Telephone: (661) 274-2650
Type of Business: Chain Restaurant Operator
Total Sales: $1,228,000 (e)
Total Units: 2
Trade Names: Cold Stone Creamery (2)
Units Franchised From: 2
Primary Menu: Snacks (2)
Areas of Operation: CA
Type of Foodservice: Quick Serve (2)
Franchise Affiliation: Kahala Brands, SCOTTSDALE, AZ

Key Personnel
KEITH AXTMAN - Partner
LORY AXTMAN - Partner

El Toreo
800 East Ave
Palmdale, CA 93550

Mailing Address: PO Box 901840, Palmdale, CA, 93590-1840
Telephone: (661) 947-4177
Type of Business: Chain Restaurant Operator
Year Founded: 1972
Total Sales: $5,863,000 (e)
Alcohol Sales: 15%
Number of Employees: 30
Average Check: Dinner(24)
Total Units: 4
Trade Names: El Toreo (4)
Company-Owned Units: 4
Preferred Square Footage: 2,500
Preferred Location Types: Freestanding; Regional Mall; Strip Mall
Alcohol Served: Beer, Wine, Liquor
Primary Menu: Mexican (4)
Areas of Operation: CA
Type of Foodservice: Casual Dining (4)

Key Personnel
RITA MURILLO - VP Information Systems, Supply Chain; General Buyer

Asian Box
855 El Camino Real Ste 21
Palo Alto, CA 94301-2326

Telephone: (650) 391-9305
Fax Number: (650) 521-0183
Internet Homepage: asianbox.com
Company Email: info@asianbox.com
Type of Business: Chain Restaurant Operator
Year Founded: 2012
Total Sales: $11,470,000 (e)
Average Check: Lunch(14); Dinner(14)
Total Units: 10
Trade Names: Asian Box (10)
Company-Owned Units: 10
Alcohol Served: Beer, Wine, Liquor
Primary Menu: Asian (10)
Projected Openings: 2
Areas of Operation: CA
Type of Foodservice: Fast Casual (10)

Key Personnel
GRACE NGUYEN - Partner; General Manager; Executive Chef
FRANK KLEIN - Partner
CHUCK IMERSON - COO
WENDY MARTINEZ - General Manager
LOLA LOCKYEAR - Director; Office Manager

Bon Appetit Management Co.
100 Hamilton Ave Ste 400
Palo Alto, CA 94301-1651

Telephone: (650) 798-8000
Fax Number: (650) 798-8090
Internet Homepage: bamco.com
Company Email: info@bamco.com
Type of Business: Foodservice Management Operator
Year Founded: 1987
Total Sales: $717,255,000 (e)
Number of Employees: 12,000
Number of Locations Served: 400
Total Foodservice Mgmt Accounts: 150
Areas of Operation: CA, DC, IL, MD, MN, MO, NC, OH, OR, TX, VA, WA
Type of Foodservice: Cafeteria (400)
Foodservice Management Venues: Business & Industry; College & University
Primary Distributors: (Food) Performance Food Group, RICHMOND, VA
Parent Company: Compass Group PLC, LONDON, ENG
Headquarters: Compass Group The Americas, CHARLOTTE, NC

Key Personnel
FEDELE BAUCCIO - CEO
MICHAEL BAUCCIO - President; COO
ELIZABETH BALDWIN - CFO; Chief Accounting Officer
MAISIE GANZLER - Chief Brand Officer; Chief Strategy Officer
MARCOS UECHI - Director Information Systems
MARISSA LAMALFA - Director Catering
DOWE JOSEPH - Director Restaurant Operations
PEGGY HAUSSER - Director Sales
CHRISTINE BOLTON - Senior Manager Human Resources

It's a Wonderfood Life Inc.
4115 El Camino Real
Palo Alto, CA 94306-4004

Telephone: (650) 424-9400
Internet Homepage: pizzachicago.com
Type of Business: Chain Restaurant Operator
Year Founded: 1991
Systemwide Sales: $6,995,000 (e)
Total Sales: $777,000 (e)
Alcohol Sales: 5%
Number of Employees: 55
Average Check: Lunch(10); Dinner(14)
Internet Order Processing: Yes
Internet Sales: 5.00%
Total Units: 1
Trade Names: Pizza Chicago (1)
Company-Owned Units: 1
Preferred Location Types: Freestanding
Alcohol Served: Beer, Wine
Primary Menu: Pizza (1)
Areas of Operation: CA
Type of Foodservice: Casual Dining (1)
Primary Distributors: (Full Line) BiRite Foodservice Distributors, BRISBANE, CA

Key Personnel
JUAN LORENZO - President; Executive Chef; Manager Information Systems, Supply Chain, Real Estate, Design; General Buyer
ARTURO PEREZ - Manager Operations

Mar Pizza Inc.
15198 Downey Ave
Paramount, CA 90723-4594

Telephone: (562) 663-1400
Fax Number: (562) 630-0011
Internet Homepage: marpizza.com
Company Email: info@marpizza.com
Type of Business: Chain Restaurant Operator
Year Founded: 2001
Total Sales: $153,853,000 (e)
Number of Employees: 684
Average Check: Lunch(16); Dinner(30)
Internet Order Processing: Yes
Total Units: 75
Trade Names: Domino's (75)
Units Franchised From: 75
Preferred Square Footage: 1,000; 1,300
Preferred Location Types: Freestanding; Strip Mall
Primary Menu: Pizza (75)
Areas of Operation: CA
Type of Foodservice: Quick Serve (75)
Foodservice Management Venues: Schools
Franchise Affiliation: Domino's Pizza Inc, ANN ARBOR, MI
Primary Distributors: (Food) US Foods, CORONA, CA

Key Personnel
ANTHONY MANOS - President; Partner; Director Finance; General Buyer
MAHMOOD SAALABI - Partner; Controller; Director Purchasing, Real Estate
ROBERT SCHEIPER - Partner; VP; Director Operations, Facility/Maintenance, Design
LINDSAY ABBETT - Director Training

Blaze Pizza LLC
35 N Lake Ave Ste 710
Pasadena, CA 91101-4185

Telephone: (626) 584-5880
Fax Number: (844) 270-1480
Internet Homepage: blazepizza.com
Company Email: info@blazepizza.com
Type of Business: Chain Restaurant Operator
Year Founded: 2012
Systemwide Sales: $566,005,000 (e)
Total Sales: $78,250,000 (e)
Average Check: Lunch(12); Dinner(14)
Internet Order Processing: Yes
Total Units: 342
Trade Names: Blaze Fast-Fire'd Pizza (342)
Company-Owned Units: 5
Units Franchised To: 337
Preferred Square Footage: 600; 1,500; 2,000; 2,400; 3,000
Preferred Location Types: Downtown; Institution (college/hospital); Lifestyle Center; Office Complex; Regional Mall; Strip Mall
Alcohol Served: Beer, Wine, Liquor
Primary Menu: Pizza (342)
Projected Openings: 7
Areas of Operation: AR, AZ, CA, CT, FL, IA, ID, IL, IN, KY, LA, MD, MI, MN, NC, NJ, NV, NY, OH, OK, OR, PA, SC, SD, TN, TX, UT, VA, WA, WI, AB, ON
Foreign Countries: CANADA
Type of Foodservice: Fast Casual (342)

Key Personnel
BETO GUAJARDO - CEO; President
JOHNNY TELLEZ - COO
CHRIS DEMERY - CTO
CHRISTIAN KUHN - Chief Marketing Officer
KEVIN MORAN - Chief Development Officer
MARIE ZHANG - Chief Supply Chain Officer
JENNIFER NGUYEN - Controller
DAVID REINHART - Director Construction, Store Design
MARCIN KEDZIERSKI - Director Information

Technology
ZIMA DIAZ - Director Franchising
EDGAR VILLA - Director Operations
LANCE SALSMAN - Director Franchise Operations
KYRA NEYHART - Director Operations
CHRISTIE AYERS - Director Architecture, Information Technology, Security
STEPHANIE LEVITT - Manager Marketing
STEPHANIE XIE - Manager Design

Dave's Hot Chicken
600 Playhouse Aly
Pasadena, CA 91101

Telephone: (626) 487-7136
Internet Homepage: daveshotchicken.com
Type of Business: Chain Restaurant Operator
Year Founded: 2017
Systemwide Sales: $203,000,000 (e)
Total Sales: $583,128,000 (e)
Total Units: 293
Trade Names: Dave's Hot Chicken (293)
Company-Owned Units: 8
Units Franchised To: 285
Preferred Location Types: Strip Mall
Primary Menu: Chicken (293)
Projected Openings: 10
Areas of Operation: CA
Type of Foodservice: Fast Casual (293)

Key Personnel
DAVE KOPUSHYAN - Co-Founder
ARMAN OGANESYAN - Co-Founder
TOM RUBENYAN - Co-Founder
GARY RUBENYAN - Co-Founder
BILL PHELPS - CEO; Partner
JIM BITTICKS - President; COO
KATIE WINEGARD - Partner
JAMES MCGEHEE - CFO
AMY DAVIS - Chief Administrative Officer
LEON DAVOYAN - CTO
CAROLYNE CANADY - Chief Development Officer
ALLIE SAVVIDES - Chief of Staff
DANNON SHIFF - Senior VP Real Estate
SHANNON SWENSON - VP Franchise Development
TIFFANY VASSOS - VP Construction, Design
SCOTT PUTMAN - VP Finance
JERRY SHEN - VP Marketing
AMANDA MUENTNICH - VP Operations
JUAN LOPEZ - VP Operations-Training
ANDREA DESSERT - VP Supply Chain
EDGAR VILLA - Regional VP
JOSE AYALA - Senior Director Operations, Product Strategy
RYAN GLASENER - Director Operations
JOSEPH VILLALOBOS - Director Operations
LAWRENCE SHINBEIN - Director Operations
JEREMY JOHNSON - Director Operations
ANNE GOLDMAN - Manager Development, Real Estate

Dine Brands Global, Inc.
10 West Walnut Street
Pasadena, CA 91103

Telephone: (818) 240-6055
Fax Number: (818) 247-0694
Internet Homepage: applebees.com; dineequity.com; ihop.com
Listing Type: Corporate Office
Type of Business: Chain Restaurant Operator
Year Founded: 2007
Systemwide Sales: $15,639,033,000 (e)
Publicly Held: Yes
Total Sales: $1,327,752,000 (e)
Alcohol Sales: 1%
Number of Employees: 3,300
Foodservice Sales: $1,128,589,000 (e)
Total Units: 3,587
Trade Names: Applebee's Neighborhood Grill & Bar (1,642); Fuzzy's Taco Shop (131); IHOP Restaurant (1,814)
Company-Owned Units: 1
Units Franchised To: 3,586
Preferred Square Footage: 4,000; 4,400; 5,000
Preferred Location Types: Downtown; Freestanding; Hotel/Motel; Strip Mall
Alcohol Served: Beer, Wine, Liquor
Primary Menu: American (3,456); Mexican (131)
Projected Openings: 109
Areas of Operation: AK, AL, AR, AZ, CA, CO, CT, DC, DE, FL, GA, HI, IA, ID, IL, IN, KS, KY, LA, MA, MD, ME, MI, MN, MO, MS, MT, NC, ND, NE, NH, NJ, NM, NV, NY, OH, OK, OR, PA, PR, RI, SC, SD, TN, TX, UT, VA, VI, VT, WA, WI, WV, WY, AB, MB, NS, ON, SK
Foreign Countries: BAHRAIN; BRAZIL; CANADA; CHILE; COSTA RICA; DOMINICAN REPUBLIC; ECUADOR; EGYPT; GUATEMALA; INDIA; INDONESIA; KUWAIT; LEBANON; MEXICO; PANAMA; QATAR; SAUDI ARABIA; THE PHILIPPINES; UNITED ARAB EMIRATES
Type of Foodservice: Casual Dining (1,642); Family Restaurant (1,814); Fast Casual (131)
Primary Distributors: (Food) US Foods Holding Corp., ROSEMONT, IL
Headquarter Offices: Applebee's Services Inc., KANSAS CITY, MO; Fuzzy's Taco Shop, IRVING, TX; IHOP Restaurant System, GLENDALE, CA
Notes: The company derives approximately 15% of its total revenue from rental & financing operations.

Key Personnel
RICHARD DAHL - Chairman
VANCE CHANG - CFO
ALLISON HALL - Chief Accounting Officer; Senior VP
KEVIN CARROLL - COO; Senior VP
SARAH CANNON-FOSTER - Chief People Officer
JUSTIN SKELTON - CIO
CHRISTINE SON - Senior VP Legal; General Counsel
KAREN WILLIAMS - VP Operations
GARY DUBOIS - VP Quality Assurance
SCOTT GLADSTONE - VP Strategy, Development
MOSES KIM - VP
ADRIAN GRUBB - VP Operations, Development
SHANNON JOHNSON - VP Culinary Operations
LAURALYNN ROGERS - Executive Director Internal Audit
PETER WATSON - Executive Director Talent Acquisitions
CAROL SCHLICHTING - Executive Director Operations, Strategic Planning
MAURICE EDWARDS SR - Executive Director Quality Assurance
JIM DARBY - Executive Director Franchising
DON ROBERTS - Executive Director Architecture, Design
BETH HOURIGAN - Executive Director Administration
LINDA LYONS-MINOR - Executive Director Media
JASON HUGHES - Director Operations
CHRIS SEVERANCE - Director Development
HOWARD M. BERK - Director
CAROLINE W. NAHAS - Director
GILBERT T. RAY - Director
DOUGLAS M. PASQUALE - Director
JASON SUAREZ - Director; Project Manager
DAVID TRUJILLO - Director
COLISTA YATES - Director Quality Assurance
DENNIS RHODES - Director Accounting
KYLE BOERS - Director Finance
CHRISTIAN TALAVERA - Director Architecture, Design
ALEX BRESETTE - Director
BRYANA PIAZZA GONZALEZ - Director Foodservice
ARMINEH SARKISSIAN - Senior Manager
ANDERSON FENG - Senior Manager Finance
SHANNON KAY - Senior Manager Risk Management
CHRISTIE COOK - Senior Manager Human Resources
RYAN GROMAN - Senior Manager
JUSTINE NGO - Senior Manager
VON DAWSON - Senior Manager Franchise Development
ASHLEY MALONE - Manager Recruitment
DEIRDRE PICKETT - Manager Training
JACKIE ROBERTS - Manager Marketing
MARY BARTOLINI - Specialist International
MICHAEL MONTENEGRO - Architect

Dog Haus International LLC.
22 Central Ct
Pasadena, CA 91105-2060

Telephone: (626) 796-4287
Internet Homepage: doghaus.com
Company Email: social@doghaus.com
Type of Business: Chain Restaurant Operator
Year Founded: 2010
Total Sales: $62,520,000 (e)
Average Check: Lunch(12); Dinner(16)
Internet Order Processing: Yes
Total Units: 52
Trade Names: Dog Haus (52)
Company-Owned Units: 1
Units Franchised To: 51
Alcohol Served: Beer, Wine, Liquor
Primary Menu: Hot Dogs (52)
Projected Openings: 10
Areas of Operation: AZ, CA, CO, CT, FL, IL, IN, MA, MD, MO, NV, NY, TN, TX, UT
Type of Foodservice: Fast Casual (52)

Key Personnel
MICHAEL MONTAGANO - CEO
ANDRE VENER - Partner; Director Finance, Marketing
QUASIM RIAZ - Partner; General Manager
HAGOP GIRAGOSSIAN - Partner; Director Franchise Development
CHRISTOPHER RAMIREZ - VP Marketing; Director
ERIK HARTUNG - Director Franchise Development
TIM PERREIRA - Consultant Supply Chain

EM Pizza Inc
1935 E Colorado Blvd
Pasadena, CA 91107-3505

Telephone: (626) 281-5200
Fax Number: (626) 281-5201
Type of Business: Chain Restaurant Operator
Total Sales: $118,370,000 (e)
Number of Employees: 170
Average Check: Lunch(8); Dinner(8)
Total Units: 61
Trade Names: Domino's (61)
Units Franchised From: 61
Preferred Square Footage: 1,000; 1,500
Preferred Location Types: Freestanding; Strip Mall
Primary Menu: Pizza (61)
Areas of Operation: CA
Type of Foodservice: Quick Serve (61)
Franchise Affiliation: Domino's Pizza Inc, ANN ARBOR, MI

Key Personnel
MATT LESSA - Director Operations
EMILY RAO - Manager Payroll
AMBER LESSA - Manager Human Resources

Lawry's Restaurants Inc.
225 S Lake Ave Ste 1150
Pasadena, CA 91101-3036

Telephone: (626) 440-5234
Internet Homepage: lawrysonline.com
Type of Business: Chain Restaurant Operator
Year Founded: 1922
Total Sales: $68,690,000 (e)
Alcohol Sales: 20%
Number of Employees: 391
Average Check: Breakfast(6); Lunch(8); Dinner(10)
Total Units: 9
Trade Names: Five Crowns (1); Lawry's Carvery (1); Lawry's The Prime Rib (4); SideDoor (2); The Tam O'Shanter (1)
Company-Owned Units: 19
Preferred Square Footage: 11,000; 16,000
Preferred Location Types: Freestanding; Regional Mall
Alcohol Served: Beer, Wine, Liquor
Primary Menu: American (4); Sandwiches/Deli (1); Steak (4)
Areas of Operation: CA, IL, NV, TX, FC
Foreign Countries: HONG KONG; JAPAN; SINGAPORE; TAIWAN
Type of Foodservice: Casual Dining (2); Fast Casual (1); Fine Dining (6)
Catering Services: Yes
Primary Distributors: (Full Line) US Foods, CORONA, CA

Key Personnel
RYAN O'MELVENY WILSON - CEO; Executive Chef
TIFFANY STITH - President; COO
PHIL CROWLEY - VP Finance
JOYCE LISI - Director Human Resources
LAURA RATNER - Director Operations
ALISON ROBBINS - Manager Marketing

M. Pernecky Management
2826 E Foothill Blvd Ste 101
Pasadena, CA 91107-3400

Telephone: (626) 744-5778
Fax Number: (626) 744-5778
Type of Business: Chain Restaurant Operator
Total Sales: $55,690,000 (e)
Number of Employees: 765
Total Units: 12
Trade Names: McDonald's (12)
Units Franchised From: 12
Preferred Square Footage: 2,500
Preferred Location Types: Discount Dept. Stores; Freestanding; Regional Mall
Primary Menu: Hamburger (12)
Projected Remodelings: 2
Areas of Operation: CA
Type of Foodservice: Quick Serve (12)
Franchise Affiliation: McDonald's Corporation, CHICAGO, IL

Key Personnel
MICHAEL PERNECKY - President; General Buyer

Shogun Teppan Steak & Sushi
470 N Halstead St
Pasadena, CA 91107-3124

Telephone: (626) 351-8945
Fax Number: (626) 351-8026
Internet Homepage: restaurantshogun.com
Type of Business: Chain Restaurant Operator
Year Founded: 1980
Total Sales: $13,300,000 (e)
Alcohol Sales: 25%
Number of Employees: 245
Average Check: Lunch(12); Dinner(30)
Total Units: 9
Trade Names: Shogun Restaurant (9)
Company-Owned Units: 9
Preferred Location Types: Freestanding
Alcohol Served: Beer, Wine, Liquor
Primary Menu: Japanese (9)
Areas of Operation: CA
Type of Foodservice: Fine Dining (9)
Primary Distributors: (Food) US Foods-Los Angeles, LA MIRADA, CA

Key Personnel
BRUCE KANENOBU - President; General Manager; General Buyer

Smith Bros. Restaurant Corp.
100 Corson St Ste 320
Pasadena, CA 91103-3872

Telephone: (626) 577-2400
Fax Number: (626) 577-8330
Internet Homepage: smithbrothersrestaurants.com
Company Email: smithbrothers@sbcglobal.net
Type of Business: Chain Restaurant Operator
Year Founded: 1997
Total Sales: $29,193,000 (e)
Alcohol Sales: 24%
Number of Employees: 400
Average Check: Lunch(30); Dinner(60)
Total Units: 3
Trade Names: Arroyo Chop House (1); Parkway Grill (1); Smitty's Grill (1)
Company-Owned Units: 3
Preferred Square Footage: 8,500
Preferred Location Types: Freestanding

Alcohol Served: Beer, Wine, Liquor
Primary Menu: American (2); Steak (1)
Areas of Operation: CA
Type of Foodservice: Casual Dining (3)
Primary Distributors: (Full Line) US Foods - San Diego, VISTA, CA

Key Personnel
BOB SMITH - President; Partner; Director Finance, Operations, Franchise Development; General Buyer
GREGG SMITH - Partner; VP; Director Purchasing, Facility/Maintenance, Information Systems, Real Estate, Design; General Buyer

Domino's Franchisee
2138 Spring St
Paso Robles, CA 93446-1454

Telephone: (805) 239-8505
Type of Business: Chain Restaurant Operator
Total Sales: $12,229,000 (e)
Total Units: 6
Trade Names: Domino's (6)
Units Franchised From: 6
Primary Menu: Pizza (6)
Areas of Operation: CA
Type of Foodservice: Quick Serve (6)
Franchise Affiliation: Domino's Pizza Inc, ANN ARBOR, MI

Key Personnel
MARK D. TALARICO - Owner; General Buyer

Emjo, Inc.
266 Orange Ave
Patterson, CA 95363-9720

Mailing Address: PO Box 1026, PATTERSON, CA, 95363-1026
Telephone: (209) 892-2483
Type of Business: Chain Restaurant Operator
Total Sales: $10,066,000 (e)
Total Units: 2
Trade Names: McDonald's (2)
Units Franchised From: 2
Preferred Location Types: Freestanding
Primary Menu: Hamburger (2)
Areas of Operation: CA
Type of Foodservice: Quick Serve (2)
Franchise Affiliation: McDonald's Corporation, CHICAGO, IL

Key Personnel
ARNOLD REGALADO - President; General Buyer

Domino's Franchisee
2560 N Perris Blvd Ste G5
Perris, CA 92571-3253

Telephone: (951) 943-4443
Type of Business: Chain Restaurant Operator
Total Sales: $6,003,000 (e)
Total Units: 3
Trade Names: Domino's (3)
Units Franchised From: 3
Primary Menu: Pizza (3)
Areas of Operation: CA
Type of Foodservice: Quick Serve (3)
Franchise Affiliation: Domino's Pizza Inc, ANN ARBOR, MI

Key Personnel
RUSSELL L. VARNER - Owner; General Buyer

Cinema West Theatres
PO Box 750595
Petaluma, CA 94975-0595

Telephone: (707) 762-0990
Fax Number: (707) 762-3969
Internet Homepage: cinemawest.com
Type of Business: Foodservice Operations - Movie Theatre
Total Sales: $33,250,000 (e)
Number of Employees: 253
Average Check: Lunch(5); Dinner(5)
Total Units: 16
Trade Names: Cinema West Theatres (16)
Company-Owned Units: 16
Preferred Location Types: Freestanding
Primary Menu: Snacks (16)
Areas of Operation: CA
Type of Foodservice: In-Store Feeder (16)

Key Personnel
DAVE CORKILL - President; Director Real Estate
JANEICE MAINARIS - Manager Accounting, Human Resources

Shahmun Corporation
1401 N McDowell Blvd
Petaluma, CA 94954-6516

Telephone: (707) 664-1021
Type of Business: Chain Restaurant Operator
Total Sales: $5,481,000 (e)
Total Units: 2
Trade Names: Jack in the Box (2)
Units Franchised From: 2
Primary Menu: Hamburger (2)
Areas of Operation: CA
Type of Foodservice: Quick Serve (2)
Franchise Affiliation: Jack in the Box Restaurants, SAN DIEGO, CA

Key Personnel
S. NAJM JAFRI - Owner; General Buyer

Domino's Franchisee
8522 Whittier Blvd
Pico Rivera, CA 90660

Telephone: (562) 692-9591
Type of Business: Chain Restaurant Operator
Total Sales: $6,146,000 (e)
Total Units: 3
Trade Names: Domino's (3)
Units Franchised From: 3
Primary Menu: Pizza (3)
Areas of Operation: CA
Type of Foodservice: Quick Serve (3)
Franchise Affiliation: Domino's Pizza Inc, ANN ARBOR, MI

Key Personnel
JOSE I. CUESTA - Owner; General Buyer

Asfour Family Corporation
183 E Yorba Linda Blvd
Placentia, CA 92870-3328

Telephone: (714) 993-3498
Internet Homepage: subwayplacentia.net
Type of Business: Chain Restaurant Operator
Total Sales: $6,782,000 (e)
Total Units: 12
Trade Names: Subway (12)
Units Franchised From: 12
Primary Menu: Sandwiches/Deli (12)
Areas of Operation: CA
Type of Foodservice: Quick Serve (12)
Franchise Affiliation: Doctor's Associates Inc., MILFORD, CT

Key Personnel
JOHN ASFOUR - Partner
REHAM ASFOUR - Partner; General Buyer

Frisbie Management Inc.
1060 Ortega Way Ste A
Placentia, CA 92870-7125

Telephone: (714) 630-9430
Fax Number: (714) 630-0280
Internet Homepage: mcdfmi.com
Type of Business: Chain Restaurant Operator
Year Founded: 1967
Total Sales: $68,050,000 (e)
Number of Employees: 700
Average Check: Breakfast(8); Lunch(12); Dinner(12)
Total Units: 14

Trade Names: McDonald's (14)
Units Franchised From: 14
Preferred Square Footage: 2,500; 3,000
Preferred Location Types: Community Mall; Discount Dept. Stores; Freestanding
Primary Menu: Hamburger (15)
Areas of Operation: CA
Type of Foodservice: Quick Serve (14)
Franchise Affiliation: McDonald's Corporation, CHICAGO, IL
Primary Distributors: (Food) The Martin-Brower Co., PHOENIX, AZ; (Supplies) The Martin-Brower Co., PHOENIX, AZ

Key Personnel
SCOTT FRISBIE - President; Director Real Estate; General Buyer
BRIAN FRISBIE - VP; Director Finance
JOANN MCBETH - Manager Human Resources
DEBRA VOLL - Manager Accounting

Eastbay Equities Inc.
399 Taylor Blvd Ste 103
Pleasant Hill, CA 94523-2200

Telephone: (925) 686-2911
Fax Number: (925) 687-5938
Company Email: ebethomassen@aol.com
Type of Business: Chain Restaurant Operator
Year Founded: 1976
Total Sales: $45,960,000 (e)
Number of Employees: 495
Average Check: Lunch(8); Dinner(8)
Total Units: 17
Trade Names: Wendy's Old Fashioned Hamburgers (17)
Units Franchised From: 17
Preferred Square Footage: 2,300
Preferred Location Types: Freestanding
Primary Menu: Hamburger (17)
Areas of Operation: CA
Type of Foodservice: Quick Serve (17)
Franchise Affiliation: The Wendy's Company, DUBLIN, OH
Primary Distributors: (Food) SYSCO Food Services of San Francisco Inc., FREMONT, CA

Key Personnel
BILL CASTO - President
MARDELLE JOHNSON - Controller; Director Finance, Human Resources

Auntie Anne's Franchise
1212 Stoneridge Mall Rd
Pleasanton, CA 94588-3220

Telephone: (925) 463-7927
Type of Business: Chain Restaurant Operator
Total Sales: $1,532,000 (e)
Total Units: 2

Trade Names: Auntie Anne's Hand-Rolled Soft Pretzels (2)
Units Franchised From: 2
Primary Menu: Snacks (2)
Areas of Operation: CA
Type of Foodservice: Quick Serve (2)
Franchise Affiliation: Auntie Anne's Inc., LANCASTER, PA

Key Personnel
ERIC TAYLOR - Owner; General Buyer

Faz Restaurants Management
5121 Hopyard Rd
Pleasanton, CA 94588-3303

Telephone: (925) 469-1600
Fax Number: (925) 469-1604
Internet Homepage: fazrestaurants.com
Company Email: faz@fazrestaurants.com
Type of Business: Chain Restaurant Operator
Year Founded: 1985
Total Sales: $26,580,000 (e)
Alcohol Sales: 10%
Number of Employees: 350
Average Check: Lunch(12); Dinner(18)
Total Units: 7
Trade Names: Faz Bakery & Coffee Bar (1); Faz Restaurant & Catering (5); MacArthur Park (1)
Company-Owned Units: 7
Preferred Square Footage: 8,000
Preferred Location Types: Downtown; Freestanding
Alcohol Served: Beer, Wine, Liquor
Primary Menu: Greek/Mediterranean (6); Snacks (1)
Areas of Operation: CA
Type of Foodservice: Fine Dining (6); Quick Serve (1)
Foodservice Management Venues: Business & Industry
Catering Services: Yes

Key Personnel
FAZ POURSOHI - President; Executive Chef; Director Loss Prevention, Real Estate, Menu Development; General Buyer
REMZI DEGERLI - General Manager

Ghai Management Services, Inc.
1904 Via Di Salerno
Pleasanton, CA 94566-2117

Telephone: (510) 573-5905
Fax Number: (510) 490-5001
Internet Homepage: pacificcascade.us
Type of Business: Chain Restaurant Operator

Year Founded: 1999
Total Sales: $243,730,000 (e)
Total Units: 106
Trade Names: Burger King (106)
Units Franchised From: 106
Preferred Location Types: Convenience Store/Gas Station; Freestanding
Primary Menu: Hamburger (106)
Areas of Operation: CA, KS, MO, OR
Type of Foodservice: Quick Serve (106)
Franchise Affiliation: Burger King Worldwide Inc., MIAMI, FL; CBC Restaurant Corp., DALLAS, TX; Taco Bell Corp., IRVINE, CA

Key Personnel
SUNNY GHAI - CEO
HARSH GHAI - President; COO; General Buyer
STEVE THOMAS - VP
BERNADETTE LUNA - General Manager
VICTORIA NALL - Director Loss Prevention
ARMANDO PADILLA - Director Operations
MUSHTARI PADILLA - Director Operations
SILVIA WYTKIND - Director Development
JENNIFER FRICK - Director Human Resources
CONNIE BROWN - Director Safety, Risk Management
STEPHEN HART - Regional Director Operations
ROGER HUDSON - District Manager
JEREMY GORDON - District Manager
ILIANA CASTRO - Manager Information Technology
BRIAN MARTINEZ - Manager Operations, District

R.W. Forsum Enterprises
101 W Foothill Blvd
Pomona, CA 91767

Telephone: (909) 596-0029
Type of Business: Chain Restaurant Operator
Total Sales: $28,140,000 (e)
Total Units: 11
Trade Names: Jack in the Box (11)
Units Franchised From: 11
Primary Menu: Hamburger (11)
Areas of Operation: CA
Type of Foodservice: Quick Serve (11)
Franchise Affiliation: Jack in the Box Restaurants, SAN DIEGO, CA

Key Personnel
REYNOLD FORSUM - Owner; General Buyer

Rice Garden Inc.
981 Corporate Center Dr Ste 150
Pomona, CA 91768-2632

Telephone: (909) 629-7423
Fax Number: (626) 281-6692
Internet Homepage: thericegarden.com
Company Email: info@thericegarden.com

Type of Business: Chain Restaurant Operator
Year Founded: 1994
Systemwide Sales: $13,300,000 (e)
Total Sales: $8,102,000 (e)
Number of Employees: 255
Average Check: Lunch(10); Dinner(10)
Total Units: 15
Trade Names: The Rice Garden (15)
Company-Owned Units: 15
Preferred Square Footage: 500; 800; 2,000
Preferred Location Types: Airports; Downtown; Grocery Stores; Institution (college/hospital); Office Complex; Other; Strip Mall
Primary Menu: Chinese (15)
Areas of Operation: AZ, CA, TX, UT
Type of Foodservice: Quick Serve (15)
Foodservice Management Venues: College & University
Catering Services: Yes
Primary Distributors: (Full Line) McLane Company, Inc., TEMPLE, TX
Parent Company: Arbor Private Investment Co., CHICAGO, IL

Key Personnel
KEVIN DUNN - President; General Buyer
JAVIER DAVILA - Area Manager

Cheeseburger Restaurants Inc.
73875 State Route 70
Portola, CA 96122-7071

Telephone: (530) 832-6871
Fax Number: (530) 832-6876
Internet Homepage: cheeseburgernation.com; waikikibrewing.com
Type of Business: Chain Restaurant Operator
Year Founded: 1989
Total Sales: $42,580,000 (e)
Alcohol Sales: 15%
Number of Employees: 668
Average Check: Lunch(20); Dinner(20)
Internet Order Processing: Yes
Internet Sales: 1.00%
Total Units: 8
Trade Names: Cheeseburger In Paradise (2); Waikiki Brewing Company (4)
Company-Owned Units: 6
Preferred Square Footage: 5,500; 6,000
Preferred Location Types: Freestanding; Hotel/Motel; Regional Mall
Alcohol Served: Beer, Wine, Liquor
Primary Menu: Hamburger (6)
Areas of Operation: HI
Type of Foodservice: Casual Dining (6)
Primary Distributors: (Food) US Foods, NORTH LAS VEGAS, NV
Notes: The company derives approximately 8% of its revenue from retail operations.

Key Personnel
LAREN GARTNER - CEO; Partner; Director Facility/Maintenance, Real Estate, Design
EDNA BAYLIFF - President; Partner; Director Finance, Purchasing, Marketing, Menu Development
ROBERT KASKIE - Exec VP
DOUG RAINEY - VP

QSC Ventures Inc.
12424 Poway Rd
Poway, CA 92064-4303

Telephone: (858) 486-1170
Type of Business: Chain Restaurant Operator
Total Sales: $15,410,000 (e)
Total Units: 6
Trade Names: Jack in the Box (6)
Units Franchised From: 6
Primary Menu: Hamburger (6)
Areas of Operation: CA
Type of Foodservice: Quick Serve (6)
Franchise Affiliation: Jack in the Box Restaurants, SAN DIEGO, CA

Key Personnel
CHARLES STAUFFER - Owner; General Buyer

LC 3S Inc.
11135 Folsom Blvd
Rancho Cordova, CA 95670-6132

Telephone: (916) 638-0733
Fax Number: (916) 635-1395
Internet Homepage: brookrest.com
Company Email: president@brookrest.com
Type of Business: Chain Restaurant Operator
Year Founded: 1981
Total Sales: $18,296,000 (e)
Alcohol Sales: 3%
Number of Employees: 280
Average Check: Lunch(10); Dinner(12)
Internet Order Processing: Yes
Total Units: 3
Trade Names: Brookfield's Family Restaurant (3)
Company-Owned Units: 3
Preferred Square Footage: 7,000
Preferred Location Types: Freestanding
Alcohol Served: Beer, Wine
Primary Menu: American (3)
Projected Remodelings: 1
Areas of Operation: CA
Type of Foodservice: Casual Dining (3)

Key Personnel
SAM MANOLAKAS - President; Executive Chef; Manager Advertising; General Buyer
STACY MARR - VP Operations

Pizza Guys Franchises Inc.
2731 Citrus Rd Ste A
Rancho Cordova, CA 95742-6303

Telephone: (916) 852-2222
Fax Number: (916) 852-5555
Internet Homepage: pizzaguys.com
Company Email: feedback@pizzaguys.com
Type of Business: Chain Restaurant Operator
Year Founded: 1986
Systemwide Sales: $109,834,000 (e)
Total Sales: $29,010,000 (e)
Number of Employees: 276
Average Check: Lunch(22); Dinner(36)
Internet Order Processing: Yes
Internet Sales: 5.00%
Total Units: 82
Trade Names: Pizza Guys (82)
Company-Owned Units: 11
Units Franchised To: 71
Preferred Square Footage: 1,200
Preferred Location Types: Strip Mall
Primary Menu: Pizza (82)
Projected Openings: 3
Areas of Operation: CA, NV
Type of Foodservice: Quick Serve (82)
Primary Distributors: (Full Line) Saladino's Inc., FRESNO, CA

Key Personnel
REZA KALANTARI - Co-Founder; CFO
SHAHPOUR NEJAD - Co-Founder; CEO; President; General Buyer
DAN M. ZAMREY - VP Finance
REZA KAMALIAN - Director Operations
KAMIAR NEJAD - Director Marketing
KIM BUI - Director Human Resources

Foster's Freeze LLC
8360 Red Oak St Ste 102
Rancho Cucamonga, CA 91730-0608

Telephone: (909) 944-0815
Fax Number: (909) 944-0895
Internet Homepage: fostersfreeze.com
Company Email: info@fostersfreeze.com
Type of Business: Chain Restaurant Operator
Year Founded: 1946
Systemwide Sales: $61,007,000 (e)
Total Sales: $908,000 (e)
Number of Employees: 4
Average Check: Lunch(5); Dinner(5)
Total Units: 71
Trade Names: Fosters Freeze (71)
Units Franchised To: 71
Preferred Square Footage: 1,500
Preferred Location Types: Community Mall; Freestanding; Regional Mall; Strip Mall
Primary Menu: Snacks (71)
Areas of Operation: CA
Type of Foodservice: Quick Serve (71)

Primary Distributors: (Full Line) US Foods-San Francisco, LIVERMORE, CA

Key Personnel
RANDY FRITCHIE - CEO; President; Partner; CFO; Director Finance, Operations, Purchasing, Facility/Maintenance, Information Systems, Supply Chain, Ethnic Marketing, Real Estate, Design, Human Resources, Store Fixtures, Menu Development
URMESH DAHYA - Partner
SHANE ARNOLD - Manager Marketing

JM Foods, Inc.
8880 Foothill Blvd
Rancho Cucamonga, CA 91730-7198

Telephone: (909) 944-3400
Type of Business: Chain Restaurant Operator
Total Sales: $85,020,000 (e)
Total Units: 63
Trade Names: Jersey Mike's Subs (63)
Units Franchised From: 63
Primary Menu: Sandwiches/Deli (63)
Areas of Operation: CA
Type of Foodservice: Quick Serve (63)
Franchise Affiliation: Jersey Mike's Franchise Systems, MANASQUAN, NJ

Key Personnel
ALVARO GARCIA - Owner; General Buyer
RICK BUCKLEY - Director Construction
BILL NEWELL - Director Operations
ERIN MACDONALD - Regional Director Marketing

The C & C Organization
8689 9th St
Rancho Cucamonga, CA 91730

Telephone: (909) 982-7108
Fax Number: (909) 981-9734
Internet Homepage: thesycamoreinn.com, caskncleaver.com
Company Email: info@caskncleaver.com
Type of Business: Chain Restaurant Operator
Year Founded: 1967
Total Sales: $14,815,000 (e)
Alcohol Sales: 25%
Number of Employees: 260
Average Check: Lunch(14); Dinner(32)
Total Units: 2
Trade Names: Cask 'n Cleaver Steakhouse (1); Sycamore Inn (1)
Company-Owned Units: 2
Preferred Square Footage: 4,000
Preferred Location Types: Freestanding
Alcohol Served: Beer, Wine, Liquor
Primary Menu: Steak/Seafood (2)
Areas of Operation: CA
Type of Foodservice: Casual Dining (2)

Primary Distributors: (Food) SYSCO Food Services of San Diego Inc., POWAY, CA

Key Personnel
GEORGE FRANOV - General Manager

Yogurtland Franchisee
10798 Foothill Blvd Ste 110
Rancho Cucamonga, CA 91730-7617

Telephone: (909) 941-3337
Type of Business: Chain Restaurant Operator
Total Sales: $2,085,000 (e)
Total Units: 2
Trade Names: Yogurtland (2)
Units Franchised From: 2
Primary Menu: Snacks (2)
Areas of Operation: CA
Type of Foodservice: Quick Serve (2)
Franchise Affiliation: Yogurtland Franchising Inc., FARMERS BRANCH, TX

Key Personnel
MARCUS CHAN - Owner; General Buyer

CGE Management
430 Silver Spur Rd Ste 101
Rancho Palos Verdes, CA 90275-3577

Telephone: (310) 541-7878
Fax Number: (310) 541-2308
Internet Homepage: chinese-gourmet-express.com
Company Email: info@cgemgmt.com
Type of Business: Chain Restaurant Operator
Year Founded: 1989
Total Sales: $19,970,000 (e)
Number of Employees: 305
Average Check: Lunch(12); Dinner(12)
Total Units: 62
Trade Names: Chinese Gourmet Express (48); Sansei Japanese Gourmet (14)
Company-Owned Units: 62
Preferred Square Footage: 800; 1,300
Preferred Location Types: Community Mall; Regional Mall; Strip Mall
Primary Menu: Chinese (48); Japanese (14)
Areas of Operation: AR, CA, CO, CT, HI, IA, IL, IN, KY, LA, MI, MN, NC, NM, NV, NY, OH, OK, OR, PA, SC, TX, UT, VA, WA, WI
Type of Foodservice: Quick Serve (62)

Key Personnel
DENNIS PUN - President
SAMUEL SIM - President; Director Marketing, Advertising, Real Estate, Design, Human Resources, Menu Development
MONICA SIM - VP Operations, Purchasing; Director Facility/Maintenance, Supply Chain, Store Fixtures

KATE CHAN - Controller; Director Information Systems, Loss Prevention, Human Resources
KELLY SIM - Manager Information Technology
SIMIAO YU - Analyst Operations

Trump National Golf Club
1 Trump National Dr
Rancho Palos Verdes, CA 90275-6173

Telephone: (310) 265-5525
Fax Number: (310) 265-5522
Internet Homepage: trumpnationallosangeles.com
Company Email: contact@trumpnational.com
Type of Business: Chain Restaurant Operator
Year Founded: 2006
Total Sales: $4,022,000 (e)
Alcohol Sales: 10%
Number of Employees: 100
Average Check: Dinner(42)
Total Units: 2
Trade Names: Cafe Pacific (1); Golfer's Lounge (1)
Company-Owned Units: 2
Preferred Location Types: Other
Alcohol Served: Beer, Wine, Liquor
Primary Menu: American (2)
Areas of Operation: CA
Type of Foodservice: Fine Dining (1)
Primary Distributors: (Full Line) SYSCO Food Services of Central California Inc., MODESTO, CA
Notes: The company derives approximately 60% of its revenue from retail and golf club operations.

Key Personnel
DONALD J. TRUMP - President
DEAN MICHELLE-TRUMP - Director Sales, Catering
CARINE HERNANDEZ - Manager
DANIELLE ISOM - Manager
KATIE KIMOSE - Manager Event Planning

Mille Fleurs
6009 Paseo Delicias
Rancho Santa Fe, CA 92067

Mailing Address: PO Box 2548, RANCHO SANTA FE, CA, 92067-2548
Telephone: (858) 756-3085
Fax Number: (858) 756-9945
Internet Homepage: millefleurs.com; asrestaurant.com
Company Email: info@MilleFleurs.com
Type of Business: Chain Restaurant Operator
Year Founded: 1984
Total Sales: $13,684,000 (e)
Alcohol Sales: 30%
Number of Employees: 80
Average Check: Lunch(48); Dinner(90)

Internet Order Processing: Yes
Total Units: 2
Trade Names: Bertrand at Mister A's (1); Mille Fleurs (1)
Company-Owned Units: 2
Preferred Location Types: Downtown; Freestanding
Alcohol Served: Beer, Wine, Liquor
Primary Menu: French/Continental (2)
Areas of Operation: CA
Type of Foodservice: Fine Dining (2)

Key Personnel
BERTRAND HUG - President; General Manager
ANGELA OSBORNE - Controller

Bowl of Heaven Franchise Group LLC
29851 Aventura Ste N
Rancho Santa Margarita, CA 92688-2014

Telephone: (949) 459-1170
Internet Homepage: bowlofheaven.com
Company Email: rsm@bowlofheaven.com
Type of Business: Chain Restaurant Operator
Year Founded: 2010
Total Sales: $3,600,000 (e)
Total Units: 10
Trade Names: Bowl of Heaven (10)
Company-Owned Units: 2
Units Franchised To: 8
Preferred Square Footage: 1,000; 1,400
Preferred Location Types: Downtown; Strip Mall
Primary Menu: Health Foods (10)
Areas of Operation: CA, UT, WI
Type of Foodservice: Fast Casual (10)

Key Personnel
DAN MCCORMICK - Co-Founder; President
MARILYN MCCORMICK - Co-Founder; Treasurer

Cotti Foods
29889 Santa Margarita Pkwy
Rancho Santa Margarita, CA 92688-3609

Telephone: (949) 858-9191
Fax Number: (949) 858-9199
Type of Business: Chain Restaurant Operator
Year Founded: 1990
Total Sales: $476,120,000 (e)
Number of Employees: 1,650
Average Check: Lunch(5); Dinner(6)
Total Units: 184
Trade Names: Pieology (10); Taco Bell (78); Wendy's Old Fashioned Hamburgers (96)
Units Franchised From: 184

Preferred Square Footage: 3,000
Preferred Location Types: Freestanding
Primary Menu: Hamburger (96); Pizza (10); Taco (78)
Areas of Operation: CA, HI, KS, TX
Type of Foodservice: Quick Serve (189)
Franchise Affiliation: Pizza Hut Inc., PLANO, TX; Taco Bell Corp., IRVINE, CA; The Wendy's Company, DUBLIN, OH
Primary Distributors: (Full Line) McLane/Riverside, RIVERSIDE, CA

Key Personnel
PETER CAPRIOTTI II - CEO; President
HOLDEN CAPRIOTTI - CFO
SCOTT MILLER - CFO
RYAN ZACCHE - Chief Development Officer
STEVE SIGLIN - Exec VP; General Counsel
FRED COOK - Senior VP
STEVEN EVANS - VP Development, Engineering
SHANE GRAY - VP Marketing
KELLY SOLARU - VP Leasing
BLAKE TRIVISON - VP Marketing
VALERIE KEMP - VP Real Estate
SOCRATES LEYVA - Director Facility/Maintenance
DREW HANSEN - Director Operations
BASHAR HITO - Director Information Technology
ESPERANZA VILLALPANDO - Director Operations
ED GARRIGUES - Director Operations
ARTURO ZUNIGA - Director Operations
DEREK NOVOTNY - Director Operations
JAMIE RILEY - Manager Information Technology
PILAR PARSONS - Administrator Payroll
CANDICE CAPONE - Administrator Payroll
WENDY GRAY - Coordinator Operations

GCP Enterprises, Inc.
28562 Oso Pkwy Ste D236
Rancho Santa Margarita, CA 92688-5595

Telephone: (949) 887-1343
Type of Business: Chain Restaurant Operator
Total Sales: $32,850,000 (e)
Total Units: 13
Trade Names: Jack in the Box (13)
Units Franchised From: 13
Primary Menu: Hamburger (13)
Areas of Operation: CA
Type of Foodservice: Quick Serve (13)
Franchise Affiliation: Jack in the Box Restaurants, SAN DIEGO, CA

Key Personnel
CHRISTINA PERUCCI - Owner; General Buyer

Golden Spoon Franchising Inc.
30212 Tomas Suite 365
Rancho Santa Margarita, CA 92688-2118

Telephone: (949) 709-2750
Internet Homepage: goldenspoon.com
Company Email: info@goldenspoon.com
Type of Business: Chain Restaurant Operator
Year Founded: 1983
Systemwide Sales: $14,536,000 (e)
Total Sales: $232,000 (e)
Number of Employees: 3
Average Check: Lunch(8); Dinner(8)
Total Units: 23
Trade Names: Golden Spoon Frozen Yogurt (23)
Units Franchised To: 23
Preferred Square Footage: 1,000; 1,500
Preferred Location Types: Freestanding; Kiosk; Strip Mall
Primary Menu: Snacks (23)
Areas of Operation: AZ, CA
Foreign Countries: JAPAN; QATAR; THE PHILIPPINES
Type of Foodservice: Quick Serve (23)
Primary Distributors: (Full Line) Southwest Traders Inc., TEMECULA, CA

Key Personnel
ROGER L. CLAWSON - CEO; Owner
CHRISSY EBLIN - Director Communications

JIPC Management
22342 Avenida Empresa Ste 220
Rancho Santa Margarita, CA 92688-2161

Telephone: (949) 916-2000
Fax Number: (949) 916-2600
Internet Homepage: johnspizza.com
Company Email: info@johnspizza.com
Type of Business: Chain Restaurant Operator
Year Founded: 1997
Total Sales: $11,500,000 (e)
Alcohol Sales: 3%
Number of Employees: 1,680
Average Check: Lunch(12); Dinner(12)
Total Units: 14
Trade Names: John's Incredible Pizza Co. (14)
Company-Owned Units: 14
Preferred Square Footage: 50,000
Preferred Location Types: Downtown; Freestanding; Regional Mall; Strip Mall
Alcohol Served: Beer, Wine
Primary Menu: Pizza (14)
Projected Openings: 1
Areas of Operation: CA, NV, OR
Type of Foodservice: Casual Dining (14)
Primary Distributors: (Full Line) SYSCO Food

Services of Sacramento Inc., PLEASANT GROVE, CA
Notes: The company derives approximately 50% of its revenue from games and entertainment.

Key Personnel
JOHN PARLET - Founder; President; Director Real Estate, Design, Menu Development; General Buyer
LORI STOWE - VP Operations; Controller; Manager Finance, Supply Chain
DENINA EVANS - Director Human Resources
NICK OSINSKI - Manager Information Technology

Pieology Pizzeria
30242 Esperanza
Rancho Santa Margarita, CA 92688-2121

Telephone: (949) 800-8314
Internet Homepage: pieology.com
Company Email: info@pieology.com
Type of Business: Chain Restaurant Operator
Year Founded: 2011
Systemwide Sales: $193,936,000 (e)
Total Sales: $39,220,000 (e)
Internet Order Processing: Yes
Internet Sales: 1.00%
Total Units: 116
Trade Names: Pieology Pizzeria (116)
Company-Owned Units: 33
Units Franchised To: 83
Primary Menu: Pizza (133)
Areas of Operation: AZ, CA, CO, FL, GA, HI, KY, MD, MN, MO, NC, NV, OH, OR, SC, TX
Type of Foodservice: Fast Casual (133)

Key Personnel
SHAWN THOMPSON - CEO
RYAN FESSLER - CFO
NESS BALZANO - VP Human Resources
RICHARD LONG - Director Information Technology
JEREMY BONK - Director Operations
JUAN RIVERA - Director Operations
SHAUNA HAY VIETSVEETS - Manager Development-Training

Simply Tacos Inc.
PO Box 80939
Rancho Santa Margarita, CA 92688-0939

Telephone: (949) 218-2367
Fax Number: (949) 218-2368
Type of Business: Chain Restaurant Operator
Year Founded: 1999
Total Sales: $56,130,000 (e)
Number of Employees: 440
Average Check: Lunch(12); Dinner(12)
Total Units: 20
Trade Names: Taco Bell (20)
Units Franchised From: 20
Preferred Square Footage: 3,000
Preferred Location Types: Freestanding
Primary Menu: Taco (20)
Areas of Operation: CA
Type of Foodservice: Quick Serve (20)
Franchise Affiliation: Taco Bell Corp., IRVINE, CA
Primary Distributors: (Full Line) McLane/Tracy, TRACY, CA

Key Personnel
LEE MITCHELL JR - President; General Manager; Director Real Estate; General Buyer
MICHAEL SHEPHERD - Manager Operations, Purchasing, Supply Chain

Domino's Franchisee
333 S Main St Ste A
Red Bluff, CA 96080-4352

Telephone: (530) 529-5555
Type of Business: Chain Restaurant Operator
Total Sales: $4,148,000 (e)
Total Units: 2
Trade Names: Domino's (2)
Units Franchised From: 2
Primary Menu: Pizza (2)
Areas of Operation: CA
Type of Foodservice: Quick Serve (2)
Franchise Affiliation: Domino's Pizza Inc, ANN ARBOR, MI

Key Personnel
CRAIG SCHUBERT - Owner; General Buyer

Black Bear Diners Inc.
1880 Shasta St
Redding, CA 96001-0417

Telephone: (530) 243-2327
Fax Number: (530) 243-8931
Internet Homepage: blackbeardiner.com
Company Email: blackbeardiner@blackbeardiner.com
Type of Business: Chain Restaurant Operator
Year Founded: 1995
Systemwide Sales: $508,216,000 (e)
Total Sales: $43,620,000 (e)
Alcohol Sales: 5%
Number of Employees: 290
Average Check: Breakfast(12); Lunch(16); Dinner(20)
Internet Order Processing: Yes
Internet Sales: 10.00%
Total Units: 148
Trade Names: Black Bear Diner (148)
Company-Owned Units: 8
Units Franchised To: 140
Preferred Square Footage: 5,000; 5,500
Preferred Location Types: Freestanding
Alcohol Served: Beer, Wine
Primary Menu: American (148)
Projected Openings: 9
Areas of Operation: AZ, CA, CO, ID, MO, MT, NV, OK, OR, TX, UT, WA
Type of Foodservice: Family Restaurant (148)

Key Personnel
BRUCE DEAN - Executive Chairman; Co-Founder
BOB MANLEY - Co-Founder; President
ANITA ADAMS - CEO; President
DAVID L. DOTY - Partner; Chief Marketing Officer
STEVE SPARKS - CFO
ROBIN YOSHIMURA - CFO
JEFF GUIDO - COO
TAMMY JOHNS - Chief People Officer
JOLISA JOHNSON - VP Marketing, Communications
SAUNDRA CLEVELAND - VP Finance; Controller
CHAD CORRIGAN - VP Franchise Development, Franchise Sales
CHUCK RISKE - VP Operations
ROBERT SIMPSON - Director Human Resources, Training
ROBBIE MCLAUGHLIN - Senior Manager Information Technology
ANDREA MILLER - Manager Franchise Development, Franchise Sales

Dave's Mac Inc
2269 Hartnell Ave
Redding, CA 96002-2323

Telephone: (530) 221-7414
Fax Number: (530) 221-4953
Type of Business: Chain Restaurant Operator
Total Sales: $10,009,000 (e)
Average Check: Dinner(12)
Total Units: 2
Trade Names: McDonald's (2)
Units Franchised From: 2
Primary Menu: Hamburger (2)
Areas of Operation: CA
Type of Foodservice: Quick Serve (2)
Franchise Affiliation: McDonald's Corporation, CHICAGO, IL

Key Personnel
DAVID L. MCGEORGE - President; General Buyer

J & A Foodservices Inc.
400 Redcliff Dr
Redding, CA 96002-0116

Telephone: (530) 222-1311
Fax Number: (530) 222-1317
Internet Homepage: jafoods.com
Type of Business: Chain Restaurant Operator
Year Founded: 1993
Total Sales: $68,450,000 (e)
Alcohol Sales: 12%
Number of Employees: 5,700
Average Check: Breakfast(8); Lunch(16); Dinner(28)
Total Units: 31
Trade Names: Applebee's (10); Burger King (13); Logan's Roadhouse (7); Marie Callender's (1)
Company-Owned Units: 2
Units Franchised From: 29
Preferred Square Footage: 2,200; 2,800
Preferred Location Types: Freestanding; Regional Mall; Strip Mall
Alcohol Served: Beer, Wine, Liquor
Primary Menu: American (18); Hamburger (13)
Areas of Operation: CA, OR
Type of Foodservice: Casual Dining (18); Quick Serve (13)
Franchise Affiliation: Burger King Worldwide Inc., MIAMI, FL
Primary Distributors: (Full Line) SYSCO Food Services of Los Angeles Inc., WALNUT, CA
Notes: The Applebee's restaurants operate as AB Enterprises.

Key Personnel
JOSEPH K. WONG - President; Manager Real Estate
ZACH SYLVIA - VP Operations; General Buyer

JM Subs North Four, L.P.
835 Browning St Ste 102
Redding, CA 96003-3873

Telephone: (530) 276-8850
Type of Business: Chain Restaurant Operator
Total Sales: $4,403,000 (e)
Total Units: 3
Trade Names: Jersey Mike's Subs (3)
Units Franchised From: 3
Primary Menu: Sandwiches/Deli (3)
Areas of Operation: CA
Type of Foodservice: Quick Serve (3)
Franchise Affiliation: Jersey Mike's Franchise Systems, MANASQUAN, NJ

Key Personnel
BEV MILLS - Partner
MICHAEL MILLLS - Partner

Lumberjacks Franchises, Inc.
410 Hemsted Dr Ste 200
Redding, CA 96002-0164

Telephone: (530) 224-1872
Fax Number: (530) 224-1863
Internet Homepage: lumberjacksrestaurant.com
Type of Business: Chain Restaurant Operator
Year Founded: 2008
Total Sales: $8,057,000 (e)
Number of Employees: 350
Total Units: 9
Trade Names: Lumberjacks Restaurant (9)
Company-Owned Units: 4
Units Franchised To: 5
Preferred Location Types: Freestanding
Alcohol Served: Beer, Wine
Primary Menu: American (9)
Projected Openings: 1
Areas of Operation: CA, NV
Type of Foodservice: Casual Dining (9)

Key Personnel
JEFF GARRETT - CEO; President
SUSAN GARRETT - Corporate Secretary

Good Stuff Restaurants
1617 S Pacific Coast Hwy Ste 102
Redondo Beach, CA 90277-5612

Telephone: (310) 316-0262
Internet Homepage: eatgoodstuff.com
Company Email: rb@eatgoodstuff.com
Type of Business: Chain Restaurant Operator
Year Founded: 1980
Total Sales: $6,267,000 (e)
Alcohol Sales: 10%
Number of Employees: 110
Average Check: Breakfast(12); Lunch(14); Dinner(22)
Internet Order Processing: Yes
Total Units: 4
Trade Names: Good Stuff Eatery (4)
Company-Owned Units: 4
Preferred Location Types: Freestanding
Alcohol Served: Beer, Wine
Primary Menu: American (4)
Areas of Operation: CA
Foreign Countries: SAUDI ARABIA
Type of Foodservice: Casual Dining (4)
Catering Services: Yes
Primary Distributors: (Full Line) SYSCO Food Services of Los Angeles Inc., WALNUT, CA

Key Personnel
CRIS BENNETT - President; Partner; Executive Chef; Director Operations, Information Systems, Menu Development, Catering
SPIKE MENDELSOHN - Partner

JAIRO GUTIERREZ - General Manager
COURTNEY BATTISTA - Manager Business Development

Hennessey's Tavern Inc.
1845 S Elena Ave Ste 300
Redondo Beach, CA 90277-5708

Telephone: (310) 540-2274
Fax Number: (310) 316-2534
Internet Homepage: hennesseystavern.com; mickiefinnzlasvegas.com
Company Email: info@hennesseystavern.com
Type of Business: Chain Restaurant Operator
Year Founded: 1976
Total Sales: $47,260,000 (e)
Alcohol Sales: 20%
Number of Employees: 830
Average Check: Breakfast(12); Lunch(12); Dinner(18)
Internet Order Processing: Yes
Total Units: 11
Trade Names: Hennessey's Tavern (10); Mickie Finnz (1)
Company-Owned Units: 11
Preferred Square Footage: 3,000
Preferred Location Types: Freestanding
Alcohol Served: Beer, Wine, Liquor
Primary Menu: American (11)
Projected Openings: 1
Areas of Operation: CA, NV
Type of Foodservice: Casual Dining (11)
Primary Distributors: (Full Line) US Foods-Los Angeles, LA MIRADA, CA

Key Personnel
PAUL HENNESSEY - CEO; Owner; Director Operations, Purchasing, Real Estate; General Buyer
NICOLE FAY - CFO

Galco Foods
864 W Manning Ave
Reedley, CA 93654-2430

Telephone: (559) 638-1041
Type of Business: Chain Restaurant Operator
Total Sales: $3,794,000 (e)
Total Units: 2
Trade Names: KFC (2)
Units Franchised From: 2
Primary Menu: Chicken (2)
Areas of Operation: CA
Type of Foodservice: Quick Serve (2)
Franchise Affiliation: KFC Corporation, LOUISVILLE, KY

Key Personnel
MANUEL GALHARDO - President; General Buyer

Valley Management Associates
18747 Sherman Way
Reseda, CA 91335-4055

Telephone: (818) 881-6801
Fax Number: (818) 881-2478
Type of Business: Chain Restaurant Operator
Year Founded: 1968
Total Sales: $27,640,000 (e)
Number of Employees: 260
Average Check: Breakfast(8); Lunch(10); Dinner(12)
Total Units: 6
Trade Names: McDonald's (6)
Units Franchised From: 6
Preferred Square Footage: 3,000
Preferred Location Types: Freestanding
Primary Menu: Hamburger (6)
Areas of Operation: CA
Type of Foodservice: Quick Serve (6)
Franchise Affiliation: McDonald's Corporation, CHICAGO, IL

Key Personnel
KENNETH LOPATY - President; Director Operations, Real Estate; General Buyer
RON LOPATY - VP; Director Information Systems
ROBERT DEOBLER - Treasurer; Director Finance
STEVEN EIFERT - Director Marketing, Human Resources

Jose's Mexican Food Inc.
1188 Leiske Dr
Rialto, CA 92376-8643

Telephone: (909) 879-0004
Fax Number: (909) 879-0005
Internet Homepage: josesmexicanfood.com; mitortillamexicangrill.com
Company Email: comments@jose-s.com
Type of Business: Chain Restaurant Operator
Year Founded: 1989
Total Sales: $8,788,000 (e)
Alcohol Sales: 10%
Number of Employees: 133
Average Check: Lunch(8); Dinner(14)
Total Units: 6
Trade Names: Jose's Mexican Food (5); Mi Tortilla Mexican Grill (1)
Company-Owned Units: 6
Preferred Square Footage: 1,500; 2,500; 3,500
Preferred Location Types: Freestanding; Regional Mall; Strip Mall
Alcohol Served: Beer, Wine, Liquor
Primary Menu: Mexican (6)
Areas of Operation: CA
Type of Foodservice: Casual Dining (6)
Catering Services: Yes
Primary Distributors: (Food) Tapia Brothers Company, MAYWOOD, CA

Key Personnel
JOSE JARA - CEO; President; Director Finance, Facility/Maintenance, Risk Management, Real Estate, Human Resources
LINDA JARA - Director
MAGGIE HAMILTON - Director Information Systems, Human Resources

Lappert's Gourmet Ice Cream
223 Ohio Ave
Richmond, CA 94804-2142

Telephone: (510) 231-2340
Fax Number: (510) 231-2344
Internet Homepage: lapperts.com
Type of Business: Chain Restaurant Operator
Total Sales: $12,720,000 (e)
Number of Employees: 35
Average Check: Dinner(5)
Internet Order Processing: Yes
Internet Sales: 1.00%
Total Units: 20
Trade Names: Lappert's Ice Cream (20)
Company-Owned Units: 4
Units Franchised To: 16
Preferred Square Footage: 2,500
Preferred Location Types: Airports; Downtown; Hotel/Motel; Regional Mall; Strip Mall
Primary Menu: Snacks (20)
Areas of Operation: CA
Type of Foodservice: Quick Serve (20)
Primary Distributors: (Full Line) Dairyland, The Chef's Warehouse, CITY OF INDUSTRY, CA

Key Personnel
MICHAEL LAPPERT - President; Manager Menu Development; General Buyer

Subway Franchise
815 N China Lake Blvd
Ridgecrest, CA 93555-3515

Telephone: (760) 384-4784
Type of Business: Chain Restaurant Operator
Total Sales: $2,792,000 (e)
Total Units: 4
Trade Names: Subway (4)
Company-Owned Units: 4
Primary Menu: Sandwiches/Deli (4)
Areas of Operation: CA
Type of Foodservice: Quick Serve (4)
Franchise Affiliation: Doctor's Associates Inc., MILFORD, CT

Key Personnel
JAGDEEP DHILLON - President; General Buyer

Cookie Plug
2915 Van Buren Blvd Ste J1
Riverside, CA 92503

Telephone: (951) 505-0146
Internet Homepage: cookieplug.com
Type of Business: Chain Restaurant Operator
Total Units: 35
Trade Names: Cookie Plug (35)
Company-Owned Units: 35
Primary Menu: Snacks (35)
Areas of Operation: AZ, CA, NV, OR, TX, UT
Type of Foodservice: Fast Casual (35)

Key Personnel
ERIK MARTINEZ - Founder
CHRIS WYLAND - CEO

Domino's Franchisee
4100 Central Ave Ste 105
Riverside, CA 92506-2930

Telephone: (951) 787-9999
Type of Business: Chain Restaurant Operator
Total Sales: $21,923,000 (e)
Total Units: 11
Trade Names: Domino's (11)
Units Franchised From: 11
Primary Menu: Pizza (11)
Areas of Operation: CA
Type of Foodservice: Quick Serve (11)
Franchise Affiliation: Domino's Pizza Inc, ANN ARBOR, MI

Key Personnel
GHOLAMHOSSEIN MOLLAGHASEMI-TABRIZI - Owner; General Buyer

Farmer Boys Food Inc.
3452 University Ave
Riverside, CA 92501-3327

Telephone: (951) 275-9900
Fax Number: (951) 275-9930
Internet Homepage: farmerboys.com
Company Email: info@farmerboys.com
Type of Business: Chain Restaurant Operator
Year Founded: 1981
Systemwide Sales: $50,829,000 (e)
Total Sales: $17,763,000 (e)
Number of Employees: 500
Average Check: Lunch(10); Dinner(12)
Total Units: 101
Trade Names: Farmer Boys (101)

Company-Owned Units: 31
Units Franchised To: 70
Preferred Square Footage: 2,800; 3,200
Preferred Location Types: Freestanding
Primary Menu: Hamburger (101)
Projected Openings: 3
Areas of Operation: CA, NV
Type of Foodservice: Fast Casual (101)
Primary Distributors: (Full Line) SYSCO Food Services of Los Angeles Inc., WALNUT, CA

Key Personnel
JOSEPH ORTIZ - President; COO
HUNTLEY CASTNER - CFO
NOAH CHILLINGWORTH - Chief Marketing Officer
JOE ADNEY - Chief Marketing Officer; VP
KRISTY FOSTER - VP Supply Chain
JOHN LUCAS - VP Branding, Quality Control
ANNE MARIE DOWELL - General Manager
DAISY ALVAREZ - Senior Director Marketing
MICHAEL BERUMEN - Senior Director Operations
GLEN RUTTER - Senior Director Development
JOYCE DERY - Director Real Estate
RONA GRIEGO - Director Construction
ERIC SMITH - Manager Information Technology

M Kyrro Foods, Inc.
497 E Alessandro Blvd Ste A
Riverside, CA 92508-5024

Telephone: (951) 776-2494
Type of Business: Chain Restaurant Operator
Total Sales: $9,772,000 (e)
Total Units: 7
Trade Names: Jersey Mike's Subs (7)
Units Franchised From: 7
Primary Menu: Sandwiches/Deli (7)
Areas of Operation: CA
Type of Foodservice: Quick Serve (7)
Franchise Affiliation: Jersey Mike's Franchise Systems, MANASQUAN, NJ

Key Personnel
SAMEH SAMAAN - Partner; General Buyer
WAHID KARAS - Partner

National Casting Company Inc
3760 Tyler St
Riverside, CA 92503-4161

Telephone: (951) 687-4222
Type of Business: Chain Restaurant Operator
Total Sales: $1,233,000 (e)
Total Units: 3
Trade Names: Baskin-Robbins (3)
Company-Owned Units: 3
Primary Menu: Snacks (3)
Areas of Operation: CA
Type of Foodservice: Quick Serve (3)
Franchise Affiliation: BR IP Holder LLC, CANTON, MA

Key Personnel
ARSHAD JAMIL - Owner; General Buyer

Preferred Hospitality Inc.
7119 Indiana Ave
Riverside, CA 92504-4543

Telephone: (951) 682-9850
Fax Number: (951) 276-9975
Internet Homepage: marketbroiler.com
Type of Business: Chain Restaurant Operator
Year Founded: 1989
Total Sales: $25,470,000 (e)
Alcohol Sales: 20%
Number of Employees: 350
Average Check: Lunch(20); Dinner(32)
Internet Order Processing: Yes
Total Units: 7
Trade Names: Market Broiler (7)
Company-Owned Units: 7
Preferred Square Footage: 5,500; 6,000
Preferred Location Types: Freestanding
Alcohol Served: Beer, Wine, Liquor
Primary Menu: Seafood (7)
Areas of Operation: CA
Type of Foodservice: Casual Dining (7)
Foodservice Management Venues: College & University
Catering Services: Yes
Primary Distributors: (Food) US Foods-Los Angeles, LA MIRADA, CA

Key Personnel
RODNEY K. COUCH - Founder; CEO
AARON PERCOCO - President
RAJESH MEHTA - CFO; Controller
LENORE VLASIC - Chief Marketing Officer
ROBIN HIGA - Corporate Chef; General Buyer
SERGIO MENDEZ - Manager District

Yogurtland Franchisee
1242 University Ave Ste A
Riverside, CA 92507-8810

Telephone: (951) 683-1950
Type of Business: Chain Restaurant Operator
Total Sales: $3,242,000 (e)
Total Units: 3
Trade Names: Yogurtland (3)
Units Franchised From: 3
Primary Menu: Snacks (3)
Areas of Operation: CA
Type of Foodservice: Quick Serve (3)
Franchise Affiliation: Yogurtland Franchising Inc., FARMERS BRANCH, TX

Key Personnel
SANG JUN LEE - Owner; General Buyer

Star Acquisitions Inc
3389 Parkside Dr
Rocklin, CA 95677-2572

Telephone: (916) 632-9263
Type of Business: Chain Restaurant Operator
Total Sales: $12,830,000 (e)
Total Units: 6
Trade Names: Carl's Jr. (6)
Units Franchised From: 6
Primary Menu: Hamburger (6)
Areas of Operation: CA
Type of Foodservice: Quick Serve (6)
Franchise Affiliation: Carl's Jr., FRANKLIN, TN

Key Personnel
NANETTE OLSON - President; General Buyer

TJLM Food Services, Inc.
6299 Commerce Blvd
Rohnert Park, CA 94928-2105

Telephone: (707) 585-3515
Type of Business: Chain Restaurant Operator
Total Sales: $12,730,000 (e)
Total Units: 5
Trade Names: Jack in the Box (5)
Units Franchised From: 5
Primary Menu: Hamburger (5)
Areas of Operation: CA
Type of Foodservice: Quick Serve (5)
Franchise Affiliation: Jack in the Box Restaurants, SAN DIEGO, CA

Key Personnel
THEODORE TOM - Owner; General Buyer

Panda Restaurant Group Inc.
1683 Walnut Grove Ave
Rosemead, CA 91770-3711

Telephone: (626) 799-9898
Fax Number: (626) 403-8600
Internet Homepage: hibachisan.com; pandaexpress.com; pandainn.com; pandarg.com
Company Email: guestrelations@pandarg.com
Type of Business: Chain Restaurant Operator
Year Founded: 1973
Systemwide Sales: $6,379,205,000 (e)
Total Sales: $5,730,473,000 (e)
Alcohol Sales: 0.20%
Number of Employees: 4,700
Average Check: Lunch(12); Dinner(12)
Total Units: 2,460
Trade Names: Hibachi-San (10); Panda

Express (2,446); Panda Inn (4)
Company-Owned Units: 2,351
Units Franchised To: 109
Preferred Square Footage: 800; 1,000; 2,000; 2,600
Preferred Location Types: Airports; Community Mall; Downtown; Freestanding; Grocery Stores; Institution (college/hospital); Lifestyle Center; Mobile Unit; Office Complex; Other; Outlet Mall; Regional Mall; Stadiums; Strip Mall; Travel Plazas
Alcohol Served: Beer, Wine, Liquor
Primary Menu: Chinese (2,450); Japanese (10)
Projected Openings: 50
Areas of Operation: AL, AR, AZ, CA, CO, CT, DC, DE, FL, GA, GU, HI, IA, ID, IL, IN, KS, KY, LA, MA, MD, ME, MI, MN, MO, MS, MT, NC, ND, NE, NH, NJ, NM, NV, NY, OH, OK, OR, PA, PR, RI, SC, SD, TN, TX, UT, VA, WA, WI, WV, WY
Foreign Countries: MEXICO; UNITED ARAB EMIRATES
Type of Foodservice: Casual Dining (4); Quick Serve (2,456)
Foodservice Management Venues: Business & Industry; College & University
Catering Services: Yes
Primary Distributors: (Full Line) The SYGMA Network Inc. - Southern California, LANCASTER, CA
Notes: Systemwide sales reflect results for Panda Express units.

Key Personnel
PEGGY T. CHERNG - Chairman; CEO; Treasurer
ANDREW CHERNG - Co-Chairman; Founder; CEO; Co-CEO
DAVID F. LANDSBERG - CFO
LEONARD YIP - Chief People Officer; CIO; Senior VP
ANDREA CHERNG - Chief Marketing Officer
PHILLINE ZITIN - Chief Diversity Officer
MONTE BAIER - Senior VP; General Counsel
GLENN INANAGA - Senior VP
JEFF WANG - Senior VP Operations
WILLIE WANG - Senior VP Operations
STANLEY LIU - VP Operations
BRYAN LIM - VP Information Systems
HECTOR CORONEL - VP Strategy
HELEN LIN - VP Operations
ROBERT LUSTIG - VP Operations, Supply Chain, Innovation, Business Development
JAYE YOUNG - VP Legal
DAVE RITTENBERRY - VP Real Estate
DAVID WANG - Executive Director Construction
CALEB MITSVOTAI - Executive Director Information Systems
ANI AVANESSIAN - Executive Director Human Resources
ROGER GOLDSTEIN - Executive Director Facility/Maintenance
BRIAN JARVIS - Executive Director Business Development
SHAUN JACKSON - Executive Director Risk Management
MIKE EVERAGE - Executive Director Real Estate
DORA LEE - Executive Director Employee Development
ED LODGEN - Executive Director Legal, Real Estate
ALBERTO RIVASPLATA - Executive Director Tax
ELAINE S. BARTLETT - Creative Director
LUTHER KWOK - Director Event Planning, Catering
CHRIS FUNG - Director Security
GABY ABIKHALIL - Director Construction
ELIZABETH HOLLENDONER - Director Human Resources
JEFFREY LO - Director Information Systems, Security
HAKIM YALA - Director Construction
FANNY HU - Director Purchasing
ALAN CHEUNG - Director Information Technology
TOM LYKINS - Director
JIMMY WANG - Director Innovation
DAVID KIM - Director Legal
KIM MILLER - Director Development
KEVIN YANG - Director Operations
CHRIS POPE - Director Architecture, Design
ANDRES ORTIZ - Director Human Resources
SUNIL MIRPURI - Director Human Resources
TOBY SELOADJI - Director Supply Chain, International
NIKHIL PATEL - Director Finance
AMANDA CHEN - Regional Director Operations
SEAN CHUAH - Regional Director Operations
JUAN CERDA - Regional Director Operations
LILY LIU - Regional Director Operations
JENNY CHEA - Senior Manager Human Resources
MANEE COE - Senior Manager Human Resources
BRUCE HEARD - Senior Manager Operations
ELIZABETH WU - Senior Manager Human Resources
XING MING - Senior Manager Information Systems; Client Services
GREG PENA - Senior Manager
LAURA LUND - Regional Manager Real Estate
JAIME DE BEERS - Manager Facility/Maintenance, Loss Prevention
PRISCILLA AMARO - Manager
SALI BARAKAT - Manager Human Resources
HARVEY CHEN - Manager
NOLAN DYO - Manager
JASON HURST - Manager Security
DANIEL LOZANO - Manager
NICK MYERS - Manager Innovation, International
HILL ZHOU - Manager Information Technology
ADRIANNA DELGADO - Manager Legal
JOHN DIBERNARDO - Manager Real Estate
DIANA HUANG - Brand Manager Marketing, Communications
MALY MANALANG - Senior Project Manager Information Technology
DOROTHY SHIH - Project Manager Information Systems
CATHERINE DAM - Project Manager Information Technology, Systems
SHASHANK DHOND - Project Manager Information Systems, Area
STEVE BLEVINS CRFP - Project Manager

Adventist Health
2100 Douglas Blvd
Roseville, CA 95661-3804

Telephone: (916) 781-2000
Fax Number: (916) 774-3326
Internet Homepage: adventisthealth.org
Type of Business: Foodservice Management Operator
Year Founded: 1973
Total Sales: $46,791,000 (e)
Number of Employees: 200
Number of Locations Served: 17
Total Foodservice Mgmt Accounts: 17
Areas of Operation: CA
Type of Foodservice: Cafeteria (17)
Foodservice Management Venues: Health Care
Primary Distributors: (Full Line) US Foods, CORONA, CA

Key Personnel
JOYCE NEWMEYER - CEO; President
RYAN ASHLOCK - President
TODD HOFHEINS - COO
JOYCE NEWMYER - Chief People Officer
JENNIFER STEMMLER - Chief Digital Officer
TIFFANY ETTEDGUI - Area Director Information Technology
JOHN BEAMAN - VP Finance
MICHAEL NELSON - VP Technology, People
PATRICK MILLER - Director Technology, Applications
DAVID NASH - Director Information Technology, Area
AHMAD KAKAR - Director Information Technology
RYAN LOWN - Director Network
RAMAN SINGH - Director Operations
VICTOR POLSTON - Director Technology
MARILYN LITTY - Manager Data Quality
DAN COOK - Manager Information Technology
CHRIS FLANNERY - Program Manager
MATTHEW EASTERBROOK - Administrator Information Systems
KATIE WEEDMAN - Administrator Information Systems
KATIE SILVA - Specialist Human Resources
STEVEN FELTY - Coordinator Human Resources
PETER HOLLISTER - Analyst Information Systems
CRISTINA MATEO - Analyst Applications

Beach Hut LLC
2220 Douglas Blvd Ste 180
Roseville, CA 95661-3822

Telephone: (916) 749-0257
Internet Homepage: beachhutdeli.com
Type of Business: Chain Restaurant Operator
Year Founded: 1981
Systemwide Sales: $15,683,000 (e)
Total Sales: $1,909,000 (e)
Alcohol Sales: 5%
Internet Order Processing: Yes
Total Units: 43
Trade Names: Beach Hut Deli (43)
Units Franchised To: 43
Preferred Square Footage: 1,200; 1,800; 2,200
Preferred Location Types: Community Mall; Freestanding; Lifestyle Center
Alcohol Served: Beer
Primary Menu: Sandwiches/Deli (43)
Projected Openings: 2
Areas of Operation: CA, NV, OR, TX
Type of Foodservice: Fast Casual (43)
Catering Services: Yes

Key Personnel
MONICA LYNCH - CFO; Corporate Secretary
DAVID REEVES - COO; General Buyer
JUSTIN BROWN - Manager Operations

J.M.J. Seekers, Inc.
424 Vernon St
Roseville, CA 95678-2637

Telephone: (916) 789-9350
Company Email: jmjseekers@gmail.com
Type of Business: Chain Restaurant Operator
Total Sales: $27,860,000 (e)
Number of Employees: 240
Total Units: 6
Trade Names: McDonald's (6)
Units Franchised From: 6
Preferred Square Footage: 2,500
Preferred Location Types: Discount Dept. Stores; Freestanding
Primary Menu: Hamburger (6)
Areas of Operation: CA
Type of Foodservice: Quick Serve (6)
Franchise Affiliation: McDonald's Corporation, CHICAGO, IL

Key Personnel
MAX RUIZ - Owner; General Buyer

Aureflam Corporation
1420 Fulton Ave Ste B
Sacramento, CA 95825-3616

Telephone: (916) 779-8800
Fax Number: (916) 484-3837
Internet Homepage: phohoa.com
Company Email: contact@phohoa.com
Type of Business: Chain Restaurant Operator
Year Founded: 1983
Systemwide Sales: $82,502,000 (e)
Total Sales: $9,422,000 (e)
Number of Employees: 300
Average Check: Lunch(8); Dinner(12)
Total Units: 67
Trade Names: Pho Hoa (67)
Company-Owned Units: 13
Units Franchised To: 54
Preferred Square Footage: 2,000; 3,000; 4,000
Preferred Location Types: Freestanding; Regional Mall
Primary Menu: Asian (67)
Areas of Operation: CA, FL, MA, MN, NC, UT, WA, FC, AB, BC
Foreign Countries: CANADA; INDONESIA; MACAO; MALAYSIA; SINGAPORE; SOUTH KOREA; THE PHILIPPINES
Type of Foodservice: Fast Casual (67)
On-site Distribution Center: Yes
Primary Distributors: (Full Line) Reinhart FoodService, AUSTELL, GA
Notes: Also operates as South Bay Soup Corporation. This company is the largest Vietnamese restaurant chain in North America.

Key Personnel
QUOC PHAN - CEO; President; CFO; Executive Chef; Manager Real Estate; General Buyer
SINICH P. KEM - Director Operations
CHUNG NGUYEN - Director Operations

D.G. Smith Enterprises
5435 Madison Ave
Sacramento, CA 95841-3111

Telephone: (916) 338-7770
Fax Number: (916) 338-7766
Type of Business: Chain Restaurant Operator
Year Founded: 1985
Total Sales: $85,490,000 (e)
Number of Employees: 225
Average Check: Lunch(8); Dinner(8)
Total Units: 31
Trade Names: Taco Bell (31)
Units Franchised From: 31
Preferred Square Footage: 2,100
Preferred Location Types: Freestanding
Primary Menu: Taco (31)
Areas of Operation: CA
Type of Foodservice: Quick Serve (31)
Franchise Affiliation: Taco Bell Corp., IRVINE, CA
Primary Distributors: (Full Line) McLane/Riverside, RIVERSIDE, CA

Key Personnel
DAVID SMITH - President; General Manager; Director Operations, Facility/Maintenance, Real Estate, Design; General Buyer

Fat City Inc.
2500 Natomas Park Dr
Sacramento, CA 95833-2938

Telephone: (916) 441-4184
Fax Number: (916) 447-3900
Internet Homepage: fatsrestaurants.com; lovemyfats.com
Company Email: info@fatsrestaurants.com
Type of Business: Chain Restaurant Operator
Year Founded: 1973
Total Sales: $16,074,000 (e)
Alcohol Sales: 25%
Number of Employees: 300
Average Check: Lunch(18); Dinner(24)
Total Units: 4
Trade Names: Fat City Bar & Cafe (1); Fat's Asia Bistro (2); Frank Fat's (1)
Company-Owned Units: 4
Preferred Location Types: Freestanding
Alcohol Served: Beer, Wine, Liquor
Primary Menu: American (1); Asian (3)
Areas of Operation: CA
Type of Foodservice: Casual Dining (4)
Catering Services: Yes
Primary Distributors: (Full Line) SYSCO Food Services of Sacramento Inc., PLEASANT GROVE, CA

Key Personnel
JERRY FAT - CEO; President; Partner; Treasurer
COLLIN FAT - Partner; Director Operations, Food and Beverage
KEVIN FAT - COO; VP
TROY BALLARD - Controller
MICHAEL TRIGLIA - General Manager
NGOC TRUONG - General Manager
JEFFREY RYAN - General Manager
VICKI SCOTT - Manager
LINDA CHIELLI - Manager Catering

Fire Wings
1700 15th St
Sacramento, CA 95811

Telephone: (916) 243-7159
Internet Homepage: firewings.com
Type of Business: Chain Restaurant Operator
Year Founded: 2015
Total Sales: $6,234,000 (e)

Total Units: 28
Trade Names: Fire Wings (28)
Units Franchised To: 28
Primary Menu: Chicken (28)
Projected Openings: 20
Areas of Operation: CA, NV, TX
Type of Foodservice: Fast Casual (28)

Key Personnel
BILLY PHONG - Owner
DAVID TRAN - Manager Branch

Godlove Enterprises Inc
4121 Marconi Ave
Sacramento, CA 95821-4213

Telephone: (916) 482-8467
Fax Number: (916) 484-7219
Type of Business: Chain Restaurant Operator
Total Sales: $43,250,000 (e)
Total Units: 9
Trade Names: McDonald's (9)
Units Franchised From: 9
Primary Menu: Hamburger (9)
Areas of Operation: CA
Type of Foodservice: Quick Serve (9)
Franchise Affiliation: McDonald's Corporation, CHICAGO, IL

Key Personnel
MICHAEL GODLOVE - President

Jack's Urban Eats LLC
1230 20th St
Sacramento, CA 95811-4204

Telephone: (916) 444-0307
Internet Homepage: jacksurbaneats.com
Company Email: contact@jacksurbaneats.com
Type of Business: Chain Restaurant Operator
Total Units: 12
Trade Names: Jack's Urban Eats (12)
Company-Owned Units: 12
Primary Menu: American (12)
Areas of Operation: CA
Type of Foodservice: Cafeteria (12)

Key Personnel
TONY BABCOCK - Partner; General Buyer
JEREMY GOEBEL - General Manager

Pizza Twist
1441 Howe Ave Suite 200
Sacramento, CA 95825

Telephone: (916) 905-5353
Internet Homepage: pizzatwist.com
Type of Business: Chain Restaurant Operator
Year Founded: 2014
Number of Employees: 1,000
Total Units: 92
Trade Names: Pizza Twist (92)
Units Franchised To: 92
Primary Menu: Pizza (92)
Projected Openings: 10
Areas of Operation: AZ, CA, ID, IL, IN, NC, NJ, NV, NY, OK, PA, TN, TX, UT, VA, WA, BC, ON
Foreign Countries: CANADA; INDONESIA
Type of Foodservice: Quick Serve (92)

Key Personnel
HARPREET DAHYIA - Director Franchising
TJ KONNER - Director Franchising

Sbm Food Corporation
7229 Stockton Blvd
Sacramento, CA 95823-2703

Telephone: (916) 392-0701
Fax Number: (916) 421-1488
Type of Business: Chain Restaurant Operator
Total Sales: $5,613,000 (e)
Average Check: Dinner(14)
Total Units: 2
Trade Names: Popeyes Louisiana Kitchen (2)
Units Franchised From: 2
Primary Menu: Chicken (2)
Areas of Operation: CA
Type of Foodservice: Quick Serve (2)
Franchise Affiliation: Popeyes Louisiana Kitchen Inc., ATLANTA, GA

Key Personnel
DAVID W. MARQUEZ - President; General Buyer
DENNIS TURCO - VP

Thai Basil
2431 J St
Sacramento, CA 95816-4805

Telephone: (916) 442-7690
Fax Number: (916) 442-7681
Internet Homepage: thaibasilrestaurant.com; vegmidtown.com
Company Email: thaibasilmidtown@mac.com
Type of Business: Chain Restaurant Operator
Year Founded: 1995
Total Sales: $6,266,000 (e)
Number of Employees: 25
Average Check: Lunch(10); Dinner(14)
Internet Order Processing: Yes
Total Units: 4
Trade Names: Thai Basil (3); Veg Cafe (1)
Company-Owned Units: 4
Alcohol Served: Beer, Wine
Primary Menu: Thai (4)
Areas of Operation: CA
Type of Foodservice: Casual Dining (4)
Catering Services: Yes

Primary Distributors: (Food) SYSCO Food Services of Los Angeles Inc., WALNUT, CA

Key Personnel
RAMON RAFFS - Partner; General Manager; General Buyer
WANNI RAFFS - Partner; Executive Chef; Director Catering; General Buyer
SULEKA SUN-LINDLEY - Partner
WANNIPA SUNUNSANGTHONG - Partner; Executive Chef; General Buyer

World of Good Tastes
8109 Fruitridge Rd Ste 1
Sacramento, CA 95820-6750

Telephone: (916) 386-1515
Fax Number: (916) 387-8929
Internet Homepage: labou.com
Company Email: customerservice@labou.com
Type of Business: Chain Restaurant Operator
Year Founded: 1981
Systemwide Sales: $16,458,000 (e)
Total Sales: $31,760,000 (e)
Alcohol Sales: 100%
Number of Employees: 300
Average Check: Lunch(8); Dinner(12)
Total Units: 14
Trade Names: La Bou Bakery & Cafe (14)
Units Franchised To: 14
Preferred Square Footage: 6,000
Preferred Location Types: Freestanding; Regional Mall; Strip Mall
Primary Menu: American (14)
Areas of Operation: CA
Type of Foodservice: Casual Dining (14)
Catering Services: Yes
Primary Distributors: (Food) Tony's Fine Foods, WEST SACRAMENTO, CA; (Supplies) Cresco Restaurant Equipment, SACRAMENTO, CA

Key Personnel
TRONG NGUYEN - CEO; President; Owner; Manager Operations, Purchasing, Facility/Maintenance, Advertising, Real Estate, Design; General Buyer
ANNIE NGO - VP Operations; Executive Chef; Supervisor Human Resources

Meadowood Napa Valley Resort
900 Meadowood Ln
Saint Helena, CA 94574-9620

Telephone: (707) 963-3646
Fax Number: (707) 963-3532
Internet Homepage: meadowood.com
Company Email: amconover@meadowood.com

Type of Business: Foodservice Operations - Hotel/Motels
Year Founded: 1982
Total Sales: $19,318,000 (e)
Alcohol Sales: 10%
Number of Employees: 25
Average Check: Breakfast(20); Lunch(34); Dinner(72)
Total Units: 1
Restaurants in Hotels: 2
Trade Names: Meadowood Napa Valley (1)
Company-Owned Units: 2
Preferred Square Footage: 5,000
Preferred Location Types: Hotel/Motel
Alcohol Served: Beer, Wine, Liquor
Primary Menu: Californian (2)
Areas of Operation: CA
Type of Foodservice: Casual Dining (1); Fine Dining (1)
Catering Services: Yes
Primary Distributors: (Full Line) US Foods - San Diego, VISTA, CA

Key Personnel
CHRISTOPHER KOSTOW - Executive Chef; General Buyer

Gary and Becky Vick Inc
40 Winham St
Salinas, CA 93901-3315

Telephone: (831) 796-0105
Type of Business: Chain Restaurant Operator
Total Sales: $17,320,000 (e)
Total Units: 8
Trade Names: Carl's Jr. (8)
Units Franchised From: 8
Primary Menu: Hamburger (8)
Areas of Operation: CA
Type of Foodservice: Quick Serve (8)
Franchise Affiliation: Carl's Jr., FRANKLIN, TN

Key Personnel
GARY VICK - President; General Buyer

Baker's Burgers
1875 Business Center Dr Ste 100
San Bernardino, CA 92408-3416

Telephone: (909) 884-7241
Fax Number: (909) 885-4059
Internet Homepage: bakersdrivethru.com
Company Email: bakers@bakersdrivethru.com
Type of Business: Chain Restaurant Operator
Year Founded: 1952
Total Sales: $77,817,000 (e)
Number of Employees: 1,626
Average Check: Breakfast(8); Lunch(8); Dinner(8)
Total Units: 39
Trade Names: Baker's Drive-Thru (39)

Company-Owned Units: 39
Preferred Square Footage: 2,000; 3,000; 5,000
Preferred Location Types: Freestanding
Primary Menu: Hamburger (39)
Areas of Operation: CA
Type of Foodservice: Quick Serve (39)

Key Personnel
MIKE WILSON - Manager Facility/Maintenance

Juan Pollo Inc.
383 S J St
San Bernardino, CA 92410

Telephone: (909) 885-6324
Fax Number: (909) 381-3175
Internet Homepage: juanpollo.com
Company Email: info@juanpollo.com
Type of Business: Chain Restaurant Operator
Year Founded: 1984
Total Sales: $46,080,000 (e)
Number of Employees: 500
Average Check: Lunch(12); Dinner(28)
Total Units: 28
Trade Names: Juan Pollo (28)
Company-Owned Units: 3
Units Franchised To: 25
Preferred Square Footage: 3,000
Preferred Location Types: Freestanding
Primary Menu: Chicken (28)
Areas of Operation: CA
Type of Foodservice: Quick Serve (28)
Catering Services: Yes
Distribution Centers: SAN BERNARDINO, CA
On-site Distribution Center: Yes

Key Personnel
ALBERT OKURA - President; Controller; Director Finance, Purchasing, Facility/Maintenance, Marketing, Real Estate, Design, Store Planning
LILIA RAMOS - Director Operations, Information Systems, Risk Management, Human Resources
MELANIE WILLE - Manager

Yogurtland Franchisee
4235 University Pkwy Ste 103
San Bernardino, CA 92407-7039

Telephone: (909) 683-6053
Type of Business: Chain Restaurant Operator
Total Sales: $2,094,000 (e)
Total Units: 2
Trade Names: Yogurtland (2)
Units Franchised From: 2
Primary Menu: Snacks (2)
Areas of Operation: CA
Type of Foodservice: Quick Serve (2)
Franchise Affiliation: Yogurtland Franchising

Inc., FARMERS BRANCH, TX

Key Personnel
TOBIAS MILLER - Owner; General Buyer

Central California Connection, LLC
899 Cherry Ave
San Bruno, CA 94066-2949

Telephone: (650) 583-6491
Fax Number: (650) 583-6492
Type of Business: Chain Restaurant Operator
Year Founded: 1984
Total Sales: $519,860,000 (e)
Number of Employees: 2,575
Average Check: Breakfast(8); Lunch(10); Dinner(12)
Total Units: 239
Trade Names: Carl's Jr. (43); Carl's Jr./Green Burrito (98)
Units Franchised From: 239
Preferred Square Footage: 2,500
Preferred Location Types: Downtown; Freestanding
Primary Menu: Hamburger (239)
Projected Openings: 14
Areas of Operation: CA
Type of Foodservice: Quick Serve (239)
Foodservice Management Venues: Schools
Franchise Affiliation: Carl's Jr., FRANKLIN, TN
Primary Distributors: (Full Line) McLane/Rocky Mount, ROCKY MOUNT, NC

Key Personnel
JEFF CASARETTO - Partner; VP Operations; Director Operations, Security, Inventory, Loss Prevention, Risk Management, Quality Assurance, Real Estate, Human Resources, Food Safety
C. THOMAS THOMPSON - Partner; Director Finance; General Buyer
SHABBIR SIDDIQUI - VP Region
MIKE REDMOND - Director Operations

Tai Wah, Inc
590 El Camino Real
San Bruno, CA 94066-4347

Telephone: (650) 588-8344
Fax Number: (650) 616-9397
Type of Business: Chain Restaurant Operator
Total Sales: $38,250,000 (e)
Total Units: 12
Trade Names: IHOP (12)
Units Franchised From: 12
Primary Menu: American (12)
Areas of Operation: CA
Type of Foodservice: Family Restaurant (12)
Franchise Affiliation: IHOP Restaurant

System, GLENDALE, CA

Key Personnel
CHRISTOPHER HSIUNG - President

Avenir Restaurant Group
716 Laurel St Ste 2
San Carlos, CA 94070-3155

Telephone: (650) 631-8813
Fax Number: (650) 631-8816
Internet Homepage: avenir-rg.com
Company Email: contact@avenirrestaurants.com
Type of Business: Chain Restaurant Operator
Year Founded: 1993
Total Sales: $4,460,000 (e)
Alcohol Sales: 30%
Number of Employees: 350
Average Check: Lunch(22); Dinner(36)
Total Units: 3
Trade Names: Milagros (1); NOLA (1); Town (1)
Company-Owned Units: 3
Preferred Location Types: Freestanding
Alcohol Served: Beer, Wine, Liquor
Primary Menu: American (1); Mexican (1); Steak/Seafood (1)
Areas of Operation: CA
Type of Foodservice: Casual Dining (1); Fine Dining (2)

Key Personnel
GREG ST. CLAIRE - President; Owner; General Manager
KRISTIN BONDS - Controller; Manager Finance, Information Systems
MICHELLE MONTERROSA - Manager Operations-Beverages

Evolution Hospitality LLC
1211 Puerta Del Sol Ste 170
San Clemente, CA 92673-6353

Telephone: (949) 325-1350
Fax Number: (949) 325-1349
Internet Homepage: evolutionhospitality.com
Company Email: info@evolutionhospitality.com
Type of Business: Foodservice Operations - Hotel/Motels
Year Founded: 1976
Total Sales: $229,920,000 (e)
Alcohol Sales: 12%
Number of Employees: 3,400
Total Units: 25
Restaurants in Hotels: 25
Trade Names: Comfort Inn (1); Courtyard (5); Desert Princess Golf Resort (1); DoubleTree by Hilton (2); Fairfield Inn (1); Hampton Inn (1); Hard Rock Hotel(1); Hilton (2); Holday Inn (1); Homewood Suites (1); Hotel Adagio (1); Hotel MDR (1); Hyatt (1); Jolly Roger Inn (1); Marriott (1); Padre Trail Inn (1); Portofino Inn & Suites (1); Queen Mary (1); The Anza (1)
Company-Owned Units: 25
Alcohol Served: Beer, Wine, Liquor
Areas of Operation: CA
Type of Foodservice: Casual Dining (1); Fine Dining (10)
Primary Distributors: (Food) SYSCO Food Services of Los Angeles Inc., WALNUT, CA
Notes: The company derives approximately 87% of its revenue from hotel operations.

Key Personnel
WILL LOUGHRAN - Senior VP Operations
MARY-CATHERINE SEXTON - Senior VP Human Resources
JON EYER - Executive Chef
KONSTANTIONOS LALIOTIS - Director Food and Beverage

Oggi's Pizza & Brewing Co.
1245 Puerta Del Sol
San Clemente, CA 92673-6310

Telephone: (949) 218-3961
Fax Number: (949) 481-0845
Internet Homepage: oggis.com
Company Email: contactus@oggis.com
Type of Business: Chain Restaurant Operator
Year Founded: 1991
Systemwide Sales: $28,233,000 (e)
Total Sales: $3,387,000 (e)
Alcohol Sales: 25%
Number of Employees: 65
Average Check: Lunch(20); Dinner(24)
Internet Order Processing: Yes
Total Units: 15
Trade Names: Oggis (15)
Company-Owned Units: 1
Units Franchised To: 14
Preferred Location Types: Downtown; Freestanding
Alcohol Served: Beer, Wine, Liquor
Primary Menu: Italian (15)
Areas of Operation: AZ, CA
Type of Foodservice: Casual Dining (15)
Catering Services: Yes

Key Personnel
JOHN HADJIS - Partner; VP; Director Menu Development; General Buyer
ESTELLA FERRERA - VP Marketing, Sales

Pedro's Tacos
2313 S El Camino Real
San Clemente, CA 92672-3256

Telephone: (949) 498-5904
Internet Homepage: pedrostacos.com
Type of Business: Chain Restaurant Operator
Total Units: 4
Trade Names: Pedro's Tacos (4)
Company-Owned Units: 2
Units Franchised To: 2
Primary Menu: Taco (4)
Areas of Operation: CA
Type of Foodservice: Quick Serve (4)

Key Personnel
ED MCNARY - Owner; General Buyer

Atlas Hotels Inc.
500 Hotel Cir N
San DiEgo, CA 92108-3005

Telephone: (619) 291-7131
Fax Number: (619) 291-3584
Internet Homepage: towncountry.com
Type of Business: Foodservice Operations - Hotel/Motels
Year Founded: 1955
Total Sales: $59,505,000 (e)
Alcohol Sales: 14%
Number of Employees: 900
Total Units: 1
Restaurants in Hotels: 3
Trade Names: Town and Country Resort (1)
Company-Owned Units: 3
Alcohol Served: Beer, Wine, Liquor
Areas of Operation: CA
Type of Foodservice: Casual Dining (3)
Primary Distributors: (Food) SYSCO Food Services of San Diego Inc., POWAY, CA
Notes: The company derives approximately 80% of its revenue from hotel operations.

Key Personnel
PAUL MCCABE - Executive Chef
APRIL SHUTE - Director Area, Region

Burger Lounge
1917 India St Ste C
San DiEgo, CA 92101

Telephone: (858) 456-0196
Internet Homepage: burgerlounge.com
Company Email: info@burgerlounge.com
Type of Business: Chain Restaurant Operator
Total Sales: $22,420,000 (e)
Total Units: 25
Trade Names: Burger Lounge (25)
Company-Owned Units: 25
Primary Menu: Hamburger (25)
Areas of Operation: CA, NV
Type of Foodservice: Fast Casual (25)
Parent Company: KarpReilly LLC, GREENWICH, CT

Key Personnel
DEAN LORING - President; General Manager; General Buyer

TIMOTHY ESCOVER - Area Director
DANIEL HOFFMAN - Director Information Technology
KELLY MCCRAY - Director Employee Development

Busalacchi Restaurants
1917 India St
San DiEgo, CA 92101-2250

Telephone: (619) 238-1917
Internet Homepage: busalacchirestaurants.com
Type of Business: Chain Restaurant Operator
Total Sales: $4,655,000 (e)
Alcohol Sales: 12%
Average Check: Dinner(18)
Total Units: 2
Trade Names: Busalacchi's (2)
Company-Owned Units: 2
Alcohol Served: Beer, Wine, Liquor
Primary Menu: Italian (2)
Areas of Operation: CA
Type of Foodservice: Casual Dining (2)

Key Personnel
JOE BUSALACCHI - Partner; Executive Chef; General Buyer
JOEY BUSALACCHI - General Manager

Champagne French Bakery Cafe
11925 Carmel Mountain Rd
San DiEgo, CA 92128

Telephone: (858) 613-7767
Internet Homepage: champagnebakery.com
Company Email: contactus@champagnebakery.com
Type of Business: Chain Restaurant Operator
Year Founded: 1987
Total Sales: $15,510,000 (e)
Alcohol Sales: 20%
Number of Employees: 200
Average Check: Breakfast(12); Lunch(16); Dinner(22)
Internet Order Processing: Yes
Total Units: 7
Trade Names: Champagne French Bakery Cafe (7)
Company-Owned Units: 7
Preferred Square Footage: 5,500; 6,000
Preferred Location Types: Freestanding; Regional Mall; Strip Mall
Primary Menu: French/Continental (7)
Areas of Operation: CA
Type of Foodservice: Casual Dining (7)
Catering Services: Yes
Primary Distributors: (Full Line) US Foods-San Francisco, LIVERMORE, CA

Key Personnel
RON WILLIAMS - Controller
IAN REISCHL SR - Director Operations

Cohn Restaurant Group
2225 Hancock St
San DiEgo, CA 92110-2033

Telephone: (619) 236-1299
Fax Number: (619) 236-1300
Internet Homepage: dinecrg.com
Company Email: contactus@dinecrg.com
Type of Business: Chain Restaurant Operator
Year Founded: 1989
Total Sales: $94,730,000 (e)
Alcohol Sales: 25%
Number of Employees: 2,392
Average Check: Lunch(36); Dinner(54)
Internet Order Processing: Yes
Total Units: 26
Trade Names: 333 Pacific (1); BO Beau (4); Castaway Cafe (1); Coaster Saloon (1); Coasterra (1); Coin Haus (1); Con Pane (1); Corvette Diner (1); Del's Hideout (1); Draft Republic (2); Island Prime (1); Libertad Tacos (1); Pacific Social (1); Sea 180 Coastal Tavern (1); Surf Rider Pizza Co. (1); Tea Pavilion (1);The Melting Pot (1); The Plantation House (1); The Prado (1); Vin De Syrah (1); Vintana (1); Zig Zag Pizza (1)
Company-Owned Units: 26
Preferred Square Footage: 2,000; 8,000
Preferred Location Types: Downtown; Freestanding; Hotel/Motel; Mobile Unit; Parks
Alcohol Served: Beer, Wine, Liquor
Primary Menu: American (6); Bar-B-Q (1); Californian (2); French/Continental (3); Japanese (1); Mexican (2); Miscellaneous (3); Pizza (1); Seafood (1); Southwest/Tex-Mex (1); Steak (2); Steak/Seafood (2)
Areas of Operation: CA, HI
Type of Foodservice: Casual Dining (26)
Primary Distributors: (Food) SYSCO Food Services of San Diego Inc., POWAY, CA

Key Personnel
LESLEY COHN - Co-Founder; Partner
DAVID COHN - President; Partner; Director Finance, Real Estate, Research & Development, Menu Development; General Buyer
JEREMY COHN - Partner
JESSICA COHN - Partner
PATTI URTADO - General Manager
FRANCESCO DOMINGUEZ - General Manager
ESTRELLA GEIDNER - General Manager
MIKE SUTTLES - Corporate Chef
JAMES STEPHENSON - Executive Chef; Manager Operations
ANDREW HENKEMEYER - Director Beverages
LILY JOYA - Manager Food and Beverage
DEBORAH LAMOUREUX - Manager Operations
JAMES LAMOUREUX - Manager Operations
LAUREN PETERSEN - Manager Catering
JEFF PITTROF - Manager Operations
JONATHAN BOYLE - Manager Operations
MARIO CORTEZ - Manager Event Planning

Epic Wings
8660 Rio San Diego Dr Suite 102
San DiEgo, CA 92108

Telephone: (619) 230-5998
Internet Homepage: epicwingsnthings.com
Type of Business: Chain Restaurant Operator
Year Founded: 1982
Systemwide Sales: $24,068,000 (e)
Total Sales: $19,110,000 (e)
Total Units: 24
Trade Names: Epic Wings (24)
Company-Owned Units: 23
Units Franchised To: 1
Primary Menu: Chicken (24)
Projected Openings: 39
Areas of Operation: AZ, CA
Type of Foodservice: Quick Serve (24)

Key Personnel
DAVID GROSSMAN - CEO; President

Farooqi Restaurant Management, Inc.
4751 El Cajon Blvd
San DiEgo, CA 92115-4520

Telephone: (619) 583-6942
Type of Business: Chain Restaurant Operator
Total Sales: $32,800,000 (e)
Total Units: 13
Trade Names: Jack in the Box (13)
Units Franchised From: 13
Primary Menu: Hamburger (13)
Areas of Operation: CA
Type of Foodservice: Quick Serve (13)
Franchise Affiliation: Jack in the Box Restaurants, SAN DIEGO, CA

Key Personnel
NASIR FAROOQI - Owner; General Buyer

Filippi's Pizza Grottos
9969 Mira Mesa Blvd
San DiEgo, CA 92131-1065

Telephone: (858) 695-1441
Fax Number: (858) 695-8591
Internet Homepage: realcheesepizza.com
Type of Business: Chain Restaurant Operator
Year Founded: 1950
Total Sales: $26,790,000 (e)
Alcohol Sales: 12%
Number of Employees: 460

Average Check: Lunch(10); Dinner(20)
Total Units: 15
Trade Names: Filippi's Pizza Grottos (15)
Company-Owned Units: 15
Preferred Square Footage: 4,000
Preferred Location Types: Community Mall; Freestanding
Alcohol Served: Beer, Wine, Liquor
Primary Menu: Pizza (15)
Areas of Operation: CA
Type of Foodservice: Casual Dining (15)
Primary Distributors: (Full Line) US Foods, CORONA, CA

Key Personnel
ALFRED DEPHILIPPIS - Partner; VP
KAREN DEPHILIPPIS - General Manager
DAN MOCERI - Manager Purchasing

GSAHTC, Inc.
6906 Miramar Rd
San DiEgo, CA 92121-2666

Telephone: (858) 527-7140
Type of Business: Chain Restaurant Operator
Total Sales: $6,887,000 (e)
Total Units: 5
Trade Names: Jersey Mike's Subs (5)
Units Franchised From: 5
Primary Menu: Sandwiches/Deli (5)
Areas of Operation: CA
Type of Foodservice: Quick Serve (5)
Franchise Affiliation: Jersey Mike's Franchise Systems, MANASQUAN, NJ

Key Personnel
TYLOR RASMUSSEN - Director Operations, Training

Hotcakes Inc.
8400 Juniper Creek Ln
San DiEgo, CA 92126

Telephone: (858) 695-2440
Fax Number: (858) 695-2861
Type of Business: Chain Restaurant Operator
Year Founded: 1989
Total Sales: $95,370,000 (e)
Number of Employees: 674
Average Check: Breakfast(8); Lunch(8); Dinner(8)
Total Units: 30
Trade Names: IHOP Restaurant (30)
Units Franchised From: 30
Preferred Square Footage: 4,400; 5,000
Preferred Location Types: Freestanding
Primary Menu: American (30)
Areas of Operation: CA
Type of Foodservice: Family Restaurant (30)
Franchise Affiliation: IHOP Restaurant

System, GLENDALE, CA

Key Personnel
ROBERT ROSENBERG - CEO; Partner
MICHAEL SZAWIELENKO - President; Partner; Director Finance, Operations, Real Estate; General Buyer
TERESITA MONTON-DEL VALLE - General Manager
CHARLES CARUAL - Director Operations
JENNIFER STEGER - Director Information Systems, Human Resources

J.S. Foods, Inc.
9350 Waxie Way Ste 560
San DiEgo, CA 92123-1056

Telephone: (858) 642-0064
Fax Number: (858) 642-1932
Type of Business: Chain Restaurant Operator
Year Founded: 1978
Total Sales: $71,100,000 (e)
Number of Employees: 450
Average Check: Breakfast(8); Lunch(10); Dinner(12)
Total Units: 32
Trade Names: Burger King (32)
Units Franchised From: 32
Preferred Square Footage: 3,000
Preferred Location Types: Freestanding
Primary Menu: Hamburger (32)
Areas of Operation: CA
Type of Foodservice: Quick Serve (32)
Franchise Affiliation: Burger King Worldwide Inc., MIAMI, FL
Primary Distributors: (Full Line) McLane/Riverside, RIVERSIDE, CA

Key Personnel
JULIAN JOSEPHSON - President; Director Purchasing, Real Estate; General Buyer
TONY STOKES - VP Operations
ISHMEL GONZALEZ - Manager Distribution

Jack in the Box Inc.
9357 Spectrum Center Blvd
San DiEgo, CA 92123

Telephone: (858) 571-2121
Fax Number: (858) 571-2101
Internet Homepage: jackinthebox.com
Company Email: info@jackinthebox.com
Type of Business: Chain Restaurant Operator
Year Founded: 1951
Systemwide Sales: $5,530,430,000 (e)
Publicly Held: Yes
Total Sales: $1,735,053,000 (e)
Alcohol Sales: 0.50%
Number of Employees: 22,000
Total Units: 2,778
Trade Names: Del Taco (592); Jack in the Box (2,186)
Company-Owned Units: 313
Units Franchised To: 2,465
Preferred Location Types: Airports; Convenience Store/Gas Station; Downtown; Freestanding; Lifestyle Center; Office Complex; Other; Outlet Mall; Regional Mall; Strip Mall; Travel Plazas
Alcohol Served: Beer, Wine, Liquor
Primary Menu: Hamburger (2,186); Taco (592)
Projected Openings: 30
Areas of Operation: AK, AR, AZ, CA, CO, CT, DC, DE, FL, GA, HI, IA, ID, IL, IN, KS, KY, LA, MA, MD, ME, MI, MN, MO, MS, MT, NC, ND, NE, NJ, NM, NV, NY, OH, OK, OR, PA, SC, SD, TN, TX, UT, VA, WA, WI, WV, WY, ON
Foreign Countries: CANADA
Type of Foodservice: Quick Serve (2,778)
Headquarter Offices: Del Taco Restaurants Inc., LAKE FOREST, CA
Notes: Jack in the Box Inc. agreed to sell its fast-casual Qdoba Restaurant Corp. to Apollo Global Management LLC in a $305 million deal which closed in March 2018

Key Personnel
DAWN HOOPER - CFO Interim; Senior VP; Principal Finance
KEVIN CARROLL - COO
STEVE PIANO - Chief People Officer
DOUG COOK - CTO; Senior VP
RYAN OSTROM - Chief Marketing Officer
TIM LINDERMAN - Chief Development Officer; Senior VP
SARAH SUPER - Chief Legal Officer; Senior VP
TERRENCE WEEKES - Chief Information Security Officer
DEAN GORDON - Chief Supply Chain Officer; Senior VP
ANNA GABELE - VP Marketing, Innovation
RUDY ROBLES - VP Operations
TIM FREE - Director Operations
KATHY KOVACEVICH - Director Communications
MARK BECKERMAN - Director Franchising
KIM SKOLNICK - Senior Manager Training, Business Development
SIMEON BRETT - Manager Information Technology
SUE BURTCHETT - Manager Design
MIKIM LUU - Manager Product Development
CINDY PERSON - Manager Franchising
KYLE MARTIN - Manager Facility/Maintenance
HEIDI LAMBERT - Manager Real Estate
CAROL WOOD - Coordinator Human Resources
AIMEE THORNE - Coordinator Accounting
MARILEE SANTOS - Designer Graphic Design
KARINE YEREVANIAN-LACY - Senior Analyst Finance

Karl Strauss Breweries
5985 Santa Fe St
San DiEgo, CA 92109-1623

Telephone: (858) 273-2739
Fax Number: (858) 581-5691
Internet Homepage: karlstrauss.com
Company Email: karl@karlstrauss.com
Type of Business: Chain Restaurant Operator
Year Founded: 1989
Total Sales: $23,740,000 (e)
Alcohol Sales: 40%
Number of Employees: 780
Average Check: Lunch(12); Dinner(12)
Internet Order Processing: Yes
Internet Sales: 1.00%
Total Units: 11
Trade Names: Karl Strauss Brewery Gardens (1); Karl Strauss Brewery Restaurant (10)
Company-Owned Units: 11
Preferred Square Footage: 5,500; 6,000
Preferred Location Types: Freestanding; Strip Mall
Alcohol Served: Beer, Wine, Liquor
Primary Menu: American (11)
Areas of Operation: CA
Type of Foodservice: Casual Dining (11)
On-site Distribution Center: Yes
Primary Distributors: (Food) US Foods - San Diego, VISTA, CA

Key Personnel
CHRISTOPHER CRAMER - CEO
MATTHEW RATTNER - President; Director Facility/Maintenance, Real Estate, Design
COLLEEN HARVEY - CFO
CHAD HEATH - VP Marketing, Sales

Kelly Companies
12730 High Bluff Dr Ste 250
San DiEgo, CA 92130

Telephone: (619) 687-5000
Internet Homepage: kellycompanies.com; foxandhound.com
Type of Business: Chain Restaurant Operator
Total Sales: $68,680,000 (e)
Total Units: 81
Trade Names: Brick House Tavern + Tap (9); Bubba Gump (1); Champps Kitchen & Bar (4); Claim Jumper (24); Craft Republic Bar & Grill (3); Fox and Hound Bar & Grill (12); Grady's Bar-B-Q (4); Guac Amigos (1); Joe's Crab Shack (7); Kings Family Restaurant (14); Lucky Bastard (1); McCormick & Schmick's Seafood & Steaks (1)
Company-Owned Units: 81
Primary Menu: American (67); Bar-B-Q (4); Seafood (9)
Type of Foodservice: Casual Dining (67); Family Restaurant (14)

Headquarter Offices: Fox & Hound Restaurant Group, DALLAS, TX; Grady's Bar-B-Q, NORTH VERSAILLES, PA

Key Personnel
MICHAEL KELLY - CEO
ERIC LOFGRAN - Senior VP

McDonalds Franchise
8929 Clairemont Mesa Blvd
San DiEgo, CA 92123-1103

Telephone: (858) 569-8386
Fax Number: (858) 259-0538
Type of Business: Chain Restaurant Operator
Total Sales: $41,550,000 (e)
Number of Employees: 400
Average Check: Breakfast(8); Lunch(8); Dinner(8)
Total Units: 9
Trade Names: McDonald's (9)
Units Franchised From: 9
Preferred Square Footage: 2,500; 3,000
Preferred Location Types: Freestanding
Primary Menu: Hamburger (9)
Areas of Operation: CA
Type of Foodservice: Quick Serve (9)
Franchise Affiliation: McDonald's Corporation, CHICAGO, IL
Primary Distributors: (Food) The Martin-Brower Co., CITY OF INDUSTRY, CA

Key Personnel
RAMZI AWAD - Owner; General Buyer

MZM Foods, Inc.
1905 Garnet Ave
San DiEgo, CA 92109-3523

Telephone: (310) 341-9696
Type of Business: Chain Restaurant Operator
Total Sales: $22,600,000 (e)
Total Units: 9
Trade Names: Jack in the Box (9)
Units Franchised From: 9
Primary Menu: Hamburger (9)
Areas of Operation: CA
Type of Foodservice: Quick Serve (9)
Franchise Affiliation: Jack in the Box Restaurants, SAN DIEGO, CA

Key Personnel
ZAKARIA SAMAAN - Partner; General Buyer

NuYo Frozen Yogurt, Inc.
2172 Blackmore Ct
San DiEgo, CA 92109-1420

Mailing Address: PO Box 2823, GRANITE BAY, CA, 95746
Telephone: (916) 780-1333
Fax Number: (619) 342-8533
Internet Homepage: nuyofrozenyogurt.com
Company Email: corporate@nuyofrozenyogurt.com
Type of Business: Chain Restaurant Operator
Total Sales: $1,720,000 (e)
Number of Employees: 35
Total Units: 5
Trade Names: NuYo Frozen Yogurt (5)
Company-Owned Units: 2
Units Franchised To: 3
Primary Menu: Snacks (5)
Areas of Operation: CA
Type of Foodservice: Quick Serve (5)

Key Personnel
MACKENZIE HARDER - CEO; President; General Buyer

Out West Restaurant Group, Inc.
8885 Rio Suite 360
San DiEgo, CA 92108

Telephone: (858) 456-2703
Fax Number: (858) 456-1302
Internet Homepage: outwestrg.com
Type of Business: Chain Restaurant Operator
Year Founded: 1992
Total Sales: $566,920,000 (e)
Alcohol Sales: 20%
Number of Employees: 5,000
Average Check: Dinner(24)
Total Units: 104
Trade Names: Outback Steakhouse (104)
Units Franchised From: 104
Preferred Square Footage: 6,200
Preferred Location Types: Freestanding; Strip Mall
Alcohol Served: Beer, Wine, Liquor
Primary Menu: Steak (104)
Areas of Operation: AZ, CA, CO, NM, NV
Type of Foodservice: Casual Dining (104)
Franchise Affiliation: Outback Steakhouse Restaurants, TAMPA, FL
Parent Company: H.I.G. Capital LLC, MIAMI, FL
Notes: Previously T-Bird Restaurant Group.

Key Personnel
DAVID GORONKIN - CEO
STEVE MUHLBAUM - COO
JENNIFER SMALL - Director Leasing
SUZANNE MANKOUSKI - Director Human Resources
MATTHEW VITORINO - Director Financial Planning
DOUG SOUTHIDA - Manager Information Technology
ROCHELLE PRESTON - Coordinator Real

Estate
KYLE LUCAS - Analyst Financial Planning

Paradigm Investment Group, LLC
4510 Executive Dr Ste 330
San DiEgo, CA 92121-3082

Telephone: (858) 458-9748
Fax Number: (866) 783-4079
Internet Homepage: paradigminvest.com
Type of Business: Chain Restaurant Operator
Year Founded: 1999
Total Sales: $180,620,000 (e)
Number of Employees: 2,500
Average Check: Breakfast(8); Lunch(8); Dinner(8)
Total Units: 94
Trade Names: Blaze Pizza (10); Hardee's (81); Jersey Mike's (3)
Units Franchised From: 94
Preferred Square Footage: 3,000; 3,500
Preferred Location Types: Freestanding
Primary Menu: Hamburger (81); Pizza (10); Sandwiches/Deli (3)
Projected Openings: 3
Areas of Operation: AL, FL, LA, MS, TN
Type of Foodservice: Fast Casual (10); Quick Serve (84)
Subsidiaries: JMTX, LLC, AMARILLO, TX
Franchise Affiliation: Blaze Pizza LLC, PASADENA, CA; Hardee's Food Systems Inc., FRANKLIN, TN; Jersey Mike's Franchise Systems, MANASQUAN, NJ
Primary Distributors: (Food) McLane/Lagrange, LAGRANGE, GA

Key Personnel
DON WOLLAN - President; General Buyer
ADRIAN DE LA ROSA - COO
GREG MAY - CTO
DOMINIQUE ROBERTS - Director Operations
ANN CAULEY - Director Operations
SUSAN DUCK - Director
JOSH HARRISON - District Manager
TOMMY CARTER - District Manager
HEATH HOLDER - Manager Information Technology

Paragon Hospitality Enterprises
2445 Hotel Circle Pl
San DiEgo, CA 92108-2813

Telephone: (619) 291-8074
Fax Number: (619) 291-5168
Internet Homepage: huntersteakhouse.com
Company Email: missionvalley@huntersteakhouse.com
Type of Business: Chain Restaurant Operator
Total Sales: $8,227,000 (e)
Alcohol Sales: 19%
Number of Employees: 120
Average Check: Lunch(16); Dinner(34)
Total Units: 2
Trade Names: Hunter Steakhouse (2)
Company-Owned Units: 2
Preferred Location Types: Freestanding
Alcohol Served: Beer, Wine, Liquor
Primary Menu: Steak (2)
Areas of Operation: CA
Type of Foodservice: Fine Dining (2)
Catering Services: Yes
Primary Distributors: (Full Line) US Foods Holding Corp., ROSEMONT, IL

Key Personnel
MIKE SCHNEIDER - Owner; VP Operations, Marketing; General Buyer
JOHN ROSSOTTO - General Manager
KIRK SHUMATE - Assistant Manager

PKD Raj & Associates, Inc.
2401 Truxtun Rd Ste 103
San DiEgo, CA 92106-6149

Telephone: (619) 221-8291
Type of Business: Chain Restaurant Operator
Total Sales: $1,302,000 (e)
Total Units: 2
Trade Names: Cold Stone Creamery (2)
Units Franchised From: 2
Primary Menu: Snacks (2)
Areas of Operation: CA
Type of Foodservice: Quick Serve (2)
Franchise Affiliation: Kahala Brands, SCOTTSDALE, AZ

Key Personnel
AJAY SHAH - Partner
PUNITA SHAH - Partner

Poke Go
3614 5th Ave
San DiEgo, CA 92103-4220

Telephone: (619) 230-5549
Internet Homepage: pokesd.com
Company Email: info@pokesd.com
Type of Business: Chain Restaurant Operator
Year Founded: 2015
Total Units: 2
Trade Names: Poke Go (2)
Company-Owned Units: 2
Primary Menu: American (2)
Areas of Operation: CA
Type of Foodservice: Fast Casual (2)

Key Personnel
CHRIS PARK - Owner; General Buyer

Premier Food Concepts, LLC
9255 Towne Centre Dr Ste 950
San DiEgo, CA 92121-3067

Telephone: (858) 450-1188
Fax Number: (858) 450-1186
Internet Homepage: lunagrill.com
Type of Business: Chain Restaurant Operator
Year Founded: 2005
Total Sales: $107,030,000 (e)
Number of Employees: 492
Total Units: 51
Trade Names: Luna Grill (51)
Company-Owned Units: 51
Preferred Location Types: Freestanding; Regional Mall; Strip Mall
Alcohol Served: Beer, Wine
Primary Menu: Greek/Mediterranean (51)
Projected Openings: 10
Areas of Operation: CA, TX
Type of Foodservice: Fast Casual (51)

Key Personnel
SEAN POURTEYMOUR - Co-Founder; CEO; Partner
RICH PINNELLA - President
MARIA POURTEYMOUR - Partner; COO; Executive Chef
BOB BARTLETT - CFO
STEVE HOLLIDAY - COO
BILLY GRENHAM - Chief Marketing Officer
GREG THORBURN - VP Real Estate
ROBERT KACZMARCZYK - Director Operations, West Region
SUZANNE MANKOUSKI - Director Human Resources
JACK AHRENS - Director Technology
DOMINICK DELEONE - District Manager
SHAUN-CASEY REYES - Manager Human Resources

Puesto Mexican Restaurants
789 W Harbor Dr
San DiEgo, CA 92101

Telephone: (619) 233-8880
Internet Homepage: eatpuesto.com
Company Email: hello@eatpuesto.com
Type of Business: Chain Restaurant Operator
Total Units: 6
Trade Names: Puesto Mexican Restaurants (6)
Company-Owned Units: 6
Primary Menu: Mexican (6)
Areas of Operation: CA
Type of Foodservice: Casual Dining (6)

Key Personnel
ERIC ADLER - Partner; General Buyer

ISIDORO LOMBROZO - Partner; General Buyer
ALAN ADLER - Partner
LUISTEEN GONZALEZ - Partner; Executive Chef

Qdoba Mexican Eats
350 Camino de La Reina Suite 400
San DiEgo, CA 92108

Telephone: (866) 500-0094
Fax Number: (720) 898-2396
Internet Homepage: qdoba.com
Type of Business: Chain Restaurant Operator
Year Founded: 1995
Systemwide Sales: $1,028,981,000 (e)
Total Sales: $815,702,000 (e)
Alcohol Sales: 2%
Number of Employees: 3,800
Average Check: Lunch(14); Dinner(14)
Total Units: 778
Trade Names: Qdoba Mexican Grill (778)
Company-Owned Units: 233
Units Franchised To: 545
Preferred Square Footage: 2,200; 2,400
Preferred Location Types: Freestanding; Lifestyle Center; Outlet Mall; Regional Mall; Strip Mall
Alcohol Served: Beer, Liquor
Primary Menu: Mexican (778)
Projected Openings: 35
Areas of Operation: AK, AR, AZ, CA, CO, CT, DC, DE, FL, GA, IA, ID, IL, IN, KS, KY, LA, MA, MD, ME, MI, MN, MO, MS, MT, NC, ND, NE, NH, NJ, NM, NV, NY, OH, OK, OR, PA, RI, SC, SD, TN, TX, UT, VA, WA, WI, WV, WY, FC, MB, ON
Foreign Countries: CANADA
Type of Foodservice: Fast Casual (778)
Catering Services: Yes
Primary Distributors: (Full Line) Shamrock Foods Colorado Division, COMMERCE CITY, CO
Parent Company: Apollo Global Management LLC, NEW YORK, NY

Key Personnel
KEVIN CARROLL - COO
PAM JOHNSON - Chief Human Resources Officer
JEREMY VITARO - Chief Development Officer
CHARLES SEIGEL III - Chief Legal Officer; Corporate Secretary
PAUL SINOWITZ - Chief Supply Chain Officer
JILL ADAMS - Senior VP Marketing
SANJAY SHASTRI - VP Human Resources
KATY VELAZQUEZ - Executive Chef
GARY BURGESS - Director Infrastructure, Security
BRIAN URANOWSKI - Director Distribution, Logistics
LAURIE MACALUSO - Director Development
KYLE MOSES - Director Development-Training
KARAN GOGRI - Director Operations
PAULINE CASTANEDA - Director Procurement
BRIAN COLE - Director Catering
MATTHEW GRISWOLD - Senior Manager
JESUS ALVAREZ - Senior Manager Safety, Risk Management, Asset Protection
JENIFER DAY-LAKE - Regional Manager Catering
ALEXANDRIA EVANS - Manager
EVA GALA - Manager
LARA AUBIN - Manager Purchasing
MICHAEL LAGMAN - Manager Information Technology-Help Desk
CHRISTOPHER THEILEN - Manager Media
PHAYZON TRICE - Manager Software; Developer
JANET VOUGA - Manager Franchising
MARCY MURPHY - Senior Project Manager

Rockin' Baja Inc.
310 5th Ave
San DiEgo, CA 92101-6910

Telephone: (619) 234-6333
Fax Number: (619) 234-6372
Internet Homepage: rockinbaja.com
Company Email: comments@rockinbaja.com
Type of Business: Chain Restaurant Operator
Year Founded: 1983
Total Sales: $15,040,000 (e)
Alcohol Sales: 20%
Average Check: Lunch(30); Dinner(42)
Total Units: 6
Trade Names: Rockin' Baja Coastal Cantina (6)
Company-Owned Units: 6
Preferred Location Types: Freestanding; Strip Mall
Alcohol Served: Beer, Wine, Liquor
Primary Menu: Seafood (6)
Areas of Operation: CA
Type of Foodservice: Casual Dining (6)

Key Personnel
RICK DIRIENZO - Owner
ELFA FRANCO - Executive Chef; General Buyer
ADRIAN HINOJOSA - Director Operations
STEVEN ROBERTS - Director

San Diego Restaurant Management Co.
831 W Harbor Dr
San DiEgo, CA 92101-7707

Telephone: (619) 232-0292
Fax Number: (619) 232-7981
Internet Homepage: edgewatergrill.com; harborhouse-sandiego.com; piercafe.com
Company Email: manager@harborhousesd.com
Type of Business: Chain Restaurant Operator
Year Founded: 1980
Total Sales: $10,124,000 (e)
Alcohol Sales: 10%
Number of Employees: 500
Average Check: Lunch(24); Dinner(30)
Total Units: 3
Trade Names: Egdewater Grill (1); Harbor House Marina San Diego (1); San Diego Pier Cafe (1)
Company-Owned Units: 3
Preferred Square Footage: 3,500; 20,000
Preferred Location Types: Freestanding
Alcohol Served: Beer, Wine, Liquor
Primary Menu: Steak/Seafood (3)
Areas of Operation: CA
Type of Foodservice: Casual Dining (3)

Key Personnel
LOUIS REZZONICO - Chairman; Director Facility/Maintenance, Real Estate, Construction, Design, Store Planning
MIKE FRY - CEO; President; CFO; Controller; Director Finance, Risk Management
KEN COOKE - Executive Chef; Manager Menu Development
JOE NADER - Executive Chef

SeaWorld of California
500 Sea World Dr
San DiEgo, CA 92109-7904

Telephone: (619) 222-6363
Fax Number: (619) 226-3996
Company Email: comments@seaworldsandiego.com
Listing Type: Divisional Office
Type of Business: Foodservice Operations - Theme Parks
Year Founded: 1957
Total Units: 8
Areas of Operation: CA
Parent Company: SeaWorld Entertainment Inc., ORLANDO, FL

Key Personnel
MARILYN HANNES - President
MARC SWANSON - CFO
G. ANTHONY TAYLOR - Chief Legal Officer; Corporate Secretary; General Counsel
CHRIS DODD - Chief Talent Officer
ANDREW NGO - VP Culinary Operations
VALERIE PUGH - Director Human Resources
MITCHEL WILSON - Director Marketing
THOMAS SIECK - Manager Culinary Operations

Simsim Outstanding Shawarma
11640 Carmel Mountain Rd
San DiEgo, CA 92128

Telephone: (858) 618-5948
Internet Homepage: eatsimsim.com

Type of Business: Chain Restaurant Operator
Year Founded: 2018
Total Units: 2
Trade Names: Simsim Outstanding Shawarma (2)
Company-Owned Units: 2
Primary Menu: Greek/Mediterranean (2)
Areas of Operation: CA
Type of Foodservice: Fast Casual (2)

Key Personnel
ALI ALMATROUK - Co-Founder
HASAN ALMATROUK - Co-Founder
IBRAHIM ALSHARIEF - Executive Chef

Subway Development of San Diego
6863 Friars Rd Ste 200
San DiEgo, CA 92108-1121

Telephone: (619) 688-9255
Fax Number: (619) 688-9291
Type of Business: Chain Restaurant Operator
Year Founded: 1983
Total Sales: $7,445,000 (e)
Number of Employees: 4,140
Average Check: Lunch(10); Dinner(12)
Total Units: 13
Trade Names: Subway (13)
Units Franchised From: 13
Preferred Square Footage: 1,500
Preferred Location Types: Freestanding; Strip Mall
Primary Menu: Sandwiches/Deli (13)
Projected Openings: 10
Areas of Operation: CA
Type of Foodservice: Quick Serve (13)
Foodservice Management Venues: Schools
Franchise Affiliation: Doctor's Associates Inc., MILFORD, CT
Primary Distributors: (Full Line) Saladino's Inc., FRESNO, CA

Key Personnel
RAGHU MARWAHA - CEO

Tajima Restaurant Group
4681 Convoy St
San DiEgo, CA 92111-2330

Telephone: (858) 576-7244
Internet Homepage: tajimasandiego.com
Type of Business: Chain Restaurant Operator
Year Founded: 2001
Total Units: 7
Trade Names: Tajima (7)
Company-Owned Units: 7
Primary Menu: Japanese (7)
Areas of Operation: CA
Type of Foodservice: Casual Dining (7)

Key Personnel
ISAMU MORIKIZONO - Owner

The Baked Bear
4516 Mission Blvd STE C
San DiEgo, CA 92109

Telephone: (858) 886-7433
Internet Homepage: thebakedbear.com
Company Email: info@thebakedbear.com
Type of Business: Chain Restaurant Operator
Year Founded: 2013
Total Units: 25
Trade Names: The Baked Bear (25)
Company-Owned Units: 2
Units Franchised To: 23
Primary Menu: Snacks (25)
Projected Openings: 7
Areas of Operation: AL, AZ, CA, MD, MO, OK, TX
Type of Foodservice: Quick Serve (25)

Key Personnel
SHANE STANGER - Co-Founder; President; Partner; General Buyer
ROBBIE ROBBINS - Co-Founder; Partner

The Bali Hai Restaurant
2230 Shelter Island Dr
San DiEgo, CA 92106-3108

Telephone: (619) 222-1181
Fax Number: (619) 222-4081
Internet Homepage: balihairestaurant.com; tomhamslighthouse.com
Company Email: sbbalihai@aol.com
Type of Business: Chain Restaurant Operator
Year Founded: 1971
Total Sales: $7,882,000 (e)
Alcohol Sales: 22%
Number of Employees: 130
Average Check: Lunch(12); Dinner(20)
Total Units: 2
Trade Names: Bali Hai Restaurant (1); Tom Ham's Lighthouse (1)
Company-Owned Units: 2
Preferred Location Types: Freestanding
Alcohol Served: Beer, Wine, Liquor
Primary Menu: Asian (1); Steak/Seafood (1)
Areas of Operation: CA
Type of Foodservice: Casual Dining (1); Fine Dining (1)
Primary Distributors: (Full Line) SYSCO Food Services of San Diego Inc., POWAY, CA

Key Personnel
LARRY BAUMANN - Partner
TOM BAUMANN - General Manager; General Buyer
GRANT BAUMANN - General Manager; General Buyer
DION MORALES - Executive Chef; General Buyer

The Brigantine Restaurant Corp.
7889 Ostrow St
San DiEgo, CA 92111-3602

Telephone: (858) 268-1030
Fax Number: (858) 268-5727
Internet Homepage: brigantine.com; miguels-cocina.com
Company Email: info@brigantine.com
Type of Business: Chain Restaurant Operator
Year Founded: 1969
Total Sales: $44,900,000 (e)
Alcohol Sales: 30%
Number of Employees: 900
Average Check: Breakfast(12); Lunch(26); Dinner(42)
Internet Order Processing: Yes
Internet Sales: 1.00%
Total Units: 14
Trade Names: Brigantine Restaurant (8); Miguel's Cocina (6)
Company-Owned Units: 14
Preferred Square Footage: 6,000; 10,000
Preferred Location Types: Community Mall; Freestanding; Strip Mall
Alcohol Served: Beer, Wine, Liquor
Primary Menu: Mexican (6); Seafood (8)
Areas of Operation: CA
Type of Foodservice: Casual Dining (6); Family Restaurant (8)
Catering Services: Yes
Primary Distributors: (Full Line) SYSCO Food Services of Los Angeles Inc., WALNUT, CA

Key Personnel
MIKE MORTON SR - Chairman
MIKE MORTON JR - CEO; President; Director Real Estate
PATRICK WALSH - General Manager
MATT MORTON - Director Store Fixtures
JACOB MCBRIDE - Director Menu Development
MICHELLE HORN - Director Sales

The Broken Yolk Cafe
1851 Garnet Ave
San DiEgo, CA 92109-3353

Telephone: (858) 740-9554
Internet Homepage: thebrokenyolkcafe.com
Company Email: info@thebrokenyolkcafe.com
Type of Business: Chain Restaurant Operator
Total Units: 31
Trade Names: Broken Yolk Cafe (32)
Company-Owned Units: 32

Primary Menu: American (32)
Projected Openings: 7
Areas of Operation: CA, FL, IL
Type of Foodservice: Casual Dining (32)

Key Personnel
JOHN GELASTOPOULOS - President
DIMITRA O'ROURKE - VP Franchising

The Crack Shack
2266 Kettner Blvd
San DiEgo, CA 92101

Telephone: (619) 795-3299
Internet Homepage: crackshack.com
Company Email: info@crackshack.com
Type of Business: Chain Restaurant Operator
Year Founded: 2015
Total Units: 5
Trade Names: The Crack Shack (5)
Company-Owned Units: 5
Primary Menu: Chicken (5)
Projected Openings: 1
Areas of Operation: CA
Type of Foodservice: Fast Casual (5)

Key Personnel
MICHAEL ROSEN - CEO; Partner
RICHARD BLAIS - Partner
NICOLE ROGERS - Director Marketing

TKS Restaurants, LLC
630 9th Avenue
San DiEgo, CA 92101

Telephone: (619) 525-0055
Internet Homepage: thekebabshop.com
Company Email: info@thekebabshop.com
Type of Business: Chain Restaurant Operator
Total Units: 14
Trade Names: The Kebab Shop (14)
Company-Owned Units: 14
Primary Menu: Middle Eastern (14)
Areas of Operation: CA
Type of Foodservice: Fast Casual (14)

Key Personnel
ANTHONY FARMAND - Co-Founder; Partner; COO
ARIAN BARYALAI - CEO; CFO
AJMAL AKBAR - Partner; Chief Development Officer
OMAR NAZIHI - VP Operations

Urban Kitchen Group
505 Laurel St
San DiEgo, CA 92101-1634

Telephone: (619) 239-2222
Internet Homepage: urbankitchengroup.com
Type of Business: Chain Restaurant Operator
Year Founded: 1995
Total Sales: $12,630,000 (e)
Alcohol Sales: 35%
Number of Employees: 60
Average Check: Lunch(10); Dinner(26)
Total Units: 5
Trade Names: Cuccina Enoteca -Del Mar (1); Cucina Enoteca - Newport Beach (1); Cucina Enoteca -Irvine (1); Cucina Sorella Kensington (1); Cucina Urbana - Banker's Hill (1)
Company-Owned Units: 5
Preferred Location Types: Freestanding
Alcohol Served: Beer, Wine, Liquor
Primary Menu: Italian (5)
Areas of Operation: CA
Type of Foodservice: Fine Dining (5)
Catering Services: Yes
Primary Distributors: (Food) US Foods - San Diego, VISTA, CA
Notes: Company also operates a catering business under the name of Urban Kitchen Catering.

Key Personnel
TRACY BORKUM - Owner; General Manager; Executive Chef; Principal; General Buyer
JOE MAGNANELLI - Executive Chef

Yogurtland Franchisee
8872 Navajo Rd Unit 20
San DiEgo, CA 92119-2100

Telephone: (619) 464-1339
Type of Business: Chain Restaurant Operator
Total Sales: $2,108,000 (e)
Total Units: 2
Trade Names: Yogurtland (2)
Units Franchised From: 2
Primary Menu: Snacks (2)
Areas of Operation: CA
Type of Foodservice: Quick Serve (2)
Franchise Affiliation: Yogurtland Franchising Inc., FARMERS BRANCH, TX

Key Personnel
RAGHU ROHIT - Owner; General Buyer

Zoological Society of San Diego
2920 Zoo Dr
San DiEgo, CA 92101-1646

Mailing Address: PO Box 120551, SAN DIEGO, CA, 92112-0551
Telephone: (619) 231-1515
Fax Number: (619) 557-3970
Internet Homepage: sandiegozoo.org; shopzoo.com
Company Email: publicrelations@sandiegozoo.org
Type of Business: Foodservice Operations - Theme Parks
Year Founded: 1916
Total Sales: $22,630,000 (e)
Alcohol Sales: 5%
Number of Employees: 459
Average Check: Lunch(8); Dinner(8)
Internet Order Processing: Yes
Internet Sales: 1.00%
Total Units: 17
Trade Names: Albert's (1); Front Street Cafe (1); Hua Mei Cafe (1); Ituri Hut (1); Jungle Java (1); Kettle Corn (1); Lagoon Terrace (1); Poppy's Patio (1); Rocks Box (1); Sabertooth Grill (1); Safari Kitchen (1); San Diego Sandwich Co. (1); Sydney's Grill (1); The Bridge (1); The Pagoda (1); Treetops Cafe (1); Zoo Brew(1)
Company-Owned Units: 17
Preferred Square Footage: 2,500; 5,500; 6,000
Preferred Location Types: Parks
Alcohol Served: Beer, Wine, Liquor
Primary Menu: Coffee (1); Mexican (1); Sandwiches/Deli (1); Snacks (8)
Areas of Operation: CA
Type of Foodservice: Cafeteria (2); Quick Serve (14)
Primary Distributors: (Food) US Foods-Los Angeles, LA MIRADA, CA; (Supplies) San Diego Restaurant Supply, SAN DIEGO, CA
Notes: Total sales represents foodservice operations only.

Key Personnel
DOUGLAS G. MYERS - CEO
DAVID FRANCO - CFO
TED MOLTER - Chief Marketing Officer; Director Marketing
DAVID MILLER - Chief Marketing Officer
LIANNE HEDDITCH - VP Communications
EAMONN FARRELL - VP Construction
DAVID PAGE - Controller; Director Finance, Accounting
ROY MAYOR - Director Marketing
BOB DILLON - Director Operations
DONNA DAMSON - Director Government Affairs
J.D. PARRISH - Director Human Resources
BRAD WILLIAMS - Director Operations, Information Technology, Global
KELLY CRAIG - Assistant Director Corporate Affairs
DENISE CABALLERO - Associate Director Payroll
DAMIEN LASATER - Associate Director Marketing
STEPHANIEJ CRISE - Senior Manager Human Resources
JUDI BOWES - Manager Marketing
MELISSA DIMARTINO - Manager E-Commerce
CHRISTINE METCALF - Manager Merchandising
MICHELLE SNOW - Manager Accounting

JOHN PUENTE - Manager Applications
KIMBERLY TURNER - Manager Design
MELISSA RUSSO - Manager Procurement
SUE SINCAVAGE - Coordinator Inventory

Foothill Pizza Inc
702 E Foothill Blvd Ste 2
San DiMas, CA 91773

Telephone: (909) 592-2806
Type of Business: Chain Restaurant Operator
Total Sales: $10,315,000 (e)
Total Units: 5
Trade Names: Domino's (5)
Units Franchised From: 5
Primary Menu: Pizza (5)
Areas of Operation: CA
Type of Foodservice: Quick Serve (5)
Franchise Affiliation: Domino's Pizza Inc, ANN ARBOR, MI

Key Personnel
BRUCE GIBSON - CEO; General Buyer

Klatch Roasting
806 W Arrow Hwy Ste A
San DiMas, CA 91773-2497

Telephone: (909) 599-0452
Internet Homepage: klatchroasting.com
Type of Business: Chain Restaurant Operator
Total Sales: $4,693,000 (e)
Total Units: 6
Trade Names: Klatch Coffee (6)
Company-Owned Units: 6
Preferred Location Types: Strip Mall
Primary Menu: Coffee (6)
Areas of Operation: CA
Type of Foodservice: Quick Serve (6)

Key Personnel
MIKE PERRY - CEO
CINDY PERRY - CFO
HOLLY PERRY - Director Retail Operations

Absinthe Group
368 Hayes St
San Francisco, CA 94102-4421

Telephone: (415) 864-2693
Fax Number: (415) 864-2794
Internet Homepage: arlequincafe.com; comstocksaloon.com; absinthe.com; bellotasf.com; barcinosf.com
Company Email: EAT@ABSINTHEGROUP.COM
Type of Business: Chain Restaurant Operator
Year Founded: 1998
Total Sales: $21,554,000 (e)
Alcohol Sales: 30%
Number of Employees: 90
Average Check: Breakfast(10); Lunch(22); Dinner(54)
Total Units: 4
Trade Names: Absinthe Brasserie & Bar (1); Barcino (1); Bellota Spanish Restaurant (1); Comstock Saloon (1)
Company-Owned Units: 4
Preferred Location Types: Downtown; Freestanding
Alcohol Served: Beer, Wine, Liquor
Primary Menu: American (1); French/Continental (1); Spanish (2)
Areas of Operation: CA
Type of Foodservice: Casual Dining (3); Fine Dining (1)
Catering Services: Yes
Primary Distributors: (Food) Greenleaf Produce, BRISBANE, CA

Key Personnel
BILL RUSSELL-SHAPIRO - Owner; General Buyer
ERIC VREEDE - VP Operations
KAT WOMER - Director Catering

Alioto's Fish Co.
360 Jefferson St Ste A
San Francisco, CA 94133-1108

Telephone: (415) 673-8300
Fax Number: (415) 931-6792
Internet Homepage: aliotos.com; waterfrontsf.com
Company Email: info@aliotos.com
Type of Business: Chain Restaurant Operator
Year Founded: 1928
Total Sales: $10,576,000 (e)
Alcohol Sales: 25%
Number of Employees: 350
Average Check: Lunch(14); Dinner(20)
Total Units: 2
Trade Names: Alioto's (1); Waterside Cafe (1)
Company-Owned Units: 2
Preferred Location Types: Strip Mall
Alcohol Served: Beer, Wine, Liquor
Primary Menu: Italian (1); Seafood (1)
Areas of Operation: CA
Type of Foodservice: Casual Dining (2)
On-site Distribution Center: Yes
Primary Distributors: (Full Line) BiRite Foodservice Distributors, BRISBANE, CA

Key Personnel
NUNZIO ALIOTO - President
TREVAR BOOKER - Manager Marketing, Public Relations, Menu Development
AL SPADARO - Manager Purchasing

Back of the House, Inc.
1829 Union St
San Francisco, CA 94123-4307

Telephone: (415) 550-8626
Internet Homepage: backofthehouseinc.com
Type of Business: Chain Restaurant Operator
Year Founded: 2009
Total Units: 28
Trade Names: a Mano (1); Barvale (1); Belga (1); Beretta (1); Delarosa (2); El Techo (1); Flores (2); Lolinda (1); Starbelly (1); Super Duper Burgers (15); The Bird (1); Uno Dos Tacos (1)
Company-Owned Units: 28
Primary Menu: American (1); French/Continental (1); Hamburger (15); Italian (1); Latin American/Cuban (1); Pizza (2); Spanish (1); Steak (1); Taco (1)
Projected Openings: 2
Areas of Operation: CA
Type of Foodservice: Casual Dining (11); Fast Casual (17)

Key Personnel
ADRIANO PAGANINI - Founder; CEO
EDMONDO SARTI - Founder; Partner
EDMUNDO ONAS - VP Operations
LESLIE WU - VP Technology, Digital Marketing
ED ONAS - Director Operations
JESSICA SPENCER-FLORES - Director Human Resources
RODRIGO MOREIRA - Director Information Technology
ISRAEL BERDOUGO - Director Operations
KHALID MUSHASHA - Director Operations
LAURA KWAN ROSENBUSH - Manager Marketing, Public Relations
KRISTINA VERNALE - Manager Accounting

Bamboo Asia
41 Montgomery St
San Francisco, CA 94104

Telephone: (415) 772-9134
Internet Homepage: bambooasia.com
Type of Business: Chain Restaurant Operator
Year Founded: 2011
Total Sales: $7,102,000 (e)
Total Units: 4
Trade Names: Bamboo Asia (4)
Company-Owned Units: 4
Primary Menu: Asian (4)
Areas of Operation: CA
Type of Foodservice: Fast Casual (4)

Key Personnel
SEBASTIAAN VAN DE RIJT - Founder; CEO
MARIELISHA GARCIA - General Manager

Beach Chalet Brewery & Restaurant
1000 Great Hwy
San Francisco, CA 94121-3268

Telephone: (415) 386-8439
Internet Homepage: beachchalet.com; parkchalet.com; honoremeryville.com; thelakechalet.com
Company Email: info@beachchalet.com
Type of Business: Chain Restaurant Operator
Year Founded: 1997
Total Sales: $14,592,000 (e)
Alcohol Sales: 10%
Number of Employees: 125
Average Check: Breakfast(8); Lunch(12); Dinner(14)
Total Units: 4
Trade Names: Beach Chalet Brewery & Restaurant (1); Honor Bar & Kitchen (1); Lake Chalet Garden Restaurant (1); Park Chalet Garden Restaurant (1)
Company-Owned Units: 4
Preferred Location Types: Freestanding
Alcohol Served: Beer, Wine, Liquor
Primary Menu: American (4)
Areas of Operation: CA
Type of Foodservice: Casual Dining (4)

Key Personnel
GAR TRUPELLI - President; Partner; General Buyer

Boba Guys
3491 19th St
San Francisco, CA 94110

Telephone: (415) 967-2622
Internet Homepage: bobaguys.com
Type of Business: Chain Restaurant Operator
Year Founded: 2013
Total Sales: $18,840,000 (e)
Total Units: 16
Trade Names: Boba Guys (16)
Company-Owned Units: 16
Areas of Operation: CA, NY

Key Personnel
BIN CHEN - Co-Founder; Partner
ANDREW CHAU - Co-Founder; Partner
KATHRYN BOWMAN - Director Finance, Operations

Boudin Bakery
50 Francisco St Ste 200
San Francisco, CA 94133-2132

Telephone: (415) 913-1849
Fax Number: (415) 913-1818
Internet Homepage: boudinbakery.com
Company Email: boudin@boudinbakery.com
Type of Business: Chain Restaurant Operator
Year Founded: 1849
Total Sales: $46,120,000 (e)
Alcohol Sales: 5%
Number of Employees: 336
Internet Order Processing: Yes
Internet Sales: 1.00%
Total Units: 23
Trade Names: Boudin Bistro (1); Boudin Sourdough Bakery & Cafe (21); Boudins Airport (1)
Company-Owned Units: 22
Preferred Square Footage: 1,800
Preferred Location Types: Airports; Community Mall; Downtown; Freestanding; Regional Mall
Alcohol Served: Beer, Wine, Liquor
Primary Menu: American (1); Sandwiches/Deli (22)
Projected Openings: 1
Areas of Operation: CA
Type of Foodservice: Casual Dining (1); Fast Casual (22)
Catering Services: Yes
Primary Distributors: (Full Line) SYSCO Food Services of San Francisco Inc., FREMONT, CA
Parent Company: GESD Capital Partners, SAN FRANCISCO, CA

Key Personnel
GAYLE DEBROSSE - Chief Brand Officer
ROBERTA BARBIERI - VP Human Resources
GENA ANDERSON - General Manager District
SIMON AMOS - General Manager
BRIAN WINSOR - Senior Director Operations
PAUL MILLER - Director Operations
DOUG ABBOTT - Director Operations
MICHAEL BAMRICK - Director Sales, Catering
DEAN C - Director Technology, Information Systems
NICOLE JACK - Manager Product Development, Catalog/Mail Order

Caffe Trieste
601 Vallejo Street
San Francisco, CA 94133

Telephone: (415) 392-6739
Internet Homepage: caffetrieste.com
Company Email: caffetriestenorthbeach@yahoo.com
Type of Business: Chain Restaurant Operator
Year Founded: 1956
Total Sales: $7,644,000 (e)
Total Units: 2
Trade Names: Caffe Trieste (2)
Company-Owned Units: 2
Primary Menu: Coffee (2)
Areas of Operation: CA
Type of Foodservice: Quick Serve (2)

Key Personnel
ADRIENNE GIOTTA - Owner
IDA PANTALEO ZOUBI - Owner

Cha Cha Cha
1801 Haight St
San Francisco, CA 94117-2711

Telephone: (415) 386-5758
Fax Number: (415) 386-0417
Internet Homepage: cha3.com
Company Email: cha3catering@gmail.com
Type of Business: Chain Restaurant Operator
Total Sales: $4,646,000 (e)
Alcohol Sales: 12%
Number of Employees: 20
Average Check: Lunch(14); Dinner(20)
Total Units: 2
Trade Names: Cha Cha Cha (2)
Company-Owned Units: 2
Preferred Location Types: Freestanding
Alcohol Served: Beer, Wine, Liquor
Primary Menu: Caribbean (2)
Areas of Operation: CA
Type of Foodservice: Casual Dining (2)
Catering Services: Yes
Primary Distributors: (Food) SYSCO Food Services of San Francisco Inc., FREMONT, CA

Key Personnel
PHILLIP HIGGINS - Owner; General Manager; Executive Chef; General Buyer

Curry Up Now
659 Valencia St
San Francisco, CA 94110-1150

Telephone: (415) 504-3631
Internet Homepage: curryupnow.com
Company Email: info@curryupnow.com
Type of Business: Chain Restaurant Operator
Year Founded: 2009
Total Units: 11
Trade Names: Curry Up Now (11)
Company-Owned Units: 11
Primary Menu: Indian (11)
Projected Openings: 10
Areas of Operation: CA
Type of Foodservice: Fast Casual (11)

Key Personnel
AKASH KAPOOR - Co-Founder; CEO
AMIR HOSSEINI - Co-Founder; VP Operations

D.O.C. Restaurant Group LLC, 7 Hills Restaurant L
2355 Chestnut St
San Francisco, CA 94123-2609

Telephone: (415) 771-2216
Internet Homepage: a16sf.com; spqrsf.com
Company Email: info@a16sf.com
Type of Business: Chain Restaurant Operator
Year Founded: 2004
Total Units: 3
Trade Names: A16 (2); SPQR (1)
Company-Owned Units: 3
Alcohol Served: Beer, Wine, Liquor
Primary Menu: Italian (3)
Areas of Operation: CA
Type of Foodservice: Casual Dining (3)

Key Personnel
SHELLEY LINDGREN - Partner; Director Alcoholic Beverages
VICTORIA LIBIN - Partner
MATTHEW ACCARRRINO - Executive Chef; General Buyer
CHRISTOPHER THOMPSON - Executive Chef
ROCKY MASELLI - Executive Chef; General Buyer
BRIAN BITTNER - Executive Chef; General Buyer

Deem Sum International Inc.
101 Spear St
San Francisco, CA 94105-1559

Mailing Address: PO Box 192960, SAN FRANCISCO, CA, 94119
Telephone: (415) 957-9990
Fax Number: (415) 957-9899
Internet Homepage: yanksing.com
Company Email: hotsauces@yanksing.com
Type of Business: Chain Restaurant Operator
Year Founded: 1988
Total Sales: $2,789,000 (e)
Alcohol Sales: 15%
Number of Employees: 50
Average Check: Lunch(14); Dinner(22)
Total Units: 2
Trade Names: Yank-Sing Dim Sum (2)
Company-Owned Units: 2
Preferred Location Types: Freestanding
Alcohol Served: Beer, Wine, Liquor
Primary Menu: Chinese (2)
Areas of Operation: CA
Type of Foodservice: Fine Dining (2)
Catering Services: Yes
Primary Distributors: (Food) Richmond Wholesale Meat Co., RICHMOND, CA

Key Personnel
HENRY CHAN - Owner; General Manager; General Buyer

Flynn Restaurant Group LLC
225 Bush St Suite 1800
San Francisco, CA 94140

Telephone: (216) 525-2775
Fax Number: (216) 328-1873
Internet Homepage: appleamerican.com; bellamerican.com; flynnrestaurantgroup.com; panamericangroup.com
Company Email: info@appleamerican.com
Type of Business: Chain Restaurant Operator
Year Founded: 1998
Total Sales: $3,980,232,000 (e)
Alcohol Sales: 6.80%
Number of Employees: 47,650
Average Check: Lunch(12); Dinner(16)
Total Units: 2,718
Trade Names: Applebee's Neighborhood Grill & Bar (461); Arby's (369); Panera Bread (127); Pizza Hut (1,202); Taco Bell (282); Wendy's Old Fashioned Hamburgers (277)
Units Franchised From: 2,718
Preferred Square Footage: 5,000
Preferred Location Types: Freestanding
Alcohol Served: Beer, Wine, Liquor
Primary Menu: American (461); Hamburger (277); Pizza (1,202); Sandwiches/Deli (496); Taco (282)
Projected Openings: 10
Areas of Operation: AL, CA, CO, DE, GA, ID, IL, IN, KY, MA, ME, MN, MO, NH, NJ, NM, NV, NY, OH, OR, PA, RI, VT, WA, WI, WV
Type of Foodservice: Casual Dining (461); Fast Casual (127); Quick Serve (2,130)
Franchise Affiliation: Applebee's Services Inc., KANSAS CITY, MO; Arby's Restaurant Group, ATLANTA, GA; Panera Bread Company, SAINT LOUIS, MO; Pizza Hut Inc., PLANO, TX; Taco Bell Corp., IRVINE, CA; The Wendy's Company, DUBLIN, OH
Primary Distributors: (Food) The SYGMA Network Inc. - Columbus, COLUMBUS, OH

Key Personnel
GREG FLYNN - Chairman; Founder; CEO; President
BILL MITCHELL - President
MARK ROMANO - President Group
LORIN CORTINA - CFO; Exec VP
RONALD BELLAMY - COO
BRAD PETTINGER - COO
RON BELLAMY - Exec VP Operations, Business Development
KELLY COOK - Senior VP Division
BO DAVIS - Senior VP Operations, Division
SARAT KONERU - Senior VP Group
JP WIEDEMER - Senior VP Finance
JOHN ROE - VP Technology
JAMES VEAZEY - VP Development
DAN KREBSBACH - VP Operations
BOB LACH - VP Real Estate
AARON KIRKMAN - VP Operations
BRENT MANGES - VP Financial Planning
KASEY MANIA - VP Procurement
BETSY MERCADO - VP Human Resources
PATRICK EULBERG - VP Real Estate
TIM FLATEY - VP Division
MIKE HEBERT - VP Operations
JEREMY BISER - VP Strategy
JEFF BARANCO - VP Operations
ADAM PIERCE - Controller; Director
JACQUELINE LEE - General Counsel
NORRIS WASHINGTON - Senior Director Licensing
JENNIFER ZIKA - Senior Director Human Resources
BRENT SALZWEDEL - Director Operations
BRIAN SHEPARD - Director Finance, Customer Analytics
KATY SIENKO - Director Operations
JASON SVEDBERG - Director Operations
DAVID LOMBARDY - Director Enterprise Solutions
GINA GHIGLIERI-FLORES - Director Operations
CHRISTOPHER GRIFFIN - Director Operations
JENNIFER LAVELLE - Director Benefits
SAL MIELE - Director Loss Prevention
BRIDGET O'BRIEN - Director Accounting
BEN ADAMS - Director Infrastructure, Networking
DOUG BACKUS - Director Applications
ANDREW CHENKUS - Director Risk Management
RON IGARASHI - Director Finance
SCOTT KELLER - Director Accounting
BETH KILPATRICK - Director Human Resources
CHRISTOPHER EUBANKS - Director Operations
GREG SWAINO - Manager Information Systems
MATT BOYNTON - Project Manager Construction
MORGAN MURRAY - Administrator Leasing

Focaccia Market & Bakery
119 Sacramento St
San Francisco, CA 94111-4001

Telephone: (415) 397-2900
Internet Homepage: focacciacatering.com
Company Email: info@focaccia.com
Type of Business: Chain Restaurant Operator
Total Units: 5
Trade Names: Focaccia (5)
Company-Owned Units: 5
Primary Menu: American (5)
Areas of Operation: CA
Type of Foodservice: Casual Dining (5)

Key Personnel
DAVID DAVARI - CEO; President
JEAN VALDES - Executive Chef

FOMO Investments LLC
555 4th St Unit 517
San Francisco, CA 94107-1626

Telephone: (725) 696-3663
Type of Business: Chain Restaurant Operator
Total Units: 5
Trade Names: The Halal Guys (5)
Units Franchised From: 5
Primary Menu: Middle Eastern (5)
Projected Openings: 2
Areas of Operation: CA, NV
Type of Foodservice: Quick Serve (5)
Franchise Affiliation: The Halal Guys Inc., ASTORIA, NY

Key Personnel
BINH TRAN - CEO; Partner
TOM NGUYEN - Partner

Gaspare's Pizza House and Italian Restaurant
5546 Geary Blvd
San Francisco, CA 94121-2209

Telephone: (415) 387-5025
Internet Homepage: gasparespizza.com
Company Email: daniel.indelicato@gmail.com
Type of Business: Chain Restaurant Operator
Year Founded: 1985
Total Units: 2
Trade Names: Gaspare's Pizza House & Italian Restaurant (1); Gaspare's Pizzeria Ristorante & Bar (1)
Company-Owned Units: 2
Alcohol Served: Beer, Wine
Primary Menu: Italian (2)
Areas of Operation: CA
Type of Foodservice: Casual Dining (2)

Key Personnel
DANIEL INDELICATO - Owner; General Buyer

Good Food Guys
99 Osgood Pl 3rd Floor
San Francisco, CA 94133

Telephone: (415) 296-8009
Internet Homepage: mixt.com; spliteats.com
Company Email: feedback@spliteats.com
Type of Business: Chain Restaurant Operator
Year Founded: 2012
Total Sales: $15,460,000 (e)
Total Units: 18
Trade Names: Mixt Greens (16); Split (2)
Company-Owned Units: 18
Primary Menu: American (2); Health Foods (16)
Projected Openings: 1
Areas of Operation: CA, TX
Type of Foodservice: Fast Casual (18)

Key Personnel
LESLIE SILVERGLIDE - Co-Founder; CEO
ANDREW SWALLOW - Co-Founder
JAKE KATZ - VP Finance, Operations
JULIO GUERRERO - VP Real Estate
SARAH EGDAL - General Counsel
GABRIELA GOMEZ - Specialist Talent Acquisitions

Java Detour Inc.
172 Golden Gate Ave
San Francisco, CA 94102

Telephone: (415) 241-8020
Fax Number: (415) 241-9120
Internet Homepage: javadetour.com
Company Email: info@javadetour.com
Type of Business: Chain Restaurant Operator
Year Founded: 1995
Systemwide Sales: $4,890,000 (e)
Total Sales: $3,887,000 (e)
Number of Employees: 34
Average Check: Breakfast(5); Lunch(5); Dinner(5)
Total Units: 9
Trade Names: Java Detour (9)
Company-Owned Units: 9
Preferred Square Footage: 650; 1,450
Preferred Location Types: Freestanding; Strip Mall
Primary Menu: Coffee (9)
Areas of Operation: CA
Type of Foodservice: Quick Serve (9)
Primary Distributors: (Full Line) SYSCO Food Services of Central California Inc., MODESTO, CA

Key Personnel
MICHAEL BINNINGER - Chairman; President; General Buyer
HARRY R. KRAATZ - CEO
GEORGE SHAW - Director Accounting
KIM KEEN - Director Human Resources

JDV Collection
530 Bush St Ste 501
San Francisco, CA 94108-3633

Telephone: (415) 835-0300
Fax Number: (415) 835-0317
Internet Homepage: jvdhotels.com
Company Email: info@jdvhospitality.com
Type of Business: Foodservice Operations - Hotel/Motels
Year Founded: 1987
Total Sales: $63,930,000 (e)
Alcohol Sales: 20%
Number of Employees: 400
Total Units: 22
Restaurants in Hotels: 22
Trade Names: Americano Restaurant & Bar (1); Aquarius (1); Bytes Cafe (1); Chambers (1); Deck33 (1); Distrito (1); El Jefe (1); Grange (1); J. Parker (1); Library Bar (1); Lodge Restaurant (1); Mums Restaurant (1); O Izakaya (1); Perennial Virant (1); Saha Restaurant (1); Swank (1); The Bungalows (1); The Deck(1); The Park Bar & Grill Restaurant (1); The Restaurant at Ventana (1); Tinto (1); Zimzala Restaurant (1)
Company-Owned Units: 22
Alcohol Served: Beer, Wine, Liquor
Areas of Operation: CA, HI
Type of Foodservice: Fast Casual (6); Fine Dining (9)
Primary Distributors: (Food) US Foods Holding Corp., ROSEMONT, IL
Parent Company: Geolo Capital, SAN FRANCISCO, CA

Key Personnel
NIKI LEONDAKIS - CEO

Keenwawa Inc
121 Spear St
San Francisco, CA 94105-1581

Telephone: (628) 333-9571
Internet Homepage: eatsa.com
Company Email: info@eatsa.com
Type of Business: Chain Restaurant Operator
Total Units: 2
Trade Names: Eatsa (2)
Company-Owned Units: 2
Primary Menu: Miscellaneous (2)
Areas of Operation: CA, DC, NY
Type of Foodservice: Fast Casual (2)

Key Personnel
SCOTT DRUMMOND - Co-Founder; Partner; Executive Chef; General Buyer
TIM YOUNG - Co-Founder; Partner; CTO

Kimpton Hotel & Restaurant Group LLC
222 Kearny St Ste 200
San Francisco, CA 94108-4537

Telephone: (415) 397-5572
Fax Number: (415) 296-8031
Internet Homepage: kimptonhotels.com
Company Email: info@kimptongroup.com
Listing Type: Subsidiary
Type of Business: Foodservice Operations - Hotel/Motels
Year Founded: 1981
Total Sales: $530,310,000 (e)
Alcohol Sales: 30%

Number of Employees: 2,240
Total Units: 70
Restaurants in Hotels: 54
Trade Names: Kimpton Hotels (70)
Company-Owned Units: 54
Alcohol Served: Beer, Wine, Liquor
Areas of Operation: AZ, CA, CO, DC, FL, IL, MA, NY, OR, TX, UT, VA, WA, BC
Foreign Countries: CANADA
Type of Foodservice: Casual Dining; Fine Dining
Primary Distributors: (Food) SYSCO Food Services of San Francisco Inc., FREMONT, CA
Parent Company: InterContinental Hotels Group (The Americas), ATLANTA, GA
Notes: The company derives approximately 65% of its revenue from hotel operations.

Key Personnel
MIKE DEFRINO - CEO
KATHLEEN REIDENBACH - Chief Commercial Officer
AVE BRADLEY - Senior VP Design
PETE KOERNER - Senior VP Member Services
CHRIS PORT - VP Development
TELESA VIA - VP Sales
SCOTT GINGERICH - Regional VP Restaurant Operations
KYLE ROURKE - Executive Chef Division
CONNOR SMITH - Senior Director Branding
CESAR HERRERA - Senior Director Construction

Kokkari Estiatorio
200 Jackson St
San Francisco, CA 94111-1806

Telephone: (415) 981-0983
Fax Number: (415) 982-0983
Internet Homepage: evvia.net; kokkari.com
Company Email: kokkari@kokkari.com
Type of Business: Chain Restaurant Operator
Year Founded: 1985
Total Sales: $19,782,000 (e)
Alcohol Sales: 30%
Number of Employees: 160
Average Check: Lunch(34); Dinner(54)
Internet Order Processing: Yes
Total Units: 2
Trade Names: Evvia Estiatorio (1); Kokkari Estiatorio (1)
Company-Owned Units: 2
Preferred Location Types: Freestanding
Alcohol Served: Beer, Wine, Liquor
Primary Menu: Greek/Mediterranean (2)
Areas of Operation: CA
Type of Foodservice: Fine Dining (2)
Primary Distributors: (Food) BiRite Foodservice Distributors, BRISBANE, CA

Key Personnel
ERIK COSSELMON - Partner; Executive Chef; General Buyer
JUDY MARCUS - Partner

La Boulangerie de San Francisco
2325 Pine St
San Francisco, CA 94115-2714

Telephone: (415) 840-4381
Internet Homepage: laboulangeriesf.com; lovingcup.com
Company Email: catering@laboulangeriesf.com
Type of Business: Chain Restaurant Operator
Year Founded: 2015
Total Sales: $9,144,000 (e)
Internet Order Processing: Yes
Total Units: 11
Trade Names: La Boulangerie de San Francisco (6); Loving Cup (5)
Company-Owned Units: 11
Primary Menu: Snacks (11)
Areas of Operation: CA
Type of Foodservice: Quick Serve (11)
Notes: La Boulangerie acquired Loving Cup, a frozen yogurt company based in San Francisco during September 2018.

Key Personnel
PASCAL RIGO - Founder; Partner; Executive Chef; General Buyer
MICHAEL STAENBERG - Partner
JAMES PARK - Partner
CRYSTAL MARQUEZ - Director Operations
ROBERT CUBBERLY - Director Product Development

Lori's Diner
500 Sutter St
San Francisco, CA 94102

Telephone: (415) 981-1950
Fax Number: (415) 981-1952
Internet Homepage: searsfinefood.com; lorisdiner.com
Company Email: info@lorisdiner.com
Type of Business: Chain Restaurant Operator
Year Founded: 1986
Total Sales: $5,346,000 (e)
Alcohol Sales: 5%
Number of Employees: 160
Average Check: Breakfast(10); Lunch(10); Dinner(18)
Total Units: 3
Trade Names: Golden Grill (1); Lori's Diner (1); Sear's Fine Foods (1)
Company-Owned Units: 3
Preferred Square Footage: 5,500; 6,000
Preferred Location Types: Airports; Freestanding
Alcohol Served: Beer, Wine
Primary Menu: American (2); Bar-B-Q (1)
Areas of Operation: CA
Type of Foodservice: Casual Dining (3)
Primary Distributors: (Full Line) BiRite Foodservice Distributors, BRISBANE, CA

Key Personnel
MAN J. KIM - Owner; Director Finance, Real Estate, Design; General Buyer
MIHO IIDA - General Manager

MAC'D
3347 Fillmore St
San Francisco, CA 94123

Internet Homepage: getmacd.com
Company Email: hello@getmacd.com
Type of Business: Chain Restaurant Operator
Year Founded: 2017
Total Units: 3
Trade Names: MAC'D (3)
Company-Owned Units: 3
Primary Menu: American (3)
Areas of Operation: CA, OR
Type of Foodservice: Fast Casual (3)

Key Personnel
CHEN-CHEN HUO - Co-Founder
LINDA BRAUN - Manager
VANESSA WILLIAMS - Supervisor

Mel's Drive-In
3355 Geary Blvd
San Francisco, CA 94118-3323

Telephone: (415) 387-2244
Fax Number: (415) 387-1259
Internet Homepage: melsdrive-in.com
Company Email: mels@att.net
Type of Business: Chain Restaurant Operator
Year Founded: 1980
Total Sales: $36,430,000 (e)
Alcohol Sales: 2%
Number of Employees: 376
Average Check: Breakfast(12); Lunch(12); Dinner(14)
Internet Order Processing: Yes
Total Units: 8
Trade Names: Mel's Drive-In (8)
Company-Owned Units: 8
Preferred Square Footage: 4,000; 5,500; 6,000
Preferred Location Types: Freestanding
Alcohol Served: Beer, Wine, Liquor
Primary Menu: American (8)
Projected Openings: 1
Areas of Operation: CA
Type of Foodservice: Casual Dining (8)
Primary Distributors: (Full Line) BiRite Foodservice Distributors, BRISBANE, CA

Key Personnel
GABRIEL MENDEZ - President; Owner; VP Information Systems, Advertising, Human Resources; Controller; General Buyer

Mina Group
244 California St Ste 410
San Francisco, CA 94111-4359

Telephone: (415) 359-0791
Fax Number: (415) 627-0981
Internet Homepage: michaelmina.net
Type of Business: Chain Restaurant Operator
Total Sales: $58,400,000 (e)
Alcohol Sales: 5%
Number of Employees: 942
Average Check: Dinner(60)
Total Units: 40
Trade Names: Bardot Brasserie (1); Bourbon Pub (2); Bourbon Steak (7); International Smoke (4); LOCALE MARKET & FARMTABLE KITCHEN (1); Margeaux Brasserie (1); Mi Almita Cantina (1); Michael Mina (2); Mina Brasserie (1); Mina's Fish House (1); Osteria Cal Mare (1); Pabu (2); Pizza & Burger (1);Pub 1842 (1); Ramen Bar (1); Restaurant Michael Mina (3); RN74 (3); Stonehill Tavern (1); Stripsteak (3); The Handle Bar (1); Trailblazer Tavern (1); Wit &Wisdom (1)
Company-Owned Units: 40
Preferred Location Types: Freestanding; Hotel/Motel
Alcohol Served: Beer, Wine, Liquor
Primary Menu: American (35); Caribbean (1); Japanese (2); Mexican (1); Steak/Seafood (1)
Areas of Operation: AZ, CA, DC, FL, HI, IL, MA, MD, NV, TN, WA, WY
Type of Foodservice: Casual Dining (16); Fine Dining (24)
Primary Distributors: (Food) SYSCO Food Services of San Francisco Inc., FREMONT, CA

Key Personnel
MICHAEL MINA - Founder; Executive Chef
JASON HIMBER - CEO
JESSICA LEE - Chief Strategy Officer
ZOE MADUROS - VP Human Resources
MARK POLITZER - VP Operations
PAULA KADUCE - Controller
GIOVANNI PUGLIESE - General Manager
NANCY ZAMMIT - General Manager
RAJ DIXIT - Executive Chef
ADAM SOBEL - Executive Chef
CORI TAHARA - Director
TAMARA VOLKER - Director Finance
STACEY MORRONE - Manager Development
JENNA STRANGE - Manager Operations

Nice Ventures, Inc.
4104 24th St
San Francisco, CA 94114-3615

Telephone: (415) 956-5596
Fax Number: (415) 956-0799
Internet Homepage: rosescafesf.com; terzosf.com; niceventures.com
Type of Business: Chain Restaurant Operator
Year Founded: 1996
Total Sales: $5,999,000 (e)
Alcohol Sales: 15%
Number of Employees: 110
Average Check: Lunch(20); Dinner(38)
Total Units: 2
Trade Names: Rose's Cafe (1); Terzo (1)
Company-Owned Units: 2
Preferred Location Types: Mixed-use Center
Alcohol Served: Beer, Wine, Liquor
Primary Menu: Italian (2)
Areas of Operation: CA
Type of Foodservice: Casual Dining (2)
Primary Distributors: (Food) A. La Rocca Sea Food Inc., SAN FRANCISCO, CA

Key Personnel
LAURIE THOMAS - CEO; President; General Buyer

OOC Inc.
1062 Folsom St
San Francisco, CA 94103-4071

Mailing Address: P O Box 20670, El Sobrante , CA, 94820
Telephone: (415) 703-8123
Fax Number: (415) 503-1633
Internet Homepage: extremepizza.com
Company Email: contactus@extremepizza.com
Type of Business: Chain Restaurant Operator
Year Founded: 1994
Systemwide Sales: $24,584,000 (e)
Total Sales: $9,020,000 (e)
Number of Employees: 447
Average Check: Lunch(12); Dinner(18)
Internet Order Processing: Yes
Internet Sales: 1.00%
Total Units: 33
Trade Names: Extreme Pizza (36)
Company-Owned Units: 8
Units Franchised To: 28
Preferred Square Footage: 1,400; 1,800; 2,500
Preferred Location Types: Downtown; Freestanding; Strip Mall
Alcohol Served: Beer, Wine
Primary Menu: Pizza (36)
Areas of Operation: CA, CO, MI, OR, VA, WA
Type of Foodservice: Fast Casual (36)
Primary Distributors: (Food) US Foods-San Francisco, LIVERMORE, CA

Key Personnel
TODD PARENT - CEO; President; General Buyer
DERRICK WILEY - VP Operations, Business Development
SUZANNE DUHIG - VP Human Resources
NICOLE LOMANACO - Director Marketing

Pan Pacific Hotel & Resorts
177 Post St Ste 800
San Francisco, CA 94108-4729

Telephone: (415) 732-5807
Fax Number: (415) 732-5800
Internet Homepage: panpacific.com
Company Email: info@panpacific.com
Type of Business: Foodservice Operations - Hotel/Motels
Year Founded: 1990
Total Sales: $720,340,000 (e)
Alcohol Sales: 25%
Number of Employees: 360
Total Units: 40
Restaurants in Hotels: 40
Trade Names: Pan Pacific Hotel & Resort (25); ParkRoyal Hotel & Resort (15)
Company-Owned Units: 40
Alcohol Served: Beer, Wine, Liquor
Areas of Operation: WA, BC
Foreign Countries: AUSTRALIA; BANGLADESH; CANADA; CHINA; INDONESIA; JAPAN; MALAYSIA; SINGAPORE; THAILAND; THE PHILIPPINES
Type of Foodservice: Casual Dining; Fine Dining
Primary Distributors: (Food) SYSCO Food Services of Los Angeles Inc., WALNUT, CA
Parent Company: Hotel Plaza Ltd., SINGAPORE, CHN
Notes: The company derives approximately 70% of its revenue from hotel operations; all but four of their locations are located in Asia.

Key Personnel
CHOE PENG SUM - CEO
CINN TAN - Chief Marketing Officer; Chief Sales Officer
KEVIN CROLEY - Senior VP Business Development
ANDREAS SUNGAIMIN - Senior VP Employee Development
SCOTT SOMBATPANIT - Manager Marketing, Sales

Pat Kuleto's Restaurant Development & Management
450 Post St Fl 4
San Francisco, CA 94102-1530

Telephone: (415) 474-9669
Fax Number: (415) 474-9159
Internet Homepage: boulevardrestaurant.com; epicroasthouse.com; farallonrestaurant.com; kuleto.com
Company Email: info@kuleto.com
Type of Business: Chain Restaurant Operator
Year Founded: 1988
Total Sales: $11,652,000 (e)
Alcohol Sales: 30%
Number of Employees: 300
Average Check: Lunch(36); Dinner(84)
Total Units: 2
Trade Names: Epic Roasthouse (1); Waterbar (1)
Company-Owned Units: 2
Preferred Location Types: Freestanding; Regional Mall; Strip Mall
Alcohol Served: Beer, Wine, Liquor
Primary Menu: American (2)
Areas of Operation: CA
Type of Foodservice: Fine Dining (2)
Primary Distributors: (Full Line) SYSCO Food Services of Sacramento Inc., PLEASANT GROVE, CA

Key Personnel
PAT KULETO - President; Executive Chef; Manager Menu Development
PETE SITTNICK - Director Business Development

Perry's
1944 Union St
San Francisco, CA 94123-4205

Telephone: (415) 922-9022
Fax Number: (415) 922-0843
Internet Homepage: perryssf.com
Type of Business: Chain Restaurant Operator
Year Founded: 1969
Total Sales: $11,497,000 (e)
Alcohol Sales: 20%
Number of Employees: 36
Average Check: Breakfast(12); Lunch(12); Dinner(18)
Internet Order Processing: Yes
Total Units: 3
Trade Names: Perry's Embarcadero (1); Perry's Union St (1); Perrys Larkspur (1)
Company-Owned Units: 3
Preferred Location Types: Freestanding
Alcohol Served: Beer, Wine, Liquor
Primary Menu: American (3)
Areas of Operation: CA
Type of Foodservice: Casual Dining (3)

Primary Distributors: (Food) BiRite Foodservice Distributors, BRISBANE, CA

Key Personnel
PERRY BUTLER - President; General Manager; Executive Chef; General Buyer
NITIN V. K. - Owner
ALDY BUTLER - Manager
MARGIE BUTLER - Manager Development, Marketing

Philz Coffee
3101 24th St
San Francisco, CA 94110

Telephone: (415) 875-9370
Internet Homepage: philzcoffee.com
Type of Business: Chain Restaurant Operator
Year Founded: 2003
Total Sales: $47,090,000 (e)
Total Units: 59
Trade Names: Philz Coffee (59)
Company-Owned Units: 59
Primary Menu: Coffee (59)
Projected Openings: 1
Areas of Operation: CA, DC, IL, MD, VA
Type of Foodservice: Quick Serve (59)

Key Personnel
PHIL JABER - Founder
JACOB JABER - CEO
ADAM STANSBERRY - COO
KRISTINE GAMBLE - Area Director
TIFFANY MINE - Creative Director
JENNIFER TETER - Director People
ANDI MERSCH - Director Sustainability
ASHLEY GARCIA - Director Finance, Real Estate
LAUREN JACKSON - Director Finance
GREGORY AHLBACH - Director Wholesale
DANNY ESTRADA - Director Store Design
ALEXANDER RIHA - Manager Human Resources
JOLIE MESCHI - Manager Marketing, Social Media, Event Planning
THOMAS HINDERLIE - Manager Recruitment
NATHANIEL ALLEN - Coordinator
ALEC ZAWACKI - Analyst

Piperade
1015 Battery St
San Francisco, CA 94111-1220

Telephone: (415) 391-2555
Fax Number: (415) 391-1159
Internet Homepage: piperade.com
Company Email: info@piperade.com
Type of Business: Chain Restaurant Operator
Year Founded: 1996
Total Sales: $4,526,000 (e)
Alcohol Sales: 25%

Number of Employees: 50
Average Check: Lunch(30); Dinner(54)
Total Units: 1
Trade Names: Piperade (1)
Company-Owned Units: 1
Preferred Location Types: Downtown; Freestanding
Alcohol Served: Beer, Wine, Liquor
Primary Menu: Spanish (1)
Areas of Operation: CA
Type of Foodservice: Fine Dining (1)
Primary Distributors: (Food) BiRite Foodservice Distributors, BRISBANE, CA

Key Personnel
CAMERON HIRIGOYEN - Partner; General Buyer
GERALD HIRIGOYEN - Partner; General Buyer

PlumpJack Group
3138 Fillmore St
San Francisco, CA 94123-3452

Telephone: (415) 346-5712
Fax Number: (415) 474-8792
Internet Homepage: plumpjack.com
Company Email: info@plumpjack.com
Type of Business: Chain Restaurant Operator
Total Sales: $7,555,000 (e)
Alcohol Sales: 8%
Number of Employees: 175
Average Check: Breakfast(10); Lunch(18); Dinner(30)
Internet Order Processing: Yes
Total Units: 5
Trade Names: Balboa Cafe (1); Forgery (1); Melvyn's Restaurant (1); PlumpJack Cafe (1); Wildhawk (1)
Company-Owned Units: 5
Preferred Square Footage: 5,500; 6,000
Preferred Location Types: Freestanding; Hotel/Motel
Alcohol Served: Beer, Wine, Liquor
Primary Menu: American (5)
Areas of Operation: CA, CO
Type of Foodservice: Casual Dining (5)
Catering Services: Yes

Key Personnel
GAVIN NEWSOM - Founder; Partner
HILARY NEWSOM - Co-President; Partner
JEREMY SCHERER - Co-President; Partner
JOHN CONOVER - Partner; General Manager
MILHAM WAKIN - CFO; VP Finance
MCKENZIE WARD - VP Marketing
DEE ANN GRAFFIGNA - VP Human Resources
HILLARY NINNER - VP Business Development
KEN LUCIANO - General Manager
MACKENZIE WARD - Director Marketing
RICO AVILA - Director Design, Business Development
KRISTINA JETTON - Director Human Resources

NICHOLAS GREENE - Manager
DANIEL HENRY - Manager
CECILE FRANCISCO - Manager Finance, Accounting
SCOT GAFFNEY - Manager Sales

Ritual Coffee Roasters
1050 Howard Street
San Francisco, CA 94103

Telephone: (415) 641-1024
Internet Homepage: ritualcoffee.com
Type of Business: Chain Restaurant Operator
Year Founded: 2005
Total Sales: $4,835,000 (e)
Total Units: 5
Trade Names: Ritual Coffee (5)
Company-Owned Units: 5
Primary Menu: Coffee (5)
Areas of Operation: CA
Type of Foodservice: Quick Serve (5)

Key Personnel
EILEEN HASSI RINALDI - Owner
APRIL KAVAN - Director Sales, Business Development
TIMOTHY SCHOFIELD - Director Marketing, Communications
DARIA WHALEN - Director Beverages

SFS 39 Inc
420 Columbus Ave
San Francisco, CA 94133-3902

Telephone: (415) 781-7673
Fax Number: (415) 392-7044
Internet Homepage: crabhouse39.com; ossosteakhouse.com; calzonesf.com; deadfish.com; franciscancrabrestaurant.com; salitoscrabhouse.com; thestinkingrose.com
Type of Business: Chain Restaurant Operator
Year Founded: 1957
Total Sales: $38,470,000 (e)
Alcohol Sales: 25%
Number of Employees: 350
Average Check: Lunch(24); Dinner(42)
Internet Order Processing: Yes
Internet Sales: 1.00%
Total Units: 9
Trade Names: Calzone's (1); Crab House (1); Osso Steakhouse (1); Salito's (1); The Dead Fish (1); The Franciscan Crab Restaurant (1); The Old Clam House (1); The Stinking Rose (2)
Company-Owned Units: 9
Preferred Location Types: Downtown; Freestanding; Other
Alcohol Served: Beer, Wine, Liquor
Primary Menu: Italian (1); Seafood (5); Steak (1); Steak/Seafood (2)
Areas of Operation: CA
Type of Foodservice: Casual Dining (6); Fine Dining (3)
Catering Services: Yes

Key Personnel
JERRY DAL BOZZO - President; Owner; Director Information Systems, Real Estate
ANDRE ASTABIE - General Manager
BRANDY MARTS - Manager Marketing

Simco Group
Pier 39 Ste 213
San Francisco, CA 94133-1030

Telephone: (415) 982-5872
Fax Number: (415) 982-3764
Internet Homepage: fogharbor.com; piermarket.com; wipeoutbarandgrill.com; biscoffcoffeecorner.com; simcorestaurants.com
Company Email: simco@simcorestaurants.com
Type of Business: Chain Restaurant Operator
Year Founded: 1978
Total Sales: $31,512,000 (e)
Alcohol Sales: 10%
Number of Employees: 120
Average Check: Breakfast(10); Lunch(16); Dinner(24)
Total Units: 4
Trade Names: Biscoff Coffee Corner (1); Fog Harbor Fish House Restaurant (1); Pier Market Restaurant (1); Wipeout Bar & Grill (1)
Company-Owned Units: 4
Preferred Location Types: Other
Alcohol Served: Beer, Wine, Liquor
Primary Menu: Coffee (1); Seafood (3)
Areas of Operation: CA
Type of Foodservice: Casual Dining (3); Quick Serve (1)
Primary Distributors: (Food) SYSCO Food Services of San Francisco Inc., FREMONT, CA

Key Personnel
SANDRA FLETCHER - President; General Manager
WARREN SIMMONS JR - Owner
ROBERT PARTRITE - COO; Executive Chef; Director Operations; General Buyer

Souvla
517 Hayes St
San Francisco, CA 94102-4213

Telephone: (415) 400-5458
Internet Homepage: souvla.com
Company Email: hello@souvla.com
Type of Business: Chain Restaurant Operator
Internet Order Processing: Yes
Total Units: 6
Trade Names: Souvla (6)
Company-Owned Units: 6
Primary Menu: Greek/Mediterranean (6)
Areas of Operation: CA
Type of Foodservice: Casual Dining (6)

Key Personnel
CHARLES BILILIES - Founder; CEO; Partner
TONY CERVONE - Partner; Executive Chef
MARIA BERDOUGO - Controller
ROSS WUNDERLICH - Senior Manager Culinary Operations
JULIANA FERNANDEZ - Senior Manager Restaurant Operations
ZEPHYR BAKER - Manager People
RAUL OROPEZA - Manager Training
MATT AYLARD - Manager Safety

Sushirrito
475 Sansome St
San Francisco, CA 94111-3103

Telephone: (415) 393-9905
Internet Homepage: sushirrito.com
Company Email: eat@sushirrito.com
Type of Business: Chain Restaurant Operator
Year Founded: 2011
Total Units: 8
Trade Names: Sushirrito (8)
Company-Owned Units: 8
Primary Menu: Californian (6)
Areas of Operation: CA
Type of Foodservice: Fast Casual (8)

Key Personnel
PETER YEN - Founder; Owner; General Buyer
TY MAHLER - Owner; General Buyer
ARTURO MOSCOSO - VP Culinary Operations

The Cliff House
1090 Point Lobos Ave
San Francisco, CA 94121-1449

Telephone: (415) 386-3330
Fax Number: (415) 387-7837
Internet Homepage: cliffhouse.com
Company Email: lisa@cliffhouse.com
Type of Business: Chain Restaurant Operator
Year Founded: 1863
Total Sales: $20,855,000 (e)
Alcohol Sales: 28%
Number of Employees: 200
Average Check: Breakfast(10); Lunch(10); Dinner(14)
Internet Order Processing: Yes
Internet Sales: 1.00%
Total Units: 2
Trade Names: Bistro (1); Sutro's Restaurant at the Cliff Hose (1)
Company-Owned Units: 2
Preferred Location Types: Freestanding

Alcohol Served: Beer, Wine, Liquor
Primary Menu: American (2)
Areas of Operation: CA
Type of Foodservice: Casual Dining (2)
Primary Distributors: (Full Line) SYSCO Food Services of Los Angeles Inc., WALNUT, CA

Key Personnel
DAN HOUNTALAS - President
MARY HOUNTALAS - CFO
RALPH BURGIN - VP; General Manager; Buyer Foodservice Equip/Supplies
KEVIN J. WEBER - Executive Chef; Buyer Food
MARY RYAN - Director

The Melt
925 Market St
San Francisco, CA 94103

Telephone: (515) 999-6358
Internet Homepage: themelt.com
Type of Business: Chain Restaurant Operator
Year Founded: 2011
Total Units: 7
Trade Names: The Melt (7)
Company-Owned Units: 7
Alcohol Served: Beer, Wine
Primary Menu: American (7)
Areas of Operation: CA, CO, TX
Type of Foodservice: Fast Casual (7)
Catering Services: Yes

Key Personnel
RALPH BOWER - CEO
LOU LEIDELMEYER - VP Administration
CHARLES WALTER - Creative Director
CHARLENE ABREU - Senior Manager Marketing

The Organic Coup
224 Kearny St
San Francisco, CA 94108

Telephone: (628) 444-3163
Internet Homepage: theorganiccoup.com
Type of Business: Chain Restaurant Operator
Year Founded: 2015
Total Sales: $9,755,000 (e)
Total Units: 11
Trade Names: The Organic Coup (11)
Company-Owned Units: 11
Primary Menu: Chicken (11)
Projected Openings: 2
Areas of Operation: CA
Type of Foodservice: Fast Casual (11)

Key Personnel
ERICA WELTON - Founder; General Buyer
DENNIS HOOVER - Founder
AMY JOHNSON - Manager Communications, Branding

The Stinking Rose
325 Columbus Ave
San Francisco, CA 94133-3907

Telephone: (415) 781-7673
Fax Number: (415) 392-0744
Internet Homepage: thestinkingrose.com
Company Email: sfcomments@thestinkingrose.com
Type of Business: Chain Restaurant Operator
Total Sales: $1,515,000 (e)
Alcohol Sales: 5%
Number of Employees: 60
Average Check: Dinner(18)
Total Units: 2
Trade Names: The Stinking Rose (2)
Company-Owned Units: 2
Preferred Location Types: Freestanding
Alcohol Served: Beer, Wine, Liquor
Primary Menu: Italian (2)
Areas of Operation: CA
Type of Foodservice: Casual Dining (2)

Key Personnel
DANTE SERAFINI - Partner; General Buyer
KATY DUKE CHAMBERLIN - Director Human Resources
ADRIANA AYALA - Manager Sales

VeganBurg Inc.
1466 Haight St
San Francisco, CA 94117

Telephone: (415) 548-8000
Internet Homepage: veganburg.com
Company Email: HELLO@VEGANBURG.COM
Type of Business: Chain Restaurant Operator
Year Founded: 2010
Total Sales: $3,153,000 (e)
Average Check: Lunch(22); Dinner(22)
Total Units: 2
Trade Names: VeganBurg (2)
Company-Owned Units: 2
Primary Menu: Health Foods (2)
Projected Openings: 1
Areas of Operation: CA, FC
Foreign Countries: SINGAPORE
Type of Foodservice: Quick Serve (2)
Catering Services: Yes

Key Personnel
ALEX TAN - Founder; CEO
ROUSSELL PACHECO - General Manager
TROY FRANKLIN - Consultant Franchise Development

Ike's Love & Sandwiches
901 Polk St
San Francsico, CA 94109

Mailing Address: PO Box 24069, San Jose, CA, 95154
Telephone: (415) 351-1972
Internet Homepage: loveandsandwiches.com
Company Email: ikesmarketing@loveandsandwiches.com
Type of Business: Chain Restaurant Operator
Year Founded: 2007
Total Sales: $50,880,000 (e)
Total Units: 104
Trade Names: Ike's Love & Sandwiches (104)
Company-Owned Units: 59
Units Franchised To: 45
Preferred Location Types: Community Mall; Downtown; Strip Mall
Primary Menu: Sandwiches/Deli (104)
Projected Openings: 15
Areas of Operation: AZ, CA, HI, NV, TX
Type of Foodservice: Fast Casual (104)

Key Personnel
IKE SHEHADEH - Founder; President
ROBERT LANE - Chief Marketing Officer
WILLIAM COULEHAN - VP Operations
SHREYAS PATEL - Director
IRENE CHAO - Director Digital Marketing
JESSE ARRIOLA - Area Manager
JESSICA JIMENEZ - Administrator Human Resources

CAM-BAS, INC.
2040 N 1st St
San Jose, CA 95131

Telephone: (408) 436-0760
Type of Business: Chain Restaurant Operator
Year Founded: 1985
Total Sales: $60,960,000 (e)
Number of Employees: 577
Average Check: Breakfast(8); Lunch(12); Dinner(12)
Total Units: 13
Trade Names: McDonald's (13)
Units Franchised From: 13
Preferred Square Footage: 2,500; 3,000
Preferred Location Types: Freestanding; Regional Mall
Primary Menu: Hamburger (13)
Areas of Operation: CA
Type of Foodservice: Quick Serve (13)
Franchise Affiliation: McDonald's Corporation, CHICAGO, IL
Primary Distributors: (Full Line) The Martin-Brower Co., STOCKTON, CA

Key Personnel
COSME FAGUNDO - President

RUANI TAFOLLA - Director Operations; General Buyer
TOM MATHEWS - Manager Operations

Canteen Vending Services
3870 Charter Park Dr
San Jose, CA 95136-1388

Telephone: (408) 979-8170
Fax Number: (408) 979-8192
Listing Type: Branch Office
Type of Business: Foodservice Management Operator
Year Founded: 1929
Number of Employees: 60
Number of Locations Served: 300
Total Foodservice Mgmt Accounts: 7
Areas of Operation: CA
Type of Foodservice: Vending machines (300)
Foodservice Management Venues: Business & Industry; College & University; Health Care; Lodging; Military Feeding; Schools; Travel Plazas
Parent Company: Compass Group The Americas, CHARLOTTE, NC
Headquarters: Canteen Vending Services, CHARLOTTE, NC

Key Personnel
BILL JOERING - VP Region; General Buyer

Erik's DeliCafe Inc.
1550 the Alameda Ste 330
San Jose, CA 95126-2329

Telephone: (831) 458-1818
Fax Number: (831) 458-9797
Internet Homepage: eriksdelicafe.com
Type of Business: Chain Restaurant Operator
Year Founded: 1973
Systemwide Sales: $25,967,000 (e)
Total Sales: $1,910,000 (e)
Alcohol Sales: 1%
Number of Employees: 55
Average Check: Lunch(12); Dinner(12)
Total Units: 30
Trade Names: Erik's DeliCafe (30)
Company-Owned Units: 4
Units Franchised To: 26
Preferred Square Footage: 2,000; 2,400
Preferred Location Types: Freestanding; Strip Mall
Primary Menu: Sandwiches/Deli (30)
Areas of Operation: CA
Type of Foodservice: Fast Casual (30)
Catering Services: Yes

Key Personnel
JUDY JOHNSON - Treasurer

Fresh On The Grill Inc
2306 Almaden Rd Ste 150
San Jose, CA 95125

Telephone: (408) 979-0251
Internet Homepage: sanjoseoph.com
Company Email: info@sanjoseoph.com
Type of Business: Chain Restaurant Operator
Total Sales: $1,866,000 (e)
Total Units: 1
Trade Names: The Original Pancake House (1)
Company-Owned Units: 1
Primary Menu: American (1)
Areas of Operation: CA
Type of Foodservice: Family Restaurant (1)
Franchise Affiliation: The Original Pancake House Franchising Inc., PORTLAND, OR

Key Personnel
DIANA KHOURI - Owner; General Buyer

Happi House Restaurants, LLC
2780 Alum Rock Ave
San Jose, CA 95127-2801

Telephone: (408) 929-2113
Fax Number: (408) 929-2116
Internet Homepage: happihouse.com
Company Email: hhgeneral@happihouse.com
Type of Business: Chain Restaurant Operator
Year Founded: 1975
Total Sales: $28,474,000 (e)
Number of Employees: 288
Average Check: Lunch(12); Dinner(14)
Total Units: 16
Trade Names: Happi House Restaurant (3); Taco Bell (13)
Company-Owned Units: 6
Preferred Square Footage: 1,200
Preferred Location Types: Freestanding
Primary Menu: Japanese (3); Taco (13)
Areas of Operation: CA
Type of Foodservice: Quick Serve (16)
Catering Services: Yes
Primary Distributors: (Full Line) BiRite Foodservice Distributors, BRISBANE, CA

Key Personnel
TAMI MASON - Co-CEO; General Buyer

Henley Restaurants Ltd
6830 Via Del Oro Ste 101
San Jose, CA 95119-1353

Telephone: (408) 227-3900
Fax Number: (408) 227-3003
Type of Business: Chain Restaurant Operator
Total Sales: $46,730,000 (e)
Total Units: 10
Trade Names: McDonald's (10)
Units Franchised From: 10
Primary Menu: Hamburger (10)
Areas of Operation: CA
Type of Foodservice: Quick Serve (10)
Franchise Affiliation: McDonald's Corporation, CHICAGO, IL

Key Personnel
JAMES C. HENLEY - President; General Buyer
ARTURO MEJIA - Director Operations

Hobee's California Restaurants
173 N Morrison Ave Ste E
San Jose, CA 95126

Telephone: (650) 493-7823
Fax Number: (650) 493-0756
Internet Homepage: hobees.com
Type of Business: Chain Restaurant Operator
Year Founded: 1974
Systemwide Sales: $12,299,000 (e)
Total Sales: $12,450,000 (e)
Alcohol Sales: 6%
Number of Employees: 190
Average Check: Breakfast(12); Lunch(14); Dinner(24)
Internet Order Processing: Yes
Internet Sales: 1.50%
Total Units: 6
Trade Names: Hobee's Restaurant (6)
Company-Owned Units: 6
Preferred Square Footage: 5,000
Preferred Location Types: Freestanding
Alcohol Served: Beer, Wine
Primary Menu: Californian (6)
Areas of Operation: CA
Type of Foodservice: Casual Dining (6)
Primary Distributors: (Food) SYSCO Food Services of Los Angeles Inc., WALNUT, CA

Key Personnel
CAMILLE CHIJATE - President
GIGI CHIJATE - Administrative Assistant
ED FIKE - Advisor
BETTY WEINER - Bookkeeper

Lee*s Sandwiches International Inc.
660 E Gish Rd
San Jose, CA 95112-2707

Telephone: (408) 280-1595
Fax Number: (408) 275-0416
Internet Homepage: leesandwiches.com
Company Email: info@leesandwiches.com
Type of Business: Chain Restaurant Operator
Year Founded: 1983

Systemwide Sales: $65,573,000 (e)
Total Sales: $10,150,000 (e)
Internet Order Processing: Yes
Total Units: 64
Trade Names: Lee*s Sandwiches (64)
Company-Owned Units: 4
Units Franchised To: 60
Preferred Square Footage: 1,500; 3,000; 5,000
Preferred Location Types: Freestanding; Regional Mall; Strip Mall
Primary Menu: Sandwiches/Deli (64)
Areas of Operation: AZ, CA, NC, NV, OK, OR, SC, TX, VA
Foreign Countries: TAIWAN; VIETNAM
Type of Foodservice: Quick Serve (64)
Notes: Lee*s Sandwiches businesses located in northern California are not affiliated with Lee*s Sandwiches International.

Key Personnel
CHIEU VAN LE - CEO; President
JIMMY M. LE - VP Sales
YEN NGOC QUACH - Corporate Secretary

Loving Hut USA
2300 Zanker Rd Suite B
San Jose, CA 95131

Internet Homepage: lovinghut.us
Company Email: usa@lovinghut.us
Type of Business: Chain Restaurant Operator
Total Sales: $27,710,000 (e)
Total Units: 38
Trade Names: Loving Hut USA (38)
Units Franchised To: 38
Primary Menu: Health Foods (38)
Areas of Operation: AZ, CA, FL, GA, HI, MA, NJ, NY, OH, OR, TX, VA, WA
Type of Foodservice: Casual Dining (38)
Notes: Loving Hut in it's entirety operates in 35+ countries with 140 locations. Only the U.S. locations have been reflected. Each franchise is individually operated with its own unique menu and hours

Key Personnel
CHING HAI - Founder
HARRY MAI - CEO; President

Nick The Greek
5765 Winfield Blvd
San Jose, CA 95126

Telephone: (408) 780-4976
Internet Homepage: nickthegreek.com
Type of Business: Chain Restaurant Operator
Year Founded: 2014
Number of Employees: 500
Total Units: 62
Trade Names: Nick The Greek (62)
Company-Owned Units: 1
Units Franchised To: 61
Primary Menu: Greek/Mediterranean (62)
Projected Openings: 10
Areas of Operation: AZ, CA, KS, MO, NV, TX, UT
Type of Foodservice: Fast Casual (62)

Key Personnel
NICK B. TSIGARIS - Chief Marketing Officer

O M, Inc
1079 Lincoln Ave
San Jose, CA 95125-3154

Telephone: (408) 882-0250
Fax Number: (408) 882-0269
Internet Homepage: aquicalmex.com
Company Email: aquicalmex@aquicalmex.com
Type of Business: Chain Restaurant Operator
Total Sales: $6,751,000 (e)
Total Units: 5
Trade Names: Aqui Cal-Mex Company (5)
Company-Owned Units: 5
Primary Menu: Californian (5)
Projected Openings: 1
Areas of Operation: CA
Type of Foodservice: Casual Dining (5)

Key Personnel
DAVID M. O'MARA - CEO; President; General Buyer

One Olive Group, LLC
81 Curtner Ave
San Jose, CA 95125

Telephone: (408) 610-9471
Type of Business: Chain Restaurant Operator
Total Units: 2
Trade Names: The Halal Guys (2)
Units Franchised From: 2
Primary Menu: Middle Eastern (2)
Projected Openings: 1
Areas of Operation: CA
Type of Foodservice: Quick Serve (2)
Franchise Affiliation: The Halal Guys Inc., ASTORIA, NY
Notes: Franchise Commitment: 20 units
  Territory: Parts of San Francisco and the rest of NoCal
  Territory Note: FOMO Investments is the other San Fran franchisee
  Address Note: Current address is owner's home address
  Phone Note: Current phone number is San Jose HG location.

Key Personnel
PATRICK MOCK - CEO

Pizza Eureka
5313 Prospect Rd
San Jose, CA 95129-5028

Telephone: (408) 253-3030
Type of Business: Chain Restaurant Operator
Total Sales: $12,062,000 (e)
Total Units: 6
Trade Names: Domino's (6)
Units Franchised From: 6
Primary Menu: Pizza (6)
Areas of Operation: CA
Type of Foodservice: Quick Serve (6)
Franchise Affiliation: Domino's Pizza Inc, ANN ARBOR, MI

Key Personnel
ALI H. IQBAL - Owner; General Buyer

Smoking Pig BBQ Company
1144 N 4th St
San Jose, CA 95112

Telephone: (408) 380-4784
Internet Homepage: smokingpigbbq.net
Type of Business: Chain Restaurant Operator
Year Founded: 2011
Total Units: 3
Trade Names: Smoking Pig BBQ (3)
Company-Owned Units: 3
Preferred Location Types: Freestanding; Stadiums
Primary Menu: Bar-B-Q (3)
Areas of Operation: CA
Type of Foodservice: Casual Dining (3)

Key Personnel
PAUL REDDICK - Founder; Owner

Tabellco Inc.
2780 Alum Rock Ave
San Jose, CA 95127-2801

Telephone: (408) 929-2113
Fax Number: (408) 929-2116
Internet Homepage: happihouse.com
Company Email: tabellco@pacbell.net
Type of Business: Chain Restaurant Operator
Year Founded: 1967
Total Sales: $26,520,000 (e)
Number of Employees: 320
Average Check: Lunch(10); Dinner(10)
Total Units: 16
Trade Names: Happi House Teriyaki Express (4); Taco Bell (12)
Company-Owned Units: 4

Units Franchised From: 12
Preferred Square Footage: 1,800
Preferred Location Types: Freestanding; Strip Mall
Primary Menu: Japanese (4); Taco (12)
Areas of Operation: CA
Type of Foodservice: Quick Serve (16)
Franchise Affiliation: Taco Bell Corp., IRVINE, CA

Key Personnel
GARY LAABS - President; Director Information Systems, Real Estate
TAMMY LAABS-MASON - VP
ALAN LAABS - Controller; Manager Human Resources
DAN CARTER - Director Operations

Togo's Eateries LLC
18 N San Pedro St
San Jose, CA 95110-2413

Telephone: (408) 280-6585
Fax Number: (408) 280-5067
Internet Homepage: togos.com
Type of Business: Chain Restaurant Operator
Year Founded: 1972
Systemwide Sales: $163,400,000 (e)
Total Sales: $42,850,000 (e)
Number of Employees: 35
Average Check: Lunch(12); Dinner(16)
Total Units: 197
Trade Names: Togo's (197)
Units Franchised To: 197
Preferred Square Footage: 1,500; 2,200
Preferred Location Types: Downtown; Freestanding; Institution (college/hospital); Regional Mall; Strip Mall
Alcohol Served: Beer, Wine
Primary Menu: Sandwiches/Deli (197)
Areas of Operation: AZ, CA, CO, ID, NV, OR, UT, WA
Type of Foodservice: Quick Serve (275)
Catering Services: Yes
Primary Distributors: (Full Line) VISTAR Specialty, ENGLEWOOD, CO
Parent Company: Nimes Capital Group, LOS ANGELES, CA

Key Personnel
MATT DOWLING - CEO; CFO
ANNA NERO - Senior VP Marketing
FARID BIGLARI - VP Operations

Una Mas Restaurants Inc.
90 Great Oaks Blvd Ste 208
San Jose, CA 95119-1314

Telephone: (408) 629-1402
Fax Number: (408) 629-1407
Internet Homepage: unamas.com
Company Email: info@unamas.com
Type of Business: Chain Restaurant Operator
Year Founded: 2003
Systemwide Sales: $8,235,000 (e)
Total Sales: $2,774,000 (e)
Alcohol Sales: 5%
Number of Employees: 4
Average Check: Lunch(10); Dinner(10)
Internet Order Processing: Yes
Total Units: 16
Trade Names: Una Mas Mexican Grille (16)
Units Franchised To: 16
Preferred Square Footage: 1,800
Preferred Location Types: Community Mall; Freestanding; Strip Mall
Alcohol Served: Beer
Primary Menu: Mexican (16)
Areas of Operation: CA
Type of Foodservice: Fast Casual (16)
Catering Services: Yes
Parent Company: Heritage Ventures, SAN JOSE, CA

Key Personnel
MIKE DIPIETRO - CEO; General Manager; Director Finance, Operations, Facility/Maintenance, Information Systems, Supply Chain, Ethnic Marketing, Real Estate, Design, Store Fixtures, Menu Development; General Buyer
SHALINI KHANNA - Owner

Yogurtland Franchisee
2742 Aborn Rd
San Jose, CA 95121-1204

Telephone: (408) 531-0200
Type of Business: Chain Restaurant Operator
Total Sales: $1,029,000 (e)
Total Units: 1
Trade Names: Yogurtland (1)
Units Franchised From: 1
Primary Menu: Snacks (1)
Areas of Operation: CA
Type of Foodservice: Quick Serve (1)
Franchise Affiliation: Yogurtland Franchising Inc., FARMERS BRANCH, TX

Key Personnel
JIM CHUN - Owner; General Buyer

Domino's Franchisee
32211 Camino Capistrano Ste E102
San Juan Capistrano, CA 92675-3738

Telephone: (949) 493-3030
Type of Business: Chain Restaurant Operator
Total Sales: $6,083,000 (e)
Total Units: 3
Trade Names: Domino's (3)
Units Franchised From: 3
Primary Menu: Pizza (3)
Areas of Operation: CA
Type of Foodservice: Quick Serve (3)
Franchise Affiliation: Domino's Pizza Inc, ANN ARBOR, MI

Key Personnel
CINDY L. GAGLIARDI - Partner; General Buyer
RICH ADAMS - Partner; General Buyer

ITNA Group, Inc.
31262 Avenida Madrid
San Juan Capistrano, CA 92675-5391

Telephone: (949) 233-6434
Type of Business: Chain Restaurant Operator
Total Sales: $5,382,000 (e)
Total Units: 2
Trade Names: Jack in the Box (2)
Units Franchised From: 2
Primary Menu: Hamburger (2)
Areas of Operation: CA
Type of Foodservice: Quick Serve (2)
Franchise Affiliation: Jack in the Box Restaurants, SAN DIEGO, CA

Key Personnel
ABDUL SADRUDDIN - Owner; General Buyer

Aryzta LLC
14490 Catalina St
San Leandro, CA 94577

Telephone: (888) 275-6847
Internet Homepage: labreabakery.com
Type of Business: Chain Restaurant Operator
Total Units: 6
Trade Names: La Brea Bakery (6)
Company-Owned Units: 6
Primary Menu: Snacks (6)
Areas of Operation: CA
Type of Foodservice: Fast Casual (6)

Key Personnel
ROBERT MINA - Senior VP Store Operations
LES ECHEVERRIA - Director Operations
LINDA BOUD - Senior Manager Sales-Foodservice Equip/Supplies

Bobcar Partnership
222 Juana Ave
San Leandro, CA 94577-4839

Telephone: (510) 667-9439
Fax Number: (510) 667-9839
Type of Business: Chain Restaurant Operator
Year Founded: 1991
Total Sales: $20,389,000 (e)
Number of Employees: 140

Average Check: Breakfast(8); Lunch(8); Dinner(8)
Total Units: 4
Trade Names: McDonald's (4)
Units Franchised From: 4
Preferred Square Footage: 2,500
Preferred Location Types: Freestanding
Primary Menu: Hamburger (4)
Areas of Operation: CA
Type of Foodservice: Quick Serve (4)
Franchise Affiliation: McDonald's Corporation, CHICAGO, IL
Primary Distributors: (Full Line) The Martin-Brower Co., STOCKTON, CA

Key Personnel
BOBBY HAYNES - President; Director Finance, Operations, Facility/Maintenance, Information Systems, Supply Chain, Real Estate, Design, Human Resources; General Buyer
MICHELLE WATTS - General Manager

Ghirardelli Chocolate Company
1111 139th Ave
San Leandro, CA 94578-2616

Telephone: (510) 483-6970
Fax Number: (510) 297-2649
Internet Homepage: ghirardelli.com
Company Email: consumerservice-gh@ghirardelli.com
Type of Business: Nontraditional Foodservice Operator
Year Founded: 1852
Total Sales: $260,465,000 (e)
Number of Employees: 975
Foodservice Sales: $78,139,000 (e)
Internet Order Processing: Yes
Total Units: 19
Trade Names: Chocolate Chocolate (19)
Company-Owned Units: 19
Preferred Location Types: Community Mall; Strip Mall
Primary Menu: Snacks (19)
Areas of Operation: AZ, CA, FL, IL, MA, NV, WI
Type of Foodservice: Quick Serve (19)
On-site Distribution Center: Yes
Primary Distributors: (Food) US Foods-San Francisco, LIVERMORE, CA
Parent Company: Lindt & Sprungli AG, KILCHBERG, CHE
Notes: The company derives approximately 70% of its revenue from retail operations.

Key Personnel
MANUELE FABBIANE - CFO
STEVE GENZOLI - VP Quality Assurance, Research & Development
SAMUEL BERNEGGER - VP Operations

ROB BUDOWSKI - VP Sales

Loco Ventures
2000 Wayne Ave
San Leandro, CA 94577-3333

Telephone: (510) 351-4131
Fax Number: (510) 351-2562
Internet Homepage: loards.com
Company Email: info@loards.com
Type of Business: Chain Restaurant Operator
Year Founded: 1950
Systemwide Sales: $5,948,000 (e)
Total Sales: $2,151,000 (e)
Number of Employees: 19
Average Check: Lunch(8); Dinner(8)
Total Units: 21
Trade Names: Loard's Ice Cream & Candies (21)
Company-Owned Units: 1
Units Franchised To: 20
Preferred Square Footage: 1,250
Preferred Location Types: Freestanding; Strip Mall
Primary Menu: Snacks (21)
Areas of Operation: CA
Type of Foodservice: Quick Serve (21)
Catering Services: Yes
On-site Distribution Center: Yes

Key Personnel
STEVEN COHAN - President; Director Finance, Real Estate, Design, Human Resources
ERNIE ENCELAN - Manager Inventory, Loss Prevention, Quality Assurance, Supply Chain, Food Safety

Heritage Restaurant Brands
51 Zaca Ln Ste 140
San Luis Obispo, CA 93401

Telephone: (805) 269-6090
Internet Homepage: coolhandlukes.com; huckleberrys.org; heritagerb.com; perkos.com
Company Email: inquiries@heritagerb.com
Type of Business: Chain Restaurant Operator
Year Founded: 1969
Systemwide Sales: $52,020,000 (e)
Total Sales: $25,450,000 (e)
Alcohol Sales: 5%
Number of Employees: 3,023
Average Check: Breakfast(8); Lunch(18); Dinner(30)
Total Units: 33
Trade Names: Cool Hand Luke's Steakhouse & Saloon (6); Huckleberry (9); Perko's Cafe Grill (18)
Units Franchised To: 33
Preferred Square Footage: 3,000
Preferred Location Types: Community Mall; Freestanding

Alcohol Served: Beer, Wine, Liquor
Primary Menu: American (24); Steak (7)
Projected Openings: 2
Areas of Operation: CA
Type of Foodservice: Casual Dining (33)
On-site Distribution Center: Yes

Key Personnel
GREG GRABER - CEO
CHIP ANDERSON - CFO
DAVID GLENNON - COO
REEM ATKINS - Director Marketing

The Graduate Restaurants Inc.
2701 McMillan Ave
San Luis Obispo, CA 93401-4739

Telephone: (805) 541-0700
Fax Number: (805) 548-8480
Internet Homepage: thegraduatestockton.com; slograd.com
Company Email: chico.grad@att.net
Type of Business: Chain Restaurant Operator
Year Founded: 1970
Total Sales: $8,832,000 (e)
Alcohol Sales: 50%
Number of Employees: 175
Average Check: Lunch(5); Dinner(10)
Total Units: 2
Trade Names: Graduate (2)
Company-Owned Units: 2
Preferred Square Footage: 11,000
Preferred Location Types: Freestanding
Alcohol Served: Beer, Wine, Liquor
Primary Menu: American (2)
Areas of Operation: CA
Type of Foodservice: Casual Dining (2)
Primary Distributors: (Full Line) Shamrock Foods Co., PHOENIX, AZ

Key Personnel
WILLIAM C. EVERETT - VP Purchasing, Information Systems, Controller; Director Construction, Store Planning
BRITTANY SONS - General Manager; General Buyer
MIKE CASSESE - Director Operations
RICHARD SIMONEAU - General Buyer

Yogurt Creations, Inc.
4251 S Higuera St Ste 800K
San Luis Obispo, CA 93401-7700

Telephone: (805) 543-1198
Internet Homepage: iloveyogurtcreations.com
Company Email: info@iloveyogurtcreations.com
Type of Business: Chain Restaurant Operator
Year Founded: 2004

Total Units: 6
Trade Names: Yogurt Creations (6)
Company-Owned Units: 6
Primary Menu: Snacks (6)
Areas of Operation: CA
Type of Foodservice: Quick Serve (6)

Key Personnel
JOHN BOLTON - Founder; Owner

PFS Management Co. Inc.
485 E Carmel St
San Marcos, CA 92078-4362

Telephone: (760) 471-8720
Fax Number: (760) 471-8725
Company Email: office@mcdh.com
Type of Business: Chain Restaurant Operator
Year Founded: 1989
Total Sales: $75,140,000 (e)
Number of Employees: 750
Average Check: Breakfast(8); Lunch(10); Dinner(12)
Total Units: 16
Trade Names: McDonald's (16)
Units Franchised From: 16
Preferred Square Footage: 2,400; 3,000
Preferred Location Types: Discount Dept. Stores; Freestanding
Primary Menu: Hamburger (16)
Areas of Operation: CA
Type of Foodservice: Quick Serve (16)
Franchise Affiliation: McDonald's Corporation, CHICAGO, IL
Primary Distributors: (Full Line) The Martin-Brower Co., STOCKTON, CA

Key Personnel
PAUL SCHMID - President; Director Finance; Manager Information Systems, Real Estate; General Buyer
ROCHELLE JOHNSON - Assistant Controller
MARY ANN KORPI - Controller
DEBBIE ELLIOTT - Director Operations, Facility/Maintenance

UltraStar Cinemas
1531 Grand Ave Ste B
San Marcos, CA 92078-2463

Telephone: (760) 597-5777
Fax Number: (760) 768-4209
Internet Homepage: ultrastarmovies.com
Company Email: guestcom@ultrastarmovies.com
Type of Business: Foodservice Operations - Movie Theatre
Year Founded: 1999
Total Sales: $9,347,000 (e)
Number of Employees: 6
Average Check: Lunch(6); Dinner(6)

Total Units: 2
Trade Names: UltraStar Movies (2)
Company-Owned Units: 2
Preferred Location Types: Regional Mall; Strip Mall
Primary Menu: Snacks (2)
Projected Openings: 1
Areas of Operation: AZ, CA
Type of Foodservice: In-Store Feeder (2)
Notes: The company derives approximately 60% of its revenue from movie theatre operations.

Key Personnel
JOHN ELLISON - Owner; Senior VP
JULIE BRAVO - VP Marketing

Amici East Coast Pizzeria
69 E 3rd Ave
San Mateo, CA 94401-4010

Telephone: (650) 373-3440
Fax Number: (650) 342-7762
Internet Homepage: amicis.com
Company Email: peter@amicis.com
Type of Business: Chain Restaurant Operator
Internet Order Processing: Yes
Total Units: 10
Trade Names: Amici's East Coast Pizzeria (10)
Company-Owned Units: 10
Alcohol Served: Beer, Wine
Primary Menu: Pizza (10)
Areas of Operation: CA
Type of Foodservice: Casual Dining (10)

Key Personnel
MIKE FORTER - Partner; General Buyer
PETER COOPERSTEIN - Partner; General Buyer

Amici's
69 E 3rd Ave
San Mateo, CA 94401-4010

Telephone: (650) 373-3440
Internet Homepage: amicis.com
Company Email: peter@amicis.com
Type of Business: Chain Restaurant Operator
Year Founded: 1981
Total Sales: $35,340,000 (e)
Alcohol Sales: 10%
Number of Employees: 455
Average Check: Lunch(14); Dinner(24)
Internet Order Processing: Yes
Total Units: 10
Trade Names: Amici's East Coast Pizzeria (10)
Company-Owned Units: 10
Preferred Square Footage: 2,500
Preferred Location Types: Freestanding
Alcohol Served: Beer, Wine
Primary Menu: Pizza (10)

Areas of Operation: CA
Type of Foodservice: Casual Dining (10)
Primary Distributors: (Full Line) BiRite Foodservice Distributors, BRISBANE, CA

Key Personnel
PETER COOPERSTEIN - Partner; Director Finance, Operations, Information Systems, Human Resources, Store Fixtures
MIKE FORTER - Partner; Director Real Estate, Design, Menu Development
ALEXIS THIBODEAU - Director Digital Marketing

Guckenheimer Enterprises
1850 Gateway Dr Ste 500
San Mateo, CA 94404-4064

Telephone: (650) 592-3800
Internet Homepage: guckenheimer.com
Company Email: info@guckenheimer.com
Type of Business: Foodservice Management Operator
Year Founded: 1968
Total Sales: $451,000,000 (e)
Number of Employees: 3,500
Number of Locations Served: 400
Total Foodservice Mgmt Accounts: 400
Areas of Operation: CA
Type of Foodservice: Cafeteria (400)
Foodservice Management Venues: Business & Industry
Primary Distributors: (Food) SYSCO Food Services of Chicago Inc., DES PLAINES, IL

Key Personnel
PAUL FAIRHEAD - COO

Pacific Hotel Management LLC
400 S El Camino Real Ste 200
San Mateo, CA 94402-1731

Telephone: (650) 347-8260
Fax Number: (650) 347-8261
Internet Homepage: phmhotels.com
Company Email: info@phmhotels.com
Type of Business: Foodservice Operations - Hotel/Motels
Year Founded: 1963
Total Sales: $126,790,000 (e)
Alcohol Sales: 20%
Number of Employees: 1,410
Total Units: 15
Restaurants in Hotels: 15
Trade Names: 4 Point by Sheraton (2); Clement Monterey (3); Homewood Suites (2); Residents Inn (2); Sheraton (3); Westin Palo Alto (3)
Company-Owned Units: 15

Alcohol Served: Beer, Wine, Liquor
Areas of Operation: CA
Type of Foodservice: Casual Dining (11); Fine Dining (4)
Primary Distributors: (Food) Systems Services of America, MILPITAS, CA
Parent Company: Clement Chen & Associates, SAN FRANCISCO, CA
Notes: The company derives approximately 80% of its revenue from hotel operations.

Key Personnel
CLEMENT CHEN III - CEO; President; Director Finance
RANDY LACY - VP Operations, Food and Beverage; Director Purchasing; General Buyer
SUZANNE MURDOCH - VP Marketing, Sales
KRESS FISCHER - Executive Director Construction, Design
STEPHANIE JOHNSON - Director Information Systems, Human Resources

Pokeatery
407 S B St
San Mateo, CA 94401-4118

Telephone: (650) 389-2672
Internet Homepage: pokeatery.com
Company Email: catering@pokeatery.com
Type of Business: Chain Restaurant Operator
Total Units: 6
Trade Names: Pokeatery (6)
Company-Owned Units: 6
Primary Menu: Seafood (6)
Areas of Operation: CA, TX
Type of Foodservice: Fast Casual (6)

Key Personnel
DEREK CHUNG - Partner; Executive Chef
JOANN CHUNG - Partner; Executive Chef

Straits Restaurant LLC
1122 7th Ave
San Mateo, CA 94402-1323

Telephone: (650) 340-9333
Fax Number: (650) 340-9668
Internet Homepage: rootsandrye.com; straitsrestaurants.com
Company Email: info@straitsrestaurants.com
Type of Business: Chain Restaurant Operator
Year Founded: 1987
Total Sales: $5,363,000 (e)
Alcohol Sales: 20%
Number of Employees: 55
Average Check: Lunch(22); Dinner(38)
Total Units: 5
Trade Names: Roots and Rye (1); Sino (1); Straits Cafe (3)
Company-Owned Units: 5

Preferred Square Footage: 2,000
Preferred Location Types: Freestanding; Regional Mall
Alcohol Served: Beer, Wine, Liquor
Primary Menu: American (1); Asian (4)
Areas of Operation: CA, TX
Type of Foodservice: Casual Dining (5)
Catering Services: Yes
Primary Distributors: (Food) SYSCO Food Services of Los Angeles Inc., WALNUT, CA

Key Personnel
CHRIS YEO - CEO; President; Partner
JULIAN YEO - Partner
KELLY YEO - Partner
ANDREW YEO - Partner
HEATHER CONNERY - General Manager
EDDIE LAM - Executive Chef; General Buyer
LILLIAN NGUYEN - Director Marketing

Subway Franchise
13501 San Pablo Ave Ste A
San Pablo, CA 94806-3869

Telephone: (510) 233-9498
Internet Homepage: subway.com
Type of Business: Chain Restaurant Operator
Total Sales: $2,142,000 (e)
Total Units: 3
Trade Names: Subway (3)
Units Franchised From: 3
Primary Menu: Sandwiches/Deli (3)
Areas of Operation: CA
Type of Foodservice: Quick Serve (3)
Franchise Affiliation: Doctor's Associates Inc., MILFORD, CT

Key Personnel
JUNG PANNU - President; General Buyer

Kalaveras Inc.
San Pedro, CA 90731

Telephone: (909) 727-3 49
Internet Homepage: kalaveras.com
Company Email: info@kalaveras.com
Type of Business: Chain Restaurant Operator
Year Founded: 2016
Total Units: 28
Trade Names: Kalaveras (28)
Company-Owned Units: 28
Primary Menu: Mexican (28)
Areas of Operation: CA
Type of Foodservice: Casual Dining (28)

Key Personnel
JOSE BRITO - Co-Founder
FRANCISCO BRITO - Co-Founder
ISAIAS OCAMPO BRITO - Partner

ANGEL BAHENA - Partner
DANIEL BRITO - Partner
ELICIA DURAN - Director Development

San Pedro Fish Market Grille
1190 Nagoya Way
San Pedro, CA 90731

Telephone: (310) 265-2260
Internet Homepage: sanpedrofish.com
Company Email: info@spfishgrille.com
Type of Business: Chain Restaurant Operator
Year Founded: 1956
Total Units: 3
Trade Names: San Pedro Fish Market Grille (3)
Company-Owned Units: 3
Preferred Location Types: Downtown; Strip Mall
Primary Menu: Seafood (3)
Areas of Operation: CA
Type of Foodservice: Fast Casual (3)

Key Personnel
MICHAEL UNGARO - Partner
MICHAEL DIBERNARDO - Partner
LOUIS MESTAZ - General Manager
JENNIFER UNGARO - Director Finance, Human Resources
ANNETTE GUESS - Manager Operations
MICHAEL MORI - Manager Operations, Logistics

Green Beans Coffee Company LLC
4300 Redwood Hwy Ste 100
San Rafael, CA 94903-2103

Telephone: (415) 461-4023
Fax Number: (415) 461-4723
Internet Homepage: greenbeanscoffee.com
Type of Business: Chain Restaurant Operator
Total Sales: $3,281,000 (e)
Number of Employees: 613
Average Check: Dinner(5)
Total Units: 70
Trade Names: Green Beans Coffee World Cafe (70)
Company-Owned Units: 70
Primary Menu: Coffee (70)
Areas of Operation: CO, GA, HI, KY, MD, NE, PA, SC, TN, TX, VA, FC
Foreign Countries: AFGHANISTAN; DJIBOUTI; IRAQ; IRELAND; JAPAN; JORDAN; KUWAIT; QATAR; UNITED ARAB EMIRATES
Type of Foodservice: Casual Dining (70)
Notes: An affiliated company, Green Beans Coffee Company Inc., operates businesses similar to this on foreign military bases.

Key Personnel
H. JASON ARAGHI - CEO; President; General Buyer
LINDA JUNGQUIST - Regional Manager
ANGELITA VELASCO - Area Manager
KALESH REJILA - Manager Logistics, International

Moana Restaurant Group
835 5th Ave
San Rafael, CA 94901-3204

Telephone: (415) 755-2000
Fax Number: (415) 755-2035
Internet Homepage: basaltnapa.com; eldoradosonoma.com; moanarestaurantgroup.com; ollacocina.com; pgrestaurant.com; piatti.com; thefarmersunion.com
Company Email: moanainfo@moanarestaurantgroup.com
Type of Business: Chain Restaurant Operator
Year Founded: 1987
Total Sales: $59,740,000 (e)
Alcohol Sales: 15%
Number of Employees: 1,932
Average Check: Lunch(18); Dinner(36)
Internet Order Processing: Yes
Internet Sales: 1.00%
Total Units: 17
Trade Names: Joinery (1); Larks Creek (1); Olla Cocina (1); Parcel 104 (1); Piatti Ristorante & Bar (9); Roundhouse (1); Sam's Anchor Cafe (1); San Pedro Square Market (1); Yankee Pier (1)
Company-Owned Units: 17
Preferred Square Footage: 5,500
Preferred Location Types: Freestanding; Strip Mall
Alcohol Served: Beer, Wine, Liquor
Primary Menu: American (4); Asian (1); Californian (1); Italian (10); Mexican (1); Pizza (5); Seafood (3)
Areas of Operation: CA, HI, OR, FC
Foreign Countries: MEXICO
Type of Foodservice: Casual Dining (17); Family Restaurant (1); Fine Dining (1)
Catering Services: Yes
Primary Distributors: (Full Line) SYSCO Food Services of San Francisco Inc., FREMONT, CA
Parent Company: Palisades Hospitality Group, SAN RAFAEL, CA

Key Personnel
JON SWANSON - President
COLLEEN GRAY - VP Finance; Controller
OLYA BOWLAND - Manager Marketing
MELANIE CHAO - Supervisor Payroll

NBR Tomatina LLC
150 Pelican Way
San Rafael, CA 94901-5550

Telephone: (415) 448-8300
Fax Number: (415) 448-8345
Internet Homepage: tomatina.com
Company Email: info@tomatina.com
Type of Business: Chain Restaurant Operator
Year Founded: 1997
Total Sales: $13,330,000 (e)
Alcohol Sales: 10%
Number of Employees: 320
Average Check: Lunch(16); Dinner(22)
Internet Order Processing: Yes
Total Units: 7
Trade Names: Tomatina (7)
Company-Owned Units: 7
Preferred Location Types: Downtown; Strip Mall
Alcohol Served: Beer, Wine
Primary Menu: Italian (7)
Areas of Operation: CA
Type of Foodservice: Casual Dining (7)
Primary Distributors: (Food) US Foods-San Francisco, LIVERMORE, CA

Key Personnel
PATRICK LACAVA - Senior VP Operations; General Manager; General Buyer
ROGELIO JACINTO - Executive Chef

Bay Area Restaurant Management
2268 Camino Ramon
San Ramon, CA 94583-1353

Telephone: (925) 277-0563
Fax Number: (925) 830-0771
Type of Business: Chain Restaurant Operator
Year Founded: 1967
Total Sales: $167,960,000 (e)
Number of Employees: 1,388
Average Check: Breakfast(8); Lunch(10); Dinner(12)
Total Units: 36
Trade Names: McDonald's (36)
Units Franchised From: 36
Preferred Square Footage: 2,500
Preferred Location Types: Community Mall; Freestanding
Primary Menu: Hamburger (36)
Projected Remodelings: 5
Areas of Operation: CA
Type of Foodservice: Quick Serve (36)
Foodservice Management Venues: Schools
Franchise Affiliation: McDonald's Corporation, CHICAGO, IL
Primary Distributors: (Full Line) The Martin-Brower Co., STOCKTON, CA

Key Personnel
HOWARD GOLDBLATT - President; Partner; Director Real Estate, Design
BRAD GOLDBLATT - Partner; CFO; General Manager
GAY FROST - Director Finance, Information Systems, Human Resources
JOANNE JONES - Director Operations, Purchasing, Facility/Maintenance, Supply Chain

Gold Coast Holdings
3000 Executive Pkwy Ste 515
San Ramon, CA 94583-2399

Telephone: (305) 567-3582
Fax Number: (925) 328-3333
Internet Homepage: gchrestaurants.com
Type of Business: Chain Restaurant Operator
Year Founded: 1992
Total Sales: $48,340,000 (e)
Alcohol Sales: 3%
Number of Employees: 7,800
Average Check: Breakfast(5); Lunch(8); Dinner(8)
Total Units: 18
Trade Names: Wendy's Old Fashioned Hamburgers (18)
Units Franchised From: 18
Preferred Square Footage: 3,000
Preferred Location Types: Freestanding
Alcohol Served: Beer, Wine, Liquor
Primary Menu: Hamburger (18)
Areas of Operation: FL
Type of Foodservice: Quick Serve (18)
Franchise Affiliation: T.G.I. Friday's Inc., DALLAS, TX; The Wendy's Company, DUBLIN, OH
Primary Distributors: (Food) Performance Foodservice - Batesville, BATESVILLE, MS; (Supplies) Performance Foodservice - Batesville, BATESVILLE, MS
Parent Company: Cerberus Capital Management LP, NEW YORK, NY

Key Personnel
JOE GODBEY - CEO; President
MIKE MASON - VP Real Estate
JOE RECAREY - Director
DENNIS ANDRA - Director Purchasing

Pacific Meritage
2236 Camino Ramon
San Ramon, CA 94583-1351

Mailing Address: PO Box 1547, SAN RAMON, CA, 94583-6547
Telephone: (925) 854-5160
Fax Number: (925) 866-8426
Internet Homepage: ontheborder-norcal.com
Type of Business: Chain Restaurant Operator

Year Founded: 1975
Total Sales: $40,890,000 (e)
Alcohol Sales: 2%
Number of Employees: 360
Average Check: Breakfast(5); Lunch(8); Dinner(16)
Total Units: 10
Trade Names: Chili's Grill & Bar (5); On the Border Mexican Grill & Cantina (5)
Units Franchised From: 10
Preferred Square Footage: 3,000; 6,000
Preferred Location Types: Freestanding
Alcohol Served: Beer, Wine, Liquor
Primary Menu: Mexican (5); Southwest/Tex-Mex (5)
Areas of Operation: CA, HI, VA
Type of Foodservice: Casual Dining (10)
Franchise Affiliation: Chili's Grill & Bar, DALLAS, TX; On The Border LLC, IRVING, TX
Primary Distributors: (Full Line) SYSCO Food Services of Los Angeles Inc., WALNUT, CA

Key Personnel
KELLY SCARBROUGH - President Group
GREGG HARP - Area Director
KATHY DEXTER - Director Training, Recruitment

PacPizza LLC
220 Porter Dr Ste 100
San Ramon, CA 94583-9206

Telephone: (925) 838-8567
Fax Number: (925) 838-5801
Internet Homepage: pacpizza.com
Type of Business: Chain Restaurant Operator
Year Founded: 1997
Total Sales: $154,900,000 (e)
Alcohol Sales: 1%
Number of Employees: 2,830
Average Check: Lunch(20); Dinner(20)
Total Units: 126
Trade Names: Pizza Hut (126)
Units Franchised From: 126
Preferred Square Footage: 2,500
Preferred Location Types: Community Mall; Downtown; Freestanding; Regional Mall; Strip Mall
Alcohol Served: Beer
Primary Menu: Pizza (126)
Areas of Operation: CA, NV, OR
Type of Foodservice: Quick Serve (126)
Foodservice Management Venues: Schools
Franchise Affiliation: Pizza Hut Inc., PLANO, TX
Primary Distributors: (Full Line) McLane Foodservice, CARROLLTON, TX

Key Personnel
BRIAN THOMPSON - President; Partner
MIKE LONG - Partner
JAQUELINE CLOUD - Director Marketing, Training

ALAN FUSS - Director Finance
LISA HOUGH - Director Human Resources
CHRISTINA STEPHAN - Director Human Resources
BRUCE MCKINNON - Manager Operations, Real Estate

Straw Hat Restaurants Inc.
18 Crow Canyon Ct Ste 270
San Ramon, CA 94583-1774

Telephone: (925) 837-3400
Fax Number: (925) 820-1080
Internet Homepage: strawhatpizza.com
Company Email: admin@strawhatpizza.com
Type of Business: Chain Restaurant Operator
Year Founded: 1959
Systemwide Sales: $21,975,000 (e)
Total Sales: $2,342,000 (e)
Alcohol Sales: 5%
Number of Employees: 5
Average Check: Lunch(16); Dinner(18)
Internet Order Processing: Yes
Total Units: 29
Trade Names: Straw Hat Grill (1); Straw Hat Pizza (28)
Units Franchised To: 29
Preferred Square Footage: 3,500
Preferred Location Types: Community Mall; Downtown; Freestanding; Regional Mall; Strip Mall
Alcohol Served: Beer, Wine
Primary Menu: Pizza (29)
Areas of Operation: CA, MT, NV, TX
Type of Foodservice: Casual Dining (28); Quick Serve (1)
Catering Services: Yes

Key Personnel
SAL LISTEK - Chairman; President
SCOTT MASON - Director Operations, Region
LISA PARTLOW - Director Finance
DENISE JONGERIUS - Director

Vitality Bowls
211 Market Pl
San Ramon, CA 94583-4743

Telephone: (925) 804-6012
Fax Number: (925) 833-1167
Internet Homepage: vitalitybowls.com
Company Email: info@vitalitybowls.com
Type of Business: Chain Restaurant Operator
Year Founded: 2011
Total Sales: $58,590,000 (e)
Total Units: 74
Trade Names: Vitality Bowls (71)
Company-Owned Units: 6
Units Franchised To: 65
Primary Menu: Health Foods (71)
Projected Openings: 2

Areas of Operation: CA, CO, FL, GA, IN, KS, MO, NC, NE, NV, NY, OH, OR, PA, TX, VA, WA
Type of Foodservice: Quick Serve (71)

Key Personnel
TARA GILAD - Co-Founder
ROY GILAD - Co-Founder; CEO
URIAH BLUM - VP Operations

Wenwest Inc
495 Elder Ave Ste C
Sand City, CA 93955-3547

Telephone: (831) 393-1185
Type of Business: Chain Restaurant Operator
Year Founded: 1976
Total Sales: $11,807,000 (e)
Number of Employees: 150
Average Check: Lunch(8); Dinner(8)
Total Units: 4
Trade Names: Wendy's Old Fashioned Hamburgers (4)
Units Franchised From: 4
Preferred Square Footage: 2,100; 2,900
Preferred Location Types: Freestanding
Primary Menu: Hamburger (4)
Areas of Operation: CA
Type of Foodservice: Quick Serve (4)
Franchise Affiliation: The Wendy's Company, DUBLIN, OH
Primary Distributors: (Full Line) Systems Services of America, FONTANA, CA

Key Personnel
EUGENE DOWLEN - Owner; General Buyer

Javier Torres Inc.
295 Academy Ave
Sanger, CA 93657-2128

Telephone: (559) 875-9119
Fax Number: (559) 875-8319
Type of Business: Chain Restaurant Operator
Total Sales: $61,400,000 (e)
Number of Employees: 325
Average Check: Breakfast(6); Lunch(8); Dinner(8)
Total Units: 13
Trade Names: McDonald's (13)
Units Franchised From: 13
Preferred Square Footage: 2,500; 3,000
Preferred Location Types: Freestanding
Primary Menu: Hamburger (13)
Areas of Operation: CA
Type of Foodservice: Quick Serve (13)
Franchise Affiliation: McDonald's Corporation, CHICAGO, IL
Primary Distributors: (Full Line) The Martin-Brower Co., STOCKTON, CA

Key Personnel
JAVIER TORRES - President; Partner; General Manager; General Buyer
BETTY TORRES - Partner

Far West Restaurant Group LLC
3720 S Susan St Ste 120
Santa Ana, CA 92704-6957

Telephone: (714) 868-7000
Fax Number: (714) 868-7011
Type of Business: Chain Restaurant Operator
Total Sales: $105,770,000 (e)
Total Units: 53
Trade Names: Wingstop (53)
Units Franchised From: 53
Primary Menu: Chicken (53)
Projected Openings: 3
Areas of Operation: CA
Type of Foodservice: Fast Casual (53)
Franchise Affiliation: Wingstop Restaurants Inc., DALLAS, TX

Key Personnel
DANIEL SONENSHINE - President
PATRICK GOITIA - CFO
JORGE ORTIZ - Exec VP Operations
KERRI SONENSHINE - VP Marketing
DEEPAK DAKIL - VP Finance
RAJNESH SINGH - Director Development
BIBIANA BECERRIL - District Manager

Nekter Franchise Inc.
1844 Carnegie Ave
Santa Ana, CA 92705-5545

Telephone: (800) 385-1650
Internet Homepage: nekterjuicebar.com
Company Email: info@nekterjuicebar.com
Type of Business: Chain Restaurant Operator
Year Founded: 2010
Systemwide Sales: $186,580,000 (e)
Total Units: 158
Trade Names: Nekter Juice Bar (142)
Company-Owned Units: 42
Units Franchised To: 100
Preferred Square Footage: 1,200
Primary Menu: Health Foods (142)
Projected Openings: 75
Areas of Operation: AZ, CA, CO, IN, MN, NC, NV, OH, OR, TX, UT, WA
Type of Foodservice: Fast Casual (142)

Key Personnel
STEVE SCHULZE - Co-Founder; CEO; President
ALEXIS SCHULZE - Co-Founder; Chief Development Officer
JOHN ASHER - Director Digital Marketing

ALANA HAMADA - Executive Assistant

Poke-Ria
1935 E 17th St Ste C
Santa Ana, CA 92705-6859

Telephone: (714) 285-9221
Internet Homepage: poke-ria.com
Company Email: info@poke-ria.com
Type of Business: Chain Restaurant Operator
Total Units: 3
Trade Names: Poke-Ria (3)
Company-Owned Units: 3
Primary Menu: American (3)
Areas of Operation: CA
Type of Foodservice: Fast Casual (3)

Key Personnel
MIKE JOHER - Partner; General Buyer
CHADE JOHER - Partner

Tay Ho Food Corp.
2430 Cape Cod Way
Santa Ana, CA 92703-3540

Telephone: (714) 973-2286
Fax Number: (714) 541-0683
Internet Homepage: tayho.com
Company Email: info@tayho.com
Type of Business: Chain Restaurant Operator
Year Founded: 1986
Systemwide Sales: $3,548,000 (e)
Total Sales: $681,000 (e)
Number of Employees: 50
Average Check: Breakfast(10); Lunch(10); Dinner(10)
Total Units: 7
Trade Names: Banh Cuon Tay Ho (7)
Units Franchised To: 7
Preferred Location Types: Freestanding
Primary Menu: Asian (7)
Areas of Operation: CA
Type of Foodservice: Fast Casual (7)
On-site Distribution Center: Yes

Key Personnel
JAYCE YENSON - Owner; General Manager; Executive Chef; Director Operations; General Buyer

The Kickin' Crab
3611 S Bristol St Ste C
Santa Ana, CA 92704-7311

Telephone: (714) 754-8888
Internet Homepage: thekickincrab.com
Company Email: info@kickincrab.com
Type of Business: Chain Restaurant Operator
Total Units: 18

Trade Names: Kickin' Crab (18)
Company-Owned Units: 18
Primary Menu: Seafood (18)
Areas of Operation: CA
Type of Foodservice: Casual Dining (18)

Key Personnel
JANE NGUYEN - President
VIVIAN NGUYEN - Supervisor

Wahoo's Fish Taco LLC
2855 Pullman St
Santa Ana, CA 92705-5713

Telephone: (949) 222-0670
Fax Number: (949) 222-0750
Internet Homepage: wahoos.com
Company Email: info@wahoos.com
Type of Business: Chain Restaurant Operator
Year Founded: 1988
Systemwide Sales: $45,899,000 (e)
Total Sales: $40,680,000 (e)
Alcohol Sales: 3%
Number of Employees: 535
Average Check: Lunch(10); Dinner(12)
Internet Order Processing: Yes
Internet Sales: 1.00%
Total Units: 46
Trade Names: Wahoo's Fish Taco (47)
Company-Owned Units: 22
Units Franchised To: 25
Preferred Square Footage: 2,500
Preferred Location Types: Freestanding; Strip Mall
Alcohol Served: Beer, Wine
Primary Menu: Taco (47)
Areas of Operation: CA, CO, HI, NE, NV, PA, TX
Foreign Countries: JAPAN
Type of Foodservice: Fast Casual (47)
Catering Services: Yes
Primary Distributors: (Full Line) SYSCO Food Services of San Francisco Inc., FREMONT, CA
Notes: Company-owned stores operate as Lamkone Restaurants Inc.

Key Personnel
RENATO "MINGO" LEE - President; Partner; Director Finance, Risk Management, Design
WING LAM - Partner; VP Information Systems, Marketing
EDUARDO LEE - Partner; VP Real Estate, Construction, Strategic Planning, Store Fixtures; Corporate Secretary
JOE LEE - Partner; Director Purchasing, Facility/Maintenance, Supply Chain, Menu Development
STEVE KARFARIDIS - COO
TOM ORBE - VP Franchise Development
MARY ANN GROSSANO - Controller; Manager Information Technology

LISA KIM - Director Catering

Yogurtland Franchisee
2800 N Mam Street 1028
Santa Ana, CA 92705

Telephone: (714) 550-9322
Type of Business: Chain Restaurant Operator
Total Sales: $4,607,000 (e)
Total Units: 5
Trade Names: Yogurtland (5)
Units Franchised From: 5
Primary Menu: Snacks (5)
Areas of Operation: CA
Type of Foodservice: Quick Serve (5)
Franchise Affiliation: Yogurtland Franchising Inc., FARMERS BRANCH, TX

Key Personnel
SUNG OK - Owner; General Buyer

Harbor Santa Barbara Inc.
3313 State St Ste B
Santa Barbara, CA 93105-2697

Telephone: (805) 682-7108
Fax Number: (805) 682-7810
Internet Homepage: harborsb.com; harryssb.com; longboardsgrillsb.com; teeoffsb.com
Type of Business: Chain Restaurant Operator
Year Founded: 1988
Total Sales: $24,720,000 (e)
Alcohol Sales: 30%
Number of Employees: 475
Average Check: Lunch(28); Dinner(42)
Total Units: 6
Trade Names: El Paseo (1); Harbor Restaurant (1); Harry's Plaza Cafe (1); Longboard Grill (1); Scotch and Sirloin (1); Tee-off (1)
Company-Owned Units: 6
Preferred Square Footage: 5,500; 6,000
Preferred Location Types: Freestanding
Alcohol Served: Beer, Wine, Liquor
Primary Menu: Mexican (1); Seafood (1); Steak (2)
Areas of Operation: CA
Type of Foodservice: Fine Dining (3)
Catering Services: Yes
Primary Distributors: (Full Line) Jordano's Inc., SANTA BARBARA, CA

Key Personnel
DAVE PERRY - CFO; General Manager Human Resources
GESA HEGEMAN - General Manager
PAUL JAKUBOWSI - Director Operations, Purchasing, Supply Chain, Menu Development, Catering
TAMMY CORDERO - Manager Information Systems

Rusty's Pizza Parlors Inc.
228 W Carrillo St
Santa Barbara, CA 93101-3793

Telephone: (805) 963-9127
Fax Number: (805) 962-5054
Internet Homepage: rustyspizza.com
Company Email: comments@rustyspizza.com
Type of Business: Chain Restaurant Operator
Year Founded: 1968
Systemwide Sales: $20,099,000 (e)
Total Sales: $12,530,000 (e)
Alcohol Sales: 7%
Number of Employees: 250
Average Check: Lunch(12); Dinner(18)
Internet Order Processing: Yes
Total Units: 17
Trade Names: Rusty's Pizza Parlor (17)
Company-Owned Units: 8
Units Franchised To: 9
Preferred Square Footage: 3,000
Preferred Location Types: Freestanding; Strip Mall
Alcohol Served: Beer, Wine
Primary Menu: Pizza (17)
Areas of Operation: CA
Type of Foodservice: Casual Dining (17)
Primary Distributors: (Full Line) Jordano's Inc., SANTA BARBARA, CA

Key Personnel
TYLER DUNCAN - CEO; Partner
ROGER P. DUNCAN - President; Director Finance, Operations, Facility/Maintenance, Information Systems, Real Estate, Design, Franchising, Menu Development; General Buyer
CAROL J. DUNCAN - Partner; VP; Manager Risk Management, Advertising

Domino's Franchisee
3207 Cabrillo Ave
Santa Clara, CA 95051-2226

Telephone: (408) 241-2828
Type of Business: Chain Restaurant Operator
Total Sales: $45,059,000 (e)
Total Units: 22
Trade Names: Domino's (22)
Units Franchised From: 22
Primary Menu: Pizza (22)
Areas of Operation: CA
Type of Foodservice: Quick Serve (22)
Franchise Affiliation: Domino's Pizza Inc, ANN ARBOR, MI

Key Personnel
FARNAD FERDOWS - Owner; General Buyer

GR8 Subs Corporation
3937 Rivermark Plz
Santa Clara, CA 95054-4156

Telephone: (408) 477-2690
Type of Business: Chain Restaurant Operator
Total Sales: $5,987,000 (e)
Total Units: 4
Trade Names: Jersey Mike's Subs (4)
Units Franchised From: 4
Primary Menu: Sandwiches/Deli (4)
Areas of Operation: CA
Type of Foodservice: Quick Serve (4)
Franchise Affiliation: Jersey Mike's Franchise Systems, MANASQUAN, NJ

Key Personnel
CATHY BROWN - Partner; Area Director
MIKE BROWN - Partner

GPK Enterprises, Inc.
24783 Valley St
Santa Clarita, CA 91321-2628

Telephone: (661) 254-3877
Fax Number: (661) 799-0590
Company Email: garykehal@yahoo.com
Type of Business: Chain Restaurant Operator
Total Sales: $2,757,000 (e)
Total Units: 4
Trade Names: Subway (4)
Units Franchised From: 4
Primary Menu: Sandwiches/Deli (4)
Areas of Operation: CA
Type of Foodservice: Quick Serve (4)
Franchise Affiliation: Doctor's Associates Inc., MILFORD, CT

Key Personnel
GURDAS KEHAL - President; General Buyer

Schutz Organization
26370 Diamond Pl Unit 500
Santa Clarita, CA 91350-2986

Telephone: (661) 253-5033
Fax Number: (661) 253-0317
Company Email: amjd@sbcglobal.net
Type of Business: Chain Restaurant Operator
Total Sales: $28,850,000 (e)
Total Units: 6
Trade Names: McDonald's (6)
Units Franchised From: 6
Preferred Location Types: Discount Dept. Stores; Freestanding
Primary Menu: Hamburger (6)
Areas of Operation: CA
Type of Foodservice: Quick Serve (6)
Franchise Affiliation: McDonald's Corporation,

CHICAGO, IL

Key Personnel
MARK SCHUTZ - President; Partner; General Buyer
JAY SCHUTZ - Partner

McDonald's Franchise
1421 Mission St
Santa Cruz, CA 95060-4738

Telephone: (408) 847-3588
Type of Business: Chain Restaurant Operator
Total Sales: $70,910,000 (e)
Total Units: 15
Trade Names: McDonald's (15)
Units Franchised From: 15
Primary Menu: Hamburger (15)
Areas of Operation: CA
Type of Foodservice: Quick Serve (15)
Franchise Affiliation: McDonald's Corporation, CHICAGO, IL

Key Personnel
STEVE PEAT - Partner; General Buyer
JAN PEAT - Partner; General Buyer

Santa Cruz Seaside Co. Inc.
400 Beach St
Santa Cruz, CA 95060-5416

Telephone: (831) 423-5590
Fax Number: (831) 460-3335
Internet Homepage: beachboardwalk.com
Company Email: guest.services@scseaside.com
Type of Business: Chain Restaurant Operator
Year Founded: 1915
Total Sales: $30,420,000 (e)
Alcohol Sales: 11%
Number of Employees: 140
Average Check: Lunch(8); Dinner(10)
Internet Order Processing: Yes
Internet Sales: 0.50%
Total Units: 20
Trade Names: Barbary Coast (1); Barnacle Bill's (1); BBQ Grill (1); Beach Tacos & Nachos (1); Boardwok (1); California Wraps (1); Captains Galley (1); Corndogs & Fries (1); Cruzin' Crepes (1); Dipper Diner (1); Fish N Fry (1); Fisherman's Galley (1); Hot Dawgs (1); Hot Dog on a Stick (1); Pizza Now (2); SenorTeds (2); Surf City Grill (1); World Grill (1)
Company-Owned Units: 18
Units Franchised From: 2
Preferred Location Types: Freestanding
Alcohol Served: Beer, Wine
Primary Menu: American (2); Asian (1); Californian (1); Chicken (1); Hamburger (2); Hot Dogs (4); Pizza (2); Sandwiches/Deli (1); Seafood (3); Taco (3)
Areas of Operation: CA
Type of Foodservice: Casual Dining (2); Quick Serve (18)
On-site Distribution Center: Yes

Key Personnel
CHARLES CANFIELD - Chairman
KARL RICE - President; VP Finance; Controller; General Buyer
DONNA MEKIS - President
TOM CANFIELD - Exec VP
OMID AMINIFARD - VP Operations
MERRY CROWEN - VP
MAGGIE KLINE - Assistant VP
DEREK WOLF - Controller
LELA VASQUEZ - General Manager
EVERARD SIMONPILLAI - Director Foodservice
SONDRA WOODS - Director Advertising
ROB KNIGHT - Director Digital
SCOTT HERNANDEZ-JASON - Director Public Relations
LISA AKESON - Director Real Estate
TODD ANDERSON - Director Development
ERIC SUMMERS - Director Finance
JESSICA ALFARO - Director Operations
PAUL SCHELL - Assistant Director Procurement
ABBI DAVIS - Associate Director Development
GEOFFREY SMITH - Manager Engineering, Construction
CHRIS SALERNO - Manager Facility/Maintenance; Coordinator Event Planning
TRACI TAKEUCHI - Manager Sales, Catering
CAROLINA DACOSTA - Manager; Administrative Assistant
ANNA BARRINGER - Manager Administration
JENNY BROWN - Manager Administration
CAMERON DE LEON - Manager Administration
CAITLIN MCCORMICK - Manager Business Development
BRETT EYMARD - Manager Catering
BRIGID FULLER - Manager Communications
IVAN DITMARS - Manager Compliance
AMANDA MARSHALL - Manager Design
WOODY CARROLL - Manager Digital Media
MARLENE ROBINSON - Manager Engineering
KELLY SAUDER - Manager Finance
ROGELIO GUZMAN - Manager Food and Beverage
ROSE WHITE - Manager Foodservice
AARON MELGARES - Manager Help Desk
GILLIAN MCGUIRE - Manager Human Resources
DIANE SCHMIDT - Manager Human Resources
ROBIN REID - Manager Operations
COLE STEELE - Manager Operations
RILEY JORDAN - Manager Promotion
STEVE DAVIS - Manager Purchasing
PAUL HOUGHTALING - Manager Research & Development
AMY FIGEL - Manager
SUSAN LEACH - Manager
MARK HERSEY - Manager Technology
KEVIN SAMSON - Manager Sales

El Gallo Giro
12764 Florence Ave
Santa Fe Springs, CA 90670-3906

Telephone: (562) 904-7088
Fax Number: (562) 904-7085
Internet Homepage: gallogiro.com
Company Email: comments@gallogiro.com
Type of Business: Chain Restaurant Operator
Year Founded: 1987
Total Sales: $14,110,000 (e)
Number of Employees: 40
Average Check: Breakfast(12); Lunch(12); Dinner(12)
Total Units: 11
Trade Names: El Gallo Giro (11)
Company-Owned Units: 11
Preferred Square Footage: 5,500; 6,000
Preferred Location Types: Freestanding; Strip Mall
Primary Menu: Mexican (11)
Areas of Operation: CA
Type of Foodservice: Family Restaurant (11)
Catering Services: Yes
Primary Distributors: (Full Line) SYSCO Food Services of Sacramento Inc., PLEASANT GROVE, CA

Key Personnel
CHARLES BONAPARTE - CEO; Executive Chef; Director Purchasing, Real Estate, Design, Menu Development, Catering
JUDITH HERNANDEZ - Director Human Resources
MIGUEL SOLIS - Director Operations

La Pizza Loca Distribution Center
12251 Florence Ave
Santa Fe Springs, CA 90670-3805

Telephone: (562) 946-1972
Fax Number: (562) 946-3702
Listing Type: Distribution Center
Type of Business: Chain Restaurant Operator
Areas of Operation: CA
Parent Company: Meruelo Group, SANTA FE SPRINGS, CA

Key Personnel
JUAN JAMES - General Manager; General Buyer

Meruelo Group
12251 Florence Ave
Santa Fe Springs, CA 90670

Telephone: (562) 946-1972
Fax Number: (562) 862-7989
Internet Homepage: lapizzaloca.com
Company Email: contacts@lapizzaloca.com
Type of Business: Chain Restaurant Operator
Year Founded: 1986
Systemwide Sales: $26,798,000 (e)
Total Sales: $16,170,000 (e)
Number of Employees: 620
Average Check: Lunch(8); Dinner(8)
Internet Order Processing: Yes
Total Units: 32
Trade Names: La Pizza Loca (32)
Company-Owned Units: 23
Units Franchised To: 9
Preferred Square Footage: 800; 1,200
Preferred Location Types: Freestanding; Strip Mall
Primary Menu: Pizza (32)
Areas of Operation: CA
Type of Foodservice: Quick Serve (32)
Foodservice Management Venues: Schools
Distribution Centers: SANTA FE SPRINGS, CA
On-site Distribution Center: Yes
Primary Distributors: (Full Line) SYSCO Food Services of Los Angeles Inc., WALNUT, CA

Key Personnel
JAVIER BENCOMO - President Operations
BRYAN TELLADO - President Finance; CFO
ALEX MERUELO - Owner
AL STOLLER - CFO
DAVID GRAY - VP Engineering
DEAN LIUZZI - Controller
DIANA SINCLARE - Supervisor Risk Management, Human Resources

Praise IAG Franchisor LLC
14071 Stage Rd
Santa Fe Springs, CA 90670-5225

Telephone: (949) 752-5282
Fax Number: (949) 752-5283
Internet Homepage: gloriajeans.com; itsagrind.com
Company Email: customerservice@gloriajeans.com
Type of Business: Chain Restaurant Operator
Year Founded: 2009
Total Sales: $1,911,000 (e)
Number of Employees: 40
Average Check: Breakfast(8); Lunch(8); Dinner(10)
Internet Order Processing: Yes
Internet Sales: 20.00%
Total Units: 79
Trade Names: Gloria Jean's Gourmet Coffee (60); It's A Grind Coffee House (19)
Company-Owned Units: 1
Units Franchised To: 78
Preferred Square Footage: 1,200; 1,700; 3,500
Preferred Location Types: Grocery Stores; Other; Strip Mall; Travel Plazas
Primary Menu: Coffee (79)
Areas of Operation: AZ, CA, CO, CT, FL, GA, IL, IN, KY, MA, MI, MO, NC, ND, NH, NJ, NV, NY, OH, PA, SC, TN, TX, UT, WI, WV
Type of Foodservice: Fast Casual (79)
Catering Services: Yes
Distribution Centers: IRVINE, CA
On-site Distribution Center: Yes

Key Personnel
SAM SERRERIA - CEO; President

Milt Guggia Enterprises Inc.
719 S McClelland St
Santa Maria, CA 93454-5122

Mailing Address: PO Box 5459, SANTA MARIA, CA, 93456-5459
Telephone: (805) 925-1594
Fax Number: (805) 925-1794
Internet Homepage: the-pantry-on-park.cafes-city.com; ajspurs.com; crackedcrab.com; pappysseafood.com; peasoupandersens.net
Type of Business: Chain Restaurant Operator
Year Founded: 1978
Total Sales: $20,603,000 (e)
Alcohol Sales: 25%
Number of Employees: 338
Average Check: Breakfast(6); Lunch(10); Dinner(20)
Total Units: 12
Trade Names: A J Spurs (3); Crumbles Bake Shop (1); Jetty's (1); Pantry on Park (1); Pappy's (1); Pea Soup Andersen's (2); Pepper Garcia's (1); Shaw's Restaurant (1); The Cracked Crab (1)
Company-Owned Units: 11
Units Franchised From: 1
Preferred Square Footage: 15,000; 17,000; 20,000
Preferred Location Types: Freestanding
Alcohol Served: Beer, Wine, Liquor
Primary Menu: American (7); Mexican (1); Seafood (1); Steak (3)
Areas of Operation: CA
Type of Foodservice: Casual Dining (11); Quick Serve (1)
On-site Distribution Center: Yes
Primary Distributors: (Full Line) Jordano's Inc., SANTA BARBARA, CA

Key Personnel
MILT GUGGIA - President; Executive Chef; Director Operations, Real Estate; General Buyer
ANGELA GUGGIA - VP
KEVIN GALVIN - Manager Advertising

Elite Restaurant Concepts
1531 12th St Unit 105
Santa Monica, CA 90401-3035

Telephone: (310) 430-3171
Type of Business: Chain Restaurant Operator
Total Sales: $9,465,000 (e)
Total Units: 6
Trade Names: Rally's Hamburgers (6)
Units Franchised From: 6
Primary Menu: Hamburger (6)
Areas of Operation: CA
Type of Foodservice: Quick Serve (6)
Franchise Affiliation: Checkers Drive-In Restaurants Inc., TAMPA, FL

Key Personnel
FARIDA DELAWALLA - Partner
NOORALI DELAWALLA - Partner; General Buyer

House of An
2700 Colorado Ave
Santa Monica, CA 90404-3553

Telephone: (323) 460-4387
Fax Number: (310) 828-4042
Internet Homepage: houseofan.com
Type of Business: Chain Restaurant Operator
Year Founded: 1971
Total Sales: $56,090,000 (e)
Alcohol Sales: 25%
Number of Employees: 90
Average Check: Lunch(36); Dinner(78)
Total Units: 6
Trade Names: ANQI (1); Crustacean Beverly Hills (1); Crustacean San Francisco (1); Da Lat Rose (1); Thanh Long (1); Tiato Santa Monica (1)
Company-Owned Units: 6
Preferred Location Types: Freestanding; Strip Mall
Alcohol Served: Beer, Wine, Liquor
Primary Menu: Asian (6)
Projected Openings: 1
Areas of Operation: CA
Type of Foodservice: Fine Dining (6)
Catering Services: Yes
Primary Distributors: (Full Line) US Foods-Los Angeles, LA MIRADA, CA

Key Personnel
ELIZABETH AN - CEO; Partner
MONIQUE AN - Partner
HELENE AN - Executive Chef; Director Menu Development

Michael's Restaurant
1147 3rd St
Santa Monica, CA 90403-5005

Telephone: (310) 451-0843
Fax Number: (310) 394-1830
Internet Homepage: michaelsnewyork.com; michaelssantamonica.com
Company Email: info@michaelssantamonica.com
Type of Business: Chain Restaurant Operator
Year Founded: 1979
Total Sales: $12,134,000 (e)
Alcohol Sales: 10%
Number of Employees: 50
Average Check: Breakfast(24); Lunch(30); Dinner(90)
Internet Order Processing: Yes
Total Units: 2
Trade Names: Michael's Restaurant (2)
Company-Owned Units: 2
Preferred Location Types: Freestanding; Other
Alcohol Served: Beer, Wine, Liquor
Primary Menu: Californian (2)
Areas of Operation: CA, NY
Type of Foodservice: Fine Dining (2)
Catering Services: Yes
Primary Distributors: (Full Line) SYSCO Food Services of San Francisco Inc., FREMONT, CA

Key Personnel
MICHAEL MCCARTY - President; Partner; General Buyer
CHAS MCCARTY - Partner
STEVE MILLINGTON - General Manager; General Buyer
KYUNG UP LIM - Executive Chef
JEFF LUSTRE - Executive Chef

Sweetfin Poke
829 Broadway
Santa Monica, CA 90401-3500

Telephone: (310) 395-1097
Internet Homepage: sweetfinpoke.com
Company Email: info@sweetfin.com
Type of Business: Chain Restaurant Operator
Total Units: 10
Trade Names: Sweetfin Poke (10)
Company-Owned Units: 10
Primary Menu: Californian (10)
Projected Openings: 3
Areas of Operation: CA
Type of Foodservice: Fast Casual (10)

Key Personnel
SETH COHEN - Founder; Co-Founder
BRETT NESTADT - Co-Founder; Partner

ALAN NATHAN - Partner

The Enterprise Fish Company
174 Kinney St
Santa Monica, CA 90405-5302

Telephone: (310) 392-8366
Fax Number: (310) 392-8017
Internet Homepage: enterprisefishco.com; hurrycurryoftokyo.com
Type of Business: Chain Restaurant Operator
Year Founded: 1978
Total Sales: $12,244,000 (e)
Alcohol Sales: 20%
Number of Employees: 85
Average Check: Lunch(18); Dinner(30)
Total Units: 4
Trade Names: Hurry Curry of Tokyo (2); The Enterprise Fish Company (2)
Company-Owned Units: 4
Preferred Location Types: Freestanding
Alcohol Served: Beer, Wine, Liquor
Primary Menu: Japanese (2); Seafood (2)
Areas of Operation: CA
Type of Foodservice: Casual Dining (4)
Primary Distributors: (Full Line) SYSCO Food Services of Los Angeles Inc., WALNUT, CA

Key Personnel
RANDY LAFERR - Partner; Executive Chef
FRED SERRA - COO

Cattlemens Inc.
250 Dutton Ave
Santa Rosa, CA 95407-6805

Telephone: (707) 528-1040
Fax Number: (707) 571-7762
Internet Homepage: cattlemens.com/restaurants
Type of Business: Chain Restaurant Operator
Year Founded: 1968
Total Sales: $35,540,000 (e)
Alcohol Sales: 15%
Number of Employees: 650
Average Check: Dinner(32)
Internet Order Processing: Yes
Internet Sales: 0.50%
Total Units: 8
Trade Names: Cattlemens (8)
Company-Owned Units: 8
Preferred Square Footage: 10,000
Preferred Location Types: Freestanding
Alcohol Served: Beer, Wine, Liquor
Primary Menu: Steak (8)
Areas of Operation: CA
Type of Foodservice: Casual Dining (8)
Catering Services: Yes
Primary Distributors: (Food) US Foods - San Diego, VISTA, CA

Key Personnel
WAYNE HOLLOWAY - CEO; President
KATHIE BURNS - Director Human Resources
LUCAS SURBURG - Director Operations

Subway Franchise
1435 Santa Rosa Ave Ste C1
Santa Rosa, CA 95404-5400

Telephone: (707) 542-2000
Type of Business: Chain Restaurant Operator
Total Sales: $3,444,000 (e)
Total Units: 6
Trade Names: Subway (6)
Units Franchised From: 6
Primary Menu: Sandwiches/Deli (6)
Areas of Operation: CA
Type of Foodservice: Quick Serve (6)
Franchise Affiliation: Doctor's Associates Inc., MILFORD, CT

Key Personnel
KAMAL GREWAR - President; General Buyer

Takeg Enterprises, Inc.
2280 Mendocino Ave Ste B4
Santa Rosa, CA 95403

Telephone: (707) 571-1888
Type of Business: Chain Restaurant Operator
Total Sales: $1,884,000 (e)
Total Units: 3
Trade Names: Cold Stone Creamery (3)
Units Franchised From: 3
Primary Menu: Snacks (3)
Areas of Operation: CA
Type of Foodservice: Quick Serve (3)
Franchise Affiliation: Kahala Brands, SCOTTSDALE, AZ

Key Personnel
TRUDY A. GRABENAUER - Partner

Wyvern Restaurants, Inc
575 W College Ave Ste 201
Santa Rosa, CA 95401-5079

Telephone: (707) 545-7447
Fax Number: (707) 545-4386
Internet Homepage: rtwyvern.com
Type of Business: Chain Restaurant Operator
Total Sales: $12,170,000 (e)
Total Units: 11
Trade Names: Round Table Pizza (11)
Units Franchised From: 11
Primary Menu: Pizza (11)
Areas of Operation: CA, WA

Type of Foodservice: Casual Dining (11)
Franchise Affiliation: Round Table Franchise Corp., CONCORD, CA

Key Personnel
MICHAEL CARNEY - President; General Buyer

Subs Enterprises, Inc.
9331 Mission Gorge Rd Ste 110
Santee, CA 92071-3883

Telephone: (619) 456-9577
Type of Business: Chain Restaurant Operator
Total Sales: $4,506,000 (e)
Total Units: 3
Trade Names: Jersey Mike's Subs (3)
Units Franchised From: 3
Primary Menu: Sandwiches/Deli (3)
Areas of Operation: CA
Type of Foodservice: Quick Serve (3)
Franchise Affiliation: Jersey Mike's Franchise Systems, MANASQUAN, NJ

Key Personnel
RAY IBRAHIM - Owner; General Buyer

Sushma Gupta
15000 Blue Gum Ct
Saratoga, CA 95070-6268

Telephone: (408) 621-6784
Type of Business: Chain Restaurant Operator
Total Sales: $8,237,000 (e)
Total Units: 3
Trade Names: Jack in the Box (3)
Units Franchised From: 3
Primary Menu: Hamburger (3)
Areas of Operation: CA
Type of Foodservice: Quick Serve (3)
Franchise Affiliation: Jack in the Box Restaurants, SAN DIEGO, CA

Key Personnel
SUSHMA GUPTA - Owner; General Buyer

Jacara Restaurants, Inc.
26510 Bouquet Canyon Rd
Saugus, CA 91350-2353

Telephone: (661) 296-1910
Type of Business: Chain Restaurant Operator
Total Sales: $6,733,000 (e)
Total Units: 5
Trade Names: Jersey Mike's Subs (5)
Units Franchised From: 5
Primary Menu: Sandwiches/Deli (5)
Areas of Operation: CA
Type of Foodservice: Quick Serve (5)
Franchise Affiliation: Jersey Mike's Franchise Systems, MANASQUAN, NJ

Key Personnel
STEPHEN J. YOULIOS - Partner
LAURA YOULIOS - Partner

Taco Surf
115 Main St
Seal Beach, CA 90740

Telephone: (562) 594-0600
Internet Homepage: tacosurf.com
Company Email: contact@tacosurf.com
Type of Business: Chain Restaurant Operator
Total Units: 5
Trade Names: Taco Surf (5)
Company-Owned Units: 5
Primary Menu: Mexican (5)
Areas of Operation: CA
Type of Foodservice: Casual Dining (5)

Key Personnel
SAM MCLARTY - Partner

F. McLintocks Inc.
750 Mattie Rd
Shell Beach, CA 93449-2059

Mailing Address: PO Box 239, PISMO BEACH, CA, 93448-0239
Telephone: (805) 773-1892
Fax Number: (805) 773-5183
Internet Homepage: mclintocks.com
Company Email: fmc@mclintocks.com
Type of Business: Chain Restaurant Operator
Year Founded: 1973
Total Sales: $13,802,000 (e)
Alcohol Sales: 18%
Number of Employees: 260
Average Check: Breakfast(10); Lunch(12); Dinner(24)
Internet Order Processing: Yes
Internet Sales: 2.00%
Total Units: 4
Trade Names: F. McLintocks Dining House (1), F. McLintocks Saloon (3)
Company-Owned Units: 4
Preferred Square Footage: 25,000
Preferred Location Types: Downtown; Freestanding
Alcohol Served: Beer, Wine, Liquor
Primary Menu: American (3); Steak/Seafood (1)
Areas of Operation: CA
Type of Foodservice: Casual Dining (4)
Distribution Centers: SAN LUIS OBISPO, CA
On-site Distribution Center: Yes
Primary Distributors: (Food) Jordano's Inc., SANTA BARBARA, CA

Key Personnel
TONEY BREAULT - President; Director Facility/Maintenance, Store Fixtures; Buyer Beverages
JAY BRITTON - VP
BILL WHITE - Director Human Resources
VICTOR ALBARRAN - Manager Purchasing; General Buyer

Angry Chickz
15301 Ventura Boulevard Building B
Suite 250
Sherman Oaks, CA 91403

Telephone: (818) 578-4394
Internet Homepage: angrychickz.com
Type of Business: Chain Restaurant Operator
Year Founded: 2018
Systemwide Sales: $36,059,000 (e)
Total Sales: $22,254,000 (e)
Total Units: 27
Trade Names: Angry Chickz (27)
Company-Owned Units: 1
Units Franchised To: 26
Primary Menu: Chicken (27)
Areas of Operation: AZ, CA, NV
Type of Foodservice: Quick Serve (27)

Key Personnel
DAVID MKHITARYAN - Founder; CEO; Owner
JOHN SCOTT - CFO
MIKE LARUE - VP Franchise Development
WILLIAM LOPEZ - VP Operations
CHRISTOPHER WADLEIGH - VP Development
TONYA MCCOY - VP Marketing

Domino's Franchisee
4467 Van Nuys Blvd
Sherman Oaks, CA 91403-2911

Telephone: (818) 783-3900
Type of Business: Chain Restaurant Operator
Total Sales: $4,167,000 (e)
Total Units: 2
Trade Names: Domino's (2)
Units Franchised From: 2
Primary Menu: Pizza (2)
Areas of Operation: CA
Type of Foodservice: Quick Serve (2)
Franchise Affiliation: Domino's Pizza Inc, ANN ARBOR, MI

Key Personnel
PAUL M. MAHONEY - Owner; General Buyer

Galaxy Theatres, LLC
15060 Ventura Blvd Ste 350
Sherman Oaks, CA 91403-2484

Telephone: (818) 986-9000
Internet Homepage: galaxytheatres.com
Company Email: corpinfo@galaxytheatres.com
Type of Business: Foodservice Operations - Movie Theatre
Year Founded: 1998
Total Sales: $21,939,000 (e)
Average Check: Dinner(8)
Internet Order Processing: Yes
Total Units: 15
Trade Names: Galaxy Theatres (15)
Company-Owned Units: 15
Primary Menu: Snacks (15)
Areas of Operation: CA, NV, TX, WA
Type of Foodservice: In-Store Feeder (15)

Key Personnel
FRANK RIMKUS - CEO
RAFE COHEN - President; COO
ROBERT HILL - Director Software
ROSIE RAMIREZ - Manager Marketing

Louise's Trattoria Inc.
15335 Morrison St Ste 240
Sherman Oaks, CA 91403-6701

Telephone: (818) 788-0500
Fax Number: (818) 501-5186
Internet Homepage: holycowbbq.com; louises.com; messhallkitchen.com
Company Email: cmorris@louises.com
Type of Business: Chain Restaurant Operator
Year Founded: 1985
Total Sales: $9,035,000 (e)
Alcohol Sales: 15%
Number of Employees: 290
Average Check: Lunch(18); Dinner(42)
Internet Order Processing: Yes
Total Units: 6
Trade Names: Holy Cow BB-Q (2); Louise's Trattoria (3); Messhall (1)
Company-Owned Units: 6
Preferred Square Footage: 3,000
Preferred Location Types: Freestanding; Strip Mall
Alcohol Served: Beer, Wine, Liquor
Primary Menu: American (1); Bar-B-Q (2); Italian (3)
Areas of Operation: CA
Type of Foodservice: Casual Dining (6)
Catering Services: Yes
Primary Distributors: (Full Line) SYSCO Food Services of Sacramento Inc., PLEASANT GROVE, CA

Key Personnel
ROBERT SERRITELLA - Owner; Executive Chef; Director Purchasing, Real Estate, Design, Menu Development

Lucky Strike Entertainment
15260 Ventura Blvd Ste 1110
Sherman Oaks, CA 91403-5346

Telephone: (818) 933-3752
Fax Number: (818) 933-3750
Internet Homepage: bowlluckystrike.com
Company Email: info@bowlluckystrike.com
Type of Business: Foodservice Operations - Bowling Alley
Year Founded: 2003
Total Sales: $160,070,000 (e)
Alcohol Sales: 5%
Number of Employees: 122
Average Check: Lunch(12); Dinner(12)
Total Units: 20
Trade Names: Lucky Strike Lanes (20)
Company-Owned Units: 20
Preferred Square Footage: 2,500
Preferred Location Types: Freestanding; Strip Mall
Alcohol Served: Beer, Wine, Liquor
Primary Menu: American (20)
Areas of Operation: CA, CO, DC, KY, MA, MI, NY, PA, ON
Foreign Countries: CANADA
Type of Foodservice: In-Store Feeder (20)
Primary Distributors: (Full Line) SYSCO Food Services of San Diego Inc., POWAY, CA
Notes: The company derives approximately 75% of its revenue from bowling operations.

Key Personnel
STEVEN FOSTER - CEO; Partner; Director Real Estate, Design
BRIAN ELIAS - Owner
GILLIAN FOSTER - Partner; Director Information Systems
KEVIN TROY - Partner
SEAN DAVIS - General Manager; Regional Director Operations
JENNIFER BURCHFIELD - Director Sales
JOSHUA MILLS - Senior Manager Event Planning
JONATHAN BLOOM - Manager Information Technology

Hofman Hospitality Group
2601 E Willow St
Signal Hill, CA 90755-2214

Telephone: (562) 596-0200
Fax Number: (562) 430-0480
Internet Homepage: saintandsecond.com; hofmangroup.com; hofshut.com; lucillesbbq.com; mightykitchen.com; spinpizza.com
Company Email: info@hofmangroup.com
Type of Business: Chain Restaurant Operator
Year Founded: 1951
Total Sales: $241,810,000 (e)
Alcohol Sales: 15%
Number of Employees: 2,580
Average Check: Breakfast(10); Lunch(10); Dinner(14)
Internet Order Processing: Yes
Total Units: 30
Trade Names: Hof's Hut Restaurant (3); Lucille's Smokehouse Bar-B-Que (26); Saint & Second (1)
Company-Owned Units: 30
Preferred Square Footage: 5,000
Preferred Location Types: Freestanding; Lifestyle Center
Alcohol Served: Beer, Wine, Liquor
Primary Menu: American (4); Bar-B-Q (26)
Areas of Operation: AZ, CA, NE, NV
Type of Foodservice: Casual Dining (29); Fine Dining (1)
On-site Distribution Center: Yes
Primary Distributors: (Full Line) US Foods-Los Angeles, LA MIRADA, CA

Key Personnel
BRAD HOFMAN - President
CHRISTOPHER CRAWLEY - CFO
JIM BERNACCHI - VP Operations
THERESA DECASAS - Controller
CRAIG HOFMAN - Director Finance, Real Estate
RYAN HOFMAN - Director Construction
JASON SININGER-WORD - Director Human Resources
DIRK HOFMAN - Director
JOAN HANSEN - Director Marketing
BRYCE RENN - Director Operating Systems
BRUCE GALLION - Director Customer Analytics
REBEKAH IRWIN - Manager Marketing
JENNIFER CHEA - Manager Finance

Flippin' Pizza International LLC
107 S Cedros Ave Ste 220
Solana Beach, CA 92075-1994

Telephone: (833) 346-3547
Fax Number: (855) 511-3777
Internet Homepage: flippinpizza.com
Company Email: info@flippinpizza.com
Type of Business: Chain Restaurant Operator
Year Founded: 2007
Systemwide Sales: $7,836,000 (e)
Total Sales: $279,000 (e)
Total Units: 20
Trade Names: Flippin' Pizza (20)
Company-Owned Units: 2
Units Franchised To: 18
Preferred Square Footage: 1,000; 1,500
Preferred Location Types: Downtown; Lifestyle Center; Mobile Unit; Office Complex; Regional Mall

Primary Menu: Pizza (20)
Areas of Operation: CA, DC, FL, GA, MD, TX, VA, FC
Foreign Countries: MEXICO; UNITED ARAB EMIRATES
Type of Foodservice: Quick Serve (20)
Catering Services: Yes

Key Personnel
HERMINIO LLEVAT - Chairman
CARLOS DURAZO - Partner
RICHARD WRIGHT - General Manager

Diversified Restaurant Group, LLC
465 1st St W Floor 2
Sonoma, CA 95476

Telephone: (707) 935-3700
Fax Number: (702) 880-5819
Internet Homepage: drgfood.com
Type of Business: Chain Restaurant Operator
Year Founded: 1967
Total Sales: $640,940,000 (e)
Number of Employees: 4,300
Average Check: Lunch(8); Dinner(8)
Internet Order Processing: Yes
Total Units: 248
Trade Names: Arby's (16); Taco Bell (226); Taco Bell Cantina (6)
Units Franchised From: 248
Preferred Square Footage: 3,400
Preferred Location Types: Community Mall; Freestanding
Primary Menu: Mexican (6); Sandwiches/Deli (16); Taco (226)
Areas of Operation: CA, KS, MO, NV
Type of Foodservice: Fast Casual (6); Quick Serve (242)
Franchise Affiliation: Taco Bell Corp., IRVINE, CA
Primary Distributors: (Food) McLane/Riverside, RIVERSIDE, CA

Key Personnel
DAVID GRIEVE - Chairman; CEO
SG ELLISON - President
TODD KELLY - CFO
BEN MARMOR - CFO
DANIEL PACKER - CIO; Exec VP
JAMES AMAN - Area Director
BOB SCHALOW - Senior VP
TOM DOUGLAS - VP
JOHN HOFFMAN - VP Business Development
KARA RAMIREZ - VP Operations
LAURY KETCHAM - Controller
RICH WIERZBOWSKI - Director Operations
GEORGE PSAROS - Director Loss Prevention
TRAVIS MASON - Director Operations
AMY LOYA - Director Human Resources
ISAIAH RITCHIE - Director Operations
BRANDON BECKER - Director Operations
CHRISTIE GLAESER - Director Operations
GURSIMRAN GHUMMAN - Director Operations
SEAN MCGUIRE - Director Operations
RONALD ROWE - Director Operations
SHANE GRANT - Director Operations
PATRICK THANTACHEVA - Director Risk Management, Legal, Human Resources, Compliance
MIKE SMITH - Director Facility/Maintenance
KEN PAROLINI - District Manager
GENO WOOLARD - District Manager
JON CASTRO - Manager Information Technology
BRITTANY PACKER - Coordinator Benefits

Mary's Pizza Shack of California Corp.
19327 Highway 12 STE 200
Sonoma, CA 95476-5445

Telephone: (707) 938-3602
Fax Number: (707) 938-5976
Internet Homepage: maryspizzashack.com
Company Email: info@maryspizzashack.com
Type of Business: Chain Restaurant Operator
Year Founded: 1959
Systemwide Sales: $32,312,000 (e)
Total Sales: $2,513,000 (e)
Alcohol Sales: 7%
Number of Employees: 714
Average Check: Lunch(14); Dinner(14)
Internet Order Processing: Yes
Total Units: 17
Trade Names: Mary's Pizza Shack (17)
Company-Owned Units: 13
Units Franchised To: 4
Preferred Square Footage: 3,600
Preferred Location Types: Freestanding; Strip Mall
Alcohol Served: Beer, Wine, Liquor
Primary Menu: Pizza (17)
Areas of Operation: CA
Type of Foodservice: Casual Dining (17)
Primary Distributors: (Equipment) Castino Restaurant Equipment & Supply Inc., ROHNERT PARK, CA; (Food) Saladino's Inc., FRESNO, CA; (Supplies) Castino Restaurant Equipment & Supply Inc., ROHNERT PARK, CA

Key Personnel
BRUCE LANE - Director Information Technology
VINCE DITO - Director Purchasing, Supply Chain, Menu Development, Food and Beverage
MIKE SHEPPARD - Manager Purchasing

Mangen Group
10814 Fawcett Ave
South El Monte, CA 91733

Telephone: (310) 417-8225
Fax Number: (949) 582-7031
Type of Business: Chain Restaurant Operator
Total Sales: $4,788,000 (e)
Total Units: 2
Trade Names: Burger King (2)
Units Franchised From: 2
Preferred Square Footage: 2,500
Primary Menu: Hamburger (2)
Areas of Operation: CA
Type of Foodservice: Quick Serve (2)
Franchise Affiliation: Burger King Worldwide Inc., MIAMI, FL

Key Personnel
HOWARD MANGEN - Owner; General Buyer
RYAN JACKSON - VP Operations
LEE JUCKETT - VP

Tapioca Express Inc.
1908 Central Ave
South El Monte, CA 91733-3324

Telephone: (626) 453-0777
Fax Number: (626) 453-0778
Internet Homepage: tapiocaexpress.com
Type of Business: Chain Restaurant Operator
Year Founded: 1999
Systemwide Sales: $21,425,000 (e)
Total Sales: $2,518,000 (e)
Number of Employees: 50
Average Check: Lunch(8); Dinner(8)
Total Units: 33
Trade Names: Tapioca Express (33)
Units Franchised To: 33
Preferred Square Footage: 2,500
Preferred Location Types: Freestanding; Regional Mall; Strip Mall
Primary Menu: Snacks (33)
Areas of Operation: CA, NV
Foreign Countries: CANADA
Type of Foodservice: Quick Serve (33)
On-site Distribution Center: Yes
Primary Distributors: (Food) MBM Corporation, PLEASANTON, CA

Key Personnel
CHENG-WEI LIN - CEO; President; Manager Menu Development; General Buyer
STEPHANIE HSUEH - CFO

Heidi's Family Restaurants Inc.
3485 Lake Tahoe Blvd
South Lake Tahoe, CA 96150-8950

Telephone: (530) 544-8113
Internet Homepage: heidisfamilyrestaurants.com; bearbeachcafe.com
Company Email: tellheidi@msn.com
Type of Business: Chain Restaurant Operator
Year Founded: 1963
Total Sales: $4,346,000 (e)
Alcohol Sales: 8%
Number of Employees: 150
Average Check: Breakfast(14); Lunch(16); Dinner(26)
Total Units: 2
Trade Names: Bear Beach Cafe (1); Heidi's Family Restaurant (1)
Company-Owned Units: 2
Preferred Square Footage: 3,500
Preferred Location Types: Freestanding; Hotel/Motel; Mixed-use Center; Strip Mall
Alcohol Served: Beer, Wine, Liquor
Primary Menu: American (2)
Areas of Operation: CA
Type of Foodservice: Casual Dining (1); Family Restaurant (1)
Primary Distributors: (Full Line) US Foods-Los Angeles, LA MIRADA, CA

Key Personnel
DONALD ROSENTHAL - Treasurer; Manager Finance, Information Systems, Supply Chain, Human Resources

V & K Food Corporation
2264 Lake Tahoe Blvd
South Lake Tahoe, CA 96150-7112

Telephone: (530) 542-1529
Fax Number: (530) 541-5559
Company Email: kfcpk@aol.com
Type of Business: Chain Restaurant Operator
Year Founded: 1984
Total Sales: $22,040,000 (e)
Number of Employees: 300
Average Check: Lunch(10); Dinner(10)
Total Units: 12
Trade Names: KFC (12)
Units Franchised From: 12
Preferred Square Footage: 2,000
Preferred Location Types: Community Mall; Freestanding
Primary Menu: Chicken (12)
Areas of Operation: CA, NV
Type of Foodservice: Quick Serve (12)
Franchise Affiliation: KFC Corporation, LOUISVILLE, KY

Key Personnel
WILLIAM VOLLENHALS - President; Controller
LISA KERN - CFO; Director Finance, Human Resources
PAT KERN - VP; Director Purchasing; General Buyer
CHRIS PORTER - General Manager; Director Operations

California Banquet Corp.
601 Fair Oaks Ave
South Pasadena, CA 91030-2601

Telephone: (626) 796-8866
Fax Number: (626) 796-8887
Internet Homepage: centralgrille.net; dineronmainrestaurant.net; shakersrestaurant.net; canoehouserestaurant.com; centralparkrestaurant.net
Company Email: calbanquet@sbcglobal.net
Type of Business: Chain Restaurant Operator
Year Founded: 1972
Total Sales: $17,220,000 (e)
Alcohol Sales: 10%
Number of Employees: 290
Average Check: Breakfast(8); Lunch(16); Dinner(20)
Total Units: 5
Trade Names: Canoe House (1); Central Grille (1); Central Park (1); Diner on Main (1); Shakers (1)
Company-Owned Units: 5
Preferred Square Footage: 4,000
Preferred Location Types: Freestanding
Alcohol Served: Beer, Wine, Liquor
Primary Menu: American (5)
Areas of Operation: CA
Type of Foodservice: Casual Dining (5)
Primary Distributors: (Full Line) SYSCO Food Services of Los Angeles Inc., WALNUT, CA

Key Personnel
DAVID YOST - President; Partner; Executive Chef; Director Operations, Facility/Maintenance, Information Systems, Real Estate, Design; General Buyer
RANDY HOFFMAN - Partner; CFO; VP; Director Finance, Purchasing, Human Resources

Max's Restaurants
120 E Grand Ave
South San Francisco, CA 94080-4803

Telephone: (650) 873-6297
Fax Number: (650) 873-6461
Internet Homepage: maxsworld.com
Type of Business: Chain Restaurant Operator
Year Founded: 1978
Total Sales: $36,220,000 (e)
Alcohol Sales: 15%
Number of Employees: 500
Average Check: Lunch(12); Dinner(18)
Total Units: 5
Trade Names: Max's Auburn (1); Max's Cafe (1); Max's Diner & Bar (1); Max's Opera Cafe (1); Max's Restaurant & Bar (1)
Company-Owned Units: 5
Preferred Square Footage: 1,500; 7,000
Preferred Location Types: Downtown; Freestanding
Alcohol Served: Beer, Wine, Liquor
Primary Menu: American (5)
Areas of Operation: CA
Type of Foodservice: Casual Dining (5)
Catering Services: Yes
Primary Distributors: (Full Line) BiRite Foodservice Distributors, BRISBANE, CA

Key Personnel
BILL BEROWITZ - Director Operations

Pacific Concessions Inc.
1819 Polk St Ste 372
South San Francisco, CA 94109

Telephone: (650) 794-9494
Fax Number: (650) 794-9490
Internet Homepage: pacificconcessions.com
Company Email: info@pacificconcessions.com
Type of Business: Foodservice Management Operator
Year Founded: 1974
Total Sales: $25,436,000 (e)
Number of Employees: 144
Number of Locations Served: 48
Total Foodservice Mgmt Accounts: 48
Areas of Operation: CA
Type of Foodservice: Quick Serve (48)
Foodservice Management Venues: Other

Key Personnel
DAN LIVAK - President
JOAN NAKANO - Controller
WOODY MIRAGLIA - Director Operations, Purchasing, Information Systems, Foodservice, Food Safety

Bambu Desserts & Drinks, Inc.
1304 E Hammer Ln
Stockton, CA 95210

Telephone: (888) 224-2469
Internet Homepage: drinkbambu.com
Type of Business: Chain Restaurant Operator
Year Founded: 2008
Systemwide Sales: $81,425,000 (e)
Total Sales: $63,390,000 (e)
Number of Employees: 700
Total Units: 66

Trade Names: Bambu Desserts & Drinks (66)
Company-Owned Units: 66
Units Franchised To: 66
Primary Menu: Coffee (66)
Areas of Operation: CA, CO, FL, IL, IN, KS, ME, MI, MN, NC, NJ, NV, NY, OR, PA, TX, UT, VA, WA, WI, AB, BC
Foreign Countries: CANADA
Type of Foodservice: Fast Casual (66)

Key Personnel
ANH NGUYEN - Founder; Partner
KELLY NGUYEN - Founder; Partner
JENNY NGUYEN - Founder; Partner
JULIE NGUYEN - Founder; Partner

Gus Chima
1540 E March Ln Ste 3
Stockton, CA 95210-5670

Telephone: (209) 951-9698
Fax Number: (209) 951-9699
Type of Business: Chain Restaurant Operator
Total Sales: $2,479,000 (e)
Total Units: 4
Trade Names: Subway (4)
Units Franchised From: 4
Primary Menu: Sandwiches/Deli (4)
Areas of Operation: CA
Type of Foodservice: Quick Serve (4)
Franchise Affiliation: Doctor's Associates Inc., MILFORD, CT

Key Personnel
GUS CHIMA - President; General Buyer

R Brothers Enterprises, LLC
874 W Benjamin Holt Dr
Stockton, CA 95207-3652

Telephone: (209) 475-1191
Type of Business: Chain Restaurant Operator
Total Sales: $1,920,000 (e)
Total Units: 5
Trade Names: Cold Stone Creamery (5)
Units Franchised From: 5
Primary Menu: Snacks (5)
Areas of Operation: CA
Type of Foodservice: Quick Serve (5)
Franchise Affiliation: Kahala Brands, SCOTTSDALE, AZ

Key Personnel
PRABHDEEP MANN - Partner; General Buyer
RAMNEEK SINGH - Partner; General Buyer

Redarhcs Inc.
4502 Georgetown Pl
Stockton, CA 95207-6202

Telephone: (209) 478-0234
Fax Number: (209) 478-5734
Type of Business: Chain Restaurant Operator
Year Founded: 1966
Total Sales: $158,290,000 (e)
Number of Employees: 1,320
Average Check: Breakfast(10); Lunch(12); Dinner(12)
Total Units: 34
Trade Names: McDonald's (34)
Units Franchised From: 34
Preferred Square Footage: 2,500; 3,000
Preferred Location Types: Freestanding; Regional Mall; Strip Mall
Primary Menu: Hamburger (34)
Areas of Operation: CA
Type of Foodservice: Quick Serve (34)
Franchise Affiliation: McDonald's Corporation, CHICAGO, IL
Primary Distributors: (Full Line) The Martin-Brower Co., STOCKTON, CA

Key Personnel
BECKY HARVEY - Director Purchasing
CINDY JONES - Director Operations, Facility/Maintenance
GRACIE RODRIGUEZ - Supervisor Accounting

Subway Sandwiches & Salads
4663 Pacific Ave
Stockton, CA 95207-7643

Telephone: (209) 473-4744
Internet Homepage: subway.com
Type of Business: Chain Restaurant Operator
Year Founded: 1998
Total Sales: $8,249,000 (e)
Number of Employees: 85
Average Check: Lunch(8); Dinner(8)
Total Units: 6
Trade Names: Subway (6)
Units Franchised From: 6
Preferred Square Footage: 300; 1,200; 2,000
Preferred Location Types: Freestanding; Strip Mall
Primary Menu: Sandwiches/Deli (6)
Areas of Operation: CA
Type of Foodservice: Quick Serve (6)
Catering Services: Yes
Franchise Affiliation: Doctor's Associates Inc., MILFORD, CT
Primary Distributors: (Full Line) Saladino's Inc., FRESNO, CA

Key Personnel
VINCE TIWANA - Owner; General Buyer

Kazi Foods Inc.
3671 Sunswept Dr
Studio City, CA 91604-2325

Mailing Address: PO Box 1378, STUDIO CITY, CA, 91604
Telephone: (818) 980-1185
Fax Number: (818) 980-9264
Company Email: info@kazifoods.com
Type of Business: Chain Restaurant Operator
Year Founded: 1993
Total Sales: $149,230,000 (e)
Number of Employees: 7,400
Average Check: Breakfast(8); Lunch(8); Dinner(10)
Total Units: 75
Trade Names: Burger King (25); KFC (50)
Units Franchised From: 75
Preferred Square Footage: 2,500
Preferred Location Types: Community Mall; Freestanding
Primary Menu: Chicken (50); Hamburger (25)
Areas of Operation: CA, CO, DC, FL, HI, LA, MD, MI, NJ, NY, PA, VI
Foreign Countries: FIJI
Type of Foodservice: Quick Serve (75)
Franchise Affiliation: Burger King Worldwide Inc., MIAMI, FL; KFC Corporation, LOUISVILLE, KY
Primary Distributors: (Food) McLane/Riverside, RIVERSIDE, CA
Regional Offices: Kazi Foods, HERSHEY, PA; Kazi Foods, HONOLULU, HI
Notes: IT Functions are handled by the Hershey PA regional office, and financial operations are handled by the Virgin Islands regional office.

Key Personnel
ZUBAIR KAZI - Chairman
BRIAN BURR - CEO; President
GRETA ZAKHARIAN - Area Director
JUAN MUJICA - General Manager
ALI ALII IEMMAT - Director Operations
FATIMA KAZI - Business Manager
STEPHEN POLUDNIAK - Manager Legal
IRENE KOSASIH - Administrator Leasing; Coordinator

Mendocino Farms
13103 Ventura Blvd Ste 100
Studio City, CA 91604-2244

Telephone: (310) 722-1935
Internet Homepage: mendocinofarms.com
Company Email: Molly@MendocinoFarms.com
Type of Business: Chain Restaurant Operator
Year Founded: 2005

Total Sales: $112,870,000 (e)
Average Check: Lunch(14); Dinner(14)
Total Units: 75
Trade Names: Blue Cow Kitchen & Bar (1); Mendocino Farms (74)
Company-Owned Units: 75
Preferred Location Types: Freestanding; Grocery Stores; Strip Mall
Primary Menu: American (1); Sandwiches/Deli (74)
Projected Openings: 2
Areas of Operation: CA, IL, TX
Type of Foodservice: Casual Dining (1); Fast Casual (74)
Catering Services: Yes

Key Personnel
MARIO DEL PERO - Founder
ELLEN CHEN - Co-Founder; CFO
KEVIN MILES - CEO
SEAN KRAJEWSKI - President; Partner
JONATHAN GARCIA - Partner
KEVIN KLIPFEL - CFO
REID TUSSING - VP Development
JIM RICH - VP Training
RIKI SWINDLER - VP Marketing
LOREN REYNOSO - VP People
BOB SALESSI - VP Operations
MATTHEW MAZZEO - VP; Controller
JEREMY BRINGARDNER - Executive Chef
JACOB LEAGUE - Senior Director Operations
GENE DAVIS - Senior Director Facility/Maintenance
BRANDI SANDERS - Director Marketing
BRADY SHERARD - Director Operations
SPENCER TROMBLEY - Director Architecture, Construction
TED STATHAKIS - Director
CHRIS BENTON - Director Finance
JOHN KISOW - Director Information Technology
LAUREN JOHNSON - Director Marketing
ROBERT MUTTON - Director Operations
CHRISTIN SPORNY - Director Operations
SCOTT FINE - Director Operations
LEE KOCIELA - Director Operations
SHERI SHOEMAKER - Director Operations
EUGENE OCHOA - Director Operations
DANIELLI MARFORI - Director Operations
KELSEY GUIETTE - Art Director
JOSE MENDOZA - Manager Culinary Operations
ROSALIN CURIEL - Manager
RYAN UMEMOTO - Manager Restaurant Operations
KAITLIN KAN - Manager Marketing
CASEY LEDWITH - Manager New Store Development

Poquito Mas
3701 Cahuenga Blvd Ste 1
Studio City, CA 91604-3503

Telephone: (818) 840-1177
Fax Number: (818) 840-1137
Internet Homepage: poquitomas.com
Company Email: mr.mas@poquitomas.com
Type of Business: Chain Restaurant Operator
Year Founded: 1984
Systemwide Sales: $23,433,000 (e)
Total Sales: $16,060,000 (e)
Alcohol Sales: 10%
Number of Employees: 225
Average Check: Lunch(16); Dinner(20)
Internet Order Processing: Yes
Internet Sales: 10.00%
Total Units: 10
Trade Names: Poquito Mas (10)
Company-Owned Units: 5
Units Franchised To: 4
Preferred Square Footage: 1,900; 2,500
Preferred Location Types: Freestanding; Strip Mall
Alcohol Served: Beer, Wine
Primary Menu: Mexican (10)
Areas of Operation: CA
Type of Foodservice: Fast Casual (10)
Catering Services: Yes
Primary Distributors: (Full Line) SYSCO Food Services of Central California Inc., MODESTO, CA

Key Personnel
KEVIN MCCARNEY - President; Executive Chef; Manager Finance, Operations, Facility/Maintenance, Real Estate, Design; General Buyer
PATTI RAVELLIS - VP; Director Customer Service, Catering

Ashria LLC
1200 Anderson Dr
Suisun City, CA 94585-3766

Telephone: (707) 425-9858
Fax Number: (707) 425-9857
Company Email: management@ashria.com
Type of Business: Chain Restaurant Operator
Total Sales: $39,060,000 (e)
Number of Employees: 102
Average Check: Lunch(12); Dinner(12)
Total Units: 15
Trade Names: Popeyes Louisiana Kitchen (15)
Units Franchised From: 15
Preferred Square Footage: 1,500
Preferred Location Types: Freestanding
Alcohol Served: Beer, Wine
Primary Menu: Chicken (15)
Areas of Operation: CA
Type of Foodservice: Quick Serve (15)
Franchise Affiliation: Popeyes Louisiana Kitchen Inc., ATLANTA, GA
Primary Distributors: (Food) SYSCO Food Services of San Francisco Inc., FREMONT, CA

Key Personnel
CAMRAN NOJOOMI - President; General Buyer

Dish Dash, LLC
190 S Murphy Ave
Sunnyvale, CA 94086-6112

Telephone: (408) 774-1889
Internet Homepage: dishdash.com
Company Email: info@dishdash.com
Type of Business: Chain Restaurant Operator
Year Founded: 2001
Total Units: 6
Trade Names: Dish N Dash (2); Dish n'Dash (2); Dishdash (2)
Company-Owned Units: 6
Primary Menu: Middle Eastern (6)
Areas of Operation: CA
Type of Foodservice: Casual Dining (2); Fast Casual (2); Fine Dining (2)

Key Personnel
EMAD IBRAHIM - Founder; Partner
NADIA MASHASHA - Founder; Partner; Director Marketing

Kia Tang
757 E El Camino Real Ste D
Sunnyvale, CA 94087-2919

Telephone: (408) 739-4420
Type of Business: Chain Restaurant Operator
Total Sales: $1,199,000 (e)
Total Units: 2
Trade Names: Cold Stone Creamery (2)
Units Franchised From: 2
Primary Menu: Snacks (2)
Areas of Operation: CA
Type of Foodservice: Quick Serve (2)
Franchise Affiliation: Kahala Brands, SCOTTSDALE, AZ

Key Personnel
KIA TANG - Owner

BMW Management
43172 Business Park Dr Ste 101
Temecula, CA 92590-3623

Telephone: (951) 676-8616
Fax Number: (951) 676-9246
Company Email: front.desk@bmwmanagement.com
Type of Business: Chain Restaurant Operator
Total Sales: $73,680,000 (e)
Number of Employees: 175
Average Check: Lunch(12); Dinner(26)
Total Units: 26
Trade Names: Richie's Real American Diner

(2); Sizzler (24)
Company-Owned Units: 2
Units Franchised From: 24
Preferred Square Footage: 5,000; 6,000
Preferred Location Types: Downtown; Freestanding; Strip Mall
Alcohol Served: Beer, Wine
Primary Menu: American (2); Steak (24)
Areas of Operation: CA
Type of Foodservice: Casual Dining (24); Family Restaurant (2)
Franchise Affiliation: Sizzler USA Inc., MISSION VIEJO, CA
Primary Distributors: (Full Line) SYSCO Food Services of Los Angeles Inc., WALNUT, CA

Key Personnel
GARY MYERS - Partner; General Manager; General Buyer
SALLY MYERS - Partner; Director Operations
AIMEE PATTON - CFO
SHANNON MURDAUGH - Coordinator Marketing

California Burgers and Fries Inc.
40426 Winchester Rd
Temecula, CA 92591-5502

Telephone: (951) 296-1955
Type of Business: Chain Restaurant Operator
Total Sales: $8,420,000 (e)
Total Units: 4
Trade Names: Five Guys Burgers and Fries (4)
Units Franchised From: 4
Primary Menu: Hamburger (4)
Areas of Operation: CA
Type of Foodservice: Fast Casual (4)
Franchise Affiliation: Five Guys Holdings Inc., LORTON, VA

Key Personnel
BRAD MURRELL - Owner

DFIT Subs, LLC
32068 Temecula Pkwy Ste 300
Temecula, CA 92592-6920

Telephone: (951) 303-3600
Type of Business: Chain Restaurant Operator
Total Sales: $18,110,000 (e)
Total Units: 13
Trade Names: Jersey Mike's Subs (13)
Units Franchised From: 13
Primary Menu: Sandwiches/Deli (13)
Areas of Operation: CA
Type of Foodservice: Quick Serve (13)
Franchise Affiliation: Jersey Mike's Franchise Systems, MANASQUAN, NJ

Key Personnel
STEVE LEONARD - Partner
FRED DOWNEY - Partner

Pechanga Resort & Casino
45000 Pechanga Pkwy
Temecula, CA 92592-5810

Mailing Address: PO Box 9041, TEMECULA, CA, 92589-9041
Telephone: (951) 693-1819
Fax Number: (951) 695-7410
Internet Homepage: pechanga.com
Type of Business: Foodservice Operations - Casinos
Total Sales: $42,567,000 (e)
Alcohol Sales: 10%
Number of Employees: 5,500
Total Units: 1
Restaurants in Hotels: 16
Trade Names: Pechanga Resort & Casino (1)
Company-Owned Units: 16
Alcohol Served: Beer, Wine, Liquor
Areas of Operation: CA
Type of Foodservice: Casual Dining (5); Fine Dining (4); Quick Serve (7)
Notes: The company derives approximately 90% of its revenue from resort and casino operations.

Key Personnel
TJEERD BRINK - CFO; VP Finance
JOHN KENEFICK - CIO; VP
BILL ANDERSON - Chief Marketing Officer
THOMAS A. MUELLER - VP Operations
PAM TOSCANO - VP Food and Beverage
JOHN FLAHERTY - VP Facility/Maintenance
HOWARD HERMANN - Director Purchasing
RICHARD J. DOMINGUEZ - Director Information Technology
COLIN WINGATE - Director Finance

Subway
27636 Ynez Rd Ste L11
Temecula, CA 92591-4639

Telephone: (951) 672-2773
Fax Number: (951) 699-6176
Internet Homepage: subway.com
Type of Business: Chain Restaurant Operator
Total Sales: $22,110,000 (e)
Total Units: 36
Trade Names: Subway (36)
Units Franchised From: 36
Primary Menu: Sandwiches/Deli (36)
Areas of Operation: CA
Type of Foodservice: Quick Serve (36)
Franchise Affiliation: Doctor's Associates Inc., MILFORD, CT

Key Personnel
ILENE KOBERT - Chief Legal Officer
ARTURO JIMENEZ - General Manager
PURUSHOTTAM BHOSLE - Director Technology
PAUL DAVIS - Regional Director Marketing
JAIS KURIAN - Senior Manager Customer Analytics
JEREMY HALL - Manager Operations, Infrastructure
JEFFREY SCHIROTA - Manager Technology; Engineer

JM West, Inc.
3435 E Thousand Oaks Blvd
Thousand Oaks, CA 91362-3653

Telephone: (805) 777-7167
Type of Business: Chain Restaurant Operator
Total Sales: $15,140,000 (e)
Total Units: 11
Trade Names: Jersey Mike's Subs (11)
Units Franchised From: 11
Primary Menu: Sandwiches/Deli (11)
Areas of Operation: CA
Type of Foodservice: Quick Serve (11)
Franchise Affiliation: Jersey Mike's Franchise Systems, MANASQUAN, NJ

Key Personnel
DAN BURRELL - Owner; General Buyer

CLK Inc.
72295 Manufacturing Rd
Thousand Palms, CA 92276-6615

Telephone: (760) 341-2992
Fax Number: (760) 423-5690
Type of Business: Chain Restaurant Operator
Year Founded: 1985
Total Sales: $125,482,000 (e)
Number of Employees: 1,070
Average Check: Breakfast(6); Lunch(8); Dinner(8)
Total Units: 59
Trade Names: Carl's Jr. (59)
Units Franchised From: 59
Preferred Square Footage: 2,500; 3,000; 4,000
Preferred Location Types: Freestanding
Primary Menu: Hamburger (59)
Projected Openings: 2
Areas of Operation: AZ, CA, NM, TX
Type of Foodservice: Quick Serve (59)
Franchise Affiliation: Carl's Jr., FRANKLIN, TN
Primary Distributors: (Full Line) McLane/Rocky Mount, ROCKY MOUNT, NC

Key Personnel
CARL L. KARCHER - President; Director Real Estate, Menu Development

KELLY KARCHER - VP
DOMENIC BONACCI - VP Finance
ANGELIQUE MCGILLEN - District Manager
KANDYCE OJEDA - District Manager

California Subshine, Inc.
24631 Crenshaw Blvd Ste M
Torrance, CA 90505-5359

Telephone: (310) 530-5888
Type of Business: Chain Restaurant Operator
Total Sales: $8,252,000 (e)
Total Units: 6
Trade Names: Jersey Mike's Subs (6)
Units Franchised From: 6
Primary Menu: Sandwiches/Deli (6)
Areas of Operation: CA
Type of Foodservice: Quick Serve (6)
Franchise Affiliation: Jersey Mike's Franchise Systems, MANASQUAN, NJ

Key Personnel
GAREN KHODAVERDIAN - Partner; General Buyer
ARTIE MAIDMAN - Partner

WDI International Inc.
21171 S Western Ave Ste 250
Torrance, CA 90501-1731

Telephone: (310) 533-3201
Fax Number: (310) 533-3202
Internet Homepage: wdiinternational.com
Type of Business: Chain Restaurant Operator
Year Founded: 1979
Total Sales: $25,090,000 (e)
Alcohol Sales: 15%
Number of Employees: 600
Average Check: Lunch(26); Dinner(48)
Total Units: 9
Trade Names: Inakaya (1); Ristorante Italiano Capricciosa (3); Taormina Sicilian Cuisine (1); Tony Roma's (3); Wolfgang's Steak House (1)
Company-Owned Units: 6
Units Franchised From: 3
Preferred Square Footage: 8,000
Preferred Location Types: Freestanding; Other
Alcohol Served: Beer, Wine, Liquor
Primary Menu: American (3); Italian (4); Japanese (1); Steak/Seafood (1)
Areas of Operation: CA, GU, HI, NY
Foreign Countries: INDONESIA; JAPAN; THE PHILIPPINES
Type of Foodservice: Casual Dining (12); Fine Dining (1)
Catering Services: Yes
Franchise Affiliation: Romacorp Inc., ORLANDO, FL
Primary Distributors: (Full Line) SYSCO Food Services of Alaska Inc., ANCHORAGE, AK

Parent Company: WDI Corporation, TOKYO, JAPAN
Notes: Total stores reflect US operations only; the company operates 150+ locations in Asia.

Key Personnel
JUN HORIUCHI - President
YOJI SHIMIZU - Director
KEN SHIMIZU - Director
SUGURU ISHIGURO - Director Operations

Yoshinoya America Inc.
991 Knox St
Torrance, CA 90502-1006

Telephone: (310) 527-6060
Fax Number: (310) 527-6050
Internet Homepage: yoshinoyaamerica.com
Company Email: cr@yoshinoya.us
Type of Business: Chain Restaurant Operator
Year Founded: 1979
Systemwide Sales: $154,921,000 (e)
Total Sales: $150,760,000 (e)
Number of Employees: 1,400
Average Check: Lunch(10); Dinner(12)
Total Units: 102
Trade Names: Yoshinoya Restaurant (102)
Company-Owned Units: 78
Units Franchised To: 24
Preferred Square Footage: 1,800; 2,500
Preferred Location Types: Downtown; Freestanding; Strip Mall
Primary Menu: Japanese (102)
Projected Openings: 10
Projected Remodelings: 3
Areas of Operation: AZ, CA, NV, NY
Foreign Countries: AUSTRALIA; CHINA; HONG KONG; JAPAN; MALAYSIA; SINGAPORE; TAIWAN; THE PHILIPPINES
Type of Foodservice: Quick Serve (102)
Parent Company: Yoshinoya D & C Co. Ltd., TOKYO, JAPAN

Key Personnel
JON GILLIAM - CEO
HARRY GANI - VP Store Planning
VINNIE CALCAGNI - VP Operations
JANET FISHER - VP People
HECTOR RAMIREZ - Director Supply Chain
ROCIO HERNANDEZ - Director Risk Management
GLORIA PIMENTEL - Director Operations
ARRON BRUESKE - Director Operations
MERARI UTRIA - Director Marketing
CAROLINE BASDAKIS - Coordinator Marketing

Domino's Franchisee
461 Skymaster Cir Bldg 650
Travis Afb, CA 94535-1909

Telephone: (707) 419-6100

Type of Business: Chain Restaurant Operator
Total Sales: $10,024,000 (e)
Total Units: 5
Trade Names: Domino's (5)
Units Franchised From: 5
Primary Menu: Pizza (5)
Areas of Operation: CA
Type of Foodservice: Quick Serve (5)
Franchise Affiliation: Domino's Pizza Inc, ANN ARBOR, MI

Key Personnel
ISSA J. SHEHADEH - Owner; General Buyer

Camida Inc
2400 Geer Rd
Turlock, CA 95382-1426

Mailing Address: PO Box 2395, TURLOCK, CA, 95381-2395
Telephone: (209) 632-6874
Fax Number: (209) 632-6874
Type of Business: Chain Restaurant Operator
Total Sales: $9,832,000 (e)
Total Units: 2
Trade Names: McDonald's (2)
Units Franchised From: 2
Primary Menu: Hamburger (2)
Areas of Operation: CA
Type of Foodservice: Quick Serve (2)
Franchise Affiliation: McDonald's Corporation, CHICAGO, IL

Key Personnel
CARL M. JEVERT - Owner; General Buyer

The Crab Cooker
17260 17th St
Tustin, CA 92780

Telephone: (714) 573-1077
Fax Number: (949) 675-8445
Internet Homepage: crabcooker.com
Type of Business: Chain Restaurant Operator
Year Founded: 1951
Total Sales: $12,326,000 (e)
Alcohol Sales: 7%
Number of Employees: 140
Average Check: Lunch(12); Dinner(18)
Total Units: 1
Trade Names: The Crab Cooker (1)
Company-Owned Units: 1
Preferred Location Types: Freestanding
Alcohol Served: Beer, Wine
Primary Menu: Seafood (1)
Areas of Operation: CA
Type of Foodservice: Casual Dining (1)
Primary Distributors: (Food) SYSCO Food Services of Los Angeles Inc., WALNUT, CA

Key Personnel
JIM WASKO - Owner; General Buyer
JIMMY WASKO - General Manager
CHRIS MANGAN - General Manager

J.A. Sutherland Inc.
1199 N State St
Ukiah, CA 95482-3415

Telephone: (707) 462-1147
Fax Number: (707) 462-1172
Company Email: tcoleman@jasutherland.com
Type of Business: Chain Restaurant Operator
Year Founded: 1978
Total Sales: $82,710,000 (e)
Number of Employees: 840
Average Check: Lunch(12); Dinner(12)
Total Units: 31
Trade Names: KFC (1); Taco Bell (30)
Units Franchised From: 31
Preferred Square Footage: 3,000
Preferred Location Types: Freestanding
Primary Menu: Chicken (1); Taco (30)
Areas of Operation: CA, OR
Type of Foodservice: Quick Serve (31)
Franchise Affiliation: KFC Corporation, LOUISVILLE, KY; Taco Bell Corp., IRVINE, CA
Primary Distributors: (Full Line) McLane Company, Inc., TEMPLE, TX

Key Personnel
JAN SUTHERLAND - President; Manager Purchasing, Loss Prevention, Supply Chain, Marketing
KATHERINE BURRIS - VP; Controller; Director Information Systems, Food Safety
CASEY BURRIS - Director Operations
ART MCCHASNEY - Manager Facility/Maintenance, Store Fixtures
STEPHEN O'DONNELL - Manager Training
LES SHANK - Manager Operations, Real Estate, Store Planning
STACY SHANK - Manager Human Resources

Bronco Billy's Pizza Palace
3940 Smith St
Union City, CA 94587-2616

Telephone: (510) 489-4601
Fax Number: (510) 489-3072
Internet Homepage: broncobillyspizza.com
Type of Business: Chain Restaurant Operator
Year Founded: 1988
Total Sales: $1,899,000 (e)
Alcohol Sales: 10%
Number of Employees: 75
Average Check: Lunch(16); Dinner(24)
Total Units: 2
Trade Names: Bronco Billy's Pizza Palace (2)
Company-Owned Units: 2
Preferred Location Types: Freestanding
Alcohol Served: Beer, Wine
Primary Menu: Pizza (2)
Areas of Operation: CA
Type of Foodservice: Casual Dining (2)
On-site Distribution Center: Yes

Key Personnel
SAM RODRIGUEZ - Owner; Treasurer; General Buyer
MARLENE TEEHAN - Owner
JON RODRIGUEZ - General Manager

Harman Management Corp.
2846 Volpey Way
Union City, CA 94587

Telephone: (415) 508-1829
Listing Type: Regional Office
Type of Business: Chain Restaurant Operator
Total Units: 32
Areas of Operation: CA
Parent Company: Harman Management Corp., LOS ALTOS, CA

Key Personnel
LOURDES FAJARDO - General Manager; General Buyer
MICHELE SHERIDAN - Director Operations
LINDA STRONG-BROWN - Regional Director
CLAY PATTERSON - Regional Director
ERIC CALDWELL - Regional Director

Universal Studios Hollywood
100 Universal City Plz
Universal City, CA 91608-1002

Telephone: (818) 622-9841
Fax Number: (818) 622-0137
Internet Homepage: universalstudios.com
Type of Business: Foodservice Operations - Theme Parks
Total Sales: $883,060,000 (e)
Alcohol Sales: 10%
Foodservice Sales: $88,306,000 (e)
Total Units: 27
Trade Names: Bumblebee Man's Taco Truck (1); Cinnabon (1); Cletus' Checken Shack (1); Cocina Mexicana (1); Despicable Delights (1); Duff Brewery Beer Garden (1); French Street Bistro (1); Gru's Lab Cafe (1); Hog's Head Pub (1); Hollywood & Dine (1); Jurassic Cafe (1); Krusty Burger (1); Lard Lad Donuts (1);Luigi's Pizza (1); Mel's Diner (1); Moe's Tavern (1); Mulligan's Irish Pub (1); Palace Theatre Cafe (1); Panda Express (1); Phineas Q. Butterfat's Ice Cream (1); Starbucks Coffee (2); Studio Cafe (1); Studio Scoop (1); Suds McDuff's Hot dogs (1); Three Broomsticks (1); Universal Tower Snack Bar (1)
Company-Owned Units: 24
Units Franchised From: 3
Preferred Square Footage: 1,200; 2,500
Preferred Location Types: Parks
Alcohol Served: Beer, Wine, Liquor
Primary Menu: American (11)
Areas of Operation: CA
Type of Foodservice: Casual Dining (7)
Primary Distributors: (Full Line) SYSCO Food Services of Central California Inc., MODESTO, CA
Parent Company: Comcast Corporation, PHILADELPHIA, PA
Headquarters: NBCUniversal Media, LLC, NEW YORK, NY

Key Personnel
KAREN IRWIN - President; COO
NICK BUONOME - CFO; Senior VP
HILARY HOFFMAN - Exec VP Marketing
DENNIS QUINN - Senior VP Sales
GLEN CONNALLY - Senior VP Technology
SCOTT STROBL - Senior VP Operations
MARVIN CORTEZ - VP Finance
CINDY GARDNER - VP Communications
DAVID HAMANO - VP Operations-Food
PETER SCHADE - VP Customer Service
JAMES MCNAMARA - VP Business Development
ALFREDO MONTANO - VP Operations
MARK HALPERIN - Executive Director Operations
SCOTT MCQUOWN - Controller
ERIC A. KOPELOW - Executive Chef
JOHN MURDY - Creative Director
JOHN PEREZ - Director
APRIL PETERSON - Director Accounting
JEFFREY LILLY - Director Operations
STAN SCOGGINS - Director Operations
ERIC SHEPPARD - Director Sales
ISMAEL AGUIRRE - Director Retail Operations
MAT WEIG - Director Marketing
KENNETH ROSENBERG - Senior Manager Security
JOEL SMITH - Senior Manager Production
RAMIRO B. CEJA - Senior Manager Quality Assurance
OSSIE COLLINS - Senior Manager Operations
HERNAN MOJARRO - Area Manager
SILVIA LOZANO - Manager Visual Merchandising
JASON MASSIATT - Manager Finance
KAMBER MOEN - Manager Production
OLIVER BENNETT - Manager Information Technology
C.J. LETCHWORTH - Manager Brand Marketing, Licensing
DIVA KAMINSKY - Manager Human Resources
JENNIFER FORD - Supervisor Technology
JESSICA REDISCH - Supervisor Live Nursery
CARLOS VANEGAS - Supervisor Compliance
ANDREW SKOWRON PMP - Project Manager
RAYMOND CHAN - Project Manager Construction
VICTOR ESTIVILL - Engineer Hardware, Software

PAOLA GUERIN - Executive Assistant

Pickapple Franchise LLC
301 County Airport Rd Ste 214
Vacaville, CA 95688-3108

Telephone: (707) 446-1713
Fax Number: (707) 446-1721
Internet Homepage: tritipgrill.com; buckhorngrill.com
Company Email: marketing@buckhorngrill.com
Type of Business: Chain Restaurant Operator
Number of Employees: 210
Total Units: 14
Trade Names: Buckhorn Grill (11); Tri-Tip Grill (3)
Company-Owned Units: 10
Units Franchised To: 4
Alcohol Served: Beer, Wine
Primary Menu: American (14)
Projected Remodelings: 2
Areas of Operation: CA, NY, TX
Type of Foodservice: Casual Dining (14)

Key Personnel
JOHN PICKEREL - President; Executive Chef
DAVID MARIA - COO
JARED RAYMOND - Director Restaurant Operations

Yin McDonald's
185 Butcher Rd
Vacaville, CA 95687-5656

Telephone: (707) 451-0130
Fax Number: (707) 451-0131
Type of Business: Chain Restaurant Operator
Year Founded: 1984
Total Sales: $61,650,000 (e)
Number of Employees: 425
Average Check: Breakfast(5); Lunch(8); Dinner(8)
Total Units: 13
Trade Names: McDonald's (13)
Units Franchised From: 13
Preferred Square Footage: 2,500
Preferred Location Types: Downtown; Freestanding
Primary Menu: Hamburger (13)
Areas of Operation: CA
Type of Foodservice: Quick Serve (13)
Franchise Affiliation: McDonald's Corporation, CHICAGO, IL
Primary Distributors: (Full Line) The Martin-Brower Co., SALT LAKE CITY, UT

Key Personnel
C.C. YIN - President; Partner; Director Operations, Real Estate
REGINA YIN - Partner; Director Information Systems; General Buyer

Mr. Stax Inc.
25060 Avenue Stanford Ste 200
Valencia, CA 91355-3993

Telephone: (661) 294-8877
Fax Number: (661) 294-8878
Internet Homepage: mrstaxinc.com
Company Email: reception@mrstaxinc.com
Type of Business: Chain Restaurant Operator
Total Sales: $66,340,000 (e)
Number of Employees: 2,400
Average Check: Breakfast(12); Lunch(14); Dinner(16)
Total Units: 21
Trade Names: IHOP Restaurant (21)
Units Franchised From: 21
Preferred Square Footage: 4,400; 5,000
Preferred Location Types: Freestanding
Primary Menu: American (21)
Areas of Operation: CA, DE, MA, NH, NV, NY, PA
Type of Foodservice: Family Restaurant (21)
Franchise Affiliation: IHOP Restaurant System, GLENDALE, CA
Primary Distributors: (Food) MBM Corporation, PLEASANTON, CA

Key Personnel
ROD MACPHERSON - Partner
RICHARD SANDNES - Partner
MARC JUSTICE - Exec VP; VP Finance, Operations; General Buyer
ANDREW MONICO - General Manager
PAPA SOUMARE - Director Development-Training

CG Yogurt LLC
7755 Haskell Ave
Van Nuys, CA 91406-1906

Telephone: (818) 981-3392
Type of Business: Chain Restaurant Operator
Total Sales: $22,770,000 (e)
Total Units: 17
Trade Names: Yogurtland (17)
Units Franchised From: 17
Primary Menu: Snacks (17)
Areas of Operation: CA
Type of Foodservice: Quick Serve (17)
Franchise Affiliation: Yogurtland Franchising Inc., FARMERS BRANCH, TX

Key Personnel
BEHZAD COHAN - Partner; General Buyer
PAUL GILL - Partner; General Buyer

Domino's Franchisee
6805 Sepulveda Blvd
Van Nuys, CA 91405-4402

Telephone: (818) 909-0088
Type of Business: Chain Restaurant Operator
Total Sales: $26,116,000 (e)
Total Units: 13
Trade Names: Domino's (13)
Units Franchised From: 13
Primary Menu: Pizza (13)
Areas of Operation: CA
Type of Foodservice: Quick Serve (13)
Franchise Affiliation: Domino's Pizza Inc, ANN ARBOR, MI

Key Personnel
DOYLE LA MOUNTAIN - Owner; General Buyer

Gurbachan, Grewal
6800 Balboa Blvd Ste A
Van Nuys, CA 91406-4578

Telephone: (818) 786-7828
Fax Number: (818) 786-7829
Type of Business: Chain Restaurant Operator
Total Sales: $2,862,000 (e)
Total Units: 4
Trade Names: Subway (4)
Units Franchised From: 4
Primary Menu: Sandwiches/Deli (4)
Areas of Operation: CA
Type of Foodservice: Quick Serve (4)
Franchise Affiliation: Doctor's Associates Inc., MILFORD, CT

Key Personnel
RAJA BOKHREL - President; General Buyer

Katsu-Ya Group
15819 Stagg St
Van Nuys, CA 91406-1922

Telephone: (818) 789-4114
Fax Number: (818) 789-4191
Internet Homepage: katsu-yagroup.com
Company Email: info@katsu-yagroup.com
Type of Business: Chain Restaurant Operator
Year Founded: 1998
Total Sales: $5,903,000 (e)
Alcohol Sales: 5%
Number of Employees: 154
Average Check: Lunch(30); Dinner(48)
Total Units: 9
Trade Names: Izaka-Ya by Katsu-Ya (2); Katsu-Ya (4); KIWAMI (1); Little Izaka-ya by Katsu-ya (1); Washoku of LA (1)
Company-Owned Units: 9
Preferred Location Types: Strip Mall

Alcohol Served: Beer, Wine
Primary Menu: Japanese (9)
Areas of Operation: CA
Type of Foodservice: Casual Dining (9)
Catering Services: Yes
Primary Distributors: (Food) International Marine Products Inc., LOS ANGELES, CA

Key Personnel
KATSUYA UECHI - CEO; Owner; Executive Chef
SATOMI NAGAI - VP
LARRY CRUCKSON - Manager Facility/Maintenance

Western Bagel Baking Corp.
7814 Sepulveda Blvd
Van Nuys, CA 91405-1020

Telephone: (818) 786-5847
Fax Number: (818) 787-3221
Internet Homepage: westernbagel.com
Company Email: wbinfo@westernbagel.com
Type of Business: Chain Restaurant Operator
Year Founded: 1947
Total Sales: $12,160,000 (e)
Number of Employees: 220
Average Check: Breakfast(5); Lunch(8);
Internet Order Processing: Yes
Internet Sales: 1.00%
Total Units: 11
Trade Names: Western Bagel (11)
Company-Owned Units: 11
Preferred Square Footage: 2,500
Preferred Location Types: Freestanding
Primary Menu: Bagels (11)
Areas of Operation: CA
Type of Foodservice: Quick Serve (11)
Primary Distributors: (Full Line) Dairyland, The Chef's Warehouse, CITY OF INDUSTRY, CA

Key Personnel
STEVE USTIN - CEO; President; Executive Chef; Director Facility/Maintenance, Real Estate, Design; General Buyer
PETER SCHEIDT - CFO; Director Information Systems, Supply Chain
JEFF USTIN - VP Production
GREG LINZNER - VP Sales
DAVID BELTRAN - Controller
MARK WEISNER - Manager Information Technology

American Gonzo Food Corp
1905 Lincoln Blvd
Venice, CA 90291-3909

Telephone: (310) 598-2070
Fax Number: (310) 861-0406
Internet Homepage: americangonzofoodcorp.com; pitfirepizza.com
Company Email: listening@pitfirepizza.com
Type of Business: Chain Restaurant Operator
Year Founded: 1997
Total Sales: $34,620,000 (e)
Alcohol Sales: 7%
Average Check: Dinner(26)
Total Units: 9
Trade Names: Pitfire Artisan Pizza (7); Superba (2)
Company-Owned Units: 9
Preferred Square Footage: 3,500; 4,000; 5,600
Alcohol Served: Beer, Wine
Primary Menu: American (2); Pizza (7)
Areas of Operation: CA
Type of Foodservice: Casual Dining (9)
Catering Services: Yes

Key Personnel
PAUL HIBLER - Founder
JEFF GOODMAN - CEO
ALEX NOVAK - VP Finance
VINIT SINGH - Director Finance
MITCHELL WONG - Director Operations

Hishmeh Enterprises
1811 Knoll Dr Ste A
Ventura, CA 93003-7321

Telephone: (805) 650-9946
Fax Number: (805) 650-9301
Company Email: hishmehenterprises@sbcglobal.net
Type of Business: Chain Restaurant Operator
Year Founded: 1988
Total Sales: $168,819,000 (e)
Number of Employees: 1,640
Average Check: Lunch(14); Dinner(22)
Total Units: 81
Trade Names: Domino's (81)
Units Franchised From: 81
Preferred Square Footage: 1,000; 1,300
Preferred Location Types: Freestanding
Primary Menu: Pizza (81)
Areas of Operation: CA
Type of Foodservice: Quick Serve (81)
Franchise Affiliation: Domino's Pizza Inc, ANN ARBOR, MI
Primary Distributors: (Food) Domino's Distribution Center, ONTARIO, CA

Key Personnel
SAM HISHMEH - President; Director Purchasing, Facility/Maintenance, Marketing
LENA HISHMEH - Partner; Director Human Resources
NICK HISHMEH - Partner; Director Finance, Information Systems
WYEL HISHMEH - Director Operations, Real Estate

Miles Management Corp
1771 S Victoria Ave
Ventura, CA 93003-6503

Telephone: (805) 650-8002
Internet Homepage: mmilescorp.com
Company Email: milesmamagementco@gmail.com
Type of Business: Chain Restaurant Operator
Year Founded: 1986
Total Sales: $28,110,000 (e)
Total Units: 9
Trade Names: IHOP (9)
Units Franchised From: 9
Primary Menu: American (9)
Areas of Operation: AK, CA
Type of Foodservice: Family Restaurant (9)
Franchise Affiliation: IHOP Restaurant System, GLENDALE, CA

Key Personnel
DON GORDON - President; General Buyer

Urbane Cafe
78 N Ash St
Ventura, CA 93001-2902

Telephone: (805) 648-2500
Fax Number: (805) 654-1509
Internet Homepage: urbanecafe.com
Company Email: info@urbanecafe.com
Type of Business: Chain Restaurant Operator
Total Sales: $16,660,000 (e)
Number of Employees: 249
Average Check: Lunch(10); Dinner(10)
Internet Order Processing: Yes
Internet Sales: 1.00%
Total Units: 18
Trade Names: Urbane Cafe (18)
Company-Owned Units: 18
Preferred Square Footage: 2,800
Preferred Location Types: Strip Mall
Primary Menu: Sandwiches/Deli (18)
Areas of Operation: CA
Type of Foodservice: Fast Casual (18)
Catering Services: Yes

Key Personnel
TOM HOLT - CEO; Owner; General Buyer
EUGENIA BATES - Director Human Resources
RAFAEL AMEZCUA - District Manager

Yolanda's Inc.
1363 Donlon St Ste 20
Ventura, CA 93003-5638

Telephone: (805) 656-6231
Fax Number: (805) 658-1960
Internet Homepage:

snapperjackstacoshack.com;
yolandasmexicancafe.com
Company Email:
mainoffice@yolandasmexicancafe.com
Type of Business: Chain Restaurant Operator
Year Founded: 1982
Total Sales: $14,650,000 (e)
Alcohol Sales: 25%
Number of Employees: 320
Average Check: Lunch(8); Dinner(14)
Total Units: 8
Trade Names: Snapper Jack's Taco Shack (4); Yolanda's Mexican Cafe (4)
Company-Owned Units: 8
Preferred Location Types: Freestanding
Alcohol Served: Beer, Wine, Liquor
Primary Menu: Mexican (8)
Projected Remodelings: 3
Areas of Operation: CA
Type of Foodservice: Casual Dining (8)
Catering Services: Yes
Primary Distributors: (Food) Jordano's Inc., SANTA BARBARA, CA

Key Personnel
ROD GIETZEN - President
GUSTAVO SORIA - Executive Chef; Manager Catering; General Buyer

Go Get Em Tiger (GGET)
4609 Hampton St
Vernon, CA 90058

Telephone: (323) 543-4321
Internet Homepage: gget.com
Type of Business: Chain Restaurant Operator
Total Sales: $8,914,000 (e)
Total Units: 8
Trade Names: Go Get Em Tiger (GGET) (8)
Company-Owned Units: 8
Primary Menu: Coffee (8)
Areas of Operation: CA
Type of Foodservice: Quick Serve (8)

Key Personnel
CHARLES BABINSKI - Co-Founder
KYLE GLANVILLE - Co-Founder; CEO

Zankou Chicken Inc.
2360 E 48th St
Vernon, CA 90058

Telephone: (818) 291-9528
Fax Number: (818) 291-4530
Internet Homepage: zankouchicken.com
Company Email: lena@zankouchicken.com
Type of Business: Chain Restaurant Operator
Year Founded: 1984
Total Sales: $4,582,000 (e)
Number of Employees: 110
Average Check: Dinner(14)
Total Units: 9
Trade Names: Zankou Chicken (9)
Company-Owned Units: 9
Preferred Location Types: Freestanding
Primary Menu: Chicken (9)
Areas of Operation: CA
Type of Foodservice: Quick Serve (9)

Key Personnel
RITA ISKENDERIAN - Owner; Executive Chef; General Buyer
DIKRAN ISKENDERIAN - Director Marketing
VARTKES ISKENDERIAN - Principal

Envision Foods, LLC
14173 Green Tree Blvd Ste J
Victorville, CA 92395

Telephone: (760) 245-5073
Internet Homepage: socaljack.com
Type of Business: Chain Restaurant Operator
Total Sales: $290,970,000 (e)
Total Units: 120
Trade Names: Jack in the Box (120)
Units Franchised From: 120
Primary Menu: Hamburger (120)
Areas of Operation: CA, IL, MO
Type of Foodservice: Quick Serve (120)
Franchise Affiliation: Jack in the Box Restaurants, SAN DIEGO, CA

Key Personnel
TERRY SHINDLE - President; General Buyer
HAMID SHARAFATIAN - CFO

L.A. Italian Kitchen Management Inc.
17853 Santiago Blvd Ste 107-482
Villa Park, CA 92861-4113

Telephone: (714) 258-2100
Fax Number: (714) 258-7614
Internet Homepage: laitaliankitchen.com; sociallifepizza.com
Company Email: admin@laitaliankitchen.com
Type of Business: Chain Restaurant Operator
Year Founded: 1991
Systemwide Sales: $4,927,000 (e)
Total Sales: $6,736,000 (e)
Number of Employees: 100
Average Check: Lunch(8); Dinner(10)
Total Units: 5
Trade Names: L.A. Italian Kitchen (4); Social Life Pizza (1)
Company-Owned Units: 5
Preferred Square Footage: 800
Preferred Location Types: Freestanding; Regional Mall
Primary Menu: Italian (4); Pizza (1)
Areas of Operation: CA, NV
Type of Foodservice: Casual Dining (5)

Key Personnel
JOSEPH R. DE SANTIS - CEO; President; Director Operations, Purchasing, Facility/Maintenance, Supply Chain, Human Resources, Menu Development; General Buyer

R-U Hungry
PO Box 7180
Visalia, CA 93290-7180

Telephone: (559) 738-8476
Fax Number: (559) 738-8732
Internet Homepage: bk.com
Type of Business: Chain Restaurant Operator
Year Founded: 1996
Total Sales: $50,580,000 (e)
Number of Employees: 660
Average Check: Breakfast(5); Lunch(6); Dinner(8)
Total Units: 23
Trade Names: Burger King (23)
Units Franchised From: 23
Preferred Square Footage: 3,000
Preferred Location Types: Convenience Store/Gas Station; Freestanding
Primary Menu: Hamburger (23)
Areas of Operation: CA
Type of Foodservice: Quick Serve (23)
Franchise Affiliation: Burger King Worldwide Inc., MIAMI, FL
Primary Distributors: (Full Line) Reinhart FoodService, AUSTELL, GA

Key Personnel
GARY GEIGER - President; General Buyer

RLMK Inc.
7043 W Pershing Ct
Visalia, CA 93291-7939

Telephone: (559) 738-8588
Fax Number: (559) 738-8586
Internet Homepage: rlmkinc.com
Type of Business: Chain Restaurant Operator
Year Founded: 1997
Total Sales: $99,720,000 (e)
Number of Employees: 625
Average Check: Breakfast(8); Lunch(8); Dinner(8)
Total Units: 21
Trade Names: McDonald's (21)
Units Franchised From: 21
Preferred Square Footage: 2,400; 3,000
Preferred Location Types: Freestanding; Regional Mall
Primary Menu: Hamburger (21)
Areas of Operation: CA
Type of Foodservice: Quick Serve (21)

Franchise Affiliation: McDonald's Corporation, CHICAGO, IL
Primary Distributors: (Full Line) The Martin-Brower Co., STOCKTON, CA

Key Personnel
ROGER DELPH - President; Director Facility/Maintenance, Real Estate, Store Fixtures; General Buyer
PHIL WHITE - Director Operations, Information Systems, Supply Chain, Human Resources

The Vintage Press Restaurante
216 N Willis St
Visalia, CA 93291-6006

Mailing Address: PO Box 1534, VISALIA, CA, 93279-1534
Telephone: (559) 733-3033
Fax Number: (559) 738-5262
Internet Homepage: depotvisalia.com; jackandcharlies.com; thevintagepress.com
Type of Business: Chain Restaurant Operator
Year Founded: 1966
Total Sales: $9,394,000 (e)
Alcohol Sales: 2%
Number of Employees: 45
Average Check: Lunch(18); Dinner(36)
Total Units: 3
Trade Names: Jack & Charlies (1); Southern Pacific Depot (1); The Vintage Press Restaurant (1)
Company-Owned Units: 3
Alcohol Served: Beer, Wine, Liquor
Primary Menu: American (3)
Areas of Operation: CA
Type of Foodservice: Casual Dining (1); Fine Dining (2)
Catering Services: Yes
Primary Distributors: (Food) SYSCO Food Services of San Francisco Inc., FREMONT, CA

Key Personnel
DAVID VARTANIAN - Partner; Executive Chef; General Buyer
GREGORY VARTANIAN - Partner; General Manager
JOHN G. VARTANIAN JR - Partner

Better Buzz Coffee Company
1150 Joshua Way
Vista, CA 92081-7836

Telephone: (619) 269-7249
Internet Homepage: betterbuzzcoffee.com
Company Email: info@betterbuzzcoffee.com
Type of Business: Chain Restaurant Operator
Number of Employees: 70
Internet Order Processing: Yes
Total Units: 8
Trade Names: Better Buzz Coffee (8)
Company-Owned Units: 8
Preferred Location Types: Freestanding; Kiosk; Office Complex
Primary Menu: Coffee (8)
Areas of Operation: CA
Type of Foodservice: Quick Serve (8)

Key Personnel
TIM LANGDON - CEO; President; Partner; Director Real Estate
AMANDA CAMERON - Director Marketing

Everbowl
1300 Specialty Drive #100
Vista, CA 92081

Telephone: (760) 330-9001
Internet Homepage: everbowl.com
Type of Business: Chain Restaurant Operator
Year Founded: 2016
Systemwide Sales: $52,150,000 (e)
Total Sales: $56,170,000 (e)
Total Units: 70
Trade Names: Everbowl (70)
Units Franchised To: 70
Primary Menu: Health Foods (70)
Areas of Operation: AR, AZ, CA, CO, FL, GA, IA, IN, KS, LA, MO, NC, NV, OH, OR, SC, TN, TX, UT, VA
Type of Foodservice: Fast Casual (70)

Key Personnel
JEFF FENSTER - Founder; CEO

McDonald's USA LLC
2999 Oak Rd Ste 900
Walnut Creek, CA 94597-2099

Telephone: (925) 949-4000
Fax Number: (925) 949-4100
Listing Type: Regional Office
Type of Business: Chain Restaurant Operator
Total Units: 1,200
Areas of Operation: CA, NV
Parent Company: McDonald's Corporation, CHICAGO, IL

Key Personnel
JON GOODBRAND - VP
CHRISTIAN BRYZINSKI - Senior Director Finance, Business Development
NICK FLETCHER - Director Marketing
KEITH ROMINE - Director Real Estate
KARA SCHMIDT - Director Digital
COURTNEY MCBURNEY - Director Development
ALEXA MORSE - Director People
DIONNE GOMEZ - Director Communications
MARK SMITH - Director Marketing, Data Security
ADEL ALMOHTADI - Director Development, Franchising
JENA HESS - Director Database, Customer Analytics
KAITLIN LABRUZZO - Senior Manager Marketing; Manager Marketing, Social Media
SANA MOHAMMED - Manager Field Marketing
ALISE FLORES - Manager Media; Coordinator Recruitment
SARA SMUDA - Manager Consumer Insights
ERIC MOORE - Manager Digital
KAREN NOVAK - Manager Marketing; Senior Product Manager
DANIEL MACDADE - Product Director

Skipolini's Pizza
1535 Giammona Dr
Walnut Creek, CA 94596-4130

Telephone: (925) 280-1100
Fax Number: (925) 280-8828
Internet Homepage: skipolinispizza.com
Type of Business: Chain Restaurant Operator
Year Founded: 1974
Total Units: 7
Trade Names: Skipolini's Pizza (7)
Company-Owned Units: 7
Primary Menu: Pizza (7)
Areas of Operation: CA, NV
Type of Foodservice: Casual Dining (7)

Key Personnel
KENT IPSEN - Founder; President; Owner

Double G Partners
2548 S Azusa Ave
West Covina, CA 91792-1642

Telephone: (626) 912-0784
Type of Business: Chain Restaurant Operator
Total Sales: $5,549,000 (e)
Total Units: 2
Trade Names: Jack in the Box (2)
Units Franchised From: 2
Primary Menu: Hamburger (2)
Areas of Operation: CA
Type of Foodservice: Quick Serve (2)
Franchise Affiliation: Jack in the Box Restaurants, SAN DIEGO, CA

Key Personnel
GARREN GRIEVE - Owner; General Buyer

Jollibee Foods Corporation
100 North Barranca Street Suite 1200
West Covina, CA 91791

Telephone: (626) 369-7118
Internet Homepage: jollibeefoods.com
Listing Type: Corporate Office
Type of Business: Chain Restaurant Operator
Total Units: 75
Trade Names: Jollibee (75)
Units Franchised To: 75
Primary Menu: Chicken (75)
Type of Foodservice: Fast Casual (75)
Headquarter Offices: Honeybee Foods Corporation, CITY OF INDUSTRY, CA; International Coffee & Tea LLC, LOS ANGELES, CA; Smashburger Master LLC, DENVER, CO

Key Personnel
TONY T. CAKTIONG - Chairman; CEO

RNB Sanchez Inc.
1000 Lakes Dr Ste 165
West Covina, CA 91790-2914

Telephone: (626) 918-7435
Fax Number: (626) 918-8502
Company Email: mcarchez@aol.com
Type of Business: Chain Restaurant Operator
Year Founded: 1977
Total Sales: $76,990,000 (e)
Number of Employees: 800
Average Check: Breakfast(8); Lunch(10); Dinner(12)
Total Units: 16
Trade Names: McDonald's (16)
Units Franchised From: 16
Preferred Square Footage: 2,500; 3,000
Preferred Location Types: Freestanding
Primary Menu: Hamburger (16)
Areas of Operation: CA
Type of Foodservice: Quick Serve (16)
Franchise Affiliation: McDonald's Corporation, CHICAGO, IL
Primary Distributors: (Food) The Martin-Brower Co., STOCKTON, CA

Key Personnel
ROBERT SANCHEZ - President; Director Finance, Supply Chain; General Buyer
ROBYN SANCHEZ - Director Marketing
ROBERT ALT - Director Operations, Facility/Maintenance, Real Estate, Design, Store Fixtures
LETTY QUEZADA - Manager Human Resources
DEAN SANCHEZ - Manager Information Systems

The Hummus Republic
6700 Fallbrook Ave
West Hills, CA 91307

Telephone: (310) 999-1696
Internet Homepage: thehummusrepublic.com
Company Email: INFO@THEHUMMUSREPUBLIC.COM
Type of Business: Chain Restaurant Operator
Year Founded: 2013
Total Units: 4
Trade Names: The Hummus Republic (4)
Company-Owned Units: 2
Units Franchised To: 2
Preferred Square Footage: 1,100
Preferred Location Types: Community Mall; Strip Mall
Primary Menu: Greek/Mediterranean (4)
Projected Openings: 18
Areas of Operation: CA
Type of Foodservice: Fast Casual (4)

Key Personnel
NIR GIAT - CEO; Partner
JORDYN WEEKLY - Partner; Director Development

Hamburger Mary's International LLC
8288 Santa Monica Blvd
West Hollywood, CA 90046-5915

Mailing Address: PO Box 456, Corona Del Mar, CA, 92625-0456
Telephone: (323) 654-3800
Fax Number: (323) 654-3808
Internet Homepage: hamburgermarys.net
Company Email: info@hamburgermarys.com
Type of Business: Chain Restaurant Operator
Year Founded: 1972
Systemwide Sales: $18,526,000 (e)
Total Sales: $1,143,000 (e)
Alcohol Sales: 40%
Number of Employees: 3
Average Check: Dinner(26)
Total Units: 17
Trade Names: Hamburger Mary's Bar & Grille (17)
Units Franchised To: 17
Preferred Square Footage: 3,500; 4,000; 5,000; 6,000
Preferred Location Types: Freestanding
Alcohol Served: Beer, Wine, Liquor
Primary Menu: American (17)
Areas of Operation: CA, CO, FL, IL, WI
Foreign Countries: GERMANY
Type of Foodservice: Casual Dining (19)
Catering Services: Yes
Primary Distributors: (Food) US Foods-Los Angeles, LA MIRADA, CA; (Food) SYSCO Food Services of Los Angeles Inc., WALNUT, CA
Notes: The company derives approximately 5% of its revenue from private label.

Key Personnel
STAN SAX - CEO; President; CFO; Director Supply Chain, Ethnic Marketing, Real Estate, Design, Menu Development; General Buyer
DARREN WOOLSEY - VP; Director Finance, Facility/Maintenance, Information Systems, Marketing, Real Estate, Design, Store Fixtures
CHETT HOLLANDER - Director Operations, Purchasing, Human Resources
MARTIN GARCIA - Director Security

Innovative Dining Group
9200 W Sunset Blvd Ste 650
West Hollywood, CA 90069-3613

Telephone: (310) 271-6000
Fax Number: (310) 271-6006
Internet Homepage: boaabudhabi.ae; innovativedining.com
Company Email: info@innovativedining.com
Type of Business: Chain Restaurant Operator
Total Sales: $23,440,000 (e)
Alcohol Sales: 20%
Number of Employees: 340
Average Check: Breakfast(20); Lunch(14); Dinner(22)
Internet Order Processing: Yes
Internet Sales: 10.00%
Total Units: 15
Trade Names: Blind Dragon (2); BOA (3); Katana (3); Robata Bar (1); Roku (1); Sushi Roku (5)
Company-Owned Units: 13
Preferred Square Footage: 5,500; 6,000
Preferred Location Types: Freestanding; Hotel/Motel
Alcohol Served: Beer, Wine, Liquor
Primary Menu: Japanese (10); Snacks (2); Steak (3)
Areas of Operation: AZ, CA, IL, NV, FC
Foreign Countries: UNITED ARAB EMIRATES
Type of Foodservice: Casual Dining (15)
Primary Distributors: (Full Line) SYSCO Food Services of Los Angeles Inc., WALNUT, CA

Key Personnel
LEE MAEN - Founder; Partner
PHILIP CUMMINS - Partner
JOHN DILAZZARO - CFO
JILLIAN DUKES - VP Marketing
DAVID FICKLEN - Director Operations
MARK JOAQUIN - Director Strategic Planning
EIJI MORI - Director Operations
CHRISTIAN CORBEN - Director Operations

Poke Bar
8539 W Sunset Blvd
West Hollywood, CA 90069-2334

Telephone: (310) 657-4294
Internet Homepage: ilovepokebar.com
Company Email: Info@ilovepokebar.com
Type of Business: Chain Restaurant Operator
Year Founded: 2015
Total Units: 65
Trade Names: Poke Bar (76)
Company-Owned Units: 76
Primary Menu: Seafood (76)
Projected Openings: 15
Areas of Operation: AZ, CA, CO, GA, NC, NY, TX, WA
Type of Foodservice: Fast Casual (76)

Key Personnel
YOON JU - Co-Founder; Co-CEO; Partner; General Buyer
JASON PARK - Co-Founder; Co-CEO; Partner
CHRIS LIM - Co-Founder; Partner

RFD Inc.
414 N La Cienega Blvd
West Hollywood, CA 90048-1907

Telephone: (310) 289-9916
Fax Number: (310) 289-9911
Internet Homepage: realfood.com
Company Email: inquiry@realfood.com
Type of Business: Chain Restaurant Operator
Total Sales: $8,702,000 (e)
Alcohol Sales: 3%
Number of Employees: 100
Average Check: Lunch(18); Dinner(24)
Internet Order Processing: Yes
Total Units: 3
Trade Names: Real Food Daily (2); Real Food Daily - LAX (1)
Company-Owned Units: 3
Preferred Location Types: Freestanding
Alcohol Served: Beer, Wine
Primary Menu: Health Foods (3)
Areas of Operation: CA
Type of Foodservice: Casual Dining (3)
Catering Services: Yes
Primary Distributors: (Full Line) SYSCO Food Services of Los Angeles Inc., WALNUT, CA

Key Personnel
PAUL BETTCHER - CEO; President; General Buyer
SCOTT GLOVER - COO
JEREMY SCULLIN - Executive Chef; General Buyer
ERIK DIETZ - Director Development

Sprinkles Cupcakes CA Inc.
422 N La Cienega Blvd
West Hollywood, CA 90048-1907

Telephone: (310) 657-4102
Internet Homepage: sprinkles.com
Company Email: eat@sprinkles.com
Type of Business: Chain Restaurant Operator
Year Founded: 2005
Total Sales: $25,340,000 (e)
Number of Employees: 307
Internet Order Processing: Yes
Total Units: 32
Trade Names: Sprinkles Cupcakes (32)
Company-Owned Units: 32
Preferred Location Types: Downtown; Lifestyle Center; Mobile Unit
Primary Menu: Snacks (32)
Projected Openings: 2
Areas of Operation: AZ, CA, DC, GA, IL, NV, NY, TX
Type of Foodservice: Quick Serve (32)

Key Personnel
CANDACE NELSON - Owner
JAMES SZETO - Director Information Technology

The Lucques Group
8474 Melrose Ave
West Hollywood, CA 90069-5313

Telephone: (323) 655-6277
Fax Number: (323) 655-3925
Internet Homepage: lucques.com
Company Email: info@lucques.com
Type of Business: Chain Restaurant Operator
Year Founded: 1998
Total Sales: $5,693,000 (e)
Alcohol Sales: 15%
Number of Employees: 144
Average Check: Breakfast(18); Lunch(54); Dinner(96)
Total Units: 6
Trade Names: A.O.C. (1); Lucques (1); Tavern (1); The Larder (2); The Larder Baking Company (1)
Company-Owned Units: 6
Preferred Location Types: Freestanding; Office Complex; Other
Alcohol Served: Beer, Wine, Liquor
Primary Menu: Californian (1); French/Continental (1); Sandwiches/Deli (2); Snacks (1); Steak/Seafood (1)
Areas of Operation: CA
Type of Foodservice: Casual Dining (4); Fine Dining (2)

Key Personnel
SUZANNE GOIN - Partner; Executive Chef
CAROLINE STYNE - Partner; General Manager; General Buyer

Creighton Enterprises Inc.
825 Jefferson Blvd
West Sacramento, CA 95691-3205

Telephone: (916) 730-6293
Fax Number: (916) 685-1242
Type of Business: Chain Restaurant Operator
Year Founded: 1987
Total Sales: $15,810,000 (e)
Number of Employees: 290
Average Check: Lunch(12); Dinner(16)
Total Units: 13
Trade Names: Little Caesars Pizza (13)
Units Franchised From: 13
Preferred Square Footage: 1,600; 3,000
Preferred Location Types: Other; Strip Mall
Primary Menu: Pizza (13)
Areas of Operation: CA
Type of Foodservice: Quick Serve (13)
Franchise Affiliation: Little Caesar Enterprises Inc., DETROIT, MI

Key Personnel
BILL CREIGHTON - President; Manager Real Estate; General Buyer

Engen Enterprises
31192 La Baya Dr Ste B
Westlake Village, CA 91362-6393

Telephone: (818) 991-4174
Fax Number: (818) 991-5033
Type of Business: Chain Restaurant Operator
Year Founded: 1965
Total Sales: $75,540,000 (e)
Number of Employees: 650
Average Check: Lunch(8); Dinner(8)
Total Units: 27
Trade Names: Taco Bell (27)
Units Franchised From: 27
Preferred Square Footage: 2,500
Preferred Location Types: Freestanding
Primary Menu: Taco (27)
Areas of Operation: CA
Type of Foodservice: Quick Serve (27)
Franchise Affiliation: Taco Bell Corp., IRVINE, CA
Primary Distributors: (Full Line) McLane/Pacific, MERCED, CA

Key Personnel
BRENT FLYNN - CEO
DAVE ENGEN - President; CFO; Manager Finance, Marketing, Human Resources, Store Planning
JODI FLYNN - Owner

GFJ Hospitality Group, Inc.
928 S Westlake Blvd #2
Westlake Village, CA 91361

Telephone: (805) 230-9950
Internet Homepage: finneyscrafthouse.com
Company Email: greg@finneyscrafthouse.com
Type of Business: Chain Restaurant Operator
Year Founded: 2016
Total Units: 3
Trade Names: Finney's Crafthouse + Kitchen (3)
Company-Owned Units: 3
Preferred Location Types: Downtown; Strip Mall
Primary Menu: American (3)
Projected Openings: 1
Areas of Operation: CA
Type of Foodservice: Casual Dining (3)

Key Personnel
ERIC BOSRAU - Executive Chef
DAVID ANNAGUEY - Director Operations

PizzaRev
2535 Townsgate Rd Ste 101
Westlake Village, CA 91361-5967

Telephone: (805) 418-5269
Fax Number: (805) 379-9081
Internet Homepage: pizzarev.com
Company Email: info@pizzarev.com
Type of Business: Chain Restaurant Operator
Year Founded: 2012
Total Sales: $1,773,000 (e)
Total Units: 12
Trade Names: PizzaRev (33)
Company-Owned Units: 19
Units Franchised To: 17
Preferred Location Types: Freestanding; Regional Mall
Alcohol Served: Beer, Wine
Primary Menu: Pizza (33)
Projected Openings: 7
Areas of Operation: CA, CO, FL, LA, NV, NY, SD, TN, TX, FC
Foreign Countries: MEXICO
Type of Foodservice: Fast Casual (33)
Catering Services: Yes
Parent Company: Cleveland Avenue LLC, ,
Notes: Buffalo Wild Wings holds a minority interest in PizzaRev.

Key Personnel
NICHOLAS A. ECKERMAN - Partner
MATT AVILA - Director Operations

Sharky's Franchise Group LLC
780 Lakefield Rd Ste C
Westlake Village, CA 91361-2653

Telephone: (805) 496-8489
Fax Number: (805) 777-7235
Internet Homepage: sharkys.com
Type of Business: Chain Restaurant Operator
Year Founded: 1991
Systemwide Sales: $63,333,000 (e)
Total Sales: $57,420,000 (e)
Alcohol Sales: 3%
Number of Employees: 172
Average Check: Dinner(18)
Total Units: 29
Trade Names: Sharky's Woodfired Mexican Grill (29)
Company-Owned Units: 6
Units Franchised To: 23
Preferred Location Types: Freestanding; Strip Mall
Alcohol Served: Beer, Wine
Primary Menu: Mexican (29)
Projected Openings: 2
Areas of Operation: AR, CA, NV, OR
Type of Foodservice: Fast Casual (29)

Key Personnel
STEVEN PAPERNO - CEO
DAVID GOLDSTEIN - COO; Director Operations, Sales, Franchising
STEVEN GOLDSTEIN - Chief Marketing Officer

StoneFire Grill Management
5655 Lindero Canyon Rd Ste 204
Westlake Village, CA 91362-4044

Telephone: (818) 991-4054
Fax Number: (818) 991-6514
Internet Homepage: stonefiregrill.com
Type of Business: Chain Restaurant Operator
Year Founded: 2000
Total Sales: $8,869,000 (e)
Alcohol Sales: 7%
Number of Employees: 1,063
Average Check: Lunch(12); Dinner(12)
Total Units: 13
Trade Names: StoneFire Grill (13)
Company-Owned Units: 13
Preferred Square Footage: 2,500
Preferred Location Types: Freestanding
Alcohol Served: Beer, Wine
Primary Menu: American (13)
Projected Openings: 1
Areas of Operation: CA
Type of Foodservice: Fast Casual (13)
Catering Services: Yes
Primary Distributors: (Food) US Foods-Los Angeles, LA MIRADA, CA

Key Personnel
JUSTIN LOPEZ - CEO
MARY HARRIGAN - Partner; Director Real Estate
MICHAEL RUBKE - CFO
MATTHEW CALABRESE - CFO
CHRIS NICHOLSON - General Manager
LISA ORTEGA - Assistant Director Human Resources
ROBERT GRADY - Manager Information Technology

Wood Ranch BBQ & Grill Inc.
2835 Townsgate Rd Ste 200
Westlake Village, CA 91361-3079

Telephone: (805) 719-9000
Internet Homepage: woodranch.com
Company Email: info@woodranch.com
Type of Business: Chain Restaurant Operator
Total Sales: $16,850,000 (e)
Number of Employees: 122
Average Check: Dinner(30)
Internet Order Processing: Yes
Total Units: 18
Trade Names: Wood Ranch BBQ & Grill (18)
Company-Owned Units: 18
Preferred Square Footage: 7,000
Preferred Location Types: Freestanding; Strip Mall
Alcohol Served: Beer, Wine, Liquor
Primary Menu: Bar-B-Q (18)
Projected Openings: 2
Areas of Operation: CA
Type of Foodservice: Casual Dining (18)
Catering Services: Yes

Key Personnel
ERIC ANDERS - CEO; Partner
OFER SHEMTOV - Partner; General Buyer
MARK QUANDT - CFO
JILL SERUP - Coordinator Catering

Denco Family, Inc
15051 Leffingwell Rd Ste 201
Whittier, CA 90604-2159

Telephone: (562) 777-2249
Fax Number: (562) 777-2250
Internet Homepage: dencofamily.com
Company Email: info@dencofamily.com
Type of Business: Chain Restaurant Operator
Year Founded: 1996
Total Sales: $49,790,000 (e)
Number of Employees: 1,080
Average Check: Breakfast(6); Lunch(8); Dinner(8)
Total Units: 20
Trade Names: Denny's (17); Popeyes Louisiana Kitchen (1); Subway (2)
Units Franchised From: 20

Preferred Square Footage: 1,000; 2,000; 3,000; 5,000
Preferred Location Types: Freestanding; Strip Mall
Primary Menu: American (17); Chicken (1); Sandwiches/Deli (2)
Areas of Operation: CA, NY, TX
Type of Foodservice: Family Restaurant (17); Quick Serve (3)
Franchise Affiliation: Denny's Corporation, SPARTANBURG, SC; Doctor's Associates Inc., MILFORD, CT; Popeyes Louisiana Kitchen Inc., ATLANTA, GA
Primary Distributors: (Food) McLane/Rancho Cucamonga, RANCHO CUCAMONGA, CA

Key Personnel
RAI MARWAH - President; Director Finance, Operations, Real Estate, Training; General Buyer
RITU PORTUGAL - President
MONIKA SHERBURNE - General Manager
BOBBY KANG - Director Operations

Lascari's & Sons Inc.
10432 Bogardus Ave
Whittier, CA 90603-2642

Telephone: (714) 693-1199
Fax Number: (562) 315-5464
Internet Homepage: lascarisdeli.com
Company Email: info@lascarisdeli.com
Type of Business: Chain Restaurant Operator
Year Founded: 1970
Total Sales: $2,052,000 (e)
Total Units: 6
Trade Names: Lascari's Deli (1); Lascari's Italian Cucina (3); Lascaris Restaurant Whittier (1); Tempo Urban Kitchen (1)
Company-Owned Units: 6
Alcohol Served: Beer, Wine, Liquor
Primary Menu: Italian (5); Miscellaneous (1)
Areas of Operation: CA
Type of Foodservice: Casual Dining (6)

Key Personnel
JOHN LASCARI - Chairman; President
ASHLEY CARPENTER - Director Catering

Mobro Enterprises Inc
9719 Carmenita Rd
Whittier, CA 90605-3248

Telephone: (562) 698-5574
Type of Business: Chain Restaurant Operator
Total Units: 3
Trade Names: Del Taco (3)
Units Franchised From: 3
Primary Menu: Taco (3)
Areas of Operation: CA
Type of Foodservice: Quick Serve (3)
Franchise Affiliation: Del Taco Restaurants Inc., LAKE FOREST, CA

Key Personnel
RAFFI MOMJIAN - President; General Buyer

Yogurtland Franchisee
13582 Whittier Blvd Ste A
Whittier, CA 90605-4414

Telephone: (562) 698-1909
Type of Business: Chain Restaurant Operator
Total Sales: $4,053,000 (e)
Total Units: 4
Trade Names: Yogurtland (4)
Units Franchised From: 4
Primary Menu: Snacks (4)
Areas of Operation: CA
Type of Foodservice: Quick Serve (4)
Franchise Affiliation: Yogurtland Franchising Inc., FARMERS BRANCH, TX

Key Personnel
STEVE YANG - Owner; General Buyer

Ashish Subway Inc.
23975 Clinton Keith Rd
Wildomar, CA 92595

Telephone: (951) 461-8930
Type of Business: Chain Restaurant Operator
Total Sales: $3,956,000 (e)
Total Units: 7
Trade Names: Subway (7)
Units Franchised From: 7
Primary Menu: Sandwiches/Deli (7)
Areas of Operation: CA
Type of Foodservice: Quick Serve (7)
Franchise Affiliation: Doctor's Associates Inc., MILFORD, CT

Key Personnel
ONKAR SUD - Owner; General Buyer

Grill Concepts, Inc.
6300 Canoga Ave Ste 600
Woodland Hills, CA 91367-8022

Telephone: (818) 251-7000
Fax Number: (818) 999-4745
Internet Homepage: dailygrill.com; grillconcepts.com; thegrill.com; theritzprimeseafood.com
Company Email: info@thegrill.com
Type of Business: Chain Restaurant Operator
Year Founded: 1984
Total Sales: $118,540,000 (e)
Alcohol Sales: 10%
Number of Employees: 2,041
Average Check: Breakfast(16); Lunch(18); Dinner(36)
Total Units: 22
Trade Names: Daily Grill (13); Public School on Tap (7); The Grill on the Alley (2)
Company-Owned Units: 22
Preferred Square Footage: 3,500; 7,600; 8,000
Preferred Location Types: Airports; Freestanding; Hotel/Motel; Regional Mall
Alcohol Served: Beer, Wine, Liquor
Primary Menu: American (27); Seafood (2)
Projected Openings: 3
Areas of Operation: CA, CO, DC, IL, TX
Type of Foodservice: Casual Dining (23); Fine Dining (6)
Catering Services: Yes
Primary Distributors: (Food) SYSCO Food Services of Los Angeles Inc., WALNUT, CA
Notes: The number of company-owned stores includes several that are managed operations.

Key Personnel
TOMIKA BROWN - VP Brand Marketing
CLAUDE COGNIAN - Director
WILL WHITE - Director Operations
JESSICA KASILIAN - Director Employee Development-Training
JESSICA PIKE - Director Human Resources

RDR Foods
22611 Ventura Blvd
Woodland Hills, CA 91364-1416

Telephone: (818) 225-1038
Company Email: flipburgers@sbcglobal.net
Type of Business: Chain Restaurant Operator
Total Sales: $11,521,000 (e)
Number of Employees: 100
Average Check: Breakfast(8); Lunch(8); Dinner(8)
Total Units: 4
Trade Names: Wendy's Old Fashioned Hamburgers (4)
Units Franchised From: 4
Preferred Square Footage: 2,100; 2,900
Preferred Location Types: Freestanding
Primary Menu: Hamburger (4)
Areas of Operation: CA
Type of Foodservice: Quick Serve (4)
Franchise Affiliation: The Wendy's Company, DUBLIN, OH
Primary Distributors: (Full Line) Systems Services of America, FONTANA, CA

Key Personnel
RONALD ROSS - President; General Manager; General Buyer

Creamistry, Inc.
22755 Savi Ranch Pkwy Ste G
Yorba Linda, CA 92887-4618

Telephone: (657) 224-9602
Internet Homepage: creamistry.com
Company Email: info@creamistry.com
Type of Business: Chain Restaurant Operator
Systemwide Sales: $29,795,000 (e)
Total Sales: $3,293,000 (e)
Total Units: 48
Trade Names: Creamistry (48)
Units Franchised To: 48
Primary Menu: Snacks (48)
Projected Openings: 3
Areas of Operation: AZ, CA, GA, LA, NV, TX
Type of Foodservice: Quick Serve (48)
Notes: Made-to-order flash-frozen (liquid nitrogen) ice cream concept.

Key Personnel
KATIE YIM - Owner
STEPHEN BOUD - COO

Delaware North Parks & Resorts At Yosemite
PO Box 578
Yosemite National Park, CA 95389-0578

Telephone: (209) 372-1000
Fax Number: (209) 372-1364
Internet Homepage: yosemitepark.com
Company Email: info@yosemitepark.com
Type of Business: Foodservice Operations - Hotel/Motels
Year Founded: 1899
Total Sales: $152,686,000 (e)
Alcohol Sales: 22%
Number of Employees: 1,400
Total Units: 19
Restaurants in Hotels: 19
Trade Names: Curry Village (5); Glacier Point Snack Stand (1); Happy Isles Snack Stand (1); The Ahwahnee (1); The Mountain Room (1); Tuolumne Lodge(1); Tuolumne Meadows Grill (1); Wawona Hotel (2); White Wolf Lodge (2); Yosemite Village (4)
Company-Owned Units: 19
Alcohol Served: Beer, Wine, Liquor
Areas of Operation: CA
Type of Foodservice: Cafeteria; Casual Dining; Fine Dining; Quick Serve
Primary Distributors: (Food) SYSCO Food Services of Los Angeles Inc., WALNUT, CA
Parent Company: Delaware North Companies Inc., BUFFALO, NY
Headquarters: Delaware North, BUFFALO, NY
Notes: The company derives approximately 75% of its revenue from hotel operations.

Key Personnel
ROLAND HENIN - Corporate Chef; Director Menu Development, Food Safety, Food and Beverage; General Buyer
JOE RABON - Director Human Resources

Mustards Grill
7399 Saint Helena Hwy
Yountville, CA 94558

Telephone: (707) 944-2424
Fax Number: (707) 944-0828
Internet Homepage: mustardsgrill.com
Company Email: info@mustardsgrill.com
Type of Business: Chain Restaurant Operator
Total Sales: $2,329,000 (e)
Alcohol Sales: 15%
Number of Employees: 35
Average Check: Lunch(14); Dinner(24)
Total Units: 1
Trade Names: Mustards Grill (1)
Company-Owned Units: 1
Preferred Location Types: Freestanding
Alcohol Served: Beer, Wine, Liquor
Primary Menu: American (1)
Areas of Operation: CA
Type of Foodservice: Casual Dining (1)

Key Personnel
SEAN KNIGHT - Partner
JIM LEIKEN - Executive Chef; General Buyer

Thomas Keller Restaurant Group
6540 Washington St
Yountville, CA 94599-1315

Telephone: (707) 944-8768
Fax Number: (707) 944-8754
Internet Homepage: adhocrestaurant.com; bouchon.com; frenchlaundry.com; tkrg.org
Type of Business: Chain Restaurant Operator
Year Founded: 1994
Total Sales: $80,810,000 (e)
Alcohol Sales: 30%
Average Check: Dinner(500)
Total Units: 13
Trade Names: Ad Hoc (1); Bouchon Bakery (5); Bouchon Bistro (2); La Calenda (1); Per Se (1); Surf Club (1); TakRoom (1); The French Laundry (1)
Company-Owned Units: 13
Alcohol Served: Beer, Wine, Liquor
Primary Menu: American (2); French/Continental (10); Mexican (1)
Areas of Operation: CA, NV, NY
Type of Foodservice: Casual Dining (11); Fine Dining (2)
Notes: The average dinner check reflects The French Laundry restaurant. In addition to the restaurants, the company operates Bouchon Bakeries in Yountville CA, New York NY, Beverly Hills CA, and Las Vegas NV.

Key Personnel
THOMAS KELLER - Owner; Executive Chef; General Buyer
DAVID CIABATTARI - CFO
LAURA CUNNINGHAM - VP Development, Branding
MICHAEL MINNILLO - General Manager
LARRY NADEAU - General Manager Division
DAVID BREEDEN - Executive Chef Division
MICHAEL SANDOVAL - Executive Chef Division
ERIK JOHNSON - Director Alcoholic Beverages
BRIAN COCHRAN - Director Operations
PAUL PETERSON - Director Alcoholic Beverages
LAUREN PRYATEL-TUCKER - Manager Restaurant Operations
RACHAEL BOVA - Manager Retail Operations

DeClerck Enterprises
303 N Oregon St
Yreka, CA 96097-2413

Telephone: (530) 842-4827
Fax Number: (530) 842-3607
Internet Homepage: tacobell.com
Company Email: declerckoffice@yahoo.com
Type of Business: Chain Restaurant Operator
Year Founded: 1983
Total Sales: $40,440,000 (e)
Number of Employees: 150
Average Check: Lunch(8); Dinner(8)
Total Units: 15
Trade Names: Taco Bell (15)
Units Franchised From: 15
Preferred Square Footage: 2,500
Preferred Location Types: Freestanding
Primary Menu: Taco (15)
Areas of Operation: CA, OR
Type of Foodservice: Quick Serve (15)
Franchise Affiliation: Taco Bell Corp., IRVINE, CA
Primary Distributors: (Full Line) McLane/Tualatin, TUALATIN, OR

Key Personnel
STEVEN DECLERCK - Owner; General Manager; Director Operations, Facility/Maintenance, Real Estate, Design; General Buyer

Kauai Restaurants, Inc.
1547 Starr Dr Ste G
Yuba City, CA 95993-2663

Telephone: (530) 742-3726
Fax Number: (530) 742-1857
Type of Business: Chain Restaurant Operator
Total Sales: $28,360,000 (e)

Number of Employees: 200
Total Units: 6
Trade Names: McDonald's (6)
Units Franchised From: 6
Preferred Square Footage: 2,500
Preferred Location Types: Discount Dept. Stores; Freestanding
Primary Menu: Hamburger (6)
Areas of Operation: CA
Type of Foodservice: Quick Serve (6)
Franchise Affiliation: McDonald's Corporation, CHICAGO, IL

Key Personnel
JOHN COOK - President; General Buyer

COLORADO

Ice Cream Fun, LLC
15400 W 64th Ave Bldg E
Arvada, CO 80007-6852

Telephone: (303) 487-0505
Type of Business: Chain Restaurant Operator
Total Sales: $1,195,000 (e)
Total Units: 3
Trade Names: Cold Stone Creamery (3)
Units Franchised From: 3
Primary Menu: Snacks (3)
Areas of Operation: CO
Type of Foodservice: Quick Serve (3)
Franchise Affiliation: Kahala Brands, SCOTTSDALE, AZ

Key Personnel
DEAN GERONDALE - Partner
MIKE BERGER - Partner

Backyard Breeze, Inc.
6770 S Cornerstar Way Unit 8C
Aurora, CO 80016-1575

Telephone: (303) 400-1997
Type of Business: Chain Restaurant Operator
Total Sales: $1,205,000 (e)
Total Units: 2
Trade Names: Cold Stone Creamery (2)
Units Franchised From: 2
Primary Menu: Snacks (2)
Areas of Operation: CO
Type of Foodservice: Quick Serve (2)
Franchise Affiliation: Kahala Brands, SCOTTSDALE, AZ

Key Personnel
ALAN WELDON - Partner
KAREN E. WELDON - Partner

Great American Restaurant Properties Inc.
3538 Peoria St Ste 508
Aurora, CO 80010-1411

Telephone: (303) 792-3088
Fax Number: (303) 792-9350
Internet Homepage: bennettsbbq.com
Company Email: info@bennettsbbq.com
Type of Business: Chain Restaurant Operator
Year Founded: 1984
Systemwide Sales: $9,011,000 (e)
Total Sales: $8,749,000 (e)
Alcohol Sales: 10%
Number of Employees: 100
Average Check: Lunch(10); Dinner(16)
Total Units: 1
Trade Names: Bennett's Pit Bar-B-Que (1)
Company-Owned Units: 1
Preferred Square Footage: 7,000
Preferred Location Types: Freestanding
Alcohol Served: Beer, Wine, Liquor
Primary Menu: Bar-B-Q (1)
Areas of Operation: CO
Type of Foodservice: Casual Dining (1)
Catering Services: Yes
Primary Distributors: (Food) SYSCO Food Services of Denver, DENVER, CO; (Supplies) SYSCO Food Services of Denver, DENVER, CO

Key Personnel
TREY WOESSNER - Owner

OM Management, Inc.
14132 E Cedar Ave Unit A
Aurora, CO 80012-1418

Telephone: (303) 340-8200
Type of Business: Chain Restaurant Operator
Total Sales: $1,229,000 (e)
Total Units: 2
Trade Names: Cold Stone Creamery (2)
Units Franchised From: 2
Primary Menu: Snacks (2)
Areas of Operation: CO
Type of Foodservice: Quick Serve (2)
Franchise Affiliation: Kahala Brands, SCOTTSDALE, AZ

Key Personnel
ALOK SARWAL - Partner
ANJALI SARWAL - Partner

Papa John's Distribution Center
3451 Fraser St
Aurora, CO 80011-1250

Telephone: (303) 371-6788
Fax Number: (303) 371-6792
Listing Type: Distribution Center
Type of Business: Chain Restaurant Operator
Number of Employees: 35
Areas of Operation: CO, ID, MT, NE, NM, SD, UT, WY
Parent Company: Papa Johns International Inc., LOUISVILLE, KY

Key Personnel
PAT COVEY - Director Distribution
JEFF MURRAY - Manager Distribution

The Wendy's Company
12200 E Iliff Ave Ste 208
Aurora, CO 80014-5375

Telephone: (303) 338-8008
Fax Number: (303) 338-9090
Listing Type: Divisional Office
Type of Business: Chain Restaurant Operator
Number of Employees: 23
Total Units: 43
Areas of Operation: CO
Parent Company: The Wendy's Company, DUBLIN, OH

Key Personnel
CHRISTY JONES - Area Director

Big Red F Restaurant Group
5440 Conestoga Ct
Boulder, CO 80301-2724

Telephone: (303) 448-9182
Internet Homepage: bigredf.com; jaxfishhouse.com; zologrill.com
Company Email: info@zologrill.com
Type of Business: Chain Restaurant Operator
Year Founded: 1994
Total Sales: $15,160,000 (e)
Alcohol Sales: 30%
Number of Employees: 132
Average Check: Lunch(14); Dinner(20)
Total Units: 11
Trade Names: Centro (1); Jax Fish House (6); Lola Mexican Fish House (1); The Post Brewing Company (1); West End Tavern (1); Zolo Grill (1)
Company-Owned Units: 11
Preferred Square Footage: 5,500; 6,000
Preferred Location Types: Freestanding
Alcohol Served: Beer, Wine, Liquor

Primary Menu: American (2); Mexican (2); Seafood (6); Southwest/Tex-Mex (1)
Areas of Operation: CO
Type of Foodservice: Casual Dining (11)
Catering Services: Yes
Primary Distributors: (Food) US Foods, CENTENNIAL, CO

Key Personnel
DAVE QUERY - Owner; General Buyer
TIFFANY RICHARDS - CFO
BRENT BEDARD - General Manager
ADAM REED - Director Operations
NIK HANKS - Manager Public Relations

● ▲
Capstone Restaurant Group
7490 Clubhouse Rd Ste 200
Boulder, CO 80301-3720

Mailing Address: P.O. Box 11110, Boulder, CO, 80301
Telephone: (303) 530-2900
Fax Number: (303) 254-5529
Internet Homepage: capstonerestaurants.com
Company Email: info@capstonerestaurants.com
Type of Business: Chain Restaurant Operator
Total Sales: $502,920,000 (e)
Total Units: 262
Trade Names: Carl's Jr. (8); Hardee's (152); Hardee's/Red Burrito (102)
Units Franchised From: 262
Areas of Operation: CO, FL, GA, IA, IL, KS, MO, MT, OH, PA, SC, TN, VA, WV, WY
Type of Foodservice: Quick Serve (262)
Franchise Affiliation: Carl's Jr., FRANKLIN, TN; DD IP Holder, CANTON, MA; Hardee's Food Systems Inc., FRANKLIN, TN; Pizza Hut Inc., PLANO, TX; Taco Bell Corp., IRVINE, CA

Key Personnel
BUDDY BROWN - CEO
TODD PAHL - President; Partner; CFO
MAX SORIA - Partner
BOBBY MEDLEN - Partner Operations
MELISSA WOLF - VP Accounting
MEGAN WILLIS - VP Operations
RANDY RIPPETOE - Regional VP
JASON WILLIS - Director Operations
KAITLYNN FINLEON - Director Payroll, Human Resources
MARIO VALDEZ - Director Information Technology
JONATHAN TWOMEY - Director Operations
KEVIN POLLOCK - Regional Director Operations
MIKE MCLENDON - Regional Director Operations
BENJAMIN EVERS - Senior Manager Accounting
BILL HOPPER - District Manager
MILTON WYNN - District Manager
CHAD SCRUGGS - District Manager

SHANNON PHIPPS - Manager Marketing
ERIN RAINEY - Manager Payroll
JEREMIAH NUHN - Manager Information Technology
LISA SHANNON - Manager Marketing
SCOTT SCHAEFER - Project Manager
TONI GUTIERREZ - Specialist Administration
SHAWN GLASS - Coordinator Training, Recruitment

Escoffier School of Culinary Arts Boulder
637 S Broadway St Ste H
Boulder, CO 80305-5961

Telephone: (877) 249-0305
Internet Homepage: escoffier.edu/locations/boulder
Company Email: admissionsboulder@escoffier.edu
Type of Business: Culinary Schools
Areas of Operation: CO

Key Personnel
KIRK BACHMAN - President
TOM EHRHARDT - Chief Marketing Officer

Hapa Group Inc
948 North St Ste 1
Boulder, CO 80304-3385

Telephone: (303) 938-9335
Fax Number: (303) 938-9334
Internet Homepage: hapasushi.com
Company Email: hapasushi@hapasushi.com
Type of Business: Chain Restaurant Operator
Total Sales: $7,062,000 (e)
Alcohol Sales: 8%
Number of Employees: 60
Average Check: Lunch(18); Dinner(30)
Internet Order Processing: Yes
Total Units: 4
Trade Names: Hapa Sushi Grill and Sake Bar (4)
Company-Owned Units: 4
Preferred Location Types: Community Mall; Downtown
Alcohol Served: Beer, Wine, Liquor
Primary Menu: Japanese (4)
Areas of Operation: CO
Type of Foodservice: Casual Dining (4)
Primary Distributors: (Food) SYSCO Food Services of Denver, DENVER, CO

Key Personnel
MARK VAN GRACK - President; Director Information Systems, Menu Development; General Buyer
JESSICA BROOKHART - COO
MICHAEL LAGUNA - General Manager

AARON NAKAMICHI - Director Operations

● ▲
JAR Inc. Ltd.
1002 Walnut St Ste 203A
Boulder, CO 80302-5199

Telephone: (303) 449-7101
Fax Number: (303) 449-7103
Type of Business: Chain Restaurant Operator
Year Founded: 1981
Total Sales: $105,739,000 (e)
Number of Employees: 1,480
Average Check: Lunch(12); Dinner(12)
Total Units: 53
Trade Names: Domino's (53)
Units Franchised From: 53
Preferred Square Footage: 1,000
Preferred Location Types: Institution (college/hospital); Office Complex; Strip Mall
Primary Menu: Pizza (53)
Areas of Operation: CO, TX
Type of Foodservice: Quick Serve (53)
Franchise Affiliation: Domino's Pizza Inc, ANN ARBOR, MI
Primary Distributors: (Full Line) SYSCO Food Services of Denver, DENVER, CO

Key Personnel
JOSEPH ROMANO - President; Partner; CFO; Director Loss Prevention, Real Estate; General Buyer
RICHARD HAFNER - Partner

● ▲
McDonald's of Boulder
2400 Central Ave Ste P1
Boulder, CO 80301-2843

Telephone: (303) 415-1805
Fax Number: (303) 443-1021
Type of Business: Chain Restaurant Operator
Total Sales: $33,610,000 (e)
Number of Employees: 120
Average Check: Breakfast(5); Lunch(8); Dinner(8)
Total Units: 7
Trade Names: McDonald's (7)
Units Franchised From: 7
Preferred Square Footage: 2,500; 3,000
Preferred Location Types: Freestanding
Primary Menu: Hamburger (7)
Areas of Operation: CO
Type of Foodservice: Quick Serve (7)
Franchise Affiliation: McDonald's Corporation, CHICAGO, IL
Primary Distributors: (Food) Mile Hi Foods, DENVER, CO

Key Personnel
AARON HOLLAND - President; General Manager; General Buyer
DAMITA HOLLAND - Owner; VP Finance

MARIA LECHUGA - Director Human Resources

Modern Restaurant Concepts
1600 28th St Unit 1212
Boulder, CO 80301-1008

Telephone: (303) 440-0476
Internet Homepage: modmarket.com
Company Email: info@modmarket.com
Type of Business: Chain Restaurant Operator
Year Founded: 2009
Total Sales: $37,930,000 (e)
Average Check: Lunch(14); Dinner(14)
Internet Order Processing: Yes
Total Units: 48
Trade Names: Lemonade (20); Modern Market (28)
Company-Owned Units: 48
Preferred Location Types: Airports; Strip Mall
Primary Menu: American (28); Californian (20)
Projected Openings: 10
Areas of Operation: AZ, CA, CO, DC, MD, TX
Type of Foodservice: Fast Casual (48)
Catering Services: Yes
Parent Company: Butterfly Equity, ,

Key Personnel
ROB MCCOLGAN - Co-CEO; Partner
NATE WEIR - Corporate Chef
ERINN MCCULLY - Director Catering
JOEL PAULSON - Manager Facility/Maintenance

Nor-Mar Management Services Inc.
6550 Gunpark Dr
Boulder, CO 80301-3596

Telephone: (303) 581-0300
Fax Number: (303) 581-0686
Type of Business: Chain Restaurant Operator
Year Founded: 1909
Total Sales: $56,420,000 (e)
Number of Employees: 650
Average Check: Breakfast(8); Lunch(8); Dinner(8)
Total Units: 25
Trade Names: Burger King (25)
Units Franchised From: 25
Preferred Square Footage: 3,000
Preferred Location Types: Community Mall; Freestanding; Strip Mall
Primary Menu: Hamburger (25)
Areas of Operation: CO, WY
Type of Foodservice: Quick Serve (25)
Franchise Affiliation: Burger King Worldwide Inc., MIAMI, FL
Primary Distributors: (Full Line) Mile Hi Foods,

DENVER, CO

Key Personnel
JOE LUKAS - President; Director Finance, Purchasing, Facility/Maintenance, Supply Chain, Real Estate, Design, Human Resources, Store Fixtures
JOHN KAY - Controller

Pasta Jay's
1001 Pearl St
Boulder, CO 80302-5110

Telephone: (303) 444-5800
Internet Homepage: pastajays.com
Type of Business: Chain Restaurant Operator
Year Founded: 1988
Total Sales: $5,452,000 (e)
Alcohol Sales: 18%
Number of Employees: 75
Average Check: Lunch(10); Dinner(22)
Total Units: 2
Trade Names: Pasta Jay's (2)
Company-Owned Units: 2
Preferred Square Footage: 2,300
Preferred Location Types: Downtown; Freestanding
Alcohol Served: Beer, Wine, Liquor
Primary Menu: Italian (2)
Areas of Operation: CO, KS, UT
Type of Foodservice: Casual Dining (3)
Catering Services: Yes
Primary Distributors: (Full Line) US Foods, CENTENNIAL, CO

Key Personnel
JAY L. ELOWSKY - Owner; General Manager; Corporate Chef; General Buyer

Rush Bowls
7490 Clubhouse Rd Fl 2
Boulder, CO 80301-3720

Telephone: (720) 485-6868
Internet Homepage: rushbowls.com
Company Email: wholesale@rushbowls.com
Type of Business: Chain Restaurant Operator
Total Units: 11
Trade Names: Rush Bowls (11)
Company-Owned Units: 3
Units Franchised To: 8
Primary Menu: Snacks (11)
Projected Openings: 3
Areas of Operation: CA, CO, MO, OH, TN, TX, FC
Type of Foodservice: Quick Serve (11)

Key Personnel
ANDREW PUDALOV - CEO; Partner
BUDDY BROWN - Partner

NICOLE MCCRAY - Senior VP

Salvaggio's Italian Deli
2609 Pearl St
Boulder, CO 80302-3820

Telephone: (303) 938-1981
Fax Number: (303) 938-1987
Internet Homepage: salvaggiosdeli.us
Type of Business: Chain Restaurant Operator
Year Founded: 1994
Total Sales: $3,156,000 (e)
Number of Employees: 36
Average Check: Breakfast(6); Lunch(12); Dinner(12)
Total Units: 2
Trade Names: Salvaggio's Italian Deli (2)
Company-Owned Units: 2
Preferred Square Footage: 3,000
Preferred Location Types: Freestanding; Mixed-use Center; Strip Mall
Primary Menu: Sandwiches/Deli (2)
Areas of Operation: CO
Type of Foodservice: Family Restaurant (2)
Primary Distributors: (Food) US Foods, OGDEN, UT

Key Personnel
STEPHEN SALVAGGIO - President; Executive Chef; Director Menu Development, Catering
JAMES LAVOIE - General Manager; General Buyer

The Kitchen
1039 Pearl St
Boulder, CO 80302-5110

Telephone: (303) 544-5973
Fax Number: (303) 544-0092
Internet Homepage: thekitchen.com
Type of Business: Chain Restaurant Operator
Year Founded: 2004
Total Sales: $66,620,000 (e)
Alcohol Sales: 20%
Total Units: 15
Trade Names: Hedge Row (1); Next Door Boulder (1); Next Door Glendale (1); Next Door Highlands Ranch (1); Next Door Indianapolis (1); Next Door Memphis (1); Next Door Orange Village (1); Next Door Stapleton (1); Next Door Union Station (1); Next Door Vernon Hills (1); The Kitchen Boulder (1); The Kitchen Chicago (1); The Kitchen Denver (1); The Kitchen Fort Collins (1); Upstairs Boulder (1)
Company-Owned Units: 15
Primary Menu: American (13); Californian (1)
Projected Openings: 1
Areas of Operation: CO, IL, TN
Type of Foodservice: Casual Dining (13); In-Store Feeder (1)

Catering Services: Yes

Key Personnel
KIMBAL MUSK - Co-Founder; Executive Chef
DON DEGNAN - President
KYLE MENDENHALL - Executive Chef

Beaver Run Resort
620 Village Rd
Breckenridge, CO 80424

Mailing Address: PO Box 2115, BRECKENRIDGE, CO, 80424-2115
Telephone: (970) 453-6000
Fax Number: (970) 453-4284
Internet Homepage: beaverrun.com
Company Email: stay@beaverrun.com
Type of Business: Foodservice Operations - Hotel/Motels
Year Founded: 1982
Total Sales: $22,531,000 (e)
Alcohol Sales: 30%
Number of Employees: 100
Total Units: 1
Restaurants in Hotels: 4
Trade Names: Beaver Run Resort & Conference Center (1)
Company-Owned Units: 4
Alcohol Served: Beer, Wine, Liquor
Areas of Operation: CO
Type of Foodservice: Casual Dining (3); Quick Serve (1)
Primary Distributors: (Food) SYSCO Food Services of Denver, DENVER, CO
Notes: The company derives approximately 67% of its revenue from resort operations

Key Personnel
JOE SHACKELTON - CEO; President; General Manager
RICH NELSON - VP
PHIL DILKS - Executive Chef
DAVE FELLER - Manager Sales
RACHEL FOLLENDER - Manager Marketing
KELLY VIRGIN RIX - Manager Sales

Famous Brands International
8001 Arista Pl Unit 600
Broomfield, CO 80021-4135

Telephone: (720) 599-3350
Internet Homepage: famousbrandsintl.com; mrsfields.com; tcby.com
Company Email: info@famousbrandsintl.com
Listing Type: Corporate Office
Type of Business: Nontraditional Foodservice Operator
Year Founded: 1977
Total Sales: $51,380,000 (e)
Number of Employees: 6,500
Average Check: Breakfast(8); Lunch(8); Dinner(8)
Internet Order Processing: Yes
Internet Sales: 10.00%
Total Units: 293
Trade Names: Mrs. Fields Cookies (145); TCBY (222)
Units Franchised To: 367
Preferred Square Footage: 200; 500; 800; 1,000; 1,500
Preferred Location Types: Airports; Community Mall; Freestanding; Hotel/Motel; Kiosk; Lifestyle Center; Outlet Mall; Regional Mall; Strip Mall; Travel Plazas
Primary Menu: Snacks (367)
Areas of Operation: AK, AL, AR, AZ, CA, CO, CT, DC, DE, FL, GA, HI, IA, ID, IL, IN, KS, KY, LA, MA, MD, ME, MI, MN, MO, MS, MT, NC, ND, NE, NH, NJ, NM, NV, NY, OH, OK, OR, PA, SC, SD, TN, TX, UT, VA, WA, WI, WV, WY
Type of Foodservice: Quick Serve (367)
On-site Distribution Center: Yes
Primary Distributors: (Food) VISTAR Specialty, ENGLEWOOD, CO
Parent Company: Z Capital Partners LLC, LAKE FOREST, IL
Headquarter Offices: TCBY Systems LLC, BROOMFIELD, CO
Notes: The company derives approximately 75% of its revenue from catalog/e-tailing & other retail sales.

Key Personnel
RICHARD HANKINS - Senior Director Development, Real Estate
KRISTIN MCKEEHAN - Coordinator Human Resources

Noodles & Company
520 Zang St Ste D
Broomfield, CO 80021-8239

Telephone: (720) 214-1900
Fax Number: (720) 214-1934
Internet Homepage: noodles.com
Company Email: thechef@noodles.com
Type of Business: Chain Restaurant Operator
Year Founded: 1995
Systemwide Sales: $740,844,000 (e)
Publicly Held: Yes
Total Sales: $503,405,000 (e)
Alcohol Sales: 3%
Number of Employees: 8,900
Average Check: Lunch(10); Dinner(10)
Total Units: 470
Trade Names: Noodles & Company (470)
Company-Owned Units: 380
Units Franchised To: 90
Preferred Square Footage: 2,600; 2,700
Preferred Location Types: Community Mall; Downtown; Freestanding; Lifestyle Center; Office Complex; Regional Mall; Strip Mall
Alcohol Served: Beer, Wine
Primary Menu: Miscellaneous (470)
Projected Openings: 19
Areas of Operation: AZ, CA, CO, CT, DC, FL, IA, ID, IL, IN, KS, KY, MD, MI, MN, MO, MT, NC, ND, NE, NY, OH, OR, PA, SD, TN, UT, VA, WA, WI
Foreign Countries: CANADA
Type of Foodservice: Fast Casual (470)
Catering Services: Yes
Primary Distributors: (Food) VISTAR Specialty, ENGLEWOOD, CO; (Supplies) VISTAR Specialty, ENGLEWOOD, CO
Parent Company: Catterton Partners, GREENWICH, CT

Key Personnel
DREW MADSEN - CEO
MIKE HYNES - CFO
BRAD WEST - COO
SCOTT DAVIS - Chief Design Officer
MITCHELL MYLEK - Area Director
MELISSA M. HEIDMAN - Exec VP; Corporate Secretary; General Counsel
STEPHEN KENNEDY - Exec VP Marketing
COREY KLINE - Exec VP Technology
WILLIAM KNOPF - VP
MIKE HERRMANN - VP Finance
CARLY HABEIN - VP Franchise Operations, Sales
FRED DUDLEY - VP Supply Chain
JOHN RAMSAY - VP Franchise Sales
DAWN RHEINLANDER - VP Real Estate
RYAN RICHARD - VP Operations
FRANK RODRIGUEZ - VP Operations
NADINE RODRIGUEZ - VP; Director Procurement
DAVID LEHN - VP Information Technology
KATHY LOCKHART - VP; Controller
STACY MOSS - Director Brand Marketing
COLIN PROTCH - Director Finance
TOM FINLEY - Director Digital Media
GREGORY BURNTHORN - Director Real Estate
STEVE CALAMARIS - Director Quality Assurance, Safety-Food
KIM DICKERSON - Director Franchise Development
MARISA KOWALSKI - Regional Director Operations
MARK THOMPSON - Regional Director Operations
DEREK RUNGE - Regional Director Operations
MATT JOHNSON - Regional Director Operations
DALE MATLOSZ - Manager Leasing
JENNIFER MCVAY - Manager Licensing
KATIE A. JOHNSON - Manager Finance
CARRIE STENGER - Manager Operations
SAMANTHA BARSTOW - Manager Quality Assurance
DARCY DEES - Manager HRIS
CHELSEA BLACKMAN - Project Manager Store Design

Pbjd Enterprises Inc
7634 US Highway 287
Broomfield, CO 80020-2227

Telephone: (303) 469-2431
Type of Business: Chain Restaurant Operator
Total Sales: $4,536,000 (e)
Total Units: 3
Trade Names: Dairy Queen Store (3)
Units Franchised From: 3
Primary Menu: Snacks (3)
Areas of Operation: CO
Type of Foodservice: Quick Serve (3)
Franchise Affiliation: International Dairy Queen Inc., BLOOMINGTON, MN

Key Personnel
BRUCE SMITH - President; General Buyer

TCBY Systems LLC
8001 Arista Pl Unit 600
Broomfield, CO 80021-4135

Telephone: (720) 599-3350
Internet Homepage: tcby.com
Company Email: reception@famousbrandsintl.com
Type of Business: Chain Restaurant Operator
Year Founded: 1976
Systemwide Sales: $151,512,000 (e)
Total Sales: $7,501,000 (e)
Number of Employees: 180
Average Check: Lunch(8); Dinner(8)
Internet Sales: 1.00%
Total Units: 365
Trade Names: TCBY (365)
Company-Owned Units: 1
Units Franchised To: 364
Preferred Square Footage: 800; 1,500
Preferred Location Types: Airports; Community Mall; Convenience Store/Gas Station; Downtown; Freestanding; Institution (college/hospital); Kiosk; Mobile Unit; Office Complex; Regional Mall; Stadiums; Strip Mall; Travel Plazas
Primary Menu: Snacks (365)
Areas of Operation: AL, AR, AZ, CA, CO, CT, DC, DE, FL, GA, HI, IA, ID, IL, IN, KS, LA, MA, MD, MI, MN, MO, MS, NC, ND, NE, NH, NJ, NM, NV, NY, OR, PA, SC, SD, TN, TX, UT, VA, WA, WI, WV, WY
Type of Foodservice: Quick Serve (365)
Primary Distributors: (Full Line) SYSCO Intermountain Food Services Inc., WEST JORDAN, UT
Parent Company: Z Capital Partners LLC, LAKE FOREST, IL
Headquarters: Famous Brands International, BROOMFIELD, CO

Key Personnel
JONATHAN STRINGHAM - Manager Operations

Vail Resorts Inc.
390 Interlocken Cres Ste 1000
Broomfield, CO 80021-8056

Telephone: (303) 404-1800
Internet Homepage: parkcitymountain.com; rockresorts.com; snow.com; vailresorts.com; vrc.com
Type of Business: Foodservice Operations - Hotel/Motels
Year Founded: 1960
Publicly Held: Yes
Total Sales: $3,219,700,000 (e)
Alcohol Sales: 20%
Number of Employees: 17,553
Total Units: 24
Restaurants in Hotels: 24
Trade Names: Breckenridge Mountain Lodge (1); Colter Bay Village (1); Hotel Jerome (1); Inn at Beaver Creek (1); Inn at Keystone (1); Jackson Lake Lodge(1); Jenny Lake Lodge (1); La Posada de Santa Fe (1); Northstar-at-Tahoe (1); Park City Mountain Resort (1); Perisher Ski Resort (1); Ritz-Carlton, Bachelor Gulch (1); Rosario Resort & Spa (1); Ski Tip Lodge (1); Sundial Lodge (1); The Equinox (1); The Equinox Resort & Spa (1); The Great Divide (1); The Keystone Lodge (1); The Lodge & Spa at Cordillera (1); The Lodge at Rancho Mirage (1); The Lodge at Vail (1); The Pines Lodge (1); Village Hotel (1)
Company-Owned Units: 24
Alcohol Served: Beer, Wine, Liquor
Areas of Operation: CA, CO, FL, MI, NM, NV, UT, VT, WA, WY
Foreign Countries: AUSTRALIA
Type of Foodservice: Casual Dining; Fast Casual; Fine Dining
Primary Distributors: (Food) SYSCO Food Services of Denver, DENVER, CO; (Specialty Foods) Shamrock Foods Colorado Division, COMMERCE CITY, CO
Notes: Included in the total number of units are locations managed by Vail Resorts in addition to those owned by the company. The company derives approximately 89% of its revenue from resort activities; total revenue excludes revenue from real estate operations.

Key Personnel
ROBERT A. KATZ - Chairman; CEO; President Division
JOHN M. GARNSEY - President International Division
BETH HOWARD - COO; VP; General Manager Division
BILL ROCK - COO Division; Senior VP
LYNANNE J. KUNKEL - Chief Human Resources Officer; Exec VP
ROBERT URWILER - CIO; Exec VP Information Systems
KIRSTEN A. LYNCH - Chief Marketing Officer; Exec VP
DAVID T. SHAPIRO - Exec VP; General Counsel
TIMOTHY APRIL - Senior VP
PAUL WADE - Executive Chef
STEVE NGUYEN - Executive Chef
GABRIELLE LERNER KEOWN - Senior Director Real Estate Development
NICKY DEFORD - Manager Communications, Division

Japetto, Inc.
4625 Trail Boss Dr Ste B
Castle Rock, CO 80104-2803

Telephone: (303) 688-2131
Type of Business: Chain Restaurant Operator
Total Sales: $1,546,000 (e)
Total Units: 2
Trade Names: Little Caesars Pizza (2)
Units Franchised From: 2
Primary Menu: Pizza (2)
Areas of Operation: CO
Type of Foodservice: Quick Serve (2)
Franchise Affiliation: Little Caesar Enterprises Inc., DETROIT, MI

Key Personnel
ADAM SCRUGGS - Partner; General Buyer
BRIAN SCRUGGS - Partner

Bell Brand Ranches, Inc
15373 E Hinsdale Cir Ste A
Centennial, CO 80112-4247

Telephone: (303) 429-6394
Type of Business: Chain Restaurant Operator
Total Sales: $20,670,000 (e)
Total Units: 15
Trade Names: Dairy Queen Store (15)
Units Franchised From: 15
Primary Menu: American (15)
Areas of Operation: CO
Type of Foodservice: Quick Serve (15)
Franchise Affiliation: International Dairy Queen Inc., BLOOMINGTON, MN

Key Personnel
STEVE DOTY - President; General Buyer
JEFFREY MILLER - Manager Operations

Bullshark Inc.
7200 S Alton Way Ste A320
Centennial, CO 80112-2254

Telephone: (303) 745-7717

Fax Number: (303) 755-6219
Internet Homepage: jasonsdeli.com
Type of Business: Chain Restaurant Operator
Year Founded: 1993
Total Sales: $18,090,000 (e)
Alcohol Sales: 2%
Number of Employees: 300
Average Check: Breakfast(8); Lunch(10); Dinner(10)
Internet Order Processing: Yes
Total Units: 8
Trade Names: Jason's Deli (8)
Units Franchised From: 8
Preferred Square Footage: 4,100
Preferred Location Types: Strip Mall
Primary Menu: Sandwiches/Deli (8)
Areas of Operation: CO
Type of Foodservice: Family Restaurant (8)
Catering Services: Yes
Franchise Affiliation: Deli Management Inc., BEAUMONT, TX
Primary Distributors: (Full Line) JDD - Jason's Deli Distribution Center, GRAND PRAIRIE, TX

Key Personnel
STANLEY LYONS - CEO; Partner; Controller
ANNE ROWLAND - Partner; Director Loss Prevention, Human Resources
DEBBIE LYONS - Partner
AHMAD ABOADAS - General Manager; Director Operations

Reinerth Enterprises Inc.
6855 S Havana St
Centennial, CO 80112-3837

Telephone: (303) 757-8787
Fax Number: (303) 757-0202
Type of Business: Chain Restaurant Operator
Year Founded: 1990
Total Sales: $51,790,000 (e)
Number of Employees: 700
Average Check: Breakfast(8); Lunch(10); Dinner(12)
Total Units: 11
Trade Names: McDonald's (11)
Units Franchised From: 11
Preferred Square Footage: 2,500
Preferred Location Types: Freestanding
Primary Menu: Hamburger (11)
Areas of Operation: CO
Type of Foodservice: Quick Serve (11)
Franchise Affiliation: McDonald's Corporation, CHICAGO, IL
Primary Distributors: (Food) Mile Hi Foods, DENVER, CO

Key Personnel
LARRY REINERTH - President; Director Purchasing, Real Estate; General Buyer
MARIA REINERTH - VP; General Manager; Director Finance
PAUL SPANGLER - Director Operations

ALEJANDRE VARGAS - Manager Risk Management, Human Resources

Yogurtland Franchisee
7535 S University Blvd Ste 5
Centennial, CO 80122-3179

Telephone: (303) 798-5644
Type of Business: Chain Restaurant Operator
Total Sales: $4,101,000 (e)
Total Units: 4
Trade Names: Yogurtland (4)
Units Franchised From: 4
Primary Menu: Snacks (4)
Areas of Operation: CO
Type of Foodservice: Quick Serve (4)
Franchise Affiliation: Yogurtland Franchising Inc., FARMERS BRANCH, TX

Key Personnel
JOHN HUGHES - Owner; General Buyer

C K C Inc
6660 Delmonico Dr Ste A
Colorado Springs, CO 80919-1966

Telephone: (719) 548-1991
Type of Business: Chain Restaurant Operator
Total Sales: $1,526,000 (e)
Total Units: 2
Trade Names: Subway (2)
Units Franchised From: 2
Primary Menu: Sandwiches/Deli (2)
Areas of Operation: CO
Type of Foodservice: Quick Serve (2)
Franchise Affiliation: Doctor's Associates Inc., MILFORD, CT

Key Personnel
JAMES PINES - President; General Buyer
SARAH KINCAID - President

Century Casinos Inc.
455 E Pikes Peak Ave Ste 210
Colorado Springs, CO 80903-3673

Telephone: (719) 527-8300
Fax Number: (719) 213-2643
Internet Homepage: cnty.com
Company Email: info@cnty.com
Type of Business: Foodservice Operations - Hotel/Motels
Year Founded: 1992
Publicly Held: Yes
Total Sales: $493,680,000 (e)
Number of Employees: 1,757
Total Units: 8
Restaurants in Hotels: 8
Trade Names: Century Casino & Hotel (8)
Company-Owned Units: 8
Areas of Operation: CO, FC, AB
Foreign Countries: CANADA
Notes: In addition to its four North American casinos, Century Casinos also has equity investments in four casinos in Poland and has agreements to operate casinos on several cruise line ships.

Key Personnel
ERWIN HAITZMANN - Chairman; CEO
PETER HOESZINGER - Vice Chairman; Co-CEO; President
MARGARET STAPLETON - CFO
TIMOTHY WRIGHT - Chief Accounting Officer; Controller
ANDREAS TERLER - CIO
GEOFF SMITH - Senior VP Operations
ERIC ROSE - VP Operations

Colomex Inc.
717 N Tejon St
Colorado Springs, CO 80903-1011

Telephone: (719) 633-2500
Fax Number: (719) 633-9610
Type of Business: Chain Restaurant Operator
Year Founded: 1983
Total Sales: $72,750,000 (e)
Number of Employees: 1,054
Average Check: Lunch(6); Dinner(8)
Total Units: 26
Trade Names: Taco Bell (26)
Units Franchised From: 26
Preferred Square Footage: 3,000
Preferred Location Types: Discount Dept. Stores; Freestanding; Regional Mall
Primary Menu: Taco (26)
Areas of Operation: CO
Type of Foodservice: Quick Serve (26)
Franchise Affiliation: Taco Bell Corp., IRVINE, CA
Primary Distributors: (Food) McLane /Aurora, COMMERCE CITY, CO

Key Personnel
JERRY GRAGE - Chairman; General Buyer
MARV KORF - Vice Chairman
MATT GRAGE - President; Manager Real Estate
KELLY BUNYEA - CFO

Concept Restaurants
15 S Tejon St Ste 206
Colorado Springs, CO 80903-1505

Telephone: (719) 635-8190
Fax Number: (719) 475-0531
Internet Homepage: mackenzieschophouse.com; conceptrestaurants.net; ritzgrill.com

Type of Business: Chain Restaurant Operator
Year Founded: 1987
Total Sales: $12,460,000 (e)
Alcohol Sales: 15%
Number of Employees: 120
Average Check: Breakfast(18); Lunch(22); Dinner(42)
Internet Order Processing: Yes
Internet Sales: 1.00%
Total Units: 5
Trade Names: Flatiron's Grill (1); Jose Muldoon's (1); MacKenzie's Chop House (1); Ritz Grill (1); Southside Johnny's (1)
Company-Owned Units: 5
Preferred Location Types: Freestanding
Alcohol Served: Beer, Wine, Liquor
Primary Menu: American (2); Mexican (1); Steak (2)
Areas of Operation: CO
Type of Foodservice: Casual Dining (3); Fine Dining (2)
Primary Distributors: (Food) Shamrock Foods Colorado Division, COMMERCE CITY, CO

Key Personnel
DAVE LOCK - President; Partner
LUKE TRAVINS - Partner; VP Operations; General Manager
SCOTT SULTZBAUGH - General Manager
CINDY BIONDO - General Manager
MARK BIONDO - General Manager
PETE MORENO - Executive Chef

Domino's Franchisee
205 W Rockrimmon Blvd Ste C
Colorado Springs, CO 80919-1760

Telephone: (719) 260-9595
Type of Business: Chain Restaurant Operator
Total Sales: $28,342,000 (e)
Total Units: 14
Trade Names: Domino's (14)
Units Franchised From: 14
Primary Menu: Pizza (14)
Areas of Operation: CO
Type of Foodservice: Quick Serve (14)
Franchise Affiliation: Domino's Pizza Inc, ANN ARBOR, MI

Key Personnel
CRAIG K. WILLIAMS - Owner; General Buyer

Drifter's Hamburgers
1485 Jamboree Dr
Colorado Springs, CO 80920-3939

Telephone: (719) 598-9058
Internet Homepage: driftershamburgers.com
Company Email: info@driftershamburgers.com
Type of Business: Chain Restaurant Operator
Year Founded: 2008
Total Units: 3
Trade Names: Drifter's Hamburgers (3)
Company-Owned Units: 3
Primary Menu: Hamburger (3)
Areas of Operation: CO
Type of Foodservice: Quick Serve (3)

Key Personnel
RICHARD BEAVEN - Owner; Executive Chef; General Buyer

J H Foods Ltd
4820 Rusina Rd Ste A
Colorado Springs, CO 80907-8127

Telephone: (719) 598-5457
Type of Business: Chain Restaurant Operator
Total Sales: $23,720,000 (e)
Number of Employees: 218
Total Units: 11
Trade Names: Carl's Jr. (11)
Units Franchised From: 11
Primary Menu: Hamburger (11)
Areas of Operation: CO
Type of Foodservice: Quick Serve (11)
Franchise Affiliation: Carl's Jr., FRANKLIN, TN

Key Personnel
JAMES A. HAFEMEISTER - President; General Buyer
JAY HAFEMEISTER - Director Marketing

L & S Enterprise # 2 Inc.
640 Southpointe Ct Ste 230
Colorado Springs, CO 80906-3884

Telephone: (719) 302-0110
Fax Number: (719) 219-5179
Company Email: macsprings3@aol.com
Type of Business: Chain Restaurant Operator
Year Founded: 1990
Total Sales: $19,722,000 (e)
Number of Employees: 315
Average Check: Breakfast(8); Lunch(8); Dinner(8)
Total Units: 4
Trade Names: McDonald's (4)
Units Franchised From: 4
Preferred Square Footage: 2,500; 3,000
Preferred Location Types: Freestanding
Primary Menu: Hamburger (4)
Areas of Operation: CO
Type of Foodservice: Quick Serve (4)
Franchise Affiliation: McDonald's Corporation, CHICAGO, IL
Primary Distributors: (Full Line) Mile Hi Foods, DENVER, CO

Key Personnel
LESLIE LOUZON - President; Owner; General Buyer

Sierra Monterey Restaurant Systems, Inc.
3654 Austin Bluffs Pkwy
Colorado Springs, CO 80918-6631

Telephone: (775) 360-2623
Type of Business: Chain Restaurant Operator
Total Sales: $10,858,000 (e)
Total Units: 4
Trade Names: Jack in the Box (4)
Units Franchised From: 4
Primary Menu: Hamburger (4)
Areas of Operation: CO
Type of Foodservice: Quick Serve (4)
Franchise Affiliation: Jack in the Box Restaurants, SAN DIEGO, CA

Key Personnel
ADAM GONZALES - Owner; General Buyer

The Broadmoor
1 Lake Ave
Colorado Springs, CO 80906-4269

Mailing Address: PO Box 1439, COLORADO SPRINGS, CO, 80901-1439
Telephone: (719) 634-7711
Fax Number: (719) 577-5779
Internet Homepage: broadmoor.com
Company Email: info@broadmoor.com
Type of Business: Foodservice Operations - Hotel/Motels
Year Founded: 1918
Total Sales: $53,190,000 (e)
Alcohol Sales: 30%
Number of Employees: 1,600
Total Units: 10
Restaurants in Hotels: 10
Trade Names: The Broadmoor (10)
Company-Owned Units: 10
Alcohol Served: Beer, Wine, Liquor
Areas of Operation: CO
Type of Foodservice: Casual Dining (10)
Primary Distributors: (Food) US Foods, CENTENNIAL, CO
Notes: The company derives approximately 60% of its revenue from hotel operations.

Key Personnel
JACK DAMIOLI - CEO; President
LARRY KELBERG - CFO
TIM HANSEN - VP Finance
ROBERT SCHWARTZ - Controller
SASHA BURKE - General Manager
DAVID PATTERSON - Executive Chef
JUSTIN MILLER - Executive Chef
MARK MUSIAL - Executive Chef
CARLA MCAULIFFE - Executive Chef

AUSTIN HILTY - Executive Chef
MARIO VIGUIE - Executive Chef
ALLISON SCOTT - Director Communications
SAM BUMGARNER - Director Purchasing
JOHN MILLER - Director Information Technology
FRED DICKMAN - Director Facility/Maintenance
JULI JAMISON - Director Graphic Design
TAMMY PAGE BOETTNER - Director Sales
JEREMY WILSON - Director Sales
KEN MILLER - Director
DAVID DRISCOLL - Assistant Director Food and Beverage
KARI ALLS - Manager Benefits
NORA JOHNSON - Manager Catering
BECKY BRUNET - Manager Catering
ELLENA RINALDI - Manager Retail Operations
SANDY GARCIA - Manager Risk Management
KEVIN MEYER - Manager Communications
JERRY HOMZY - Manager Customer Service
AK RAJ - Manager Food and Beverage
PANNI EBAUGH - Manager Recruitment
ASHLEY CHASE - Manager Restaurant Operations
KRISTA HEINICKE - Manager Communications, Public Relations
SARA SCOTT - Manager Marketing
JAMES GOODING - Supervisor Loss Prevention
PETER ORINAK - Supervisor
NEIL RODEN - Supervisor Catering
EDWARD SHIPP - Supervisor Customer Service
ELIZABETH BROWN - Coordinator Production
KELLY SANTORO - Agent Sales
FELICIA MARINO - Agent
TOM SCHMIDT - Consultant

The Pepper Tree Restaurant
888 W Moreno Ave
Colorado Springs, CO 80905-1732

Telephone: (719) 471-4888
Fax Number: (719) 471-0997
Internet Homepage: peppertreecs.com; swisschaletofwoodlandpark.com
Type of Business: Chain Restaurant Operator
Year Founded: 1983
Total Sales: $3,758,000 (e)
Alcohol Sales: 10%
Number of Employees: 25
Average Check: Lunch(18); Dinner(28)
Internet Order Processing: Yes
Total Units: 2
Trade Names: Swiss Chalet (1); The Pepper Tree (1)
Company-Owned Units: 2
Preferred Square Footage: 1,500
Preferred Location Types: Freestanding
Alcohol Served: Beer, Wine, Liquor
Primary Menu: Eastern European (2)
Areas of Operation: CO
Type of Foodservice: Fine Dining (2)
Primary Distributors: (Food) Shamrock Foods

Colorado Division, COMMERCE CITY, CO

Key Personnel
PAULA LEVY - Owner

Butcher Block
4605 E 74th Ave
Commerce City, CO 80022-1421

Telephone: (303) 289-2055
Internet Homepage: butcherblockcafe.com
Company Email: butcherblockcafe@gmail.com
Type of Business: Chain Restaurant Operator
Year Founded: 1980
Total Sales: $2,092,000 (e)
Number of Employees: 50
Average Check: Lunch(8); Dinner(10)
Total Units: 3
Trade Names: Butcher Block (3)
Company-Owned Units: 3
Preferred Square Footage: 2,000
Preferred Location Types: Freestanding
Primary Menu: American (3)
Areas of Operation: CO
Type of Foodservice: Family Restaurant (3)

Key Personnel
KIRK MICHEL - President
MICKEY MICHEL - Treasurer; Manager Operations, Marketing; General Buyer
AUSTIN MICHEL - General Manager

Pudge Brothers Pizza
6170 E 49th Dr
Commerce City, CO 80022-4503

Telephone: (303) 287-1551
Internet Homepage: pudgebrotherspizza.com
Company Email: pudgebros@msn.com
Type of Business: Chain Restaurant Operator
Year Founded: 1991
Total Sales: $4,884,000 (e)
Average Check: Dinner(16)
Total Units: 9
Trade Names: Pudge Brothers Pizza (9)
Units Franchised To: 9
Preferred Location Types: Community Mall; Downtown; Office Complex; Strip Mall
Primary Menu: Pizza (9)
Areas of Operation: CO
Type of Foodservice: Quick Serve (9)

Key Personnel
ALEX KURTSER - Owner; General Buyer

Domino's Franchisee
1111 W Victory Way
Craig, CO 81625-2950

Telephone: (970) 824-4855
Type of Business: Chain Restaurant Operator
Total Sales: $14,018,000 (e)
Total Units: 7
Trade Names: Domino's (7)
Units Franchised From: 7
Primary Menu: Pizza (7)
Areas of Operation: CO
Type of Foodservice: Quick Serve (7)
Franchise Affiliation: Domino's Pizza Inc, ANN ARBOR, MI

Key Personnel
JAMES HAYDON - Owner

Alvarado Concepts/Palo Alto Inc.
924 W Colfax Ave Ste 302
Denver, CO 80204-2629

Telephone: (303) 745-0555
Fax Number: (303) 745-0188
Internet Homepage: teamhungry.com
Company Email: malbornov@paloaltoinc.com
Type of Business: Chain Restaurant Operator
Year Founded: 1984
Total Sales: $330,200,000 (e)
Number of Employees: 3,000
Average Check: Lunch(12); Dinner(16)
Total Units: 213
Trade Names: KFC; Long John Silver's; Pizza Hut; Taco Bell
Units Franchised From: 213
Preferred Square Footage: 2,500
Preferred Location Types: Community Mall; Downtown; Freestanding; Institution (college/hospital); Stadiums; Strip Mall
Alcohol Served: Beer
Projected Openings: 15
Areas of Operation: CA, CO, NM, VA
Foreign Countries: MEXICO
Type of Foodservice: Quick Serve (213)
Franchise Affiliation: KFC Corporation, LOUISVILLE, KY; Long John Silver's Inc., LOUISVILLE, KY; Pizza Hut Inc., PLANO, TX; Taco Bell Corp., IRVINE, CA
Primary Distributors: (Food) McLane /Aurora, COMMERCE CITY, CO

Key Personnel
ROB ALVARADO - Chairman; CEO; Owner; Exec VP; Director Operations, Purchasing, Supply Chain, Design
LINDA ALVARADO - President
JEFF GELLER - VP Business Development
RENE RENTERIA - Director Facility/Maintenance, Loss Prevention, Risk

Management, Human Resources
KRISTI PETERSON - Director Training
STEPHEN YAGER - Manager Information Technology

Anthony's Pizza & Pasta International
210 Saint Paul St Ste 200
Denver, CO 80206-5100

Telephone: (720) 932-1800
Fax Number: (720) 941-6267
Internet Homepage: anthonyspizzaandpasta.com
Company Email: info@anthonyspizzaandpasta.com
Type of Business: Chain Restaurant Operator
Systemwide Sales: $13,266,000 (e)
Total Sales: $1,952,000 (e)
Alcohol Sales: 8%
Number of Employees: 4
Average Check: Lunch(6); Dinner(10)
Internet Order Processing: Yes
Total Units: 23
Trade Names: Anthony's Pizza & Pasta (23)
Units Franchised To: 23
Preferred Square Footage: 2,500
Preferred Location Types: Freestanding
Alcohol Served: Beer, Wine, Liquor
Primary Menu: Pizza (23)
Areas of Operation: CO
Type of Foodservice: Casual Dining (23)
Primary Distributors: (Full Line) US Foods, CENTENNIAL, CO

Key Personnel
JOHN LEBEL - President; General Manager; Director Operations; General Buyer
JEREMY BETLACH - Director Information Technology; Manager Operations

Bacon Social House
2434 W 44th Ave
Denver, CO 80211

Telephone: (720) 550-7065
Internet Homepage: baconsocialhouse.com
Company Email: info@baconsocialhouse.com
Type of Business: Chain Restaurant Operator
Year Founded: 2015
Total Units: 3
Trade Names: Bacon Social House (3)
Company-Owned Units: 3
Preferred Square Footage: 4,200
Preferred Location Types: Downtown; Freestanding
Primary Menu: American (3)
Projected Openings: 1
Areas of Operation: CO, MN
Type of Foodservice: Casual Dining (3)

Key Personnel
DAVID DILL - Founder; Owner
CALEB BENTON - VP Operations

Biju's Little Curry Shop
1441 E 26th Ave
Denver, CO 80205

Telephone: (303) 292-3500
Internet Homepage: littlecuryshop.com
Company Email: info@littlecuryshop.com
Type of Business: Chain Restaurant Operator
Internet Order Processing: Yes
Total Units: 2
Trade Names: Biju's Little Curry Shop (2)
Company-Owned Units: 2
Areas of Operation: CO

Key Personnel
BIJU THOMAS - Co-Founder; President; Executive Chef; General Buyer
CAITI ROWE - Co-Founder

Birdcall
25 E Dakota Ave
Denver, CO 80209

Telephone: (720) 458-0886
Internet Homepage: eatbirdcall.com
Type of Business: Chain Restaurant Operator
Year Founded: 2017
Total Units: 3
Trade Names: Birdcall (3)
Company-Owned Units: 3
Primary Menu: Chicken (3)
Areas of Operation: CO
Type of Foodservice: Fast Casual (3)

Key Personnel
PETER NEWLIN - President
JASON WILEY - Director Operations

Black Shamrock Partners
3900 E Mexico Ave Ste 1350
Denver, CO 80210

Telephone: (303) 592-3800
Internet Homepage: consumercp.com; tomsurban.com; livebasilpizza.com
Company Email: feedback@smashburger.com
Type of Business: Chain Restaurant Operator
Total Units: 6
Trade Names: Live Basil Pizza (1); Tom's Urban (5)
Company-Owned Units: 5
Preferred Location Types: Airports; Downtown; Hotel/Motel
Primary Menu: American (1); Pizza (1)
Projected Openings: 1
Areas of Operation: CA, CT, NV, OR
Type of Foodservice: Casual Dining (4); Fast Casual (1)

Key Personnel
RICK SCHADEN - Chairman; Partner
BROOKS SCHADEN - CEO; Partner
SHANNON MCNIEL - President; COO
TOM RYAN - Partner
DOUG WINTER - Exec VP Operations
JOANNA SANCHEZ - VP Event Planning, Sales
JANE CROUSE - Director Training
LORI BELLOIR - Director Communications, Design

Bonanno Concepts
701 N Grant St
Denver, CO 80203

Telephone: (303) 832-4778
Fax Number: (303) 832-3532
Internet Homepage: bonannoconcepts.com; mizunadenver.com
Company Email: info@mizunadenver.com
Type of Business: Chain Restaurant Operator
Year Founded: 2001
Total Sales: $26,030,000 (e)
Alcohol Sales: 28%
Number of Employees: 488
Average Check: Lunch(18); Dinner(46)
Internet Sales: 3.00%
Total Units: 11
Trade Names: Bones (1); Denver Milk Market (1); French 75 (1); Green Russell (1); Luca d' Italia (1); Mizuna (1); Osteria Marco (1); Russell's Smokehouse (1); Salt & Grinder (1); Vesper Lounge (1); Wednesday's Pie (1)
Company-Owned Units: 11
Preferred Square Footage: 5,000
Preferred Location Types: Downtown; Freestanding; Strip Mall
Alcohol Served: Beer, Wine, Liquor
Primary Menu: American (7); Asian (1); French/Continental (2); Italian (1)
Areas of Operation: CO
Type of Foodservice: Casual Dining (8); Fine Dining (3)
Primary Distributors: (Food) Shamrock Foods Colorado Division, COMMERCE CITY, CO

Key Personnel
FRANK BONANNO - CEO; Owner; General Manager; Executive Chef; General Buyer
NICK M. GRAY - President; CFO; Director Finance
PHILLIP COSTAS - Executive Chef
JACQUELINE BONANNO - Creative Director
PAIGE DUNGAN - Director Public Relations
LAURA SOSNOWSKI - Director Event Planning, Sales, Catering
LIZA ZIMMERMAN - Director Sales

Breckenridge-Wynkoop LLC
155 S Madison St Ste 226
Denver, CO 80209-3013

Telephone: (303) 595-3500
Fax Number: (303) 595-3902
Internet Homepage: breckbrew.com; cherrycricket.com; gaetanositalian.com; goosetowntavern.com; mainlinefoco.com; phantomcanyon.com; wazeesupperclub.com; wynkoop.com
Company Email: management@wynkoop.com
Type of Business: Chain Restaurant Operator
Year Founded: 1988
Total Sales: $51,260,000 (e)
Alcohol Sales: 40%
Number of Employees: 770
Average Check: Lunch(22); Dinner(30)
Total Units: 12
Trade Names: Breckenridge Brewery & Pub (1); Breckenridge Colorado Craft (1); Cherry Cricket (1); Goosetown Tavern (1); MainLine (1); Phantom Canyon Brewing Company (1); Session Kitchen (1); The Ale House (1); The Ale House at Amato's (1); The Breckenridge Brewery Bar-B-Que (1); Wazee Supper Club (1); Wynkoop Brewing Company (1)
Company-Owned Units: 12
Preferred Square Footage: 5,000
Preferred Location Types: Freestanding
Alcohol Served: Beer, Wine, Liquor
Primary Menu: American (11); Bar-B-Q (1)
Areas of Operation: CO
Type of Foodservice: Casual Dining (12)
Primary Distributors: (Food) Shamrock Foods Colorado Division, COMMERCE CITY, CO

Key Personnel
EDWARD A. CERKOVNIK JR - Founder; President
LEE DRISCOLL - CEO; Director Real Estate
CALLEY MCCUE - CFO
MELISSA BROOKS - Director Human Resources
ALEX BUNN - Director Marketing

Brooklyn's
2644 W Colfax Ave
Denver, CO 80204-2344

Telephone: (303) 572-3999
Fax Number: (303) 572-0245
Internet Homepage: milwaukee-st-tavern.com
Company Email: gm@milwaukeestreettavern.com
Type of Business: Chain Restaurant Operator
Year Founded: 1982
Total Sales: $3,078,000 (e)
Alcohol Sales: 20%
Number of Employees: 35
Average Check: Lunch(14); Dinner(18)
Total Units: 3
Trade Names: Brooklyn's (2); Milwaukee Street Tavern (1)
Company-Owned Units: 3
Preferred Location Types: Freestanding
Alcohol Served: Beer, Wine, Liquor
Primary Menu: American (3)
Areas of Operation: CO
Type of Foodservice: Casual Dining (3)
Primary Distributors: (Full Line) US Foods, CENTENNIAL, CO

Key Personnel
DIANE KEEFE - General Manager; Executive Chef

Canteen Vending Services
123 Yuma St
Denver, CO 80223-1205

Telephone: (303) 722-2861
Fax Number: (303) 722-0455
Listing Type: Branch Office
Type of Business: Foodservice Management Operator
Year Founded: 1929
Number of Employees: 50
Number of Locations Served: 500
Total Foodservice Mgmt Accounts: 500
Areas of Operation: CO
Type of Foodservice: Vending machines (500)
Foodservice Management Venues: Business & Industry; College & University; Schools; Travel Plazas
Parent Company: Compass Group The Americas, CHARLOTTE, NC
Headquarters: Canteen Vending Services, CHARLOTTE, NC

Key Personnel
JOHN CREWS - General Manager; General Buyer

Colorado Bagel Co LLC
2000 S University Blvd Unit A
Denver, CO 80210-4368

Telephone: (303) 777-7600
Type of Business: Chain Restaurant Operator
Year Founded: 2001
Total Sales: $3,288,000 (e)
Average Check: Dinner(10)
Total Units: 3
Trade Names: Bruegger's Bagel Bakery (3)
Units Franchised From: 3
Preferred Location Types: Strip Mall
Primary Menu: Bagels (3)
Projected Openings: 2
Projected Remodelings: 1
Areas of Operation: CO
Type of Foodservice: Fast Casual (3)
Franchise Affiliation: Bruegger's Enterprises Inc., DALLAS, TX

Key Personnel
BEN CARTER - President; General Buyer

Dazbog Franchising, LLC
1090 Yuma St
Denver, CO 80204-3838

Telephone: (303) 892-9999
Internet Homepage: dazbog.com
Company Email: coffee@dazbog.com
Type of Business: Chain Restaurant Operator
Total Units: 25
Trade Names: Dazbog Coffee (25)
Company-Owned Units: 25
Primary Menu: Coffee (25)
Areas of Operation: CO, WY
Type of Foodservice: Quick Serve (25)

Key Personnel
ANATOLY YUFFA - Co-Founder; Partner
LEONID YUFFA - Co-Founder; Partner

DC PIE CO.
2223 E Colfax Ave
Denver, CO 80206

Telephone: (303) 537-4240
Internet Homepage: dcpieco.com
Company Email: info@dcpieco.com
Type of Business: Chain Restaurant Operator
Total Units: 2
Trade Names: DC PIE CO. (2)
Company-Owned Units: 2
Preferred Location Types: Downtown; Strip Mall
Primary Menu: Pizza (2)
Projected Openings: 1
Areas of Operation: CO, FL
Type of Foodservice: Casual Dining (2)

Key Personnel
DOMINIC CAVAGNUOLO - Partner

Dividend Restaurant Group
1855 Blake St Ste 200
Denver, CO 80202

Telephone: (720) 699-0274
Internet Homepage: macaronigrill.com
Company Email: info@macaronigrill.com
Type of Business: Chain Restaurant Operator
Year Founded: 1988
Systemwide Sales: $170,763,000 (e)
Total Sales: $230,750,000 (e)
Alcohol Sales: 15%
Number of Employees: 10,605

Average Check: Lunch(20); Dinner(22)
Internet Order Processing: Yes
Internet Sales: 15.00%
Total Units: 69
Trade Names: Eddie Merlots (13); Romano's Macaroni Grill (42); Sullivan's Steakhouse (14)
Company-Owned Units: 50
Units Franchised To: 19
Preferred Square Footage: 6,300; 7,000; 7,200
Preferred Location Types: Community Mall; Downtown; Freestanding; Lifestyle Center; Regional Mall; Strip Mall
Alcohol Served: Beer, Wine, Liquor
Primary Menu: Italian (42); Steak (14); Steak/Seafood (13)
Areas of Operation: AK, AL, AR, AZ, CA, CO, DE, FL, GA, HI, IL, IN, KS, KY, LA, MA, MD, ME, MI, NC, NE, NM, NV, NY, OH, PA, SC, TN, TX, UT, VA, WA, FC
Foreign Countries: BAHRAIN; EGYPT; GERMANY; JAPAN; MEXICO; QATAR; TAIWAN; UNITED ARAB EMIRATES
Type of Foodservice: Casual Dining (42); Fine Dining (27)
Catering Services: Yes
Primary Distributors: (Food) US Foods, GARLAND, TX
Parent Company: Redrock Partners LLC, PHOENIX, AZ

Key Personnel
NISHANT MOCHADO - CEO
NICOLE TRIPPS - CFO
LISA BACHICHA - VP Human Resources
RYAN JOHNSON - VP Operations
JEFFREY MEYER - VP Purchasing, Culinary Operations
JENNY LYNCH - Senior Director Event Planning, Sales
CHRISTIAN KNOX - Director Operations
BRYANT BURNS - Director Operations
MARTY DANNER - Director Payroll, Benefits, Human Resources
TONY FATTAHI - Director Operations
KELLY GIBBONS - Director Operations
DERREN NFAMOVER - Manager Culinary Operations

Domino's Distribution Center
10252 E 51st Ave
Denver, CO 80239-2426

Telephone: (303) 373-0330
Fax Number: (303) 371-0386
Internet Homepage: dominos.com
Listing Type: Distribution Center
Type of Business: Chain Restaurant Operator
Number of Employees: 60
Areas of Operation: CO, KS, MT, NE, NM, SD, UT, WY
Parent Company: Domino's Pizza Inc, ANN ARBOR, MI

Key Personnel
PIPER TATUM - General Manager

E&I Holdings Inc.
1391 Speer Blvd Ste 720
Denver, CO 80204

Telephone: (303) 768-8883
Internet Homepage: theeggandirestaurants.com
Company Email: customer_care@eggandi.org
Listing Type: Subsidiary
Type of Business: Chain Restaurant Operator
Year Founded: 1987
Systemwide Sales: $67,002,000 (e)
Total Sales: $7,240,000 (e)
Number of Employees: 119
Average Check: Breakfast(10); Lunch(10);
Total Units: 55
Trade Names: THE EGG & I (55)
Company-Owned Units: 15
Preferred Square Footage: 3,300; 4,000
Preferred Location Types: Freestanding; Strip Mall
Primary Menu: American (55)
Areas of Operation: AL, AR, AZ, CO, FL, GA, IL, IN, KS, ME, MO, NC, NE, NM, TN, TX, UT, VA, WI, WY
Type of Foodservice: Family Restaurant (55)
Primary Distributors: (Food) SYSCO Food Services of Denver, DENVER, CO
Parent Company: First Watch Restaurants Inc., BRADENTON, FL

Key Personnel
RAYNO SEASER - Co-Founder
NICK MARTINEZ - Director Operations

Elway's
3900 E Mexico Ave Ste 820
Denver, CO 80210

Telephone: (303) 399-3230
Fax Number: (303) 399-4379
Internet Homepage: elways.com; haciendacolorado.com
Company Email: info@elways.com
Type of Business: Chain Restaurant Operator
Year Founded: 2007
Total Sales: $53,850,000 (e)
Alcohol Sales: 25%
Total Units: 10
Trade Names: Elway's (4); Hacienda Colorado (6)
Company-Owned Units: 10
Alcohol Served: Beer, Wine, Liquor
Primary Menu: Mexican (6); Steak (4)
Areas of Operation: CO
Type of Foodservice: Casual Dining (6); Fine Dining (4)
Notes: Hacienda Colorado provides management services to the Elway's chain.

Key Personnel
TIM SCHMIDT - President; Partner
JOHN ELWAY - President; Partner; General Buyer
ANDREW CHAPMAN - General Manager

Family Restaurants Inc.
2706 W Colfax Ave
Denver, CO 80204-2346

Telephone: (303) 534-3773
Fax Number: (303) 534-3774
Internet Homepage: lovevi.com
Type of Business: Chain Restaurant Operator
Year Founded: 1994
Total Sales: $47,180,000 (e)
Alcohol Sales: 1%
Number of Employees: 1,340
Average Check: Breakfast(10); Lunch(14); Dinner(24)
Total Units: 19
Trade Names: Qdoba Mexican Grill (9); Village Inn (10)
Units Franchised From: 19
Preferred Square Footage: 5,000
Preferred Location Types: Freestanding
Alcohol Served: Beer, Wine
Primary Menu: American (10); Mexican (9)
Areas of Operation: AK, CO
Type of Foodservice: Casual Dining (10); Fast Casual (9)
Franchise Affiliation: Qdoba Mexican Eats, SAN DIEGO, CA; Village Inn, MINNETONKA, MN
Primary Distributors: (Full Line) US Foods, CENTENNIAL, CO
Notes: The company also does business in Alaska as Alaska Inns; these locations are included in the total Village Inn count. The Qdoba restaurant operates as Flavors West LLC.

Key Personnel
MICHAEL SCOTT - President; Director Finance, Operations, Purchasing, Real Estate; General Buyer

Hacienda Colorado
3900 E Mexico Ave Ste 820
Denver, CO 80210

Telephone: (303) 399-3230
Fax Number: (303) 399-4379
Internet Homepage: haciendacolorado.com; elways.com
Company Email: gene@haciendacolorado.com
Type of Business: Chain Restaurant Operator

Year Founded: 1998
Internet Order Processing: Yes
Total Units: 11
Trade Names: Elways Steak House (4); Hacienda Colorado (7)
Company-Owned Units: 5
Alcohol Served: Beer, Wine, Liquor
Primary Menu: Mexican (7); Steak (4)
Projected Openings: 2
Areas of Operation: CO
Type of Foodservice: Casual Dining (7); Fine Dining (4)
Catering Services: Yes
Parent Company: Uncle Julio's Corp, IRVING, TX

Key Personnel
TIM SCHMIDT - Owner
RAYANNE GUILFORD - Supervisor Area
RHONDA KNOL - Consultant Beverages

Ink! Coffee Co. of Colorado
2851 Larimer St
Denver, CO 80205

Telephone: (303) 292-7369
Fax Number: (720) 214-2222
Internet Homepage: inkcoffee.com
Company Email: info@inkcoffee.com
Type of Business: Chain Restaurant Operator
Year Founded: 1994
Total Sales: $9,119,000 (e)
Number of Employees: 160
Internet Order Processing: Yes
Total Units: 15
Trade Names: Ink Coffee Company (15)
Company-Owned Units: 15
Preferred Location Types: Downtown; Office Complex; Other
Primary Menu: Coffee (15)
Areas of Operation: CO
Type of Foodservice: Fast Casual (15)
Catering Services: Yes

Key Personnel
ANDREW SALTONSTALL - Co-Founder; Partner
KEITH HERBERT - CEO; President; Partner
BRENT ELLIOTT - VP Operations

JJD Subway Inc
1050 W Colfax Ave Ste B
Denver, CO 80204-2071

Telephone: (303) 572-3700
Fax Number: (303) 572-3708
Type of Business: Chain Restaurant Operator
Total Sales: $2,928,000 (e)
Total Units: 4
Trade Names: Subway (4)
Units Franchised From: 4
Primary Menu: Sandwiches/Deli (4)
Areas of Operation: CO
Type of Foodservice: Quick Serve (4)
Franchise Affiliation: Doctor's Associates Inc., MILFORD, CT

Key Personnel
KRISTEN DONHOWE - Partner; General Buyer

Johnson & Wales University Denver Campus
7150 Montview Blvd
Denver, CO 80220-1800

Telephone: (877) 598-3368
Internet Homepage: jwu.edu/denver
Type of Business: Culinary Schools
Areas of Operation: CO

Key Personnel
RICHARD WISCOTT PHD - President

KTM Restaurant Group, LLC
1514 York St
Denver, CO 80206-1425

Telephone: (720) 475-1337
Internet Homepage: ktmrestaurantgroup.com; tacostequilawhiskey.com
Company Email: info@ktmrestaurantgroup.com
Type of Business: Chain Restaurant Operator
Year Founded: 2011
Total Units: 4
Trade Names: Tacos Tequila Whiskey (4)
Company-Owned Units: 4
Primary Menu: Taco (4)
Areas of Operation: AZ, CO
Type of Foodservice: Casual Dining (4)

Key Personnel
KEVIN MORRISON - Owner; Executive Chef

La Fogata
5670 E Evans Ave Ste 100
Denver, CO 80222-5321

Telephone: (303) 753-9458
Fax Number: (303) 753-0834
Internet Homepage: la-fogata.com
Company Email: dacalhoun@la-fogata.com
Type of Business: Chain Restaurant Operator
Year Founded: 1991
Total Sales: $2,511,000 (e)
Alcohol Sales: 12%
Number of Employees: 20
Average Check: Breakfast(8); Lunch(10); Dinner(12)
Internet Order Processing: Yes
Total Units: 2
Trade Names: La Fogata (2)
Company-Owned Units: 2
Preferred Location Types: Freestanding
Alcohol Served: Beer, Wine, Liquor
Primary Menu: Mexican (2)
Areas of Operation: CO
Type of Foodservice: Casual Dining (2)
Catering Services: Yes

Key Personnel
DANETTE A. CALHOUN - President; Executive Chef; General Buyer
JACKIE MOUTSARISE - General Manager

LaMar's Donuts
3600 S Yosemite St Ste 750
Denver, CO 80237-1851

Telephone: (303) 771-9999
Fax Number: (303) 771-9991
Internet Homepage: lamars.com
Company Email: customerservice@lamars.com
Type of Business: Chain Restaurant Operator
Year Founded: 1960
Systemwide Sales: $19,546,000 (e)
Total Sales: $7,928,000 (e)
Number of Employees: 94
Average Check: Breakfast(6); Lunch(6); Dinner(6)
Internet Order Processing: Yes
Total Units: 25
Trade Names: LaMar's Donuts (25)
Company-Owned Units: 8
Units Franchised To: 17
Preferred Square Footage: 2,000
Preferred Location Types: Freestanding; Strip Mall
Primary Menu: Snacks (25)
Areas of Operation: AZ, CO, KS, MO, NE
Type of Foodservice: Quick Serve (25)
Catering Services: Yes
Primary Distributors: (Food) Performance Foodservice, RICE, MN

Key Personnel
MATT JOSLIN - CEO; Director Operations, Facility/Maintenance, Information Systems, Real Estate, Site Selection, Design
TEMI OSIFODUNRIN - Director Marketing, Advertising
CAMERON ANAYA - Director Company Operations

Larkburger
621 Kalamath St
Denver, CO 80204-4424

Mailing Address: P O Box 12031, DENVER,

CO, 80212
Telephone: (720) 285-1998
Internet Homepage: larkburger.com
Company Email: feedback@larkburger.com
Type of Business: Chain Restaurant Operator
Year Founded: 2006
Internet Order Processing: Yes
Total Units: 8
Trade Names: Larkburger (8)
Company-Owned Units: 8
Alcohol Served: Beer, Wine
Primary Menu: Hamburger (8)
Projected Openings: 2
Areas of Operation: CO
Type of Foodservice: Fast Casual (8)

Key Personnel
THOMAS SALAMUNOVICH - Co-Founder; Corporate Chef; General Buyer

Lime An American Cantina
500 16th St
Denver, CO 80202

Telephone: (303) 629-5463
Internet Homepage: limecolorado.com; eatatlime.com
Company Email: info@eatatlime.com
Type of Business: Chain Restaurant Operator
Year Founded: 2001
Total Sales: $3,942,000 (e)
Alcohol Sales: 30%
Number of Employees: 50
Average Check: Dinner(30)
Total Units: 2
Trade Names: Lime An American Cantina (2)
Company-Owned Units: 2
Preferred Location Types: Downtown; Mixed-use Center; Strip Mall
Alcohol Served: Beer, Wine, Liquor
Primary Menu: Mexican (2)
Areas of Operation: CO
Type of Foodservice: Casual Dining (2)
Catering Services: Yes

Key Personnel
CURT SIMS - Owner; General Manager; General Buyer

Little India Restaurant
1533 Champa St
Denver, CO 80202-2908

Telephone: (303) 629-5777
Fax Number: (303) 629-5778
Internet Homepage: littleindiaofdenver.com
Type of Business: Chain Restaurant Operator
Total Sales: $1,282,000 (e)
Alcohol Sales: 5%
Average Check: Lunch(12); Dinner(18)
Internet Order Processing: Yes
Total Units: 2
Trade Names: Little India (2)
Company-Owned Units: 2
Alcohol Served: Beer, Wine, Liquor
Primary Menu: Indian (2)
Areas of Operation: CO
Type of Foodservice: Casual Dining (2)
Catering Services: Yes
Primary Distributors: (Food) SYSCO Food Services of Denver, DENVER, CO

Key Personnel
SIMERAN S. BAIDWAN - Partner; Executive Chef; General Buyer
VINNY MALHOTRA - Partner; General Buyer
ALEXANDRIA COHEE - Chief Marketing Officer

Lodo Restaurant Group
1946 Market St
Denver, CO 80202-1420

Telephone: (303) 293-2290
Fax Number: (303) 436-9427
Internet Homepage: lodosbarandgrill.com
Company Email: info@lodosbarandgrill.com
Type of Business: Chain Restaurant Operator
Year Founded: 1992
Total Sales: $9,098,000 (e)
Alcohol Sales: 45%
Number of Employees: 60
Average Check: Lunch(12); Dinner(14)
Internet Order Processing: Yes
Total Units: 3
Trade Names: Lodo's Bar & Grill (3)
Company-Owned Units: 3
Preferred Location Types: Downtown; Freestanding
Alcohol Served: Beer, Wine, Liquor
Primary Menu: American (3)
Projected Openings: 1
Areas of Operation: CO
Type of Foodservice: Casual Dining (3)
Catering Services: Yes
Primary Distributors: (Food) SYSCO Food Services of Denver, DENVER, CO
Notes: Also operates a banquet facility, "Mattie's House of Mirrors".

Key Personnel
CHRIS MYERS - President
KATHY PUEPPKE - Controller
IAN MACCLURE - General Manager

Maria Empanada
1298 S Broadway
Denver, CO 80210

Telephone: (303) 934-2221
Internet Homepage: mariaempanada.com
Type of Business: Chain Restaurant Operator
Year Founded: 2010
Total Units: 4
Trade Names: Maria Empanada (4)
Company-Owned Units: 4
Primary Menu: Sandwiches/Deli (4)
Areas of Operation: CO
Type of Foodservice: Quick Serve (4)

Key Personnel
LORENA CANTAROVICI - Owner; General Buyer

Mici Handcrafted Italian
2373 Central Park Blvd
Denver, CO 80238-2300

Telephone: (303) 355-6424
Internet Homepage: miciitalian.com
Company Email: catering@miciitalian.com
Type of Business: Chain Restaurant Operator
Year Founded: 2004
Total Units: 5
Trade Names: Mici Handcrafted Italian (5)
Company-Owned Units: 5
Primary Menu: Pizza (5)
Areas of Operation: CO
Type of Foodservice: Casual Dining (5)

Key Personnel
ELLIOT SCHIFFER - CEO
JEFF MICELI - Partner
KIM MICELI - Partner
MICHAEL MICELI - Partner
JOE MELTON - Senior VP Operations

Park Burger
1890 S Pearl St
Denver, CO 80210

Telephone: (720) 242-9951
Internet Homepage: parkburger.com
Company Email: info@parkburger.com
Type of Business: Chain Restaurant Operator
Year Founded: 2009
Total Units: 5
Trade Names: Park Burger (5)
Company-Owned Units: 5
Primary Menu: Hamburger (5)
Areas of Operation: CO
Type of Foodservice: Casual Dining (5)

Key Personnel
JEAN-PHILIPPE FAILYAU - Owner

Pete's Restaurants
300 S Pearl St
Denver, CO 80209-2020

Telephone: (303) 778-6675
Internet Homepage: petesrestaurants.com;

petesrestaurantstoo.com
Company Email:
info@petesrestaurantstoo.com
Type of Business: Chain Restaurant Operator
Year Founded: 1962
Total Sales: $9,597,000 (e)
Alcohol Sales: 20%
Number of Employees: 14
Average Check: Breakfast(12); Lunch(14); Dinner(18)
Total Units: 6
Trade Names: Pete's Central One Restaurant (1); Pete's Greek Town Cafe (1); Pete's Gyros Place (1); Pete's Kitchen (1); Pete's Satire Restaurant & Lounge(1); Pete's University Park Cafe (1)
Company-Owned Units: 6
Preferred Square Footage: 5,500; 6,000
Alcohol Served: Beer, Wine, Liquor
Primary Menu: Greek/Mediterranean (4); Mexican (1); Snacks (1)
Areas of Operation: CO
Type of Foodservice: Casual Dining (6)
Catering Services: Yes
Primary Distributors: (Full Line) US Foods, CENTENNIAL, CO

Key Personnel
DEAN CONTOS - General Manager; General Buyer

Protos Pizza
2401 15th St Ste 190
Denver, CO 80202-1141

Telephone: (720) 855-9400
Fax Number: (720) 855-9401
Internet Homepage: protospizza.com
Company Email: protos.denver@gmail.com
Type of Business: Chain Restaurant Operator
Year Founded: 1999
Total Sales: $30,500,000 (e)
Number of Employees: 350
Total Units: 6
Trade Names: Proto's Pizzeria Napoletana (6)
Company-Owned Units: 6
Alcohol Served: Beer, Wine, Liquor
Primary Menu: Pizza (6)
Areas of Operation: CO
Type of Foodservice: Casual Dining (6)

Key Personnel
PAM PROTO - Owner; General Buyer
JOHN COX - General Manager
LEAH-KIM BROWN - Director Finance
JAMIE LOUTH - Assistant Manager

Punch Bowl Social
4411 E Kentucky Ave
Denver, CO 80246-2009

Telephone: (720) 458-1514
Internet Homepage: punchbowlsocial.com
Type of Business: Chain Restaurant Operator
Year Founded: 2012
Total Sales: $77,720,000 (e)
Total Units: 16
Trade Names: Punch Bowl Social (16)
Company-Owned Units: 16
Preferred Square Footage: 12,500; 25,000
Primary Menu: American (16)
Projected Openings: 5
Areas of Operation: CA, CO, GA, IL, IN, MI, MN, OH, OR, TX, VA, WI
Type of Foodservice: Casual Dining (16)

Key Personnel
JOHN HAYWOOD - CEO
RICHARD FLAHERTY - Co-CEO
MEGAN FRECKELTON - Director Design
LEAH HANSON - Director Training
CHARLIE BOOM - Manager POS/Scanning, Systems

Red Lion Hotels Corporation
1550 Market St Ste 350
Denver, CO 80202

Telephone: (509) 459-6100
Fax Number: (509) 325-7324
Internet Homepage: guesthouseintl.com; redlion.com; settleinn.com
Company Email: info@redlion.com
Listing Type: Subsidiary
Type of Business: Foodservice Operations - Hotel/Motels
Year Founded: 1936
Total Sales: $196,360,000 (e)
Alcohol Sales: 15%
Number of Employees: 4,200
Internet Order Processing: Yes
Total Units: 1,327
Trade Names: America's Best Inns & Suites; America's Best Value; Canada's Best Value; Country Hearth Inn & Suites; GuestHouse International; Hotel RL; Jameson Inn; Leo Hotel; Lexington; Palms Hotels & Resorts; Red Lion; Settle Inn & Suites; Signature Inn
Company-Owned Units: 1,082
Alcohol Served: Beer, Wine, Liquor
Projected Remodelings: 2
Areas of Operation: AK, AL, AR, CA, CO, FL, GA, IA, ID, IL, IN, KS, KY, MI, MN, MO, MT, NC, NM, NV, OR, SD, TN, TX, UT, WA, BC
Foreign Countries: CANADA
Type of Foodservice: Casual Dining; Fine Dining; Quick Serve
Primary Distributors: (Food) US Foods, FIFE, WA
Parent Company: Sonesta International Hotels Corp., NEWTON, MA
Notes: Red Lion operates/manages several hotels which do not offer in-hotel dining. The company also operates TicketsWest, an entertainment services provider, and other activities; these operations are excluded from total sales for purposes of this listing. The company derives approximately 75% of its revenuefrom hotel operations.

Key Personnel
ROBERT G. WOLFE - Chairman
GARY SIMS - COO; Exec VP
THOMAS L. MCKEIRNAN - Exec VP; General Counsel
AMANDA MARCELLO - Senior VP
JORDAN LANGLOIS - Senior VP Franchise Operations
DAVID WRIGHT - VP Accounting
STEVE BENNETT - Controller
KIMBERLEY A. BEST - General Manager
AMANDA ANDERSON - Director Sales, Catering
SARAH FRANK - Director Marketing
DEEDEE LEWIS - Director Marketing, Sales
LAURIE WILSON - Director Sales
DON BINKLEY - Manager Sales

REGO Restaurant Group
4700 S Syracuse St Ste 640
Denver, CO 80237

Telephone: (720) 359-3300
Internet Homepage: quiznos.com; tacodelmar.com
Listing Type: Corporate Office
Type of Business: Chain Restaurant Operator
Systemwide Sales: $350,929,000 (e)
Total Sales: $249,220,000 (e)
Total Units: 1,672
Trade Names: Churchs Chicken (904); Quiznos (215); Taco Del Mar (96); Texas Chicken (457)
Company-Owned Units: 100
Units Franchised To: 1,572
Primary Menu: Chicken (1,361); Sandwiches/Deli (215); Taco (96)
Areas of Operation: AK, AL, AR, AZ, CA, CO, CT, DC, DE, FL, GA, HI, IA, ID, IL, IN, KS, KY, LA, MA, MI, MN, MO, MS, MT, NC, ND, NJ, NM, NV, NY, OH, OK, OR, PA, SD, TN, TX, UT, VA, WA, WI, WV, WY, AB, BC, MB, NB, NL, NS, NT, ON, PE, QC, SK, YT
Foreign Countries: CANADA
Type of Foodservice: Quick Serve (1,672)
Subsidiaries: The Quiznos Master LLC, DENVER, CO

Key Personnel
ANANAD GOWDA - Executive Chairman
TIM CASEY - CEO; President
JOE GUITH - CEO Division

TOM KURRIKOFF - CFO
VANESSA FOX - Chief Development Officer
GREGORY BOUDREAUX - VP Restaurant Operations
GREGORY BOURDREAUX - Director Operations, Training
AMY MARZAN - Director Supply Chain
KEVIN BROWNE - Director Operations
DANA ABOOD - Director

Restaurants of America Inc.
300 S Jackson St Ste 400
Denver, CO 80209-3131

Telephone: (720) 493-4668
Fax Number: (720) 529-1357
Internet Homepage: hooterscolorado.com
Type of Business: Chain Restaurant Operator
Year Founded: 1990
Total Sales: $17,620,000 (e)
Alcohol Sales: 5%
Number of Employees: 1,200
Average Check: Lunch(14); Dinner(18)
Total Units: 5
Trade Names: Hooters (5)
Units Franchised From: 5
Preferred Square Footage: 3,800; 5,000
Preferred Location Types: Freestanding; Strip Mall
Alcohol Served: Beer, Wine, Liquor
Primary Menu: American (5)
Areas of Operation: CO
Type of Foodservice: Casual Dining (5)
Franchise Affiliation: HOA Restaurant Group LLC, ATLANTA, GA

Key Personnel
BRIAN WESTON - CEO; President; Director Supply Chain, Menu Development; General Buyer
ERIC WILLY - Director Information Technology- POS Systems
AMBER BARTZ - Director Training

Richard Sandoval Restaurants
3377 Blake St Ste 106
Denver, CO 80205-2463

Telephone: (646) 285-0796
Fax Number: (646) 285-0799
Internet Homepage: richardsandoval.com
Company Email: info@richardsandoval.com
Type of Business: Chain Restaurant Operator
Year Founded: 1997
Total Sales: $62,730,000 (e)
Alcohol Sales: 15%
Number of Employees: 459
Average Check: Lunch(30); Dinner(54)
Internet Order Processing: Yes
Internet Sales: 5.00%
Total Units: 42
Trade Names: Anchor and Brine (1); Aqimero (1); Bahia (1); Baptist & Bottle (1); Bayou & Bottle (1); Brisas (1); Ciclo (1); El Centro (2); El Centro DF (1); El Puerto (1); Ironwood (1); La Biblioteca (1); La Hacienda (1); La Laguna (1); La Sandia (2); Latincity (1); Live Oak (1); Masa 14 (1); Maya (4); Pampano (1); Pesce (1); Raya (1); Richard Sandoval's Toro Gastrobar (2); Tamayo (1); Toro Latin Gastrobar (2); Toro Latin Kitchen and Bar (2); Toro Toro (5); Venga Venga(1); Zengo (1); Zocalo (1)
Company-Owned Units: 42
Preferred Square Footage: 5,500; 6,000
Preferred Location Types: Freestanding
Alcohol Served: Beer, Wine, Liquor
Primary Menu: American (4); Italian (1); Latin American/Cuban (13); Mexican (17); Miscellaneous (1); Seafood (1); Spanish (2); Steak/Seafood (3)
Areas of Operation: AZ, CA, CO, DC, FL, NV, NY, PA, VA, FC
Foreign Countries: MEXICO; UNITED ARAB EMIRATES; YUGOSLAVIA
Type of Foodservice: Casual Dining (27); Fine Dining (15)

Key Personnel
RICHARD SANDOVAL - Chairman; CEO; Executive Chef
ELI JUSHVAEV - Exec VP; Director Finance

Rightway Brands, Inc.
1800 Glenarm Pl Ste 101
Denver, CO 80202

Telephone: (303) 530-2700
Fax Number: (303) 531-0018
Type of Business: Chain Restaurant Operator
Systemwide Sales: $10,346,000 (e)
Total Sales: $4,069,000 (e)
Total Units: 10
Trade Names: Smiling Moose Rocky Mountain Deli (9); Zopc Epiq Sandwiches (1)
Units Franchised To: 10
Preferred Square Footage: 2,000
Primary Menu: Sandwiches/Deli (10)
Areas of Operation: CO, IN, MT, ND, OH, SD, TX, WI, WY
Type of Foodservice: Fast Casual (10)

Key Personnel
RICHARD EISENBERG - President
JOHN BROWN JR - Chief Business Development Officer; VP
KEVIN BRUTSCH - VP Operations
STEVEN CHAVEZ - Senior Director Logistics

Sage Hospitality Resources LLC
1575 Welton St Ste 300
Denver, CO 80202-4218

Telephone: (303) 405-8394
Fax Number: (303) 595-7219
Internet Homepage: sagehospitality.com
Company Email: info@sagehospitality.com
Type of Business: Foodservice Operations - Hotel/Motels
Year Founded: 1983
Total Sales: $386,670,000 (e)
Alcohol Sales: 20%
Number of Employees: 56,000
Total Units: 32
Restaurants in Hotels: 20
Trade Names: AC Hotel (2); Courtyard (2); DoubleTree (3); Embassy Suites (1); Hilton Garden Inn (1); Homewood Suites (3); Hotel Commonwealth (1); Hotel Nia (1); Hutton Hotel (1); Hyatt Place (1); Marriott (2); Morrison House (1); Perry Lane (1); Renaissance (2); Springhill Suites (1); The Alexandrian (1); TheCrawford Hotel (1); The Elizabeth Hotel (1); The Hotel Zags (1); The Logan (1); The Maven Hotel (1); The Nines (1); The Ritz Carlton (1); Westin (1)
Company-Owned Units: 15
Units Franchised From: 5
Alcohol Served: Beer, Wine, Liquor
Projected Openings: 10
Areas of Operation: CA, CO, FL, IL, PA, UT
Type of Foodservice: Casual Dining (10); Fine Dining (5); Quick Serve (5)
Franchise Affiliation: Dividend Restaurant Group, DENVER, CO; Starbucks Corporation, SEATTLE, WA
Primary Distributors: (Food) SYSCO Food Services of Denver, DENVER, CO
Notes: The company derives approximately 70% of its revenue from hotel operations.

Key Personnel
ZACHARY T. NEWMEYER - Chairman
PETER KARPINSKI - Co-Founder; COO
WALTER ISENDERG - CEO, President
KENNETH GEIST - Exec VP Business Development
BRAD A. ROBINETTE - Senior VP Marketing, Sales
VINCENT PIRO - VP Operations, Group
JAN LUCAS - VP Operations, Region, Division
PAUL MCCORMICK - VP Operations

Sage Restaurant Group
1575 Welton St Ste 300
Denver, CO 80202-4218

Telephone: (303) 595-7264
Internet Homepage: sagerestaurantgroup.com

Company Email:
info@sagerestaurantgroup.com
Type of Business: Chain Restaurant Operator
Total Units: 12
Trade Names: Departure Restaurant + Lounge (1); Emporium Kitchen (1); Hello Betty Fish House (1); Kachina Southwestern Grill (2); Mercat a la Planxa (1); The Corner Office Restaurant + Martini Bar (1); The Original (1); Urban Farmer Steakhouse (4)
Company-Owned Units: 12
Primary Menu: American (1); Asian (2); Caribbean (1); Seafood (1); Southwest/Tex-Mex (2); Spanish (1); Steak (4)
Areas of Operation: CO, IL, MI, OR, PA, RI
Type of Foodservice: Casual Dining (11); Quick Serve (1)

Key Personnel
WALTER ISENBERG - CEO; President
JESSICA WERNER - VP Procurement, Business Development

Sam's No. 3
1500 Curtis St
Denver, CO 80202-2343

Telephone: (303) 534-1927
Fax Number: (303) 534-9934
Internet Homepage: samsno3.com
Company Email: downtown@samsno3.com
Type of Business: Chain Restaurant Operator
Year Founded: 1927
Total Sales: $3,046,000 (e)
Alcohol Sales: 30%
Number of Employees: 40
Average Check: Breakfast(6); Lunch(10); Dinner(14)
Total Units: 3
Trade Names: Sam's No. 3 (3)
Company-Owned Units: 3
Preferred Location Types: Downtown; Freestanding
Alcohol Served: Beer, Wine, Liquor
Primary Menu: Miscellaneous (3)
Areas of Operation: CO
Type of Foodservice: Casual Dining (3)
Primary Distributors: (Full Line) Shamrock Foods Colorado Division, COMMERCE CITY, CO

Key Personnel
SPERO ARMATAS - President; General Buyer
ALEX ARMATAS - Partner; Director Menu Development; General Buyer
PATRICK ARMATAS - Partner; General Manager; General Buyer
BRANDY RAE - Coordinator Social Media

▲ Smashburger Master LLC
3900 E Mexico Ave Ste 1200
Denver, CO 80210-3956

Telephone: (303) 633-1500
Internet Homepage: smashburger.com
Company Email: frontdeskdesk@smashburger.com
Type of Business: Chain Restaurant Operator
Year Founded: 2007
Systemwide Sales: $312,941,000 (e)
Total Sales: $183,850,000 (e)
Average Check: Lunch(10); Dinner(10)
Total Units: 221
Trade Names: Smashburger (221)
Company-Owned Units: 175
Units Franchised To: 46
Preferred Square Footage: 1,600; 2,000; 2,500; 3,000
Preferred Location Types: Airports; Freestanding; Lifestyle Center; Regional Mall; Strip Mall
Alcohol Served: Beer, Wine
Primary Menu: Hamburger (221)
Projected Openings: 15
Areas of Operation: AL, AZ, CA, CO, FL, GA, IA, ID, IL, KS, KY, LA, MI, MN, MO, NC, ND, NE, NJ, NM, NV, NY, OH, OK, PA, SC, TN, TX, UT, VA, FC, AB, ON
Foreign Countries: CANADA; COSTA RICA; EL SALVADOR; ENGLAND; KUWAIT; PANAMA; SAUDI ARABIA
Type of Foodservice: Fast Casual (221)
Parent Company: Jollibee Foods Corporation, WEST COVINA, CA
Headquarters: Icon Burger Development Company LLC, DENVER, CO

Key Personnel
DENISE NELSEN - CEO
THOMAS PRATHER - Chief Marketing Officer
JIM SULLIVAN - Chief Development Officer
TY LUFMAN - Senior VP; General Counsel
ROB BOYER - VP Operations, Franchise Operations, Training
ROD BOYER - VP International
KELLY SAUNDERS - VP Training
JENNIFER SCHADEN - Director Operations, Communications
KYLE TRINKAUS - Director Accounting, Payroll
RYAN HEDLUND - Director Purchasing
MALLORY O'LEARY - Director Operations
JENNIFFER BROWN - Regional Manager Operations-Training
JULIE BECK - Manager Payroll
KATY MICHAEL - Manager Media
ALISON STUART - Manager Information Technology
EMILY ROMME - Manager

Snarf's Sandwiches
2762 Walnut St
Denver, CO 80205-2233

Telephone: (720) 389-7920
Fax Number: (303) 727-9838
Internet Homepage: eatsnarfs.com
Company Email: marketing@eatsnarfs.com
Type of Business: Chain Restaurant Operator
Year Founded: 1996
Total Sales: $9,922,000 (e)
Total Units: 23
Trade Names: Snarf's Sandwiches (23)
Company-Owned Units: 23
Preferred Location Types: Institution (college/hospital); Mixed-use Center; Outlet Mall
Primary Menu: Sandwiches/Deli (23)
Projected Openings: 2
Areas of Operation: CO, IL, MO, TX
Type of Foodservice: Fast Casual (23)
Catering Services: Yes

Key Personnel
JIMMY SEIDEL - Founder; CEO
NATALIE BRILLIANT - Director Operations, Business Development
BRITTANY LIRTZMAN - Director Operations
HELEN WOOD - Director Marketing
CARA GREENE - Manager Human Resources

Snooze Import Export LLC
3001 Brighton Blvd Ste 303
Denver, CO 80216-5082

Telephone: (303) 296-6344
Internet Homepage: SnoozeEatery.com
Company Email: eggme@SnoozeEatery.com
Type of Business: Chain Restaurant Operator
Year Founded: 2006
Total Sales: $67,470,000 (e)
Average Check: Breakfast(14);
Total Units: 30
Trade Names: Snooze: an AM Eatery (30)
Company-Owned Units: 30
Preferred Location Types: Downtown; Strip Mall
Alcohol Served: Beer, Wine, Liquor
Primary Menu: American (30)
Projected Openings: 3
Areas of Operation: AZ, CA, CO, TX
Type of Foodservice: Casual Dining (30)
Catering Services: Yes

Key Personnel
DAVID BIRZON - CEO
JON SCHLEGEL - Partner
ADAM SCHLEGEL - Partner
BILL LONG - CFO
BRIANNA BORIN - VP Training

BETH COCHRAN - Manager Region

TAG Restaurant Group
1441 Larimer Street
Denver, CO 80202

Telephone: (303) 996-9985
Internet Homepage: tagrestaurantgroup.com
Type of Business: Chain Restaurant Operator
Year Founded: 2009
Total Sales: $11,380,000 (e)
Total Units: 12
Trade Names: BuBu (2); Done Deal (1); Guard and Grace (2); Hashtag (2); Los Chingones (5)
Company-Owned Units: 12
Primary Menu: American (2); Asian (2); Mexican (5); Snacks (1); Steak (2)
Areas of Operation: CO
Type of Foodservice: Casual Dining (8); Fast Casual (2); Fine Dining (2)

Key Personnel
JAMES PARK - CEO
TROY GUARD - Partner; Executive Chef
NIKKI GUARD - Partner; Director Beverages

Teriyaki Madness LLC
1660 S Albion St Ste 800
Denver, CO 80222-4045

Telephone: (303) 997-0719
Internet Homepage: franchise.teriyakimadness.com; teriyakimadness.com
Company Email: realestate@teriyakimadness.com
Type of Business: Chain Restaurant Operator
Year Founded: 2003
Systemwide Sales: $77,484,000 (e)
Total Sales: $19,220,000 (e)
Average Check: Dinner(12)
Total Units: 96
Trade Names: Teriyaki Madness (97)
Company-Owned Units: 16
Units Franchised To: 81
Preferred Location Types: Freestanding, Strip Mall
Primary Menu: Asian (97)
Projected Openings: 8
Areas of Operation: AZ, CA, CO, FL, GA, IA, MD, MI, MT, NC, NE, NV, NY, TX, VA
Type of Foodservice: Fast Casual (97)
Catering Services: Yes

Key Personnel
MICHAEL HAITH - Chairman; CEO
ERIN HICKS - COO
JODI BOYCE - VP Marketing
KEVIN MCCARTHY - VP Operations-Training
KEITH SPECHT - Controller
LIZ WORLEY - Director Marketing

ZANE PASCHAL - Manager Supply Chain
ALISON SATRIANA - Manager Franchise Development
KRISTIN SIMPSON - Manager Development, Real Estate
SHANLEE KASSON - Manager Training
JAMES JOHNSON - Coordinator Franchise Development

The Delectable Egg Restaurants
1625 Court Pl Ste 2
Denver, CO 80202-4520

Telephone: (303) 892-5720
Fax Number: (303) 892-5821
Internet Homepage: delectableegg.com
Type of Business: Chain Restaurant Operator
Year Founded: 1982
Total Sales: $2,598,000 (e)
Number of Employees: 80
Average Check: Breakfast(18); Lunch(18);
Total Units: 5
Trade Names: The Delectable Egg (5)
Company-Owned Units: 5
Preferred Location Types: Downtown; Freestanding; Strip Mall
Alcohol Served: Liquor
Primary Menu: American (5)
Areas of Operation: CO
Type of Foodservice: Fast Casual (5)

Key Personnel
KEN THIESEN - Owner; General Manager; Executive Chef; General Buyer
WHITNEY SHEAR - General Manager

The Quiznos Master LLC
4700 S Syracuse St Ste 640
Denver, CO 80237-3008

Telephone: (720) 359-3300
Fax Number: (720) 359-3399
Internet Homepage: realestate.quiznos.com; quiznos.com
Listing Type: Subsidiary
Type of Business: Chain Restaurant Operator
Year Founded: 1981
Systemwide Sales: $80,883,000 (e)
Total Sales: $4,839,000 (e)
Number of Employees: 800
Average Check: Lunch(8); Dinner(8)
Total Units: 215
Trade Names: Quiznos (215)
Units Franchised To: 215
Preferred Square Footage: 1,200; 1,600
Preferred Location Types: Airports; Community Mall; Convenience Store/Gas Station; Downtown; Freestanding; Institution (college/hospital); Lifestyle Center; Outlet Mall; Regional Mall; Stadiums; Strip Mall

Primary Menu: Sandwiches/Deli (215)
Areas of Operation: AK, AL, AR, AZ, CA, CO, CT, DC, DE, FL, GA, GU, HI, IA, ID, IL, IN, KS, KY, LA, MA, MD, ME, MI, MN, MO, MT, NC, ND, NE, NH, NJ, NM, NV, NY, OH, OK, OR, PA, PR, RI, SC, SD, TN, TX, UT, VT, WA, WI, WV, AB, BC, MB, NB, NL, NS, NT, ON, QC, SK, YT
Foreign Countries: AUSTRALIA; BAHAMAS; BAHRAIN; CANADA; COSTA RICA; EGYPT; EL SALVADOR; ENGLAND; GREAT BRITAIN; GUATEMALA; GUYANA; HONDURAS; INDIA; IRELAND; JAPAN; JORDAN; MALAYSIA; MEXICO; PANAMA; PARAGUAY; RUSSIA; SAUDI ARABIA; SOUTH KOREA; TAIWAN; TRINIDAD & TOBAGO; TURKEY; UNITED ARAB EMIRATES
Type of Foodservice: Quick Serve (215)
Foodservice Management Venues: Parks & Recreation
Catering Services: Yes
Primary Distributors: (Full Line) SYSCO Food Services of Denver, DENVER, CO
Parent Company: High Bluff Capital Partners, ,
Headquarters: REGO Restaurant Group, DENVER, CO

Key Personnel
TIM CASEY - CEO

The Taco House
581 S Federal Blvd
Denver, CO 80219-2939

Telephone: (303) 936-3633
Fax Number: (303) 279-6207
Internet Homepage: tacohouse.org
Type of Business: Chain Restaurant Operator
Year Founded: 1957
Systemwide Sales: $8,377,000 (e)
Total Sales: $3,503,000 (e)
Number of Employees: 130
Average Check: Breakfast(8); Lunch(10); Dinner(12)
Total Units: 2
Trade Names: Taco House (2)
Company-Owned Units: 2
Preferred Square Footage: 2,500
Preferred Location Types: Freestanding
Primary Menu: Mexican (2)
Areas of Operation: CO
Type of Foodservice: Family Restaurant (2)
Primary Distributors: (Full Line) SYSCO Food Services of Denver, DENVER, CO

Key Personnel
NANCY RISCH - Owner; Director Real Estate, Design, Store Fixtures
GREG RISCH - General Manager

Trangen Inc.
1340 W Bayaud Ave Unit 2
Denver, CO 80223-1245

Telephone: (303) 722-2149
Fax Number: (303) 722-2074
Internet Homepage: thesandwichboard.com
Company Email:
  philb@thesandwichboard.com
Type of Business: Chain Restaurant Operator
Year Founded: 1970
Total Sales: $6,279,000 (e)
Number of Employees: 90
Average Check: Breakfast(8); Lunch(8); Dinner(8)
Total Units: 12
Trade Names: Sandwich Board (12)
Company-Owned Units: 12
Preferred Square Footage: 1,700; 3,000
Preferred Location Types: Office Complex
Primary Menu: Sandwiches/Deli (12)
Areas of Operation: CO
Type of Foodservice: Quick Serve (12)
Foodservice Management Venues: Business & Industry
Primary Distributors: (Full Line) US Foods, PHOENIX, AZ

Key Personnel
PHILLIP BOOGHIER - CEO; VP; General Manager; Director Finance, Operations, Facility/Maintenance, Supply Chain, Design
PAM DANIELS - President; Controller; Director Purchasing, Information Systems, Human Resources, Franchise Development; Manager Real Estate; General Buyer

Washington Park Grille
1096 S Gaylord St
Denver, CO 80209-4636

Telephone: (303) 777-0707
Fax Number: (303) 777-0247
Internet Homepage: agavetacobar.com; washparkgrille.com
Type of Business: Chain Restaurant Operator
Year Founded: 1985
Total Sales: $6,964,000 (e)
Alcohol Sales: 25%
Number of Employees: 80
Average Check: Breakfast(12); Lunch(18); Dinner(36)
Total Units: 3
Trade Names: Agave Taco Bar (1); Max Gill & Grill (1); Washington Park Grille (1)
Company-Owned Units: 3
Preferred Location Types: Downtown; Freestanding; Strip Mall
Alcohol Served: Beer, Wine, Liquor
Primary Menu: Italian (1); Mexican (1); Seafood (1)
Areas of Operation: CO
Type of Foodservice: Casual Dining (3)
Primary Distributors: (Food) Shamrock Foods Colorado Division, COMMERCE CITY, CO

Key Personnel
JEFF ESTEY - President; Partner; Buyer Beverages
GREG SAUBER - Partner; General Manager; Buyer Beverages
RAFAEL NAJERA - Executive Chef; General Buyer

Yampa Sandwich Company
1617 Wazee St
Denver, CO 80202

Telephone: (303) 534-7900
Internet Homepage: yampasandwichco.com
Type of Business: Chain Restaurant Operator
Year Founded: 1999
Average Check: Lunch(22); Dinner(24)
Total Units: 5
Trade Names: Yampa Sandwich Company
Company-Owned Units: 5
Primary Menu: Sandwiches/Deli (5)
Areas of Operation: CO
Type of Foodservice: Casual Dining (5)
Catering Services: Yes

Key Personnel
PETER BONIFACE - Co-Founder
DAVID PEPIN - Co-Founder
DAVE MISCHELL - CEO

Cherry Berry
265 Turner Dr
Durango, CO 81303-7941

Telephone: (702) 586-8700
Fax Number: (702) 586-8700
Internet Homepage: cherryberryyogurtbar.com; thefuzzypeach.com; yogurtini.com
Company Email:
  info@cherryberryyogurtbar.com
Type of Business: Chain Restaurant Operator
Total Sales: $36,557,000 (e)
Total Units: 39
Trade Names: Aspen Leaf (5); Cherry Berry Yogurt Bar (46); Fuzzy Peach (4); U Swirl (21); Yoglimogli (13); Yokgurtini (17)
Company-Owned Units: 5
Units Franchised To: 101
Primary Menu: Snacks (106)
Areas of Operation: AR, CT, GA, IA, IL, KS, KY, MI, MN, MO, MT, NC, ND, NE, NM, OK, SD, TX, UT, WI, WY, BC, NS
Foreign Countries: CANADA
Type of Foodservice: Quick Serve (106)
Parent Company: U-Swirl, Inc, DURANGO, CO

Key Personnel
FRANK CRAIL - President

McDonald's of Durango
555 S Camino Del Rio
Durango, CO 81303-6826

Telephone: (970) 247-9391
Fax Number: (970) 247-9041
Type of Business: Chain Restaurant Operator
Year Founded: 1992
Total Sales: $20,689,000 (e)
Number of Employees: 250
Average Check: Breakfast(8); Lunch(10); Dinner(12)
Total Units: 4
Trade Names: McDonald's (4)
Units Franchised From: 4
Preferred Square Footage: 2,500; 3,000
Preferred Location Types: Freestanding
Primary Menu: Hamburger (4)
Areas of Operation: CO, NM
Type of Foodservice: Quick Serve (4)
Franchise Affiliation: McDonald's Corporation, CHICAGO, IL

Key Personnel
BUD LORD - Senior Director Operations
JOHN WENDEL - Senior Director Development
JEFF DONAHUE - Area Manager

U-Swirl, Inc
265 Turner Dr
Durango, CO 81303-7941

Telephone: (702) 586-8700
Fax Number: (970) 259-5895
Internet Homepage: aspenleafyogurt.com; U-SWIRL.com; yogurtini.com; yoglimogli.com
Company Email: info@U-SWIRL.com
Type of Business: Chain Restaurant Operator
Total Sales: $4,295,000 (e)
Number of Employees: 62
Average Check: Lunch(8); Dinner(5)
Total Units: 97
Trade Names: Aspen Leaf Yogurt (4); CherryBerry (45); Fuzzy Peach (4); Let's Yo! (3); U-Swirl Frozen Yogurt (19); Yogli Mogli (5); Yogurtini (17)
Units Franchised To: 97
Preferred Square Footage: 1,800; 3,000
Preferred Location Types: Strip Mall
Primary Menu: Snacks (97)
Areas of Operation: AZ, CA, CO, FL, GA, IA, ID, IL, KS, MO, MT, NE, NM, NV, NY, PA, SC, TN, TX, UT, VA, WA
Type of Foodservice: Quick Serve (97)
Parent Company: Rocky Mountain Chocolate Factory Inc., DURANGO, CO
Headquarter Offices: Cherry Berry,

DURANGO, CO

Key Personnel
BRYAN MERRYMAN - Chairman; CEO
ALAN STRIBLING - President
JEREMY KINNEY - Controller

Basic Food Group Inc.
45 Inverness Dr E
Englewood, CO 80112-5412

Telephone: (303) 861-2937
Fax Number: (303) 861-2962
Internet Homepage: basicfoodgroup.com; avenuegrill.com; gntavern.com
Company Email: eat@avenuegrill.com
Type of Business: Chain Restaurant Operator
Year Founded: 1988
Total Sales: $28,330,000 (e)
Alcohol Sales: 35%
Number of Employees: 177
Average Check: Lunch(20); Dinner(36)
Total Units: 8
Trade Names: Avenue Grill (1); Famous Dave's (6); Great Northern Tavern (1)
Company-Owned Units: 3
Units Franchised From: 6
Preferred Location Types: Downtown; Freestanding
Alcohol Served: Beer, Wine, Liquor
Primary Menu: American (2); Bar-B-Q (6)
Areas of Operation: CO
Type of Foodservice: Casual Dining (5); Fine Dining (3)
Franchise Affiliation: BBQ Holdings, Inc., MINNETONKA, MN
Primary Distributors: (Food) US Foods, CENTENNIAL, CO

Key Personnel
WILLIAM FERGUSON JR - President; General Manager
JOHN BROKOS - CFO; Controller; Manager Accounting
ANDREW LUBATTY - Executive Chef; Manager Menu Development; General Buyer

Destination Hotels & Resorts Inc.
10333 E Dry Creek Rd Ste 450
Englewood, CO 80112-1562

Telephone: (303) 799-3830
Fax Number: (303) 799-6011
Internet Homepage: mountaindestination.com; destinationhotels.com; loweenterprises.com
Type of Business: Foodservice Operations - Hotel/Motels
Year Founded: 1973
Total Sales: $812,790,000 (e)
Alcohol Sales: 10%
Number of Employees: 8,200
Total Units: 37
Restaurants in Hotels: 37
Trade Names: Destination Resorts Hawaii; Destination Resorts Snowmass; Destination Resorts Vail; Embassy Suites at Chevy Chase Pavilion; Estancia La Jolla Hotel & Spa; Hamilton Park Hotel & Conference Center; Hotel Icon; Inverness Hotel & Conference Center; L'Auberge Del Mar; Manor Vail Lodge; Miramonte Resort & Spa; Mountain Lodge at Telluride; Resort at Squaw Creek; Rizzo Conference Center; Royal Palms Resort and Spa; Santa Fe; Sheraton Universal; Skamania Lodge; Stowe Mountain Lodge; Sunriver Resort & Conference Center; Tarrytown House Estate & Conference Center; Tempe MissionPalms Hotel; Terrance Resort; Teton Mountain Lodge; The Carolina Inn; The Driskill Hotel; The Gant Hotel; The Hotel Telluride; The Inn at Suncadia; The Madison; The Richardson Hotel; The Stonebridge Inn; The Wigwam Golf Resort & Spa; Top of the Village; Vail Cascade Resort & Spa; Wailea Beach Villas; Wild Dunes Resort
Company-Owned Units: 37
Alcohol Served: Beer, Wine, Liquor
Projected Remodelings: 3
Areas of Operation: AZ, CA, CO, DC, FL, NJ, NY, OR, SC, TX, WY
Type of Foodservice: Casual Dining; Fine Dining
Primary Distributors: (Food) SYSCO Food Services of Denver, DENVER, CO
Parent Company: Lowe Enterprises, LOS ANGELES, CA
Notes: The company derives approximately 70% of its revenue from hotel operations.

Key Personnel
ANDRE FOURNIER - Exec VP Marketing, Sales

Red Robin Gourmet Burgers Inc.
10000 E. Geddes Avenue Suite 500
Englewood, CO 80112

Telephone: (303) 846-6000
Fax Number: (303) 846-6013
Internet Homepage: redrobin.com; rrburgerworks.com
Type of Business: Chain Restaurant Operator
Year Founded: 1969
Systemwide Sales: $3,843,632,000 (e)
Publicly Held: Yes
Total Sales: $1,675,347,000 (e)
Alcohol Sales: 10%
Number of Employees: 22,483
Average Check: Lunch(14); Dinner(14)
Internet Order Processing: Yes
Internet Sales: 1.00%
Total Units: 506
Trade Names: Red Robin Gourmet Burgers & Spirits (506)
Company-Owned Units: 415
Units Franchised To: 91
Preferred Square Footage: 2,000; 4,000; 5,600; 5,800; 6,350
Preferred Location Types: Community Mall; Downtown; Freestanding; Regional Mall; Strip Mall
Alcohol Served: Beer, Wine, Liquor
Primary Menu: Hamburger (506)
Areas of Operation: AK, AL, AR, AZ, CA, CO, CT, DE, FL, GA, IA, ID, IL, IN, KS, KY, MA, MD, ME, MI, MN, MO, MT, NC, NE, NH, NJ, NM, NV, NY, OH, OK, OR, PA, RI, SC, TN, TX, UT, VA, WA, WI, AB, BC
Foreign Countries: CANADA
Type of Foodservice: Casual Dining (506); Fast Casual (0)
Primary Distributors: (Equipment) Trimark Strategic, LEWISVILLE, TX; (Full Line) SYSCO Food Services of Los Angeles Inc., WALNUT, CA
Notes: The company has received a formal offer to be bought by Vintage Capital Management LLC and the terms are currently being reviewed.

Key Personnel
DAVID PACE - Chairman
G. J. HART - CEO
LYNN SCHWEINFURTH - CFO; Exec VP
PHYLLIS ROSELLO MERCURIO - COO
JAMIE REEVES - COO
MEGHAN SPULER - Chief People Officer
CYRUS KELLEY - VP Consumer Insights
AMY JONES-HOM - VP Operations
STEVE CANADA - Regional VP Real Estate
AL HANSEN - Regional VP
KAREN KAEHLER - Executive Chef
MEREDITH STEVENS - Director Digital Marketing, Loyalty Program
GLENN PICKARTS - Director Construction
PAUL BROWN - Director Finance, Operations
JASON MOUNTS - Director Innovation
ERIN LEMBKE - Director Brand Marketing
MELANIE HAMM - Director Accounting
STEVE VINCENT - Director Transformation
SUSAN FEICHTER - Director Restaurant Operations
MO MORRILL - Director Franchise Operations
MIKE THUNELL - Director Technology
RICK MATTHEWS - Director Operations
RON PERROTTA - Regional Director Operations
JEFFREY TINKER - Regional Director Operations
GLEN ALLEN - Regional Manager Facility/Maintenance
MARK DUBBERLY - Manager Real Estate
KARA ANDERSON - Manager Marketing
LINDSEY BRADISH - Manager Marketing, National
CLAIRE SIMPSON - Manager Human Resources

ELLIE ZUCCARELLI - Project Manager Supply Chain; Buyer
BRANDY MACAULEY - Project Manager Innovation

Tokyo Joe's
10111 Inverness Main St Ste O
Englewood, CO 80112

Telephone: (303) 796-7318
Fax Number: (303) 796-9198
Internet Homepage: tokyojoes.com
Type of Business: Chain Restaurant Operator
Year Founded: 1996
Total Sales: $18,760,000 (e)
Alcohol Sales: 2%
Number of Employees: 375
Average Check: Lunch(10); Dinner(10)
Total Units: 33
Trade Names: Tokyo Joe's (33)
Company-Owned Units: 28
Units Franchised To: 5
Preferred Square Footage: 3,000
Preferred Location Types: Freestanding; Strip Mall
Alcohol Served: Beer, Wine
Primary Menu: Japanese (33)
Areas of Operation: AZ, CA, CO, TX
Type of Foodservice: Fast Casual (33)
Primary Distributors: (Full Line) Shamrock Foods Colorado Division, COMMERCE CITY, CO
Parent Company: Gridiron Capital LLC, NEW CANAAN, CT

Key Personnel
LARRY LEITH - Founder; CIO; Director Menu Development; General Buyer
TOM EICHENBERGER - CFO
MARCI LEITH - VP Operations, Human Resources
BETSY WAYNE - Director Marketing, Advertising

Tasty's Fresh Burgers and Fries
710 Centre St
Fernandina Beach, CO 32034

Telephone: (904) 321-0409
Internet Homepage: tastysfreshburgersandfries.com
Type of Business: Chain Restaurant Operator
Year Founded: 2011
Total Sales: $2,306,000 (e)
Number of Employees: 30
Total Units: 2
Trade Names: Tasty's Fresh Burgers and Fries (2)
Company-Owned Units: 2
Primary Menu: Hamburger (2)
Projected Openings: 2
Areas of Operation: FL
Type of Foodservice: Fast Casual (2)

Key Personnel
CHAD DOUGHERTY - Co-Founder; Partner
KATY DOUGHERTY - Co-Founder; Partner
JUSTIN SOUTHWELL - Executive Chef

Ice Station Zebra & Associates
3600 Magrath Ave
Fort Carson, CO 80913

Telephone: (719) 579-7827
Type of Business: Chain Restaurant Operator
Total Sales: $5,266,000 (e)
Total Units: 4
Trade Names: Jimmy John's Gourmet Sandwich Shop (4)
Units Franchised From: 4
Areas of Operation: CO
Franchise Affiliation: Jimmy John's Franchise LLC, CHAMPAIGN, IL

Key Personnel
DEREK COHN - Owner

Austin's American Grill
109 N College Ave Ste 220
Fort Collins, CO 80524-2605

Telephone: (970) 266-2612
Fax Number: (970) 266-2613
Internet Homepage: bigalsburgersanddogs.com; austinsamericangrill.com; themoothouse.com
Type of Business: Chain Restaurant Operator
Total Sales: $9,689,000 (e)
Alcohol Sales: 10%
Number of Employees: 100
Average Check: Lunch(14); Dinner(18)
Total Units: 5
Trade Names: Austin's American Grill (2); Big Al's Burgers & Dogs (1); Comet Chicken (1); Moot House (1)
Company-Owned Units: 5
Preferred Location Types: Freestanding
Alcohol Served: Beer, Wine, Liquor
Primary Menu: American (2); Chicken (1); Hamburger (1); Miscellaneous (1)
Areas of Operation: CO
Type of Foodservice: Casual Dining (4); Quick Serve (1)
Primary Distributors: (Full Line) SYSCO Food Services of Denver, DENVER, CO

Key Personnel
STEVE TAYLOR - Owner; General Manager; General Buyer

Berry Blendz Juice Enterprises Inc.
1112 Oakridge Dr Unit 112
Fort Collins, CO 80525-6242

Telephone: (970) 797-2855
Fax Number: (970) 229-9015
Internet Homepage: berryblendz.com
Company Email: info@berryblendz.com
Type of Business: Chain Restaurant Operator
Year Founded: 1997
Systemwide Sales: $20,100,000 (e)
Total Sales: $796,000 (e)
Number of Employees: 200
Average Check: Dinner(6)
Total Units: 15
Trade Names: Berry Blendz (15)
Units Franchised To: 15
Preferred Location Types: Community Mall; Discount Dept. Stores; Freestanding
Primary Menu: Snacks (15)
Projected Openings: 1
Areas of Operation: CO, MN, OH
Type of Foodservice: Quick Serve (15)
On-site Distribution Center: Yes
Primary Distributors: (Full Line) Dairyland, The Chefs' Warehouse, BRONX, NY

Key Personnel
RICHARD B. PICKETT - CEO; President
HEATH B. PICKETT - COO; Senior VP
BERKLEY L. FULLER III - VP Marketing, Sales
BARBARA B. MCCLELLAND - VP Finance
DANIEL PURDY - VP Supply Chain, Real Estate
JENNIFER WERTH - VP Operations
KENDRA FRANK - Director Store Operations, Training

Cheba Hut Franchising Inc.
406 N College Ave
Fort Collins, CO 80524

Telephone: (970) 420-3358
Internet Homepage: chebahut.com
Company Email: corp@chebahut.com
Type of Business: Chain Restaurant Operator
Year Founded: 2001
Systemwide Sales: $11,194,000 (e)
Total Sales: $2,834,000 (e)
Number of Employees: 734
Average Check: Lunch(10); Dinner(20)
Internet Order Processing: Yes
Total Units: 54
Trade Names: Cheba Hut (54)
Company-Owned Units: 3
Units Franchised To: 51
Primary Menu: Hamburger (0); Sandwiches/Deli (54)
Areas of Operation: AZ, CA, CO, NM, NV, OR,

WI
Type of Foodservice: Casual Dining (0); Quick Serve (54)
Catering Services: Yes

Key Personnel
DORIAN LENZ - CEO; Owner; COO; General Buyer
MARC TORRES - COO
BRIAN LOEB - VP Marketing

Domino's Franchisee
2649 E Mulberry St Suite 5
Fort Collins, CO 80524

Telephone: (970) 416-8868
Type of Business: Chain Restaurant Operator
Total Sales: $59,849,000 (e)
Total Units: 29
Trade Names: Domino's (29)
Units Franchised From: 29
Primary Menu: Pizza (29)
Areas of Operation: CO, OK, WY
Type of Foodservice: Quick Serve (29)
Franchise Affiliation: Domino's Pizza Inc, ANN ARBOR, MI

Key Personnel
CHARLES S. DOLAN - Owner; General Buyer

Rio Grande Mexican Restaurants
149 W Mountain Ave
Fort Collins, CO 80524-2822

Telephone: (970) 224-1009
Fax Number: (970) 224-0315
Internet Homepage: riograndemexican.com
Company Email: marketing@riograndemexican.com
Type of Business: Chain Restaurant Operator
Year Founded: 1986
Total Sales: $25,300,000 (e)
Alcohol Sales: 25%
Number of Employees: 500
Average Check: Lunch(12); Dinner(18)
Total Units: 5
Trade Names: Rio Grande Mexican Restaurant (5)
Company-Owned Units: 5
Preferred Location Types: Downtown; Freestanding; Regional Mall; Stadiums; Strip Mall
Alcohol Served: Beer, Wine, Liquor
Primary Menu: Mexican (5)
Projected Openings: 1
Areas of Operation: CO
Type of Foodservice: Casual Dining (5)

Key Personnel
PAT MCGAUGHRAN - Owner; General Buyer
STEVE RICHTER - COO
JOSH FAY - Controller
CHRIS JUMPER - Director Food and Beverage
ERICH WHISENHUNT - Manager Operations
NINA EMERY - Coordinator Facility/Maintenance
SARAH NILSTOFT - Generalist Human Resources

Silver Mine Subs Inc.
8010 S County Road 5 Unit 203
Fort Collins, CO 80528-9004

Telephone: (970) 266-2600
Fax Number: (970) 267-3538
Internet Homepage: silverminesubs.com
Company Email: silverminesubs@silverminesubs.com
Type of Business: Chain Restaurant Operator
Year Founded: 1996
Systemwide Sales: $14,083,000 (e)
Total Sales: $8,032,000 (e)
Alcohol Sales: 5%
Number of Employees: 82
Average Check: Lunch(8); Dinner(8)
Internet Order Processing: Yes
Total Units: 12
Trade Names: Silver Mine Subs (12)
Units Franchised To: 12
Preferred Square Footage: 3,000
Preferred Location Types: Freestanding; Strip Mall
Primary Menu: Sandwiches/Deli (12)
Areas of Operation: AZ, CO, WI, WY
Type of Foodservice: Fast Casual (12)
Catering Services: Yes
Primary Distributors: (Full Line) Vistar Rocky Mountain, DENVER, CO

Key Personnel
LANCE JONES - Co-Founder; VP
JOHN LANGRECK - Co-Founder; VP Finance, Store Development; Treasurer
KIT DESLACK - VP Franchise Development, Menu Development, Catering

Sonic Drive-In Franchise
1301 W Elizabeth St
Fort Collins, CO 80521-4510

Telephone: (970) 493-4766
Type of Business: Chain Restaurant Operator
Total Sales: $6,998,000 (e)
Total Units: 3
Trade Names: Sonic America's Drive-In (3)
Units Franchised From: 3
Primary Menu: Hamburger (3)
Areas of Operation: CO
Type of Foodservice: Quick Serve (3)

Franchise Affiliation: Sonic Corp., OKLAHOMA CITY, OK

Key Personnel
SCOTT BEARD - Owner; General Buyer

The Lost Cajun
110 2nd Ave
Frisco, CO 80443

Telephone: (970) 485-6123
Internet Homepage: thelostcajun.com
Company Email: franchiseinfo@thelostcajun.com
Type of Business: Chain Restaurant Operator
Year Founded: 2010
Systemwide Sales: $73,466,000 (e)
Total Sales: $66,960,000 (e)
Total Units: 26
Trade Names: The Lost Cajun (26)
Company-Owned Units: 25
Units Franchised To: 1
Primary Menu: Cajun/Creole (26)
Projected Openings: 7
Areas of Operation: CO, LA, NC, SC, TN, TX
Type of Foodservice: Casual Dining (26)

Key Personnel
RAYMOND GRIFFIN - CEO; Partner; General Buyer
JON ESPEY - President; Partner
RICHARD BERNS - COO
RICHARD LEVEILLE - Chief Development Officer

JJNJ, Inc
3112 S Glen Ave
Glenwood Springs, CO 81601-4443

Mailing Address: PO Box 1329, GLENWOOD SPRINGS, CO, 81602-1329
Telephone: (970) 945-1571
Fax Number: (970) 384-2592
Type of Business: Chain Restaurant Operator
Year Founded: 1999
Total Sales: $60,860,000 (e)
Number of Employees: 415
Average Check: Breakfast(8); Lunch(8); Dinner(10)
Total Units: 13
Trade Names: McDonald's (13)
Units Franchised From: 13
Preferred Square Footage: 2,500; 3,000
Preferred Location Types: Freestanding
Primary Menu: Hamburger (13)
Areas of Operation: CO
Type of Foodservice: Quick Serve (13)
Franchise Affiliation: McDonald's Corporation, CHICAGO, IL
Primary Distributors: (Full Line) Mile Hi Foods,

DENVER, CO

Key Personnel
PAUL NELSON - President; Director Supply Chain; General Buyer
KLAUS MINTER - Director Operations

Jacobs Entertainment, Inc.
17301 W Colfax Ave Ste 250
Golden, CO 80401-4800

Telephone: (303) 215-5200
Fax Number: (303) 215-5120
Internet Homepage: gdwcasino.com; jacobsentertainmentinc.com; thegilpincasino.com; thelodgecasino.com
Type of Business: Foodservice Operations - Casinos
Year Founded: 1991
Total Sales: $624,360,000 (e)
Alcohol Sales: 30%
Number of Employees: 1,744
Average Check: Lunch(14); Dinner(26)
Total Units: 15
Trade Names: Gold Dust West Casino - Carson City (3); Gold Dust West Casino - Elko (1); Gold Dust West Casino - Reno (1); Sands Regency (5); The Gilpin Casino (1); The Lodge Casino (4)
Company-Owned Units: 15
Preferred Location Types: Hotel/Motel
Alcohol Served: Beer, Wine, Liquor
Primary Menu: American (12); Asian (1); Mexican (1); Snacks (1)
Areas of Operation: CO, NV
Type of Foodservice: Casual Dining (14); Quick Serve (1)
Primary Distributors: (Food) US Foods, CENTENNIAL, CO
Notes: The company derives approximately 92% of its revenue from casinos, truck stops, pari-mutuel, fuel and other operations.

Key Personnel
JEFFREY P. JACOBS - Chairman; CEO; Owner; Treasurer; Corporate Secretary
BRETT A. KRAMER - CFO
CHRIS MAZANEC - CFO
JOHN EAST - COO
JONATHAN BOULWARE - VP Operations
J GARCIA - VP; General Manager
TRACY HANSEN - Director Finance
ROBERT JANIS - Director Operations
SHEILA BROWN - Director Human Resources
BRANDON DREXLER - Director Compliance
STEVE EDWARDS - Director Information Technology
SAMANTHA FRYBERGER - Director Marketing
MARC ANDERSON - Director Operations
DONNA VOTAW - Director Facility/Maintenance
BEN WHITE - Director Operations
TARA GORACKE - Manager Accounting
AMANDA HETTINGER - Assistant Manager Payroll
TRACY BASURTO - Assistant Manager
DANIEL LUNSFORD - Project Manager Information Technology
KEITH ALLEN JONES - Corporate Director Safety, Human Resources
GEORGE BARGISEN - Corporate Director Food
JUAN SAA - Corporate Director Operations

Salad Collective
112 N Rubey Dr Ste. 220
Golden, CO 80403

Telephone: (303) 355-2499
Internet Homepage: saladcollective.com
Company Email: marketing@madgreens.com
Type of Business: Chain Restaurant Operator
Year Founded: 2019
Total Sales: $34,190,000 (e)
Total Units: 39
Trade Names: Mad Greens (26); Snappy Salads (13)
Company-Owned Units: 39
Preferred Square Footage: 2,300
Preferred Location Types: Downtown; Freestanding
Primary Menu: Health Foods (39)
Areas of Operation: AZ, CO, TX, UT
Type of Foodservice: Fast Casual (39)

Key Personnel
DARDEN COORS - CEO
JOHN MONTGOMERY - President
JENN RUPPERT - VP Marketing
WENDY HULL - VP Human Resources
NICK D'ANTONIO - VP Information Technology
SARA VONGILLERN - Manager Marketing

The Naples Group
2495 Youngfield St Ste 1
Golden, CO 80401-0204

Telephone: (303) 458-0997
Fax Number: (303) 433-4956
Internet Homepage: heidisbrooklyndeli.com
Company Email: heidi@heidisbrooklyndeli.com
Type of Business: Chain Restaurant Operator
Year Founded: 1994
Total Sales: $27,020,000 (e)
Number of Employees: 43
Average Check: Breakfast(6); Lunch(8); Dinner(10)
Total Units: 15
Trade Names: Heidi's Brooklyn Deli (15)
Units Franchised To: 15
Preferred Location Types: Freestanding; Office Complex; Strip Mall
Primary Menu: Sandwiches/Deli (15)
Areas of Operation: AZ, CA, CO, MD, ME, NV, WY
Type of Foodservice: Fast Casual (15)
Catering Services: Yes
Primary Distributors: (Full Line) SYSCO Food Services of Denver, DENVER, CO

Key Personnel
HEIDI NAPLES - Partner; CFO; Director Operations
STEVE NAPLES - Partner; General Buyer
KOURTNEY RICHARDS - Manager Communications, Franchise Development

ColCal Inc
607 25 Rd
Grand Junction, CO 81505

Telephone: (970) 245-0898
Fax Number: (970) 208-8339
Internet Homepage: colcal.net
Type of Business: Chain Restaurant Operator
Year Founded: 1986
Total Sales: $13,820,000 (e)
Number of Employees: 204
Average Check: Lunch(12); Dinner(12)
Total Units: 5
Trade Names: Taco Bell (5)
Units Franchised From: 5
Preferred Square Footage: 2,500
Preferred Location Types: Freestanding
Primary Menu: Taco (5)
Areas of Operation: CO
Type of Foodservice: Quick Serve (5)
Franchise Affiliation: Taco Bell Corp., IRVINE, CA
Primary Distributors: (Full Line) McLane/Western, LONGMONT, CO

Key Personnel
KENNETH BASINGER - CEO; President; Manager Finance, Operations, Purchasing, Real Estate, Store Planning

Inflated Dough Inc
2249 Broadway Ste 102A
Grand Junction, CO 81507-1157

Telephone: (970) 243-3639
Type of Business: Chain Restaurant Operator
Total Sales: $14,523,000 (e)
Total Units: 7
Trade Names: Domino's (7)
Units Franchised From: 7
Primary Menu: Pizza (7)
Areas of Operation: CO
Type of Foodservice: Quick Serve (7)
Franchise Affiliation: Domino's Pizza Inc, ANN ARBOR, MI

Key Personnel
ANTHONY TRELEVEN - Owner; General Buyer

King Enterprises
1305 Glenwood Ave
Grand Junction, CO 81501-4329

Mailing Address: PO Box 2738, GRAND JUNCTION, CO, 81502-2738
Telephone: (970) 245-6420
Fax Number: (970) 243-9836
Type of Business: Chain Restaurant Operator
Year Founded: 1989
Total Sales: $23,750,000 (e)
Number of Employees: 250
Average Check: Breakfast(8); Lunch(10); Dinner(12)
Total Units: 5
Trade Names: McDonald's (5)
Units Franchised From: 5
Preferred Square Footage: 3,000
Preferred Location Types: Discount Dept. Stores; Freestanding
Primary Menu: Hamburger (5)
Areas of Operation: CO, UT
Type of Foodservice: Quick Serve (5)
Franchise Affiliation: McDonald's Corporation, CHICAGO, IL
Primary Distributors: (Food) Mile Hi Foods, DENVER, CO

Key Personnel
DOUGLAS KING - Partner; Director Operations, Facility/Maintenance; General Buyer
SHANE KING - Partner; Director Finance, Information Systems, Real Estate; General Buyer

Jardel Enterprises Inc.
7935 E Prentice Ave Ste 108
Greenwood Village, CO 80111-2711

Telephone: (720) 529-0121
Fax Number: (720) 529-5865
Type of Business: Chain Restaurant Operator
Year Founded: 1995
Total Sales: $9,597,000 (e)
Number of Employees: 80
Average Check: Breakfast(8); Lunch(10); Dinner(12)
Total Units: 4
Trade Names: Burger King (4)
Units Franchised From: 4
Preferred Square Footage: 2,500; 4,000
Preferred Location Types: Airports; Freestanding
Primary Menu: Hamburger (4)
Projected Remodelings: 1
Areas of Operation: CO
Type of Foodservice: Quick Serve (4)
Franchise Affiliation: Burger King Worldwide Inc., MIAMI, FL
Primary Distributors: (Full Line) Shamrock Foods Colorado Division, COMMERCE CITY, CO

Key Personnel
CARLOS DE LA ROSA - President; Partner; Director Real Estate, Design
MICHAEL DE LA ROSA - Partner; General Buyer
MARY DE LA ROSA - Director Human Resources

Original Pancake House
5900 S University Blvd Ste D
Greenwood Village, CO 80121-2886

Telephone: (303) 795-0573
Internet Homepage: ophdenver.com
Company Email: choph@comcast.net
Type of Business: Chain Restaurant Operator
Total Units: 2
Trade Names: The Original Pancake House (2)
Units Franchised From: 2
Primary Menu: American (2)
Areas of Operation: CO
Type of Foodservice: Family Restaurant (2)
Franchise Affiliation: The Original Pancake House Franchising Inc., PORTLAND, OR

Key Personnel
SARA HUENEKE ERNST - President; General Buyer
DAVID DENNISON - Director Operations

Renzios Inc.
4690 S Yosemite St Unit A
Greenwood Village, CO 80111-1246

Telephone: (303) 267-0300
Internet Homepage: renziosgreekfood.com
Type of Business: Chain Restaurant Operator
Year Founded: 1979
Systemwide Sales: $6,901,000 (e)
Total Sales: $3,032,000 (e)
Alcohol Sales: 1%
Number of Employees: 80
Average Check: Lunch(10); Dinner(10)
Internet Order Processing: Yes
Internet Sales: 1.00%
Total Units: 8
Trade Names: Cafe Athens (2); Renzios (5); The Athenian (1)
Company-Owned Units: 8
Preferred Square Footage: 1,200; 1,800
Preferred Location Types: Freestanding; Regional Mall; Strip Mall
Alcohol Served: Beer, Wine, Liquor
Primary Menu: Greek/Mediterranean (8)
Areas of Operation: CO, MT, WY
Type of Foodservice: Casual Dining (2); Quick Serve (6)
Catering Services: Yes
Primary Distributors: (Food) Grecian Delight Foods Inc., ELK GROVE VILLAGE, IL

Key Personnel
THOMAS RENTZIOS - President; CFO; Director Information Systems, Loss Prevention, Marketing, Menu Development, Catering
CHRIS RENTZIOS - Director Finance, Operations, Purchasing, Facility/Maintenance, POS/Scanning, Marketing, Real Estate, Design, Store Fixtures, Store Planning

RMR Colorado LLC
5347 S Valentia Way Ste 320
Greenwood Village, CO 80111-3146

Telephone: (303) 586-8285
Fax Number: (303) 586-8288
Internet Homepage: blackeyedpeacolorado.com
Company Email: comments@blackeyedpeacolorado.com
Type of Business: Chain Restaurant Operator
Total Sales: $58,090,000 (e)
Alcohol Sales: 15%
Number of Employees: 500
Average Check: Lunch(12); Dinner(18)
Internet Order Processing: Yes
Internet Sales: 1.00%
Total Units: 10
Trade Names: Black-Eyed Pea (10)
Company-Owned Units: 10
Preferred Square Footage: 2,400; 5,400
Preferred Location Types: Freestanding
Alcohol Served: Beer, Wine, Liquor
Primary Menu: American (10)
Areas of Operation: CO
Type of Foodservice: Casual Dining (10)
Primary Distributors: (Full Line) US Foods, CENTENNIAL, CO

Key Personnel
JIM SHAW - Partner
STEVE SHAW - Partner; COO; VP Operations
ANDY MUELLER - Manager Human Resources

Skyport Companies Inc./First Meridian Services
8231 E Prentice Ave
Greenwood Village, CO 80111-2901

Telephone: (303) 342-9000
Fax Number: (303) 806-9805
Type of Business: Foodservice Management Operator
Year Founded: 1992
Total Sales: $49,945,000 (e)
Number of Employees: 500
Number of Locations Served: 55
Total Foodservice Mgmt Accounts: 40
Total Units: 25

Trade Names: Aviators Club, dba Airport Lounges (2); Cantina JV, dba Cantina Grill (1); Dos Amigos, dba La Casita (1); F & B Concessions (5); FM Bakery(1); FM Juice, dba Jamba Juice (1); FM Paradise (6); Lounge 5280 (1); Skyport (6); Woody Creek, dba Caribou Coffee (1)
Company-Owned Units: 25
Areas of Operation: CO
Type of Foodservice: Quick Serve (40)
Foodservice Management Venues: Transportation
Primary Distributors: (Full Line) US Foods, CENTENNIAL, CO

Key Personnel
DAVID MOSTELLER - President; Controller; Manager Purchasing, Real Estate, Research & Development, Store Planning

Venice Ristorante
5946 S Holly St
Greenwood Village, CO 80111-4221

Telephone: (720) 482-9191
Fax Number: (720) 482-1995
Internet Homepage: veniceristorante.com
Company Email: veniceristorante@hotmail.com
Type of Business: Chain Restaurant Operator
Total Sales: $8,188,000 (e)
Alcohol Sales: 30%
Number of Employees: 60
Average Check: Dinner(38)
Total Units: 3
Trade Names: Chianti Ristorante & Winebar (1); Venice Italiano Ristorante & Winebar (1); Venice Ristorante & Winebar (1)
Company-Owned Units: 3
Alcohol Served: Beer, Wine, Liquor
Primary Menu: Italian (3)
Areas of Operation: CO
Type of Foodservice: Fine Dining (3)
Primary Distributors: (Food) SYSCO Food Services of Denver, DENVER, CO

Key Personnel
ALESSANDRO CAROLLO - Partner; Executive Chef; General Buyer
SARA CAROLLO - Partner; General Buyer
NUNZIO MARINO - General Manager; General Buyer
CHRISTIAN DELLE FAVE - Executive Chef; General Buyer

Xanterra Parks & Resorts
6312 S Fiddlers Green Cir Ste 600N
Greenwood Village, CO 80111-4920

Telephone: (303) 600-3400
Fax Number: (303) 600-3600
Internet Homepage: xanterra.com
Company Email: info-corp@xanterra.com
Type of Business: Foodservice Operations - Hotel/Motels
Year Founded: 1968
Total Sales: $70,350,000 (e)
Alcohol Sales: 18%
Number of Employees: 8,500
Total Units: 29
Restaurants in Hotels: 29
Trade Names: Bright Angel Lodge (1); Bryce Canyon Lodge (1); Burr Oak Resort (1); Canyon Lodge (1); Crater Lake Lodge (1); El Tovar Hotel (1); Furnace Creek Inn & Ranch (1); Grant Village (1); Hueston Woods Resort (1); Kachina & Thunderbird Lodge (1); Kingsmill Resort (1); Lake Yellowstone Hotel (1); Mammoth Hot Springs Hotel (1); Maswik Lodge (1); Maumee Bay Resort (1); Mazama Village Motor Inn (1); Mohican Resort (1); Old Faithful Inn (1); Old Faithful Lodge (1); Old Faithful Snow Lodge (1); Phantom Ranch (1); Punderson Manor Resort (1); Roosevelt Lodge (1); Salt Fork Resort (1); Shawnee Resort (1); Silverado Resort (1); Stovepipe Well Village (1); Yavapai Lodge (1); Zion Lodge (1)
Company-Owned Units: 29
Alcohol Served: Beer, Wine, Liquor
Projected Remodelings: 2
Areas of Operation: AZ, CA, CO, OH, OR, UT, VA, WY
Type of Foodservice: Casual Dining; Fine Dining
Notes: The company derives approximately 70% of its revenue from hotel operations.

Key Personnel
ANDREW N. TODD - CEO; President; Executive Chef; Director Operations, Real Estate; General Buyer
HANS DESAI - VP
GORDON TAYLOR - VP
SHANNON DIERENBACH - VP Human Resources

Pizza Hut of the Rockies
8149 State Highway 135
Gunnison, CO 81230-9620

Telephone: (970) 641-1703
Fax Number: (970) 641-2017
Type of Business: Chain Restaurant Operator
Year Founded: 1985
Total Sales: $3,891,000 (e)
Alcohol Sales: 2%
Number of Employees: 90
Average Check: Lunch(10); Dinner(12)
Total Units: 3
Trade Names: Pizza Hut (3)
Units Franchised From: 3
Preferred Square Footage: 3,500
Preferred Location Types: Community Mall; Freestanding; Strip Mall
Alcohol Served: Beer
Primary Menu: Pizza (3)
Areas of Operation: OR, WA
Type of Foodservice: Casual Dining (3)
Foodservice Management Venues: Schools
Franchise Affiliation: Pizza Hut Inc., PLANO, TX
Primary Distributors: (Full Line) McLane Foodservice, CARROLLTON, TX

Key Personnel
NANCY RIEMER - President; Director Finance, Operations, Purchasing, Facility/Maintenance, Risk Management, Real Estate, Site Selection
KAREN MCDONOUGH - Administrative Assistant

Brown Family Restaurants, LLC
9362 S Colorado Blvd Ste D-4
Highlands Ranch, CO 80126-5201

Telephone: (303) 683-3066
Type of Business: Chain Restaurant Operator
Total Sales: $9,656,000 (e)
Total Units: 7
Trade Names: Jersey Mike's Subs (7)
Units Franchised From: 7
Primary Menu: Sandwiches/Deli (7)
Areas of Operation: CO
Type of Foodservice: Quick Serve (7)
Franchise Affiliation: Jersey Mike's Franchise Systems, MANASQUAN, NJ

Key Personnel
JASON BROWN - Partner; General Buyer
IRENE BROWN - Partner

Culver's Frozen Custard Franchisee
4890 Thompson Pkwy
Johnstown, CO 80534-6424

Telephone: (970) 667-2475
Type of Business: Chain Restaurant Operator
Total Sales: $12,988,000 (e)
Total Units: 3
Trade Names: Culver's Frozen Custard (3)
Units Franchised From: 3
Areas of Operation: CO
Franchise Affiliation: Culver Franchising System Inc., PRAIRIE DU SAC, WI

Key Personnel
JEROME SCHUMACHER - Owner; General Buyer

Domino's Franchisee
28 S Parish Ave
Johnstown, CO 80534-7800

Telephone: (970) 587-7887
Type of Business: Chain Restaurant Operator
Total Sales: $6,028,000 (e)
Total Units: 3
Trade Names: Domino's (3)
Units Franchised From: 3
Primary Menu: Pizza (3)
Areas of Operation: CO
Type of Foodservice: Quick Serve (3)
Franchise Affiliation: Domino's Pizza Inc, ANN ARBOR, MI

Key Personnel
BRIAN DELGRASSO - Owner; General Buyer

KT Napier Investments LLC
27680 Frontage Rd
La Junta, CO 81050-9707

Mailing Address: P. O. Box 8267, Pueblo, CO, 81008
Telephone: (719) 542-7625
Type of Business: Chain Restaurant Operator
Total Sales: $23,850,000 (e)
Number of Employees: 120
Total Units: 5
Trade Names: McDonald's (5)
Units Franchised From: 5
Preferred Square Footage: 2,500
Preferred Location Types: Freestanding
Primary Menu: Hamburger (5)
Areas of Operation: CO
Type of Foodservice: Quick Serve (5)
Franchise Affiliation: McDonald's Corporation, CHICAGO, IL

Key Personnel
KEVIN NAPIER - President; Owner; General Buyer

Boselli Brothers
790 Niwot Ridge Ln
Lafayette, CO 80026-3426

Telephone: (303) 499-9861
Type of Business: Chain Restaurant Operator
Year Founded: 1998
Total Sales: $20,357,000 (e)
Number of Employees: 150
Average Check: Breakfast(8); Lunch(8); Dinner(8)
Total Units: 4
Trade Names: McDonald's (4)
Units Franchised From: 4
Preferred Square Footage: 2,500; 3,000
Preferred Location Types: Freestanding
Primary Menu: Hamburger (4)
Areas of Operation: CO
Type of Foodservice: Quick Serve (4)
Franchise Affiliation: McDonald's Corporation, CHICAGO, IL
Primary Distributors: (Full Line) US Foods, CENTENNIAL, CO

Key Personnel
RICHARD WILLIAM BOSELLI - President; General Manager; General Buyer

Renaissance Entertainment Corporation
2335 High Lonesome Trl Ste 101
Lafayette, CO 80026-9397

Telephone: (303) 664-0300
Fax Number: (303) 664-0303
Internet Homepage: renfair.com; renfair.com/forestoffear
Type of Business: Nontraditional Foodservice Operator
Total Sales: $18,023,000 (e)
Alcohol Sales: 3%
Average Check: Dinner(30)
Total Units: 4
Trade Names: Bristol Renaissance Faire (1); Forest of Fear (1); New York Renaissance Faire (1); Southern California Renaissance Pleasure Faire (1)
Company-Owned Units: 4
Preferred Location Types: Other; Parks
Alcohol Served: Beer, Wine
Primary Menu: American (4)
Areas of Operation: CA, NY, WI
Type of Foodservice: Quick Serve (4)
Primary Distributors: (Full Line) SYSCO Food Services of Denver, DENVER, CO
Parent Company: Ellora Entertainment LLC, LOUISVILLE, CO
Notes: All food concessions are run by independent vendors; foodservice sales reflect beverage revenue only. The company derives approximately 76% of its revenue from admissions, vendor fees, souvenir revenues, and other sources related to the operations of the Renaissance Faires.

Key Personnel
DEB JOHNSON - Chief Administrative Officer; Corporate Secretary; Controller

Boston Market Corporation
14103 Denver West Pkwy Ste 100
Lakewood, CO 80401-3124

Telephone: (303) 278-9500
Fax Number: (303) 216-5338
Internet Homepage: bostonmarket.com; chefspage.com
Company Email: realestateinfo@bost.com
Listing Type: Subsidiary
Type of Business: Chain Restaurant Operator
Year Founded: 1992
Systemwide Sales: $655,670,000 (e)
Total Sales: $658,390,000 (e)
Number of Employees: 12,260
Average Check: Lunch(8); Dinner(10)
Internet Order Processing: Yes
Internet Sales: 0.50%
Total Units: 350
Trade Names: Boston Market (350)
Company-Owned Units: 331
Units Franchised To: 19
Preferred Square Footage: 3,000
Preferred Location Types: Downtown; Freestanding; Grocery Stores; Strip Mall; Travel Plazas
Primary Menu: Chicken (350)
Areas of Operation: AZ, CA, CO, CT, DE, FL, GA, IL, IN, KS, MA, MD, MI, MN, MO, NC, NH, NJ, NM, NV, NY, OH, PA, RI, TX, VA, WI
Type of Foodservice: Fast Casual (350)
Catering Services: Yes
Primary Distributors: (Full Line) The Martin-Brower Co. LLC, ROSEMONT, IL
Parent Company: Rohan Group of Companies, FEASTERVILLE TREVOSE, PA

Key Personnel
JUDY CANTRELL - Chief Brand Officer
MICHELLE GLANDER - Senior Director Marketing
RICHARD DAVIS - Senior Director Innovation
STACI HENRY - Director Supply Chain
SARAH PRINZI - Director Risk Management
MIKE DANIEL - Director Operations
KARINA BERRETH - Manager Information Technology
COURTNEY JOHNSON - Manager Operations, Human Resources
LIZ FOX - Manager Innovation
SHAWNA DORSEY - Developer

Coffee & Bagel Brands
555 Zang St Ste 300
Lakewood, CO 80228-1013

Telephone: (303) 568-8000
Fax Number: (888) 964-5454
Internet Homepage: einsteinbros.com; einsteinnoah.com; manhattanbagel.com; noahs.com
Listing Type: Corporate Office
Type of Business: Chain Restaurant Operator
Year Founded: 1993
Systemwide Sales: $2,347,961,000 (e)
Total Sales: $1,291,627,000 (e)
Number of Employees: 6,900
Average Check: Breakfast(6); Lunch(6);
Total Units: 866

Trade Names: Bruegger's Bagel Bakery (182); Einstein Bros Bagels (553); Manhattan Bagel (75); Noah's New York Bagels (56)
Units Franchised To: 866
Preferred Square Footage: 1,400; 1,800; 2,300; 2,400; 2,700
Preferred Location Types: Airports; Downtown; Freestanding; Hotel/Motel; Institution (college/hospital); Lifestyle Center; Other; Regional Mall; Strip Mall; Travel Plazas
Primary Menu: Bagels (866)
Projected Openings: 50
Areas of Operation: AL, AR, AZ, CA, CO, CT, DC, DE, FL, GA, IA, ID, IL, IN, KS, KY, LA, MA, MD, MI, MN, MO, MS, MT, NC, NH, NJ, NM, NV, NY, OH, OK, OR, PA, SC, SD, TN, TX, UT, VA, VT, WA, WI
Type of Foodservice: Fast Casual (866)
Catering Services: Yes
Subsidiaries: Bruegger's Enterprises Inc., DALLAS, TX
Primary Distributors: (Food) Systems Services of America, SCOTTSDALE, AZ; (Food) Performance Foodservice - Temple, TEMPLE, TX
Parent Company: JAB Holding Company, LUDWIGSHAFEN, GER
Notes: The company derives approximately 8% of its revenue from wholesale and manufacturing operations.

Key Personnel
JOSE ALBERTO DUENAS - CEO; President
JOSE A. DUENAS - CEO; President
JESSICA DEPETRO - President; CFO
MARKUS LONNQUIST - CIO
MIKE DAVIS - Senior VP; Corporate Secretary; General Counsel
TEKA O'ROURKE - VP Marketing
WILL MACINTOSH - Senior Director Operations
LYNNE HANDLIN - Senior Director Human Resources
ANDREW HEALD - Senior Director Wholesale
JESSICA LEE - Director; Data Production
FRED LEON - Director Facility/Maintenance
KELSEY ARTES - Director Finance
RANDY MCCRAY - Director Operations
JULIO GARCIA - Director Information Technology
BRENDA PEREA - Director Operations
JON STANLEY - Director Operations, Southeast Region
ANNE WILDE - Director Innovation, Menu Development
ANDREW WORRELL - Director Sales
FITZ-DAVID SMITH - Buyer Beverages
DARLENE GRAZIANO - Coordinator Catering
JEANNIE BUSSCHER - Coordinator Distribution

Good Times Restaurants Inc.
141 Union Blvd Ste 400
Lakewood, CO 80228-1879

Telephone: (303) 384-1400
Fax Number: (303) 273-0177
Internet Homepage: goodtimesburgers.com; baddaddysburgerbar.com
Company Email: info@gtrestaurants.com
Type of Business: Chain Restaurant Operator
Year Founded: 1986
Systemwide Sales: $224,879,000 (e)
Publicly Held: Yes
Total Sales: $181,855,000 (e)
Number of Employees: 2,230
Average Check: Lunch(8); Dinner(10)
Total Units: 72
Trade Names: Bad Daddy's Burger Bar (41); Good Times Burgers & Frozen Custard (31)
Company-Owned Units: 47
Units Franchised To: 25
Preferred Square Footage: 880; 1,900; 2,400; 2,700
Preferred Location Types: Freestanding
Alcohol Served: Beer, Wine, Liquor
Primary Menu: Hamburger (72)
Projected Openings: 3
Areas of Operation: CO, NC, SC, TN, WY
Type of Foodservice: Casual Dining (41); Quick Serve (31)
Subsidiaries: Bad Daddy's International, HUNTERSVILLE, NC
Franchise Affiliation: Taco John's International Inc., CHEYENNE, WY
Primary Distributors: (Full Line) US Foods, LOVELAND, CO
Parent Company: Small Island Investments Ltd., BOSTON, MA

Key Personnel
RYAN ZINK - CEO Interim; CFO
SCOTT G. LEFEVER - COO
SCOTT SOMES - COO Group
DON STACK - Senior VP Operations
BILL MCCLINTOCK - VP Franchise Development
KERI AUGUST - VP Accounting
SUSAN M. KNUTSON - Treasurer; Controller
CHRIS DEVORE - Controller
GARY STATON - Director Risk Management, Human Resources, Food Safety
KIT MITCHELL - Director Franchise Operations
TIM TAYLOR - Director Information Technology
NICHOLAS CORBISHLEY - Director Store Development
NICHOLAS G. BIEGEL - Director Purchasing, Product Development
WILLIAM K. MITCHELL - Director Facility/Maintenance
BROCK DAVIS - Director Information Technology
KATIE ANDERSEN - Manager Digital Marketing

RMC Inc.
12345 W Alameda Pkwy Ste 210
Lakewood, CO 80228-2827

Mailing Address: PO Box 280548, LAKEWOOD, CO, 80228
Telephone: (303) 237-1340
Fax Number: (303) 237-0824
Internet Homepage: tucanos.com
Company Email: corporate@tucanos.com
Type of Business: Chain Restaurant Operator
Total Sales: $6,100,000 (e)
Number of Employees: 585
Internet Order Processing: Yes
Total Units: 9
Trade Names: Tucanos Brazilian Grill (9)
Company-Owned Units: 9
Preferred Square Footage: 7,000; 7,500
Preferred Location Types: Freestanding; Strip Mall
Alcohol Served: Beer, Wine, Liquor
Primary Menu: Latin American/Cuban (9)
Areas of Operation: CO, ID, IN, MO, NM, UT, VA
Type of Foodservice: Casual Dining (9)

Key Personnel
STEVE OLDHAM - Founder; President
MICKEY PADILLA - Partner; Director Design
JOE HEEB - Partner; CFO
JEANETTE HEEB - Partner

Wend Colorado LLP
1536 Cole Blvd Ste 325
Lakewood, CO 80401-3413

Telephone: (303) 825-4009
Fax Number: (303) 232-5077
Type of Business: Chain Restaurant Operator
Year Founded: 1985
Total Sales: $43,280,000 (e)
Number of Employees: 660
Average Check: Lunch(8); Dinner(12)
Total Units: 16
Trade Names: Wendy's Old Fashioned Hamburgers (16)
Units Franchised From: 16
Preferred Square Footage: 2,100
Preferred Location Types: Freestanding; Strip Mall
Primary Menu: Hamburger (16)
Areas of Operation: CO
Type of Foodservice: Quick Serve (16)
Franchise Affiliation: The Wendy's Company, DUBLIN, OH

Key Personnel
SARA TRUDO - Controller; Director Human Resources; Manager Personnel
PAT SEE - Director Marketing; Manager Human Resources

ANDREA CHRISTNER - Manager Accounting
DAVID SEE - General Buyer

DJTC Corp.
8 W Dry Creek Cir Ste 207
Littleton, CO 80120-8082

Telephone: (303) 794-3098
Fax Number: (303) 794-0034
Type of Business: Chain Restaurant Operator
Year Founded: 1994
Total Sales: $10,275,000 (e)
Number of Employees: 120
Average Check: Breakfast(8); Lunch(8); Dinner(10)
Total Units: 2
Trade Names: McDonald's (2)
Units Franchised From: 2
Preferred Square Footage: 2,500; 3,000
Preferred Location Types: Freestanding
Primary Menu: Hamburger (2)
Areas of Operation: CO
Type of Foodservice: Quick Serve (2)
Franchise Affiliation: McDonald's Corporation, CHICAGO, IL
Primary Distributors: (Food) Mile Hi Foods, DENVER, CO

Key Personnel
THOMAS CARLSON - President; Director Operations; Manager Real Estate; General Buyer

H.W. Holdings Corporation
7761 Shaffer Pkwy Ste 102
Littleton, CO 80127-3729

Telephone: (303) 730-6300
Internet Homepage: lepeep.com
Type of Business: Chain Restaurant Operator
Year Founded: 1981
Systemwide Sales: $26,242,000 (e)
Total Sales: $4,164,000 (e)
Alcohol Sales: 1%
Number of Employees: 4
Average Check: Breakfast(24); Lunch(24);
Total Units: 46
Trade Names: Le Peep Restaurant (46)
Units Franchised To: 46
Preferred Square Footage: 3,200
Preferred Location Types: Downtown; Freestanding; Hotel/Motel; Regional Mall; Strip Mall
Primary Menu: American (46)
Areas of Operation: CA, CO, ID, IL, IN, KS, MO, NC, NE, NJ, NM, OH, SC, TN, TX
Type of Foodservice: Casual Dining (46)
Catering Services: Yes

Key Personnel
KEVIN WESSEL - CEO; President; General Buyer
KATE WESSEL - Owner; VP
AMANDA RHOADS - VP Licensing
TYRONE MACK - VP Operations
SUE VALENTINE - Director Operations; Manager Risk Management, Human Resources

Rob-Kraft Inc.
8117 Southpark Cir
Littleton, CO 80120-5666

Mailing Address: PO Box 270008, LITTLETON, CO, 80227-0008
Telephone: (303) 628-2200
Fax Number: (303) 480-2198
Internet Homepage: robkraftinc.com
Type of Business: Chain Restaurant Operator
Year Founded: 1983
Total Sales: $41,140,000 (e)
Number of Employees: 783
Average Check: Breakfast(8); Lunch(10); Dinner(12)
Total Units: 18
Trade Names: Burger King (18)
Units Franchised From: 18
Preferred Square Footage: 2,000; 2,500; 4,000
Preferred Location Types: Freestanding
Primary Menu: Hamburger (18)
Areas of Operation: CO
Type of Foodservice: Quick Serve (18)
Franchise Affiliation: Burger King Worldwide Inc., MIAMI, FL
Primary Distributors: (Food) Shamrock Foods Colorado Division, COMMERCE CITY, CO

Key Personnel
NICK KRAFT - President; Partner
GARY ROBISON - Partner; VP Operations
SCOTT BUCHLER - VP Restaurant Operations
BRIAN ROBISON - VP Human Resources

Triple "J" Management, LLC
7421 W Bowles Ave Ste 10
Littleton, CO 80123-3096

Telephone: (303) 948-1000
Company Email: triplejmanagement@gmail.com
Type of Business: Chain Restaurant Operator
Total Sales: $1,172,000 (e)
Total Units: 2
Trade Names: Cold Stone Creamery (2)
Units Franchised From: 2
Primary Menu: Snacks (2)
Areas of Operation: CO
Type of Foodservice: Quick Serve (2)
Franchise Affiliation: Kahala Brands, SCOTTSDALE, AZ

Key Personnel
JEFFREY SCHIFANO - Owner

Ultra Mac Corporation
5105 S Santa Fe Dr
Littleton, CO 80120-1040

Telephone: (303) 794-3540
Fax Number: (303) 794-0035
Type of Business: Chain Restaurant Operator
Year Founded: 1984
Total Sales: $52,200,000 (e)
Number of Employees: 555
Average Check: Breakfast(8); Lunch(8); Dinner(8)
Total Units: 11
Trade Names: McDonald's (11)
Units Franchised From: 11
Preferred Square Footage: 2,500; 3,000
Preferred Location Types: Convenience Store/Gas Station; Freestanding
Primary Menu: Hamburger (11)
Areas of Operation: CO
Type of Foodservice: Quick Serve (11)
Franchise Affiliation: McDonald's Corporation, CHICAGO, IL
Primary Distributors: (Full Line) Mile Hi Foods, DENVER, CO

Key Personnel
KATHLEEN LINNEMAN - President; Manager Real Estate; General Buyer
JON COSBY - Director Operations

Aspen Food Service, Inc
10863 W I25 Frontage Rd
Longmont, CO 80504-9564

Mailing Address: 1822 Skyway Dr, Unit N, LONGMONT, CO, 80504
Telephone: (303) 682-9566
Fax Number: (303) 682-9567
Type of Business: Chain Restaurant Operator
Total Sales: $23,610,000 (e)
Total Units: 5
Trade Names: McDonald's (5)
Units Franchised From: 5
Primary Menu: Hamburger (5)
Areas of Operation: CO
Type of Foodservice: Quick Serve (5)
Franchise Affiliation: McDonald's Corporation, CHICAGO, IL

Key Personnel
GARY T. KOENIG - President; General Buyer
SHARON KOENIG - President

Dq Treat Franchisee
1945 Main St
Longmont, CO 80501-1913

Telephone: (303) 776-6552
Type of Business: Chain Restaurant Operator
Total Sales: $6,908,000 (e)
Total Units: 5
Trade Names: Dairy Queen Store (5)
Units Franchised From: 5
Primary Menu: Snacks (5)
Areas of Operation: CO
Type of Foodservice: Quick Serve (5)
Franchise Affiliation: International Dairy Queen Inc., BLOOMINGTON, MN

Key Personnel
JUDITH LINDBERG - President; Partner; General Buyer
JULIE STOCKETT - Partner

Twin Arches Mc Donald's
1900 Main St
Longmont, CO 80501-1914

Telephone: (303) 684-9426
Fax Number: (303) 772-1043
Type of Business: Chain Restaurant Operator
Total Sales: $19,769,000 (e)
Total Units: 4
Trade Names: McDonald's (4)
Units Franchised From: 4
Primary Menu: Hamburger (4)
Areas of Operation: CO
Type of Foodservice: Quick Serve (4)
Franchise Affiliation: McDonald's Corporation, CHICAGO, IL

Key Personnel
JAY MCAVOY - President; General Buyer
LISA WAGNER - Supervisor Operations

Ziggi's Coffee
400 Main St
Longmont, CO 80501

Telephone: (303) 800-0517
Internet Homepage: ziggiscoffee.com
Company Email: info@ziggiscoffee.com
Type of Business: Chain Restaurant Operator
Year Founded: 2004
Total Sales: $57,970,000 (e)
Number of Employees: 250
Total Units: 27
Trade Names: Ziggi's Coffee (27)
Company-Owned Units: 27
Primary Menu: Coffee (21)
Type of Foodservice: Quick Serve (21)

Key Personnel
BRANDON KNUDSEN - Founder; CEO
ANDY LINKE - Creative Director
KATHRYN BLEEKER - Director Marketing
NIKKI RIVERA - Director Operations
JEFF DEESE - Director Operations

Tri Taco Inc.
2050 S Townsend Ave
Montrose, CO 81401-6402

Mailing Address: PO Box 1709, MONTROSE, CO, 81402-1709
Telephone: (970) 249-2620
Fax Number: (972) 970-0892
Type of Business: Chain Restaurant Operator
Year Founded: 1989
Total Sales: $8,943,000 (e)
Number of Employees: 65
Average Check: Lunch(8); Dinner(8)
Total Units: 3
Trade Names: Taco Bell (3)
Units Franchised From: 3
Preferred Location Types: Freestanding
Primary Menu: Taco (3)
Areas of Operation: CO
Type of Foodservice: Quick Serve (3)
Franchise Affiliation: Taco Bell Corp., IRVINE, CA
Primary Distributors: (Full Line) McLane /Aurora, COMMERCE CITY, CO

Key Personnel
PATRICIA ROTHE - President; General Buyer
MICHELLE ROTHE - VP Operations, Distribution
TROY ROTHE - Manager Region

Domino's Franchisee
481 W Highway 105 Unit 200
Monument, CO 80132-9128

Telephone: (719) 219-0603
Type of Business: Chain Restaurant Operator
Total Sales: $22,884,000 (e)
Total Units: 11
Trade Names: Domino's (11)
Units Franchised From: 11
Primary Menu: Pizza (11)
Areas of Operation: CO
Type of Foodservice: Quick Serve (11)
Franchise Affiliation: Domino's Pizza Inc, ANN ARBOR, MI

Key Personnel
ANTHONY S. MAND - Owner; General Buyer

Cinzetti's Italian Market Restaurants
281 W 104th Ave
Northglenn, CO 80234-4103

Telephone: (303) 451-7300
Fax Number: (303) 451-8300
Internet Homepage: slatebridge.com; cinzzettis.com
Type of Business: Chain Restaurant Operator
Average Check: Lunch(8); Dinner(20)
Total Units: 5
Trade Names: Cinzetti's Italian Market Restaurant (2); The White Chocolate Grill (3)
Company-Owned Units: 5
Preferred Location Types: Freestanding; Strip Mall
Alcohol Served: Beer, Wine, Liquor
Primary Menu: American (3); Italian (2)
Areas of Operation: AZ, CO, KS
Type of Foodservice: Casual Dining (5)

Key Personnel
DAVID MEREDITH - General Manager; General Buyer
BRYANT CROSS - Executive Chef; General Buyer

Homer's Pizza, INC.
PO Box 497
Pueblo, CO 81002-0497

Telephone: (719) 545-8437
Fax Number: (719) 543-8620
Company Email: lcp238@aol.com
Type of Business: Chain Restaurant Operator
Total Sales: $4,189,000 (e)
Number of Employees: 150
Total Units: 7
Trade Names: Little Caesars Pizza (7)
Units Franchised From: 7
Preferred Location Types: Strip Mall
Primary Menu: Pizza (7)
Areas of Operation: CO
Type of Foodservice: Quick Serve (7)
Catering Services: Yes
Franchise Affiliation: Little Caesar Enterprises Inc., DETROIT, MI

Key Personnel
DAVE FEAMSTER - Owner; Executive Chef; General Buyer

Napier Enterprises Inc.
3901 Outlook Blvd Ste B
Pueblo, CO 81008-1696

Telephone: (719) 542-2913
Fax Number: (719) 542-2936

Type of Business: Chain Restaurant Operator
Year Founded: 1986
Total Sales: $20,058,000 (e)
Number of Employees: 170
Average Check: Breakfast(6); Lunch(8); Dinner(8)
Total Units: 4
Trade Names: McDonald's (4)
Units Franchised From: 4
Preferred Square Footage: 2,500; 3,000
Preferred Location Types: Freestanding
Primary Menu: Hamburger (4)
Areas of Operation: CO
Type of Foodservice: Quick Serve (4)
Franchise Affiliation: McDonald's Corporation, CHICAGO, IL
Primary Distributors: (Food) Mile Hi Foods, DENVER, CO

Key Personnel
DAVID M. NAPIER - President; General Manager; General Buyer

Stan Rivera Inc
1707 S Pueblo Blvd
Pueblo, CO 81005-2103

Telephone: (719) 561-1228
Type of Business: Chain Restaurant Operator
Total Sales: $4,372,000 (e)
Total Units: 2
Trade Names: Village Inn (2)
Units Franchised From: 2
Primary Menu: American (2)
Areas of Operation: CO
Type of Foodservice: Family Restaurant (2)
Franchise Affiliation: Village Inn, MINNETONKA, MN

Key Personnel
STANLEY RIVERA - President; General Buyer

Subway Franchise
3216 W Northern Ave
Pueblo, CO 81005-2250

Telephone: (719) 564-8121
Internet Homepage: subway.com
Type of Business: Chain Restaurant Operator
Total Sales: $2,745,000 (e)
Total Units: 4
Trade Names: Subway (4)
Units Franchised From: 4
Primary Menu: Sandwiches/Deli (4)
Areas of Operation: CO
Type of Foodservice: Quick Serve (4)
Franchise Affiliation: Doctor's Associates Inc., MILFORD, CT

Key Personnel
JOE DELAO - President

CAH Enterprises
214 W Main St
Sterling, CO 80751-3143

Telephone: (970) 522-1407
Fax Number: (970) 522-4561
Type of Business: Chain Restaurant Operator
Total Sales: $15,163,000 (e)
Total Units: 3
Trade Names: McDonald's (3)
Units Franchised From: 3
Primary Menu: Hamburger (3)
Areas of Operation: CO
Type of Foodservice: Quick Serve (3)
Franchise Affiliation: McDonald's Corporation, CHICAGO, IL

Key Personnel
DIANE SPAURGE - Owner; General Buyer
RACHELLE FONG - Director

Desert Dough Company, Inc.
5781 E 128th Ave Ste 110
Thornton, CO 80602-8058

Telephone: (720) 542-8026
Type of Business: Chain Restaurant Operator
Total Sales: $2,010,000 (e)
Total Units: 3
Trade Names: Little Caesars Pizza (3)
Units Franchised From: 3
Primary Menu: Pizza (3)
Areas of Operation: CO
Type of Foodservice: Quick Serve (3)
Franchise Affiliation: Little Caesar Enterprises Inc., DETROIT, MI

Key Personnel
BRIAN FLEMING - President; General Buyer
NICK SCHOLL - General Manager

Moe's Original Franchise System
PO Box 2512
Vail, CO 81658-2512

Telephone: (970) 328-0177
Internet Homepage: moesoriginalbbq.com
Company Email: info@moesoriginalbbq.com
Type of Business: Chain Restaurant Operator
Year Founded: 2001
Average Check: Lunch(14); Dinner(14)
Total Units: 65
Trade Names: Moe's Original Bar B Que (65)
Company-Owned Units: 65
Alcohol Served: Beer, Wine, Liquor
Primary Menu: Bar-B-Q (65)
Projected Openings: 2
Areas of Operation: AL, CA, CO, FL, GA, LA, ME, MS, MT, NC, NM, OH, SC, TN, VA, WY, FC
Type of Foodservice: Quick Serve (65)
Catering Services: Yes

Key Personnel
BEN GILBERT - Co-Founder
MIKE FERNANDEZ - Co-Founder
JEFF KENNEDY - Co-Founder
ARIN OLIVER - Coordinator Marketing

Sonnenalp Resort
20 Vail Rd
Vail, CO 81657-5010

Telephone: (970) 476-5656
Fax Number: (970) 479-5422
Internet Homepage: sonnenalp.com
Company Email: info@sonnenalp.com
Type of Business: Foodservice Operations - Hotel/Motels
Year Founded: 1978
Total Sales: $17,794,000 (e)
Alcohol Sales: 15%
Number of Employees: 450
Total Units: 1
Restaurants in Hotels: 4
Trade Names: Sonnenalp Hotel (1)
Company-Owned Units: 4
Alcohol Served: Beer, Wine, Liquor
Areas of Operation: CO
Foreign Countries: GERMANY
Type of Foodservice: Casual Dining (4)
Primary Distributors: (Food) SYSCO Food Services of Denver, DENVER, CO; (Specialty Foods) US Foods, CENTENNIAL, CO
Notes: The company derives approximately 80% of its revenue from resort operations. Restaurants within the hotel include: Swiss Chalet, Bully Ranch, Balata and Ludwig's.

Key Personnel
JOHANNES FAESSLER - Owner; General Manager; Director Purchasing; General Buyer
JOHN MILLS - CFO; Controller; Manager Finance
SARAH BRENT - Director Advertising, Promotion

Blackjack Pizza Franchising, Inc.
9070 Marshall Ct
Westminster, CO 80031-2920

Telephone: (303) 426-1921
Fax Number: (303) 428-0174

Internet Homepage: blackjackpizza.com
Type of Business: Chain Restaurant Operator
Year Founded: 1983
Systemwide Sales: $49,652,000 (e)
Total Sales: $3,962,000 (e)
Number of Employees: 15
Average Check: Lunch(12); Dinner(20)
Internet Order Processing: Yes
Internet Sales: 1.00%
Total Units: 42
Trade Names: Blackjack Pizza (42)
Units Franchised To: 42
Preferred Square Footage: 2,500
Preferred Location Types: Strip Mall
Primary Menu: Pizza (42)
Projected Openings: 2
Areas of Operation: AZ, CO, MT, WY
Type of Foodservice: Quick Serve (42)
Primary Distributors: (Full Line) Shamrock Foods Colorado Division, COMMERCE CITY, CO

Key Personnel
MARK MALSAM - Director Operations, Purchasing, Facility/Maintenance, Marketing, Menu Development
AMBER RUDIN - Director Accounting
DANIEL ZUK - Regional Manager Operations

Bodan Inc./Group W Partners LLC
960 W 124th Ave Ste 400
Westminster, CO 80234-1722

Telephone: (303) 530-3515
Fax Number: (303) 530-3516
Type of Business: Chain Restaurant Operator
Total Sales: $114,010,000 (e)
Number of Employees: 1,615
Average Check: Lunch(8); Dinner(12)
Total Units: 42
Trade Names: Wendy's Old Fashioned Hamburgers (42)
Units Franchised From: 42
Preferred Square Footage: 3,000
Preferred Location Types: Freestanding
Primary Menu: Hamburger (42)
Areas of Operation: CO, OR, WA
Type of Foodservice: Quick Serve (42)
Franchise Affiliation: The Wendy's Company, DUBLIN, OH

Key Personnel
DANIEL O'BRIEN - President; Partner; Director Finance, Operations, Purchasing, Facility/Maintenance, Information Systems, Real Estate
HOWARD O'BRIEN - Partner
STEVE HARRIS - COO
DOUG RICH - Director Operations, Technology

Boselli Investments
1130 W 124th Ave Ste 1100
Westminster, CO 80234-1714

Telephone: (303) 427-0915
Fax Number: (303) 428-6480
Company Email: rlundmcd@gmail.com
Type of Business: Chain Restaurant Operator
Year Founded: 1997
Total Sales: $66,560,000 (e)
Number of Employees: 800
Average Check: Breakfast(8); Lunch(10); Dinner(10)
Total Units: 14
Trade Names: McDonald's (14)
Units Franchised From: 14
Preferred Square Footage: 2,500
Preferred Location Types: Convenience Store/Gas Station; Discount Dept. Stores; Freestanding
Primary Menu: Hamburger (14)
Projected Remodelings: 4
Areas of Operation: CO
Type of Foodservice: Quick Serve (14)
Franchise Affiliation: McDonald's Corporation, CHICAGO, IL
Primary Distributors: (Food) The Martin-Brower Co., SALT LAKE CITY, UT

Key Personnel
DON ANTHONY BOSELLI - President; Director Supply Chain, Real Estate, Design; General Buyer
ALEXANDRA RIOS - Manager Customer Service

Clara Corporation
4855 Ward Rd Ste 600
Wheat Ridge, CO 80033-1953

Telephone: (303) 232-3390
Fax Number: (303) 232-9756
Type of Business: Chain Restaurant Operator
Year Founded: 1980
Total Sales: $37,860,000 (e)
Number of Employees: 400
Average Check: Breakfast(8); Lunch(10); Dinner(10)
Total Units: 8
Trade Names: McDonald's (8)
Units Franchised From: 8
Preferred Square Footage: 2,500; 3,000
Preferred Location Types: Discount Dept. Stores; Freestanding
Primary Menu: Hamburger (8)
Areas of Operation: CO
Type of Foodservice: Quick Serve (8)
Franchise Affiliation: McDonald's Corporation, CHICAGO, IL
Primary Distributors: (Food) Mile Hi Foods, DENVER, CO

Key Personnel
FRANK SANDOVAL - Owner; General Buyer

Mountainside Pizza Inc.
3890 Kipling St Ste B
Wheat Ridge, CO 80033-4141

Telephone: (303) 989-8390
Type of Business: Chain Restaurant Operator
Year Founded: 1976
Total Sales: $86,783,000 (e)
Number of Employees: 872
Average Check: Lunch(16); Dinner(30)
Total Units: 42
Trade Names: Domino's (42)
Units Franchised From: 42
Preferred Square Footage: 1,750
Preferred Location Types: Freestanding; Stadiums; Strip Mall
Primary Menu: Pizza (42)
Areas of Operation: CO, TX
Type of Foodservice: Quick Serve (42)
Franchise Affiliation: Domino's Pizza Inc, ANN ARBOR, MI
Primary Distributors: (Full Line) Domino's Distribution Center, DENVER, CO

Key Personnel
BRENT HAMILL - President; General Buyer
STEVE JONES - VP Operations

Domino's Franchisee
1555 Main St Unit A1
Windsor, CO 80550-5999

Telephone: (970) 686-5500
Type of Business: Chain Restaurant Operator
Total Sales: $16,017,000 (e)
Total Units: 8
Trade Names: Domino's (8)
Units Franchised From: 8
Primary Menu: Pizza (8)
Areas of Operation: CO
Type of Foodservice: Quick Serve (8)
Franchise Affiliation: Domino's Pizza Inc, ANN ARBOR, MI

Key Personnel
BRIAN DELGROSSO - Owner; General Buyer

Rocky Mountain Business Ventures
1220 W Ash St Unit B
Windsor, CO 80550-4611

Telephone: (970) 686-2949

Fax Number: (970) 686-2959
Company Email: rockymtnbv@msn.com
Type of Business: Chain Restaurant Operator
Total Sales: $1,482,000 (e)
Alcohol Sales: 20%
Number of Employees: 46
Average Check: Breakfast(12); Lunch(12); Dinner(12)
Total Units: 3
Trade Names: Subway (3)
Units Franchised From: 3
Preferred Square Footage: 2,200; 2,400
Preferred Location Types: Freestanding; Strip Mall
Primary Menu: Sandwiches/Deli (3)
Areas of Operation: CO
Type of Foodservice: Quick Serve (3)
Catering Services: Yes
Franchise Affiliation: Doctor's Associates Inc., MILFORD, CT

Key Personnel
STEVE LAUER - President; General Buyer

CONNECTICUT

Domino's Franchisee
137 N Main St
Ansonia, CT 06401-1629

Telephone: (203) 732-3030
Company Email: nbspizza@yahoo.com
Type of Business: Chain Restaurant Operator
Total Sales: $4,019,000 (e)
Total Units: 2
Trade Names: Domino's (2)
Units Franchised From: 2
Primary Menu: Pizza (2)
Areas of Operation: CT
Type of Foodservice: Quick Serve (2)
Franchise Affiliation: Domino's Pizza Inc, ANN ARBOR, MI

Key Personnel
NASIR U. AHMAD - Owner; General Buyer

McDonald's Franchise
185 New Britain Rd
Berlin, CT 06037-1353

Telephone: (860) 224-0501
Type of Business: Chain Restaurant Operator
Total Sales: $23,410,000 (e)
Average Check: Dinner(12)
Total Units: 5
Trade Names: McDonald's (5)
Units Franchised From: 5
Preferred Square Footage: 2,500
Preferred Location Types: Downtown; Freestanding

Primary Menu: Hamburger (5)
Areas of Operation: CT
Type of Foodservice: Quick Serve (5)
Franchise Affiliation: McDonald's Corporation, CHICAGO, IL

Key Personnel
NICHOLAS HASKOS - President; Partner; General Buyer
JOHN HASKOS - Partner

DM Burritos, LLC
1060 W Main St
Branford, CT 06405-3441

Telephone: (203) 433-4092
Type of Business: Chain Restaurant Operator
Total Sales: $6,844,000 (e)
Total Units: 4
Trade Names: Moe's Southwest Grill (4)
Units Franchised From: 4
Primary Menu: Southwest/Tex-Mex (4)
Areas of Operation: CT
Type of Foodservice: Fast Casual (4)
Franchise Affiliation: Moe's Southwest Grill LLC, ATLANTA, GA

Key Personnel
MATTHEW RUSCONI - Owner; General Buyer

Dunkin' Donuts Franchise
529 North Ave Ste D
Bridgeport, CT 06606-5746

Telephone: (203) 331-1945
Internet Homepage: dunkindonuts.com
Type of Business: Chain Restaurant Operator
Total Sales: $10,900,000 (e)
Number of Employees: 100
Average Check: Dinner(8)
Total Units: 7
Trade Names: Dunkin' Donuts (7)
Units Franchised From: 7
Preferred Square Footage: 1,500; 2,200
Preferred Location Types: Freestanding; Strip Mall
Primary Menu: Snacks (7)
Areas of Operation: CT
Type of Foodservice: Quick Serve (7)
Franchise Affiliation: DD IP Holder, CANTON, MA

Key Personnel
BANGALORE MAHESH - President; General Manager; General Buyer

Trefz Corporation
10 Middle St Ste 17
Bridgeport, CT 06604-4257

Telephone: (203) 367-3621
Fax Number: (203) 339-4141
Type of Business: Chain Restaurant Operator
Year Founded: 1964
Total Sales: $227,100,000 (e)
Number of Employees: 2,440
Average Check: Breakfast(8); Lunch(8); Dinner(8)
Total Units: 48
Trade Names: McDonald's (48)
Units Franchised From: 48
Preferred Square Footage: 4,000
Preferred Location Types: Freestanding; Strip Mall
Primary Menu: Hamburger (48)
Areas of Operation: CT, NY
Type of Foodservice: Quick Serve (48)
Distribution Centers: STRATFORD, CT
Franchise Affiliation: McDonald's Corporation, CHICAGO, IL
Primary Distributors: (Food) SYSCO Food Services of Connecticut Inc., ROCKY HILL, CT

Key Personnel
CHRISTIAN C. TREFZ - CEO; President
ROBERT J. HULL JR - CFO; VP Loss Prevention, Risk Management, Quality Assurance, Supply Chain, Real Estate
PAUL TREFZ - Exec VP
MICHELE HUDSON - General Manager
MARIA CARLOS - Director Human Resources, Training; Manager Information Systems

Wenconn Inc.
75 John St Ste 2
Bridgeport, CT 06604-4330

Telephone: (203) 366-6442
Fax Number: (203) 368-6632
Type of Business: Chain Restaurant Operator
Year Founded: 1985
Total Sales: $20,372,000 (e)
Number of Employees: 230
Average Check: Lunch(8); Dinner(10)
Total Units: 7
Trade Names: Wendy's Old Fashioned Hamburgers (7)
Units Franchised From: 7
Preferred Square Footage: 1,500; 2,500
Preferred Location Types: Freestanding
Primary Menu: Hamburger (7)
Areas of Operation: CT
Type of Foodservice: Quick Serve (7)
Franchise Affiliation: The Wendy's Company, DUBLIN, OH
Primary Distributors: (Equipment) The

Wasserstrom Co., COLUMBUS, OH; (Food) The SYGMA Network Inc. - Pennsylvania, HARRISBURG, PA; (Supplies) The Wasserstrom Co., COLUMBUS, OH

Key Personnel
MARK LEVY - President; General Manager Finance, Human Resources; Manager Real Estate; General Buyer
JOHN TERWILLGER - Director Operations
CHRISTINA HEY - Manager Administration

WestConn Ltd
2308 Main St
Bridgeport, CT 06606-5321

Telephone: (203) 334-3030
Type of Business: Chain Restaurant Operator
Total Sales: $55,345,000 (e)
Total Units: 27
Trade Names: Domino's (27)
Units Franchised From: 27
Preferred Square Footage: 1,200
Primary Menu: Pizza (27)
Areas of Operation: CT, NY
Type of Foodservice: Quick Serve (27)
Franchise Affiliation: Domino's Pizza Inc, ANN ARBOR, MI

Key Personnel
ROB COOKSTON - President; General Manager

Domino's Franchisee
656 Farmington Ave
Bristol, CT 06010

Telephone: (860) 582-5100
Type of Business: Chain Restaurant Operator
Total Sales: $8,256,000 (e)
Total Units: 4
Trade Names: Domino's (4)
Units Franchised From: 4
Primary Menu: Pizza (4)
Areas of Operation: CT
Type of Foodservice: Quick Serve (4)
Franchise Affiliation: Domino's Pizza Inc, ANN ARBOR, MI

Key Personnel
MOHAMMED IQBAL - Owner; General Buyer

Dunkin' Donuts Franchise
855 Farmington Ave
Bristol, CT 06010-3922

Telephone: (860) 589-6002
Internet Homepage: dunkindonuts.com
Type of Business: Chain Restaurant Operator
Total Sales: $19,990,000 (e)
Average Check: Dinner(8)
Total Units: 13
Trade Names: Dunkin' Donuts (13)
Units Franchised From: 13
Preferred Square Footage: 1,500; 2,200
Preferred Location Types: Freestanding; Strip Mall
Primary Menu: Snacks (13)
Areas of Operation: CT
Type of Foodservice: Quick Serve (13)
Franchise Affiliation: DD IP Holder, CANTON, MA

Key Personnel
WILLIAM GHIO - President; General Buyer
JANET GHIO - VP; General Buyer

CT Heros
187 Highland Ave
Cheshire, CT 06410-2520

Telephone: (203) 250-9933
Type of Business: Chain Restaurant Operator
Total Sales: $1,525,000 (e)
Total Units: 2
Trade Names: Subway (2)
Units Franchised From: 2
Primary Menu: Sandwiches/Deli (2)
Areas of Operation: CT
Type of Foodservice: Quick Serve (2)
Franchise Affiliation: Doctor's Associates Inc., MILFORD, CT

Key Personnel
AAMIR ARIS - Owner; General Buyer
JIM HACKETT - General Manager

Jake's Franchising LLC
716 S Main St
Cheshire, CT 06410-3472

Telephone: (203) 439-7991
Fax Number: (203) 439-7992
Internet Homepage: unclewilliesbarbecue.com; waybackburgers.com
Company Email: comments@jakeshamburgers.com
Type of Business: Chain Restaurant Operator
Year Founded: 1991
Systemwide Sales: $11,658,000 (e)
Total Sales: $15,170,000 (e)
Number of Employees: 40
Average Check: Dinner(12)
Internet Order Processing: Yes
Total Units: 158
Trade Names: Uncle Willie's BBQ (2); Wayback Burgers (156)
Units Franchised To: 158
Preferred Square Footage: 1,200; 1,800
Primary Menu: Bar-B-Q (2); Hamburger (156)
Areas of Operation: CA, CO, CT, DE, FL, GA, IL, IN, MA, MD, MI, MN, NC, NH, NJ, NY, OH, OK, OR, PA, SC, TN, TX, VA, WA, WY, FC
Foreign Countries: ARGENTINA; BRUNEI; KUWAIT; MALAYSIA; MOROCCO; PAKISTAN; SAUDI ARABIA; SUDAN; THE NETHERLANDS
Type of Foodservice: Family Restaurant (2); Quick Serve (156)

Key Personnel
JOHN G. CARTER - Founder; CEO; Treasurer
JOHN EUCALITTO - President
JADE GIAMATTEI - Manager Marketing; Coordinator Marketing

Domino's Franchisee
142 E Putnam Ave
Cos Cob, CT 06807-2701

Telephone: (203) 661-2202
Company Email: goldcoastdominos@gmail.com
Type of Business: Chain Restaurant Operator
Total Sales: $4,133,000 (e)
Total Units: 2
Trade Names: Domino's (2)
Units Franchised From: 2
Primary Menu: Pizza (2)
Areas of Operation: CT
Type of Foodservice: Quick Serve (2)
Franchise Affiliation: Domino's Pizza Inc, ANN ARBOR, MI

Key Personnel
GEOSSREL CRUME - Owner; General Buyer

Green & Tonic
7 Strickland Rd
Cos Cob, CT 06807

Telephone: (855) 464-2638
Internet Homepage: greenandtonic.com
Company Email: hello@greenandtonic.com
Type of Business: Chain Restaurant Operator
Year Founded: 2010
Internet Order Processing: Yes
Total Units: 5
Trade Names: Green & Tonic (5)
Company-Owned Units: 5
Primary Menu: Health Foods (5)
Areas of Operation: CT
Type of Foodservice: Fast Casual (5)

Key Personnel
FAUSTO MIERES - President

EatRamen Holdings LLC
46 Mill Plain Road
Danbury, CT 06810

Telephone: (833) 333-7577
Internet Homepage: mechanoodlebar.com
Company Email: consummerrequest@mechanoodlebar.com
Type of Business: Chain Restaurant Operator
Year Founded: 2013
Total Sales: $8,810,000 (e)
Total Units: 10
Trade Names: Mecha Noolde Bar (10)
Company-Owned Units: 10
Primary Menu: Asian (10)
Areas of Operation: CO, CT, DC, MD, OH
Type of Foodservice: Fast Casual (10)

Key Personnel
RICHARD REYES - Founder; CEO
SCOTT PAVLICA - VP Finance, Accounting
MATTHEW T. NEHRENZ - Director Operations
BRIAN REILLY - Director Development
KELLY ZOLAD - Director Human Resources
JONATHAN RODRIGUEZ - Director Beverages

Salsa Fresca Mexican Grill
109 Federal Rd
Danbury, CT 06811

Telephone: (203) 456-3448
Internet Homepage: salsafrescagrill.com
Type of Business: Chain Restaurant Operator
Year Founded: 2008
Total Units: 10
Trade Names: Salsa Fresca Mexican Grill (10)
Company-Owned Units: 10
Primary Menu: Mexican (10)
Projected Openings: 98
Areas of Operation: CT, NY
Type of Foodservice: Fast Casual (10)

Key Personnel
SETH HIRSCHEL - Co-Founder
JOHN TUCKER - Co-Founder
ERIC FRIEDMAN - COO
LYNETTE MCKEE - Director Franchising
SARAH MILES - Manager

Cedar Mountain Management, Inc.
70 Old Kings Hwy N
Darien, CT 06820-4725

Telephone: (203) 656-3661
Fax Number: (203) 656-3668
Type of Business: Chain Restaurant Operator
Total Sales: $56,340,000 (e)
Total Units: 12
Trade Names: McDonald's (12)
Units Franchised From: 12
Preferred Square Footage: 2,500
Preferred Location Types: Downtown; Freestanding
Primary Menu: Hamburger (12)
Areas of Operation: NJ, NY
Type of Foodservice: Quick Serve (12)
Franchise Affiliation: McDonald's Corporation, CHICAGO, IL

Key Personnel
JIM LEWIS - President; General Buyer

Coromandel
25 Old Kings Hwy N #11
Darien, CT 06820

Telephone: (203) 662-1213
Fax Number: (203) 662-1215
Internet Homepage: coromandelcuisine.com
Company Email: jose@coromandelcuisine.com
Type of Business: Chain Restaurant Operator
Total Sales: $6,191,000 (e)
Average Check: Dinner(24)
Internet Order Processing: Yes
Total Units: 6
Trade Names: Coromandel (6)
Company-Owned Units: 6
Preferred Location Types: Downtown; Freestanding; Strip Mall
Alcohol Served: Beer, Wine, Liquor
Primary Menu: Indian (6)
Areas of Operation: CT, NY
Type of Foodservice: Casual Dining (6)
Catering Services: Yes

Key Personnel
NARASIMHA KOTHAPALLI - Senior VP; Global Operations

Domino's Distribution Center
14 International Dr
East Granby, CT 06026-9718

Telephone: (860) 653-8900
Fax Number: (860) 653-8914
Internet Homepage: dominos.com
Listing Type: Distribution Center
Type of Business: Chain Restaurant Operator
Number of Employees: 70
Areas of Operation: CT, MA, NH, NJ, NY, PA, RI, VT
Parent Company: Domino's Pizza Inc, ANN ARBOR, MI

Key Personnel
JOE ZIMMERMAN - Manager Warehouse

Dunkin' Donuts Franchise
1084 Main St
East Hartford, CT 06108-2240

Telephone: (860) 291-0677
Internet Homepage: dunkindonuts.com
Type of Business: Chain Restaurant Operator
Total Sales: $12,380,000 (e)
Number of Employees: 100
Average Check: Dinner(8)
Total Units: 8
Trade Names: Dunkin' Donuts (8)
Units Franchised From: 8
Preferred Square Footage: 1,500; 2,200
Preferred Location Types: Freestanding; Strip Mall
Primary Menu: Snacks (8)
Areas of Operation: CT
Type of Foodservice: Quick Serve (8)
Franchise Affiliation: DD IP Holder, CANTON, MA

Key Personnel
JIM ZAFIRIS - President; General Buyer

US Foods Companies
330 Roberts St Ste 100
East Hartford, CT 06108-3654

Telephone: (860) 290-1844
Type of Business: Chain Restaurant Operator
Year Founded: 1981
Total Sales: $19,030,000 (e)
Number of Employees: 400
Average Check: Breakfast(5); Lunch(8); Dinner(8)
Total Units: 6
Trade Names: Red Robin Gourmet Burgers & Spirits (6)
Units Franchised From: 6
Preferred Square Footage: 4,000
Preferred Location Types: Freestanding
Alcohol Served: Beer, Wine, Liquor
Primary Menu: Hamburger (6)
Areas of Operation: CT, MA
Type of Foodservice: Casual Dining (6)
Franchise Affiliation: Plamondon Companies Inc., FREDERICK, MD; Red Robin Gourmet Burgers Inc., ENGLEWOOD, CO; Sbarro Holdings LLC, COLUMBUS, OH
Primary Distributors: (Full Line) MBM Corporation, LANCASTER, PA

Key Personnel
RICHARD SHELDON - President; Controller; Director Finance, Purchasing, Marketing, Real Estate
ALTA BUTLER - Manager Human Resources

Alex Mercuri
1996 Post Rd
Fairfield, CT 06824-5720

Telephone: (203) 254-0321
Type of Business: Chain Restaurant Operator
Total Sales: $2,096,000 (e)
Total Units: 3
Trade Names: Subway (3)
Units Franchised From: 3
Primary Menu: Sandwiches/Deli (3)
Areas of Operation: CT
Type of Foodservice: Quick Serve (3)
Franchise Affiliation: Doctor's Associates Inc., MILFORD, CT

Key Personnel
ALEX MERCURI - President; General Buyer

Fairfield Creamery, LLC
2323 Black Rock Tpke
Fairfield, CT 06825-3220

Telephone: (203) 371-4111
Type of Business: Chain Restaurant Operator
Total Sales: $1,278,000 (e)
Total Units: 2
Trade Names: Cold Stone Creamery (2)
Units Franchised From: 2
Primary Menu: Snacks (2)
Areas of Operation: CT
Type of Foodservice: Quick Serve (2)
Franchise Affiliation: Kahala Brands, SCOTTSDALE, AZ

Key Personnel
ABID HUSSAIN - Partner
USMAN ASYED - Partner

G.F. Vasey Holdings, LLC
118 Conyers Farm Dr
Greenwich, CT 06831-2735

Telephone: (315) 292-8283
Type of Business: Chain Restaurant Operator
Total Sales: $56,320,000 (e)
Total Units: 28
Trade Names: Five Guys Burgers and Fries (28)
Units Franchised From: 28
Preferred Square Footage: 3,000
Primary Menu: Hamburger (28)
Areas of Operation: CT, MA, VT
Type of Foodservice: Fast Casual (28)
Franchise Affiliation: Five Guys Holdings Inc., LORTON, VA

Key Personnel
ROGER VASEY - Partner
SANDRA VASEY - Partner

Skal Restaurant Group
64 Greenwich Ave
Greenwich, CT 06830-5504

Telephone: (203) 861-6400
Fax Number: (203) 861-9009
Internet Homepage: caskrepublic.com; gingermanct.com; skalrestaurants.com; gingermangreenwich.com
Company Email: info@gingermangreenwich.com
Type of Business: Chain Restaurant Operator
Total Sales: $78,103,000 (e)
Alcohol Sales: 20%
Number of Employees: 90
Average Check: Lunch(14); Dinner(30)
Total Units: 4
Trade Names: Cask Republic (3); The Ginger Man (1)
Company-Owned Units: 4
Preferred Location Types: Freestanding
Alcohol Served: Beer, Wine, Liquor
Primary Menu: American (1); Miscellaneous (3)
Areas of Operation: CT
Type of Foodservice: Casual Dining (4)
Primary Distributors: (Full Line) Dairyland, The Chefs' Warehouse, BRONX, NY

Key Personnel
CHRISTIAN BURNS - Partner; General Manager; General Buyer
STEVEN SCHIFF - Partner
CHRISTY ZIRNHELD - CFO
STEVEN BEAN - Executive Chef; General Buyer
CARL CARRION - Director Culinary Operations
MARIO CONTACESSI - Director Operations

Abbott's Lobsters in the Rough
117 Pearl St
Groton, CT 06340-5763

Telephone: (860) 536-7719
Internet Homepage: costellosclamshack.com; abbottslobster.com
Company Email: info@abbottslobster.com
Type of Business: Chain Restaurant Operator
Year Founded: 1947
Total Sales: $5,758,000 (e)
Number of Employees: 60
Average Check: Lunch(24); Dinner(36)
Total Units: 2
Trade Names: Abbott's Lobsters in the Rough (1); Costello's Clam Company (1)
Company-Owned Units: 2
Preferred Location Types: Freestanding
Primary Menu: Seafood (2)
Areas of Operation: CT
Type of Foodservice: Family Restaurant (2)
Primary Distributors: (Food) US Foods, NORWICH, CT

Key Personnel
DEIDRA MEARS - Owner; General Manager; Executive Chef; Manager Menu Development; Buyer Beverages, Food, Foodservice Equip/Supplies

David Vorchheimer LLC
220 State Road 12
Groton, CT 06340

Telephone: (860) 405-9661
Type of Business: Chain Restaurant Operator
Total Sales: $14,530,000 (e)
Total Units: 9
Trade Names: Moe's Southwest Grill (9)
Units Franchised From: 9
Primary Menu: Southwest/Tex-Mex (9)
Areas of Operation: CT
Type of Foodservice: Fast Casual (9)
Franchise Affiliation: Moe's Southwest Grill LLC, ATLANTA, GA

Key Personnel
DAVID VORCHHEIMER - Owner; General Buyer

Ashley's Ice Cream Cafe Inc.
942 Boston Post Rd
Guilford, CT 06437-2750

Telephone: (203) 458-3040
Fax Number: (203) 458-3040
Internet Homepage: ashleysicecream.net
Type of Business: Chain Restaurant Operator
Year Founded: 1979
Total Sales: $3,689,000 (e)
Number of Employees: 45
Total Units: 5
Trade Names: Ashley's Ice Cream Cafe (5)
Company-Owned Units: 5
Preferred Location Types: Office Complex
Primary Menu: Snacks (5)
Areas of Operation: CT
Type of Foodservice: Quick Serve (5)
Catering Services: Yes
Distribution Centers: HAMDEN, CT
Primary Distributors: (Supplies) Gordon Food Service, TAUNTON, MA

Key Personnel
JOE AMETRANO - President; Executive Chef; Manager Franchising; General Buyer
BRIAN ANDERSON - Manager Quality Assurance, Food Safety

Domino's Franchisee
312 Farmington Ave
Hartford, CT 06105-3302

Telephone: (860) 246-8333
Type of Business: Chain Restaurant Operator
Total Sales: $6,238,000 (e)
Total Units: 3
Trade Names: Domino's (3)
Units Franchised From: 3
Primary Menu: Pizza (3)
Areas of Operation: CT
Type of Foodservice: Quick Serve (3)
Franchise Affiliation: Domino's Pizza Inc, ANN ARBOR, MI

Key Personnel
RAHMAN CHOWDHURY - Owner; General Buyer

Hartford Restaurant Group
30R Bartholomew Ave
Hartford, CT 06106

Telephone: (860) 206-6284
Fax Number: (860) 206-6251
Internet Homepage: hartfordrestaurantgroup.com
Type of Business: Chain Restaurant Operator
Year Founded: 2002
Total Sales: $25,430,000 (e)
Alcohol Sales: 12%
Number of Employees: 126
Total Units: 9
Trade Names: Wood-N-Tap (9)
Company-Owned Units: 9
Preferred Location Types: Downtown; Freestanding
Alcohol Served: Beer, Wine, Liquor
Primary Menu: American (9)
Areas of Operation: CT
Type of Foodservice: Casual Dining (9)

Key Personnel
PHIL BARNETT - Partner; Director Marketing
MIKE HAMLIN - Partner; Director Real Estate, Construction
DENISE VOJNICH - CFO
BRYAN DEMERS - Director Operations

J.D.S. Foods, Inc.
76 Brainard Rd
Hartford, CT 06114-1604

Telephone: (860) 524-9345
Fax Number: (860) 246-8856
Type of Business: Chain Restaurant Operator
Total Sales: $20,390,000 (e)
Number of Employees: 130
Total Units: 4
Trade Names: McDonald's (4)
Units Franchised From: 4
Preferred Square Footage: 2,500
Primary Menu: Hamburger (4)
Areas of Operation: CT
Type of Foodservice: Quick Serve (4)
Franchise Affiliation: McDonald's Corporation, CHICAGO, IL

Key Personnel
JUDY YOUNG - President; General Buyer

Locals 8 Restaurant Group
484 Farmington Ave
Hartford, CT 06105-3106

Telephone: (860) 231-9928
Internet Homepage: burgersbeerbourbon.com; locals8.com; mytisane.com; thehalfdoor.com
Company Email: guestrelations@burgersbeerbourbon.com
Type of Business: Chain Restaurant Operator
Total Sales: $12,090,000 (e)
Total Units: 13
Trade Names: b Restaurants (10); Butchers & Bakers (1); The Half Door (1); Tisane (1)
Company-Owned Units: 13
Primary Menu: American (3); Hamburger (10)
Areas of Operation: CT, DC, MA, VA
Type of Foodservice: Casual Dining (13)

Key Personnel
ALLIE GAMBLE - Founder; CEO
DARYL DEMARCO - VP Human Resources

Max Restaurant Group
249 Pearl St Fl 2
Hartford, CT 06103-2112

Telephone: (860) 522-9806
Fax Number: (860) 522-5705
Internet Homepage: maxrestaurantgroup.com
Company Email: maxmail@mrgct.com
Type of Business: Chain Restaurant Operator
Year Founded: 1986
Total Sales: $74,580,000 (e)
Alcohol Sales: 35%
Number of Employees: 565
Average Check: Lunch(28); Dinner(46)
Internet Order Processing: Yes
Internet Sales: 2.00%
Total Units: 11
Trade Names: Max A Mia (1); Max Amore (1); Max Burger (2); Max Downtown (1); Max Fish (1); Max's Oyster Bar (1); Max's Tavern (1); Savoy Pizzrria (1); The Cooper Restaurant (1); Trumbull Kitchen (1)
Company-Owned Units: 11
Preferred Square Footage: 5,500; 6,000
Preferred Location Types: Downtown; Freestanding; Other
Alcohol Served: Beer, Wine, Liquor
Primary Menu: American (3); Hamburger (2); Italian (2); Pizza (1); Seafood (2); Steak (1)
Areas of Operation: CT, FL, MA
Type of Foodservice: Casual Dining (1); Fast Casual (2); Fine Dining (8)
Foodservice Management Venues: Business & Industry
Catering Services: Yes
Primary Distributors: (Full Line) SYSCO of Boston, PLYMPTON, MA

Key Personnel
STEVEN ABRAMS - Partner; General Manager
MARK CONLEY - Partner; General Manager; Director Facility/Maintenance, Real Estate, Design
BRAD KARSKY - Partner; General Manager
VICKI ROSENTHAL - Partner
SCOTT SMITH - Partner; VP; Director Operations, Purchasing, Risk Management, Food Safety
JOHN THOMAS - Partner
KEVIN GILLESPIE - General Manager
ELISABETH GUARINO - General Manager
STEPHEN LUNDGREN - Executive Chef
CHRIS SHEEHAN - Executive Chef
HUNTER MORTON - Executive Chef
NATHANIEL WAUGAMAN - Executive Chef
BOBBY VENETIANER - Director Operations, Purchasing, Inventory
JILL WALLER - Director Human Resources
BRIAN MITCHELL - Director Beverages
SCOTT MONTEMERLO - Director Catering
JESSICA STALMACH - Manager Restaurant Operations; Coordinator Event Planning
AMY PURCELL - Manager Restaurant Operations
LAURA SLACK - Manager Event Planning

Peppercorn's Grill
357 Main St
Hartford, CT 06106-1824

Telephone: (860) 547-1714
Fax Number: (860) 724-7612
Internet Homepage: peppercornsgrill.com; piccoloarancio.com
Company Email: dcialfi@aol.com
Type of Business: Chain Restaurant Operator
Year Founded: 1989
Total Sales: $2,335,000 (e)
Alcohol Sales: 15%
Number of Employees: 25
Average Check: Lunch(18); Dinner(36)
Total Units: 2
Trade Names: Peppercorn's Grill (1); Piccolo Arancio Restaurant (1)
Company-Owned Units: 2
Preferred Location Types: Downtown
Alcohol Served: Beer, Wine, Liquor
Primary Menu: Italian (2)

Areas of Operation: CT
Type of Foodservice: Fine Dining (2)
Catering Services: Yes

Key Personnel
DINO CIALFI - President; Partner; General Manager; Executive Chef; General Buyer
SAL CIALFI - Partner; Executive Chef

The First & Last Tavern
939 Maple Ave
Hartford, CT 06114-2730

Telephone: (860) 956-5000
Fax Number: (860) 956-9783
Internet Homepage: firstandlasttavern.com
Company Email: thefirstandlasttavern@yahoo.com
Type of Business: Chain Restaurant Operator
Year Founded: 1932
Total Sales: $6,215,000 (e)
Alcohol Sales: 20%
Number of Employees: 85
Average Check: Lunch(10); Dinner(18)
Total Units: 6
Trade Names: The First & Last Bakery (1); The First & Last Tavern (5)
Company-Owned Units: 2
Units Franchised To: 4
Preferred Location Types: Freestanding
Alcohol Served: Beer, Wine, Liquor
Primary Menu: Italian (6)
Areas of Operation: CT
Type of Foodservice: Casual Dining (6)
Catering Services: Yes
Primary Distributors: (Food) SYSCO Food Services of Connecticut Inc., ROCKY HILL, CT

Key Personnel
CURT NEMARICH - Partner; Director Menu Development; General Buyer
RICH NEMARICH - Partner; General Buyer
JAIMIE KEHOE - General Manager

The Whole Donut Group
894 New Britain Ave
Hartford, CT 06106-3921

Telephone: (860) 953-3569
Fax Number: (860) 953-1692
Internet Homepage: thewholedonut.tripod.com
Company Email: thewholedonut@msn.com
Type of Business: Chain Restaurant Operator
Year Founded: 1950
Systemwide Sales: $1,482,000 (e)
Total Sales: $755,000 (e)
Number of Employees: 55
Average Check: Breakfast(6);
Total Units: 9
Trade Names: Whole Donut (9)

Units Franchised To: 9
Preferred Square Footage: 1,500; 2,000
Preferred Location Types: Freestanding; Strip Mall
Primary Menu: Snacks (9)
Areas of Operation: CT, MA
Type of Foodservice: Quick Serve (9)
Primary Distributors: (Full Line) US Foods, NORWICH, CT

Key Personnel
JOHN ALGIERE - President; VP Operations, Store Planning; Director Finance, Real Estate, Design, Human Resources
FRANK KROPF - CIO; Controller; Director Information Systems

The Boathouse at Lakeville
349 Main St
Lakeville, CT 06039

Telephone: (860) 435-2111
Fax Number: (860) 435-4543
Internet Homepage: fourbrotherspizzainn.com; theboathouseatlakeville.com
Type of Business: Chain Restaurant Operator
Year Founded: 1976
Total Sales: $9,002,000 (e)
Alcohol Sales: 5%
Number of Employees: 110
Average Check: Lunch(24); Dinner(42)
Total Units: 12
Trade Names: Four Brothers Pizzeria (9); The Boathouse at Lakeville (1); The Millerton Inn (1); Yiannis (1)
Company-Owned Units: 12
Preferred Square Footage: 5,500; 6,000
Preferred Location Types: Freestanding
Alcohol Served: Beer, Wine, Liquor
Primary Menu: American (3); Pizza (9)
Areas of Operation: CT, MA, NY
Type of Foodservice: Casual Dining (9); Fine Dining (3)
Catering Services: Yes
Primary Distributors: (Food) Ginsberg's Foods, HUDSON, NY

Key Personnel
PETER STEFANOPOULOS - Owner; Executive Chef; Manager Facility/Maintenance, Information Systems, Real Estate, Design, Menu Development, Catering; General Buyer
KEVIN HOHLA - General Manager

R&K Spero McDonald's
35 Cottage Rd
Madison, CT 06443-3426

Telephone: (203) 245-1604
Company Email: dickspero@aol.com
Type of Business: Chain Restaurant Operator

Total Sales: $46,370,000 (e)
Number of Employees: 402
Average Check: Dinner(12)
Total Units: 10
Trade Names: McDonald's (10)
Units Franchised From: 10
Preferred Square Footage: 2,500
Preferred Location Types: Downtown; Freestanding
Primary Menu: Hamburger (10)
Areas of Operation: CT
Type of Foodservice: Quick Serve (10)
Franchise Affiliation: McDonald's Corporation, CHICAGO, IL

Key Personnel
RICHARD SPERO - President; General Buyer
ELISE MINEO - Manager Administration

Batista Companies
57 S Broad St
Meriden, CT 06450-6544

Telephone: (203) 238-3482
Fax Number: (203) 238-3548
Type of Business: Chain Restaurant Operator
Total Sales: $23,380,000 (e)
Number of Employees: 380
Average Check: Breakfast(5); Lunch(8); Dinner(8)
Total Units: 15
Trade Names: Dunkin' Donuts (15)
Units Franchised From: 15
Preferred Square Footage: 1,500; 2,200
Preferred Location Types: Freestanding; Strip Mall
Primary Menu: Snacks (15)
Areas of Operation: CT
Type of Foodservice: Quick Serve (15)
Franchise Affiliation: DD IP Holder, CANTON, MA

Key Personnel
MICHAEL BATISTA - CEO; President; General Buyer
A.J. CORTEZ - Director Operations
MELISSA CORTEZ - Director Human Resources, Training
KRISTY PEREZ - Manager Information Technology

Frank Pepe's Development Company LLC
130 Research Pkwy Ste 212
Meriden, CT 06450-7152

Telephone: (203) 440-1924
Fax Number: (203) 440-0693
Internet Homepage: pepespizzeria.com
Company Email: kberry@pepespizzeria.com

Type of Business: Chain Restaurant Operator
Total Sales: $7,157,000 (e)
Alcohol Sales: 5%
Average Check: Dinner(14)
Total Units: 11
Trade Names: Frank Pepe Pizzeria Napoletana (11)
Company-Owned Units: 11
Alcohol Served: Beer, Wine
Primary Menu: Pizza (11)
Areas of Operation: CT, MA, NY
Type of Foodservice: Casual Dining (11)

Key Personnel
KEN BERRY - CEO; President; Partner; Executive Chef; General Buyer

Doctor's Associates Inc.
325 Sub Way
Milford, CT 06461-3081

Telephone: (203) 877-4281
Internet Homepage: subway.com
Company Email: franchise@subway.com
Type of Business: Chain Restaurant Operator
Year Founded: 1965
Systemwide Sales: $27,868,455,000 (e)
Total Sales: $1,420,402,000 (e)
Number of Employees: 400
Average Check: Breakfast(8); Lunch(8); Dinner(8)
Total Units: 35,982
Trade Names: Subway (35,982)
Units Franchised To: 35,982
Preferred Square Footage: 300; 800; 1,200; 1,500; 2,000
Preferred Location Types: Airports; Community Mall; Convenience Store/Gas Station; Discount Dept. Stores; Downtown; Freestanding; Grocery Stores; Hotel/Motel; Institution (college/hospital); Kiosk; Lifestyle Center; Mobile Unit; Office Complex; Other; Outlet Mall; Parks; Regional Mall; Stadiums; Strip Mall; Travel Plazas
Primary Menu: Sandwiches/Deli (35,982)
Projected Openings: 100
Projected Remodelings: 1,500
Areas of Operation: AK, AL, AR, AZ, CA, CO, CT, DC, DE, FL, GA, GU, HI, IA, ID, IL, IN, KS, KY, LA, MA, MD, ME, MI, MN, MO, MS, MT, NC, ND, NE, NH, NJ, NM, NV, NY, OH, OK, OR, PA, PR, RI, SC, SD, TN, TX, UT, VA, VI, VT, WA, WI, WV, WY, AB, BC, MB, NB, NL, NS, NT, ON, PE, QC, SK, YT
Foreign Countries: AFGHANISTAN; ANGUILLA; ANTIGUA; ARGENTINA; ARUBA; AUSTRALIA; AUSTRIA; BAHAMAS; BAHRAIN; BARBADOS; BELGIUM; BOLIVIA; BONAIRE; BRAZIL; BULGARIA; CANADA; CAYMAN ISLANDS; CHILE; CHINA; COLOMBIA; COSTA RICA; CURACAO; CYPRUS; CZECHREPUBLIC; DENMARK; DJIBOUTI; DOMINICA; DOMINICAN REPUBLIC; ECUADOR; EGYPT; EL SALVADOR; ENGLAND; FINLAND; FRANCE; GERMANY; GRENADA; GUATEMALA; HONDURAS; HONG KONG; HUNGARY; ICELAND; INDIA; IRELAND; ISLE OF MAN; ISRAEL; ITALY; JAMAICA; JAPAN;JORDAN; KENYA; KUWAIT; LEBANON; LIECHTENSTEIN; LITHUANIA; LUXEMBOURG; MACAO; MALAYSIA; MALTA; MARTINIQUE; MAURITIUS; MEXICO; NEW ZEALAND; NICARAGUA; NORTHERN IRELAND; NORWAY; OMAN; PAKISTAN; PANAMA; PERU; POLAND; PORTUGAL; QATAR; ROMANIA; RUSSIA; SAINT EUSTATIUS; SAINT KITTS AND NEVIS; SAINT MAARTEN; SAINT MARTIN; SAUDI ARABIA; SCOTLAND; SINGAPORE;SLOVAKIA; SLOVENIA; SOUTH AFRICA; SOUTH KOREA; SPAIN; ST. LUCIA; ST. VINCENT; SURINAME; SWEDEN; SWITZERLAND; TAIWAN; TANZANIA; THAILAND; THE NETHERLANDS; THE PHILIPPINES; TRINIDAD & TOBAGO; TURKEY; UNITED ARAB EMIRATES; URUGUAY; VENEZUELA; VIETNAM;WALES; ZAMBIA
Type of Foodservice: Quick Serve (35,982)
Foodservice Management Venues: Business & Industry; College & University; Health Care; Lodging; Military Feeding; Recreational; Schools; Transportation
Primary Distributors: (Full Line) SYSCO Food Services of Connecticut Inc., ROCKY HILL, CT

Key Personnel
CARRIE WALSH - CEO Interim; President International Division
CLAIRE SORABELLA - President Franchise Development
BEN WELLS - CFO; VP Consumer Insights
MIKE KAPPITT - COO
DAVE BLANKENSHIP - CIO
BILL MCCANE - Chief Development Officer
MIKE KEHOE - Chief Development Officer Global
ILENE KOLBERT - Chief Legal Officer
JOHN SCOTT - Chief Transformation Officer
MILLIE SHINN - Exec VP
PAUL FABRE - Senior VP Innovation
CHRISTINA WELLS - Senior VP Marketing
LISA SHEA - VP Human Resources
MICHELE DINELLO - VP Communications, Public Relations
NEVILLE HAMILTON - VP Strategy
MICHELE KLOTZER DINELLO - VP Communications, Public Relations
BRYAN HOOPER - VP Technology, Digital, Consumer Insights
TAYLOR BENNETT - VP Development
BARBARA MILLETTE - Senior Director
JEN MYERS - Director Marketing
LAURA SHEEHY - Director Talent Acquisitions
PATRICK ROSE - Director Design
JOE WAGNER - Director Franchise Sales
FEI YU - Director Digital
BARBARA BARTHOLOMEW - Director Accounting
MICHELLE CORDIAL - Director
DOUG LUCE - Director Operations, Infrastructure
DOUGLAS FRY - Director Canada
SANDRA LARKIN - Senior Manager Employee Development
KALONI ARCIDIACONO - Senior Manager Operations
MICHELLE FUOCO - Senior Manager Finance, Global
AMANDA JABLON - Senior Manager Human Resources, Compliance
KEVIN KANE - Manager Public Relations
ALISON GOLDBERG - Manager Communications
AMY COOPER - Manager Franchise Development
DAN TROXELL - Manager Information Systems, Information Technology
CARRIE FISCHER - Manager
DAVE CASWELL - Product Manager Digital
TIM MILLER - Project Manager Operations, International Division

American Steakhouse
477 Main St Unit 212
Monroe, CT 06468-1175

Telephone: (203) 261-4811
Fax Number: (203) 261-4070
Internet Homepage: americansteakhouse.com
Type of Business: Chain Restaurant Operator
Year Founded: 1968
Total Sales: $8,451,000 (e)
Alcohol Sales: 12%
Number of Employees: 250
Average Check: Lunch(12); Dinner(22)
Total Units: 3
Trade Names: American Steakhouse (3)
Company-Owned Units: 3
Preferred Square Footage: 5,500; 6,000
Preferred Location Types: Freestanding; Strip Mall
Alcohol Served: Beer, Wine
Primary Menu: Steak (3)
Areas of Operation: CT
Type of Foodservice: Casual Dining (3)
Primary Distributors: (Full Line) City Line Distributors, WEST HAVEN, CT

Key Personnel
ISABEL TARTAGLIA - CEO; Partner; Director Finance, Operations, Facility/Maintenance, Information Systems, Supply Chain, Real Estate, Human Resources
REMO TARTAGLIA - President; Partner; Director Purchasing, Menu Development
LORRAINE TARTAGLIA - Partner; VP

CK Restaurant Group
20 E Main St
Mystic, CT 06355-2646

Telephone: (860) 536-3228
Internet Homepage: olioct.com; bravobravoct.com; ckrestaurantgroup.com/olio
Company Email: info@bravobravoct.com
Type of Business: Chain Restaurant Operator
Total Sales: $4,532,000 (e)
Alcohol Sales: 15%
Number of Employees: 20
Average Check: Lunch(36); Dinner(60)
Internet Order Processing: Yes
Total Units: 2
Trade Names: Bravo Bravo (1); Olio's (1)
Company-Owned Units: 2
Preferred Location Types: Downtown; Freestanding
Alcohol Served: Beer, Wine, Liquor
Primary Menu: Italian (2)
Areas of Operation: CT
Type of Foodservice: Casual Dining (2)
Primary Distributors: (Food) SYSCO Food Services of Connecticut Inc., ROCKY HILL, CT

Key Personnel
CAROL KANABIS - President; General Manager
ANGELA KANABIS - General Manager; Executive Chef; General Buyer
JASON KOWALSKI - Corporate Chef
WILLIAM HALL - Executive Chef; General Buyer

New Haven Donuts Inc
255 Kimberly Ave
New Haven, CT 06519-2828

Telephone: (203) 789-0655
Type of Business: Chain Restaurant Operator
Total Sales: $46,760,000 (e)
Number of Employees: 100
Average Check: Dinner(8)
Total Units: 30
Trade Names: Dunkin' Donuts (30)
Units Franchised From: 30
Preferred Square Footage: 1,500; 2,200
Preferred Location Types: Freestanding; Strip Mall
Primary Menu: Snacks (30)
Areas of Operation: CT
Type of Foodservice: Quick Serve (30)
Franchise Affiliation: DD IP Holder, CANTON, MA

Key Personnel
PETER PACHECO - President; Partner; General Buyer
DALIA PACHECO - Partner; VP

The Halal Way CT LLC
906 Chapel St
New Haven, CT 06511

Telephone: (203) 691-5166
Type of Business: Chain Restaurant Operator
Total Units: 5
Trade Names: The Halal Guys (5)
Company-Owned Units: 5
Primary Menu: Middle Eastern (5)
Projected Openings: 2
Areas of Operation: CT, GA, NJ
Type of Foodservice: Quick Serve (5)
Franchise Affiliation: The Halal Guys Inc., ASTORIA, NY
Notes: Franchise Commitment: 10-15 Stores
Territory: CT, Northern NJ
Next Opening: Newark, NJ.
Targeted Area: Stamford, CT
Note: Partner Jack Yeung owns pharmacies in Southbury, Danbury and one in the Bronx.
Note: Owneship group consists of a dozen+ investors. Yeungs and Huda are the managing partners.
Phone Note: Number for New Haven HG location.

Key Personnel
JENAH YEUNG - Partner
NAZMUL HUDA - Partner

Domino's Franchisee
938 Bank St Ste 7
New London, CT 06320-2793

Telephone: (860) 442-9383
Type of Business: Chain Restaurant Operator
Total Sales: $6,134,000 (e)
Total Units: 3
Trade Names: Domino's (3)
Units Franchised From: 3
Primary Menu: Pizza (3)
Areas of Operation: CT
Type of Foodservice: Quick Serve (3)
Franchise Affiliation: Domino's Pizza Inc, ANN ARBOR, MI

Key Personnel
NUNO M. AMARAL - Owner; General Buyer

New Britain Donuts
66 Cedar St
Newington, CT 06111-2633

Telephone: (860) 666-1890
Fax Number: (860) 666-1034
Internet Homepage: jobsnewbritain.com
Type of Business: Chain Restaurant Operator
Year Founded: 1987
Total Sales: $31,090,000 (e)
Number of Employees: 150
Average Check: Breakfast(8); Lunch(8); Dinner(8)
Total Units: 20
Trade Names: Dunkin' Donuts (20)
Units Franchised From: 20
Preferred Location Types: Freestanding; Strip Mall
Primary Menu: Snacks (20)
Areas of Operation: CT
Type of Foodservice: Quick Serve (20)
Franchise Affiliation: DD IP Holder, CANTON, MA
Primary Distributors: (Food) SYSCO Food Services of Connecticut Inc., ROCKY HILL, CT

Key Personnel
CARY GAGNON - President; Controller; General Manager; General Buyer

Subway Subs of Connecticut Incorporated
75 Washington Ave Ste 1
North Haven, CT 06473-1728

Telephone: (203) 239-9659
Type of Business: Chain Restaurant Operator
Total Sales: $9,698,000 (e)
Total Units: 17
Trade Names: Subway (17)
Units Franchised From: 17
Primary Menu: Sandwiches/Deli (17)
Areas of Operation: CT
Type of Foodservice: Quick Serve (17)
Franchise Affiliation: Doctor's Associates Inc., MILFORD, CT

Key Personnel
AMIR ARIS - Owner; General Buyer

Cain Management Inc.
195 East Ave
Norwalk, CT 06855-1109

Telephone: (203) 854-9783
Fax Number: (203) 854-0323
Company Email: cmi@cainmanagementinc.com
Type of Business: Chain Restaurant Operator
Year Founded: 1975
Total Sales: $59,360,000 (e)
Number of Employees: 1,320
Average Check: Breakfast(14); Lunch(10); Dinner(10)
Total Units: 38
Trade Names: Dunkin' Donuts (38)
Units Franchised From: 38
Preferred Square Footage: 1,500

Preferred Location Types: Freestanding
Primary Menu: Snacks (38)
Projected Openings: 1
Areas of Operation: CT, NY
Type of Foodservice: Quick Serve (38)
Franchise Affiliation: BR IP Holder LLC, CANTON, MA; DD IP Holder, CANTON, MA
Primary Distributors: (Full Line) Dunkin' Donuts Distribution Center, BELLINGHAM, MA

Key Personnel
MARY CAIN - Partner; VP Operations, Information Systems, Supply Chain, Human Resources; General Buyer
SHEIKH MUNIRUZZAMAN - Director Operations

HEI Hotels and Resorts
101 Merritt 7 Ste 1
Norwalk, CT 06851-1060

Telephone: (203) 849-8844
Fax Number: (203) 849-5918
Internet Homepage: heihotels.com
Company Email: info@heihotels.com
Type of Business: Foodservice Operations - Hotel/Motels
Total Units: 72
Restaurants in Hotels: 81
Trade Names: Aloft (2); Crowne Plaza (1); Embassy Suites (5); Envue (1); Hilton (8); Holiday Inn Express (2); Hotel at Avalon (1); Hotel Chicago (1); Hotel Republic (1); Hotel RL (2); Hyatt (1); LE MÉRIDIEN (5); Marriott (4); Pullman (1); Red Lion Hotel (1); Residence Inn (1); Royal Palm South Beach (1); Sheraton (6); The Brown Palace Hotel (1); The Gwen (1); The Highland (1); The Inn (1); THE KIMPTON BRICE HOTEL (1); The Liberty (1); The Westshore Grand (1);The Whitley (1); W Chicago (1); W Hollywood (1); Westin (17)
Company-Owned Units: 72
Alcohol Served: Beer, Wine, Liquor
Projected Openings: 2
Projected Remodelings: 6
Areas of Operation: CA, CO, DC, FL, IL, IN, LA, MA, MN, MO, NJ, NV, NY, PA, TN, TX, VA, VT, WA
Type of Foodservice: Casual Dining; Fine Dining

Key Personnel
GARY MENDELL - Chairman
TED DARNALL - CEO Division
ANTHONY RUTLEDGE - CEO; Partner
STEVE MENDELL - President Business Development
CLARK HANRATTIE - Partner; CFO
NIGEL HURST - Exec VP Human Resources; Senior VP Human Resources
DAN WALWORTH - Exec VP
MARCUS HARRIS - Exec VP

BRIAN RUSSO - Senior VP Finance
BRAD KOCH - VP Information Technology

Bow Tie Cinemas LLC
641 Danbury Rd
Ridgefield, CT 06877-2738

Telephone: (203) 659-2600
Fax Number: (203) 659-2601
Internet Homepage: bowtiecinemas.com
Company Email: comments@bowtiecinemas.com
Type of Business: Foodservice Operations - Movie Theatre
Year Founded: 1936
Total Sales: $96,700,000 (e)
Internet Order Processing: Yes
Total Units: 32
Trade Names: Bow Tie Cinema (32)
Company-Owned Units: 32
Primary Menu: Snacks (32)
Projected Openings: 2
Areas of Operation: CO, CT, MD, NJ, NY, VA
Type of Foodservice: In-Store Feeder (32)

Key Personnel
CHARLES B. MOSS JR - Chairman; Partner
BEN MOSS - CEO; Partner
JOSEPH MASHER - COO
JENIFER PELLEGRINO - VP Human Resources

Golden Hawk LLC
2 Corporate Dr Ste 238
Shelton, CT 06484-6250

Telephone: (203) 926-6014
Type of Business: Chain Restaurant Operator
Total Sales: $82,970,000 (e)
Number of Employees: 750
Total Units: 18
Trade Names: McDonald's (18)
Units Franchised From: 18
Preferred Square Footage: 2,500
Primary Menu: Hamburger (18)
Areas of Operation: CT
Type of Foodservice: Quick Serve (18)
Franchise Affiliation: McDonald's Corporation, CHICAGO, IL

Key Personnel
ROGER FACEY - President; General Buyer

New Castle Hotels & Resorts
2 Corporate Dr Ste 154
Shelton, CT 06484-6246

Telephone: (203) 925-8370
Fax Number: (203) 925-8376

Internet Homepage: newcastlehotels.com
Company Email: info@newcastlehotels.com
Type of Business: Foodservice Operations - Hotel/Motels
Year Founded: 1980
Total Sales: $256,540,000 (e)
Alcohol Sales: 30%
Number of Employees: 3,344
Total Units: 22
Restaurants in Hotels: 22
Trade Names: Algonquin Resort (1); Cambria Hotel (1); Courtyard (2); Digby Pines Golf Resort and Spa (1); Digby Pines Resort (1); Fairfield Inn & Suites (1); Four Points (1); Hampton Inn (2); Hilton (1); Holiday Inn (1); Homewood Suites (1); Liscombe Lodge (1); Residence Hotel (3); SpringHill Suites (1); TheCraftsman Inn (1); Westin (2); Westport Inn (1)
Company-Owned Units: 22
Alcohol Served: Beer, Wine, Liquor
Projected Remodelings: 2
Areas of Operation: CT, ME, NJ, NY, OH, PA, VA, VT, WI, NS
Foreign Countries: CANADA
Type of Foodservice: Casual Dining (22)
Primary Distributors: (Food) SYSCO Food Services of Connecticut Inc., ROCKY HILL, CT
Notes: The company derives approximately 75% of its revenue from hotel operations.

Key Personnel
DAVID J. BUFFAM - Chairman; Founder
JEREMY BUFFAM - Partner
JULIAN BUFFAM - Partner
JUDI SCOFIELD - CFO; VP
BRYAN WOODHOUSE - VP; Controller
MARIAN R. BARBIERI - VP Human Resources
ANNA BARKER - VP Accounting
LISA BESESCHECK - Corporate Secretary; Manager Administration
BRIAN REYNOLDS - Controller Region
JOHN WILSON - Controller Region
NINA SELVAGGI - Director Accounting
DANIELA BURGA - Director Human Resources
GLENN BOWIE - Regional Director Marketing, Sales

Southport Brewing Company
819 Bridgeport Ave
Shelton, CT 06484-4714

Telephone: (203) 225-7734
Internet Homepage: sbcrestaurants.com; sittingducktavern.com; southportbrewing.com
Type of Business: Chain Restaurant Operator
Total Sales: $15,159,000 (e)
Alcohol Sales: 12%
Number of Employees: 144
Total Units: 4
Trade Names: Burrata Italian Kitchen (1); SBC Restaurant & Brewery (2); The Sitting Duck

Tavern (1)
Company-Owned Units: 4
Preferred Location Types: Freestanding; Strip Mall
Alcohol Served: Beer, Wine, Liquor
Primary Menu: American (4)
Areas of Operation: CT
Type of Foodservice: Casual Dining (4)
Catering Services: Yes

Key Personnel
BILL DASILVA - CEO; Partner; General Buyer
MARK DASILVA - President; Partner
DAVID RUTIGLIANO - Partner; Executive Chef

Between Rounds Franchise Corp.
19 John Fitch Blvd Ste A
South Windsor, CT 06074-4006

Telephone: (860) 291-0323
Fax Number: (860) 289-2732
Internet Homepage: betweenroundsbagels.com
Type of Business: Chain Restaurant Operator
Year Founded: 1990
Systemwide Sales: $9,939,000 (e)
Total Sales: $5,734,000 (e)
Number of Employees: 50
Average Check: Breakfast(8); Lunch(8); Dinner(8)
Total Units: 4
Trade Names: Between Rounds Bagel Deli & Bakery (4)
Company-Owned Units: 3
Units Franchised To: 1
Preferred Square Footage: 2,000; 2,500; 3,000
Preferred Location Types: Freestanding; Strip Mall
Primary Menu: Bagels (4)
Areas of Operation: CT
Type of Foodservice: Family Restaurant (4)
Catering Services: Yes
Primary Distributors: (Food) Thurston Foods Inc., WALLINGFORD, CT

Key Personnel
JERRY PUIIA - Owner; Executive Chef; Director Purchasing; General Buyer
JOSEPH PUIIA - VP; Director Finance, Operations, Supply Chain; Manager Information Systems
LAURIE PUIIA - Manager Operations

†
Centerplate Inc.
2187 Atlantic St Ste 6
Stamford, CT 06902-6890

Telephone: (203) 975-5900
Internet Homepage: centerplate.com
Company Email: info@centerplate.com
Type of Business: Foodservice Management Operator
Year Founded: 1929
Total Sales: $1,222,885,000 (e)
Number of Employees: 28,000
Number of Locations Served: 140
Total Foodservice Mgmt Accounts: 140
Trade Names: John Harvard's Brewery & Ale House (5); Sophie's (2)
Areas of Operation: CA, CO, CT, FL, IL, LA, MI, NY, SC, WA, FC, BC
Type of Foodservice: Full-service sit-down dining (140)
Foodservice Management Venues: Other; Sports Venues
Primary Distributors: (Food) SYSCO Corporation, HOUSTON, TX
Parent Company: Kohlberg & Co., MOUNT KISCO, NY
Notes: Centerplate's principal executive office is in Stamford CT, while the corporate headquarters is in Spartanburg SC.

Key Personnel
DAVID WINARSKI - Senior VP Human Resources
ERIC WOODEN - Senior VP
GIL LOGAN - Executive Chef

● ▲
Katsos Management
979 E Main St
Stamford, CT 06902-4109

Telephone: (203) 569-0156
Company Email: katsos979@yahoo.com
Type of Business: Chain Restaurant Operator
Total Sales: $15,530,000 (e)
Average Check: Lunch(6); Dinner(8)
Total Units: 10
Trade Names: Dunkin' Donuts (10)
Units Franchised From: 10
Preferred Square Footage: 1,500; 2,200
Preferred Location Types: Freestanding
Primary Menu: Snacks (10)
Areas of Operation: CT
Type of Foodservice: Quick Serve (10)
Franchise Affiliation: DD IP Holder, CANTON, MA

Key Personnel
LOUIS KATSOS - President; General Buyer

Marchetti Management Services
207 Main St
Stamford, CT 06901-2918

Telephone: (203) 967-3116
Fax Number: (203) 967-4724
Internet Homepage: marchettimanagement.com; tarantinorestaurant.com
Company Email: info@marchettimanagement.com
Type of Business: Chain Restaurant Operator
Year Founded: 1983
Total Sales: $8,303,000 (e)
Alcohol Sales: 25%
Number of Employees: 60
Average Check: Lunch(20); Dinner(38)
Total Units: 3
Trade Names: Columbus Park Trattoria's (1); Osteria Applausi (1); Tarantino's (1)
Company-Owned Units: 3
Preferred Location Types: Freestanding
Alcohol Served: Beer, Wine, Liquor
Primary Menu: Italian (3)
Areas of Operation: CT
Type of Foodservice: Casual Dining (3)
Catering Services: Yes
Primary Distributors: (Equipment) Best Restaurant Equipment Co., STRATFORD, CT; (Food) Jeraci Food Distributors Inc., ELMSFORD, NY; (Supplies) Jeraci Food Distributors Inc., ELMSFORD, NY

Key Personnel
MARIA MARCHETTI - President; Partner; Manager Human Resources
MICHAEL MARCHETTI - Partner; General Manager; Executive Chef; Director Food Safety, Catering; General Buyer
FRANK MARCHETTI - Partner; Director Food and Beverage
ANTONIO MARCHETTI SR - Partner; Director Facility/Maintenance

Siena
519 Summer St
Stamford, CT 06901-1314

Telephone: (203) 351-0898
Internet Homepage: sienastamford.com
Type of Business: Chain Restaurant Operator
Year Founded: 1997
Total Sales: $1,435,000 (e)
Total Units: 2
Trade Names: Siena (2)
Company-Owned Units: 2
Primary Menu: Italian (2)
Type of Foodservice: Fine Dining (2)

Key Personnel
PASQUALE CONTE - President; General Manager
EUGENE JEROME - Executive Chef; General Buyer

JTK Management Restaurants
3 Main St
Stonington, CT 06378-1411

Mailing Address: PO Box 203, MYSTIC, CT, 06355-0203
Telephone: (860) 536-3369
Internet Homepage: jtkmanagement.com
Company Email: info@jtkmanagement.com
Type of Business: Chain Restaurant Operator
Year Founded: 1973
Total Sales: $20,370,000 (e)
Alcohol Sales: 15%
Average Check: Lunch(14); Dinner(32)
Total Units: 4
Trade Names: Breakwater (1); Dock & Dine (1); Go Fish (1); Steak Loft (1)
Company-Owned Units: 4
Preferred Location Types: Freestanding
Alcohol Served: Beer, Wine, Liquor
Primary Menu: Seafood (3); Steak/Seafood (1)
Areas of Operation: CT
Type of Foodservice: Casual Dining (4)
Primary Distributors: (Full Line) SYSCO Food Services of Connecticut Inc., ROCKY HILL, CT

Key Personnel
JON KODAMA - President; General Manager; General Buyer
MARI KODAMA - General Manager
ANNIE BARNES - General Manager

Domino's Franchisee
1244 Storrs Rd
Storrs Mansfield, CT 06268-2200

Telephone: (860) 429-7969
Type of Business: Chain Restaurant Operator
Total Sales: $8,026,000 (e)
Total Units: 4
Trade Names: Domino's (4)
Units Franchised From: 4
Primary Menu: Pizza (4)
Areas of Operation: CT
Type of Foodservice: Quick Serve (4)
Franchise Affiliation: Domino's Pizza Inc, ANN ARBOR, MI

Key Personnel
NEIL A. WARREN - Owner; General Buyer

Trefz Distribution Center
849 Honeyspot Rd
Stratford, CT 06615-7140

Telephone: (203) 377-8955
Fax Number: (203) 375-6149
Listing Type: Distribution Center
Type of Business: Chain Restaurant Operator
Number of Employees: 14
Areas of Operation: CT, NY
Parent Company: Trefz Corporation, BRIDGEPORT, CT

Key Personnel
TERRY ROTAS - General Manager; Director Purchasing, Distribution, Transportation

Dunkin' Donuts Franchise
369 E Main St
Thomaston, CT 06787-1614

Telephone: (860) 283-6763
Internet Homepage: dunkindonuts.com
Type of Business: Chain Restaurant Operator
Total Sales: $30,000,000 (e)
Number of Employees: 160
Average Check: Dinner(8)
Total Units: 19
Trade Names: Dunkin' Donuts (19)
Units Franchised From: 19
Preferred Square Footage: 1,500; 2,200
Preferred Location Types: Freestanding; Strip Mall
Primary Menu: Snacks (19)
Areas of Operation: CT
Type of Foodservice: Quick Serve (19)
Franchise Affiliation: DD IP Holder, CANTON, MA

Key Personnel
MARIA ROCHA - President; General Buyer

Dunkin' Donuts Franchise
2210 Norwich New London Tpke
Uncasville, CT 06382

Telephone: (860) 848-1833
Internet Homepage: dunkindonuts.com
Type of Business: Chain Restaurant Operator
Total Sales: $7,693,000 (e)
Number of Employees: 145
Average Check: Dinner(8)
Total Units: 5
Trade Names: Dunkin' Donuts (5)
Units Franchised From: 5
Preferred Square Footage: 1,500; 2,200
Preferred Location Types: Freestanding
Primary Menu: Snacks (5)
Areas of Operation: CT
Type of Foodservice: Quick Serve (5)
Franchise Affiliation: DD IP Holder, CANTON, MA

Key Personnel
JANE COUTO - President; General Buyer

Mohegan Tribal Gaming Authority
1 Mohegan Sun Blvd
Uncasville, CT 06382-1355

Telephone: (860) 862-8000
Fax Number: (860) 862-3901
Internet Homepage: mohegansun.com
Company Email: information@mohegansun.com
Type of Business: Foodservice Operations - Casinos
Year Founded: 1990
Total Sales: $1,781,800,000 (e)
Alcohol Sales: 20%
Number of Employees: 10,635
Average Check: Breakfast(12); Lunch(28); Dinner(46)
Foodservice Sales: $124,726,000 (e)
Total Units: 41
Trade Names: Ballo Italian Restaurant & Social Club (1); Bean & Vine Cafe (1); Ben & Jerry's (1); Bobby Flay's Bar Americain (1); Bobby's Burger Palace (1); Bow & Arrow Sports Bar (1); Carlo's Bakery Sweet Room (1); Chick-fil-A (1); Chief's Deli (1); Comix (1); Dunkin' Donuts (2); Frank Pepe Pizzeria Napoletana (1); Geno's Bagels, Sweets and Subs (1); Geno's Fast Break (1); Geno's Pub (1); Hash House A Go Go (1); Imus Ranch Coffee (1); Jasper White's Summer Shack (1); Jasper White's Summer Shack Express (1); Jersey Mike's Subs (1); Jimmy Buffet's Margaritaville (1); Johnny Rockets (1); Johnny Rockets Express (1); Jumbo Oriental (1); Krispy Kreme Doughnuts (3); Landsdowne Irish Pub (1); Michael Jordan's 23 Sportscafe (1); Michael Jordan's Steak House (1); Pasta Vita (1); Seasons Buffet (1); SolToro Tequila Grill (1); Starbucks Coffee (1); Sticks & Stones (1); Sunrise Square (1); The Original SoupMan (1); Todd English'sTuscany (1); Tom's Urban (1); Wok On (1)
Company-Owned Units: 20
Units Franchised From: 21
Preferred Square Footage: 2,500; 5,500; 6,000
Preferred Location Types: Freestanding; Hotel/Motel; Other
Alcohol Served: Beer, Wine, Liquor
Primary Menu: American (11); Asian (2); Chicken (1); Coffee (2); Hamburger (2); Italian (4); Mexican (1); Miscellaneous (3); Pizza (1); Sandwiches/Deli (2); Seafood (2); Snacks (5); Steak (1)
Areas of Operation: CT, PA
Type of Foodservice: Casual Dining (16); Family Restaurant (5); Fast Casual (1); Fine Dining (4); Quick Serve (14)
Franchise Affiliation: Ben & Jerry's Franchising Inc., SOUTH BURLINGTON, VT; Jimmy Buffett's Margaritaville, KEY WEST, FL; Krispy Kreme Doughnut Corporation,

CHARLOTTE, NC; Ruth's Hospitality Group Inc., WINTER PARK, FL; Starbucks Corporation, SEATTLE, WA; The Johnny Rockets Group Inc., LAKE FOREST, CA; Wolfgang Puck Inc., LAS VEGAS, NV
Primary Distributors: (Full Line) SYSCO Food Services of Connecticut Inc., ROCKY HILL, CT
Headquarter Offices: Niagra Casinos, NIAGRA FALLS, ON CANADA
Notes: The company derives 93.5% of its revenue from casino & retail operations.

Key Personnel
KEVIN P. BROWN - Chairman
MARILYNN R. MALERBA - Chairman
RALPH JAMES GESSNER JR - Vice Chairman
ROBERT J. SOPER - CEO Division; President Division
ANTHONY MCGOWAN - CFO Division
RAY PINEAULT - COO Division; Exec VP Division
PATRICIA SMITH - Chief Human Resources Officer
KAWEL LAUBACH - Chief Human Resources Officer; Senior VP
TOM SMOCK - Chief Legal Officer; Senior VP
MICHAEL PALERMO - Senior VP Marketing
GARY LUDERITZ - Senior VP Business Development
GEORGE GALINSKY - Senior VP Marketing, Communications
TIM BAKER - Senior VP Architecture
JENNIFER BALLESTER - VP Communications
ANN BEINERT - VP Human Resources
JEFF HAMILTON - VP Human Resources
MIKE HAMILTON - VP Operations
SCOTT WELLS - VP; General Counsel
ERICA TESSIER - VP Marketing
BETHANY SEIDEL - VP Marketing, Promotion
HELEN ANN SHOCKEY - VP Supply Chain
PETER J. ROBERTI - VP Finance
DAVID ROME - VP; General Counsel
THAYNE D. HUTCHINS JR - Treasurer
DONALD ASSALONE - Director Global
SEAN MCMANUS - Director Finance
PAULA TYCIENSKI - Director Brand Marketing
JOHN WARE - Director Information Technology, Global
PAUL SURPRENANT - Director Purchasing
TRACEY WILSON - Director Compliance
LIZ JONES - Manager Communications
JACK CUMMINGS - Manager Purchasing
PETER SCHULTZ - Project Manager
AMY MONTGOMERY - Corporate Director Marketing

Domino's Franchisee
600 N Colony Rd
Wallingford, CT 06492-3168

Telephone: (203) 284-0500
Type of Business: Chain Restaurant Operator
Total Sales: $12,315,000 (e)
Total Units: 6
Trade Names: Domino's (6)
Units Franchised From: 6
Primary Menu: Pizza (6)
Areas of Operation: CT
Type of Foodservice: Quick Serve (6)
Franchise Affiliation: Domino's Pizza Inc, ANN ARBOR, MI

Key Personnel
MOHAMMED J. UDDIN - Owner; General Buyer

S & Z Enterprises
170 N Plains Industrial Rd
Wallingford, CT 06492-2337

Telephone: (203) 265-9798
Type of Business: Chain Restaurant Operator
Year Founded: 1975
Total Sales: $15,393,000 (e)
Number of Employees: 125
Average Check: Breakfast(8); Lunch(10); Dinner(12)
Total Units: 3
Trade Names: McDonald's (3)
Units Franchised From: 3
Preferred Square Footage: 2,500; 3,000
Preferred Location Types: Freestanding
Primary Menu: Hamburger (3)
Areas of Operation: CT
Type of Foodservice: Quick Serve (3)
Franchise Affiliation: McDonald's Corporation, CHICAGO, IL
Primary Distributors: (Full Line) The Martin-Brower Co., ENFIELD, CT

Key Personnel
THEODORE ZAFIRIS - President; General Buyer

Domino's Franchisee
77 Meriden Rd
Waterbury, CT 06705-1933

Telephone: (203) 755-8110
Type of Business: Chain Restaurant Operator
Total Sales: $16,607,000 (e)
Total Units: 8
Trade Names: Domino's (8)
Units Franchised From: 8
Primary Menu: Pizza (8)
Areas of Operation: CT
Type of Foodservice: Quick Serve (8)
Franchise Affiliation: Domino's Pizza Inc, ANN ARBOR, MI

Key Personnel
DAVID KEITHBELL - Owner; General Buyer

Frankie's Franchise Systems
378 Chase Ave Ste 302
Waterbury, CT 06704-1948

Telephone: (203) 756-2935
Fax Number: (203) 757-5361
Internet Homepage: frankieshotdogs.com
Type of Business: Chain Restaurant Operator
Year Founded: 1932
Systemwide Sales: $14,556,000 (e)
Total Sales: $7,827,000 (e)
Number of Employees: 69
Average Check: Lunch(12); Dinner(12)
Total Units: 8
Trade Names: Frankie's Family Restaurant (8)
Company-Owned Units: 2
Units Franchised To: 6
Preferred Square Footage: 3,000
Preferred Location Types: Freestanding; Strip Mall
Primary Menu: American (8)
Areas of Operation: CT
Type of Foodservice: Family Restaurant (8)
Primary Distributors: (Full Line) US Foods, NORWICH, CT

Key Personnel
FRANCIS CAIAZZO - General Manager

Wing It On Franchising, LLC
516 Frost Rd
Waterbury, CT 06705-2304

Telephone: (203) 574-2781
Internet Homepage: wingiton.com
Company Email: wio@wingiton.com
Type of Business: Chain Restaurant Operator
Year Founded: 2011
Total Units: 7
Trade Names: Wing It On! (7)
Company-Owned Units: 6
Units Franchised To: 1
Primary Menu: Chicken (7)
Projected Openings: 2
Areas of Operation: CT, NH, NJ
Type of Foodservice: Fast Casual (7)

Key Personnel
MATT ENSERO - Founder; CEO; Partner
MARC ROMANOW - VP Franchising

Sweet Dreams, LLC
909 Hartford Tpke Ste D7B
Waterford, CT 06385-4267

Telephone: (860) 447-0530
Type of Business: Chain Restaurant Operator
Total Sales: $1,175,000 (e)
Total Units: 2

Trade Names: Cold Stone Creamery (2)
Units Franchised From: 2
Primary Menu: Snacks (2)
Areas of Operation: CT
Type of Foodservice: Quick Serve (2)
Franchise Affiliation: Kahala Brands, SCOTTSDALE, AZ

Key Personnel
CHRIS ANATRA - Partner
CHRISTINE ANATRA - Partner

Waterford Hotel Group Inc.
914 Hartford Tpke Ste 100
Waterford, CT 06385-4276

Mailing Address: PO Box 715, WATERFORD, CT, 06385-0715
Telephone: (860) 442-4559
Fax Number: (860) 437-7752
Internet Homepage: waterfordhotelgroup.com
Company Email: info@waterfordhotelgroup.com
Type of Business: Foodservice Operations - Hotel/Motels
Year Founded: 1984
Total Sales: $67,560,000 (e)
Alcohol Sales: 10%
Number of Employees: 1,560
Total Units: 39
Restaurants in Hotels: 12
Trade Names: Aloft Beachwood (1); Andover Inn (1); Comfort Inn Piqua (1); Courtyard by Marriott (7); DoubleTree by Hilton (4); Fairfield Inn & Suites (2); Gettysburg Hotel (1); Hilton (3); Holiday Inn Express (1); Homewood Suites (1); Hyatt House (3); Inn on Boltwood (1); Marriott (1); Microtel Inn & Suites by Wyndham Uncasville (1); New Bedford Harbor Hotel (1); New Haven Village Suites (1); Ramada West Palm Beach Airport (1); Residence Inn (2); Sheraton (2); SpringHill Suites (1); The Williams Inn (1); Towne Place Suites (1); Westin Columbus (1)
Company-Owned Units: 11
Units Franchised From: 1
Alcohol Served: Beer, Wine, Liquor
Projected Remodelings: 6
Areas of Operation: AR, CT, FL, MA, NY, PA, RI
Type of Foodservice: Casual Dining (11); Quick Serve (1)
Franchise Affiliation: Starbucks Corporation, SEATTLE, WA
Primary Distributors: (Food) SYSCO Food Services of Connecticut Inc., ROCKY HILL, CT
Notes: The company derives approximately 70% of its revenue from hotel operations.

Key Personnel
LEN WOLMAN - Chairman; CEO
KAREN BACHOFNER - VP Sales
LISA BEERS - VP Public Relations
JOHN DELGROSSO - VP Technology, Engineering, Construction
MICHAEL HEATON - VP Operations; Director Food and Beverage
JUDY MORAN - VP Human Resources

Restaurant Bricco
78 Lasalle Rd
West Hartford, CT 06107-2303

Telephone: (860) 233-0220
Fax Number: (860) 233-7503
Internet Homepage: billygrant.com
Type of Business: Chain Restaurant Operator
Total Sales: $6,915,000 (e)
Alcohol Sales: 30%
Number of Employees: 20
Average Check: Dinner(42)
Total Units: 3
Trade Names: Bricco Trattoria (1); Grant's Restaurant and Bar (1); Restaurant Bricco (1)
Company-Owned Units: 3
Preferred Location Types: Strip Mall
Alcohol Served: Beer, Wine, Liquor
Primary Menu: American (1); Italian (2)
Areas of Operation: CT
Type of Foodservice: Fine Dining (3)
Catering Services: Yes
Primary Distributors: (Full Line) Napoli Foods Inc., CHESHIRE, CT

Key Personnel
MIKE GRANT - Partner
TONY GRANT - Partner
WILLIAM GRANT III - Partner; Executive Chef; General Buyer

ADT Pizza
20 Ketchum St
Westport, CT 06880

Telephone: (337) 289-0101
Fax Number: (866) 212-9238
Internet Homepage: pizzahut.com
Company Email: info@pizzahut.com
Type of Business: Chain Restaurant Operator
Year Founded: 1958
Total Sales: $140,750,000 (e)
Alcohol Sales: 3%
Number of Employees: 3,100
Average Check: Lunch(14); Dinner(20)
Internet Order Processing: Yes
Total Units: 115
Trade Names: Pizza Hut (115)
Units Franchised From: 115
Preferred Square Footage: 2,500
Preferred Location Types: Downtown; Freestanding; Strip Mall
Alcohol Served: Beer
Primary Menu: Pizza (115)
Projected Openings: 50
Areas of Operation: LA, NC, OH, SC, TX
Franchise Affiliation: Pizza Hut Inc., PLANO, TX
Primary Distributors: (Full Line) McLane/High Plains, LUBBOCK, TX

Key Personnel
ADAM DIAMOND - CEO; Partner
DAVID TETENS - Partner; COO
TYLER HEBERT - VP Operations
DANIELLE HUDSON - Director Training
DAVID LOCKWOOD - Director Operations
KAREN PANCZYK - Director Customer Service
ANGELA ROWE - Director Marketing, Sales
KEVIN DUNLAP - Director Loss Prevention, Risk Management
HENRY ELLIS - Director Operations
NICOLE FRANCIOL - Director Finance
WESLEY HARNETT - Director Operations
AMY YORK - Director Operations
BECKY BOCHABERI - Director Recruitment, People
SHALENA BROWN - Director Recruitment, People

Connecticut Wings Limited Partnership
1731 Berlin Tpke
Wethersfield, CT 06109-1303

Telephone: (860) 563-8083
Type of Business: Chain Restaurant Operator
Total Sales: $30,250,000 (e)
Total Units: 10
Trade Names: Hooters (10)
Units Franchised From: 10
Alcohol Served: Beer, Wine, Liquor
Primary Menu: American (10)
Areas of Operation: CT, MA, NY
Type of Foodservice: Casual Dining (10)
Franchise Affiliation: HOA Restaurant Group LLC, ATLANTA, GA

Key Personnel
MARK PHANEUF JR - President; General Buyer

Dunkin' Donuts of Wethersfield
225 Silas Deane Hwy
Wethersfield, CT 06109-1240

Telephone: (860) 563-5926
Fax Number: (860) 563-5247
Type of Business: Chain Restaurant Operator
Year Founded: 1982
Total Sales: $12,350,000 (e)
Number of Employees: 60
Average Check: Breakfast(8); Lunch(8); Dinner(8)

Total Units: 8
Trade Names: Dunkin' Donuts (8)
Units Franchised From: 8
Preferred Square Footage: 1,500; 2,200
Preferred Location Types: Freestanding
Primary Menu: Snacks (8)
Areas of Operation: CT
Type of Foodservice: Quick Serve (8)
Franchise Affiliation: DD IP Holder, CANTON, MA
Primary Distributors: (Full Line) SYSCO Food Services of Connecticut Inc., ROCKY HILL, CT

Key Personnel
MANUEL PINE - President; Partner; Controller
EDWARD PINE - Partner; General Manager; General Buyer

Hines Sudden Service
27 Town Line Rd
Wethersfield, CT 06109-4316

Telephone: (860) 563-8141
Fax Number: (860) 563-9792
Type of Business: Chain Restaurant Operator
Year Founded: 1968
Total Sales: $3,806,000 (e)
Number of Employees: 280
Average Check: Lunch(10); Dinner(12)
Total Units: 2
Trade Names: KFC (2)
Units Franchised From: 2
Preferred Square Footage: 3,000
Preferred Location Types: Freestanding
Primary Menu: Chicken (2)
Areas of Operation: CT
Type of Foodservice: Quick Serve (2)
Franchise Affiliation: KFC Corporation, LOUISVILLE, KY
Primary Distributors: (Food) McLane/Guilderland Center, GUILDERLAND CENTER, NY

Key Personnel
DAVID HINES - CEO; Director Finance, Information Systems, Real Estate; General Buyer
LOKMAN CHOWDHURY - President
ROBERT TOMLINSON - General Manager; Director Operations, Purchasing, Facility/Maintenance, Store Fixtures

Southpaw
245 Amity Rd
Woodbridge, CT 06525

Internet Homepage: southpaw.co
Type of Business: Chain Restaurant Operator
Year Founded: 2010

Key Personnel
JUDD WISHNOW - Founder; Co-CEO
ERICA S. WISHNOW - Founder; Co-CEO
JEFF STEWART - Exec VP East Division
PAUL FAUST - Exec VP West Region
DEEK VONDERHAAR - Exec VP Midwest Region, Mid-Atlantic Region

DISTRICT OF COLUMBIA

&pizza
1118 H St NE
Washington, DC 20002-4443

Telephone: (202) 733-1285
Internet Homepage: andpizza.com
Type of Business: Chain Restaurant Operator
Year Founded: 2012
Total Sales: $62,600,000 (e)
Total Units: 28
Trade Names: &pizza (28)
Company-Owned Units: 45
Preferred Location Types: Airports; Downtown; Stadiums
Primary Menu: Pizza (28)
Projected Openings: 50
Areas of Operation: DC, MA, MD, NY, PA, VA
Type of Foodservice: Fast Casual (28)

Key Personnel
MICHAEL LASTORIA - Founder
MIKE BURNS - CEO
PAUL DOUGHTY - Senior Director Facility/Maintenance, Construction
JULIAN ROBERT GONZALEZ - Director Finance
MARA FRISCH - Director People-Training

Booeymonger Inc.
3265 Prospect St NW
Washington, DC 20007-3215

Telephone: (202) 333-4810
Fax Number: (202) 333-8309
Internet Homepage: booeymonger.com
Type of Business: Chain Restaurant Operator
Year Founded: 1973
Total Sales: $7,858,000 (e)
Alcohol Sales: 10%
Number of Employees: 120
Average Check: Lunch(5); Dinner(6)
Internet Order Processing: Yes
Total Units: 4
Trade Names: Booeymonger (4)
Company-Owned Units: 4
Preferred Location Types: Freestanding
Alcohol Served: Beer, Wine
Primary Menu: Sandwiches/Deli (4)
Areas of Operation: DC, MD, VA
Type of Foodservice: Fast Casual (4)
Catering Services: Yes
Primary Distributors: (Full Line) SYSCO Food Services of Baltimore, JESSUP, MD

Key Personnel
RON VOGEL - President

Capital Restaurant Concepts Ltd.
1305 Wisconsin Ave NW Ste A
Washington, DC 20007-3346

Telephone: (202) 339-6800
Fax Number: (202) 339-6801
Internet Homepage: neyla.com; capitalrestaurants.com; gbrowns.com; j-pauls.com; oldglorybbq.com; paolosristorante.com
Company Email: crcinfo@capitalrestaurants.com
Type of Business: Chain Restaurant Operator
Year Founded: 1985
Total Sales: $30,230,000 (e)
Alcohol Sales: 30%
Number of Employees: 410
Average Check: Lunch(24); Dinner(36)
Internet Order Processing: Yes
Internet Sales: 1.00%
Total Units: 5
Trade Names: Georgia Brown's (1); J. Paul's (1); Neyla's Mediterranean Bistro (1); Old Glory (1); Paolo's (1)
Company-Owned Units: 5
Preferred Square Footage: 5,000
Preferred Location Types: Community Mall; Freestanding
Alcohol Served: Beer, Wine, Liquor
Primary Menu: American (2); Bar-B-Q (1); Greek/Mediterranean (1); Italian (1)
Areas of Operation: DC, MD, VA
Type of Foodservice: Casual Dining (5)
Catering Services: Yes
Primary Distributors: (Equipment) Adams-Burch Inc., LANDOVER, MD; (Food) SYSCO Food Services of Baltimore, JESSUP, MD; (Supplies) Adams-Burch Inc., LANDOVER, MD

Key Personnel
BECHARA NAMMOUR - Chairman; Owner; Director Information Systems
MARTIN CRAFT - CFO; Director Finance

Cava Group, Inc.
14 Ridge Square NW Suite 500
Washington, DC 20016

Telephone: (202) 400-2920
Internet Homepage: cava.com
Company Email: info@cavagrill.com

Type of Business: Chain Restaurant Operator
Year Founded: 2006
Publicly Held: Yes
Total Sales: $963,713,000 (e)
Number of Employees: 10,690
Total Units: 367
Trade Names: Cava Grill (367); Cava Mezze
Company-Owned Units: 367
Primary Menu: Greek/Mediterranean (367)
Projected Openings: 50
Areas of Operation: AL, AR, CA, CO, CT, DC, DE, FL, GA, IL, IN, KS, LA, MA, MD, MO, NC, NJ, NY, OK, PA, RI, SC, TN, TX, VA
Type of Foodservice: Fast Casual (367)

Key Personnel
TED XENOHRISTOS - Co-Founder
DIMITRI MOSHOVITIS - Co-Founder
BRETT SCHULMAN - CEO
TRICIA TOLIVAR - CFO
MARK BERINATO - Senior VP Digital
TODD BROOKS - Controller
MARA XENOHRISTOS - Director Event Planning
REED ARMSTRONG - Director Culinary Development
PARKER MIDDLETON - Senior Manager Real Estate
PARIS JACKSON - Manager Operations, Technology
MATT COIT - Coordinator Real Estate

Clyde's Restaurant Group
3236 M St NW
Washington, DC 20007-3615

Telephone: (202) 333-9180
Fax Number: (202) 625-7429
Internet Homepage: clydes.com
Company Email: info@clydes.com
Type of Business: Chain Restaurant Operator
Year Founded: 1963
Total Sales: $133,460,000 (e)
Alcohol Sales: 20%
Number of Employees: 1,500
Average Check: Breakfast(14); Lunch(18); Dinner(30)
Internet Order Processing: Yes
Internet Sales: 5.00%
Total Units: 12
Trade Names: 1789 Restaurant (1); Clyde's (7); Clyde's Willow Creek Farm (1); Old Ebbitt Grill (1); The Hamilton (1); The Tombs (1)
Company-Owned Units: 12
Preferred Square Footage: 10,000; 17,000; 25,000
Preferred Location Types: Freestanding; Office Complex
Alcohol Served: Beer, Wine, Liquor
Primary Menu: American (12)
Areas of Operation: DC, MD, VA
Type of Foodservice: Casual Dining (8); Fine Dining (4)

Primary Distributors: (Full Line) US Foods, MANASSAS, VA
Parent Company: Graham Holdings Co., ARLINGTON, VA

Key Personnel
JEFFREY OWENS - CFO
JOHN MCDONNELL - COO
KATIE BARONGAN - VP Human Resources
TAMUREI MOORE - Assistant Controller
STEPHEN LYONS - Corporate Chef
DANIEL AHN - Executive Chef
RYAN WILLIAMS - Executive Chef
KEVIN KELLER - Director Operations
BRIAN ZIPIN - Director Alcoholic Beverages
DESTINY KIBALAMA - Director Human Resources, Recruitment
JOHN FILKINS - Director
MEGAN TRUDO - Director Event Planning
ANGELA BRIMAGE - Director Human Resources
DAVE STRZEMIENSKI - Director Information Technology
BONNIE PAIGO - Director Payroll
NOEL REYES - Manager Purchasing
EMMRICK MCCADDEN - Manager Marketing

Guac & Roll, LLC
1275 1st St NE Ste B
Washington, DC 20002-3218

Telephone: (703) 727-1197
Type of Business: Chain Restaurant Operator
Total Sales: $31,440,000 (e)
Total Units: 19
Trade Names: Moe's Southwest Grill (19)
Units Franchised From: 19
Primary Menu: Southwest/Tex-Mex (19)
Areas of Operation: DC, MD, VA
Type of Foodservice: Fast Casual (19)
Franchise Affiliation: Moe's Southwest Grill LLC, ATLANTA, GA

Key Personnel
BRAD CHASTEEN - Partner; General Buyer
FRANK MARESCA - Partner
STEVE TAYLOR - Partner

Guapo's Restaurants
4515 Wisconsin Ave NW
Washington, DC 20016-4619

Telephone: (202) 686-3588
Fax Number: (202) 686-5490
Internet Homepage: guaposrestaurant.com
Type of Business: Chain Restaurant Operator
Year Founded: 1991
Total Sales: $24,250,000 (e)
Alcohol Sales: 2%
Number of Employees: 270
Average Check: Lunch(18); Dinner(26)

Internet Order Processing: Yes
Total Units: 9
Trade Names: Guapo's Mexican Restaurant (6); Guapo's Rotisseries (3)
Company-Owned Units: 9
Preferred Square Footage: 5,500; 6,000
Preferred Location Types: Freestanding; Strip Mall
Alcohol Served: Beer, Wine, Liquor
Primary Menu: Chicken (3); Mexican (6)
Areas of Operation: DC, MD, VA
Type of Foodservice: Casual Dining (6); Fast Casual (3)
Primary Distributors: (Food) US Foods, MANASSAS, VA

Key Personnel
ANGELA MUSALENA - Director Operations, Facility/Maintenance, Information Systems, Supply Chain, Real Estate
HECTOR A. RINCON - Director Purchasing, Human Resources, Menu Development; General Buyer
CARMEN ROTH - Manager Finance
DAVID MORAN - Manager Food and Beverage

Hot N Juicy Crawfish
2651 Connecticut Ave NW
Washington, DC 20008

Telephone: (202) 299-9448
Internet Homepage: hotnjuicycrawfish.com
Company Email: info@hotnjuicycrawfish.com
Type of Business: Chain Restaurant Operator
Total Sales: $14,970,000 (e)
Number of Employees: 54
Total Units: 11
Trade Names: Hot N Juicy Crawfish (11)
Company-Owned Units: 11
Alcohol Served: Beer
Primary Menu: Seafood (11)
Areas of Operation: CA, DC, FL, NV
Type of Foodservice: Casual Dining (11)

Key Personnel
QUINA NGAYN - Owner
JILLIAN SUTTON - Manager Marketing

Knightsbridge Corp.
631 D St NW Apt 127
Washington, DC 20004-2914

Telephone: (202) 393-5883
Fax Number: (202) 393-6439
Internet Homepage: ardeobardeo.com; bindaasdc.com; bombayclubdc.com; knightsbridgerestaurantgroup.com; ovalroom.com; rasikarestaurant.com
Company Email: contact@knightsbridgerestaurantgroup.com
Type of Business: Chain Restaurant Operator

Year Founded: 1987
Total Sales: $38,760,000 (e)
Alcohol Sales: 35%
Number of Employees: 450
Average Check: Lunch(30); Dinner(60)
Total Units: 9
Trade Names: Bindaas (2); Bombay Club (1); Modena (1); Olivia (1); Oval Room (1); Rasika (2); Sababa (1)
Company-Owned Units: 9
Preferred Location Types: Freestanding
Alcohol Served: Beer, Wine, Liquor
Primary Menu: American (1); Eastern European (2); Indian (5); Italian (1)
Areas of Operation: DC
Type of Foodservice: Casual Dining (2); Fine Dining (7)
Catering Services: Yes
Primary Distributors: (Equipment) Adams-Burch Inc., LANDOVER, MD; (Supplies) Adams-Burch Inc., LANDOVER, MD

Key Personnel
MATT KUHN - Executive Chef

Little Sesame
1828 L St NW
Washington, DC 20036

Internet Homepage: eatlittlesesame.com
Company Email: hello@eatlittlesesame.com
Type of Business: Chain Restaurant Operator
Total Units: 2
Trade Names: Little Sesame (2)
Company-Owned Units: 1
Primary Menu: Greek/Mediterranean (2)
Projected Openings: 1
Areas of Operation: DC
Type of Foodservice: Fast Casual (2)

Key Personnel
RONEN TENNE - Executive Chef
NICK WISEMAN - Executive Chef

Matchbox Food Group
806 7th St NW Ste 300
Washington, DC 20001-3964

Telephone: (202) 289-4403
Fax Number: (202) 289-4451
Internet Homepage: eatdc3.com; matchboxfoodgroup.com; matchboxrestaurants.com; tedsbulletin.com
Company Email: info@matchbox369.com
Type of Business: Chain Restaurant Operator
Year Founded: 2003
Number of Employees: 500
Average Check: Lunch(24); Dinner(42)
Total Units: 25
Trade Names: DC-3 (9); Matchbox (11); Ted's Bulletin (5)

Company-Owned Units: 25
Alcohol Served: Beer, Wine, Liquor
Primary Menu: American (24); Hot Dogs (1)
Projected Openings: 1
Areas of Operation: CA, DC, FL, MD, TX, VA
Type of Foodservice: Casual Dining (25)
Parent Company: Thompson Hospitality, RESTON, VA

Key Personnel
MICHAEL ESTRADA - Area Director Operations
ALLISON FINKELSTEIN - General Manager
FELIPE MUNOZ - Executive Chef
MARIO GUEVARA - Executive Chef
LAURA WILLIAMSON - Creative Director
KAYTLYN KAVLICK - Coordinator Marketing, Event Planning

Nando's USA
819 7th St NW Fl 2
Washington, DC 20001-3762

Telephone: (202) 621-9611
Fax Number: (202) 697-5226
Internet Homepage: nandosperiperi.com
Company Email: customerservice@nandosperiperi.com
Type of Business: Chain Restaurant Operator
Year Founded: 1987
Total Sales: $71,201,000 (e)
Number of Employees: 405
Average Check: Dinner(14)
Total Units: 45
Trade Names: Nando's Peri Peri (45)
Company-Owned Units: 45
Alcohol Served: Beer, Wine
Primary Menu: Chicken (45)
Projected Openings: 1
Areas of Operation: DC, GA, IL, MD, TX, VA
Type of Foodservice: Fast Casual (45)
Primary Distributors: (Equipment) Singer Equipment Co. Inc., ELVERSON, PA; (Food) SYSCO Food Services of Virginia LLC, HARRISONBURG, VA;(Supplies) Adams-Burch Inc., LANDOVER, MD

Key Personnel
JOHN FISHER - CEO
NESTOR NOVA - CFO
DEBBIE TICKNOR - CFO
LESLIE WILLIAMS - COO
SEPANTA BAGHERPOUR - VP Marketing
JESSICA RELCHER - VP Operations
BRANDON SILVER - General Manager
APRIL HACKSTALL - Director Digital Marketing
PETER WINKLER - Senior Manager Digital Marketing
TRACEY MULHERIN - Senior Manager Marketing
MICKI SCHLECHTING - Manager Training, Employee Development
MELINDA NETTELBECK - Manager Design

DAN JABLOW - Manager Purchasing

Oceanside Management Group
3000 K St NW
Washington, DC 20007-5109

Telephone: (202) 944-4545
Fax Number: (202) 944-4104
Internet Homepage: nicksriversidegrill.com; tonyandjoes.com
Company Email: info@tonyandjoes.com
Type of Business: Chain Restaurant Operator
Year Founded: 1987
Total Sales: $12,453,000 (e)
Alcohol Sales: 26%
Number of Employees: 170
Average Check: Lunch(18); Dinner(42)
Total Units: 2
Trade Names: Nick's Riverside Grille (1); Tony & Joe's (1)
Company-Owned Units: 2
Preferred Square Footage: 5,500; 6,000
Preferred Location Types: Freestanding; Stadiums
Alcohol Served: Beer, Wine, Liquor
Primary Menu: Seafood (1); Steak (1)
Areas of Operation: DC
Type of Foodservice: Casual Dining (2)
Primary Distributors: (Equipment) Adams-Burch Inc., LANDOVER, MD; (Food) US Foods, SEVERN, MD; (Supplies) Acme Paper & Supply Co., SAVAGE, MD

Key Personnel
ANTHONY B. CIBEL - Partner; Director Operations, Real Estate, Product Development, Menu Development
GREGORY CASTEN - Partner; Controller; Manager Purchasing
DAVID PERA - General Manager

Passion Food Hospitality LLC
1010 Massachusetts Ave NW Unit 1213
Washington, DC 20001-5420

Telephone: (202) 408-0201
Fax Number: (202) 408-0250
Internet Homepage: passionfoodhospitality.com
Company Email: info@passionfoodhospitality.com
Type of Business: Chain Restaurant Operator
Year Founded: 1998
Total Sales: $12,610,000 (e)
Alcohol Sales: 30%
Number of Employees: 143
Average Check: Lunch(30); Dinner(54)
Internet Order Processing: Yes

Total Units: 5
Trade Names: Burger Tap & Shake (1); District Commons (1); Passion Fish (2); TenPenh (1)
Company-Owned Units: 5
Preferred Location Types: Downtown; Freestanding; Office Complex
Alcohol Served: Beer, Wine, Liquor
Primary Menu: American (1); Asian (1); Hamburger (1); Seafood (2)
Areas of Operation: DC, MD, VA
Type of Foodservice: Casual Dining (2); Fine Dining (3)
Primary Distributors: (Food) Adams-Burch Inc., LANDOVER, MD; (Supplies) Adams-Burch Inc., LANDOVER, MD

Key Personnel
GUS DIMILLO - President; Partner
JEFF TUNKS - Partner; Executive Chef; General Buyer
DAVID WIZENBERG - Partner
TANIA LEON - Director Accounting
KATHRYN ARVIS - Director Marketing
SHARON DALY - Director Finance

RB Properties Inc.
1054 31st St NW Ste 1000
Washington, DC 20007-6030

Telephone: (202) 342-1054
Fax Number: (202) 342-0973
Internet Homepage: rbpropertiesinc.com
Company Email: corporate@rbpropertiesinc.com
Type of Business: Foodservice Operations - Hotel/Motels
Year Founded: 1980
Total Sales: $51,430,000 (e)
Alcohol Sales: 25%
Number of Employees: 700
Total Units: 5
Restaurants in Hotels: 5
Trade Names: Henley Park Hotel (1); Hotel Lombardy (1); State Plaza Hotel (1); The Morrison Clark Inn (1); Washington Plaza Hotel (1)
Company-Owned Units: 5
Alcohol Served: Beer, Wine, Liquor
Areas of Operation: DC
Primary Distributors: (Food) SYSCO Food Services of Virginia LLC, HARRISONBURG, VA
Notes: The company derives approximately 80% of its revenue from hotel operations.

Key Personnel
RICHARD BERNSTEIN - VP
LISA HORNSTEIN - VP Marketing
MIKE WILDING - VP; Controller
MILFORD EBO - Director Purchasing; General Buyer

LEIF KUROWSKI - Manager Human Resources

Sala Thai
4020 Minnesota Ave NE
Washington, DC 20019

Telephone: (202) 399-7999
Internet Homepage: salathaidc.com
Company Email: salathaidc@aol.com
Type of Business: Chain Restaurant Operator
Year Founded: 1988
Total Sales: $9,110,000 (e)
Alcohol Sales: 10%
Number of Employees: 15
Average Check: Lunch(12); Dinner(20)
Total Units: 3
Trade Names: Sala Thai (3)
Company-Owned Units: 3
Preferred Square Footage: 5,500; 6,000
Preferred Location Types: Freestanding
Alcohol Served: Beer, Wine, Liquor
Primary Menu: Thai (3)
Areas of Operation: DC, MD
Type of Foodservice: Casual Dining (3)
Catering Services: Yes
Primary Distributors: (Food) Adams-Burch Inc., LANDOVER, MD

Key Personnel
OY CHANGSILA - President; General Manager; General Buyer

Sunnyside Restaurant Group
303 Pennsylvania Ave SE
Washington, DC 20003-1148

Telephone: (202) 543-8222
Internet Homepage: goodstuffeatery.com; wethepizza.com; santarosataqueria.com
Type of Business: Chain Restaurant Operator
Year Founded: 2008
Average Check: Dinner(16)
Total Units: 8
Trade Names: Good Stuff Eatery (5); Santa Rosa Taqueria (1); We The Pizza (2)
Company-Owned Units: 8
Primary Menu: Hamburger (5); Mexican (1); Pizza (2)
Areas of Operation: DC, IL, VA
Foreign Countries: SAUDI ARABIA
Type of Foodservice: Casual Dining (6); Fast Casual (2)
Catering Services: Yes

Key Personnel
HARVEY MENDELSOHN - CEO; Partner
MICHELINE MENDELSOHN - CEO
CATHERINE MENDELSOHN - COO
KARINA WILKEY - Controller
YASER JOUDEH - Director Business Development

COURTNEY BATTISTA - Manager Operations

Takorean
1309 5th St NE
Washington, DC 20002

Telephone: (202) 543-5659
Internet Homepage: takorean.com
Company Email: eat@takorean.com
Type of Business: Chain Restaurant Operator
Year Founded: 2010
Total Units: 4
Trade Names: Takorean (4)
Company-Owned Units: 4
Primary Menu: Korean (4)
Areas of Operation: DC, PA
Type of Foodservice: Fast Casual (4)

Key Personnel
MICHAEL LENARD - CEO
LUKAS UMANA - President; CFO
ERIC LENARD - Partner; Director Franchise Development
GREG KUHN - General Manager

The Palm Restaurant Group
1730 Rhode Island Ave NW Ste 900
Washington, DC 20036-3113

Telephone: (202) 775-7256
Fax Number: (202) 775-8292
Internet Homepage: thepalm.com
Company Email: customercare@thepalm.com
Type of Business: Chain Restaurant Operator
Year Founded: 1926
Systemwide Sales: $157,976,000 (e)
Total Sales: $156,410,000 (e)
Alcohol Sales: 30%
Number of Employees: 1,713
Average Check: Dinner(76)
Internet Order Processing: Yes
Internet Sales: 3.00%
Total Units: 20
Trade Names: Palm Restaurant (20)
Company-Owned Units: 20
Preferred Square Footage: 5,800
Preferred Location Types: Freestanding; Hotel/Motel; Office Complex; Regional Mall
Alcohol Served: Beer, Wine, Liquor
Primary Menu: Steak (20)
Areas of Operation: CA, CO, DC, FL, GA, IL, MA, NC, NJ, NV, NY, PA, PR, TN, TX, VA, FC
Foreign Countries: MEXICO
Type of Foodservice: Fine Dining (24)
Primary Distributors: (Full Line) SYSCO Food Services of Albany, HALFMOON, NY

Key Personnel
JOY JONES - General Counsel
LILY COHEN - Manager Sales

JAN BONUGLI - Manager Sales

ThinkFood Group
717 D St NW Fl 6
Washington, DC 20004-2812

Telephone: (202) 638-1910
Fax Number: (202) 638-1831
Internet Homepage: beefsteakveggies.com; minibarbyjoseandreas.com; jaleo.com; oyamel.com; thinkfoodgroup.com; zaytinya.com
Type of Business: Chain Restaurant Operator
Year Founded: 1996
Total Sales: $159,950,000 (e)
Alcohol Sales: 30%
Number of Employees: 2,050
Average Check: Lunch(26); Dinner(54)
Total Units: 29
Trade Names: Beefsteak (4); Butterfly Tacos Y Tortas (1); Cafe By The River (1); China Chilcano (1); China Poblano (1); E by Jose Andres (1); Fish by Jose Andres (1); Jaleo (6); Little Spain (1); mini bar by jose andres (1); Oyamel (1); PEPE (1); Spanish Diner (2); The Bazaar by Jose Andres (4); Tres by JoseAndres (1); Zaytinya (2)
Company-Owned Units: 29
Preferred Square Footage: 5,500; 6,000
Preferred Location Types: Downtown; Freestanding
Alcohol Served: Beer, Wine, Liquor
Primary Menu: American (5); Greek/Mediterranean (2); Health Foods (4); Mexican (1); Miscellaneous (3); Seafood (1); Spanish (13)
Areas of Operation: CA, DC, FL, MD, NV, PA, VA
Type of Foodservice: Casual Dining (13); Family Restaurant (1); Fast Casual (4); Fine Dining (11)
Primary Distributors: (Equipment) Lenox-Martell Inc., BOSTON, MA; (Supplies) Lenox-Martell Inc., BOSTON, MA

Key Personnel
JOSE ANDRES - Executive Chairman; President
ROB WILDER - Vice Chairman; General Buyer
KIMBERLY GRANT - CEO
JOE RAFFA - COO Culinary Operations; Creative Director Culinary Operations
SATCHEL KAPLAN ALLEN - Chief of Staff
TERRI CUTTRINO - Corporate Chef
WILLIAM WOODSON - Senior Director
TINA LAVELLE - Senior Director Operations
CHARISSE DICKENS - Director Research & Development
MIGUEL LANCHA - Director Beverages, Culinary Development-Beverages
GREG SPIES - Director Digital Marketing
SHEA DONAHUE - Manager

Toastique
764 Maine Ave SW
Washington, DC 20024

Telephone: (202) 484-5200
Internet Homepage: toastique.com
Company Email: info@toastique.com
Type of Business: Chain Restaurant Operator
Year Founded: 2018
Systemwide Sales: $24,853,000 (e)
Total Sales: $20,504,000 (e)
Total Units: 33
Trade Names: Toastique (33)
Company-Owned Units: 6
Units Franchised To: 27
Primary Menu: Health Foods (33)
Areas of Operation: CA, CO, DC, FL, GA, KS, MD, MI, MN, NC, NJ, NV, NY, PA, SD, TN, TX, UT, VA
Type of Foodservice: Fast Casual (33)

Key Personnel
BRIANNA KEEFE - Founder; CEO
KYLE IZETT - President; CFO
SEAN KEEFE - COO
HAILEY HYDE - Director Development
NICOLE VALENTIN - Director Strategy
KELSEY FORMAN - Director Training
MORISSA GOODMAN - Director Franchise Development

DELAWARE

SoDel Concepts
PO Box 31
Bethany Beach, DE 19930-0031

Telephone: (302) 644-1200
Internet Homepage: sodelconcepts.com
Type of Business: Chain Restaurant Operator
Total Sales: $13,160,000 (e)
Total Units: 14
Trade Names: Bluecoast Seafood Grill (2); Catch54 Fish House (1); Club House at Baywood (1); Crust & Craft (1); Fish On! (1); Lupo Italian Kitchen (1); Matt's Fish Camp (3); NorthEast Seafood Kitchen (1); Ocean View Brewing Company (1); Papa Grandes (1); Thompson Island (1)
Company-Owned Units: 14
Primary Menu: American (1); Italian (1); Mexican (1); Pizza (1); Seafood (10)
Projected Openings: 1
Areas of Operation: DE
Type of Foodservice: Casual Dining (14)

Key Personnel
SCOTT KAMMERER - CEO; Partner; General Buyer
MIKE DICKINSON - VP Operations
DOUG RULEY - VP
LINDSEY BARRY - Controller
CHRISTINA DANAE EVANS - General Manager
RONNIE BURKLE - Executive Chef
ALAN LEVIN - Director
MATT PATTON - Director Operations
DANIELLE PANARELLO - Director Operations
DAN LEVIN - Director Facility/Maintenance
ANDREW DICKINSON - Director Marketing
CAROLINE JUDGE - Director Marketing
KRIS MEDFORD - Director Operations
NEILA DOLAN - Manager Marketing
LISA WHEELER - Manager Human Resources
NICOLE PANTO - Manager Marketing

Crabby Dick's
30 Clinton St
Delaware City, DE 19706-7700

Mailing Address: PO Box 527, DELAWARE CITY, DE, 19706-0527
Telephone: (302) 832-5100
Fax Number: (302) 832-2709
Internet Homepage: crabby-dicks.com
Company Email: info@crabby-dicks.com
Type of Business: Chain Restaurant Operator
Year Founded: 2006
Total Sales: $3,897,000 (e)
Alcohol Sales: 5%
Average Check: Lunch(12); Dinner(24)
Internet Order Processing: Yes
Internet Sales: 2.00%
Total Units: 2
Trade Names: Crabby Dick's (2)
Company-Owned Units: 2
Preferred Location Types: Hotel/Motel
Alcohol Served: Beer, Wine, Liquor
Primary Menu: Seafood (2)
Areas of Operation: DE
Type of Foodservice: Casual Dining (2)
Primary Distributors: (Food) US Foods, SEVERN, MD

Key Personnel
DALE SLOTTER - President; General Manager; General Buyer
JOHN CRABBYDICKS - Owner
JIMMY JOHNSON - Executive Chef

Auntie Anne's Franchise
33 Laurel Dr
Dover, DE 19901-4521

Telephone: (302) 697-4650
Internet Homepage: auntieannesfranchising.com
Type of Business: Chain Restaurant Operator
Total Sales: $1,575,000 (e)
Total Units: 2
Trade Names: Auntie Anne's Hand-Rolled Soft Pretzels (2)

Units Franchised From: 2
Primary Menu: Snacks (3)
Areas of Operation: DE
Type of Foodservice: Quick Serve (3)
Franchise Affiliation: Auntie Anne's Inc., LANCASTER, PA

Key Personnel
CATHERINE RIEHL - Owner; General Buyer

Dover Downs Gaming & Entertainment Inc.
1131 N Dupont Hwy
Dover, DE 19901-2008

Mailing Address: PO Box 1412, DOVER, DE, 19903-1412
Telephone: (302) 674-4600
Fax Number: (302) 741-8971
Internet Homepage: doverdowns.com
Type of Business: Foodservice Operations - Casinos
Year Founded: 1967
Publicly Held: Yes
Total Sales: $127,732,000 (e)
Alcohol Sales: 10%
Number of Employees: 715
Average Check: Breakfast(12); Lunch(18); Dinner(22)
Total Units: 7
Trade Names: Festival Buffet (1); Gr8 Burgers & Shakes (1); Jerry Longo's Meatballs & Martinis (1); MACAU KITCHEN EXPRESS (1); Sugar Factory (1); Sweet Perks II (1); Winner's Circle (1)
Company-Owned Units: 7
Preferred Square Footage: 2,500; 3,000; 5,500; 6,000
Preferred Location Types: Other
Alcohol Served: Beer, Wine, Liquor
Primary Menu: Asian (1); Italian (1); Snacks (1)
Areas of Operation: DE
Type of Foodservice: Casual Dining (6); Fine Dining (0)
Primary Distributors: (Full Line) SYSCO Food Services of Baltimore, JESSUP, MD
Notes: The company derives approximately 95% of its revenue from gaming, hotel, and other operations.

Key Personnel
DENIS MCGLYNN - Chairman; CEO; President
EDWARD J. SUTOR - COO; Exec VP
NANCY MCCOY - VP; General Manager; Executive Assistant
PETER BRADLEY - VP; General Manager
MELISSA CULLEN - VP Human Resources
STEVE KEENER - Assistant VP
CHARLES PALMER - Assistant VP
TERRY HERBEIN - Controller
JOE CARPENTER - Senior Director Accounting
ROBIN PRICE - Director Catering
MIKE SIMPSON - Director Information Technology
STEPHEN KEENER - Director Operations
JEROME LAWRENCE - Director Purchasing
PATRICIA BRITTINGHAM - Director
CHRISTOPHER GATTA - Manager Finance
LISA SKELLEY - Manager Sales

● ▲
R & K Management
879 N Dupont Hwy
Dover, DE 19901-2000

Telephone: (302) 674-8573
Fax Number: (302) 674-8591
Type of Business: Chain Restaurant Operator
Total Sales: $15,078,000 (e)
Number of Employees: 65
Average Check: Breakfast(8); Lunch(8); Dinner(8)
Total Units: 3
Trade Names: McDonald's (3)
Units Franchised From: 3
Preferred Square Footage: 2,500; 3,000
Preferred Location Types: Freestanding
Primary Menu: Hamburger (3)
Areas of Operation: DE
Type of Foodservice: Quick Serve (3)
Franchise Affiliation: McDonald's Corporation, CHICAGO, IL

Key Personnel
ROBERT COCOZZOLI - President; General Buyer

Hanna's Systems
39064 Harpoon Rd
Fenwick Island, DE 19944-4015

Telephone: (302) 539-3095
Fax Number: (302) 539-3066
Internet Homepage: brewriver.com; harpoonhannasrestaurant.com
Type of Business: Chain Restaurant Operator
Year Founded: 1982
Total Sales: $9,458,000 (e)
Alcohol Sales: 35%
Number of Employees: 120
Average Check: Lunch(14); Dinner(24)
Internet Order Processing: Yes
Total Units: 2
Trade Names: Brew River (1); Harpoon Hanna's (1)
Company-Owned Units: 2
Preferred Location Types: Freestanding
Alcohol Served: Beer, Wine, Liquor
Primary Menu: Seafood (2)
Areas of Operation: DE
Type of Foodservice: Casual Dining (2)
Primary Distributors: (Full Line) Sysco Eastern Maryland Inc., POCOMOKE CITY, MD

Key Personnel
FRANK HANNA - Partner; Executive Chef; General Buyer
LEIGH HANNA - Partner

Grotto's Commisary
17467 Shady Rd
Lewes, DE 19958

Telephone: (302) 645-4900
Fax Number: (302) 645-5697
Internet Homepage: grottopizza.com
Listing Type: Distribution Center
Type of Business: Chain Restaurant Operator
Number of Employees: 100
Areas of Operation: DE
Parent Company: Grotto Pizza Inc., REHOBOTH BEACH, DE

Key Personnel
RALPH GALBREATH - General Manager Distribution, Warehouse, Transportation, Human Resources
MICHAEL JONES - Director Operations

Irish Eyes
213 Anglers Rd
Lewes, DE 19958-1151

Telephone: (302) 645-6888
Fax Number: (302) 645-6830
Internet Homepage: irisheyespub.com
Type of Business: Chain Restaurant Operator
Year Founded: 1986
Total Sales: $4,748,000 (e)
Alcohol Sales: 25%
Number of Employees: 80
Average Check: Lunch(16); Dinner(28)
Total Units: 2
Trade Names: Irish Eyes (2)
Company-Owned Units: 2
Preferred Location Types: Freestanding
Alcohol Served: Beer, Wine, Liquor
Primary Menu: American (2)
Areas of Operation: DE
Type of Foodservice: Casual Dining (2)

Key Personnel
TOM JONES - Partner; General Manager

● ▲
DP Inc
156 Mullet Run
Milford, DE 19963-5367

Telephone: (302) 424-1600
Fax Number: (302) 424-7667
Type of Business: Chain Restaurant Operator
Total Sales: $24,139,000 (e)
Total Units: 12

Trade Names: Domino's (12)
Units Franchised From: 12
Primary Menu: Pizza (12)
Areas of Operation: DE
Type of Foodservice: Quick Serve (12)
Franchise Affiliation: Domino's Pizza Inc, ANN ARBOR, MI

Key Personnel
DONALD M. PROUSE - Owner; General Buyer
BRENT PROUSE - Supervisor Operations

Mama Maria's Italian Restaurant & Pizza
945 N Dupont Blvd Ste A
Milford, DE 19963-1067

Telephone: (302) 422-2661
Internet Homepage: mamamaria.com
Company Email: mamamarias@aol.com
Type of Business: Chain Restaurant Operator
Year Founded: 1981
Total Sales: $3,917,000 (e)
Alcohol Sales: 15%
Number of Employees: 24
Average Check: Lunch(18); Dinner(30)
Total Units: 2
Trade Names: Mama Maria's Italian Restaurant & Pizza (2)
Company-Owned Units: 2
Preferred Location Types: Freestanding
Alcohol Served: Beer, Wine, Liquor
Primary Menu: Italian (2)
Areas of Operation: DE
Type of Foodservice: Casual Dining (2)
Primary Distributors: (Food) SYSCO Food Services of Baltimore, JESSUP, MD; (Food) US Foods, SWEDESBORO, NJ

Key Personnel
FRANCO LARAGIONE - Partner; General Manager
GIUSEPPE LARAGIONE - Partner; Executive Chef; General Buyer
SAL LARAGIONE - Partner; General Manager

Domino's Franchisee
132 Broadkill Rd
Milton, DE 19968-1008

Telephone: (302) 684-5000
Type of Business: Chain Restaurant Operator
Total Sales: $4,103,000 (e)
Total Units: 2
Trade Names: Domino's (2)
Units Franchised From: 2
Primary Menu: Pizza (2)
Areas of Operation: DE
Type of Foodservice: Quick Serve (2)
Franchise Affiliation: Domino's Pizza Inc, ANN ARBOR, MI

Key Personnel
JAMES A. BOYD - Owner; General Buyer

Grotto's Commisary
144 Quigley Blvd Ste 102
New Castle, DE 19720-4199

Telephone: (302) 325-9682
Fax Number: (302) 325-9686
Listing Type: Distribution Center
Type of Business: Foodservice Operations - Bowling Alley
Number of Employees: 9
Areas of Operation: DE
Parent Company: Grotto Pizza Inc., REHOBOTH BEACH, DE

Key Personnel
MICHAEL JONES - Director Region

Ashby Hospitality Group
108 W Main St
Newark, DE 19711-3229

Telephone: (302) 894-1200
Fax Number: (302) 894-1255
Internet Homepage: deerparktavern.com; mcglynnspub.com; cantwells-tavern.com
Company Email: McGlynnsPub@live.com
Type of Business: Chain Restaurant Operator
Year Founded: 1983
Total Sales: $6,325,000 (e)
Alcohol Sales: 40%
Number of Employees: 200
Average Check: Lunch(14); Dinner(30)
Internet Order Processing: Yes
Total Units: 5
Trade Names: Cantwell Tavern (1); Deer Park Tavern & Restaurant (1); McGlynns Pub & Restaurant (3)
Company-Owned Units: 5
Preferred Location Types: Downtown; Freestanding; Mixed-use Center
Alcohol Served: Beer, Wine, Liquor
Primary Menu: American (5)
Areas of Operation: DE
Type of Foodservice: Casual Dining (5)
Primary Distributors: (Full Line) Sysco Eastern Maryland Inc., POCOMOKE CITY, MD

Key Personnel
MARC ASHBY - President
ROBERT ASHBY - Owner; General Manager; Executive Chef; General Buyer
JANICE MUNYAN - Controller
JEREMY HUGHES - Director Operations
JENNIFER WASSMER - Manager

Hip Stone, Inc.
2470 Pulaski Hwy
Newark, DE 19702-3971

Telephone: (302) 838-2992
Type of Business: Chain Restaurant Operator
Total Sales: $1,229,000 (e)
Total Units: 2
Trade Names: Cold Stone Creamery (2)
Units Franchised From: 2
Primary Menu: Snacks (2)
Areas of Operation: DE
Type of Foodservice: Quick Serve (2)
Franchise Affiliation: Kahala Brands, SCOTTSDALE, AZ

Key Personnel
HAYTHUM ISSA - Owner

Prunella Holdings LLC
113 Barksdale Professional Ctr
Newark, DE 19711-3258

Telephone: (302) 332-8833
Fax Number: (302) 747-5841
Internet Homepage: fracturedprune.com
Type of Business: Chain Restaurant Operator
Year Founded: 1976
Total Sales: $1,449,000 (e)
Number of Employees: 66
Average Check: Breakfast(5); Lunch(8); Dinner(8)
Total Units: 22
Trade Names: The Fractured Prune Donut Shoppe (22)
Company-Owned Units: 11
Units Franchised To: 11
Preferred Location Types: Freestanding; Strip Mall
Primary Menu: Snacks (22)
Areas of Operation: AZ, CA, CO, DE, MD, NC, NJ, PA, SC
Type of Foodservice: Quick Serve (22)

Key Personnel
DAN BRINTON - President

Seasons Pizza
1007 Church Rd
Newark, DE 19702-5101

Telephone: (302) 836-0400
Fax Number: (302) 836-6434
Internet Homepage: seasonspizza.com
Company Email: service@seasonspizza.com
Type of Business: Chain Restaurant Operator
Year Founded: 1981
Total Sales: $6,073,000 (e)
Alcohol Sales: 5%

Average Check: Dinner(10)
Total Units: 28
Trade Names: Seasons Pizza (28)
Company-Owned Units: 19
Units Franchised To: 9
Preferred Location Types: Freestanding; Strip Mall
Alcohol Served: Beer, Wine
Primary Menu: Pizza (28)
Projected Openings: 10
Areas of Operation: DE, MD, NJ, PA
Type of Foodservice: Fast Casual (28)
Catering Services: Yes

Key Personnel
ANGELO HALAKOS - President; Executive Chef; General Buyer

Two Stones Pub
2 Chesmar Plz Rt 4
Newark, DE 19713

Telephone: (302) 294-1890
Internet Homepage: 2spbrewing.com; twostonespub.com
Company Email: info@2spbrewing.com
Type of Business: Chain Restaurant Operator
Total Units: 5
Trade Names: Two Stones Pub (5)
Company-Owned Units: 5
Primary Menu: American (5)
Areas of Operation: DE
Type of Foodservice: Casual Dining (5)

Key Personnel
MICHAEL STIGLITZ - Owner; Director Operations
CHRISTOPHER MEYER - Corporate Chef; Director Culinary Operations; General Buyer

Big Fish Restaurant Group
228 Rehoboth Ave
Rehoboth Beach, DE 19971-2134

Mailing Address: PO Box 669, REHOBOTH BEACH, DE 19971-0669
Telephone: (302) 227-3895
Fax Number: (302) 227-5231
Internet Homepage: bellacoast.com; bigfishgrill.com; bigfishrestaurantgroup.com; crabhouserehoboth.com; summerhousesaloon.com
Type of Business: Chain Restaurant Operator
Year Founded: 1977
Total Sales: $12,880,000 (e)
Alcohol Sales: 25%
Number of Employees: 262
Average Check: Lunch(16); Dinner(36)
Total Units: 14
Trade Names: Barroja (1); Big Fish Grill (4); Harvest House (1); Mikimotos Asian Grill and Sushi Bar (1); Obie's by the Sea (1); Oyster House (1); Salt Air (1); Sazio (1); Stingray Restaurant (1); Summer House (1); Washington Street Ale House (1)
Company-Owned Units: 14
Preferred Location Types: Freestanding
Alcohol Served: Beer, Wine, Liquor
Primary Menu: American (3); Asian (2); Mexican (1); Seafood (8)
Areas of Operation: DE, PA
Type of Foodservice: Casual Dining (14)
Primary Distributors: (Food) Sysco Eastern Maryland Inc., POCOMOKE CITY, MD

Key Personnel
ERIC SUGRUE - Partner
NORMAN SUGRUE - Partner
KARL PETERS - CFO
HOLLY MONACO - VP; Executive Director
LISA BREEDLOVE - General Manager; Director Culinary Operations
MICHAEL MCNUTT - Director
AMY POLEND - Director Culinary Operations
MARY BETH TRYON - Director Marketing
JESSICA WHITE - Manager Accounting
KIM ROSSO - Manager
SUSAN SOKOWSKI - Manager Catering
BOB MOYER - Manager Sales-Seafood, Seafood

Dogfish Head Brewing & Eats
320 Rehoboth Ave
Rehoboth Beach, DE 19971-3108

Telephone: (302) 226-2739
Fax Number: (302) 226-0792
Internet Homepage: dogfish.com; dogfish.com/blog/milton-brewery
Company Email: dogfish@dogfish.com
Type of Business: Chain Restaurant Operator
Year Founded: 1995
Total Sales: $30,493,000 (e)
Number of Employees: 60
Average Check: Lunch(16); Dinner(22)
Total Units: 6
Trade Names: Chesapeake & Maine (1); Dogfish Head Alehouse (3); Dogfish Head Brewings & Eats (1); Milton Brewery (1)
Company-Owned Units: 3
Units Franchised To: 3
Alcohol Served: Beer, Wine, Liquor
Primary Menu: American (5); Seafood (1)
Areas of Operation: DE, MD
Type of Foodservice: Casual Dining (6)
Primary Distributors: (Food) Sysco Eastern Maryland Inc., POCOMOKE CITY, MD

Key Personnel
MATT SILVERMAN - Executive Chef; General Buyer

Grotto Pizza Inc.
20376 Coastal Hwy
Rehoboth Beach, DE 19971-8015

Telephone: (302) 227-3567
Fax Number: (302) 227-4566
Internet Homepage: grottopizza.com
Company Email: legendarytaste@grottopizza.com
Type of Business: Chain Restaurant Operator
Year Founded: 1960
Total Sales: $37,250,000 (e)
Alcohol Sales: 20%
Number of Employees: 1,351
Average Check: Lunch(24); Dinner(42)
Internet Order Processing: Yes
Internet Sales: 1.00%
Total Units: 23
Trade Names: Grotto Pizza (23)
Company-Owned Units: 23
Preferred Square Footage: 3,000
Preferred Location Types: Freestanding; Other; Strip Mall
Alcohol Served: Beer, Wine, Liquor
Primary Menu: Pizza (23)
Areas of Operation: DE, MD, PA
Type of Foodservice: Casual Dining (23)
Distribution Centers: LEWES, DE; NEW CASTLE, DE
On-site Distribution Center: Yes
Primary Distributors: (Food) SYSCO Food Services of Baltimore, JESSUP, MD

Key Personnel
DOMINICK PULIERI - President; Director Finance, Marketing, Real Estate, Design, Menu Development
FRANK ALBERO - CFO; Director Facility/Maintenance, Information Systems, Store Fixtures
GLENN BYRUM - Director Human Resources
MICHAEL JONES - Director Purchasing, Supply Chain, Foodservice, Food and Beverage

Meoli Company
19545 Camelot Dr Ste A
Rehoboth Beach, DE 19971-1197

Telephone: (302) 330-3040
Fax Number: (302) 330-3041
Internet Homepage: meolicompanies.com
Type of Business: Chain Restaurant Operator
Year Founded: 1968
Total Sales: $124,150,000 (e)
Number of Employees: 1,500
Average Check: Breakfast(8); Lunch(8); Dinner(10)
Total Units: 25
Trade Names: McDonald's (25)
Units Franchised From: 25
Preferred Square Footage: 2,500; 3,000

Preferred Location Types: Freestanding
Primary Menu: Hamburger (25)
Areas of Operation: DE, MD
Type of Foodservice: Quick Serve (25)
Franchise Affiliation: McDonald's Corporation, CHICAGO, IL

Key Personnel
MICHAEL MEOLI - President; Partner; General Buyer
ANTHONY MEOLI - Partner; General Buyer
JAMES SCHAFFER - Director Operations

●▲
First Star Partners LLC
22802 Sussex Hwy
Seaford, DE 19973-5865

Telephone: (302) 536-1542
Type of Business: Chain Restaurant Operator
Total Sales: $1,948,000 (e)
Total Units: 3
Trade Names: Little Caesars Pizza (3)
Units Franchised From: 3
Primary Menu: Pizza (3)
Areas of Operation: DE
Type of Foodservice: Quick Serve (3)
Franchise Affiliation: Little Caesar Enterprises Inc., DETROIT, MI

Key Personnel
JOHN YOHO - President; General Buyer

Authentic Mexican Restaurants Group
4147 Concord Pike
Wilmington, DE 19803

Telephone: (302) 778-4646
Fax Number: (302) 778-4946
Internet Homepage: authenticmex.com; lastoltecas.com
Type of Business: Chain Restaurant Operator
Total Sales: $37,920,000 (e)
Alcohol Sales: 10%
Number of Employees: 382
Average Check: Breakfast(6); Lunch(12); Dinner(16)
Total Units: 14
Trade Names: La Tolteca (4); La Tonalteca (10)
Company-Owned Units: 14
Preferred Square Footage: 5,500; 6,000
Preferred Location Types: Freestanding
Alcohol Served: Beer, Wine, Liquor
Primary Menu: Mexican (14)
Areas of Operation: DE, NY, PA
Type of Foodservice: Casual Dining (14)
Primary Distributors: (Food) US Foods, MANASSAS, VA

Key Personnel
NATANEL CEDILLO - President; Treasurer; General Manager Finance, Supply Chain, Real Estate, Human Resources; General Buyer

●▲
Dukart Management
2525 Concord Pike
Wilmington, DE 19803-5002

Telephone: (302) 478-9200
Fax Number: (302) 479-0192
Type of Business: Chain Restaurant Operator
Year Founded: 1980
Total Sales: $28,660,000 (e)
Number of Employees: 300
Average Check: Breakfast(8); Lunch(10); Dinner(10)
Total Units: 6
Trade Names: McDonald's (6)
Units Franchised From: 6
Preferred Square Footage: 2,500; 3,000
Preferred Location Types: Community Mall; Freestanding
Primary Menu: Hamburger (6)
Areas of Operation: DE, PA
Type of Foodservice: Quick Serve (6)
Franchise Affiliation: McDonald's Corporation, CHICAGO, IL
Primary Distributors: (Full Line) McLane/Aberdeen, ABERDEEN, MD

Key Personnel
JOEL DUKART - Partner
MICHAEL DUKART - Partner

Harry's Hospitality Group
2020 Naamans Rd
Wilmington, DE 19810-2655

Telephone: (302) 475-3000
Fax Number: (302) 475-9990
Internet Homepage: harrys-savoy.com; harryshospitalitygroup.com; harryshospitalitygroup.com/kid-shelleens
Company Email: info@harrys-savoy.com
Type of Business: Chain Restaurant Operator
Year Founded: 1988
Total Units: 2
Trade Names: Harry's Savoy Grill (1); Kid Shelleen's (1)
Company-Owned Units: 2
Alcohol Served: Beer, Wine, Liquor
Primary Menu: Steak (2)
Areas of Operation: DE
Type of Foodservice: Casual Dining (1); Fine Dining (1)

Key Personnel
XAVIER TEIXIDO - President; General Buyer
NICOLE STEPANIAK - Director Human Resources

‡
Hotel duPont
42 W 11th St
Wilmington, DE 19801

Telephone: (302) 594-3100
Fax Number: (302) 594-3108
Internet Homepage: hoteldupont.com
Company Email: info@hoteldupont.com
Type of Business: Foodservice Operations - Hotel/Motels
Year Founded: 1913
Total Sales: $51,541,000 (e)
Alcohol Sales: 15%
Number of Employees: 400
Total Units: 1
Restaurants in Hotels: 1
Trade Names: Hotel du Pont (1)
Company-Owned Units: 1
Alcohol Served: Beer, Wine, Liquor
Areas of Operation: DE
Type of Foodservice: Fine Dining (1)
Primary Distributors: (Food) SYSCO Food Services of Central Pennsylvania LLC, HARRISBURG, PA
Notes: The company derives approximately 75% of its revenue from hotel operations.

Key Personnel
EDWARD BREEN - CEO
KEITH MILLER - Executive Chef
MERELLA MERULLA - Director Marketing, Sales

The Big Pit
714 Greenbank Rd
Wilmington, DE 19808-3168

Telephone: (302) 998-8853
Fax Number: (302) 998-8853
Internet Homepage: charcoalpit.net
Company Email: comments@charcoalpit.net
Type of Business: Chain Restaurant Operator
Year Founded: 1978
Total Sales: $5,001,000 (e)
Alcohol Sales: 10%
Number of Employees: 80
Average Check: Lunch(14); Dinner(26)
Total Units: 2
Trade Names: Big Pit (1); Charcoal Pit (1)
Company-Owned Units: 2
Preferred Location Types: Freestanding; Strip Mall
Alcohol Served: Beer, Wine, Liquor
Primary Menu: American (2)
Areas of Operation: DE
Type of Foodservice: Casual Dining (2)
Primary Distributors: (Full Line) SYSCO Food Services of Baltimore, JESSUP, MD

Key Personnel
LOUIS CAPANO III - Owner; Executive Chef; General Buyer
MIKE SCIOTA - General Manager; General Buyer

Toscana Kitchen & Bar
1412 N Dupont St
Wilmington, DE 19806-4030

Telephone: (302) 654-8001
Fax Number: (302) 655-8250
Internet Homepage: bigchefguy.com; brandywineprime.com; piccolinatoscana.com; tonicbargrille.com
Type of Business: Chain Restaurant Operator
Year Founded: 1991
Total Sales: $5,271,000 (e)
Alcohol Sales: 20%
Number of Employees: 120
Average Check: Lunch(18); Dinner(42)
Internet Order Processing: Yes
Internet Sales: 10.00%
Total Units: 3
Trade Names: Brandywine Prime (1); Piccolino Toscana (1); Tonic Bar and Grill (1)
Company-Owned Units: 3
Preferred Location Types: Downtown; Freestanding; Strip Mall
Alcohol Served: Beer, Wine, Liquor
Primary Menu: Italian (1); Steak (1); Steak/Seafood (1)
Areas of Operation: DE
Type of Foodservice: Casual Dining (3)
Catering Services: Yes
Primary Distributors: (Supplies) Singer Equipment Co. Inc., ELVERSON, PA

Key Personnel
DAN BUTLER - Owner; Executive Chef; Manager Food Safety; General Buyer

ACW Corp.
2851 Creek Rd
Yorklyn, DE 19736

Telephone: (302) 427-1776
Fax Number: (302) 427-1775
Internet Homepage: acwcorp.com
Type of Business: Chain Restaurant Operator
Year Founded: 1965
Total Sales: $33,780,000 (e)
Number of Employees: 475
Average Check: Breakfast(8); Lunch(10); Dinner(10)
Total Units: 18
Trade Names: Arby's (18)
Units Franchised From: 18
Preferred Square Footage: 2,500; 3,300
Preferred Location Types: Community Mall; Freestanding

Primary Menu: Sandwiches/Deli (18)
Projected Openings: 10
Areas of Operation: DE, MD, NJ, PA, VA
Type of Foodservice: Quick Serve (18)
Franchise Affiliation: Arby's Restaurant Group, ATLANTA, GA
Primary Distributors: (Full Line) Willow Run Foods Inc., KIRKWOOD, NY

Key Personnel
CHARLES CRAWFORD - President; CFO; Director Real Estate, Franchising, Store Fixtures
CHRISTIAN GILLIGAN - VP Purchasing, Supply Chain
DANIELLE TAYLOR - Treasurer; Manager Marketing
MARIA HILGER - Controller
ANNA CRAWFORD - Manager Information Systems, Risk Management, Quality Assurance, Human Resources, Food Safety

FLORIDA

Canteen Vending Services
1050 Miller Dr
Altamonte Springs, FL 32701

Telephone: (407) 862-0800
Listing Type: Branch Office
Type of Business: Foodservice Management Operator
Year Founded: 1929
Number of Employees: 25
Number of Locations Served: 130
Total Foodservice Mgmt Accounts: 130
Areas of Operation: FL
Type of Foodservice: Vending machines (130)
Foodservice Management Venues: Business & Industry; College & University; Health Care; Lodging; Military Feeding; Prison Feeding; Schools; Travel Plazas
Parent Company: Compass Group The Americas, CHARLOTTE, NC
Headquarters: Canteen Vending Services, CHARLOTTE, NC

Key Personnel
DAVE KINSEY - Controller Southeast Division
WES GRIFFITH - General Manager; General Buyer

Firestat, LLC
931 N State Road 434 Unit # 1040
Altamonte Springs, FL 32714

Telephone: (407) 682-7827
Type of Business: Chain Restaurant Operator
Total Sales: $5,752,000 (e)
Total Units: 5

Trade Names: Firehouse Subs (5)
Units Franchised From: 5
Primary Menu: Sandwiches/Deli (5)
Areas of Operation: FL
Type of Foodservice: Fast Casual (5)
Franchise Affiliation: Firehouse Restaurant Group Inc., JACKSONVILLE, FL

Key Personnel
TOM CALATO - President; General Buyer

Kobe Japanese Steak House and Sushi Bar
468 W State Road 436
Altamonte Springs, FL 32714-4147

Telephone: (407) 389-1081
Fax Number: (866) 788-5623
Internet Homepage: kobesteakhouse.com
Company Email: Contactus@kobesteakhouse.com
Type of Business: Chain Restaurant Operator
Year Founded: 1979
Total Sales: $13,940,000 (e)
Alcohol Sales: 20%
Number of Employees: 380
Average Check: Lunch(22); Dinner(36)
Total Units: 11
Trade Names: Kobe Japanese Steak House (11)
Company-Owned Units: 11
Preferred Square Footage: 7,000
Preferred Location Types: Freestanding; Strip Mall
Alcohol Served: Beer, Wine, Liquor
Primary Menu: Japanese (11)
Areas of Operation: FL
Foreign Countries: CANADA
Type of Foodservice: Fine Dining (11)
Catering Services: Yes
Primary Distributors: (Food) SYSCO Food Services of West Coast Florida Inc., PALMETTO, FL

Key Personnel
CHAU NGUYEN - President; Controller; Executive Chef; Director Finance, Facility/Maintenance, Design, Catering; General Buyer
ANTHONY NGUYEN - VP; Director Operations, Purchasing, Information Systems, Supply Chain, Ethnic Marketing; Manager Real Estate
MINHMAN LAVIGNE - VP; Director Human Resources

Sodexo (Campus Services Division)
283 Cranes Roost Blvd Ste 260
Altamonte Springs, FL 32701-3437

Telephone: (407) 339-3230
Fax Number: (407) 260-2305
Listing Type: Divisional Office
Type of Business: Foodservice Management Operator
Number of Employees: 48,000
Number of Locations Served: 900
Total Foodservice Mgmt Accounts: 900
Areas of Operation: FL
Type of Foodservice: Cafeteria (900)
Foodservice Management Venues: College & University
Primary Distributors: (Food) SYSCO Central Florida Inc., OCOEE, FL
Parent Company: Sodexo, MONTIGNY-LE-BRETONNEUX, FRA
Headquarters: Sodexo Inc., GAITHERSBURG, MD

Key Personnel
TOM POST - President

Poppos Taqueria
212C Pine Ave
Anna Maria, FL 34216

Telephone: (941) 254-7941
Internet Homepage: poppostaqueria.com
Type of Business: Chain Restaurant Operator
Total Sales: $8,788,000 (e)
Total Units: 8
Trade Names: Poppos Taqueria (8)
Company-Owned Units: 8
Primary Menu: Mexican (8)
Areas of Operation: FL
Type of Foodservice: Fast Casual (8)

Key Personnel
PATRICK COLEMAN - Co-Founder; Partner
CASEY COLEMAN - Co-Founder; Partner
ROWEN COLEMAN - Co-Founder; Partner
MADELINE OLDENBURG - Director Communications

The Chiles Group
101 Pine Ave
Anna Maria, FL 34216

Mailing Address: PO Box 1478, ANNA MARIA, FL, 34216-1478
Telephone: (941) 778-1696
Fax Number: (941) 778-3997
Internet Homepage: groupersandwich.com
Type of Business: Chain Restaurant Operator
Year Founded: 1979
Total Sales: $27,771,000 (e)
Alcohol Sales: 20%
Number of Employees: 300
Average Check: Lunch(14); Dinner(26)
Internet Order Processing: Yes
Internet Sales: 2.00%
Total Units: 3
Trade Names: Mar-Vista (1); The Beach House (1); The Sandbar (1)
Company-Owned Units: 3
Preferred Location Types: Freestanding
Alcohol Served: Beer, Wine, Liquor
Primary Menu: Seafood (3)
Areas of Operation: FL
Type of Foodservice: Casual Dining (3)
Catering Services: Yes
Primary Distributors: (Full Line) SYSCO Food Services of West Coast Florida Inc., PALMETTO, FL

Key Personnel
EDWARD CHILES - President; General Buyer
DIANE WOJCIECHOWSKI - CFO
MARTHA WRIGHT - CFO
ANTHONY CUCCI - General Manager; Director Catering; General Buyer
DAVID GALLAGHER - General Manager; General Buyer
CARYN V. HODGE - Director Marketing, Advertising

Barbeque Integrated Inc.
2999 NE 191st St Ste 500
Aventura, FL 33180-3117

Telephone: (407) 355-5800
Fax Number: (407) 363-4763
Internet Homepage: smokeybones.com
Company Email: feedback@smokeybones.com
Type of Business: Chain Restaurant Operator
Year Founded: 1996
Total Sales: $233,870,000 (e)
Alcohol Sales: 15%
Number of Employees: 4,000
Average Check: Lunch(14); Dinner(24)
Internet Order Processing: Yes
Total Units: 62
Trade Names: Smokey Bones Bar & Fire Grill (62)
Company-Owned Units: 62
Preferred Square Footage: 7,600
Preferred Location Types: Freestanding
Alcohol Served: Beer, Wine, Liquor
Primary Menu: Bar-B-Q (62)
Areas of Operation: FL, GA, IL, IN, KY, MA, MD, MI, NC, NY, OH, PA, RI, SC, TN, VA
Type of Foodservice: Casual Dining (62)
Primary Distributors: (Full Line) McLane/Rocky Mount, ROCKY MOUNT, NC
Parent Company: Sun Capital Partners Inc., BOCA RATON, FL
Notes: Formerly known as Smokey Bones, the company name was changed following its acquisition by Sun Capital.

Key Personnel
HAL LAWLOR - President; COO
NICOLE COPPOLA MILNTHORPE - CFO
JAVIER RETAMAR - CFO
ALEX SUTTER - Senior VP Operations
NICHOLE ROBILLARD - VP Marketing
LANCE DUNAGAN - General Manager
DOUGLAS MEDINA - Director Purchasing, Supply Chain
BRITTANY WHITE - Manager Operations

Bella Luna
19575 Biscayne Blvd Ste 1097
Aventura, FL 33180-2357

Telephone: (305) 792-9330
Fax Number: (305) 792-9335
Internet Homepage: ilbellagiocityplace.com; bellalunaaventura.com
Type of Business: Chain Restaurant Operator
Year Founded: 1999
Total Sales: $7,263,000 (e)
Alcohol Sales: 10%
Number of Employees: 80
Average Check: Lunch(14); Dinner(20)
Total Units: 7
Trade Names: Bella Luna (1); Bellagio (4); Carpaccio (1); Trattoria Rosalia (1)
Company-Owned Units: 7
Preferred Square Footage: 5,500; 6,000
Preferred Location Types: Strip Mall
Alcohol Served: Beer, Wine, Liquor
Primary Menu: Italian (7)
Areas of Operation: FL
Type of Foodservice: Casual Dining (7)
Primary Distributors: (Food) SYSCO Food Services of South Florida Inc., MEDLEY, FL

Key Personnel
TOM BILLANTE - President; Director Real Estate, Design; General Buyer
MARCOS ROJAS - General Manager
JULIO BOMTEMPO - Executive Chef; General Buyer

Benihana Inc.
21500 Biscayne Blvd
Aventura, FL 33180-1260

Telephone: (305) 593-0770
Fax Number: (305) 592-6371
Internet Homepage: benihana.com; harusushi.com; rasushi.com
Company Email: info@benihana.com
Type of Business: Chain Restaurant Operator
Year Founded: 1964
Systemwide Sales: $1,362,003,000 (e)

Total Sales: $1,186,004,000 (e)
Alcohol Sales: 15%
Number of Employees: 7,400
Average Check: Dinner(34)
Internet Order Processing: Yes
Internet Sales: 15.00%
Total Units: 183
Trade Names: Benihana (90); Haru (8); RA Sushi Bar Restaurant (85)
Company-Owned Units: 173
Units Franchised To: 10
Preferred Square Footage: 5,000; 7,000; 8,000
Preferred Location Types: Downtown; Freestanding; Hotel/Motel; Lifestyle Center; Office Complex; Regional Mall; Stadiums; Strip Mall
Alcohol Served: Beer, Wine, Liquor
Primary Menu: Japanese (183)
Areas of Operation: AK, AR, AZ, CA, CO, FL, GA, HI, IL, IN, KS, MD, MI, MN, MO, NJ, NV, NY, OH, OR, PA, TN, TX, UT, VA, WI
Foreign Countries: ARUBA; BRAZIL; EL SALVADOR; PANAMA
Type of Foodservice: Casual Dining (183)
Primary Distributors: (Full Line) SYSCO Atlanta LLC, COLLEGE PARK, GA
Parent Company: Angelo, Gordon & Co., NEW YORK, NY
Notes: Systemwide sales, alcoholic beverage sales, and average check reflect Benihana concept operations only. The company also operates some 'Ghost Kitchens' for their concepts. These locations have no physical address and are delivery-only.

Key Personnel
NICOLE THAUNG - CFO
MARK LEACH - COO
JEANNIE MEANS - VP Marketing
SETH ROSE - VP Operations
KATHRYN PENDERGAST - VP Operations
FREDDY PARDO - VP People
BETH STUTE - VP Development, Real Estate
VLATA GURFINKEL - Senior Director Financial Planning
LAUREN HALL - Senior Director Marketing
ALFREDO MARTINEZ - Senior Director Beverages
VERONICA GOLDSTEIN - Creative Director
JEREMY SMITH - Director Purchasing
ALEX GONZALEZ - Director Financial Planning
CATHERINE MARQUEZ - Director Marketing
DANIEL TINSTMAN - Director Operations
EDWARD P. GRACE - Director
SARA KAMBER - Director Marketing
THOMAS SLOTNICK - Director Compliance
DAN BAUGH - Director Human Resources
LIZ POWERS - Director Talent Acquisitions
YANIA YANEZ - Manager Marketing, Social Media
WELTON WILLIAMS - Analyst Operations

Salsa Fiesta Grill
18205 Biscayne Blvd Suite 2221
Aventura, FL 33160

Telephone: (305) 358-5751
Internet Homepage: salsafiestagrill.com
Company Email: contact@salsafiestagrill.com
Type of Business: Chain Restaurant Operator
Year Founded: 2004
Total Units: 6
Trade Names: Salsa Fiesta Urban Mex Grill (6)
Company-Owned Units: 6
Preferred Location Types: Downtown; Strip Mall
Primary Menu: Mexican (6)
Areas of Operation: FL
Type of Foodservice: Fast Casual (6)

Key Personnel
CESAR OLIVO - Co-Founder; Partner
ADRIANA P. BENATAR - Co-Founder; Partner; CFO
SAMUEL P. BENATAR - Executive Director
GISEEL HURTADO - Controller
SMILE JIMINIAN - General Manager
DAMIAN PEREZ - General Manager
KAREN RUIZ - General Manager

Domino's Franchisee
1093 W Main St
Avon Park, FL 33825-3313

Telephone: (863) 452-5116
Type of Business: Chain Restaurant Operator
Total Sales: $11,939,000 (e)
Total Units: 6
Trade Names: Domino's (6)
Units Franchised From: 6
Primary Menu: Pizza (6)
Areas of Operation: FL
Type of Foodservice: Quick Serve (6)
Franchise Affiliation: Domino's Pizza Inc, ANN ARBOR, MI

Key Personnel
PAUL ZDANOWICZ - Owner; General Buyer

Action Business Corp.
324 SW 16th St
Belle Glade, FL 33430-2824

Telephone: (561) 996-6581
Fax Number: (561) 996-9155
Type of Business: Chain Restaurant Operator
Total Sales: $26,190,000 (e)
Number of Employees: 250
Average Check: Lunch(8); Dinner(8)
Total Units: 10
Trade Names: Popeyes Louisiana Kitchen (10)
Units Franchised From: 10
Preferred Square Footage: 2,000
Preferred Location Types: Freestanding; Strip Mall
Primary Menu: Chicken (10)
Areas of Operation: FL
Type of Foodservice: Quick Serve (10)
Franchise Affiliation: Popeyes Louisiana Kitchen Inc., ATLANTA, GA

Key Personnel
JIM HERRING - CEO; General Buyer
MIKE ROYAL - Owner; General Buyer
BRANDON ROYAL - Director Accounting

Royal Family Businesses
324 SW 16th St
Belle Glade, FL 33430-2824

Telephone: (561) 996-6581
Fax Number: (561) 996-2538
Internet Homepage: royalfamilybusinesses.com
Company Email: hq@royalsinc.com
Type of Business: Chain Restaurant Operator
Year Founded: 1977
Total Sales: $47,180,000 (e)
Number of Employees: 424
Average Check: Breakfast(5); Lunch(12); Dinner(12)
Total Units: 11
Trade Names: Captain D's (1); Popeyes' Louisiana Kitchen (10)
Units Franchised From: 11
Preferred Square Footage: 3,200
Preferred Location Types: Freestanding
Primary Menu: Chicken (10); Seafood (1)
Projected Openings: 3
Areas of Operation: FL
Type of Foodservice: Quick Serve (11)
Franchise Affiliation: Burger King Worldwide Inc., MIAMI, FL

Key Personnel
GEORGE M. ROYAL - President
MIKE ROYAL - VP Marketing
LUANA HAMILTON - Controller
JUVENAL BLANCO - Director Operations; Manager Purchasing, Store Planning
KIM MANN - Manager Payroll

Domino's Franchisee
1328 NW 2nd Ave
Boca Raton, FL 33432-1660

Telephone: (561) 391-9177
Type of Business: Chain Restaurant Operator
Total Sales: $58,503,000 (e)
Total Units: 29
Trade Names: Domino's (29)
Units Franchised From: 29

Primary Menu: Pizza (29)
Areas of Operation: FL
Type of Foodservice: Quick Serve (29)
Franchise Affiliation: Domino's Pizza Inc, ANN ARBOR, MI

Key Personnel
BRIAN K. JANDREW - Owner; General Buyer

Hospitality Consultants Inc.
622 Banyan Trl Suite 200
Boca Raton, FL 33431

Telephone: (561) 997-4002
Fax Number: (561) 997-4003
Internet Homepage: hcrsi.com
Company Email: bobg@hcrsi.com
Type of Business: Foodservice Operations - Hotel/Motels
Year Founded: 1978
Total Sales: $32,120,000 (e)
Alcohol Sales: 20%
Number of Employees: 112
Total Units: 8
Restaurants in Hotels: 1
Trade Names: Days Inn (1); Hilton (1); Holiday Inn (3); Independent (2); Ramada (1)
Company-Owned Units: 1
Alcohol Served: Beer, Wine, Liquor
Areas of Operation: FL, NE
Type of Foodservice: Casual Dining (1)
Primary Distributors: (Food) SYSCO Food Services of West Coast Florida Inc., PALMETTO, FL
Notes: The company derives approximately 80% of its revenue from hotel operations.

Key Personnel
THOMAS M. HENNESSY JR - Vice Chairman
WICK KELLEY - VP Real Estate

I Heart Mac & Cheese
621 NW 53rd St Suite 360
Boca Raton, FL 33487

Telephone: (561) 893-0101
Internet Homepage: iheartmacandcheese.com
Type of Business: Chain Restaurant Operator
Year Founded: 2016
Total Sales: $46,300,000 (e)
Average Check: Lunch(14); Dinner(14)
Total Units: 121
Trade Names: I Heart Mac & Cheese (121)
Company-Owned Units: 13
Units Franchised To: 108
Preferred Square Footage: 1,600
Primary Menu: Sandwiches/Deli (121)
Projected Openings: 33
Areas of Operation: FL, GA, NY
Type of Foodservice: Fast Casual (121)

Catering Services: Yes

Key Personnel
MICHAEL BLUM - Founder
STEVE GIORDANELLA - CEO
GERARDO DONATIELLO - VP Operations

Janus Hotels and Resorts Inc.
2300 NW Corporate Blvd Ste 232
Boca Raton, FL 33431-7359

Telephone: (561) 997-2325
Fax Number: (561) 997-5331
Internet Homepage: janushotels.com
Company Email: info@janushotels.com
Type of Business: Foodservice Operations - Hotel/Motels
Year Founded: 1991
Total Sales: $68,740,000 (e)
Alcohol Sales: 15%
Number of Employees: 800
Foodservice Sales: $15,810,000 (e)
Total Units: 30
Restaurants in Hotels: 30
Trade Names: Best Western; Comfort Inn; Crowne Plaza; Days Inn; Econolodge; Holiday Inn; Holiday Inn Express; Howard Johnson; Knights Inn; Radisson; Ramada Inn; Red Roof; Sleep Inn; Super 8
Company-Owned Units: 30
Alcohol Served: Beer, Wine, Liquor
Areas of Operation: AZ, CT, FL, IL, IN, KY, MA, MD, MI, MN, NC, NY, OH, OK, PA, VA, WI
Type of Foodservice: Casual Dining
Primary Distributors: (Food) SYSCO Food Services of West Coast Florida Inc., PALMETTO, FL
Notes: The company derives approximately 77% of its revenue from hotel operations & management fees.

Key Personnel
LOUIS S. BECK - Chairman; CEO
MICHAEL M. NANOSKY - President
RICHARD TONGES - CFO; VP Finance; Treasurer
GREG CAPPEL - VP Marketing, Sales
TOM MOORE - VP Operations
ERIC GLAZER - General Counsel
BURTON BONGARD - Senior Director Development
LAURA FLANNERY - Director Human Resources
BRUCE HOHENSTEIN - Regional Director Operations

Miami Subs Grill Corp.
901 Clint Moore Rd Suite A
Boca Raton, FL 33487

Telephone: (954) 973-0000
Fax Number: (954) 973-7616
Internet Homepage: saladcreations.net; miamisubs.com
Company Email: subsgril@miamisubs.com
Type of Business: Chain Restaurant Operator
Year Founded: 1983
Systemwide Sales: $82,999,000 (e)
Total Sales: $12,185,000 (e)
Alcohol Sales: 2.80%
Number of Employees: 345
Average Check: Lunch(12); Dinner(14)
Total Units: 32
Trade Names: Miami Grill (29); Salad Creations (3)
Company-Owned Units: 4
Units Franchised To: 28
Preferred Square Footage: 2,000; 3,500; 5,000
Preferred Location Types: Airports; Community Mall; Downtown; Freestanding; Office Complex; Outlet Mall; Regional Mall; Strip Mall; Travel Plazas
Primary Menu: Health Foods (3); Sandwiches/Deli (29)
Projected Openings: 2
Areas of Operation: FL, HI, IN, SC, TX, FC
Foreign Countries: GUYANA; MALAYSIA
Type of Foodservice: Quick Serve (32)
Foodservice Management Venues: Schools
Catering Services: Yes

Key Personnel
RICHARD CHWATT - CEO
BERNARD VOGEL - CEO
EVAN FRIEDMAN - Co-President; Exec VP
JONATHAN VOGEL - COO
ROBERT HAAR - VP Franchise Development
JEFF BOERGER - VP Corporate Development
ALAN BERGMAN - Executive Chef
JERRY ERNST - Director Purchasing
JACKIE MACEDA - Director Marketing
TODD LIND - Director Information Technology

Raw Juce
2200 Glades Rd Ste 403
Boca Raton, FL 33431-7348

Telephone: (561) 424-5823
Internet Homepage: rawjuce.com
Type of Business: Chain Restaurant Operator
Year Founded: 2013
Total Units: 9
Trade Names: Raw Juce (9)
Company-Owned Units: 9
Primary Menu: Health Foods (9)
Projected Openings: 2

Areas of Operation: FL
Type of Foodservice: Quick Serve (9)

Key Personnel
STEVE SHAFFER - Founder
BARRY RABKIN - Co-Founder; Partner
JEFF LEVINE - Co-Founder; Partner
CHLOE THURSTON - General Manager
TEDDY KAUFMAN - Director Operations; Manager Human Resources

Rotelli Pizza & Pasta Inc.
4755 Technology Way Ste 1-101
Boca Raton, FL 33431-3325

Telephone: (561) 826-0900
Fax Number: (561) 826-0901
Internet Homepage: rotellipizzapasta.com
Company Email: info@rotellipp.com
Type of Business: Chain Restaurant Operator
Year Founded: 1999
Systemwide Sales: $80,008,000 (e)
Total Sales: $49,540,000 (e)
Alcohol Sales: 12%
Number of Employees: 400
Average Check: Lunch(14); Dinner(22)
Total Units: 26
Trade Names: Rotelli Pizza & Pasta (26)
Company-Owned Units: 7
Units Franchised To: 19
Preferred Square Footage: 5,500; 6,000
Preferred Location Types: Community Mall; Freestanding; Regional Mall; Strip Mall
Alcohol Served: Beer, Wine, Liquor
Primary Menu: Italian (26)
Areas of Operation: CO, FL, NC, OH, PA, SC
Type of Foodservice: Casual Dining (26)
Catering Services: Yes
Primary Distributors: (Food) Cheney Bros. Inc., RIVIERA BEACH, FL

Key Personnel
JOSEPH J. BILOTTI JR - CEO; President; Director Operations, Facility/Maintenance, Sales, Real Estate, Design, Store Fixtures
PATRICK MORRIS - COO
SHARON GORANT - Office Manager

Seabreeze Pizza, LLC
5455 N Federal Hwy Ste D
Boca Raton, FL 33487-4994

Telephone: (561) 997-6622
Fax Number: (561) 995-6984
Type of Business: Chain Restaurant Operator
Total Sales: $1,521,000 (e)
Total Units: 2
Trade Names: Little Caesars Pizza (2)
Units Franchised From: 2
Primary Menu: Pizza (2)
Areas of Operation: FL
Type of Foodservice: Quick Serve (2)
Catering Services: Yes
Franchise Affiliation: Little Caesar Enterprises Inc., DETROIT, MI

Key Personnel
TERRY MAX - President; General Buyer
CHERYL GOMMEL - Manager Accounting

St Andrews Country Club
17557 Claridge Oval W
Boca Raton, FL 33496-1336

Telephone: (561) 487-1110
Fax Number: (561) 477-7217
Internet Homepage: standrewscc.com
Type of Business: Nontraditional Foodservice Operator
Year Founded: 1982
Total Sales: $10,535,000 (e)
Alcohol Sales: 15%
Number of Employees: 75
Average Check: Lunch(12); Dinner(22)
Total Units: 3
Trade Names: Cafe Blue (1); Gallery Dining Room (1); Lakeside Grill (1)
Company-Owned Units: 3
Preferred Location Types: Freestanding; Other
Alcohol Served: Beer, Wine, Liquor
Primary Menu: American (3)
Areas of Operation: FL
Type of Foodservice: Casual Dining (2); Fine Dining (1)
Primary Distributors: (Food) SYSCO Food Services of South Florida Inc., MEDLEY, FL
Notes: The company derives approximately 60% of its revenue from golf club operations.

Key Personnel
CRAIG MARTIN - CEO; General Manager; General Buyer
KEVIN LOU LOUGHNEY - Director Facility/Maintenance
ARI AJOY - Manager Food and Beverage

Tossed Franchise Corporation
851 Broken Sound Pkwy NW Ste 136
Boca Raton, FL 33487

Telephone: (561) 617-1836
Internet Homepage: tossed.com
Company Email: amt@tossed.com
Type of Business: Chain Restaurant Operator
Year Founded: 1998
Systemwide Sales: $7,148,000 (e)
Total Sales: $477,000 (e)
Number of Employees: 116
Average Check: Lunch(10); Dinner(10)
Internet Order Processing: Yes
Total Units: 4
Trade Names: Tossed (4)
Company-Owned Units: 1
Units Franchised To: 3
Preferred Square Footage: 250; 1,400; 1,600
Preferred Location Types: Airports; Freestanding; Institution (college/hospital); Kiosk
Primary Menu: American (5)
Areas of Operation: CA, FL, MA, NC, NY, BC
Foreign Countries: CANADA
Type of Foodservice: Fast Casual (4)
Catering Services: Yes

Key Personnel
A. MICHAEL TOROYAN - COO; Chief Development Officer
BRUCE CHODASH - Corporate Secretary; Director
LEAH SINGH - Director Catering

Phelan Holdings, Inc.
3820 Via Del Rey
Bonita Springs, FL 34134

Telephone: (239) 431-5504
Fax Number: (239) 260-1350
Internet Homepage: deeplagoon.com; pinchersusa.com; texastonys.com
Company Email: info@phelanbrands.com
Type of Business: Chain Restaurant Operator
Year Founded: 2004
Total Sales: $26,370,000 (e)
Alcohol Sales: 10%
Number of Employees: 776
Internet Order Processing: Yes
Internet Sales: 1.00%
Total Units: 17
Trade Names: Deep Lagoon (2); Pinchers Crab Shack (13); Texas Tony's BBQ Shack (2)
Company-Owned Units: 17
Alcohol Served: Beer, Wine, Liquor
Primary Menu: Bar-B-Q (2); Seafood (15)
Areas of Operation: FL
Type of Foodservice: Casual Dining (17)

Key Personnel
ANTHONY L. PHELAN - President; General Buyer
ADAM PHELAN - Controller
GRANT PHELAN - Director Operations

Bud's Chicken & Seafood
518 Industrial Ave Ste 12
Boynton Beach, FL 33426-3664

Telephone: (561) 736-3344
Internet Homepage: budschicken.com
Type of Business: Chain Restaurant Operator
Year Founded: 1957

Total Sales: $9,411,000 (e)
Number of Employees: 215
Average Check: Lunch(16); Dinner(16)
Total Units: 6
Trade Names: Bud's Chicken & Seafood (6)
Company-Owned Units: 6
Preferred Square Footage: 2,900
Preferred Location Types: Freestanding
Primary Menu: American (6)
Areas of Operation: FL
Type of Foodservice: Quick Serve (6)
Catering Services: Yes
Primary Distributors: (Full Line) Cheney Bros. Inc., RIVIERA BEACH, FL
Parent Company: B.T.O. Management Group, BOYNTON BEACH, FL

Key Personnel
TOM BRINKMAN - VP

Dragon House, LLC
1787 N Congress Ave Ste 2
Boynton Beach, FL 33426-8208

Telephone: (561) 739-5353
Type of Business: Chain Restaurant Operator
Total Sales: $1,192,000 (e)
Total Units: 2
Trade Names: Cold Stone Creamery (2)
Units Franchised From: 2
Primary Menu: Snacks (2)
Areas of Operation: FL
Type of Foodservice: Quick Serve (2)
Franchise Affiliation: Kahala Brands, SCOTTSDALE, AZ

Key Personnel
GERALDINE DRAGOVICH - Partner
JENNIFER DRAGOVICH - Partner

Restaurant Holdings Inc.
4600 N Ocean Blvd Ste 100
Boynton Beach, FL 33435-7365

Telephone: (561) 278-0356
Fax Number: (561) 243-3147
Internet Homepage: bananaboatboynton.com; primecatchboynton.com
Company Email: rholding@bellsouth.net
Type of Business: Chain Restaurant Operator
Year Founded: 1990
Total Sales: $4,836,000 (e)
Alcohol Sales: 20%
Number of Employees: 60
Average Check: Breakfast(18); Lunch(18); Dinner(34)
Total Units: 2
Trade Names: Banana Boat (1); Prime Catch (1)
Company-Owned Units: 2
Preferred Location Types: Freestanding

Alcohol Served: Beer, Wine, Liquor
Primary Menu: Seafood (2)
Areas of Operation: FL
Type of Foodservice: Casual Dining (2)
Primary Distributors: (Food) SYSCO Food Services of Chicago Inc., DES PLAINES, IL

Key Personnel
GILLES THERIEN - Partner; General Manager; Executive Chef; General Buyer
LUKE THERIEN - Partner; VP; General Manager
JOHN BONK - Executive Chef

Basil's Franchising
5917 Manatee Ave W
Bradenton, FL 34209-2407

Telephone: (941) 794-5222
Internet Homepage: basilschicken.com
Type of Business: Chain Restaurant Operator
Year Founded: 1987
Systemwide Sales: $4,724,000 (e)
Total Sales: $4,195,000 (e)
Number of Employees: 60
Average Check: Lunch(8); Dinner(10)
Internet Order Processing: Yes
Internet Sales: 1.00%
Total Units: 3
Trade Names: Basil Flame Broil Chicken and Ribs (3)
Company-Owned Units: 2
Units Franchised To: 1
Preferred Location Types: Freestanding
Primary Menu: Chicken (3)
Areas of Operation: FL
Type of Foodservice: Family Restaurant (3)
Catering Services: Yes

Key Personnel
NICK MALLIARAS - President; CFO; Director Catering; General Buyer
STAVROS MALLIARAS - VP; Executive Chef

Duff's Buffet
6010 14th St W
Bradenton, FL 34207-4104

Telephone: (941) 752-3666
Fax Number: (941) 752-5983
Internet Homepage: duffsbuffet.com
Type of Business: Chain Restaurant Operator
Year Founded: 1995
Total Sales: $5,170,000 (e)
Number of Employees: 400
Average Check: Lunch(12); Dinner(10)
Total Units: 3
Trade Names: Duff's Buffet (3)
Company-Owned Units: 3
Preferred Square Footage: 16,000
Preferred Location Types: Freestanding; Strip Mall
Primary Menu: American (3)
Areas of Operation: FL
Type of Foodservice: Family Restaurant (3)
Primary Distributors: (Food) Cheney Bros., PUNTA GORDA, FL

Key Personnel
RANDY KISER - Owner; General Buyer
DOUG JENSEN - General Manager; General Buyer

First Watch Restaurants Inc.
8725 Pendery Place Suite 201
Bradenton, FL 34201

Telephone: (941) 907-9800
Fax Number: (941) 907-8933
Internet Homepage: firstwatch.com; theeggandirestaurants.com; thegoodeggaz.com; sunandfork.com
Company Email: comments@firstwatch.com
Type of Business: Chain Restaurant Operator
Year Founded: 1983
Systemwide Sales: $669,118,000 (e)
Publicly Held: Yes
Total Sales: $542,321,000 (e)
Number of Employees: 2,794
Average Check: Breakfast(10); Lunch(14);
Total Units: 524
Trade Names: First Watch (523); Sun & Fork (1)
Company-Owned Units: 425
Units Franchised To: 99
Preferred Square Footage: 3,200; 4,000; 4,500
Preferred Location Types: Freestanding; Lifestyle Center; Strip Mall
Primary Menu: American (524)
Projected Openings: 3
Areas of Operation: AR, AZ, CO, FL, GA, IL, IN, KS, KY, MD, ME, MO, NC, NE, NM, OH, OK, PA, TN, TX, UT, VA, WI, WV, WY
Type of Foodservice: Family Restaurant (524)
Subsidiaries: E&I Holdings Inc., DENVER, CO
Primary Distributors: (Full Line) SYSCO Central Florida Inc., OCOEE, FL
Parent Company: Advent International Corporation, BOSTON, MA

Key Personnel
CHRISTOPHER A. TOMASSO - CEO; President; Partner
MEL HOPE - CFO
LAURA SORENSEN - Chief People Officer
ROB CONTI - CIO
ERIC HARTMAN - Chief Development Officer; Exec VP
JAY WOLSZCZAK - Chief Legal Officer; General Counsel
MATTHEW EISENACHER - Chief Brand Officer
BRIAN FISHER - Senior VP Operations
DANNY FOSTER - VP Construction, Design

DAVID LYNCH - VP Region
LILAH TAHA-RIPPETT - VP Purchasing
SHANE SCHAIBLY - Corporate Chef
JENNIFER SWAN - Senior Director Employee Development
MATTHEW LIVINGSTON - Senior Director Real Estate
JESSICA REPLOGLE - Senior Director Marketing
KARINA STASI - Director Human Resources
CHRISTOPHER MANGINO - Director Information Technology
RENEE HOOD - Director Human Resources
MARGARET FARRINGTON - Director Operations
ROBERT BAKER - Director Restaurant Operations
JOSH BERNARD - Director Operations
DAVID LOETSCHER - Regional Director Operations
ANTHONY SULLIVAN - Manager Operations
REILLEY GEIGER - Manager Operations
BRIAN VELDHEER - Manager Infrastructure
MATTHEW ARNWINE - Project Manager Construction

Mahana Fresh
4808 14th St W
Bradenton, FL 34207

Telephone: (941) 216-3890
Internet Homepage: mahanafresh.com
Type of Business: Chain Restaurant Operator
Year Founded: 2019
Systemwide Sales: $5,780,000 (e)
Total Sales: $4,298,000 (e)
Total Units: 4
Trade Names: Mahana Fresh (4)
Company-Owned Units: 1
Units Franchised To: 3
Primary Menu: Health Foods (4)
Areas of Operation: FL, NC, VA
Type of Foodservice: Fast Casual (4)

Key Personnel
JOHN THOMAS - President
DAVE BAER - COO
JEFF TARLTON - Director Franchise Development

Pat & J, Inc.
621 Cortez Rd W
Bradenton, FL 34207-1549

Telephone: (941) 727-1818
Type of Business: Chain Restaurant Operator
Total Sales: $2,463,000 (e)
Total Units: 2
Trade Names: Firehouse Subs (2)
Units Franchised From: 2
Primary Menu: Sandwiches/Deli (2)
Areas of Operation: FL
Type of Foodservice: Fast Casual (2)
Franchise Affiliation: Firehouse Restaurant Group Inc., JACKSONVILLE, FL

Key Personnel
DON FOX - CEO Division

SWS Operations
1403 57th Ave W Frnt
Bradenton, FL 34207-3641

Telephone: (941) 758-3030
Fax Number: (941) 753-6760
Type of Business: Chain Restaurant Operator
Total Sales: $55,453,000 (e)
Average Check: Dinner(28)
Total Units: 28
Trade Names: Domino's (28)
Units Franchised From: 28
Primary Menu: Pizza (28)
Areas of Operation: FL
Type of Foodservice: Quick Serve (28)
Franchise Affiliation: Domino's Pizza Inc, ANN ARBOR, MI

Key Personnel
ERIN MULLINS - President; General Buyer

3 Square Restaurant Group LLC
2042 Badlands Dr
Brandon, FL 33511

Telephone: (813) 689-1611
Fax Number: (813) 689-1411
Internet Homepage: bellasitaliancafe.com; square1burgers.com
Type of Business: Chain Restaurant Operator
Year Founded: 2006
Total Sales: $6,839,000 (e)
Alcohol Sales: 10%
Number of Employees: 159
Total Units: 3
Trade Names: Square 1 Burgers & Bar (3)
Company-Owned Units: 3
Preferred Location Types: Freestanding; Strip Mall
Alcohol Served: Beer, Wine, Liquor
Primary Menu: Hamburger (3)
Areas of Operation: FL
Type of Foodservice: Casual Dining (3)

Key Personnel
SHERRI RUTOLO - Partner

Capital Tacos
119 W Bloomingdale Ave
Brandon, FL 33511

Telephone: (813) 315-8752
Internet Homepage: capitaltacos.com
Company Email: hello@capitaltacos.com
Type of Business: Chain Restaurant Operator
Year Founded: 2013
Total Units: 6
Trade Names: Capital Tacos (6)
Company-Owned Units: 6
Primary Menu: Taco (6)
Projected Openings: 1
Areas of Operation: FL
Type of Foodservice: Fast Casual (6)

Key Personnel
KRISTEL HESKETT - Partner
BOBBY HESKETT - Partner; General Buyer
JOEL BULGER - Chief Marketing Officer

Managing Foods
1326 E Lumsden Rd
Brandon, FL 33511-6717

Telephone: (813) 684-0622
Fax Number: (813) 661-5184
Internet Homepage: kazborsgrille.com
Company Email: info@kazborsgrille.com
Type of Business: Chain Restaurant Operator
Year Founded: 1984
Total Sales: $80,590,000 (e)
Alcohol Sales: 20%
Number of Employees: 590
Average Check: Lunch(12); Dinner(14)
Total Units: 63
Trade Names: Hungry Howie's Pizza (63)
Units Franchised From: 63
Preferred Square Footage: 300; 1,000; 1,500
Preferred Location Types: Downtown; Freestanding; Strip Mall
Alcohol Served: Beer, Wine, Liquor
Primary Menu: Pizza (63)
Areas of Operation: AL, FL
Type of Foodservice: Quick Serve (63)
Franchise Affiliation: Hungry Howie's Pizza & Subs Inc., MADISON HEIGHTS, MI

Key Personnel
TOM KAZBOUR - President; Partner; General Buyer
ZIAD KAZBOUR - Partner
HABIB KAZBOUR - Partner
TAREK KAZBOUR - Partner; General Buyer

Moe's Southwest Grill Largo
2338 W Brandon Blvd
Brandon, FL 33511-4715

Telephone: (813) 681-0955
Internet Homepage: moes.com
Type of Business: Chain Restaurant Operator
Total Sales: $9,919,000 (e)
Total Units: 6
Trade Names: Moe's Southwest Grill (6)
Units Franchised From: 6
Primary Menu: Southwest/Tex-Mex (6)
Areas of Operation: FL
Type of Foodservice: Fast Casual (6)
Franchise Affiliation: Moe's Southwest Grill LLC, ATLANTA, GA

Key Personnel
ANTHONY FRIEL - Partner; General Buyer
KEN FRANKLIN - Partner

Phil Mook Enterprises
1108 W Brandon Blvd
Brandon, FL 33511-4128

Telephone: (813) 681-4841
Fax Number: (813) 654-0575
Type of Business: Chain Restaurant Operator
Year Founded: 1963
Total Sales: $16,020,000 (e)
Number of Employees: 210
Average Check: Lunch(8); Dinner(12)
Total Units: 9
Trade Names: KFC (9)
Units Franchised From: 9
Preferred Square Footage: 2,800
Preferred Location Types: Freestanding
Primary Menu: Chicken (9)
Areas of Operation: FL
Type of Foodservice: Quick Serve (9)
Franchise Affiliation: KFC Corporation, LOUISVILLE, KY
Primary Distributors: (Full Line) Kelly's Foods Inc., WINTER GARDEN, FL

Key Personnel
CHRIS MOOK - President; Director Operations, Purchasing, Real Estate, Design
JENNIFER MOOK - Director Human Resources; Manager Facility/Maintenance, Information Systems, Risk Management

Domino's Franchisee
19526 Cortez Blvd
Brooksville, FL 34601-3157

Telephone: (352) 796-8888
Type of Business: Chain Restaurant Operator
Total Sales: $6,069,000 (e)
Total Units: 3
Trade Names: Domino's (3)
Units Franchised From: 3
Primary Menu: Pizza (3)
Areas of Operation: FL
Type of Foodservice: Quick Serve (3)
Franchise Affiliation: Domino's Pizza Inc, ANN ARBOR, MI

Key Personnel
MATTHEW WACKERBARTH - Owner; General Buyer

J & J Industry Inc.
315 Howell Ave
Brooksville, FL 34601-2039

Telephone: (352) 799-6872
Fax Number: (352) 799-6874
Type of Business: Chain Restaurant Operator
Year Founded: 1974
Total Sales: $56,720,000 (e)
Number of Employees: 530
Average Check: Breakfast(8); Lunch(8); Dinner(10)
Total Units: 12
Trade Names: McDonald's (12)
Units Franchised From: 12
Preferred Square Footage: 2,500
Preferred Location Types: Discount Dept. Stores; Freestanding
Primary Menu: Hamburger (12)
Areas of Operation: FL
Type of Foodservice: Quick Serve (12)
Franchise Affiliation: McDonald's Corporation, CHICAGO, IL

Key Personnel
JOE DAVID - President; Manager Finance, Information Systems, Supply Chain, Real Estate; General Buyer

IAP Worldwide Services
7315 N Atlantic Ave
Cape Canaveral, FL 32920-3721

Telephone: (321) 784-7100
Fax Number: (321) 784-7336
Internet Homepage: iapws.com
Company Email: Barbara.A.Jerich@iapws.com
Type of Business: Foodservice Management Operator
Year Founded: 1989
Total Sales: $183,491,000 (e)
Number of Employees: 356
Number of Locations Served: 160
Total Foodservice Mgmt Accounts: 160
Areas of Operation: SC
Type of Foodservice: Cafeteria (80); Mobile units/kiosks (80)
Foodservice Management Venues: Business & Industry; Military Feeding
Primary Distributors: (Food) SYSCO Food Services of South Florida Inc., MEDLEY, FL
Notes: The company derives approximately 95% of its revenue from procurement and management operations.

Key Personnel
ROBERT HARGIS - COO
DALE THORNTON - Senior VP Business Development
LEIGHANN OWENS - VP Human Resources; Senior Director Human Resources
DANIEL RUSSELL - VP
ANNA LUEJE - General Counsel
ROBERT EGGE - Senior Director Human Resources
MARCUS WARD - Director Operations, Business Development
JENNIFER WILLIAMS - Director Talent
DENNIS SLADE - Senior Manager Logistics
LESA MADDEN - Senior Manager
KARI LACOSTE-JONES - Manager Procurement
JEFFREY MONTROY - Project Manager Architecture
PETER SCIACCA - Specialist Procurement
HENRY MATTA - Senior Analyst HRIS
CHARLES ENGASSER - Engineer Network

Domino's Franchisee
3904 Skyline Blvd
Cape Coral, FL 33914-5835

Telephone: (239) 945-0040
Company Email: dominos3884@live.com
Type of Business: Chain Restaurant Operator
Total Sales: $8,187,000 (e)
Total Units: 4
Trade Names: Domino's (4)
Units Franchised From: 4
Primary Menu: Pizza (4)
Areas of Operation: FL
Type of Foodservice: Quick Serve (4)
Franchise Affiliation: Domino's Pizza Inc, ANN ARBOR, MI

Key Personnel
NANCY DRURY - Owner; General Buyer

Guerrieri Management, Inc.
1128 Country Club Blvd
Cape Coral, FL 33990-3096

Telephone: (239) 573-3674
Fax Number: (239) 573-3679
Type of Business: Chain Restaurant Operator
Total Sales: $43,190,000 (e)
Number of Employees: 172
Total Units: 16
Trade Names: Taco Bell (16)

Units Franchised From: 16
Primary Menu: Taco (16)
Projected Openings: 2
Areas of Operation: FL
Type of Foodservice: Quick Serve (16)
Franchise Affiliation: Taco Bell Corp., IRVINE, CA

Key Personnel
GORDON GUERRIERI - President; General Buyer

Iguana Mia
1027 Cape Coral Pkwy E
Cape Coral, FL 33904-9160

Telephone: (239) 945-7755
Internet Homepage: iguanamia.com
Company Email: juan@iguana.com
Type of Business: Chain Restaurant Operator
Year Founded: 1990
Total Sales: $14,903,000 (e)
Alcohol Sales: 20%
Number of Employees: 74
Average Check: Lunch(12); Dinner(14)
Internet Order Processing: Yes
Internet Sales: 0.25%
Total Units: 3
Trade Names: Iguana Mia (3)
Company-Owned Units: 3
Preferred Location Types: Freestanding; Travel Plazas
Alcohol Served: Beer, Wine, Liquor
Primary Menu: Mexican (3)
Areas of Operation: FL
Foreign Countries: UNITED STATES OF AMERICA
Type of Foodservice: Casual Dining (3)
Catering Services: Yes
Primary Distributors: (Food) SYSCO Food Services of West Coast Florida Inc., PALMETTO, FL

Key Personnel
MICHAEL ATHERTON - President; Director Finance, Purchasing
DIRK ARTHERTON - Owner
JULIAN PRIETO - VP Quality Assurance, Menu Development, Food Safety, Catering; Executive Chef
TODD HARRISON - Director Operations

Michael Silverman, LLC
1631 Del Prado Blvd S Ste 412
Cape Coral, FL 33990-6741

Telephone: (239) 458-9303
Type of Business: Chain Restaurant Operator
Total Sales: $16,520,000 (e)
Total Units: 10
Trade Names: Moe's Southwest Grill (10)
Units Franchised From: 10
Primary Menu: Southwest/Tex-Mex (10)
Areas of Operation: FL
Type of Foodservice: Fast Casual (10)
Franchise Affiliation: Moe's Southwest Grill LLC, ATLANTA, GA

Key Personnel
MICHAEL SILVERMAN - Owner; General Buyer

3Bm Enterprises Inc
1291 State Road 436
Casselberry, FL 32707-6402

Telephone: (407) 645-3612
Type of Business: Chain Restaurant Operator
Total Sales: $28,220,000 (e)
Total Units: 6
Trade Names: McDonald's (6)
Units Franchised From: 6
Primary Menu: Hamburger (6)
Areas of Operation: FL
Type of Foodservice: Quick Serve (6)
Franchise Affiliation: McDonald's Corporation, CHICAGO, IL

Key Personnel
TIMOTHY E. WRIGHT - President; General Buyer
KIM WRIGHT - Manager Customer Service

Celebration Restaurant Group, LLC
1146 Celebration Blvd
Celebration, FL 34747-4605

Telephone: (321) 939-2924
Fax Number: (321) 939-2823
Internet Homepage: celebrationrg.com
Type of Business: Chain Restaurant Operator
Year Founded: 2009
Total Sales: $250,390,000 (e)
Alcohol Sales: 7%
Number of Employees: 4,625
Average Check: Lunch(14); Dinner(20)
Internet Order Processing: Yes
Internet Sales: 2.00%
Total Units: 163
Trade Names: KFC (3); Pizza Hut (127); Taco Bell (33)
Units Franchised From: 163
Preferred Square Footage: 2,500
Preferred Location Types: Freestanding; Strip Mall
Alcohol Served: Beer
Primary Menu: Chicken (3); Pizza (127); Taco (33)
Areas of Operation: FL, IN, KY, OH
Type of Foodservice: Fine Dining (127); Quick Serve (39)
Subsidiaries: Bravo Foods LLC, COCOA, FL
Franchise Affiliation: KFC Corporation, LOUISVILLE, KY; Pizza Hut Inc., PLANO, TX; Taco Bell Corp., IRVINE, CA
Notes: Celebration Restaurant Group is comprised of CFL Pizza (Pizza Hut franchises) and Bravo Foods (Taco Bell franchises).

Key Personnel
ANDY ROSEN - CEO; President; General Buyer
CARL VANNOSTRAND - President; COO
VIKKI HODGKINS - CFO
JANET STEWART - Chief People Officer
KRISTEN ORTON - Director Operations
MEGHAN OSBORN - Director Marketing
RUMONE TRAILL - Director Operations
RUTH CARABALLO - Manager Human Resources
JACKIE FREEMAN - Manager Human Resources
MEGHAN STRONGRICH - Manager Marketing
COURTNEY PETERS - Coordinator Marketing

GALO Enterprises
1014 Main St
Chipley, FL 32428-1927

Mailing Address: PO Box 547, CHIPLEY, FL, 32428-0547
Telephone: (850) 638-9808
Fax Number: (850) 638-9828
Type of Business: Chain Restaurant Operator
Total Sales: $4,939,000 (e)
Number of Employees: 170
Average Check: Breakfast(8); Lunch(10); Dinner(10)
Total Units: 11
Trade Names: Subway (11)
Units Franchised From: 11
Preferred Square Footage: 300; 2,000
Preferred Location Types: Freestanding; Strip Mall
Primary Menu: Sandwiches/Deli (11)
Areas of Operation: FL
Type of Foodservice: Quick Serve (11)
Franchise Affiliation: Doctor's Associates Inc., MILFORD, CT
Primary Distributors: (Full Line) Southeastern Food Merchandisers, PELHAM, AL

Key Personnel
STACI CLARK - Owner; COO; General Buyer

Auntie Anne's Franchise
27001 US Highway 19 N Ste 2008
Clearwater, FL 33761-3418

Telephone: (727) 791-3922
Type of Business: Chain Restaurant Operator
Total Sales: $5,030,000 (e)
Total Units: 7

Trade Names: Auntie Anne's Hand-Rolled Soft Pretzels (7)
Units Franchised From: 7
Primary Menu: Snacks (7)
Areas of Operation: FL
Type of Foodservice: Quick Serve (7)
Franchise Affiliation: Auntie Anne's Inc., LANCASTER, PA

Key Personnel
RALPH JUDY - Owner; General Buyer

Carmel Kitchen & Wine Bar
2548 N McMullen Booth Rd
Clearwater, FL 33761-4150

Telephone: (727) 724-4228
Internet Homepage: carmel-kitchen.com
Company Email: countryside@carmel-kitchen.com
Type of Business: Chain Restaurant Operator
Year Founded: 2011
Total Sales: $6,399,000 (e)
Average Check: Lunch(14); Dinner(30)
Total Units: 2
Trade Names: Carmel Cafe & Wine Bar (2)
Company-Owned Units: 2
Preferred Location Types: Freestanding; Strip Mall
Alcohol Served: Beer, Wine, Liquor
Primary Menu: Greek/Mediterranean (2)
Areas of Operation: FL
Type of Foodservice: Casual Dining (2)
Catering Services: Yes

Key Personnel
TAMMY DUNNE - VP
SANDAL SANDERS - Director Catering

COR Enterprises Inc.
2430 Estancia Blvd Ste 106
Clearwater, FL 33761-2607

Telephone: (727) 799-9972
Fax Number: (727) 724-8499
Internet Homepage: codysoriginalroadhouse.com
Company Email: info@codysoriginalroadhouse.com
Type of Business: Chain Restaurant Operator
Year Founded: 1971
Systemwide Sales: $33,818,000 (e)
Total Sales: $4,724,000 (e)
Alcohol Sales: 25%
Number of Employees: 40
Average Check: Lunch(14); Dinner(22)
Internet Order Processing: Yes
Total Units: 11
Trade Names: Cody's Original Roadhouse (11)
Company-Owned Units: 1
Units Franchised To: 10

Preferred Square Footage: 6,000
Preferred Location Types: Freestanding; Strip Mall
Alcohol Served: Beer, Wine, Liquor
Primary Menu: American (11)
Projected Openings: 3
Areas of Operation: FL
Type of Foodservice: Casual Dining (11)
Catering Services: Yes
Primary Distributors: (Full Line) US Foods, TAMPA, FL
Parent Company: Morrison Companies, BATON ROUGE, LA

Key Personnel
SAM MEGALLA - President; General Buyer
BRIAN CORCORAN - Owner
JAN SHENDOK - Controller
JODI MACKAY - Director Development
LYNETTE MCKEE - Director Franchise Sales

Hooters Management Corp.
107 Hampton Rd Ste 200
Clearwater, FL 33759-4960

Telephone: (727) 725-2551
Fax Number: (727) 725-4717
Internet Homepage: originalhooters.com
Type of Business: Chain Restaurant Operator
Year Founded: 1983
Total Sales: $105,500,000 (e)
Alcohol Sales: 40%
Number of Employees: 1,732
Average Check: Lunch(10); Dinner(14)
Internet Order Processing: Yes
Internet Sales: 5.00%
Total Units: 25
Trade Names: Hooters (25)
Company-Owned Units: 25
Preferred Square Footage: 3,800; 5,000
Preferred Location Types: Freestanding; Strip Mall; Travel Plazas
Alcohol Served: Beer, Wine, Liquor
Primary Menu: American (25)
Projected Openings: 1
Areas of Operation: FL, IL, NY
Type of Foodservice: Casual Dining (25)
Franchise Affiliation: HOA Restaurant Group LLC, ATLANTA, GA
Primary Distributors: (Full Line) SYSCO Food Services of West Coast Florida Inc., PALMETTO, FL

Key Personnel
GIL DIGIANNANTONIO - Co-Founder; Partner
NEIL KIEFER - CEO; President; Partner; Director Real Estate
BRUCE CLARK - CFO
JEFFREY HALL - CIO; CTO
STEVE BALDACCI - VP Operations
BILL MOORE - VP Operations
CHUCK RILEY - VP Purchasing, Supply Chain
LEAH ROBERTS - VP Marketing

SETH BAUMAN - General Manager
ANDREA HILL - Director Operations
NICOLE JOHNSTON - Director Human Resources
NICOLE ZIMMERLE - Director Human Resources
LISA ALLEN - Regional Director Operations
WAYNE CORRISTON - Manager Restaurant Operations
ROSALYNE FOLLMAN - Coordinator Training

Sunstate Restaurant Management Inc.
1777 St Pauls Dr
Clearwater, FL 33764-6461

Telephone: (727) 443-4464
Fax Number: (727) 444-4464
Type of Business: Chain Restaurant Operator
Year Founded: 1995
Total Sales: $8,899,000 (e)
Number of Employees: 170
Average Check: Lunch(8); Dinner(10)
Total Units: 6
Trade Names: Checkers (6)
Units Franchised From: 6
Preferred Square Footage: 500
Preferred Location Types: Freestanding
Primary Menu: Hamburger (6)
Areas of Operation: FL
Type of Foodservice: Quick Serve (6)
Franchise Affiliation: Checkers Drive-In Restaurants Inc., TAMPA, FL
Primary Distributors: (Food) McLane/Orlando, ORLANDO, FL

Key Personnel
R. CRAIG JOY - President; Director Information Systems, Real Estate, Human Resources; General Buyer
MELINDA SHARPE - Manager Finance
BARBARA CROUTHERS - Manager Operations

Team St. Pete Inc.
2659 Ulmerton Rd
Clearwater, FL 33762-3337

Telephone: (727) 571-1281
Type of Business: Chain Restaurant Operator
Total Sales: $30,308,000 (e)
Total Units: 15
Trade Names: Domino's (15)
Units Franchised From: 15
Preferred Square Footage: 1,000
Preferred Location Types: Strip Mall
Primary Menu: Pizza (15)
Areas of Operation: FL
Type of Foodservice: Quick Serve (15)
Franchise Affiliation: Domino's Pizza Inc, ANN ARBOR, MI

Privett Management Group
100 S Berner Rd
Clewiston, FL 33440

Telephone: (863) 805-0720
Internet Homepage: privettmg.com
Company Email: ken@daniamg.com
Type of Business: Chain Restaurant Operator
Total Sales: $9,327,000 (e)
Number of Employees: 134
Average Check: Breakfast(5); Lunch(5); Dinner(5)
Total Units: 6
Trade Names: Dunkin' Donuts (6)
Units Franchised From: 6
Preferred Square Footage: 1,500; 2,200
Preferred Location Types: Freestanding; Strip Mall
Primary Menu: Snacks (6)
Areas of Operation: FL, TN
Type of Foodservice: Quick Serve (6)
Franchise Affiliation: DD IP Holder, CANTON, MA

Key Personnel
KEN PRIVETT - CEO; President
JAMES KENNEDY - VP Operations, Development

Subway of Clewiston Inc
940 W Sugarland Hwy
Clewiston, FL 33440-2701

Telephone: (863) 983-9138
Type of Business: Chain Restaurant Operator
Total Sales: $2,406,000 (e)
Total Units: 4
Trade Names: Subway (4)
Units Franchised From: 4
Primary Menu: Sandwiches/Deli (4)
Areas of Operation: FL
Type of Foodservice: Quick Serve (4)
Franchise Affiliation: Doctor's Associates Inc., MILFORD, CT

Key Personnel
MO PATEL - President; General Buyer

Westgate Resorts
401 Meade Ave
Cocoa Beach, FL 32931-3775

Telephone: (321) 783-7549
Fax Number: (321) 868-1820
Internet Homepage: cocoabeachpier.com
Type of Business: Chain Restaurant Operator
Year Founded: 1962
Total Sales: $6,490,000 (e)
Alcohol Sales: 80%
Number of Employees: 55
Average Check: Lunch(14); Dinner(18)
Total Units: 5
Trade Names: Keith's Oyster Bar (1); Pelican (1); Rikki Tiki Tavern (1); Sea Dogs (1); The Boardwalk (1)
Company-Owned Units: 5
Preferred Square Footage: 5,000
Preferred Location Types: Freestanding; Other
Alcohol Served: Beer, Wine, Liquor
Primary Menu: Miscellaneous (1); Sandwiches/Deli (1); Snacks (1); Steak/Seafood (2)
Areas of Operation: FL
Type of Foodservice: Casual Dining (2); Family Restaurant (1)
Primary Distributors: (Full Line) SYSCO Food Services of South Florida Inc., MEDLEY, FL
Parent Company: The Cocoa Beach Pier, COCOA BEACH, FL
Notes: The company derives approximately 20% of its revenue from gift shops.

Key Personnel
DAVID SIEGEL - Founder; CEO; President
MARK WALTRIP - COO
MICHAEL MCLEAN - Chief Engineering Officer
BRIAN WALTRIP - Senior VP Development
TOM SPARKS - Senior VP Operations
JOEL SCHEID - VP Finance
JESUS RODRIGUEZ - VP Customer Service
TRICIA ENGEL-BETHEL - VP Talent, Talent Acquisitions
GARY PEARCE - VP Marketing, Sales
LISA LEVERT - Executive Director
HENOLD MONDELUS - Executive Director
KEVIN KROGMAN - Executive Director Customer Analytics
JUAN CALDERON - Senior Director Marketing
TANYA WOLAN - Director Operations
LISA GHAI - Director Sourcing, Procurement
JIM GOSLIN - Regional Director Sales
JANICE NUNEZ - Regional Manager Sales
JOSEPH THOMAS - Manager Product Development

Bru's Room Sports Grill
5460 W Hillsboro Blvd Ste B
Coconut Creek, FL 33073-4307

Telephone: (954) 968-1050
Fax Number: (954) 935-5600
Internet Homepage: brusroom.com
Company Email: corporate@brusroom.com
Type of Business: Chain Restaurant Operator
Year Founded: 1989
Total Sales: $7,241,000 (e)
Alcohol Sales: 20%
Number of Employees: 225
Average Check: Lunch(14); Dinner(18)
Internet Order Processing: Yes
Total Units: 9
Trade Names: Bru's Room Sports Grill (9)
Company-Owned Units: 9
Preferred Square Footage: 5,500; 6,000
Preferred Location Types: Freestanding; Strip Mall
Alcohol Served: Beer, Wine, Liquor
Primary Menu: American (9)
Areas of Operation: FL
Type of Foodservice: Casual Dining (9)
Catering Services: Yes
Primary Distributors: (Full Line) US Foods, TAMPA, FL

Key Personnel
BOB BRUDZINSKI - CEO; President; Exec VP Operations, Supply Chain; General Manager; General Buyer
MELIPA PRAHL - CFO
TRAVIS COX - Senior Director Operations, Development

MK Restaurant Concepts, LLC
3190 Commodore Plz
Coconut Grove, FL 33133-5818

Telephone: (305) 422-3377
Internet Homepage: lokalmiami.com
Company Email: info@kushhospitality.com
Type of Business: Chain Restaurant Operator
Total Units: 4
Trade Names: Kush (1); Lokal (1); The Spillover (1); Vicky's House (1)
Company-Owned Units: 4
Primary Menu: American (2); Hamburger (1); Seafood (1)
Areas of Operation: FL
Type of Foodservice: Casual Dining (4)

Key Personnel
MATT KUSCHER - Founder; Partner
PRISCILLA KUSCHER - Partner
ZENOBIA BHAIJEE - General Manager
ZUNIEL MELENDEZ - General Manager

Snowball Pizza Inc
9116 Griffin Rd
Cooper City, FL 33328-3540

Telephone: (954) 680-7759
Type of Business: Chain Restaurant Operator
Total Sales: $34,675,000 (e)
Total Units: 17
Trade Names: Domino's (17)
Units Franchised From: 17
Primary Menu: Pizza (17)

Key Personnel
PHIL RANDS - President; General Manager; General Buyer

Areas of Operation: FL
Type of Foodservice: Quick Serve (17)
Franchise Affiliation: Domino's Pizza Inc, ANN ARBOR, MI

Key Personnel
RICHARD C. TRAENKNER - Owner; Director Real Estate; General Buyer
JOSE ALEJANDRO - General Manager

Chill-N Nitrogen Ice Cream
255 Giralda Ave Suite 500
Coral Gables, FL 33134

Telephone: (305) 925-7530
Internet Homepage: chillnicecream.com
Company Email: Nitrogenninja@ChillNIceCream.com
Type of Business: Chain Restaurant Operator
Year Founded: 2012
Total Units: 8
Trade Names: Chill-N Nitrogen Ice Cream (8)
Company-Owned Units: 8
Primary Menu: Snacks (8)
Areas of Operation: FL
Type of Foodservice: Fast Casual (8)

Key Personnel
DANNY GOLIK - Co-Founder; COO
DONNA GOLIK - Co-Founder; Chief Brand Officer
DAVID LEONARDO - CEO

International Restaurant Management Group
4531 Ponce De Leon Blvd Ste 300
Coral Gables, FL 33146-1832

Telephone: (305) 476-1611
Fax Number: (305) 476-9622
Internet Homepage: irmgusa.com
Company Email: info@irmgusa.com
Type of Business: Chain Restaurant Operator
Year Founded: 1975
Total Sales: $154,960,000 (e)
Alcohol Sales: 1%
Number of Employees: 2,600
Average Check: Lunch(10); Dinner(14)
Total Units: 91
Trade Names: Argentina Grill (1); Basil Thai (1); BURGER KING (12); Chicken Connection (3); Cilantro Fresh Mex (1); Kelly's Cajun Grill (31); Latin Grill (4); Popeyes (5); Suki Hana (15); WOK A HOLIC (4); Yeung's Lotus Express (14)
Units Franchised To: 74
Units Franchised From: 17
Preferred Square Footage: 750; 2,500
Preferred Location Types: Airports; Community Mall; Regional Mall; Strip Mall; Travel Plazas
Alcohol Served: Beer, Wine
Primary Menu: American (12); Asian (19); Cajun/Creole (31); Californian (0); Chicken (9); Chinese (14); Latin American/Cuban (4); Pizza (0); Thai (1)
Areas of Operation: AL, AZ, CA, CO, DC, DE, FL, GA, IA, ID, IL, IN, KS, KY, LA, MD, MI, MS, NC, NJ, NV, NY, OH, OR, PA, PR, TN, TX, UT, VA, WA
Foreign Countries: MEXICO; VENEZUELA
Type of Foodservice: Fast Casual (38); Quick Serve (53)
Primary Distributors: (Food) SYSCO Food Services of South Florida Inc., MEDLEY, FL

Key Personnel
KELLY YEUNG - CEO; President
ALLY HO - CFO; Controller
MARTIN NUNEZ - Area Director
KEN CHOQUETTE - Senior VP Development, Real Estate
NITA YEUNG - VP
ANTHONY NAPOLIELLO - VP
TONG ESTRADA - General Manager
SALVADOR ARELLANO - Director Operations
STEPHANIE YEUNG - Director Development
GEORGE TSESMETZIS - Director Operations
JOHANNA WADE - Director Risk Management
OMAR FRANCO - Regional Manager
LEONARD BOORD - Manager Information Technology
MARTY SUDUT - Project Manager
MATTHEW LAU - Consultant

Montes Enterprises Inc
3280 Coral Way
Coral Gables, FL 33145-2234

Telephone: (305) 444-5466
Fax Number: (305) 444-1177
Type of Business: Chain Restaurant Operator
Total Sales: $28,740,000 (e)
Total Units: 6
Trade Names: McDonald's (6)
Units Franchised From: 6
Primary Menu: Hamburger (6)
Areas of Operation: FL
Type of Foodservice: Quick Serve (6)
Franchise Affiliation: McDonald's Corporation, CHICAGO, IL

Key Personnel
JOSE MONTES - Owner; General Buyer

Pincho Factory
30 Giralda Ave
Coral Gables, FL 33134-5303

Telephone: (305) 446-5666
Internet Homepage: pinchofactory.com
Type of Business: Chain Restaurant Operator
Year Founded: 2010
Total Sales: $10,150,000 (e)
Total Units: 10
Trade Names: Pincho Factory (10)
Company-Owned Units: 7
Units Franchised To: 3
Preferred Location Types: Stadiums; Strip Mall
Primary Menu: Hamburger (10)
Projected Openings: 2
Areas of Operation: FL
Type of Foodservice: Fast Casual (10)

Key Personnel
OTTO OTHMAN - Executive Chairman; Co-Founder; Chief Marketing Officer
NIZAR AHMAD - Co-Founder

D'Lites Enterprises Inc.
10897 NW 6th St
Coral Springs, FL 33071-7941

Telephone: (954) 340-1131
Fax Number: (954) 340-1933
Internet Homepage: dlitesemporium.com
Company Email: info@dlitesemporium.com
Type of Business: Chain Restaurant Operator
Year Founded: 1982
Systemwide Sales: $3,217,000 (e)
Total Sales: $2,521,000 (e)
Number of Employees: 5
Average Check: Lunch(5); Dinner(5)
Internet Order Processing: Yes
Internet Sales: 2.00%
Total Units: 10
Trade Names: D'Lites Emporium (10)
Units Franchised To: 10
Preferred Square Footage: 1,200
Preferred Location Types: Strip Mall
Primary Menu: Snacks (10)
Areas of Operation: FL, GA, NJ, NY, TX, VA, FC
Foreign Countries: HONDURAS; MEXICO
Type of Foodservice: In-Store Feeder (10)

Key Personnel
JERRY CORSOVER - President; Manager Franchising, Menu Development

The Starboard Group
12540 W Atlantic Blvd
Coral Springs, FL 33071-4085

Telephone: (954) 255-2266
Fax Number: (954) 255-2299
Internet Homepage: starboardwendys.com
Type of Business: Chain Restaurant Operator
Total Sales: $258,850,000 (e)
Number of Employees: 2,962
Total Units: 96

Trade Names: Wendy's Old Fashioned Hamburgers (96)
Units Franchised From: 96
Primary Menu: Hamburger (96)
Areas of Operation: AL, FL, IL, MI, MO, VA, WI
Type of Foodservice: Quick Serve (96)
Franchise Affiliation: The Wendy's Company, DUBLIN, OH

Key Personnel
ANDREW LEVY - CEO
SANDI ADLER - VP Legal, Human Resources
NANCY EVANS - VP Operations
BOB CAL - Director Information Technology
KEVIN RODRIGUEZ - Director Financial Planning
BRIAN JOHNSON - Director Operations
HENDRIK EMANUELS - Manager District

All Stores Management
9170 W State Road 84
Davie, FL 33324-4458

Telephone: (954) 652-0208
Fax Number: (954) 689-8598
Type of Business: Chain Restaurant Operator
Total Sales: $21,860,000 (e)
Number of Employees: 256
Average Check: Breakfast(6); Lunch(6); Dinner(8)
Total Units: 14
Trade Names: Dunkin' Donuts (14)
Units Franchised From: 14
Preferred Square Footage: 1,500; 2,200
Preferred Location Types: Freestanding; Office Complex; Strip Mall
Primary Menu: Snacks (14)
Areas of Operation: FL
Type of Foodservice: Quick Serve (14)
Franchise Affiliation: DD IP Holder, CANTON, MA

Key Personnel
MEHRDAD FALLAH-MOGHADDAM - President; General Buyer

Char-Hut of America Inc.
4395 SW 60th Ave
Davie, FL 33314-3619

Telephone: (954) 472-3330
Fax Number: (954) 641-0645
Internet Homepage: charhutrestaurants.com
Company Email: chcorporate@charhut.com
Type of Business: Chain Restaurant Operator
Year Founded: 1976
Total Sales: $7,204,000 (e)
Number of Employees: 265
Average Check: Lunch(12); Dinner(14)
Internet Order Processing: Yes
Total Units: 4
Trade Names: Char-Hut (4)
Company-Owned Units: 3
Units Franchised To: 1
Preferred Square Footage: 2,200; 2,700; 3,000
Preferred Location Types: Freestanding
Primary Menu: Hamburger (4)
Areas of Operation: FL
Type of Foodservice: Quick Serve (4)
Catering Services: Yes
Primary Distributors: (Food) SYSCO Food Services of Southeast Florida LLC, RIVIERA BEACH, FL

Key Personnel
TONY CAMMISA - President; COO; General Manager; Director Menu Development, Catering
JUDY CAMMISA - Corporate Secretary; General Buyer
STEVEN KAMELHAIR - Director Franchise Development

Insei, Inc.
15641 Sheridan St Ste 500
Davie, FL 33331-3493

Telephone: (954) 880-0014
Type of Business: Chain Restaurant Operator
Total Sales: $1,248,000 (e)
Total Units: 2
Trade Names: Cold Stone Creamery (2)
Units Franchised From: 2
Primary Menu: Snacks (2)
Areas of Operation: FL
Type of Foodservice: Quick Serve (2)
Franchise Affiliation: Kahala Brands, SCOTTSDALE, AZ

Key Personnel
SIMON LEON - Partner
WENDY SWA - Partner

Stonewood Holdings LLC
810 Fentress Ct Ste 130B
Daytona Beach, FL 32117-5118

Telephone: (386) 677-1167
Fax Number: (386) 677-9133
Internet Homepage: peachvalleycafe.com; stonewoodgrill.com
Type of Business: Chain Restaurant Operator
Year Founded: 1999
Total Sales: $43,643,000 (e)
Alcohol Sales: 23.75%
Number of Employees: 700
Average Check: Breakfast(10); Lunch(16); Dinner(42)
Total Units: 14
Trade Names: Peach Valley Cafe (6); Stonewood Grill & Tavern (8)
Company-Owned Units: 14
Preferred Square Footage: 5,500; 6,000
Preferred Location Types: Freestanding; Strip Mall
Alcohol Served: Beer, Wine, Liquor
Primary Menu: American (6); Steak/Seafood (8)
Areas of Operation: FL
Type of Foodservice: Casual Dining (8); Family Restaurant (6)
Primary Distributors: (Food) Food Supply Inc., SOUTH DAYTONA, FL

Key Personnel
VANESSA GASIOR - Controller

Domino's Franchisee
210 N Federal Hwy
Deerfield Beach, FL 33441-3612

Telephone: (954) 574-9994
Type of Business: Chain Restaurant Operator
Total Sales: $4,027,000 (e)
Total Units: 2
Trade Names: Domino's (2)
Units Franchised From: 2
Primary Menu: Pizza (2)
Areas of Operation: FL
Type of Foodservice: Quick Serve (2)
Franchise Affiliation: Domino's Pizza Inc, ANN ARBOR, MI

Key Personnel
NEAL T. CORCORAN - Owner; General Buyer

Domino's Franchisee
209 N Amelia Ave
Deland, FL 32724-4319

Telephone: (386) 738-1500
Type of Business: Chain Restaurant Operator
Total Sales: $8,192,000 (e)
Total Units: 4
Trade Names: Domino's (4)
Units Franchised From: 4
Primary Menu: Pizza (4)
Areas of Operation: FL
Type of Foodservice: Quick Serve (4)
Franchise Affiliation: Domino's Pizza Inc, ANN ARBOR, MI

Key Personnel
ANTHONY S. REULBACH - Owner; General Buyer

Boston's on the Beach
40 S Ocean Blvd
Delray Beach, FL 33483-6932

Telephone: (561) 278-3364
Fax Number: (561) 278-3328
Internet Homepage: bostonsonthebeach.com
Company Email:
 info@bostonsdelraybeach.com
Type of Business: Chain Restaurant Operator
Year Founded: 1979
Total Sales: $11,072,000 (e)
Alcohol Sales: 20%
Number of Employees: 110
Average Check: Breakfast(8); Lunch(12); Dinner(18)
Internet Order Processing: Yes
Internet Sales: 2.00%
Total Units: 3
Trade Names: 50 Ocean (1); Bostons on the Beach (1); Sandbar (1)
Company-Owned Units: 3
Preferred Location Types: Freestanding
Alcohol Served: Beer, Wine, Liquor
Primary Menu: American (1); Seafood (2)
Areas of Operation: FL
Type of Foodservice: Casual Dining (2); Fine Dining (1)
Primary Distributors: (Food) Cheney Bros. Inc., RIVIERA BEACH, FL; (Supplies) Edward Don & Co., MIRAMAR, FL
Notes: Owned by Ocean Properties.

Key Personnel
MARK PISARRI - Director
JENNIFER HESSER - Manager Catering

Brooklyn Water Enterprises Inc.
1450 SW 10th St Ste 2
Delray Beach, FL 33444-1200

Telephone: (561) 455-7490
Internet Homepage: brooklynwaterbagels.com
Company Email:
 brooklynwaterbagels@thelevelup.com
Type of Business: Chain Restaurant Operator
Year Founded: 2007
Total Sales: $14,710,000 (e)
Number of Employees: 243
Total Units: 16
Trade Names: The Original Brooklyn Water Bagel Co. It's All About The Water (16)
Company-Owned Units: 2
Units Franchised To: 14
Preferred Square Footage: 450; 3,700; 5,000
Preferred Location Types: Freestanding; Lifestyle Center; Strip Mall
Primary Menu: Bagels (16)
Areas of Operation: CA, FL, MA

Type of Foodservice: Fast Casual (16)

Key Personnel
KARI REYNOLDS - CFO; Controller

Fresh Dining Concepts
601 N Congress Ave
Delray Beach, FL 33445-4621

Telephone: (561) 265-5779
Type of Business: Chain Restaurant Operator
Total Sales: $29,080,000 (e)
Total Units: 40
Trade Names: Auntie Anne's Hand-Rolled Soft Pretzels (39); Cinnabon (1)
Units Franchised From: 40
Primary Menu: Snacks (40)
Areas of Operation: FL
Type of Foodservice: Quick Serve (40)
Franchise Affiliation: Auntie Anne's Inc., LANCASTER, PA

Key Personnel
LUIS SAN MIGUEL - Owner; General Buyer
YILDRIS RODRIGUEZ-ROSS - CFO
KEVIN BUSH - Chief Strategy Officer
NATALYA OKSENGORN - Director Operations
DANIELLE GODLEWSKI - Director Operations
STEVE JOHANNES - Director Operations

David Costa Enterprises
4300 Legendary Dr Ste 220
Destin, FL 32541-8605

Telephone: (850) 897-3169
Fax Number: (866) 870-2376
Internet Homepage: costamcd.com
Type of Business: Chain Restaurant Operator
Total Sales: $112,220,000 (e)
Number of Employees: 917
Total Units: 24
Trade Names: McDonald's (24)
Units Franchised From: 24
Preferred Square Footage: 2,500
Preferred Location Types: Discount Dept. Stores; Freestanding
Primary Menu: Hamburger (17)
Areas of Operation: FL
Type of Foodservice: Quick Serve (17)
Franchise Affiliation: McDonald's Corporation, CHICAGO, IL

Key Personnel
DAVID COSTA SR - President; Partner; General Buyer
DAVID COSTA JR - Partner; General Buyer
ALBERTO COSTA - Director

Fudpuckers Beachside Bar & Grill
20001 Emerald Coast Pkwy
Destin, FL 32541-3410

Telephone: (850) 654-1544
Fax Number: (850) 837-8226
Internet Homepage: fudpucker.com
Company Email: fudpucker@fudpucker.com
Type of Business: Chain Restaurant Operator
Year Founded: 1983
Total Sales: $1,868,000 (e)
Alcohol Sales: 37%
Number of Employees: 300
Average Check: Lunch(12); Dinner(18)
Internet Order Processing: Yes
Total Units: 1
Trade Names: Fudpuckers Beachside Bar & Grill (1)
Company-Owned Units: 1
Preferred Location Types: Freestanding
Alcohol Served: Beer, Wine, Liquor
Primary Menu: Steak/Seafood (1)
Areas of Operation: FL
Type of Foodservice: Casual Dining (1)
Catering Services: Yes
Primary Distributors: (Food) SYSCO Central Florida Inc., OCOEE, FL

Key Personnel
CHESTER KROEGER - Partner; General Buyer

Island Wing Company
12598 US Highway 98 W
Destin, FL 32550

Telephone: (877) 628-9001
Internet Homepage: islandwing.com
Type of Business: Chain Restaurant Operator
Total Sales: $8,998,000 (e)
Total Units: 8
Trade Names: Island Wing Company (8)
Company-Owned Units: 8
Primary Menu: Chicken (8)
Areas of Operation: AL, FL
Type of Foodservice: Casual Dining (8)

Key Personnel
SAM OSBORNE - CEO

Southern Restaurant Group Inc.
1771 Scenic Highway 98 Fl 2
Destin, FL 32541-3312

Mailing Address: PO Box 99, DESTIN, FL, 32540-0099
Telephone: (850) 837-1637

Fax Number: (850) 654-5839
Internet Homepage: srgcorp.net
Type of Business: Chain Restaurant Operator
Year Founded: 1979
Total Sales: $33,990,000 (e)
Alcohol Sales: 22%
Number of Employees: 680
Average Check: Breakfast(8); Lunch(24); Dinner(38)
Total Units: 6
Trade Names: Back Porch (2); Louisiana Lagniappe (2); Pompano Joe's (2)
Company-Owned Units: 6
Preferred Square Footage: 3,000; 5,500; 6,000
Preferred Location Types: Freestanding; Lifestyle Center
Alcohol Served: Beer, Wine, Liquor
Primary Menu: Seafood (6)
Areas of Operation: AL, FL
Type of Foodservice: Casual Dining (3); Fast Casual (1); Fine Dining (2)
Catering Services: Yes
Primary Distributors: (Full Line) SYSCO Food Services of Central Alabama Inc., CALERA, AL

Key Personnel
JOHN COMER - CEO; President; Director Operations, Purchasing
MARYLOU COWGILL - CFO; Exec VP; Controller; Manager Finance, Facility/Maintenance, Real Estate, Design, Human Resources
ROBERTO HERNANDEZ - Executive Chef
DAVID SMITH - Director Marketing
HOWARD COWGILL - Director Accounting
LINDA WESTCOTT - Manager Payroll, Benefits

Centurion Restaurant Group
8899 NW 18th Ter Ste. 200
Doral, FL 33172

Telephone: (305) 798-3002
Internet Homepage: centurionrestaurantgroup.com
Company Email: info@centurionrestaurantgroup.com
Type of Business: Chain Restaurant Operator
Total Sales: $10,700,000 (e)
Total Units: 13
Trade Names: Beehive Kitchen (2); Bulla Gastrobar (8); Pisco Y Nazca (3)
Company-Owned Units: 13
Primary Menu: Miscellaneous (2); Spanish (11)
Areas of Operation: DC, FL, GA, NC, TX
Type of Foodservice: Casual Dining (11); Fast Casual (2)

Key Personnel
MILCIADES PACHAS - Director Finance

Graziano's Group
2678 NW 112th Ave
Doral, FL 33172-1818

Telephone: (305) 591-8115
Fax Number: (305) 591-8114
Internet Homepage: grazianosgroup.com
Company Email: info@grazianosgroup.com
Type of Business: Chain Restaurant Operator
Total Sales: $47,250,000 (e)
Alcohol Sales: 25%
Number of Employees: 145
Average Check: Lunch(36); Dinner(60)
Total Units: 10
Trade Names: Graziano's Market (6); Graziano's Restaurant (4)
Company-Owned Units: 10
Alcohol Served: Beer, Wine, Liquor
Primary Menu: Latin American/Cuban (10)
Areas of Operation: FL
Type of Foodservice: Casual Dining (6); Fine Dining (4)
Primary Distributors: (Food) SYSCO Food Services of South Florida Inc., MEDLEY, FL

Key Personnel
LEO GRAZIANO - CEO
MARIO GRAZIANO - Owner; General Manager; Executive Chef; General Buyer
MICHELE GRAZIANO - Owner

Domino's Franchisee
1289 San Christopher Dr
Dunedin, FL 34698-5334

Telephone: (727) 736-3030
Type of Business: Chain Restaurant Operator
Total Sales: $6,177,000 (e)
Total Units: 3
Trade Names: Domino's (3)
Units Franchised From: 3
Primary Menu: Pizza (3)
Areas of Operation: FL
Type of Foodservice: Quick Serve (3)
Franchise Affiliation: Domino's Pizza Inc, ANN ARBOR, MI

Key Personnel
ELIZABETH A. MCDERMOTT - Partner; General Buyer
MIKE MCDERMOTT - Partner

Domino's Franchisee
3502 N Access Rd Ste 3
Englewood, FL 34224-8510

Telephone: (941) 475-5691
Type of Business: Chain Restaurant Operator
Total Sales: $13,917,000 (e)
Total Units: 7
Trade Names: Domino's (7)
Units Franchised From: 7
Primary Menu: Pizza (7)
Areas of Operation: FL
Type of Foodservice: Quick Serve (7)
Franchise Affiliation: Domino's Pizza Inc, ANN ARBOR, MI

Key Personnel
PAUL J. ZDANOWICZ - Owner; General Buyer

Bahia Bowls
20301 Grande Oak Blvd Suite 118-24
Estero, FL 33928

Telephone: (239) 908-3543
Internet Homepage: bahiabowls.com
Type of Business: Chain Restaurant Operator
Year Founded: 2017
Number of Employees: 125
Total Units: 14
Trade Names: Bahia Bowls Acai Cafe (14)
Units Franchised To: 14
Primary Menu: Health Foods (14)
Projected Openings: 1
Areas of Operation: FL, OH, PA, TN, TX
Type of Foodservice: Fast Casual (14)

Key Personnel
BEN CASEY - Co-Founder
VAN HATZIYIANIS - Co-Founder

Domino's Franchisee
1936 N Highway 19
Eustis, FL 32726-6729

Telephone: (352) 483-4688
Type of Business: Chain Restaurant Operator
Total Sales: $6,122,000 (e)
Total Units: 3
Trade Names: Domino's (3)
Units Franchised From: 3
Primary Menu: Pizza (3)
Areas of Operation: FL
Type of Foodservice: Quick Serve (3)
Franchise Affiliation: Domino's Pizza Inc, ANN ARBOR, MI

Key Personnel
JOSEPH C. CRULL - Owner; General Buyer

Lake Culinary Institute
2001 Kurt St
Eustis, FL 32726-6164

Telephone: (352) 589-2250
Fax Number: (352) 483-2611
Internet Homepage: lake.k12.fl.us;

laketech.org
Company Email: laketechnical@gmail.com
Type of Business: Culinary Schools
Areas of Operation: FL

Key Personnel
KEN KOENIG - Director Culinary Development

Dcfljji, Llc
33550 S Dixie Hwy
Florida City, FL 33034-5602

Telephone: (305) 246-0504
Type of Business: Chain Restaurant Operator
Total Sales: $2,645,000 (e)
Total Units: 2
Trade Names: Jimmy John's Gourmet Sandwich Shop (2)
Units Franchised From: 2
Areas of Operation: FL
Franchise Affiliation: Jimmy John's Franchise LLC, CHAMPAIGN, IL

Key Personnel
DARRYL COPELAND - Partner
RACHEL BRAUNSTEIN - Partner

American Social
721 E Las Olas Blvd
Fort Lauderdale, FL 33301-2236

Telephone: (954) 715-1134
Internet Homepage: americansocialbar.com
Type of Business: Chain Restaurant Operator
Year Founded: 2012
Total Units: 3
Trade Names: American Social (3)
Company-Owned Units: 3
Alcohol Served: Beer, Wine, Liquor
Primary Menu: American (3)
Projected Openings: 1
Areas of Operation: FL
Type of Foodservice: Casual Dining (3)

Key Personnel
RICK J. MIJARES - Partner
PAUL GREENBERG - Partner
ADAM PERHOSKY - Director Marketing
MADDIE GARVIA - Director Marketing

CAO Bakery & Cafe
1535 N Federal Hwy
Fort Lauderdale, FL 33304

Telephone: (954) 530-2266
Internet Homepage: caobakerycafe.com
Type of Business: Chain Restaurant Operator
Total Sales: $14,080,000 (e)
Total Units: 11
Trade Names: CAO Bakery & Cafe (11)
Company-Owned Units: 11
Primary Menu: Sandwiches/Deli (11)
Type of Foodservice: Casual Dining (11)

Key Personnel
ANTONIO CAO - Founder; President
YVETTE RODRIGUEZ CAO - Partner; Chief Marketing Officer
YVETTE R. CAO - Chief Marketing Officer

Chima Brazilian Steakhouse
2400 E Las Olas Blvd Ste C
Fort Lauderdale, FL 33301-1529

Telephone: (954) 712-0581
Fax Number: (954) 712-0599
Internet Homepage: chimasteakhouse.com
Company Email:
 chima.web@chimasteakhouse.com
Type of Business: Chain Restaurant Operator
Year Founded: 2004
Total Units: 4
Trade Names: Chima Brazilian Steakhouse (4)
Company-Owned Units: 4
Alcohol Served: Beer, Wine, Liquor
Primary Menu: Steak (4)
Areas of Operation: FL, NC, PA, VA
Type of Foodservice: Fine Dining (4)

Key Personnel
LUCAS SILVA - Owner; General Buyer
GONZALO GARCIA - General Manager
THIAGO CASTRO - Director Development
BETSY MILLSON - Manager Marketing, Sales
ASHLEY WILLIAMS - Manager Sales

Domino's Franchisee
3416 N Ocean Blvd
Fort Lauderdale, FL 33308-6902

Telephone: (954) 565-3030
Internet Homepage: dominos.com
Type of Business: Chain Restaurant Operator
Total Sales: $4,081,000 (e)
Internet Order Processing: Yes
Total Units: 2
Trade Names: Domino's (2)
Units Franchised From: 2
Primary Menu: Pizza (2)
Areas of Operation: FL
Type of Foodservice: Quick Serve (2)
Franchise Affiliation: Domino's Pizza Inc, ANN ARBOR, MI

Key Personnel
WILLIAM DAWSON - Owner; General Buyer

Flanigan's Enterprises Inc.
5059 NE 18th Ave
Fort Lauderdale, FL 33334-5724

Telephone: (954) 377-1961
Fax Number: (954) 377-1980
Internet Homepage: flanigans.net
Company Email: chris@flanigans.net
Type of Business: Chain Restaurant Operator
Year Founded: 1959
Systemwide Sales: $268,548,000 (e)
Publicly Held: Yes
Total Sales: $178,075,000 (e)
Alcohol Sales: 22%
Number of Employees: 525
Average Check: Lunch(14); Dinner(18)
Foodservice Sales: $146,021,000 (e)
Internet Order Processing: Yes
Internet Sales: 2.00%
Total Units: 36
Trade Names: Flanigan's Seafood Bar & Grill (36)
Company-Owned Units: 31
Units Franchised To: 5
Preferred Square Footage: 5,000
Preferred Location Types: Freestanding
Alcohol Served: Beer, Wine, Liquor
Primary Menu: Seafood (36)
Areas of Operation: FL
Type of Foodservice: Casual Dining (36)
Primary Distributors: (Full Line) SYSCO Food Services of South Florida Inc., MEDLEY, FL
Notes: The company derives approximately 22% of its revenue from the Big Daddy's retail liquor-store chain and other business ventures. Four of the "Franchised To" units are joint venture operations. Systemwide sales reflect restaurant operations only.

Key Personnel
JAMES G. FLANIGAN - Chairman; CEO; President
JEFFREY KASTNER - CFO; Corporate Secretary; General Counsel
JEAN PICARD - VP Retail Operations
PETER BRUCE - Director Operations
WILFRID BENECHE - Manager Restaurant Operations
CRISTOFER MARTINEZ - Manager Restaurant Operations

Gyroville
6341 N Andrews Ave
Fort Lauderdale, FL 33309-2143

Telephone: (954) 634-9767
Internet Homepage: gyroville.com
Company Email: info@gyroville.com
Type of Business: Chain Restaurant Operator
Year Founded: 2010
Total Sales: $7,873,000 (e)

Total Units: 9
Trade Names: Gyroville (9)
Company-Owned Units: 9
Primary Menu: Sandwiches/Deli (9)
Projected Openings: 2
Areas of Operation: FL, KS, MI, FC
Type of Foodservice: Fast Casual (9)

Key Personnel
LAMBROS KOKKINELIS - Founder; CEO; Owner
DAVID KURLANDER - Director Operations

Lester's Diner
250 W State Road 84
Fort Lauderdale, FL 33315-2545

Telephone: (954) 525-5641
Fax Number: (954) 525-9853
Internet Homepage: lestersdiner.com
Company Email: lestersdiner@bellsouth.net
Type of Business: Chain Restaurant Operator
Year Founded: 1967
Total Sales: $7,404,000 (e)
Number of Employees: 105
Average Check: Breakfast(12); Lunch(18); Dinner(24)
Total Units: 4
Trade Names: Lester's Diner (4)
Company-Owned Units: 4
Preferred Square Footage: 5,000
Preferred Location Types: Freestanding; Mixed-use Center
Primary Menu: American (4)
Areas of Operation: FL
Type of Foodservice: Casual Dining (4)
Primary Distributors: (Full Line) SYSCO Food Services of South Florida Inc., MEDLEY, FL

Key Personnel
PETER DOGAGIS - President; Executive Chef
GERONIMO DOGAGIS - General Manager
PADALISE DOGAGIS - General Manager; General Buyer

LTP Management Group
436 S Andrews Ave
Fort Lauderdale, FL 33301-2830

Telephone: (954) 766-8197
Fax Number: (954) 766-8195
Internet Homepage: adobegilas.com; lulusbaitshack.com; royalpigpub.com
Type of Business: Chain Restaurant Operator
Year Founded: 1993
Total Sales: $73,440,000 (e)
Alcohol Sales: 20%
Number of Employees: 1,454
Average Check: Lunch(18); Dinner(24)
Total Units: 21
Trade Names: Adobe Gilas (3); Hooters (16); Lulu's Bait Shack (1); Royal Pig Pub and Kitchen (1)
Units Franchised From: 21
Preferred Square Footage: 5,000
Preferred Location Types: Freestanding; Strip Mall
Alcohol Served: Beer, Wine, Liquor
Primary Menu: American (17); Mexican (3); Seafood (1)
Areas of Operation: FL, IL, NV, OH
Type of Foodservice: Casual Dining (21)
Catering Services: Yes
Franchise Affiliation: HOA Restaurant Group LLC, ATLANTA, GA
Primary Distributors: (Full Line) Cheney Bros. Inc., RIVIERA BEACH, FL; (Supplies) Louis Wohl & Sons Inc., TAMPA, FL

Key Personnel
TERRY BRAWNER - President
PAUL LYNCH - CFO; VP Risk Management, Quality Assurance, Food Safety; Executive Chef
BILL BECKER - COO
DALE REGNIER - VP Marketing; Director Purchasing
RICHARD COREY - General Manager
LISA BURGS - Director Human Resources, Training, Recruitment
JOE UPCHURCH - Director Operations, Facility/Maintenance
JOHN WALLACE - Manager Information Systems, E-Commerce, Internet Development

Quarterdeck Seafood Bar & Neighborhood Grill
1015 SE 16th St Ste 1
Fort Lauderdale, FL 33316-6103

Telephone: (954) 525-8042
Fax Number: (954) 765-1902
Internet Homepage: quarterdeckrestaurants.com
Company Email: info@quarterdeckrestaurants.com
Type of Business: Chain Restaurant Operator
Year Founded: 1966
Total Sales: $26,620,000 (e)
Alcohol Sales: 15%
Number of Employees: 200
Average Check: Lunch(24); Dinner(24)
Total Units: 5
Trade Names: Quarterdeck Seafood Bar & Neighborhood Grill (5)
Company-Owned Units: 5
Preferred Square Footage: 5,500; 6,000
Preferred Location Types: Freestanding; Strip Mall
Alcohol Served: Beer, Wine, Liquor
Primary Menu: Steak/Seafood (5)
Areas of Operation: FL
Type of Foodservice: Casual Dining (5)
Catering Services: Yes

Key Personnel
JAMES FLANIGAN - Partner
PAUL B. FLANIGAN - Partner; Executive Chef; Director Real Estate, Design, Catering; General Buyer
FRANK D. ZAFFERE - Partner; Director Operations, Information Systems
JOE ZEBROWSKI - Partner
MIKE JIN - Executive Chef

Rio Vista Management Group Inc.
113 SW 11th Ct Ste C
Fort Lauderdale, FL 33315-1271

Telephone: (954) 766-9800
Fax Number: (954) 766-9904
Type of Business: Chain Restaurant Operator
Year Founded: 1986
Total Sales: $51,150,000 (e)
Number of Employees: 400
Average Check: Breakfast(5); Lunch(8); Dinner(8)
Total Units: 11
Trade Names: McDonald's (11)
Units Franchised From: 11
Preferred Square Footage: 2,500; 3,000
Preferred Location Types: Freestanding
Primary Menu: Hamburger (11)
Areas of Operation: FL
Type of Foodservice: Quick Serve (11)
Franchise Affiliation: McDonald's Corporation, CHICAGO, IL
Primary Distributors: (Food) The Martin-Brower Co., POMPANO BEACH, FL

Key Personnel
DANIEL ASHLIN - President; Director Finance, Operations, Facility/Maintenance, Information Systems, Supply Chain, Real Estate, Design, Store Fixtures; General Buyer
JEANNIE TERBENI - CFO
JOHN SPICCI - Director Operations

Bowling Management Associates
14513 Global Pkwy
Fort Myers, FL 33913-8829

Telephone: (239) 947-2111
Internet Homepage: bowlandcenters.com
Type of Business: Foodservice Operations - Bowling Alley
Total Sales: $16,200,000 (e)
Alcohol Sales: 10%
Number of Employees: 200
Average Check: Lunch(5); Dinner(5)
Total Units: 6

Trade Names: Bowland (6)
Company-Owned Units: 6
Preferred Location Types: Freestanding
Alcohol Served: Beer, Wine, Liquor
Primary Menu: American (6)
Projected Openings: 1
Areas of Operation: FL
Type of Foodservice: In-Store Feeder (6)

Key Personnel
PATRICK CINIELLO - CEO; President; General Buyer
DONNA CESARE - Director
PAUL CLARK - Manager Accounting

Broadway Palm Dinner Theatre Inc.
1380 Colonial Blvd
Fort Myers, FL 33907-1015

Telephone: (239) 278-4422
Fax Number: (239) 278-5664
Internet Homepage: broadwaypalm.com; dutchapple.com
Company Email: tickets@broadwaypalm.com
Type of Business: Chain Restaurant Operator
Year Founded: 1993
Total Sales: $15,482,000 (e)
Alcohol Sales: 19%
Number of Employees: 125
Average Check: Lunch(48); Dinner(54)
Internet Order Processing: Yes
Internet Sales: 3.00%
Total Units: 2
Trade Names: Broadway Palm Dinner Theatre (1); Dutch Apple Dinner Theatre (1)
Company-Owned Units: 2
Preferred Location Types: Strip Mall
Alcohol Served: Beer, Wine, Liquor
Primary Menu: American (2)
Areas of Operation: FL, PA
Type of Foodservice: Casual Dining (2)
Catering Services: Yes
Primary Distributors: (Food) SYSCO Food Services of South Florida Inc., MEDLEY, FL

Key Personnel
MARY LAWTON - General Manager; General Buyer
CHRISTIAN MENDIVIL - General Manager
TED JENKINS - Executive Chef; General Buyer
KATHY BERNIER - Director Food and Beverage
PATTY STALLSMITH - Director Sales

Domino's Franchisee
4550 Palm Beach Blvd
Fort Myers, FL 33905-3455

Telephone: (239) 693-1600
Type of Business: Chain Restaurant Operator
Total Sales: $8,314,000 (e)
Total Units: 4
Trade Names: Domino's (4)
Units Franchised From: 4
Primary Menu: Pizza (4)
Areas of Operation: FL
Type of Foodservice: Quick Serve (4)
Franchise Affiliation: Domino's Pizza Inc, ANN ARBOR, MI

Key Personnel
ALVARAO FARACE - Owner; General Buyer

Rib City Inc.
2122 2nd St
Fort Myers, FL 33901-3013

Telephone: (239) 334-8634
Fax Number: (239) 332-7232
Internet Homepage: ribcity.com; verandarestaurant.com
Company Email: comments@ribcity.com
Type of Business: Chain Restaurant Operator
Year Founded: 1978
Systemwide Sales: $28,701,000 (e)
Total Sales: $26,480,000 (e)
Alcohol Sales: 10%
Number of Employees: 316
Average Check: Dinner(24)
Total Units: 26
Trade Names: Rib City (25); Veranda (1)
Company-Owned Units: 14
Units Franchised To: 12
Preferred Square Footage: 5,000
Preferred Location Types: Freestanding; Strip Mall
Alcohol Served: Beer, Wine, Liquor
Primary Menu: Bar-B-Q (25); Southern (1)
Areas of Operation: CO, FL, IL, MO, OH, TN, VA, WA
Type of Foodservice: Casual Dining (25); Fine Dining (1)
Catering Services: Yes
Primary Distributors: (Full Line) SYSCO Food Services of West Coast Florida Inc., PALMETTO, FL
Notes: Company also operates as FM Veranda Inc.

Key Personnel
PAUL PEDEN - CEO; General Manager; Executive Chef; Director Purchasing, Real Estate, Franchise Development, Catering; General Buyer
CRAIG PEDEN - President; Treasurer; Director Operations, Facility/Maintenance; Manager Supply Chain, Design
DINA GREEN - Controller

SouthWest Florida Restaurant Investments Inc.
6710 Winkler Rd Ste 7
Fort Myers, FL 33919-7274

Telephone: (239) 936-5556
Fax Number: (239) 936-1061
Internet Homepage: swfri.com
Company Email: comments@swfri.com
Type of Business: Chain Restaurant Operator
Total Sales: $6,164,000 (e)
Alcohol Sales: 5%
Number of Employees: 110
Average Check: Breakfast(10); Lunch(10); Dinner(10)
Total Units: 2
Trade Names: Denny's (2)
Units Franchised From: 2
Preferred Square Footage: 3,000; 5,000
Preferred Location Types: Freestanding
Alcohol Served: Beer, Wine
Primary Menu: American (2)
Areas of Operation: FL
Type of Foodservice: Casual Dining (2)
Franchise Affiliation: Denny's Corporation, SPARTANBURG, SC
Primary Distributors: (Food) McLane/Orlando, ORLANDO, FL

Key Personnel
SCOTT BROWN - CEO

Lee's Famous Recipes Inc.
171 Brooks St SE Ste F
Fort Walton Beach, FL 32548-3718

Telephone: (850) 244-6575
Fax Number: (850) 244-6131
Internet Homepage: leesfamousrecipe.com
Type of Business: Chain Restaurant Operator
Year Founded: 1967
Systemwide Sales: $229,048,000 (e)
Total Sales: $231,840,000 (e)
Number of Employees: 1,064
Average Check: Breakfast(5); Lunch(5); Dinner(8)
Total Units: 130
Trade Names: Lee's Famous Recipe Chicken (130)
Units Franchised To: 130
Preferred Square Footage: 2,100
Preferred Location Types: Convenience Store/Gas Station; Freestanding
Primary Menu: Chicken (130)
Areas of Operation: AL, FL, IL, IN, KY, MI, MO, OH, TN, VA, WI, BC
Foreign Countries: CANADA
Type of Foodservice: Quick Serve (130)
Primary Distributors: (Full Line) PFG - Customized Support Services, LEBANON, TN

Key Personnel
LORI SEERING - VP Marketing
BILL SPARKS - VP Operations
DAN SOKOLIK - VP Marketing
JESSICA CROUCH - Director Marketing
OLIVER WHEELER - District Manager

Shula's Restaurant Group
3020 NE 32nd Ave Ste 347
Ft Lauderdale, FL 33308-7221

Telephone: (954) 393-1920
Fax Number: (954) 537-3313
Internet Homepage: shulas.com
Company Email: info@shula.com
Type of Business: Chain Restaurant Operator
Year Founded: 1989
Systemwide Sales: $77,180,000 (e)
Total Sales: $6,448,000 (e)
Alcohol Sales: 30%
Number of Employees: 16
Average Check: Dinner(90)
Internet Order Processing: Yes
Internet Sales: 5.50%
Total Units: 21
Trade Names: Shula Burger (3); Shula's 2 (2); Shula's 347 (5); Shula's America's Steak House (8); Shula's Bar & Grill (3)
Units Franchised To: 21
Preferred Square Footage: 5,500; 6,000
Preferred Location Types: Hotel/Motel
Alcohol Served: Beer, Wine, Liquor
Primary Menu: American (2); Hamburger (3); Steak (16)
Projected Openings: 2
Areas of Operation: AZ, FL, IL, OH, TX, UT, VA
Type of Foodservice: Casual Dining (8); Fast Casual (4); Fine Dining (8)
Primary Distributors: (Food) SYSCO Food Services of South Florida Inc., MEDLEY, FL
Notes: Average dinner check reflects the Shula's Steak House operations; average check for Shula's 347 is $38 and for Shula's 2 is $22.

Key Personnel
MARY ANNE SHULA - Chairman; Partner
DAVE SHULA - President; Partner; Director Operations, Facility/Maintenance, Franchise Development; General Buyer
DEMETRIO ZAVALA - Corporate Chef; Director Culinary Development

GC Southwest Holding Company
5091 Okeechobee Rd
Ft Pierce, FL 34947

Telephone: (772) 489-8004
Type of Business: Chain Restaurant Operator
Total Sales: $13,750,000 (e)
Total Units: 9
Trade Names: Golden Corral Buffet & Grill (9)
Units Franchised From: 9
Preferred Square Footage: 5,500; 6,000
Preferred Location Types: Freestanding
Primary Menu: American (9)
Projected Remodelings: 5
Areas of Operation: AZ, IL, NM, WI
Type of Foodservice: Family Restaurant (9)
Franchise Affiliation: Golden Corral Corp., RALEIGH, NC

Key Personnel
MICHAEL J. PETROLINE - President; General Buyer
SHIRLEY PETROLINE - Director Human Resources

Canteen Vending Services
3009 NE 19th Dr
Gainesville, FL 32609-3362

Telephone: (352) 377-0510
Fax Number: (352) 376-5870
Listing Type: Branch Office
Type of Business: Foodservice Management Operator
Year Founded: 1929
Number of Employees: 31
Number of Locations Served: 100
Total Foodservice Mgmt Accounts: 100
Areas of Operation: FL
Type of Foodservice: Vending machines (100)
Foodservice Management Venues: Business & Industry; College & University; Health Care; Lodging; Schools; Travel Plazas
Parent Company: Compass Group The Americas, CHARLOTTE, NC
Headquarters: Canteen Vending Services, CHARLOTTE, NC

Key Personnel
RAY MARTIGNETTI - General Manager; Director Operations, Purchasing

Five Star Pizza
210 SW 2nd Ave
Gainesville, FL 32601

Telephone: (352) 375-5600
Internet Homepage: fivestarpizza.com
Type of Business: Chain Restaurant Operator
Year Founded: 1988
Total Units: 21
Trade Names: Five Star Pizza (21)
Company-Owned Units: 21
Primary Menu: Pizza (21)
Areas of Operation: FL
Type of Foodservice: Quick Serve (21)

Key Personnel
JOHN GILLESPIE - Founder; Owner

Gator Domino's Pizza
3201 SW 42nd St
Gainesville, FL 32608-2360

Mailing Address: PO Box 141858, GAINESVILLE, FL, 32614-4858
Telephone: (352) 373-3343
Fax Number: (352) 337-0525
Internet Homepage: gatordominos.com
Company Email: office@gatordominos.com
Type of Business: Chain Restaurant Operator
Year Founded: 1970
Total Sales: $20,544,000 (e)
Number of Employees: 180
Average Check: Lunch(16); Dinner(26)
Internet Order Processing: Yes
Total Units: 10
Trade Names: Domino's (10)
Units Franchised From: 10
Preferred Square Footage: 1,000; 1,300
Preferred Location Types: Strip Mall
Primary Menu: Pizza (10)
Areas of Operation: FL
Type of Foodservice: Quick Serve (10)
Foodservice Management Venues: Schools
Franchise Affiliation: Domino's Pizza Inc, ANN ARBOR, MI
Primary Distributors: (Food) Domino's Distribution Center, GROVELAND, FL

Key Personnel
GRAHAM BALLARD - Owner

McDonald's Franchise
1030 E University Ave
Gainesville, FL 32601

Telephone: (352) 376-0830
Internet Homepage: mcdjax.com
Company Email: gnvmcd@jcurt.com
Type of Business: Chain Restaurant Operator
Total Sales: $37,820,000 (c)
Total Units: 8
Trade Names: McDonald's (8)
Units Franchised From: 8
Preferred Square Footage: 2,500
Primary Menu: Hamburger (8)
Areas of Operation: FL
Type of Foodservice: Quick Serve (8)
Franchise Affiliation: McDonald's Corporation, CHICAGO, IL

Key Personnel
JACQUELYN PARIS - President; General Buyer

Shivstone Inc
3822 Newberry Rd Ste B
Gainesville, FL 32607-4835

Telephone: (352) 271-7437
Company Email: coldstone20156@gmail.com
Type of Business: Chain Restaurant Operator
Total Sales: $1,232,000 (e)
Total Units: 2
Trade Names: Cold Stone Creamery (2)
Units Franchised From: 2
Primary Menu: Snacks (2)
Areas of Operation: FL
Type of Foodservice: Quick Serve (2)
Franchise Affiliation: Kahala Brands, SCOTTSDALE, AZ

Key Personnel
NEERU CHAUDHARI - Partner
DHAIRYA R. CHAUDHARI - Partner

The Bento Group
3841 SW Archer Rd
Gainesville, FL 32608

Telephone: (352) 224-5123
Internet Homepage: chelatacos.com; avenuegastrobar.com; eatatbento.com
Type of Business: Chain Restaurant Operator
Year Founded: 2002
Total Sales: $40,960,000 (e)
Total Units: 18
Trade Names: Avenue Gastrobar (1); Bento Asian Kitchen + Sushi (14); Chela Tequila & Tacos (1); Sticky Rice Lao Street Food (1); Sushi CHAO (1)
Company-Owned Units: 18
Primary Menu: American (1); Asian (15); Japanese (1); Mexican (1)
Areas of Operation: FL
Type of Foodservice: Casual Dining (1); Fast Casual (17)

Key Personnel
JIMMY TUNG - Partner
JOHHNY TUNG - Partner
DAVID YU - Partner
TAMMY LANEY - Director Operations
ANDREINA RIVAS - Director Human Resources
NICOLE STANULEWICH - Manager Human Resources

Domino's Distribution Center
7600 American Way
Groveland, FL 34736-8649

Telephone: (352) 429-5555
Fax Number: (352) 429-5998
Internet Homepage: dominos.com
Listing Type: Distribution Center
Type of Business: Chain Restaurant Operator
Number of Employees: 74
Areas of Operation: FL, GA
Parent Company: Domino's Pizza Inc, ANN ARBOR, MI

Key Personnel
JOHN PEOPLES - General Manager; Director Supply Chain
DAN FENBERS - Supervisor Warehouse

Domino's Franchisee
1200 W Broad St Ste A
Groveland, FL 34736-2023

Telephone: (352) 429-4500
Type of Business: Chain Restaurant Operator
Total Sales: $6,233,000 (e)
Total Units: 3
Trade Names: Domino's (3)
Units Franchised From: 3
Primary Menu: Pizza (3)
Areas of Operation: FL
Type of Foodservice: Quick Serve (3)
Franchise Affiliation: Domino's Pizza Inc, ANN ARBOR, MI

Key Personnel
KEITH W. SHERRICK - Owner; General Buyer

Concept Acquisitions II, LLC
1515 International Pkwy Ste 2013
Heathrow, FL 32746-7635

Mailing Address: PO Box 950759, LAKE MARY, FL, 32795
Telephone: (407) 574-8363
Fax Number: (407) 333-8852
Internet Homepage: mannysgrills.com; ohohburrito.com; tendersucf.com
Company Email: info@flamersgrill.com
Type of Business: Chain Restaurant Operator
Year Founded: 1987
Systemwide Sales: $106,926,000 (e)
Total Sales: $28,150,000 (e)
Number of Employees: 70
Average Check: Lunch(12); Dinner(12)
Total Units: 30
Trade Names: Flamers Burgers & Chicken; Manny's Mediterranean Cafe; Manny's Neighborhood Grille; Oh!Oh! Burrito; Quickfire Grille; Quickfire Sub Station; Tenders
Company-Owned Units: 70
Preferred Square Footage: 600; 1,000; 1,200
Preferred Location Types: Community Mall; Downtown; Freestanding; Strip Mall
Areas of Operation: DC, FL, GA, MA, MD, MI, NC, OH, PA, PR, VA
Foreign Countries: EGYPT; MEXICO; THE PHILIPPINES
Type of Foodservice: Quick Serve
Primary Distributors: (Full Line) SYSCO Atlanta LLC, COLLEGE PARK, GA

Key Personnel
LEN PFUNTNER - VP Operations; Director Operations
NICK KNOTT - Director Franchise Sales

Domino's Franchisee
2488 N Heritage Oaks Path
Hernando, FL 34442-6332

Telephone: (352) 527-1240
Type of Business: Chain Restaurant Operator
Total Sales: $4,165,000 (e)
Total Units: 2
Trade Names: Domino's (2)
Units Franchised From: 2
Primary Menu: Pizza (2)
Areas of Operation: FL
Type of Foodservice: Quick Serve (2)
Franchise Affiliation: Domino's Pizza Inc, ANN ARBOR, MI

Key Personnel
SCOTT A. MOORE - Owner; General Buyer

The Grill Room
505 E Hartford St
Hernando, FL 34442-3347

Telephone: (352) 746-6855
Fax Number: (352) 746-9863
Internet Homepage: thevillagesofcitrushills.com
Type of Business: Chain Restaurant Operator
Total Sales: $3,139,000 (e)
Alcohol Sales: 30%
Number of Employees: 460
Average Check: Breakfast(10); Lunch(10); Dinner(36)
Total Units: 2
Trade Names: Skyview (1); The Grill Room (1)
Company-Owned Units: 2
Preferred Location Types: Other
Alcohol Served: Beer, Wine, Liquor
Primary Menu: French/Continental (1); Steak (1)
Areas of Operation: FL
Type of Foodservice: Casual Dining (1); Fine Dining (1)
Primary Distributors: (Food) SYSCO Central Florida Inc., OCOEE, FL
Notes: Located in the Citrus Hill Golf & Country Club.

Key Personnel
JERRY NASH - Partner; VP Operations
STEVE TAMPOSI - Partner

ANTHONY LAMBERT - General Manager;
  General Buyer
DWAYNE ZIMMERMAN - Executive Chef;
  General Buyer

Jerry & Joe's Pizza
1772 W 68th St
Hialeah, FL 33014-4437

Telephone: (305) 821-5555
Fax Number: (305) 362-5109
Internet Homepage: jerryandjoes.com
Company Email: jandjpizz@aol.com
Type of Business: Chain Restaurant Operator
Year Founded: 1958
Systemwide Sales: $15,659,000 (e)
Total Sales: $5,376,000 (e)
Number of Employees: 88
Average Check: Lunch(14); Dinner(22)
Internet Order Processing: Yes
Total Units: 4
Trade Names: Jerry & Joe's Pizza (4)
Company-Owned Units: 2
Units Franchised To: 2
Preferred Square Footage: 1,000
Preferred Location Types: Convenience
  Store/Gas Station; Strip Mall
Primary Menu: Pizza (4)
Areas of Operation: FL
Type of Foodservice: Quick Serve (4)
Primary Distributors: (Food) Palermos
  Wholesale Italian Foods Inc., MIAMI LAKES,
  FL

Key Personnel
HENRY CRUZ - President; Manager Menu
  Development; General Buyer

Palm Springs Chicken Take-Out Inc
811 W 49th St
Hialeah, FL 33012-3544

Telephone: (305) 821-8661
Type of Business: Chain Restaurant Operator
Total Sales: $5,795,000 (e)
Total Units: 3
Trade Names: KFC (3)
Units Franchised From: 3
Primary Menu: Chicken (3)
Areas of Operation: FL
Type of Foodservice: Quick Serve (3)
Franchise Affiliation: KFC Corporation,
  LOUISVILLE, KY

Key Personnel
DANIEL YAGODA - President; General Buyer
MICHAEL MATHEWS - Director; Community
  Relations

STEVEN BILLER - Director Media

E.A.P. Management Corp.
2501 Hollywood Blvd Ste 200
Hollywood, FL 33020-6632

Telephone: (954) 920-1802
Fax Number: (954) 920-3043
Type of Business: Chain Restaurant Operator
Total Sales: $72,130,000 (e)
Total Units: 35
Trade Names: KFC (25); Taco Bell (10)
Units Franchised From: 35
Primary Menu: Chicken (25); Taco (10)
Areas of Operation: FL
Type of Foodservice: Quick Serve (35)
Franchise Affiliation: KFC Corporation,
  LOUISVILLE, KY; Taco Bell Corp., IRVINE, CA

Key Personnel
BURT SREBRENIK - President; General Buyer

Sheridan Technical Center
5400 Sheridan St
Hollywood, FL 33021-3346

Telephone: (754) 321-5410
Fax Number: (754) 321-5680
Internet Homepage: sheridantechnical.com
Company Email:
  kim.curry@browardschools.com
Type of Business: Culinary Schools
Areas of Operation: FL

Key Personnel
MICHAEL MCDONNELL - Chairman

Taverna Opa
800 N Ocean Dr
Hollywood, FL 33019-1230

Telephone: (954) 922-2256
Fax Number: (954) 922-2258
Internet Homepage: giorgiosbakery.com;
  tavernaopa.com
Company Email: info@tavernaopa.com
Type of Business: Chain Restaurant Operator
Year Founded: 1996
Total Sales: $13,210,000 (e)
Alcohol Sales: 40%
Number of Employees: 104
Average Check: Dinner(20)
Total Units: 5
Trade Names: Giorgio's Bakery & Bistro (1);
  Taverna Kyma (1); Taverna Opa (3)
Company-Owned Units: 4
Units Franchised To: 1
Preferred Square Footage: 5,500; 6,000
Preferred Location Types: Freestanding

Alcohol Served: Beer, Wine, Liquor
Primary Menu: Greek/Mediterranean (5)
Areas of Operation: FL
Type of Foodservice: Casual Dining (5)
Catering Services: Yes
On-site Distribution Center: Yes
Primary Distributors: (Food) SYSCO Food
  Services of South Florida Inc., MEDLEY, FL

Key Personnel
PETER TSIALIAMANIS - President; General
  Manager; Executive Chef; General Buyer

Vilarino's Inc.
6015 Garfield St
Hollywood, FL 33024-6017

Telephone: (954) 981-6777
Fax Number: (954) 981-3060
Internet Homepage:
  lasvegascubancuisine.com
Company Email:
  emailus@lasvegascubancuisine.com
Type of Business: Chain Restaurant Operator
Total Sales: $10,560,000 (e)
Total Units: 15
Trade Names: La Casita Cuban Cuisine (1);
  Las Vegas Cuban Cuisine (13); Vila's
  Restaurant (1)
Company-Owned Units: 15
Primary Menu: Latin American/Cuban (15)
Areas of Operation: FL, NV
Type of Foodservice: Casual Dining (15)

Key Personnel
ANTONIO VILARINO - Partner; General
  Manager; General Buyer
NILDA VILARINO - Partner

Show Palace Dinner Theatre
16128 US Highway 19
Hudson, FL 34667-4303

Telephone: (727) 863-7949
Fax Number: (727) 819-1209
Internet Homepage: showpalace.net
Company Email: info@showpalace.net
Type of Business: Chain Restaurant Operator
Year Founded: 1997
Total Sales: $11,390,000 (e)
Alcohol Sales: 10%
Number of Employees: 50
Average Check: Dinner(54)
Internet Order Processing: Yes
Total Units: 2
Trade Names: Palace Grand (1); Show Palace
  Dinner Theatre (1)
Company-Owned Units: 2
Preferred Location Types: Freestanding
Alcohol Served: Beer, Wine, Liquor
Primary Menu: American (2)

Areas of Operation: FL
Type of Foodservice: Casual Dining (2)
Primary Distributors: (Food) SYSCO Food Services of West Coast Florida Inc., PALMETTO, FL

Key Personnel
VICTORIA MARA - Owner
TOMMY COGHILL - General Manager; General Buyer
JENNIFER MARA - Business Manager

The Original Crabby Bill's Seafood Inc.
401 Gulf Blvd
Indian Rocks Beach, FL 33785-2539

Telephone: (727) 595-4825
Fax Number: (727) 593-5997
Internet Homepage: jakesmexicancantina.com; lulusoysterbar.com; ready-set-yo.com; seabreezeislandgrill.com; crabbybills.com; crabbybillsirb.com
Company Email: crabbygifts@crabbybillsirb.com
Type of Business: Chain Restaurant Operator
Year Founded: 1983
Systemwide Sales: $27,288,000 (e)
Total Sales: $29,180,000 (e)
Alcohol Sales: 100%
Number of Employees: 465
Average Check: Breakfast(10); Lunch(16); Dinner(24)
Internet Sales: 2.00%
Total Units: 9
Trade Names: Bon Appetit (1); Cabanas Grill (1); Evy's Terrace Bar (1); Guilty Sea Sports Bar (1); Jake's Costal Cantina (1); JD's Restaurant & Lounge (1); Pipo N Betty's Bakery (1); The Original Crabby Bill's (1); The SeaBreeze Island Grill and Raw Bar (1)
Company-Owned Units: 9
Preferred Square Footage: 4,500; 7,000
Preferred Location Types: Freestanding; Hotel/Motel
Alcohol Served: Beer, Wine, Liquor
Primary Menu: Mexican (1); Seafood (7); Snacks (1)
Areas of Operation: FL
Type of Foodservice: Casual Dining (9); Quick Serve (0)
Catering Services: Yes
Primary Distributors: (Food) Cheney Bros. Inc., RIVIERA BEACH, FL

Key Personnel
MATT LODER - CEO; President; Executive Chef
LUIS CAMPUZANO - CFO
PAUL JENKINS - VP Operations, Facility/Maintenance, Supply Chain, Store Fixtures; Director Information Systems; General Buyer

BayStar Restaurant Group
19325 Gulf Blvd
Indian Shores, FL 33785-2214

Telephone: (727) 391-4052
Internet Homepage: baystarrestaurantgroup.com; islandwaygrill.com; rumbaislandgrill.com; saltrockgrill.com
Company Email: baystarrestaurantgroup@gmail.com
Type of Business: Chain Restaurant Operator
Total Sales: $12,140,000 (e)
Alcohol Sales: 15%
Total Units: 9
Trade Names: Island Way Grill (1); Marina Cantina (1); Poke Havana (1); Rumba Island Bar & Grill (2); Salt Cracker Fish Camp (1); Salt Rock Grill (1); Salt Rock Tavern (1); SeaWead (1)
Company-Owned Units: 9
Preferred Location Types: Community Mall; Freestanding
Alcohol Served: Beer, Wine, Liquor
Primary Menu: Caribbean (2); Mexican (1); Miscellaneous (1); Southern (1); Steak/Seafood (4)
Areas of Operation: FL
Type of Foodservice: Casual Dining (9)
Catering Services: Yes

Key Personnel
FRANK CHIVAS - President; General Buyer
SHERI AQUILA - General Manager; Director Catering
DAVID NOVAK - General Manager

Effin Egg
13123 E EMERALD COAST PKWY
Inlet Beach, FL 32461

Telephone: (678) 974-7562
Internet Homepage: effinegg.com
Company Email: effinegg@gmail.com
Type of Business: Chain Restaurant Operator
Year Founded: 2019
Systemwide Sales: $4,000,000 (e)
Total Sales: $3,508,000 (e)
Total Units: 5
Trade Names: Effin Egg (5)
Units Franchised To: 5
Primary Menu: American (5)
Projected Openings: 3
Areas of Operation: GA, IL, NJ, NY, TX
Type of Foodservice: Fast Casual (5)

Key Personnel
JEFF MARTIN - Founder; President

Pierre's
81600 Overseas Hwy
Islamorada, FL 33036-3700

Telephone: (305) 664-3225
Fax Number: (305) 664-3304
Internet Homepage: moradabay.com
Company Email: info@moradabay.com
Type of Business: Chain Restaurant Operator
Total Sales: $3,058,000 (e)
Alcohol Sales: 35%
Number of Employees: 125
Average Check: Lunch(24); Dinner(36)
Total Units: 2
Trade Names: Morada Bay Cafe (1); Pierres at Morada Bay (1)
Company-Owned Units: 2
Preferred Location Types: Freestanding
Alcohol Served: Beer, Wine, Liquor
Primary Menu: American (1); French/Continental (1)
Areas of Operation: FL
Type of Foodservice: Casual Dining (2)
Primary Distributors: (Food) SYSCO Food Services of South Florida Inc., MEDLEY, FL

Key Personnel
HUBERT BODWIN - President; General Buyer

Bono's Pit Bar-B-Q
10645 Philips Hwy Bldg 200
Jacksonville, FL 32256-6507

Telephone: (904) 880-8310
Fax Number: (904) 880-8373
Internet Homepage: williejewells.com; bonosbarbq.com
Company Email: info@bonosbarbq.com
Type of Business: Chain Restaurant Operator
Year Founded: 1949
Systemwide Sales: $51,935,000 (e)
Total Sales: $23,310,000 (e)
Alcohol Sales: 5%
Number of Employees: 395
Average Check: Lunch(8); Dinner(14)
Total Units: 35
Trade Names: Bono's Pit Bar-B-Q (20); Willie Jewell's Old School Bar-B-Q (15)
Company-Owned Units: 10
Units Franchised To: 25
Preferred Square Footage: 3,700
Preferred Location Types: Freestanding; Strip Mall
Alcohol Served: Beer, Wine
Primary Menu: Bar-B-Q (35)
Projected Openings: 3
Areas of Operation: CO, FL, GA, SC
Type of Foodservice: Casual Dining (20); Fast Casual (15)
Catering Services: Yes
Primary Distributors: (Full Line) Manna

Provisions, JACKSONVILLE, FL

Key Personnel
JOE ADEEB - CEO; Director Finance, Real Estate, Design, Menu Development, Catering
JOSH MARTINO - President; Director Operations, Purchasing, Facility/Maintenance, Marketing, Research & Development; General Buyer
ANGELA MCCREARY - Controller
DEBORAH MALINIS - Director Catering

DCC Lee Enterprises
12276 San Jose Blvd Ste 601
Jacksonville, FL 32223-8672

Telephone: (904) 288-6750
Fax Number: (904) 288-6978
Internet Homepage: mcdjax.com
Company Email: office@mcdjax.com
Type of Business: Chain Restaurant Operator
Year Founded: 1994
Total Sales: $94,530,000 (e)
Number of Employees: 950
Average Check: Breakfast(6); Lunch(8); Dinner(8)
Total Units: 20
Trade Names: McDonald's (20)
Units Franchised From: 20
Preferred Square Footage: 3,000
Preferred Location Types: Discount Dept. Stores; Freestanding
Primary Menu: Hamburger (20)
Areas of Operation: FL
Type of Foodservice: In-Store Feeder (20); Quick Serve (20)
Franchise Affiliation: McDonald's Corporation, CHICAGO, IL

Key Personnel
DAVID MULLINS SR - Partner; Director Real Estate; General Buyer
DAVID MULLINS JR - Partner; VP; Director Human Resources
GENE MULLINS - Manager Operations
SARAH MARTIN - Manager Finance
AMANDA MERNAGH - Manager Human Resources
WILLIE BRANTLEY - Supervisor Operations

Dmor Inc
10250 Normandy Blvd Ste 602
Jacksonville, FL 32221

Telephone: (904) 693-1188
Company Email: mcdonaldscare@dmor.net
Type of Business: Chain Restaurant Operator
Total Sales: $32,300,000 (e)
Average Check: Dinner(12)
Total Units: 7
Trade Names: McDonald's (7)
Units Franchised From: 7
Preferred Square Footage: 2,500
Preferred Location Types: Downtown; Freestanding
Primary Menu: Hamburger (7)
Areas of Operation: FL
Type of Foodservice: Quick Serve (7)
Franchise Affiliation: McDonald's Corporation, CHICAGO, IL

Key Personnel
DEBORAH MORELAND - President; General Buyer

Famous Amos Restaurants Inc.
9310 Old Kings Rd S Ste 1101
Jacksonville, FL 32257-6196

Telephone: (904) 731-3396
Fax Number: (904) 731-3421
Internet Homepage: famousamos.bz
Company Email: tiffany.FamousAmos@aol.com
Type of Business: Chain Restaurant Operator
Year Founded: 1967
Total Sales: $5,467,000 (e)
Number of Employees: 400
Average Check: Breakfast(6); Lunch(12); Dinner(14)
Total Units: 2
Trade Names: Famous Amos Restaurant (2)
Company-Owned Units: 2
Preferred Square Footage: 3,600
Preferred Location Types: Freestanding
Primary Menu: American (2)
Areas of Operation: FL
Type of Foodservice: Family Restaurant (2)
Catering Services: Yes
On-site Distribution Center: Yes
Primary Distributors: (Full Line) SYSCO Food Services of Jacksonville Inc., JACKSONVILLE, FL

Key Personnel
JOSEPHINE PHELAN - Partner; Executive Chef; General Buyer
JOHN PHELAN - Partner; General Buyer

Firehouse Restaurant Group Inc.
12735 Gran Bay Pkwy W Ste 150
Jacksonville, FL 32258-4889

Telephone: (904) 886-8300
Fax Number: (904) 886-2111
Internet Homepage: firehousesubs.com
Company Email: mail@firehousesubs.com
Type of Business: Chain Restaurant Operator
Year Founded: 1994
Systemwide Sales: $1,282,878,000 (e)
Total Sales: $198,427,000 (e)
Number of Employees: 857
Average Check: Lunch(10); Dinner(10)
Total Units: 1,282
Trade Names: Firehouse Subs (1,282)
Company-Owned Units: 37
Units Franchised To: 1,245
Preferred Square Footage: 1,400; 1,600; 1,800; 2,000
Preferred Location Types: Airports; Freestanding; Strip Mall
Primary Menu: Sandwiches/Deli (1,282)
Projected Openings: 80
Areas of Operation: AL, AZ, CA, CO, FL, GA, IA, ID, IL, IN, KS, KY, LA, MA, MD, ME, MI, MN, MO, MS, NC, NE, NM, NV, NY, OH, OK, PA, PR, SC, SD, TN, TX, UT, VA, WA, WI, WV
Type of Foodservice: Fast Casual (1,282)
Catering Services: Yes
Primary Distributors: (Full Line) The SYGMA Network Inc.- Florida, ORLANDO, FL
Parent Company: Restaurant Brands International, TORONTO, ON CANADA

Key Personnel
CHRIS SORENSEN - Co-Founder; Partner; VP
DON FOX - CEO
MIKE HANCOCK - COO
MIKE BRANSON - Area Director Franchising
GREGORY P. DELKS - VP Franchise Development, Global Development
ROB JAKOBY - VP Information Technology
JOHN L. RAULERSON - VP Quality Assurance
MELISSA SIMPSON - Director Digital Media
LINDSAY WILLIAMS - Director Development
JAY MILLER - Director Product Development
NASLI HEERAMANEK - Director Brand Marketing
RISA RAPPAPORT - Director Catering
ANGELA DIBENEDETTO - Director Communications
RICHARD ELKINS - Director Construction
DAVID BERLIN - Director Franchise Operations
BOB MAY - Senior Manager Real Estate
GINA HARDY - Senior Manager Real Estate
JEFFREY SALLS - Senior Manager Supply Chain
CHRISTINE STAHL - Senior Manager
ADAM STOKES - Manager Real Estate
SCOTT SCHALK - Manager Communications
BRITT MITCHELL - Manager Real Estate
BRITTANY BERSANI - Manager Real Estate
CRAIG GARWOOD - Manager Real Estate
RICHARD GRIGGS - Manager Franchising

Harry's of America
9995 Gate Pkwy N Ste 400B
Jacksonville, FL 32246-1897

Telephone: (904) 642-2165
Fax Number: (904) 642-7918
Internet Homepage: hookedonharrys.com

Type of Business: Chain Restaurant Operator
Year Founded: 1987
Total Sales: $17,840,000 (e)
Alcohol Sales: 25%
Number of Employees: 280
Average Check: Lunch(14); Dinner(22)
Internet Order Processing: Yes
Internet Sales: 1.00%
Total Units: 5
Trade Names: Harry's Seafood Bar & Grille (5)
Company-Owned Units: 5
Preferred Square Footage: 5,500
Preferred Location Types: Downtown; Freestanding; Strip Mall
Alcohol Served: Beer, Wine, Liquor
Primary Menu: Seafood (5)
Areas of Operation: FL
Type of Foodservice: Casual Dining (5)
Catering Services: Yes
Primary Distributors: (Equipment) Edward Don & Co., MIRAMAR, FL; (Food) SYSCO Food Services of Jacksonville Inc., JACKSONVILLE, FL; (Supplies) Edward Don & Co., MIRAMAR, FL

Key Personnel
LOUIS SAIG - CEO; President; Partner; Director Real Estate, Business Development, Internet Development
JEFF JABOT - Partner
JESSE JABOT - Partner; COO; VP Operations; Director Marketing
GREGORY SAIG - Partner; Treasurer
JUSTIN GRIFFIN - Director Operations; General Buyer
BROOKE BLYSTONE - Manager Accounting
DOMINIC HERRING - Specialist

♦

Jacksonville Coffee Company
12620 Beach Blvd Ste 7
Jacksonville, FL 32246

Telephone: (904) 551-1671
Internet Homepage: jacksonvillecoffeecompany.com
Company Email: info@jacksonvillecoffeecompany.com
Type of Business: Chain Restaurant Operator
Year Founded: 1910
Total Sales: $6,022,000 (e)
Total Units: 2
Trade Names: Jacksonville Coffee Company (2)
Company-Owned Units: 2
Primary Menu: Coffee (2)
Areas of Operation: FL
Type of Foodservice: Quick Serve (2)

Key Personnel
JOSE PARADA - Owner

ZACHARY PROEHL - General Manager

Jenkins Quality Barbecue Inc.
4255 Camellia Cir E
Jacksonville, FL 32207-7022

Telephone: (904) 448-5868
Internet Homepage: jenkinsqualitybarbecue.com
Company Email: info@jenkinsqualitybarbecue.com
Type of Business: Chain Restaurant Operator
Year Founded: 1945
Total Sales: $3,006,000 (e)
Number of Employees: 30
Average Check: Lunch(12); Dinner(14)
Internet Order Processing: Yes
Total Units: 3
Trade Names: Jenkins Quality Barbecue (3)
Company-Owned Units: 3
Preferred Location Types: Freestanding
Primary Menu: Bar-B-Q (3)
Areas of Operation: FL
Type of Foodservice: Quick Serve (3)
On-site Distribution Center: Yes

Key Personnel
JOBON BROWN - General Manager

●

JRVL Inc
PO Box 7466
Jacksonville, FL 32238-0466

Telephone: (904) 781-1197
Fax Number: (904) 777-6748
Company Email: jrvloffice@gmail.com
Type of Business: Chain Restaurant Operator
Total Sales: $42,640,000 (e)
Average Check: Lunch(8); Dinner(12)
Total Units: 9
Trade Names: McDonald's (9)
Units Franchised From: 9
Preferred Square Footage: 2,500
Preferred Location Types: Downtown; Freestanding
Primary Menu: Hamburger (9)
Areas of Operation: FL
Type of Foodservice: Quick Serve (9)
Franchise Affiliation: McDonald's Corporation, CHICAGO, IL

Key Personnel
JAMES VAN LAERE - President; General Buyer
EMERSON MCDONALDS - General Manager

▲

Larry's Giant Subs Inc.
4479 Deerwood Lake Pkwy Ste 1
Jacksonville, FL 32216-2250

Telephone: (904) 739-9069
Fax Number: (904) 739-1218
Internet Homepage: larryssubs.com
Company Email: bigone@larryssubs.com
Type of Business: Chain Restaurant Operator
Year Founded: 1982
Systemwide Sales: $23,879,000 (e)
Total Sales: $3,264,000 (e)
Alcohol Sales: 0.50%
Number of Employees: 330
Average Check: Lunch(8); Dinner(8)
Total Units: 47
Trade Names: Larry's Giant Subs (47)
Company-Owned Units: 5
Units Franchised To: 42
Preferred Square Footage: 1,200; 1,400
Preferred Location Types: Freestanding; Strip Mall
Alcohol Served: Beer
Primary Menu: Sandwiches/Deli (47)
Projected Openings: 3
Areas of Operation: FL, GA, SC, TX
Type of Foodservice: Quick Serve (47)
Catering Services: Yes
Primary Distributors: (Full Line) SYSCO Food Services of Jacksonville Inc., JACKSONVILLE, FL

Key Personnel
LARRY RAIKES - CEO; President; CFO; CIO; Executive Chef; Director Facility/Maintenance, Advertising, Real Estate
MITCHELL RAIKES - COO; VP; Director Operations, Information Systems; General Buyer
JENNIFER POIRIER - Manager Finance, Operations, Purchasing, Inventory, Human Resources, Food Safety

● ▲

Lee Wesley Restaurants, LLC
210 State St E
Jacksonville, FL 32202-3053

Telephone: (904) 354-7886
Fax Number: (904) 551-0184
Internet Homepage: leewesley.com
Company Email: info@LeeWesley.com
Type of Business: Chain Restaurant Operator
Total Sales: $11,370,000 (e)
Total Units: 8
Trade Names: Burger King (5); Panda Express (2); Shula's Bar & Grill (1)
Units Franchised From: 8
Primary Menu: Chinese (2); Hamburger (5); Steak (1)
Areas of Operation: FL

Type of Foodservice: Casual Dining (1); Quick Serve (7)
Franchise Affiliation: Burger King Worldwide Inc., MIAMI, FL; Panda Restaurant Group Inc., ROSEMEAD, CA; Shula's Restaurant Group, FT LAUDERDALE, FL

Key Personnel
ARTHUR J. LEE - CEO; President
CAMILLE J. LEE-JOHNSON - Exec VP
BRANDON W. LEE - Director Finance

Loop Restaurant Group Inc.
3721 San Jose Pl Ste 1
Jacksonville, FL 32257-2430

Telephone: (904) 268-2609
Fax Number: (904) 268-5809
Internet Homepage: looppizzagrill.com
Type of Business: Chain Restaurant Operator
Year Founded: 1981
Systemwide Sales: $18,022,000 (e)
Total Sales: $9,002,000 (e)
Alcohol Sales: 10%
Number of Employees: 217
Average Check: Lunch(12); Dinner(14)
Internet Order Processing: Yes
Total Units: 16
Trade Names: The Loop Pizza Grill (16)
Company-Owned Units: 5
Units Franchised To: 11
Preferred Square Footage: 1,500
Preferred Location Types: Downtown; Freestanding; Strip Mall
Alcohol Served: Beer, Wine
Primary Menu: Pizza (16)
Areas of Operation: FL, NC
Type of Foodservice: Fast Casual (16)
Catering Services: Yes

Key Personnel
MIKE SCHNEIDER - CEO; Director Risk Management, Real Estate, Menu Development
CHRIS HARTLEY - COO; Director Operations, Human Resources

M Hospitality
2107 Hendricks Ave
Jacksonville, FL 32207-3370

Telephone: (904) 396-1213
Fax Number: (904) 396-5222
Internet Homepage: matthewsrestaurant.com; mshackburgers.com; restaurantmedure.us
Company Email: info@matthews.com
Type of Business: Chain Restaurant Operator
Total Sales: $14,960,000 (e)
Alcohol Sales: 12%
Number of Employees: 20
Average Check: Lunch(26); Dinner(90)
Total Units: 6
Trade Names: M Shack (4); Matthew's Restaurant (1); Restaurant Medure (1)
Company-Owned Units: 6
Preferred Location Types: Downtown; Other
Alcohol Served: Beer, Wine, Liquor
Primary Menu: American (2); Hamburger (4)
Projected Openings: 1
Areas of Operation: FL
Type of Foodservice: Fast Casual (4); Fine Dining (2)
Catering Services: Yes
Primary Distributors: (Food) SYSCO Food Services of Jacksonville Inc., JACKSONVILLE, FL

Key Personnel
MATTHEW MEDURE - President; Partner; General Manager; Executive Chef; General Buyer
DAVID MEDURE - Partner; Executive Chef

Roly Poly Franchise Systems
13245 Atlantic Blvd Ste 4-399
Jacksonville, FL 32225

Telephone: (904) 739-7659
Fax Number: (305) 295-9371
Internet Homepage: rolypoly.com
Company Email: rolypolyhq@aol.com
Type of Business: Chain Restaurant Operator
Year Founded: 1996
Systemwide Sales: $33,551,000 (e)
Total Sales: $621,000 (e)
Number of Employees: 6
Average Check: Lunch(12); Dinner(12)
Internet Order Processing: Yes
Internet Sales: 0.50%
Total Units: 25
Trade Names: Roly Poly (25)
Units Franchised To: 25
Preferred Square Footage: 800; 1,200
Preferred Location Types: Downtown; Strip Mall
Primary Menu: Sandwiches/Deli (25)
Areas of Operation: AL, CT, GA, IL, IN, KY, LA, MD, MI, NC, NJ, NY, OH, PA, SC, TX
Type of Foodservice: Quick Serve (25)
Catering Services: Yes

Key Personnel
LINDA L. WOLF - CEO; President; Executive Chef; Director Information Systems; General Buyer
JANE FERGUSON - COO; VP Operations; Director Purchasing, Human Resources, Training

The Sheik Restaurant
9720 Atlantic Blvd
Jacksonville, FL 32225-8223

Telephone: (904) 721-2660
Fax Number: (904) 721-2668
Internet Homepage: thesheiksandwiches.com
Type of Business: Chain Restaurant Operator
Year Founded: 1971
Total Sales: $6,909,000 (e)
Number of Employees: 160
Average Check: Lunch(8); Dinner(12)
Total Units: 8
Trade Names: Sheik Restaurant (8)
Company-Owned Units: 8
Preferred Square Footage: 2,000
Preferred Location Types: Freestanding
Primary Menu: Sandwiches/Deli (8)
Areas of Operation: FL
Type of Foodservice: Quick Serve (8)
Primary Distributors: (Full Line) US Foods, TAMPA, FL

Key Personnel
ELIAS SALAMEH - President; Partner; Manager Finance, Information Systems, Real Estate, Design, Human Resources
MIKE SALAMEH - Partner; Executive Chef; Director Purchasing, Human Resources; General Buyer
SAM SALAMEH - Partner; VP Operations, Facility/Maintenance, Supply Chain, Human Resources, Store Fixtures; General Manager

Welcome To Moe's, Inc
450 State Road 13 Ste 106
Jacksonville, FL 32259-3863

Telephone: (904) 382-0375
Internet Homepage: welcometomoes.com
Type of Business: Chain Restaurant Operator
Total Sales: $30,780,000 (e)
Alcohol Sales: 5%
Average Check: Dinner(14)
Total Units: 19
Trade Names: Moe's Southwest Grill (19)
Units Franchised From: 19
Preferred Square Footage: 2,000; 2,800
Alcohol Served: Beer
Primary Menu: Southwest/Tex-Mex (19)
Areas of Operation: FL
Type of Foodservice: Fast Casual (19)
Franchise Affiliation: Moe's Southwest Grill LLC, ATLANTA, GA
Notes: Also operates 14 Moe's Southwest Grill locations in DC, Maryland and Virginia under Guac & Roll, LLC.

Key Personnel
BRAD CHASTEEN - President
GORDON HAYWARD - Regional Manager

CATHY COULTER - Manager Sales, Catering

Woody's Bar-B-Q Inc.
4745 Sutton Park Ct Ste 301
Jacksonville, FL 32224-0254

Telephone: (904) 992-0556
Fax Number: (904) 992-0551
Internet Homepage: woodys.com
Company Email: admin@woodysbarbq.com
Type of Business: Chain Restaurant Operator
Year Founded: 1980
Systemwide Sales: $30,959,000 (e)
Total Sales: $11,730,000 (e)
Alcohol Sales: 10%
Number of Employees: 96
Average Check: Lunch(14); Dinner(14)
Internet Order Processing: Yes
Internet Sales: 1.00%
Total Units: 16
Trade Names: Woody's Bar-B-Q (16)
Units Franchised To: 16
Preferred Square Footage: 1,000; 1,500; 2,500; 2,800; 3,000; 5,000
Preferred Location Types: Freestanding; Strip Mall
Alcohol Served: Beer, Wine, Liquor
Primary Menu: Bar-B-Q (16)
Projected Openings: 5
Areas of Operation: FL, PA
Foreign Countries: CANADA
Type of Foodservice: Casual Dining (16)
Catering Services: Yes
Primary Distributors: (Full Line) SYSCO Central Florida Inc., OCOEE, FL

Key Personnel
WOODY MILLS - President; Partner
YOLANDA MILLS-MAWMAN - Partner; Senior VP; Treasurer; Director Information Systems, Human Resources
BILL ARNOLD - Area Director
JAY VAIL - VP Operations
PAUL MCALLISTER - Director Purchasing

Adventure Holdings LLC
2315 Beach Blvd Ste 203
Jacksonville Beach, FL 32250-4033

Telephone: (904) 246-4555
Fax Number: (904) 270-8822
Internet Homepage: adventurelanding.com
Type of Business: Foodservice Operations - Theme Parks
Total Sales: $30,640,000 (e)
Number of Employees: 56
Average Check: Lunch(16); Dinner(16)
Total Units: 18
Trade Names: Adventure Landing (18)
Company-Owned Units: 18
Preferred Square Footage: 2,500

Preferred Location Types: Parks
Primary Menu: American (18)
Areas of Operation: FL, NC, NY, TX
Type of Foodservice: Quick Serve (18)
Primary Distributors: (Full Line) SYSCO Central Florida Inc., OCOEE, FL
Notes: The company derives approximately 20% of its revenue from games.

Key Personnel
HANK WOODBURN - CEO; President; Director Real Estate
MATT LOEB - VP Operations
BECKY KOHLHAAS - Controller

Frank Entertainment
1003 W Indiantown Rd Ste 210
Jupiter, FL 33458-6851

Telephone: (561) 776-4747
Fax Number: (561) 776-2340
Internet Homepage: franktheatres.com; superplayusa.com
Company Email: info@frankcompanies.com
Type of Business: Foodservice Operations - Movie Theatre
Year Founded: 1921
Total Sales: $141,530,000 (e)
Alcohol Sales: 3%
Number of Employees: 970
Average Check: Lunch(12); Dinner(14)
Internet Order Processing: Yes
Internet Sales: 1.00%
Total Units: 29
Trade Names: Cinebowl and Grill (3); Frank's Theatres (20); Revolutions Bowling Bar & Grill (5); Superplay USA (1)
Company-Owned Units: 29
Preferred Square Footage: 35,000; 70,000
Preferred Location Types: Community Mall; Freestanding; Regional Mall; Strip Mall
Alcohol Served: Beer, Wine, Liquor
Primary Menu: American (8); Miscellaneous (21)
Projected Openings: 2
Areas of Operation: FL, NC, NJ, NY, PA, SC, TN
Type of Foodservice: Casual Dining (8); In-Store Feeder (21)
Primary Distributors: (Full Line) SYSCO Food Services of Metro New York, JERSEY CITY, NJ
Notes: The company derives approximately 72% of its revenue from theater admissions, on-screen advertising, and other sales.

Key Personnel
DEBORAH FRANK - Partner; VP Real Estate; Director Finance, Supply Chain, Design
JOYCE FRANK - Senior VP
ALAIN LEBEL - VP Operations
RICK ALBERTSON - Director Real Estate, Site Selection

JACK BERNOWITZ - Director Food and Beverage

Jetty's
1075 N Highway A1A
Jupiter, FL 33477-4429

Telephone: (561) 743-8166
Fax Number: (561) 743-5566
Internet Homepage: jettysjupiter.com; keegrillbocaraton.com; utikibeach.com
Type of Business: Chain Restaurant Operator
Year Founded: 1991
Total Sales: $4,068,000 (e)
Alcohol Sales: 12%
Number of Employees: 60
Average Check: Dinner(38)
Total Units: 3
Trade Names: Jetty's (1); Kee Grill (1); U Tiki Beach (1)
Company-Owned Units: 3
Preferred Location Types: Freestanding
Alcohol Served: Beer, Wine, Liquor
Primary Menu: American (3)
Areas of Operation: FL
Type of Foodservice: Casual Dining (3)
Primary Distributors: (Equipment) SYSCO Food Services of South Florida Inc., MEDLEY, FL; (Food) Cheney Bros. Inc., RIVIERA BEACH, FL; (Supplies) Edward Don & Co., MIRAMAR, FL

Key Personnel
PATRICK KOENIG - Partner
RICHARD JOHNSON JR - Partner
SCOTT JOHNSON - Partner

Jupiter Beach Resort & Spa
5 N Highway A1A
Jupiter, FL 33477-5145

Telephone: (561) 746-2511
Fax Number: (561) 744-1741
Internet Homepage: jupiterbeachresort.com
Type of Business: Chain Restaurant Operator
Year Founded: 1984
Total Sales: $4,410,000 (e)
Alcohol Sales: 17%
Number of Employees: 40
Average Check: Breakfast(14); Lunch(18); Dinner(36)
Total Units: 2
Trade Names: Sinclairs Ocean Lounge & Grill (1); The Sandbar (1)
Company-Owned Units: 2
Preferred Location Types: Freestanding
Alcohol Served: Beer, Wine, Liquor
Primary Menu: American (2)
Areas of Operation: FL
Type of Foodservice: Casual Dining (2)
Catering Services: Yes

Primary Distributors: (Food) SYSCO Food Services of South Florida Inc., MEDLEY, FL

Key Personnel
SUSAN REEVES - Controller
JUSTIN EARLE - General Manager; General Buyer
RICKY GOPEESINGH - Executive Chef; General Buyer
ARLENE PACILLO - Director Human Resources

Nature's Way Cafe Franchising LLC
10541 SE Le Parc
Jupiter, FL 33469-8147

Telephone: (561) 714-4500
Internet Homepage: natureswaycafe.com
Type of Business: Chain Restaurant Operator
Year Founded: 1979
Systemwide Sales: $4,402,000 (e)
Total Sales: $264,000 (e)
Number of Employees: 3
Average Check: Breakfast(5); Lunch(8); Dinner(10)
Total Units: 3
Trade Names: Nature's Way Cafe (3)
Units Franchised To: 3
Preferred Square Footage: 1,200
Preferred Location Types: Office Complex; Strip Mall
Primary Menu: Health Foods (3)
Areas of Operation: FL
Type of Foodservice: Family Restaurant (3)
Catering Services: Yes
Primary Distributors: (Food) Cheney Bros. Inc., RIVIERA BEACH, FL

Key Personnel
GARY BODLEY - CEO; Partner; Manager Real Estate, Catering
LILIANA BATISTA - President; Partner; General Manager; General Buyer

Ocean Reef Club
35 Ocean Reef Dr Ste 200
Key Largo, FL 33037-5259

Telephone: (305) 367-5855
Fax Number: (305) 367-2224
Internet Homepage: oceanreef.com
Company Email: info@oceanreef.com
Type of Business: Chain Restaurant Operator
Year Founded: 1950
Total Sales: $32,190,000 (e)
Alcohol Sales: 20%
Number of Employees: 500
Average Check: Breakfast(14); Lunch(18); Dinner(40)
Total Units: 15
Trade Names: Clubhouse Prime (1); Fitness Cafe (1); Gianni Ristorante (1); Palm Court (1); Reef Hut (1); Reef Lounge (1); Reef Treats (1); Rum Runner (1); The 19th Hole (1); The Beach Grill (1); The Burgee Bar (1); The Islander (1); The Ocean Room (1); The Point (1); The Raw Bar (1)
Company-Owned Units: 15
Preferred Square Footage: 5,000; 6,000
Preferred Location Types: Freestanding
Alcohol Served: Beer, Wine, Liquor
Primary Menu: American (7); Italian (1); Miscellaneous (2); Sandwiches/Deli (1); Seafood (2); Snacks (1); Steak (1)
Areas of Operation: FL
Type of Foodservice: Casual Dining (10); Fine Dining (1); Quick Serve (4)
Catering Services: Yes
Primary Distributors: (Food) SYSCO Food Services of West Coast Florida Inc., PALMETTO, FL

Key Personnel
ALEX TONARELLI - President
RICHARD WEINSTEIN - President Membership; COO Marketing; Senior VP
ERWIN PALS - VP Food
MIC O'KEEFFE - VP
RYAN STEELE - VP Facility/Maintenance
LAURA CHIAMPA - VP Human Resources, Training
FORD FRANKLIN - VP Finance
LAUREN MOUSE - Executive Director Finance
ISLANDE DILLON - Executive Director Membership
MOLLY CARROLL - Executive Director Communications
JUAN ACEVEDO - Executive Director Information Technology
DAN TANNER - Executive Director Operations
CHRISTOPHER PATTERSON - Executive Director Food and Beverage
LLOYD VAN - Executive Director Operations
DIANA DARDIO - General Manager
CRAIG HOROWITZ - General Manager
ROBBIE FELSTEAD - Director National Accounts
MANDA AIKEN - Director Food
SEAN CARROLL - Director Operations
PHILIPPE REYNAUD - Director Culinary Operations
DAN TAYLOR - Director Purchasing
JOHN RILEY - Assistant Director Event Planning
AARON ODONNELL - Manager Restaurant Operations
AMY CORNAIRE - Manager; Community Relations
NICOLE BODCHON - Manager Membership
ELIZABETH BOVILL - Manager Group
JOANN FORTE - Manager Engineering
JACQUELINE DOBSON - Manager Food
KAELI HOTTINGER - Coordinator Development
CHRISTINA SARMIENTO - Coordinator Human Resources
KATIE SALVATO - Designer

Senor Frijoles Inc.
103900 Overseas Hwy
Key Largo, FL 33037-2816

Telephone: (305) 451-4502
Fax Number: (305) 453-9661
Internet Homepage: fkrm.com; ballyhoosrestaurant.com; houseofsubsdeli.com; senorfrijolesrestaurant.com; sundownerskeylargo.com
Company Email: r.stoky@fkrm.com
Type of Business: Chain Restaurant Operator
Year Founded: 1978
Total Sales: $11,930,000 (e)
Alcohol Sales: 10%
Number of Employees: 200
Average Check: Lunch(14); Dinner(22)
Total Units: 5
Trade Names: Ballyhoo's (1); Cactus Jack's Pub (1); Marker 88 Restaurant (1); Senor Frijoles (1); Sundowners (1)
Company-Owned Units: 4
Units Franchised From: 1
Preferred Square Footage: 5,700
Preferred Location Types: Freestanding
Alcohol Served: Beer, Wine, Liquor
Primary Menu: American (2); Mexican (1); Steak/Seafood (2)
Areas of Operation: FL
Type of Foodservice: Casual Dining (4); Fine Dining (1)
Catering Services: Yes
Primary Distributors: (Equipment) Edward Don & Co., MIRAMAR, FL; (Food) SYSCO Food Services of South Florida Inc., MEDLEY, FL

Key Personnel
SALVADOR BARRIOS - Executive Chef; Manager Facility/Maintenance, Catering; General Buyer

Domino's Franchisee
2704 N Roosevelt Blvd
Key West, FL 33040

Telephone: (305) 296-7795
Type of Business: Chain Restaurant Operator
Total Sales: $5,974,000 (e)
Total Units: 3
Trade Names: Domino's (3)
Units Franchised From: 3
Primary Menu: Pizza (3)
Areas of Operation: FL
Type of Foodservice: Quick Serve (3)
Franchise Affiliation: Domino's Pizza Inc, ANN ARBOR, MI

Key Personnel
MURPHY D. RANSON - Owner; General Buyer

Southernmost Restaurant Group
700 Front St Ste 105
Key West, FL 33040-6689

Telephone: (305) 294-4902
Fax Number: (305) 296-7742
Internet Homepage: alonzosoysterbar.com; aandblobsterhouse.com
Company Email: ablobsterhouse@gmail.com
Type of Business: Chain Restaurant Operator
Total Sales: $22,014,000 (e)
Alcohol Sales: 30%
Average Check: Breakfast(14); Lunch(20); Dinner(26)
Total Units: 3
Trade Names: A & B Lobster House (1); Alonzo's Oyster Bar (1); White Tarpon Deli (1)
Company-Owned Units: 3
Preferred Location Types: Freestanding
Alcohol Served: Beer, Wine, Liquor
Primary Menu: Sandwiches/Deli (1); Seafood (2)
Areas of Operation: FL
Type of Foodservice: Casual Dining (2); Quick Serve (1)
Catering Services: Yes
Primary Distributors: (Full Line) US Foods, BOCA RATON, FL

Key Personnel
GENE SMITH - Owner; General Buyer

The Pier House Resort & Caribbean Spa
1 Duval St
Key West, FL 33040-6610

Telephone: (305) 296-4600
Fax Number: (305) 296-7569
Internet Homepage: pierhouse.com
Company Email: info@pierhouse.com
Type of Business: Foodservice Operations - Hotel/Motels
Year Founded: 1965
Total Sales: $48,847,000 (e)
Alcohol Sales: 30%
Number of Employees: 150
Average Check: Lunch(18); Dinner(30)
Total Units: 1
Restaurants in Hotels: 3
Trade Names: Pier House Resort (1)
Company-Owned Units: 3
Alcohol Served: Beer, Wine, Liquor
Areas of Operation: FL
Type of Foodservice: Casual Dining (3)
Primary Distributors: (Food) SYSCO Food Services of South Florida Inc., MEDLEY, FL
Parent Company: Remington Hotels, DALLAS, TX
Notes: The company derives approximately 60% of its revenue from hotel operations.

Key Personnel
JOY SMATT - CEO
TERESA RUSSELL - CFO; Director Finance
JOSEPH DANTONI - General Manager
BLANCA LAMBERSON - Director Purchasing, Foodservice, Food Safety, Food and Beverage

Nisbet Enterprises
21 W Hickpochee Ave
Labelle, FL 33935-5019

Mailing Address: PO Box 1920, Labelle, FL, 33975
Telephone: (863) 612-0333
Type of Business: Chain Restaurant Operator
Total Sales: $32,790,000 (e)
Average Check: Dinner(12)
Total Units: 7
Trade Names: McDonald's (7)
Units Franchised From: 7
Preferred Location Types: Freestanding
Primary Menu: Hamburger (7)
Areas of Operation: FL
Type of Foodservice: Quick Serve (7)
Franchise Affiliation: McDonald's Corporation, CHICAGO, IL

Key Personnel
STEVEN NISBET - President; General Buyer

Bumbly, LLC
674 N US Highway 441
Lady Lake, FL 32159-3777

Telephone: (352) 633-9744
Type of Business: Chain Restaurant Operator
Total Sales: $4,378,000 (e)
Total Units: 3
Trade Names: Jersey Mike's Subs (3)
Units Franchised From: 3
Primary Menu: Sandwiches/Deli (3)
Areas of Operation: FL
Type of Foodservice: Quick Serve (3)
Franchise Affiliation: Jersey Mike's Franchise Systems, MANASQUAN, NJ

Key Personnel
JACOB RICHARD - Owner; General Buyer

Chicken Guy!
1506 E Buena Vista Dr Suite A
Lake Buena Vista, FL 32830

Telephone: (407) 560-8180
Internet Homepage: chickenguy.com
Type of Business: Chain Restaurant Operator
Year Founded: 2018
Total Sales: $9,875,000 (e)
Total Units: 9
Trade Names: Chicken Guy! (9)
Company-Owned Units: 9
Preferred Location Types: Community Mall; Strip Mall
Primary Menu: Chicken (9)
Projected Openings: 2
Areas of Operation: FL
Type of Foodservice: Fast Casual (9)
Parent Company: Earl Enterprises, ORLANDO, FL

Key Personnel
GUY FIERI - Co-Founder; Executive Chef
ROBERT EARL - Co-Founder

Disney's Hollywood Studios
351 S Studio Dr
Lake Buena Vista, FL 32830

Telephone: (407) 824-2222
Fax Number: (407) 560-4359
Listing Type: Divisional Office
Type of Business: Foodservice Operations - Theme Parks
Total Units: 17
Areas of Operation: FL
Parent Company: Walt Disney World Co., LAKE BUENA VISTA, FL

Key Personnel
PERRY CRAWLEY - General Manager

Millennium Management Group
1494 E Buena Vista Dr Fl 3
Lake Buena Vista, FL 32830-8521

Mailing Address: PO Box 692469, ORLANDO, FL, 32869-2469
Telephone: (407) 425-6826
Fax Number: (407) 828-6082
Internet Homepage: splitsvillelanes.com
Type of Business: Foodservice Operations - Bowling Alley
Year Founded: 1992
Total Sales: $19,980,000 (e)
Alcohol Sales: 75%
Number of Employees: 505
Average Check: Lunch(16); Dinner(24)

Total Units: 6
Trade Names: Splitsville (5); Splitsville at Disney (1)
Company-Owned Units: 6
Preferred Square Footage: 4,000; 20,000
Preferred Location Types: Freestanding; Lifestyle Center; Strip Mall
Alcohol Served: Beer, Wine, Liquor
Primary Menu: American (6)
Areas of Operation: FL, MA, OH, TX, VA
Type of Foodservice: In-Store Feeder (6)
Primary Distributors: (Food) SYSCO Atlanta LLC, COLLEGE PARK, GA

Key Personnel
MARK GIBSON - President; Director Finance, Real Estate, Design, Menu Development
GUY REVELLE - VP Operations; Director Facility/Maintenance; General Buyer
TONY MASTROBUONO - Controller
SHERRY CIOFFI - Controller; Manager Operations, Information Systems, Human Resources
TOM BUZYNISKI - General Manager Region; Director Purchasing

The Magic Kingdom
1180 Seven Seas Dr
Lake Buena Vista, FL 32830

Mailing Address: PO Box 10000, LAKE BUENA VISTA, FL, 32830-1000
Telephone: (407) 824-2222
Fax Number: (407) 824-5530
Listing Type: Divisional Office
Type of Business: Foodservice Operations - Theme Parks
Number of Employees: 28
Total Units: 28
Areas of Operation: FL
Parent Company: Walt Disney World Co., LAKE BUENA VISTA, FL

Key Personnel
DAN COCKERELL - VP Operations
MARY ANN SMITH - General Manager Food and Beverage
ROBERT GILBERT - Executive Chef; General Buyer

Walt Disney World Co.
1375 E Buena Vista Dr
Lake Buena Vista, FL 32830-8402

Mailing Address: PO Box 10000, LAKE BUENA VISTA, FL, 32830-1000
Telephone: (407) 824-2222
Fax Number: (407) 560-3109
Internet Homepage: disney.com
Type of Business: Foodservice Operations - Theme Parks
Year Founded: 1971
Publicly Held: Yes
Total Sales: $19,311,900,000 (e)
Alcohol Sales: 20%
Number of Employees: 56,500
Foodservice Sales: $3,862,380,000 (e)
Total Units: 407
Trade Names: Disney Boardwalk (11); Disney Springs (68); Disney's 23 Resorts (134); Disney's Animal Kingdom Theme Park (40); Disney's Blizzard Beach Water Park (9); Disney's Hollywood Studios (32); Disney's Typhoon Lagoon (7); Epcot (67); Magic Kingdom Park (39)
Company-Owned Units: 407
Preferred Square Footage: 2,500; 3,000; 5,500; 6,000
Preferred Location Types: Hotel/Motel; Kiosk; Mobile Unit; Parks; Stadiums
Alcohol Served: Beer, Wine, Liquor
Primary Menu: Miscellaneous (407)
Areas of Operation: FL
Type of Foodservice: Casual Dining; Family Restaurant; Fast Casual; Fine Dining; Quick Serve
Distribution Centers: LAKE BUENA VISTA, FL
On-site Distribution Center: Yes
Parent Company: The Walt Disney Company, BURBANK, CA
Divisional Offices: Disney's Hollywood Studios, LAKE BUENA VISTA, FL; The Magic Kingdom, LAKE BUENA VISTA, FL
Notes: The company derives approximately 80% of its revenue from theme park attractions, hotel/resort operations, and sales of merchandise in these locations. Restaurant counts exclude kiosks & carts. Total location counts includes all restaurants in all venues inside the park, including all hotels and resorts.

Key Personnel
ROBERT "BOB" A. IGER - Executive Chairman
PHIL HOLMES - VP Operations, Group
RICK WERTSCHING - VP Sourcing, Procurement
ROBERT ADAMS - Executive Chef Division
MICHAEL PYTHOUD - Director Culinary Development
SARAH SINOFF - Director Marketing
SCOTT HENDERSON - Director Technology
SHAJI GEORGE - Manager Food Safety
BETSY HUMMEL - Specialist Sourcing

Ellianos Coffee
426 SW Commerce Dr Ste 130
Lake City, FL 32025

Telephone: (386) 755-5828
Internet Homepage: ellianos.com
Type of Business: Chain Restaurant Operator
Year Founded: 2002
Total Units: 63
Trade Names: Ellianos Coffee (63)
Company-Owned Units: 63
Primary Menu: Coffee (63)
Areas of Operation: AL, FL, GA
Type of Foodservice: Fast Casual (63)

Key Personnel
SCOTT STEWART - Co-Founder; Owner
PAM STEWART - Co-Founder
MIKE STEWART - VP
CHAD STEWART - VP Franchise Development
GREG PRUITT - VP Strategic Services, Marketing, Communications
MALLORY PRUITT - Executive Director
DALLAS STE-MARIE - Controller
JONATHAN MORGAN - Director Franchise Sales
ERIC PRESTON - Director Operations, Logistics
MEGAN CADY - Director Store Operations, Training
JIM ZUBER - Director Construction
DEBI BENNEFIELD - Director Real Estate
ABBY BENTON - Manager Marketing
KYLE ANDERSON - Project Manager Development

Helms Foodservice
PO Box 2375
Lake City, FL 32056-2375

Telephone: (386) 754-1555
Fax Number: (386) 755-0504
Type of Business: Chain Restaurant Operator
Year Founded: 1994
Total Sales: $3,911,000 (e)
Number of Employees: 45
Average Check: Lunch(12); Dinner(14)
Total Units: 2
Trade Names: KFC (2)
Units Franchised From: 2
Preferred Location Types: Freestanding
Primary Menu: Chicken (2)
Areas of Operation: FL
Type of Foodservice: Quick Serve (2)
Franchise Affiliation: KFC Corporation, LOUISVILLE, KY
Primary Distributors: (Full Line) Kelly's Foods Inc., WINTER GARDEN, FL

Key Personnel
LAWRENCE HELMS - President; General Manager; General Buyer

Momex Foods Inc
798 SW Main Blvd
Lake City, FL 32025-5742

Telephone: (386) 755-9673
Fax Number: (386) 755-2296
Internet Homepage: teammomex.com
Company Email: info@teammomex.com

Type of Business: Chain Restaurant Operator
Total Sales: $11,960,000 (e)
Total Units: 7
Trade Names: Krystal (2); Taco Bell (4); Wing Stop (1)
Units Franchised From: 7
Primary Menu: Chicken (1); Hamburger (2); Taco (4)
Areas of Operation: FL
Type of Foodservice: Quick Serve (7)
Franchise Affiliation: Taco Bell Corp., IRVINE, CA; The Krystal Co., DUNWOODY, GA

Key Personnel
MICHAEL C. MOSES - President; General Buyer
TERA DICKS - Controller

Domino's Franchisee
3801 W Lake Mary Blvd Unit 107
Lake Mary, FL 32746-6160

Telephone: (407) 322-9060
Type of Business: Chain Restaurant Operator
Total Sales: $18,305,000 (e)
Total Units: 9
Trade Names: Domino's (9)
Units Franchised From: 9
Primary Menu: Pizza (9)
Areas of Operation: FL
Type of Foodservice: Quick Serve (9)
Franchise Affiliation: Domino's Pizza Inc, ANN ARBOR, MI

Key Personnel
THOMAS R. LEWIS - Owner; General Buyer

Gators Dockside Group
1331 S International Pkwy Ste 1291
Lake Mary, FL 32746-1405

Telephone: (407) 333-3278
Fax Number: (407) 333-3198
Internet Homepage: gatorsdockside.com
Type of Business: Chain Restaurant Operator
Year Founded: 1991
Total Sales: $59,290,000 (e)
Alcohol Sales: 30%
Number of Employees: 588
Average Check: Lunch(14); Dinner(20)
Total Units: 27
Trade Names: Gator's Dockside (27)
Company-Owned Units: 10
Units Franchised To: 17
Preferred Square Footage: 6,500
Preferred Location Types: Freestanding; Strip Mall
Alcohol Served: Beer, Wine, Liquor
Primary Menu: American (27)
Areas of Operation: FL
Type of Foodservice: Casual Dining (27)

Catering Services: Yes
Primary Distributors: (Food) SYSCO Food Services of West Coast Florida Inc., PALMETTO, FL

Key Personnel
PAUL CIPPARONE - President; COO; Director Finance, Purchasing, Design, Human Resources
SANDRA CLARK - Director Operations, Human Resources, Menu Development; General Buyer

Russo's Inc.
1246 Lake Blvd
Lake Park, FL 33403

Telephone: (561) 845-7722
Internet Homepage: russossubs.com
Type of Business: Chain Restaurant Operator
Year Founded: 1947
Total Sales: $2,648,000 (e)
Alcohol Sales: 1%
Number of Employees: 35
Average Check: Lunch(8); Dinner(10)
Total Units: 2
Trade Names: Russo's (2)
Company-Owned Units: 2
Preferred Location Types: Strip Mall
Alcohol Served: Beer
Primary Menu: Sandwiches/Deli (2)
Areas of Operation: FL
Type of Foodservice: Fast Casual (2)
Primary Distributors: (Full Line) Cheney Bros. Inc., RIVIERA BEACH, FL

Key Personnel
DAN RUSSO - President; General Manager; Executive Chef; General Buyer

Duffy's Management Inc.
1926 10th Ave N Ste 300
Lake Worth, FL 33461-3300

Telephone: (561) 585-6685
Fax Number: (561) 585-6670
Internet Homepage: duffysmvp.com
Company Email: info@duffysmvp.com
Type of Business: Chain Restaurant Operator
Year Founded: 1985
Total Sales: $184,570,000 (e)
Alcohol Sales: 30%
Number of Employees: 3,193
Average Check: Lunch(22); Dinner(30)
Internet Order Processing: Yes
Internet Sales: 50.00%
Total Units: 34
Trade Names: Duffy's Sports Grill (34)
Company-Owned Units: 34
Preferred Square Footage: 7,500
Preferred Location Types: Freestanding; Strip Mall
Alcohol Served: Beer, Wine, Liquor
Primary Menu: American (34)
Projected Openings: 3
Areas of Operation: FL
Type of Foodservice: Casual Dining (34)
Primary Distributors: (Food) SYSCO Food Services of South Florida Inc., MEDLEY, FL; (Supplies) SYSCO Food Services of South Florida Inc., MEDLEY, FL

Key Personnel
JOE WEBB - President
FRANCISCO GIL - Treasurer
CHRIS MARRERO - Regional Director Operations
ALLISON PETERSON - Manager Human Resources
MEGHAN WELCH - Manager Marketing
JOAN CHEESMAN - Manager Accounting

Crispers Restaurants LLC
1476 Town Center Dr Ste 219
Lakeland, FL 33803-7971

Telephone: (863) 646-2102
Fax Number: (863) 413-1876
Internet Homepage: crispers.com
Type of Business: Chain Restaurant Operator
Year Founded: 1989
Total Sales: $17,030,000 (e)
Number of Employees: 415
Average Check: Lunch(10); Dinner(10)
Internet Order Processing: Yes
Total Units: 13
Trade Names: Crispers (13)
Company-Owned Units: 13
Preferred Square Footage: 5,000
Preferred Location Types: Freestanding; Strip Mall
Primary Menu: American (13)
Areas of Operation: FL
Type of Foodservice: Fast Casual (13)
Primary Distributors: (Food) US Foods, LAKELAND, FL
Parent Company: Boyne Capital LLC, MIAMI, FL

Key Personnel
BILL RADEBAUGH - CEO; President
SARA PEOPLES - Manager Information Systems

Double A Foods Inc.
4510 US Highway 98 N
Lakeland, FL 33809-3601

Telephone: (863) 816-9900
Company Email: lakeland09701@zaxbys.com
Type of Business: Chain Restaurant Operator
Total Sales: $20,670,000 (e)

Total Units: 6
Trade Names: Zaxby's (6)
Units Franchised From: 6
Primary Menu: Chicken (6)
Areas of Operation: FL, NC
Type of Foodservice: Fast Casual (6)
Franchise Affiliation: Zaxby's Franchising Inc., ATHENS, GA

Key Personnel
DAVID W. ABBOTT - President; Owner

Florida Pizza Management
2115 S Florida Ave
Lakeland, FL 33803-7224

Telephone: (863) 682-4170
Fax Number: (863) 688-1819
Type of Business: Chain Restaurant Operator
Year Founded: 1984
Total Sales: $9,145,000 (e)
Number of Employees: 75
Average Check: Lunch(16); Dinner(28)
Total Units: 7
Trade Names: Hungry Howie's Pizza & Subs (7)
Units Franchised From: 7
Preferred Square Footage: 300; 1,500
Preferred Location Types: Freestanding; Strip Mall
Primary Menu: Pizza (7)
Areas of Operation: FL
Type of Foodservice: Quick Serve (7)
Franchise Affiliation: Hungry Howie's Pizza & Subs Inc., MADISON HEIGHTS, MI

Key Personnel
JACK CLEGHORN - President; Director Finance, Information Systems, Supply Chain, Real Estate, Design, Human Resources; General Buyer

Hungry Howie's Distribution
3710 New Tampa Hwy
Lakeland, FL 33815-3332

Telephone: (863) 683-4292
Fax Number: (863) 683-9891
Listing Type: Distribution Center
Type of Business: Foodservice Operations - Bowling Alley
Number of Employees: 20
Areas of Operation: AL, FL, GA
Parent Company: Hungry Howie's Pizza & Subs Inc., MADISON HEIGHTS, MI

Key Personnel
SCOTT TRAVERS - General Manager

Raving Fans Restaurant Group
1326 Town Center Dr
Lakeland, FL 33803-7953

Telephone: (863) 616-9700
Type of Business: Chain Restaurant Operator
Total Sales: $28,480,000 (e)
Total Units: 17
Trade Names: Moe's Southwest Grill (17)
Units Franchised From: 17
Primary Menu: Southwest/Tex-Mex (17)
Areas of Operation: FL
Type of Foodservice: Fast Casual (17)
Franchise Affiliation: Moe's Southwest Grill LLC, ATLANTA, GA

Key Personnel
FRIEL FRANKLIN - Owner; General Buyer

Vandalay Pizza Industries, Inc
2936 S Florida Ave
Lakeland, FL 33803-4044

Telephone: (863) 937-9222
Type of Business: Chain Restaurant Operator
Total Sales: $9,609,000 (e)
Total Units: 8
Trade Names: Little Caesars Pizza (8)
Units Franchised From: 8
Primary Menu: Pizza (8)
Areas of Operation: FL
Type of Foodservice: Quick Serve (8)
Franchise Affiliation: Little Caesar Enterprises Inc., DETROIT, MI

Key Personnel
ANTHONY SHAMOUN - Owner; General Buyer

Wen-Lake Corporation
2240 Griffin Rd
Lakeland, FL 33810-5565

Telephone: (863) 853-8838
Internet Homepage: wenlake.com
Type of Business: Chain Restaurant Operator
Total Sales: $22,040,000 (e)
Total Units: 8
Trade Names: Wendy's Old Fashioned Hamburgers (8)
Units Franchised From: 8
Primary Menu: Hamburger (8)
Areas of Operation: FL
Type of Foodservice: Quick Serve (8)
Franchise Affiliation: The Wendy's Company, DUBLIN, OH

Key Personnel
MARTIN PHILLIPS - VP Operations

Charter One Hotels & Resorts
6731 Professional Pkwy Ste 100
Lakewood Ranch, FL 34240-8491

Telephone: (941) 364-9224
Fax Number: (941) 907-9854
Internet Homepage: charteronehotels.com
Company Email: info@charteronehotels.com
Type of Business: Foodservice Operations - Hotel/Motels
Year Founded: 1980
Total Sales: $122,230,000 (e)
Alcohol Sales: 15%
Number of Employees: 420
Total Units: 35
Restaurants in Hotels: 7
Trade Names: Allamanda Villas (1); Best Western Cobleskill Hotel (3); Bristol Harbor (1); Candlewood Suites (1); Capri (1); Cohutta Lodge (1); Comfort Inn (1); Coquina On The Beach (1); Crystal Palms Beach Resort (1); Four Winds Resort (1); Glidden House Case Western University (1); Grande Bay Resort (1);Hampton Inn & Suites (3); Hilton Hotel (1); Holiday Inn (3); Holiday Inn Express & Suites (4); Inn at the Beach (1); Lido Beach Resort (1); Quality Inn (1); Radisson Hotel (2); Safari Resort Inn (1); Sandbar Beach Resort (1); Stanley Hotel (1); The Litchfield Inn (1); Tropical Breeze (1)
Company-Owned Units: 7
Alcohol Served: Beer, Wine, Liquor
Areas of Operation: FL, NC, NY, OH
Type of Foodservice: Casual Dining (7)
Primary Distributors: (Food) SYSCO Food Services of West Coast Florida Inc., PALMETTO, FL
Notes: The company derives approximately 80% of its revenue from hotel operations.

Key Personnel
JOHN BALLIETT - Chairman; CEO
PAMELA CHAISSON - VP Human Resources
DAWN MILHOUS - Director Marketing
SHANNON WARD - Director Operations

Santa Fe Mexican Grill
800 Clearwater Largo Rd N
Largo, FL 33770-4125

Telephone: (727) 270-7378
Internet Homepage: greenwoodsantafe.com
Type of Business: Chain Restaurant Operator
Year Founded: 1998
Total Units: 3
Trade Names: Santa Fe Mexican Grill (3)
Company-Owned Units: 3

Primary Menu: Mexican (3)
Projected Openings: 1
Areas of Operation: FL, SC
Type of Foodservice: Casual Dining (3)

Key Personnel
ESTANISLAO ROMAN - Founder; Owner; General Buyer
DAVID ROMAN - General Manager

Winghouse, Inc.
7491 Ulmerton Rd Ste 3B
Largo, FL 33771-4504

Telephone: (727) 535-2939
Fax Number: (727) 535-2827
Internet Homepage: winghouse.com; winghousefranchising.com
Company Email: info@winghouse.com
Listing Type: Subsidiary
Type of Business: Chain Restaurant Operator
Year Founded: 1994
Total Sales: $51,230,000 (e)
Alcohol Sales: 30%
Number of Employees: 948
Average Check: Lunch(10); Dinner(14)
Internet Order Processing: Yes
Internet Sales: 5.00%
Total Units: 24
Trade Names: WingHouse Bar & Grill (24)
Company-Owned Units: 24
Preferred Square Footage: 6,000
Preferred Location Types: Freestanding; Strip Mall
Alcohol Served: Beer, Wine, Liquor
Primary Menu: Chicken (24)
Projected Openings: 2
Areas of Operation: FL
Type of Foodservice: Casual Dining (24)
Catering Services: Yes
Primary Distributors: (Food) SYSCO Food Services of West Coast Florida Inc., PALMETTO, FL; (Supplies) SYSCO Food Services of West Coast Florida Inc., PALMETTO, FL
Parent Company: ARC Group Inc., ORANGE PARK, FL

Key Personnel
JOHN NOVAK - Director Facility/Maintenance

Domino's Franchisee
2009 Citrus Blvd
Leesburg, FL 34748-3838

Telephone: (352) 787-2600
Type of Business: Chain Restaurant Operator
Total Sales: $7,954,000 (e)
Total Units: 4
Trade Names: Domino's (4)
Units Franchised From: 4
Primary Menu: Pizza (4)
Areas of Operation: FL
Type of Foodservice: Quick Serve (4)
Franchise Affiliation: Domino's Pizza Inc, ANN ARBOR, MI

Key Personnel
JOSE Y. RAMIA - Owner; General Buyer

Bam-B Enterprises of Central Florida Inc.
6820 N Orange Blossom Trl
Lockhart, FL 32810

Telephone: (407) 291-7352
Type of Business: Chain Restaurant Operator
Year Founded: 1992
Total Sales: $14,851,000 (e)
Number of Employees: 300
Average Check: Breakfast(8); Lunch(8); Dinner(8)
Total Units: 3
Trade Names: McDonald's (3)
Units Franchised From: 3
Preferred Square Footage: 2,500; 3,000
Preferred Location Types: Freestanding
Primary Menu: Hamburger (3)
Areas of Operation: FL
Type of Foodservice: Quick Serve (3)
Franchise Affiliation: McDonald's Corporation, CHICAGO, IL
Primary Distributors: (Full Line) The Martin-Brower Co., POMPANO BEACH, FL

Key Personnel
BOB ALLEGROE - President; Director Operations, Real Estate
BILL LANGMAN - Controller; Director Finance
MARK ALLEGROE - Director Information Systems, Customer Service
ERIC FIDDLER - Supervisor District; General Buyer

Food Systems Unlimited Inc.
750 Florida Central Pkwy Ste 100
Longwood, FL 32750-7590

Telephone: (407) 830-5338
Fax Number: (407) 830-4443
Internet Homepage: asianchao.com; foodsystemsunlimited.com
Company Email: info@foodsystemsunlimited.com
Type of Business: Chain Restaurant Operator
Year Founded: 1991
Systemwide Sales: $142,178,000 (e)
Total Sales: $82,290,000 (e)
Number of Employees: 712
Average Check: Breakfast(12); Lunch(14); Dinner(14)
Total Units: 72
Trade Names: Asian Chao (40); Chao Cajun (7); Maki of Japan (16); Sushi Fuji (3); Tobu (6)
Company-Owned Units: 45
Units Franchised To: 27
Preferred Square Footage: 750
Preferred Location Types: Airports; Community Mall
Primary Menu: Asian (46); Cajun/Creole (7); Japanese (19)
Projected Openings: 2
Areas of Operation: FL, GA, IL, IN, KY, MA, MD, MN, NC, NJ, NY, OH, PA, TN, TX, VA, WA
Type of Foodservice: Quick Serve (72)
Catering Services: Yes
Primary Distributors: (Full Line) SYSCO Food Services of South Florida Inc., MEDLEY, FL

Key Personnel
BIAGIO SCHIANO - Chairman; CEO; President; Executive Chef
ARSENIO HINOJOSA - VP Operations
JENNIFER WALSH - Director Administration, Legal, Leasing, Human Resources
FION YEUNG - Manager Operations

Sobik's Corporation
620 Crown Oak Centre Dr Ste 104
Longwood, FL 32750-6188

Telephone: (407) 671-2600
Fax Number: (407) 530-0253
Internet Homepage: sobiks.com
Company Email: info@sobiks.com
Type of Business: Chain Restaurant Operator
Year Founded: 1969
Systemwide Sales: $4,072,000 (e)
Total Sales: $1,560,000 (e)
Number of Employees: 80
Average Check: Dinner(10)
Total Units: 8
Trade Names: Sobik's Subs (8)
Units Franchised To: 8
Preferred Square Footage: 1,600; 2,000
Preferred Location Types: Freestanding; Office Complex; Strip Mall
Primary Menu: Sandwiches/Deli (8)
Areas of Operation: FL
Type of Foodservice: Quick Serve (8)
Foodservice Management Venues: Business & Industry
Catering Services: Yes
Primary Distributors: (Food) US Foods, LAKELAND, FL

Key Personnel
JODI KOBRIN - CEO; President

Domino's Franchisee
7070 Seminole Pratt Whitney Rd Ste 1
Loxahatchee, FL 33470-3491

Telephone: (561) 333-1415
Type of Business: Chain Restaurant Operator
Total Sales: $15,989,000 (e)
Total Units: 8
Trade Names: Domino's (8)
Units Franchised From: 8
Primary Menu: Pizza (8)
Areas of Operation: FL
Type of Foodservice: Quick Serve (8)
Franchise Affiliation: Domino's Pizza Inc, ANN ARBOR, MI

Key Personnel
MOHAMMAD A. ZEBIB - Owner; General Buyer

Frost Management
18582 N Dale Mabry Hwy
Lutz, FL 33548-7900

Telephone: (813) 961-8083
Fax Number: (813) 961-6467
Type of Business: Chain Restaurant Operator
Year Founded: 1985
Total Sales: $37,390,000 (e)
Number of Employees: 400
Average Check: Breakfast(8); Lunch(8); Dinner(8)
Total Units: 8
Trade Names: McDonald's (8)
Units Franchised From: 8
Preferred Square Footage: 1,600
Preferred Location Types: Freestanding
Primary Menu: Hamburger (8)
Areas of Operation: FL
Type of Foodservice: Quick Serve (8)
Franchise Affiliation: McDonald's Corporation, CHICAGO, IL

Key Personnel
JACK FROST - President; Partner; Director Purchasing; Manager Information Systems; General Buyer
JOHN FROST - Partner; VP Operations; Director Finance, Supply Chain, Real Estate
AMY JOHNSON - Manager Administration
JIM SESSLAR - Manager Facility/Maintenance

Coastal Southern Inc
2240 S Highway 77
Lynn Haven, FL 32444-4620

Telephone: (850) 763-5114
Type of Business: Chain Restaurant Operator
Total Sales: $8,625,000 (e)
Total Units: 3
Trade Names: Sonny's Real Pit Bar-B-Q (3)
Units Franchised From: 3
Primary Menu: Bar-B-Q (3)
Areas of Operation: FL
Type of Foodservice: Casual Dining (3)
Franchise Affiliation: Sonny's Franchise Company, MAITLAND, FL

Key Personnel
WAYNE LINDSEY - Owner; General Buyer

St. Clair Restaurant Management Inc.
2300 S Highway 77
Lynn Haven, FL 32444-4600

Telephone: (850) 271-5550
Type of Business: Chain Restaurant Operator
Total Sales: $17,900,000 (e)
Total Units: 5
Trade Names: Zaxby's (5)
Units Franchised From: 5
Primary Menu: Chicken (5)
Areas of Operation: AL, FL
Type of Foodservice: Fast Casual (5)
Franchise Affiliation: Zaxby's Franchising Inc., ATHENS, GA

Key Personnel
KENNETH G. CLARK - President

RGMS, Inc.
1620 S 6th St
Macclenny, FL 32063-5040

Telephone: (904) 259-1616
Type of Business: Chain Restaurant Operator
Total Sales: $4,773,000 (e)
Total Units: 2
Trade Names: Burger King (2)
Units Franchised From: 2
Preferred Location Types: Freestanding
Primary Menu: Hamburger (2)
Areas of Operation: FL, GA
Type of Foodservice: Quick Serve (2)
Franchise Affiliation: Burger King Worldwide Inc., MIAMI, FL

Key Personnel
RICKY DAVIS - President; Owner; General Buyer

Johnson and Johnson
PO Box 157
Madison, FL 32341-0157

Telephone: (850) 973-2277
Fax Number: (850) 973-3702
Internet Homepage: jj-fuel.com
Company Email: Info@JJ-Fuel.com
Type of Business: Chain Restaurant Operator
Total Sales: $20,660,000 (e)
Average Check: Dinner(12)
Total Units: 9
Trade Names: Burger King (9)
Units Franchised From: 9
Preferred Location Types: Convenience Store/Gas Station; Freestanding
Primary Menu: Hamburger (9)
Areas of Operation: FL
Type of Foodservice: Quick Serve (9)
Franchise Affiliation: Burger King Worldwide Inc., MIAMI, FL

Key Personnel
ELIZABETH JOHNSON-WARING - President; General Buyer
KEVIN DOYLE - Director Quality Assurance

Antonio's
611 S Orlando Ave
Maitland, FL 32751-5611

Telephone: (407) 645-5523
Fax Number: (407) 645-1053
Internet Homepage: antoniosonline.com
Company Email: mail@antoniosonline.com
Type of Business: Chain Restaurant Operator
Year Founded: 1990
Total Sales: $22,851,000 (e)
Alcohol Sales: 4.67%
Number of Employees: 75
Average Check: Lunch(22); Dinner(36)
Internet Order Processing: Yes
Total Units: 3
Trade Names: Antonio's (1); Antonio's Cafe & Deli (1); Cafe D'Antonio (1)
Company-Owned Units: 3
Preferred Location Types: Freestanding
Alcohol Served: Beer, Wine, Liquor
Primary Menu: Italian (3)
Areas of Operation: FL
Type of Foodservice: Casual Dining (1); Fast Casual (1); Fine Dining (1)
Primary Distributors: (Food) SYSCO Central Florida Inc., OCOEE, FL; (Supplies) Louis Wohl & Sons Inc., TAMPA, FL
Notes: The company also owns and operates Antonio's Wine & Spirits.

Key Personnel
GREGORY GENTILE - Owner; Director Finance, Operations, Human Resources; General Buyer

Jeremiah's Italian Ice
433 S Orlando Ave
Maitland, FL 32751

Telephone: (407) 559-9991
Internet Homepage: jeremiahsice.com
Type of Business: Chain Restaurant Operator
Year Founded: 1996
Systemwide Sales: $45,964,000 (e)
Total Sales: $45,790,000 (e)
Total Units: 71
Trade Names: Jeremiah's Italian Ice (71)
Company-Owned Units: 18
Units Franchised To: 53
Primary Menu: Snacks (71)
Projected Openings: 96
Areas of Operation: AZ, FL, GA, LA, NC, TX
Type of Foodservice: Quick Serve (71)
Parent Company: Pivotal Growth Partners, CHICAGO, IL

Key Personnel
MICHAEL KELLER - CEO; President
RENE NAVARRO - Controller
JULIANNA VOYLES - Senior Director Franchise Operations
IRVING FORESTIER - Director Franchise Operations
CASEY COOLEY - Director Real Estate, Franchise Development
LINDSAY HANNA - Director Operations
DEVIN SCHNEIDER - Director Branding
ERIN BUONO - Director Research & Development
ADAM HING - Director Supply Chain

Sonny's Franchise Company
850 Concourse Pkwy S Ste 150
Maitland, FL 32751-6145

Telephone: (407) 660-8888
Fax Number: (407) 725-7678
Internet Homepage: sonnysbbq.com
Company Email: corporate@sonnysbbq.com
Type of Business: Chain Restaurant Operator
Year Founded: 1968
Systemwide Sales: $239,422,000 (e)
Total Sales: $35,170,000 (e)
Alcohol Sales: 2%
Number of Employees: 658
Average Check: Lunch(8); Dinner(8)
Internet Order Processing: Yes
Internet Sales: 0.50%
Total Units: 94
Trade Names: Sonny's Real Pit Bar-B-Q (99)
Company-Owned Units: 1
Units Franchised To: 98
Preferred Square Footage: 5,700
Preferred Location Types: Freestanding
Alcohol Served: Beer, Wine, Liquor
Primary Menu: Bar-B-Q (99)
Areas of Operation: AL, FL, GA, KY, LA, MS, NC, SC, TN
Type of Foodservice: Casual Dining (99)
Catering Services: Yes
Primary Distributors: (Full Line) SYSCO Central Florida Inc., OCOEE, FL; (Supplies) Louis Wohl & Sons Inc., TAMPA, FL

Key Personnel
KENNON ADKINSON - Chief Culture Officer
GEORGE MCALLAN - Chief Growth Officer
CHRISTIE SCHATZ - VP Human Resources; Director Training
BILLY BREWER - Director Operations

The Pike Corporation
1801 N Maitland Ave
Maitland, FL 32751-3322

Telephone: (407) 622-8800
Fax Number: (407) 622-1420
Internet Homepage: samsneadstavern.com
Company Email: samsneadstavern@gmail.com
Type of Business: Chain Restaurant Operator
Year Founded: 1998
Systemwide Sales: $31,626,000 (e)
Total Sales: $6,267,000 (e)
Alcohol Sales: 25%
Number of Employees: 562
Average Check: Lunch(18); Dinner(32)
Total Units: 10
Trade Names: Sam Snead's Tavern (10)
Company-Owned Units: 2
Units Franchised To: 8
Preferred Square Footage: 5,500; 6,000
Preferred Location Types: Airports; Freestanding; Hotel/Motel; Office Complex; Strip Mall
Alcohol Served: Beer, Wine, Liquor
Primary Menu: American (10)
Areas of Operation: FL, GA, VA, WV, NB
Foreign Countries: CANADA
Type of Foodservice: Casual Dining (10)
Catering Services: Yes
Primary Distributors: (Food) SYSCO Central Florida Inc., OCOEE, FL

Key Personnel
MATT FISHER - Senior VP
CHARLES MANSIR - Executive Chef; Director Menu Development; General Buyer

Tijuana Flats Burrito Company
2300 Maitland Center Pkwy #306
Maitland, FL 32751

Telephone: (407) 339-2222
Fax Number: (407) 704-2171
Internet Homepage: tijuanaflats.com
Type of Business: Chain Restaurant Operator
Year Founded: 1995
Systemwide Sales: $190,473,000 (e)
Total Sales: $194,640,000 (e)
Alcohol Sales: 10%
Number of Employees: 2,769
Average Check: Lunch(10); Dinner(14)
Internet Order Processing: Yes
Internet Sales: 1.00%
Total Units: 128
Trade Names: Tijuana Flats (128)
Company-Owned Units: 109
Units Franchised To: 19
Preferred Square Footage: 1,800; 2,000; 2,500
Preferred Location Types: Freestanding; Power Center; Strip Mall
Alcohol Served: Beer, Wine
Primary Menu: Mexican (128)
Projected Openings: 15
Areas of Operation: FL, GA, IN, NC, VA
Type of Foodservice: Fast Casual (128)
Catering Services: Yes
Primary Distributors: (Food) Cheney Bros. Inc., RIVIERA BEACH, FL

Key Personnel
CAMP FITCH - Chairman
JAMES GRECO - CEO
LOUIE PSALLIDAS - CFO
RICK BOUFFARD - Regional Director
GABRIEL RODRIGUEZ - Senior Manager Information Technology
ANDY SOVA - Manager Information Systems; Analyst Systems

Bagel 13
1301 S Babcock St
Melbourne, FL 32901-3068

Telephone: (321) 802-6627
Internet Homepage: bagel13.com
Type of Business: Chain Restaurant Operator
Total Units: 5
Trade Names: Bagel 13 (5)
Company-Owned Units: 5
Primary Menu: Bagels (5)
Areas of Operation: FL
Type of Foodservice: Fast Casual (5)

Key Personnel
LEONARD WALKER - Owner; General Buyer

Domino's Franchisee
2480 Aurora Rd
Melbourne, FL 32935-3340

Telephone: (321) 242-2202
Type of Business: Chain Restaurant Operator
Total Sales: $30,374,000 (e)

Total Units: 15
Trade Names: Domino's (15)
Units Franchised From: 15
Primary Menu: Pizza (15)
Areas of Operation: FL
Type of Foodservice: Quick Serve (15)
Franchise Affiliation: Domino's Pizza Inc, ANN ARBOR, MI

Key Personnel
RICHARD W. PRICE - Owner; General Buyer

Keiser University Center Culinary Arts Melbourne
900 S Babcock St
Melbourne, FL 32901-1853

Telephone: (321) 409-4800
Fax Number: (321) 725-3766
Internet Homepage: keiseruniversity.edu
Type of Business: Culinary Schools
Areas of Operation: FL

Key Personnel
JAMES MCGINNESS - Executive Chef; General Buyer

Schuckers Inc.
1500 S Babcock St
Melbourne, FL 32901-3034

Telephone: (321) 723-3626
Type of Business: Chain Restaurant Operator
Year Founded: 1987
Total Sales: $2,807,000 (e)
Number of Employees: 100
Average Check: Lunch(6); Dinner(8)
Total Units: 5
Trade Names: Subway (5)
Units Franchised From: 5
Preferred Square Footage: 200; 500
Preferred Location Types: Downtown; Freestanding; Regional Mall
Primary Menu: Sandwiches/Deli (5)
Areas of Operation: FL
Type of Foodservice: Quick Serve (5)
Franchise Affiliation: Doctor's Associates Inc., MILFORD, CT
Primary Distributors: (Full Line) US Foods, BOCA RATON, FL

Key Personnel
CINDY SCHUCKERS - Owner; General Manager

Taste of India
606 N Wickham Rd Ste C
Melbourne, FL 32935-8845

Telephone: (321) 751-4191
Internet Homepage: tasteofindiamelbourne.com
Company Email: Anil_72usa@yahoo.com
Type of Business: Chain Restaurant Operator
Total Sales: $3,161,000 (e)
Alcohol Sales: 4%
Average Check: Dinner(36)
Total Units: 2
Trade Names: Taste of India (2)
Company-Owned Units: 2
Alcohol Served: Beer, Wine, Liquor
Primary Menu: Indian (2)
Areas of Operation: FL
Type of Foodservice: Fine Dining (2)
Catering Services: Yes

Key Personnel
ANIL VADAPARAMBIL - President; Owner

Yen Brevard, LLC
1515 Palm Bay Rd Ste 160
Melbourne, FL 32905-3815

Telephone: (321) 473-8996
Type of Business: Chain Restaurant Operator
Total Sales: $9,751,000 (e)
Total Units: 7
Trade Names: Jersey Mike's Subs (7)
Units Franchised From: 7
Primary Menu: Sandwiches/Deli (7)
Areas of Operation: FL
Type of Foodservice: Quick Serve (7)
Franchise Affiliation: Jersey Mike's Franchise Systems, MANASQUAN, NJ

Key Personnel
BRYAN PRICE - Owner; General Buyer

100 MONTADITOS
1450 Brickell Ave
Miami, FL 33131-3444

Telephone: (305) 415-6283
Internet Homepage: us.100montaditos.com
Company Email: customercare@100montaditos.com
Type of Business: Chain Restaurant Operator
Year Founded: 2000
Total Units: 4
Trade Names: 100 MONTADITOS (4)
Company-Owned Units: 4
Alcohol Served: Beer, Wine, Liquor
Primary Menu: Sandwiches/Deli (4)
Projected Openings: 1
Areas of Operation: DC, FL, NY
Foreign Countries: CHILE; COLOMBIA; ITALY; MEXICO; PORTUGAL; SPAIN
Type of Foodservice: Fast Casual (4)
Catering Services: Yes

Key Personnel
FRANCISCO JAVIER CERNUDA - CEO
DAVID GALLARDO - COO
PIERRE LLANIO - General Manager
IGNACIO GARCIA NIETO - Director Operations

50 Eggs, Inc.
7350 Biscayne Blvd
Miami, FL 33138-5151

Telephone: (786) 360-2553
Internet Homepage: 50eggsinc.com; eatspringchicken.com; runchickenrun.com; runpigrun.com
Company Email: info@runchickenrun.com
Type of Business: Chain Restaurant Operator
Total Units: 7
Trade Names: Ad Lib (1); Chica (1); Spring Chicken (1); Yardbird Southern Table & Bar (4)
Company-Owned Units: 7
Primary Menu: American (4); Chicken (2); Latin American/Cuban (1)
Areas of Operation: FL, NV
Type of Foodservice: Casual Dining (6); Fine Dining (1)

Key Personnel
JOHN KUNKEL - CEO; Owner

Anacapri
12669 S Dixie Hwy
Miami, FL 33156-5958

Telephone: (305) 232-8001
Fax Number: (305) 232-4006
Internet Homepage: anacaprifood.com
Company Email: anacaprifood@bellsouth.net
Type of Business: Chain Restaurant Operator
Year Founded: 1990
Total Sales: $1,505,000 (e)
Number of Employees: 12
Average Check: Lunch(8); Dinner(18)
Internet Order Processing: Yes
Total Units: 2
Trade Names: Anacapri (2)
Company-Owned Units: 2
Preferred Location Types: Freestanding
Alcohol Served: Beer, Wine
Primary Menu: Italian (2)
Areas of Operation: FL
Type of Foodservice: Fine Dining (2)
Catering Services: Yes

Key Personnel
GUISEPPE ZUOZO - President; General Manager; General Buyer
DAVID GONZALEZ - Director Operations

Areas USA, Inc.
5301 Blue Lagoon Dr Ste 600
Miami, FL 33126-2098

Telephone: (305) 267-8510
Internet Homepage: areasusa.com
Type of Business: Chain Restaurant Operator
Total Sales: $13,490,000 (e)
Total Units: 166
Trade Names: Auntie Anne's Hand-Rolled Soft Pretzels; BGrill; Big Bowl; Carl's Jr; Champs; Cheerburger Cheerburger; Citrus Market; City Point Bar; Corona Beach House; Currito; Dunkin' Donuts; Earl of Sandwich; Ford's Filling Station; Freshens Fresh Food Studio; Homeboy Cafe & Bakery; Hub 51; Island ChickenGrill; Jamba Juice; Jerry's Subs & Pizza; KFC; La Pausa; Lamill Coffee; McGinleys; Mezza Mediterranean Grille; Nathan's; Natural Break; Nature's Table; Orange Optix; Peet's; Phillips Seafood Express; Pizza Hut; Qdoba Mexican Grill; RJ Grunts; Ruby Tuesday; Sam & Harry's; Sammy's Pizza; Subway; Sunshine Market; The Coffee Bean & Tea Leaf; tocco; Tony Roma's; Tortas Frontera; Urban Olive; Villa; Wendys; Wow Bao
Units Franchised From: 166
Projected Openings: 10
Areas of Operation: CA, FL, GA
Type of Foodservice: Quick Serve

Key Personnel
SERGIO RODRIGUEZ - CEO
CARLOS BERNAL - CEO
ROBERT NEGRON - CFO; VP
ALBERTO SERRATOS - VP Finance
HUY PHAM - VP Business Development
JAIME BARBANOJ - VP Purchasing, Construction
VANESSA PEÑARANDA - Executive Director Corporate Affairs, Legal
VALENTINA ELLISON - Executive Director Business Development
GUY DIMARIA - General Manager; Director Operations
PAULA ANTICH - Director Marketing, Communications
DERRICK CHIN - Director Construction
CARLOS J. DE JESUS - Director Operations
CARY SELF - Director Customer Service, Training
PAULA LOPEZ - Director Purchasing
GEORGE GARCIA - Director Human Resources
MARIA MARTINEZ - Director Business Development
ANTHONY PASERCHIA - Director Risk Management, Asset Protection
MARWAN WANNA - Director Construction, Design
FILINTO GALBAN - Regional Director Operations
KENYA SMITH - Regional Manager Human Resources
JENNIFER BIENES - Manager Accounting
PATRICIA LOMBILLO - Manager Communications
MARGARITA NUNEZ - Manager Human Resources
JONATHAN VARGAS - Manager Operations, Information Technology
ALEX RODRIQUEZ - Administrator Information Technology
DIMITRA BRACKIN - Coordinator Accounting

Argo Management
4961 SW 74th Ct
Miami, FL 33155-4471

Telephone: (305) 661-0024
Fax Number: (305) 669-0836
Type of Business: Chain Restaurant Operator
Total Sales: $48,090,000 (e)
Total Units: 10
Trade Names: McDonald's (10)
Units Franchised From: 10
Preferred Square Footage: 2,500
Primary Menu: Hamburger (10)
Projected Remodelings: 2
Areas of Operation: FL
Type of Foodservice: Quick Serve (10)
Franchise Affiliation: McDonald's Corporation, CHICAGO, IL

Key Personnel
ALEX RODRIGUEZ - Partner; General Buyer
ISA RODRIGUEZ - Partner; Corporate Secretary; General Buyer
VIVIAN RODRIGUEZ - Manager Branch

Balrod Enterprises Inc.
13530 SW 152nd St
Miami, FL 33177-1111

Telephone: (305) 251-6787
Type of Business: Chain Restaurant Operator
Year Founded: 1993
Total Sales: $13,250,000 (e)
Number of Employees: 216
Total Units: 5
Trade Names: Wendy's Old Fashioned Hamburgers (5)
Units Franchised From: 5
Primary Menu: Hamburger (5)
Areas of Operation: FL
Type of Foodservice: Fast Casual (5)
Franchise Affiliation: The Wendy's Company, DUBLIN, OH

Key Personnel
SERGIO BALSINDE - Owner; General Buyer
FRANCISCO RIZO - Manager District

Burbowl
117 SE 3rd Ave
Miami, FL 33131

Telephone: (786) 558-4244
Internet Homepage: bur-bowl.com
Company Email: info@bur-bowl.com
Type of Business: Chain Restaurant Operator
Year Founded: 2014
Total Units: 4
Trade Names: Burbowl (4)
Company-Owned Units: 1
Units Franchised To: 3
Preferred Square Footage: 1,500; 1,800
Preferred Location Types: Institution (college/hospital); Strip Mall
Primary Menu: Hamburger (4)
Projected Openings: 30
Areas of Operation: FL
Type of Foodservice: Fast Casual (4)

Key Personnel
ANGEL BENITEZ JR - Founder; Partner
RENE PRATS - Partner

Burger King Worldwide Inc.
5505 Blue Lagoon Dr
Miami, FL 33126-2029

Telephone: (305) 378-3000
Fax Number: (305) 378-7910
Internet Homepage: bk.com; burgerking.com
Type of Business: Chain Restaurant Operator
Year Founded: 1954
Systemwide Sales: $27,819,299,000 (e)
Publicly Held: Yes
Total Sales: $1,335,417,000 (e)
Number of Employees: 11,000
Average Check: Breakfast(6); Lunch(8); Dinner(8)
Internet Order Processing: Yes
Total Units: 19,384
Trade Names: Burger King (19,383); WHOPPER Bar (1)
Company-Owned Units: 52
Units Franchised To: 18,322
Preferred Square Footage: 1,900; 4,300
Preferred Location Types: Airports; Community Mall; Convenience Store/Gas Station; Downtown; Freestanding; Institution (college/hospital); Kiosk; Mobile Unit; Office Complex; Other; Outlet Mall; Parks; Regional Mall; Stadiums; Travel Plazas
Primary Menu: Hamburger (19,384)
Projected Openings: 50
Projected Remodelings: 800
Areas of Operation: AK, AL, AR, AZ, CA, CO,

CT, DC, DE, FL, GA, GU, HI, IA, ID, IL, IN, KS, KY, LA, MA, MD, ME, MI, MN, MO, MS, MT, NC, ND, NE, NH, NJ, NM, NV, NY, OH, OK, OR, PA, PR, RI, SC, SD, TN, TX, UT, VA, VT, WA, WI, WV, WY, AB, BC, MB, NB, NL, NS, ON, PE, QC, SK

Foreign Countries: ANDORRA; ANTIGUA; ARGENTINA; ARUBA; AUSTRALIA; AUSTRIA; BAHAMAS; BAHRAIN; BOLIVIA; BRAZIL; BRUNEI; CAMBODIA; CANADA; CAYMAN ISLANDS; CHILE; CHINA; COLOMBIA; COSTA RICA; CURACAO; CYPRUS; CZECH REPUBLIC; DENMARK; DOMINICAN REPUBLIC; EL SALVADOR; ENGLAND; FRANCE; GERMANY; GIBRALTAR; GUATEMALA; HONDURAS; HONG KONG; HUNGARY; ICELAND; INDIA; INDONESIA; ISRAEL; ITALY; JAMAICA; JAPAN; JORDAN; KUWAIT; LATVIA; LEBANON; LITHUANIA; MALAYSIA; MALTA; MEXICO; NEW ZEALAND; NICARAGUA; NORTHERN IRELAND; NORWAY; PAKISTAN; PANAMA; PARAGUAY; PERU; PORTUGAL; QATAR; RUSSIA; SAINT MAARTEN; SAUDI ARABIA; SINGAPORE; SOUTH KOREA; SPAIN; SRI LANKA; ST. LUCIA; SURINAME; SWEDEN; SWITZERLAND; TAIWAN; THAILAND; THE NETHERLANDS; THE PHILIPPINES; TRINIDAD & TOBAGO; TURKEY; UNITED ARAB EMIRATES; URUGUAY; VENEZUELA

Type of Foodservice: Quick Serve (19,384)
Foodservice Management Venues: College & University; Military Feeding
Primary Distributors: (Full Line) Restaurant Services Inc., MIAMI, FL
Parent Company: Restaurant Brands International, TORONTO, ON CANADA

Key Personnel
ALEXANDRE BEHRING - Chairman
MARIA TERREROS - CEO
DAVID SHEAR - President International Division
DIEGO BEAMONTE - President Global
ANNE CHWAT - President; General Counsel
AMY KNIGHTS - President Real Estate
CARLOS SARRIA - President Company Operations, EMEA
TOM CURTIS - President United States, Canada
JOSHUA KOBZA - COO
VICENTE TOME - VP; General Counsel
ANNETTE RODRIGUEZ - VP Development
ROBIN SCHAFER - General Counsel; Director
CHRISTOPHER PADOAN - General Manager Southeast Division
BETTY BLANDON - Senior Director Internal Audit
ALEX CORDERO - Senior Director Finance
CHARLES MORERA - Senior Director Accounting, Global
JOHN HEFTY - Director Business Development
KOMAL DESAI - Director Finance
LUCY GRIMM - Director Finance
MARIO BOJORQUEZ - Director Operations
MATTHEW BRESNAHAN - Director Digital
RENATO ROSSI - Director Marketing, North America
GORDON TAM - Director Finance, Development
ANA CECILIA DIAZ - Director Procurement, Global
IVETTE DIAZ - Director
ERIC MAUST - Director Strategy, Marketing
CARLOS NUNEZ - Director Marketing
MARY PICHARDO - Director Operations
SHAMBRIKA SAUNDERS - Director Training
COLLIN SCHOPFER - Director Restaurant Operations
ANA SILVA - Director Communications, Digital Marketing
CHRISTOPHER SMITH - Director
ROSEY SUAREZ - Director Operations
STEVE TAKAHASHI - Director Finance, Operations
JILL TYSON - Director
BEBE ZICHA - Director Food
ALEXANDRE ANTONELLO - Director Marketing, Division
CHLOE HART - Director Innovation
JACK MCCLUSKEY - Director Operations
GUILLERMO CUE - Director Innovation
OLGA FUENTES - Senior Manager Global
JOSE LUIS SANCHEZ - Senior Manager Operations-Training
SERGIO RODRIGUEZ - Senior Manager Finance
JOHN SCHMEROLD - Senior Manager Finance, Global
DAVID WILSON - Regional Manager
ALLISON THOMAS - District Manager
DOUGLAS LITTLEJOHN - Manager Promotion
GRACIELA BARRERA - Manager Operations
MARSHA BEWLEY - Manager Development, Talent
LILIA DUARTE - Manager Tax
ROSARIO GALVEZ-BARREIRO - Manager Accounting, Global
LOURDES GARCES - Manager Accounting
HENRY GARRIGA - Manager Development
ENRIQUE GARRIGA - Manager Development
FLÁVIA GUETTER - Manager Social Media, Digital Marketing, North America
ALLISON LAU - Manager Operations; Global Operations
LEILA MCCLEARY - Manager Development, Innovation
KARLA PATINO - Manager Strategy, Field Marketing
LUIS RIVERA - Manager Construction
WILLIAM WASHINGTON - Manager Development
CHRISTIAN DESCOUBET - Assistant Manager

Chicken Kitchen USA LLC
524 Arthur Godfrey Rd
Miami, FL 33140

Telephone: (305) 531-1888
Internet Homepage: chickenkitchen.com
Type of Business: Chain Restaurant Operator
Year Founded: 1983
Systemwide Sales: $30,457,000 (e)
Total Sales: $19,915,000 (e)
Number of Employees: 220
Average Check: Lunch(12); Dinner(16)
Total Units: 28
Trade Names: Chicken Kitchen (28)
Company-Owned Units: 19
Units Franchised To: 9
Preferred Square Footage: 1,200; 2,400
Preferred Location Types: Strip Mall
Primary Menu: Chicken (28)
Areas of Operation: FL, TX
Foreign Countries: PANAMA
Type of Foodservice: Quick Serve (18)
Catering Services: Yes
Primary Distributors: (Food) Cheney Bros. Inc., RIVIERA BEACH, FL
Notes: The company derives approximately 11% of its revenue from commissary sales to franchisees.

Key Personnel
CHRISTIAN DE BERDOUARE - President; Executive Chef; Manager Real Estate, Franchise Development
HOWARD ETTELMAN - CFO; Controller

CrepeMaker, Inc.
14365 SW 142nd St
Miami, FL 33186-6726

Telephone: (305) 233-1113
Fax Number: (305) 252-3100
Internet Homepage: crepemaker.com
Company Email: info@crepemaker.com
Type of Business: Chain Restaurant Operator
Year Founded: 1992
Total Sales: $1,833,000 (e)
Average Check: Dinner(12)
Total Units: 6
Trade Names: Crepemaker (6)
Units Franchised To: 6
Alcohol Served: Beer, Wine
Primary Menu: French/Continental (6)
Areas of Operation: CA, FL, PR, TN
Type of Foodservice: Casual Dining (6)
Catering Services: Yes

Key Personnel
CHRIS HOFFMAN - President
MARIA SUNE - President; Owner

Domino's Franchisee
8737 SW 24th St
Miami, FL 33165-2005

Telephone: (305) 227-0551
Type of Business: Chain Restaurant Operator

Total Sales: $4,116,000 (e)
Total Units: 2
Trade Names: Domino's (2)
Units Franchised From: 2
Primary Menu: Pizza (2)
Areas of Operation: FL
Type of Foodservice: Quick Serve (2)
Franchise Affiliation: Domino's Pizza Inc, ANN ARBOR, MI

Key Personnel
ISSA A. BADER - Owner; General Buyer

Don Pan International Bakery
6925 NW 52nd St
Miami, FL 33166-4844

Telephone: (877) 936-6726
Fax Number: (305) 834-6540
Internet Homepage: donpan.com
Company Email: info@donpan.com
Type of Business: Chain Restaurant Operator
Year Founded: 1995
Total Units: 12
Trade Names: Don Pan International Bakery (12)
Company-Owned Units: 12
Primary Menu: Sandwiches/Deli (12)
Areas of Operation: FL, FC
Type of Foodservice: Quick Serve (12)

Key Personnel
ALVARO GORRIN SR - Partner; General Buyer
JUAN GORRIN - Partner
CAROLINA GORRIN - COO

Dr Smood Group Inc
2230 NW 2nd Ave
Miami, FL 33127-4854

Telephone: (786) 334-4420
Internet Homepage: drsmood.com
Company Email: hello@drsmood.com
Type of Business: Chain Restaurant Operator
Year Founded: 2012
Total Sales: $6,979,000 (e)
Internet Order Processing: Yes
Total Units: 8
Trade Names: Dr Smood (8)
Company-Owned Units: 8
Primary Menu: Health Foods (8)
Projected Openings: 3
Areas of Operation: FL, NY
Type of Foodservice: Fast Casual (8)

Key Personnel
RENE SINDLEV - Chairman; Founder
DIDIER CHOUKROUN - CEO; President
FRANCESCO PERILLO - Chief Growth Officer

Giardino Enterprises
8000 SW 117th Ave Ste PH-D
Miami, FL 33183

Telephone: (305) 595-4495
Fax Number: (305) 595-4496
Internet Homepage: giardinosalads.com
Company Email: info@giardinosalads.com
Type of Business: Chain Restaurant Operator
Year Founded: 2004
Total Sales: $12,210,000 (e)
Total Units: 15
Trade Names: Giardino Gourmet Salads (15)
Company-Owned Units: 1
Units Franchised To: 14
Primary Menu: American (15)
Areas of Operation: FL, NC, TN
Type of Foodservice: Fast Casual (15)

Key Personnel
ODY LUGO - Partner; Director Operations, Marketing; General Buyer
KENNETH LUGO - Partner; Director Franchise Development

Global Miami J.V.
3663 SW 8th St
Miami, FL 33135-4133

Telephone: (305) 446-4914
Fax Number: (305) 445-9469
Internet Homepage: globalmia.com
Company Email: info@globalmia.com
Type of Business: Chain Restaurant Operator
Year Founded: 1971
Total Sales: $104,710,000 (e)
Alcohol Sales: 10%
Number of Employees: 1,472
Average Check: Breakfast(10); Lunch(14); Dinner(24)
Total Units: 27
Trade Names: Au Bon Pain (4); Cafe La Carreta (1); Cafe Versailles (6); Clubhouse One (1); Islander Bar & Grill (2); La Carreta Restaurant (1); Manchu Wok(2); Nathan's Famous (3); Sushi Maki (3); The Clover (1); Villa Pizza (3)
Company-Owned Units: 11
Units Franchised From: 16
Preferred Square Footage: 8,000
Preferred Location Types: Airports; Community Mall; Freestanding; Strip Mall
Alcohol Served: Beer, Wine, Liquor
Primary Menu: American (1); Caribbean (2); Chinese (2); Hot Dogs (4); Japanese (3); Latin American/Cuban (8); Miscellaneous (1); Pizza (3); Sandwiches/Deli (4)
Areas of Operation: FL
Type of Foodservice: Casual Dining (7); Fast Casual (4); Quick Serve (16)
Franchise Affiliation: ABP Corporation, BOSTON, MA; MTY Food Group Inc., SAINT-LAURENT, QC; Nathan's Famous Inc., JERICHO, NY; Villa Restaurant Group, MORRISTOWN, NJ
Primary Distributors: (Full Line) SYSCO Central Florida Inc., OCOEE, FL

Key Personnel
NICOLE VALLS - VP Operations

J R One Inc
12150 SW 128th Ct Ste 120
Miami, FL 33186-4672

Telephone: (305) 253-8155
Type of Business: Chain Restaurant Operator
Total Sales: $8,249,000 (e)
Total Units: 5
Trade Names: Johnny Rockets (5)
Units Franchised From: 5
Primary Menu: Hamburger (5)
Areas of Operation: FL
Type of Foodservice: Family Restaurant (5)
Franchise Affiliation: The Johnny Rockets Group Inc., LAKE FOREST, CA

Key Personnel
KENNETH ELDRIDGE - President; General Buyer

LCL Food Services Inc.
13349 SW 131st St
Miami, FL 33186-5816

Telephone: (305) 252-8961
Fax Number: (305) 252-8962
Type of Business: Chain Restaurant Operator
Year Founded: 1989
Total Sales: $42,500,000 (e)
Number of Employees: 432
Average Check: Breakfast(8); Lunch(8); Dinner(8)
Total Units: 9
Trade Names: McDonald's (9)
Units Franchised From: 9
Preferred Square Footage: 2,500
Preferred Location Types: Freestanding
Primary Menu: Hamburger (9)
Areas of Operation: FL
Type of Foodservice: Quick Serve (9)
Franchise Affiliation: McDonald's Corporation, CHICAGO, IL
Primary Distributors: (Full Line) The Martin-Brower Co., POMPANO BEACH, FL

Key Personnel
ANTHONY LOPEZ - President; General Manager Finance, Operations,

Facility/Maintenance, Information Systems, Supply Chain, Real Estate, Store Fixtures; General Buyer
SOPHIA LOPEZ - Director Marketing
NIKKI PEREZ - Director Operations; Manager Customer Service
KIM HELLRIEGEL - Manager Human Resources, Branch

Los Ranchos Restaurants Inc.
135 SW 107th Ave
Miami, FL 33174-1417

Telephone: (305) 229-7002
Internet Homepage: losranchossteakhouse.com
Type of Business: Chain Restaurant Operator
Year Founded: 1981
Total Sales: $11,248,000 (e)
Alcohol Sales: 20%
Number of Employees: 150
Average Check: Lunch(18); Dinner(30)
Internet Order Processing: Yes
Total Units: 4
Trade Names: Los Ranchos Restaurant (4)
Company-Owned Units: 4
Preferred Square Footage: 5,500; 6,000
Preferred Location Types: Regional Mall
Alcohol Served: Beer, Wine, Liquor
Primary Menu: Steak (4)
Areas of Operation: FL
Type of Foodservice: Casual Dining (4)
Catering Services: Yes
Primary Distributors: (Full Line) SYSCO Central Florida Inc., OCOEE, FL

Key Personnel
MYRNA SOMOZA - President; Executive Chef; Director Real Estate, Design, Catering
MARK CLARK - President
RAPHAEL WONG - Exec VP; Treasurer; Corporate Secretary; Director Information Systems

Martinez Distributors
7379 NW 31st St
Miami, FL 33122

Telephone: (305) 882-8282
Fax Number: (305) 882-8686
Internet Homepage: mdist.us
Type of Business: Foodservice Management Operator
Total Sales: $143,285,000 (e)
Number of Locations Served: 100
Total Foodservice Mgmt Accounts: 100

Key Personnel
JESUS MARTINEZ - Owner

LAZARO NUNEZ - General Manager

McDonald's Franchise
599 NW 62nd St
Miami, FL 33150-4499

Telephone: (305) 665-1888
Fax Number: (305) 397-1889
Type of Business: Chain Restaurant Operator
Total Sales: $52,290,000 (e)
Number of Employees: 600
Total Units: 11
Trade Names: McDonald's (11)
Units Franchised From: 11
Preferred Square Footage: 2,500
Primary Menu: Hamburger (11)
Areas of Operation: FL
Type of Foodservice: Quick Serve (11)
Franchise Affiliation: McDonald's Corporation, CHICAGO, IL

Key Personnel
ANTHONY GREENWOOD - President; General Buyer

McDonald's Franchise
7148 SW 47th St
Miami, FL 33155-4642

Telephone: (305) 793-0313
Type of Business: Chain Restaurant Operator
Total Sales: $27,800,000 (e)
Average Check: Dinner(12)
Total Units: 6
Trade Names: McDonald's (6)
Units Franchised From: 6
Preferred Location Types: Freestanding
Primary Menu: Hamburger (6)
Areas of Operation: FL
Type of Foodservice: Quick Serve (6)
Franchise Affiliation: McDonald's Corporation, CHICAGO, IL

Key Personnel
ROSELINA RODRIGUEZ - President; General Buyer

Panther Coffee
2390 NW 2nd Ave
Miami, FL 33127-4302

Telephone: (305) 677-3952
Internet Homepage: panthercoffee.com
Company Email: panther@panthercoffee.com
Type of Business: Chain Restaurant Operator
Year Founded: 2010
Total Units: 5
Trade Names: Panther Coffee (5)
Company-Owned Units: 5

Primary Menu: Coffee (5)
Projected Openings: 1
Areas of Operation: FL
Type of Foodservice: Quick Serve (5)

Key Personnel
LETICIA POLLOCK - Founder; Partner
JOEL POLLOCK - Founder; Partner

Pizzerias LLC
10756 SW 72nd St
Miami, FL 33173

Telephone: (305) 596-7272
Type of Business: Chain Restaurant Operator
Year Founded: 2003
Total Sales: $42,910,000 (e)
Number of Employees: 500
Average Check: Lunch(20); Dinner(32)
Total Units: 32
Trade Names: Papa John's Pizza (32)
Units Franchised From: 32
Preferred Square Footage: 1,100; 1,500
Preferred Location Types: Freestanding; Strip Mall
Primary Menu: Pizza (32)
Areas of Operation: FL
Type of Foodservice: Quick Serve (32)
Franchise Affiliation: Papa Johns International Inc., LOUISVILLE, KY
Primary Distributors: (Full Line) McLane/Lagrange, LAGRANGE, GA

Key Personnel
RICKY WARMAN - CEO; President; General Manager; General Buyer

Pollo Tropical Operations Inc.
7255 NW 19th St Suite C
Miami, FL 33126

Telephone: (305) 670-7696
Fax Number: (305) 670-6403
Internet Homepage: pollotropical.com
Company Email: contact@pollotropical.com
Type of Business: Chain Restaurant Operator
Year Founded: 1988
Systemwide Sales: $1,166,194,000 (e)
Publicly Held: Yes
Total Sales: $520,421,000 (e)
Alcohol Sales: 2%
Number of Employees: 3,500
Average Check: Lunch(12); Dinner(12)
Total Units: 495
Trade Names: Pollo Tropical (495)
Company-Owned Units: 172
Units Franchised To: 323
Preferred Square Footage: 2,800; 3,200
Preferred Location Types: Downtown;

Freestanding; Institution (college/hospital); Outlet Mall; Strip Mall
Alcohol Served: Beer, Wine
Primary Menu: Chicken (495)
Projected Openings: 2
Areas of Operation: FL, PR
Foreign Countries: BAHAMAS; GUYANA; PANAMA
Type of Foodservice: Fast Casual (495)
Catering Services: Yes
Primary Distributors: (Equipment) N. Wasserstrom & Sons, COLUMBUS, OH; (Food) Performance Food Group, RICHMOND, VA; (Supplies) Performance Food Group, RICHMOND, VA
Parent Company: El Pollo Loco Holdings, Inc., DALLAS, TX

Key Personnel
TIM TAFT - CEO; President
JEFF WEBB - VP Purchasing, Research & Development, Product Development
ALAN JACOBS - Senior Director
MAURO LEDER - Director Franchise Operations
EDO LICINA - Director Finance
JOANNA JIMENEZ - Senior Manager Brand Marketing
HERNAN ROLDAN - District Manager
CARMEN OCHOA - District Manager
MAURO HERNANDEZ - Manager Training
FELIPE IZQUIERDO - Manager Construction
MITCHELL NISBETH - Manager Purchasing
SALLY THROCKMORTON - Manager Human Resources
VERONICA BRAVO - Manager
LOWRANDY DEMAS - Assistant Manager Catering
AILEEN CASADEVALL - Project Manager Operations

Rey's Pizza
2480 SW 137th Ave
Miami, FL 33175-6330

Mailing Address: PO Box 940398, Miami, FL, 33194-0398
Telephone: (305) 207-1711
Fax Number: (305) 207-1703
Internet Homepage: reypizza.com
Company Email: gerencia@reypizza.com
Type of Business: Chain Restaurant Operator
Year Founded: 1980
Total Sales: $17,370,000 (e)
Alcohol Sales: 1%
Number of Employees: 100
Average Check: Lunch(8); Dinner(12)
Total Units: 9
Trade Names: Rey's Pizza (9)
Company-Owned Units: 9
Preferred Square Footage: 3,400
Preferred Location Types: Freestanding; Office Complex
Alcohol Served: Beer, Wine
Primary Menu: Pizza (9)
Areas of Operation: FL
Type of Foodservice: Casual Dining (9)

Key Personnel
MARGARITTE RODRIGUEZ - Owner; General Buyer
JULIO GUTIERREZ - General Counsel; Director Human Resources
RAMON RODRIGUEZ JR - Director Operations, Marketing; General Buyer
PEDRO RAMOS - Manager Purchasing

Rice Mediterranean Kitchen
50 SW 10th St
Miami, FL 33130

Telephone: (305) 755-9588
Internet Homepage: ricekitchen.com
Company Email: info@ricekitchen.com
Type of Business: Chain Restaurant Operator
Year Founded: 2005
Total Units: 7
Trade Names: Rice House of Kebob (2); Rice Mediterranean Kitchen (5)
Company-Owned Units: 7
Preferred Square Footage: 3,500
Preferred Location Types: Downtown; Strip Mall
Primary Menu: Greek/Mediterranean (7)
Areas of Operation: FL
Type of Foodservice: Fast Casual (7)

Key Personnel
ESI SHABANI - Partner
JAFAR SHEBANI - Partner
REZA SHEBANI - Partner

Sergio's Restaurants
12380 SW 130th St
Miami, FL 33186-6229

Telephone: (305) 552-9623
Fax Number: (305) 552-7735
Internet Homepage: sergios.com
Company Email: info@sergios.com
Type of Business: Chain Restaurant Operator
Year Founded: 1975
Internet Order Processing: Yes
Total Units: 7
Trade Names: Sergio's Cuban (2); Sergio's Restaurant (5)
Company-Owned Units: 5
Units Franchised To: 2
Preferred Location Types: Airports; Freestanding; Strip Mall
Alcohol Served: Beer, Wine
Primary Menu: Latin American/Cuban (7)
Projected Openings: 2
Areas of Operation: FL
Type of Foodservice: Casual Dining (5); Fast Casual (2)
Catering Services: Yes

Key Personnel
CARLOS GAZITUA - President; General Buyer

Shorty's Inc.
9150 SW 87th Ave Ste 205
Miami, FL 33176-2313

Telephone: (305) 595-1622
Fax Number: (305) 279-2159
Internet Homepage: shortys.com
Company Email: info@Shortys.com
Type of Business: Chain Restaurant Operator
Year Founded: 1951
Systemwide Sales: $23,475,000 (e)
Total Sales: $22,240,000 (e)
Alcohol Sales: 3%
Number of Employees: 120
Average Check: Lunch(14); Dinner(22)
Internet Order Processing: Yes
Internet Sales: 1.00%
Total Units: 4
Trade Names: Shorty's Bar-B-Q (4)
Company-Owned Units: 4
Preferred Location Types: Freestanding
Alcohol Served: Beer, Wine
Primary Menu: Bar-B-Q (4)
Areas of Operation: FL
Type of Foodservice: Casual Dining (4)
Catering Services: Yes
Primary Distributors: (Full Line) SYSCO Food Services of South Florida Inc., MEDLEY, FL

Key Personnel
MARK VASTURO - CEO; President; Director Menu Development; General Buyer
ARTIE IGLESIAS - Controller
EVETTE PARRA - Director Catering
BAILEY DAVIS - Director Marketing

Surfside Coffee LLC
3252 NE 1st Ave Ste 205
Miami, FL 33137

Telephone: (855) 336-6887
Internet Homepage: surfsidecoffee.net
Company Email: info@surfsidecoffee.net
Type of Business: Chain Restaurant Operator
Year Founded: 2014
Total Sales: $107,760,000 (e)
Total Units: 70
Trade Names: Dunkin' Donuts (70); PizzaRev
Units Franchised From: 70
Primary Menu: Snacks (70)
Areas of Operation: FL
Type of Foodservice: Quick Serve (70)
Franchise Affiliation: DD IP Holder, CANTON, MA

Key Personnel
DEANA BAKER - General Manager
SUNNIE WILCOX - General Manager

Sushi Sake
261 SW 8th St
Miami, FL 33130

Telephone: (305) 285-3232
Internet Homepage: sushisakemiami.com
Company Email: franchise@sushisakemiami.com
Type of Business: Chain Restaurant Operator
Year Founded: 2009
Total Sales: $15,300,000 (e)
Total Units: 16
Trade Names: Sushi Sake (16)
Company-Owned Units: 16
Primary Menu: Asian (16)
Projected Openings: 2
Areas of Operation: FL
Type of Foodservice: Casual Dining (16)

Key Personnel
JAMES AGUAYO - Co-Founder
ARGELIO AGUAYO JR - Co-Founder
ANGEL AGUAYO - Director Operations

Wendium of Florida, LLC
12000 SW 49th St
Miami, FL 33175-5606

Telephone: (305) 458-6343
Type of Business: Chain Restaurant Operator
Year Founded: 1995
Total Sales: $16,070,000 (e)
Number of Employees: 150
Average Check: Lunch(10); Dinner(10)
Total Units: 6
Trade Names: Wendy's Old Fashioned Hamburgers (6)
Units Franchised From: 6
Preferred Square Footage: 2,100; 2,900
Preferred Location Types: Freestanding
Primary Menu: Hamburger (6)
Areas of Operation: FL
Type of Foodservice: Quick Serve (6)
Franchise Affiliation: The Wendy's Company, DUBLIN, OH

Key Personnel
RAUL DOMINGUEZ - President; General Manager; Manager Information Systems, Real Estate; General Buyer

Global Italian Food LLC
333 23rd St
Miami Beach, FL 33139

Telephone: (786) 362-5165
Internet Homepage: piola.it
Company Email: piolausa@piola.com
Type of Business: Chain Restaurant Operator
Total Units: 10
Trade Names: Piola (10)
Company-Owned Units: 10
Primary Menu: Italian (10)
Areas of Operation: DC, FL, NC, TX, VA
Type of Foodservice: Casual Dining (13)

Key Personnel
STEFANO CARNIATO - Owner; General Buyer

Myles Restaurant Group
157 Collins Ave
Miami Beach, FL 33139-7242

Telephone: (305) 538-9996
Fax Number: (305) 532-8982
Internet Homepage: bigpinktakeout.com; mylesrestaurantgroup.com
Company Email: info@mylesrestaurantgroup.com
Type of Business: Chain Restaurant Operator
Year Founded: 1994
Total Sales: $40,262,000 (e)
Alcohol Sales: 20%
Number of Employees: 350
Average Check: Lunch(20); Dinner(36)
Total Units: 4
Trade Names: Big Pink (1); Prime 112 (1); Prime Fish (1); Prime Italian (1)
Company-Owned Units: 4
Preferred Location Types: Freestanding
Alcohol Served: Beer, Wine, Liquor
Primary Menu: American (1); Italian (1); Steak (1); Steak/Seafood (1)
Areas of Operation: FL
Type of Foodservice: Casual Dining (1); Fine Dining (3)
Primary Distributors: (Full Line) SYSCO Food Services of South Florida Inc., MEDLEY, FL

Key Personnel
MYLES CHEFETZ - Owner; General Manager; Director Menu Development; General Buyer
MICHAEL SABIN - Corporate Chef

Vida and Estilo Corporation
1370 Washington Ave Ste 307
Miami Beach, FL 33139-8123

Telephone: (305) 604-9060
Internet Homepage: ohmexicorestaurant.com; verestaurants.com; havana1957.com
Company Email: info@cafenuvo.com
Type of Business: Chain Restaurant Operator
Total Sales: $28,160,000 (e)
Alcohol Sales: 10%
Number of Employees: 90
Average Check: Lunch(12); Dinner(22)
Total Units: 17
Trade Names: Cafe Americano (1); Havana 1957 (5); La Cerveceria (2); Mercato Della Pescheria (2); MIT Steak Bar (1); Oh Mexico (1); Tapas & Tintos (1); Tapas y Tintos (1); Taqueria (2); Terraza (1)
Company-Owned Units: 17
Alcohol Served: Beer, Wine, Liquor
Areas of Operation: FL, NV, FC
Foreign Countries: MEXICO
Type of Foodservice: Casual Dining (17)
Primary Distributors: (Full Line) Reinhart FoodService, JACKSONVILLE, FL

Key Personnel
EDUARDO ARAOZ - President; General Manager; General Buyer

BPH Burger
4727 NW 167th St
Miami Gardens, FL 33055-4242

Telephone: (305) 624-7041
Type of Business: Chain Restaurant Operator
Total Sales: $13,760,000 (e)
Average Check: Dinner(12)
Total Units: 6
Trade Names: Burger King (6)
Units Franchised From: 6
Preferred Location Types: Freestanding
Primary Menu: Hamburger (6)
Areas of Operation: FL
Type of Foodservice: Quick Serve (6)
Franchise Affiliation: Burger King Worldwide Inc., MIAMI, FL

Key Personnel
LARISSA ARONSON - VP Operations
MICHAEL ARONSON - VP Operations; General Buyer
JUAN LEAL - Controller
EDUARD PERALTA - General Manager

Koning Restaurants International
15600 NW 15th Ave Ste C
Miami Gardens, FL 33169-5609

Telephone: (305) 430-1200
Fax Number: (305) 663-9027
Type of Business: Chain Restaurant Operator
Year Founded: 1992
Total Sales: $71,490,000 (e)

Alcohol Sales: 3%
Number of Employees: 1,965
Average Check: Lunch(14); Dinner(20)
Total Units: 60
Trade Names: Pizza Hut (60)
Units Franchised From: 60
Preferred Square Footage: 2,500; 3,200
Preferred Location Types: Downtown; Freestanding; Strip Mall
Alcohol Served: Beer
Primary Menu: Pizza (60)
Areas of Operation: FL
Type of Foodservice: Quick Serve (60)
Catering Services: Yes
Franchise Affiliation: Pizza Hut Inc., PLANO, TX
Primary Distributors: (Full Line) SYSCO Food Services of South Florida Inc., MEDLEY, FL

Key Personnel
ALFREADO SALAS - CEO; President; Director Finance, Real Estate
ROMAY MARTINEZ - General Manager Restaurant Operations
PRIAMO PLASENCIA - Director Information Systems, Information Technology
GABY BERRIDO - Director Human Resources, Training
ELSIE DAVILA - Director Operations, Purchasing, Facility/Maintenance, Supply Chain, Design, Store Fixtures
MAURICIO DAVILA - Director Operations, Catering

Spiegel Investment CC
6723 Main St
Miami Lakes, FL 33014-2071

Telephone: (786) 639-0004
Type of Business: Chain Restaurant Operator
Total Sales: $2,806,000 (e)
Total Units: 5
Trade Names: Cold Stone Creamery (5)
Units Franchised From: 5
Primary Menu: Snacks (5)
Areas of Operation: FL
Type of Foodservice: Quick Serve (5)
Franchise Affiliation: Kahala Brands, SCOTTSDALE, AZ

Key Personnel
FREDERICK SPIEGEL - Partner
RUTH SPIEGEL - Partner
STEPHEN SPIEGEL - Partner

Cuisine Management
1300 3rd St S
Naples, FL 34102-7220

Telephone: (239) 262-5500
Fax Number: (239) 262-5500
Internet Homepage: baysideseafoodgrillandbar.com; tonysoffthird.com; ridgwaybarandgrill.com
Company Email: info@baysideseafoodgrillandbar.com
Type of Business: Chain Restaurant Operator
Year Founded: 1972
Total Sales: $7,326,000 (e)
Alcohol Sales: 23%
Number of Employees: 300
Average Check: Lunch(24); Dinner(60)
Internet Order Processing: Yes
Total Units: 3
Trade Names: Bayside Seafood Grill & Bar (1); Ridgway Bar & Grill (1); Tony's Off Third Wine & Bakery (1)
Company-Owned Units: 3
Preferred Location Types: Freestanding
Alcohol Served: Beer, Wine, Liquor
Primary Menu: American (1); Seafood (2)
Areas of Operation: FL
Type of Foodservice: Casual Dining (1); Fine Dining (2)
Primary Distributors: (Equipment) Edward Don & Co., MIRAMAR, FL; (Food) SYSCO Corporation, HOUSTON, TX; (Supplies) Edward Don & Co., MIRAMAR, FL

Key Personnel
SUKIE HONEYCUTT - Partner; General Buyer
JOHN EVERDING - Partner
CAROLINE RIDGWAY - Manager Marketing, Media

Domino's Franchisee
15275 Collier Blvd Ste 208
Naples, FL 34119-6750

Telephone: (239) 304-3040
Type of Business: Chain Restaurant Operator
Total Sales: $8,298,000 (e)
Total Units: 4
Trade Names: Domino's (4)
Units Franchised From: 4
Primary Menu: Pizza (4)
Areas of Operation: FL
Type of Foodservice: Quick Serve (4)
Franchise Affiliation: Domino's Pizza Inc, ANN ARBOR, MI

Key Personnel
CHARLES SPERO - Owner; General Buyer

IC Naples, Inc.
6420 Naples Blvd Ste 105
Naples, FL 34109-2058

Telephone: (239) 592-1600
Type of Business: Chain Restaurant Operator
Total Sales: $1,219,000 (e)
Total Units: 2
Trade Names: Cold Stone Creamery (2)
Units Franchised From: 2
Primary Menu: Snacks (2)
Areas of Operation: FL
Type of Foodservice: Quick Serve (2)
Franchise Affiliation: Kahala Brands, SCOTTSDALE, AZ

Key Personnel
HITESH BARVALIYA - Owner; General Buyer

Domino's Franchisee
1844 Renzulli Rd
New Smyrna Beach, FL 32168-1726

Telephone: (386) 428-2021
Type of Business: Chain Restaurant Operator
Total Sales: $9,977,000 (e)
Total Units: 5
Trade Names: Domino's (5)
Units Franchised From: 5
Primary Menu: Pizza (5)
Areas of Operation: FL
Type of Foodservice: Quick Serve (5)
Franchise Affiliation: Domino's Pizza Inc, ANN ARBOR, MI

Key Personnel
RICHARD T. CEIDE - Owner; General Buyer

Gyarmathy & Associates Inc.
13180 N Cleveland Ave Ste 111
North Fort Myers, FL 33903-6230

Telephone: (239) 997-1992
Fax Number: (239) 997-2891
Company Email: corporatequarters1#gmail.com
Type of Business: Chain Restaurant Operator
Total Sales: $16,200,000 (e)
Alcohol Sales: 8%
Number of Employees: 275
Average Check: Lunch(14); Dinner(14)
Total Units: 9
Trade Names: KFC (9)
Units Franchised From: 9
Preferred Square Footage: 1,500
Preferred Location Types: Freestanding; Strip Mall
Alcohol Served: Beer, Wine, Liquor
Primary Menu: Chicken (9)
Areas of Operation: FL
Type of Foodservice: Quick Serve (9)
Catering Services: Yes
Franchise Affiliation: BBQ Holdings, Inc., MINNETONKA, MN; KFC Corporation, LOUISVILLE, KY
Primary Distributors: (Full Line) US Foods, BOCA RATON, FL

Key Personnel
JIM GYARMATHY - President; General Buyer
BONNIE BAILEY - Senior VP
MONICA MONTGOMERY - VP Finance, Information Systems, Real Estate, Human Resources, Store Fixtures, Menu Development

Sliderz, MG Inc.
1817 NE 123rd St
North Miami, FL 33181-2805

Telephone: (786) 703-7415
Internet Homepage: sliderz.com
Type of Business: Chain Restaurant Operator
Year Founded: 2015
Total Sales: $1,509,000 (e)
Total Units: 2
Trade Names: Sliderz Restaurants (2)
Units Franchised To: 2
Primary Menu: Hamburger (2)
Projected Openings: 5
Areas of Operation: FL
Type of Foodservice: Fast Casual (2)

Key Personnel
BUZZY SKLAR - Founder; CEO; Director Franchise Development; General Buyer

BurgerFi International, Inc.
105 US Highway 1
North Palm Beach, FL 33408-5401

Telephone: (561) 844-5528
Fax Number: (561) 844-5522
Internet Homepage: theofficedelray.com; burgerfi.com; vicandangelos.com
Company Email: info@BurgerFi.com
Type of Business: Chain Restaurant Operator
Year Founded: 1999
Systemwide Sales: $166,012,000 (e)
Publicly Held: Yes
Total Sales: $44,830,000 (e)
Alcohol Sales: 10%
Total Units: 177
Trade Names: Anthony's Coal Fired Pizza (61); BurgerFi (116)
Company-Owned Units: 61
Units Franchised To: 116
Preferred Square Footage: 2,500; 3,000
Preferred Location Types: Freestanding; Strip Mall
Alcohol Served: Beer, Wine, Liquor
Primary Menu: American (0); Hamburger (116); Italian (0); Pizza (61)
Projected Openings: 10
Areas of Operation: AL, AZ, CA, CO, CT, DC, FL, GA, IL, KS, MA, MD, MI, NC, NJ, NY, OH, PA, SC, TN, TX, VA
Type of Foodservice: Casual Dining (61); Fast Casual (116); Fine Dining (0)

Parent Company: OPES Acquisition Corp., MIAMI, FL
Notes: Systemwide sales reflect BurgerFi restaurants only.

Key Personnel
CHRISTOPHER JONES - CFO
MICHELLE ZAVOLTA - Chief People Officer
STEVE LIEBER - Director Franchising
PAUL GRIFFIN - Director Culinary Development
BRITTANY DEBAPTISTE - Director Marketing
MICHAEL HENRY - Director Operations
HALEY WINANT - Director Supply Chain
JONATHAN MOY - Director Training

The Chen Group
17945 Tamiami Trl
Northport, FL 34287

Telephone: (941) 426-5866
Internet Homepage: kumojapanesesteakhouse.com
Type of Business: Chain Restaurant Operator
Total Units: 6
Trade Names: Kumo Japanese Steakhouse (2); Mr. & Mrs. Crab (4)
Company-Owned Units: 6
Primary Menu: Cajun/Creole (4); Japanese (2)
Projected Openings: 3
Areas of Operation: FL
Type of Foodservice: Casual Dining (6)

Key Personnel
ZHAO K. CHEN - Owner
LILY REN - Manager

Offerdahl's Cafe Grille Inc.
979 NE 45th St
Oakland Park, FL 33334-3809

Telephone: (954) 492-2842
Internet Homepage: offerdahls.com
Company Email: info@offerdahls.com
Type of Business: Chain Restaurant Operator
Total Sales: $3,800,000 (e)
Alcohol Sales: 2%
Number of Employees: 51
Average Check: Breakfast(5); Lunch(10); Dinner(12)
Internet Order Processing: Yes
Total Units: 6
Trade Names: Offerdahl's Cafe and Grille (6)
Company-Owned Units: 5
Units Franchised To: 1
Preferred Square Footage: 3,000
Preferred Location Types: Strip Mall
Alcohol Served: Beer, Wine
Primary Menu: American (6)
Areas of Operation: FL
Type of Foodservice: Fast Casual (6)
Primary Distributors: (Food) Cheney Bros.

Inc., RIVIERA BEACH, FL

Key Personnel
JOHN OFFERDAHL - President; Partner; General Manager; Director Menu Development; General Buyer
LYNN OFFERDAHL - Partner
RITA FINNEGAN - District Manager; Manager Operations, Human Resources

Domino's Franchisee
3855 E Silver Springs Blvd Ste 101
Ocala, FL 34470-4929

Telephone: (352) 368-6868
Type of Business: Chain Restaurant Operator
Total Sales: $6,184,000 (e)
Total Units: 3
Trade Names: Domino's (3)
Units Franchised From: 3
Primary Menu: Pizza (3)
Areas of Operation: FL
Type of Foodservice: Quick Serve (3)
Franchise Affiliation: Domino's Pizza Inc, ANN ARBOR, MI

Key Personnel
MICHAEL W. WALKER - Owner; General Buyer

Great American Holding Co.
943 E Fort King St
Ocala, FL 34471-2354

Mailing Address: PO Box 3778, OCALA, FL, 34478-3778
Telephone: (352) 732-8060
Fax Number: (352) 351-8586
Type of Business: Chain Restaurant Operator
Year Founded: 1978
Total Sales: $27,100,000 (e)
Number of Employees: 750
Average Check: Breakfast(8); Lunch(8); Dinner(8)
Total Units: 12
Trade Names: Burger King (12)
Units Franchised From: 12
Preferred Square Footage: 2,500
Preferred Location Types: Freestanding
Primary Menu: Hamburger (12)
Areas of Operation: FL, TN
Type of Foodservice: Quick Serve (12)
Franchise Affiliation: Burger King Worldwide Inc., MIAMI, FL
Primary Distributors: (Full Line) Reinhart FoodService, AUSTELL, GA

Key Personnel
GENE CAMP - President; Partner
MERRITT FORE - Partner; CFO; Treasurer
RUSS SUES - Director Operations

RANDY CRUZE - Director Operations
KRISTEN CLIFFORD - Manager Marketing

Jax Bbq, LLC
2605 SW 33rd St
Ocala, FL 34471-7810

Telephone: (352) 620-2514
Fax Number: (352) 620-2531
Company Email:
  bbqm@heritagemanagement.net
Type of Business: Chain Restaurant Operator
Total Sales: $50,500,000 (e)
Total Units: 20
Trade Names: Sonny's Real Pit Bar-B-Q (20)
Units Franchised From: 20
Primary Menu: Bar-B-Q (20)
Areas of Operation: FL
Type of Foodservice: Casual Dining (20)
Franchise Affiliation: Sonny's Franchise Company, MAITLAND, FL

Key Personnel
KENNETH B. KIRKPATRICK - President; General Buyer
PAUL AYOUB - Controller
JOSH MCCALL - Director Operations

Lalo Enterprises Inc.
2900 SW 27th Ave
Ocala, FL 34471-8952

Telephone: (352) 861-9234
Fax Number: (352) 861-9659
Type of Business: Chain Restaurant Operator
Total Sales: $35,430,000 (e)
Number of Employees: 200
Average Check: Lunch(8); Dinner(10)
Total Units: 10
Trade Names: Zaxby's (10)
Units Franchised From: 10
Preferred Location Types: Freestanding
Primary Menu: Chicken (10)
Projected Openings: 1
Areas of Operation: FL
Type of Foodservice: Fast Casual (10)
Franchise Affiliation: Zaxby's Franchising Inc., ATHENS, GA

Key Personnel
CHRISTIE HARPER - President; General Buyer

Our Family Franchise, Inc.
16333 Nikki Ln
Odessa, FL 33556-6003

Telephone: (727) 494-4588
Company Email: ilmconsultant@aol.com
Type of Business: Chain Restaurant Operator
Total Sales: $1,560,000 (e)
Total Units: 2
Trade Names: Little Caesars Pizza (2)
Units Franchised From: 2
Primary Menu: Pizza (2)
Areas of Operation: FL
Type of Foodservice: Quick Serve (2)
Franchise Affiliation: Little Caesar Enterprises Inc., DETROIT, MI

Key Personnel
LARRY R. PROODIAN - President; Partner; General Buyer
MARIA PROODIAN - Partner

ARC Group Inc.
1409 Kingsley Ave Ste 2
Orange Park, FL 32073

Telephone: (904) 741-5500
Fax Number: (904) 741-5577
Internet Homepage: bakedwingsarebetter.com; arcgrpinc.com; dickswingsandgrill.com
Type of Business: Chain Restaurant Operator
Year Founded: 2000
Systemwide Sales: $18,958,000 (e)
Total Sales: $13,450,000 (e)
Alcohol Sales: 10%
Total Units: 67
Trade Names: Dick's Wings & Grill (19); Fat Patty's (4); Tilted Kilt Pub & Eatery (12); Wing Nutz (10); WingHouse Bar & Grill (22)
Company-Owned Units: 30
Units Franchised To: 37
Preferred Square Footage: 1,200; 1,500; 3,000; 4,000; 5,000
Preferred Location Types: Downtown; Stadiums
Alcohol Served: Beer, Wine, Liquor
Primary Menu: American (16); Chicken (51)
Projected Openings: 2
Areas of Operation: AZ, CA, CO, FL, GA, ID, IL, KY, LA, MA, ME, NJ, NV, PA, TN, TX, UT, VA, WV, ON
Foreign Countries: CANADA
Type of Foodservice: Casual Dining (67)
Subsidiaries: Tilted Kilt Franchise Operating LLC, TEMPE, AZ; Winghouse, Inc., LARGO, FL

Key Personnel
SEENU KASTURI - Chairman; CEO; CFO
KHURRAM JAMIL - Executive Director Information Technology
SANDY HOLLEY - Director Quality Assurance, Training
MICHAEL SMALL - Director Business Development

Maple Street Biscuit Company
340 Corporate Way STE 300
Orange Park, FL 32073

Telephone: (904) 398-1004
Internet Homepage: maplestreetbiscuits.com
Company Email:
  info@maplestreetbiscuits.com
Listing Type: Subsidiary
Type of Business: Chain Restaurant Operator
Year Founded: 2012
Total Sales: $65,870,000 (e)
Total Units: 40
Trade Names: Maple Street Biscuit Company (40)
Company-Owned Units: 1
Units Franchised To: 39
Primary Menu: American (40)
Projected Openings: 3
Areas of Operation: FL, GA, NC, SC, TN, TX
Type of Foodservice: Casual Dining (40)
Parent Company: Cracker Barrel Old Country Store Inc., LEBANON, TN

Key Personnel
SCOTT MOORE - Co-Founder; CEO

SBB Enterprises, Inc.
661 Blanding Blvd Ste 514
Orange Park, FL 32073-5041

Telephone: (904) 710-1941
Type of Business: Chain Restaurant Operator
Total Sales: $2,998,000 (e)
Total Units: 5
Trade Names: Little Caesars Pizza (5)
Units Franchised From: 5
Primary Menu: Pizza (5)
Areas of Operation: FL
Type of Foodservice: Quick Serve (5)
Franchise Affiliation: Little Caesar Enterprises Inc., DETROIT, MI

Key Personnel
SIMON BAGOUS - President; General Buyer

The King Group
372 Blanding Blvd Ste 1
Orange Park, FL 32073-4351

Telephone: (904) 272-7004
Fax Number: (904) 272-7009
Company Email: king0097@bellsouth.net
Type of Business: Chain Restaurant Operator
Total Sales: $15,348,000 (e)
Number of Employees: 75
Average Check: Breakfast(8); Lunch(8); Dinner(8)

Total Units: 3
Trade Names: McDonald's (3)
Units Franchised From: 3
Preferred Square Footage: 2,500; 3,000
Preferred Location Types: Freestanding
Primary Menu: Hamburger (3)
Areas of Operation: FL
Type of Foodservice: Quick Serve (3)
Franchise Affiliation: McDonald's Corporation, CHICAGO, IL

Key Personnel
KAREN KING - President; Partner; General Buyer
JOE KING - Partner

Another Broken Egg of America Inc.
5955 T G Lee Blvd Suite 100
Orlando, FL 32822

Telephone: (407) 440-0450
Fax Number: (850) 424-5905
Internet Homepage: anotherbrokenegg.com
Company Email: info@anotherbrokenegg.com
Type of Business: Chain Restaurant Operator
Year Founded: 1996
Systemwide Sales: $105,322,000 (e)
Total Sales: $18,830,000 (e)
Number of Employees: 1,238
Average Check: Breakfast(16); Lunch(16);
Total Units: 79
Trade Names: Another Broken Egg Cafe (79)
Company-Owned Units: 2
Units Franchised To: 77
Preferred Square Footage: 3,500; 4,000
Preferred Location Types: Freestanding; Strip Mall
Alcohol Served: Liquor
Primary Menu: American (79)
Projected Openings: 1
Areas of Operation: AL, CA, FL, GA, IN, KY, LA, MS, NC, OH, SC, TN, TX
Type of Foodservice: Casual Dining (79)
Parent Company: The Beekman Group, NEW YORK, NY

Key Personnel
CHRIS ARTINIAN - President
BRAD CAMERON - CFO
BRANDY BLACKWELL - VP Marketing; Senior Director Marketing

Bahama Breeze
1000 Darden Center Dr
Orlando, FL 32837-4032

Mailing Address: PO Box 695011, ORLANDO, FL, 32869
Telephone: (407) 245-4000
Fax Number: (407) 241-6996
Internet Homepage: bahamabreeze.com
Company Email: info@bahamabreeze.com
Type of Business: Chain Restaurant Operator
Year Founded: 1995
Publicly Held: Yes
Total Sales: $277,942,000 (e)
Alcohol Sales: 23%
Number of Employees: 1,800
Average Check: Lunch(26); Dinner(32)
Internet Order Processing: Yes
Internet Sales: 0.50%
Total Units: 44
Trade Names: Bahama Breeze (44)
Company-Owned Units: 43
Units Franchised To: 1
Preferred Square Footage: 9,000; 12,000
Preferred Location Types: Freestanding
Alcohol Served: Beer, Wine, Liquor
Primary Menu: Caribbean (44)
Areas of Operation: DE, FL, GA, IL, MA, MD, MI, NC, NJ, NV, NY, OH, PA, TN, VA, WA
Type of Foodservice: Casual Dining (44)
Primary Distributors: (Full Line) McLane/Rocky Mount, ROCKY MOUNT, NC
Parent Company: Darden Restaurants Inc., ORLANDO, FL

Key Personnel
CHRIS BASS - General Manager
TOM MCFARLAND - General Manager
RON MONTILLIANO - General Manager
RICH JEFFERS - Senior Director Communications
ATHI KRISHNAMURTHY - Director Digital, Innovation
ANANDKUMAR PARTHASARATHY - Director Information Systems
PAUL TULLOCH - Senior Manager Quality Assurance
CLARYSSA PONCE - Manager
LUIS GUASCH - Manager Facility/Maintenance, National
ERIK HANSEN - Manager Restaurant Operations

Bar Harbor Lobster Co.
2000 Premier Row
Orlando, FL 32809-6208

Telephone: (407) 851-4001
Fax Number: (407) 857-1314
Internet Homepage: barharborseafood.com; bostonlobsterfeast.com
Company Email: info@bostonlobsterfeast.com
Type of Business: Chain Restaurant Operator
Year Founded: 1985
Total Sales: $18,703,000 (e)
Alcohol Sales: 25%
Number of Employees: 240
Average Check: Lunch(22); Dinner(42)
Internet Order Processing: Yes
Total Units: 2
Trade Names: Boston Lobster Feast (2)
Company-Owned Units: 2
Preferred Location Types: Freestanding
Alcohol Served: Beer, Wine, Liquor
Primary Menu: Seafood (2)
Areas of Operation: FL
Type of Foodservice: Casual Dining (2)
Primary Distributors: (Food) SYSCO Central Florida Inc., OCOEE, FL

Key Personnel
JEFF HAZELL - President; Owner
DENNIS MCGRATH - VP Finance; Controller
LYNN CONLEY - Administrator Accounting

Basich Inc
7409 E Colonial Dr
Orlando, FL 32807-6315

Telephone: (407) 281-6606
Fax Number: (407) 281-0277
Type of Business: Chain Restaurant Operator
Total Sales: $10,020,000 (e)
Total Units: 2
Trade Names: McDonald's (2)
Units Franchised From: 2
Preferred Location Types: Freestanding
Primary Menu: Hamburger (2)
Areas of Operation: FL
Type of Foodservice: Quick Serve (2)
Franchise Affiliation: McDonald's Corporation, CHICAGO, IL

Key Personnel
MICHAEL YONTZ - General Buyer

BUCA Inc.
4700 Millenia Blvd Ste 400
Orlando, FL 32839-6020

Telephone: (407) 903-5500
Internet Homepage: bucadibeppo.com
Type of Business: Chain Restaurant Operator
Year Founded: 1996
Systemwide Sales: $286,310,000 (e)
Total Sales: $281,370,000 (e)
Alcohol Sales: 19%
Number of Employees: 5,100
Average Check: Lunch(14); Dinner(22)
Internet Order Processing: Yes
Internet Sales: 15.00%
Total Units: 72
Trade Names: Buca di Beppo (72)
Company-Owned Units: 67
Units Franchised To: 5
Preferred Square Footage: 4,400; 8,000; 11,000
Preferred Location Types: Downtown; Freestanding; Lifestyle Center; Regional Mall
Alcohol Served: Beer, Wine, Liquor
Primary Menu: Italian (72)

Areas of Operation: AZ, CA, CO, DC, FL, GA, HI, IL, IN, KY, MD, MI, MN, MO, NC, NJ, NM, NV, NY, OH, PA, TN, TX, UT, WA, WI
Foreign Countries: ENGLAND; THE PHILIPPINES; UNITED ARAB EMIRATES
Type of Foodservice: Casual Dining (72)
Catering Services: Yes
Parent Company: Earl Enterprises, ORLANDO, FL

Key Personnel
RICHARD SAULTZ - CEO; President
EMILY BISHOP - COO
TRISH GIORDANO - Exec VP Marketing, Sales
SARAH LOVELL - VP
JEREMY COLEMAN - VP
STEPHANIE BIEBEL - VP
ALLISON SWEENEY - Director Operations, Sales
AMANDA RUSH - Regional Manager Marketing, Sales
LENIX WRIGHT - Coordinator Facility/Maintenance

Buena Vista Hospitality Group
6675 Westwood Blvd Ste 170
Orlando, FL 32821-6015

Telephone: (407) 352-7161
Fax Number: (407) 429-3832
Internet Homepage: bvhg.com
Company Email: info@bvhg.com
Type of Business: Foodservice Operations - Hotel/Motels
Year Founded: 1986
Total Sales: $267,820,000 (e)
Alcohol Sales: 15%
Number of Employees: 450
Total Units: 6
Restaurants in Hotels: 6
Trade Names: Chateau Gartier (1); Holiday Inn Sunspree Resort Hotel (2); Lakeland Hotel (1); LPGA International (1); Pelican Point Golf & Country Club (1)
Company-Owned Units: 6
Units Franchised From: 1
Alcohol Served: Beer, Wine, Liquor
Areas of Operation: FL, QC
Foreign Countries: CANADA
Type of Foodservice: Fine Dining (6)
Primary Distributors: (Food) SYSCO Central Florida Inc., OCOEE, FL
Notes: The company derives approximately 80% of its revenue from hotel/management/development operations.

Key Personnel
MICHAEL H. FROST - President; Partner
CHAD A. MARTIN - Partner; VP Marketing, Sales
FLORIAN MOREL - Partner; Senior VP Food and Beverage; Executive Chef
COLIN WRIGHT - Partner; Exec VP
JIM HAUGHNEY - VP Operations
CAROLE MARTIN - VP Human Resources
BASIL TROWBRIDGE - Director Operations

Cheddar's Restaurant Holding Corp.
1000 Darden Center Dr
Orlando, FL 32837

Telephone: (407) 245-4000
Fax Number: (972) 871-0679
Internet Homepage: cheddars.com
Company Email: cheddars@cheddars.com
Type of Business: Chain Restaurant Operator
Year Founded: 1978
Systemwide Sales: $851,034,000 (e)
Total Sales: $810,550,000 (e)
Alcohol Sales: 10%
Number of Employees: 3,512
Average Check: Lunch(10); Dinner(22)
Total Units: 184
Trade Names: Cheddar's Scratch Kitchen (184)
Company-Owned Units: 181
Units Franchised To: 3
Preferred Square Footage: 7,800; 8,000
Preferred Location Types: Freestanding; Regional Mall
Alcohol Served: Beer, Wine, Liquor
Primary Menu: American (184)
Projected Openings: 3
Areas of Operation: AL, AR, AZ, CO, DE, FL, GA, IA, IL, IN, KS, KY, LA, MD, MI, MO, NC, NE, NM, OH, OK, PA, SC, TN, TX, VA, WI, WV
Type of Foodservice: Casual Dining (184)
Primary Distributors: (Full Line) US Foods, HOUSTON, TX
Parent Company: Darden Restaurants Inc., ORLANDO, FL

Key Personnel
PAUL HAWKINS - Area Director
CHRIS ALBANESE - VP Finance
MELINDA R. ANDERSON - Director Human Resources
JAY MICHALEC - Director Culinary Operations
SCOTT GWARTNEY - Director Operations
GARY NELSON - Director Operations
BILL STREBER - Director Operations
DONALD WILLIAMS - Director Operations
GLENN NEUMAN - Manager Talent Acquisitions
MARTIN SORIA - Manager Culinary Operations
DEREK HAGUE - Manager Operations
JENNY MOREIRA - Manager Operations
KEDRAN BELL - Manager Operations
MARK BLOOM - Manager
DARREN CARDUCCI - Manager Human Resources
HEATHER CHAMBERS - Manager
JOHN FELTON - Brand Manager

Darden Restaurants Inc.
1000 Darden Center Dr
Orlando, FL 32837-4032

Mailing Address: PO Box 695011, ORLANDO, FL, 32869-5011
Telephone: (407) 245-4000
Fax Number: (407) 245-5310
Internet Homepage: bahamabreeze.com; darden.com; eddiev.com; longhornsteakhouse.com; olivegarden.com; seasons52.com; thecapitalgrille.com; wildfishseafoodgrille.com
Company Email: dardeninfo@darden.com
Listing Type: Corporate Office
Type of Business: Chain Restaurant Operator
Year Founded: 1968
Publicly Held: Yes
Total Sales: $10,854,768,000 (e)
Alcohol Sales: 10%
Number of Employees: 185,000
Total Units: 2,181
Trade Names: Bahama Breeze (44); Cheddar's Scratch Kitchen (184); Eddie V's Prime Seafood (30); LongHorn Steakhouse (594); Olive Garden Italian Restaurant (967); Ruth's Chris Steakhouse (158); Seasons 52 (44); The Capital Burger (4); The Capital Grille (68); Yard House (88)
Company-Owned Units: 2,035
Units Franchised To: 146
Preferred Location Types: Community Mall; Downtown; Freestanding; Lifestyle Center; Regional Mall; Strip Mall
Alcohol Served: Beer, Wine, Liquor
Primary Menu: American (272); Caribbean (44); Hamburger (4); Italian (967); Seafood (74); Steak (752); Steak/Seafood (68)
Projected Openings: 37
Areas of Operation: AK, AL, AR, AZ, CA, CO, CT, DC, DE, FL, GA, HI, IA, ID, IL, IN, KS, KY, LA, MA, MD, ME, MI, MN, MO, MS, MT, NC, ND, NE, NH, NJ, NM, NV, NY, OH, OK, OR, PA, RI, SC, SD, TN, TX, UT, VA, VT, WA, WI, WV, WY, AB, MB, ON, SK
Foreign Countries: CANADA
Type of Foodservice: Casual Dining (1,925); Fine Dining (256)
Primary Distributors: (Full Line) McLane/Rocky Mount, ROCKY MOUNT, NC
Headquarter Offices: Bahama Breeze, ORLANDO, FL; Cheddar's Restaurant Holding Corp., ORLANDO, FL; LongHorn Steakhouse, ORLANDO, FL; Olive Garden, ORLANDO, FL; Ruth's Hospitality Group Inc., WINTER PARK, FL; The Capital Grille, ORLANDO, FL; Yard House USA Inc., IRVINE, CA
Notes: Location counts only reflect company-owned stores in the U.S. and Canada. The company also operates a small number of franchised locations in Latin America and the

Middle East that are not reflected here.

Key Personnel
JOHN MARTIN - President
TODD BURROWES - President Group
RICK CARDENAS - President; COO
MICHAEL KNEIDINGER - President
DAN KIERNAN - President Division
JOHN WILKERSON - President
RAJESH VENNAM - CFO
SARAH KING - Chief Human Resources Officer; Senior VP
CHRIS CHANG - CIO; Senior VP
JENNIFER ARGUELLO - Chief Marketing Officer; Exec VP
DOUGLAS MILANES - Chief Development Officer; Senior VP Supply Chain
RICH RENNINGER - Chief Development Officer; Senior VP
SUSAN CONNELLY - Chief Communications Officer
MATT BROAD - Chief Compliance Officer; Senior VP; Corporate Secretary; General Counsel
CHARLES FLOR - Senior VP Operations
RICHARD HERNANDEZ - Senior VP Operations
JORDAN LOMAS - Senior VP Information Technology
ANGELA SIMMONS - Senior VP Tax
JUSTIN SIKORA - Senior VP Communications
JOHN MADONNA - Senior VP; Controller
BRADLEY SMITH - Senior VP Franchising
JOE CULELLA - Senior VP Marketing
CHRISTINE WILSON - Senior VP Human Resources
MELINDA REZMER ANDERSON - Senior VP Human Resources
JASON MOGG - Senior VP Purchasing
MICHAEL SENICH - VP; Corporate Chef
DIANA GARCIA-LORENZANA - VP Digital Marketing, Customer Communications
LAUREEN SUSTACHEK - VP Asset Management
RANDY BABITT - VP Human Resources
KRISTY KIERNAN - VP Human Resources
DEBBY WALKER - VP Purchasing
JOHN FELTON - VP Marketing
SETH N. RIVERA - General Counsel; Director
LAUREN GIUDICE - General Counsel Legal; Director
RICH JEFFERS - Senior Director Communications
LORI VAN DUYNE - Senior Director Strategy
PHILIP CARR - Senior Director
BARBARA THOMASON - Senior Director Human Resources
RACHELLE PETERSON - Senior Director Human Resources
JOANNE HENDERSON - Senior Director Human Resources
JESSICA DINON - Senior Director
MARC GRAVITZ - Director Development, Training
JEFF HANNIFORD - Director Customer Analytics
CHRIS HARRINGTON - Director Recruitment; Manager Talent Acquisitions
COLLEEN HUNTER - Director Licensing
SCOTT WILLIAMS - Director Talent Acquisitions
ATHI KRISHNAMURTHY - Director Digital, Innovation
LOU SPEAKS - Director Operations
LAUREN WILKINSON - Director Digital Marketing
MATT REDLING - Director Digital Media
SOLUNA SHAH - Director Digital
KEVIN SHAW - Director Security
JENNIFER WHITE - Director Marketing
PAUL TULLOCH - Senior Manager Quality Assurance
JASON WADDINGHAM - Manager Purchasing
TRACEY RANDALL - Manager Food and Beverage, Purchasing-Alcoholic Beverages, Purchasing-Beverages
JIM ROEGER - Manager Facility/Maintenance
MARK WIRNOWSKI - Manager Information Technology
ROBERT RANAUDO - Manager Information Systems, Information Technology
PAULA BUTLER - Manager Field Marketing, Sales, National
CHRIS FORD - Manager Purchasing-Produce
STEVEN LEONARD - Manager Finance, Information Technology
HEIDI METCALF - Manager
GREG WATTS - Manager Data Security
LEIGHANNE LATTIN - Manager Finance
DARYL L. CUNNINGHAM - Manager Human Resources, Division
RANGA SURPANENI - Manager Business Development
RACHELLE KENNEDY - Manager Digital Marketing
ADITYA RAJPAL - Associate Manager Consumer Insights
MATTHEW SIMEONE - Brand Manager
KYLE COMINSKY - Brand Manager
JENNY WILSON - Brand Manager
CHRIS ROTH - Project Manager Systems
NATALIN DAY - Project Manager Information Technology
KORI GREEN - Project Manager Information Technology, Digital
JEFF FOSTER - Architect

●▲
Dattani Management Corp
12441 S Orange Blossom Trl
Orlando, FL 32837

Mailing Address: P O Box 590524, Orlando, FL, 32859
Telephone: (407) 492-1880
Fax Number: (407) 251-0111
Internet Homepage: coldstoneparty.com
Company Email: cs@dattanicorp.com
Type of Business: Chain Restaurant Operator
Total Sales: $3,375,000 (e)
Total Units: 8
Trade Names: Cold Stone Creamery (8)
Units Franchised From: 8
Primary Menu: Snacks (8)
Areas of Operation: FL
Type of Foodservice: Quick Serve (8)
Franchise Affiliation: Kahala Brands, SCOTTSDALE, AZ

Key Personnel
BIREN DATTANI - Partner
LABHU DATTANI - Partner
HASMUKH DATTANI - Partner
VIJAY DATTAINI - Partner

●▲
Domino's Franchisee
6101 Silver Star Rd
Orlando, FL 32808-4242

Telephone: (407) 291-6676
Type of Business: Chain Restaurant Operator
Total Sales: $6,101,000 (e)
Total Units: 3
Trade Names: Domino's (3)
Units Franchised From: 3
Primary Menu: Pizza (3)
Areas of Operation: FL
Type of Foodservice: Quick Serve (3)
Franchise Affiliation: Domino's Pizza Inc, ANN ARBOR, MI

Key Personnel
ANDY HAVENER - Owner; General Buyer

Earl of Sandwich LLC
4700 Millenia Blvd Ste 400
Orlando, FL 32839-6020

Telephone: (877) 426-3275
Fax Number: (407) 992-2987
Internet Homepage: earlofsandwichusa.com
Company Email: info@earlofsandwichusa.com
Type of Business: Chain Restaurant Operator
Year Founded: 2004
Systemwide Sales: $126,618,000 (e)
Total Sales: $56,842,000 (e)
Alcohol Sales: 5%
Number of Employees: 345
Average Check: Breakfast(10); Lunch(10); Dinner(10)
Total Units: 37
Trade Names: Earl of Sandwich (37)
Company-Owned Units: 14
Units Franchised To: 23
Preferred Square Footage: 240; 1,800; 6,000
Preferred Location Types: Freestanding; Regional Mall; Strip Mall
Alcohol Served: Beer, Wine
Primary Menu: Sandwiches/Deli (37)
Areas of Operation: AZ, CA, FL, MA, MD, MI, NC, NV, NY, PA, TX

Foreign Countries: ENGLAND; FRANCE
Type of Foodservice: Fast Casual (37)
Catering Services: Yes
Primary Distributors: (Food) SYSCO Central Florida Inc., OCOEE, FL
Parent Company: Earl Enterprises, ORLANDO, FL

Key Personnel
ROBERT EARL - Founder
THOMAS AVALLONE - Vice Chairman
ANTHONY BURNHAM - Controller

EverFresh Endeavors, LLC
9547 Blandford Rd
Orlando, FL 32827

Mailing Address: 4316 Clearbrook Lane, Kensington, MD, 20895
Telephone: (305) 947-8844
Internet Homepage: limefreshmexicangrill.com; mandalaholdings.com
Company Email: info@mandalaholdings.com
Type of Business: Chain Restaurant Operator
Year Founded: 2016
Total Units: 8
Trade Names: Lime Fresh Mexican Grill (10)
Units Franchised To: 10
Primary Menu: Mexican (11)
Projected Openings: 1
Areas of Operation: FL
Type of Foodservice: Fast Casual (10)
Parent Company: Mandala Hodlings, ,

Key Personnel
NICK CASTALDO - Partner; Chief Marketing Officer
LEE BABCOCK - Partner; CFO
JOHN TIMS - VP Operations
JANIE FRASER - Director Marketing, Catering

Flippers Pizzeria Franchising LLC
10832 Satellite Blvd Ste A
Orlando, FL 32837-8401

Telephone: (407) 938-9614
Fax Number: (407) 938-9615
Internet Homepage: flipperspizzeria.com
Company Email: contactus@flipperspizzeria.com
Type of Business: Chain Restaurant Operator
Year Founded: 1987
Total Sales: $16,300,000 (e)
Alcohol Sales: 11%
Number of Employees: 288
Average Check: Lunch(18); Dinner(18)
Total Units: 13
Trade Names: Flippers Pizzeria (13)

Company-Owned Units: 10
Units Franchised To: 3
Preferred Square Footage: 1,800; 2,200; 5,500; 6,000
Preferred Location Types: Strip Mall
Alcohol Served: Beer, Wine
Primary Menu: Pizza (13)
Areas of Operation: FL
Type of Foodservice: Casual Dining (13)
Distribution Centers: ORLANDO, FL
On-site Distribution Center: Yes
Primary Distributors: (Food) US Foods, TAMPA, FL

Key Personnel
TODD DENNIS - Chairman; Co-Founder; Chief Marketing Officer; Exec VP
SCOTT KOUSAIE - Chairman; Co-Founder; Owner; COO; Exec VP
BRETT DENNIS - Co-Founder; COO Foodservice; Exec VP Foodservice
DON HOWARD - President
BEN RICHARDSON - COO
IAN SCHNEIDER - VP Franchising
JOSH HOGAN - VP Operations
SUSAN LAWLESS - Coordinator Human Resources

FoodFirst Global Restaurants Inc.
4700 Millenia Blvd #400
Orlando, FL 32839

Telephone: (407) 903-5500
Fax Number: (614) 326-7943
Internet Homepage: bon-vie.com; bravoitalian.com; brioitalian.com
Type of Business: Chain Restaurant Operator
Year Founded: 1992
Total Sales: $447,910,000 (e)
Alcohol Sales: 20%
Number of Employees: 10,000
Average Check: Lunch(22); Dinner(30)
Internet Order Processing: Yes
Internet Sales: 20.00%
Total Units: 73
Trade Names: Bon Vie (1); Bravo Cucina Italiana (45); Bravo Italian Kitchen (27)
Company-Owned Units: 73
Preferred Square Footage: 7,200
Preferred Location Types: Freestanding; Lifestyle Center; Regional Mall
Alcohol Served: Beer, Wine, Liquor
Primary Menu: French/Continental (1); Italian (72)
Areas of Operation: AL, AR, AZ, CA, CO, CT, DE, FL, GA, IA, IL, IN, KS, KY, LA, MA, MD, MI, MO, NC, NE, NJ, NM, NV, NY, OH, OK, PA, TN, TX, UT, VA, WI
Type of Foodservice: Fine Dining (73)
Catering Services: Yes
Primary Distributors: (Food) Gordon Food Service, SPRINGFIELD, OH; (Full Line) US Foods Holding Corp., ROSEMONT, IL
Parent Company: Earl Enterprises, ORLANDO, FL
Notes: Guest check averages reflect BRAVO! operations; BRIO check averages are several dollars higher.

Key Personnel
ANTONIO BONCHRISTIANO - Vice Chairman
DARREN TAPP - Manager Operations
JESSICA WILLIAMS - Manager Corporate Affairs

Gilchrist Enterprises
1711 35th St Ste 108
Orlando, FL 32839-8860

Telephone: (407) 428-0961
Fax Number: (407) 428-0966
Type of Business: Chain Restaurant Operator
Year Founded: 2000
Total Sales: $43,510,000 (e)
Number of Employees: 300
Average Check: Breakfast(8); Lunch(10); Dinner(10)
Total Units: 9
Trade Names: McDonald's (9)
Units Franchised From: 9
Preferred Square Footage: 1,500
Preferred Location Types: Freestanding
Primary Menu: Hamburger (9)
Areas of Operation: FL
Type of Foodservice: Quick Serve (9)
Franchise Affiliation: McDonald's Corporation, CHICAGO, IL

Key Personnel
JAMES GILCHRIST - President; Director Finance; Manager Real Estate; General Buyer
HOWARD HUGHES - Director Operations, Facility/Maintenance; Manager Information Systems

Graffiti Junktion
700 E Washington St
Orlando, FL 32801

Telephone: (321) 424-5800
Internet Homepage: graffitijunktion.com
Type of Business: Chain Restaurant Operator
Year Founded: 2008
Total Sales: $13,534,000 (e)
Alcohol Sales: 20%
Number of Employees: 50
Total Units: 3
Trade Names: Graffiti Junktion (3)
Units Franchised To: 3
Alcohol Served: Beer, Wine, Liquor
Primary Menu: American (3)
Areas of Operation: FL

Type of Foodservice: Casual Dining (3)

Key Personnel
GREG PETERS - President; Partner
THOMAS S. HUGHES - Partner

Hawkers Asian Street Fare
54 W Church St Ste 250
Orlando, FL 32801

Telephone: (407) 810-9046
Internet Homepage: eathawkers.com
Company Email: info@eathawkers.com
Type of Business: Chain Restaurant Operator
Total Units: 8
Trade Names: Hawkers Asian Street Fare (8)
Company-Owned Units: 8
Areas of Operation: FL

Key Personnel
KALEB HARRELL - Co-Founder; CEO
WAYNE YUNG - Co-Founder
ALLEN LO - Co-Founder

LongHorn Steakhouse
1000 Darden Center Dr
Orlando, FL 32837-4032

Mailing Address: PO Box 695011, ORLANDO, FL, 32869-5011
Telephone: (407) 245-4000
Fax Number: (407) 245-4336
Internet Homepage: longhornsteakhouse.com
Type of Business: Chain Restaurant Operator
Year Founded: 1981
Systemwide Sales: $2,435,717,000 (e)
Publicly Held: Yes
Total Sales: $2,806,200,000 (e)
Alcohol Sales: 10%
Number of Employees: 18,000
Average Check: Lunch(20); Dinner(24)
Internet Order Processing: Yes
Total Units: 594
Trade Names: LongHorn Steakhouse (594)
Company-Owned Units: 575
Units Franchised To: 19
Preferred Square Footage: 5,000; 6,008
Preferred Location Types: Freestanding
Alcohol Served: Beer, Wine, Liquor
Primary Menu: Steak (594)
Projected Openings: 10
Areas of Operation: AL, AR, AZ, CO, CT, DE, FL, GA, IA, IL, IN, KS, KY, LA, MA, MD, ME, MI, MO, MS, NC, NE, NH, NJ, NY, OH, OK, PA, PR, RI, SC, TN, TX, UT, VA, VT, WI, WV
Type of Foodservice: Casual Dining (594)
Primary Distributors: (Full Line) US Foods Holding Corp., ROSEMONT, IL
Parent Company: Darden Restaurants Inc., ORLANDO, FL

Key Personnel
TODD BURROWES - President
ELIZABETH KIRKUS - Partner
MONIKA SAXENA - Exec VP Brand Marketing
THOMAS HALL - Exec VP Operations
KURT HANKINS - Senior VP
JANICKA GREEN - Senior VP Operations
JENNIFER PIERCE - Senior VP Human Resources
PAULA MANCHESTER - Senior VP Human Resources
LAURA WILLIAMSON - Senior VP Finance
SHANE BROOKS - Regional VP
STEPHEN KING - Director Operations
VALERIE NAUER - Director Operations
JENI NIKOLETICH - Director Operations
ROB POLING - Director Operations
CHRISTINE WILSON - Director Employee Benefits
DAVE ZEHNER - Director Operations
JASON SMITH - Director Operations
DAVID STAGG - Director Operations
DANIELLE SCHNESKE - Manager Human Resources
WENDY MCKOWN - Manager
NICHOLAS HUBER - Manager
ELIZABETH APPLEGARTH - Manager
MORGAN HANKINSON - Associate Manager

Margaritaville Enterprises
6800 Lakewood Plaza Dr
Orlando, FL 32819-5580

Telephone: (407) 224-3149
Fax Number: (407) 224-3229
Internet Homepage: margaritaville.com
Company Email: info@margaritaville.com
Type of Business: Chain Restaurant Operator
Year Founded: 1987
Systemwide Sales: $408,028,000 (e)
Total Sales: $176,630,000 (e)
Alcohol Sales: 30%
Number of Employees: 1,695
Average Check: Lunch(26); Dinner(42)
Internet Order Processing: Yes
Internet Sales: 5.00%
Total Units: 65
Trade Names: 5 O'Clock Somewhere Bar (11); Air Margaritaville (6); Jimmy Buffetts Margaritaville Cafe (29); Land Shark Bar & Grille (19)
Company-Owned Units: 35
Units Franchised To: 30
Preferred Square Footage: 5,500; 6,000
Preferred Location Types: Downtown; Freestanding; Other
Alcohol Served: Beer, Wine, Liquor
Primary Menu: American (65)
Projected Openings: 3
Areas of Operation: AL, AZ, CT, FL, IL, LA, MS, NJ, NV, OK, SC, TN, TX, FC
Foreign Countries: AUSTRALIA; BRITISH OVERSEAS TERRITORIES; CANADA; CAYMAN ISLANDS; JAMAICA; MEXICO
Type of Foodservice: Casual Dining (65)
Distribution Centers: ORLANDO, FL
On-site Distribution Center: Yes
Primary Distributors: (Full Line) SYSCO Food Services of South Florida Inc., MEDLEY, FL

Key Personnel
DAN LEONARD - President
LAURA MCCONNELL - CFO
BRAD SCHWAEBLE - COO
TAMARA BALDANZA-DEKKER - Chief Marketing Officer
CATE FARMER - Senior VP
RYAN GARCIA - Senior VP Beverages
JOE GINEL - VP
CLAUDIA INFANTE - VP Strategy
TOM FAUST - VP Marketing, Sales
MELISSA BARTLE - VP Development
ELYSE CURTIS - VP Marketing
MEAGHAN WALSH - VP Operations
COURTNEY WATKINS - VP Marketing
ART SINGLEY - General Manager
NORA SWIRE - Senior Director Marketing, International
PAUL FRASER - Senior Director Database
HEATHER JONES - Senior Director Marketing
TOM KEMPSEY - Director Culinary Operations
MICHELLE DROZ - Director Finance
CHRIS BLATZ - Director Marketing
ADAM BOCKEN - Director Human Resources-Training
BRET BROWN - Director Operations, International
PHILLIP TAYLOR - Director Food
JIM WISEMAN - Director Business Development
BETH MOOREFIELD - Director Marketing, Business Development
DUSTIN MATHEWS - Director Sales
MARTA BERGSTROM - Regional Director Operations
ERIN LANNON-LYNCH - Manager Sales
ANDREA MACFARLAND - Manager Product Development
MELISSA ROBINSON - Manager Sales
MERCEDES BLACKWOOD - Specialist Development, Marketing

Miller's Ale House Inc.
5750 Major Blvd Ste 400
Orlando, FL 32819-7971

Telephone: (407) 547-1120
Internet Homepage: millersalehouse.com
Company Email: customerservice@millersalehouse.com
Type of Business: Chain Restaurant Operator
Year Founded: 1988
Systemwide Sales: $690,575,000 (e)
Total Sales: $743,390,000 (e)
Alcohol Sales: 30%
Number of Employees: 6,246
Average Check: Lunch(8); Dinner(14)

Total Units: 93
Trade Names: Miller's Ale House Restaurant (93)
Company-Owned Units: 93
Preferred Square Footage: 7,200; 7,500; 9,500
Preferred Location Types: Community Mall; Freestanding; Strip Mall
Alcohol Served: Beer, Wine, Liquor
Primary Menu: American (93)
Projected Openings: 1
Areas of Operation: DE, FL, GA, IL, MA, MD, NJ, NV, NY, OH, PA, TN, VA
Type of Foodservice: Casual Dining (93)
Catering Services: Yes
Primary Distributors: (Full Line) Cheney Bros. Inc., RIVIERA BEACH, FL
Parent Company: Roark Capital Group, ATLANTA, GA

Key Personnel
CHUCK ARNOTT - President Real Estate
LYNDA BARR - CFO
THOMAS ARCHER - VP; General Counsel
KENNETH BROOKS - VP Information Technology
DOUG JACKSON - VP Purchasing
MITCHELL KOENIG - VP Operations, Division
PAUL LIVRIERI - VP Operations, Division
PATTI NASH - VP Human Resources
LARRY HEISS - General Manager
JOHN HOLMES - General Manager
KURT BLOM - General Manager
COLLEEN HUGHES - Senior Director Recruitment
MARY LOWE - Senior Director Training
SHANE FEEMSTER - Senior Director Construction, Design
PAULA THROOP - Director Training
SUSAN PASTINE - Director Training, Recruitment
NEELAM SINGH - Director Accounting
TIM KOPLIN - Director Real Estate
SAM KELLY - Director Information Technology, Infrastructure, Security
JIMMEY CHICO - Director Operations
JOSEPH AMORE - Director Operations
CHRIS BENDEL - Director New Store Development
TOSHA ELLIS - Senior Manager
HARRY DECKER - Regional Manager
JASON TESTA - Regional Manager
LALITA RAMKISON - Manager Payroll
SEAN LINDSEY - Manager

Natures Table Franchise Co.
545 Delaney Ave Ste 2
Orlando, FL 32801-3866

Telephone: (407) 481-2544
Fax Number: (407) 843-6057
Internet Homepage: naturestable.com
Company Email: info@naturestable.com
Type of Business: Chain Restaurant Operator
Year Founded: 1977
Systemwide Sales: $46,900,000 (e)
Total Sales: $9,945,000 (e)
Number of Employees: 20
Average Check: Breakfast(6); Lunch(12); Dinner(12)
Internet Order Processing: Yes
Total Units: 77
Trade Names: Nature's Table Cafe (71); Natures Table Bistro (6)
Company-Owned Units: 4
Units Franchised To: 73
Preferred Square Footage: 500; 2,000
Preferred Location Types: Community Mall; Institution (college/hospital); Office Complex
Primary Menu: Health Foods (77)
Areas of Operation: CA, FL, GA, KS, OK, TX, VA, WA
Type of Foodservice: Quick Serve (77)
Catering Services: Yes
Primary Distributors: (Full Line) US Foods Holding Corp., ROSEMONT, IL
Notes: The company specializes in unconventional locations such as the BWI Airport, Atlanta Airport, Orlando Airport, medical complexes, military bases, etc.

Key Personnel
RICH WAGNER - CEO; Senior VP; Controller; Director Facility/Maintenance, Design
BRYAN BUFFALO - CIO; VP Operations, Information Systems; General Manager; General Buyer
LISA ODOM - VP Operations

New York Pizza Development, LLC
2589 S Hiawassee Rd
Orlando, FL 32835-6316

Telephone: (407) 293-2199
Internet Homepage: nypdpizzeria.com
Company Email: franchisenypd@aol.com
Type of Business: Chain Restaurant Operator
Year Founded: 1996
Total Sales: $3,463,000 (e)
Alcohol Sales: 5%
Number of Employees: 21
Average Check: Dinner(14)
Total Units: 6
Trade Names: NYPD Pizza (6)
Company-Owned Units: 2
Units Franchised To: 4
Preferred Square Footage: 1,400; 3,000
Preferred Location Types: Downtown; Freestanding; Strip Mall
Alcohol Served: Beer, Wine
Primary Menu: Pizza (6)
Projected Openings: 1
Areas of Operation: AR, FL
Type of Foodservice: Casual Dining (6)
Catering Services: Yes
Notes: AKA Baby Brother Brands LLC

Key Personnel
PAUL RUSSO - CEO; CFO
SHAWN LYNCH - Director Operations, Training

Oerther Foods Inc.
8150 Presidents Dr
Orlando, FL 32809-7625

Telephone: (407) 859-7123
Fax Number: (407) 859-1568
Internet Homepage: mcfun.com
Company Email: comments@oertherfoods.com
Type of Business: Chain Restaurant Operator
Year Founded: 1960
Total Sales: $116,130,000 (e)
Number of Employees: 1,100
Average Check: Breakfast(8); Lunch(8); Dinner(10)
Total Units: 24
Trade Names: McDonald's (24)
Units Franchised From: 24
Preferred Square Footage: 2,500
Preferred Location Types: Convenience Store/Gas Station; Discount Dept. Stores; Freestanding
Primary Menu: Hamburger (24)
Areas of Operation: FL
Type of Foodservice: Quick Serve (24)
Franchise Affiliation: McDonald's Corporation, CHICAGO, IL

Key Personnel
GARY OERTHER - Chairman; CEO; Partner
GREGG OERTHER - CEO; Partner
JEANIE OERTHER - Partner; General Buyer
MARK SHERBONDY - VP Operations
GEORGETTE LEMIEUX - VP Operations
KATHLEEN THOMASON - Director Finance
PAULA MAYFIELD-RICHARDS - Manager Accounting
CARLOS GUERRERO - Manager

Olive Garden
1000 Darden Center Dr
Orlando, FL 32837-4032

Mailing Address: PO Box 695011, ORLANDO, FL, 32869
Telephone: (407) 245-4000
Fax Number: (407) 245-5189
Internet Homepage: olivegarden.com
Type of Business: Chain Restaurant Operator
Year Founded: 1982
Systemwide Sales: $5,572,611,000 (e)
Publicly Held: Yes
Total Sales: $5,067,000,000 (e)
Alcohol Sales: 7%
Number of Employees: 95,000

Average Check: Lunch(20); Dinner(20)
Total Units: 967
Trade Names: Olive Garden Italian Restaurant (967)
Company-Owned Units: 920
Units Franchised To: 47
Preferred Square Footage: 7,500; 7,700
Preferred Location Types: Freestanding; Strip Mall
Alcohol Served: Beer, Wine, Liquor
Primary Menu: Italian (967)
Projected Openings: 3
Areas of Operation: AK, AL, AR, AZ, CA, CO, CT, DE, FL, GA, IA, ID, IL, IN, KS, KY, LA, MA, MD, ME, MI, MN, MO, MS, MT, NC, ND, NE, NH, NJ, NM, NV, NY, OH, OK, OR, PA, RI, SC, SD, TN, TX, UT, VA, VT, WA, WI, WV, WY, FC, AB, BC, MB
Foreign Countries: CANADA
Type of Foodservice: Casual Dining (967)
Primary Distributors: (Full Line) McLane/Rocky Mount, ROCKY MOUNT, NC
Parent Company: Darden Restaurants Inc., ORLANDO, FL

Key Personnel
DAN KIERNAN - President
BRYAN CLEMENTS - Exec VP
JENNY HANSON - Senior VP Operations
THERESA WILLINGS - Senior VP Human Resources
DARRELL SULLIVAN - General Manager
TREY HAMM - General Manager
TERRENCE TOOKES - Executive Chef Research & Development
JENNIFER TREPTOW - Executive Chef
RICH JEFFERS - Senior Director Communications
KIM SELLGREN - Director Operations
WINSTON WILLIAMS - Director Operations
JUSTIN ISBELL - Director Operations
DOUG ESTES - Director
MARC GRAVITZ - Director Development, Training
LIDIA PEREZ - Manager Social Media
OMAR PORTER - Manager Culinary Development
MARIBEL HILL - Designer Graphic Design

Papa John's Distribution Center
9600 Delegates Dr
Orlando, FL 32837-8355

Telephone: (407) 851-3595
Listing Type: Distribution Center
Type of Business: Chain Restaurant Operator
Number of Employees: 100
Areas of Operation: FL, GA, SC
Parent Company: Papa Johns International Inc., LOUISVILLE, KY

Key Personnel
SCOTT DALZELL - Manager Distribution

Planet Hollywood International Inc.
4700 Millenia Blvd Ste 400
Orlando, FL 32839-6020

Telephone: (407) 903-5500
Internet Homepage: planethollywoodintl.com
Company Email: general-information@planethollywood.com
Type of Business: Chain Restaurant Operator
Year Founded: 1991
Systemwide Sales: $64,314,000 (e)
Total Sales: $63,430,000 (e)
Alcohol Sales: 15%
Number of Employees: 2,500
Average Check: Lunch(12); Dinner(30)
Internet Order Processing: Yes
Internet Sales: 1.00%
Total Units: 7
Trade Names: Planet Hollywood (6); Tequila Taqueria (1)
Company-Owned Units: 1
Units Franchised To: 6
Preferred Square Footage: 10,000
Preferred Location Types: Downtown; Freestanding; Regional Mall
Alcohol Served: Beer, Wine, Liquor
Primary Menu: Californian (6); Mexican (1)
Projected Remodelings: 2
Areas of Operation: FL, NV, NY, ON
Foreign Countries: CANADA; FRANCE
Type of Foodservice: Casual Dining (7)
Catering Services: Yes
Distribution Centers: ORLANDO, FL
On-site Distribution Center: Yes
Primary Distributors: (Food) SYSCO Central Florida Inc., OCOEE, FL
Parent Company: Earl Enterprises, ORLANDO, FL
Notes: Planet Hollywood derives approximately 30% of revenue from retail operations. Systemwide sales reflects foodservice operations only.

Key Personnel
ROBERT I. EARL - Chairman; Founder
JOHN THALL - President
TRISH GIORDANO - Exec VP Marketing, Sales
BOB CHARLES - VP Distribution
JOSEPH FISCHER - General Manager
DANNY ACAMPADO - Director Human Resources
PETER MAGGIO - Director Marketing, Sales
SHANNON GLIDEWELL - Director Human Resources
LINDA VASKOVSKY - Director National Accounts
CHRIS KLECKNER - Director Web Development
WILLIAM GARVEY - Director Technology
DONNA MUCHEL - Manager Recruitment
PAUL VEGA - Manager Facility/Maintenance
IAN DUFFY - Manager Finance, Strategic Services
ERIC RAMOS - Manager Restaurant Operations
SHANNON WARD - Corporate Director Human Resources

Red Lobster Seafood Co.
450 S Orange Ave
Orlando, FL 32801-3383

Telephone: (407) 734-9000
Fax Number: (407) 245-5733
Internet Homepage: redlobster.ca; redlobster.com
Company Email: website@redlobster.com
Type of Business: Chain Restaurant Operator
Year Founded: 1968
Systemwide Sales: $2,600,000,000 (e)
Total Sales: $2,600,000,000 (e)
Alcohol Sales: 8%
Number of Employees: 65,000
Average Check: Lunch(18); Dinner(26)
Internet Order Processing: Yes
Internet Sales: 1.00%
Total Units: 536
Trade Names: Red Lobster (536)
Company-Owned Units: 536
Preferred Square Footage: 5,700; 7,195
Preferred Location Types: Community Mall; Downtown; Freestanding; Regional Mall; Strip Mall
Alcohol Served: Beer, Wine, Liquor
Primary Menu: Seafood (536)
Areas of Operation: AL, AR, AZ, CA, CO, CT, DE, FL, GA, HI, IA, ID, IL, IN, KS, KY, LA, MD, MI, MN, MO, MS, MT, NC, ND, NE, NJ, NM, NV, NY, OH, OK, OR, PA, SC, SD, TN, TX, UT, VA, WA, WI, WV, WY, AB, MB, ON, SK
Foreign Countries: CANADA
Type of Foodservice: Casual Dining (536)
Primary Distributors: (Full Line) McLane/Rocky Mount, ROCKY MOUNT, NC; (Full Line) Systems Services of America, SCOTTSDALE, AZ; (Full Line) The SYGMA Network Inc. - Denver, DENVER, CO; (Supplies) Maines Paper & Food Service Inc., CONKLIN, NY; (Supplies) Systems Services of America, SCOTTSDALE, AZ
Parent Company: Thai Union Group PCL, TAMBON TARSRAI, THA

Key Personnel
DAMOLA ADAMOLEKUN - CEO
LILLIAN MURPHY - President
BOB BAKER - CFO
LARRY KONECNY - COO
CIJOY OLICKAL - CIO
NICHOLE ROBILLARD - Chief Marketing Officer
JACK MCNERTNEY - VP Facility/Maintenance, Development, Asset Management

JENNA MACKLETON - VP Operations
MICHAEL LADUKE - Executive Chef
DAVID MASONE - Director Facility/Maintenance
JEFF MATRAY - Director Marketing
MICHAEL MACDONALD - Director Operations
MEERA PEREIRA - Director Tax
BETSY BONAWITZ - Director Operations
NICOLE BOTT - Director Communications
KENNAN BURCH - Director Marketing
ROBERT CHUHAK - Director Purchasing, Sourcing
JEFFREY COUTURIER - Director Employee Compensation
ELIZABETH CRAGO - Director Real Estate
BARRY FULGHUM - Director Operations
ANA GULACSY - Director Accounting
JEWEL TAYLOR - Director Benefits, Compensation
KIM BRAVAR - Senior Manager Employee Development
MIKE DENNIS - Manager Information/Data Security, Compliance
STEVE HILDE - Manager Operations
JOHN KILIANY - Manager Facility/Maintenance
KATE ACOSTA - Manager Tax
JOCELYN FERNANDES - Manager Strategic Sourcing
PAT RACETTE - Manager Marketing
NORMA RIVERA - Manager Licensing
TARA MITCHELL - Manager Human Resources
AARON MAXWELL - Manager HRIS
JASON A LEWIS - Manager Infrastructure
BILLY KREBSBACH - Manager Infrastructure, Network
JANICE YATES - Manager Information Technology, HRIS
LICHENYANG ZHOU - Manager Supply Chain, International Division
KATHLEEN GRAY - Associate Manager Strategic Sourcing
DIANE DRISCOLL - Project Manager
ALANA HERNDON - Project Manager
ABE KONDAMUDI - Agent Information Technology
MIKE HALPERIN - Engineer Information Systems

Restaurant Partners Inc.
1030 N Orange Ave Ste 200
Orlando, FL 32801-1030

Telephone: (407) 839-5070
Fax Number: (407) 839-3388
Internet Homepage: restaurantpartnersinc.com
Company Email: contact@restaurantpartnersinc.com
Type of Business: Chain Restaurant Operator
Year Founded: 1992
Total Sales: $16,330,000 (e)
Alcohol Sales: 25%
Number of Employees: 300
Average Check: Breakfast(14); Lunch(16); Dinner(30)
Total Units: 6
Trade Names: Dixie Dave's (1); Grille 29 (2); Market Street Cafe (1); Sloppy Joe's On The Beach (1); Upper Crust Pizza Cafe (1)
Company-Owned Units: 6
Preferred Square Footage: 3,000
Preferred Location Types: Freestanding; Strip Mall
Alcohol Served: Beer, Wine, Liquor
Primary Menu: American (2); Pizza (1); Steak/Seafood (2)
Areas of Operation: AL, FL
Type of Foodservice: Casual Dining (6)
Primary Distributors: (Full Line) SYSCO Food Services of West Coast Florida Inc., PALMETTO, FL
Notes: The company also operates Starlite Ballroom, a private-function facility.

Key Personnel
DAVID MANUCHIA - CEO; President; Director Facility/Maintenance, Real Estate, Menu Development
BILL DOYLE - Corporate Chef; General Buyer
MINDY BADOLATO - Director
DJ MARIELLO - Director Operations

Romacorp Inc.
11315 Corporate Blvd Ste 100
Orlando, FL 32817

Telephone: (214) 343-7800
Internet Homepage: tonyromas.com
Company Email: guest.relation@romacorp.com
Type of Business: Chain Restaurant Operator
Year Founded: 1972
Systemwide Sales: $283,929,000 (e)
Total Sales: $87,060,000 (e)
Alcohol Sales: 15%
Number of Employees: 544
Average Check: Lunch(14); Dinner(26)
Internet Order Processing: Yes
Internet Sales: 1.00%
Total Units: 101
Trade Names: Tony Roma's (101)
Company-Owned Units: 5
Units Franchised To: 96
Preferred Square Footage: 8,000
Preferred Location Types: Downtown; Freestanding; Regional Mall; Strip Mall
Alcohol Served: Beer, Wine, Liquor
Primary Menu: American (101)
Areas of Operation: CA, FL, HI, IA, IL, MN, MO, NJ, NV, NY, TX, WA, WI, AB, BC, MB, ON, SK
Foreign Countries: ARUBA; AUSTRALIA; BAHRAIN; BRAZIL; CANADA; CHILE; COSTA RICA; CURACAO; DOMINICAN REPUBLIC; ECUADOR; EL SALVADOR; ENGLAND; GERMANY; GUATEMALA; INDONESIA; JAPAN; MALAYSIA; MEXICO; NORTHERN IRELAND; PANAMA; PERU; SAUDI ARABIA; SINGAPORE; SOUTH KOREA; SPAIN; THAILAND; UNITED ARAB EMIRATES; UNITED STATES OF AMERICA; VENEZUELA
Type of Foodservice: Casual Dining (101)
Catering Services: Yes
Primary Distributors: (Full Line) SYSCO Corporation, HOUSTON, TX
Parent Company: Highland Capital Management LP, DALLAS, TX

Key Personnel
MOHAIMINA HAQUE - CEO
RAMON BOURGEOIS - COO
BOB GALLAGHER - Senior VP Culinary Operations, Purchasing-Beverages
ALEXIS KOBERNYK - VP Region
SARAH JACKSON - VP Human Resources
HUGO MORAN - Regional VP Operations
ALOKANANDA SAHA - Controller
BUDDY HALL - Senior Director Human Resources, Training
ALEXANDRA GIERBOLINI - Director Training

Rosen Plaza Hotel
9700 International Dr
Orlando, FL 32819-8100

Telephone: (407) 996-9700
Fax Number: (407) 996-9111
Internet Homepage: rosenhotels.com; rosenhotelsandresorts.com; rosenplaza.com
Type of Business: Chain Restaurant Operator
Year Founded: 1991
Total Sales: $7,163,000 (e)
Alcohol Sales: 18%
Number of Employees: 60
Average Check: Breakfast(14); Lunch(14); Dinner(26)
Total Units: 5
Trade Names: Cafe Matisse (1); Jacks Place (1); Lite Bite Express (1); Poolside Bar & Grill (1); Smoooth Java (1)
Company-Owned Units: 5
Preferred Square Footage: 1,500; 1,900
Preferred Location Types: Hotel/Motel
Alcohol Served: Beer, Wine, Liquor
Primary Menu: American (2); Coffee (1); Snacks (1); Steak/Seafood (1)
Areas of Operation: FL
Type of Foodservice: Casual Dining (3); Quick Serve (2)
Primary Distributors: (Full Line) SYSCO Central Florida Inc., OCOEE, FL

Key Personnel
HARRIS ROSEN - President; COO
DEREK BAUM - General Manager
JAY FINKELSTEIN - General Manager
MICHAEL MCMULLEN - Executive Chef; General Buyer
AHLAM SAKOUT - Director Training
PATRICK VANBENTHUSEN - Director Security

DOREA MAYS - Director Human Resources
KARI BINA - Manager Catering
JANICE MIDDLESTADT - Manager Sales
RONALD BRANTNER - Engineer

SeaWorld Entertainment Inc.
9205 Southpark Center Loop Ste 400
Orlando, FL 32819-8651

Telephone: (407) 226-5011
Fax Number: (407) 226-5136
Internet Homepage: adventureisland.com; aquaticabyseaworld.com; buschgardens.com; discoverycove.com; seaworld.com; seaworldparks.com; sesameplace.com; shamu.com; watercountryusa.com
Type of Business: Foodservice Operations - Theme Parks
Year Founded: 1957
Publicly Held: Yes
Total Sales: $732,546,000 (e)
Alcohol Sales: 3.50%
Number of Employees: 14,200
Average Check: Breakfast(8); Lunch(16); Dinner(18)
Foodservice Sales: $146,509,000 (e)
Total Units: 12
Trade Names: Adventure Island (1); Aquatica Orlando (1); Aquatica San Antonio and Discovery Point (1); Aquatica San Diego (1); Busch Gardens Tampa Bay (1); Busch Gardens Williamsburg (1); Discovery Cove (1); SeaWorld of California (1); SeaWorld of Florida (1); SeaWorld of San Antonio (1); Sesame Place (1); Water Country USA (1)
Company-Owned Units: 12
Preferred Location Types: Parks
Alcohol Served: Beer, Wine
Areas of Operation: CA, FL, PA, TX, VA
Type of Foodservice: Cafeteria; Casual Dining; Fine Dining; Quick Serve
Catering Services: Yes
Primary Distributors: (Full Line) SYSCO Central Florida Inc., OCOEE, FL
Parent Company: The Blackstone Group, NEW YORK, NY
Divisional Offices: Busch Gardens Tampa Bay & Adventure Island, TAMPA, FL; Busch Gardens Williamsburg & Water Country USA, WILLIAMSBURG, VA; SeaWorld of California, SAN DIEGO, CA; SeaWorld of Florida, ORLANDO, FL; SeaWorld of San Antonio Inc., SAN ANTONIO, TX; Sesame Place, LANGHORNE, PA
Notes: The company derives approximately 80% of its revenue from amusement park operations and merchandise sales.

Key Personnel
ELIZABETH GULACSY - Chief Accounting Officer
TONY TAYLOR - Chief Legal Officer; Senior VP; Corporate Secretary; General Counsel
CHRISTOPHER DOLD - Chief Business Development Officer
MIKE DENNINGER - Senior VP Environment
CATHERINE MARSHBURN - VP Marketing
JEREMY WILLIAMS - VP Human Resources
DAN MAYER - VP Benefits, Compensation
QUINN DOYLE - VP Consumer Insights
GENARO CASTRO - VP Culinary Operations
ROLAND GARCIA - VP
JIM FORRESTER - VP Finance
BYRON SURRETT - VP Merchandising
JEFF HORNICK - Senior Director Development
BRENT VESCOGNI - Director Information Technology
SHEKUFEH BOYLE - Director Accounting
ANDREW SCHAFFER - Director Engineering, Design
SCOTT GASS - Director Communications
MICHELLE WOODS - Director Talent
SANDRA RESENDEZ - Director Merchandising
DAVID SKELTON - Director Operations
TIMOTHY DARLING - Director Finance
FATIMA GUENNOUNI - Director Quality Assurance
STEPHANIE BARRETO - Manager Finance
TIM CARRIER - Corporate Manager Information Technology
ANDREW WHEELER - Corporate Director

SeaWorld of Florida
7007 Sea Harbor Dr
Orlando, FL 32821-8009

Telephone: (407) 351-3600
Listing Type: Divisional Office
Type of Business: Foodservice Operations - Theme Parks
Total Units: 9
Areas of Operation: FL
Parent Company: SeaWorld Entertainment Inc., ORLANDO, FL

Key Personnel
JON SURGUINE - Supervisor Purchasing; General Buyer
ANN RAINEY - Supervisor Accounting

▲ Seminole Hard Rock Entertainment Inc.
6100 Old Park Ln
Orlando, FL 32835-2466

Telephone: (407) 445-7625
Fax Number: (407) 445-9709
Internet Homepage: hardrock.com
Company Email: customer-care@hardrock.com
Type of Business: Chain Restaurant Operator
Year Founded: 1971
Systemwide Sales: $1,181,953,000 (e)
Total Sales: $518,420,000 (e)
Alcohol Sales: 50%
Number of Employees: 8,000
Average Check: Lunch(18); Dinner(18)
Foodservice Sales: $269,578,000 (e)
Internet Order Processing: Yes
Internet Sales: 15.00%
Total Units: 172
Trade Names: Hard Rock Cafe (170)
Company-Owned Units: 48
Units Franchised To: 122
Preferred Location Types: Airports; Downtown; Freestanding; Hotel/Motel; Regional Mall; Strip Mall
Alcohol Served: Beer, Wine, Liquor
Primary Menu: American (170)
Projected Openings: 2
Areas of Operation: AK, AZ, CA, CO, CT, DC, FL, GA, GU, HI, IL, KY, LA, MA, MD, MI, MN, MS, NJ, NV, NY, PA, PR, SC, TN, TX, WA, FC, ON
Foreign Countries: ANDORRA; ARGENTINA; ARUBA; AUSTRALIA; AUSTRIA; AZERBAIJAN; BAHAMAS; BELGIUM; BOLIVIA; BRAZIL; CAMBODIA; CANADA; CAYMAN ISLANDS; CHILE; COLOMBIA; COSTA RICA; CYPRUS; CZECH REPUBLIC; DENMARK; DOMINICAN REPUBLIC; EGYPT; ENGLAND;FIJI; FINLAND; FRANCE; GEORGIA; GERMANY; GREECE; GUYANA; HONG KONG; HUNGARY; ICELAND; INDIA; INDONESIA; IRELAND; ITALY; JAMAICA; JAPAN; KAZAKHSTAN; MALAYSIA; MALTA; MEXICO; MONGOLIA; NEPAL; NICARAGUA; NIGERIA; NORWAY; PANAMA; PARAGUAY;POLAND; PORTUGAL; ROMANIA; RUSSIA; SAINT MARTIN; SCOTLAND; SINGAPORE; SOUTH AFRICA; SPAIN; SWEDEN; THAILAND; THE NETHERLANDS; THE PHILIPPINES; TRINIDAD & TOBAGO; TUNISIA; UNITED ARAB EMIRATES; URUGUAY; VENEZUELA; VIETNAM
Type of Foodservice: Casual Dining (170)
Catering Services: Yes
Primary Distributors: (Full Line) SYSCO Food Services of South Florida Inc., MEDLEY, FL; (Supplies) Louis Wohl & Sons Inc., TAMPA, FL
Parent Company: Seminole Tribe of Florida, HOLLYWOOD, FL
Notes: The company derives approximately 48% of its revenue from retail operations. Systemwide sales are based on foodservice operations only.

Key Personnel
JIM ALLEN - Chairman; CEO
EDWARD TRACY - CEO
GEORGE GOLDHOFF - President
JON LUCAS - COO; Exec VP Operations
ANTONIO BAUTISTA - Senior VP Franchise Operations, Franchise Development
JOSEPH EMANUELE - Senior VP Construction, Design
VICKIE KUNKLE - Senior VP Merchandising
DALE HIPSH - Senior VP

KRESIMIR SPAJIC - Senior VP Gaming/Entertainment
ANIBAL FERNANDEZ - VP Franchise Operations, Franchise Development
PETR SUCHANEK - VP Development
STEFANO PANDIN - Area VP
TOM PEREZ - Area VP; Senior Director
LINDA NELSON - Senior Director
LORI NESS - Director Store Systems
MARIA CARRILLO - Director Design
TRENT CALL - Director Development
GIOVANNI TALIAFERRO - Director Design
ALLISON JORDAN - Director Digital
LISA HENDRIXSON - Manager Marketing, Sales
VELIA LEE - Manager Marketing, Sales
ZULEIKA SOTO - Manager Marketing, Sales
LUCY URDANETA - Manager Marketing, Sales
RONALD MOREY - Manager Retail Operations
MICHAEL MCCLOUD - Product Manager Information Technology

Talk of the Town Restaurant Group
1260 Central Florida Pkwy
Orlando, FL 32837-9259

Telephone: (407) 851-8400
Fax Number: (407) 851-8401
Internet Homepage: talkofthetownrestaurants.com
Type of Business: Chain Restaurant Operator
Year Founded: 1974
Total Sales: $52,250,000 (e)
Alcohol Sales: 20%
Number of Employees: 525
Total Units: 10
Trade Names: Charley's Steakhouse (3); Fish Bones (2); Johnnie's Hideaway (1); MoonFish (1); Texas Cattle Co. (2); Vito's Italian Chophouse (1)
Company-Owned Units: 10
Preferred Square Footage: 8,000
Preferred Location Types: Freestanding; Strip Mall
Alcohol Served: Beer, Wine, Liquor
Primary Menu: Seafood (2); Steak (6); Steak/Seafood (2)
Areas of Operation: FL
Type of Foodservice: Casual Dining (10)
Catering Services: Yes
Primary Distributors: (Full Line) SYSCO Food Services of Jacksonville Inc., JACKSONVILLE, FL

Key Personnel
CHARLES WOODSBY - Chairman; Founder; Director Finance, Facility/Maintenance, Supply Chain
RONALD WOODSBY - CEO; President; Executive Chef; Director Real Estate, Design, Human Resources; General Buyer
SETH MILLER - Partner; COO
ADAM SANTORELLI - Partner
TODD BOWLING - Director Information Systems, Beverages
IMANE TAZI - Director Restaurant Operations
BRITTANIE OLAVARRIA - Manager Marketing
ANDREA SUTTON - Manager Event Planning

Tavistock Restaurants LLC
4705 S Apopka Vineland Rd Ste 210
Orlando, FL 32819

Telephone: (407) 909-7101
Fax Number: (510) 654-8292
Internet Homepage: abeandlouies.com; abeandlouies.com; aquaknox.net; atlanticfishco.com; atlasrestaurant.com; blackhawkgrille.com; cafedelreymarina.com; californiacafe.com; canonita.com; coachgrillrestaurant.com; freebirds.com; joesamerican.com; napavalleygrille.com; sapporoscottsdale.com; tavistockrestaurants.com; timpanochophouse.net; zed451.com
Company Email: info@tavistockrestaurants.com
Type of Business: Chain Restaurant Operator
Year Founded: 2003
Total Sales: $111,410,000 (e)
Alcohol Sales: 20%
Number of Employees: 3,100
Average Check: Lunch(18); Dinner(54)
Total Units: 70
Trade Names: Abe & Louie's (2); Atlantic Fish (1); Atlas (1); Canonita (1); Canvas Restaurant & Market (1); Chroma Modern Bar + Kitchen (1); Coach Grill (1); FREEBIRDS World Burrito (55); Joe's American Bar & Grill (2); Napa Valley Grille (1); Park Pizza & Brewing Company (1); The Garden Room (1); Timpano (2)
Company-Owned Units: 70
Preferred Square Footage: 3,000; 6,000; 8,000
Preferred Location Types: Freestanding; Regional Mall
Alcohol Served: Beer, Wine, Liquor
Primary Menu: American (5); Californian (56); Italian (2); Japanese (1); Mexican (2); Pizza (1); Seafood (2); Steak (2); Steak/Seafood (1)
Projected Openings: 2
Areas of Operation: AR, AZ, CA, CT, FL, IN, KS, MA, MD, MN, MO, NH, NJ, OK, PA, RI, TX
Type of Foodservice: Casual Dining (11); Fast Casual (55); Fine Dining (8)
Catering Services: Yes
Subsidiaries: Freebirds World Burrito, AUSTIN, TX
Primary Distributors: (Full Line) US Foods-San Francisco, LIVERMORE, CA
Parent Company: Tavistock Group, WINDERMERE, FL

Key Personnel
CAROL SPIROS - Area Director
LISA HELMKE - VP Construction, Design
TOM O'BRIEN - VP Operations
MICHAEL FERRARO - VP Food
PIPER HOOD - VP Sales
STEVEN FELDMAN - VP Finance
TIM FANNIN - VP Operations
WES SMITH - Senior Director Training
KASEY ANDERSEN - Director Sales
MARTIN EILER - Director Operations
JULIEN GOBIN - Director Event Planning
LUIS MARTINEZ - Director Finance
MARISSA REAGAN - Director Sales
GINA SAIA - Director Sales
TYLER BLUM - Manager Training

The Capital Grille
1000 Darden Center Dr
Orlando, FL 32837-4032

Mailing Address: PO Box 695011, ORLANDO, FL, 32869-5011
Telephone: (407) 245-4000
Fax Number: (407) 245-4336
Internet Homepage: thecapitalgrille.com
Type of Business: Chain Restaurant Operator
Year Founded: 1996
Systemwide Sales: $627,718,000 (e)
Publicly Held: Yes
Total Sales: $620,275,000 (e)
Alcohol Sales: 29%
Average Check: Lunch(66); Dinner(90)
Total Units: 72
Trade Names: The Capital Burger (4); The Capital Grille (68)
Company-Owned Units: 70
Units Franchised To: 2
Preferred Location Types: Freestanding; Lifestyle Center
Alcohol Served: Beer, Wine, Liquor
Primary Menu: Hamburger (4); Steak/Seafood (68)
Areas of Operation: AZ, CA, CO, CT, DC, FL, GA, IL, IN, MA, MD, MI, MN, MO, NC, NJ, NV, NY, OH, PA, RI, TN, TX, VA, WA, WI
Type of Foodservice: Casual Dining (4); Fine Dining (68)
Primary Distributors: (Full Line) US Foods Holding Corp., ROSEMONT, IL
Parent Company: Darden Restaurants Inc., ORLANDO, FL

Key Personnel
M. JOHN MARTIN - President
RON ADELMAN - Senior VP Operations
PAUL MUSZYNSKI - Director Operations
KEN OSGOOD - Director Operations
KELLY PAYNE - Director Operations
GWEN ZIMMER - Director Operations

Thornton Park Restaurant Group

800 N Orange Ave Ste 200
Orlando, FL 32801-1170

Telephone: (407) 650-9151
Fax Number: (407) 649-9421
Internet Homepage: socothorntonpark.com; urbanlifemanagement.com; reyesmex.com
Type of Business: Chain Restaurant Operator
Year Founded: 1994
Total Sales: $3,515,000 (e)
Alcohol Sales: 10%
Number of Employees: 50
Average Check: Breakfast(10); Lunch(24); Dinner(42)
Total Units: 2
Trade Names: Reyes Mezcaleria (1); Soco Restaurant (1)
Company-Owned Units: 2
Preferred Location Types: Freestanding; Other
Alcohol Served: Beer, Wine, Liquor
Primary Menu: American (1); Mexican (1)
Projected Openings: 1
Areas of Operation: FL
Type of Foodservice: Casual Dining (2)
Catering Services: Yes
Primary Distributors: (Food) SYSCO Central Florida Inc., OCOEE, FL

Key Personnel
GREG RICHIE - Partner; Executive Chef
CRAIG USTLER - Partner; Executive Chef; Director Catering

Universal Orlando Resort

1000 Universal Studios Plz
Orlando, FL 32819-7601

Telephone: (407) 363-8000
Fax Number: (407) 224-4329
Internet Homepage: universalorlando.com
Type of Business: Foodservice Operations - Theme Parks
Year Founded: 1992
Total Sales: $2,397,400,000 (e)
Alcohol Sales: 25%
Number of Employees: 12,000
Average Check: Breakfast(26); Lunch(28); Dinner(104)
Foodservice Sales: $287,688,000 (e)
Internet Order Processing: Yes
Total Units: 69
Trade Names: Antojitos Authentic Mexican Food (1); Big Kahuna Pizza (1); Bigfire (1); BK Whopper Bar (1); Blondies (1); Bob Marley: Tribute to Freedom (1); Bone Chillin' (1); Bubba Gump Shrimp Co. (1); Cafe 4 (1); Cafe La Bamba (1); Captain America Diner (1); Cathy's Ice Cream (1); Cinnabon (1); CircusMcGurkus (1); Comic Strip Cafe (1); Confisco (1); Cowfish (1); Croissant Moon Bakery (1); Finnegan's Bar & Grill (1); Fire Eater's Grill (1); Galaxy Bar (1); Green Eggs and Ham Cafe (1); Hard Rock Cafe (1); Hard Rock Hotel (6); Hop On Pop Ice Cream Shope (1); Jimmy Buffett's Margaritaville (1); Kid Zone Pizza Co (1); Latin Quarter Express (1); Loews Portofino Bay Hotel (7); Loews Royal Pacific Resort (6); Lombard's Seafood Grille (1); Louie's Italian Restaurant (1); Mel's Drive-In (1); Moe's Southwest Grill (1); Moose Juice, Goose Juice (1); Mythos (1); NASCAR Sports Grill (1); NBC Sports Grill & Brew (1); Panda Express (1); Pat O'Brien's (1); Pizza Predattoria (1); Richter's Burger Co. (1); Schwab's Pharmacy (1); Starbucks Cafe (1); Starbucks Coffee (1); The Burger Digs (1);The Frozen Dessert (1); The Watering Hole (1); Thunder Falls Terrace (1); Toothsome Chocolate Emporium and Savory Feast Kitchen (1); Universal Studios' Classic Monster Cafe (1); VIVO Italian Kitchen (1); Wimpy's (1)
Company-Owned Units: 60
Units Franchised From: 9
Preferred Square Footage: 500
Preferred Location Types: Freestanding; Kiosk; Mobile Unit; Parks
Alcohol Served: Beer, Wine, Liquor
Primary Menu: American (19); Asian (0); Cajun/Creole (0); Caribbean (1); Chinese (1); Coffee (2); Hamburger (4); Italian (3); Latin American/Cuban (1); Mexican (1); Miscellaneous (20); Pizza (3); Sandwiches/Deli (1); Seafood (2); Snacks (8); Southwest/Tex-Mex (2)
Areas of Operation: FL
Type of Foodservice: Casual Dining (22); Fast Casual (1); Fine Dining (3); Quick Serve (24)
Primary Distributors: (Food) SYSCO Food Services of Jacksonville Inc., JACKSONVILLE, FL
Parent Company: Comcast Corporation, PHILADELPHIA, PA
Headquarters: NBCUniversal Media, LLC, NEW YORK, NY
Notes: The company derives approximately 88% of its total revenue from theme park operations.

Key Personnel
THOMAS L. WILLIAMS - Chairman Group; CEO Group; Director Real Estate
WILLIAM A. DAVIS - President; COO
TRACEY STOCKWELL - CFO
JOHN R. SPROULS - Exec VP Human Resources
JIM TIMON - Senior VP Gaming/Entertainment
DONNA MIRUS BATES - Senior VP Strategic Planning
DEVIN ELMORE - Senior VP
MICHAEL FILANDRO - Senior VP Finance
RICHARD T. FLORELL - Senior VP Operations; General Manager Operations
CHARLIE GUNDACKER - Senior VP Development
SCOT LAFERTE - Senior VP Human Resources
MAFRENE LISBOA - VP Architecture, Information Technology
VICTOR MEENA - VP Training
STACY HOWARD - VP Digital, Media
MARY KNAPP - VP Global Marketing
SHARON FOLEY - VP Talent Acquisitions
TRISH ENGLER - VP Operations
JENNIFER ADAMSON - VP Media
ALLISON OLOFSON - VP Finance
SHAWN SHARMA - VP Sales
XIOMARA WILEY - VP Marketing, Sales
KIMBERLY WEEDMARK - VP Event Planning
AMY SLATER - General Manager
ASHLEY BETEMIT - General Manager
LAURA MCINTYRE - General Manager
TREVOR KNOTT - Senior Director Finance
TINA INGRAM - Senior Director Human Resources
ROB KANTOR - Senior Director Engineering
REID CARLSON - Senior Director
JENNIFER ADDEO - Senior Director Finance
CHAD ADAMS - Senior Director Finance
CAESAR ESPEARANZA - Senior Director Customer Analytics
DAN DONOVAN - Senior Director
JEFF FERENBACH - Senior Director Operations
MATTHEW RYAN - Senior Director Marketing
MANDY PENN - Senior Director Marketing
FRITZ WOJDYLA - Senior Director Marketing
TYLER PENN - Director Finance
JULIE SIMON-WHITTAKER - Director National Accounts
LAURA DEL VECCHIO - Director Customer Service
MARK DARWISH - Director Technology
KRISTIN CHASE - Director Development
TAKIS. CHONDROGIANNIS - Director National Accounts
ROBERT GOLDBERG - Director Finance
LINDSAY LISZEWSKI - Director Omnichannel
JOANNA LANEAVE - Director Sales, Group
TODD LEE - Director Event Planning
DAVID MATHEWS - Assistant Director Human Resources
JEFF KUJAWA - Senior Manager Finance
KEVIN LOTTER - Senior Manager Operations
JESSICA GOLSON - Senior Manager Consumer Insights
MATT EITEL - Senior Manager
PATRICK GLASSBURN - Senior Manager Sales
ZACH HARIG - Senior Manager Operations
ONOME HARRIS - Senior Manager Marketing, Sales
ROXANA CASTILLO - Senior Manager Information Technology
VICKI BOWLIN - Senior Manager Development
STEFANIE DAVIS - Senior Manager Talent
JEREMY SCHEINBERG - Senior Manager Marketing
LORA SALAZAR - Senior Manager Marketing
TOM PALLANDER - Senior Manager Purchasing

PHAEDRA POHL - Manager Marketing
RAFAEL SARDINA - Manager Strategic Sourcing
LOU REPASSY - Manager Sales
PHILLIP SHAW - Manager Technology
PATTY SLABAUGH - Manager Fulfillment
LAURIE WEST - Manager Operations
COURTNEY WALTER - Manager Employee Development-Training
BIRGIT TURMAN - Manager Facility/Maintenance
ROBERT COUSIN - Manager Branding
PATTI COLETTI - Manager Finance
BRETT CONROY - Manager Marketing
STEVEN FIELDS - Manager Sales
WANDA FORD CRUMPLER - Manager Human Resources, Employee Benefits
GLENN FORTE - Manager Visual Merchandising
ROBERT GAUGHAN - Manager Transportation
AARON GAYHART - Manager Marketing
CHERYL GEIGER - Manager Marketing
MEGAN BODSHAUG - Manager Sales
DOUG CHANSKY - Manager Operations
ANGELINA CAMISE - Manager Security
MICHELLE BAILEY - Manager Sales
NICHOLAS BEERBOWER - Manager Operations
ALEJANDRA AGREDA - Manager Operations
ANISA ALI - Manager Development
KATELYN HABER - Manager Restaurant Operations
FELIPE HERNANDEZ - Manager Sales
CARLOS GUZMAN - Manager Information Technology
YOLANDA GONZALEZ - Manager Human Resources
JENNIFER JACOBSON - Manager Event Planning
SARAH KNORP - Manager Restaurant Operations
KELLY KERRIGAN - Manager Sales
OMAR KHALID - Manager Finance
CELINA MALDONADO - Manager Operations
KRISTIN MANFREDI - Manager Operations
LISA LEWIS - Manager Purchasing
LISA LEYVA - Manager Sales
BILL LINDELOF - Manager Operations
MICHAEL MCGAFFIGAN - Manager Sales
MIKE MCGOVERN - Manager Sales
MORGAN LLOYD - Manager Human Resources
DAN MCLEAR - Manager Media
TONY MASTROIANNI - Manager Technology
CHRIS MEUSHAW - Manager Event Planning
MARISSA MIKOLENKO - Manager Operations
DERRICK MOORE - Manager Technology
GLENN MOSHER - Manager Production
MICHELLE MUGNAINI - Manager Sales
CAROLINE BENNETT - Assistant Manager Development, Talent
MICHAEL ARMIJO - Supervisor Transportation
DANIELLE ACEVEDO - Supervisor Operations
ARCHIE BAYLEY - Supervisor Live Nursery
ASHLEY BICKERT - Supervisor Operations
JUSTIN BROWN - Supervisor Quality Assurance
TONY FARFAN - Supervisor Operations
CHARLENE COTHRAN - Supervisor Sales
JOHN CHWALISZ - Supervisor Operations
TOM CIESZYNSKI - Supervisor Live Nursery
PAUL CUOZZO - Supervisor
SHERRI MEYER - Supervisor Human Resources
STEVEN MARCHETTI - Supervisor Loss Prevention, E-Commerce
RICHARD LITTLEJOHN - Supervisor Security
KYLA KLUTSARITS - Supervisor Transportation
JAMES UGARTE - Supervisor Operations
MARK WALLPE - Supervisor
BOB WARREN - Supervisor
KATHERINE TOWER - Supervisor Operations
JUSTIN TERZO - Supervisor Operations
BENJAMIN THOMPSON - Supervisor Operations
LAURA ROOT - Supervisor Operations
KAREN SMIZMAUL - Supervisor Human Resources
CJ RIVERA - Supervisor
CAROL POWELL - Supervisor
MELISSA PEREZ - Supervisor Operations
MICHELLE PINA - Supervisor
ROBERT MONNERAT - Supervisor
MICHAEL NEWMAN - Supervisor Technology
APRIL STUART - Project Manager Marketing
KELSEA MULROY - Project Manager
PAUL MEENA - Project Manager
HEATHER FRENCH - Project Manager Marketing
MICHAEL AUMAN - Administrator Fulfillment
CAROL MEEHAN - Administrator
MATTHEW LOPEZ - Administrator Development
PATTY KRYWANCZYK - Administrator Human Resources
PATTI HILL - Administrator
ANANDHI PONNUSAMY - Administrator Database
JOSHUA RAWLINS - Administrator Information Systems
BRENDA SLOCKI - Specialist Human Resources
GLADYS SEPULVEDA - Specialist Payroll
RACHEL TRACE - Specialist Operations
SUSAN SOMERVILLE - Specialist Marketing, Sales
STEVE HARD - Specialist Technology
YURIKO ALMONTE - Specialist Training
JOY STEARNS - Buyer
MARLA STEVENS - Coordinator Communications
CHRISTINA TRILLO - Coordinator Operations
VICTORIA SMITH - Coordinator Production
DEREK OSTREM - Coordinator Production
ALBERTO PENA - Coordinator Operations, Technology
ROXANNE RODRIGUEZ - Coordinator Member Services
KATHLEEN PARRISH - Coordinator Facility/Maintenance
NICOLE BUSH - Coordinator Marketing, Sales
DAVID BRESCIA - Coordinator Administration
AMY BOND - Coordinator Training
DANIEL BOOTH - Coordinator Media
WENDY CHMELAR - Coordinator Operations
MICHELLE GLASS - Coordinator Sales
KERI CLARK - Coordinator Development
CLAIRE COMMONS - Coordinator Sales
VICTORIA JOHNSON - Coordinator Operations
CHRISTINA HAIMES - Coordinator Marketing
KESSIE HARTSFIELD - Coordinator Sales
NICK LABER - Coordinator Sales
SARAH MUTH - Coordinator Communications
JULIE KENNEDY-RICK - Representative Licensing
LEEANN LAMB - Representative Human Resources
ELYSSA MARTINEZ - Representative Marketing, Sales
MATTHEW HEIDEN - Representative E-Commerce
JENNIFER GRIZZELL - Representative Human Resources
ERIN KAPUT - Representative Marketing
CRISTINA COONS - Representative Marketing
HEATHER FRONK - Representative Sales
MATT DONOVAN - Representative Sales
BRITTANY BROOKINS - Representative Sales
MADELYN OSMUN - Representative Sales
SARAH PIZZO - Representative Communications
TIM SHELTON - Representative National Accounts
JORDAN WAGNER - Representative Marketing
KRISTEN TRECO - Representative Human Resources
FATIH SWANK - Representative Sales
ALI SNYDER - Designer
NICK COLLINS - Designer
DYLAN KOLLATH - Designer
TERESA GUZMAN - Senior Analyst
FELIPE MIRANDA - Senior Analyst Sourcing
PATRICK DAYHOFF - Senior Analyst Finance
MORGAN AMORE - Senior Analyst Procurement
ALDOUS ACACIO - Senior Analyst Data Quality
CHARLENE SPENCE - Senior Analyst Procurement
DEBBIE PEARLMAN - Senior Analyst Procurement
AARON MOODY - Senior Analyst
JUSTIN PORTER - Analyst Sales
LISA PORTERFIELD - Analyst Procurement
NEELEY ABRUZZESE - Analyst Sales
ALEXANDER DAVIS - Analyst Information Technology
THOMAS CHRISTENSEN - Architect
KATHI LADONICZKI - Senior Engineer
CHRIS HIGHTOWER - Engineer
SARAH KELLEY - Engineer
AUSTIN KELLY - Engineer
ALEX ABDALA - Engineer Network
NICHOLAS AMORE - Engineer
ALAN ARMOR - Engineer Network, Communications
CASEY BARRETO-BOYLE - Engineer
ANTHONY NORROW - Engineer

JEREMIAH STENBERG - Engineer

Domino's Franchisee
343 W Granada Blvd Ste H
Ormond Beach, FL 32174-6275

Telephone: (386) 677-3030
Type of Business: Chain Restaurant Operator
Total Sales: $4,165,000 (e)
Total Units: 2
Trade Names: Domino's (2)
Units Franchised From: 2
Primary Menu: Pizza (2)
Areas of Operation: FL
Type of Foodservice: Quick Serve (2)
Franchise Affiliation: Domino's Pizza Inc, ANN ARBOR, MI

Key Personnel
STEVEN P. BROOKS - Owner; General Buyer

Purple Submarine
1474 W Granada Blvd Ste 25
Ormond Beach, FL 32174-9187

Telephone: (386) 265-1933
Type of Business: Chain Restaurant Operator
Total Sales: $12,430,000 (e)
Total Units: 9
Trade Names: Jersey Mike's Subs (9)
Units Franchised From: 9
Primary Menu: Sandwiches/Deli (9)
Areas of Operation: FL
Type of Foodservice: Quick Serve (9)
Franchise Affiliation: Jersey Mike's Franchise Systems, MANASQUAN, NJ

Key Personnel
DREW MAIDER - Partner; General Buyer
MARK DEBIASE - Partner

Huey Magoo's Restaurants LLC.
4293 Alafaya Trl
Oviedo, FL 32765-9410

Telephone: (407) 732-4635
Internet Homepage: hueymagoos.com
Company Email: travis@hueymagoos.com
Type of Business: Chain Restaurant Operator
Year Founded: 2004
Total Sales: $37,930,000 (e)
Total Units: 50
Trade Names: Huey Magoos Chicken Tenders (71)
Company-Owned Units: 1
Units Franchised To: 70
Primary Menu: Chicken (71)
Projected Openings: 50

Areas of Operation: FL
Type of Foodservice: Quick Serve (71)

Key Personnel
ANDY HOWARD - CEO; Partner
MICHAEL SUTTER - COO; Exec VP Training
DAN COLLINS - Consultant Franchise Development
PAUL ZIELINSKI - Consultant Franchise Development

Domino's Franchisee
4571 Watkins St
Pace, FL 32571-2511

Telephone: (850) 995-8889
Type of Business: Chain Restaurant Operator
Total Sales: $4,096,000 (e)
Total Units: 2
Trade Names: Domino's (2)
Units Franchised From: 2
Primary Menu: Pizza (2)
Areas of Operation: FL
Type of Foodservice: Quick Serve (2)
Franchise Affiliation: Domino's Pizza Inc, ANN ARBOR, MI

Key Personnel
ERIC S. SMITH - Owner; General Buyer

Firebox, LLC
4367 Highway 90
Pace, FL 32571-2004

Telephone: (850) 994-1666
Type of Business: Chain Restaurant Operator
Total Sales: $3,691,000 (e)
Total Units: 3
Trade Names: Firehouse Subs (3)
Units Franchised From: 3
Primary Menu: Sandwiches/Deli (3)
Type of Foodservice: Fast Casual (3)
Franchise Affiliation: Firehouse Restaurant Group Inc., JACKSONVILLE, FL

Key Personnel
ANTHONY PIETSCH - President; General Buyer

Loroam, Inc.
4222 Highway 90
Pace, FL 32571-2000

Telephone: (850) 995-9500
Type of Business: Chain Restaurant Operator
Total Sales: $2,683,000 (e)
Total Units: 5
Trade Names: Little Caesars Pizza (5)
Units Franchised From: 5

Primary Menu: Pizza (5)
Areas of Operation: FL
Type of Foodservice: Quick Serve (5)
Franchise Affiliation: Little Caesar Enterprises Inc., DETROIT, MI

Key Personnel
SARAH CASSADY - Manager

The Breakers
1 S County Rd
Palm Beach, FL 33480-4023

Telephone: (877) 724-3188
Fax Number: (561) 659-8403
Internet Homepage: thebreakers.com
Company Email: info@thebreakers.com
Type of Business: Foodservice Operations - Hotel/Motels
Year Founded: 1896
Total Sales: $167,661,000 (e)
Alcohol Sales: 20%
Number of Employees: 1,800
Total Units: 1
Restaurants in Hotels: 9
Trade Names: The Breakers Palm Beach (1)
Company-Owned Units: 9
Alcohol Served: Beer, Wine, Liquor
Areas of Operation: FL
Type of Foodservice: Casual Dining (7); Fine Dining (2)
Primary Distributors: (Equipment) General Hotel & Restaurant Supply Corp., MIAMI LAKES, FL; (Food) Cheney Bros. Inc., RIVIERA BEACH, FL; (Supplies) General Hotel & Restaurant Supply Corp., MIAMI LAKES, FL
Parent Company: Flagler System Inc., PALM BEACH, FL
Notes: The company derives approximately 70% of its revenue from hotel operations.

Key Personnel
JAMES KENAN III - Chairman
PAUL N. LEONE - President; COO
ALEX GILMURRAY - CFO; Director Finance
ATESH C. CHANDRA - Chief Administrative Officer
TRICIA TAYLOR - Senior VP; General Manager
JOANN SCHULZ - VP Foodservice; Executive Chef; Director Purchasing, Risk Management, Food Safety, Food and Beverage; Buyer Beverages, Food
JIM MOSTAD - VP Sales
DENISE BOBER - VP Human Resources
KRISTY PRESSLY - General Counsel
KIRK BELL - General Manager
JEFF SIMMS - Executive Chef; Manager Menu Development
SHARI MANTEGNA - Director Marketing
ARTHUR BIRMELIN - Director Security, Loss Prevention
JOHN WEBSTER - Director Training

DARREN HIRSOWITZ - Director Finance
MARK GERSTNER - Assistant Director Food and Beverage
GABRIELLE PEARLBERG - Assistant Director Food and Beverage
MARGUERITE BEAU - Assistant Director Sales
JOHN ZOLLER - Manager Quality Assurance
CAITLIN SCHILKIE - Manager Business Development
ISAAC JAQUEZ - Manager Operations
CHARLI KING - Manager Accounting
RYAN GARCIA - Manager Operations
BRUCE LEET - Manager Sales
CARA PREGADIO - Manager Sales
TIMOTHY THORNTON - Manager Customer Service
JIM FREBRARO - Manager Restaurant Operations
SHANNON FAVOLE - Manager Sales
ELLEN AKWA - Buyer Jewelry

Cutting Edge Pizza LLC
3801 Pga Blvd Ste 600
Palm Beach Gardens, FL 33418

Telephone: (860) 951-7999
Fax Number: (860) 951-0234
Internet Homepage: cepizza.com
Company Email: marketing@cepizza.com
Type of Business: Chain Restaurant Operator
Year Founded: 2001
Total Sales: $77,240,000 (e)
Number of Employees: 1,400
Average Check: Lunch(22); Dinner(34)
Total Units: 63
Trade Names: Little Caesars Pizza (63)
Units Franchised From: 63
Preferred Square Footage: 1,500
Preferred Location Types: Freestanding; Strip Mall
Primary Menu: Pizza (63)
Projected Openings: 2
Areas of Operation: MD, NC, SC, VA
Type of Foodservice: Quick Serve (63)
Franchise Affiliation: Little Caesar Enterprises Inc., DETROIT, MI
Primary Distributors: (Food) Blue Line Foodservice Distribution, SAN ANTONIO, TX

Key Personnel
JAMES BANISTER - CFO; Director Finance

Manero's Restaurant
2851 SW High Meadows Ave
Palm City, FL 34990-2682

Telephone: (772) 220-3011
Internet Homepage: jarthurs.com; maneros.com
Company Email: info@maneros.com
Type of Business: Foodservice Operations - Movie Theatre
Year Founded: 1986
Total Sales: $5,523,000 (e)
Alcohol Sales: 14%
Number of Employees: 35
Average Check: Lunch(12); Dinner(20)
Total Units: 2
Trade Names: J. Arthur's Restaurant (1); Manero's (1)
Company-Owned Units: 2
Preferred Square Footage: 7,100
Preferred Location Types: Freestanding
Alcohol Served: Beer, Wine, Liquor
Primary Menu: Steak (2)
Areas of Operation: FL, NC
Type of Foodservice: Casual Dining (2)
Catering Services: Yes
Primary Distributors: (Full Line) SYSCO Food Services of Southeast Florida LLC, RIVIERA BEACH, FL

Key Personnel
JAY MAHONEY - President; General Manager; Executive Chef; Manager Menu Development; General Buyer
JOHN MAHONEY - Owner
JOYCE THOMAS - Manager Administration

C&P Restaurant Group, Inc.
1475 Palm Coast Pkwy NW Ste 101
Palm Coast, FL 32137-4736

Telephone: (386) 986-2800
Type of Business: Chain Restaurant Operator
Total Sales: $3,818,000 (e)
Total Units: 3
Trade Names: Firehouse Subs (3)
Units Franchised From: 3
Primary Menu: Sandwiches/Deli (3)
Areas of Operation: FL
Type of Foodservice: Fast Casual (3)
Franchise Affiliation: Firehouse Restaurant Group Inc., JACKSONVILLE, FL

Key Personnel
DAVID HAUSE - President; General Buyer

Perfect Pizza Pie Inc
4879 Palm Coast Pkwy NW Unit 2
Palm Coast, FL 32137-3673

Telephone: (386) 597-2825
Type of Business: Chain Restaurant Operator
Total Sales: $65,010,000 (e)
Total Units: 32
Trade Names: Domino's (32)
Units Franchised From: 32
Primary Menu: Pizza (32)
Areas of Operation: FL
Type of Foodservice: Quick Serve (32)
Franchise Affiliation: Domino's Pizza Inc, ANN ARBOR, MI

Key Personnel
AHSAN M. SHEIKH - Partner; General Buyer
LISA SHEIKH - Partner; General Buyer
ASHLEY CHALKER - Manager
TAI BITNER - Specialist Information Technology

Grain & Berry
33840 US Highway 19 N
Palm Harbor, FL 34684

Telephone: (727) 771-7795
Internet Homepage: grainandberry.com
Company Email: info@grainandberry.com
Type of Business: Chain Restaurant Operator
Year Founded: 2017
Total Units: 7
Trade Names: Grain & Berry (7)
Company-Owned Units: 7
Primary Menu: Health Foods (7)
Projected Openings: 5
Areas of Operation: FL
Type of Foodservice: Fast Casual (7)

Key Personnel
TREY KESSLER - Co-Founder; CEO
DOUGLAS LANG - Co-Founder; COO
KIRSTEN LANG - Co-Founder; Chief Development Officer

Innisbrook Golf Resort
36750 US Highway 19 N
Palm Harbor, FL 34684-1239

Telephone: (727) 942-2000
Fax Number: (727) 942-5578
Internet Homepage: innisbrookgolfresort.com
Type of Business: Foodservice Operations - Hotel/Motels
Year Founded: 1971
Total Sales: $47,749,000 (e)
Alcohol Sales: 15%
Number of Employees: 800
Total Units: 1
Restaurants in Hotels: 5
Trade Names: Innisbrook Golf Resort (1)
Company-Owned Units: 5
Alcohol Served: Beer, Wine, Liquor
Areas of Operation: FL
Type of Foodservice: Casual Dining (5)
Primary Distributors: (Food) SYSCO Food Services of Jacksonville Inc., JACKSONVILLE, FL; (Specialty Foods) Fishman & Associates Inc., VENICE, FL
Notes: The company derives approximately 60% of its revenue from hotel operations.

Key Personnel
SHEILA C. JOHNSON - CEO; Owner

JOSEPH MEYER - Director Purchasing
ABBIE MARINO - Director Finance
DARIN RIGGIO - Director Marketing, Sales

DeBest Pizza, Inc.
812 White Oak Ct
Panama City, FL 32408-5237

Telephone: (850) 819-3333
Fax Number: (850) 249-0303
Internet Homepage: debestpizza.com
Company Email: office@debestpizza.com
Type of Business: Chain Restaurant Operator
Total Sales: $10,036,000 (e)
Internet Order Processing: Yes
Total Units: 5
Trade Names: Domino's (5)
Units Franchised From: 5
Primary Menu: Pizza (5)
Areas of Operation: FL
Type of Foodservice: Quick Serve (5)
Franchise Affiliation: Domino's Pizza Inc, ANN ARBOR, MI

Key Personnel
DOUG DEGOOD - President

Norsco Management Inc
1302 W 15th St
Panama City, FL 32401-2049

Telephone: (850) 785-8845
Fax Number: (850) 785-6931
Type of Business: Chain Restaurant Operator
Total Sales: $8,159,000 (e)
Average Check: Dinner(14)
Total Units: 3
Trade Names: Popeyes Louisiana Kitchen (3)
Units Franchised From: 3
Primary Menu: Chicken (3)
Areas of Operation: FL
Type of Foodservice: Quick Serve (3)
Franchise Affiliation: Popeyes Louisiana Kitchen Inc., ATLANTA, GA

Key Personnel
J. C. SCOTT - President; General Buyer
STEVE BUMP - Director Operations
BARRY CRAVEN - Manager Operations

Vittles Company
508 Harmon Ave
Panama City, FL 32401-3044

Telephone: (850) 763-0501
Fax Number: (850) 872-0072
Internet Homepage: pofolks.com; triplejsteakhouse.com
Company Email: info@triplejsteakhouse.com
Type of Business: Chain Restaurant Operator
Year Founded: 1985
Systemwide Sales: $22,801,000 (e)
Total Sales: $16,950,000 (e)
Alcohol Sales: 10%
Number of Employees: 270
Average Check: Breakfast(10); Lunch(16); Dinner(24)
Total Units: 8
Trade Names: PoFolk's (7); Triple "J" Steakhouse (1)
Company-Owned Units: 1
Units Franchised From: 7
Preferred Square Footage: 4,000; 6,000
Preferred Location Types: Freestanding
Alcohol Served: Beer, Wine, Liquor
Primary Menu: American (7); Steak/Seafood (1)
Areas of Operation: AL, FL
Type of Foodservice: Casual Dining (1); Family Restaurant (7)
Catering Services: Yes
Primary Distributors: (Food) US Foods, NORCROSS, GA

Key Personnel
PETER SOSTHEIM - Chairman; President; Director Purchasing, Real Estate, Menu Development
ARLESS POOLE - Director Finance, Operations, Ethnic Marketing, Human Resources; Manager Security, Inventory, Loss Prevention, Risk Management, Quality Assurance, District, Menu Development, Food Safety, Catering

Spell Restaurant Group
11040 Hutchison Blvd
Panama City Beach, FL 32407

Telephone: (850) 230-2739
Internet Homepage: spellrestaurantgroup.com
Company Email: info@saltwatergrillpcb.com
Type of Business: Chain Restaurant Operator
Year Founded: 2004
Number of Employees: 300
Total Units: 12
Trade Names: Bahalu Tapas & Tacos (5); Brookhaven Pub & Grill (1); Edward's Fine Food & Wine (1); George's at Alys Beach (1); Grits & Grind (1); La Cocina Mexican Grill & Bar (1); La Crema Tapas & Chocolate (1); Saltwater Grill (1)
Company-Owned Units: 12
Primary Menu: American (2); Mexican (1); Seafood (3); Spanish (6)
Areas of Operation: AL, FL, MS, TN
Type of Foodservice: Casual Dining (12)

Key Personnel
RICK SPELL - Co-Founder; Partner
CHRISTY S. TERRY - Co-Founder; Partner
DREW TERRY - Partner

CAMILLE WITHALL - Executive Chef
ANGELA POE - Executive Chef
WILL HAMPTON - Project Manager

Ferber & Sons Inc.
15429 Mulholland Rd
Parrish, FL 34219-1832

Telephone: (941) 745-5855
Fax Number: (941) 747-0641
Type of Business: Chain Restaurant Operator
Year Founded: 1973
Total Sales: $9,143,000 (e)
Number of Employees: 90
Average Check: Lunch(8); Dinner(8)
Total Units: 5
Trade Names: KFC (4); KFC/Long John Silver's (1)
Units Franchised From: 5
Preferred Square Footage: 2,400
Preferred Location Types: Freestanding
Primary Menu: Chicken (5); Seafood (1)
Areas of Operation: FL
Type of Foodservice: Quick Serve (5)
Franchise Affiliation: KFC Corporation, LOUISVILLE, KY; Long John Silver's Inc., LOUISVILLE, KY
Primary Distributors: (Full Line) Kelly's Foods Inc., WINTER GARDEN, FL

Key Personnel
DAN FERBER SR - President; General Buyer
PAULETTE K. FERBER - VP
LYNN MCSWAIN - Treasurer
LYNN FERBER - Director Purchasing, Supply Chain, Human Resources

Bri'chae, LLC
5010 Bayou Blvd
Pensacola, FL 32503-2551

Telephone: (850) 478-9861
Type of Business: Chain Restaurant Operator
Total Sales: $3,735,000 (e)
Total Units: 3
Trade Names: Firehouse Subs (3)
Units Franchised From: 3
Primary Menu: Sandwiches/Deli (3)
Areas of Operation: FL
Type of Foodservice: Fast Casual (3)
Franchise Affiliation: Firehouse Restaurant Group Inc., JACKSONVILLE, FL

Key Personnel
SCOTT ESTY - President; General Buyer

Captain D's of Pensacola Inc
6387 Pensacola Blvd
Pensacola, FL 32505-1901

Telephone: (850) 332-2407
Type of Business: Chain Restaurant Operator
Total Sales: $5,594,000 (e)
Total Units: 4
Trade Names: Captain D's Seafood Kitchen (4)
Units Franchised From: 4
Primary Menu: Seafood (4)
Areas of Operation: FL
Type of Foodservice: Quick Serve (4)
Franchise Affiliation: Captain D's LLC, NASHVILLE, TN

Key Personnel
JOE BORTONE - President; General Buyer
KEVIN CLAUSEY - Store Manager

McGuire's Irish Pub
600 E Gregory St
Pensacola, FL 32502-4140

Telephone: (850) 433-2849
Fax Number: (850) 434-5400
Internet Homepage: mcguiresirishpub.com
Company Email: michelle@mcguiresirishpub.com
Type of Business: Chain Restaurant Operator
Year Founded: 1977
Total Sales: $30,812,000 (e)
Alcohol Sales: 30%
Number of Employees: 400
Average Check: Lunch(18); Dinner(32)
Total Units: 2
Trade Names: McGuire's Irish Pub (1); McGuire's Irish Pub of Destin (1)
Company-Owned Units: 2
Preferred Location Types: Freestanding
Alcohol Served: Beer, Wine, Liquor
Primary Menu: Steak/Seafood (2)
Areas of Operation: FL
Type of Foodservice: Casual Dining (2)
Primary Distributors: (Food) SYSCO Food Services of West Coast Florida Inc., PALMETTO, FL

Key Personnel
BILLY MARTIN - Partner; COO; General Buyer
MCGUIRE MARTIN - Partner; Executive Chef; General Buyer

Nowak Enterprises, Inc
3695 N L St
Pensacola, FL 32505-5216

Telephone: (850) 438-5133
Fax Number: (850) 432-6365
Internet Homepage: nowakenterprises.com
Company Email: service@nowakent.com
Type of Business: Chain Restaurant Operator
Year Founded: 1991
Total Sales: $28,200,000 (e)
Number of Employees: 300
Total Units: 6
Trade Names: McDonald's (6)
Units Franchised From: 6
Preferred Square Footage: 2,500
Preferred Location Types: Freestanding; Strip Mall
Primary Menu: Hamburger (6)
Areas of Operation: FL
Type of Foodservice: Quick Serve (6)
Franchise Affiliation: McDonald's Corporation, CHICAGO, IL

Key Personnel
PETER J. NOWAK - CEO; President; General Buyer
CAROLINE PATE - Director Operations
DICK RIZZO - Director Communications
SUZANNE JOHNSON - Director Payroll, Human Resources
SHARON DIEHL - Bookkeeper

O'Connor Management Group
1110 N 9th Ave
Pensacola, FL 32501-3236

Telephone: (850) 470-9555
Fax Number: (850) 470-0079
Company Email: office@omg.gccoxmail.com
Type of Business: Chain Restaurant Operator
Total Sales: $33,540,000 (e)
Number of Employees: 465
Total Units: 7
Trade Names: McDonald's (7)
Units Franchised From: 7
Preferred Square Footage: 2,500
Primary Menu: Hamburger (7)
Areas of Operation: FL
Type of Foodservice: Quick Serve (7)
Franchise Affiliation: McDonald's Corporation, CHICAGO, IL

Key Personnel
JOHN O'CONNOR - President; General Buyer
ANDREA WALLACE - Director Operations

Shrimp Basket
7282 Plantation Rd Ste 301
Pensacola, FL 32504

Mailing Address: P. O. Box 904, Gulf Shores, AL, 36547
Telephone: (251) 968-8639
Fax Number: (850) 475-2615
Internet Homepage: shrimpbasket.com
Type of Business: Chain Restaurant Operator
Year Founded: 1993
Total Units: 30
Trade Names: Shrimp Basket (30)
Company-Owned Units: 30
Primary Menu: Seafood (30)
Areas of Operation: AL, FL, GA, LA, MS
Type of Foodservice: Casual Dining (30)

Key Personnel
SIDNEY FIQUETTE - General Manager
STEPHANIE LOWERY - Director Administration

Padrino's
801 S University Dr Ste J105
Plantation, FL 33324-3367

Telephone: (954) 723-9156
Fax Number: (954) 476-8289
Internet Homepage: padrinos.com
Type of Business: Chain Restaurant Operator
Year Founded: 1992
Total Sales: $8,356,000 (e)
Alcohol Sales: 12%
Number of Employees: 45
Average Check: Lunch(12); Dinner(14)
Total Units: 6
Trade Names: Padrino's (6)
Company-Owned Units: 6
Preferred Location Types: Freestanding
Alcohol Served: Beer, Wine
Primary Menu: Spanish (6)
Areas of Operation: FL
Type of Foodservice: Casual Dining (6)
Catering Services: Yes
Primary Distributors: (Food) US Foods, BOCA RATON, FL

Key Personnel
MARIO PADRINO - President; Partner; Executive Chef; General Buyer
NAYADE PADRINO - Partner; Executive Chef
LAURA CORREDOIRA - Director Marketing, Public Relations

Domino's Franchisee
104 Commonwealth Ave N Ste 2
Polk City, FL 33868-9500

Telephone: (863) 874-4888
Type of Business: Chain Restaurant Operator
Total Sales: $3,996,000 (e)
Total Units: 2
Trade Names: Domino's (2)
Units Franchised From: 2
Primary Menu: Pizza (2)
Areas of Operation: FL
Type of Foodservice: Quick Serve (2)
Franchise Affiliation: Domino's Pizza Inc, ANN

ARBOR, MI

Key Personnel
JARRED S. FISCHLER - Owner; General Buyer

Domino's Franchisee
2201 W Sample Rd Bldg A
Pompano Beach, FL 33073-3082

Telephone: (954) 974-3399
Type of Business: Chain Restaurant Operator
Total Sales: $4,124,000 (e)
Total Units: 2
Trade Names: Domino's (2)
Units Franchised From: 2
Primary Menu: Pizza (2)
Areas of Operation: FL
Type of Foodservice: Quick Serve (2)
Franchise Affiliation: Domino's Pizza Inc, ANN ARBOR, MI

Key Personnel
CARLOS H. MARTINEZ - Owner; General Buyer

JAE Restaurant Group
1100 Park Central Blvd S Ste 3300
Pompano Beach, FL 33064-2246

Telephone: (561) 997-6002
Fax Number: (561) 997-6045
Internet Homepage: jaerestaurantgroup.com
Type of Business: Chain Restaurant Operator
Total Sales: $602,590,000 (e)
Total Units: 222
Trade Names: Wendys Old Fashioned Hamburgers (222)
Units Franchised From: 222
Primary Menu: Hamburger (222)
Projected Openings: 2
Areas of Operation: FL, NM, TN, TX
Type of Foodservice: Quick Serve (222)

Key Personnel
EDDIE RODRIGUEZ - Chairman; Partner
ANDRES GARCIA - Co-Chairman; Partner
ED AUSTIN - CEO
BEN MANSOOR - COO
ARTURO VAZQUEZ - COO
ANTONETT RODRIGUEZ - Chief People Officer
MICHAEL RODRIGUEZ - VP Operations
LUIS RIVERA - VP Facility/Maintenance, Construction
KRISTI WHITAKER - Director Training
ROB PHAM - Director Information Technology
EHAB NESSIM - Director Operations, Area
SORAYA WARD - Manager Accounting
REGINA BUTLER - Manager Administration

Upchurch Management
1439 SW 26th Ave
Pompano Beach, FL 33069-4315

Telephone: (954) 972-2004
Fax Number: (954) 972-2792
Type of Business: Chain Restaurant Operator
Year Founded: 1978
Total Sales: $150,660,000 (e)
Number of Employees: 900
Average Check: Breakfast(6); Lunch(8); Dinner(10)
Total Units: 32
Trade Names: McDonald's (32)
Units Franchised From: 32
Preferred Square Footage: 4,000
Preferred Location Types: Downtown; Freestanding
Primary Menu: Hamburger (32)
Projected Openings: 10
Areas of Operation: FL
Type of Foodservice: Quick Serve (32)
Franchise Affiliation: McDonald's Corporation, CHICAGO, IL

Key Personnel
BRENT U - President
JAMES UPCHURCH JR - President; Director Supply Chain, Real Estate; General Buyer
MARY GRIESEMER - CFO; Director Finance
SUE LASKOWITZ - Director Human Resources
JODI ALEXANDER - Director Marketing
STEVE EDWARDS - Director Operations
CATHIE CLARK - Manager Human Resources
NILDA RENTAS - Supervisor Accounting

Ponte Vedra Beach Resorts
200 Ponte Vedra Blvd
Ponte Vedra Beach, FL 32082-1810

Telephone: (904) 285-1111
Fax Number: (904) 285-2111
Internet Homepage: pontevedra.com; pvresorts.com
Company Email: info@pvresorts.com
Type of Business: Foodservice Operations - Hotel/Motels
Year Founded: 1928
Total Sales: $60,842,000 (e)
Alcohol Sales: 25%
Number of Employees: 800
Total Units: 2
Restaurants in Hotels: 11
Trade Names: Beach Side Snack Bar (1); Sea Hoarse Grill (1); Sea View Grille (1); Seafoam Room (1); Surf Club Patio (1); Surf Deck Grille (1); The Gourmet Shop (1); The Gulf Club (1); The Inn Dining (1); The Oasis (1); The Tavern (1)
Company-Owned Units: 11
Alcohol Served: Beer, Wine, Liquor
Areas of Operation: FL
Type of Foodservice: Casual Dining (7); Fine Dining (4)
Primary Distributors: (Food) SYSCO Food Services of Jacksonville Inc., JACKSONVILLE, FL
Notes: The company derives approximately 60% of its revenue from hotel operations.

Key Personnel
MICHAEL GORDON - VP; General Manager
HERMANN MULLER - Executive Chef
ERIK OSOL - Executive Chef
CRAIG SCHONINGER - Director Marketing
AARON STILES - Director Food and Beverage
SHAUN O'DONNELL - Director Operations
LAURA CAPOBIANCO - Director Catering
BILL DAVID - Director Development, Training
STEFANIE HARRISON - Manager Human Resources
ANTHONY CARUSO - Coordinator Group

T.L. Cannon Management Corp.
220 Ponte Vedra Park Dr Ste 100
Ponte Vedra Beach, FL 32082-6616

Telephone: (904) 273-9558
Fax Number: (904) 273-6061
Internet Homepage: tlcannon.com
Company Email: info@tlcannon.com
Type of Business: Chain Restaurant Operator
Year Founded: 1991
Total Sales: $238,530,000 (e)
Alcohol Sales: 10%
Number of Employees: 4,000
Average Check: Lunch(14); Dinner(20)
Total Units: 61
Trade Names: Applebee's Neighborhood Grill & Bar (60); Table 1 (1)
Company-Owned Units: 1
Units Franchised From: 60
Preferred Square Footage: 4,900
Preferred Location Types: Community Mall; Downtown; Freestanding; Regional Mall
Alcohol Served: Beer, Wine, Liquor
Primary Menu: American (63)
Areas of Operation: CT, FL, NY, PA
Type of Foodservice: Casual Dining (63)
Catering Services: Yes
Franchise Affiliation: Applebee's Services Inc., KANSAS CITY, MO
Primary Distributors: (Full Line) Maines Paper & Food Service Inc., CONKLIN, NY

Key Personnel
MATTHEW FAIRBAIRN - CEO; Partner
JOHN A. PERRY JR - President
DAVID STEIN - Partner
RITCH MABRY - CFO; VP Finance
RICK GAGLIASTRI - Executive Director Operations

CLYDE BRANT - Controller
DENISE CANTLAY - Director Real Estate
JAMES MILLER - Director Operations
BOB PATTERSON - Director Information Technology; Manager Information Systems
STEPHANIE GRIFFIN - Director Marketing
STEVE BELL - Director Facility/Maintenance, Construction
DEB QUIGGLE-SHULTIS - Director Operations
SUSAN SABIO - Director Human Resources
MARK HEINZMANN - Manager Purchasing, Security, Inventory, Loss Prevention, Quality Assurance, Food Safety; General Buyer
KAITLYN CZERWONKA - Manager Marketing, Social Media

Coastal QSR
1720 El Jobean Rd Unit 102
Port Charlotte, FL 33948-1286

Telephone: (941) 255-5405
Fax Number: (941) 255-9528
Company Email: hr@theborder.com
Type of Business: Chain Restaurant Operator
Year Founded: 2008
Total Sales: $282,820,000 (e)
Number of Employees: 2,140
Average Check: Lunch(14); Dinner(18)
Total Units: 135
Trade Names: Long John Silver's/Taco Bell (1); Taco Bell (130); Taco Bell/KFC (4)
Units Franchised From: 135
Preferred Square Footage: 2,500; 3,200
Preferred Location Types: Freestanding
Primary Menu: Chicken (4); Seafood (1); Taco (130)
Areas of Operation: FL
Type of Foodservice: Quick Serve (135)
Franchise Affiliation: KFC Corporation, LOUISVILLE, KY; Long John Silver's Inc., LOUISVILLE, KY; Taco Bell Corp., IRVINE, CA
Primary Distributors: (Food) McLane/Arlington, ARLINGTON, TX

Key Personnel
NICK PETERS - President; Director Finance, Real Estate; General Buyer
WILEY TURNER - CFO
CARLOS SILVA - COO

Domino's Franchisee
1940 Kings Hwy Unit 1
Port Charlotte, FL 33980-4298

Telephone: (941) 624-3030
Type of Business: Chain Restaurant Operator
Total Sales: $4,063,000 (e)
Total Units: 2
Trade Names: Domino's (2)
Units Franchised From: 2
Primary Menu: Pizza (2)
Areas of Operation: FL
Type of Foodservice: Quick Serve (2)
Franchise Affiliation: Domino's Pizza Inc, ANN ARBOR, MI

Key Personnel
PAUL ZDANOWICZ - Owner

YSS, Inc.
12531 S McCall Rd
Port Charlotte, FL 33981

Telephone: (941) 698-7559
Type of Business: Chain Restaurant Operator
Total Sales: $9,488,000 (e)
Total Units: 4
Trade Names: Burger King (4)
Units Franchised From: 4
Preferred Location Types: Freestanding
Primary Menu: Hamburger (4)
Areas of Operation: FL
Type of Foodservice: Quick Serve (4)
Franchise Affiliation: Burger King Worldwide Inc., MIAMI, FL

Key Personnel
ANDREW ALLEN - CEO; President
MURRAWAT H. SAYED - President; General Buyer
SHAUKED SAYED - Exec VP
DAN KING - Director Information Technology

Darrel Pereida
1769 NW Saint Lucie West Blvd
Port Saint Lucie, FL 34986-2501

Telephone: (772) 344-3920
Type of Business: Chain Restaurant Operator
Total Sales: $3,489,000 (e)
Total Units: 2
Trade Names: Moe's Southwest Grill (2)
Units Franchised From: 2
Primary Menu: Southwest/Tex-Mex (2)
Areas of Operation: FL
Type of Foodservice: Fast Casual (2)
Franchise Affiliation: Moe's Southwest Grill LLC, ATLANTA, GA

Key Personnel
DARREL PEREIDA - Owner; General Buyer

BF Fort Myers Inc
25450 Airport Rd
Punta Gorda, FL 33950-5746

Telephone: (941) 637-8865
Listing Type: Divisional Office
Type of Business: Chain Restaurant Operator
Total Units: 41

Trade Names: Wendy's Old Fashioned Hamburgers (41)
Units Franchised From: 41
Primary Menu: Hamburger (41)
Areas of Operation: FL
Type of Foodservice: Quick Serve (41)
Parent Company: Manna Inc., LOUISVILLE, KY

Key Personnel
GLENN BLACKMON - Director Human Resources
MICHAEL ROBINSON - Director Operations; General Buyer
DAVE SHEEN - Director Operations; General Buyer
ROWENE SHEEN - District Manager
CHERI DAHLBERG - Office Manager Payroll, Administration, Benefits

Laxmi-Bhavan Inc.
27690 Bermont Rd Unit 4
Punta Gorda, FL 33982-1904

Telephone: (941) 505-2444
Type of Business: Chain Restaurant Operator
Total Sales: $14,870,000 (e)
Total Units: 26
Trade Names: Subway (26)
Units Franchised From: 26
Primary Menu: Sandwiches/Deli (26)
Areas of Operation: FL
Type of Foodservice: Quick Serve (26)
Franchise Affiliation: Doctor's Associates Inc., MILFORD, CT

Key Personnel
CHETAN PATEL - President

River City Grill Inc.
131 W Marion Ave
Punta Gorda, FL 33950-4412

Telephone: (941) 639-9080
Fax Number: (941) 639-9765
Internet Homepage: italiapg.com; rivercitygrillpg.com
Company Email: dine@rivercitygrillpg.com
Type of Business: Chain Restaurant Operator
Total Sales: $4,611,000 (e)
Alcohol Sales: 5%
Average Check: Dinner(24)
Total Units: 2
Trade Names: Italia (1); River City Grill (1)
Company-Owned Units: 2
Preferred Location Types: Downtown
Alcohol Served: Beer, Wine, Liquor
Primary Menu: American (1); Italian (1)
Areas of Operation: FL
Type of Foodservice: Casual Dining (2)

Key Personnel
DIANE AMARAL - Partner; CFO
DOUG AMARAL - Partner; Executive Chef; General Buyer

Smugglers Enterprises, Inc.
1200 W Retta Esplanade Ste 55
Punta Gorda, FL 33951-1289

Telephone: (941) 637-1177
Internet Homepage: smugglers.com; smugglersculinarycatering.com
Company Email: captainstable@smugglers.com
Type of Business: Chain Restaurant Operator
Year Founded: 1992
Total Sales: $7,240,000 (e)
Total Units: 5
Trade Names: Captain's Table (1); Harpoon Harry's (1); Harpoon Harry's Crab House (2); Laishley Crab House (1)
Company-Owned Units: 5
Primary Menu: Seafood (5)
Projected Openings: 1
Areas of Operation: FL, TN
Type of Foodservice: Casual Dining (5)

Key Personnel
RON EVANS - CEO; President
KELLY LISCUM - VP
RODNEY MONROIG - VP; Director Operations
JERRY CLEFFI - General Manager Event Planning
CORINNE WIMBERLY - General Manager Restaurant Operations
DAVE KASS - General Manager
PHIL ROBERTSON - General Manager
SAMANTHA KNIGHT - Director Event Planning

Sunway Restaurant Corporation
9870 US Highway 301 S
Riverview, FL 33578-5809

Telephone: (813) 677-6556
Fax Number: (813) 672-2443
Type of Business: Chain Restaurant Operator
Total Sales: $20,650,000 (e)
Total Units: 4
Trade Names: McDonald's (4)
Units Franchised From: 4
Primary Menu: Hamburger (4)
Areas of Operation: FL
Type of Foodservice: Quick Serve (4)
Franchise Affiliation: McDonald's Corporation, CHICAGO, IL

Key Personnel
FRED J. SCARCELL III - President

Andreams Corp
100 Main St Ste 102
Safety Harbor, FL 34695-3668

Telephone: (727) 725-3696
Type of Business: Chain Restaurant Operator
Total Sales: $1,169,000 (e)
Total Units: 2
Trade Names: Cold Stone Creamery (2)
Units Franchised From: 2
Primary Menu: Snacks (2)
Areas of Operation: FL
Type of Foodservice: Quick Serve (2)
Franchise Affiliation: Kahala Brands, SCOTTSDALE, AZ

Key Personnel
ANDREA MONTOYA - Owner

Gypsy Cab Co.
828 Anastasia Blvd
Saint Augustine, FL 32080-4660

Telephone: (904) 824-8244
Fax Number: (904) 829-9080
Internet Homepage: thecornerbar.gypsycab.com; gypsycab.com
Company Email: info@gypsycab.com
Type of Business: Chain Restaurant Operator
Year Founded: 1983
Total Sales: $5,109,000 (e)
Alcohol Sales: 7%
Number of Employees: 55
Average Check: Lunch(12); Dinner(22)
Total Units: 2
Trade Names: Gypsy Cab Co. (1); The Corner Bar & Grill (1)
Company-Owned Units: 2
Preferred Square Footage: 120; 150
Preferred Location Types: Freestanding
Alcohol Served: Beer, Wine, Liquor
Primary Menu: Miscellaneous (2)
Areas of Operation: FL
Type of Foodservice: Casual Dining (2)
Catering Services: Yes
Primary Distributors: (Food) Food Supply Inc., SOUTH DAYTONA, FL

Key Personnel
PATRICK MORISSEY - Owner; Executive Chef; General Buyer
JEFF HERR - Manager Food and Beverage; Buyer Beverages

Tennyson Foods Inc
162 San Marco Ave Ste 3
Saint Augustine, FL 32084-3291

Telephone: (904) 829-1468

Fax Number: (904) 826-1805
Type of Business: Chain Restaurant Operator
Total Sales: $3,950,000 (e)
Total Units: 7
Trade Names: Subway (7)
Units Franchised From: 7
Primary Menu: Sandwiches/Deli (7)
Areas of Operation: FL
Type of Foodservice: Quick Serve (7)
Franchise Affiliation: Doctor's Associates Inc., MILFORD, CT

Key Personnel
JAMES TENNYSON - President; General Buyer

Ramp Industries, Inc.
4123 Neptune Rd
Saint Cloud, FL 34769-6741

Telephone: (407) 892-7878
Type of Business: Chain Restaurant Operator
Total Sales: $20,005,000 (e)
Total Units: 4
Trade Names: McDonald's (4)
Units Franchised From: 4
Preferred Location Types: Freestanding
Primary Menu: Hamburger (4)
Areas of Operation: FL
Type of Foodservice: Quick Serve (4)
Franchise Affiliation: McDonald's Corporation, CHICAGO, IL

Key Personnel
MIKE BEATTY - President; General Buyer

2B Hospitality
200 Beach Drive NE Suite #3
Saint Petersburg, FL 33701

Telephone: (727) 408-6920
Internet Homepage: 2bhospitality.com
Type of Business: Chain Restaurant Operator
Total Units: 4
Trade Names: BellaBrava (3); Stillwaters Tavern (1)
Company-Owned Units: 4
Primary Menu: American (1); Italian (3)
Areas of Operation: FL
Type of Foodservice: Fine Dining (4)

Key Personnel
TARYN NICHOLS - General Manager

G.A. Food Services
12200 32nd Ct N
Saint Petersburg, FL 33716-1803

Telephone: (727) 573-2211
Fax Number: (727) 572-8209

Internet Homepage: gafoods.com; sunmeadow.com
Type of Business: Foodservice Management Operator
Year Founded: 1973
Total Sales: $167,579,000 (e)
Number of Employees: 400
Number of Locations Served: 400
Total Foodservice Mgmt Accounts: 400
Areas of Operation: FL
Type of Foodservice: Cafeteria (400)
Foodservice Management Venues: Health Care; Parks & Recreation; Schools
Primary Distributors: (Food) SYSCO Food Services of West Coast Florida Inc., PALMETTO, FL; (Supplies) Imperial Dade Orlando, ORLANDO, FL

Key Personnel
KENNETH LOBIANCO - CEO
ANNETTE HENRY - Manager Human Resources

Jai Kapi, LLC
4949 4th St N
Saint Petersburg, FL 33703-3800

Telephone: (727) 521-0640
Type of Business: Chain Restaurant Operator
Total Sales: $2,480,000 (e)
Total Units: 2
Trade Names: Firehouse Subs (2)
Units Franchised From: 2
Primary Menu: Sandwiches/Deli (2)
Areas of Operation: FL
Type of Foodservice: Fast Casual (2)
Franchise Affiliation: Firehouse Restaurant Group Inc., JACKSONVILLE, FL

Key Personnel
COOPER SHANAHAN - General Manager

Lazy Flamingo Inc.
6520 Pine Ave Apt A
Sanibel, FL 33957-2001

Telephone: (239) 472-8484
Fax Number: (239) 472-0555
Internet Homepage: lazyflamingo.com; sunsetgrillsanibel.com
Company Email: lazyusa@aol.com
Type of Business: Chain Restaurant Operator
Year Founded: 1987
Total Sales: $7,759,000 (e)
Alcohol Sales: 20%
Number of Employees: 75
Average Check: Breakfast(12); Lunch(24); Dinner(24)
Internet Order Processing: Yes
Total Units: 5
Trade Names: Lazy Flamingo (4); Sunset Grill (1)
Company-Owned Units: 5
Preferred Location Types: Freestanding
Alcohol Served: Beer, Wine
Primary Menu: Seafood (5)
Areas of Operation: FL
Type of Foodservice: Casual Dining (5)
Catering Services: Yes
Primary Distributors: (Full Line) SYSCO Food Services of South Florida Inc., MEDLEY, FL

Key Personnel
LARRY C. THOMPSON - Owner; Director Finance, Information Systems, Real Estate, Design
KATHY THOMPSON - Executive Chef; Manager Operations; General Buyer

Sanibel Majik Inc.
1200 Periwinkle Way
Sanibel, FL 33957-4702

Telephone: (239) 489-2226
Fax Number: (239) 395-8646
Internet Homepage: prawnbroker.com
Type of Business: Chain Restaurant Operator
Year Founded: 1978
Total Sales: $43,420,000 (e)
Alcohol Sales: 10%
Number of Employees: 350
Average Check: Lunch(12); Dinner(24)
Total Units: 10
Trade Names: Black Marlin (1); Magic Oyster (1); Matzaluna (1); Palm City Grill (1); Prawn Broker (2); Sanibel Grill (1); Shrimpers (1); Timbers (1); University Grill (1)
Company-Owned Units: 10
Preferred Square Footage: 8,000
Preferred Location Types: Freestanding
Alcohol Served: Beer, Wine, Liquor
Primary Menu: Italian (1); Seafood (9)
Projected Remodelings: 2
Areas of Operation: FL
Type of Foodservice: Casual Dining (10)
Primary Distributors: (Full Line) SYSCO Food Services of West Coast Florida Inc., PALMETTO, FL

Key Personnel
MATT ASEN - President; Partner; Controller
JIM FOSTER - Partner
KIPP FOSTER - Partner
MICHAEL SCHILLING - Partner; Director Risk Management
MARK BLUST - General Manager; Director Finance, Operations, Facility/Maintenance, Information Systems, Real Estate, Human Resources, Menu Development; General Buyer

Joe D and Ka Investments, LLC
1425 E Nursery Rd
Santa Rosa Beach, FL 32459-5210

Mailing Address: P.O. Box 1024, SANTA ROSA BEACH, FL, 32459
Telephone: (248) 310-4502
Type of Business: Chain Restaurant Operator
Total Sales: $2,470,000 (e)
Total Units: 4
Trade Names: Little Caesars Pizza (4)
Units Franchised From: 4
Primary Menu: Pizza (4)
Areas of Operation: FL
Type of Foodservice: Quick Serve (4)
Franchise Affiliation: Little Caesar Enterprises Inc., DETROIT, MI

Key Personnel
KAREN ANGELOSANTE - Partner; General Buyer
JOE DAVENPORT - Partner; General Buyer

Domino's Franchisee
4080 Cattlemen Rd
Sarasota, FL 34233-5033

Telephone: (941) 378-0030
Type of Business: Chain Restaurant Operator
Total Sales: $4,143,000 (e)
Total Units: 2
Trade Names: Domino's (2)
Units Franchised From: 2
Primary Menu: Pizza (2)
Areas of Operation: FL
Type of Foodservice: Quick Serve (2)
Franchise Affiliation: Domino's Pizza Inc, ANN ARBOR, MI

Key Personnel
RENATO DE GUIA - Owner; General Buyer

Gecko's Hospitality Group
4870 S Tamiami Trl
Sarasota, FL 34231-4352

Telephone: (941) 921-3924
Internet Homepage: geckosgrill.com
Company Email: office@geckoshospitality.com
Type of Business: Chain Restaurant Operator
Year Founded: 1992
Total Units: 10
Trade Names: Dockside Waterfront Grill (1); Dry Dock Waterside Grill (1); Gecko's Grill & Pub (6); Red Barn Bar (1); S'macks Burgers & Shakes (1)
Company-Owned Units: 10
Primary Menu: American (9); Hamburger (1)

Areas of Operation: FL
Type of Foodservice: Casual Dining (10)

Key Personnel
MIKE QUILLEN - Partner; General Buyer
MIKE GOWAN - Partner; General Buyer

Le Macaron French Pastries
382 Saint Armands Cir
Sarasota, FL 34236-1313

Telephone: (941) 552-8872
Internet Homepage: lemacaron-us.com
Company Email: lemacaronfranchise@gmail.com
Type of Business: Chain Restaurant Operator
Year Founded: 2009
Total Units: 50
Trade Names: Le Macaron (50)
Company-Owned Units: 2
Units Franchised To: 48
Preferred Square Footage: 800; 1,000
Areas of Operation: AZ, CA, FL, GA, NC, NV, NY, TX
Type of Foodservice: Quick Serve (50)

Key Personnel
ROSALIE GUILLEM - Partner
AUDREY SABA - Partner; General Buyer
LOAN LUCAS - Director Web Design

Mi Pueblo, Inc.
4436 Bee Ridge Rd
Sarasota, FL 34233-2502

Telephone: (941) 379-2880
Internet Homepage: mipueblomexican.com
Company Email: info@mipueblomexican.com
Type of Business: Chain Restaurant Operator
Year Founded: 1999
Total Sales: $3,315,000 (e)
Alcohol Sales: 5%
Total Units: 3
Trade Names: mi Pueblo el Restaurante Mexicano & Cantina (3)
Company-Owned Units: 3
Preferred Location Types: Freestanding
Alcohol Served: Beer, Wine, Liquor
Primary Menu: Mexican (3)
Areas of Operation: FL
Type of Foodservice: Casual Dining (3)
Catering Services: Yes

Key Personnel
HUGO C. NUNEZ - President; Executive Chef; Director Menu Development; General Buyer

●▲
Robroy Restaurants Inc.
1663 Mound St
Sarasota, FL 34236-7715

Telephone: (941) 365-7891
Fax Number: (941) 951-0389
Type of Business: Chain Restaurant Operator
Year Founded: 1959
Total Sales: $58,870,000 (e)
Number of Employees: 720
Average Check: Breakfast(6); Lunch(6); Dinner(14)
Total Units: 26
Trade Names: Burger King (26)
Units Franchised From: 26
Preferred Square Footage: 2,800
Preferred Location Types: Freestanding
Primary Menu: Hamburger (26)
Projected Remodelings: 2
Areas of Operation: FL
Type of Foodservice: Quick Serve (26)
Franchise Affiliation: Burger King Worldwide Inc., MIAMI, FL
Primary Distributors: (Full Line) Reinhart FoodService, JACKSONVILLE, FL

Key Personnel
ROBERT FURMAN - President; Director Finance, Operations, Purchasing, Information Systems, Supply Chain, Real Estate, Design
JENNIFER FAIRLY - VP Operations; General Buyer

Tableseide Restaurant Group
1235 N Gulfstream Ave
Sarasota, FL 34236

Telephone: (941) 538-7330
Internet Homepage: tableseide.com
Type of Business: Chain Restaurant Operator
Year Founded: 2008
Total Units: 7
Trade Names: Lemon Tree Kitchen (1); Libby's Neighborhood Brasserie (2); Muse at the Ringling (1); Oak & Stone (3)
Company-Owned Units: 7
Primary Menu: American (3); Miscellaneous (1); Pizza (3)
Projected Openings: 2
Areas of Operation: FL
Type of Foodservice: Casual Dining (7)

Key Personnel
JOE SEIDENSTICKER - CEO
CLAUDIA CH - Controller
ALEXANDRA S. SIMPSON - Specialist Marketing

●▲
3 Carter's Subway Inc
3212 US Highway 27 S Sebring, FL 33870
Sebring, FL 33870

Telephone: (863) 664-2014
Type of Business: Chain Restaurant Operator
Total Sales: $2,943,000 (e)
Total Units: 5
Trade Names: Subway (5)
Units Franchised From: 5
Primary Menu: Sandwiches/Deli (5)
Areas of Operation: FL
Type of Foodservice: Quick Serve (5)
Franchise Affiliation: Doctor's Associates Inc., MILFORD, CT

Key Personnel
LEWIS CARTER - Partner; General Buyer
SANDRA R. CARTER - Partner; General Buyer

JOTO Inc.
12932 Lois Ave
Seminole, FL 33776-1807

Telephone: (727) 319-0204
Internet Homepage: jotospizza.com
Company Email: jotos@jotospizza.com
Type of Business: Chain Restaurant Operator
Year Founded: 1981
Total Sales: $3,006,000 (e)
Total Units: 2
Trade Names: JOTO's Pizza (2)
Company-Owned Units: 2
Primary Menu: Pizza (2)
Type of Foodservice: Casual Dining (2)

Key Personnel
JODI WHITCOMB - Owner; General Buyer

Seminole Lanes and Sunrise Lanes
8668 Park Blvd Ste K
Seminole, FL 33777-4348

Telephone: (727) 397-6490
Fax Number: (727) 393-9077
Internet Homepage: semimolelanes.com; sunriselanes.com
Type of Business: Foodservice Operations - Bowling Alley
Total Sales: $5,991,000 (e)
Alcohol Sales: 5%
Number of Employees: 40
Average Check: Lunch(8); Dinner(8)
Total Units: 2
Trade Names: Seminole Lanes (1); Sunrise Lanes (1)
Company-Owned Units: 2

Preferred Location Types: Other
Alcohol Served: Beer, Wine, Liquor
Primary Menu: American (2)
Areas of Operation: FL
Type of Foodservice: In-Store Feeder (2)
Primary Distributors: (Food) SYSCO Central Florida Inc., OCOEE, FL
Notes: The company derives approximately 70% of its revenue from bowling center operations.

Key Personnel
CORY KRAUSS - Partner; General Manager; General Buyer
GERALD KRAUSS - Partner; General Buyer
KEVIN KRAUSS - Partner; General Manager
RYNE PODLAS - General Manager; General Buyer

NCB, Inc.
7301 SW 57th Ct Ste 520
South Miami, FL 33143-5339

Telephone: (305) 661-4460
Fax Number: (305) 661-0053
Internet Homepage: ncbinc.net
Type of Business: Chain Restaurant Operator
Total Sales: $129,490,000 (e)
Number of Employees: 700
Total Units: 27
Trade Names: McDonald's (27)
Units Franchised From: 27
Preferred Square Footage: 2,500
Primary Menu: Hamburger (27)
Areas of Operation: FL
Type of Foodservice: Quick Serve (27)
Franchise Affiliation: McDonald's Corporation, CHICAGO, IL

Key Personnel
ANGEL VELIZ - President; Partner; General Buyer
RENE VELIZ - Partner; General Buyer
MICHAEL LAVINE - VP Operations
SUZANNE FOX - Controller
AYLIN MORALES - Manager Payroll

Starlite Cruises
3400 Pasadena Ave S
South Pasadena, FL 33707-4489

Mailing Address: 25 Causeway Blvd, Slip 58, CLEARWATER, FL, 33767
Telephone: (727) 462-2628
Fax Number: (727) 446-4814
Internet Homepage: starlitecruises.com
Company Email: info@starlitecruises.com
Type of Business: Chain Restaurant Operator
Total Sales: $7,673,000 (e)
Alcohol Sales: 25%
Number of Employees: 65

Average Check: Lunch(20); Dinner(36)
Internet Order Processing: Yes
Internet Sales: 5.00%
Total Units: 3
Trade Names: Calypso Queen (1); Starlite Majesty (1); Starlite Sapphire (1)
Company-Owned Units: 3
Preferred Location Types: Mixed-use Center; Mobile Unit; Other
Alcohol Served: Beer, Wine, Liquor
Primary Menu: American (3)
Areas of Operation: FL
Type of Foodservice: Cafeteria (1); Fine Dining (2)
Primary Distributors: (Full Line) Florida Food Service Inc., GAINESVILLE, FL

Key Personnel
PHIL HENDERSON - President
CHARLIE WARD - General Manager; General Buyer
TERESA BRUCE - Manager Sales
JUNE O'BRIEN - Manager Sales

Domino's Franchisee
13081 Spring Hill Dr
Spring Hill, FL 34609-5050

Telephone: (352) 686-2100
Type of Business: Chain Restaurant Operator
Total Sales: $5,957,000 (e)
Total Units: 3
Trade Names: Domino's (3)
Units Franchised From: 3
Primary Menu: Pizza (3)
Areas of Operation: FL
Type of Foodservice: Quick Serve (3)
Franchise Affiliation: Domino's Pizza Inc, ANN ARBOR, MI

Key Personnel
JERRY CAMPBELL - Owner

Domino's Franchisee
8381 Northcliffe Blvd
Spring Hill, FL 34606-1141

Telephone: (352) 684-0005
Type of Business: Chain Restaurant Operator
Total Sales: $4,102,000 (e)
Total Units: 2
Trade Names: Domino's (2)
Units Franchised From: 2
Primary Menu: Pizza (2)
Areas of Operation: FL
Type of Foodservice: Quick Serve (2)
Franchise Affiliation: Domino's Pizza Inc, ANN ARBOR, MI

Key Personnel
JERRY W. CAMPBELL - Owner; General Buyer

Tradewinds Island Resorts On Saint Pete Beach
5500 Gulf Blvd
St Pete Beach, FL 33706-2323

Telephone: (727) 367-6461
Fax Number: (727) 363-2275
Internet Homepage: tradewindsresort.com
Company Email: reservations@twresort.com
Type of Business: Foodservice Operations - Hotel/Motels
Year Founded: 1985
Total Sales: $43,661,000 (e)
Alcohol Sales: 25%
Number of Employees: 500
Total Units: 1
Restaurants in Hotels: 6
Trade Names: TradeWinds Island Resorts on St. Pete Beach (1)
Company-Owned Units: 6
Alcohol Served: Beer, Wine, Liquor
Areas of Operation: FL
Primary Distributors: (Food) SYSCO Food Services of West Coast Florida Inc., PALMETTO, FL; (Supplies) SYSCO Food Services of West Coast Florida Inc., PALMETTO, FL
Notes: The company derives approximately 70% of its revenue from resort operations.

Key Personnel
JEFFERY FREDRICKSON - VP Food and Beverage
TRAVIS JOHNSON - VP Marketing
LYNDA WATERS - VP Marketing
DON WOOLDRIDGE - VP Human Resources
JUSTIN HARRY - Executive Chef

Banyan Cafe & Catering, Inc.
701 Central Ave
St Petersburg, FL 33701-3627

Telephone: (727) 896-6100
Internet Homepage: banyancoffee.com
Company Email: banyancoffee@yahoo.com
Type of Business: Chain Restaurant Operator
Year Founded: 2009
Total Units: 2
Trade Names: Banyan Cafe & Catering (2)
Company-Owned Units: 2
Primary Menu: Sandwiches/Deli (2)
Areas of Operation: FL
Type of Foodservice: Fast Casual (2)
Catering Services: Yes

Key Personnel
HERMAN NOVA - Owner; General Manager;

General Buyer
TESS BROWN - Owner

Go To Steve's
300 Beach Dr NE Ste 104
St Petersburg, FL 33701-3403

Telephone: (727) 896-3463
Fax Number: (727) 896-3463
Internet Homepage: gotosteves.com
Type of Business: Chain Restaurant Operator
Total Sales: $3,058,000 (e)
Total Units: 4
Trade Names: 400 Beach Seafood & Tap House (1); Cafe Gala (1); Parkshore Grill (1); The Hangar Restaurant & Flight Lounge (1)
Company-Owned Units: 4
Alcohol Served: Beer, Wine, Liquor
Primary Menu: American (2); Seafood (1); Steak/Seafood (1)
Areas of Operation: FL
Type of Foodservice: Casual Dining (3); Fine Dining (1)

Key Personnel
STEVE WESTPHAL - Owner; General Buyer

Kahwa Coffee Roasting Company
3070 44th Ave N
St Petersburg, FL 33714

Telephone: (727) 388-1340
Fax Number: (727) 388-1353
Company Email: info@kahwacoffee.com
Type of Business: Chain Restaurant Operator
Year Founded: 2006
Total Units: 14
Trade Names: Kahwa Coffee (14)
Company-Owned Units: 14
Primary Menu: Snacks (14)
Projected Openings: 3
Areas of Operation: Fl
Type of Foodservice: Quick Serve (14)

Key Personnel
RAPHAEL PERRIER - Owner; General Buyer
KATIE SENKOVICH - Regional Manager

Beachside Hospitality Group
11201 Corporate Circle North Suite 100
St. Petersburg, FL 33716

Telephone: (727) 210-0987
Internet Homepage: bshgrp.com
Type of Business: Chain Restaurant Operator
Total Sales: $11,374,000 (e)
Total Units: 12
Trade Names: Crabby's Bar & Grill Clearwater (1); Crabby's Bar & Grill NSB (1); Crabby's Beachside (1); Crabby's Dockside (1); Crabby's Dockside Ft. Pierce(1); Crabby's Hideaway (1); Crabby's Oceanside (1); Crabby's On The Pass (1); Crabby's St. Cloud (1); Salty's Island Bar & Grille (1); The Salty Crab Bar & Grill (1); The Salty Crab North Beach (1)
Company-Owned Units: 12
Primary Menu: Seafood (12)
Type of Foodservice: Casual Dining (12)

Key Personnel
GREG POWERS - CEO
EDDIE WRIGHT - COO
JULIA CASSINO - Director Marketing

Noble Crust
8300 4th St N
St. Petersburg, FL 33702

Telephone: (727) 329-6041
Internet Homepage: noble-crust.com
Company Email: info@noble-crust.com
Type of Business: Chain Restaurant Operator
Year Founded: 2015
Total Units: 3
Trade Names: Noble Crust (3)
Company-Owned Units: 3
Primary Menu: Pizza (3)
Areas of Operation: FL
Type of Foodservice: Casual Dining (3)

Key Personnel
TIM CURCI - Partner
TJ THIELBAR - Partner
ROB REINSMITH - Partner; Executive Chef
JEFF STROUSE - Partner

Mulligan's Beach House
1038 SE Ocean Blvd Ste D
Stuart, FL 34996-2599

Telephone: (772) 600-7368
Internet Homepage: mulligansbeachhouse.com
Type of Business: Chain Restaurant Operator
Year Founded: 1997
Internet Order Processing: Yes
Total Units: 8
Trade Names: Mulligan's Beach House (8)
Company-Owned Units: 8
Primary Menu: American (8)
Areas of Operation: FL
Type of Foodservice: Casual Dining (8)

Key Personnel
GEORGE HART - CEO; President; General Buyer

Auntie Anne's Franchise
12555 W Sunrise Blvd
Sunrise, FL 33323-0900

Telephone: (954) 845-1133
Type of Business: Chain Restaurant Operator
Total Sales: $4,130,000 (e)
Total Units: 6
Trade Names: Auntie Anne's Hand-Rolled Soft Pretzels (2); Subway (4)
Units Franchised To: 6
Units Franchised From: 6
Primary Menu: Sandwiches/Deli (4); Snacks (2)
Areas of Operation: FL
Type of Foodservice: Quick Serve (6)
Franchise Affiliation: Auntie Anne's Inc., LANCASTER, PA

Key Personnel
MELINDA ACORD - Partner; General Buyer
LINDA ACORD - Partner; General Buyer

Pure Green Juice & Smoothies
4635 N.W. 103rd Ave
Sunrise, FL 33351

Telephone: (917) 382-9174
Internet Homepage: puregreenfranchise.com
Type of Business: Chain Restaurant Operator
Year Founded: 2014
Total Sales: $17,490,000 (e)
Total Units: 31
Trade Names: Pure Green Juice & Smoothies (31)
Company-Owned Units: 31
Primary Menu: American (31); Health Foods (31)
Type of Foodservice: Casual Dining (31); Fast Casual (31)

Key Personnel
ROSS FRANKLIN - Founder; CEO

Sunshine Restaurant Partners
13650 NW 8th St Ste 103
Sunrise, FL 33325-6239

Telephone: (305) 931-5454
Fax Number: (954) 618-6472
Internet Homepage: ihopsrp.com
Type of Business: Chain Restaurant Operator
Year Founded: 1961
Total Sales: $426,890,000 (e)
Number of Employees: 3,500
Average Check: Breakfast(5); Lunch(6);

Dinner(8)
Total Units: 155
Trade Names: IHOP Restaurant (155)
Units Franchised From: 155
Preferred Square Footage: 3,500
Preferred Location Types: Freestanding; Strip Mall
Primary Menu: American (155)
Areas of Operation: FL, GA
Type of Foodservice: Family Restaurant (155)
Franchise Affiliation: IHOP Restaurant System, GLENDALE, CA
Parent Company: Argonne Capital Group LLC, ATLANTA, GA
Headquarters: Summit Restaurant Group LLC, ATLANTA, GA

Key Personnel
MIKE BISOGNO - Area Director
BOB BURNS - Area Director
AMANDA MAHLER - Area Director Operations
CLAUDIA RODRIGUEZ - VP Human Resources
JANET ALEXANDER - Director Marketing
CHRISTOPHER HOWARD - Director Construction
JASON ULRICH - Director Area
CRIS GUERRA - Director Information Technology
MELISSA EGAN - Director Marketing, Communications
BILL GOWANLOCH - Director
WILLIAM GOWANLOCH - Regional Director
LARRY BRAKEFIELD - Regional Director Operations
JOEL DREHER - Manager Facility/Maintenance

The Grapevine Inc.
1342 SW 160th Ave
Sunrise, FL 33326-1907

Telephone: (954) 660-0470
Fax Number: (954) 660-0490
Internet Homepage: vignetos.com
Type of Business: Chain Restaurant Operator
Year Founded: 2001
Total Sales: $3,076,000 (e)
Alcohol Sales: 10%
Number of Employees: 35
Average Check: Lunch(40); Dinner(60)
Total Units: 2
Trade Names: Vignetos Italian Grill (2)
Company-Owned Units: 2
Preferred Location Types: Freestanding; Strip Mall
Alcohol Served: Beer, Wine, Liquor
Primary Menu: Italian (2)
Areas of Operation: FL
Type of Foodservice: Family Restaurant (1); Fine Dining (1)
Primary Distributors: (Food) SYSCO Food Services of South Florida Inc., MEDLEY, FL

Key Personnel
FRANK CASTIGLIONE - Partner
JOSEPH CASTIGLIONE - Partner
MICHAEL CASTIGLIONE - Partner; Executive Chef; General Buyer
ANGELO DI PIAZZA - Partner

Yonutz! Fantastical Donuts and Ice Cream
121 NW 136th St
Sunrise, FL 33325

Telephone: (954) 372-7179
Internet Homepage: yonutz.com
Company Email: info@yonutz.com
Type of Business: Chain Restaurant Operator
Year Founded: 2021
Number of Employees: 250
Total Units: 17
Units Franchised To: 17
Primary Menu: Donut (17)
Areas of Operation: AZ, CO, FL, ID, NM, NV, OK, TX, UT
Type of Foodservice: Quick Serve (17)

Key Personnel
TONY BAHU - Founder; CEO
DAVE VANHOOSE - Director Franchise Development

D.D. & H. Usry, Inc.
2415 N Monroe St Ste 1108
Tallahassee, FL 32303-4129

Telephone: (850) 553-4560
Company Email: coldstonetally@gmail.com
Type of Business: Chain Restaurant Operator
Total Sales: $1,216,000 (e)
Total Units: 2
Trade Names: Cold Stone Creamery (2)
Units Franchised From: 2
Primary Menu: Snacks (2)
Areas of Operation: FL
Type of Foodservice: Quick Serve (2)
Franchise Affiliation: Kahala Brands, SCOTTSDALE, AZ

Key Personnel
HUSTON USRY III - Partner
DELILAH SPATES - Partner

Domino's Franchisee
1528 W Tennessee St
Tallahassee, FL 32304-3405

Telephone: (850) 222-6363
Type of Business: Chain Restaurant Operator
Total Sales: $10,160,000 (e)
Total Units: 5
Trade Names: Domino's (5)
Units Franchised From: 5
Primary Menu: Pizza (5)
Areas of Operation: FL
Type of Foodservice: Quick Serve (5)
Franchise Affiliation: Domino's Pizza Inc, ANN ARBOR, MI

Key Personnel
DENNIS V. TRAN - Owner; General Buyer

K & A Subs Gainesville I, LLC
1355 Market St Ste A6
Tallahassee, FL 32312-1753

Telephone: (850) 320-6210
Fax Number: (850) 320-6211
Type of Business: Chain Restaurant Operator
Total Sales: $17,890,000 (e)
Total Units: 13
Trade Names: Jersey Mike's Subs (13)
Units Franchised From: 13
Primary Menu: Sandwiches/Deli (13)
Areas of Operation: FL
Type of Foodservice: Quick Serve (13)
Franchise Affiliation: Jersey Mike's Franchise Systems, MANASQUAN, NJ

Key Personnel
KIMBERLY A. CROWELL - Partner; General Buyer
ANGELO CROWELL - Partner

Keiser University Center Culinary Arts Tallahassee
1700 Halstead Blvd Ste 2
Tallahassee, FL 32309-3484

Telephone: (850) 906-9494
Internet Homepage: keiseruniversity.edu
Type of Business: Culinary Schools
Areas of Operation: FL

Key Personnel
DEBORAH MILLER - Executive Chef

Lindy's Fried Chicken Inc.
2785 S Monroe St
Tallahassee, FL 32301-6365

Telephone: (850) 878-6700
Internet Homepage: lindys-chicken.com
Type of Business: Chain Restaurant Operator
Year Founded: 1968
Systemwide Sales: $8,442,000 (e)
Total Sales: $3,324,000 (e)

Number of Employees: 75
Average Check: Lunch(10); Dinner(12)
Total Units: 7
Trade Names: Lindy's Fried Chicken (7)
Company-Owned Units: 2
Units Franchised To: 5
Preferred Square Footage: 2,500
Preferred Location Types: Freestanding
Primary Menu: Chicken (7)
Areas of Operation: FL
Type of Foodservice: Quick Serve (7)
Primary Distributors: (Full Line) Reinhart FoodService, LOUISVILLE, TN

Key Personnel
RAY SALIS JR - President; Controller; Executive Chef; Director Facility/Maintenance, Supply Chain, Real Estate, Design, Store Fixtures, Menu Development
TERRI ROBINSON - Owner; Manager
SAMUEL WASHINGTON - General Manager; Manager Operations; General Buyer

Soul Provider, Inc.
3491 Thomasville Rd
Tallahassee, FL 32309-3499

Telephone: (850) 906-0007
Type of Business: Chain Restaurant Operator
Total Sales: $4,906,000 (e)
Total Units: 4
Trade Names: Firehouse Subs (4)
Units Franchised From: 4
Primary Menu: Sandwiches/Deli (4)
Areas of Operation: FL
Type of Foodservice: Fast Casual (4)
Franchise Affiliation: Firehouse Restaurant Group Inc., JACKSONVILLE, FL

Key Personnel
MATT HOLMES - President; General Buyer
KELLY RYE - General Manager

23 Restaurant Services
505 E Jackson St
Tampa, FL 33602-4989

Telephone: (800) 767-0882
Internet Homepage: fordsgarageusa.com; yeomanscaskandlion.com
Company Email: office@23restaurants.com
Type of Business: Chain Restaurant Operator
Year Founded: 2012
Total Sales: $3,051,000 (e)
Total Units: 14
Trade Names: Capone's Coal Fired Pizza (1); Ford's Garage (11); Yeoman's Cask & Lion (2)
Company-Owned Units: 14
Primary Menu: American (11); Miscellaneous (2); Pizza (1)
Projected Openings: 2
Areas of Operation: FL
Type of Foodservice: Casual Dining (14)

Key Personnel
MIKE MCGUIGAN - Co-Founder
MARC BROWN - President; Partner
BILLY DOWNS - President
BILLY DIAMOND - Exec VP Operations
JEFF GABRIEL - VP Strategy
TERESA MCNAMARA - VP Accounting
JENNIFER PACI - Director New Store Development

ABC Pizza House Inc.
1242 W Hillsborough Ave
Tampa, FL 33603-1314

Telephone: (813) 237-3324
Fax Number: (813) 239-1089
Internet Homepage: abcpizza.com
Type of Business: Chain Restaurant Operator
Year Founded: 1965
Total Sales: $9,306,000 (e)
Alcohol Sales: 10%
Number of Employees: 74
Average Check: Lunch(10); Dinner(12)
Internet Order Processing: Yes
Total Units: 8
Trade Names: ABC Pizza Restaurant (8)
Company-Owned Units: 8
Preferred Square Footage: 5,000
Preferred Location Types: Freestanding
Alcohol Served: Beer, Wine
Primary Menu: Pizza (8)
Areas of Operation: FL
Type of Foodservice: Casual Dining (8)
Primary Distributors: (Food) Cheney Bros. Inc., RIVIERA BEACH, FL; (Food) Gordon Food Service, MIAMI, FL

Key Personnel
ANTHONY FOTOPOULOS - President; Controller; Manager Operations, Purchasing, Real Estate, Construction, Design, Store Planning
DIANE FOTOPOULOS - CFO; Director Finance, Information Systems, Human Resources
JAMES FOTOPOULOS - VP
GEORGE FOTOPOULOS - General Manager

Bern's Steak House
1208 S Howard Ave
Tampa, FL 33606-3102

Telephone: (813) 251-2421
Fax Number: (813) 251-5001
Internet Homepage: haventampa.com; bernssteakhouse.com; elevagerestaurant.com; sweetchocolatepi.com; epicureanhotel.com/taste
Company Email: bshcontact@bernssteakhouse.com
Type of Business: Chain Restaurant Operator
Year Founded: 1953
Total Sales: $23,367,000 (e)
Alcohol Sales: 25%
Number of Employees: 250
Average Check: Dinner(60)
Total Units: 4
Trade Names: Bern's Steak House (1); Chocolate Pi (1); Elevage (1); Haven (1)
Company-Owned Units: 4
Preferred Location Types: Freestanding
Alcohol Served: Beer, Wine, Liquor
Primary Menu: American (2); Snacks (1); Steak (1)
Areas of Operation: FL
Type of Foodservice: Casual Dining (1); Fine Dining (3)
Primary Distributors: (Food) SYSCO Food Services of West Coast Florida Inc., PALMETTO, FL

Key Personnel
DAVID LAXER - President; General Manager; General Buyer
HABTEAB HAMDE - Executive Chef
CHAD JOHNSON - Executive Chef Division
BROOKE P. KUHL - Director Public Relations
KEVIN PELLEY - Director Alcoholic Beverages
NATHANIEL WILSON - Director Food and Beverage
R FRANK RUSSO - Manager

Bloomin' Brands Inc.
2202 N West Shore Blvd Ste 500
Tampa, FL 33607-5754

Telephone: (813) 282-1225
Fax Number: (813) 282-1209
Internet Homepage: bloominbrands.com; bonefishgrill.com; carrabbas.com; flemingssteakhouse.com; outback.com
Listing Type: Corporate Office
Type of Business: Chain Restaurant Operator
Year Founded: 1988
Publicly Held: Yes
Total Sales: $4,143,224,000 (e)
Alcohol Sales: 17%
Number of Employees: 93,000
Internet Order Processing: Yes
Total Units: 1,480
Trade Names: Abbraccio (Carrabas International) (83); Aussie Grill (5); Bonefish Grill (176); Carrabba's Italian Grill (217); Fleming's Prime Steakhouse and Wine Bar (64); Outback Steakhouse (688); Outback Steakhouse (International) (247)
Company-Owned Units: 1,189
Units Franchised To: 291
Preferred Location Types: Airports; Downtown; Freestanding; Hotel/Motel; Kiosk; Lifestyle Center; Stadiums; Strip Mall

Alcohol Served: Beer, Wine, Liquor
Primary Menu: Italian (300); Sandwiches/Deli (5); Seafood (176); Steak (999)
Areas of Operation: AK, AL, AR, AZ, CA, CO, CT, DE, FL, GA, GU, HI, IA, ID, IL, IN, KS, KY, LA, MA, MD, MI, MN, MO, MS, MT, NC, NE, NH, NJ, NM, NV, NY, OH, OK, OR, PA, PR, RI, SC, SD, TN, TX, UT, VA, VI, VT, WA, WI, WV, WY, FC, AB, ON
Foreign Countries: AUSTRALIA; BAHAMAS; BRAZIL; CANADA; CHINA; COSTA RICA; DOMINICAN REPUBLIC; ECUADOR; HONG KONG; INDONESIA; JAPAN; MALAYSIA; MEXICO; QATAR; SAUDI ARABIA; SINGAPORE; SOUTH KOREA; TAIWAN; THAILAND; THE PHILIPPINES; UNITED ARAB EMIRATES
Type of Foodservice: Casual Dining (1,235); Fast Casual (5); Fine Dining (240)
Catering Services: Yes
Primary Distributors: (Full Line) PFG - Customized Support Services, LEBANON, TN
Headquarter Offices: Bonefish Grill, TAMPA, FL; Carrabba's Italian Grill Inc., TAMPA, FL; Outback Steakhouse Restaurants, TAMPA, FL
Notes: Store counts include international locations.

Key Personnel
MIKE SPANOS - CEO
BRETT PATTERSON - President Division
PAT HAFNER - President Division
FRANK LATORRE - Partner
MICHAEL HEALY - CFO; Exec VP
SUZANN TREVISAN - Chief Human Resources Officer
GAGAN SINHA - CIO
SUK SINGH - Chief Development Officer; Exec VP Franchising
KELLY BRAUN LEFFERTS - Chief Legal Officer; Exec VP; Corporate Secretary
S. ALLISON HICKS - Chief Compliance Officer; VP; General Counsel; Senior Director
PHIL PACE - Group VP; Controller
MARK GRAFF - VP Finance, Investor Relations
CATHIE KOCH - VP Communications
DEREK KOLANO - VP Internal Audit
CRYSTAL BIASI - VP Database
LISA DAWSON - Senior Director Design
TINA LEWIS - Senior Director Procurement, Global
BRITTANY MATTINGLY - Senior Director Finance
NICOLE MCMICKLE - Senior Director Integration, Training
CORD MCLEAN - Director Development, Diversity
BRIAN MARSHALL - Director Employee Compensation
KEVIN ELLIOTT - Director Finance
JAMIE BUTLER - Director Site Selection
ELIZABETH DALY - Director Media; Community Relations
VICKI BOYD - Director Employee Benefits
MICHAEL BELLOMO - Director Risk Management
JAMIESON BUMP - Director Finance
CHRIS LAKEY - Director Production
SCOTT O'DONOGHUE - Director Finance
ALEXANDER OSTROWSKI - Director Supply Chain
STEVEN ROSINSKI - Director Customer Analytics
MARK RUSSELL - Director Construction, Design
SCOTT SELF - Director Procurement
ALEX POSSON - Director Human Resources
JEFFREY WESSELS - Director Supply Chain
CINDY ZIEGLER - Director Supply Chain
TIMOTHY MOORE - Senior Manager Design
SAMANTHA KOLODZIEJ - Manager Marketing
ANGELA KILLINGS - Manager Procurement, Global
KELLY HENNESSEY - Manager Procurement, Global-Food
SAMIRA HASAN - Manager Accounting
KEVIN BUNCH - Manager Real Estate
YVONNE BRYANT - Manager Site Selection
COLEEN ALBRITTON - Manager POS/Scanning
KATHRYN DAVIS - Manager Data Quality
CARRIE CHADBOURNE - Manager Licensing
JULIE GOLDENBERG - Manager Human Resources, HRIS
ROBERT GORMAN - Manager Marketing
LEAH SUNG BURGESS - Manager Field Marketing
KYLE REDDING - Manager Security
DANIEL SENDRAL - Manager Tax
BARRY HERMAN - Senior Project Manager
TYLER JACKSON - Project Manager Information Technology
LANI DUCKWORTH - Project Manager Design
ADAM SHOOLBRED - Project Manager Design
WESLEY SYKES - Project Manager

Bonefish Grill
2202 N West Shore Blvd Ste 500
Tampa, FL 33607-5754

Telephone: (813) 282-1225
Fax Number: (813) 282-1209
Internet Homepage: bonefishgrill.com
Company Email: customerservice@bonefishgrill.com
Type of Business: Chain Restaurant Operator
Systemwide Sales: $778,994,000 (e)
Total Sales: $933,420,000 (e)
Alcohol Sales: 22%
Average Check: Dinner(28)
Total Units: 176
Trade Names: Bonefish Grill (176)
Company-Owned Units: 169
Units Franchised To: 7
Preferred Square Footage: 5,500
Preferred Location Types: Freestanding
Alcohol Served: Beer, Wine, Liquor
Primary Menu: Seafood (176)
Areas of Operation: AL, AR, CA, CO, CT, FL, GA, IA, ID, IL, IN, KS, KY, LA, MA, MD, MI, MO, MS, NC, NE, NJ, NV, NY, OH, OK, PA, RI, SC, TN, TX, VA, WA, WI
Type of Foodservice: Fine Dining (176)
Parent Company: Bloomin' Brands Inc., TAMPA, FL

Key Personnel
JEFF CARCARA - President; Exec VP
DIANE HARTZEL - VP Operations
CHRIS ARREOLA - VP Development, Training
PENNY TABOLT - Regional VP
AMANDA TRAVAGLINI - Director Marketing
RICHARD RUSH - Director Operations
MARRIAH BARBER - Manager Marketing
APRIL KELLY - Manager Culinary Operations

Brock's Eatery
10117 Princess Palm Ave Ste 375
Tampa, FL 33610-8300

Telephone: (813) 629-4397
Type of Business: Chain Restaurant Operator
Year Founded: 1996
Total Sales: $9,746,000 (e)
Number of Employees: 16
Average Check: Breakfast(5); Lunch(8); Dinner(10)
Total Units: 4
Trade Names: Brock's Eatery (4)
Company-Owned Units: 4
Preferred Square Footage: 3,000
Primary Menu: American (4)
Areas of Operation: FL
Type of Foodservice: Casual Dining (4)
Primary Distributors: (Food) US Foods, TAMPA, FL

Key Personnel
MELISSA BROCK - President; General Buyer
JACKIE ZIMMERMAN - Manager Operations

Brock's Foodservice Management
10117 Princess Palm Ave Ste 375
Tampa, FL 33610-8300

Telephone: (813) 629-4397
Type of Business: Foodservice Management Operator
Total Sales: $14,881,000 (e)
Number of Locations Served: 10
Total Foodservice Mgmt Accounts: 10
Trade Names: Brock's (10)
Areas of Operation: FL
Type of Foodservice: Quick Serve (20)
Foodservice Management Venues: College & University

Key Personnel
MELISSA BROCK - Owner

Burger 21 Inc.
8810 Twin Lakes Blvd
Tampa, FL 33614-1767

Telephone: (813) 327-7870
Internet Homepage: burger21.com
Company Email: info@burger21.com
Type of Business: Chain Restaurant Operator
Year Founded: 2010
Total Sales: $36,520,000 (e)
Average Check: Lunch(18); Dinner(24)
Total Units: 26
Trade Names: Burger 21 (26)
Company-Owned Units: 4
Units Franchised To: 22
Preferred Location Types: Airports; Downtown
Alcohol Served: Beer, Wine
Primary Menu: Hamburger (26)
Areas of Operation: AZ, FL, GA, IL, NC, NJ, NY, PA, TX, VA
Type of Foodservice: Fast Casual (26)
Catering Services: Yes
Headquarter Offices: GrillSmith LLC, TAMPA, FL

Key Personnel
MARK T. JOHNSTON - President; Partner
ARLENE JOHNSTON - Partner; Director Marketing, Business Development
SHAKON TURNER - Director Franchise Development
ROBBIE SMITH - Director Operations
ANNETTE KARAYANES - Director

BurgerMonger LLC
10412 N Dale Mabry Hwy
Tampa, FL 33618-4134

Telephone: (813) 968-6860
Internet Homepage: burgermonger.com
Type of Business: Chain Restaurant Operator
Year Founded: 2011
Total Sales: $7,573,000 (e)
Alcohol Sales: 5%
Total Units: 5
Trade Names: BurgerMonger (5)
Company-Owned Units: 5
Alcohol Served: Beer, Wine
Primary Menu: Hamburger (5)
Areas of Operation: FL
Type of Foodservice: Fast Casual (5)

Key Personnel
JAKE HICKTON - Co-Founder; Partner; Executive Director; Executive Chef
BOB SLANE - Co-Founder; Partner
JEFF SMITH - General Manager
LISA DEPTULA - Manager Operations; General

Buyer
AURIANNA RICE - Manager Sales, Catering

Busch Gardens Tampa Bay & Adventure Island
10165 N McKinley Drive,
Tampa, FL 33612

Mailing Address: PO Box 9158, TAMPA, FL, 33674-9158
Telephone: (813) 884-4386
Company Email: comments@buschgardens.com
Listing Type: Divisional Office
Type of Business: Foodservice Operations - Theme Parks
Year Founded: 1957
Total Units: 14
Areas of Operation: FL
Parent Company: SeaWorld Entertainment Inc., ORLANDO, FL

Key Personnel
RICK LAMPHIER - VP Operations
FRED ZIELINSKI - Director Foodservice
LAUREANO QUINTA - Director Foodservice

Carrabba's Italian Grill Inc.
2202 N West Shore Blvd Ste 500
Tampa, FL 33607-5754

Telephone: (813) 282-1225
Fax Number: (813) 288-1779
Internet Homepage: carrabbas.com
Company Email: info@carrabbas.com
Type of Business: Chain Restaurant Operator
Year Founded: 1995
Systemwide Sales: $823,327,000 (e)
Total Sales: $1,047,800,000 (e)
Alcohol Sales: 15%
Number of Employees: 11,360
Average Check: Lunch(14); Dinner(26)
Internet Order Processing: Yes
Internet Sales: 0.50%
Total Units: 217
Trade Names: Carrabba's Italian Grill (217)
Company-Owned Units: 204
Units Franchised To: 13
Preferred Square Footage: 5,500; 6,000; 6,500
Preferred Location Types: Community Mall; Freestanding; Strip Mall
Alcohol Served: Beer, Wine, Liquor
Primary Menu: Italian (217)
Areas of Operation: AL, AR, AZ, CO, CT, FL, GA, IL, IN, KS, KY, LA, MA, MD, MI, MO, NC, NE, NH, NJ, NV, NY, OH, OK, PA, RI, SC, TN, TX, UT, VA, WI
Type of Foodservice: Casual Dining (217)
Catering Services: Yes
Primary Distributors: (Full Line) PFG - Customized Support Services, LEBANON, TN
Parent Company: Bloomin' Brands Inc., TAMPA, FL

Key Personnel
KEREY ANDRADE - Partner
AMANDA DOVE - Partner
PAT HAFNER - VP Operations
JOEL BARKER - VP Research & Development, Culinary Development, Menu Development
JAY SMITH - Senior Director Research & Development
KEVIN POWERS - Director Marketing, Sales

Caspers Company
4908 W Nassau St
Tampa, FL 33607-3827

Telephone: (813) 287-2231
Fax Number: (813) 289-7850
Internet Homepage: casperscompany.com
Company Email: info@casperscompany.com
Type of Business: Chain Restaurant Operator
Year Founded: 1958
Total Sales: $301,690,000 (e)
Number of Employees: 3,800
Average Check: Breakfast(5); Lunch(6); Dinner(6)
Total Units: 64
Trade Names: McDonald's (63); Oxford Exchange (1)
Units Franchised From: 64
Preferred Square Footage: 500; 3,000
Preferred Location Types: Community Mall; Freestanding; Institution (college/hospital)
Primary Menu: American (1); Hamburger (53)
Areas of Operation: FL
Type of Foodservice: Casual Dining (1); Quick Serve (53)
Distribution Centers: TAMPA, FL
Franchise Affiliation: McDonald's Corporation, CHICAGO, IL
Notes: Caspers Company also owns Oxford Exchange in Tampa, FL.

Key Personnel
BLAKE J. CASPER - Chairman; CEO
RUDY GARCIA - President
ADRIENNE MCQUOID HANSON - CFO
BOB CONIGLIARO - VP Marketing
BRIAN WISCHNACK - VP; Director Information Technology
ROBBIE OBERLE - VP Training
KIM SCOTT - VP Human Resources
RACHAEL CAGLE - Director Finance
MARC DORTCH - Supervisor Area

Checkers Drive-In Restaurants Inc.
4300 W Cypress St Ste 600
Tampa, FL 33607-4157

Telephone: (813) 283-7000
Fax Number: (813) 283-7001
Internet Homepage: checkers.com; checkerscompany.com; checkersfranchising.com; rallys.com
Company Email: automail@checkers.com
Type of Business: Chain Restaurant Operator
Year Founded: 1985
Systemwide Sales: $1,422,304,000 (e)
Total Sales: $412,091,000 (e)
Number of Employees: 5,500
Average Check: Lunch(8); Dinner(8)
Total Units: 862
Trade Names: Checkers (559); Rally's Hamburgers (303)
Company-Owned Units: 259
Units Franchised To: 603
Preferred Square Footage: 760; 800; 980
Preferred Location Types: Airports; Convenience Store/Gas Station; Downtown; Freestanding; Institution (college/hospital); Mobile Unit; Regional Mall; Stadiums; Strip Mall
Primary Menu: Hamburger (862)
Areas of Operation: AL, AR, AZ, CA, DC, DE, FL, GA, IA, IL, IN, KY, LA, MD, MI, MN, MO, MS, NC, NJ, NV, NY, OH, PA, SC, TN, TX, VA, WI, WV
Type of Foodservice: Quick Serve (862)
Primary Distributors: (Food) Willow Run Foods Inc., KIRKWOOD, NY
Parent Company: Oak Hill Capital Partners, L.P., NEW YORK, NY

Key Personnel
MICHAEL BLAIR - CFO
SCOTT JOHNSON - Chief Marketing Officer
MINH LE - Chief Information Security Officer
VINCE BROCKMAN - Senior VP; General Counsel
CHRIS WARD - VP Supply Chain
RYAN JOY - Senior Director Research & Development
PATTI DUMARS - Senior Director Supply Chain
KRIS MCDONALD - Senior Director Real Estate, Construction, Design
LAUREN AXE - Director Branding
RUSSELL BERNSTINE - Director Construction, Design
MARY MELVIN - Director Restaurant Operations
RON KATTNER - Senior Manager Loss Prevention
RAY BONN - Senior Manager Payroll
CHERI BISHOP - Senior Manager Operations
KRISTI SHAW - Senior Manager Merchandising
CAROL MANICK - District Manager
JOHN LAVERTY - Manager Construction
RON SALERNO - Manager Operations
STEPHANIE GRANT - Manager Real Estate
RODNEY JONES - Manager Information Technology

Ciccio Restaurant Group
1015 S Howard Ave
Tampa, FL 33606-2431

Telephone: (813) 251-8406
Fax Number: (813) 254-5039
Internet Homepage: cicciorestaurantgroup.com
Company Email: info@ciccioandtonys.com
Type of Business: Chain Restaurant Operator
Year Founded: 1996
Total Sales: $18,790,000 (e)
Alcohol Sales: 18%
Number of Employees: 274
Average Check: Breakfast(14); Lunch(18); Dinner(22)
Internet Order Processing: Yes
Total Units: 19
Trade Names: Better Byrd (1); Ciccio's California (4); Ciccio's/Water Unique Sushi (1); Daily Eats (1); Fresh Kitchen (9); Green Lemon (1); Sweet Soul (1); Taco Dirty (1)
Company-Owned Units: 19
Preferred Square Footage: 2,500
Preferred Location Types: Downtown; Freestanding
Alcohol Served: Beer, Wine, Liquor
Primary Menu: American (10); Californian (5); Chicken (1); Mexican (1); Snacks (1); Taco (1)
Projected Openings: 2
Areas of Operation: FL
Type of Foodservice: Casual Dining (8); Fast Casual (10); Quick Serve (1)
Catering Services: Yes
Primary Distributors: (Food) SYSCO Food Services of West Coast Florida Inc., PALMETTO, FL

Key Personnel
JAMES LANZA - President; Partner; Director Information Systems, Real Estate; General Buyer
MATTHEW LANZA - Partner
JEFF GIGANTI - Partner; General Manager; Director Catering

Ciro's
2109 Bayshore Blvd
Tampa, FL 33606-2113

Telephone: (813) 251-0022
Internet Homepage: atlanticbeerandoyster.com; bocatampa.com; cirostampa.com
Company Email: bocatampa@be1concepts.com
Type of Business: Chain Restaurant Operator
Year Founded: 2010
Total Sales: $26,683,000 (e)
Alcohol Sales: 15%
Average Check: Lunch(22); Dinner(34)
Total Units: 2
Trade Names: Atlantic Beer & Oyster (1); Ciro's Speakeasy and Supper Club (1)
Company-Owned Units: 2
Alcohol Served: Beer, Wine, Liquor
Primary Menu: American (4); Miscellaneous (2); Seafood (1)
Projected Openings: 2
Areas of Operation: FL
Type of Foodservice: Casual Dining (7)

Key Personnel
KEVIN ENDERLE - President; Owner; General Buyer
FRANK SCALFARO - CFO
DAWN FERGUSON - General Manager
MARSHALL HAMILTON - General Manager
SCOTT WENGER - General Manager

Columbia Restaurant Group
2025 E 7th Ave
Tampa, FL 33605-3901

Telephone: (813) 248-3000
Fax Number: (813) 247-5881
Internet Homepage: chacha-coconuts.com; columbiarestaurant.com; ulele.com
Company Email: comments@columbiarestaurant.com
Type of Business: Chain Restaurant Operator
Year Founded: 1905
Total Sales: $34,480,000 (e)
Alcohol Sales: 20%
Number of Employees: 1,003
Average Check: Lunch(10); Dinner(14)
Internet Order Processing: Yes
Internet Sales: 2.00%
Total Units: 9
Trade Names: Cha Cha Coconuts (1); Columbia Restaurant (7); Ulele (1)
Company-Owned Units: 9
Preferred Square Footage: 2,700
Preferred Location Types: Downtown; Freestanding
Alcohol Served: Beer, Wine, Liquor
Primary Menu: American (1); Caribbean (1); Spanish (7)
Areas of Operation: FL
Type of Foodservice: Casual Dining (9)
Catering Services: Yes
Primary Distributors: (Full Line) US Foods, LAKELAND, FL
Notes: The company derives approximately 5% of its revenue from retail operations.

Key Personnel
MARK RUSS - Controller; Manager Accounting
MICHAEL HEAD - Senior Director Operations
JEFF HOUCK - Manager Marketing, Public

ConSul Hospitality Group
1511 N West Shore Blvd
Tampa, FL 33607

Telephone: (813) 498-2618
Internet Homepage: metrodiner.com
Company Email: info@metrodiner.com
Type of Business: Chain Restaurant Operator
Year Founded: 2000
Systemwide Sales: $36,627,000 (e)
Total Sales: $33,550,000 (e)
Total Units: 58
Trade Names: Metro Diner (58)
Company-Owned Units: 12
Units Franchised To: 46
Primary Menu: American (58)
Projected Openings: 20
Areas of Operation: AL, DE, FL, GA, IN, KY, NC, NV, OK, PA, TN, VA
Type of Foodservice: Casual Dining (58)

Key Personnel
HUGH CONNERTY - Co-Chairman; Partner
CHRIS SULLIVAN - Co-Chairman; Partner
MARK DAVOLI - Founder
CARL SAHLSTEN - CEO
JOHN KUNKEL - CFO
STANLEY GOODMAN - COO
DEBORAH ROVEGNO - Controller
CASEY HINSON - Director Training
CRAFTON BRYANT - Director Marketing
TRAVIS GRAPPO - Director Operations
MORGAN GRIFFIN - Manager Purchasing
ANDREW LOPER - Program Manager Construction, Design
JENNY EURTON - Executive Assistant

Datz Restaurant Group
2616 S Macdill Ave
Tampa, FL 33619

Telephone: (813) 831-7000
Internet Homepage: datzrestaurantgroup.com
Company Email: ownero@datztampa.com
Type of Business: Chain Restaurant Operator
Year Founded: 2009
Total Units: 6
Trade Names: Datz (2); Dough (1); Dr. BBQ (1); Roux (1); The Canyon at the James Museum (1)
Company-Owned Units: 6
Preferred Location Types: Freestanding; Strip Mall
Primary Menu: American (3); Bar-B-Q (1); Cajun/Creole (1); Snacks (1)
Areas of Operation: FL
Type of Foodservice: Casual Dining (2); Fast Casual (4)

Key Personnel
SUZANNE PERRY - Co-Founder
ROGER PERRY - Co-Founder

Domino's Franchisee
1005 N Tampa St
Tampa, FL 33602-3710

Telephone: (813) 221-1611
Type of Business: Chain Restaurant Operator
Total Sales: $28,806,000 (e)
Total Units: 14
Trade Names: Domino's (14)
Units Franchised From: 14
Primary Menu: Pizza (14)
Areas of Operation: FL
Type of Foodservice: Quick Serve (14)
Franchise Affiliation: Domino's Pizza Inc, ANN ARBOR, MI

Key Personnel
STEVEN A. LONGEN - Owner; General Buyer

Dow Sherwood Corporation
5404 Hoover Blvd Ste 23
Tampa, FL 33634-5351

Telephone: (813) 885-5434
Fax Number: (813) 888-9539
Internet Homepage: dowsherwood.com
Company Email: info@dowsherwood.com
Type of Business: Chain Restaurant Operator
Year Founded: 1960
Total Sales: $14,580,000 (e)
Number of Employees: 415
Average Check: Breakfast(12); Lunch(12); Dinner(12)
Total Units: 11
Trade Names: Village Inn (11)
Units Franchised From: 11
Preferred Square Footage: 3,000; 12,000
Preferred Location Types: Freestanding
Primary Menu: American (11)
Areas of Operation: FL
Type of Foodservice: Family Restaurant (11)
Franchise Affiliation: Village Inn, MINNETONKA, MN
Primary Distributors: (Full Line) US Foods, TAMPA, FL

Key Personnel
PAUL WALKER - President; Manager Operations, Purchasing, Real Estate
MIKE DENUNZIO - General Manager Restaurant Operations
ELAINE GRAU - Director Finance, Information Systems
JIM WALKER - Director Operations; Manager Advertising, Human Resources
JOSEPH BARBA - Manager

EVOS Holdings, LLC
609 S Howard Ave
Tampa, FL 33606-2412

Telephone: (813) 258-0005
Fax Number: (813) 258-9899
Internet Homepage: evos.com
Company Email: comments@evos.com
Type of Business: Chain Restaurant Operator
Total Sales: $1,884,000 (e)
Average Check: Lunch(8); Dinner(14)
Total Units: 4
Trade Names: EVOS (4)
Company-Owned Units: 4
Preferred Location Types: Freestanding; Strip Mall
Primary Menu: Health Foods (4)
Areas of Operation: FL
Type of Foodservice: Fast Casual (4)

Key Personnel
ALKIS CRASSAS - President; Partner
MICHAEL JEFFERS - Partner; VP; Treasurer; Corporate Secretary

FSC Franchise Co., LLC
5660 W Cypress St Ste A
Tampa, FL 33607-1777

Telephone: (813) 226-2333
Fax Number: (813) 226-0030
Internet Homepage: beefobradys.com; beefobradysfranchise.com
Type of Business: Chain Restaurant Operator
Year Founded: 1985
Systemwide Sales: $267,987,000 (e)
Total Sales: $17,580,000 (e)
Alcohol Sales: 15%
Number of Employees: 50
Average Check: Lunch(14); Dinner(18)
Internet Order Processing: Yes
Internet Sales: 1.00%
Total Units: 178
Trade Names: Beef'O'Brady's Family Sports Pub (172); The Brass Tap (50)
Company-Owned Units: 15
Units Franchised To: 207
Preferred Square Footage: 2,500; 3,000; 3,400; 4,000
Preferred Location Types: Downtown; Freestanding; Strip Mall
Alcohol Served: Beer, Wine, Liquor
Primary Menu: American (222)
Areas of Operation: AL, AR, CO, FL, GA, IA, IL, IN, KY, LA, MD, MI, MN, MO, MS, NC, OH, SC, TN, TX, VA
Foreign Countries: KUWAIT
Type of Foodservice: Casual Dining (222)
Catering Services: Yes

Primary Distributors: (Food) Performance Foodservice - Florida, DOVER, FL
Parent Company: CapitalSpring Partners,,
Headquarter Offices: Newk's Franchise Company, JACKSON, MS

Key Personnel
CHRIS ELLIOTT - CEO
SCOTT SIRLOUIS - COO
HEATHER BOGGS - Chief Marketing Officer
JEAN BAUDRAND - Chief Development Officer
MIKE PATRON - VP Operations; Senior Director Operations
JAMIE CECIL - VP Franchise Development
STAN DORSEY - Executive Chef; Director Research & Development
JESSICA BUCHTA - Senior Director Marketing
CAROL DECANIO - Director Training
JEFF LIDDIC - Manager Quality Assurance
LINDA MENKE - Manager Marketing, Social Media
KARLEE BOYD - Manager Marketing, Catering
VANESSA JAURIQUE-MARQUIS - Manager Research & Development, Culinary Development

GI Entertainment and Restaurant Group Inc.
5214 W Tyson Ave
Tampa, FL 33611-3224

Mailing Address: PO Box 13109, TAMPA, FL, 33681
Telephone: (813) 242-0565
Fax Number: (813) 242-9658
Internet Homepage: thelocaltampa.com; greeniguana.com; hulabayclub.com
Company Email: comments@greeniguana.com
Type of Business: Chain Restaurant Operator
Total Sales: $15,374,000 (e)
Alcohol Sales: 20%
Total Units: 3
Trade Names: Green Iguana (1); Hula Bay (1); The Local (1)
Company-Owned Units: 3
Preferred Location Types: Freestanding; Strip Mall
Alcohol Served: Beer, Wine, Liquor
Primary Menu: American (2); Seafood (1)
Areas of Operation: FL
Type of Foodservice: Casual Dining (3)

Key Personnel
ALAN FOSCO - COO

GrillSmith LLC
8810 Twin Lakes Blvd
Tampa, FL 33614-1767

Telephone: (813) 327-7870
Internet Homepage: grillsmith.com
Type of Business: Chain Restaurant Operator
Year Founded: 2004
Total Sales: $18,569,000 (e)
Number of Employees: 68
Average Check: Lunch(12); Dinner(22)
Internet Order Processing: Yes
Total Units: 5
Trade Names: GrillSmith (5)
Company-Owned Units: 5
Preferred Location Types: Lifestyle Center
Alcohol Served: Beer, Wine, Liquor
Primary Menu: Steak (5)
Areas of Operation: FL
Type of Foodservice: Casual Dining (5)
Catering Services: Yes
Primary Distributors: (Food) Cheney Bros. Inc., RIVIERA BEACH, FL
Parent Company: Burger 21 Inc., TAMPA, FL

Key Personnel
PACO PARES - Corporate Chef

H.I. Development Corporation
111 W Fortune St
Tampa, FL 33602-3206

Telephone: (813) 229-6686
Fax Number: (813) 223-9734
Internet Homepage: hidevelopment.com
Company Email: mailbox@hidevelopment.com
Type of Business: Foodservice Operations - Hotel/Motels
Year Founded: 1959
Total Sales: $81,360,000 (e)
Alcohol Sales: 15%
Number of Employees: 624
Total Units: 8
Restaurants in Hotels: 7
Trade Names: Caribe Hotel (1); Guy Harvey Oceanfront Resort (1); Holiday Inn (5); The Barrymore Hotel (1)
Company-Owned Units: 7
Alcohol Served: Beer, Wine, Liquor
Areas of Operation: FL, PR
Type of Foodservice: Casual Dining (7)
Primary Distributors: (Food) US Foods, LAKELAND, FL
Notes: The company derives approximately 75% of its revenue from hotel operations.

Key Personnel
ANDRE CALLEN - CEO; President
MARGARET BRITT - Controller
LARRY COLLIER - Director Operations

Holy Hog Barbecue Franklin LLC
302 E Kennedy Blvd
Tampa, FL 33602

Telephone: (813) 223-4464
Internet Homepage: holyhogbbq.com
Type of Business: Chain Restaurant Operator
Year Founded: 2010
Internet Order Processing: Yes
Total Units: 5
Trade Names: Holy Hog Barbecue (5)
Company-Owned Units: 5
Alcohol Served: Beer, Wine
Primary Menu: Bar-B-Q (5)
Areas of Operation: FL
Type of Foodservice: Fast Casual (5)

Key Personnel
DANNY HERNANDEZ - Founder; Partner
DAVE BURTON - Partner

Illas Management
6948 W Linebaugh Ave
Tampa, FL 33625

Telephone: (813) 265-2910
Internet Homepage: ourmcdonalds.com
Type of Business: Chain Restaurant Operator
Total Sales: $130,930,000 (e)
Total Units: 27
Trade Names: McDonald's (27)
Units Franchised From: 27
Preferred Square Footage: 2,500
Preferred Location Types: Freestanding; Strip Mall
Primary Menu: Hamburger (27)
Areas of Operation: FL
Type of Foodservice: Quick Serve (27)
Franchise Affiliation: McDonald's Corporation, CHICAGO, IL

Key Personnel
JUAN ILLAS - President; Partner; General Buyer
JAVI ILLAS - Partner
TIMOTHY RATULOWSKI - General Manager
ROB ROBERTS - Director Operations
RAMONA JACKSON - Director Training
MIKAELA DEDIOS - Manager Payroll, Human Resources

Impact FHS Restaurants, LLC
7627 W Courtney Campbell Cswy
Tampa, FL 33607-1431

Telephone: (813) 287-0907
Internet Homepage: impact-properties.com
Type of Business: Chain Restaurant Operator
Total Sales: $11,480,000 (e)
Total Units: 11
Trade Names: Aqua (1); BurgerFi (3); Firehouse Subs (6); Starbucks Coffee (1)
Company-Owned Units: 1
Units Franchised From: 10
Preferred Square Footage: 1,500
Primary Menu: Coffee (1); Hamburger (3); Miscellaneous (1); Sandwiches/Deli (6)
Areas of Operation: FL
Type of Foodservice: Casual Dining (4); Quick Serve (7)
Franchise Affiliation: Firehouse Restaurant Group Inc., JACKSONVILLE, FL

Key Personnel
DILIP KANJI - CEO; President; General Buyer
SHIRIN KANJI - Chief Investment Officer; Senior VP
NASH KANJI - Exec VP; Director Development
KISH KANJI - Exec VP
MARY MATHIEU - Senior VP

Jane King Enterprises
2513 N 50th St
Tampa, FL 33619-2738

Telephone: (813) 247-6269
Type of Business: Chain Restaurant Operator
Total Sales: $11,470,000 (e)
Total Units: 5
Trade Names: Burger King (5)
Units Franchised From: 5
Primary Menu: Hamburger (5)
Areas of Operation: FL
Type of Foodservice: Quick Serve
Franchise Affiliation: Burger King Worldwide Inc., MIAMI, FL

Key Personnel
JANE KING - Owner; General Buyer

Little Greek Franchise Development LLC
9280 Bay Plaza Blvd Ste 726
Tampa, FL 33619-4481

Telephone: (813) 245-3934
Internet Homepage: littlegreekrestaurant.com
Type of Business: Chain Restaurant Operator
Year Founded: 2012
Systemwide Sales: $15,334,000 (e)
Total Sales: $12,640,000 (e)
Number of Employees: 286
Internet Order Processing: Yes
Total Units: 44
Trade Names: Little Greek Fresh Grill (44)
Company-Owned Units: 1
Units Franchised To: 44
Preferred Location Types: Mobile Unit; Strip Mall
Alcohol Served: Beer, Wine
Primary Menu: Greek/Mediterranean (44)
Projected Openings: 1
Areas of Operation: AR, FL, GA, KY, OH, TX
Type of Foodservice: Fast Casual (36)
Primary Distributors: (Food) Roma Food Enterprises Inc., RICHMOND, VA; (Full Line) SYSCO Corporation, HOUSTON, TX

Key Personnel
SIGRID BRATIC - Founder; Partner
NICK VOJNOVIC - CEO; President; Partner
BRYAN ST. GEORGE - COO
CHUCK WINSHIP - Director
JEN BUJALSKI - Manager Marketing

McKibbon Hotel Management Inc.
5315 Avion Park Dr Ste 120
Tampa, FL 33607-1461

Telephone: (813) 241-2399
Fax Number: (813) 241-2399
Internet Homepage: mckibbon.com
Company Email: info@mckibbon.com
Type of Business: Foodservice Operations - Hotel/Motels
Year Founded: 1950
Total Sales: $70,490,000 (e)
Number of Employees: 300
Total Units: 80
Restaurants in Hotels: 10
Trade Names: Various Names (80)
Company-Owned Units: 80
Areas of Operation: AL, AR, AZ, FL, GA, IL, NC, NY, PA, SC, TN, TX, VA
Primary Distributors: (Food) SYSCO Atlanta LLC, COLLEGE PARK, GA; (Specialty Foods) SYSCO Atlanta LLC, COLLEGE PARK, GA
Notes: The company derives approximately 90% of its revenue from hotel operations.

Key Personnel
JOHN B. MCKIBBON III - Chairman
VANN HERRING - CEO; Director Operations, Purchasing, Information Systems, Real Estate, Menu Development, Food and Beverage; General Buyer
RANDY HASSEN - President
BRUCE BAERWALDE - Exec VP Operations
LYNN PRATER - VP Marketing, Sales
KRISTY RUFF - Director Information Systems

Mr.Empanada Franchise Corp
4029 W South Ave
Tampa, FL 33614-6555

Telephone: (813) 879-6233
Fax Number: (813) 879-6233
Internet Homepage: mrempanada.com
Company Email: admin@mrempanada.com
Type of Business: Chain Restaurant Operator
Year Founded: 2003
Total Sales: $13,190,000 (e)
Average Check: Dinner(5)
Total Units: 9
Trade Names: Mr. Empanada (9)
Company-Owned Units: 5
Units Franchised To: 4
Primary Menu: Latin American/Cuban (9)
Areas of Operation: FL
Type of Foodservice: Fast Casual (9)

Key Personnel
ALBERT PEREZ - Partner
AUDREY PEREZ - Partner
LISA PEREZ - Partner; General Buyer

MVP Restaurant Partners LLC
4343 Anchor Plaza Pkwy Ste 1
Tampa, FL 33634-7513

Telephone: (844) 328-1737
Fax Number: (813) 443-5344
Internet Homepage: eatpdq.com
Company Email: info@eatpdq.com
Type of Business: Chain Restaurant Operator
Total Sales: $58,010,000 (e)
Total Units: 57
Trade Names: PDQ (67)
Company-Owned Units: 67
Primary Menu: Chicken (60)
Projected Openings: 15
Areas of Operation: AL, FL, GA, NC, NJ, NV, OK, SC, TX, UT
Type of Foodservice: Quick Serve (67)

Key Personnel
KEP SWEENEY - CEO
STEPHEN ERICKSON - President; General Buyer
BOB BASHAM - Partner
NICK READER - Partner
ANNE ANSLEY - CFO
NINA FRANCHINA - Chief People Officer
JEFF KAMIS - VP Public Relations, Media
ANDREW MCADAMS - VP Business Development

Outback Steakhouse Restaurants
2202 N West Shore Blvd Ste 500
Tampa, FL 33607-5754

Telephone: (813) 282-1225
Fax Number: (813) 282-1209
Internet Homepage: outback.com
Company Email: news@outback.com
Type of Business: Chain Restaurant Operator
Year Founded: 1988
Systemwide Sales: $2,631,885,000 (e)
Publicly Held: Yes
Total Sales: $3,493,990,000 (e)
Alcohol Sales: 10%
Number of Employees: 49,000
Average Check: Dinner(26)
Internet Order Processing: Yes
Internet Sales: 1.00%
Total Units: 940
Trade Names: Aussie Grill (5); Outback (International) (247); Outback Steakhouse (688)
Company-Owned Units: 727
Units Franchised To: 213
Preferred Square Footage: 700; 6,000; 6,200
Preferred Location Types: Airports; Downtown; Freestanding; Lifestyle Center; Stadiums; Strip Mall
Alcohol Served: Beer, Wine, Liquor
Primary Menu: Sandwiches/Deli (5); Steak (935)
Projected Openings: 20
Projected Remodelings: 35
Areas of Operation: AK, AL, AR, AZ, CA, CO, CT, DE, FL, GA, GU, HI, IA, ID, IL, IN, KS, KY, LA, MA, MD, MI, MN, MO, MS, MT, NC, ND, NE, NH, NJ, NM, NV, NY, OH, OK, OR, PA, PR, RI, SC, SD, TN, TX, UT, VA, VT, WA, WI, WV, WY, AB, ON
Foreign Countries: AUSTRALIA; BRAZIL; CANADA; CHINA; COSTA RICA; DOMINICAN REPUBLIC; EGYPT; HONG KONG; INDONESIA; JAPAN; MALAYSIA; MEXICO; QATAR; SAUDI ARABIA; SINGAPORE; SOUTH KOREA; TAIWAN; THAILAND; THE PHILIPPINES; UNITED ARAB EMIRATES
Type of Foodservice: Casual Dining (935); Fast Casual (5)
Catering Services: Yes
Primary Distributors: (Equipment) Strategic Equipment & Supply Reynolds Division, TAMPA, FL
Parent Company: Bloomin' Brands Inc., TAMPA, FL
Notes: Franchised To includes some international development joint venture locations.

Key Personnel
TIM GANNON - Founder
TRUDY COOPER - Co-Founder
DAVID DENO - CEO
BRETT PATTERSON - President; Group VP
TIMOTHY MARTIN - President Development, Real Estate
JIM MOREY - President Finance, Strategy
BOBBY SILVEST - President Marketing
PAT HAFNER - President
GREG . SCARLETT - COO
STEVE ERICKSON - Senior VP
JOSEPH JACKSON - VP
MOISES LARREGUI - Regional VP Operations
SUSAN CLINE - Senior Director Operations-Training
RONI LLOYD - Senior Director Business Development
BECKY BOYD - Director Beverages
DEVIASHA SHARP - Director Marketing
WILLIAM GRIMM - Director
ADAM JAYNE - Senior Manager
SHAREN ROBINSON - Manager Talent Acquisitions
TIM DUNN - Manager
MARC VIGLIO - Manager Accounting
MATTHEW LEWIS - Manager Operations-Training
LORI BASSINGER - Project Manager Development, Training
HERB BOWER - Systems Engineer

PinChasers
4847 N Armenia Ave
Tampa, FL 33603-1438

Telephone: (813) 877-7418
Fax Number: (813) 877-1872
Internet Homepage: pinchasers.net
Type of Business: Foodservice Operations - Bowling Alley
Total Sales: $9,342,000 (e)
Alcohol Sales: 10%
Number of Employees: 50
Average Check: Breakfast(6); Lunch(6); Dinner(10)
Total Units: 3
Trade Names: PinChaser East Pasco (1); PinChaser Midtown (1); PinChaser Veterans (1)
Company-Owned Units: 3
Preferred Location Types: Other
Alcohol Served: Beer, Wine, Liquor
Primary Menu: American (3)
Areas of Operation: FL
Type of Foodservice: In-Store Feeder (3)
Primary Distributors: (Full Line) US Foods, TAMPA, FL
Notes: The company derives approximately 60% of its revenue from bowling center operations.

Key Personnel
ANTHONY PERRONE - CEO; President; Partner; Manager Menu Development; General Buyer
ROBIN PERRONE - Partner; Manager Purchasing, Sales; Specialist Customer Service
ROBBY MARTIN - General Manager; Director Human Resources; Manager Operations

Pita's Republic
11239 Causeway Blvd
Tampa, FL 33511

Telephone: (813) 960-4976
Internet Homepage: pitasrepublic.com
Type of Business: Chain Restaurant Operator
Year Founded: 1991
Total Sales: $10,440,000 (e)
Number of Employees: 32
Average Check: Lunch(8); Dinner(8)
Total Units: 9
Trade Names: Pita's Republic (9)
Company-Owned Units: 7
Units Franchised To: 2
Preferred Square Footage: 2,500
Preferred Location Types: Freestanding; Strip Mall
Primary Menu: Sandwiches/Deli (9)
Areas of Operation: FL
Type of Foodservice: Quick Serve (9)
Catering Services: Yes
Primary Distributors: (Food) SYSCO Food Services of West Coast Florida Inc., PALMETTO, FL; (Full Line) US Foods, TAMPA, FL

Key Personnel
MOE ELKASRI - President; Executive Chef; Director Catering; General Buyer

Proper House Group
6500 N Florida Ave
Tampa, FL 33604

Telephone: (813) 374-8940
Internet Homepage: gallitotampa.com; nebraskaminimart.com; properhousegroup.com; roosterandthetill.com
Company Email: phgtampa@gmail.com
Type of Business: Chain Restaurant Operator
Year Founded: 2013
Total Units: 3
Trade Names: Gallito Taqueria (1); Nebraska Mini-Mart (1); Rooster & the Till (1)
Company-Owned Units: 3
Preferred Location Types: Downtown; Freestanding; Strip Mall
Primary Menu: American (2); Taco (1)
Areas of Operation: FL
Type of Foodservice: Casual Dining (1); Quick Serve (2)

Key Personnel
TY RODRIGUEZ - Co-Founder; Partner
FERRELL ALVAREZ - Co-Founder; Partner

MYLES GALLAGHER - General Manager
BRIAN LAMPE - Executive Chef

Restaurant BT
2507 S Macdill Ave
Tampa, FL 33629-7255

Telephone: (813) 258-1916
Internet Homepage: restaurantbt.com
Company Email: bt@restaurantbt.com
Type of Business: Chain Restaurant Operator
Total Units: 4
Trade Names: Bistro BT (1); BT IN A Box (1); BT to Go (1); Restaurant BT (1)
Company-Owned Units: 4
Primary Menu: Asian (4)
Areas of Operation: FL
Type of Foodservice: Fast Casual (3); Fine Dining (1)

Key Personnel
BT NGUYEN - Owner; Executive Chef

S.M.A.K. Creamery, LLC
2774 E Fowler Ave
Tampa, FL 33612-6200

Telephone: (813) 975-0102
Type of Business: Chain Restaurant Operator
Total Sales: $1,843,000 (e)
Total Units: 3
Trade Names: Cold Stone Creamery (3)
Units Franchised From: 3
Primary Menu: Snacks (3)
Areas of Operation: FL
Type of Foodservice: Quick Serve (3)
Franchise Affiliation: Kahala Brands, SCOTTSDALE, AZ

Key Personnel
SHAWN WILLIAMS - CEO; Owner
MILDRED WRIGHT - Partner
CHERRI SCOGGIN - Regional Director Operations

Salem's Gyros & Subs
8409 Laurel Fair Cir Ste 102
Tampa, FL 33610-7396

Telephone: (813) 898-2848
Fax Number: (813) 898-2850
Internet Homepage: salemsgyrosandsubs.com
Company Email: info@salemsgyros.com
Type of Business: Chain Restaurant Operator
Year Founded: 1988
Total Sales: $23,350,000 (e)
Average Check: Dinner(16)
Total Units: 14
Trade Names: Salem's Gyros & Subs (14)
Company-Owned Units: 14
Preferred Square Footage: 4,000
Preferred Location Types: Freestanding
Primary Menu: Sandwiches/Deli (14)
Projected Openings: 2
Areas of Operation: FL
Type of Foodservice: Quick Serve (14)
Primary Distributors: (Full Line) SYSCO Food Services of West Coast Florida Inc., PALMETTO, FL

Key Personnel
SALEM GHARSALLI - CEO; President; Owner; General Buyer

SoFresh
2774 E Fowler Ave
Tampa, FL 33612

Telephone: (813) 977-4477
Internet Homepage: lovesofresh.com
Company Email: hello@lovesofresh.com
Type of Business: Chain Restaurant Operator
Year Founded: 2013
Total Units: 7
Trade Names: SoFresh (7)
Company-Owned Units: 6
Units Franchised To: 1
Preferred Location Types: Strip Mall
Primary Menu: Health Foods (7)
Projected Openings: 1
Areas of Operation: FL, PA
Type of Foodservice: Fast Casual (7)

Key Personnel
JOHN WILLIAMS - Co-Founder; CEO
TYLER BERLINGERI - Director Branding

Soho Leisure Group
2408 W Kennedy Blvd
Tampa, FL 33609-3304

Telephone: (813) 259-9669
Internet Homepage: soholeisuregroup.com; cheapinsoho.com; thehydeparkcafe.com; thekennedysoho.com
Type of Business: Chain Restaurant Operator
Total Units: 3
Trade Names: Cheap Restaurant and Bar (1); Hyde Park Cafe (1); The Kennedy (1)
Company-Owned Units: 3
Alcohol Served: Beer, Wine, Liquor
Primary Menu: Miscellaneous (3)
Areas of Operation: FL
Type of Foodservice: Casual Dining (3)

Key Personnel
TOMMY ORTIZ - Founder; Partner
CHRIS SCOTT - Partner

BLAIR JOHNSON - General Manager

Subway Management Corporation
300 E Madison St
Tampa, FL 33602-4813

Telephone: (813) 985-7899
Fax Number: (813) 984-8283
Internet Homepage: subway.com
Type of Business: Chain Restaurant Operator
Year Founded: 1976
Total Sales: $17,290,000 (e)
Number of Employees: 200
Average Check: Lunch(12); Dinner(12)
Total Units: 21
Trade Names: Subway (21)
Units Franchised From: 21
Preferred Square Footage: 900; 1,500
Preferred Location Types: Strip Mall
Primary Menu: Sandwiches/Deli (21)
Areas of Operation: FL
Type of Foodservice: Quick Serve (21)
Franchise Affiliation: Doctor's Associates Inc., MILFORD, CT
Primary Distributors: (Food) US Foods, LAKELAND, FL

Key Personnel
KHALID KHAN - VP; Director Finance, Operations, Purchasing, Facility/Maintenance, Information Systems, Real Estate

Surf Shack Coastal Kitchen LLC
12217 W Linebaugh Ave
Tampa, FL 33626-1743

Telephone: (813) 475-5916
Internet Homepage: surfshackkitchen.com; terraceatsurfshack.com
Type of Business: Chain Restaurant Operator
Total Units: 3
Trade Names: Surf Shack Coastal Kitchen (2); The Terrace at Surf Shack (1)
Company-Owned Units: 3
Primary Menu: American (3)
Areas of Operation: FL
Type of Foodservice: Casual Dining (3)

Key Personnel
STEVE BISHOP - CEO
RON FULLER - Chief Development Officer; Principal; General Buyer

Taco Bus
3914 N US Highway 301 Ste 400
Tampa, FL 33619

Telephone: (813) 372-0461
Internet Homepage: taco-bus.com
Type of Business: Chain Restaurant Operator
Year Founded: 1996
Total Sales: $10,620,000 (e)
Average Check: Lunch(10); Dinner(14)
Internet Order Processing: Yes
Total Units: 12
Trade Names: Taco Bus (12)
Company-Owned Units: 12
Preferred Location Types: Downtown; Freestanding; Travel Plazas
Primary Menu: Mexican (12)
Projected Openings: 3
Areas of Operation: FL
Type of Foodservice: Fast Casual (12)
Catering Services: Yes

Key Personnel
OMAR CHAUDHRY - Partner; General Buyer
ALISON CHAUDHRY - Partner
HEATHER CHAUDHRY - Director Operations, Marketing
PABLO PERALES - Manager Purchasing

The Melting Pot Restaurants Inc.
7886 Woodland Center Blvd
Tampa, FL 33614-2409

Telephone: (813) 881-0055
Fax Number: (813) 889-9361
Internet Homepage: frontburnerbrands.com; meltingpot.com
Company Email: info@meltingpot.com
Type of Business: Chain Restaurant Operator
Year Founded: 1975
Systemwide Sales: $249,546,000 (e)
Total Sales: $15,330,000 (e)
Alcohol Sales: 25%
Number of Employees: 89
Average Check: Dinner(50)
Foodservice Sales: $11,498,000 (e)
Internet Order Processing: Yes
Internet Sales: 1.00%
Total Units: 97
Trade Names: The Melting Pot Restaurant (97)
Company-Owned Units: 4
Units Franchised To: 93
Preferred Square Footage: 5,000; 6,000
Preferred Location Types: Community Mall; Downtown; Freestanding; Hotel/Motel; Lifestyle Center; Office Complex; Regional Mall; Strip Mall
Alcohol Served: Beer, Wine, Liquor
Primary Menu: American (97)
Areas of Operation: AL, AZ, CA, CO, CT, DC, DE, FL, GA, HI, ID, IL, IN, LA, MA, MD, MI, MN, MO, NC, NJ, NM, NV, NY, OH, OK, OR, PA, SC, TN, TX, UT, VA, WA, WI
Foreign Countries: CANADA; MEXICO; QATAR
Type of Foodservice: Fine Dining (97)
Primary Distributors: (Equipment) Beltram Foodservice Group, TAMPA, FL; (Food) The Bruss Co., CHICAGO, IL; (Food) Reinhart FoodService, LOUISVILLE, TN; (Food) Labatt Food Service, SAN ANTONIO, TX; (Food) Nicholas & Co. Inc., SALT LAKE CITY, UT; (Food) Reinhart FoodService LLC, CHICAGO, IL; (Food) US Foods Holding Corp., ROSEMONT, IL; (Food) Jacmar Foodservice Distribution, CITY OF INDUSTRY, CA; (Supplies) Edward Don & Co., MIRAMAR, FL
Parent Company: Front Burner, TAMPA, FL
Notes: The total of "Franchised To" restaurants includes several that are owned by corporations whose shareholders are also shareholders of The Melting Pot. The company derives approximately 25% of its revenue from the sale of food, equipment & supplies to its franchisees.

Key Personnel
MICHAEL M. JOHNSTON - President
SCOTT PIERCE - CFO; Treasurer
DANIEL D. STONE - Chief People Officer; Chief Business Development Officer
JAY WALDEN - VP Construction, Design
WILLIAM MURPHY - Controller
BUD CULP - General Counsel
LAUREN MULHERN - Director Public Relations
CARMEN MURRILLO - Director Marketing
DAN AMMEN - Director Purchasing, Distribution
ANDREW SKEINS - Manager Operations, Training
CINDY SMITH - Manager Data Quality
ROBIN DAVIS - Manager Restaurant Operations
JOHN MARTIN - Manager Restaurant Operations
KYLE WRAY - Manager Beverages
BRANDY HARDY - Administrator Legal, Franchising

The Wendy's Company
4631 Woodland Corporate Blvd Ste 109
Tampa, FL 33614-2404

Telephone: (813) 371-3360
Fax Number: (813) 886-6361
Listing Type: Divisional Office
Type of Business: Chain Restaurant Operator
Total Units: 95
Areas of Operation: FL
Parent Company: The Wendy's Company, DUBLIN, OH

Key Personnel
TODD A. PENEGOR - CEO; President; Director
ADAM HOLLAND - Chief Information Security Officer; VP
RICHARD HOPKINS - VP Division
RODRIGO BARBOSA - Senior Director Construction, International
ALLAN CAMPBELL - Director Operations, Area, Canada
TARA FITZPATRICK - Director Operations-Training
GENE FERRARO - Director Financial Planning
ANDREW VICKS - Director Systems, Operations-Integration
SOPHIE CHOGOVADZE - Regional Manager Marketing; Manager Marketing, International
MICHELLE GOETZ - Manager Finance, Information Technology
GREG CORNISH - Manager Finance

Valenti Management Inc.
3930 Premier North Dr
Tampa, FL 33618

Telephone: (813) 935-8777
Fax Number: (813) 935-6446
Company Email: info@valentims.com
Type of Business: Chain Restaurant Operator
Year Founded: 1996
Total Sales: $49,150,000 (e)
Alcohol Sales: 5%
Number of Employees: 394
Average Check: Breakfast(5); Lunch(10); Dinner(12)
Total Units: 12
Trade Names: Chili's Grill & Bar (12)
Units Franchised From: 12
Preferred Square Footage: 2,800; 3,500
Preferred Location Types: Freestanding; Regional Mall; Strip Mall
Alcohol Served: Beer, Wine, Liquor
Primary Menu: Southwest/Tex-Mex (12)
Projected Openings: 3
Projected Remodelings: 6
Areas of Operation: AL, MS
Type of Foodservice: Casual Dining (12)
Franchise Affiliation: Chili's Grill & Bar, DALLAS, TX
Primary Distributors: (Equipment) The Wasserstrom Co., COLUMBUS, OH; (Food) The SYGMA Network Inc. - Columbus, COLUMBUS, OH; (Supplies) The SYGMA Network, Inc., DUBLIN, OH

Key Personnel
DARRELL VALENTI - CEO; President
STEVE NESBITT - CFO
SHARON RITCH - Chief Accounting Officer
PETER GRANT - COO; Senior VP; General Buyer
TROY G. VALENTI - Senior VP Real Estate
JOANNE COX - Manager Human Resources

Webe Subs Inc
10049 E Adamo Dr
Tampa, FL 33619-2619

Telephone: (813) 879-5489
Type of Business: Chain Restaurant Operator
Total Sales: $11,810,000 (e)
Total Units: 20
Trade Names: Subway (20)
Units Franchised From: 20
Primary Menu: Sandwiches/Deli (20)
Areas of Operation: FL
Type of Foodservice: Quick Serve (20)
Franchise Affiliation: Doctor's Associates Inc., MILFORD, CT

Key Personnel
THOMAS R. CLASEN - President

World of Beer Franchising Inc.
10910 Sheldon Rd
Tampa, FL 33626-4701

Telephone: (813) 926-9300
Fax Number: (813) 920-0801
Internet Homepage: worldofbeer.com
Company Email: info@worldofbeerusa.com
Type of Business: Chain Restaurant Operator
Year Founded: 2007
Systemwide Sales: $134,004,000 (e)
Total Sales: $8,627,000 (e)
Alcohol Sales: 75%
Total Units: 65
Trade Names: World of Beer (65)
Units Franchised To: 65
Preferred Square Footage: 2,000; 2,700
Preferred Location Types: Freestanding; Strip Mall
Alcohol Served: Beer, Wine
Projected Openings: 3
Areas of Operation: AL, AZ, CA, CO, CT, DC, FL, GA, IL, KY, LA, MD, NC, NJ, NY, OH, SC, TN, TX, VA, WI
Notes: World of Beer locations do not operate kitchens and derive approximately 5% of total revenue from the retail sale of beer and tobacco products.

Key Personnel
SCOTT D. ZEPP - Co-Founder; Partner
MATTHEW L. LAFON - Co-Founder; Partner; VP Franchise Development
PAUL E. AVERY - CEO; President
BENJAMIN P. NOVELLO - Partner; Chief Development Officer
JAMES R. POLLARD - Partner
JAMES BUELL - Chief Brand Officer; Chief Innovation Officer
MARC VIGLIO - Controller
JOHN BIRD - General Manager
RYAN MCCARTHY - Director Business Development
MARC SAWYER - Director
JASON KALICHAK - Director Information Technology
CINDY FRANZESE - Director Human Resources
BARBARA KRAMER - Director Marketing-Integration
DAVID BELLIVEAU - Director
CORI ROSECRANS - Manager Brand Marketing
CHESLEIGH SLAYTON - Manager Marketing, Design

Yogurtology Franchising, LLC
3641 W Kennedy Blvd Ste A
Tampa, FL 33609-2849

Telephone: (813) 867-8628
Fax Number: (813) 353-2221
Internet Homepage: yogurtology.com
Company Email: email@yogurtology.com
Type of Business: Chain Restaurant Operator
Systemwide Sales: $10,720,000 (e)
Total Sales: $3,152,000 (e)
Total Units: 13
Trade Names: Yogurtology (13)
Units Franchised From: 13
Primary Menu: Snacks (13)
Projected Openings: 2
Areas of Operation: AZ, FL
Type of Foodservice: Quick Serve (13)

Key Personnel
JORDAN LEVY - President
EAN MENDELSOHN - VP
JENNIFER DUFEK - Director Marketing

Louis Pappas Restaurants Group
731 Wesley Ave
Tarpon Springs, FL 34689-6711

Telephone: (727) 937-1770
Fax Number: (727) 937-1788
Internet Homepage: louispappas.com
Company Email: info@louispappas.com
Type of Business: Chain Restaurant Operator
Year Founded: 2001
Total Sales: $6,007,000 (e)
Alcohol Sales: 20%
Number of Employees: 45
Average Check: Lunch(10); Dinner(10)
Internet Order Processing: Yes
Internet Sales: 4.00%
Total Units: 5
Trade Names: Louis Pappas Market Cafe (5)
Company-Owned Units: 5
Preferred Square Footage: 2,500; 3,000
Preferred Location Types: Freestanding; Strip Mall
Alcohol Served: Beer, Wine
Primary Menu: Greek/Mediterranean (5)
Areas of Operation: FL
Type of Foodservice: Fast Casual (5)
Primary Distributors: (Full Line) Cheney Bros. Inc., RIVIERA BEACH, FL

Key Personnel
LOUIS L. PAPPAS - CEO; Partner; Executive Chef; Director Operations
NANCY PAPPAS - Partner
FLORINDA WILLIAMS - Director Purchasing; General Buyer

3Natives: Acai and Juicery
251 U S 1
Tequesta, FL 33469

Telephone: (561) 203-7980
Internet Homepage: 3natives.com
Type of Business: Chain Restaurant Operator
Year Founded: 2013
Total Units: 12
Trade Names: 3Natives: Acai and Juicery (12)
Company-Owned Units: 12
Preferred Location Types: Strip Mall
Primary Menu: Health Foods (12)
Projected Openings: 3
Areas of Operation: FL
Type of Foodservice: Fast Casual (12)

Key Personnel
ANTHONY BAMBINO - Founder

Domino's Franchisee
1850 Knox McRae Dr Ste 102
Titusville, FL 32780-5421

Telephone: (321) 268-8008
Type of Business: Chain Restaurant Operator
Total Sales: $10,257,000 (e)
Total Units: 5
Trade Names: Domino's (5)
Units Franchised From: 5
Primary Menu: Pizza (5)
Areas of Operation: FL
Type of Foodservice: Quick Serve (5)
Franchise Affiliation: Domino's Pizza Inc, ANN ARBOR, MI

Key Personnel
WILLIAM D. BLALOCK - Owner; General Buyer

Beard Papa's
2856 Columbia St
Torrance, FL 90503

Telephone: (131) 064-26542
Internet Homepage: beardpapas.com
Type of Business: Chain Restaurant Operator
Year Founded: 1999
Total Units: 42
Trade Names: Beard Papa's (42)
Company-Owned Units: 10
Units Franchised To: 32
Primary Menu: Snacks (42)
Areas of Operation: AZ, CA, CO, GA, IL, MA, MN, NC, NV, NY, OR, SC, TX, UT, WA
Type of Foodservice: Casual Dining (0); Fast Casual (42)

Key Personnel
YUJI HIROTA - Founder; Owner
PAMELA FAZIO - CEO United States; President United States
JARON LINDSAY - VP Operations
MARK NATHAN - Director Marketing

Paradise Pizza Inc
437 S John Sims Pkwy
Valparaiso, FL 32580-1409

Mailing Address: PO Box 5306, NICEVILLE, FL, 32578-5306
Telephone: (850) 678-1161
Fax Number: (850) 678-4531
Type of Business: Chain Restaurant Operator
Total Sales: $14,544,000 (e)
Total Units: 7
Trade Names: Domino's (7)
Units Franchised From: 7
Primary Menu: Pizza (7)
Areas of Operation: FL
Type of Foodservice: Quick Serve (7)
Franchise Affiliation: Domino's Pizza Inc, ANN ARBOR, MI

Key Personnel
FRANK L. PICHARDO - President
ERIK LANDERS - General Manager

Fast Food Enterprises
144 Vista Royale Sq
Vero Beach, FL 32962-3057

Telephone: (772) 569-3420
Fax Number: (772) 569-5365
Internet Homepage: fastfoodent.com
Type of Business: Chain Restaurant Operator
Year Founded: 1972
Total Sales: $22,230,000 (e)
Number of Employees: 800
Average Check: Breakfast(5); Lunch(8); Dinner(8)
Total Units: 10
Trade Names: Burger King (10)
Units Franchised From: 10
Preferred Square Footage: 2,500; 4,000
Preferred Location Types: Freestanding
Primary Menu: Hamburger (10)
Areas of Operation: PA
Type of Foodservice: Quick Serve (22)
Franchise Affiliation: Burger King Worldwide Inc., MIAMI, FL

Key Personnel
MARK HOLM - President
TRISHA COOK - Controller
REBECCA FOREMAN - Manager

Pereira Holdings, LLC
2605 S State Road 7 Ste 410
Wellington, FL 33414-9374

Telephone: (561) 792-5712
Type of Business: Chain Restaurant Operator
Total Sales: $19,300,000 (e)
Total Units: 12
Trade Names: Moe's Southwest Grill (12)
Units Franchised From: 12
Primary Menu: Southwest/Tex-Mex (12)
Areas of Operation: FL, GA
Type of Foodservice: Fast Casual (12)
Franchise Affiliation: Moe's Southwest Grill LLC, ATLANTA, GA

Key Personnel
THIAGO PEREIRA - Partner; General Buyer
NANCY PANOZ - Partner
ANDREA PEREIRA - Partner

Apple Investors Group (Anand Enterprises Inc.)
1503 Belvedere Rd
West Palm Beach, FL 33406-1501

Telephone: (561) 242-4907
Internet Homepage: appleig.com
Type of Business: Chain Restaurant Operator
Total Sales: $176,500,000 (e)
Alcohol Sales: 10%
Total Units: 75
Trade Names: Applebee's Neighborhood Grill & Bar (46); IHOP Restaurant (7); Pizza Hut (18); Stevi B's Pizza (4)
Units Franchised From: 75
Preferred Location Types: Freestanding
Alcohol Served: Beer, Wine, Liquor
Primary Menu: American (53); Pizza (22)
Areas of Operation: AL, FL, GA, MO, NM, TN, VA
Type of Foodservice: Casual Dining (68); Family Restaurant (7)
Franchise Affiliation: ACG Pizza Partners LLC, DUNWOODY, GA; Applebee's Services Inc., KANSAS CITY, MO; IHOP Restaurant System, GLENDALE, CA

Key Personnel
URMESH DAHYA - Co-Founder; Senior Director Information Technology
ANAND PATEL - President; Principal; General Buyer
NIMESH DAYHA - CFO
ELIZABETH MARKHAM - Area Director
JOHANNAH ESTEP - VP Operations
EDUARDO HAQUEO - VP Operations
MARQ MARSHALL - VP Operations
STEVE HUBBARD - VP Operations
STEVE SHABAZIAN - VP Operations
KEVIN JONES - General Manager
JUSTIN JAMES - General Manager
MATT PALANZA - Director Marketing
BRYAN J. BARCLAY - Director Human Resources
JACKIE BROWN - Director Human Resources

Big Time Restaurant Group
400 Clematis St Ste 205
West Palm Beach, FL 33401-5322

Telephone: (561) 659-1940
Fax Number: (561) 659-3588
Internet Homepage: bigtimerestaurants.com
Type of Business: Chain Restaurant Operator
Year Founded: 1997
Total Sales: $15,020,000 (e)
Alcohol Sales: 10%
Number of Employees: 566
Average Check: Lunch(12); Dinner(24)
Total Units: 16
Trade Names: Big City Tavern (1); City Cellar Wine Bar & Grill (1); City Oyster (1); Grease (1); Louie Bossi's Ristorante, Bar & Pizzeria (2); Rocco's Tacos & Tequila Bar (10)
Company-Owned Units: 16
Preferred Square Footage: 5,500; 6,000
Preferred Location Types: Freestanding; Strip Mall
Alcohol Served: Beer, Wine, Liquor
Primary Menu: American (3); Italian (2); Seafood (1); Taco (10)
Projected Openings: 1
Areas of Operation: FL
Type of Foodservice: Casual Dining (16)

Key Personnel
LOUIE BOSSI - Partner; Executive Chef
TODD HERBST - Partner; General Buyer
LISABET SUMMA - Partner; Executive Director Culinary Development
WILLIAM WATSON - Partner; Director Finance
CHRISTIE BELLINO PHR - Director Development, Training
SYDNEY LAX - Director Event Planning

BARBARA DILLON - Director Operations

Bolay Restaurant Partners
1880 Okeechobee Blvd Suite A
West Palm Beach, FL 33409

Telephone: (561) 815-5185
Internet Homepage: bolay.com
Company Email: marketing@bolay.com
Type of Business: Chain Restaurant Operator
Year Founded: 2016
Total Sales: $14,770,000 (e)
Total Units: 20
Trade Names: Bolay | So Fresh. So Bold. (20)
Company-Owned Units: 20
Preferred Square Footage: 2,500
Preferred Location Types: Strip Mall
Primary Menu: Health Foods (20)
Projected Openings: 2
Areas of Operation: FL
Type of Foodservice: Fast Casual (20)

Key Personnel
CHRIS GANNON - Co-Founder; CEO
TIM GANNON - Co-Founder
CLAUDE DELUCIA - Partner Operations
DAN RISICK - Partner Operations
JORGE BERLINGERI - Partner Operations
COLLEEN BRADY - Partner Operations
JOSE HERNANDEZ - Partner
DANIEL MARTIN - Partner
ROBERT PUGH - VP Food
OWEN BRADY - VP Supply Chain
ANDREA L. CASE - Senior Director Talent
DALY K. REBACK - Director Marketing
ENRIQUE MARTINEZ - Manager Restaurant Operations

Great Service Restaurants LLC
2101 Vista Pkwy Ste 274
West Palm Beach, FL 33411-2706

Telephone: (561) 228-6212
Fax Number: (561) 228-6214
Internet Homepage: greatservicerestaurants.com; jambajuice.com
Company Email: info@greatsr.com
Type of Business: Chain Restaurant Operator
Year Founded: 2010
Total Sales: $13,500,000 (e)
Average Check: Breakfast(12); Lunch(12); Dinner(12)
Internet Order Processing: Yes
Total Units: 13
Trade Names: Jamba Juice (13)
Units Franchised From: 13
Preferred Square Footage: 1,200
Primary Menu: Health Foods (13)
Areas of Operation: FL
Type of Foodservice: Quick Serve (13)

Franchise Affiliation: Jamba Inc., FRISCO, TX

Key Personnel
GUILLERMO PEREZ-VARGAS - Partner; General Buyer
ANGEL HERRERA - Partner; General Buyer

Hurricane AMT LLC
1800 Okeechobee Rd Ste 100
West Palm Beach, FL 33409-5207

Telephone: (310) 319-1850
Fax Number: (561) 932-1074
Internet Homepage: hurricanewings.com
Company Email: info@hurricanewings.com
Listing Type: Subsidiary
Type of Business: Chain Restaurant Operator
Year Founded: 1995
Systemwide Sales: $117,964,000 (e)
Total Sales: $7,059,000 (e)
Alcohol Sales: 7%
Number of Employees: 174
Average Check: Dinner(14)
Total Units: 47
Trade Names: Hurrican BTW (1); Hurricane Grill and Wings (48)
Units Franchised To: 49
Preferred Square Footage: 2,500; 4,500
Preferred Location Types: Freestanding
Alcohol Served: Beer, Wine, Liquor
Primary Menu: American (49); Seafood (0)
Projected Openings: 10
Areas of Operation: AL, AZ, CO, FL, GA, KS, MD, NY, TX
Type of Foodservice: Casual Dining (0); Fast Casual (49)
Parent Company: Fat Brands, Inc., BEVERLY HILLS, CA

Key Personnel
WALTER HENRY - VP Real Estate
STEPHEN SANTOS - Director Operations

JAHA Chicken Inc
980 N Military Trl
West Palm Beach, FL 33415-1320

Telephone: (561) 274-4161
Fax Number: (561) 687-0915
Type of Business: Chain Restaurant Operator
Total Sales: $32,260,000 (e)
Total Units: 18
Trade Names: KFC (18)
Units Franchised From: 18
Preferred Location Types: Freestanding
Primary Menu: Chicken (18)
Areas of Operation: FL
Type of Foodservice: Quick Serve (18)
Franchise Affiliation: KFC Corporation, LOUISVILLE, KY

Key Personnel
JUAN GAVILAN - President; Partner

Jon Smith Subs
2121 Vista Pkwy
West Palm Beach, FL 33411-2706

Telephone: (561) 425-6829
Fax Number: (561) 640-6062
Internet Homepage: jonsmithsubs.com
Company Email: info@jonsmithsubfranchise.com
Type of Business: Chain Restaurant Operator
Year Founded: 1986
Systemwide Sales: $16,850,000 (e)
Total Units: 20
Trade Names: Jon Smith Subs (20)
Company-Owned Units: 15
Units Franchised From: 5
Primary Menu: Sandwiches/Deli (20)
Projected Openings: 15
Areas of Operation: FL, NV, OH, TX, VA
Type of Foodservice: Fast Casual (20)
Parent Company: United Franchise Group, WEST PALM BEACH, FL
Notes: The Greek Greek concept is operated by United Franchise Group. See that listing for more information, including contacts.

Key Personnel
RAY TITUS - CEO
JIM BUTLER - President

Palm Beach Kennel Club
1111 N Congress Ave
West Palm Beach, FL 33409-6317

Telephone: (561) 683-2222
Fax Number: (561) 684-9121
Internet Homepage: pbkennelclub.com
Company Email: info@PBKennelClub.com
Type of Business: Chain Restaurant Operator
Year Founded: 1968
Total Sales: $4,696,000 (e)
Alcohol Sales: 20%
Number of Employees: 60
Average Check: Lunch(12); Dinner(30)
Total Units: 2
Trade Names: Paddock Room Restaurant (1); The Terrace Room (1)
Company-Owned Units: 2
Preferred Location Types: Other
Alcohol Served: Beer, Wine, Liquor
Primary Menu: American (2)
Areas of Operation: FL
Type of Foodservice: Casual Dining (1); Fine Dining (1)
Primary Distributors: (Food) SYSCO Food Services of Southeast Florida LLC, RIVIERA BEACH, FL

Key Personnel
PATRICK J. ROONEY SR - CEO
JOSEPH ROONEY - VP
WAN YOU LAURENT - Executive Chef
ALEXIS BARBISH-SOMMER - Director Marketing
DAVID GRIEDER - Director Food and Beverage; General Buyer
RENEE LAMPMAN - Director Human Resources
DAN LAUGHLIN - Manager Operations
EDWARD GRAY - Manager Security
KAITLYN TRUPIA - Manager Sales
JUDY FRANKLYN - Specialist Customer Service

RREMC Restaurants LLC
1280 N Congress Ave Ste 107
West Palm Beach, FL 33409

Telephone: (561) 684-2101
Fax Number: (561) 584-5799
Internet Homepage: rremcrestaurants.com
Company Email: debbie@rremc.com
Type of Business: Chain Restaurant Operator
Year Founded: 2002
Total Sales: $159,410,000 (e)
Average Check: Dinner(10)
Total Units: 55
Trade Names: Denny's (55)
Units Franchised From: 55
Alcohol Served: Beer
Primary Menu: American (55)
Areas of Operation: FL, GA, VA
Type of Foodservice: Family Restaurant (55)
Franchise Affiliation: Denny's Corporation, SPARTANBURG, SC

Key Personnel
JOHN METZ - CEO; Partner
KATHY CUDA - Partner
VICTOR CUDA - COO; General Buyer
LAUNDA BOLDEN - Regional VP
JENNY FRANCO - Director Human Resources

Sloan's Franchise LLC
1100 Technology Pl Ste 116
West Palm Beach, FL 33407-4634

Telephone: (561) 839-3000
Internet Homepage: sloansicecream.com
Company Email: info@sloansicecream.com
Type of Business: Chain Restaurant Operator
Year Founded: 1999
Total Units: 16
Trade Names: Sloan's (16)
Company-Owned Units: 5
Units Franchised To: 11
Primary Menu: Snacks (16)
Projected Openings: 2
Areas of Operation: CA, FL, NV
Foreign Countries: KUWAIT; SAUDI ARABIA

Type of Foodservice: Quick Serve (16)

Key Personnel
SLOAN KAMENSTEIN - Founder; CEO
DAVID WILD - Director Franchise Operations, Franchise Development

The Great Greek Mediterranean Grill
2121 Vista Pkwy
West Palm Beach, FL 33411

Telephone: (561) 567-0258
Fax Number: (561) 640-6062
Internet Homepage: thegreatgreekgrill.com
Type of Business: Chain Restaurant Operator
Year Founded: 2018
Systemwide Sales: $7,750,000 (e)
Total Units: 22
Trade Names: The Great Greek Grill (22)
Company-Owned Units: 1
Units Franchised To: 21
Primary Menu: Greek/Mediterranean (22)
Projected Openings: 5
Areas of Operation: FL, NV
Type of Foodservice: Fast Casual (22)
Parent Company: United Franchise Group, WEST PALM BEACH, FL
Notes: The Greek Greek concept is operated by United Franchise Group. See that listing for more information, including contacts.

Key Personnel
RAY TITUS - CEO
BOB ANDERSEN - President Branding
ANGELO FREITES - VP Operations

TooJay's Management Corporation
3654 Georgia Ave
West Palm Beach, FL 33405-2121

Telephone: (561) 659-9011
Fax Number: (561) 659-9703
Internet Homepage: toojays.com
Company Email: info@toojays.com
Type of Business: Chain Restaurant Operator
Year Founded: 1981
Total Sales: $79,050,000 (e)
Alcohol Sales: 1%
Number of Employees: 401
Average Check: Breakfast(5); Lunch(8); Dinner(8)
Internet Order Processing: Yes
Total Units: 21
Trade Names: TooJay's, Original Gourmet Deli (21)
Company-Owned Units: 21
Preferred Square Footage: 4,000
Preferred Location Types: Strip Mall

Alcohol Served: Beer, Wine
Primary Menu: Sandwiches/Deli (21)
Areas of Operation: FL
Type of Foodservice: Casual Dining (21)
Catering Services: Yes
On-site Distribution Center: Yes

Key Personnel
JAY TRUNGALE - Chairman; Partner
MARK KIRKE - CEO
KEVIN GAGNON - Chief Accounting Officer; VP Finance
ALAN NUCKLES - Senior VP Operations, Purchasing, Construction
ART SANDERS - VP Human Resources
TOM SEEKER - Director Information Technology
JENNELL PICCOLO - Manager Purchasing
PETER COWLEY - Supervisor Central Region

United Franchise Group
2121 Vista Pkwy
West Palm Beach, FL 33411

Telephone: (561) 425-6829
Fax Number: (561) 640-6062
Listing Type: Corporate Office
Type of Business: Chain Restaurant Operator
Year Founded: 2005
Total Sales: $21,770,000 (e)
Total Units: 31
Trade Names: Jon Smith Subs (12); The Great Greek Grill (19)
Company-Owned Units: 13
Units Franchised To: 18
Primary Menu: Greek/Mediterranean (19); Sandwiches/Deli (12)
Projected Openings: 21
Areas of Operation: FL, NV, OH, TX, VA
Type of Foodservice: Fast Casual (31)
Headquarter Offices: Jon Smith Subs, WEST PALM BEACH, FL; The Great Greek Mediterranean Grill, WEST PALM BEACH, FL
Notes: United Franchise Group houses a group of franchise systems, most of which are not in the foodservice industry. United Franchise Group's Signarama brand is the world's largest sign franchise.

Key Personnel
RAY TITUS - Founder; CEO
TODD NEWTON - CFO
DAVID BAXTER - COO
BRADY LEE - COO
STEPHEN SELTZER - Chief Marketing Officer Legal; Director
ANTHONY MICHAEL FOLEY - Global VP Sales
PAULA MERCER - VP Administration
MICHAEL WHITE - VP Franchise Sales
BRIAN GOSS - Regional VP Franchise Sales
PAT IPPOLITO - Regional VP Franchise Sales
DAN NEMUNAITIS - Regional VP Franchise Sales
ALAN VAN CAMPEN - Regional VP Franchise

Sales
MARIA LOBOSCO - Regional VP Franchise Sales
SEAN PALMER - Regional VP Franchise Sales
BOB ANDERSEN - Director Sales
CASEY MATTHEWS - Regional Manager Franchise Sales
MATT SZAFARYN - Regional Manager Franchise Sales
FRANK YOUNG - Manager Finance

DelVecchio's Pizzeria
1675 N Commerce Pkwy
Weston, FL 33326

Telephone: (954) 385-1350
Fax Number: (954) 384-44838
Internet Homepage: delvecchiospizza.com
Company Email: social@delvecchiospizza.com
Type of Business: Chain Restaurant Operator
Year Founded: 2000
Total Sales: $7,683,000 (e)
Alcohol Sales: 8%
Total Units: 3
Trade Names: DelVecchio's Pizzeria & Italian Restaurant (3)
Company-Owned Units: 3
Alcohol Served: Beer, Wine
Primary Menu: Pizza (3)
Projected Openings: 1
Areas of Operation: FL
Type of Foodservice: Casual Dining (3)
Catering Services: Yes
Parent Company: JEM4, WESTON, FL

Key Personnel
JAMES E. MCDONNELL IV - Founder; CEO
STEPHEN FELLER - Director Marketing, Social Media

Green Apple Ventures
1555 Bonaventure Blvd
Weston, FL 33326

Telephone: (786) 472-2868
Type of Business: Chain Restaurant Operator
Total Sales: $9,944,000 (e)
Total Units: 11
Trade Names: Yogurtland (11)
Units Franchised From: 11
Primary Menu: Snacks (11)
Areas of Operation: FL
Type of Foodservice: Quick Serve (11)
Franchise Affiliation: Yogurtland Franchising Inc., FARMERS BRANCH, TX

Key Personnel
ENRIQUE ALTAMIRANO - Owner; General Buyer

The Cheese Course, Inc.
1555 Bonaventure Blvd STE 200
Weston, FL 33326

Telephone: (786) 472-2868
Internet Homepage: thecheesecourse.com
Company Email: info@thecheesecourse.com
Type of Business: Chain Restaurant Operator
Total Sales: $4,104,000 (e)
Alcohol Sales: 5%
Average Check: Dinner(16)
Total Units: 6
Trade Names: The Cheese Course (6)
Company-Owned Units: 6
Alcohol Served: Beer, Wine
Primary Menu: Sandwiches/Deli (6)
Projected Openings: 2
Areas of Operation: CO, FL, TX
Type of Foodservice: Fast Casual (6)
Primary Distributors: (Full Line) Cheney Bros. Inc., RIVIERA BEACH, FL

Key Personnel
ENRIQUE ALTAMIRANO - President; VP Operations; General Buyer

Topper's Craft Creamery
4750 the Grove Dr Suite 290
Windermere, FL 34786

Telephone: (813) 767-9644
Type of Business: Chain Restaurant Operator
Year Founded: 2006
Total Units: 12
Trade Names: Topper's Craft Creamery (12)
Company-Owned Units: 7
Units Franchised To: 5
Preferred Location Types: Airports; Freestanding; Hotel/Motel; Parks
Primary Menu: Snacks (12)
Areas of Operation: FL
Type of Foodservice: Quick Serve (12)

Key Personnel
WADE ONEY - Chairman; Co-Founder

Manny's Original Chophouse
132 Avenue E SW
Winter Haven, FL 33880

Telephone: (863) 875-8999
Fax Number: (863) 875-8940
Internet Homepage: mannyschophouse.com
Company Email: mannyschophouse@yahoo.com
Type of Business: Chain Restaurant Operator
Total Sales: $21,400,000 (e)
Alcohol Sales: 15%
Total Units: 6
Trade Names: Manny's Original Chophouse (6)
Company-Owned Units: 6
Alcohol Served: Beer, Wine, Liquor
Primary Menu: American (6)
Areas of Operation: FL
Type of Foodservice: Casual Dining (6)

Key Personnel
EMMANUEL NIKOLAIDIS - Owner; Executive Chef

Raysway Inc
642 Pope Ave NW
Winter Haven, FL 33881-4665

Telephone: (863) 293-4531
Type of Business: Chain Restaurant Operator
Total Sales: $15,470,000 (e)
Total Units: 3
Trade Names: McDonald's (3)
Units Franchised From: 3
Preferred Location Types: Freestanding
Primary Menu: Hamburger (3)
Areas of Operation: FL
Type of Foodservice: Quick Serve (3)
Franchise Affiliation: McDonald's Corporation, CHICAGO, IL

Key Personnel
GARY MOULTON - President; General Buyer

4R Restaurant Group LLC
1600 W Fairbanks Ave
Winter Park, FL 32789-4604

Telephone: (407) 474-8377
Internet Homepage: 4rspecialtycakes.com; asouthernaffair.com; 4rsmokehouse.com
Company Email: pitmaster@4rsmokehouse.com
Type of Business: Chain Restaurant Operator
Year Founded: 2009
Total Sales: $51,550,000 (e)
Average Check: Lunch(14); Dinner(14)
Total Units: 15
Trade Names: 4 Rivers Smokehouse (14); The COOP (1)
Company-Owned Units: 15
Primary Menu: Bar-B-Q (14); Southern (1)
Projected Openings: 1
Areas of Operation: FL
Type of Foodservice: Casual Dining (1); Fast Casual (14)
Catering Services: Yes

Key Personnel
JOHN RIVERS - Founder; CEO; Partner; Executive Chef
JEFF PALERMO - Partner; Senior VP Operations

MONIQUE WALDROP - Chief Marketing Officer
ANDREW BURNS - Creative Director
KRISTIN GALICZ - Director Operations, Training
ALLEN REJONIS - Director Human Resources
BOBBIE DEVERALL - Director Operations, Catering
JENNY HERBERT - Manager Culinary Development

Artistry Restaurants
201 N New York Ave Suite 200
Winter Park, FL 32789

Telephone: (407) 553-3525
Internet Homepage: artistryrestaurants.com
Type of Business: Chain Restaurant Operator
Total Sales: $49,538,000 (e)
Total Units: 29
Trade Names: Atlantic Beer and Oyster (1); Boca (2); Oak & Stone (7); Sandbar Amelia Island (1); Shrimp Basket (18)
Company-Owned Units: 29
Primary Menu: American (2); Pizza (7); Seafood (20)
Areas of Operation: AL, FL, MS
Type of Foodservice: Casual Dining (29)

Key Personnel
BRYAN LOCKWOOD - CEO; Partner
BARRY GOFF - Partner
MIKE WOOD - Partner
CHIP HEADLEY - Partner
JOHN MASSARI - CFO
JASON BROOKS - COO
DANIEL HARF - Chief Concept Officer

DiPasqua Enterprises Inc.
2277 Lee Rd
Winter Park, FL 32789-1887

Telephone: (407) 644-8578
Fax Number: (407) 539-0563
Internet Homepage: subwaydipasqua.com
Type of Business: Chain Restaurant Operator
Year Founded: 1976
Total Sales: $64,650,000 (e)
Number of Employees: 1,100
Average Check: Breakfast(8); Lunch(12); Dinner(12)
Total Units: 109
Trade Names: Subway (109)
Units Franchised From: 109
Preferred Square Footage: 1,500
Preferred Location Types: Freestanding; Regional Mall; Strip Mall
Primary Menu: Sandwiches/Deli (109)
Projected Openings: 3
Projected Remodelings: 6
Areas of Operation: FL
Type of Foodservice: Quick Serve (109)
Franchise Affiliation: Doctor's Associates Inc., MILFORD, CT
Primary Distributors: (Food) US Foods, LAKELAND, FL

Key Personnel
LINA DEL ROSARIO - CEO; COO; Executive Assistant
PETER DIPASQUA - CEO
PAUL VANORDEN - Director Construction, Leasing
JESSIE DOMINGUEZ - Manager Human Resources
MICHELLE HILLARD - Manager

Jimmy Hula's Licensing, LLC
2522 Aloma Ave
Winter Park, FL 32792-3402

Telephone: (407) 790-7838
Internet Homepage: jimmyhulas.com
Type of Business: Chain Restaurant Operator
Year Founded: 2013
Total Sales: $11,580,000 (e)
Total Units: 10
Trade Names: Jimmy Hula's (10)
Units Franchised To: 10
Primary Menu: American (10)
Projected Openings: 1
Areas of Operation: FL
Type of Foodservice: Family Restaurant (10); Fast Casual (15)

Key Personnel
JIM HARTMAN - Founder; CEO
ZACH HARTMAN - VP; Director Operations

JM Hospitality Group
310 S Park Ave
Winter Park, FL 32789

Telephone: (407) 647-7277
Internet Homepage: jmhospitality.net
Company Email: info@bluontheavenue.com
Type of Business: Chain Restaurant Operator
Year Founded: 1994
Total Units: 5
Trade Names: 310 Restaurants New American Cuisine (3); Blu on the Avenue (1); Bovine Steakhouse (1)
Company-Owned Units: 5
Preferred Location Types: Downtown
Primary Menu: American (3); Seafood (1); Steak (1)
Areas of Operation: FL
Type of Foodservice: Casual Dining (5)

Key Personnel
JOANNE MCMAHON - Owner
TONY KRUEGER - Executive Chef
HILLARY JOVI-HASEMANN - Director Event Planning
BOB CARTER - Manager Operations

Metro Corral Partners Inc.
1069 W Morse Blvd Ste 100
Winter Park, FL 32789-3780

Telephone: (407) 629-9311
Fax Number: (407) 629-2513
Company Email: apemail@metrocorral.com
Type of Business: Chain Restaurant Operator
Year Founded: 1989
Total Sales: $118,380,000 (e)
Alcohol Sales: 5%
Number of Employees: 1,493
Average Check: Breakfast(10); Lunch(14); Dinner(16)
Total Units: 24
Trade Names: Golden Corral Buffet & Grill (24)
Units Franchised From: 24
Preferred Square Footage: 2,000; 5,000
Preferred Location Types: Freestanding
Alcohol Served: Beer, Wine
Primary Menu: American (24)
Areas of Operation: FL, GA
Type of Foodservice: Casual Dining (24)
Catering Services: Yes
Franchise Affiliation: Golden Corral Corp., RALEIGH, NC
Primary Distributors: (Equipment) Coastal Equipment, JACKSONVILLE, NC; (Food) McLane/Rocky Mount, ROCKY MOUNT, NC; (Supplies) Coastal Equipment, JACKSONVILLE, NC

Key Personnel
ERIC HOLM - President; Partner; Director Operations, Information Systems, Real Estate, Store Fixtures
DIANE HOLM - Partner; VP; Director Purchasing
JEFF CHEATHAM - VP Operations
ELIZABETH LI - Controller Group; Manager Human Resources
DOUG KOSKEY - Director
WANDA DELGADO - Manager

Prestige Worldwide S&A, LLC
4004 N Goldenrod Rd
Winter Park, FL 32792-8999

Telephone: (407) 671-0053
Type of Business: Chain Restaurant Operator
Total Sales: $5,874,000 (e)
Total Units: 4
Trade Names: Jersey Mike's Subs (4)
Units Franchised From: 4
Primary Menu: Sandwiches/Deli (4)
Areas of Operation: FL
Type of Foodservice: Quick Serve (4)

Franchise Affiliation: Jersey Mike's Franchise Systems, MANASQUAN, NJ

Key Personnel
SEAN GILLESPIE - Owner; General Buyer

Ruth's Hospitality Group Inc.
1030 W Canton Ave Ste 100
Winter Park, FL 32789-3050

Telephone: (407) 333-7440
Fax Number: (407) 833-9625
Internet Homepage: rhgi.com; ruthschris.com
Company Email: info@rhgi.com
Type of Business: Chain Restaurant Operator
Year Founded: 1965
Systemwide Sales: $1,999,593,000 (e)
Publicly Held: Yes
Total Sales: $543,797,000 (e)
Alcohol Sales: 25%
Number of Employees: 5,740
Average Check: Lunch(50); Dinner(92)
Internet Order Processing: Yes
Internet Sales: 5.00%
Total Units: 158
Trade Names: Ruth's Chris Steak House (158)
Company-Owned Units: 84
Units Franchised To: 74
Preferred Square Footage: 7,000; 8,000; 9,000
Preferred Location Types: Community Mall; Downtown; Freestanding; Hotel/Motel; Regional Mall
Alcohol Served: Beer, Wine, Liquor
Primary Menu: Steak/Seafood (158)
Projected Openings: 2
Areas of Operation: AL, AR, AZ, CA, CO, CT, DC, FL, GA, HI, ID, IL, IN, KY, LA, MA, MD, MI, MN, MO, MS, NC, NJ, NV, NY, OH, OR, PA, PR, RI, SC, TN, TX, UT, VA, WA, WI, AB, ON
Foreign Countries: ARUBA; CANADA; CHINA; HONG KONG; INDONESIA; JAPAN; MEXICO; SINGAPORE; TAIWAN
Type of Foodservice: Fine Dining (158)
Catering Services: Yes
Primary Distributors: (Full Line) Gordon Food Service Inc., WYOMING, MI; (Full Line) Gordon Food Service, HOUSTON, TX; (Full Line) Reinhart FoodService LLC, CHICAGO, IL
Parent Company: Darden Restaurants Inc., ORLANDO, FL
Notes: Average check values and system-wide sales reflect Ruth's Chris Steak House restaurant operations only.

Key Personnel
LAURA KIMBROUGH - VP People
NIK TALWAR - Regional VP
ABDIEL ALEMAN - Senior Director Culinary Development
KATIE FEROLDI - Director

SHERRI BRYANT - Director Payroll, Benefits, Compensation
KARRY EDMONDS - Director Infrastructure, Security
JOHN M ZIMMERMAN - Manager Quality Assurance

SM Restaurants Inc.
108 S Park Ave
Winter Park, FL 32789

Telephone: (407) 644-8609
Internet Homepage: bosphorousrestaurant.com
Company Email: info@BosphorousRestaurant.com
Type of Business: Chain Restaurant Operator
Year Founded: 2004
Number of Employees: 200
Total Units: 4
Trade Names: Bosphorous Turkish Cuisine (4)
Company-Owned Units: 4
Preferred Square Footage: 3,000
Preferred Location Types: Community Mall; Downtown
Primary Menu: Middle Eastern (4)
Areas of Operation: FL
Type of Foodservice: Casual Dining (4)

Key Personnel
DOVED SEXTER - Partner
TAMMY SEXTER - Partner
NADIA LAKOMKINA - General Manager

GEORGIA

Williams Investment Co.
1221 W 4th St Ste 11
Adel, GA 31620-2918

Telephone: (229) 896-4511
Fax Number: (229) 896-4710
Internet Homepage: wincohotels.com
Company Email: winco2@windstream.net
Type of Business: Foodservice Operations - Hotel/Motels
Year Founded: 1963
Total Sales: $85,140,000 (e)
Number of Employees: 1,224
Total Units: 17
Restaurants in Hotels: 7
Trade Names: Candlewood Suites (1); Comfort Inn & Suites (3); Country Inn & Suites (2); Days Inn (4); Holiday Inn (1); Holiday Inn Express (2); Howard Johnson (1); Super 8 (3)
Company-Owned Units: 1
Units Franchised From: 6
Areas of Operation: GA
Type of Foodservice: Family Restaurant (3); Quick Serve (4)

Franchise Affiliation: IHOP Restaurant System, GLENDALE, CA; Shoney's North America Corp., NASHVILLE, TN
Primary Distributors: (Food) SYSCO Atlanta LLC, COLLEGE PARK, GA
Notes: The company derives approximately 80% of its revenue from hotel operations.

Key Personnel
MIKE WILLIAMS - President; Director Finance, Real Estate
RICK WILLIAMS - VP Operations, Real Estate; Executive Chef; Director Information Systems, Human Resources, Menu Development, Food and Beverage; General Buyer
STEVE WILLIAMS - VP Marketing
PAUL MCNEAL - VP Operations

EDN Inc.
2203 Trowbridge Rd
Albany, GA 31721-2136

Telephone: (229) 888-3372
Type of Business: Chain Restaurant Operator
Year Founded: 1984
Total Sales: $13,330,000 (e)
Number of Employees: 250
Average Check: Breakfast(10); Lunch(12); Dinner(12)
Total Units: 6
Trade Names: Burger King (6)
Units Franchised From: 6
Preferred Square Footage: 2,500; 4,000
Preferred Location Types: Freestanding
Primary Menu: Hamburger (6)
Areas of Operation: GA
Type of Foodservice: Quick Serve (6)
Franchise Affiliation: Burger King Worldwide Inc., MIAMI, FL

Key Personnel
EDWARD NORTHROP - President; Partner; Director Operations
JOAN NORTHROP - Partner; Manager Real Estate
TODD E. NORTHROP - Partner; VP Purchasing, Supply Chain, General Buyer
BRENT A. NORTHROP - Partner; Manager Finance, Information Systems

Flying Buffalo Inc.
2801 Pointe North Blvd
Albany, GA 31721-1588

Telephone: (229) 431-1900
Type of Business: Chain Restaurant Operator
Total Sales: $11,118,000 (e)
Total Units: 3
Trade Names: Zaxby's (3)
Units Franchised From: 3
Primary Menu: Chicken (3)

Areas of Operation: GA
Type of Foodservice: Fast Casual (3)
Franchise Affiliation: Zaxby's Franchising Inc., ATHENS, GA

Key Personnel
DEBORAH G. DURDEN - President; General Buyer

Blazing Buns, L.L.C.
1000 N Point Cir
Alpharetta, GA 30022-4853

Telephone: (770) 667-8637
Type of Business: Chain Restaurant Operator
Total Sales: $7,990,000 (e)
Total Units: 11
Trade Names: Auntie Anne's Hand-Rolled Soft Pretzels (10); Cinnabon (1)
Units Franchised From: 11
Primary Menu: Snacks (11)
Areas of Operation: GA
Type of Foodservice: Quick Serve (11)
Franchise Affiliation: Auntie Anne's Inc., LANCASTER, PA; Cinnabon Inc., ATLANTA, GA

Key Personnel
DANIEL TRICKEL - Owner; General Buyer

Celtic Group, Inc.
872 N Brookshade Pkwy
Alpharetta, GA 30004-0837

Telephone: (404) 307-2628
Type of Business: Chain Restaurant Operator
Total Sales: $8,486,000 (e)
Total Units: 4
Trade Names: Five Guys Burgers and Fries (4)
Units Franchised From: 4
Primary Menu: Hamburger (4)
Areas of Operation: IN
Type of Foodservice: Fast Casual (4)
Franchise Affiliation: Five Guys Holdings Inc., LORTON, VA

Key Personnel
MARY WALSH - Partner; General Buyer
PATRICK WALSH - Partner; General Buyer

Conglomerated Host Ltd.
14485 Hopewell Rd
Alpharetta, GA 30004-6931

Mailing Address: PO Box 1229, ALPHARETTA, GA, 30009-1229
Telephone: (770) 521-0808
Fax Number: (770) 521-0809
Internet Homepage: provinos.com; scalinis.com
Company Email: service@provinos.com
Type of Business: Chain Restaurant Operator
Year Founded: 1977
Systemwide Sales: $19,380,000 (e)
Total Sales: $19,910,000 (e)
Alcohol Sales: 18%
Number of Employees: 405
Average Check: Lunch(16); Dinner(24)
Total Units: 9
Trade Names: Provino's (8); Scalini's (1)
Company-Owned Units: 8
Units Franchised To: 1
Preferred Square Footage: 5,000
Preferred Location Types: Freestanding; Strip Mall
Alcohol Served: Beer, Wine, Liquor
Primary Menu: Italian (9)
Areas of Operation: GA, TN
Type of Foodservice: Casual Dining (9)
Primary Distributors: (Food) Performance Foodservice - Milton's, OAKWOOD, GA

Key Personnel
JOHN BOGINO - Chairman; Partner; Controller; Director Menu Development
TRACY RAY - President; VP Operations, Purchasing, Supply Chain; Manager Marketing
LARRY FISHER - Partner; Treasurer; Manager Human Resources
HAROLD GERLITSCH - Partner; Senior VP
SCOTT GARNER - VP Facility/Maintenance, Real Estate, Design, Research & Development, Franchising, Store Fixtures
SHELLEE SMITH - Manager Accounting, Information Systems

Cowabunga Inc.
3585 Trotter Dr
Alpharetta, GA 30004-7701

Telephone: (770) 777-2217
Fax Number: (770) 777-2218
Internet Homepage: cowabungainc.com
Type of Business: Chain Restaurant Operator
Year Founded: 1989
Total Sales: $221,870,000 (e)
Number of Employees: 1,819
Total Units: 109
Trade Names: Domino's (109)
Units Franchised From: 109
Preferred Square Footage: 1,000
Primary Menu: Pizza (107)
Projected Openings: 10
Areas of Operation: AL, GA, SC
Type of Foodservice: Quick Serve (107)
Franchise Affiliation: Domino's Pizza Inc, ANN ARBOR, MI

Key Personnel
JILL ULP - Chief Culture Officer
MICHAEL L. ORCUTT - CEO
JULIE GEOGHAN - CFO
JAY GAINES - VP Operations
JOHN MINICK - VP Operations
JOHN SANDFORD - General Manager
MIKE LOREN - Regional Director
RANDY THOMPSON - Regional Director Operations
BILL WISE - Manager Information Technology
TABITHA GRANT - Manager Marketing
REBECCA STRANGE - Manager Administration, Human Resources

Marlow's Tavern
3719 Old Alabama Rd Ste 200-H
Alpharetta, GA 30022-8677

Telephone: (770) 475-1800
Internet Homepage: marlowstavern.com
Type of Business: Chain Restaurant Operator
Year Founded: 2004
Total Sales: $60,000,000 (e)
Alcohol Sales: 15%
Average Check: Lunch(24); Dinner(24)
Total Units: 17
Trade Names: Marlow's Tavern (17)
Company-Owned Units: 17
Alcohol Served: Beer, Wine, Liquor
Primary Menu: American (17)
Areas of Operation: FL, GA
Type of Foodservice: Casual Dining (17)
Catering Services: Yes

Key Personnel
JOHN C. METZ - CEO; Partner; Executive Chef
TOM DIGIORGIO - Partner
RICHARD E. RIVERA - Partner
MEG POTTS - VP Finance
CHRIS KOST - Manager Beverages

QS America
8460 Holcomb Bridge Rd Ste 200
Alpharetta, GA 30022-6868

Telephone: (770) 594-8644
Fax Number: (770) 594-9430
Internet Homepage: brookwoodgrill.com; freshtoorder.com; qsamerica.com
Company Email: info@qsamerica.com
Type of Business: Chain Restaurant Operator
Total Sales: $18,230,000 (e)
Alcohol Sales: 5%
Internet Order Processing: Yes
Total Units: 12
Trade Names: Brookwood Grill (1); Fresh To Order (11)
Company-Owned Units: 12
Preferred Location Types: Airports; Downtown; Mixed-use Center
Alcohol Served: Beer, Wine, Liquor
Primary Menu: American (12)
Projected Openings: 2

Areas of Operation: AL, FL, GA, SC, TN, TX
Type of Foodservice: Casual Dining (1); Quick Serve (12)
Notes: Fresh To Order (f2o) operates as f2o Holding LLC.

Key Personnel
PIERRE PANOS - CEO
DAVID STEENEKAMP - President; COO

Roasters Inc.
1360 Union Hill Rd Ste 3B
Alpharetta, GA 30004-8454

Telephone: (770) 753-2988
Fax Number: (770) 753-2989
Internet Homepage: roastersfresh.com
Type of Business: Chain Restaurant Operator
Year Founded: 1990
Total Sales: $7,580,000 (e)
Alcohol Sales: 5%
Number of Employees: 200
Average Check: Lunch(12); Dinner(14)
Total Units: 3
Trade Names: Roasters (3)
Company-Owned Units: 3
Preferred Location Types: Freestanding; Strip Mall
Alcohol Served: Beer, Wine
Primary Menu: Chicken (3)
Areas of Operation: GA
Type of Foodservice: Casual Dining (3)
Catering Services: Yes
Primary Distributors: (Full Line) SYSCO Atlanta LLC, COLLEGE PARK, GA

Key Personnel
STEVE LESLIE - President; Director Finance, Operations, Menu Development; General Buyer

Southern Legacy Waffles, LLC
1021 Cambridge Sq
Alpharetta, GA 30009-1860

Telephone: (770) 664-4339
Fax Number: (770) 664-1641
Internet Homepage: slwllc.net
Type of Business: Chain Restaurant Operator
Year Founded: 1967
Total Sales: $62,630,000 (e)
Number of Employees: 1,595
Average Check: Breakfast(8); Lunch(8); Dinner(10)
Total Units: 71
Trade Names: Waffle House (71)
Units Franchised From: 71
Preferred Square Footage: 1,900
Preferred Location Types: Freestanding
Primary Menu: American (71)
Areas of Operation: GA, MS, TN
Type of Foodservice: Family Restaurant (71)
Franchise Affiliation: Waffle House Inc., NORCROSS, GA
Primary Distributors: (Full Line) US Foods, MEMPHIS, TN

Key Personnel
STEVE HUTCHENS - President; Director Operations, Purchasing; General Buyer
KIRK LEWIS - Exec VP
STEVEN GOWER - Senior VP
JEFF ALLEN - VP; Director Human Resources
MANDY ALLEN - VP Risk Management, Human Resources

Taco Mac Restaurant Group
6220 Shiloh Rd Ste 100
Alpharetta, GA 30005-8347

Telephone: (678) 679-1210
Fax Number: (678) 679-1211
Internet Homepage: tacomac.com
Company Email: info@tmacrestaurants.com
Type of Business: Chain Restaurant Operator
Year Founded: 1980
Total Sales: $23,470,000 (e)
Alcohol Sales: 42%
Number of Employees: 146
Average Check: Lunch(8); Dinner(8)
Internet Order Processing: Yes
Internet Sales: 1.00%
Total Units: 26
Trade Names: Taco Mac (24)
Company-Owned Units: 21
Units Franchised To: 2
Preferred Square Footage: 2,000
Preferred Location Types: Freestanding; Strip Mall
Alcohol Served: Beer, Wine, Liquor
Primary Menu: American (24)
Areas of Operation: GA, NC, TN
Type of Foodservice: Casual Dining (24)
Primary Distributors: (Full Line) US Foods, FAIRBURN, GA; (Full Line) Ben E. Keith Foods, FORT WORTH, TX
Parent Company: Fresh Hospitality LLC, NASHVILLE, TN

Key Personnel
HAROLD MARTIN - CEO
JOHN BAKKEGARD - CFO
JASON EVERETT - VP Operations
LAURA GRUNWALD - Senior Director Human Resources
ALEX RENER - Director Operations
BRYAN CANNON - Director Culinary Operations, Food Safety
ADAM ANACKER - Director Beverages

The Wendy's Company-Atlanta Division
1145 Sanctuary Pkwy Ste 225
Alpharetta, GA 30009-4735

Telephone: (770) 283-3700
Fax Number: (770) 283-3808
Listing Type: Divisional Office
Type of Business: Chain Restaurant Operator
Number of Employees: 14
Total Units: 800
Areas of Operation: FL, GA, NC, SC, TN
Parent Company: The Wendy's Company, DUBLIN, OH

Key Personnel
TAMMY BRANHAM - VP Restaurant Operations
ASHLEY SPERLING - Manager Real Estate

Your Pie Corporate
13010 Morris Rd Suite 100
Alpharetta, GA 30004

Telephone: (706) 850-5304
Internet Homepage: yourpie.com
Company Email: info@yourpie.com
Type of Business: Chain Restaurant Operator
Year Founded: 2008
Systemwide Sales: $44,077,000 (e)
Total Sales: $23,770,000 (e)
Alcohol Sales: 15%
Number of Employees: 584
Internet Order Processing: Yes
Total Units: 79
Trade Names: Your Pie (79)
Company-Owned Units: 2
Units Franchised To: 77
Preferred Location Types: Strip Mall
Alcohol Served: Beer, Wine
Primary Menu: Pizza (79)
Projected Openings: 10
Areas of Operation: AL, CO, FL, GA, IA, IL, KS, LA, MS, NC, OK, SC, TN, TX, VA
Type of Foodservice: Fast Casual (79)

Key Personnel
DREW FRENCH - Founder
LISA DIMSON - Chief Marketing Officer
KEN CALDWELL - VP Franchise Development
CRISTINA T - Senior Director Finance, Accounting
ASHLEY WILLIAMS - Director Training
MICHELE CAVENAUGH - Director Operations
ASHLEY TRAIL - Manager Digital Marketing
PEARSON CLARK - Manager Franchise Operations
COURTNEY BROWN - Manager Franchise Development

Avants Management Group
1091 Founders Blvd Ste D
Athens, GA 30606-6177

Telephone: (706) 316-9888
Fax Number: (706) 316-9222
Type of Business: Chain Restaurant Operator
Year Founded: 1998
Total Sales: $66,100,000 (e)
Number of Employees: 525
Average Check: Lunch(8); Dinner(8)
Total Units: 19
Trade Names: Zaxby's (19)
Units Franchised From: 19
Preferred Square Footage: 3,500
Preferred Location Types: Freestanding
Primary Menu: Chicken (19)
Areas of Operation: AL, GA, NC, TN, TX
Type of Foodservice: Fast Casual (19)
Catering Services: Yes
Franchise Affiliation: Zaxby's Franchising Inc., ATHENS, GA

Key Personnel
GARY AVANTS - President; Director Operations, Information Systems, Real Estate; General Buyer
JORDAN AVANTS - Director Human Resources
MELISSA CROWE - Director Operations
RYAN DOSS - Director Finance
MARYSTUART HULSEY - Director Marketing
HALEY GRESHAM - Manager District

Barberitos Inc.
1090 S Milledge Ave
Athens, GA 30605-1336

Telephone: (610) 947-5644
Fax Number: (706) 316-0834
Internet Homepage: barberitos.com
Company Email: comments@barberitos.com
Type of Business: Chain Restaurant Operator
Year Founded: 2000
Systemwide Sales: $13,399,000 (e)
Total Sales: $2,922,000 (e)
Alcohol Sales: 1%
Number of Employees: 24
Average Check: Lunch(10); Dinner(10)
Total Units: 48
Trade Names: Barberitos, a Southwestern Grille & Cantina (48)
Company-Owned Units: 3
Units Franchised To: 45
Preferred Square Footage: 3,000
Preferred Location Types: Freestanding; Regional Mall; Strip Mall
Alcohol Served: Beer
Primary Menu: Southwest/Tex-Mex (48)
Projected Openings: 3
Areas of Operation: FL, GA, NC, SC, TN
Type of Foodservice: Fast Casual (48)

Catering Services: Yes
Primary Distributors: (Full Line) Reinhart FoodService, LOUISVILLE, TN

Key Personnel
DOWNING BARBER - CEO; President; General Manager; Executive Chef; Director Facility/Maintenance, Real Estate, Design, Store Fixtures; General Buyer
CANDICE BARBER - CFO; VP Finance, Information Systems; Treasurer
JULIE JORDAN - Director Operations

Bush and Associates Investments, Inc.
1040 Founders Blvd
Athens, GA 30606

Telephone: (334) 749-9733
Type of Business: Chain Restaurant Operator
Total Sales: $7,511,000 (e)
Total Units: 2
Trade Names: Zaxby's (2)
Units Franchised From: 2
Primary Menu: Chicken (2)
Areas of Operation: AL
Type of Foodservice: Fast Casual (2)
Franchise Affiliation: Zaxby's Franchising Inc., ATHENS, GA

Key Personnel
JOHN BUSH - CEO
THOMAS P. BUSH - President

Jittery Joe's Coffee Franchising, LLC
1480 Baxter St Ste C
Athens, GA 30606-6393

Telephone: (187) 743-85637
Fax Number: (706) 227-6189
Internet Homepage: jitteryjoes.com
Company Email: info@jitteryjoes.com
Type of Business: Chain Restaurant Operator
Year Founded: 1994
Total Sales: $10,100,000 (e)
Internet Order Processing: Yes
Total Units: 17
Trade Names: Jittery Joes (17)
Company-Owned Units: 17
Primary Menu: Coffee (17)
Areas of Operation: GA, NY, TN, FC
Type of Foodservice: Quick Serve (17)

Key Personnel
BOB GOOGE - CEO; General Manager

Locos Franchise Company, Inc.
1091 Founders Blvd Ste A
Athens, GA 30605

Telephone: (706) 548-7277
Fax Number: (706) 548-7244
Internet Homepage: kebagrill.com; locosgrill.com
Company Email: info@locosgrill.com
Type of Business: Chain Restaurant Operator
Year Founded: 1988
Systemwide Sales: $28,145,000 (e)
Total Sales: $4,341,000 (e)
Alcohol Sales: 15%
Number of Employees: 40
Average Check: Lunch(14); Dinner(14)
Internet Order Processing: Yes
Internet Sales: 0.50%
Total Units: 9
Trade Names: Keba (3); Locos Grill & Pub (6)
Company-Owned Units: 3
Units Franchised To: 6
Preferred Square Footage: 4,500
Preferred Location Types: Freestanding; Strip Mall
Alcohol Served: Beer, Wine, Liquor
Primary Menu: American (6); Middle Eastern (3)
Areas of Operation: AL, GA, MO
Type of Foodservice: Casual Dining (6); Quick Serve (3)
Catering Services: Yes
Primary Distributors: (Full Line) US Foods, FAIRBURN, GA

Key Personnel
JAMEY LOFTIN - President; COO; Director Purchasing, Marketing
COURTNEY GARRETT - Specialist Business Development
DOROTHY MURFIN - Executive Assistant

Zaxby's Franchising Inc.
1040 Founders Blvd
Athens, GA 30606-6138

Telephone: (706) 353-8107
Fax Number: (706) 433-2330
Internet Homepage: zaxbys.com; zaxbysfranchising.com
Company Email: info@zaxbys.com
Type of Business: Chain Restaurant Operator
Year Founded: 1990
Systemwide Sales: $2,756,285,000 (e)
Total Sales: $471,970,000 (e)
Number of Employees: 350
Average Check: Lunch(10); Dinner(12)
Total Units: 928
Trade Names: Zaxby's (929)
Company-Owned Units: 145

Units Franchised To: 784
Preferred Square Footage: 3,300; 3,500; 3,800
Preferred Location Types: Freestanding; Institution (college/hospital); Regional Mall; Strip Mall
Primary Menu: Chicken (929)
Projected Openings: 2
Areas of Operation: AL, AR, FL, GA, IN, KY, LA, MO, MS, NC, OK, SC, TN, TX, UT, VA
Type of Foodservice: Fast Casual (929)
Primary Distributors: (Full Line) Performance Foodservice - Milton's, OAKWOOD, GA
Parent Company: Goldman, Sachs & Co. (GS Capital Partners), NEW YORK, NY
Notes: The company-owned stores reflect operations of affiliated companies; Zaxby's Franchising operates no restaurants.

Key Personnel
ZACHARY W. MCLEROY - Chairman; CEO; President; Partner
BERNARD ACOCA - CEO
ROB COLVIN - President
TONY D. TOWNLEY - Partner; Exec VP
DONNY LAU - CFO
SHARLENE SMITH - COO
MICHELLE MORGAN - Chief People Officer
MIKE NETTLES - CTO; Chief Digital Officer
PATRICK SCHWING - Chief Marketing Officer; Chief Strategy Officer
MIKE METTLER - Chief Development Officer
VANESSA FOX - Chief Development Officer
CARL MOUNT - Chief Supply Chain Officer
STEPHANIE P. GAMBLE - VP Menu Development
JON GARDNER - VP Financial Planning
ALAN LUDLOFF - VP Brand Marketing
AMY CAMP PRITCHETT - VP Franchise Development
BRENDA B. TRICKEY - General Counsel
MICHAEL SOBEL - Senior Director Purchasing, Distribution
VANCE W. SNOW - Director Franchise Development
BRIAN COLEMAN - Director Operations
GARY NASH - Director Purchasing
NICK PETROCCI - Director Digital
STEVE MILLER - Director Distribution
PAT JOHNSON - Director Applications
LAUREN HEAVERN - Director Franchising
STEPHEN GANEM - Director
CHERYL WOOD - Director Franchise Sales
L. DIANNE MASON - Senior Manager Purchasing
KEVIN MASTERS - Senior Manager Accounting
ERIN TODD - Senior Manager Branding
CHRIS REESE - Manager Real Estate
JILL SMITH - Manager Training
KAMI K - Manager Communications
ANDREW JOHNSON - Manager Design
REED CHANDLER - Manager Financial Planning
EVAN CONNORS - Manager Social Media
ALEXA FOWLER - Manager Training
EMILY ADAMS - Manager Training
ROB ADKISSON - Manager Quality Assurance
CHERYL ANNARELLI - Manager Safety-Food
CAROLINE BENNETT - Manager Operations
DUSTIN QUINN - Project Manager

● ▲
Zaxby's Houston LLC
2500 Daniells Bridge Rd Bldg 200 Ste 2B
Athens, GA 30606

Telephone: (281) 955-8865
Internet Homepage: zaxbys.com/locations/tx/houston
Type of Business: Chain Restaurant Operator
Total Sales: $28,380,000 (e)
Total Units: 8
Trade Names: Zaxby's (8)
Units Franchised From: 8
Primary Menu: Chicken (8)
Areas of Operation: TX
Type of Foodservice: Fast Casual (8)
Franchise Affiliation: Zaxby's Franchising Inc., ATHENS, GA

Key Personnel
SHAWN TAYLOR - CEO; President; Owner
JOEL BULGER - Chief Marketing Officer

101 Concepts
4969 Roswell Rd Ste 200
Atlanta, GA 30342-2680

Telephone: (404) 497-9700
Fax Number: (404) 497-9770
Internet Homepage: ciboatlanta.com; food101atl.com; meehanssandysprings.com; 101concepts.com
Type of Business: Chain Restaurant Operator
Year Founded: 1999
Total Sales: $12,910,000 (e)
Alcohol Sales: 5%
Number of Employees: 30
Average Check: Lunch(16); Dinner(24)
Total Units: 5
Trade Names: 101 Steak (1); Meehan's Public House (3); Restaurant Paradis (1)
Company-Owned Units: 5
Preferred Square Footage: 5,500; 6,000
Preferred Location Types: Freestanding
Alcohol Served: Beer, Wine, Liquor
Primary Menu: American (4); Steak (1)
Areas of Operation: FL, GA
Type of Foodservice: Casual Dining (4); Fine Dining (1)
Catering Services: Yes
On-site Distribution Center: Yes
Primary Distributors: (Full Line) US Foods, NORCROSS, GA

Key Personnel
STEVE BUERO - President; Partner; Executive Chef; Director Information Systems; General Buyer
PHIL RONESS - Partner; Director Real Estate, Design; General Buyer
CHRIS SEGAL - Partner; Director Supply Chain; General Buyer
J.D. DOYLE - Manager Food and Beverage
SHONDA LEWIS - Executive Assistant

● ▲
755 Restaurant Corporation
3466 Buffington Ctr
Atlanta, GA 30349-2948

Telephone: (404) 766-2727
Fax Number: (404) 766-2221
Internet Homepage: 755restaurant.com
Company Email: info@755restaurant.com
Type of Business: Chain Restaurant Operator
Year Founded: 1995
Total Sales: $77,290,000 (e)
Number of Employees: 752
Average Check: Breakfast(8); Lunch(8); Dinner(8)
Total Units: 29
Trade Names: Krispy Kreme Doughnuts (2); Popeyes Louisiana Kitchen (27)
Units Franchised From: 29
Preferred Square Footage: 2,000
Preferred Location Types: Freestanding
Primary Menu: Chicken (27); Snacks (2)
Areas of Operation: GA
Type of Foodservice: Quick Serve (29)
Catering Services: Yes
Franchise Affiliation: Krispy Kreme Doughnut Corporation, CHARLOTTE, NC; Popeyes Louisiana Kitchen Inc., ATLANTA, GA

Key Personnel
BILLYE AARON - Co-Founder
HENRY L. AARON - Co-Founder
VICTOR HAYDEL - CEO; President; Director Finance, Real Estate
JAY HYDEL - Director Operations
KAREN WEST - Director Accounting
DAWN COFF - Manager Accounting
LOUIS TANENBAUM - Manager Compliance
DORINDA AARON-BOWEN - Manager Human Resources; Supervisor Operations
TOD FRASER - Supervisor Operations

● ▲
A&R Pars, Inc.
3393 Peachtree Rd NE Ste 2043
Atlanta, GA 30326-1109

Telephone: (404) 429-0239
Type of Business: Chain Restaurant Operator
Total Sales: $4,867,000 (e)
Total Units: 3
Trade Names: Checkers (3)

Units Franchised From: 3
Primary Menu: Hamburger (3)
Areas of Operation: GA
Type of Foodservice: Quick Serve (3)
Franchise Affiliation: Checkers Drive-In Restaurants Inc., TAMPA, FL

Key Personnel
ALI PARSA - President; General Buyer

American Deli International
2716 Northeast Expy NE
Atlanta, GA 30345-1807

Telephone: (404) 254-3444
Fax Number: (404) 228-6147
Internet Homepage: iloveamericandeli.com
Company Email: info@iloveamericandeli.com
Type of Business: Chain Restaurant Operator
Year Founded: 1989
Systemwide Sales: $112,824,000 (e)
Total Sales: $4,837,000 (e)
Number of Employees: 537
Average Check: Lunch(12); Dinner(12)
Total Units: 178
Trade Names: American Deli (178)
Units Franchised To: 178
Preferred Location Types: Freestanding; Strip Mall
Primary Menu: Sandwiches/Deli (178)
Projected Openings: 8
Areas of Operation: AL, CA, FL, GA, LA, MS, NC, SC, TX
Type of Foodservice: Quick Serve (178)

Key Personnel
YONSUK KIM - CEO; President; VP Purchasing
JAMES HAN - CFO; VP
YOUNG KIM - VP; Director POS/Scanning
DONGHEE KIM - Director Franchise Development

Arby's Restaurant Group
3 Glenlake Pkwy
Atlanta, GA 30328

Telephone: (678) 514-4100
Fax Number: (678) 514-5339
Internet Homepage: arbys.com
Type of Business: Chain Restaurant Operator
Year Founded: 1964
Systemwide Sales: $5,615,170,000 (e)
Total Sales: $2,467,700,000 (e)
Number of Employees: 50,000
Average Check: Breakfast(5); Lunch(10); Dinner(12)
Total Units: 3,436
Trade Names: Arby's (3,436)
Company-Owned Units: 1,130
Units Franchised To: 2,306
Preferred Square Footage: 1,400; 2,500; 3,000; 3,200; 3,500
Preferred Location Types: Airports; Community Mall; Convenience Store/Gas Station; Downtown; Freestanding; Office Complex; Other; Regional Mall; Stadiums; Strip Mall; Travel Plazas
Primary Menu: Sandwiches/Deli (3,436)
Projected Openings: 100
Areas of Operation: AK, AL, AR, AZ, CA, CO, CT, DE, FL, GA, HI, IA, ID, IL, IN, KS, KY, LA, MA, MD, ME, MI, MN, MO, MS, MT, NC, ND, NE, NH, NJ, NM, NV, NY, OH, OK, OR, PA, SC, SD, TN, TX, UT, VA, WA, WI, WV, WY, AB, BC, MB, NB, NS, ON, SK
Foreign Countries: CANADA; EGYPT; KUWAIT; QATAR; TURKEY; UNITED ARAB EMIRATES
Type of Foodservice: Quick Serve (3,436)
Primary Distributors: (Equipment) The Wasserstrom Co., COLUMBUS, OH; (Food) Willow Run Foods Inc., KIRKWOOD, NY; (Food) McLane/Lagrange, LAGRANGE, GA; (Supplies) Willow Run Foods Inc., KIRKWOOD, NY
Parent Company: Inspire Brands, ATLANTA, GA
Divisional Offices: Arby's Restaurant Group, INDIANAPOLIS, IN

Key Personnel
PAUL BROWN - Co-Founder; CEO
ROLAND SMITH - CEO; President
JIM TAYLOR - President
SUSAN BAUER - President Finance, Tax
MATT COSSON - President Sourcing, Distribution, Logistics
DAVID GRAVES - President
JOHN KELLY - COO
CHRISTOPHER FULLER - Chief Communications Officer
STEPHANIE SENTELL - Senior VP
KAREN SHELLEDY - VP Franchise Development
DARRELL KINKAID - VP Information Technology
TARA PIERCE - VP Tax
WADE COOPER - VP Architecture, Design
DAVID PELLETIER - VP Division
DAVE EMBERTON - VP Human Resources
NEVILLE CRAW - VP Product Development; Corporate Chef
BRIAN PATTERSON - VP Information Technology
BILL NORTON - VP Fulfillment
BILL DUFFY - VP Acquisitions, Mergers
TIM WADDELL - VP International Division
JEFF COBB - VP Brand Marketing
GENE SANTOVENIA - VP Real Estate
MELISSA NUSS ESHPETER - VP Leasing
DEMON DELOATCH - General Manager
JEWELL MICHAEL - Corporate Chef Development, Innovation
JOHN MECUM - Senior Director Training
ERIC BALLANCE - Senior Director Operations
KEITH ENGLER - Senior Director Franchise Development
JUDITH BADER - Senior Director Training
MARCUS PHILLIPS - Senior Director Operations
FRANK INOA - Senior Director Operations, Engineering
EUGENE KLIBANOFF - Senior Director Tax
ROSS MARTIN - Director Accounting
DINA WESTERBY - Director Recruitment, Talent
MICHAEL MCGUIRE - Director Infrastructure
TIFFANY STEFFES - Director Communications
JUSTIN PAPE - Director
TONY TOURVILLE - Director Real Estate
KERI RHODES - Director Risk Management
JANNE MIZE - Director Facility/Maintenance
MICHAEL DEE - Director Real Estate
TREVOR RODABAUGH - Director Operations
ROBERT DIMSON - Director Media
MAI GIRTON - Director Product Development, International
JAMES MCCOLLUM - Director International
BETH OLSON - Director Training
JENNA RANKIN - Director
JACKYE WATKINS - Director Operations
JON GILL - Director Operations
STACIE SANDERS - Senior Manager
LISA INGRAHAM - Manager Consumer Insights
LINDSEY JOYNER - Manager Advertising
SUZANNE PEARSON - Manager Human Resources
JACKIE SANGSTER - Manager Accounting
SEAN MIGNECO - Manager POS/Scanning
HEIDI GREENSPAN - Manager Business Development
MARSHA ETHERIDGE - Manager Customer Service
CINDY HALLIDAY - Manager Franchise Development
TREY PARKER - Manager Systems
WALLIS BAXTER - Manager Operations
JEREMY NAVARRO - Manager Finance
SCOTT BADER - Manager
SHEILA CARROLL - Manager Legal
MELODY COOK-BLOUNT - Manager Quality Assurance
VICKY HUNTER CHUSTZ - Manager Operations-Integration
JOSH MCNELLY - Manager Innovation, Product Development
GEORGE NIX - Manager
ANDRE RENFROE - Manager
BIANCA ROBERTS - Manager Operations, Design-Training
MONICA SIMPSON - Manager Accounting
DAYE STUART - Manager Risk Management
PETER SULLIVAN - Manager Architecture
ED WESSEL - Manager Financial Planning
ANTHONY GRANTHAM - Manager Training
WENDY BULGER - Manager Operations
DOUGLAS PARKS - Associate Manager Digital
KENNETH ORKE - Product Manager Systems
REBECCA GRAUERT - Project Manager
JENNIFER TODD - Analyst Development
STACY B. HANSARD - Executive Assistant

Auntie Anne's Franchise
3393 Peachtree Rd NE
Atlanta, GA 30326-1162

Telephone: (404) 816-1438
Internet Homepage: auntieannesfranchising.com
Type of Business: Chain Restaurant Operator
Total Sales: $5,129,000 (e)
Total Units: 7
Trade Names: Auntie Anne's Hand-Rolled Soft Pretzels (7)
Units Franchised From: 7
Primary Menu: Snacks (7)
Areas of Operation: GA
Type of Foodservice: Quick Serve (7)
Franchise Affiliation: Auntie Anne's Inc., LANCASTER, PA

Key Personnel
WILLIAM RENTON - Owner; General Buyer

Big Game Brands, Inc.
1801 Peachtree St NE Ste 130
Atlanta, GA 30309

Telephone: (404) 351-3500
Fax Number: (815) 377-3683
Internet Homepage: flyingbiscuit.com; italianpie.com; monkeyjoes.com
Type of Business: Chain Restaurant Operator
Year Founded: 1995
Systemwide Sales: $84,016,000 (e)
Total Sales: $5,139,000 (e)
Alcohol Sales: 0.50%
Number of Employees: 83
Total Units: 55
Trade Names: Flying Biscuit Cafe (20); Monkey Joe's (33); The Original Italian Pie (7)
Units Franchised To: 60
Preferred Location Types: Airports; Community Mall; Downtown; Freestanding; Office Complex; Other; Regional Mall; Strip Mall
Alcohol Served: Beer, Wine
Primary Menu: American (20), Pizza (7); Snacks (33)
Areas of Operation: AL, CT, FL, GA, IA, IL, IN, KY, MA, MD, MO, NC, PA, SC, TN, TX, VA, WI
Type of Foodservice: Casual Dining (7); Fast Casual (20); Quick Serve (33)
Catering Services: Yes
Primary Distributors: (Full Line) Reinhart FoodService, LOUISVILLE, TN

Key Personnel
DARYL DOLLINGER - Co-Founder; President
SONNY CRUMPTON - Senior VP
BRENT FULLER - VP Operations; Brand Manager
REGINA COOPER - Controller Finance
RANDY JEFFIRS - Director Operations
SHONNA LESTER - Director Marketing
SCOTT NICELY - Director Training
MILA PHINNEY - Manager Franchise Sales; Administrator
JENN CANNON - Manager

Buckhead Life Restaurant Group
265 Pharr Rd NE
Atlanta, GA 30305-2225

Telephone: (404) 237-2060
Fax Number: (404) 237-2160
Internet Homepage: buckheadrestaurants.com
Company Email: dish@buckheadrestaurants.com
Type of Business: Chain Restaurant Operator
Year Founded: 1979
Total Sales: $97,010,000 (e)
Alcohol Sales: 25%
Number of Employees: 2,500
Average Check: Breakfast(18); Lunch(30); Dinner(60)
Total Units: 10
Trade Names: Atlanta Fish Market (1); Bistro Niko (1); Buckhead Diner (1); Chops Lobster Bar (2); City Fish Market (1); Corner Cafe/Buckhead Bread (1); Kyma (1); Lobster Bar Sea Grille (1); Pricci (1)
Company-Owned Units: 12
Preferred Square Footage: 2,200; 8,000
Preferred Location Types: Freestanding; Office Complex; Strip Mall
Alcohol Served: Beer, Wine, Liquor
Primary Menu: American (2); French/Continental (1); Greek/Mediterranean (1); Italian (1); Seafood (3); Steak/Seafood (2)
Projected Openings: 1
Areas of Operation: FL, GA
Type of Foodservice: Casual Dining (4); Fine Dining (6)
Foodservice Management Venues: Parks & Recreation
Primary Distributors: (Equipment) Edward Don & Co., NORCROSS, GA

Key Personnel
EMILO SARDINAS - Chief Engineering Officer
EDWIN D'SOUZA - General Manager
JON SKINNER - General Manager
PAUL SCIMEME - General Manager
SAM THAN - General Manager
BOBBY ASARE - General Manager
RYAN SCARPA - General Manager
GEORGE MOLLAS - General Manager
HEIDI SANDATE - Director Event Planning
BETHANY VINCENT - Director Sales
ERIC CUTILLO - Director Purchasing
ANNE SYMBAS - Manager Payroll
BARRY ZIEMBA - Manager Information Systems
ERIKA HAVRON - Manager Customer Service
THORSTEN HORRMANN - Manager Event Planning
SCOTT HAVRON - Manager Alcoholic Beverages
TAHO ROSSLOW - Manager Beverages
CHELSEA HINDES - Coordinator Marketing
VANESSA STANGER - Coordinator Marketing
MARY HARFOOT - Analyst Database
BRYAN CHANCELLOR - Developer

Buffalo Wild Wings Inc.
3 Glenlake Pkwy
Atlanta, GA 55416-1237

Telephone: (678) 514-4100
Fax Number: (952) 593-9787
Internet Homepage: franchiseinfo.buffalowildwings.com; buffalowildwings.com
Company Email: info@buffalowildwings.com
Type of Business: Chain Restaurant Operator
Year Founded: 1982
Systemwide Sales: $6,031,621,000 (e)
Total Sales: $3,401,400,000 (e)
Alcohol Sales: 21%
Number of Employees: 26,000
Average Check: Lunch(10); Dinner(14)
Internet Order Processing: Yes
Internet Sales: 1.00%
Total Units: 1,312
Trade Names: B-Dubs Express (1); Buffalo Wild Wings (1,279); Rusty Taco (32)
Company-Owned Units: 702
Units Franchised To: 610
Preferred Square Footage: 4,500; 5,000; 6,400; 7,600; 9,800
Preferred Location Types: Freestanding; Lifestyle Center; Office Complex; Strip Mall
Alcohol Served: Beer, Wine, Liquor
Primary Menu: Chicken (1,280); Taco (32)
Projected Openings: 1
Areas of Operation: AK, AL, AR, AZ, CA, CO, CT, DE, FL, GA, HI, IA, ID, IL, IN, KS, KY, LA, MA, MD, ME, MI, MN, MO, MS, MT, NC, ND, NE, NH, NJ, NM, NV, NY, OH, OK, OR, PA, RI, SC, SD, TN, TX, UT, VA, VT, WA, WI, WV, WY, FC, AB, ON
Foreign Countries: CANADA; MEXICO; THE PHILIPPINES; UNITED ARAB EMIRATES
Type of Foodservice: Casual Dining (1,279); Fast Casual (33)
Primary Distributors: (Full Line) McLane Foodservice, CARROLLTON, TX
Parent Company: Inspire Brands, ATLANTA, GA

Key Personnel
STEVE DUNN - Founder; CEO Division
PAUL BORWN - CEO
LYLE TICK - President
JOHN BOWIE - COO
RITA PATEL - Chief Marketing Officer
KATHLEEN M. BENNING - Chief Brand Officer;

Chief Strategy Officer; Exec VP Business
  Development
GREG DARUS - VP Real Estate
JAMIE CARAWAN - VP Menu Development;
  Executive Chef
JEFF BAKER - VP Marketing, Advertising
MICHAEL KROMER - VP Risk Management,
  Compliance
TRISTAN MELINE - VP Marketing
PHIL ALBANESE - Regional VP
JOSH MARTIN - Senior Director
JOHN L - Director Digital
BRETT FRY - Director Human Resources
CHAD GLIDEWELL - Director Branding
CARL CHEANEY - Director Real Estate
KIM SOBASKY - Director Loyalty Program
HOMER VASQUEZ - Director Operations
JOY WOLNEY - Director Human Resources
MELANY TERRAZAS - Manager Menu
  Development
CAROLINE BURLESON - Manager Public
  Relations
VALERIE HOGAN - Manager Purchasing
KELLY KESTON - Manager Innovation

Cartel Restaurants, Inc.
340 E Paces Ferry Rd NE
Atlanta, GA 30305-2352

Telephone: (404) 237-2972
Fax Number: (404) 237-6927
Internet Homepage: littleazio.com
Type of Business: Chain Restaurant Operator
Year Founded: 1977
Total Sales: $5,244,000 (e)
Alcohol Sales: 15%
Number of Employees: 175
Average Check: Lunch(12); Dinner(20)
Internet Sales: 1.00%
Total Units: 2
Trade Names: Ltttle Azio (2)
Company-Owned Units: 2
Preferred Square Footage: 5,500; 6,000
Preferred Location Types: Downtown;
  Freestanding; Strip Mall
Alcohol Served: Beer, Wine, Liquor
Primary Menu: Italian (3)
Areas of Operation: GA
Type of Foodservice: Casual Dining (2)
Primary Distributors: (Food) SYSCO Atlanta
  LLC, COLLEGE PARK, GA

Key Personnel
GEORGE MATT ROHRIG - President
AL ROHRIG - Partner; Exec VP; Director Real
  Estate
MATT ROHRIG - Partner; VP
SUSIE CARLETON - Controller
SUZIE CARLTON - Controller; Director
  Information Systems
ABBIE PEPPER - Director Operations

Carvel Corporation
5620 Glenridge Dr
Atlanta, GA 30342-1334

Telephone: (404) 255-3250
Fax Number: (404) 255-4978
Internet Homepage: carvel.com
Company Email: customerservice@carvel.com
Type of Business: Chain Restaurant Operator
Year Founded: 1934
Systemwide Sales: $198,141,000 (e)
Total Sales: $113,310,000 (e)
Number of Employees: 381
Average Check: Lunch(5); Dinner(5)
Total Units: 304
Trade Names: Carvel Ice Cream (418)
Units Franchised To: 418
Preferred Square Footage: 1,000
Preferred Location Types: Airports;
  Community Mall; Downtown; Freestanding;
  Grocery Stores; Institution (college/hospital);
  Lifestyle Center; Regional Mall; Stadiums;
  Strip Mall; Travel Plazas
Primary Menu: Snacks (418)
Projected Openings: 3
Areas of Operation: AK, AL, AZ, CA, CT, DC,
  FL, GA, IL, IN, MA, MD, MI, MO, MS, NC, NH,
  NJ, NV, NY, OH, PA, PR, RI, SC, TN, TX, VA,
  VT, WI, WV
Foreign Countries: ARUBA; EGYPT;
  JORDAN; SAUDI ARABIA; SOUTH AFRICA
Type of Foodservice: Quick Serve (418)
Foodservice Management Venues: College &
  University; Military Feeding; Schools;
  Transportation
Catering Services: Yes
Primary Distributors: (Food) Blue Line
  Foodservice Distribution, ORLANDO, FL
Parent Company: Roark Capital Group,
  ATLANTA, GA
Headquarters: GoTo Foods, ATLANTA, GA
Notes: The company derives approximately
  69% of its revenue from wholesale operations;
  systemwide sales are based on retail
  operations only.

Key Personnel
RICHARD STAKOFSKY - President; Owner
MIKE DIXON - CFO
JIM SALERNO - VP Operations
DAVE FENNER - Executive Chef; Director
  Research & Development
KENZIE KUEHNLE - Director Operations, Sales
GREG STILES - Director Information
  Technology
WAYNE BROWN - Director Operations

Chick-fil-A Inc.
5200 Buffington Rd
Atlanta, GA 30349-2945

Telephone: (404) 765-8000
Fax Number: (404) 765-8140
Internet Homepage: chick-fil-a.com;
  truettsgrill.com
Type of Business: Chain Restaurant Operator
Year Founded: 1967
Systemwide Sales: $21,434,206,000 (e)
Total Sales: $5,946,361,000 (e)
Number of Employees: 1,928
Average Check: Breakfast(5); Lunch(6);
  Dinner(6)
Internet Order Processing: Yes
Internet Sales: 0.50%
Total Units: 3,059
Trade Names: Chick-fil-A (3,051); Chick-fil-A
  Dwarf House (5); Truett's Grill (3)
Company-Owned Units: 30
Units Franchised To: 3,029
Preferred Square Footage: 1,000; 4,000
Preferred Location Types: Airports;
  Downtown; Freestanding; Grocery Stores;
  Institution (college/hospital); Mobile Unit;
  Regional Mall
Primary Menu: Chicken (3,059)
Projected Openings: 100
Areas of Operation: AL, AR, AZ, CA, CO, CT,
  DC, DE, FL, GA, IA, ID, IL, IN, KS, KY, LA,
  MA, MD, MI, MN, MO, MS, NC, NE, NH, NJ,
  NM, NY, OH, OK, PA, RI, SC, SD, TN, TX, UT,
  VA, WA, WI, WV, WY
Type of Foodservice: Family Restaurant (8);
  Quick Serve (3,051)
Catering Services: Yes
Primary Distributors: (Full Line)
  McLane/Rocky Mount, ROCKY MOUNT, NC;
  (Supplies) Maines Paper & Food Service
  Tennessee, ARLINGTON, TN
Notes: Chick-fil-A derives approximately 16% of
  total revenue from rental income and other
  activities.

Key Personnel
ANDREW CATHY - CEO
DONALD M. CATHY - President; Exec VP
SUSANNAH W. FROST - President
BRENT RAGSDALE - CFO; Senior VP
CLIFFORD T. ROBINSON - COO; Chief People
  Officer; Senior VP
ALLYSSA PRIESTER - Chief People Officer
MICHAEL E. ERBRICK - CIO; VP Information
  Technology
JONATHAN B. BRIDGES - Chief Marketing
  Officer; Senior VP Marketing
ROBERT P. DUGAS - Chief Procurement
  Officer; VP Supply Chain
ERWIN REID - Senior VP Development,
  International
WILLIAM F. FAULK JR - VP Innovation
DAVID B. FARMER - VP Menu Development

WILLIAM J. DUNPHY JR - VP Talent
ONOME OKUMA - VP Customer Service
JANET BRIDGES - VP Finance
KELLY LUDWICK - VP Labor Relations
TAMMY PEARSON - VP; General Counsel
SANDI MOODY - VP Finance, Risk Management
LIBBY WANAMAKER - VP Talent
DON PERRY - VP Public Relations
CARRIE KURLANDER - VP Public Affairs, Public Relations
JOE SARACINO - VP Strategy, Advertising, Media
PAUL TROTTI - VP Supply Chain
JOHN STEPHENSON - VP
MEYER SKALAK - Executive Director Supply Chain
ED RINDERLE - Executive Director IT Applications
LINDSEY BARRON - Executive Director Enterprise Solutions
SHANNON J. GARDNER - Executive Director Risk Management
JAY FILE - Executive Director Northeast Region
AMY ROOKS - General Counsel; Director Real Estate
MARK L. BRACKETT - Senior Director Information Technology
BRIAN T. GRADY - Senior Director
CHERYL B. DICK - Senior Director Operations
TODD GRUBBS - Senior Director Company Operations
M. ANDERSON PIPER - Senior Director Strategic Planning
DANIEL STRAIN - Senior Director Information Systems, Information Technology
MICHAEL GARRISON - Senior Director Innovation
JOSH FIGARETTI - Senior Director Technology; Director Operations
DAVID LAUGHLIN - Senior Director Technology; Director Information Technology
ROBERT MCLAUGHLIN - Senior Director Branding
SALEITHA L. CHAMPION - Senior Director Finance
MARK MORAITAKIS - Senior Director Consumer Insights
JODEE MORGAN - Senior Director Operations, Talent
GREGG LOLLIS - Senior Director Development, Construction
AMY M. OHDE - Senior Director Development
ASHLEY CALLAHAN - Senior Director Marketing
REBECCA SILLS - Senior Director Talent
SARAH BLACKMON - Senior Director Supply Chain, Quality Control
DAVE FADER - Senior Director
ANGIE NAPIER - Senior Director Tax
DAVID RABON - Senior Director Information Technology, Innovation
MIKE LEDFORD - Senior Director Sourcing, Supply Chain, Logistics
THOMAS A. NOLAN - Director Development

COLIN GROMLEY - Director Real Estate
JOSEPH LATIMER - Director Strategic Planning
KRISTEN CLEVER - Director Strategic Planning
PETER ABERNATHY - Director Operations
TYRONE DILLARD - Director Real Estate
TODD SWEATT - Director Operations
TOM A. MORDER - Director Consumer Insights
SCOTT THIGPEN - Director Development
TONY GAYDA - Director Information Systems
ALEX B. DOVERSPIKE - Director Supply Chain
AMANDA NORRIS - Director Training
JOHN MATTIOLI - Director Training
SEAN WARREN - Director Development, Licensing
KEVIN P. MALONE - Director Operations
CHRISTOPHER W. TAYLOR - Director Information Technology
JASON B. FISCHER - Director Supply Chain
DON L. IKELER III - Director Development
JIMMY OLIVER - Director Software Engineering
BRYAN GINSBERG - Director Operations
CHAD HERRING - Director Inventory
TODD KOPRIVA - Director Supply Chain
HEATHER BEAUBIEN - Director Sustainability
TJ HAMMOND - Director Development, Talent
JASON HILL - Director Development, Construction
JASON JOYNER - Director
COURTNEY LAVALLEE - Director Marketing
DEE REID - Director Information Technology
SARA STORCK - Director Strategy
DANIEL J STRAIN - Director Information Technology
SUSAN WEST - Director Marketing, Sales
JAY DUFF - Director Engineering
DANIEL SNEAD - Director Development, Construction, International
TERRY DOUGLAS - Director Operations, Warehouse
TONY LETTS - Senior Manager
MAUREEN BEDIENT-ROGERS - Senior Manager Information Technology, Communications, Training
JENNIFER CUMMINGS - Senior Manager Information Technology, Database, Customer Analytics
TRENT GILLEY - Senior Manager Design
KANIKA PATRICK - Senior Manager Digital Experience
DAVID ROWE - Senior Manager Advertising
JEFFREY DEASON - Senior Manager Information Technology
BRIAN KOLODZIEJ - Senior Manager
MICHAEL LAGE - Senior Manager Digital Experience
KEVIN PURCER - Senior Manager Strategy, Digital
PACE SWEATT - Manager Business Development
BRIAN WRAY - Manager Design, Strategic Planning
FRANKLIN COOK - Manager Information Systems
LAUREN MCGUIRE - Manager
JODIE WORRELL - Manager Marketing

ANGELA SAVAGE - Manager Digital Marketing
DALE WESSON - Manager Information Technology
STEPHEN CHANG - Manager Systems, Talent
TEDDY CRAVENS - Manager
ROBERT DAVIS - Manager Operations, Engineering, Security
SARAH GRIESENAUER - Manager Strategy, Development
MARCUS HUNT - Manager
JOHN MACKE - Manager Communications, Information Technology-Training
MATT RIFE - Manager Information Technology
RYAN P WALKER - Manager Information Technology
TERRI WHIGHAM - Manager Sourcing
REX POWELL - Program Manager Development
GAIL ROBINSON - Supervisor Development, Design
NICOLE KOVZEL - Senior Project Manager
TARA BALDISSEROTTO - Project Manager Information Technology
PAULA TURNER - Consultant
EREN PAGE - Consultant
ALBERT YANG - Senior Analyst Real Estate
CHRIS LEVINE - Engineer Data Quality
MIKE MIDDENDORF - Engineer Applications

▲
Church's Chicken
980 Hammond Dr Ste 1100
Atlanta, GA 30328-8187

Telephone: (770) 350-3800
Fax Number: (770) 512-3920
Internet Homepage: churchs.com; churchsfranchise.com
Company Email: info@churchs.com
Type of Business: Chain Restaurant Operator
Year Founded: 1952
Systemwide Sales: $1,583,961,000 (e)
Total Sales: $271,830,000 (e)
Number of Employees: 4,800
Average Check: Breakfast(10); Lunch(10); Dinner(12)
Total Units: 1,361
Trade Names: Church's Chicken (904); Texas Chicken (457)
Company-Owned Units: 100
Units Franchised To: 1,261
Preferred Square Footage: 1,850
Preferred Location Types: Airports; Community Mall; Convenience Store/Gas Station; Downtown; Freestanding; Grocery Stores; Institution (college/hospital); Kiosk; Mobile Unit; Parks; Regional Mall; Strip Mall; Travel Plazas
Primary Menu: Chicken (1,361)
Projected Openings: 60
Areas of Operation: AL, AR, AZ, CA, CO, FL, GA, HI, IL, IN, KS, LA, MI, MO, MS, NC, NJ, NM, NV, NY, OH, OK, PA, PR, SC, TN, TX, VA, VI, WA, WI, BC, ON

Foreign Countries: BAHRAIN; BELARUS; BULGARIA; CANADA; CURACAO; GUYANA; HONDURAS; INDONESIA; IRAQ; JORDAN; LAOS; MALAYSIA; MEXICO; OMAN; PAKISTAN; SAUDI ARABIA; SINGAPORE; THAILAND; TRINIDAD & TOBAGO; UNITED ARAB EMIRATES; VENEZUELA; VIETNAM
Type of Foodservice: Quick Serve (1,361)
Catering Services: Yes
Primary Distributors: (Food) Performance Foodservice - Temple, TEMPLE, TX; (Food) Kelly's Foods Inc., WINTER GARDEN, FL; (Food) PFD Supply Corp., ST PETERS, MO; (Food) Southwest Traders Inc., TEMECULA, CA; (Full Line) I Supply Co., FAIRBORN, OH
Parent Company: REGO Restaurant Group, DENVER, CO
Headquarters: Cajun Global LLC, ATLANTA, GA
Notes: Franchised Church's operations are handled by Cajun Global LLC and company-operated Church's restaurants are controlled by Cajun Restaurants LLC.

Key Personnel
JOE GUITH - CEO
CRAIG PRUSHER - President; Chief Legal Officer; Exec VP
KAREN BRANDENBURG VIERA - President Global; Chief People Officer
LOUIS "DUSTY" J. PROFUMO - CFO; Exec VP
KAREN VIERA - Chief People Officer; Senior VP
NAVIN SHARMA - Chief Marketing Officer
ALISA P. CLEEK - Chief Legal Officer
BEN WAITES - VP Finance
PAUL BROWN - VP
RANDALL LAWRENCE - VP Supply Chain
ALAN MAGEE - VP Technology, Digital Marketing
BILL MITCHELL - VP Restaurant Operations
LAKKITHA SILVA - Controller; Director Financial Planning
TERI ASKERNEESE-HOOD - Controller
WILBERT MEDE - General Manager
KEVIN HOUSTON - Senior Director Research & Development
JOYCE MESSER - Senior Director Facility/Maintenance, Kitchen Equipment, Supply Chain-Kitchen Equipment
GEORGIA MARGESON - Senior Director Advertising
TRACY LINDSEY - Senior Director Construction
DALE BENNETT - Senior Director Operations
STEVE LASH - Senior Director Distribution, Logistics
SARAH MINTON - Senior Director Media
AMANDA ROBBINS - Director Field Marketing
ADRIENNE BREALOND - Director Human Resources
WAYNE STUBBS - Director Construction
MUHAMMAD KHAN - Director Operations
DIANE GRANT - Senior Manager Supply Chain
PAMIE BANSI - Senior Manager Advertising
EMILY KONG - Senior Manager Finance
RACHEL BACKUS - Senior Manager Construction, Design
COURTNEY BATCHELLER - Senior Manager; Product Strategy
CARMEN GARCIA - Manager Construction
MELANIE HOWELL - Manager Marketing; Merchandise Manager
JACKIE ROSS - Manager Research & Development, Product Development
DANA MOORE - Manager Accounting
GARDY LEANDRE - Manager Finance
SHERRY MORELAND - Manager Advertising
TAMIRRA TURNER - Manager
RAEI-LEIGH RHODES - Manager HRIS
DANIEL ROBINSON - Manager
JUSTIN LEMAZKOUR - Senior Analyst Systems

▲

Cinnabon Inc.
200 Glenridge Cmn Ste 200
Atlanta, GA 30328

Telephone: (404) 255-3250
Fax Number: (404) 255-4978
Internet Homepage: cinnabon.com
Type of Business: Chain Restaurant Operator
Year Founded: 1985
Systemwide Sales: $439,480,000 (e)
Total Sales: $55,370,000 (e)
Number of Employees: 100
Average Check: Breakfast(6); Lunch(6); Dinner(6)
Total Units: 521
Trade Names: Cinnabon (1,600)
Units Franchised To: 1,600
Preferred Square Footage: 750
Preferred Location Types: Airports; Community Mall; Downtown; Grocery Stores; Institution (college/hospital); Kiosk; Office Complex; Other; Outlet Mall; Parks; Regional Mall; Strip Mall; Travel Plazas
Primary Menu: Snacks (1,600)
Projected Openings: 30
Projected Remodelings: 10
Areas of Operation: AK, AL, AR, AZ, CA, CO, CT, DC, DE, FL, GA, HI, IA, IL, IN, KS, KY, LA, MA, MD, MI, MN, MO, MT, NC, NH, NJ, NM, NV, NY, OH, OK, OR, PA, PR, SC, SD, TN, TX, UT, VA, WA, WI, WV, WY, BC, NS, ON, QC
Foreign Countries: ARUBA; AUSTRALIA; BAHRAIN; CANADA; COLOMBIA; COSTA RICA; CYPRUS; DOMINICAN REPUBLIC; ECUADOR; EGYPT; EL SALVADOR; GERMANY; GREAT BRITAIN; GREECE; GUATEMALA; HONDURAS; INDONESIA; ITALY; JAMAICA; JAPAN; JORDAN; KUWAIT; LIBYA; MALAYSIA; MALTA; MEXICO; MOROCCO; OMAN; PAKISTAN; PANAMA; PERU; QATAR; ROMANIA; RUSSIA; SAUDI ARABIA; SOUTH AFRICA; SOUTHKOREA; SYRIA; THAILAND; THE PHILIPPINES; TRINIDAD & TOBAGO; TURKEY; UNITED ARAB EMIRATES; VENEZUELA
Type of Foodservice: Quick Serve (1,600)
Foodservice Management Venues: College & University; Military Feeding
Primary Distributors: (Full Line) McLane Company, Inc., TEMPLE, TX
Parent Company: Roark Capital Group, ATLANTA, GA
Headquarters: GoTo Foods, ATLANTA, GA
Notes: Total units reflects worldwide operations.

Key Personnel
JIM HOLTHOUSER - CEO
JIMMY TCHEOU - Owner
MICHAEL ALBERICI - VP Marketing
TIM GOODMAN - VP Franchising
HEATHER LANE - Director Training
SUSANA TAFUR - Director Art
TESHURAH YISRAEL - Manager Human Resources
ABBY ROWELL - Specialist Marketing

Cinnaholic Franchising LLC
1567 Mount Vernon Rd Suite 112
Atlanta, GA 30338

Telephone: (833) 246-3726
Internet Homepage: cinnaholic.com
Company Email: contact@cinnaholic.com
Type of Business: Chain Restaurant Operator
Year Founded: 2010
Systemwide Sales: $39,200,000 (e)
Total Sales: $35,970,000 (e)
Total Units: 56
Trade Names: Cinnaholic Gourmet Cinnamon Rolls (56)
Company-Owned Units: 1
Units Franchised To: 55
Preferred Location Types: Downtown; Strip Mall
Primary Menu: Snacks (56)
Projected Openings: 100
Areas of Operation: AZ, CA, FL, GA, ID, MD, NC, NJ, NV, OH, PA, TN, TX, UT, WA
Foreign Countries: CANADA
Type of Foodservice: Fast Casual (56)

Key Personnel
SPENCER REID - Partner
LEANNE CAVALLARO - Manager Franchise Operations
MELANIE CROW-PUTNAM - Supervisor

Concentrics Restaurants
1579 Monroe Dr NE Suite F#520
Atlanta, GA 30324

Telephone: (404) 888-0659
Fax Number: (404) 888-9566
Internet Homepage: concentricsrestaurants.com
Type of Business: Chain Restaurant Operator
Year Founded: 2002

Total Sales: $227,650,000 (e)
Alcohol Sales: 13.33%
Average Check: Dinner(36)
Total Units: 45
Trade Names: 30Tables (1); 360 (1); Allora (1); Basso (1); Boundary (1); Brasserie (1); Brim House (1); Bully Boy (1); Central (1); Cibo Matto (1); Dockery's; Eight Up (1); Flip (1); GBD (1); HDT (1); IOS Greek Kitchen (1); Juniper and Ivy (1); Keep (1); LPC (1); Luma on the Park (1); Max's Coal Oven Pizzeria (1); Moly B's (1); Murphy's (1); Nexto (1); OffShore (1); ONE. Midtown Kitchen (1); Piebar (1); Plough (1); Prato (1); Roof (1); Room At Twelve (1); Slate (1); State &Lake (1); Stats (1); Tap (1); The Bakeshop (1); The Establishment (1); The Exchange (1); The Market at Cheshire (1); The Painted Pin (1); The Restaurant (1); The Spence (1); Trois (1); TWO. Urban Licks (1); Upstairs (1); VU (1)
Company-Owned Units: 45
Alcohol Served: Beer, Wine, Liquor
Primary Menu: American (28); French/Continental (1); Greek/Mediterranean (1); Hamburger (1); Hot Dogs (1); Italian (3); Pizza (3); Seafood (3)
Areas of Operation: AL, CA, FL, GA, IL, KY, MO
Type of Foodservice: Casual Dining (45)

Key Personnel
ROBERT AMICK - Founder; Partner; General Buyer
TODD RUSHING - Partner
MARISA ANDERSON - VP Marketing
BRODIE LANG - General Manager
NICK MELVIN - Executive Chef
JOE NASH - Director Sales
KAREN SINGLETARY - Director Training
MARCUS MARSHALL - Regional Director Operations
HAYDEN GUNN - Manager Event Planning
MICHELE RIVERA - Manager Training

†

Concessions International
566 Wells St SW
Atlanta, GA 30312-2426

Telephone: (404) 681-0300
Fax Number: (404) 653-8151
Internet Homepage: cintl.com
Company Email: bbbanko@cintl.com
Type of Business: Foodservice Management Operator
Year Founded: 1978
Total Sales: $113,754,000 (e)
Number of Employees: 1,500
Number of Locations Served: 180
Total Foodservice Mgmt Accounts: 180
Trade Names: Concessions International
Areas of Operation: GA
Type of Foodservice: Quick Serve (180)
Foodservice Management Venues: Other; Transportation
Primary Distributors: (Full Line) SYSCO Atlanta LLC, COLLEGE PARK, GA

Key Personnel
DONATA MAJOR - Vice Chairman
MICHAEL RUSSELL - Vice Chairman
DONATA RUSSELL-ROSS - CEO
CHARLES BLUEMLE - Partner
CHARLES JOHNSON - VP Corporate Affairs
MARCO RODGERS - VP Information Technology
KENNETH SIMON - Regional VP Operations
ANDRE WIGGINS - Controller; Director Compliance
VAGN NIELSEN - Executive Chef
AARON ALLEN - Executive Chef; Director Culinary Operations
AKOSUA NYANNOR FMP, PHR - Director Human Resources, Training
GERARD BLUNT - Director Finance, Accounting
AKOSUA NYANNOR - Director Training
ALAIN ZEMMOUR - Director Operations
DEBORAH CONKLIN - Business Manager Accounting
MICHAEL RODGERS - Manager Information Technology
SHARON HERNDON - Manager HRIS
CONCESSIONS SOCIAL - Manager Social Media
SARETHA HOLT - Manager
KATHLEEN GLYNN - Project Manager
TOMIKO MOORE - Coordinator Payroll
EDWARD WOOD - Analyst Purchasing

Dantanna's
3400 Around Lenox Rd NE Ste 304
Atlanta, GA 30326-1408

Telephone: (404) 760-8873
Internet Homepage: dantannas.com
Company Email: info@dantannas.com
Type of Business: Chain Restaurant Operator
Total Sales: $11,322,000 (e)
Alcohol Sales: 28%
Average Check: Lunch(26); Dinner(48)
Internet Order Processing: Yes
Total Units: 1
Trade Names: Dantanna's (1)
Company-Owned Units: 1
Preferred Location Types: Downtown; Freestanding
Alcohol Served: Beer, Wine, Liquor
Primary Menu: Steak/Seafood (1)
Areas of Operation: GA
Type of Foodservice: Casual Dining (1)

Key Personnel
JAY KAZLOW - President; Partner; COO
CHANTEL SAINSBURY - Specialist Event Planning

‡

Davidson Hotels & Resorts
1 Ravinia Dr Ste 1600
Atlanta, GA 30346-2109

Telephone: (678) 349-0909
Fax Number: (678) 349-0908
Internet Homepage: davidsonhotels.com
Company Email: info@davidsonhotels.com
Type of Business: Foodservice Operations - Hotel/Motels
Year Founded: 1974
Total Sales: $316,180,000 (e)
Alcohol Sales: 20%
Number of Employees: 2,610
Total Units: 30
Restaurants in Hotels: 30
Trade Names: DoubleTree by Hilton (1); Embassy Suites (1); Hilton (5); Holiday Inn (2); Hyatt (2); Marriott (3); Park Vista (1); Radisson (2); Renaissance (3); Sheraton (7); The Camby (1); Westin (2)
Company-Owned Units: 30
Units Franchised From: 2
Alcohol Served: Beer, Wine, Liquor
Projected Remodelings: 5
Areas of Operation: AL, AR, AZ, CA, CO, DC, FL, GA, IL, MD, MO, NC, OH, OR, PA, TN, TX, VA
Type of Foodservice: Casual Dining (30)
Primary Distributors: (Food) SYSCO Food Services of Louisville, LOUISVILLE, KY
Notes: The company derives approximately 80% of its revenue from hotel operations.

Key Personnel
JOHN A. BELDEN - CEO; President Real Estate
BARRY WABLER - CFO; Exec VP
THOM GESHAY - COO
STEVEN A. MARGOL - Chief Investment Officer; Exec VP Business Development
BERNIE MURPHY - Senior VP Business Development
STEVE KILROY - VP Beverages, Food
KATHY HOOD - VP Marketing, Sales
DWAYNE DEAN - General Manager
STEPHEN KILROY - Director Food and Beverage
MICHAEL YOUSIF - Director Business Development
RON STEVENSON - Director E-Commerce
DEDRA THOMPSON - Director Employee Development
CYNDI NORWOOD - Manager Marketing, Communications, Promotion
KERRI HINES BROWN - Manager Administration
ROBERT MCLEROY - Agent Customer Service
COLE MCCORMACK - Analyst Finance

Dtox Juice
3850 Roswell Rd NE
Atlanta, GA 30342

Telephone: (404) 812-0819
Internet Homepage: dtoxjuice.com
Type of Business: Chain Restaurant Operator
Year Founded: 2011
Total Sales: $2,889,000 (e)
Total Units: 4
Trade Names: Dtox Jucie (4)
Company-Owned Units: 4
Primary Menu: Health Foods (4)
Areas of Operation: FL, GA, TN
Type of Foodservice: Quick Serve (4)

Key Personnel
KAREN SPENCER - Partner
JENNY FORST - Partner

Experiential Brands
Atlanta, GA 30188

Internet Homepage: experientialbrands.com; inkedtacos.com; oghotchicken.com; pinsaromanpizza.com
Type of Business: Chain Restaurant Operator
Year Founded: 2023
Number of Employees: 200
Total Units: 16
Trade Names: Inked Tacos (2); Pinsa Roman Pizza (1); The Original Hot Chicken (13)
Company-Owned Units: 16
Primary Menu: Chicken (13); Pizza (1); Taco (2)
Areas of Operation: GA, KY, OH
Type of Foodservice: Fast Casual (16)
Parent Company: NRD Capital Management II LLC, BROOKHAVEN, GA

Key Personnel
AZIZ HASHIM - CEO
JAMES WALKER - Chief Concept Officer; Chief Culinary Officer
TOM MALLINDINE - VP Operations
BRITTINEY TAYLOR - Director New Store Development, Training
SCOTT HASKEN - Director Finance

Fado Pubs Inc.
2964 Peachtree Rd NW Ste 600
Atlanta, GA 30305-2123

Telephone: (404) 848-8433
Fax Number: (404) 848-9984
Internet Homepage: fadoirishpub.com; tiginirishpub.com
Type of Business: Chain Restaurant Operator
Year Founded: 1996
Total Sales: $55,400,000 (e)
Alcohol Sales: 75%
Number of Employees: 470
Average Check: Breakfast(10); Lunch(18); Dinner(24)
Internet Order Processing: Yes
Internet Sales: 1.00%
Total Units: 13
Trade Names: Fado Irish Pub (10); Tigin Irish Pub (3)
Company-Owned Units: 13
Preferred Square Footage: 5,000; 5,500
Preferred Location Types: Freestanding
Alcohol Served: Beer, Wine, Liquor
Primary Menu: Miscellaneous (12)
Areas of Operation: CO, CT, DC, FL, GA, IL, MD, MO, OH, PA, TX, WA
Type of Foodservice: Casual Dining (13)
Primary Distributors: (Food) US Foods, NORCROSS, GA

Key Personnel
KIERAN MCGILL - CEO; President; Partner; General Manager; Executive Chef; Director Purchasing, Facility/Maintenance, Supply Chain, Real Estate, Design
ERIC PETERSON - Partner; Director Operations
CINDY COPLEN - Controller; Director Information Systems, Asset Protection, Human Resources; Manager Asset Protection
HELÉN KIRK - Manager Marketing, Sales

Fellini's Pizza Inc.
1610 Dekalb Ave NE
Atlanta, GA 30307-2112

Telephone: (404) 371-1485
Fax Number: (404) 371-1487
Internet Homepage: fellinisatlanta.com; greatergoodbbq.com
Company Email: .fellinispizza@earthlink.net
Type of Business: Chain Restaurant Operator
Year Founded: 1980
Total Sales: $18,440,000 (e)
Alcohol Sales: 10%
Number of Employees: 305
Average Check: Lunch(8); Dinner(14)
Total Units: 14
Trade Names: Fellini's Pizza (7); Greater Good BBQ (2); La Fonda Latina (5)
Company-Owned Units: 14
Preferred Square Footage: 5,500; 6,000
Preferred Location Types: Freestanding
Alcohol Served: Beer, Wine
Primary Menu: Bar-B-Q (2); Pizza (7); Spanish (5)
Areas of Operation: GA
Type of Foodservice: Casual Dining (9); Family Restaurant (5)
Primary Distributors: (Full Line) SYSCO Atlanta LLC, COLLEGE PARK, GA

Key Personnel
JOHN HARPER - Partner; Director Finance, Operations, Purchasing, Information Systems; General Buyer
MICHAEL NELSON - Partner; Director Facility/Maintenance, Supply Chain, Real Estate, Design, Store Fixtures, Menu Development

Fifth Group Restaurants
229 Peachtree St NE Ste 600
Atlanta, GA 30303-1619

Telephone: (404) 815-4700
Fax Number: (678) 302-3222
Internet Homepage: fifthgroup.com; latavolatrattoria.com; southcitykitchen.com
Type of Business: Chain Restaurant Operator
Year Founded: 1993
Total Sales: $22,970,000 (e)
Alcohol Sales: 8%
Number of Employees: 325
Average Check: Lunch(16); Dinner(34)
Total Units: 13
Trade Names: Alma Cocina (2); Ecco (3); El Taco (2); La Tavola Trattoria (1); Lure (1); South City Kitchen (4)
Company-Owned Units: 11
Units Franchised To: 2
Preferred Square Footage: 5,500; 6,000
Alcohol Served: Beer, Wine, Liquor
Primary Menu: French/Continental (3); Italian (1); Latin American/Cuban (2); Mexican (2); Seafood (1); Southern (4)
Areas of Operation: GA
Type of Foodservice: Casual Dining (6); Fine Dining (7)
Catering Services: Yes
Primary Distributors: (Equipment) Atlanta Fixture & Sales Co., ATLANTA, GA
Notes: Company also operates a catering company "Bold American Catering".

Key Personnel
KRIS REINHARD - Partner; General Manager Catering, Division
STEVE SIMON - Partner; Director Human Resources
JENNIFER SCOTT - VP People
RICHARD SHIRLEY - VP Finance
JASON PRISTASH - Controller
KATIE PECHARICH - General Manager
PAUL HYMEL - General Manager
ELIZABETH KIRKHOPE - General Manager
STUART FIERMAN - General Manager; Director Operations; General Buyer
CHET GREEN - General Manager
JONATHAN BEATTY - Executive Chef
JUSTIN JORDAN - Executive Chef
CHIP ULBRICH - Executive Chef
CHUCK SOBCZUK - Director Facility/Maintenance
IAN MENDELSOHN - Director Operations

PAULA OWENS - Director Operations
JONATHAN BARKELL - Director Operations
LAUREN AKERS - Manager Corporate Affairs
JAMIE HILLYER - Manager Operations
ALLYSON BROWN - Manager Sales
ADAM BURKHART - Manager Logistics
KACEY CARELSON - Manager Sales
KELLIE CULVER - Manager
MONIQUE JOYCE - Manager Sales
PHIL RUGARI - Manager
ALLISON WHITE - Manager Sales
ALLISON WILLIAMS - Manager Sales
JASON PEDERSEN - Engineer Facility/Maintenance

Freshens Quality Brands
1750 the Exchange SE
Atlanta, GA 30339-2024

Telephone: (678) 627-5400
Fax Number: (678) 627-5454
Internet Homepage: freshens.com
Company Email: custservice@freshens.com
Type of Business: Chain Restaurant Operator
Year Founded: 1985
Systemwide Sales: $26,012,000 (e)
Total Sales: $20,680,000 (e)
Number of Employees: 400
Average Check: Breakfast(6); Lunch(6); Dinner(6)
Total Units: 402
Trade Names: Freshens Smoothie Company (402)
Company-Owned Units: 5
Units Franchised To: 397
Preferred Square Footage: 500
Preferred Location Types: Airports; Community Mall; Downtown; Institution (college/hospital); Kiosk; Lifestyle Center; Office Complex; Outlet Mall; Stadiums; Strip Mall
Primary Menu: Snacks (402)
Areas of Operation: AR, KS, MO, OK
Type of Foodservice: Quick Serve (402)
Foodservice Management Venues: College & University
Primary Distributors: (Food) Performance Foodservice - Milton's, OAKWOOD, GA
Notes: In addition to the 30 Freshens locations, the company has more than 1200 licensed locations which are primarily run by foodservice management operators; revenues from this sector are included in total sales but not included in systemwide sales.

Key Personnel
MELINDA MEREDITH - Controller; Director Human Resources, Personnel
KEVIN TRUESDALE - Director Communications, Training
PAMELA HEDRICK - Director Store Development

ANDREA WILLIAMS - Manager Operations

Global Concessions, Inc.
9770 Spine Rt SW
Atlanta, GA 30320

Mailing Address: PO Box 20905, Airport Mail Facility, ATLANTA, GA, 30320-0905
Telephone: (404) 209-0907
Fax Number: (404) 209-0407
Internet Homepage: globalconcessions.com; sweetgeorgiasjukejoint.com
Company Email: info@globalconcessions.com
Type of Business: Foodservice Management Operator
Year Founded: 1990
Total Sales: $44,474,000 (e)
Number of Employees: 500
Number of Locations Served: 13
Total Foodservice Mgmt Accounts: 1
Trade Names: Coffee Beanery (1); Fresh Healthy Cafe (1); Ihop Express (1); Jekyll Island Seafood Company (1); One Flew South (1); Purple Leaf Cafe (1); Shane's Rib Shack (1); Sojourner's Cafe (1); Sweet Georgia's Juke Joint (2); SweetWater Brewing Co (1); Teriyaki Experience (1)
Units Franchised From: 1
Areas of Operation: GA
Type of Foodservice: Full-service sit-down dining (5); Quick Serve (8)
Foodservice Management Venues: Transportation
Franchise Affiliation: Ben & Jerry's Franchising Inc., SOUTH BURLINGTON, VT; Great Wraps Inc., ATLANTA, GA; Nathan's Famous Inc., WESTBURY, NY; TRUFOODS, LLC, NEW YORK, NY

Key Personnel
TERRANCE HARPS - President
CRAIG HACKLANDER - Director Operations
JACQUELINE EVANS - Director Human Resources

Goldberg's Bagel Co. & Deli
4385 Roswell Rd NE
Atlanta, GA 30342-3315

Telephone: (404) 266-2644
Fax Number: (404) 255-3444
Internet Homepage: goldbergbagel.com
Company Email: goldberg-bagels@bellsouth.net
Type of Business: Chain Restaurant Operator
Year Founded: 1971
Total Sales: $18,810,000 (e)
Number of Employees: 135
Average Check: Breakfast(10); Lunch(12);
Internet Order Processing: Yes
Total Units: 12

Trade Names: Braves All Star Grill (2); Goldberg's Bagel & Deli (10)
Company-Owned Units: 12
Preferred Square Footage: 2,500
Preferred Location Types: Freestanding; Mixed-use Center; Strip Mall
Primary Menu: American (2); Bagels (10)
Projected Openings: 1
Areas of Operation: GA
Type of Foodservice: Casual Dining (2); Quick Serve (10)
Catering Services: Yes
On-site Distribution Center: Yes
Primary Distributors: (Full Line) SYSCO Atlanta LLC, COLLEGE PARK, GA

Key Personnel
WAYNE SAXE - President; Partner; Director Advertising; General Buyer
HOWARD AARON - Partner; General Manager; Executive Chef; Director Catering; General Buyer
DEBRA KIRKWOOD - Manager Human Resources

GoTo Foods
5620 Glenridge Point Pkwy NE
Atlanta, GA 30342

Telephone: (404) 255-3250
Fax Number: (404) 255-4978
Internet Homepage: focusbrands.com
Listing Type: Corporate Office
Type of Business: Chain Restaurant Operator
Systemwide Sales: $3,934,775,000 (e)
Total Sales: $478,510,000 (e)
Total Units: 6,247
Trade Names: Auntie Anne's Hand-Rolled Soft Pretzels (1,947); Carvel Ice Cream (400); Cinnabon (1,513); Jamba Juice (864); McAlister's Deli (452); Moe's Southwest Grill (718); Schlotzsky's Austin Eatery (353)
Company-Owned Units: 80
Units Franchised To: 6,167
Primary Menu: Health Foods (864); Sandwiches/Deli (805); Snacks (3,860); Southwest/Tex-Mex (718)
Areas of Operation: AK, AL, AR, AZ, CA, CO, CT, DC, DE, FL, GA, HI, IA, ID, IL, IN, KS, KY, LA, MA, MD, ME, MI, MN, MO, MS, MT, NC, ND, NE, NH, NJ, NM, NV, NY, OH, OK, OR, PA, PR, RI, SC, SD, TN, TX, UT, VA, VT, WA, WI, WV, WY, FC, ON, QC
Foreign Countries: ARUBA; BONAIRE; BRUNEI; CAMBODIA; CANADA; COSTA RICA; EGYPT; ENGLAND; GERMANY; GREECE; GUATEMALA; HONDURAS; INDIA; INDONESIA; IRELAND; JAPAN; JORDAN; LEBANON; MALAYSIA; NICARAGUA; PARAGUAY; QATAR; RUSSIA; SAUDI ARABIA; SOUTH AFRICA; SOUTH KOREA; THAILAND; THE PHILIPPINES; TRINIDAD & TOBAGO; TURKEY; UKRAINE; UNITED

ARAB EMIRATES; VIETNAM
Type of Foodservice: Fast Casual (1,523); Quick Serve (4,724)
Parent Company: Roark Capital Group, ATLANTA, GA
Headquarter Offices: Auntie Anne's Inc., LANCASTER, PA; Carvel Corporation, ATLANTA, GA; Cinnabon Inc., ATLANTA, GA; Jamba Inc., FRISCO, TX; McAlister's Corporation, ATLANTA, GA; Moe's Southwest Grill LLC, ATLANTA, GA; Schlotzsky's Ltd., ATLANTA, GA

Key Personnel
JIM HOLTHOUSER - CEO
DAVE MIKITA - President Global
MIKE DIXON - CFO
GUILLERMO CREMER - Chief People Officer
BRIAN KRAUSE - Chief Development Officer
JIM SALERNO - Chief Brand Officer Division
DONNA SPANGLER-JOSEPHSON - Chief Brand Officer Division
TRACEY YOUNG - Chief Brand Officer Division
KIERAN DONAHUE - Chief Commercial Officer
JAMES BAIRD - Chief Information Security Officer
SARAH POWELL - Exec VP; General Counsel
DAWN RAY - Senior VP Communications
STEVE CORP - Senior VP Franchise Sales
MICHAEL BARRET - VP; Controller
JUAN CARLOS BANDERAS - VP Quality Assurance
TIM GOODMAN - VP Franchise Operations
ERIC FRANKLIN - VP Payroll, Benefits, HRIS
SEAN WOODEN - VP; Director International
MIKE DESTEFANO - Regional VP Operations
CHERYL AYERS - Director Talent
GARRETT FADDEN - Director Information Technology, Systems
DAVID FENNER - Director Development
BOOKER WASHINGTON - Director Talent
LINDSAY HAYNES - Senior Manager Communications
BRENDA MCGRANAHAN - Manager Development
MATTHEW GAYHART - Manager Training
ERIC VERDUCI - Manager Information Technology, Systems

Gourmet Services Inc.
260 Peachtree St NW Ste 1500
Atlanta, GA 30303-1245

Telephone: (404) 876-5700
Fax Number: (404) 876-2240
Internet Homepage: gourmetservicesinc.com
Type of Business: Foodservice Management Operator
Year Founded: 1975
Total Sales: $49,881,000 (e)
Number of Employees: 1,500
Number of Locations Served: 21
Total Foodservice Mgmt Accounts: 21

Areas of Operation: GA
Type of Foodservice: Cafeteria (21)
Foodservice Management Venues: Business & Industry; College & University; Schools
Primary Distributors: (Food) US Foods, NORCROSS, GA

Key Personnel
NATHANIEL R. GOLDSTON III - Founder; CEO
GIL JONES - President; COO
ALFRED BAKER - Senior VP Operations, Purchasing; Director Menu Development
KIM GOLDSTON-MARTIN - Senior VP Corporate Development

GPS Hospitality, LLC
2100 Riveredge Pkwy Ste 850
Atlanta, GA 30328-4656

Telephone: (770) 933-5023
Fax Number: (770) 933-5024
Internet Homepage: gpshospitality.com
Type of Business: Chain Restaurant Operator
Year Founded: 2012
Total Sales: $1,102,000,000 (e)
Number of Employees: 2,045
Total Units: 476
Trade Names: Burger King (394); Pizza Hut (63); Popeye's (19)
Units Franchised From: 476
Preferred Location Types: Freestanding
Primary Menu: Chicken (19); Hamburger (394); Pizza (63)
Projected Openings: 10
Projected Remodelings: 40
Areas of Operation: AL, AR, FL, GA, IN, KY, LA, MD, MI, MS, NJ, OH, PA, WV
Type of Foodservice: Quick Serve (476)
Franchise Affiliation: Burger King Worldwide Inc., MIAMI, FL; Popeyes Louisiana Kitchen Inc., ATLANTA, GA

Key Personnel
TOM GARRETT - Founder; CEO
MICHAEL LIPPERT - President; COO
SCOTT JASINSKI - CFO
BRIAN ARNOLD - Chief Development Officer
CHRIS PHILLIPS - Chief Strategy Officer
MIKE KOVAC - Senior VP Operations
GARY THOMAS - VP Operations
HEATHER DARDEN - VP Legal
JOE WALLER - VP Operations
TRISH FARLEY - VP Finance
VICKIE VOLAN - VP Human Resources
CARMEN GIANGUZZO - VP Operations
TAYON SEALS - General Manager
CHRIS JASINSKI - Director Marketing
JERMAINE WALKER - Director Operations
JAY RIKER - Director Training
TED BRENNEN - Director Construction
JEN FORBES - Director Development
TOM DAVIS - Director Construction
TODD JACKSON - Director Real Estate

ANGIE OCCHIPINTI - Director Development
ROGER WOOD - Director Operations
DANIEL K. LEE - Director Strategy
SKIDMORE STEPHANIE - Director Legal
LISA GRIER - Director Communications
CASSANDRA FISCHELS - Director Human Resources
REID NEUMANN - Director Marketing
TOM BRADLEY - Director Leasing
STEPHANIE SKIDMORE - Director Legal
JULIE HENSHAW - Director Licensing
NICK MYHRE - Director Operations
TOM WILSON - Director Operations
CHRISTINE WASDIN - Director Payroll, HRIS
BRYAN ROHR - Director Accounting
CASSIE FISCHELS - Director Human Resources
BOBBY GARNER - Director Operations
GREG COMER - Director Operations
JESSICA SOMMERFELDT - Director Operations
TROY THERIOT - Director Operations
SHELLY MCKINNON - Director Operations
KEVIN RAY - Director Operations
PAUL BURKE - Director District
NIKKI RANDOLPH - District Manager
CARLA BARAHONA - District Manager
GEORGIANNA INGRAM - Manager
SHANE PEIRIS - Manager Information Technology
LAUREN BOOTH - Manager Training

Great Wraps Inc.
17 Executive Park East NE Ste 150
Atlanta, GA 30329

Telephone: (404) 248-9900
Fax Number: (404) 248-0180
Internet Homepage: greatwraps.com
Company Email: comments@greatwraps.com
Type of Business: Chain Restaurant Operator
Year Founded: 1981
Systemwide Sales: $62,834,000 (e)
Total Sales: $3,596,000 (e)
Alcohol Sales: 10%
Number of Employees: 600
Average Check: Breakfast(6); Lunch(10); Dinner(10)
Total Units: 48
Trade Names: Blue Sky Cafe (1); Gorin's Homemade Cafe & Grill (1); Great Wraps Grill (45); T.J (1)
Company-Owned Units: 1
Units Franchised To: 47
Preferred Square Footage: 600; 800; 1,400; 1,700
Preferred Location Types: Airports; Community Mall; Downtown; Freestanding; Institution (college/hospital); Regional Mall; Strip Mall
Alcohol Served: Beer
Primary Menu: Sandwiches/Deli (48)
Areas of Operation: AL, AR, DC, FL, GA, IL,

LA, MD, MI, NC, NE, NJ, NV, SC, TN, TX, VA, WI
Type of Foodservice: Quick Serve (48)
Catering Services: Yes

Key Personnel
MARK KAPLAN - Chairman; CEO; Manager Supply Chain, Marketing, Sales, Real Estate, Design, Franchising
CHRIS BEWLEY - Director Operations

Hilton Atlanta Airport
1031 Virginia Ave
Atlanta, GA 30354-1319

Telephone: (404) 767-9000
Fax Number: (404) 559-6889
Internet Homepage: hilton.com
Type of Business: Foodservice Operations - Hotel/Motels
Year Founded: 1987
Total Sales: $60,421,000 (e)
Alcohol Sales: 15%
Number of Employees: 300
Total Units: 1
Restaurants in Hotels: 4
Trade Names: Hilton Atlanta Airport (1)
Company-Owned Units: 4
Alcohol Served: Beer, Wine, Liquor
Areas of Operation: GA
Type of Foodservice: Casual Dining (3); Quick Serve (1)
Primary Distributors: (Food) SYSCO Atlanta LLC, COLLEGE PARK, GA
Notes: The company derives approximately 75% of its revenue from hotel operations.

Key Personnel
LESLIE PCHOLA - VP Area
TINA NALAMPOON - Executive Chef
YAN PORTNOY - Director MIS
TROY SMITH - Director Real Estate
PETRONA VICENTE - Director Finance
EDITH DEAR - Manager Event Planning

HOA Restaurant Group LLC
1815 the Exchange SE
Atlanta, GA 30339-2027

Telephone: (770) 951-2040
Fax Number: (770) 618-7032
Internet Homepage: hooters.com; originalhooters.com
Company Email: hooterspr@hooters.com
Type of Business: Chain Restaurant Operator
Year Founded: 1983
Systemwide Sales: $1,609,838,000 (e)
Total Sales: $734,520,000 (e)
Alcohol Sales: 20%
Number of Employees: 25,500
Average Check: Lunch(16); Dinner(16)
Internet Order Processing: Yes
Internet Sales: 1.00%
Total Units: 424
Trade Names: Hooters (420); Hoots (4)
Company-Owned Units: 203
Units Franchised To: 221
Preferred Square Footage: 4,400; 5,500
Preferred Location Types: Airports; Community Mall; Downtown; Freestanding; Hotel/Motel; Hotel/Motel; Outlet Mall; Strip Mall
Alcohol Served: Beer, Wine, Liquor
Primary Menu: American (424)
Projected Openings: 2
Areas of Operation: AL, AR, AZ, CA, CO, CT, DC, DE, FL, GA, HI, IA, ID, IL, IN, KS, KY, LA, MA, MD, MI, MN, MO, MS, MT, NC, ND, NE, NJ, NM, NV, NY, OH, OK, OR, PA, RI, SC, TN, TX, UT, VA, VI, WA, WI, WV, AB, MB, NS, ON, QC
Foreign Countries: ARUBA; AUSTRALIA; AUSTRIA; BRAZIL; CANADA; CHINA; COLOMBIA; COSTA RICA; CZECH REPUBLIC; DOMINICAN REPUBLIC; GERMANY; GRENADA; GUATEMALA; HUNGARY; JAPAN; MEXICO; PANAMA; RUSSIA; SAO TOME & PRINCIPE; SINGAPORE; SOUTH AFRICA; SOUTHKOREA; SWITZERLAND; TAIWAN; THAILAND
Type of Foodservice: Casual Dining (420); Fast Casual (4)
Catering Services: Yes
Parent Company: Nord Bay Capital/TriArtisan Capital Advisors LLC, TAMPA, FL
Notes: The company derives approximately 5% of its revenue from retail operations.

Key Personnel
CHERYL WHITING-KISH - Chief People Officer
BRUCE SKALA - Chief Marketing Officer
LARRY LINEN - Senior VP Global Operation
FRED SIGMUND - VP Development
TIM BAUM - VP Operations
DAN BABBITT - VP Human Resources
JAY ROSS - Director Sourcing
ROBBY FICHTEL - Manager Facility/Maintenance, Store Fixtures
CAROLINE PERRY - Manager Employee Development, Division

Hojeij Branded Foods
1750 the Exchange SE Ste 200
Atlanta, GA 30339-2024

Telephone: (770) 953-3300
Fax Number: (770) 953-8383
Internet Homepage: hbfairports.com
Company Email: contactus.hbfairports@gmail.com
Type of Business: Foodservice Management Operator
Year Founded: 1999
Total Sales: $21,566,000 (e)
Number of Employees: 350
Number of Locations Served: 30
Total Foodservice Mgmt Accounts: 30
Total Units: 27
Trade Names: Abica Coffee (1); Arby's (1); Caribou Coffee (1); Crystal Hamburgers (1); Freshens Smoothie Company (7); Java City (1); mamma ilardo's pizzeria (2); Nature's Table Cafe (1); Qdoba Mexican Grill (2); Seattle's Best Coffee (3); The Bar (1); Villa Pizza (1); Wendy's Old Fashioned Hamburgers (5)
Company-Owned Units: 27
Areas of Operation: CA, DC, FL, GA, MD, MI, NJ, PA, TX, UT
Type of Foodservice: Quick Serve (30)
Foodservice Management Venues: Business & Industry; Transportation
Franchise Affiliation: Burger King Worldwide Inc., MIAMI, FL; Caribou Coffee Co., BROOKLYN CENTER, MN; Freshens Quality Brands, ATLANTA, GA; Gosh Enterprises Inc., COLUMBUS, OH; Piezzetta, TOWSON, MD; Starbucks Corporation, SEATTLE, WA

Key Personnel
J STEPHEN OLSEN - Co-Founder
REGYNALD WASHINGTON - CEO
MARK BEIDEL - CFO
DAVID HO - VP Information Technology
MIA SPIVEY - VP Finance
SEBLE SACCHINELLI - General Manager
ROMEO MITITEANU - Director Operations
BETH COBURN - Director Construction
JOELLEN GREEN - Manager Accounting
AUDREY HARDY JOHNSON - Manager Sales
SHEILA BUCKLEY - Manager
KELLY QUINDLEN - Manager Business Development
ERICA ROWDEN - Supervisor
RODNEY ZUBERBIER - Analyst POS/Scanning

Home-Grown Industries Of Georgia
150 Great Southwest Pkwy SW
Atlanta, GA 30336-2300

Telephone: (404) 505-2806
Internet Homepage: mellowmushroom.com
Type of Business: Chain Restaurant Operator
Year Founded: 1974
Systemwide Sales: $266,815,000 (e)
Total Sales: $52,460,000 (e)
Alcohol Sales: 20%
Number of Employees: 400
Average Check: Lunch(18); Dinner(24)
Internet Order Processing: Yes
Internet Sales: 1.00%
Total Units: 175
Trade Names: Mellow Mushroom (175)
Company-Owned Units: 2
Units Franchised To: 173
Preferred Square Footage: 2,500; 4,000;

5,000
Preferred Location Types: Freestanding; Strip Mall
Alcohol Served: Beer, Wine, Liquor
Primary Menu: Pizza (175)
Areas of Operation: AL, AR, AZ, CO, DC, FL, GA, IN, KY, LA, MD, MS, NC, NE, OH, OR, SC, TN, TX, UT, VA
Type of Foodservice: Casual Dining (175)
Primary Distributors: (Full Line) US Foods, FAIRBURN, GA
Notes: The company derives approximately 23% of total revenue from commissary operations.

Key Personnel
MARC WEINSTEIN - Chairman; Partner; Director Marketing, Design, Franchising
MIKE NICHOLSON - Partner
JEFFREY L. WIGGINS - CFO
MIKE FOSTER - COO
CHARLES KEVIN BRIDGES - Senior VP Finance, Accounting; Corporate Secretary
JANINE TEPROVICH - Director Human Resources
KEVIN A. SUGARMAN - Director Training
NICKK WILLIS - Director Information Technology

Homegrown Restaurant Concepts
1424 N Highland Ave NE Ste M
Atlanta, GA 30306-3307

Telephone: (404) 888-0777
Internet Homepage: doccheys.com; dragonbowlatl.com; homegrownrestaurants.com
Company Email: rchey@doccheys.com
Type of Business: Chain Restaurant Operator
Year Founded: 1997
Systemwide Sales: $15,424,000 (e)
Total Sales: $10,282,000 (e)
Alcohol Sales: 3%
Number of Employees: 120
Average Check: Lunch(6); Dinner(10)
Total Units: 4
Trade Names: Doc Chey's Asian Kitchen (2); Dragon Bowl (1); Osteria 832 (1)
Company-Owned Units: 4
Preferred Square Footage: 3,000
Preferred Location Types: Regional Mall; Strip Mall
Alcohol Served: Beer, Wine, Liquor
Primary Menu: Asian (3); Italian (1)
Areas of Operation: GA, NC
Type of Foodservice: Fast Casual (4)
Catering Services: Yes
Primary Distributors: (Food) SYSCO Atlanta LLC, COLLEGE PARK, GA

Key Personnel
RICHARD CHEY - CEO; President
MELANIE VAUGHN - CFO; VP Operations, Construction; Director Finance, Marketing, Franchise Development
BROOK MESSINA - Executive Chef; Manager Purchasing

Hopkins and Company
2277 Peachtree Rd NE
Atlanta, GA 30309-1168

Telephone: (404) 355-0321
Internet Homepage: hfbreadco.com; hfburger.com; holeman-finch.com; hopschicken.com; lintonsinthegarden.com; restauranteugene.com; resurgenshg.com
Company Email: media@resurgenshg.com
Type of Business: Chain Restaurant Operator
Year Founded: 2012
Total Units: 7
Trade Names: C. Ellet's (1); H & F Burger (2); Holeman and Finch Bottle Shop (1); Holeman and Finch Public House (1); Hop's Chicken (1); Restaurant Eugene (1)
Company-Owned Units: 7
Primary Menu: American (3); Chicken (1); Hamburger (2); Steak/Seafood (1)
Areas of Operation: GA
Type of Foodservice: Casual Dining (2); Fine Dining (2); Quick Serve (3)

Key Personnel
LINTON HOPKINS - CEO; Partner; Executive Chef
GINA HOPKINS - Partner
ALESSANDRIA STRUEBING - Manager Marketing
COURTNEY RAINES - Generalist Human Resources

Hsu's at Peachtree Center
192 Peachtree Center Ave NE
Atlanta, GA 30303-1712

Telephone: (404) 659-2788
Fax Number: (404) 577-3456
Internet Homepage: aznrestaurant.com; hsus.com; pacificrimbistro.com
Company Email: info@hsus.com
Type of Business: Chain Restaurant Operator
Year Founded: 1992
Total Sales: $11,342,000 (e)
Alcohol Sales: 25%
Number of Employees: 22
Average Check: Lunch(22); Dinner(42)
Total Units: 3
Trade Names: AZN Azian Cuisine (1); Hsu's Gourmet Chinese Restaurant (1); Pacific Rim Bistro (1)
Company-Owned Units: 3
Preferred Location Types: Downtown; Office Complex
Alcohol Served: Beer, Wine, Liquor
Primary Menu: Asian (2); Chinese (1)
Areas of Operation: FL, GA
Type of Foodservice: Casual Dining (1); Fine Dining (2)
Catering Services: Yes
Primary Distributors: (Full Line) SYSCO Atlanta LLC, COLLEGE PARK, GA

Key Personnel
ANNA HSU - Owner; Manager Food and Beverage; General Buyer

Huddle House Distribution Center
3655 Southside Industrial Pkwy SE Ste 103
Atlanta, GA 30354-3204

Telephone: (404) 682-9000
Fax Number: (888) 483-3539
Internet Homepage: huddlehouse.com
Listing Type: Distribution Center
Type of Business: Chain Restaurant Operator
Number of Employees: 50
Areas of Operation: GA, IL, IN, KS, MD, OH, OK, PA, TX
Parent Company: Huddle House Inc., ATLANTA, GA

Key Personnel
DON ROSE - Director Distribution

Huddle House Inc.
5901 Peachtree Dunwoody Rd Ste B450
Atlanta, GA 30328-5348

Telephone: (770) 325-1300
Fax Number: (770) 394-1970
Internet Homepage: huddlehouse.com; huddlehousefranchising.com
Company Email: customerservice@huddlehouse.com
Type of Business: Chain Restaurant Operator
Year Founded: 1964
Systemwide Sales: $515,980,000 (e)
Total Sales: $151,990,000 (e)
Number of Employees: 4,500
Average Check: Breakfast(6); Lunch(8); Dinner(8)
Total Units: 617
Trade Names: Huddle House (328); Perkins Restaurant & Bakery (289)
Company-Owned Units: 149
Units Franchised To: 468
Preferred Square Footage: 1,500; 1,700; 2,000; 4,000

Preferred Location Types: Convenience Store/Gas Station; Freestanding; Hotel/Motel; Strip Mall
Primary Menu: American (617)
Areas of Operation: AL, GA, IL, IN, KS, KY, LA, MO, MS, NC, OH, OK, SC, TN, TX, VA, WV
Foreign Countries: CANADA
Type of Foodservice: Family Restaurant (617)
Distribution Centers: ATLANTA, GA
Subsidiaries: Perkins Restaurant & Bakery, MEMPHIS, TN
Primary Distributors: (Food) SYSCO Atlanta LLC, COLLEGE PARK, GA
Notes: The company derives approximately 74% of its total revenue from the sale of food, supplies, and equipment to its franchisees.

Key Personnel
JAMES O'REILLY - CEO
BLAIN SHORTREED - President
ROBERT HESS - CIO
PETER ORTIZ - Chief Development Officer
NATHAN BALLARD - Chief Supply Chain Officer
JAMES ROBINSON - Area Director Franchising
MATTHEW LOOVIS - Area Director Franchising
JAMIL SPENCER - Senior VP Operations; Director Operations
JORGE PEDERZINI - VP Marketing
KIRK BIONDI - Executive Chef; Director Menu Development
JEREMY LEE - Senior Director Field Marketing
MEGAN AMODIO - Senior Director Operations-Training
MARTY KONOVALSKI - Director Franchising
ROBERT BROWN - Director Franchise Operations
MALINDA REDDIE - Manager Brand Marketing
NICHOLAS STEPHEN - Manager Training

Inspire Brands
3 Glenlake Pkwy
Atlanta, GA 30328

Telephone: (678) 514-4100
Internet Homepage: inspirebrands.com
Company Email: hello@inspirebrands.com
Listing Type: Corporate Office
Type of Business: Chain Restaurant Operator
Systemwide Sales: $47,285,564,000 (e)
Total Sales: $38,539,308,000 (e)
Number of Employees: 325,000
Total Units: 31,493
Trade Names: Arby's (3,395); B-Dubs Express (2); Baskin Robbins (7,800); Buffalo Wild Wings (1,295); Dunkin Donuts (12,776); Jimmy John's Gourmet Sandwich Shop (2,671); Rusty Taco (35); Sonic America's Drive-In (3,519)
Company-Owned Units: 2,036
Units Franchised To: 29,457
Primary Menu: Chicken (1,297); Hamburger (3,519); Sandwiches/Deli (6,066); Snacks (20,576); Taco (35)
Type of Foodservice: Casual Dining (1,295); Fast Casual (37); Quick Serve (30,161)
Subsidiaries: Jimmy John's Franchise LLC, CHAMPAIGN, IL
Parent Company: Roark Capital Group, ATLANTA, GA
Headquarter Offices: Arby's Restaurant Group, ATLANTA, GA; BR IP Holder LLC, CANTON, MA; Buffalo Wild Wings Inc., ATLANTA, GA; DD IP Holder, CANTON, MA; Sonic Corp., OKLAHOMA CITY, OK
Divisional Offices: Arby's Restaurant Group, INDIANAPOLIS, IN

Key Personnel
DAN LYNN - Chief Restaurant Operations Officer; Chief Commercial Officer
PAUL BROWN - Co-Founder; CEO
BRENDAN MAURI - President Division
JIM TAYLOR - President Division
JAMES NORTH - President
MICHAEL HALEY - President International; Director Global Development
RYAN DICKERSON - President Digital, Branding, E-Commerce
BRIAN PRUITT - President Strategy, Media
DAVID GRAVES - President Division
KATE JASPON - CFO
JOHN BOWIE - COO Group
NATALIE ROTHMAN - Chief People Officer
NILS OKESON - Chief Administrative Officer; General Counsel
YASIR ANWAR - CTO
ELLEN ROSE - Chief Marketing Officer
FRANK SICKELSMITH - Chief Development Officer
JASON MACEDA - Chief Development Officer
CHRISTOPHER FULLER - Chief Communications Officer
SCOTT MURPHY - Chief Brand Officer
CHRISTIAN CHARNAUX - Chief Growth Officer
CHRISTOPHER HELD - Chief Supply Chain Officer
BRAD ORSCHEL - Senior VP; General Counsel
STEPHANIE SENTELL - Senior VP Restaurant Operations, Innovation
ASHLEY LAWRENCE - VP Facility/Maintenance
MELISSA NUSS ESHPETER - VP Leasing
MEG BENDER - VP Digital, Strategic Planning
DAVID KATZMAN - VP Integration
SAI ADIVI - VP Technology, Infrastructure
DAVE KATZMAN - VP Business Development
JAMIE CARAWAN - VP Menu Development; Executive Chef
ANDREW KOHN - VP Information Technology
GARY MELKUMOV - VP Architecture, Innovation
PATRICK DOGAN - Senior Director Data Production
SHAWN CLABORN - Senior Director Procurement
LYNDON CEREJO - Senior Director Customer Service
SANJAY CHATTERJEE - Senior Director Digital Marketing
HEATHER LINK - Senior Director Human Resources
STEPHEN GALLOWAY - Senior Director Information Technology
JOHN MECUM - Senior Director Operations
LINDSAY ROBERTSON - Senior Director Human Resources
BECKY FELIS - Director Marketing
ERIC BROWN - Director Franchise Development
HARRY WISHNOW - Director Compliance
ALEXANDER NIXON - Director Consumer Insights
RICHARD LUSK - Director
ABRINA MATTHEWS - Director Architecture, Design
DAPHNE MCMANUS - Director Franchise Development
LUCIANA BELLINI GREENE - Director Design
HILARY COOPER - Director Marketing
ALBERT LIWOSO - Director Marketing
DANIEL HOPKINS - Director Training
POLLY ANDERSEN - Director Procurement, Information Technology
SUSAN WATSON - Senior Manager Digital Marketing
WILLIAM JOHNSTON - Senior Manager Business Development
CHARLES SCHUPPAN - Manager Infrastructure
CRYSTAL MCDUFFIE - Manager Digital
CHARITY BELL - Manager Human Resources, Compliance
JESSIE PARSONS - Manager Human Resources, Compliance
DENISE FENTON - Brand Manager

InterContinental Hotels Group (The Americas)
3 Ravinia Dr Ste 100
Atlanta, GA 30346-2121

Telephone: (770) 604-2000
Internet Homepage: ihg.com
Type of Business: Foodservice Operations - Hotel/Motels
Year Founded: 1952
Publicly Held: Yes
Total Sales: $3,824,700,000 (e)
Alcohol Sales: 20%
Number of Employees: 12,812
Total Units: 5,603
Restaurants in Hotels: 5603
Trade Names: Avid Hotels (1); Candlewood Suites (396); Crowne Plaza Hotel and Resort (429); EVEN Hotels (10); Holiday Inn Express (2,726); Holiday Inn Hotels and Resorts (1,251); Hotel Indigo (102); Hualuxe (8); InterContinental Hotel (204); Kimpton (66); Other (126); Regent (6); Staybridge Suites (276); Voco (2)
Company-Owned Units: 302
Units Franchised To: 3,354

Alcohol Served: Beer, Wine, Liquor
Projected Openings: 1
Areas of Operation: AK, AL, AR, AZ, CA, CO, CT, DC, DE, FL, GA, HI, IA, ID, IL, IN, KS, KY, LA, MA, MD, ME, MI, MN, MO, MS, MT, NC, ND, NE, NH, NJ, NM, NV, NY, OH, OK, OR, PA, PR, RI, SC, SD, TN, TX, UT, VA, VT, WA, WI, WV, WY, AB, BC, MB, NB, NL, NS, ON, PE, QC
Foreign Countries: CANADA
Type of Foodservice: Cafeteria; Casual Dining; Family Restaurant; Fast Casual; Fine Dining; Quick Serve
Subsidiaries: Kimpton Hotel & Restaurant Group LLC, SAN FRANCISCO, CA
Primary Distributors: (Food) SYSCO Atlanta LLC, COLLEGE PARK, GA
Parent Company: InterContinental Hotels Group PLC, LONDON, ENG
Headquarter Offices: Campbell House Gift Shop, LEXINGTON, KY
Notes: Total sales represent revenues from locations in the Americas only; the company-owned total also includes managed locations. The company derives approximately 70% of its revenue from hotel operations and has a large number of locations which do not offer foodservice.

Key Personnel
KEITH BARR - CEO
ELIE MAALOUF - CEO Division
PAUL EDGECLIFFE-JOHNSON - CFO
ERIC PEARSON - CTO; Chief Commercial Officer
DAVID JORDAN - Chief Security Officer; Senior VP
HEATHER BALSLEY - Senior VP Global Marketing
GINA LABARRE - VP Marketing, Group
TIMOTHY GENOVESE - VP Quality Assurance
TIM HORAN - Director Marketing, Sales
CHRIS BRADLEY - Director Finance
YOLA MARSHALL - Director Operations
STELA MURAT - Director Digital Designs
ARTURO ORTIZ - Manager Operations, Social Media
GENNA PANAGOPOULOS - Manager Development
KETAN SURI - Manager Finance
SCOTT CHAPMAN - Manager Branding
RUY AGUILAR SSLP, CMP - Manager Operations, Sales
LAURA AHERN - Manager Finance
JOE BARRY - Manager Marketing
DANIEL BAUTISTA - Manager Information Technology
VIRGINIA BIANCHETTI - Manager Digital Marketing
TINA BRADBERRY BARLAN - Manager Finance
MICHELLE MACON - Manager Sales, Business Development
TERESA LEGATE - Manager Finance
COLLIER LESTER - Manager Operations

TRACY SLAVITSKY - Associate Manager

Jackmont Hospitality
1760 Peachtree St NW Ste 200
Atlanta, GA 30309-2335

Telephone: (404) 523-5744
Fax Number: (404) 523-8006
Internet Homepage: jackmont.com
Company Email: information@jackmont.com
Type of Business: Foodservice Management Operator
Year Founded: 1994
Total Sales: $108,121,000 (e)
Number of Employees: 1,900
Number of Locations Served: 38
Total Foodservice Mgmt Accounts: 38
Trade Names: T.G.I. Friday's (38)
Units Franchised From: 38
Areas of Operation: DC, FL, GA, MD, NC, PA, SC
Foodservice Management Venues: Business & Industry; College & University; Health Care
Franchise Affiliation: T.G.I. Friday's Inc., DALLAS, TX
Primary Distributors: (Full Line) SYSCO Atlanta LLC, COLLEGE PARK, GA

Key Personnel
VALERIE RICHARDSON JACKSON - Chairman
DANIEL J. HALPERN - Co-Founder; CEO; President; General Buyer
BROOKE R. JACKSON-EDMOND - Co-Founder; Exec VP; Senior VP Marketing
JEFF RITSON - President; COO
PETE MCKNIGHT - CFO
CRAIG HACKLANDER - VP Operations
CHARLYE BATTEN - VP Human Resources
BRENDA BRANCH - VP Operations
ANTONIO JOHNSON - Controller
KRISTA CHESHIRE - General Manager
DREW SPENCER - General Manager
SCOTT PENNINGTON - Director Training
ANDREW PIERSON - Director Operations
DAKITA PLANT - Director Operations
JOHN FAISON - Director Operations
NANCY FOURNIER - Director Training
CHARLES BRYANT - Manager Food and Beverage
DONALD BERGER - Manager Food and Beverage
DAVE ORR - Manager Facility/Maintenance, Construction

Kale Me Crazy Franchising, Inc.
3167 Peachtree Rd Suite F
Atlanta, GA 30305

Internet Homepage: kalemecrazy.net
Type of Business: Chain Restaurant Operator
Year Founded: 2013
Number of Employees: 250
Total Units: 24
Trade Names: Kale Me Crazy (24)
Units Franchised To: 24
Primary Menu: Health Foods (24)
Areas of Operation: AL, CA, FL, GA, MS, NC, TX
Type of Foodservice: Fast Casual (24)

Key Personnel
ROI SHLOMO - Founder; CEO
MARIA ROVAYO - Director Art

Katsu International
5600 Roswell Rd Ste M100
Atlanta, GA 30342-1161

Telephone: (404) 256-1173
Fax Number: (404) 256-6462
Internet Homepage: kobesteaks.net
Type of Business: Chain Restaurant Operator
Year Founded: 1975
Total Sales: $5,674,000 (e)
Alcohol Sales: 10%
Number of Employees: 144
Average Check: Lunch(14); Dinner(34)
Total Units: 2
Trade Names: Kobe Steaks (2)
Company-Owned Units: 2
Preferred Location Types: Freestanding
Alcohol Served: Beer, Wine, Liquor
Primary Menu: Japanese (2)
Areas of Operation: TN, TX
Type of Foodservice: Fine Dining (2)
Catering Services: Yes
Primary Distributors: (Equipment) Atlanta Fixture & Sales Co., ATLANTA, GA; (Supplies) Atlanta Fixture & Sales Co., ATLANTA, GA

Key Personnel
MIKE KOMACHI - President; General Manager; Director Operations-Beverages; General Buyer
KATSUHIKO WATANABE - Owner

Killer Concepts Management Inc.
2100 Powers Ferry Rd SE Ste 120
Atlanta, GA 30339-5104

Telephone: (770) 984-6350
Fax Number: (770) 612-2473
Internet Homepage: raysrestaurants.com
Company Email: info@raysrestaurants.com
Type of Business: Chain Restaurant Operator
Year Founded: 1985
Total Sales: $31,166,000 (e)
Alcohol Sales: 15%
Number of Employees: 300

Average Check: Lunch(14); Dinner(42)
Internet Order Processing: Yes
Total Units: 3
Trade Names: Ray's In The City (1); Ray's Killer Creek (1); Ray's On The River (1)
Company-Owned Units: 3
Preferred Location Types: Freestanding; Other
Alcohol Served: Beer, Wine, Liquor
Primary Menu: Steak/Seafood (3)
Areas of Operation: GA
Type of Foodservice: Fine Dining (3)
Catering Services: Yes

Key Personnel
JEREMY MILLER - Executive Chef
ALEX BEBIAK - Director Operations; General Buyer
UGO OKPAREKE - Director Purchasing
JOHN SCHADL - Director Human Resources, Training
TIMOTHY THIEL - Director Food and Beverage
PAULA NUCKOLLS - Manager Accounting
ERIN FREEDMAN - Coordinator Marketing

La Cima Restaurants LLC
3365 Piedmont Rd NE Ste 1050
Atlanta, GA 30305-1708

Telephone: (404) 961-8946
Internet Homepage: twinpeaksrestaurant.com
Company Email: gmbucket@lacimallc.com
Type of Business: Chain Restaurant Operator
Year Founded: 2011
Total Units: 87
Trade Names: Twin Peaks Restaurant (87)
Units Franchised From: 87
Primary Menu: American (87)
Areas of Operation: AL, FL, GA, NC, SC, TN
Type of Foodservice: Casual Dining (87)
Franchise Affiliation: Twin Restaurant Holding LLC, DALLAS, TX

Key Personnel
COBY BROOKS - CEO; President
DAVE HADELMAN - Partner Operations; VP Operations
JIM TESSMER - Partner; CFO
PATTI FREDERICK - Chief Administrative Officer
JAMES PORCELLO - VP Operations
SAM ADAMS - Director Training
STEVEN YI - Director Information Technology
FRANK RODRIGUEZ - Director Operations
KAAN YILMAZ - Director Training
FABIOLA RAMIREZ - Manager Marketing

Levy Restaurants
285 Andrew Young International Blvd NW
Atlanta, GA 30313-1513

Telephone: (404) 223-4500
Fax Number: (404) 223-4511
Internet Homepage: levyrestaurants.com
Listing Type: Divisional Office
Type of Business: Foodservice Management Operator
Year Founded: 1985
Total Sales: $81,399,000 (e)
Number of Employees: 350
Number of Locations Served: 150
Total Foodservice Mgmt Accounts: 12
Trade Names: Levy Restaurants
Areas of Operation: GA
Type of Foodservice: Full-service sit-down dining (12)
Foodservice Management Venues: Business & Industry
Primary Distributors: (Full Line) SYSCO Atlanta LLC, COLLEGE PARK, GA
Parent Company: Levy Restaurants, CHICAGO, IL

Key Personnel
MERIDITH LAMBERT - Area Director Marketing, Sales
KEN GEORGE - VP Finance, Operations
PAULA MEYER - Regional VP Human Resources; Regional Director Human Resources
MOLLY DALE - General Manager
STEVE COVEY - Director Operations
KELLY DUGAN - Director Operations
YOUSUF AHMED - Director Operations
ANDY AMEZCUA - Director Operations
ANTHONY BENCOMO - Director Operations
JAKE CARLISLE - Director Operations
BRIAN CHILDERS - Director Purchasing
TARA SASSER - Director Sales
ALAURA TAGGART - Director Human Resources
ERIN VICK - Director Marketing
JESSICA GOMES - Director Operations
TAMMICHELE HOLT - Director Catering
JOHN JOHNSON - Director Operations
JIMMY KRAUS - Director Operations
AMANDA CORDOVA - Regional Manager Human Resources
KEVIN DENNEY - Manager Operations
TERESA MAINS - Manager Sales, Catering

Liberty House Restaurant Corp.
3150 Piedmont Rd NE Ste C
Atlanta, GA 30305-2508

Telephone: (404) 262-3130
Fax Number: (404) 262-3784
Internet Homepage: blueridgegrill.com; bonesrestaurant.com; okcafe.com
Type of Business: Chain Restaurant Operator
Year Founded: 1981
Total Sales: $7,664,000 (e)
Alcohol Sales: 20%
Number of Employees: 180
Average Check: Breakfast(8); Lunch(22); Dinner(84)
Total Units: 3
Trade Names: Blue Ridge Grill (1); Bone's Restaurant (1); OK Cafe (1)
Company-Owned Units: 3
Preferred Location Types: Freestanding
Alcohol Served: Beer, Wine, Liquor
Primary Menu: American (2); Steak (1)
Areas of Operation: GA
Type of Foodservice: Casual Dining (1); Fine Dining (2)
Primary Distributors: (Full Line) SYSCO Atlanta LLC, COLLEGE PARK, GA

Key Personnel
SUSAN DEROSE - Partner; Director Menu Development; General Buyer
RICHARD LEWIS - Partner; General Manager; General Buyer
RUSS EBERHART - Executive Chef; General Buyer

McAlister's Corporation
5620 Glenridge Dr
Atlanta, GA 30342-1334

Telephone: (770) 360-8300
Internet Homepage: mcalistersdeli.com
Company Email: comments@mcalistersdeli.com
Type of Business: Chain Restaurant Operator
Year Founded: 1989
Systemwide Sales: $880,298,000 (e)
Total Sales: $145,840,000 (e)
Alcohol Sales: 1%
Number of Employees: 1,449
Average Check: Breakfast(6); Lunch(8); Dinner(10)
Internet Order Processing: Yes
Internet Sales: 3.00%
Total Units: 436
Trade Names: McAlister's Deli (444)
Units Franchised To: 444
Preferred Square Footage: 3,600; 4,000
Preferred Location Types: Airports; Downtown; Freestanding; Institution (college/hospital); Outlet Mall; Regional Mall; Strip Mall
Alcohol Served: Beer
Primary Menu: Sandwiches/Deli (444)
Projected Openings: 60
Areas of Operation: AL, AR, AZ, CO, FL, GA, ID, IL, IN, KS, KY, LA, MI, MO, MS, NC, NJ, NM, NY, OH, OK, SC, TN, TX, VA, WY

Type of Foodservice: Fast Casual (444)
Catering Services: Yes
Primary Distributors: (Equipment) Hotel & Restaurant Supply, MERIDIAN, MS; (Supplies) Hotel & Restaurant Supply, MERIDIAN, MS
Parent Company: Roark Capital Group, ATLANTA, GA
Headquarters: GoTo Foods, ATLANTA, GA

Key Personnel
JOE GUITH - President
MICHAEL DIXON - CFO
NATALIA FRANCO - Chief Marketing Officer
TIM GOODMAN - VP Franchise Operations
JAY W. STANCILL - VP Development-Training
KRISTEN STANCILL - VP Operations
ARON TEN EYCK - VP Operations
MIKE MOSS - Senior Director Operations
MICHAEL FREEMAN - Senior Director Training
JEFF EDMISTON - Director Operations
JASON SALISBURY - Regional Director
MEGAN GREGG - Senior Manager Training
HOWARD SILLS - Area Manager Catering
CODY MUNN - Manager Marketing, Catering
COURTNEY BUFFORD - Manager
KELSEY MOODY - Manager

Metrotainment Cafes
1119 Logan Cir NW
Atlanta, GA 30318-2854

Telephone: (404) 249-9468
Fax Number: (404) 249-9395
Internet Homepage: metrocafes.com
Type of Business: Chain Restaurant Operator
Year Founded: 1991
Total Sales: $51,790,000 (e)
Alcohol Sales: 20%
Number of Employees: 700
Average Check: Lunch(32); Dinner(36)
Total Units: 14
Trade Names: Cowtippers (1); Einstein's (1); Guaco Joe's (1); Hudson Grille (8); Joe's on Jupiter (1); Metrotainment Bakery (1); Sugar Shack at Brookhaven(1)
Company-Owned Units: 14
Preferred Square Footage: 5,500; 6,000
Preferred Location Types: Freestanding; Strip Mall
Alcohol Served: Beer, Wine, Liquor
Primary Menu: American (5); Mexican (1); Snacks (1); Steak (7)
Projected Openings: 1
Areas of Operation: GA
Type of Foodservice: Casual Dining (12); Fast Casual (1); Fine Dining (1)
Catering Services: Yes
Notes: The company derives approximately 5% of its revenue from wholesale/retail bakery operations.

Key Personnel
JEFFREY LANDAU - CEO; Partner; Director Facility/Maintenance, Real Estate, Franchise Development, Store Fixtures
CHRISTOPHER ANDERSON - Partner
JOSE CARRANZA - Partner
JIM BELLEW - CFO
AMY LANDAU - General Manager
HEATHER WATSON - General Manager
THOMAS ALBERTINI - Executive Chef
CRAIG DOWNES - Executive Chef
RAYMOND JENNINGS - Director Human Resources
RUSS ADAMS - Director Operations
RUSSELL ADAMS - Director Operations
KENNETH STORR - Director Purchasing, Supply Chain, Menu Development
SHAWN MCCLAIN - Manager
BRENDA RUSSELL - Coordinator Special Projects

Moe's Southwest Grill LLC
5620 Glenridge Dr Ste 200
Atlanta, GA 30342

Telephone: (404) 255-3250
Fax Number: (404) 255-4978
Internet Homepage: moes.com
Company Email: info@moes.com
Type of Business: Chain Restaurant Operator
Year Founded: 2000
Systemwide Sales: $998,208,000 (e)
Total Sales: $66,110,000 (e)
Alcohol Sales: 10%
Number of Employees: 175
Average Check: Lunch(10); Dinner(14)
Internet Order Processing: Yes
Internet Sales: 5.00%
Total Units: 684
Trade Names: Moe's Southwest Grill (721)
Units Franchised To: 721
Preferred Square Footage: 2,000; 2,500; 2,800
Preferred Location Types: Airports; Downtown; Freestanding; Institution (college/hospital); Lifestyle Center; Regional Mall; Strip Mall
Alcohol Served: Beer, Wine
Primary Menu: Southwest/Tex-Mex (721)
Areas of Operation: AL, AR, AZ, CO, CT, DC, DE, FL, GA, HI, IA, ID, IL, IN, KS, KY, LA, MA, MD, MI, MN, MO, NC, ND, NE, NJ, NY, OH, OK, OR, PA, SC, SD, TN, TX, UT, VA, VT, WI, WY, AB, BC, MB, NB, NS, NT, ON, PE, QC, SK, YT
Foreign Countries: CANADA; COSTA RICA; GUATEMALA; RUSSIA
Type of Foodservice: Fast Casual (721)
Catering Services: Yes
Primary Distributors: (Full Line) SYSCO Corporation, HOUSTON, TX
Parent Company: GoTo Foods, ATLANTA, GA

Key Personnel
ERIK HESS - President
MICHAEL DIXON - CFO
MIKE SMITH - Chief Brand Officer; VP Operations
STEVE PARKER - Senior VP Development
ANDY ROONEY - VP Operations, Business Development
ANISSA MANDELL - VP Distribution, Logistics
BRAD CAMERON - Treasurer; Senior Director Finance
KAREN BUSTIOS - Senior Director Strategic Planning
JOHN HENSLEY - Director Operations
MILES VANCE - Regional Director Marketing
LILIA MEEHAN - Regional Manager Catering
DANIELLE DESALVO - Regional Manager Catering
MARY AMASON - Manager Brand Marketing
JIMMY BROOKS - Manager Production
LAUREN TALIAFERRO - Manager Design
RAY K. STEWART - Consultant Franchise Development
ALAN STOLL - Consultant Franchising
JOEY COMBS - Consultant Franchising

Nakato Japanese Restaurant
1776 Cheshire Bridge Rd NE
Atlanta, GA 30324-4922

Telephone: (404) 873-6583
Fax Number: (404) 874-7897
Internet Homepage: nakatorestaurant.com
Company Email:
  http://www.nakatorestaurant.com
Type of Business: Chain Restaurant Operator
Year Founded: 1972
Total Sales: $26,970,000 (e)
Alcohol Sales: 20%
Number of Employees: 140
Average Check: Dinner(36)
Internet Order Processing: Yes
Total Units: 5
Trade Names: Nakato Japanese Restaurant (5)
Company-Owned Units: 5
Preferred Location Types: Freestanding
Alcohol Served: Beer, Wine, Liquor
Primary Menu: Japanese (5)
Areas of Operation: GA, MO, NC, SC
Type of Foodservice: Fine Dining (5)
Catering Services: Yes
Primary Distributors: (Food) US Foods, CHARLOTTE, NC

Key Personnel
KIYOSHI NAKATO - President; Executive Chef; Director Operations, Marketing, Store Planning; General Buyer
HIROE NAKATO - Exec VP; Director Finance, Human Resources
SACHI NAKATO - General Manager; Director Catering
SACHIYO NAKATO TAKAHARA - General Manager

Neighborhood Restaurant Partners
1455 Lincoln Pkwy E Ste 430
Atlanta, GA 30346-2209

Telephone: (770) 623-0360
Fax Number: (770) 623-0557
Internet Homepage: applebeesatlanta.com; nrpneighborhood.com
Type of Business: Chain Restaurant Operator
Year Founded: 1985
Total Sales: $311,780,000 (e)
Alcohol Sales: 15%
Number of Employees: 2,237
Average Check: Lunch(14); Dinner(20)
Internet Order Processing: Yes
Internet Sales: 1.00%
Total Units: 112
Trade Names: Applebee's Neighborhood Grill & Bar (112)
Units Franchised From: 112
Preferred Square Footage: 5,000; 6,800
Preferred Location Types: Community Mall; Freestanding
Alcohol Served: Beer, Wine, Liquor
Primary Menu: American (112)
Areas of Operation: AL, FL, GA, TX
Type of Foodservice: Casual Dining (112)
Franchise Affiliation: Applebee's Services Inc., KANSAS CITY, MO
Primary Distributors: (Full Line) Reinhart FoodService, LOUISVILLE, TN

Key Personnel
COYE MANN - CFO
CHRIS LEMBCKE - Area Director
RODNEY CAMPBELL - Area Director
RYAN DOYLE - Area Director
PAMELA JONES-BOVELSKY - VP Marketing
DANA BUCK - Director Human Resources
CLARE PARKER - Director Human Resources
STEVE SMITH - Regional Director Operations
ALEX FORMEY - Regional Director Operations
KAREN FINCHER - Manager Marketing
GAIL MURPHY - Manager Human Resources

Ney Nagler Weyman Corp.
1026 N Highland Ave NE
Atlanta, GA 30306-4056

Telephone: (404) 875-3673
Fax Number: (404) 875-7392
Internet Homepage: genes.beer; nightcapfoodandspirits.com; vickerys.com
Type of Business: Chain Restaurant Operator
Year Founded: 1983
Total Sales: $9,261,000 (e)
Alcohol Sales: 30%
Number of Employees: 120
Average Check: Lunch(20); Dinner(38)
Total Units: 5
Trade Names: Fontaines Oyster House (1); Gene's Haufbrau (1); Highland Tapsteak Cellar (1); Steamhouse Lounge (1); Vickery's (1)
Company-Owned Units: 5
Preferred Location Types: Freestanding; Other
Alcohol Served: Beer, Wine, Liquor
Primary Menu: American (2); Seafood (2); Steak (1)
Areas of Operation: GA, SC
Type of Foodservice: Casual Dining (4); Fine Dining (1)
Primary Distributors: (Full Line) US Foods, CHARLOTTE, NC

Key Personnel
CHIP NEY - Partner; VP; General Manager; General Buyer
SAM WEYMAN - Partner; VP; General Manager; General Buyer
MER DIMMETT - CFO
MICHAEL ZIMMERMAN - Executive Chef

Noble Investment Group LLC
3424 Peachtree Rd NE Ste 1100
Atlanta, GA 30326-1127

Telephone: (404) 262-9660
Fax Number: (404) 262-9244
Internet Homepage: nobleinvestment.com
Type of Business: Foodservice Operations - Hotel/Motels
Year Founded: 1978
Total Sales: $171,240,000 (e)
Alcohol Sales: 15%
Number of Employees: 5,000
Total Units: 44
Restaurants in Hotels: 33
Trade Names: Courtyard by Marriott (1); Embassy Suites (3); Hilton (1); Hilton Garden Inn (5); Holiday Inn (2); Hyatt Place (6); Hyatt Regency (2); Lodge and Spa (5); Marriott (13); Residence Inn (1); SpringHill Suites (1); W Hotels (2); Westin (2)
Company-Owned Units: 44
Alcohol Served: Beer, Wine, Liquor
Projected Openings: 10
Areas of Operation: AL, CA, FL, GA, KS, LA, NC, SC, TN, TX, VA, WI
Type of Foodservice: Casual Dining (28); Fine Dining (5)
Primary Distributors: (Food) SYSCO Atlanta LLC, COLLEGE PARK, GA
Notes: The company also operates a number of limited-service hotels; their sales are included in total revenue.

Key Personnel
MITESH SHAH - CEO; President
JAMES E. CONLEY JR - CFO
RODNEY S. WILLIAMS - Chief Investment Officer
STEVEN NICHOLAS - Exec VP Operations
KEVIN GRASS - Senior VP Business Development
ADITYA BHOOPATHY - VP Strategic Planning
BENJAMIN BRUNT - VP Strategic Planning

Peak Enterprises, Inc. Galeau, LLC
537 10th St NW
Atlanta, GA 30318-5713

Telephone: (404) 347-9912
Type of Business: Chain Restaurant Operator
Total Sales: $3,653,000 (e)
Total Units: 3
Trade Names: Firehouse Subs (3)
Units Franchised From: 3
Primary Menu: Sandwiches/Deli (3)
Areas of Operation: GA
Type of Foodservice: Fast Casual (3)
Franchise Affiliation: Firehouse Restaurant Group Inc., JACKSONVILLE, FL

Key Personnel
CLINT ROHLETTER - Partner; General Buyer
GRANT ROHLETTER - Partner; General Buyer

Philly Franchising Co.
2980 Cobb Pkwy SE Ste 200
Atlanta, GA 30339-3158

Telephone: (770) 955-0086
Internet Homepage: phillyconnection.com
Type of Business: Chain Restaurant Operator
Year Founded: 1987
Systemwide Sales: $24,838,000 (e)
Total Sales: $1,539,000 (e)
Alcohol Sales: 10%
Number of Employees: 7
Average Check: Lunch(14); Dinner(24)
Total Units: 14
Trade Names: The Philly Connection (14)
Units Franchised To: 14
Preferred Square Footage: 800; 1,300; 1,400
Preferred Location Types: Downtown; Freestanding; Strip Mall
Alcohol Served: Beer
Primary Menu: Sandwiches/Deli (14)
Areas of Operation: FL, GA, KY, NC, TN, TX
Type of Foodservice: Fast Casual (14)
Catering Services: Yes

Key Personnel
RAYMOND GASPART - CEO; President; Controller; Director Finance, Real Estate, Personnel, Franchising
JOHN POLLOCK - Senior VP
OLIVIER GASPART - VP Operations; Manager Facility/Maintenance, Supply Chain, Food Safety, Purchasing-Food, Purchasing-Foodservice Equip/Supplies, Purchasing-

Kitchen Equipment
DANIELLE ROBBINS - Director Marketing, Human Resources

PONKO Chicken
2896 Chamblee Tucker Rd
Atlanta, GA 30341

Telephone: (770) 451-4251
Internet Homepage: ponkochicken.com
Company Email: chamblee@ponkochicken.com
Type of Business: Chain Restaurant Operator
Year Founded: 2017
Total Units: 2
Trade Names: PONKO Chicken (2)
Company-Owned Units: 1
Units Franchised To: 1
Primary Menu: Chicken (2)
Projected Openings: 1
Areas of Operation: GA
Type of Foodservice: Fast Casual (2)

Key Personnel
PATRICK SALLARULO - Chairman; CEO
MAGGIE ANTOINE - Co-Founder; Executive Chef

Popeyes Louisiana Kitchen Inc.
400 Perimeter Center Ter NE #1000
Atlanta, GA 30346

Telephone: (404) 459-4450
Fax Number: (404) 459-4533
Internet Homepage: company.popeyes.com; popeyes.com
Type of Business: Chain Restaurant Operator
Year Founded: 1972
Systemwide Sales: $7,240,574,000 (e)
Publicly Held: Yes
Total Sales: $735,429,000 (e)
Number of Employees: 2,130
Average Check: Lunch(8); Dinner(8)
Total Units: 4,571
Trade Names: Popeyes Louisiana Kitchen (4,571)
Units Franchised To: 4,571
Preferred Square Footage: 1,500; 2,000; 2,500; 3,000
Preferred Location Types: Airports; Community Mall; Convenience Store/Gas Station; Downtown; Freestanding; Outlet Mall; Regional Mall; Strip Mall; Travel Plazas
Primary Menu: Chicken (4,571)
Projected Openings: 100
Areas of Operation: AK, AL, AR, AZ, CA, CO, CT, DC, DE, FL, GA, GU, HI, IA, ID, IL, IN, KS, KY, LA, MA, MD, ME, MI, MN, MO, MS, MT, NC, ND, NE, NH, NJ, NM, NV, NY, OH, OK, OR, PA, PR, RI, SC, SD, TN, TX, UT, VA, WA, WI, WV, FC, ON
Foreign Countries: AFGHANISTAN; CANADA; CAYMAN ISLANDS; COSTA RICA; GERMANY; HONDURAS; JAMAICA; KUWAIT; MALAYSIA; PANAMA; QATAR; SINGAPORE; SOUTH KOREA; TRINIDAD & TOBAGO; TURKEY
Type of Foodservice: Quick Serve (4,571)
Catering Services: Yes
Primary Distributors: (Full Line) US Foods, NORCROSS, GA
Parent Company: Restaurant Brands International, TORONTO, ON CANADA

Key Personnel
JOHN M. CRANOR III - Chairman
YOSEF HOJCHMAN - President
JEFF KLEIN - President
HOPE DIAZ - Chief Marketing Officer
BART LACOUNT - Chief Marketing Officer
MATT RUBIN - Chief Digital Officer
AMY ALARCON - VP Culinary Development
MIKE TASEVSKI - VP
RICHARD COATS - VP Operations
GRADY WALKER - Treasurer; Director Finance
NICK PAJOR - Corporate Chef Research & Development
BERNADETTE NEAL - Director Finance
DAVID FERNANDES - Director Brand Marketing
PETER GENNA - Director Culinary Development
MATTHEW MONHEIT - Director Innovation
KEVIN NEMETH - Director Digital Marketing
NADER SALEH - Director Operations
BOBBY KANG - Director Operations
SERENA FAULKNER - Director Operations
JOHN GARGIULO - Director Operations-Training
CRISTINA PAVON HOFFMANN - Director Field Marketing
DIMITRI JOSEPH - Manager Digital
JAMI GILLPATRICK - Manager Marketing

RiRa Group of Companies
1080 Peachtree St NE Ste 1
Atlanta, GA 30309-6800

Telephone: (404) 477-1700
Fax Number: (404) 477-1701
Internet Homepage: rira.com
Type of Business: Chain Restaurant Operator
Year Founded: 1997
Total Sales: $28,810,000 (e)
Alcohol Sales: 30%
Number of Employees: 350
Average Check: Lunch(14); Dinner(22)
Total Units: 9
Trade Names: Keegans (1); Ri-Ra's Irish Pub & Restaurant (8)
Company-Owned Units: 9
Preferred Square Footage: 5,500; 6,000
Preferred Location Types: Freestanding
Alcohol Served: Beer, Wine, Liquor
Primary Menu: Miscellaneous (9)
Areas of Operation: DC, GA, IN, ME, NC, NH, NJ, NV, VT
Type of Foodservice: Casual Dining (9)
Primary Distributors: (Food) US Foods, CLIFTON PARK, NY

Key Personnel
DAVID KELLY - Partner; Director Real Estate; General Buyer
CIARAN SHEEHAN - Partner; Director Menu Development; General Buyer

Rising Roll Gourmet Co.
7840 Roswell Rd Ste 405
Atlanta, GA 30350-6877

Telephone: (404) 202-1141
Fax Number: (678) 461-8561
Internet Homepage: risingroll.com
Type of Business: Chain Restaurant Operator
Year Founded: 1996
Systemwide Sales: $70,194,000 (e)
Total Sales: $23,310,000 (e)
Number of Employees: 45
Average Check: Lunch(12);
Total Units: 18
Trade Names: Rising Roll Gourmet (18)
Company-Owned Units: 18
Preferred Square Footage: 4,000
Preferred Location Types: Airports; Freestanding; Office Complex; Regional Mall; Strip Mall
Primary Menu: Sandwiches/Deli (18)
Areas of Operation: FL, GA, KY, TX
Type of Foodservice: Fast Casual (20)
Foodservice Management Venues: Schools
Catering Services: Yes

Key Personnel
MIKE LASSITER - CEO; President; Director Real Estate
TOMMY WILLIAMS - VP Operations, Product Development
ALICE BARNEBEE - Director Operations

RMH Franchise
1 Concourse Pkwy Suite 600
Atlanta, GA 30328

Telephone: (402) 858-8341
Internet Homepage: rmhfranchise.com
Type of Business: Chain Restaurant Operator
Total Sales: $377,800,000 (e)
Number of Employees: 6,000
Total Units: 131
Trade Names: Applebee's (131)
Units Franchised From: 131
Primary Menu: American (131)
Type of Foodservice: Casual Dining (131)
Parent Company: Sun Holdings LLC, DALLAS,

TX

Key Personnel
MITCH BLOCHER - President; CFO
HOWARD HOHMAN - COO
RYAN PILKINGTON - VP Strategic Planning
KEVIN BENNETT - Regional VP Operations
PHIL HECKATHORNE - Regional VP Operations
SCOTT HUTCHINSON - Regional VP Operations
ADAM BOGET - Regional VP
ROGER SOMERS - Executive Director Information Technology
MELANIE BARICHIVICH - Director Marketing
JEN HANSEN - Director Human Resources
MICHELLE CARLSON - Director Training
GINNI NAEGLE - Director Operations
CHAD CIRULLO - Director Operations
JON LUCAS - Director Operations
ERIC SCHLIEMAN - Director Operations
ERIC RICKARD - Director Operations
TYLER BURNAM - Director Operations
TODD ZELKO - Director Operations

Schlotzsky's Ltd.
5620 Glenridge Point Pkwy NE
Atlanta, GA 30342-1334

Telephone: (404) 255-3250
Fax Number: (404) 255-4978
Internet Homepage: schlotzskys.com
Company Email: generalinfo@focusbrand.com
Type of Business: Chain Restaurant Operator
Year Founded: 1971
Systemwide Sales: $448,857,000 (e)
Total Sales: $94,720,000 (e)
Alcohol Sales: 1.10%
Number of Employees: 1,400
Average Check: Lunch(8); Dinner(10)
Total Units: 363
Trade Names: Schlotzsky's Austin Eatery (363)
Units Franchised To: 363
Preferred Square Footage: 2,400; 2,700; 3,200; 3,400
Preferred Location Types: Airports; Community Mall; Downtown; Freestanding; Regional Mall, Strip Mall
Alcohol Served: Beer, Wine
Primary Menu: Sandwiches/Deli (363)
Projected Openings: 10
Areas of Operation: AK, AL, AR, AZ, CA, CO, DC, FL, GA, ID, IL, IN, KS, KY, LA, MI, MN, MO, NC, ND, NE, NM, NV, OH, OK, OR, SC, SD, TN, TX, UT, VA, WA, WI, WV
Foreign Countries: CHINA; COSTA RICA; GERMANY; GUATEMALA; JORDAN; MALAYSIA; MOROCCO; RUSSIA; SOUTH KOREA; TURKEY
Type of Foodservice: Fast Casual (363)
Catering Services: Yes
Parent Company: GoTo Foods, ATLANTA, GA
Notes: The company derives approximately 20% of its revenue from the sale of its branded products in grocery & other retail stores. Corporate operations are located in Atlanta GA, but franchise operations are at in Austin TX.

Key Personnel
MICHAEL DIXON - CFO
BRENDA THIBODEAUX - Director Catering

Seven Out, LLC
227 Sandy Springs Pl Ste 102
Atlanta, GA 30328-5918

Telephone: (404) 252-9898
Type of Business: Chain Restaurant Operator
Total Sales: $4,479,000 (e)
Total Units: 3
Trade Names: Jersey Mike's Subs (3)
Units Franchised From: 3
Primary Menu: Sandwiches/Deli (3)
Areas of Operation: GA
Type of Foodservice: Quick Serve (3)
Franchise Affiliation: Jersey Mike's Franchise Systems, MANASQUAN, NJ

Key Personnel
GARY DORFMAN - Owner; General Buyer

Smalls Sliders Franchising LLC
7000 Central Pkwy Suite 1100
Atlanta, GA 30328

Internet Homepage: smallssliders.com
Type of Business: Chain Restaurant Operator
Year Founded: 2019
Total Sales: $5,407,000 (e)
Total Units: 24
Trade Names: Smalls Sliders (24)
Units Franchised To: 24
Primary Menu: Hamburger (24)
Projected Openings: 10
Areas of Operation: AL, AR, FL, GA, KS, LA, MO, MS, SC, TX
Type of Foodservice: Quick Serve (24)

Key Personnel
BRANDON LANDRY - Chairman; Co-Founder
JACOB DUGAS - Co-Founder
DAN HURWITZ - CFO
JULIE HAUSER-BLANNER - COO
DON CROCKER - Chief Development Officer
MICHAEL ALBERICI - Senior VP Marketing
RICHARD LEVEILLE - VP Franchise Development
GREGORY SWAFFORD - VP Supply Chain
CARLOS LARCADA - Regional VP
VICKY CHUSTZ - Senior Director Operations
ADAM ROOF - Senior Director Financial Planning
NATE MINNIS - Director Real Estate
KIM DECAROLIS - Director Business Development
CHARNELL SMITH-LANDRY - Director Digital
MIKE TROST - Director Construction, Store Design
KRYSTAL FAIRCLOTH - Director Brand Marketing
TARA BERGER - Director Finance
AARON CHENG - Director Business Development
CARLI WEST - Senior Manager Training
JENNIFER MASSIE - District Manager
LINDY SIMMONS - Manager Social Media
JESSICA SAULS - Manager Human Resources
RACHEL TYERYAR - Manager Financial Planning
REGINALD L. WILLIAMS II - Manager Real Estate
KEYLA TARABOCHIE - Program Manager Enterprise Solutions
ALISON EDGINTON - Specialist Training

Sotto Sotto
313 N Highland Ave NE
Atlanta, GA 30307-1911

Telephone: (404) 523-6678
Fax Number: (404) 880-0462
Internet Homepage: urestaurants.net
Type of Business: Chain Restaurant Operator
Year Founded: 1998
Total Sales: $3,117,000 (e)
Number of Employees: 25
Average Check: Dinner(54)
Total Units: 4
Trade Names: Escorpion (1); Fritti (1); Novo Cucina (1); Sotto Sotto (1)
Company-Owned Units: 4
Preferred Location Types: Freestanding; Strip Mall
Alcohol Served: Beer, Wine, Liquor
Primary Menu: Italian (2); Mexican (1); Pizza (1)
Areas of Operation: GA
Type of Foodservice: Casual Dining (2); Fine Dining (2)
Catering Services: Yes

Key Personnel
RICCARDO ULLIO - Owner; Executive Chef; General Buyer
MATTHEW POWERS - Director Operations

Southern Proper Hospitality Group
2030 Powers Ferry Rd SE Ste 460
Atlanta, GA 30339

Telephone: (404) 334-0943

Internet Homepage: sphospitality.com
Company Email: info@sphospitality.com
Listing Type: Corporate Office
Type of Business: Chain Restaurant Operator
Total Sales: $17,960,000 (e)
Number of Employees: 500
Total Units: 18
Trade Names: Chido & Padre's (1); Gypsy Kitchen (1); Milton's Black Mountain (1); Milton's Cuisine & Cocktails (1); Ocean & Acre (1); The Big Ketch (1); The Blind Pig Parlour Bar (1); The Southern Gentleman (1); Tin Lizzy's Cantina (10)
Company-Owned Units: 18
Primary Menu: American (1); Mexican (11); Seafood (2); Southern (3); Spanish (1)
Areas of Operation: FL, GA
Type of Foodservice: Casual Dining (18); Fast Casual (0)
Headquarter Offices: Tin Lizzy's Cantina, ATLANTA, GA

Key Personnel
MIKE EVERTSEN - Partner
CHRIS HADERMANN - Partner
JOHN "JP" PIEMONTE - Partner
DANI ALVAREZ - Manager Marketing
KIM FONG - Designer

Star Provisions
1460 Ellsworth Industrial Blvd NW
Atlanta, GA 30318-5580

Telephone: (404) 365-0410
Fax Number: (404) 365-8020
Internet Homepage: starprovisions.com; starprovisions.com/bacchanalia; starprovisions.com/floataway-cafe; starprovisions.com/little-bacch; starprovisions.com/whstilesfish-camp
Company Email: aquatrano@eatoutoften.net
Type of Business: Chain Restaurant Operator
Total Sales: $13,240,000 (e)
Alcohol Sales: 5%
Average Check: Dinner(36)
Total Units: 5
Trade Names: Bacchanalia (1); Floatway Cafe (1); Little Star Provisions (1); Star Provisions (1); W.H. Stiles Fish Camp (1)
Company-Owned Units: 5
Preferred Location Types: Freestanding
Alcohol Served: Beer, Wine, Liquor
Primary Menu: American (3); Sandwiches/Deli (1); Seafood (1)
Areas of Operation: GA
Type of Foodservice: Casual Dining (1); Fast Casual (1); Fine Dining (3)
Primary Distributors: (Full Line) SYSCO Atlanta LLC, COLLEGE PARK, GA
Notes: The company also operates Quinones Room at Bacchanalia, a prix-fixe offshoot of its Bacchanalia restaurant.

Key Personnel
CLIFFORD R. HARRISON - Partner; Executive Chef; General Buyer
FRANCES QUATRANO - General Manager

Sterling Restaurants, LLC
2915 Peachtree Rd NE
Atlanta, GA 30305-2101

Telephone: (404) 446-1101
Type of Business: Chain Restaurant Operator
Total Sales: $87,500,000 (e)
Total Units: 54
Trade Names: Moe's Southwest Grill (53); Shane's Rib Shack (1)
Units Franchised From: 54
Primary Menu: Bar-B-Q (1); Southwest/Tex-Mex (53)
Areas of Operation: GA
Type of Foodservice: Fast Casual (53)
Franchise Affiliation: Moe's Southwest Grill LLC, ATLANTA, GA

Key Personnel
MARK MONROE - CEO; General Buyer
DAVID ORR - Director Construction

Taqueria Del Sol
1200B Howell Mill Rd NW
Atlanta, GA 30318-4346

Telephone: (404) 352-5811
Internet Homepage: taqueriadelsol.com
Company Email: admin@taqueriadelsol.com
Type of Business: Chain Restaurant Operator
Total Sales: $6,782,000 (e)
Alcohol Sales: 10%
Number of Employees: 44
Average Check: Lunch(10); Dinner(14)
Total Units: 5
Trade Names: Taqueria Del Sol (5)
Company-Owned Units: 5
Preferred Location Types: Freestanding; Strip Mall
Alcohol Served: Beer, Wine, Liquor
Primary Menu: Southwest/Tex-Mex (5)
Projected Openings: 2
Areas of Operation: GA
Type of Foodservice: Casual Dining (5)
Primary Distributors: (Food) SYSCO Atlanta LLC, COLLEGE PARK, GA

Key Personnel
MICHAEL KLANK - President; Owner
GEORGE TRUSLER - General Manager
EDDIE HERNANDEZ - Executive Chef; General Buyer

Ted's Montana Grill LLC
133 Luckie St NW
Atlanta, GA 30303-2038

Telephone: (404) 266-1344
Fax Number: (404) 233-6717
Internet Homepage: tedsmontanagrill.com
Type of Business: Chain Restaurant Operator
Year Founded: 2001
Total Sales: $153,870,000 (e)
Alcohol Sales: 3%
Number of Employees: 3,139
Average Check: Lunch(18); Dinner(28)
Internet Order Processing: Yes
Internet Sales: 3.00%
Total Units: 41
Trade Names: Ted's Montana Grill (40)
Company-Owned Units: 40
Preferred Square Footage: 5,500; 6,000
Preferred Location Types: Downtown; Freestanding; Lifestyle Center; Strip Mall
Alcohol Served: Beer, Wine, Liquor
Primary Menu: American (40)
Areas of Operation: CO, CT, FL, GA, IL, IN, KY, MA, MT, NC, NY, OH, PA, TN, VA
Type of Foodservice: Casual Dining (40)
Primary Distributors: (Food) SYSCO Atlanta LLC, COLLEGE PARK, GA

Key Personnel
TED TURNER - Chairman; Partner
GEORGE MCKERROW JR - CEO; Partner
KRISTI MARTIN - President; COO
NANCY FURR - CFO; Controller
BILL BENZ - VP Information Technology
BECKY COPELAND - VP Human Resources-Training
REBECCA COPELAND - VP Human Resources, Training
CHRIS RAUCCI - Executive Chef; Director Menu Development
JESSICA SMITH - Senior Director Marketing
ANGELA GOLDTHWAITE - Senior Director Human Resources
EDDIE HENSLEY - Director Operations
KRISTIE MANSUR - Director Operations
CHERYL BEASLEY - Director Compliance
JAMES EBERSOLD - Director Purchasing
SCOTT FRIESEN - Director Operations
DAVE CHAPMAN - Director Operations
CHAD COGHLAN - Director Operations
ERIC ADAMSON - Director Facility/Maintenance
ROBERT WEBB - Director Operations
MATTIE WILMOTH - Director Training
DAVID ROBERTE - Manager Region
JEFF RYALS - Manager Culinary Operations
LOU ANNE AMBURN - Coordinator Facility/Maintenance
ALLY NEWTON - Coordinator Training

Texas Chicken & Burgers
1180 Peachtree St NE #2280
Atlanta, GA 30309

Telephone: (404) 920-9000
Internet Homepage: texaschickenandburgers.com
Type of Business: Chain Restaurant Operator
Year Founded: 1952
Systemwide Sales: $7,740,000 (e)
Total Sales: $2,119,000 (e)
Total Units: 43
Trade Names: Texas Chicken & Burgers (43)
Units Franchised To: 43
Primary Menu: Chicken (43)
Areas of Operation: NY, PA, WA
Type of Foodservice: Fast Casual (43)

Key Personnel
REGAN MCCOOK - Founder; CEO

The International Culinary School Atlanta
6600 Peachtree Dunwoody Rd
Atlanta, GA 30328-6773

Telephone: (800) 275-4242
Internet Homepage: artinstitutes.edu/atlanta
Company Email: phorton@aii.edu
Type of Business: Culinary Schools
Areas of Operation: GA

Key Personnel
NEWTON MYVETT - President

The Varsity Inc.
61 North Ave NW
Atlanta, GA 30308-2103

Telephone: (770) 795-0802
Fax Number: (404) 881-0273
Internet Homepage: thevarsity.com
Type of Business: Chain Restaurant Operator
Year Founded: 1928
Systemwide Sales: $21,534,000 (e)
Total Sales: $24,540,000 (e)
Number of Employees: 515
Average Check: Lunch(22); Dinner(30)
Internet Order Processing: Yes
Internet Sales: 1.00%
Total Units: 7
Trade Names: The Varsity (7)
Company-Owned Units: 7
Preferred Square Footage: 20,000
Preferred Location Types: Freestanding
Primary Menu: Hot Dogs (7)
Areas of Operation: GA
Type of Foodservice: Quick Serve (7)
Catering Services: Yes

Primary Distributors: (Food) Sutherland's Foodservice/Rich & Morgan Inc., FOREST PARK, GA

Key Personnel
NANCY SIMMS - Chairman; CEO; Director Real Estate
GORDON MUIR - President; Director Operations, Information Systems, Menu Development, E-Commerce, Internet Development
CANDICE BENNETT - Controller

The Westin Peachtree Plaza
210 Peachtree St NW
Atlanta, GA 30303-1704

Telephone: (404) 589-7506
Fax Number: (404) 654-8156
Internet Homepage: sundialrestaurant.com; westinpeachtreeplazaatlanta.com
Company Email: peach-sundial@westin.com
Type of Business: Chain Restaurant Operator
Year Founded: 1980
Total Sales: $18,263,000 (e)
Alcohol Sales: 20%
Number of Employees: 50
Average Check: Breakfast(20); Lunch(26); Dinner(66)
Total Units: 4
Trade Names: Starbucks (1); Sun Dial Restaurant (1); The Bar 210 (1); The Cafe (1)
Company-Owned Units: 4
Preferred Location Types: Hotel/Motel
Alcohol Served: Beer, Wine, Liquor
Primary Menu: American (2); Coffee (1); Southern (1)
Areas of Operation: GA
Type of Foodservice: Casual Dining (2); Fine Dining (1); Quick Serve (1)
Primary Distributors: (Food) SYSCO Atlanta LLC, COLLEGE PARK, GA

Key Personnel
BRAD SCHOKNECHT - General Manager
MIKE HSIANG - Director Finance

Thumbs Up Diner
573 Edgewood Ave SE
Atlanta, GA 30312-1935

Telephone: (404) 223-0690
Internet Homepage: thumbsupdiner.com
Type of Business: Chain Restaurant Operator
Total Units: 5
Trade Names: Thumbs Up Diner (5)
Company-Owned Units: 5
Primary Menu: American (5)
Areas of Operation: GA
Type of Foodservice: Casual Dining (5)

Key Personnel
LOU LOCRICCHIO - Founder; Owner; General Buyer
CAPRICE CASEY - Owner

Tin Drum Asiacafe LLC
1117 Perimeter Ctr Ste W200
Atlanta, GA 30338-5465

Telephone: (678) 379-5048
Fax Number: (770) 821-1895
Internet Homepage: tindrumcafe.com
Type of Business: Chain Restaurant Operator
Total Sales: $8,914,000 (e)
Internet Order Processing: Yes
Total Units: 10
Trade Names: Tin Drum Asiacafe (10)
Company-Owned Units: 2
Units Franchised To: 8
Preferred Location Types: Downtown; Institution (college/hospital); Strip Mall
Primary Menu: Asian (10)
Projected Openings: 8
Areas of Operation: GA
Type of Foodservice: Fast Casual (10)

Key Personnel
ALTAF POPATIYA - COO
MATT SCHINELLI - Director Business Development

Tin Lizzy's Cantina
2030 Powers Ferry Rd SE Ste 460
Atlanta, GA 30339

Telephone: (678) 681-9503
Internet Homepage: tinlizzyscantina.com
Type of Business: Chain Restaurant Operator
Year Founded: 2006
Total Sales: $9,265,000 (e)
Total Units: 10
Trade Names: Tin Lizzy's Cantina (10)
Company-Owned Units: 10
Primary Menu: Mexican (10)
Areas of Operation: GA, SC
Type of Foodservice: Casual Dining (10)
Parent Company: Southern Proper Hospitality Group, ATLANTA, GA

Key Personnel
ALEX CURLEY - CEO
CHRIS HADERMANN - Partner
MIKE EVERTSEN - Partner
JOHN PIEMONTE - Partner

Tropical Smoothie Franchise Development Corp.
1117 Perimeter Ctr Ste W200
Atlanta, GA 30338-5465

Telephone: (770) 821-1900
Fax Number: (770) 821-1895
Internet Homepage: tropicalsmoothie.com; tropicalsmoothiecafe.com
Company Email: tsi@tropicalsmoothie.com
Type of Business: Chain Restaurant Operator
Year Founded: 1997
Systemwide Sales: $919,264,000 (e)
Total Sales: $76,540,000 (e)
Number of Employees: 60
Average Check: Breakfast(12); Lunch(12); Dinner(12)
Total Units: 837
Trade Names: Tropical Smoothie Cafe (837)
Company-Owned Units: 1
Units Franchised To: 836
Preferred Square Footage: 1,200; 1,500; 2,000; 2,400
Preferred Location Types: Community Mall; Downtown; Freestanding; Institution (college/hospital); Lifestyle Center; Office Complex; Outlet Mall; Regional Mall; Strip Mall
Primary Menu: Sandwiches/Deli (837)
Projected Openings: 174
Areas of Operation: AL, AR, AZ, CA, FL, GA, HI, IA, IL, IN, KY, LA, MA, MD, MI, MN, MS, MT, NC, NE, NJ, NV, NY, OH, PA, SC, TN, TX, VA, WA, WI
Foreign Countries: INDIA
Type of Foodservice: Quick Serve (837)
Catering Services: Yes
Primary Distributors: (Full Line) SYSCO Food Services of Jacksonville Inc., JACKSONVILLE, FL
Parent Company: Levine Leichtman Capital Partners, BEVERLY HILLS, CA

Key Personnel
H. SCOTT PRESSLY - Chairman
MAX WETZEL - CEO
CHRIS SASSER - CFO
JONATHAN BIGGS - COO
MICHAEL LAPID - CIO; Chief Digital Officer
DEBORAH VON KUTZLEBEN - Chief Marketing Officer
CHERYL FLETCHER - Chief Development Officer
KRISTI KINGERY - Senior VP Quality Assurance, Supply Chain
LORETTA SEXTON - VP People
JENNIFER FOLGER - VP Franchise Development
BRIAN BLOSSER - VP Construction, Design
PETE WARD - General Counsel
KAREN WICKLIFFE - General Counsel
KAREN GRISSOM - Senior Director Operations, Training
KRISTEN AKEL - Director Real Estate
KELSEY DOCKINS - Director Communications
RONALD PLAUCHE JR - Director Construction, Design
BRADEN TURNER - Director
MICHAEL SCHWARTZSEID - Senior Manager Customer Analytics
KATIE BARNES - Senior Manager Supply Chain
KIM HOLLIS - Senior Manager Marketing
AUSTIN SILLS - Manager Franchise Development
HALEY CROOK - Specialist Franchise Development

Twisted Taco Franchise Inc.
PO Box 467181
Atlanta, GA 31146-7181

Telephone: (404) 946-8226
Internet Homepage: twistedtaco.com
Company Email: Twistedtacofranchise@gmail.com
Type of Business: Chain Restaurant Operator
Year Founded: 2002
Total Sales: $14,210,000 (e)
Total Units: 15
Trade Names: Twisted Taco (15)
Company-Owned Units: 15
Preferred Location Types: Institution (college/hospital); Strip Mall
Alcohol Served: Beer, Wine, Liquor
Primary Menu: Southwest/Tex-Mex (15)
Areas of Operation: AR, FL, GA, KY, NY, SC, TN
Type of Foodservice: Casual Dining (15)
Catering Services: Yes

Key Personnel
PAUL GIBBS - President; Partner
RAY SIERADZKI - Partner; VP

Uncle Maddio's Pizza Joint
3303 Habersham Rd NW
Atlanta, GA 30305-1160

Telephone: (404) 392-0707
Internet Homepage: unclemaddios.com
Company Email: franchising@unclemaddios.com
Type of Business: Chain Restaurant Operator
Year Founded: 2008
Total Sales: $21,820,000 (e)
Total Units: 29
Trade Names: Uncle Maddio's Pizza Joint (29)
Company-Owned Units: 29
Preferred Location Types: Lifestyle Center; Mobile Unit
Primary Menu: Pizza (29)
Projected Openings: 2
Areas of Operation: AL, AR, CO, FL, GA, KY, NC, ND, SC, TN, VA
Type of Foodservice: Fast Casual (29)
Catering Services: Yes
Parent Company: Integrity Brands LLC, ATLANTA, GA

Key Personnel
MATTHEW R. ANDREW - Founder; CEO
OYONDA EDWARDS - General Manager
BRANDON HIGGINBOTHAM - Director Real Estate Development
GOLDEN SCOTT - Project Manager Marketing

We're Cooking Inc.
4199 Paces Ferry Rd SE Ste C
Atlanta, GA 30339-5750

Telephone: (770) 333-0957
Fax Number: (770) 433-2542
Internet Homepage: aria-atl.com; canoeatl.com
Company Email: comments@canoeatl.com
Type of Business: Chain Restaurant Operator
Year Founded: 1995
Total Sales: $13,089,000 (e)
Alcohol Sales: 30%
Number of Employees: 110
Average Check: Lunch(26); Dinner(54)
Total Units: 2
Trade Names: Aria (1); Canoe (1)
Company-Owned Units: 2
Preferred Location Types: Freestanding
Alcohol Served: Beer, Wine, Liquor
Primary Menu: American (2)
Areas of Operation: GA
Type of Foodservice: Fine Dining (2)
Primary Distributors: (Food) Inland Seafood, TUCKER, GA

Key Personnel
KEVIN CORNISH - Director

Willy's Mexicana Grill
1876 Defoor Ave NW Ste 6
Atlanta, GA 30318-3000

Telephone: (404) 252-6366
Fax Number: (404) 252-6558
Internet Homepage: willys.com
Company Email: 411@willys.com
Type of Business: Chain Restaurant Operator
Year Founded: 1995
Total Sales: $36,950,000 (e)
Alcohol Sales: 10%
Number of Employees: 465
Average Check: Breakfast(6); Lunch(8); Dinner(10)
Internet Order Processing: Yes
Internet Sales: 1.00%
Total Units: 31
Trade Names: Willy's Mexicana Grill (31)
Company-Owned Units: 31
Preferred Square Footage: 2,000
Preferred Location Types: Freestanding; Strip

Mall
Alcohol Served: Beer, Wine, Liquor
Primary Menu: Mexican (31)
Areas of Operation: GA
Type of Foodservice: Fast Casual (31)
Catering Services: Yes
Primary Distributors: (Full Line) SYSCO Atlanta LLC, COLLEGE PARK, GA

Key Personnel
WILLY BITTER - CEO; President; General Buyer
JUAN GARCIA - President
DIANA PANNIER - VP Marketing
SAMANTHA BRYAN - Senior Director Marketing, Sales
JUDI BADER - Senior Director Employee Development

Wing Zone Franchise Corp.
2120 Powers Ferry Rd SE Ste 101
Atlanta, GA 30339-5020

Telephone: (404) 875-5045
Fax Number: (404) 875-6631
Internet Homepage: wingzone.com; wingzonefranchise.com
Company Email: customer@wingzone.com
Listing Type: Subsidiary
Type of Business: Chain Restaurant Operator
Year Founded: 1992
Systemwide Sales: $54,256,000 (e)
Total Sales: $6,177,000 (e)
Number of Employees: 61
Average Check: Lunch(14); Dinner(20)
Internet Order Processing: Yes
Internet Sales: 1.00%
Total Units: 30
Trade Names: Wing Zone (61)
Company-Owned Units: 1
Units Franchised To: 60
Preferred Square Footage: 1,200; 1,500; 2,000
Preferred Location Types: Community Mall; Strip Mall
Alcohol Served: Beer
Primary Menu: Chicken (61)
Areas of Operation: AL, CO, FL, GA, IL, KS, KY, LA, MD, MS, NC, NY, OH, SC, TN, TX, VA, WA, WI, FC
Type of Foodservice: Quick Serve (61)
Primary Distributors: (Equipment) Atlanta Fixture & Sales Co., ATLANTA, GA; (Supplies) Atlanta Fixture & Sales Co., ATLANTA, GA
Parent Company: Capriotti's Sandwich Shop Inc., LAS VEGAS, NV

Key Personnel
ASHLEY MORRIS - CEO
ADAM J. SCOTT - Partner; CFO; Senior VP; Director Information Technology, Marketing
KELVIN T. JOHNSON - VP Operations, Training
JIM RIEKEL - VP Operations

GURUDEV NADKARNI - Director Marketing

Zesto Snack Shops Inc.
2963 Piedmont Rd NE
Atlanta, GA 30305-2755

Telephone: (404) 261-4497
Fax Number: (404) 261-1409
Internet Homepage: zestoatlanta.com
Company Email: zesto@aol.com
Type of Business: Chain Restaurant Operator
Year Founded: 1949
Total Sales: $6,848,000 (e)
Alcohol Sales: 8%
Number of Employees: 110
Average Check: Breakfast(6); Lunch(12); Dinner(16)
Total Units: 5
Trade Names: Zesto Drive-In (5)
Company-Owned Units: 5
Preferred Square Footage: 3,000
Preferred Location Types: Freestanding
Primary Menu: Hamburger (5)
Areas of Operation: GA
Type of Foodservice: Quick Serve (5)
Primary Distributors: (Equipment) Atlanta Fixture & Sales Co., ATLANTA, GA

Key Personnel
JAMES B. LIVADITIS - President; Partner; Executive Chef; Director Finance, Real Estate, Design; General Buyer
VICTORIA LIVADITIS - Partner

Domino's Franchisee
3100 Washington Rd
Augusta, GA 30907-3813

Telephone: (706) 863-2262
Type of Business: Chain Restaurant Operator
Total Sales: $14,332,000 (e)
Total Units: 7
Trade Names: Domino's (7)
Units Franchised From: 7
Primary Menu: Pizza (7)
Areas of Operation: GA, SC
Type of Foodservice: Quick Serve (7)
Franchise Affiliation: Domino's Pizza Inc, ANN ARBOR, MI

Key Personnel
JOHN W. ECKBURG - Owner; General Buyer

Dakota Enterprises Inc.
5875 Gore Pl
Austell, GA 30106-3283

Telephone: (770) 819-8888
Fax Number: (770) 819-0038

Type of Business: Chain Restaurant Operator
Total Sales: $7,935,000 (e)
Number of Employees: 150
Average Check: Lunch(8); Dinner(12)
Total Units: 14
Trade Names: Subway (14)
Units Franchised From: 14
Preferred Square Footage: 1,200
Preferred Location Types: Convenience Store/Gas Station; Freestanding; Strip Mall
Primary Menu: Sandwiches/Deli (14)
Areas of Operation: GA
Type of Foodservice: Quick Serve (14)
Franchise Affiliation: Doctor's Associates Inc., MILFORD, CT

Key Personnel
CARLYLE KAUFMAN - President; Partner; General Buyer
LORETTA KAUFMAN - Partner; Director Information Systems, Marketing, Human Resources
STACY WATSON - Manager Administration

Sugar Fork Foods Inc.
1945 Parkway Pointe Dr
Bethlehem, GA 30620-2161

Telephone: (770) 867-0455
Type of Business: Chain Restaurant Operator
Total Sales: $30,770,000 (e)
Total Units: 9
Trade Names: Zaxby's (9)
Units Franchised From: 9
Primary Menu: Chicken (9)
Areas of Operation: GA
Type of Foodservice: Fast Casual (9)
Franchise Affiliation: Zaxby's Franchising Inc., ATHENS, GA

Key Personnel
TODD S. FAULKNER - President

Blue Ridge Mountain Investments Inc
195 Highway 515 W
Blairsville, GA 30512-3501

Telephone: (706) 745-0092
Company Email: blairsville63801@zaxbys.com
Type of Business: Chain Restaurant Operator
Total Sales: $11,489,000 (e)
Number of Employees: 39
Average Check: Lunch(12); Dinner(14)
Total Units: 3
Trade Names: Zaxby's (3)
Units Franchised From: 3
Preferred Square Footage: 3,300; 3,800
Preferred Location Types: Freestanding
Primary Menu: Chicken (3)

Areas of Operation: GA, NC
Type of Foodservice: Fast Casual (3)
Franchise Affiliation: Zaxby's Franchising Inc., ATHENS, GA

Key Personnel
TERRY PAYNE - Owner
PATRICIA BERTUNA - General Manager; Director Operations

Perry & Brady Enterprises Inc.
3001 Monroe Hwy
Bogart, GA 30622-8513

Telephone: (770) 725-4193
Fax Number: (770) 725-4195
Type of Business: Chain Restaurant Operator
Total Sales: $21,240,000 (e)
Number of Employees: 335
Average Check: Lunch(8); Dinner(12)
Total Units: 6
Trade Names: Zaxby's (6)
Units Franchised From: 6
Preferred Square Footage: 3,500
Preferred Location Types: Freestanding; Strip Mall
Primary Menu: Chicken (6)
Areas of Operation: GA, MO, TN
Type of Foodservice: Fast Casual (6)
Franchise Affiliation: Zaxby's Franchising Inc., ATHENS, GA
Primary Distributors: (Full Line) McLane/Lagrange, LAGRANGE, GA

Key Personnel
ANDY BRADY - President; General Buyer

Chateau Elan Winery & Resort
100 Rue Charlemagne Dr
Braselton, GA 30517-2435

Telephone: (678) 425-0900
Fax Number: (678) 425-6000
Internet Homepage: chateauelan.com
Company Email: chateau@chateauelan.com
Type of Business: Chain Restaurant Operator
Year Founded: 1981
Total Sales: $16,530,000 (e)
Alcohol Sales: 27%
Number of Employees: 600
Average Check: Breakfast(16); Lunch(30); Dinner(72)
Internet Order Processing: Yes
Internet Sales: 2.00%
Total Units: 6
Trade Names: Fleur-de-Lis (1); Le Soleil Pool Bar (1); Marc (1); Paddy's Irish Pub (1); Sarazen's Bar & Grill (1); Versailles (1)

Company-Owned Units: 6
Preferred Square Footage: 5,500; 6,000
Preferred Location Types: Freestanding; Hotel/Motel
Alcohol Served: Beer, Wine, Liquor
Primary Menu: American (1); French/Continental (3); Greek/Mediterranean (1); Miscellaneous (1)
Areas of Operation: GA
Type of Foodservice: Casual Dining (4); Fine Dining (2)
Primary Distributors: (Full Line) SYSCO Atlanta LLC, COLLEGE PARK, GA

Key Personnel
HENK EVERS - CEO; President; Owner; General Manager
ERIN GRILL - General Manager
DAVE ZERFAS - Director Operations; Manager Marketing, Human Resources
JOAN GIBBS - Manager Sales
HANNAH CASSADY - Manager Catering
DEREK CORNELL - Manager Restaurant Operations
CRYSTAL DORSEY - Manager Restaurant Operations

Lucky's Burgers and Brew
305 Brookhaven Ave NE #1250
Brookhaven, GA 30319

Telephone: (678) 705-1713
Internet Homepage: luckysburgerandbrew.com
Company Email: ted@luckysburgerandbrew.com
Type of Business: Chain Restaurant Operator
Year Founded: 2010
Total Units: 3
Trade Names: Lucky's Burgers and Brew (3)
Company-Owned Units: 3
Preferred Location Types: Strip Mall
Primary Menu: American (3)
Areas of Operation: GA
Type of Foodservice: Casual Dining (3)

Key Personnel
ERNIE GEYER - Co-Founder; Partner
TED LESCHER - Co-Founder; General Manager; Executive Chef
MICHAEL LIVINGSTON - General Manager; Director

NRD Capital Management II LLC
4170 Ashford Dunwoody Rd NE Ste 390
Brookhaven, GA 30319-1419

Telephone: (404) 865-3356
Fax Number: (404) 499-1964

Internet Homepage: nrdiusa.com
Company Email: info@nrdcapital.com
Listing Type: Corporate Office
Type of Business: Chain Restaurant Operator
Year Founded: 1996
Total Sales: $1,593,366,000 (e)
Alcohol Sales: 1%
Number of Employees: 1,400
Average Check: Lunch(8); Dinner(8)
Total Units: 451
Trade Names: Frisch's Big Boy (76); Fuzzy's Taco Shop (144); Ruby Tuesday (213); The Captains Boil (18)
Company-Owned Units: 370
Units Franchised To: 81
Preferred Square Footage: 300; 1,200; 2,000; 2,500; 3,200
Preferred Location Types: Freestanding; Regional Mall; Strip Mall
Primary Menu: American (289); Steak/Seafood (18); Taco (144)
Projected Openings: 3
Areas of Operation: AL, AR, AZ, CA, CO, CT, DC, DE, FL, GA, GU, HI, IA, ID, IN, KS, KY, LA, MA, MD, ME, MI, MN, MO, MS, NC, ND, NE, NH, NJ, NM, NV, NY, OH, OK, OR, PA, RI, SC, SD, TN, TX, UT, VA, WI, WV, ON
Foreign Countries: CANADA
Type of Foodservice: Casual Dining (231); Family Restaurant (76); Fast Casual (144)
Headquarter Offices: Experiential Brands, ATLANTA, GA; Frisch's Restaurants Inc., CINCINNATI, OH; Ruby Tuesday Inc., MARYVILLE, TN
Notes: Also known as National Restaurant Development Inc.

Key Personnel
AZIZ HASHIM - CEO; President
ANWAR BHAYANI - CFO
ROZINA HAMID - Director Investor Relations
HARRISON PRICE - Principal

Seasons of Japan
701 Glynn Isle
Brunswick, GA 31525

Telephone: (912) 748-9383
Internet Homepage: seasonsofjapan.com
Type of Business: Chain Restaurant Operator
Total Units: 9
Trade Names: Seasons of Japan (9)
Company-Owned Units: 9
Primary Menu: Japanese (9)
Areas of Operation: GA, SC
Type of Foodservice: Fast Casual (9)

Key Personnel
TOSHI HIRATA - CEO

TMD Management LLC
154 Shell Dr
Brunswick, GA 31520-2803

Telephone: (912) 267-9072
Type of Business: Chain Restaurant Operator
Total Sales: $38,070,000 (e)
Number of Employees: 310
Total Units: 8
Trade Names: McDonald's (8)
Units Franchised From: 8
Preferred Square Footage: 2,500
Primary Menu: Hamburger (8)
Areas of Operation: GA
Type of Foodservice: Quick Serve (8)
Franchise Affiliation: McDonald's Corporation, CHICAGO, IL

Key Personnel
KATIE BOOTH - President; General Buyer

Folks Restaurant Management Group
1384 Buford Business Blvd Ste 500
Buford, GA 30518-9252

Telephone: (770) 904-6595
Fax Number: (770) 904-6898
Internet Homepage: folkskitchen.com
Company Email: guestservices@folkskitchen.com
Type of Business: Chain Restaurant Operator
Year Founded: 1978
Total Sales: $20,824,000 (e)
Alcohol Sales: 0.50%
Number of Employees: 185
Average Check: Lunch(12); Dinner(20)
Internet Order Processing: Yes
Internet Sales: 1.00%
Total Units: 5
Trade Names: Folks Southern Kitchen (5)
Company-Owned Units: 5
Preferred Square Footage: 3,800
Preferred Location Types: Freestanding; Strip Mall
Alcohol Served: Beer, Wine
Primary Menu: Southern (5)
Areas of Operation: GA
Type of Foodservice: Casual Dining (5)
Catering Services: Yes
Primary Distributors: (Full Line) US Foods, FAIRBURN, GA

Key Personnel
RICHARD PRATT - President; Owner; General Manager; Director Purchasing, Marketing, Real Estate

Golden Buddha
4300 Buford Dr Ste 6
Buford, GA 30518-3458

Telephone: (770) 945-1225
Fax Number: (770) 932-4202
Internet Homepage: goldenbuddhaga.com
Type of Business: Chain Restaurant Operator
Year Founded: 1984
Total Sales: $6,080,000 (e)
Alcohol Sales: 5%
Number of Employees: 200
Average Check: Breakfast(10); Lunch(10); Dinner(10)
Total Units: 4
Trade Names: Lee's Golden Buddha (2); Mo Mo Ya Japanese Restaurant (2)
Company-Owned Units: 4
Preferred Square Footage: 5,000
Preferred Location Types: Freestanding; Strip Mall
Alcohol Served: Beer, Wine, Liquor
Primary Menu: Chinese (2); Japanese (2)
Areas of Operation: GA
Type of Foodservice: Casual Dining (4)
Catering Services: Yes
Primary Distributors: (Equipment) Atlanta Fixture & Sales Co., ATLANTA, GA; (Food) US Foods, FAIRBURN, GA; (Supplies) Atlanta Fixture & Sales Co., ATLANTA, GA

Key Personnel
BEN LEE - President; CFO; Executive Chef; Director Facility/Maintenance, Information Systems, Real Estate, Design, Human Resources, Menu Development, Catering; Buyer Food, Foodservice Equip/Supplies

Harris Group Inc.
2725 Mall of Georgia Blvd
Buford, GA 30519-8791

Telephone: (770) 448-2432
Fax Number: (770) 448-9942
Type of Business: Chain Restaurant Operator
Year Founded: 1986
Total Sales: $47,480,000 (e)
Number of Employees: 800
Average Check: Breakfast(8); Lunch(10); Dinner(10)
Total Units: 10
Trade Names: Panera Bread (10)
Units Franchised From: 10
Preferred Square Footage: 2,100; 2,900; 4,480
Preferred Location Types: Freestanding
Primary Menu: Sandwiches/Deli (10)
Areas of Operation: GA
Type of Foodservice: Fast Casual (10)
Franchise Affiliation: Panera Bread Company, SAINT LOUIS, MO; The Wendy's Company, DUBLIN, OH
Primary Distributors: (Full Line) The SYGMA Network, Inc., DUBLIN, OH

Key Personnel
DON HARRIS - Partner; Director Operations, Purchasing, Information Systems, Supply Chain, Ethnic Marketing, Real Estate
SCOTT HARRIS - Partner; Director Operations, Purchasing, Information Systems, Supply Chain, Ethnic Marketing
JULIE KENDALL - Controller; Director Finance, Human Resources
SHARA M. PRADERE - Director Human Resources
DANIEL KAPRAL - Director
MARIANNE HARRIS - Director Human Resources
MIKE DUFFASEE - Director Operations, Facility/Maintenance
TONY GARBARINO - Director Technology
MATTHEW TERRY - Director Employee Development
RON THIRTYACRE - Regional Director
BRYAN WOOD - Regional Director
JEFF RYAN - Regional Director
ANGELA BATZLE - Manager Accounting, Branch

Meadowbrook Restaurant Company Inc.
156 Prominence Point Pkwy
Canton, GA 30114-9008

Telephone: (770) 479-5711
Type of Business: Chain Restaurant Operator
Total Sales: $24,290,000 (e)
Total Units: 7
Trade Names: Zaxby's (7)
Units Franchised From: 7
Primary Menu: Chicken (7)
Areas of Operation: GA
Type of Foodservice: Fast Casual (7)
Franchise Affiliation: Zaxby's Franchising Inc., ATHENS, GA

Key Personnel
FRED J. WEIR III - President; General Buyer

HLC Foods of Carrollton, LLC
1195 Bankhead Hwy
Carrollton, GA 30116-8587

Telephone: (770) 832-1050
Type of Business: Chain Restaurant Operator
Total Sales: $42,850,000 (e)
Total Units: 12
Trade Names: Zaxby's (12)
Units Franchised From: 12

Primary Menu: Chicken (12)
Areas of Operation: GA
Type of Foodservice: Fast Casual (12)
Franchise Affiliation: Zaxby's Franchising Inc., ATHENS, GA

Key Personnel
H. LINDSEY CORDELL III - President
JULIE WALKER - Director
LIZ CHADWICK - Director Marketing, Sales, Human Resources

Hotlinez of West Georgia, Inc.
1202 S Park St
Carrollton, GA 30117-4404

Telephone: (770) 832-9047
Type of Business: Chain Restaurant Operator
Total Sales: $2,523,000 (e)
Total Units: 2
Trade Names: Firehouse Subs (2)
Units Franchised From: 2
Preferred Location Types: Strip Mall
Primary Menu: Sandwiches/Deli (2)
Areas of Operation: AL, GA
Type of Foodservice: Fast Casual (2)
Franchise Affiliation: Firehouse Restaurant Group Inc., JACKSONVILLE, FL

Key Personnel
JOEL DENNIS - President; General Buyer

Michael McCorsley
1561 S Highway 27 Ste A
Carrollton, GA 30117-8927

Telephone: (770) 836-0067
Type of Business: Chain Restaurant Operator
Total Sales: $5,913,000 (e)
Total Units: 8
Trade Names: Subway (8)
Units Franchised From: 8
Primary Menu: Sandwiches/Deli (8)
Areas of Operation: GA
Type of Foodservice: Quick Serve (8)
Franchise Affiliation: Doctor's Associates Inc., MILFORD, CT

Key Personnel
JASON MCCORSLEY - Owner; General Buyer

Red Hot Stuff, LLC
1765 S Highway 27
Carrollton, GA 30117-8937

Telephone: (770) 830-7575
Type of Business: Chain Restaurant Operator
Total Sales: $3,464,000 (e)
Total Units: 2
Trade Names: Moe's Southwest Grill (2)
Units Franchised From: 2
Primary Menu: Southwest/Tex-Mex (2)
Areas of Operation: GA
Type of Foodservice: Fast Casual (2)
Franchise Affiliation: Moe's Southwest Grill LLC, ATLANTA, GA

Key Personnel
MICHAEL STEED - Owner; General Buyer

Dabney's Incorporated
135 N Main St
Cedartown, GA 30125-2645

Telephone: (678) 861-5223
Type of Business: Chain Restaurant Operator
Total Sales: $14,380,000 (e)
Total Units: 5
Trade Names: Bojangles' Famous Chicken 'N Biscuits (5)
Units Franchised From: 5
Primary Menu: Chicken (5)
Areas of Operation: GA
Type of Foodservice: Quick Serve (5)
Franchise Affiliation: Bojangles Restaurants Inc., CHARLOTTE, NC

Key Personnel
MITCH ABNEY - President; General Buyer

Domino's Franchisee
202 East Ave
Cedartown, GA 30125-3002

Telephone: (770) 748-0909
Type of Business: Chain Restaurant Operator
Total Sales: $4,052,000 (e)
Total Units: 2
Trade Names: Domino's (2)
Units Franchised From: 2
Primary Menu: Pizza (2)
Areas of Operation: GA
Type of Foodservice: Quick Serve (2)
Franchise Affiliation: Domino's Pizza Inc, ANN ARBOR, MI

Key Personnel
BRIAN F. BARGER - Owner; General Buyer

SAQ Enterprise Inc.
4906 Peachtree Blvd
Chamblee, GA 30341

Telephone: (770) 451-6447
Type of Business: Chain Restaurant Operator
Total Sales: $7,376,000 (e)
Total Units: 2
Trade Names: Zaxby's (2)
Units Franchised From: 2
Primary Menu: Chicken (2)
Areas of Operation: GA
Type of Foodservice: Fast Casual (2)
Franchise Affiliation: Zaxby's Franchising Inc., ATHENS, GA

Key Personnel
SHEILA C. WILLIAMS - President

McLeroy's Enterprises, Inc.
110 Southern Bank Dr
Clarkesville, GA 30523

Telephone: (706) 754-5152
Type of Business: Chain Restaurant Operator
Total Sales: $47,860,000 (e)
Total Units: 14
Trade Names: Zaxby's (14)
Units Franchised From: 14
Primary Menu: Chicken (14)
Areas of Operation: GA
Type of Foodservice: Fast Casual (14)
Franchise Affiliation: Zaxby's Franchising Inc., ATHENS, GA

Key Personnel
J. GREGORY MCLEROY - President
DENISE FORTNER - Manager Administration

3DC Enterprises
6190 Bradley Park Dr
Columbus, GA 31904-9201

Telephone: (706) 320-0046
Fax Number: (706) 320-0391
Type of Business: Chain Restaurant Operator
Total Sales: $6,764,000 (e)
Number of Employees: 180
Average Check: Lunch(12); Dinner(14)
Total Units: 10
Trade Names: Zaxby's (10)
Units Franchised From: 10
Preferred Square Footage: 3,500
Preferred Location Types: Freestanding
Primary Menu: Chicken (10)
Areas of Operation: AL, GA, TX
Type of Foodservice: Fast Casual (10)
Franchise Affiliation: Zaxby's Franchising Inc., ATHENS, GA

Key Personnel
DAVID YOUNG - President
TAYLOR LUCKEY - General Manager

Cinnabon Franchisee
3131 Manchester Expy
Columbus, GA 31909-6400

Telephone: (706) 327-3232
Type of Business: Chain Restaurant Operator
Total Sales: $760,000 (e)
Total Units: 2
Trade Names: Cinnabon (2)
Units Franchised From: 2
Primary Menu: Snacks (2)
Areas of Operation: GA
Type of Foodservice: Quick Serve (2)
Franchise Affiliation: Cinnabon Inc., ATLANTA, GA

Key Personnel
FRANK ROSS - Owner; General Buyer

Country's Barbecue Inc.
6298 Veterans Pkwy
Columbus, GA 31909

Telephone: (706) 660-1415
Internet Homepage: countrysbarbecue.com
Type of Business: Chain Restaurant Operator
Year Founded: 1975
Systemwide Sales: $16,377,000 (e)
Total Sales: $5,822,000 (e)
Alcohol Sales: 3%
Number of Employees: 75
Average Check: Lunch(8); Dinner(14)
Internet Order Processing: Yes
Internet Sales: 2.00%
Total Units: 7
Trade Names: Country's Barbecue (7)
Company-Owned Units: 3
Units Franchised To: 4
Preferred Square Footage: 5,500
Preferred Location Types: Freestanding
Alcohol Served: Beer
Primary Menu: Bar-B-Q (7)
Areas of Operation: AL, GA
Type of Foodservice: Casual Dining (7)
Catering Services: Yes
On-site Distribution Center: Yes
Primary Distributors: (Food) SYSCO Atlanta LLC, COLLEGE PARK, GA

Key Personnel
JAMES MORPETH - President; Executive Chef; Director Facility/Maintenance, Marketing, Advertising, Real Estate, Design, Franchising, Menu Development
KELLEY AMON - CFO; Controller; Director Finance, Information Systems, Supply Chain, Human Resources; General Buyer
SCOTT RESSMEYER - Exec VP; Manager Operations, Distribution, Food Safety
GRIFF MORPETH - VP

TERESA RARDIN - Manager Accounting

Rkj Enterprise Inc
6131 Gateway Rd
Columbus, GA 31909-5549

Telephone: (706) 327-4222
Fax Number: (706) 327-0003
Type of Business: Chain Restaurant Operator
Total Sales: $22,340,000 (e)
Total Units: 37
Trade Names: Big E's BBQ (1); Subway (36)
Units Franchised From: 37
Primary Menu: Bar-B-Q (1); Sandwiches/Deli (36)
Areas of Operation: AL, GA
Type of Foodservice: Quick Serve (37)
Franchise Affiliation: Doctor's Associates Inc., MILFORD, CT

Key Personnel
ROBBY JONES - President; General Buyer

Schuster Enterprises Inc.
3530 Macon Rd
Columbus, GA 31907-2530

Mailing Address: PO Box 12029, COLUMBUS, GA, 31917-2029
Telephone: (706) 563-3066
Fax Number: (706) 561-6577
Type of Business: Chain Restaurant Operator
Year Founded: 1968
Total Sales: $147,760,000 (e)
Number of Employees: 2,826
Average Check: Breakfast(6); Lunch(8); Dinner(8)
Total Units: 66
Trade Names: Burger King (66)
Units Franchised From: 66
Preferred Square Footage: 2,500
Preferred Location Types: Freestanding
Primary Menu: Hamburger (66)
Areas of Operation: AL, GA
Type of Foodservice: Quick Serve (66)
Franchise Affiliation: Burger King Worldwide Inc., MIAMI, FL

Key Personnel
TODD SCHUSTER - CEO; Exec VP Real Estate
CATHY ROBERTSON - COO

Domino's Franchisee
2120 N Broad St
Commerce, GA 30529

Telephone: (470) 499-2900
Type of Business: Chain Restaurant Operator
Total Sales: $4,083,000 (e)
Total Units: 2
Trade Names: Domino's (2)
Units Franchised From: 2
Primary Menu: Pizza (2)
Areas of Operation: GA
Type of Foodservice: Quick Serve (2)
Franchise Affiliation: Domino's Pizza Inc, ANN ARBOR, MI

Key Personnel
STEVEN P. CONWAY - Owner; General Buyer

Vineyard Industries Inc.
1460 Iris Dr SW
Conyers, GA 30094-5142

Telephone: (770) 483-6760
Fax Number: (770) 483-0757
Type of Business: Chain Restaurant Operator
Year Founded: 1984
Total Sales: $47,390,000 (e)
Number of Employees: 630
Average Check: Breakfast(8); Lunch(8); Dinner(8)
Total Units: 10
Trade Names: McDonald's (10)
Units Franchised From: 10
Preferred Square Footage: 2,500
Preferred Location Types: Discount Dept. Stores; Freestanding
Primary Menu: Hamburger (10)
Areas of Operation: GA
Type of Foodservice: Quick Serve (10)
Franchise Affiliation: McDonald's Corporation, CHICAGO, IL

Key Personnel
BRUCE VINEYARD - President; Director Facility/Maintenance, Real Estate
LYNN VINEYARD MILLER - Director Operations, Information Systems, Supply Chain, Design, Store Fixtures
RANDY MILLER - Manager Finance, Purchasing, Loss Prevention, Risk Management, Ethnic Marketing, Human Resources

Keith Muller Enterprises
6220 Browns Bridge Rd
Cumming, GA 30041-4760

Telephone: (770) 886-8871
Fax Number: (770) 887-0204
Company Email: kbmuller@bellsouth.net
Type of Business: Chain Restaurant Operator
Year Founded: 1974
Total Sales: $76,890,000 (e)
Number of Employees: 920
Average Check: Breakfast(6); Lunch(8); Dinner(10)
Total Units: 21

Trade Names: McDonald's (21)
Units Franchised From: 21
Preferred Square Footage: 2,500; 3,000
Preferred Location Types: Freestanding
Primary Menu: Hamburger (21)
Areas of Operation: GA
Type of Foodservice: Quick Serve (21)
Franchise Affiliation: McDonald's Corporation, CHICAGO, IL

Key Personnel
KEITH MULLER - President; Director Finance, Operations, Facility/Maintenance, Real Estate, Human Resources; General Buyer

Bayshore Development
1111 S Thornton Ave Ste A
Dalton, GA 30720-7910

Mailing Address: PO Box 891, DALTON, GA, 30722-0891
Telephone: (706) 226-4207
Fax Number: (706) 278-8237
Company Email: bayshore1@windstream.net
Type of Business: Chain Restaurant Operator
Year Founded: 1990
Total Sales: $15,120,000 (e)
Alcohol Sales: 1%
Number of Employees: 250
Average Check: Lunch(10); Dinner(12)
Total Units: 10
Trade Names: Checkers (10)
Units Franchised From: 10
Preferred Square Footage: 1,000
Preferred Location Types: Freestanding
Primary Menu: Hamburger (10)
Areas of Operation: GA, TN
Type of Foodservice: Quick Serve (10)
Franchise Affiliation: Checkers Drive-In Restaurants Inc., TAMPA, FL

Key Personnel
LARRY ROBERTS - President; Director Information Systems, Franchising; General Buyer
COREY ROBERTS - Treasurer
LARRY FORD - Director Operations, Purchasing, Facility/Maintenance, Supply Chain, Human Resources; General Buyer

C.J. Poag Enterprises
1217 Lamar St
Dalton, GA 30720-7404

Telephone: (706) 278-1133
Internet Homepage: dineoptions.com/CremoDriveIn
Type of Business: Chain Restaurant Operator
Year Founded: 1953
Total Sales: $4,728,000 (e)
Number of Employees: 100
Average Check: Lunch(8); Dinner(10)
Total Units: 4
Trade Names: Burger Den (2); Central Drive In (1); Cremo Drive In (1)
Company-Owned Units: 4
Primary Menu: American (2); Hamburger (2)
Areas of Operation: GA
Type of Foodservice: Quick Serve (4)
Primary Distributors: (Full Line) Jacobs Wholesale Paper Co., CHATTANOOGA, TN

Key Personnel
C. J. POAG - President; Executive Chef; Manager Purchasing, Real Estate
POLLY MONTGOMERY - Manager Finance, Human Resources

Domino's Franchisee
222 W Cuyler St
Dalton, GA 30720-8209

Telephone: (706) 226-1008
Type of Business: Chain Restaurant Operator
Total Sales: $12,039,000 (e)
Total Units: 6
Trade Names: Domino's (6)
Units Franchised From: 6
Primary Menu: Pizza (6)
Areas of Operation: GA
Type of Foodservice: Quick Serve (6)
Franchise Affiliation: Domino's Pizza Inc, ANN ARBOR, MI

Key Personnel
JUSTIN S. SHOEMAKER - Owner; General Buyer

Saulat Enterprises
1129 North Way
Darien, GA 31305-9141

Mailing Address: PO Box 478, DARIEN, GA, 31305-0478
Telephone: (912) 437-2927
Fax Number: (912) 437-2962
Type of Business: Chain Restaurant Operator
Year Founded: 1997
Total Sales: $17,338,000 (e)
Number of Employees: 280
Average Check: Breakfast(8); Lunch(10); Dinner(12)
Total Units: 9
Trade Names: Hardee's (9)
Units Franchised From: 9
Preferred Square Footage: 2,500
Preferred Location Types: Freestanding
Primary Menu: Hamburger (9)
Areas of Operation: GA
Type of Foodservice: Quick Serve (9)
Franchise Affiliation: Hardee's Food Systems Inc., FRANKLIN, TN
Primary Distributors: (Food) McLane/Lagrange, LAGRANGE, GA; (Supplies) McLane/Lagrange, LAGRANGE, GA

Key Personnel
SHAKIL SAULAT - President; CFO; COO; Director Finance, Purchasing, Facility/Maintenance, Sales, Real Estate, Human Resources, Store Fixtures; General Buyer

Farm Burger LLC
410B W Ponce De Leon Ave
Decatur, GA 30030-2443

Telephone: (404) 378-5077
Internet Homepage: farmburger.net
Company Email: info@farmburger.net
Type of Business: Chain Restaurant Operator
Total Sales: $11,360,000 (e)
Total Units: 13
Trade Names: Farm Burger (13)
Company-Owned Units: 13
Primary Menu: Hamburger (13)
Areas of Operation: AL, CA, GA, NC, TN
Type of Foodservice: Fast Casual (13)

Key Personnel
GEORGE FRANGOS - Co-Founder; Partner; Advisor
PIC WALKER - Partner
MISHMA SLAUGHTER - General Manager
TARA LEDWELL - General Manager
JAMES MCFARLAND - Director Training
CAMERON THOMPSON - Director Culinary Development
TYLER FRISBEE - Regional Manager Catering
NICHOLAS HARDIN - Manager Food and Beverage
JENNIFER SISLEY - Manager Catering

Mrs. Winner's Franchising Group, LLC
4499 Glenwood Rd
Decatur, GA 30032-5157

Telephone: (404) 835-2724
Internet Homepage: lovemrswinners.com
Company Email: info@mrswinnersbrand.com
Type of Business: Chain Restaurant Operator
Year Founded: 1979
Systemwide Sales: $18,759,000 (e)
Total Sales: $13,400,000 (e)
Total Units: 14
Trade Names: Mrs. Winner's Chicken & Biscuits (14)
Units Franchised To: 14
Primary Menu: Chicken (14)
Areas of Operation: GA, NC, TN

Type of Foodservice: Quick Serve (14)

Key Personnel
JOHN E. BUTTOLPH - CEO; President; Partner
RAYMOND "JAY" BANDY - Director Operations
ADAM EDWARDS - Director Franchise Sales

Scoville Hot Chicken
2502 Blackmon Drive #830
Decatur, GA 30033

Internet Homepage: scovillechicken.com
Company Email: info@scovillechicken.com
Type of Business: Chain Restaurant Operator
Number of Employees: 80
Total Units: 6
Trade Names: Scoville Hot Chicken (6)
Units Franchised To: 6
Primary Menu: Chicken (6)
Areas of Operation: GA
Type of Foodservice: Fast Casual (6)

Key Personnel
STEVEN OH - Founder; Exec VP

Domino's Franchisee
803 Peterson Ave N Ste A
Douglas, GA 31533-4920

Telephone: (912) 384-3800
Type of Business: Chain Restaurant Operator
Total Sales: $18,205,000 (e)
Total Units: 9
Trade Names: Domino's (9)
Units Franchised From: 9
Primary Menu: Pizza (9)
Areas of Operation: GA
Type of Foodservice: Quick Serve (9)
Franchise Affiliation: Domino's Pizza Inc, ANN ARBOR, MI

Key Personnel
MICHAEL P. NAGENGAST - Owner; General Buyer

Lyon Management Company Inc.
318 Coffee Ave S
Douglas, GA 31533-0007

Telephone: (912) 384-8222
Fax Number: (912) 384-5232
Internet Homepage: lyonmgt.com
Company Email: info@lyonmgt.com
Type of Business: Chain Restaurant Operator
Year Founded: 1976
Total Sales: $19,600,000 (e)
Number of Employees: 79

Average Check: Lunch(8); Dinner(8)
Total Units: 23
Trade Names: Dairy Queen (3); KFC (14); KFC/Taco Bell (3)
Units Franchised From: 23
Preferred Square Footage: 2,500; 3,200
Preferred Location Types: Freestanding
Primary Menu: American (3); Chicken (17); Taco (3)
Areas of Operation: GA
Type of Foodservice: Quick Serve (23)
Franchise Affiliation: KFC Corporation, LOUISVILLE, KY
Primary Distributors: (Full Line) US Foods, FAIRBURN, GA

Key Personnel
WALTER LYON - President; General Buyer

Perimeter Foods, Inc.
509 Columbia Ave
Douglas, GA 31533-5021

Telephone: (912) 384-7302
Fax Number: (912) 383-8552
Type of Business: Chain Restaurant Operator
Total Sales: $7,330,000 (e)
Total Units: 3
Trade Names: Burger King (3)
Units Franchised From: 3
Preferred Location Types: Freestanding
Primary Menu: Hamburger (3)
Areas of Operation: GA
Type of Foodservice: Quick Serve (3)
Franchise Affiliation: Burger King Worldwide Inc., MIAMI, FL

Key Personnel
BRIAN VAUGHN - President; General Buyer

Davids Fast Food Inc
1829 Veterans Blvd
Dublin, GA 31021 3601

Telephone: (478) 275-0710
Type of Business: Chain Restaurant Operator
Total Sales: $14,925,000 (e)
Total Units: 3
Trade Names: McDonald's (3)
Units Franchised From: 3
Primary Menu: Hamburger (3)
Areas of Operation: GA
Type of Foodservice: Quick Serve (3)
Franchise Affiliation: McDonald's Corporation, CHICAGO, IL

Key Personnel
DAVID DAVIS - President; General Buyer

Dublin Foods Inc.
2203 Veterans Blvd
Dublin, GA 31021-2909

Telephone: (478) 275-1070
Type of Business: Chain Restaurant Operator
Total Sales: $14,573,000 (e)
Total Units: 4
Trade Names: Zaxby's (4)
Units Franchised From: 4
Primary Menu: Chicken (4)
Areas of Operation: GA
Type of Foodservice: Fast Casual (4)
Franchise Affiliation: Zaxby's Franchising Inc., ATHENS, GA

Key Personnel
D. SCOTT ROBERTS - President

Kurani Global Restaurants U.S.
2825 Breckinridge Blvd
Duluth, GA 30096-7609

Telephone: (770) 923-2313
Fax Number: (770) 923-7226
Internet Homepage: kgrus.net
Company Email: ds@goldendonut.net
Type of Business: Chain Restaurant Operator
Total Sales: $10,990,000 (e)
Number of Employees: 40
Average Check: Lunch(10); Dinner(10)
Total Units: 7
Trade Names: Dunkin' Donuts (7)
Units Franchised From: 7
Preferred Square Footage: 2,500; 3,200
Preferred Location Types: Freestanding; Strip Mall
Primary Menu: Snacks (7)
Projected Openings: 20
Areas of Operation: FL, GA
Type of Foodservice: Quick Serve (7)
Franchise Affiliation: DD IP Holder, CANTON, MA
Notes: Pizza Huts operate as Kurani Pizza Inc., Long John Silver's operate as United Seafood of America Inc.

Key Personnel
SULTAN KURANI - President
RUBY KURANI - Senior VP
KAMRAN KURANI - VP; Director Operations, Purchasing
MUNEERA BUDHANI - General Manager Communications
ANEELA KHUWAJA - General Manager Accounting
PARVEZ KHUWAJA - Director Finance
GREG COMER - Director Training, West Division
RAY LOPEZ - Director Operations

JOHN STROTHER - Director Training, East Division
AMINA BHARWANI - General Buyer

Norsan Food Group
2150 Boggs Rd Ste 500
Duluth, GA 30096-5893

Telephone: (678) 242-1654
Fax Number: (770) 414-0617
Internet Homepage: myfrontera.com; norsangroup.com; pampassteakhouse.com
Company Email: info@norsangroup.com
Type of Business: Chain Restaurant Operator
Year Founded: 1987
Total Sales: $24,260,000 (e)
Alcohol Sales: 18%
Number of Employees: 700
Average Check: Lunch(14); Dinner(26)
Internet Order Processing: Yes
Internet Sales: 0.50%
Total Units: 14
Trade Names: Frontera Mex-Mex Grill (11); Luciano's Ristorante Italiano (2); Pampas Steakhouse (1)
Company-Owned Units: 14
Preferred Square Footage: 5,000
Preferred Location Types: Freestanding; Strip Mall
Alcohol Served: Beer, Wine, Liquor
Primary Menu: Italian (2); Mexican (11); Steak (1)
Areas of Operation: GA
Type of Foodservice: Casual Dining (2); Fast Casual (11); Fine Dining (1)
Catering Services: Yes
Primary Distributors: (Food) SYSCO Atlanta LLC, COLLEGE PARK, GA

Key Personnel
NORBERTO SANCHEZ - Chairman; CEO; President; Director Real Estate, Menu Development
PAMELA SANCHEZ - VP Strategy, Development
POLO CASTRO - Regional Director Operations

Saigon Restaurant Group
3675 Satellite Blvd Ste 750
Duluth, GA 30096-2310

Telephone: (770) 368-0633
Fax Number: (770) 368-0638
Internet Homepage: saigoncafeusa.com
Company Email: info@atlsaigongroup.com
Type of Business: Chain Restaurant Operator
Total Units: 7
Trade Names: Saigon Basil (1); Saigon Cafe (6)
Company-Owned Units: 6
Units Franchised To: 1
Primary Menu: Asian (7)
Areas of Operation: GA
Type of Foodservice: Casual Dining (6); Fast Casual (1)

Key Personnel
DAVID LEE - CEO; President
PATRICIA LEE - Director Operations

The Melting Pot Franchise
8295 Royal Melbourne Way
Duluth, GA 30097-6631

Telephone: (404) 389-0099
Fax Number: (404) 389-0097
Internet Homepage: meltingpot.com
Company Email: tmpmarketing@gmail.com
Type of Business: Chain Restaurant Operator
Total Sales: $8,215,000 (e)
Alcohol Sales: 5%
Total Units: 4
Trade Names: The Melting Pot (4)
Units Franchised From: 4
Preferred Location Types: Downtown; Strip Mall
Alcohol Served: Beer, Wine, Liquor
Primary Menu: American (4)
Areas of Operation: GA
Type of Foodservice: Casual Dining (4)
Franchise Affiliation: The Melting Pot Restaurants Inc., TAMPA, FL

Key Personnel
MARK GUNN - Partner; General Manager; Director Operations; General Buyer

ACG Pizza Partners LLC
1455 Lincoln Pkwy E Ste 600B
Dunwoody, GA 30346-2209

Telephone: (770) 514-7783
Fax Number: (770) 514-7938
Internet Homepage: stevibs.com
Company Email: info@stevibs.com
Type of Business: Chain Restaurant Operator
Year Founded: 1996
Systemwide Sales: $25,281,000 (e)
Total Sales: $4,994,000 (e)
Number of Employees: 710
Average Check: Lunch(10); Dinner(10)
Total Units: 19
Trade Names: Stevi B's Pizza (19)
Company-Owned Units: 19
Preferred Square Footage: 5,500; 6,000
Preferred Location Types: Strip Mall
Primary Menu: Pizza (19)
Areas of Operation: AL, FL, GA, MI, OH, TN, VA
Type of Foodservice: Family Restaurant (19)
Parent Company: Argonne Capital Group LLC, ATLANTA, GA
Notes: Formerly known as Stevi B's Pizza Franchise Inc., the company name was changed when it was acquired by Argonne Capital Group LLC.

Key Personnel
JOHN PAVIDIS - CEO
JENNIFER ROTONDO - Chief Marketing Officer

JM of Howell Mill LLC
2458 Jett Ferry Rd Ste 220
Dunwoody, GA 30338-3060

Telephone: (770) 394-1999
Type of Business: Chain Restaurant Operator
Total Sales: $8,192,000 (e)
Total Units: 6
Trade Names: Jersey Mike's Subs (6)
Units Franchised From: 6
Primary Menu: Sandwiches/Deli (6)
Areas of Operation: GA
Type of Foodservice: Quick Serve (6)
Franchise Affiliation: Jersey Mike's Franchise Systems, MANASQUAN, NJ

Key Personnel
JEFF SPONSLER - Owner; General Buyer

The Krystal Co.
1455 Lincoln Pkwy E Ste 600
Dunwoody, GA 30346-2200

Telephone: (770) 351-4500
Internet Homepage: krystal.com
Type of Business: Chain Restaurant Operator
Year Founded: 1932
Systemwide Sales: $470,826,000 (e)
Total Sales: $293,620,000 (e)
Number of Employees: 7,120
Average Check: Breakfast(6); Lunch(8); Dinner(8)
Total Units: 286
Trade Names: Krystal (291)
Company-Owned Units: 184
Units Franchised To: 102
Preferred Square Footage: 1,700
Preferred Location Types: Airports; Community Mall; Convenience Store/Gas Station; Downtown; Freestanding; Institution (college/hospital); Mobile Unit; Regional Mall
Primary Menu: Hamburger (291)
Projected Openings: 13
Projected Remodelings: 20
Areas of Operation: AL, AR, FL, GA, KY, LA, MS, NC, SC, TN
Type of Foodservice: Quick Serve (291)
Primary Distributors: (Food) US Foods, MONTGOMERY, AL
Parent Company: Fortress Investment Group LLC, NEW YORK, NY

Key Personnel
CASEY TERRELL - Chief Marketing Officer
DAN JAMES - VP Real Estate, Construction
GLORIA DANIELS - VP Purchasing, Quality Assurance
MANNY RODRIGUEZ - VP Operations
BEVERLY DAVIS - Regional VP Operations
2 CHAINZ - Creative Director Marketing
LINDA BOLTON - Director Operations
STEVE WARE - Director Operations
FRANCOIS RUSS - Director Operations, Information Technology
ASHLEY HADLEY - Director Human Resources

Singleton Food Services Inc.
772 Maddox Dr Ste 136
East Ellijay, GA 30540-8196

Telephone: (706) 515-0013
Fax Number: (706) 635-0013
Company Email: sfsinc13@yahoo.com
Type of Business: Chain Restaurant Operator
Total Sales: $11,260,000 (e)
Total Units: 17
Trade Names: Subway (17)
Units Franchised From: 17
Primary Menu: Sandwiches/Deli (17)
Areas of Operation: GA, NC
Type of Foodservice: Quick Serve (17)
Franchise Affiliation: Doctor's Associates Inc., MILFORD, CT

Key Personnel
ED SINGLETON - President; General Buyer

JMP Pizza
4092 Olde Glen Cv
Fairborn, GA 30213

Telephone: (770) 969-0101
Type of Business: Chain Restaurant Operator
Total Sales: $47,897,000 (e)
Total Units: 23
Trade Names: Domino's (23)
Units Franchised From: 23
Primary Menu: Pizza (23)
Areas of Operation: GA
Type of Foodservice: Quick Serve (23)
Franchise Affiliation: Domino's Pizza Inc, ANN ARBOR, MI

Key Personnel
JOSEPH M. PODSEN - Owner; General Buyer

This is It! Southern BBQ
105 McIntosh Xing
Fayetteville, GA 30214-7365

Telephone: (678) 817-7757
Fax Number: (678) 817-9137
Internet Homepage: thisisitbbq.com
Company Email: thisisit@thisisitbbq.com
Type of Business: Chain Restaurant Operator
Year Founded: 1983
Systemwide Sales: $24,107,000 (e)
Total Sales: $23,200,000 (e)
Number of Employees: 148
Average Check: Lunch(12); Dinner(12)
Internet Order Processing: Yes
Internet Sales: 4.00%
Total Units: 11
Trade Names: This Is It! Bar-B-Q & Seafood (11)
Company-Owned Units: 1
Units Franchised To: 10
Preferred Square Footage: 1,500
Preferred Location Types: Community Mall; Downtown; Freestanding; Strip Mall
Primary Menu: Bar-B-Q (11)
Areas of Operation: GA
Type of Foodservice: Quick Serve (11)
Catering Services: Yes
Primary Distributors: (Full Line) US Foods, FAIRBURN, GA

Key Personnel
SHELLY ANTHONY III - Founder; CEO; President; Partner; Director Facility/Maintenance, Loss Prevention, Real Estate, Design, Menu Development, Catering
TINA DENISE ANTHONY - CEO; COO
BARBARA ANTHONY - Partner; Exec VP Purchasing, Information Systems; Director Finance
TELLEY ANTHONY - VP; Director Operations
NINA ANTHONY - Manager Training

North East Georgia Inc.
209 Boulevard
Gainesville, GA 30501-3603

Telephone: (770) 536-8781
Fax Number: (770) 536-8022
Type of Business: Chain Restaurant Operator
Year Founded: 1973
Total Sales: $57,000,000 (e)
Number of Employees: 400
Average Check: Breakfast(8); Lunch(10); Dinner(12)
Total Units: 12
Trade Names: McDonald's (12)
Units Franchised From: 12
Preferred Square Footage: 2,500
Preferred Location Types: Discount Dept. Stores; Freestanding
Primary Menu: Hamburger (12)
Areas of Operation: GA
Type of Foodservice: Quick Serve (12)
Franchise Affiliation: McDonald's Corporation, CHICAGO, IL

Key Personnel
ROBERT SWOSZOWSKI - President; Director Real Estate; General Buyer
LINDA SANDERS - Controller
KIM SCOTT - Director Operations, Facility/Maintenance
CHRISTINE KERR - Director Training
ALICIA SWOSZOWSKI - Manager Finance, Information Systems, Human Resources

Southern Baked Pie Company
748 Grove Street
Gainesville, GA 30501

Telephone: (404) 263-0656
Internet Homepage: southernbakedpie.com
Type of Business: Chain Restaurant Operator
Year Founded: 2012
Total Sales: $2,848,000 (e)
Total Units: 4
Trade Names: Southern Baked Pie Company (4)
Company-Owned Units: 4
Primary Menu: Miscellaneous (4)
Areas of Operation: GA
Type of Foodservice: Quick Serve (4)

Key Personnel
AMANDA WILBANKS - Founder; Owner

Encore Foods Inc
1931 Grayson Hwy
Grayson, GA 30017-1245

Mailing Address: PO Box 429, Bostwick, GA, 30623
Telephone: (770) 963-7855
Type of Business: Chain Restaurant Operator
Total Sales: $14,718,000 (e)
Total Units: 4
Trade Names: Zaxby's (4)
Units Franchised From: 4
Primary Menu: Chicken (4)
Areas of Operation: GA
Type of Foodservice: Fast Casual (4)
Franchise Affiliation: Zaxby's Franchising Inc., ATHENS, GA

Key Personnel
STEPHEN P. DAILEY - President

Crumbley Enterprises, Inc.
1699 N Expressway
Griffin, GA 30223-1275

Telephone: (770) 233-3322
Type of Business: Chain Restaurant Operator

Total Sales: $6,212,000 (e)
Total Units: 5
Trade Names: Little Caesars Pizza (5)
Units Franchised From: 5
Primary Menu: Pizza (5)
Areas of Operation: GA
Type of Foodservice: Quick Serve (5)
Franchise Affiliation: Little Caesar Enterprises Inc., DETROIT, MI

Key Personnel
PATRICK CRUMBLEY - President; General Buyer

Johnny's Pizza Franchise Systems Inc.
834 Virginia Ave
Hapeville, GA 30354-1943

Telephone: (404) 455-0444
Internet Homepage: johnnybruscos.com; johnnyspizza.com
Type of Business: Chain Restaurant Operator
Year Founded: 1994
Systemwide Sales: $87,407,000 (e)
Total Sales: $9,274,000 (e)
Alcohol Sales: 7%
Number of Employees: 1,217
Average Check: Lunch(16); Dinner(22)
Internet Order Processing: Yes
Total Units: 65
Trade Names: Johnny Brusco's New York Style Pizza (15); Johnny's New York Style Pizza (53)
Units Franchised To: 68
Preferred Square Footage: 2,200; 2,400
Preferred Location Types: Freestanding; Strip Mall
Alcohol Served: Beer, Wine
Primary Menu: Pizza (68)
Projected Openings: 3
Areas of Operation: AL, AR, FL, GA, KY, NC, TN
Type of Foodservice: Casual Dining (68)
Catering Services: Yes
Primary Distributors: (Full Line) US Foods, NORCROSS, GA

Key Personnel
BRUCE JACKSON - President; Partner; Director Finance, Purchasing, Supply Chain, Real Estate, Design, Franchise Development, Menu Development, Catering
SCOTT ALLEN - Partner; VP Operations, Information Systems
LUKE JACKSON - Director Operations
JOANNA O'NEIL - Specialist Operations

Mc Donald's of Hartwell
19 W Franklin St
Hartwell, GA 30643-1592

Telephone: (706) 376-2700
Internet Homepage: mcgeorgia.com
Type of Business: Chain Restaurant Operator
Total Sales: $46,750,000 (e)
Total Units: 10
Trade Names: McDonald's (10)
Units Franchised From: 10
Primary Menu: Hamburger (10)
Areas of Operation: GA, SC
Type of Foodservice: Quick Serve (10)
Franchise Affiliation: McDonald's Corporation, CHICAGO, IL

Key Personnel
TERRY S. SHUGART - President; General Buyer

Castellucci Hospitality Group
10305 Medlock Bridge Rd Ste A2
Johns Creek, GA 30097

Telephone: (770) 817-8000
Internet Homepage: cooksandsoldiers.com; castelluccihg.com; doublezeroatl.com; iberianpigatl.com; sugorestaurant.com
Company Email: info@castelluccihg.com
Type of Business: Chain Restaurant Operator
Total Units: 6
Trade Names: Bar Mercado (1); Cooks & Soldiers (1); Double Zero (1); Recess (1); Sugo Kitchen (1); The Iberian Pig (1)
Company-Owned Units: 6
Primary Menu: Health Foods (1); Italian (2); Spanish (3)
Areas of Operation: GA
Type of Foodservice: Casual Dining (6)

Key Personnel
FEDERICO CASTELLUCCI III - CEO; President; Partner
STEPHANIE CASTELLUCCI - Partner; General Manager
NANCY CASTELLUCCI - General Manager
MARISSA FRYE - General Manager
AARON JEFFERSON - General Manager
JOHN CASTELLUCCI - Executive Chef
MATTHEW RIDGWAY - Executive Chef
VICTORIA SHORE - Executive Chef
RICARDO SOTO - Executive Chef
LAUREN CASTELLUCCI - Director Marketing, Sales
RYAN BUTTNER - Director Operations
MEEKA BAXTER - Manager Accounting
SYDNEY CUMMISKEY - Manager Marketing, Social Media

Cheeseburger Bobby's Inc.
1690 Roberts Blvd NW Ste 121
Kennesaw, GA 30144-7830

Telephone: (770) 218-9962
Fax Number: (770) 218-9963
Internet Homepage: cheeseburgerbobbys.com
Company Email: info@cheeseburgerbobbys.com
Type of Business: Chain Restaurant Operator
Year Founded: 2007
Total Sales: $8,853,000 (e)
Average Check: Dinner(10)
Total Units: 12
Trade Names: Cheeseburger Bobby's (12)
Company-Owned Units: 1
Units Franchised To: 11
Preferred Square Footage: 2,000; 2,600
Primary Menu: Hamburger (12)
Areas of Operation: GA
Type of Foodservice: Fast Casual (12)

Key Personnel
ROBERT STOLL - President; Partner; General Manager; General Buyer
RICHARD STOLL - Partner
WARREN DUNCAN - Director Operations

G&H Enterprises Inc.
780 Townpark Ln NW
Kennesaw, GA 30144-5579

Telephone: (770) 429-5778
Type of Business: Chain Restaurant Operator
Total Sales: $15,315,000 (e)
Total Units: 4
Trade Names: Zaxby's (4)
Units Franchised From: 4
Primary Menu: Chicken (4)
Areas of Operation: GA
Type of Foodservice: Fast Casual (4)
Franchise Affiliation: Zaxby's Franchising Inc., ATHENS, GA

Key Personnel
TONY C. GUNTHROP - President
GERALD HUGGINS - President

Ralph Stephens
400 Ernest W Barrett Pkwy NW Ste 124
Kennesaw, GA 30144-4951

Telephone: (770) 428-9039
Fax Number: (770) 425-5144
Type of Business: Chain Restaurant Operator
Total Sales: $18,366,000 (e)
Total Units: 2

Trade Names: Chick-fil-A (2)
Company-Owned Units: 2
Primary Menu: Chicken (2)
Areas of Operation: GA
Type of Foodservice: Quick Serve (2)
Franchise Affiliation: Chick-fil-A Inc., ATLANTA, GA

Key Personnel
RALPH W. STEPHENS II - President; General Buyer

Jamsouth Inc.
1377 E King Ave
Kingsland, GA 31548-6831

Mailing Address: P.O. Box 21679, St. Simons Island, GA, 31522
Telephone: (912) 510-8500
Type of Business: Chain Restaurant Operator
Total Sales: $7,556,000 (e)
Total Units: 2
Trade Names: Zaxby's (2)
Units Franchised From: 2
Primary Menu: Chicken (2)
Areas of Operation: GA
Type of Foodservice: Fast Casual (2)
Franchise Affiliation: Zaxby's Franchising Inc., ATHENS, GA

Key Personnel
JAMES A. MAUPIN - President

Domino's Franchisee
1319 Lakes Blvd Ste A
Lake Park, GA 31636-3083

Telephone: (229) 559-9997
Type of Business: Chain Restaurant Operator
Total Sales: $14,562,000 (e)
Total Units: 7
Trade Names: Domino's (7)
Units Franchised From: 7
Primary Menu: Pizza (7)
Areas of Operation: GA
Type of Foodservice: Quick Serve (7)
Franchise Affiliation: Domino's Pizza Inc, ANN ARBOR, MI

Key Personnel
RICKY E. TEEL - Owner; General Buyer

Gandolfo's DeliBoys
1475 Buford Dr Ste 403-116
Lawrenceville, GA 30043-3719

Telephone: (770) 833-1139
Fax Number: (770) 338-2726
Internet Homepage: gandolfosdeli.com; poolsrestaurantgroup.com
Company Email: customerservice@gandolfosdeli.com
Type of Business: Chain Restaurant Operator
Year Founded: 2003
Systemwide Sales: $41,813,000 (e)
Total Sales: $2,479,000 (e)
Alcohol Sales: 5%
Number of Employees: 6
Average Check: Breakfast(8); Lunch(12); Dinner(14)
Total Units: 31
Trade Names: Gandolfo's N Y Delicatessen (31)
Units Franchised To: 31
Preferred Square Footage: 3,000
Preferred Location Types: Downtown; Strip Mall
Alcohol Served: Beer, Wine
Primary Menu: Sandwiches/Deli (31)
Areas of Operation: AZ, CA, CO, FL, GA, ID, IN, MD, MT, NC, NE, NH, NV, OR, UT
Type of Foodservice: Fast Casual (31)
Catering Services: Yes
Primary Distributors: (Food) SYSCO Intermountain Food Services Inc., WEST JORDAN, UT

Key Personnel
DAN POOL - CEO; Owner; VP Operations, Marketing, Menu Development

Mark Tredwell
680 Duluth Hwy
Lawrenceville, GA 30046-7695

Telephone: (770) 962-7844
Type of Business: Chain Restaurant Operator
Total Sales: $18,313,000 (e)
Total Units: 2
Trade Names: Chick-fil-A (2)
Units Franchised From: 2
Primary Menu: Chicken (2)
Areas of Operation: GA
Type of Foodservice: Quick Serve (2)
Franchise Affiliation: Chick-fil-A Inc., ATLANTA, GA

Key Personnel
MARK TREDWELL - President; General Buyer

Pool's Restaurant Group
1475 Buford Dr Ste 403-116
Lawrenceville, GA 30043-3719

Telephone: (770) 833-1139
Fax Number: (800) 701-9634
Internet Homepage: gandolfosdeli.com; petros.com
Type of Business: Chain Restaurant Operator
Year Founded: 1985
Systemwide Sales: $40,958,000 (e)
Total Sales: $18,806,000 (e)
Number of Employees: 110
Average Check: Lunch(12); Dinner(14)
Total Units: 31
Trade Names: Gandolfos (17); Petro's Chili & Chips (14)
Company-Owned Units: 5
Units Franchised To: 26
Preferred Square Footage: 2,500
Preferred Location Types: Downtown; Freestanding; Kiosk; Regional Mall; Strip Mall
Primary Menu: Mexican (14); Sandwiches/Deli (17)
Areas of Operation: AR, CA, NE, TN, UT, WA
Type of Foodservice: Quick Serve (31)
Foodservice Management Venues: Health Care; Schools
Catering Services: Yes
Primary Distributors: (Food) Institutional Wholesale Co., COOKEVILLE, TN; (Food) Reinhart FoodService, LOUISVILLE, TN

Key Personnel
DAN POOL - CEO; Partner
DALE WIDMER - President; Partner; Director Finance, Facility/Maintenance, Real Estate, Design, Store Fixtures, Menu Development; General Buyer
RANDY WIDMER - Partner; Exec VP Operations; VP Purchasing; General Manager
SABRINA BRIGHT - CFO
KIMBERLY WIDMER - Director Marketing
SHANNON DE LORE - Administrator Finance

Sonic Drive-Ins of North Georgia
299 Grayson Hwy
Lawrenceville, GA 30046-5726

Telephone: (770) 337-5510
Internet Homepage: sonicnorthgeorgia.com
Company Email: billy.wright@sonicpartnernet.com
Type of Business: Chain Restaurant Operator
Year Founded: 2000
Total Sales: $21,370,000 (e)
Total Units: 10
Trade Names: Sonic America's Drive-In (10)
Units Franchised From: 10
Primary Menu: Hamburger (10)
Areas of Operation: GA
Type of Foodservice: Quick Serve (10)
Franchise Affiliation: Sonic Corp., OKLAHOMA CITY, OK

Key Personnel
LANCE BURNS - Owner; General Buyer
BILLY WRIGHT - Director Marketing

RoysBoys Pizza LLC
PO Box 2628
Loganville, GA 30052-1963

Telephone: (770) 554-9747
Fax Number: (770) 554-9748
Type of Business: Chain Restaurant Operator
Year Founded: 1998
Total Sales: $13,590,000 (e)
Number of Employees: 300
Average Check: Lunch(16); Dinner(16)
Total Units: 10
Trade Names: Papa John's Pizza (10)
Units Franchised From: 10
Preferred Square Footage: 1,100; 1,500
Preferred Location Types: Freestanding; Strip Mall
Primary Menu: Pizza (10)
Areas of Operation: GA
Type of Foodservice: Quick Serve (10)
Franchise Affiliation: Papa Johns International Inc., LOUISVILLE, KY
Primary Distributors: (Full Line) Papa John's Distribution Center, LOUISVILLE, KY

Key Personnel
DEAN THOMPSON - President; Director Finance, Purchasing
ALEX LARSON - Manager Operations

Martin's Restaurant Systems Inc.
5222 Floyd Rd SW
Mableton, GA 30126-2302

Mailing Address: PO Box 689, MABLETON, GA, 30126-0689
Telephone: (770) 948-3922
Fax Number: (770) 944-3314
Internet Homepage: martinsrestaurants.com
Company Email: customercare@martinsrestaurants.com
Type of Business: Chain Restaurant Operator
Year Founded: 1962
Total Sales: $29,420,000 (e)
Number of Employees: 419
Average Check: Breakfast(8); Lunch(8);
Total Units: 17
Trade Names: Martin's (17)
Company-Owned Units: 17
Preferred Square Footage: 2,800
Preferred Location Types: Freestanding
Primary Menu: American (17)
Areas of Operation: GA
Type of Foodservice: Quick Serve (17)
Primary Distributors: (Food) Performance Foodservice - Milton's, OAKWOOD, GA; (Supplies) Southeastern Paper Group Inc., SPARTANBURG, SC

Key Personnel
MILAN SAVIC - President; Partner; Exec VP Operations; Director Facility/Maintenance, Design, Store Fixtures; Manager Training; General Buyer
JUDY STAPLETON - Manager Human Resources
KATHLEEN BOUCHER - Coordinator Marketing

C.C.H. Restaurant Management Inc.
3625 Vineville Ave Ste 2
Macon, GA 31204-1852

Telephone: (478) 476-4632
Type of Business: Chain Restaurant Operator
Year Founded: 1991
Total Sales: $48,550,000 (e)
Number of Employees: 410
Average Check: Lunch(10); Dinner(10)
Total Units: 14
Trade Names: Zaxby's (14)
Units Franchised From: 14
Preferred Square Footage: 3,500
Preferred Location Types: Freestanding
Primary Menu: Chicken (14)
Areas of Operation: GA
Type of Foodservice: Fast Casual (14)
Franchise Affiliation: Zaxby's Franchising Inc., ATHENS, GA
Primary Distributors: (Full Line) SYSCO Atlanta LLC, COLLEGE PARK, GA

Key Personnel
J. ERIC HEFNER - President; General Buyer
CHAD OLIVER - COO

Domino's Franchisee
4682 Forsyth Rd
Macon, GA 31210-4420

Telephone: (478) 757-2999
Type of Business: Chain Restaurant Operator
Total Sales: $14,011,000 (e)
Total Units: 7
Trade Names: Domino's (7)
Units Franchised From: 7
Primary Menu: Pizza (7)
Areas of Operation: GA
Type of Foodservice: Quick Serve (7)
Franchise Affiliation: Domino's Pizza Inc, ANN ARBOR, MI

Key Personnel
TODD P. DYRDA - Owner; General Buyer

Fincher's Barbecue & Catering
3947 Houston Ave
Macon, GA 31206-2515

Telephone: (478) 787-4648
Fax Number: (478) 788-1711
Internet Homepage: finchersbbqga.net
Company Email: bbqdawg@gmail.com
Type of Business: Chain Restaurant Operator
Year Founded: 1935
Total Sales: $2,981,000 (e)
Alcohol Sales: 1%
Number of Employees: 50
Average Check: Lunch(10); Dinner(16)
Total Units: 4
Trade Names: Fincher's Barbecue & Catering (4)
Company-Owned Units: 3
Units Franchised To: 1
Preferred Location Types: Freestanding
Alcohol Served: Beer
Primary Menu: Bar-B-Q (4)
Areas of Operation: GA
Type of Foodservice: Casual Dining (3); Quick Serve (1)
Catering Services: Yes
Primary Distributors: (Food) A.C.C. Distributors Inc., LEESBURG, GA

Key Personnel
DOUG FINCHER III - Co-President

Graham Crackas Inc.
3625 Vineville Ave Ste 2
Macon, GA 31204-1852

Telephone: (478) 476-4632
Type of Business: Chain Restaurant Operator
Total Sales: $51,190,000 (e)
Total Units: 15
Trade Names: Zaxby's (15)
Units Franchised From: 15
Primary Menu: Chicken (15)
Areas of Operation: GA
Type of Foodservice: Fast Casual (15)
Franchise Affiliation: Zaxby's Franchising Inc., ATHENS, GA

Key Personnel
J. ERIC HEFNER - President

Nu-Way Weiners Inc.
204 Spring St Ste G
Macon, GA 31201-0720

Telephone: (478) 743-6593
Fax Number: (478) 743-7602
Internet Homepage: nu-wayweiners.com

Company Email: nuway@nu-wayweiners.com
Type of Business: Chain Restaurant Operator
Year Founded: 1916
Systemwide Sales: $7,600,000 (e)
Total Sales: $8,242,000 (e)
Number of Employees: 150
Average Check: Lunch(6); Dinner(6)
Internet Order Processing: Yes
Internet Sales: 0.50%
Total Units: 10
Trade Names: Nu-Way Weiners (10)
Company-Owned Units: 9
Preferred Square Footage: 1,200; 1,800
Preferred Location Types: Downtown; Strip Mall
Primary Menu: Hot Dogs (10)
Areas of Operation: GA
Type of Foodservice: Quick Serve (10)
Catering Services: Yes

Key Personnel
SPYROS N. DERMATAS - Partner; Manager Finance, Operations, Information Systems, Real Estate, Design, Human Resources, Menu Development; General Buyer

S & S Cafeterias
2124 Riverside Dr
Macon, GA 31204-1747

Telephone: (478) 745-4759
Fax Number: (478) 746-8233
Internet Homepage: sscafeterias.com
Company Email: customerservice@sscafeterias.com
Type of Business: Chain Restaurant Operator
Year Founded: 1936
Total Sales: $19,530,000 (e)
Number of Employees: 377
Average Check: Lunch(14); Dinner(16)
Internet Order Processing: Yes
Internet Sales: 0.50%
Total Units: 6
Trade Names: S & S Cafeteria (6)
Company-Owned Units: 6
Preferred Square Footage: 5,500; 6,000
Preferred Location Types: Freestanding; Strip Mall
Primary Menu: American (6)
Areas of Operation: GA, SC, TN
Type of Foodservice: Cafeteria (6)
Foodservice Management Venues: Health Care; Schools
Distribution Centers: MACON, GA
On-site Distribution Center: Yes
Parent Company: Smith & Sons Foods Inc., MACON, GA

Key Personnel
RICK POGUE - CEO
J. A. SMITH IV - President
JUDSON R. SMITH - Manager District
LOUIS R. BENNETT III - Manager District

S & S Food Administrators
2626 Riverside Dr
Macon, GA 31204-17

Mailing Address: PO Box 4688, MACON, GA, 31208-4688
Telephone: (478) 745-4759
Fax Number: (478) 746-8233
Internet Homepage: sscafeterias.com
Company Email: customerservice@sscafeterias.com
Type of Business: Foodservice Management Operator
Year Founded: 1936
Total Sales: $67,048,000 (e)
Number of Employees: 800
Number of Locations Served: 25
Total Foodservice Mgmt Accounts: 25
Areas of Operation: AL, GA, SC, TN
Type of Foodservice: Cafeteria (25)
Foodservice Management Venues: Business & Industry; Health Care
Parent Company: Smith & Sons Foods Inc., MACON, GA

Key Personnel
DAVID JOHNSON - CFO; CIO; VP; Treasurer
JUDD SMITH - General Manager
MELISSA SMITH - Director Human Resources, Personnel
RITA W. KISER - Director Advertising
ANGELA FREEMAN - Manager Information Systems

J. Christopher's Restaurants LLC
1275 Powers Ferry Rd SE Ste 120
Marietta, GA 30067-9490

Telephone: (770) 738-1170
Internet Homepage: jchristophers.com
Company Email: office@jchristophers.com
Type of Business: Chain Restaurant Operator
Year Founded: 1996
Total Sales: $27,580,000 (e)
Number of Employees: 209
Total Units: 23
Trade Names: J. Christopher's (23)
Company-Owned Units: 4
Units Franchised To: 18
Preferred Square Footage: 3,500
Primary Menu: American (23)
Areas of Operation: GA, TN
Type of Foodservice: Fast Casual (23)
Notes: J. Christopher's is open for breakfast and lunch only.

Key Personnel
BARRY LENNON - Partner
JEFF MCCANN - Partner; General Buyer
TAYLOR BOLTZ - General Manager

La Cosecha Inc.
1306 Cobb Industrial Dr
Marietta, GA 30066-6607

Telephone: (678) 354-2700
Fax Number: (678) 710-3169
Internet Homepage: laparrilla.com; lacosechagroup.com
Company Email: info@laparrilla.com
Type of Business: Chain Restaurant Operator
Total Sales: $30,670,000 (e)
Alcohol Sales: 10%
Average Check: Dinner(36)
Total Units: 20
Trade Names: La Parilla (20)
Company-Owned Units: 20
Preferred Location Types: Freestanding
Alcohol Served: Beer, Wine, Liquor
Primary Menu: Mexican (20)
Areas of Operation: AL, GA
Type of Foodservice: Casual Dining (20)
Catering Services: Yes

Key Personnel
MARTIN VELAZQUEZ. - Owner; Executive Chef; General Buyer

Leaf Management
PO Box 680095
Marietta, GA 30068-0002

Telephone: (770) 993-0011
Company Email: leafmgt@gmail.com
Type of Business: Chain Restaurant Operator
Total Sales: $7,053,000 (e)
Total Units: 3
Trade Names: Burger King (3)
Units Franchised From: 3
Primary Menu: Hamburger (3)
Areas of Operation: GA
Type of Foodservice: Quick Serve (3)
Franchise Affiliation: Burger King Worldwide Inc., MIAMI, FL

Key Personnel
JOSEPH AHLZADEH - President; Owner; General Buyer

Moore & Moore Investments Inc.
2500 Barrett Creek Blvd
Marietta, GA 30066-8609

Telephone: (770) 429-3965
Type of Business: Chain Restaurant Operator
Total Sales: $7,488,000 (e)
Total Units: 2
Trade Names: Zaxby's (2)
Units Franchised From: 2
Primary Menu: Chicken (2)
Areas of Operation: GA
Type of Foodservice: Fast Casual (2)
Franchise Affiliation: Zaxby's Franchising Inc., ATHENS, GA

Key Personnel
CHRISTOPHER M. MOORE - President

PMTD Restaurants LLC
3535 Roswell Rd Ste 52
Marietta, GA 30062-8830

Telephone: (770) 578-8749
Fax Number: (770) 971-8238
Internet Homepage: pmtd.com
Type of Business: Chain Restaurant Operator
Year Founded: 1989
Total Sales: $35,600,000 (e)
Number of Employees: 521
Average Check: Lunch(8); Dinner(8)
Total Units: 27
Trade Names: KFC (19); KFC/Taco Bell (6); Taco Bell (2)
Units Franchised From: 27
Preferred Square Footage: 2,500; 3,200
Preferred Location Types: Freestanding
Primary Menu: Chicken (25); Taco (2)
Areas of Operation: AL, GA
Type of Foodservice: Quick Serve (27)
Franchise Affiliation: KFC Corporation, LOUISVILLE, KY
Primary Distributors: (Full Line) SYSCO Atlanta LLC, COLLEGE PARK, GA

Key Personnel
DAVID BARR - Chairman; CEO; Partner; General Buyer
BILL BYRD - President; Partner
JACOB EASTMAN - Director Operations

Royal Waffle King
1459 Field Park Cir
Marietta, GA 30066-5946

Telephone: (770) 528-0300
Fax Number: (877) 640-5977
Internet Homepage: royalwaffleking.com
Company Email: waffleking@bellsouth.net
Type of Business: Chain Restaurant Operator
Year Founded: 1999
Total Sales: $8,516,000 (e)
Number of Employees: 110
Average Check: Dinner(10)
Total Units: 10
Trade Names: Royal Waffle King (10)
Company-Owned Units: 7
Units Franchised To: 3
Primary Menu: American (10)
Areas of Operation: AL, GA, KY, NC
Type of Foodservice: Family Restaurant (10)

Key Personnel
CHARLIE CROWDER - President; General Buyer

The Neighborhood Dining Group Inc.
3162 Johnson Ferry Rd Ste 200
Marietta, GA 30062-7610

Mailing Address: 155 East Bay St, CHARLESTON, SC, 29401
Telephone: (770) 645-9944
Fax Number: (770) 645-9410
Internet Homepage: minerorestaurant.com; huskrestaurant.com; mccradysrestaurant.com; neighborhooddininggroup.com
Company Email: info@chicagosrestaurant.com
Type of Business: Chain Restaurant Operator
Year Founded: 1991
Total Sales: $14,630,000 (e)
Alcohol Sales: 10%
Number of Employees: 500
Average Check: Lunch(24); Dinner(30)
Total Units: 8
Trade Names: Delaney Oyster House (1); Husk Restaurant (4); McCrady's Restaurant (1); Minero (2)
Company-Owned Units: 8
Preferred Square Footage: 5,500; 6,000
Preferred Location Types: Freestanding
Alcohol Served: Beer, Wine, Liquor
Primary Menu: Mexican (2); Seafood (1); Southern (1); Steak/Seafood (4)
Areas of Operation: GA, SC, TN
Type of Foodservice: Casual Dining (7); Fine Dining (1)
Catering Services: Yes
Primary Distributors: (Full Line) SYSCO Atlanta LLC, COLLEGE PARK, GA

Key Personnel
DAVID HOWARD - President; Partner; General Manager; Executive Chef; General Buyer
KENNY LYONS - VP Operations

Troubleshooters Inc.
750 Johnson Ferry Rd
Marietta, GA 30068

Telephone: (678) 560-8100
Fax Number: (678) 560-8100
Type of Business: Chain Restaurant Operator
Total Sales: $10,964,000 (e)
Number of Employees: 50
Average Check: Lunch(8); Dinner(14)
Total Units: 3
Trade Names: Zaxby's (3)
Units Franchised From: 3
Preferred Square Footage: 3,300; 3,800
Preferred Location Types: Freestanding
Primary Menu: Chicken (3)
Areas of Operation: GA
Type of Foodservice: Fast Casual (3)
Franchise Affiliation: Zaxby's Franchising Inc., ATHENS, GA
Primary Distributors: (Full Line) SYSCO Atlanta LLC, COLLEGE PARK, GA

Key Personnel
RAY GOFF - Owner; Executive Chef
MICHELLE THOMAS - General Manager; General Buyer

Southeast QSR LLC
4107 Columbia Rd
Martinez, GA 30907

Telephone: (706) 855-6395
Fax Number: (706) 855-6982
Internet Homepage: borderattitude.com
Company Email: info@borderattitude.com
Type of Business: Chain Restaurant Operator
Year Founded: 1987
Total Sales: $169,350,000 (e)
Number of Employees: 1,860
Average Check: Lunch(8); Dinner(10)
Total Units: 63
Trade Names: Taco Bell (63)
Units Franchised From: 63
Preferred Square Footage: 1,400
Preferred Location Types: Freestanding
Primary Menu: Taco (63)
Areas of Operation: AL, FL, GA, MS, SC
Type of Foodservice: Quick Serve (63)
Franchise Affiliation: Taco Bell Corp., IRVINE, CA
Primary Distributors: (Food) McLane/Forest Park, FOREST PARK, GA

Key Personnel
NICHOLAS PETERS - President; General Manager; Director Real Estate; General Buyer
CARLOS SILVA - COO
SPENCER BASS - VP Development
ERIC VANDEN NOORT - VP Finance
TONY MOBLEY - Director Information Systems

RODNEY FIELDS - Director Real Estate
NIKI AUSTIN - Director Marketing
GREG TAYLOR - Director Talent
TRACY GILLETTE - Director Human Resources
PETER BROOKS - Director Real Estate
ANGIE ALVEAR GALVEZ - Manager
STEVE MCGEE - Project Manager Construction
SARAH MCCLAIN - Coordinator

Exceptional Restaurant Co.
155 Westridge Pkwy Ste 230
Mcdonough, GA 30253-3052

Telephone: (678) 482-5555
Fax Number: (678) 482-7991
Internet Homepage: teamerc.com
Company Email: katrina@teamerc.com
Type of Business: Chain Restaurant Operator
Year Founded: 1998
Total Sales: $21,370,000 (e)
Number of Employees: 230
Average Check: Breakfast(8); Lunch(8); Dinner(10)
Total Units: 10
Trade Names: Sonic Drive-In Restaurant (10)
Units Franchised From: 10
Preferred Square Footage: 2,500
Preferred Location Types: Freestanding; Regional Mall
Primary Menu: Miscellaneous (10)
Areas of Operation: GA
Type of Foodservice: Quick Serve (10)
Franchise Affiliation: Sonic Corp., OKLAHOMA CITY, OK
Primary Distributors: (Food) McLane/Forest Park, FOREST PARK, GA; (Supplies) McLane/Forest Park, FOREST PARK, GA

Key Personnel
DEBRA LUTHER - President; Director Finance, Facility/Maintenance, Information Systems, Risk Management, Supply Chain, Marketing, Real Estate, Store Fixtures
JEROME THOMAS - COO; Director Marketing, Real Estate, Design, Human Resources; General Buyer
GEREMIE NELSON - General Manager
JANIE MUDD - Manager Accounting, Human Resources

RPW Georgia Inc.
6516 Kitten Lake Dr
Midland, GA 31820

Telephone: (706) 225-0333
Type of Business: Chain Restaurant Operator
Total Sales: $3,582,000 (e)
Total Units: 2
Trade Names: Moe's Southwest Grill (2)
Units Franchised From: 2
Primary Menu: Southwest/Tex-Mex (2)

Areas of Operation: GA
Type of Foodservice: Fast Casual (2)
Franchise Affiliation: Moe's Southwest Grill LLC, ATLANTA, GA

Key Personnel
KEALON DRAKE - Partner
LAURA LEE - Partner

BraKat Enterprises Inc.
195 Martin Luther King Jr Blvd
Monroe, GA 30655-5621

Mailing Address: PO Box 429, Bostwick, GA, 30623
Telephone: (770) 207-0800
Type of Business: Chain Restaurant Operator
Total Sales: $35,620,000 (e)
Number of Employees: 120
Average Check: Dinner(8)
Total Units: 10
Trade Names: Zaxby's (10)
Units Franchised From: 10
Preferred Square Footage: 3,500
Preferred Location Types: Freestanding; Strip Mall
Primary Menu: Chicken (10)
Areas of Operation: GA
Type of Foodservice: Fast Casual (10)
Franchise Affiliation: Zaxby's Franchising Inc., ATHENS, GA
Primary Distributors: (Full Line) SYSCO Atlanta LLC, COLLEGE PARK, GA

Key Personnel
STEPHEN P. DAILEY - President; General Buyer
DOUG DAVIS - CFO; Director Operations

South GA Burgers, LLC
1955 Highway 34 E
Newnan, GA 30265

Telephone: (770) 251-9600
Fax Number: (770) 251-9679
Type of Business: Chain Restaurant Operator
Total Sales: $67,100,000 (e)
Number of Employees: 335
Total Units: 25
Trade Names: Taco Bell (12); Wendy's Old Fashioned Hamburgers (13)
Units Franchised From: 25
Primary Menu: Hamburger (13); Taco (12)
Areas of Operation: GA, NC
Type of Foodservice: Quick Serve (25)
Franchise Affiliation: Taco Bell Corp., IRVINE, CA; The Wendy's Company, DUBLIN, OH

Key Personnel
DOUG AUGUSTINE - President; General Buyer

MIKE BENDER - VP
CHARLES KUEHL - Controller

Great American Cookies
1346 Oakbrook Dr Ste 170
Norcross, GA 30093-2229

Telephone: (770) 514-4500
Fax Number: (770) 514-4903
Internet Homepage: globalfranchise.com; greatamericancookies.com
Company Email: customerservice@gfgmanagement.com
Type of Business: Chain Restaurant Operator
Year Founded: 1977
Systemwide Sales: $101,256,000 (e)
Total Sales: $9,880,000 (e)
Internet Order Processing: Yes
Total Units: 371
Trade Names: Great American Cookies (371)
Units Franchised To: 371
Preferred Location Types: Kiosk; Mobile Unit; Regional Mall; Strip Mall
Primary Menu: Snacks (371)
Projected Openings: 30
Projected Remodelings: 30
Areas of Operation: AL, AR, CO, FL, GA, GU, IA, IL, IN, KY, LA, MD, MI, MN, MO, MS, NC, NJ, NV, NY, OH, OK, PA, PR, SC, SD, TN, TX, VA, WI, WV
Foreign Countries: BAHRAIN; SAUDI ARABIA; UNITED ARAB EMIRATES
Type of Foodservice: Quick Serve (371)
Distribution Centers: ATLANTA, GA
Parent Company: Fat Brands, Inc., BEVERLY HILLS, CA

Key Personnel
CHRIS DULL - CEO; President
LEWIS LOEB - CFO
JENN JOHNSTON - Chief Marketing Officer
DAVID KAISER - Exec VP; Director Store Operations, Marketing, Franchise Development

JDK Foods Inc.
6895 Jimmy Carter Blvd
Norcross, GA 30071

Telephone: (404) 410-7599
Type of Business: Chain Restaurant Operator
Total Sales: $7,294,000 (e)
Total Units: 2
Trade Names: Zaxby's (2)
Units Franchised From: 2
Primary Menu: Chicken (2)
Areas of Operation: GA
Type of Foodservice: Fast Casual (2)
Franchise Affiliation: Zaxby's Franchising Inc., ATHENS, GA

Key Personnel
DANIEL L. MCCLURE - President

Pretzelmaker Inc.
1346 Oakbrook Dr Ste 170
Norcross, GA 30093-2229

Telephone: (770) 514-4500
Fax Number: (770) 514-4903
Internet Homepage: pretzelmaker.com
Company Email:
 customerservice@gfgmanagement.com
Type of Business: Chain Restaurant Operator
Year Founded: 1991
Systemwide Sales: $87,263,000 (e)
Total Sales: $81,630,000 (e)
Number of Employees: 90
Internet Order Processing: Yes
Total Units: 188
Trade Names: Pretzelmaker/Pretzel Time (188)
Units Franchised To: 188
Preferred Square Footage: 500; 800
Preferred Location Types: Community Mall; Freestanding; Regional Mall
Primary Menu: Snacks (225)
Areas of Operation: AL, AR, AZ, CA, CO, CT, DE, FL, GA, GU, HI, IA, ID, IL, IN, KS, KY, LA, MA, MD, MI, MN, MO, MS, MT, NC, ND, NE, NH, NV, NY, OH, OK, OR, PA, SC, SD, TN, TX, UT, VA, WA, WI, WV, WY, AB, MB, NB, NL, NS, QC
Foreign Countries: CANADA; MEXICO; QATAR; SAUDI ARABIA; THE PHILIPPINES
Type of Foodservice: Quick Serve (225)
Parent Company: Fat Brands, Inc., BEVERLY HILLS, CA

Key Personnel
M. CHRISTOPHER DULL - CEO; President
LEWIS LOEB - CFO
JENN JOHNSTON - COO; Chief Marketing Officer
LISA CHEATHAM - VP Marketing
LAURA NELSON - General Manager
KEVIN LIND - Director Training
HEATHER BUNTING - Manager Marketing, Communications, Branch
MIKAYLI JEPHSON - Manager Operations

Restaurant Management Group
6065 Oakbrook Pkwy
Norcross, GA 30093-1701

Telephone: (770) 248-0141
Fax Number: (770) 248-0151
Internet Homepage: louisianabistreaux.com; malonesatlanta.com
Type of Business: Chain Restaurant Operator
Year Founded: 1979
Total Sales: $15,745,000 (e)
Alcohol Sales: 15%
Number of Employees: 230
Average Check: Lunch(10); Dinner(20)
Total Units: 3
Trade Names: Louisiana Bistreaux (2); Malone's Grill & Bar (1)
Company-Owned Units: 3
Preferred Location Types: Freestanding
Alcohol Served: Beer, Wine, Liquor
Primary Menu: American (1); Cajun/Creole (2)
Areas of Operation: GA
Type of Foodservice: Casual Dining (3)
Catering Services: Yes

Key Personnel
FRED DELAWALLA - President; Executive Chef; Manager Finance, Operations, Real Estate, Design, Catering; General Buyer

Subway 1
1241 Indian Trail Lilburn Rd Ste C
Norcross, GA 30093-4587

Telephone: (770) 921-7827
Type of Business: Chain Restaurant Operator
Total Sales: $1,203,000 (e)
Total Units: 2
Trade Names: Subway (2)
Units Franchised From: 2
Primary Menu: Sandwiches/Deli (2)
Areas of Operation: GA
Type of Foodservice: Quick Serve (2)
Franchise Affiliation: Doctor's Associates Inc., MILFORD, CT

Key Personnel
JAY PATEL - President

Waffle House Inc.
5986 Financial Dr
Norcross, GA 30071-2949

Telephone: (877) 992-3353
Fax Number: (770) 729-5999
Internet Homepage: wafflehouse.com
Company Email:
 communications@wafflehouse.com
Type of Business: Chain Restaurant Operator
Year Founded: 1955
Systemwide Sales: $1,623,430,000 (e)
Total Sales: $1,047,600,000 (e)
Number of Employees: 19,000
Average Check: Breakfast(6); Lunch(8); Dinner(8)
Total Units: 1,951
Trade Names: Waffle House (1,951)
Company-Owned Units: 1,374
Units Franchised To: 577
Preferred Square Footage: 1,600; 3,000
Preferred Location Types: Freestanding
Primary Menu: American (1,951)
Projected Openings: 30
Areas of Operation: AL, AR, AZ, CO, DE, FL, GA, IL, IN, KS, KY, LA, MD, MO, MS, NC, NM, OH, OK, PA, SC, TN, TX, VA, WV
Type of Foodservice: Family Restaurant (1,951)
Primary Distributors: (Food) US Foods, FAIRBURN, GA

Key Personnel
JOE W. ROGERS JR - Chairman
WALT EHMER - CEO; President
BOB MOORE - CFO
MICHAEL HOWARD - CIO; Controller
DEB VEAL-HOOVER - Area Director People
BENJAMIN PRATT - Area Director People
ROB ABNEY - Exec VP
EMILY GREEN - Senior VP
TERRY SMITH - Senior VP Operations
JEFF CAMP - Senior VP
LOUIS TODD - VP Facility/Maintenance, Construction, Store Planning
JOHN FERVIER - VP Risk Management
GREG ROLLINGS - VP Marketing, Product Development
CRAIG KNIGHT - VP Operations
JEFF COLE - VP Real Estate, Design
WILL MIZELL - VP Human Resources
TRACY BRADSHAW - VP Human Resources
KEN WILLIAMS - VP Real Estate
BUTCH BAUR - VP Real Estate
SANDEEP MUJUMDAR - VP Information Technology
NJERI BOSS - VP Public Relations
VALENCIA PORTER - VP
CHUCK CANTRELL - VP People
ANDREW GRISSETT - Controller Operations
TERI SNOKE - Controller Operations
RACHEL SIMMONS - Director Human Resources, People, Area
KAREN WILKINS - Director Benefits, Group
LARRY SIGLER - Director Safety-Food
PHILIP PERSONETTE - Director
ISRAEL STACY - Director Recruitment
JASMINE TELLIS-CHAMBERS - Director Recruitment
ROBERT ALLEY - Director Real Estate
AMIE LEWIS - Director Recruitment
KATHERINE GASKINS - Director Employee Benefits
CHELSEA SMITH - Director Recruitment
JESSICA HERRING - Director Recruitment
SHANNON ORME - Director Recruitment
LAURA GRIMES - Director Recruitment
NATASHA BAGWILL - Director Recruitment
JOANN SEYMOUR - Director Recruitment
JADE JENKINS - Director Recruitment
SHAWN WILSON - Director People
USMAN BAJWA - Regional Manager
DEVEN KANUNGO - Regional Manager
JIMMY SHEPARD - Manager

Yogurtland Franchisee
4880 Peachtree Parkway
Norcross, GA 30092

Telephone: (770) 416-1005
Type of Business: Chain Restaurant Operator
Total Sales: $2,121,000 (e)
Total Units: 2
Trade Names: Yogurtland (2)
Units Franchised From: 2
Primary Menu: Snacks (2)
Areas of Operation: GA
Type of Foodservice: Quick Serve (2)
Franchise Affiliation: Yogurtland Franchising Inc., FARMERS BRANCH, TX

Key Personnel
RICK EVANS - Owner; General Buyer

PITA Mediterranean Street Food
312 Crosstown Dr
Peachtree City, GA 30269

Telephone: (404) 764-8858
Internet Homepage: pitastreetfood.com
Company Email: nourpita@gmail.com
Type of Business: Chain Restaurant Operator
Year Founded: 2011
Total Sales: $665,000 (e)
Total Units: 32
Trade Names: PITA Mediterranean Street Food (32)
Company-Owned Units: 3
Units Franchised To: 29
Primary Menu: Middle Eastern (32)
Type of Foodservice: Fast Casual (32)

Key Personnel
NOUR RABAI - Founder; CEO

Palmaccio Management
130 Canal St Ste 201
Pooler, GA 31322-4000

Telephone: (912) 450-3003
Fax Number: (912) 450-3013
Type of Business: Chain Restaurant Operator
Total Sales: $97,260,000 (e)
Number of Employees: 385
Total Units: 21
Trade Names: McDonald's (21)
Units Franchised From: 21
Preferred Square Footage: 2,500
Primary Menu: Hamburger (21)
Areas of Operation: GA, SC
Type of Foodservice: Quick Serve (21)
Franchise Affiliation: McDonald's Corporation, CHICAGO, IL

Key Personnel
JOHN PALMACCIO - President; General Buyer
GEORGE FELTON - Director Operations

Stoner's Pizza Joint
80 Bass Dr
Richmond Hill, GA 31324

Telephone: (843) 518-1972
Internet Homepage: stonerspizzajoint.com
Company Email: Franchise@StonersPizzaJoint.com
Type of Business: Chain Restaurant Operator
Year Founded: 2013
Total Sales: $30,560,000 (e)
Number of Employees: 350
Average Check: Dinner(24)
Total Units: 24
Trade Names: Stoner's Pizza Joint (24)
Company-Owned Units: 6
Units Franchised To: 18
Primary Menu: Pizza (24)
Projected Openings: 3
Areas of Operation: FL, GA, SC
Type of Foodservice: Casual Dining (24)
Catering Services: Yes

Key Personnel
DREW CICCARELLI - President
GLENN CYBULSKI - President; COO Culinary Operations
NICK BERGELT - Chief Concept Officer
WILLIAM CARLISI - VP Purchasing, Franchise Sales
JUDD CARLISI - VP Purchasing, Franchise Sales

Domino's Franchisee
117 Poplar Springs Rd
Ringgold, GA 30736-2808

Telephone: (706) 965-5000
Type of Business: Chain Restaurant Operator
Total Sales: $6,013,000 (e)
Total Units: 3
Trade Names: Domino's (3)
Units Franchised From: 3
Primary Menu: Pizza (3)
Areas of Operation: GA
Type of Foodservice: Quick Serve (3)
Franchise Affiliation: Domino's Pizza Inc, ANN ARBOR, MI

Key Personnel
KEVIN R. SCHWARTZ - Owner; General Buyer

HLC Foods, LLC
2415 Shorter Ave SW
Rome, GA 30165-1914

Telephone: (706) 291-9996
Type of Business: Chain Restaurant Operator
Total Sales: $17,620,000 (e)
Total Units: 5
Trade Names: Zaxby's (5)
Units Franchised From: 5
Primary Menu: Chicken (5)
Areas of Operation: GA
Type of Foodservice: Fast Casual (5)
Franchise Affiliation: Zaxby's Franchising Inc., ATHENS, GA

Key Personnel
H. LINDSEY CORDELL III - President; Owner
RAY COUEY - Manager District

Las Palmas Mexican Restaurant
246 Shorter Ave NW
Rome, GA 30165

Telephone: (706) 291-9788
Internet Homepage: laspalmasmexicanrest.com
Type of Business: Chain Restaurant Operator
Total Sales: $672,000 (e)
Total Units: 4
Trade Names: Las Palmas Mexican Restaurant (4)
Company-Owned Units: 4
Primary Menu: Mexican (4)
Areas of Operation: GA
Type of Foodservice: Casual Dining (4)

Key Personnel
EFRAIN LOPEZ - Owner

Cinco Mexican Cantina
1000 Holcomb Woods Pkwy Ste 416
Roswell, GA 30076-2585

Telephone: (678) 303-1455
Fax Number: (770) 676-6164
Internet Homepage: cincorestaurants.com
Company Email: cincocorporate@hotmail.com
Type of Business: Chain Restaurant Operator
Total Units: 4
Trade Names: Cinco Mexican Cantina (4)
Company-Owned Units: 4
Primary Menu: Mexican (4)
Projected Openings: 1
Areas of Operation: GA
Type of Foodservice: Casual Dining (4)
Catering Services: Yes

El Porton Mexican Restaurant Inc.
11190 Alpharetta Hwy
Roswell, GA 30076-1436

Telephone: (678) 393-0100
Fax Number: (678) 393-0102
Internet Homepage: elportonmexicanrestaurants.com
Company Email: el-customerservice@elportonrestaurants.com
Type of Business: Chain Restaurant Operator
Year Founded: 1990
Total Sales: $16,460,000 (e)
Alcohol Sales: 10%
Number of Employees: 120
Average Check: Lunch(14); Dinner(24)
Total Units: 12
Trade Names: El Porton Mexican Restaurant (12)
Company-Owned Units: 12
Preferred Square Footage: 3,500; 4,000
Preferred Location Types: Freestanding
Alcohol Served: Beer, Wine, Liquor
Primary Menu: Mexican (12)
Areas of Operation: AR, GA, TN
Type of Foodservice: Casual Dining (12)
Catering Services: Yes
Primary Distributors: (Full Line) SYSCO Atlanta LLC, COLLEGE PARK, GA

Key Personnel
JOSE PEREZ - President; Controller; Executive Chef; Director Operations, Supply Chain, Real Estate, Design, Foodservice, Menu Development, Catering
LESLIE AVENDANO - General Manager
JUVENAL PEREZ - Manager Facility/Maintenance, Information Systems, Human Resources; General Buyer

Ippolito's
900 Old Roswell Lakes Pkwy Ste 140
Roswell, GA 30076-8664

Telephone: (770) 992-1414
Fax Number: (770) 992-1493
Internet Homepage: ippolitos.net
Company Email: lisaatippolitos@yahoo.com
Type of Business: Chain Restaurant Operator
Year Founded: 1989
Total Sales: $7,227,000 (e)
Alcohol Sales: 1%
Number of Employees: 440
Average Check: Lunch(18); Dinner(36)
Total Units: 5

Key Personnel
MICHAEL BURANDT - Owner
BRITNEY CARTER - Coordinator Special Projects

Trade Names: Ippolito's (5)
Company-Owned Units: 5
Preferred Square Footage: 5,500; 6,000
Preferred Location Types: Freestanding; Strip Mall
Alcohol Served: Beer, Wine, Liquor
Primary Menu: Italian (5)
Areas of Operation: GA
Type of Foodservice: Casual Dining (5)
Catering Services: Yes
Primary Distributors: (Food) Roma Food Enterprises Inc., RICHMOND, VA

Key Personnel
GEORGE IPPOLITO - President; Partner; CFO; Executive Chef; Director Facility/Maintenance, Real Estate, Design, Human Resources; General Buyer
TONI IPPOLITO - Partner; General Manager
LISA REESE - Manager Accounting, Information Systems
BRANDON IPPOLITO - Manager Operations

MFP Franchise Systems Inc.
904 Bombay Ln
Roswell, GA 30076-5829

Mailing Address: PO Box 681896, MARIETTA, GA, 30068
Telephone: (800) 882-9436
Internet Homepage: myfriendsplacedeli.com
Company Email: mfp@bellsouth.net
Type of Business: Chain Restaurant Operator
Year Founded: 1980
Systemwide Sales: $7,718,000 (e)
Total Sales: $1,824,000 (e)
Number of Employees: 5
Average Check: Breakfast(8); Lunch(12); Dinner(12)
Internet Order Processing: Yes
Total Units: 6
Trade Names: My Friend's Place (6)
Units Franchised To: 6
Preferred Square Footage: 1,400; 1,600; 2,000
Preferred Location Types: Downtown; Office Complex; Strip Mall
Primary Menu: Sandwiches/Deli (6)
Areas of Operation: GA
Type of Foodservice: Quick Serve (6)
Catering Services: Yes

Key Personnel
SERGIO VALENTIN SR - CEO; President; Director Operations, Purchasing, Supply Chain, Real Estate, Design, Training, Franchise Development; General Buyer
ROSALIND C. KATZ - VP; Corporate Secretary; General Manager; Director Information Systems, Marketing, Human Resources; General Buyer

Steak-Out Franchising Inc.
2300 Holcomb Bridge Rd Ste 103-363
Roswell, GA 30076-3481

Telephone: (678) 533-6000
Fax Number: (678) 533-6010
Internet Homepage: steakout.com
Company Email: info@steakout.com
Type of Business: Chain Restaurant Operator
Year Founded: 1986
Systemwide Sales: $9,558,000 (e)
Total Sales: $1,314,000 (e)
Number of Employees: 54
Average Check: Lunch(10); Dinner(14)
Internet Order Processing: Yes
Total Units: 9
Trade Names: Steak-Out Char-Broiled Delivery (9)
Units Franchised To: 9
Preferred Square Footage: 1,500; 2,000
Preferred Location Types: Freestanding; Strip Mall
Primary Menu: Steak (9)
Areas of Operation: AL, GA, IL, SD
Type of Foodservice: Quick Serve (9)
Foodservice Management Venues: Schools
Catering Services: Yes
Primary Distributors: (Food) Reinhart FoodService, LOUISVILLE, TN; (Supplies) Reinhart FoodService, LOUISVILLE, TN

Key Personnel
DONALD R. HARKLEROAD - CEO; President; General Buyer
KELLY POSEY - Manager Marketing

V&V Foods LLC
11235 Woodstock Rd
Roswell, GA 30075-2551

Telephone: (770) 552-2245
Type of Business: Chain Restaurant Operator
Total Sales: $21,320,000 (e)
Total Units: 6
Trade Names: Zaxby's (6)
Units Franchised From: 6
Primary Menu: Chicken (6)
Areas of Operation: GA
Type of Foodservice: Fast Casual (6)
Franchise Affiliation: Zaxby's Franchising Inc., ATHENS, GA

Key Personnel
RICHARD S. VANN - Owner; General Buyer

Georgia Theatre Company
50 Cinema Ln
Saint Simons Island, GA 31522-6600

Telephone: (912) 634-5192
Fax Number: (912) 634-5195
Internet Homepage: gtcmovies.com
Type of Business: Foodservice Operations - Movie Theatre
Year Founded: 1991
Total Sales: $51,240,000 (e)
Number of Employees: 1,000
Average Check: Lunch(6); Dinner(6)
Internet Order Processing: Yes
Internet Sales: 5.00%
Total Units: 25
Trade Names: Georgia Theatre Company (25)
Company-Owned Units: 25
Preferred Location Types: Downtown; Freestanding; Strip Mall
Primary Menu: Snacks (25)
Areas of Operation: FL, GA, SC, VA
Type of Foodservice: In-Store Feeder (25)
Primary Distributors: (Full Line) SYSCO Food Services of Denver, DENVER, CO
Notes: The company derives approximately 80% of its revenue from theatre operations.

Key Personnel
BILL STEMBLER - CEO; General Buyer
BO CHAMBLISS - President
MICHAEL WARREN - CFO
JEFF MOBLEY - VP Operations

Azteca Management Inc.
5925 Roswell Rd
Sandy Springs, GA 30328-4914

Telephone: (404) 252-7347
Fax Number: (404) 252-0096
Internet Homepage: elaztecaatlanta.com
Type of Business: Chain Restaurant Operator
Year Founded: 1980
Total Sales: $7,094,000 (e)
Alcohol Sales: 15%
Number of Employees: 60
Average Check: Lunch(14); Dinner(20)
Total Units: 4
Trade Names: El Azteca (4)
Company-Owned Units: 4
Preferred Square Footage: 5,500; 6,000
Preferred Location Types: Freestanding; Strip Mall
Alcohol Served: Beer, Wine, Liquor
Primary Menu: Mexican (4)
Areas of Operation: GA
Type of Foodservice: Casual Dining (4)
Catering Services: Yes
Primary Distributors: (Food) SYSCO Atlanta LLC, COLLEGE PARK, GA

Key Personnel
MIGUEL SOTELO - Executive Chef; General Buyer

Morrison Healthcare
400 Northridge Rd Ste 600
Sandy Springs, GA 30350-3354

Telephone: (404) 845-3330
Fax Number: (404) 845-3333
Internet Homepage: iammorrison.com
Company Email: morrisoncommunications@iammorrison.com
Type of Business: Foodservice Management Operator
Year Founded: 1996
Total Sales: $4,192,176,000 (e)
Number of Employees: 24,000
Number of Locations Served: 1,850
Total Foodservice Mgmt Accounts: 900
Areas of Operation: GA
Type of Foodservice: Cafeteria; Full-service sit-down dining
Foodservice Management Venues: Health Care; Other
Parent Company: Compass Group PLC, LONDON, ENG
Headquarters: Compass Group The Americas, CHARLOTTE, NC
Notes: Morrison Healthcare is a leading national food and nutrition services company exclusively dedicated to serving more than 600 hospitals and healthcare systems.

Key Personnel
TIM PIERCE - CEO
GLENN ROBINSON - President Division
JOHN HUTSELL - President Division
ERIN MEEHAN - President Division
GINA DAMON - Senior VP Human Resources
CARY NEFF - VP Culinary Development

Carey Hilliard's Restaurants Inc.
11111 Abercorn St
Savannah, GA 31419-1829

Telephone: (912) 925-2131
Fax Number: (912) 925-1699
Internet Homepage: careyhilliards.com
Type of Business: Chain Restaurant Operator
Year Founded: 1960
Total Sales: $22,950,000 (e)
Alcohol Sales: 5%
Number of Employees: 240
Average Check: Lunch(10); Dinner(12)
Internet Order Processing: Yes
Total Units: 6
Trade Names: Carey Hilliard's Restaurant (6)
Company-Owned Units: 6
Preferred Square Footage: 2,000; 8,000
Preferred Location Types: Freestanding
Alcohol Served: Beer, Wine
Primary Menu: American (6)
Areas of Operation: GA
Type of Foodservice: Casual Dining (6)
Catering Services: Yes
Primary Distributors: (Full Line) US Foods, LEXINGTON, SC

Key Personnel
G. TIMOTHY HILLIARD - CEO; President
THOMAS EAST - Controller

Culinary Institute of Savannah
5717 White Bluff Rd
Savannah, GA 31405-5521

Telephone: (912) 443-5700
Fax Number: (912) 443-4799
Internet Homepage: savannahtech.edu
Type of Business: Culinary Schools
Areas of Operation: GA

Key Personnel
KATHY S. LOVE - President
JEAN-YVES VANDEVILLE - Executive Chef; Director Culinary Operations

Donaldson Enterprises Inc.
2801 Wicklow St
Savannah, GA 31404-4131

Telephone: (912) 354-8828
Fax Number: (912) 354-6567
Internet Homepage: johnnyharris.com
Company Email: info@johnnyharris.com
Type of Business: Chain Restaurant Operator
Year Founded: 1924
Total Sales: $30,520,000 (e)
Alcohol Sales: 9%
Number of Employees: 465
Average Check: Breakfast(10); Lunch(16); Dinner(24)
Internet Order Processing: Yes
Internet Sales: 1.00%
Total Units: 11
Trade Names: Atlanta Bread (1); Houlihans (1); Wendy's Old Fashioned Hamburgers (9)
Units Franchised From: 11
Preferred Square Footage: 3,300
Preferred Location Types: Freestanding; Strip Mall
Alcohol Served: Beer, Wine, Liquor
Primary Menu: American (1); Hamburger (9); Sandwiches/Deli (1)
Areas of Operation: GA
Type of Foodservice: Casual Dining (1); Fast Casual (1); Quick Serve (9)
Catering Services: Yes

Franchise Affiliation: Atlanta Bread Company, SMYRNA, GA; HRI Inc., LEAWOOD, KS; The Wendy's Company, DUBLIN, OH
Primary Distributors: (Food) SYSCO Atlanta LLC, COLLEGE PARK, GA
Notes: Houlihan's operates as JDL Investments.

Key Personnel
NORMAN L. HEIDT - President; General Manager; Executive Chef; Director Catering; General Buyer
B.J. LOWENTHAL - President; Owner; CFO; Director Supply Chain
JEFF EVANS - Regional Manager Sales; Manager District

Liquid Fire, LLC
8108 Abercorn St
Savannah, GA 31406-3476

Telephone: (912) 920-4161
Type of Business: Chain Restaurant Operator
Total Sales: $5,026,000 (e)
Total Units: 4
Trade Names: Firehouse Subs (4)
Units Franchised From: 4
Primary Menu: Sandwiches/Deli (4)
Areas of Operation: GA
Type of Foodservice: Fast Casual (4)
Catering Services: Yes
Franchise Affiliation: Firehouse Restaurant Group Inc., JACKSONVILLE, FL

Key Personnel
CHAD WEAVER - President; General Buyer

NTG Enterprises
2809 Roger Lacey Dr Ste A
Savannah, GA 31404-4465

Telephone: (912) 692-0021
Fax Number: (912) 692-0064
Type of Business: Chain Restaurant Operator
Total Sales: $23,820,000 (e)
Number of Employees: 150
Total Units: 5
Trade Names: McDonald's (5)
Units Franchised From: 5
Preferred Square Footage: 2,500
Preferred Location Types: Convenience Store/Gas Station; Freestanding
Primary Menu: Hamburger (5)
Areas of Operation: GA
Type of Foodservice: Quick Serve (5)
Franchise Affiliation: McDonald's Corporation, CHICAGO, IL

Key Personnel
NINA GOMPELS - President; General Buyer

River Street Riverboat Co.
9 E River St
Savannah, GA 31401-1295

Mailing Address: PO Box 10086, SAVANNAH, GA, 31412-0286
Telephone: (912) 232-6404
Fax Number: (912) 234-7881
Internet Homepage: savannahriverboat.com
Company Email: info@savannahriverboat.com
Type of Business: Foodservice Operations - Bowling Alley
Year Founded: 1991
Total Sales: $4,643,000 (e)
Alcohol Sales: 18%
Number of Employees: 70
Average Check: Lunch(22); Dinner(36)
Internet Order Processing: Yes
Internet Sales: 30.00%
Total Units: 2
Trade Names: Georgia Queen (1); Savannah River Queen (1)
Company-Owned Units: 2
Preferred Location Types: Other
Alcohol Served: Beer, Wine, Liquor
Primary Menu: American (2)
Areas of Operation: GA
Type of Foodservice: Casual Dining (2)
Primary Distributors: (Full Line) SYSCO Atlanta LLC, COLLEGE PARK, GA

Key Personnel
CHRISTINE DEGENHARDT - Controller

Savannah Restaurants Corp.
10 Mall Ct Ste A
Savannah, GA 31406-3691

Telephone: (912) 353-9090
Fax Number: (912) 355-8414
Internet Homepage: savannahbk.com
Company Email: savrest@aol.com
Type of Business: Chain Restaurant Operator
Total Sales: $24,770,000 (e)
Number of Employees: 320
Total Units: 11
Trade Names: Burger King (11)
Units Franchised From: 11
Preferred Square Footage: 2,500
Primary Menu: Hamburger (11)
Areas of Operation: GA
Type of Foodservice: Quick Serve (11)
Franchise Affiliation: Burger King Worldwide Inc., MIAMI, FL

Key Personnel
ALEX SALGUEIRO - President; General Buyer
JUSTIN J - Director Operations
JUSTIN JANNEY - Director Operations
DANIEL BYRNE - District Manager

Turner Food & Spirits Co.
112 Oatland Island Rd
Savannah, GA 31410-1155

Telephone: (912) 898-9286
Fax Number: (912) 898-0472
Internet Homepage: thepirateshouse.com
Type of Business: Chain Restaurant Operator
Year Founded: 1987
Total Sales: $13,550,000 (e)
Alcohol Sales: 28%
Number of Employees: 300
Average Check: Lunch(22); Dinner(36)
Total Units: 6
Trade Names: Barracuda Bob's (1); Cotton Exchange (1); One Eyed Lizzy's (1); Pearls Saltwater Grille (1); Pirate's House (1); The Exchange (1)
Company-Owned Units: 6
Preferred Square Footage: 5,500; 6,000
Preferred Location Types: Downtown; Freestanding; Other
Alcohol Served: Beer, Wine, Liquor
Primary Menu: Seafood (3); Steak/Seafood (3)
Areas of Operation: GA
Type of Foodservice: Casual Dining (4); Fine Dining (2)
Primary Distributors: (Food) SYSCO Atlanta LLC, COLLEGE PARK, GA

Key Personnel
JOHN R. TURNER - CEO; Owner; CFO; Executive Chef; Director Finance, Operations, Facility/Maintenance, Information Systems, Supply Chain, Real Estate, Design; General Buyer
ROBERT NACLERIO - General Manager
SHAUN CARTER - Executive Chef
CHRIS DICKAMORE - Executive Chef
JOSEPH JONES - Manager

H.J. Wings & Things
20 Thomas Grace Annex Ln Ste F
Sharpsburg, GA 30277-3569

Telephone: (770) 318-4572
Internet Homepage: homeofthescorchers.com
Company Email: wingsandthings@earthlink.net
Type of Business: Chain Restaurant Operator
Year Founded: 1988
Systemwide Sales: $19,211,000 (e)
Total Sales: $4,721,000 (e)
Alcohol Sales: 10%
Number of Employees: 70
Average Check: Lunch(8); Dinner(8)
Total Units: 7
Trade Names: H.J. Wings & Things (7)

Units Franchised To: 7
Preferred Location Types: Freestanding; Strip Mall
Alcohol Served: Beer, Wine
Primary Menu: American (7)
Areas of Operation: GA
Type of Foodservice: Fast Casual (7)
Catering Services: Yes
Primary Distributors: (Full Line) US Foods, FAIRBURN, GA

Key Personnel
SCOTT HAYGOOD - Owner; General Buyer
JILL PEREZ - Manager District

Springfield Investments, Inc.
216 Wax Rd SE
Silver Creek, GA 30173-2477

Mailing Address: PO Box 370, SILVER CREEK, GA, 30173-0370
Telephone: (706) 378-8054
Fax Number: (706) 378-8786
Company Email: sabb56@gmail.com
Type of Business: Chain Restaurant Operator
Year Founded: 1985
Total Sales: $41,140,000 (e)
Number of Employees: 500
Average Check: Lunch(8); Dinner(10)
Total Units: 15
Trade Names: Wendy's Old Fashioned Hamburgers (15)
Units Franchised From: 15
Preferred Square Footage: 2,100
Preferred Location Types: Freestanding
Primary Menu: Hamburger (15)
Areas of Operation: AL, GA, TN
Type of Foodservice: Quick Serve (15)
Franchise Affiliation: The Wendy's Company, DUBLIN, OH

Key Personnel
MOHOMMAD ABBASI - Partner; Director Finance, Real Estate, Franchising; General Buyer
SANDY ABBASI - Partner; Director Customer Service
THOMAS BRADFORD - Director Operations, Information Systems, Supply Chain
HAROLD ERWIN - Manager Facility/Maintenance

Atlanta Bread Company
1200 Wilson Way SE Ste 100
Smyrna, GA 30082-7212

Mailing Address: P.O. Box 1667, Smyrna, GA, 30081-1667
Telephone: (770) 432-0933
Fax Number: (770) 432-4489
Internet Homepage: atlantabread.com
Company Email: abc@atlantabread.com
Type of Business: Chain Restaurant Operator
Year Founded: 1993
Systemwide Sales: $25,651,000 (e)
Total Sales: $8,011,000 (e)
Alcohol Sales: 1%
Number of Employees: 73
Average Check: Breakfast(8); Lunch(8); Dinner(8)
Internet Order Processing: Yes
Internet Sales: 1.00%
Total Units: 16
Trade Names: Atlanta Bread Company Bakery Cafe (16)
Units Franchised To: 16
Preferred Square Footage: 5,000
Preferred Location Types: Airports; Freestanding; Lifestyle Center; Strip Mall
Alcohol Served: Beer, Wine
Primary Menu: Sandwiches/Deli (16)
Projected Openings: 2
Projected Remodelings: 4
Areas of Operation: AL, AR, CO, FL, GA, IL, MD, MS, NC, NJ, NV, NY, OK, PA, SC, TX, VA, WI
Type of Foodservice: Fast Casual (16)
Catering Services: Yes
Franchise Affiliation: Atlanta Bread Company, SMYRNA, GA
Primary Distributors: (Full Line) SYSCO Atlanta LLC, COLLEGE PARK, GA

Key Personnel
JERRY COUVARAS - CEO; President
BASIL COUVARAS - COO; VP
LANDRY PIERRE - General Manager
TYLER TRICE - General Manager

SJAC Food Groups LLC
3080 Highlands Pkwy SE Ste C
Smyrna, GA 30082-5183

Telephone: (678) 309-3330
Fax Number: (678) 309-3393
Internet Homepage: sjacfoodgroups.com
Company Email: info@sjacfoodgroups.com
Type of Business: Chain Restaurant Operator
Total Sales: $46,390,000 (e)
Number of Employees: 661
Average Check: Lunch(10); Dinner(14)
Total Units: 13
Trade Names: Zaxby's (13)
Units Franchised From: 13
Preferred Square Footage: 3,500
Primary Menu: Chicken (13)
Projected Openings: 1
Areas of Operation: GA, OK
Type of Foodservice: Fast Casual (13)
Franchise Affiliation: Zaxby's Franchising Inc., ATHENS, GA
Primary Distributors: (Full Line) US Foods, FAIRBURN, GA

Key Personnel
STERLING COLEMAN - President; Manager Operations; General Buyer
TRACEY STALLING - CFO
RAVEN STOKES - General Manager
SHAWNNETTA WIMES - General Manager

The Original Hot Dog Factory
1529 Spring Rd SE
Smyrna, GA 30080

Telephone: (678) 293-6099
Internet Homepage: theoriginalhotdogfactory.com
Type of Business: Chain Restaurant Operator
Year Founded: 2010
Average Check: Lunch(10); Dinner(12)
Total Units: 11
Trade Names: The Original Hot Dog Factory (11)
Units Franchised To: 11
Preferred Square Footage: 1,200
Primary Menu: Hot Dogs (11)
Projected Openings: 20
Areas of Operation: GA
Type of Foodservice: Casual Dining (11)
Catering Services: Yes
Parent Company: Pivotal Growth Partners, CHICAGO, IL

Key Personnel
SEAN FLOYD - Manager Operations, District

TME Enterprises
2400 Herodian Way SE Ste 157
Smyrna, GA 30080-8500

Telephone: (770) 984-8004
Fax Number: (770) 984-9509
Company Email: info@memelton.com
Type of Business: Chain Restaurant Operator
Total Sales: $69,580,000 (e)
Number of Employees: 840
Average Check: Lunch(8); Dinner(8)
Total Units: 27
Trade Names: Five Guys (8); Taco Bell (19)
Units Franchised From: 27
Preferred Square Footage: 2,500; 3,200
Preferred Location Types: Downtown; Freestanding; Regional Mall
Primary Menu: Hamburger (8); Taco (19)
Areas of Operation: GA
Type of Foodservice: Quick Serve (27)
Franchise Affiliation: Five Guys Holdings Inc., LORTON, VA; Taco Bell Corp., IRVINE, CA

Key Personnel
MICHAEL MELTON - President; Owner
DONELL GIBSON - CFO; Controller
MORTEZA AMIRKHANI - Director Operations; General Buyer

AYISHA WRIGHT - Director Human Resources

Falcons Restaurant Group, LLC/ Chunara Food Group
2199 Glenmore Ln
Snellville, GA 30078-5611

Telephone: (404) 936-2121
Fax Number: (770) 504-5506
Internet Homepage: chunarafoodgroup.com
Company Email: chunara@bellsouth.net
Type of Business: Chain Restaurant Operator
Total Sales: $126,560,000 (e)
Total Units: 49
Trade Names: Checkers (7); Church's Chicken (12); Dunkin' Donuts (8); Popeyes Louisiana Kitchen (7); T.G.I. Friday's (15)
Units Franchised From: 49
Primary Menu: American (15); Chicken (19); Hamburger (7); Snacks (8)
Areas of Operation: AL, GA, KY, MI, MO, OH, PA, WV
Type of Foodservice: Casual Dining (15); Quick Serve (34)
Franchise Affiliation: Checkers Drive-In Restaurants Inc., TAMPA, FL; Church's Chicken, ATLANTA, GA; DD IP Holder, CANTON, MA; Popeyes Louisiana Kitchen Inc., ATLANTA, GA; T.G.I. Friday's Inc., DALLAS, TX

Key Personnel
SHAMSU CHARANIA - CEO
KADIRALI CHUNARA - President; General Buyer
PILLAI SUNDAR - Chief Administrative Officer

Vision Foods, Inc.
1830 Scenic Hwy N
Snellville, GA 30078-2114

Telephone: (678) 344-8556
Fax Number: (678) 344-2757
Type of Business: Chain Restaurant Operator
Total Sales: $3,773,000 (e)
Total Units: 3
Trade Names: Firehouse Subs (3)
Units Franchised From: 3
Primary Menu: Sandwiches/Deli (3)
Areas of Operation: GA
Type of Foodservice: Fast Casual (3)
Franchise Affiliation: Firehouse Restaurant Group Inc., JACKSONVILLE, FL

Key Personnel
ADAM AREFIAN - President; General Buyer
MALIK REID - General Manager

Hodges Management Co.
7 N Main St
Statesboro, GA 30458-5750

Mailing Address: PO Box 637, STATESBORO, GA, 30459-0637
Telephone: (912) 764-9991
Fax Number: (912) 489-1924
Internet Homepage: thmco.com
Company Email: webmaster@thmco.com
Type of Business: Chain Restaurant Operator
Year Founded: 1963
Total Sales: $57,430,000 (e)
Number of Employees: 695
Average Check: Lunch(16); Dinner(16)
Total Units: 32
Trade Names: Dairy Queen (5); KFC (24); Taco Bell (3)
Units Franchised From: 32
Preferred Square Footage: 3,000
Preferred Location Types: Freestanding
Primary Menu: Chicken (24); Snacks (5); Taco (3)
Projected Openings: 1
Areas of Operation: GA, SC
Type of Foodservice: Quick Serve (32)
Franchise Affiliation: KFC Corporation, LOUISVILLE, KY
Primary Distributors: (Full Line) US Foods, LEXINGTON, SC

Key Personnel
LLOYD I. HODGES SR - President; General Manager; Director Purchasing, Real Estate
LLOYD HODGES JR - VP; Director Operations, Facility/Maintenance, Supply Chain, Advertising, Ethnic Marketing, Design, Store Fixtures, Food Safety; General Buyer
PAULA FREEMAN - Controller; Director Finance, Facility/Maintenance, Information Systems, Loss Prevention, Human Resources
LINDA DAVIS - Manager Human Resources
MIKE WILSON - Project Manager

Petrus Brands Inc.
829 Fairways Ct
Stockbridge, GA 30281-7219

Telephone: (678) 782-3021
Internet Homepage: shanesribshack.com
Type of Business: Chain Restaurant Operator
Year Founded: 1978
Total Sales: $24,150,000 (e)
Alcohol Sales: 15%
Number of Employees: 245
Average Check: Breakfast(6); Lunch(14); Dinner(22)
Internet Order Processing: Yes
Internet Sales: 2.00%
Total Units: 62
Trade Names: Shane's Rib Shack (66)
Units Franchised To: 66
Preferred Square Footage: 1,200; 1,500; 2,500; 2,800
Preferred Location Types: Airports; Community Mall; Convenience Store/Gas Station; Downtown; Freestanding; Kiosk; Lifestyle Center; Office Complex; Outlet Mall; Regional Mall; Stadiums; Strip Mall
Alcohol Served: Beer, Wine
Primary Menu: Bar-B-Q (66)
Areas of Operation: AL, AZ, FL, GA, LA, NC, NY, SC, TN, VA
Type of Foodservice: Fast Casual (66)
Catering Services: Yes
Primary Distributors: (Food) S & W Wholesale Foods Inc., HAMMOND, LA; (Food) Reinhart FoodService, LOUISVILLE, TN

Key Personnel
SHANE THOMPSON - CEO; President
RACHEL SETTLE - VP Marketing
ERICA LUMMUS - Creative Director; Director Brand Marketing
SUZANNE ADAMS - Director Franchise Operations, Human Resources
JUDY DEMPSEY MORRIS - Director Finance

Hillcrest Foods Inc.
50 Satellite Blvd NW Ste G
Suwanee, GA 30024-7105

Telephone: (770) 932-2068
Fax Number: (770) 932-1243
Internet Homepage: wafflehouse.com
Company Email: hillcrestfoodsinc@gmail.com
Type of Business: Chain Restaurant Operator
Year Founded: 1963
Total Sales: $44,440,000 (e)
Number of Employees: 800
Average Check: Breakfast(8); Lunch(8); Dinner(8)
Total Units: 52
Trade Names: Waffle House (52)
Units Franchised From: 52
Preferred Square Footage: 2,700
Preferred Location Types: Freestanding; Strip Mall
Primary Menu: American (52)
Projected Openings: 10
Areas of Operation: GA, NC, SC
Type of Foodservice: Family Restaurant (52)
Franchise Affiliation: Waffle House Inc., NORCROSS, GA

Key Personnel
TODD MILLER - President; VP Finance, Operations, Purchasing
STEVE ROBERTS - District Manager
MICHELLE WILLS - Coordinator Customer Service

Hoover Foods Inc.
4030 Johns Creek Pkwy
Suwanee, GA 30024-1254

Telephone: (770) 448-0300
Fax Number: (770) 497-5798
Internet Homepage: hooverfoods.com
Company Email: customerservice@hooverfoods.com
Type of Business: Chain Restaurant Operator
Year Founded: 1975
Total Sales: $130,520,000 (e)
Number of Employees: 1,300
Average Check: Lunch(8); Dinner(8)
Total Units: 49
Trade Names: Wendy's Old Fashioned Hamburgers (49)
Units Franchised From: 49
Preferred Square Footage: 3,300
Preferred Location Types: Freestanding; Outlet Mall
Primary Menu: Hamburger (49)
Areas of Operation: FL, GA
Type of Foodservice: Quick Serve (49)
Franchise Affiliation: The Wendy's Company, DUBLIN, OH
Primary Distributors: (Full Line) The SYGMA Network Inc.- San Antonio, SAN ANTONIO, TX

Key Personnel
DUANE HOOVER - CEO; President; Director Information Systems, Real Estate
CARL HOOVER - Exec VP
MARGARET COOK - VP Financial Planning; Controller
GLENN VARNER - Director Finance, Operations, Purchasing, Facility/Maintenance, Security, Inventory, Loss Prevention, Risk Management, Quality Assurance, Supply Chain, Design, Human Resources, Food Safety; General Buyer
DARRELL SLIMMON - Director Operations

La Cazuela Mexican Restaurants
4090 Jones Creek Pkwy
Suwanee, GA 30024

Telephone: (770) 623-6026
Fax Number: (770) 751-9346
Internet Homepage: lacazuela.com
Company Email: info@lacazuela.com
Type of Business: Chain Restaurant Operator
Year Founded: 1987
Total Sales: $3,832,000 (e)
Alcohol Sales: 25%
Number of Employees: 165
Average Check: Lunch(12); Dinner(20)
Total Units: 3
Trade Names: La Cazuela (3)
Company-Owned Units: 3
Preferred Square Footage: 4,500
Preferred Location Types: Strip Mall
Alcohol Served: Beer, Wine, Liquor
Primary Menu: Mexican (3)
Areas of Operation: GA
Type of Foodservice: Casual Dining (4)
Catering Services: Yes

Key Personnel
CARLOS RODRIGUEZ - CEO; President; Executive Chef; Director Facility/Maintenance, Information Systems, Real Estate, Design, Human Resources, Catering; General Buyer
MONICA MORALES - Coordinator Accounting

Spice Wing
3186 Lawrenceville Suwanee Rd
Suwanee, GA 30024

Telephone: (678) 899-6792
Internet Homepage: spicewing.com
Type of Business: Chain Restaurant Operator
Trade Names: Spice Wing (5)
Units Franchised To: 5
Primary Menu: Chicken (5)
Projected Openings: 20
Areas of Operation: GA
Type of Foodservice: Fast Casual (5)
Parent Company: Pivotal Growth Partners, CHICAGO, IL

Key Personnel
KHUSHAL PATEL - CEO
JESAL PANDYA - Director Operations
AMAN PATEL - Director Training

Joysach Inc.
234 Cherokee Rd
Thomaston, GA 30286-3402

Mailing Address: P. O. Box 1098, THOMASTON, GA, 30286-1098
Telephone: (706) 646-9678
Fax Number: (706) 646-9676
Type of Business: Chain Restaurant Operator
Year Founded: 1977
Total Sales: $32,440,000 (e)
Number of Employees: 200
Average Check: Breakfast(8); Lunch(10); Dinner(10)
Total Units: 7
Trade Names: McDonald's (7)
Units Franchised From: 7
Preferred Square Footage: 2,500; 3,000
Preferred Location Types: Convenience Store/Gas Station; Freestanding
Primary Menu: Hamburger (7)
Areas of Operation: GA
Type of Foodservice: Quick Serve (7)
Franchise Affiliation: McDonald's Corporation, CHICAGO, IL

Key Personnel
GEORGE SIZEMORE - President; Director Finance, Operations, Facility/Maintenance, Information Systems, Real Estate, Human Resources, Store Fixtures; General Buyer
JESSICA DEEN - Partner
STARLA RIDDICK - Partner
JENNIFER ROBERTS - Partner

Wen-Star, Inc
209 N Dawson St
Thomasville, GA 31792-5130

Telephone: (229) 226-9050
Type of Business: Chain Restaurant Operator
Total Sales: $40,590,000 (e)
Total Units: 15
Trade Names: Wendy's Old Fashioned Hamburgers (15)
Units Franchised From: 15
Preferred Location Types: Freestanding
Primary Menu: Hamburger (15)
Areas of Operation: AL, FL, GA, LA
Type of Foodservice: Quick Serve (15)
Franchise Affiliation: The Wendy's Company, DUBLIN, OH

Key Personnel
WAYNE ROBERTS - President; General Buyer

Domino's Franchisee
1233 Washington Rd
Thomson, GA 30824-7352

Telephone: (706) 595-9656
Type of Business: Chain Restaurant Operator
Total Sales: $39,352,000 (e)
Total Units: 19
Trade Names: Domino's (19)
Units Franchised From: 19
Primary Menu: Pizza (19)
Areas of Operation: GA, SC
Type of Foodservice: Quick Serve (19)
Franchise Affiliation: Domino's Pizza Inc, ANN ARBOR, MI

Key Personnel
KERRI-LEA SAUNDERS - Owner; General Buyer

Little Caesars of Atlanta, LLC
3201 Tucker Norcross Rd Ste A3
Tucker, GA 30084-2151

Telephone: (770) 621-2705
Type of Business: Chain Restaurant Operator
Total Sales: $1,533,000 (e)

Total Units: 2
Trade Names: Little Caesars Pizza (2)
Units Franchised From: 2
Primary Menu: Pizza (2)
Areas of Operation: GA
Type of Foodservice: Quick Serve (2)
Franchise Affiliation: Little Caesar Enterprises Inc., DETROIT, MI

Key Personnel
BRAD MOORE - President; General Buyer

SI Restaurants, LLC
4788 Jonesboro Rd Ste B3
Union City, GA 30291-1988

Telephone: (770) 969-8459
Fax Number: (770) 969-8606
Type of Business: Chain Restaurant Operator
Total Sales: $13,360,000 (e)
Total Units: 9
Trade Names: Checkers (9)
Units Franchised From: 9
Primary Menu: Hamburger (9)
Areas of Operation: GA
Type of Foodservice: Quick Serve (9)
Franchise Affiliation: Checkers Drive-In Restaurants Inc., TAMPA, FL

Key Personnel
ABID KHUTLIWALA - President; General Buyer

Kentucky Fried Chicken of Valdosta Inc.
1203 N Ashley St
Valdosta, GA 31601-4015

Telephone: (229) 247-2395
Fax Number: (229) 249-9146
Type of Business: Chain Restaurant Operator
Year Founded: 1965
Total Sales: $3,863,000 (e)
Number of Employees: 95
Average Check: Lunch(8); Dinner(8)
Total Units: 2
Trade Names: KFC (2)
Units Franchised From: 2
Preferred Location Types: Freestanding
Primary Menu: Chicken (2)
Areas of Operation: GA
Type of Foodservice: Quick Serve (2)
Franchise Affiliation: KFC Corporation, LOUISVILLE, KY
Primary Distributors: (Full Line) US Foods, NORCROSS, GA

Key Personnel
TIM HARRIS - President; Owner

G F I Inc
100 N Houston Lake Rd
Warner Robins, GA 31093

Telephone: (478) 953-4363
Type of Business: Chain Restaurant Operator
Total Sales: $4,213,000 (e)
Total Units: 7
Trade Names: Subway (7)
Units Franchised From: 7
Primary Menu: Sandwiches/Deli (7)
Areas of Operation: GA
Type of Foodservice: Quick Serve (7)
Franchise Affiliation: Doctor's Associates Inc., MILFORD, CT

Key Personnel
GENE HELMS - President

Paul Messer's McDonald's
88 W Candler St
Winder, GA 30680-2502

Mailing Address: PO Box 1568, WINDER, GA, 30680-6568
Telephone: (770) 867-3090
Fax Number: (770) 867-7272
Type of Business: Chain Restaurant Operator
Total Sales: $46,260,000 (e)
Number of Employees: 600
Average Check: Breakfast(10); Lunch(10); Dinner(10)
Total Units: 10
Trade Names: McDonald's (10)
Units Franchised From: 10
Preferred Square Footage: 2,500; 3,000
Preferred Location Types: Freestanding
Primary Menu: Hamburger (10)
Projected Openings: 3
Areas of Operation: GA
Type of Foodservice: Quick Serve (10)
Franchise Affiliation: McDonald's Corporation, CHICAGO, IL

Key Personnel
PAUL MESSER JR - President; Director Finance, Operations, Facility/Maintenance, Information Systems, Supply Chain, Real Estate, Design; General Buyer

Pizza the Pie LLC
323 Resource Pkwy
Winder, GA 30680-8364

Telephone: (770) 867-4111
Fax Number: (770) 867-2217
Type of Business: Chain Restaurant Operator
Total Sales: $82,576,000 (e)
Total Units: 41

Trade Names: Domino's (41)
Units Franchised From: 41
Preferred Square Footage: 1,000
Primary Menu: Pizza (41)
Areas of Operation: GA, SC
Type of Foodservice: Quick Serve (41)
Franchise Affiliation: Domino's Pizza Inc, ANN ARBOR, MI

Key Personnel
GREG FOX - President; General Buyer
JESY WILLIAMS - Manager Human Resources

Joseph Scripture
8979 Highway 92
Woodstock, GA 30189-3689

Telephone: (770) 926-4581
Fax Number: (770) 926-1080
Type of Business: Chain Restaurant Operator
Total Sales: $31,140,000 (e)
Total Units: 10
Trade Names: IHOP (10)
Units Franchised From: 10
Primary Menu: American (10)
Areas of Operation: GA
Type of Foodservice: Family Restaurant (10)
Franchise Affiliation: IHOP Restaurant System, GLENDALE, CA

Key Personnel
JOSEPH SCRIPTURE - President

HAWAII

Domino's Distribution Center
99-1445 Koaha Pl
Aiea, HI 96701-5601

Telephone: (808) 486-2688
Fax Number: (808) 487-6978
Listing Type: Distribution Center
Type of Business: Chain Restaurant Operator
Areas of Operation: HI
On-site Distribution Center: Yes
Parent Company: Domino's Pizza Inc, ANN ARBOR, MI

Key Personnel
TOM BAHNEMAN - General Manager

McDonald's Franchise
91-1051 Keaunui Dr
Ewa Beach, HI 96706-6351

Telephone: (808) 676-7730
Type of Business: Chain Restaurant Operator
Year Founded: 1983

Total Sales: $27,580,000 (e)
Total Units: 6
Trade Names: McDonald's (6)
Units Franchised From: 6
Preferred Square Footage: 2,500
Primary Menu: Hamburger (6)
Areas of Operation: HI
Type of Foodservice: Quick Serve (6)
Franchise Affiliation: McDonald's Corporation, CHICAGO, IL

Key Personnel
MILES ICHINOSE - President; General Buyer

Cafe Pesto
308 Kamehameha Ave Ste 101
Hilo, HI 96720-2960

Mailing Address: PO Box 44392, KAMUELA, HI, 96743-4392
Telephone: (808) 969-6640
Fax Number: (808) 969-4858
Internet Homepage: cafepesto.com
Company Email: hilo@cafepesto.com
Type of Business: Chain Restaurant Operator
Year Founded: 1988
Total Sales: $2,811,000 (e)
Alcohol Sales: 22%
Number of Employees: 40
Average Check: Lunch(14); Dinner(26)
Total Units: 1
Trade Names: Cafe Pesto Hilo Bay (1)
Company-Owned Units: 1
Preferred Location Types: Freestanding
Alcohol Served: Beer, Wine, Liquor
Primary Menu: Asian (1)
Areas of Operation: HI
Type of Foodservice: Casual Dining (1)
Catering Services: Yes
Primary Distributors: (Equipment) Bargreen-Ellingson Inc., HONOLULU, HI; (Supplies) Bargreen-Ellingson Inc., HONOLULU, HI

Key Personnel
DAVID PALMER - President; Director Purchasing, Risk Management, Food Safety; General Buyer
MICHAEL COHEN - General Manager; Buyer Beverages
MOSES TAVARES - Executive Chef

DK Restaurants
500 Ala Moana Blvd Ste 3-500
Honolulu, HI 96813-4920

Telephone: (808) 532-6286
Fax Number: (808) 532-0667
Internet Homepage: vinohawaii.com; dkrestaurants.com; sanseihawaii.com
Company Email: dflemming@dkrestaurants.com
Type of Business: Chain Restaurant Operator
Total Sales: $6,924,000 (e)
Alcohol Sales: 3%
Number of Employees: 231
Average Check: Lunch(14); Dinner(26)
Total Units: 7
Trade Names: d.k. Steakhouse (1); Sansei Seafood Restaurant and Sushi Bar (5); Vino (1)
Company-Owned Units: 7
Preferred Square Footage: 5,500; 6,000
Preferred Location Types: Freestanding; Hotel/Motel; Strip Mall
Alcohol Served: Beer, Wine, Liquor
Primary Menu: Seafood (6); Steak (1)
Areas of Operation: HI
Type of Foodservice: Casual Dining (7)
Primary Distributors: (Food) Bargreen-Ellingson Inc., HONOLULU, HI

Key Personnel
DAVE KODAMA - Owner; General Manager; Executive Chef; General Buyer

Halekulani Corp.
2222 Kalakaua Ave Ste 900
Honolulu, HI 96815-2524

Telephone: (808) 526-1186
Fax Number: (808) 536-8794
Internet Homepage: halekulani.com
Type of Business: Chain Restaurant Operator
Year Founded: 1984
Total Sales: $7,626,000 (e)
Alcohol Sales: 20%
Number of Employees: 700
Average Check: Lunch(32); Dinner(60)
Total Units: 4
Trade Names: House Without A Key (1); La Mer (1); Lewers Lounge (1); Orchids (1)
Company-Owned Units: 4
Preferred Location Types: Hotel/Motel
Alcohol Served: Beer, Wine, Liquor
Primary Menu: American (1); French/Continental (1); Seafood (1), Snacks (1)
Areas of Operation: HI
Type of Foodservice: Casual Dining (2); Fine Dining (2)
Primary Distributors: (Food) HFM FoodService, HONOLULU, HI

Key Personnel
PETER SHAINDLIN - COO
PATRICIA TAM - VP Branding
LIANA MULLEITNER - Director Internet Development
LINDA NAKAIMA - Director Human Resources

Kazi Foods
560 N Nimitz Hwy Ste 214
Honolulu, HI 96817-5380

Telephone: (808) 550-4100
Fax Number: (808) 550-4795
Company Email: info@kazifoods.com
Listing Type: Regional Office
Type of Business: Chain Restaurant Operator
Year Founded: 1993
Total Units: 33
Units Franchised From: 33
Preferred Square Footage: 2,500
Areas of Operation: HI
Parent Company: Kazi Foods Inc., STUDIO CITY, CA

Key Personnel
MIKI TRAVIS - Director Training
DENISE YAMAUCHI - Director Operations
ORLANDO IGNACIO - Project Manager

L & L Franchise Inc.
931 University Ave Ste 202
Honolulu, HI 96826-3241

Telephone: (808) 951-9888
Fax Number: (808) 951-0888
Internet Homepage: hawaiianbarbecue.com
Company Email: info@hawaiianbarbecue.com
Type of Business: Chain Restaurant Operator
Year Founded: 1976
Systemwide Sales: $163,409,000 (e)
Total Sales: $17,280,000 (e)
Number of Employees: 207
Average Check: Breakfast(10); Lunch(12); Dinner(12)
Internet Order Processing: Yes
Total Units: 199
Trade Names: L&L Hawaiian Barbecue (195)
Units Franchised To: 195
Preferred Square Footage: 1,200; 1,500
Preferred Location Types: Community Mall; Downtown; Freestanding; Institution (college/hospital); Kiosk; Regional Mall; Strip Mall
Primary Menu: Asian (195)
Areas of Operation: AK, AZ, CA, CO, GU, HI, NV, NY, OR, TN, TX, UT, WA
Foreign Countries: CHINA; INDONESIA; THE PHILIPPINES
Type of Foodservice: Fast Casual (195)
Catering Services: Yes
Primary Distributors: (Full Line) Y. Hata & Co. Ltd., HONOLULU, HI

Key Personnel
EDDIE FLORES - CEO; President
ELISIA FLORES - CEO; CFO
ELAINE FLORES - Exec VP
KARL AOKI - Executive Chef

BRANDON DELA CRUZ - Director Marketing
JOSIE AKANA - Director Information Systems, Franchising
ANDREW LEE - Director Purchasing
CAROLINE GUIRA - Assistant Director Marketing

McDonald's Restaurants of Hawaii
1132 Bishop St Ste 2000
Honolulu, HI 96813-2814

Telephone: (808) 585-8570
Fax Number: (808) 532-1580
Listing Type: Regional Office
Type of Business: Chain Restaurant Operator
Number of Employees: 20
Total Units: 85
Areas of Operation: GU, HI
Parent Company: McDonald's Corporation, CHICAGO, IL

Key Personnel
MARTIN LAU - Director Operations
MELANIE OKAZAKI - Manager Purchasing, Marketing
PAULETTE WAGE - Manager Human Resources
MORGAN NAKAMURA - Consultant

Moose Inc.
310 Lewers St
Honolulu, HI 96815-2343

Telephone: (808) 923-0751
Internet Homepage: fredsmexicancafe.com; moosemcgillycuddys.com; mooserestaurantgroup.com
Company Email: sarah.long@fredsmexicancafe.com
Type of Business: Chain Restaurant Operator
Year Founded: 1980
Total Sales: $32,510,000 (e)
Alcohol Sales: 50%
Number of Employees: 764
Total Units: 7
Trade Names: Fred's Mexican Cafe (3); Moose McGillycuddy's (2); Sandy's Beach Shack (1); Tamarindo (1)
Company-Owned Units: 7
Preferred Square Footage: 4,000
Preferred Location Types: Freestanding
Alcohol Served: Beer, Wine, Liquor
Primary Menu: American (2); Californian (1); Mexican (3); Miscellaneous (1)
Areas of Operation: CA, HI
Type of Foodservice: Casual Dining (7)
Catering Services: Yes
Primary Distributors: (Full Line) US Foods-Los Angeles, LA MIRADA, CA

Key Personnel
LEE DESHONG - President; Controller; General Buyer
GEORGE WATSON - Director Finance, Operations, Information Systems, Human Resources, Food Safety

Outrigger Enterprises
2375 Kuhio Ave
Honolulu, HI 96815-2939

Telephone: (808) 921-6600
Fax Number: (808) 921-6595
Internet Homepage: ohanahotels.com; outrigger.com
Type of Business: Foodservice Operations - Hotel/Motels
Year Founded: 1947
Total Sales: $267,700,000 (e)
Alcohol Sales: 10%
Number of Employees: 4,371
Total Units: 31
Restaurants in Hotels: 31
Trade Names: Outrigger Hotels & Resorts (31)
Company-Owned Units: 31
Alcohol Served: Beer, Wine, Liquor
Areas of Operation: GU, HI, FC
Foreign Countries: AUSTRALIA; FIJI; INDONESIA; THAILAND
Type of Foodservice: Casual Dining; Fine Dining
Primary Distributors: (Food) VIP Foodservice, KAHULUI, HI
Notes: The company derives approximately 80% of its revenue from hotel/resort operations. Company also has operations in Australia, Indonesia, & Fiji.

Key Personnel
W. DAVID P. CAREY III - CEO; President
SEAN DEE - Chief Marketing Officer; Exec VP
MEL KANESHIGE - Exec VP Real Estate
RUTHANN YAMANAKA - Senior VP Human Resources, Training, Strategic Planning
BARBARA CAMPBELL - VP Operations
WILLIAM VISSER - VP Operations
NURHAN ENUSTON - Director Catering

PJ Hawaii LLC
2875 Paa St Ste A
Honolulu, HI 96819-4462

Telephone: (808) 831-3388
Fax Number: (808) 831-3389
Type of Business: Chain Restaurant Operator
Year Founded: 1992
Total Sales: $14,990,000 (e)
Number of Employees: 280
Average Check: Lunch(16); Dinner(28)
Total Units: 11
Trade Names: Papa John's Pizza (11)
Units Franchised From: 11
Preferred Square Footage: 1,100; 1,500
Preferred Location Types: Strip Mall
Primary Menu: Pizza (11)
Areas of Operation: HI
Type of Foodservice: Quick Serve (11)
Foodservice Management Venues: Schools
Franchise Affiliation: Papa Johns International Inc., LOUISVILLE, KY
Primary Distributors: (Food) Papa John's Distribution Center, LOUISVILLE, KY

Key Personnel
MIKE DONLEY - President

Pop's Inc
Kohou St Ste 2B
Honolulu, HI 96817

Mailing Address: P O Box 17787, HONOLULU, HI, 40059
Telephone: (808) 841-6600
Fax Number: (808) 841-0700
Internet Homepage: popeyeshawaii.com
Company Email: info@popeyeshawaii.com
Type of Business: Chain Restaurant Operator
Total Sales: $12,660,000 (e)
Total Units: 5
Trade Names: Popeyes Louisiana Kitchen (5)
Units Franchised From: 5
Primary Menu: Chicken (5)
Areas of Operation: HI
Type of Foodservice: Quick Serve (5)
Franchise Affiliation: Popeyes Louisiana Kitchen Inc., ATLANTA, GA

Key Personnel
KAL UEZU - Owner
LORI UEZU - VP Sales

Prince Resorts Hawaii
100 Holomoana St
Honolulu, HI 96815-1436

Telephone: (808) 882-7222
Fax Number: (808) 944-4491
Internet Homepage: princeresortshawaii.com
Company Email: info@maunakeabeachhotel.com
Type of Business: Foodservice Operations - Hotel/Motels
Year Founded: 1965
Total Sales: $67,717,000 (e)
Alcohol Sales: 15%
Number of Employees: 1,000
Total Units: 3
Restaurants in Hotels: 14
Trade Names: Hapuna Beach Prince Hotel (1); Hawaii Prince Hotel Waikiki & Golf Club (1); Mauna Kea Beach Hotel (1)
Company-Owned Units: 14

Alcohol Served: Beer, Wine, Liquor
Areas of Operation: HI
Type of Foodservice: Casual Dining (14)
Primary Distributors: (Food) SYSCO Food Services of Los Angeles Inc., WALNUT, CA; (Specialty Foods) Wing Sing Seafood Inc., HONOLULU, HI
Notes: The company derives approximately 65% of its revenue from hotel operations. Restaurants within the hotels include: Manta & Pavilion Wine Bar, Number 3, Hau Tree, Copper Terrace, Coast Grille, Ocean Terrace, Beach Bar, Reef Lounge(2), Prince Court, Hakone, Bird of Paradise, Marina Front Cafe and Promenade Deck.

Key Personnel
SHIGEKI YAMANE - VP Strategic Planning
STACY YOSHIZAWA - Director Marketing
CINDY OKUMURA - Director Sales
RYAN DOI - Director Information Systems
EDITHA DOMINGO - Manager Accounting
YOON JUNG KIM - Manager Sales
SHIRLEY LAU CHAN - Manager Human Resources
LINDA LEUNG - Manager Sales

Scanlan Management LLC
4510 Salt Lake Blvd Ste D14
Honolulu, HI 96818-3170

Telephone: (808) 537-3300
Fax Number: (808) 537-3306
Internet Homepage: gotjack.com
Type of Business: Chain Restaurant Operator
Total Sales: $150,810,000 (e)
Total Units: 66
Trade Names: Jack in the Box (36); Jamba Juice (30)
Units Franchised From: 66
Primary Menu: Hamburger (36); Snacks (30)
Areas of Operation: HI
Type of Foodservice: Quick Serve (66)
Franchise Affiliation: Jack in the Box Restaurants, SAN DIEGO, CA

Key Personnel
CHRISTOPHER SCANLAN - Owner; General Buyer
PAUL GALANG - District Manager

Tanaka of Tokyo Restaurants Ltd.
150 Kaiulani Ave 1St Floor
Honolulu, HI 96815

Telephone: (808) 922-4233
Fax Number: (808) 922-6948
Internet Homepage: tanakaoftokyo.com
Type of Business: Chain Restaurant Operator
Year Founded: 1978
Total Sales: $21,341,000 (e)
Alcohol Sales: 25%
Number of Employees: 200
Average Check: Lunch(22); Dinner(42)
Total Units: 3
Trade Names: Tanaka of Tokyo Restaurant (3)
Company-Owned Units: 3
Preferred Location Types: Freestanding
Alcohol Served: Beer, Wine, Liquor
Primary Menu: Japanese (3)
Areas of Operation: HI
Type of Foodservice: Casual Dining (3)
Primary Distributors: (Equipment) Bargreen-Ellingson Inc., HONOLULU, HI; (Food) Y. Hata & Co. Ltd., HONOLULU, HI; (Supplies) Bargreen-Ellingson Inc., HONOLULU, HI

Key Personnel
RICHARD TANAKA - Chairman; CEO; Controller; Director Information Systems, Real Estate
CHESTER KANESHIRO - President; Manager Operations, Purchasing, Loss Prevention, Marketing
CALVIN YAMASAKI - Manager Accounting

TD Food Group Inc.
828 Fort Street Mall Ste 130
Honolulu, HI 96813-4314

Telephone: (808) 566-3200
Fax Number: (808) 566-3215
Internet Homepage: pizzahuthawaii.com; tacobellhawaii.com
Company Email: chelsea_kuriki@thdfsg.com
Type of Business: Chain Restaurant Operator
Year Founded: 1984
Total Sales: $196,200,000 (e)
Alcohol Sales: 2%
Number of Employees: 1,531
Average Check: Lunch(12); Dinner(12)
Internet Order Processing: Yes
Total Units: 74
Trade Names: Pizza Hut (36); Taco Bell (38)
Units Franchised From: 74
Preferred Square Footage: 2,500
Preferred Location Types: Community Mall; Freestanding
Primary Menu: Pizza (36); Taco (38)
Areas of Operation: HI
Type of Foodservice: Quick Serve (74)
Foodservice Management Venues: Schools
Catering Services: Yes
Franchise Affiliation: Pizza Hut Inc., PLANO, TX; Taco Bell Corp., IRVINE, CA
Primary Distributors: (Food) HFM FoodService, HONOLULU, HI
Parent Company: Nimes Capital Group, LOS ANGELES, CA
Headquarters: Pacific Island Restaurants, HONOLULU, HI

Key Personnel
KEVIN KURIHARA - CEO; President
ERIC LEE - Director Operations, Group; General Buyer
LAWTON NAKATA - Director Information Systems, Information Technology
LEAH ALLEN - Director Marketing
DAVID CHAR - Director Operations
ROMEO CORPUZ - Director Operations, Group
CINDY JULIAN - Director Operations
CAROL GRAFF - Manager Human Resources
HUGH CHUNG - Administrator Network
JANIS LAWTON - Administrator Human Resources

Teddy's Bigger Burgers
PO Box 161056
Honolulu, HI 96816-0923

Telephone: (888) 501-0393
Internet Homepage: teddysbb.com
Company Email: wecare@teddysbb.com
Type of Business: Chain Restaurant Operator
Year Founded: 1998
Total Units: 22
Trade Names: Teddy's Bigger Burgers (22)
Company-Owned Units: 13
Units Franchised To: 9
Primary Menu: Hamburger (25)
Areas of Operation: CA, HI, IA, TX, WA, FC
Foreign Countries: JAPAN; THAILAND; THE PHILIPPINES
Type of Foodservice: Casual Dining (22)

Key Personnel
RICH STULA - Co-CEO; Partner; Executive Chef
TED TSAKIRIS - Co-CEO; Partner
CLIFFORD JONES - General Manager

Westin Moana Surfrider Hotel
2365 Kalakaua Ave
Honolulu, HI 96815-5041

Telephone: (808) 922-3111
Fax Number: (808) 924-4799
Internet Homepage: moana-surfrider.com
Type of Business: Foodservice Operations - Hotel/Motels
Year Founded: 1988
Total Sales: $24,145,000 (e)
Alcohol Sales: 20%
Number of Employees: 250
Average Check: Dinner(36)
Total Units: 1
Restaurants in Hotels: 6
Trade Names: Mona Surfrider (1)
Company-Owned Units: 6
Alcohol Served: Beer, Wine, Liquor
Areas of Operation: HI

Type of Foodservice: Casual Dining (5); Family Restaurant (1)
Primary Distributors: (Food) SYSCO Food Services of San Diego Inc., POWAY, CA
Notes: The company derives approximately 70% of its revenue from hotel operations.

Key Personnel
FREDERICK ORR - General Manager; Director Operations
JASON WATANABE - Executive Chef
RYAN LOO - Executive Chef; General Buyer

Zippy's Inc.
1765 S King St Fl 2
Honolulu, HI 96826-2134

Telephone: (808) 973-0880
Fax Number: (808) 955-7043
Internet Homepage: zippys.com
Company Email: info@zippys.com
Type of Business: Chain Restaurant Operator
Year Founded: 1966
Total Sales: $29,810,000 (e)
Alcohol Sales: 5%
Number of Employees: 1,900
Average Check: Breakfast(6); Lunch(10); Dinner(12)
Internet Order Processing: Yes
Internet Sales: 1.00%
Total Units: 24
Trade Names: Zippy's (24)
Company-Owned Units: 24
Preferred Square Footage: 5,000
Preferred Location Types: Freestanding; Strip Mall
Alcohol Served: Beer, Wine
Primary Menu: American (24)
Areas of Operation: HI
Type of Foodservice: Casual Dining (24)
Catering Services: Yes
Primary Distributors: (Full Line) Y. Hata & Co. Ltd., HONOLULU, HI

Key Personnel
JASON HIGA - CEO
PAUL YOKOTA - President
DOUGLAS SHIMABUKURO - CFO; Controller; Manager Finance, Operations, Facility/Maintenance, Information Systems, Loss Prevention, Risk Management, Marketing, Real Estate

Grelyn of Maui
340 Dairy Rd
Kahului, HI 96732-2414

Telephone: (808) 877-6432
Type of Business: Chain Restaurant Operator
Total Sales: $28,020,000 (e)
Total Units: 6

Trade Names: McDonald's (6)
Units Franchised From: 6
Preferred Square Footage: 2,500
Primary Menu: Hamburger (6)
Areas of Operation: HI
Type of Foodservice: Quick Serve (6)
Franchise Affiliation: McDonald's Corporation, CHICAGO, IL

Key Personnel
LINDA ROSARIO - President; General Buyer

Leopoldino Inc.
65-1154 Mamalahoa Hwy
Kamuela, HI 96743-8431

Telephone: (808) 885-8824
Fax Number: (808) 885-2189
Type of Business: Chain Restaurant Operator
Total Sales: $23,380,000 (e)
Number of Employees: 50
Average Check: Breakfast(12); Lunch(12); Dinner(12)
Total Units: 5
Trade Names: McDonald's (5)
Units Franchised From: 5
Preferred Square Footage: 2,500; 3,000
Preferred Location Types: Freestanding
Primary Menu: Hamburger (5)
Areas of Operation: HI
Type of Foodservice: Quick Serve (5)
Franchise Affiliation: McDonald's Corporation, CHICAGO, IL
Primary Distributors: (Food) Golden State Foods, WAIPAHU, HI

Key Personnel
ROBERT LEOPOLDINO - President; General Manager; General Buyer
MARGERIE CABASAN - Manager Store Operations

Bubba Burger Hawaii Inc.
4-1435 Kuhio Hwy Ste 104
Kapaa, HI 96746-1745

Telephone: (808) 823-0069
Fax Number: (808) 821-7748
Internet Homepage: bubbaburger.com
Company Email: obubba@aloha.net
Type of Business: Chain Restaurant Operator
Year Founded: 1990
Systemwide Sales: $2,263,000 (e)
Total Sales: $2,263,000 (e)
Number of Employees: 24
Average Check: Lunch(12); Dinner(12)
Internet Order Processing: Yes
Internet Sales: 1.00%
Total Units: 3
Trade Names: Bubba Burgers (3)
Company-Owned Units: 3

Preferred Location Types: Freestanding; Strip Mall
Primary Menu: Hamburger (3)
Areas of Operation: HI
Type of Foodservice: Quick Serve (3)

Key Personnel
ANDREW HART - President; Partner; CFO; Director Menu Development; General Buyer
DEBBIE BOSSLER - Partner
JOHN GRECO - Partner; Director Operations, Menu Development; General Buyer

Fork & Salad Maui
1279 S Kihei Rd Unit 204
Kihei, HI 96732

Telephone: (808) 879-3675
Internet Homepage: forkandsaladmaui.com
Type of Business: Chain Restaurant Operator
Year Founded: 2016
Average Check: Lunch(16); Dinner(20)
Total Units: 2
Trade Names: Fork & Salad Maui (2)
Company-Owned Units: 2
Preferred Square Footage: 1,600
Primary Menu: Health Foods (2)
Areas of Operation: HI
Type of Foodservice: Casual Dining (2)
Catering Services: Yes

Key Personnel
JARON BLOSSER - Partner
CODY CHRISOPHER - Partner
TRAVIS MORRIN - Partner

Tri-Star Restaurant Group LLC
2980 S Kihei Rd
Kihei Maui, HI 96753

Telephone: (808) 875-7555
Internet Homepage: nicksfishmarketmaui.com; sonzrestaurant.com; tristarrestaurants.com
Company Email: info@tristarrestaurants.com
Type of Business: Chain Restaurant Operator
Year Founded: 1998
Total Sales: $25,516,000 (e)
Alcohol Sales: 5%
Number of Employees: 175
Average Check: Dinner(42)
Total Units: 4
Trade Names: Mannoli's Pizza Company (1); Nick's Fishmarket Maui (1); Sarento's On The Beach (1); Sonz Steakhouse (1)
Company-Owned Units: 4
Preferred Location Types: Hotel/Motel
Alcohol Served: Beer, Wine, Liquor
Primary Menu: Italian (1); Pizza (1); Seafood (2)

Areas of Operation: HI
Type of Foodservice: Casual Dining (1); Fine Dining (3)

Key Personnel
JIRO NOGUCHI - Chairman
AARON PLACOURAKIS - CEO; President
GENO SARMIENTO - Partner; Executive Chef
DON ABERNATHY - Partner; Director Operations
PAUL FENG - Executive Chef; General Buyer

Longhi's Restaurant
888 Front St Ste H
Lahaina, HI 96761-2324

Telephone: (808) 667-2288
Fax Number: (808) 661-5795
Internet Homepage: longhis.com
Type of Business: Chain Restaurant Operator
Year Founded: 1976
Total Sales: $17,614,000 (e)
Alcohol Sales: 5%
Number of Employees: 100
Average Check: Breakfast(12); Lunch(18); Dinner(40)
Internet Order Processing: Yes
Total Units: 3
Trade Names: Longhi's (3)
Company-Owned Units: 3
Alcohol Served: Beer, Wine, Liquor
Primary Menu: Greek/Mediterranean (3)
Areas of Operation: HI
Type of Foodservice: Fine Dining (3)
Catering Services: Yes

Key Personnel
PETER LONGHI - President; Director Menu Development; General Buyer
MARY ANN BOWMAN - Manager

T S Restaurants
40 Kupuohi St Ste 206
Lahaina, HI 96761-2714

Telephone: (808) 667-4000
Fax Number: (808) 667-4842
Internet Homepage: tsrestaurants.com
Type of Business: Chain Restaurant Operator
Year Founded: 1977
Total Sales: $130,170,000 (e)
Alcohol Sales: 30%
Number of Employees: 1,535
Average Check: Lunch(14); Dinner(26)
Internet Order Processing: Yes
Internet Sales: 0.50%
Total Units: 13
Trade Names: Duke's (5); Duke's Beach House (1); Hula Grill (2); Jake's Del Mar (1); Keoki's Paradise (1); Kimo's (1); Leilani's on the Beach (1); Sunnyside Restaurant & Lodge (1)
Company-Owned Units: 13
Preferred Square Footage: 7,000
Preferred Location Types: Freestanding; Hotel/Motel
Alcohol Served: Beer, Wine, Liquor
Primary Menu: Steak/Seafood (13)
Areas of Operation: CA, HI
Type of Foodservice: Casual Dining (13)
Catering Services: Yes
Primary Distributors: (Food) HFM FoodService, HONOLULU, HI

Key Personnel
SUSIE SAXTEN - Chairman
JACKIE REED - CEO
NAOMI SAUCEDA - Controller
NICHOLAS WARE - General Manager
SCOTT MCGILL - Executive Chef; Manager Menu Development
DUSTIN ANSELM - Executive Chef

Casanova
1188 Makawao Ave
Makawao, HI 96768-9448

Mailing Address: PO Box 1166, MAKAWAO, HI, 96768-1166
Telephone: (808) 572-0220
Fax Number: (808) 572-4978
Internet Homepage: casanovamaui.com
Company Email: casanovamaui@yahoo.com
Type of Business: Chain Restaurant Operator
Year Founded: 1986
Total Sales: $4,521,000 (e)
Alcohol Sales: 25%
Average Check: Breakfast(10); Lunch(14); Dinner(36)
Total Units: 2
Trade Names: Bistro Casanova (1); Casanova (1)
Company-Owned Units: 2
Alcohol Served: Beer, Wine, Liquor
Primary Menu: Italian (2)
Areas of Operation: HI
Type of Foodservice: Casual Dining (1); Fine Dining (1)
Catering Services: Yes

Key Personnel
GIOVANNI CAPPELLI - President; General Buyer
ELIAS WEINSTOCK - Chief Creative Officer; VP
GEOVAN SARTO - Executive Chef; Manager Catering
ROXANE GARZON - Director Media

Sumida & Associates Inc
2138 Main St
Wailuku, HI 96793-1637

Telephone: (808) 244-8211
Fax Number: (808) 242-6882
Type of Business: Chain Restaurant Operator
Total Sales: $20,692,000 (e)
Total Units: 4
Trade Names: McDonald's (4)
Units Franchised From: 4
Primary Menu: Hamburger (4)
Areas of Operation: HI
Type of Foodservice: Quick Serve (4)
Franchise Affiliation: McDonald's Corporation, CHICAGO, IL

Key Personnel
DIANE SUMIDA - President; General Buyer

Big City Diner
94-800 Ukee St Ste 305
Waipahu, HI 96797-4044

Telephone: (808) 678-8868
Fax Number: (808) 678-8869
Internet Homepage: bigcitydinerhawaii.com
Type of Business: Chain Restaurant Operator
Year Founded: 1998
Total Sales: $7,261,000 (e)
Number of Employees: 300
Average Check: Breakfast(14); Lunch(14); Dinner(14)
Total Units: 6
Trade Names: Big City Diner (6)
Company-Owned Units: 6
Alcohol Served: Beer, Wine
Primary Menu: American (6)
Areas of Operation: HI
Type of Foodservice: Family Restaurant (6)
Catering Services: Yes
Primary Distributors: (Full Line) Y. Hata & Co. Ltd., HONOLULU, HI

Key Personnel
LANE MURAOKA - Owner; General Buyer
JODY FRANKS - Director Operations, Catering

IOWA

Duale Industries Inc
2316 230th St
Ames, IA 50014-6307

Telephone: (515) 232-7103
Company Email: dualeindustries@gmail.com
Type of Business: Chain Restaurant Operator
Total Sales: $11,711,000 (e)
Total Units: 4
Trade Names: Wendy's Old Fashioned Hamburgers (4)
Units Franchised From: 4
Primary Menu: Hamburger (4)
Areas of Operation: IA
Type of Foodservice: Quick Serve (4)

Franchise Affiliation: The Wendy's Company, DUBLIN, OH

Key Personnel
JEFF MOSIMAN - President; General Buyer

Iowa State University Dining
1215 Friley Hall
Ames, IA 50012-0005

Telephone: (515) 294-4793
Fax Number: (515) 294-4016
Internet Homepage: dining.iastate.edu; iastate.edu
Company Email: dmohr@isstate.edu
Type of Business: Chain Restaurant Operator
Total Sales: $17,580,000 (e)
Total Units: 24
Trade Names: ABE's Harvest Cafe (1); Bookends Cafe (1); Business Cafe (1); Caribou Coffee (1); Clydes Fresh Express (1); Conversations (1); Courtyard Cafe (1); Design Cafe (1); Dinkey's (1); East Side Market (1); Friley Windows (1); Gentle Doctor Cafe (1); Global Cafe (1); Hawthorn (1); Heaping Plato (1);Lance and Ellie's (1); Memorial Union Food Court (1); MU Market & Cafe (1); Seasons Marketplace (1); South Side Market (1); Storms Dining (1); Union DriveMarketplace (1); West Side Market (1); Whirlybird's (1)
Company-Owned Units: 3
Units Franchised From: 24
Primary Menu: American (22); Miscellaneous (1)
Areas of Operation: IA
Type of Foodservice: Casual Dining (3); Quick Serve (21)
Franchise Affiliation: Godfather's Pizza, Inc., OMAHA, NE

Key Personnel
WENDY WINTERSTEEN - President; General Buyer
HANNAH DONG - CIO
CORY HARMS - Director Purchasing
MOHAMED ALI - Director
JILL ARROYO - Associate Director
DUSTIN MOHR - Agent Purchasing

JKB Restaurants
4923 Lincoln Way
Ames, IA 50014-3616

Telephone: (515) 292-1388
Fax Number: (515) 292-6410
Type of Business: Chain Restaurant Operator
Year Founded: 1971
Total Sales: $15,320,000 (e)
Number of Employees: 260
Average Check: Breakfast(8); Lunch(8); Dinner(8)
Total Units: 3
Trade Names: McDonald's (3)
Units Franchised From: 3
Preferred Square Footage: 1,600
Preferred Location Types: Freestanding
Primary Menu: Hamburger (3)
Areas of Operation: IA
Type of Foodservice: Quick Serve (3)
Franchise Affiliation: McDonald's Corporation, CHICAGO, IL
Primary Distributors: (Full Line) The Martin-Brower Co., MASON CITY, IA

Key Personnel
JIM BAKER - Owner; General Buyer

Mian Group
209 Lincoln Way
Ames, IA 50010-3325

Mailing Address: 2825 E 13th St, Ames, IA, 50010
Telephone: (515) 292-0991
Company Email: office@mianinc.com
Type of Business: Chain Restaurant Operator
Total Sales: $50,080,000 (e)
Total Units: 18
Trade Names: Burger King (7); IHOP (11)
Units Franchised From: 18
Primary Menu: American (11); Hamburger (7)
Areas of Operation: IA, IL
Type of Foodservice: Family Restaurant (11); Quick Serve (7)
Franchise Affiliation: Burger King Worldwide Inc., MIAMI, FL; IHOP Restaurant System, GLENDALE, CA
Notes: Mian Group operates IHOP, Burger King, Taco Bell and KFC franchises in Iowa and Illinois.

Key Personnel
KHURRAM MIAN - CEO; President

Domino's Franchisee
2420 18th St
Bettendorf, IA 52722

Telephone: (563) 359-7777
Company Email: dominos3030@hotmail.com
Type of Business: Chain Restaurant Operator
Total Sales: $4,121,000 (e)
Total Units: 2
Trade Names: Domino's (2)
Units Franchised From: 2
Primary Menu: Pizza (2)
Areas of Operation: IA
Type of Foodservice: Quick Serve (2)
Franchise Affiliation: Domino's Pizza Inc, ANN ARBOR, MI

Key Personnel
SCOTT A. OCEL - Owner; General Buyer

Happy Joe's Pizza & Ice Cream Parlor Inc.
2705 Happy Joe Dr
Bettendorf, IA 52722-2385

Telephone: (563) 332-8811
Fax Number: (563) 332-5822
Internet Homepage: happyjoes.com
Company Email: info@happyjoes.com
Type of Business: Chain Restaurant Operator
Year Founded: 1972
Systemwide Sales: $86,186,000 (e)
Total Sales: $23,080,000 (e)
Alcohol Sales: 10%
Number of Employees: 230
Average Check: Breakfast(8); Lunch(10); Dinner(10)
Internet Order Processing: Yes
Internet Sales: 1.00%
Total Units: 46
Trade Names: Happy Joe's Pizza & Ice Cream Parlor (46)
Company-Owned Units: 12
Units Franchised To: 34
Preferred Square Footage: 2,000, 15,000
Preferred Location Types: Convenience Store/Gas Station; Freestanding; Strip Mall
Alcohol Served: Beer, Wine
Primary Menu: Pizza (46)
Areas of Operation: IA, IL, MN, MO, ND, WI
Type of Foodservice: Fast Casual (46)
Catering Services: Yes
Primary Distributors: (Food) Performance Food Group, RICHMOND, VA

Key Personnel
HOLLIE MATTHYS - Controller; Director Finance; Manager Loss Prevention

La Rosa Enterprises Inc.
3111 Devils Glen Rd
Bettendorf, IA 52722-3361

Telephone: (563) 332-1313
Internet Homepage: rudystacos.com
Company Email: EastVillage@rudystacos.com
Type of Business: Chain Restaurant Operator
Year Founded: 1972
Systemwide Sales: $28,138,000 (e)
Total Sales: $10,980,000 (e)
Alcohol Sales: 5%
Number of Employees: 120
Average Check: Lunch(10); Dinner(14)
Total Units: 12
Trade Names: Rudy's Tacos (12)
Company-Owned Units: 2
Units Franchised To: 10
Preferred Square Footage: 6,000

Preferred Location Types: Freestanding
Alcohol Served: Beer, Wine, Liquor
Primary Menu: Mexican (12)
Projected Openings: 2
Areas of Operation: IA, IL
Type of Foodservice: Casual Dining (12)
Primary Distributors: (Equipment) Tri City Equipment Co., DAVENPORT, IA

Key Personnel
KEVIN QUIJAS - CEO
MARILYN QUIJAS - President; Director Operations, Purchasing, Facility/Maintenance, Information Systems, Marketing, Real Estate, Design, Human Resources, Food Safety
BRICE QUIJAS - VP; General Counsel; Director Finance, Loss Prevention, Product Development, Menu Development

Mann's McDonalds
610 N 4th St Ste 510
Burlington, IA 52601-5070

Telephone: (319) 753-0722
Fax Number: (319) 753-0412
Type of Business: Chain Restaurant Operator
Total Sales: $19,781,000 (e)
Total Units: 4
Trade Names: McDonald's (4)
Units Franchised From: 4
Preferred Location Types: Freestanding
Primary Menu: Hamburger (4)
Areas of Operation: IA
Type of Foodservice: Quick Serve (4)
Franchise Affiliation: McDonald's Corporation, CHICAGO, IL

Key Personnel
DONNA MANN - Owner; General Buyer

McDermott Oil Company
1501 1st Ave E
Cascade, IA 52033-7718

Telephone: (563) 852-3510
Fax Number: (563) 852-7421
Internet Homepage: mcdermottoil.com
Company Email: info@mcdermottoil.com
Type of Business: Chain Restaurant Operator
Total Sales: $2,504,000 (e)
Total Units: 4
Trade Names: Godfather's Pizza (4)
Units Franchised From: 4
Alcohol Served: Beer, Wine
Primary Menu: Pizza (4)
Areas of Operation: IA
Type of Foodservice: Casual Dining (4)
Franchise Affiliation: Godfather's Pizza, Inc., OMAHA, NE

Key Personnel
JASON MCDERMOTT - President; VP Finance, Sales; General Buyer
KEN MCDERMOTT - Owner
MONICA MCDERMOTT - Controller

Domino's Franchisee
2024 College St
Cedar Falls, IA 50613-3618

Telephone: (319) 266-3333
Type of Business: Chain Restaurant Operator
Total Sales: $12,339,000 (e)
Total Units: 6
Trade Names: Domino's (6)
Units Franchised From: 6
Primary Menu: Pizza (6)
Areas of Operation: IA
Type of Foodservice: Quick Serve (6)
Franchise Affiliation: Domino's Pizza Inc, ANN ARBOR, MI

Key Personnel
ERIC J. LOCKHART - Owner; General Buyer

The Other Place
2214 College St
Cedar Falls, IA 50613-3622

Mailing Address: PO Box 969, CEDAR FALLS, IA, 50613-0047
Telephone: (319) 287-9219
Fax Number: (319) 235-1462
Internet Homepage: pepperssportspub.com; theotherplace.com
Type of Business: Chain Restaurant Operator
Year Founded: 1970
Total Sales: $16,650,000 (e)
Alcohol Sales: 20%
Number of Employees: 200
Average Check: Lunch(10); Dinner(12)
Total Units: 14
Trade Names: Peppers (1); The Other Place (13)
Company-Owned Units: 14
Preferred Square Footage: 5,500; 6,000
Preferred Location Types: Freestanding
Alcohol Served: Beer, Wine, Liquor
Primary Menu: American (1); Italian (13)
Areas of Operation: IA, KS
Type of Foodservice: Casual Dining (14)
Catering Services: Yes
Primary Distributors: (Full Line) US Foods, CORALVILLE, IA

Key Personnel
SUE STEDMAN - Partner; Director Facility/Maintenance, Real Estate, Design; General Buyer
GREG KISNER - Partner; Director Finance, Operations, Purchasing, Menu Development
TROY STEDMAN - Partner; Director Human Resources
JOEL STEDMAN - Partner

Beaton Inc.
5805 Council St NE Ste D
Cedar Rapids, IA 52402-5807

Telephone: (319) 378-1127
Fax Number: (319) 378-1713
Internet Homepage: beatonjobs.com
Type of Business: Chain Restaurant Operator
Year Founded: 1984
Total Sales: $42,660,000 (e)
Number of Employees: 552
Average Check: Breakfast(5); Lunch(8); Dinner(8)
Total Units: 19
Trade Names: Burger King (19)
Units Franchised From: 19
Preferred Square Footage: 1,600
Preferred Location Types: Freestanding
Primary Menu: Hamburger (19)
Areas of Operation: IA, IL
Type of Foodservice: Quick Serve (19)
Franchise Affiliation: Burger King Worldwide Inc., MIAMI, FL
Primary Distributors: (Food) Reinhart FoodService, CEDAR RAPIDS, IA

Key Personnel
PERRY BEATON - President; Director Finance, Operations, Purchasing, Facility/Maintenance, Supply Chain
CAROL BEATON - VP; General Manager; Director Real Estate, Site Selection, Human Resources
KATHY FRERICHS - Controller; Manager Human Resources

Dallhaus Ltd
2405 Edgewood Rd SW
Cedar Rapids, IA 52404-3251

Telephone: (319) 390-2061
Fax Number: (319) 390-2062
Internet Homepage: culvers.com
Type of Business: Chain Restaurant Operator
Total Sales: $20,500,000 (e)
Total Units: 5
Trade Names: Culver's Frozen Custard (5)
Company-Owned Units: 5
Units Franchised From: 5
Primary Menu: Snacks (5)
Areas of Operation: IA
Type of Foodservice: Quick Serve (5)
Franchise Affiliation: Culver Franchising System Inc., PRAIRIE DU SAC, WI

Key Personnel
JACOB KENDALL - President; General Buyer

Domino's Franchisee
2460 Edgewood Rd SW
Cedar Rapids, IA 52404

Telephone: (319) 366-3030
Type of Business: Chain Restaurant Operator
Total Sales: $4,071,000 (e)
Total Units: 2
Trade Names: Domino's (2)
Units Franchised From: 2
Primary Menu: Pizza (2)
Areas of Operation: IA
Type of Foodservice: Quick Serve (2)
Franchise Affiliation: Domino's Pizza Inc, ANN ARBOR, MI

Key Personnel
HAMED SAGHAH - Owner; General Buyer

Kirkwood Community College Hospitality Arts
6301 Kirkwood Blvd SW
Cedar Rapids, IA 52404-5260

Telephone: (319) 398-5411
Internet Homepage: kirkwood.edu
Company Email: ask@kirkwood.edu
Type of Business: Culinary Schools
Areas of Operation: IA

Key Personnel
SARA SWANSON - Executive Director Applications
DAVID HORSFIELD - Executive Chef
TIERNEY KETTMANN - Associate Director Marketing

Panera Bread of Iowa
1241 Park Pl NE Ste C
Cedar Rapids, IA 52402-2022

Telephone: (319) 365-9093
Fax Number: (319) 365-9128
Internet Homepage: paneraiowa.com
Company Email: contactus@paneraiowa.com
Type of Business: Chain Restaurant Operator
Total Sales: $92,350,000 (e)
Number of Employees: 893
Total Units: 20
Trade Names: Panera Bread (20)
Units Franchised From: 20
Preferred Square Footage: 3,200; 4,800
Preferred Location Types: Freestanding
Primary Menu: Sandwiches/Deli (20)
Projected Openings: 2

Areas of Operation: IA, IL
Type of Foodservice: Fast Casual (20)
Franchise Affiliation: Panera Bread Company, SAINT LOUIS, MO

Key Personnel
MIKE YOUNG - President; General Buyer
JOHN CATALANO - Director Operations
DEB HARTLEY - Manager Training
BRIAN MCGRATH - Manager District
STEVEN RUSSELL - Manager Facility/Maintenance
KAREN BEARD - Manager Human Resources

Paul Revere's Pizza International, Ltd.
47 Kirkwood Ct SW
Cedar Rapids, IA 52404

Telephone: (319) 399-1500
Fax Number: (319) 395-9115
Internet Homepage: paulreverespizza.com
Company Email: info@paulreverespizza.com
Type of Business: Chain Restaurant Operator
Year Founded: 1975
Systemwide Sales: $7,173,000 (e)
Total Sales: $815,000 (e)
Number of Employees: 90
Average Check: Lunch(16); Dinner(16)
Internet Order Processing: Yes
Total Units: 6
Trade Names: Paul Revere's Pizza (6)
Units Franchised To: 6
Preferred Square Footage: 1,200; 1,700
Preferred Location Types: Freestanding; Strip Mall
Primary Menu: Pizza (6)
Areas of Operation: IA, TX, WI
Type of Foodservice: Quick Serve (6)
Catering Services: Yes
Primary Distributors: (Full Line) US Foods, CORALVILLE, IA

Key Personnel
LARRY SCHUSTER - CEO; President; Manager Operations, Purchasing, Loss Prevention, Risk Management, Quality Assurance, Real Estate, Design, Research & Development, Product Development, Franchising, Menu Development, Food Safety, Catering; General Buyer
TOM MUELLER - CFO; Exec VP Advertising; Director Finance, Research & Development, Product Development, Menu Development

KGB
200 N Main St Ste 6
Charles City, IA 50616-2026

Telephone: (641) 228-3822

Type of Business: Chain Restaurant Operator
Total Sales: $11,560,000 (e)
Total Units: 20
Trade Names: Subway (20)
Units Franchised From: 20
Primary Menu: Sandwiches/Deli (20)
Areas of Operation: IA
Type of Foodservice: Quick Serve (20)
Franchise Affiliation: Doctor's Associates Inc., MILFORD, CT

Key Personnel
GEORGE SLATTERY - Partner; General Buyer
BOB THOMPSON - Partner
FLORIAN GROUSSET - Director Software

McSoifer's Inc.
1010 S Grand Ave Ste 4
Charles City, IA 50616-3729

Telephone: (641) 228-2838
Fax Number: (641) 228-5370
Type of Business: Chain Restaurant Operator
Year Founded: 1978
Total Sales: $51,080,000 (e)
Number of Employees: 480
Average Check: Breakfast(8); Lunch(8); Dinner(8)
Total Units: 11
Trade Names: McDonald's (11)
Units Franchised From: 11
Preferred Square Footage: 3,500
Preferred Location Types: Convenience Store/Gas Station; Freestanding; Travel Plazas
Primary Menu: Hamburger (11)
Areas of Operation: IA
Type of Foodservice: Quick Serve (11)
Franchise Affiliation: McDonald's Corporation, CHICAGO, IL
Primary Distributors: (Food) The Martin-Brower Co. LLC, ROSEMONT, IL

Key Personnel
SCOTT SOIFER - President; General Manager; General Buyer

Cabin Coffee Company
303 Main Ave
Clear Lake, IA 50428-1824

Telephone: (641) 357-6500
Fax Number: (641) 357-6538
Internet Homepage: cabincoffeecompany.com
Company Email: info@cabincoffee.net
Type of Business: Chain Restaurant Operator
Year Founded: 2002
Total Units: 17
Trade Names: Cabin Coffee Company (17)
Company-Owned Units: 5
Units Franchised To: 12

Primary Menu: Coffee (17)
Projected Openings: 1
Areas of Operation: CO, GA, IA, IN, MN, WI
Type of Foodservice: Quick Serve (17)

Key Personnel
BRAD BARBER - Partner
ANGIE BARBER - Partner

Rivercity Dairy Queen
108 8th Ave N
Clinton, IA 52732-3816

Telephone: (563) 243-4831
Type of Business: Chain Restaurant Operator
Total Sales: $2,985,000 (e)
Total Units: 2
Trade Names: Dairy Queen Store (2)
Units Franchised From: 2
Primary Menu: Snacks (2)
Areas of Operation: IA
Type of Foodservice: Quick Serve (2)
Franchise Affiliation: International Dairy Queen Inc., BLOOMINGTON, MN

Key Personnel
MARK SMITH - Owner; General Buyer

Central Iowa KFC
14812 N Ave
Columbus Junction, IA 52738-9526

Mailing Address: PO Box 269, COLUMBUS JUNCTION, IA, 52738-0269
Telephone: (319) 728-3282
Fax Number: (319) 728-2940
Type of Business: Chain Restaurant Operator
Year Founded: 1968
Total Sales: $28,530,000 (e)
Number of Employees: 300
Average Check: Lunch(10); Dinner(10)
Total Units: 16
Trade Names: KFC (8); KFC/Long John Silver's (1); KFC/Taco Bell (7)
Units Franchised From: 16
Preferred Square Footage: 1,800
Preferred Location Types: Freestanding
Primary Menu: Chicken (16); Seafood (1); Taco (7)
Areas of Operation: IA, IL
Type of Foodservice: Quick Serve (16)
Catering Services: Yes
Franchise Affiliation: KFC Corporation, LOUISVILLE, KY; Taco Bell Corp., IRVINE, CA

Key Personnel
KEVIN SCHLUTZ - President; Director Supply Chain, Real Estate, Design, Food Safety; General Buyer
MICHELLE HUNT - Director Information Systems, Marketing

Cordes Creamery, Inc.
921 25th Ave
Coralville, IA 52241-1224

Telephone: (319) 341-7900
Type of Business: Chain Restaurant Operator
Total Sales: $1,240,000 (e)
Total Units: 2
Trade Names: Cold Stone Creamery (2)
Units Franchised From: 2
Primary Menu: Snacks (2)
Areas of Operation: IA
Type of Foodservice: Quick Serve (2)
Franchise Affiliation: Kahala Brands, SCOTTSDALE, AZ

Key Personnel
HEATHER CORDES - Partner
KENNETH CORDES - Partner

Panchero's Franchise Corporation
2475 Coral Ct Ste B
Coralville, IA 52241-2830

Telephone: (319) 545-6565
Fax Number: (319) 545-6570
Internet Homepage: pancheros.com
Company Email: pancheros@pancheros.com
Type of Business: Chain Restaurant Operator
Year Founded: 1992
Total Sales: $24,210,000 (e)
Alcohol Sales: 5%
Number of Employees: 842
Average Check: Lunch(8); Dinner(8)
Total Units: 71
Trade Names: Panchero's Mexican Grill (71)
Company-Owned Units: 26
Units Franchised To: 45
Preferred Square Footage: 1,800; 2,400
Preferred Location Types: Downtown; Lifestyle Center; Strip Mall
Alcohol Served: Beer, Wine
Primary Menu: Mexican (71)
Projected Openings: 2
Areas of Operation: AZ, CA, CT, FL, IA, IL, IN, KY, MD, MI, MN, MO, ND, NJ, PA, SD, WI
Type of Foodservice: Fast Casual (71)
Primary Distributors: (Full Line) Reinhart FoodService, CEDAR RAPIDS, IA

Key Personnel
RODNEY L. ANDERSON - President; CFO; Treasurer; Manager Information Systems, Real Estate; General Buyer
NANETTE BEINER - Chief Administrative Officer; Director Real Estate
SHANNON KRAUSS - Director Construction, Design
LISA HOBART - District Manager

GLS Investments Inc
5108 Jersey Ridge Rd Ste A
Davenport, IA 52807-3133

Telephone: (563) 355-2623
Internet Homepage: qcmaidrite.com
Type of Business: Chain Restaurant Operator
Total Sales: $3,381,000 (e)
Total Units: 5
Trade Names: Maid Rite (5)
Units Franchised From: 5
Primary Menu: American (5)
Areas of Operation: IA, IL
Type of Foodservice: Quick Serve (5)
Franchise Affiliation: Maid-Rite Corp., DES MOINES, IA

Key Personnel
LARRY SELSER - President; General Buyer

Badawi Pizza Company
3220 SE 14th St
Des Moines, IA 50320-1330

Telephone: (515) 365-5000
Type of Business: Chain Restaurant Operator
Total Sales: $3,060,000 (e)
Total Units: 5
Trade Names: Little Caesars Pizza (5)
Units Franchised From: 5
Primary Menu: Pizza (5)
Areas of Operation: IA
Type of Foodservice: Quick Serve (5)
Franchise Affiliation: Little Caesar Enterprises Inc., DETROIT, MI

Key Personnel
MOHAMED BADAOUI - Partner; General Buyer
FRED BERRY - Partner; General Buyer

Buzzard Billy's Armadillo Bar & Grill-o
615 3rd St
Des Moines, IA 50309

Telephone: (515) 844-8299
Fax Number: (254) 753-1277
Internet Homepage: buzzardbillys.com
Company Email: buzzardbillys@hotmail.com
Type of Business: Chain Restaurant Operator
Year Founded: 1992
Total Sales: $7,888,000 (e)
Alcohol Sales: 15%
Number of Employees: 170
Average Check: Lunch(18); Dinner(30)
Total Units: 3

Trade Names: Buzzard Billy's Armadillo Bar & Grill-o (3)
Company-Owned Units: 1
Units Franchised To: 2
Preferred Location Types: Freestanding
Alcohol Served: Beer, Wine, Liquor
Primary Menu: Cajun/Creole (3)
Areas of Operation: IA, NE, WI
Type of Foodservice: Casual Dining (3)
Catering Services: Yes

Key Personnel
DAN MASSOTH - President; Partner; Executive Chef; General Buyer
DIANE NOWLAIN - Partner
ANDY MASSOTH - Partner; VP; General Manager
MIKE HATAWAY - General Manager
JEFF KIRBY - General Manager

†
Consolidated Management Company
2670 106th St Ste 140
Des Moines, IA 50322-3746

Telephone: (515) 278-9774
Fax Number: (515) 254-0394
Internet Homepage: consolidatedmgmt.com
Company Email: info@consolidatedmgmt.com
Type of Business: Foodservice Management Operator
Year Founded: 1975
Total Sales: $28,446,000 (e)
Number of Employees: 200
Number of Locations Served: 68
Total Foodservice Mgmt Accounts: 68
Areas of Operation: AR, CO, IA, IL, IN, KS, KY, MN, MO, NE, OK, SD, TN, WI
Type of Foodservice: Cafeteria (68)
Foodservice Management Venues: Business & Industry; Prison Feeding; Schools
Primary Distributors: (Full Line) Martin Brothers Distribution Co. Inc., CEDAR FALLS, IA

Key Personnel
DOMINIC TRADER - President
ROSS LARSON - CFO; VP Finance
CARRIE LARSEN - Director Purchasing

Tasty Tacos Inc.
1420 E Grand Ave
Des Moines, IA 50316-3806

Telephone: (515) 262-9821
Fax Number: (515) 263-8828
Internet Homepage: tastytacos.com
Type of Business: Chain Restaurant Operator
Year Founded: 1961
Total Sales: $6,853,000 (e)
Number of Employees: 102
Average Check: Lunch(6); Dinner(8)
Internet Order Processing: Yes
Total Units: 6
Trade Names: Tasty Tacos (6)
Company-Owned Units: 6
Preferred Square Footage: 1,200
Preferred Location Types: Freestanding; Strip Mall
Primary Menu: Taco (6)
Areas of Operation: IA
Type of Foodservice: Quick Serve (6)
Primary Distributors: (Equipment) Hockenbergs, DES MOINES, IA; (Food) SYSCO Food Services of Iowa Inc., ANKENY, IA; (Supplies) SYSCO Food Services of Iowa Inc., ANKENY, IA

Key Personnel
ANTONIA MOSQUEDA - Exec VP

●▲
Parco Ltd.
998 Fremont Ave Ste UL2
Dubuque, IA 52003-0300

Telephone: (563) 557-1337
Fax Number: (563) 557-1362
Type of Business: Chain Restaurant Operator
Year Founded: 1987
Total Sales: $79,398,000 (e)
Number of Employees: 933
Average Check: Breakfast(8); Lunch(10); Dinner(10)
Total Units: 27
Trade Names: Wendy's Old Fashioned Hamburgers (27)
Units Franchised From: 27
Preferred Square Footage: 1,500
Preferred Location Types: Freestanding
Primary Menu: Hamburger (27)
Areas of Operation: IA, IL, MN, WI
Type of Foodservice: Quick Serve (27)
Franchise Affiliation: The Wendy's Company, DUBLIN, OH
Primary Distributors: (Full Line) Upper Lakes Foods Inc., CLOQUET, MN

Key Personnel
STEVE PARCO - VP
PAM PRAY - Director Human Resources
JULIET DIAZ - Manager Human Resources
KARI KROGMAN - Manager Accounting, Administration

●▲
To-Ne of Iowa, Inc.
250 S Locust St
Dubuque, IA 52003-7416

Telephone: (563) 557-5151
Fax Number: (563) 557-5152
Type of Business: Chain Restaurant Operator
Total Sales: $4,869,000 (e)
Total Units: 2
Trade Names: Burger King (2)
Units Franchised From: 2
Preferred Location Types: Freestanding
Primary Menu: Hamburger (2)
Areas of Operation: IA
Type of Foodservice: Quick Serve (2)
Franchise Affiliation: Burger King Worldwide Inc., MIAMI, FL

Key Personnel
TONY LEHMANN - President; General Buyer

●▲
Dairy Queen
1204 S Lincoln St
Knoxville, IA 50138-3177

Telephone: (641) 828-7317
Fax Number: (641) 828-7317
Internet Homepage: dairyqueen.com
Type of Business: Chain Restaurant Operator
Total Sales: $2,903,000 (e)
Total Units: 2
Trade Names: Dairy Queen Store (2)
Units Franchised From: 2
Primary Menu: Snacks (2)
Areas of Operation: IA
Type of Foodservice: Quick Serve (2)
Franchise Affiliation: International Dairy Queen Inc., BLOOMINGTON, MN

Key Personnel
JIM SPERR - President; General Buyer
LANCE GLOSEMEYER - VP Customer Analytics
MARTIN DAVIS - Director Global-Training
RAE WANG - Director Brand Marketing
JENNIFER RUDE - Director Franchise Development, Franchise Sales; Manager Development, Franchise Sales
SU BACHINGER - Manager Field Marketing

●▲
M B C Subway Inc
1205 W Main St
Manchester, IA 52057-2308

Telephone: (563) 927-3984
Type of Business: Chain Restaurant Operator
Total Sales: $2,458,000 (e)
Total Units: 4
Trade Names: Subway (4)
Units Franchised From: 4
Primary Menu: Sandwiches/Deli (4)
Areas of Operation: IA
Type of Foodservice: Quick Serve (4)
Franchise Affiliation: Doctor's Associates Inc., MILFORD, CT

Key Personnel
MICHAEL B. CRUMPTON - Owner; General Buyer

A & N River City Inc.
2010 S Federal Ave
Mason City, IA 50401-6700

Telephone: (641) 423-6710
Type of Business: Chain Restaurant Operator
Total Sales: $10,239,000 (e)
Total Units: 2
Trade Names: McDonald's (2)
Units Franchised From: 2
Preferred Location Types: Freestanding
Primary Menu: Hamburger (2)
Areas of Operation: IA
Type of Foodservice: Quick Serve (2)
Franchise Affiliation: McDonald's Corporation, CHICAGO, IL

Key Personnel
NANCY CARROLL - President; General Buyer

Domino's Franchisee
125 S Delaware Ave
Mason City, IA 50401-3908

Telephone: (641) 423-2330
Type of Business: Chain Restaurant Operator
Total Sales: $14,025,000 (e)
Total Units: 7
Trade Names: Domino's (7)
Units Franchised From: 7
Primary Menu: Pizza (7)
Areas of Operation: IA
Type of Foodservice: Quick Serve (7)
Franchise Affiliation: Domino's Pizza Inc, ANN ARBOR, MI

Key Personnel
PAUL M. GRITZ - Owner; General Buyer

Land Mark Products Inc.
1007 Okoboji Ave
Milford, IA 51351-1376

Mailing Address: PO Box 188, MILFORD, IA, 51351-0188
Telephone: (712) 338-2771
Fax Number: (712) 338-2263
Internet Homepage: pcpizza.com
Type of Business: Chain Restaurant Operator
Year Founded: 1977
Systemwide Sales: $282,914,000 (e)
Total Sales: $41,020,000 (e)
Number of Employees: 75
Average Check: Lunch(8); Dinner(8)
Total Units: 900

Trade Names: Piccadilly Circus Pizza & Subs (900)
Units Franchised To: 900
Preferred Square Footage: 600
Preferred Location Types: Convenience Store/Gas Station; Freestanding; Grocery Stores; Institution (college/hospital); Parks; Stadiums; Strip Mall; Travel Plazas
Primary Menu: Pizza (900)
Areas of Operation: AK, AL, AR, AZ, CA, CO, FL, GA, IA, ID, IL, IN, KS, KY, LA, ME, MI, MN, MO, MS, MT, NC, ND, NE, NJ, NM, NV, NY, OK, OR, PA, VA, WA, WI, WY
Type of Foodservice: Quick Serve (900)
Catering Services: Yes
Primary Distributors: (Full Line) Farner-Bocken Co., CARROLL, IA
Notes: This company has units in more than 800 convenience stores & other non-traditional locations.

Key Personnel
ROD SIMONSON - CEO
JASON FARRELL - President; Senior VP Operations, Purchasing, Menu Development
CORY ZWEIBAHMER - Director Operations

Subway, Ltd
317 S Main St
Monticello, IA 52310-1704

Telephone: (319) 465-4648
Type of Business: Chain Restaurant Operator
Total Sales: $1,502,000 (e)
Total Units: 2
Trade Names: Subway (2)
Units Franchised From: 2
Primary Menu: Sandwiches/Deli (2)
Areas of Operation: IA
Type of Foodservice: Quick Serve (2)
Franchise Affiliation: Doctor's Associates Inc., MILFORD, CT

Key Personnel
JOHN HARMS - President

A & D Management Co. Inc.
207 E Washington St
Mount Pleasant, IA 52641

Telephone: (319) 385-2214
Fax Number: (319) 385-2025
Type of Business: Chain Restaurant Operator
Year Founded: 1971
Total Sales: $7,254,000 (e)
Alcohol Sales: 2%
Number of Employees: 1,030
Average Check: Lunch(8); Dinner(10)
Total Units: 6
Trade Names: Pizza Hut (6)
Units Franchised From: 6

Preferred Square Footage: 3,000
Preferred Location Types: Freestanding
Alcohol Served: Beer, Wine
Primary Menu: Pizza (6)
Projected Remodelings: 1
Areas of Operation: CO, MN, NE
Type of Foodservice: Fast Casual (6)
Franchise Affiliation: Pizza Hut Inc., PLANO, TX
Primary Distributors: (Full Line) McLane/Memphis, MEMPHIS, TN

Key Personnel
MARVIN DAY - President; Director Operations, Facility/Maintenance, Real Estate, Design, Store Fixtures, Menu Development; General Buyer
KIM EWINGER - Director Information Systems
DIANE MAY - Manager Finance

The Pizza Ranch Inc.
204 19th St SE
Orange City, IA 51041-4400

Telephone: (712) 707-8800
Fax Number: (712) 707-8825
Internet Homepage: pizzaranch.com
Type of Business: Chain Restaurant Operator
Year Founded: 1981
Systemwide Sales: $28,690,000 (e)
Total Sales: $29,660,000 (e)
Alcohol Sales: 1%
Number of Employees: 5,088
Average Check: Lunch(8); Dinner(10)
Internet Order Processing: Yes
Total Units: 212
Trade Names: The Pizza Ranch (212)
Units Franchised To: 212
Preferred Square Footage: 1,200; 5,000
Preferred Location Types: Community Mall; Convenience Store/Gas Station; Downtown; Freestanding; Strip Mall
Alcohol Served: Beer
Primary Menu: Pizza (212)
Projected Openings: 2
Areas of Operation: IA, IL, KS, MI, MN, MT, ND, NE, SD, WI
Type of Foodservice: Casual Dining (212)
Catering Services: Yes
Primary Distributors: (Equipment) TriMark Hockenbergs, OMAHA, NE; (Food) Martin Brothers Distribution Co. Inc., CEDAR FALLS, IA; (Supplies) The Wasserstrom Co., COLUMBUS, OH
Notes: Total sales includes some revenue derived from franchise supplies and merchandise sales, financial services revenue, and volume allowance rebates.

Key Personnel
ADRIE GROENEWEG - President; General Buyer
JON MOSS - COO

MARK SOUBA - Chief Development Officer
DEAN KOOIMA - VP Finance
JEFFREY VAN SCHEPEN - VP Business Development
SCOTT GROENEWEG - VP Business Development
PERRY KROSSCHELL - VP Business Development
JEFF V. SCHEPEN - VP Business Development
BRADY GROENEWEG - General Manager
DONNIE BEAN - General Manager Marketing; Director
KYLE SCHUITEMAN - Director Information Technology
RORY LARSEN - Director Construction
JOHN VANDER STELT - Director Design
KIM JAMER - Director Food Safety
JASON LECHNER - Director Development-Training
GWEN LAHRS - Senior Manager Marketing, Advertising
SEAN LANDRUM - Manager Culinary Development
PAUL ROLLINS - Manager Franchising

Tennyson Enterprises
13133 Angle Rd
Ottumwa, IA 52501-8976

Telephone: (641) 682-8776
Fax Number: (641) 682-2377
Type of Business: Chain Restaurant Operator
Year Founded: 1966
Total Sales: $22,810,000 (e)
Alcohol Sales: 2%
Number of Employees: 725
Total Units: 19
Trade Names: Pizza Hut (17); Sirloin Stockade (2)
Units Franchised From: 19
Preferred Square Footage: 3,000; 5,000
Preferred Location Types: Freestanding
Alcohol Served: Beer, Wine, Liquor
Primary Menu: Pizza (17); Steak (2)
Areas of Operation: IA, IL, MN, MO
Type of Foodservice: Family Restaurant (2); Quick Serve (17)
Franchise Affiliation: Pizza Hut Inc., PLANO, TX; Stockade Companies LLC, ROUND ROCK, TX

Key Personnel
BOB HENDERSON - Controller; Director Information Systems
T. J. WALSH - Director Operations, Marketing, Human Resources, Menu Development

Burrito Builders
156 Gaul Dr
Sergeant Bluff, IA 51054-8963

Telephone: (712) 203-0492
Type of Business: Chain Restaurant Operator
Total Units: 15
Trade Names: Pancheros Mexican Grill (15)
Units Franchised From: 15
Primary Menu: Mexican (15)
Areas of Operation: IA, MO, NE
Type of Foodservice: Casual Dining (15)
Franchise Affiliation: Panchero's Franchise Corporation, CORALVILLE, IA

Key Personnel
DAN HISEROTE - Owner; General Buyer

SIOUX CITY DQ INC
128 Gaul Dr
Sergeant Bluff, IA 51054-8963

Telephone: (712) 943-3733
Fax Number: (712) 943-3734
Internet Homepage: siouxlanddq.com
Type of Business: Chain Restaurant Operator
Total Sales: $16,760,000 (e)
Average Check: Dinner(14)
Total Units: 12
Trade Names: Dairy Queen Store (12)
Units Franchised From: 12
Primary Menu: American (12)
Areas of Operation: IA
Type of Foodservice: Quick Serve (12)
Franchise Affiliation: International Dairy Queen Inc., BLOOMINGTON, MN

Key Personnel
DAN HISEROTE - President; General Buyer

Hueing Inc.
660 N Main Ave
Sioux Center, IA 51250-1826

Telephone: (712) 722-3663
Fax Number: (712) 722-3666
Type of Business: Chain Restaurant Operator
Total Sales: $11,120,000 (e)
Number of Employees: 90
Average Check: Dinner(12)
Total Units: 6
Trade Names: Hardee's (6)
Units Franchised From: 6
Preferred Square Footage: 3,000; 3,500
Preferred Location Types: Freestanding
Primary Menu: Hamburger (6)
Areas of Operation: IA, MN
Type of Foodservice: Quick Serve (6)
Franchise Affiliation: Hardee's Food Systems Inc., FRANKLIN, TN
Primary Distributors: (Food) McLane/Mason City, MASON CITY, IA

Key Personnel
ROD HARTWIG - President; Owner; Manager Information Systems, Supply Chain, Real Estate, Design; General Buyer

James Hanscom, LLC
2121 Hamilton Blvd
Sioux City, IA 51104-4146

Telephone: (712) 239-1683
Fax Number: (712) 239-9167
Type of Business: Chain Restaurant Operator
Total Sales: $1,666,000 (e)
Total Units: 2
Trade Names: Little Caesars Pizza (2)
Units Franchised From: 2
Primary Menu: Pizza (2)
Areas of Operation: IA, NE
Type of Foodservice: Quick Serve (2)
Franchise Affiliation: Little Caesar Enterprises Inc., DETROIT, MI

Key Personnel
JAMES HANSCOM - President; General Buyer

S.E.P. Administration LLC
90 Pierce St
Sioux City, IA 51101-1417

Mailing Address: PO Box 3085, SIOUX CITY, IA, 51102-3085
Telephone: (712) 279-0079
Fax Number: (712) 279-0213
Type of Business: Chain Restaurant Operator
Year Founded: 1997
Total Sales: $11,550,000 (e)
Number of Employees: 105
Average Check: Breakfast(8); Lunch(8); Dinner(8)
Total Units: 5
Trade Names: Burger King (5)
Units Franchised From: 5
Preferred Square Footage: 2,500
Preferred Location Types: Freestanding; Regional Mall
Primary Menu: Hamburger (5)
Areas of Operation: IA, NE
Type of Foodservice: Quick Serve (5)
Franchise Affiliation: Burger King Worldwide Inc., MIAMI, FL
Primary Distributors: (Full Line) Reinhart FoodService, CEDAR RAPIDS, IA

Key Personnel
SHENNEN SALTZMAN - President; General Buyer

JIM WILLEMS - Director Operations

Stanek Inc.
4440 Sergeant Rd
Sioux City, IA 51106-4703

Telephone: (712) 276-8395
Fax Number: (712) 276-4351
Company Email: siouxhardee@yahoo.com
Type of Business: Chain Restaurant Operator
Year Founded: 1968
Total Sales: $5,777,000 (e)
Number of Employees: 150
Average Check: Breakfast(8); Lunch(10); Dinner(10)
Total Units: 3
Trade Names: Hardee's (3)
Units Franchised From: 3
Preferred Square Footage: 3,000; 3,500
Preferred Location Types: Freestanding
Primary Menu: Hamburger (3)
Areas of Operation: IA, NE
Type of Foodservice: Quick Serve (3)
Franchise Affiliation: Hardee's Food Systems Inc., FRANKLIN, TN
Primary Distributors: (Food) McLane/Mason City, MASON CITY, IA

Key Personnel
SHAWN STANEK - President; Director Operations; Manager Finance, Purchasing, Marketing; General Buyer

Nellis Management Company
2940 104th St
Urbandale, IA 50322-3815

Telephone: (515) 252-1742
Fax Number: (515) 252-1743
Internet Homepage: nellismanagement.com
Company Email: info@nellis-nmc.com
Type of Business: Chain Restaurant Operator
Year Founded: 1964
Total Sales: $21,160,000 (e)
Number of Employees: 431
Average Check: Lunch(8); Dinner(8)
Total Units: 20
Trade Names: Long John Silver's (20)
Units Franchised From: 20
Preferred Square Footage: 2,400; 2,500
Preferred Location Types: Freestanding
Primary Menu: American (20); Seafood (20)
Areas of Operation: AZ, IA, IL
Type of Foodservice: Quick Serve (20)
Franchise Affiliation: A&W Restaurants Inc., LEXINGTON, KY; Long John Silver's Inc., LOUISVILLE, KY
Primary Distributors: (Food) McLane/Midwest, DANVILLE, IL

Key Personnel
MARK LEVITT - CEO; President

Raccoon Valley Partners
2900 100th St Ste 103
Urbandale, IA 50322-3841

Telephone: (515) 276-1526
Fax Number: (515) 276-0513
Internet Homepage: rvpmcdonalds.com
Company Email: comments@rfpmcdonalds.com
Type of Business: Chain Restaurant Operator
Year Founded: 2000
Total Sales: $65,680,000 (e)
Number of Employees: 600
Average Check: Breakfast(5); Lunch(8); Dinner(8)
Total Units: 14
Trade Names: McDonald's (14)
Units Franchised From: 14
Preferred Square Footage: 2,500; 3,000
Preferred Location Types: Freestanding
Primary Menu: Hamburger (14)
Areas of Operation: IA
Type of Foodservice: Quick Serve (14)
Franchise Affiliation: McDonald's Corporation, CHICAGO, IL
Primary Distributors: (Food) The Martin-Brower Co. LLC, ROSEMONT, IL

Key Personnel
BILL HABIG - President
STEVEN MATHSON - Partner
MICHAEL KEENAN - Director Technology

G & M Waterloo, Inc
1515 E San Marnan Dr
Waterloo, IA 50702-4300

Telephone: (319) 233-4800
Type of Business: Chain Restaurant Operator
Total Sales: $8,644,000 (e)
Total Units: 7
Trade Names: Jimmy John's Gourmet Sandwich Shop (7)
Units Franchised From: 7
Areas of Operation: IA
Franchise Affiliation: Jimmy John's Franchise LLC, CHAMPAIGN, IL

Key Personnel
MARC MOTZER - Owner

J & M Partnership
2016 Howard Ave
Waterloo, IA 50702-2726

Telephone: (319) 235-1150

Fax Number: (319) 232-5002
Type of Business: Chain Restaurant Operator
Total Sales: $38,270,000 (e)
Number of Employees: 350
Average Check: Breakfast(8); Lunch(8); Dinner(10)
Total Units: 8
Trade Names: McDonald's (8)
Units Franchised From: 8
Preferred Square Footage: 2,500
Preferred Location Types: Freestanding
Primary Menu: Hamburger (8)
Areas of Operation: IA
Type of Foodservice: Quick Serve (8)
Franchise Affiliation: McDonald's Corporation, CHICAGO, IL
Primary Distributors: (Full Line) The Martin-Brower Co. LLC, ROSEMONT, IL

Key Personnel
JOHN FREYBERGER - President; Director Finance, Operations, Purchasing, Information Systems, Supply Chain, Real Estate; General Buyer
LEAH FREYBERGER - Manager Administration

Matco of Waterloo Inc
220 W Ridgeway Ave Ste 105
Waterloo, IA 50701-4200

Telephone: (319) 291-6700
Fax Number: (319) 291-7130
Type of Business: Chain Restaurant Operator
Total Units: 9
Trade Names: Village Inn (9)
Units Franchised From: 9
Primary Menu: American (9)
Areas of Operation: IA
Type of Foodservice: Family Restaurant (9)
Franchise Affiliation: Village Inn, MINNETONKA, MN

Key Personnel
SCOTT BOYER - President

Auntie Anne's Franchise
101 Jordan Creek Pkwy
West Des Moines, IA 50266-8181

Telephone: (515) 223-1345
Type of Business: Chain Restaurant Operator
Total Sales: $2,358,000 (e)
Total Units: 3
Trade Names: Auntie Anne's Hand-Rolled Soft Pretzels (3)
Units Franchised From: 3
Primary Menu: Snacks (3)
Areas of Operation: IA
Type of Foodservice: Quick Serve (3)
Franchise Affiliation: Auntie Anne's Inc.,

LANCASTER, PA

Key Personnel
AMBER BAMBROUGH - Owner; General Buyer

B-Bop's Inc.
939 Office Park Rd Ste 333
West Des Moines, IA 50265-2566

Telephone: (515) 221-3202
Fax Number: (515) 221-3202
Internet Homepage: b-bops.com
Company Email: info@b-bops.com
Type of Business: Chain Restaurant Operator
Year Founded: 1988
Total Sales: $19,180,000 (e)
Number of Employees: 200
Average Check: Lunch(8); Dinner(8)
Total Units: 10
Trade Names: B-Bops (10)
Company-Owned Units: 10
Preferred Square Footage: 950
Preferred Location Types: Freestanding
Primary Menu: Hamburger (10)
Areas of Operation: IA
Type of Foodservice: Quick Serve (10)
Primary Distributors: (Full Line) Martin Brothers Distribution Co. Inc., CEDAR FALLS, IA

Key Personnel
ROBERT JOHNSON - President; General Manager; Executive Chef; General Buyer
JODY JONES - Manager Human Resources

†
Canteen Vending Services
519 S 18th St
West Des Moines, IA 50265-5506

Telephone: (515) 225-6060
Fax Number: (515) 225-6969
Listing Type: Branch Office
Type of Business: Foodservice Management Operator
Year Founded: 1929
Number of Employees: 30
Number of Locations Served: 100
Total Foodservice Mgmt Accounts: 100
Areas of Operation: IA
Type of Foodservice: Vending machines (100)
Foodservice Management Venues: Business & Industry; College & University; Health Care; Military Feeding; Prison Feeding; Schools
Parent Company: Compass Group The Americas, CHARLOTTE, NC
Headquarters: Canteen Vending Services, CHARLOTTE, NC

Key Personnel
MATT HOFFMAN - VP Region

Waterfront Seafood Market Restaurant
2900 University Ave Ste 130
West Des Moines, IA 50266-1203

Telephone: (515) 223-5106
Fax Number: (515) 224-9665
Internet Homepage: waterfrontseafoodmarket.com
Company Email: waterfrontseafood@msn.com
Type of Business: Chain Restaurant Operator
Year Founded: 1983
Total Sales: $3,505,000 (e)
Number of Employees: 75
Average Check: Lunch(10); Dinner(24)
Total Units: 2
Trade Names: Waterfront Seafood Market Restaurant (2)
Company-Owned Units: 2
Preferred Location Types: Freestanding; Strip Mall
Alcohol Served: Beer, Wine, Liquor
Primary Menu: Seafood (2)
Areas of Operation: IA
Type of Foodservice: Casual Dining (2)
Catering Services: Yes
Primary Distributors: (Food) US Foods, CORALVILLE, IA

Key Personnel
TED HANKE - President; General Manager
JENNIFER HAUS - Partner
BLAKE HANKE - Partner
SHAWN HANKE JR - Partner; Manager Catering; General Buyer

IDAHO

●▲
Boise Pizza Inc.
2124 S Broadway Ave
Boise, ID 83706-4205

Telephone: (208) 343-0793
Type of Business: Chain Restaurant Operator
Total Sales: $23,974,000 (e)
Total Units: 12
Trade Names: Domino's (12)
Units Franchised From: 12
Primary Menu: Pizza (12)
Areas of Operation: ID
Type of Foodservice: Quick Serve (12)
Franchise Affiliation: Domino's Pizza Inc, ANN ARBOR, MI

Key Personnel
PHILIP F. MIKELONIS - Owner; General Buyer

†
Canteen Vending Services
11875 W President Dr
Boise, ID 83713

Telephone: (208) 377-8488
Fax Number: (208) 376-9533
Listing Type: Branch Office
Type of Business: Foodservice Management Operator
Year Founded: 1929
Number of Employees: 18
Number of Locations Served: 80
Total Foodservice Mgmt Accounts: 80
Areas of Operation: ID
Type of Foodservice: Vending machines (80)
Foodservice Management Venues: Business & Industry; College & University; Health Care; Travel Plazas
Parent Company: Compass Group The Americas, CHARLOTTE, NC
Headquarters: Canteen Vending Services, CHARLOTTE, NC

Key Personnel
JEFF SEWELL - General Manager; Director Operations

Chicago Connection LLC
7766 W Lemhi St
Boise, ID 83709-2880

Telephone: (208) 323-1231
Internet Homepage: chicagoconnection.com
Type of Business: Chain Restaurant Operator
Year Founded: 1982
Total Sales: $8,440,000 (e)
Alcohol Sales: 2%
Number of Employees: 200
Average Check: Lunch(8); Dinner(12)
Total Units: 8
Trade Names: Chicago Connection (8)
Company-Owned Units: 8
Preferred Square Footage: 3,500
Preferred Location Types: Freestanding; Strip Mall
Alcohol Served: Beer, Wine
Primary Menu: Pizza (8)
Areas of Operation: ID
Type of Foodservice: Casual Dining (8)
Foodservice Management Venues: Schools
Catering Services: Yes
On-site Distribution Center: Yes
Primary Distributors: (Full Line) SYSCO Food Services of Idaho Inc., BOISE, ID

Key Personnel
JOY KEALEY - VP Operations, Marketing; Controller; Director Finance,

Darmody Enterprises
1705 S Milwaukee St
Boise, ID 83709-5149

Telephone: (208) 345-9545
Fax Number: (208) 345-2072
Type of Business: Chain Restaurant Operator
Year Founded: 1999
Total Sales: $105,920,000 (e)
Number of Employees: 1,200
Average Check: Breakfast(8); Lunch(10); Dinner(10)
Total Units: 28
Trade Names: McDonald's (28)
Units Franchised From: 28
Preferred Square Footage: 3,000
Preferred Location Types: Discount Dept. Stores; Freestanding
Primary Menu: Hamburger (28)
Areas of Operation: ID
Type of Foodservice: In-Store Feeder (4); Quick Serve (24)
Franchise Affiliation: McDonald's Corporation, CHICAGO, IL
Primary Distributors: (Full Line) The Martin-Brower Co., SUMNER, WA

Key Personnel
RICHARD DARMODY - President; Partner; Director Supply Chain, Real Estate; General Buyer
RICHARD DARMODY JR - Partner; VP Operations; Director Facility/Maintenance, Design, Store Fixtures
ALAINE BUCKLEY - CFO
DODI JOHNSON - General Manager
BECKY ALEXANDER - Director Marketing

Eddie's Restaurant
7067 W Overland Rd
Boise, ID 83709-1910

Telephone: (208) 377-3340
Fax Number: (208) 377-1097
Internet Homepage: eddies-restaurant.com
Type of Business: Chain Restaurant Operator
Year Founded: 1972
Total Sales: $2,736,000 (e)
Number of Employees: 60
Average Check: Breakfast(8); Lunch(10); Dinner(14)
Total Units: 2
Trade Names: Eddie's Diner (1); Eddie's Restaurant (1)
Company-Owned Units: 2
Preferred Location Types: Freestanding
Primary Menu: American (2)
Areas of Operation: ID
Type of Foodservice: Family Restaurant (2)
Facility/Maintenance, Design, Catering

Primary Distributors: (Food) SYSCO Food Services of Idaho Inc., BOISE, ID

Key Personnel
EDDIE BIRD JR - Partner; Executive Chef; Director Operations
PHIL BIRD - Partner; Manager Accounting, Catering; General Buyer

Subway Franchise
2550 W Explorer Dr
Boise, ID 83713

Telephone: (208) 887-9222
Internet Homepage: subway.com
Type of Business: Chain Restaurant Operator
Total Sales: $16,490,000 (e)
Total Units: 27
Trade Names: Subway (27)
Units Franchised From: 27
Primary Menu: Sandwiches/Deli (27)
Areas of Operation: ID
Type of Foodservice: Quick Serve (27)
Franchise Affiliation: Doctor's Associates Inc., MILFORD, CT

Key Personnel
BOB J. HUCKSTEP - President

The Gyro Shack
5602 W State St
Boise, ID 83703-3010

Telephone: (208) 853-5840
Type of Business: Chain Restaurant Operator
Total Units: 6
Trade Names: The Gyro Shack (6)
Company-Owned Units: 5
Units Franchised To: 1
Primary Menu: Greek/Mediterranean (6)
Areas of Operation: ID

Key Personnel
DOUG MILLER - CEO; Partner
SETH BRINK - Partner; VP Operations

Triple T Enterprises Inc.
408 E 41st St
Boise, ID 83714-6309

Telephone: (208) 433-9596
Fax Number: (208) 433-9588
Internet Homepage: smokymountainpizza.com
Type of Business: Chain Restaurant Operator
Year Founded: 1991
Total Sales: $12,130,000 (e)
Alcohol Sales: 10%
Number of Employees: 222
Average Check: Lunch(8); Dinner(12)
Total Units: 8
Trade Names: Smoky Mountain Pizza & Pasta (8)
Company-Owned Units: 8
Preferred Square Footage: 5,500; 6,000
Preferred Location Types: Freestanding; Strip Mall
Alcohol Served: Beer, Wine, Liquor
Primary Menu: Italian (9)
Areas of Operation: ID, UT
Type of Foodservice: Casual Dining (8)
Catering Services: Yes
Primary Distributors: (Full Line) SYSCO Food Services of Idaho Inc., BOISE, ID

Key Personnel
DAN TODD - President; Partner; Director Finance, Real Estate
TAMARA THIMM - Owner Accounting
GERALD B. TODD - Partner; VP Business Development; Director Purchasing; General Buyer
JOHN RYAN - VP Operations; Director Information Systems, Design, Human Resources
TOM REDING - Director Catering, Menu Development-Beverages

Westside Pizza
8489 W Overland Rd
Boise, ID 83714

Telephone: (208) 322-1000
Internet Homepage: westsidepizza.com
Type of Business: Chain Restaurant Operator
Total Sales: $24,730,000 (e)
Total Units: 40
Trade Names: Westside Pizza (40)
Units Franchised To: 40
Primary Menu: Pizza (40)
Type of Foodservice: Fast Casual (40)

Key Personnel
RODNEY NELSON - President; VP Franchise Development
AARON OLSON - COO
EVA BROWNING - Director Marketing

Pita Pit Inc.
505 E Front Ave
Coeur D Alene, ID 83814-2747

Telephone: (208) 765-3326
Fax Number: (208) 667-7694
Internet Homepage: pitapitusa.com
Company Email: contactus@pitapitusa.com
Type of Business: Chain Restaurant Operator
Year Founded: 1995
Systemwide Sales: $381,865,000 (e)
Total Sales: $12,910,000 (e)
Number of Employees: 27

Average Check: Breakfast(10); Lunch(10); Dinner(10)
Total Units: 169
Trade Names: Pita Pit (600)
Company-Owned Units: 15
Units Franchised To: 585
Preferred Square Footage: 800; 1,000; 1,500
Preferred Location Types: Community Mall; Freestanding; Regional Mall; Strip Mall
Primary Menu: Greek/Mediterranean (600)
Projected Openings: 25
Areas of Operation: AL, AZ, CA, CO, DC, DE, FL, GA, IA, ID, IL, IN, KS, KY, LA, MA, MD, MI, MN, MO, MT, NC, ND, NM, NV, NY, OH, OK, OR, PA, SC, TN, TX, UT, VA, WA, WV
Foreign Countries: AUSTRALIA; BRAZIL; CANADA; ENGLAND; FRANCE; INDIA; IRELAND; NEW ZEALAND; PANAMA; SAUDI ARABIA; SINGAPORE; TRINIDAD & TOBAGO; UNITED ARAB EMIRATES
Type of Foodservice: Quick Serve (600)
Catering Services: Yes

Key Personnel
BRADEN MARTYNIUK - VP Restaurant Operations
LEE STRAIT - VP Legal
MEGHAN HAUGEN - Director Operations

Domino's Franchisee
1700 N Whitley Dr
Fruitland, ID 83619

Telephone: (208) 452-6755
Type of Business: Chain Restaurant Operator
Total Sales: $6,004,000 (e)
Total Units: 3
Trade Names: Domino's (3)
Units Franchised From: 3
Primary Menu: Pizza (3)
Areas of Operation: OR
Type of Foodservice: Quick Serve (3)
Franchise Affiliation: Domino's Pizza Inc, ANN ARBOR, MI

Key Personnel
CHAD R. BITTNER - Owner; General Buyer

Moxie Java International LLC
4990 W Chinden Blvd
Garden City, ID 83714-1407

Telephone: (208) 322-7773
Fax Number: (208) 321-0279
Internet Homepage: moxiejava.com
Company Email: info@moxiejava.com
Type of Business: Chain Restaurant Operator
Year Founded: 1991
Systemwide Sales: $15,961,000 (e)
Total Sales: $4,097,000 (e)
Number of Employees: 18
Average Check: Breakfast(8); Lunch(8); Dinner(8)
Internet Order Processing: Yes
Internet Sales: 1.00%
Total Units: 15
Trade Names: Moxie Java (15)
Units Franchised To: 15
Preferred Square Footage: 1,500; 3,000
Preferred Location Types: Convenience Store/Gas Station; Freestanding; Hotel/Motel; Institution (college/hospital); Office Complex
Primary Menu: Coffee (15)
Areas of Operation: ID, ND, SC
Type of Foodservice: Quick Serve (15)
Distribution Centers: BOISE, ID
On-site Distribution Center: Yes
Primary Distributors: (Full Line) Shamrock Foods, MERIDIAN, ID
Parent Company: Chase Enterprises, BOISE, ID
Notes: The company derives approximately 30% of sales from wholesale coffee to franchisees.

Key Personnel
RICHARD DEAN - CEO; President
RYAN STEWART - CEO; President

Fiesta Ole Inc.
1856 N Yellowstone Hwy
Idaho Falls, ID 83401-1622

Mailing Address: PO Box 1589, IDAHO FALLS, ID, 83403-1589
Telephone: (208) 529-2662
Fax Number: (208) 529-9503
Type of Business: Chain Restaurant Operator
Year Founded: 1989
Systemwide Sales: $8,164,000 (e)
Total Sales: $9,389,000 (e)
Number of Employees: 125
Average Check: Lunch(14); Dinner(26)
Total Units: 4
Trade Names: Fiesta Ole (4)
Company-Owned Units: 2
Units Franchised To: 2
Preferred Square Footage: 1,500; 3,200
Preferred Location Types: Convenience Store/Gas Station; Freestanding
Primary Menu: Mexican (4)
Areas of Operation: ID, UT
Type of Foodservice: Quick Serve (4)
Catering Services: Yes
Primary Distributors: (Full Line) Shamrock Foods, MERIDIAN, ID; (Full Line) SYSCO Food Services of Idaho Inc., BOISE, ID

Key Personnel
JENNIFER OLSEN - President; Owner; General Buyer
TROY SAMMONS - Director Operations

Papa Kelsey's Inc.
2285 E 17th St
Idaho Falls, ID 83404-6512

Telephone: (208) 523-3136
Fax Number: (208) 523-5939
Internet Homepage: papakelseysonline.com
Company Email: papakelseysif@msn.com
Type of Business: Chain Restaurant Operator
Year Founded: 1984
Systemwide Sales: $14,865,000 (e)
Total Sales: $8,982,000 (e)
Number of Employees: 125
Average Check: Lunch(8); Dinner(10)
Total Units: 14
Trade Names: Papa Kelsey's Pizza & Subs (14)
Company-Owned Units: 2
Units Franchised To: 12
Preferred Square Footage: 2,000; 3,000
Preferred Location Types: Freestanding; Strip Mall
Primary Menu: Pizza (14)
Areas of Operation: AZ, CO, UT
Type of Foodservice: Family Restaurant (14)
Foodservice Management Venues: Schools
Primary Distributors: (Equipment) BS&R Equipment Design & Supply Co., TWIN FALLS, ID; (Food) Nicholas & Co. Inc., SALT LAKE CITY, UT; (Supplies) Nicholas & Co. Inc., SALT LAKE CITY, UT

Key Personnel
DANNY KLASSEN - President; Owner; Director Finance, Purchasing, Risk Management, Product Development, Food Safety

S.H. Myers Inc.
1600 E 17th St
Idaho Falls, ID 83404-6366

Telephone: (208) 523-0918
Fax Number: (208) 523-3710
Type of Business: Chain Restaurant Operator
Year Founded: 1994
Total Sales: $32,810,000 (e)
Number of Employees: 75
Average Check: Lunch(16); Dinner(16)
Total Units: 36
Trade Names: Papa Murphy's Take 'N' Bake Pizza (36)
Units Franchised From: 36
Preferred Square Footage: 2,000
Preferred Location Types: Freestanding
Primary Menu: Pizza (36)
Areas of Operation: IA, ID, OR, TN
Type of Foodservice: Quick Serve (36)
Franchise Affiliation: Papa Murphy's International Inc., VANCOUVER, WA

Key Personnel
DAVE MYERS - President; Partner

CLAYTON MYERS - Partner; VP Operations; Director Marketing; General Buyer

SGK Idaho, Inc.
424 S Woodruff Ave
Idaho Falls, ID 83401-4367

Telephone: (208) 528-9489
Type of Business: Chain Restaurant Operator
Total Sales: $20,280,000 (e)
Total Units: 8
Trade Names: Jack in the Box (8)
Units Franchised From: 8
Primary Menu: Hamburger (8)
Areas of Operation: ID
Type of Foodservice: Quick Serve (8)
Franchise Affiliation: Jack in the Box Restaurants, SAN DIEGO, CA

Key Personnel
SIMON KARROUM - Partner; General Buyer
GABRIEL KARROUM - Partner

Golden Cone Inc
505 S Lincoln Ave
Jerome, ID 83338-3026

Telephone: (208) 324-2500
Fax Number: (208) 324-6931
Type of Business: Chain Restaurant Operator
Total Sales: $4,537,000 (e)
Total Units: 3
Trade Names: Dairy Queen Store (3)
Units Franchised From: 3
Primary Menu: Snacks (3)
Areas of Operation: ID
Type of Foodservice: Quick Serve (3)
Franchise Affiliation: International Dairy Queen Inc., BLOOMINGTON, MN

Key Personnel
CON HAYCOCK - President; Partner
DEE HAYCOCK - Partner

Happy Day Restaurants
703 Main St
Lewiston, ID 83501-1835

Telephone: (208) 743-0583
Fax Number: (208) 746-2041
Internet Homepage: happydayrestaurants.com
Company Email: info@happydayrestaurants.com
Type of Business: Chain Restaurant Operator
Year Founded: 1961
Total Sales: $19,380,000 (e)
Alcohol Sales: 5%
Number of Employees: 450
Average Check: Lunch(10); Dinner(20)
Total Units: 13
Trade Names: A&W All American Food (1); Arby's (4); Happy Day Catering (1); Main Street Grill (1); Mystic Cafe (1); Taco Time (3); Tomato Brothers (1); Zany's (1)
Company-Owned Units: 5
Units Franchised From: 8
Preferred Square Footage: 2,300
Preferred Location Types: Freestanding; Strip Mall
Alcohol Served: Beer, Wine, Liquor
Primary Menu: American (4); Italian (1); Miscellaneous (1); Pizza (1); Sandwiches/Deli (4); Taco (3)
Areas of Operation: ID, WA
Type of Foodservice: Casual Dining (3); Family Restaurant (1); Quick Serve (9)
Catering Services: Yes
Franchise Affiliation: A&W Restaurants Inc., LEXINGTON, KY; Arby's Restaurant Group, ATLANTA, GA; Kahala Brands, SCOTTSDALE, AZ
Primary Distributors: (Food) US Foods, SPOKANE, WA; (Supplies) US Foods, SPOKANE, WA

Key Personnel
BRUCE FINCH - President; Director Finance, Operations, Purchasing, Facility/Maintenance, Loss Prevention, Supply Chain, Real Estate, Design, Franchise Development, Store Fixtures, Menu Development, Catering
TOBE FINCH - President
PAT ROGERS - VP Operations; General Buyer
LORI DUFOUR - Director Human Resources
KEN KING - Director Marketing
MIKE COOPER - Manager Information Systems

ES-O-EN Corp.
455 W Amity Rd
Meridian, ID 83642-6921

Mailing Address: PO Box 607, MERIDIAN, ID, 83680-0607
Telephone: (208) 888-6420
Fax Number: (208) 888-6313
Internet Homepage: esoen.com
Company Email: stan@esoen.com
Type of Business: Chain Restaurant Operator
Year Founded: 1976
Total Sales: $80,060,000 (e)
Number of Employees: 1,100
Average Check: Lunch(8); Dinner(8)
Total Units: 29
Trade Names: Taco Bell (29)
Units Franchised From: 29
Preferred Square Footage: 2,500
Preferred Location Types: Freestanding
Primary Menu: Taco (29)
Areas of Operation: ID, OR, UT
Type of Foodservice: Quick Serve (29)
Franchise Affiliation: Taco Bell Corp., IRVINE, CA
Primary Distributors: (Full Line) McLane/Tracy, TRACY, CA

Key Personnel
STANLEY O. NICOLAYSEN - Founder
CARL NICOLAYSEN - CEO; President; Partner; Director Facility/Maintenance, Real Estate

GoodWood Barbecue Company
965 S Industry Way Ste 107
Meridian, ID 83642-9316

Telephone: (208) 895-8640
Fax Number: (208) 362-7890
Internet Homepage: goodwoodbbq.com
Company Email: corporate@goodwoodbbq.com
Type of Business: Chain Restaurant Operator
Total Sales: $9,201,000 (e)
Alcohol Sales: 5%
Number of Employees: 65
Average Check: Lunch(10); Dinner(12)
Total Units: 4
Trade Names: GoodWood Barbecue (4)
Company-Owned Units: 4
Preferred Location Types: Freestanding
Alcohol Served: Beer, Wine, Liquor
Primary Menu: Bar-B-Q (4)
Areas of Operation: ID, UT
Type of Foodservice: Casual Dining (4)
Catering Services: Yes
Primary Distributors: (Full Line) Shamrock Foods, MERIDIAN, ID

Key Personnel
STEVE COOPER - President; Partner

Idaho Pizza Co.
PO Box 610
Meridian, ID 83680-0610

Telephone: (208) 922-1840
Internet Homepage: idahopizzacompany.com
Type of Business: Chain Restaurant Operator
Year Founded: 1998
Total Sales: $13,900,000 (e)
Alcohol Sales: 3%
Average Check: Dinner(14)
Total Units: 16
Trade Names: Idaho Pizza (16)
Company-Owned Units: 7
Units Franchised To: 9
Preferred Location Types: Freestanding; Strip Mall
Alcohol Served: Beer, Wine
Primary Menu: Pizza (16)
Areas of Operation: ID
Type of Foodservice: Casual Dining (16)

Key Personnel
JOHN MCNICHOLL - President; General Buyer
CRAIG QUINTERO - VP Marketing

Ole International Foods
3284 E Pine Ave
Meridian, ID 83642-5922

Telephone: (208) 887-3888
Internet Homepage: cafeole.com
Type of Business: Chain Restaurant Operator
Year Founded: 1981
Total Sales: $2,472,000 (e)
Alcohol Sales: 35%
Number of Employees: 75
Average Check: Lunch(8); Dinner(12)
Total Units: 4
Trade Names: Cafe Ole (2); Golden Corral (2)
Company-Owned Units: 2
Units Franchised From: 2
Preferred Location Types: Freestanding; Office Complex
Alcohol Served: Beer, Wine, Liquor
Primary Menu: American (2); Mexican (2)
Areas of Operation: ID
Type of Foodservice: Casual Dining (4)
Catering Services: Yes
Primary Distributors: (Full Line) SYSCO Food Services of Idaho Inc., BOISE, ID

Key Personnel
JEFF CASEY - President; General Manager; Executive Chef; General Buyer
BRANDT CASEY - Manager Catering

Thomas Cuisine Management
700 E Franklin Rd
Meridian, ID 83642-7992

Telephone: (208) 884-5766
Fax Number: (208) 884-8763
Internet Homepage: thomascuisine.com
Company Email: info@thomascuisine.com
Type of Business: Foodservice Management Operator
Year Founded: 1986
Total Sales: $64,036,000 (e)
Number of Employees: 197
Number of Locations Served: 50
Total Foodservice Mgmt Accounts: 50
Areas of Operation: ID
Type of Foodservice: Cafeteria (50)
Foodservice Management Venues: Business & Industry; Health Care; Other
Primary Distributors: (Full Line) US Foods, OGDEN, UT

Key Personnel
JIM COOPER - VP Business Development

GREG MALMEN - VP Information Technology
MATT THOMAS - Director Information Systems, Risk Management
CHRISTINE KING - Specialist Payroll

Ultimate Scoop, LLC
1400 N Eagle Rd Ste 103
Meridian, ID 83642-9403

Telephone: (208) 895-8336
Company Email: ultimate_scoop@hotmail.com
Type of Business: Chain Restaurant Operator
Total Sales: $2,408,000 (e)
Total Units: 4
Trade Names: Cold Stone Creamery (4)
Units Franchised From: 4
Primary Menu: Snacks (4)
Areas of Operation: ID
Type of Foodservice: Quick Serve (4)
Franchise Affiliation: Kahala Brands, SCOTTSDALE, AZ

Key Personnel
KENT LEE - Partner
NANCY LEE - Partner

Domino's Franchisee
275 Yellowstone Ave
Pocatello, ID 83201-4656

Telephone: (208) 232-4332
Type of Business: Chain Restaurant Operator
Total Sales: $4,047,000 (e)
Total Units: 2
Trade Names: Domino's (2)
Units Franchised From: 2
Primary Menu: Pizza (2)
Areas of Operation: ID
Type of Foodservice: Quick Serve (2)
Franchise Affiliation: Domino's Pizza Inc, ANN ARBOR, MI

Key Personnel
ROBERT O. MEYER - Owner; General Buyer

MMJ
831 Yellowstone Ave
Pocatello, ID 83201-4414

Telephone: (208) 234-0869
Fax Number: (208) 478-1892
Type of Business: Chain Restaurant Operator
Total Sales: $14,797,000 (e)
Total Units: 3
Trade Names: McDonald's (3)
Units Franchised From: 3
Preferred Location Types: Freestanding
Primary Menu: Hamburger (3)
Areas of Operation: ID

Type of Foodservice: Quick Serve (3)
Franchise Affiliation: McDonald's Corporation, CHICAGO, IL

Key Personnel
MARY JOHNSON - Partner; General Buyer
MIKE JOHNSON - Partner; General Buyer
TANICIA GALVAN - Department Manager

The Temple Group, Inc.
475 Yellowstone Ave Ste A
Pocatello, ID 83201-4528

Telephone: (208) 233-4312
Company Email: pocatellocoldstone@gmail.com
Type of Business: Chain Restaurant Operator
Total Sales: $1,811,000 (e)
Total Units: 3
Trade Names: Cold Stone Creamery (3)
Units Franchised From: 3
Primary Menu: Snacks (3)
Areas of Operation: ID
Type of Foodservice: Quick Serve (3)
Franchise Affiliation: Kahala Brands, SCOTTSDALE, AZ

Key Personnel
JEREMIAH TEMPLE - Partner
KASSIE TEMPLE - Partner
JAMIE JOHNSON - Director Business Development

Domino's Franchisee
15640 N Highway 41 Ste 600
Rathdrum, ID 83858-8710

Telephone: (208) 687-3480
Type of Business: Chain Restaurant Operator
Total Sales: $8,068,000 (e)
Total Units: 4
Trade Names: Domino's (4)
Units Franchised From: 4
Primary Menu: Pizza (4)
Areas of Operation: ID
Type of Foodservice: Quick Serve (4)
Franchise Affiliation: Domino's Pizza Inc, ANN ARBOR, MI

Key Personnel
MELISSA A. HIGHTOWER - Owner; General Buyer

Cichos Organization
859 S Yellowstone Hwy Ste 303
Rexburg, ID 83440-5294

Mailing Address: P.O. Box 807, Rexburg, ID, 83440-0807

Telephone: (208) 359-1995
Type of Business: Chain Restaurant Operator
Total Sales: $42,440,000 (e)
Number of Employees: 550
Total Units: 9
Trade Names: McDonald's (9)
Units Franchised From: 9
Preferred Square Footage: 2,500
Preferred Location Types: Convenience Store/Gas Station; Discount Dept. Stores; Freestanding
Primary Menu: Hamburger (9)
Areas of Operation: ID
Type of Foodservice: Quick Serve (9)
Franchise Affiliation: McDonald's Corporation, CHICAGO, IL

Key Personnel
TRENT CICHOS - President; General Buyer

Domino's Franchisee
151 W Main St
Rigby, ID 83442-1435

Telephone: (208) 745-3030
Type of Business: Chain Restaurant Operator
Total Sales: $8,073,000 (e)
Total Units: 4
Trade Names: Domino's (4)
Units Franchised From: 4
Primary Menu: Pizza (4)
Areas of Operation: ID
Type of Foodservice: Quick Serve (4)
Franchise Affiliation: Domino's Pizza Inc, ANN ARBOR, MI

Key Personnel
WESLEY K. WOOD - Owner; General Buyer

Domino's Franchisee
316 5th Ave
Sandpoint, ID 83864-1428

Telephone: (208) 263-6600
Type of Business: Chain Restaurant Operator
Total Sales: $6,219,000 (e)
Total Units: 3
Trade Names: Domino's (3)
Units Franchised From: 3
Primary Menu: Pizza (3)
Areas of Operation: ID
Type of Foodservice: Quick Serve (3)
Franchise Affiliation: Domino's Pizza Inc, ANN ARBOR, MI

Key Personnel
DARREN B. TETACHUK - Owner; General Buyer

Sun Valley Company
1 Sun Valley Rd
Sun Valley, ID 83353

Mailing Address: PO Box 10, SUN VALLEY, ID, 83353-0010
Telephone: (208) 622-4111
Fax Number: (208) 622-3700
Internet Homepage: sunvalley.com
Company Email: ski@sunvalley.com
Type of Business: Foodservice Operations - Hotel/Motels
Year Founded: 1936
Total Sales: $50,337,000 (e)
Alcohol Sales: 20%
Number of Employees: 1,800
Total Units: 1
Restaurants in Hotels: 20
Trade Names: Sun Valley Lodging (1)
Company-Owned Units: 20
Alcohol Served: Beer, Wine, Liquor
Areas of Operation: ID
Type of Foodservice: Casual Dining; Fine Dining
Primary Distributors: (Food) SYSCO Food Services of Iowa Inc., ANKENY, IA; (Specialty Foods) SYSCO Food Services of Iowa Inc., ANKENY, IA
Parent Company: Sinclair Oil Co., SALT LAKE CITY, UT
Notes: The company derives approximately 80% of its revenue from resort operations.

Key Personnel
TIMOTHY SILVA - VP; General Manager; General Buyer
KATHY KERRICK - Controller; Manager Finance, Information Systems
JACK SIBBACH - Director Marketing, Public Relations, Sales
VICTOR SCHOESSLER - Director Operations
BRENT GILLETTE - Director Sales
JUSTIN CAMBIER - Director
MATTHEW PARKE - Manager Operations, Human Resources

Kyle Inc.
261 4th Ave N
Twin Falls, ID 83301-6139

Telephone: (208) 734-5505
Fax Number: (208) 734-5559
Company Email: valley@valleyinc.net
Type of Business: Chain Restaurant Operator
Total Sales: $51,010,000 (e)
Number of Employees: 205
Total Units: 11
Trade Names: McDonald's (11)
Units Franchised From: 11
Preferred Square Footage: 2,500
Primary Menu: Hamburger (11)
Areas of Operation: ID
Type of Foodservice: Quick Serve (11)
Franchise Affiliation: McDonald's Corporation, CHICAGO, IL

Key Personnel
DONNA KYLE - Partner
WILLIAM KYLE - Partner; General Buyer

ILLINOIS

RJ Nelson Enterprises
22W421 Army Trail Rd
Addison, IL 60101-1435

Telephone: (630) 295-9208
Fax Number: (630) 295-9230
Company Email: mcdnelson@aol.com
Type of Business: Chain Restaurant Operator
Year Founded: 1986
Total Sales: $28,440,000 (e)
Number of Employees: 350
Average Check: Breakfast(8); Lunch(10); Dinner(12)
Total Units: 6
Trade Names: McDonald's (6)
Units Franchised From: 6
Preferred Square Footage: 2,500
Preferred Location Types: Freestanding
Primary Menu: Hamburger (6)
Areas of Operation: IL
Type of Foodservice: Quick Serve (6)
Franchise Affiliation: McDonald's Corporation, CHICAGO, IL
Primary Distributors: (Full Line) The Martin-Brower Co. LLC, ROSEMONT, IL

Key Personnel
RAYMOND NELSON - President; Partner; Director Finance, Operations, Facility/Maintenance, Information Systems, Supply Chain, Real Estate, Human Resources; General Buyer

The Portillo Food Service Distribution Center
380 S Rohlwing Rd
Addison, IL 60101-3030

Telephone: (630) 620-0460
Fax Number: (630) 620-5012
Listing Type: Distribution Center
Type of Business: Chain Restaurant Operator
Number of Employees: 50
Areas of Operation: IL
Parent Company: The Portillo Restaurant Group, OAK BROOK, IL

Key Personnel
JORGE BURMUDEZ - General Manager; General Buyer

PFC Classic Dining Restaurant Group
2380 Esplanade Dr Ste 203
Algonquin, IL 60102-5463

Telephone: (815) 356-8004
Fax Number: (847) 458-2446
Internet Homepage: pfcclassicdining.com
Company Email: info@pfcclassicdining.com
Type of Business: Chain Restaurant Operator
Year Founded: 1992
Total Sales: $86,984,000 (e)
Alcohol Sales: 1%
Number of Employees: 1,350
Average Check: Breakfast(12); Lunch(14); Dinner(16)
Total Units: 28
Trade Names: Denny's (27); Ruby Tuesday (1)
Units Franchised From: 28
Preferred Square Footage: 3,000; 5,000
Preferred Location Types: Freestanding
Alcohol Served: Beer, Wine, Liquor
Primary Menu: American (28)
Areas of Operation: IL, IN, WI
Type of Foodservice: Casual Dining (1); Family Restaurant (27)
Franchise Affiliation: Denny's Corporation, SPARTANBURG, SC
Primary Distributors: (Full Line) McLane/Fast Food Merchandisers, TAYLORVILLE, IL
Notes: PFC Classic Dining Restaurant Group also operates as RT Holdings of Southern Wisconsin LLC.

Key Personnel
AMY HORTON - Coordinator Human Resources

Condesa del Mar
12220 S Cicero Ave
Alsip, IL 60803-2947

Telephone: (708) 371-7000
Fax Number: (708) 371-7005
Internet Homepage: chateaudelmar.com; condesadelmar.com; hhcountryclub.com
Type of Business: Chain Restaurant Operator
Year Founded: 1975
Total Sales: $7,481,000 (e)
Alcohol Sales: 35%
Number of Employees: 200
Average Check: Breakfast(14); Lunch(20); Dinner(26)
Total Units: 2
Trade Names: Hickory Hills Country Club (1); PGN Village Inn (1)
Company-Owned Units: 2
Preferred Location Types: Freestanding; Mixed-use Center
Alcohol Served: Beer, Wine, Liquor
Primary Menu: American (2)
Areas of Operation: IL
Type of Foodservice: Casual Dining (2)
Foodservice Management Venues: Schools
Primary Distributors: (Equipment) Edward Don & Co., WOODRIDGE, IL; (Food) SYSCO Food Services of Chicago Inc., DES PLAINES, IL; (Supplies) Edward Don & Co., WOODRIDGE, IL

Key Personnel
NANCY GIANNAKAS - President; Controller; Manager Human Resources
ELIZABETH ANGOBALDO - Manager Culinary Operations-Beverages

JV Enterprises of Illinois, Inc.
101 S East St Ste C
Annawan, IL 61234-7710

Mailing Address: P.O. Box 308, Annawan, IL, 61234
Telephone: (309) 935-5959
Fax Number: (309) 935-5969
Internet Homepage: jvpizzahut.com
Company Email: tlay@jvpizzahut.com
Type of Business: Chain Restaurant Operator
Year Founded: 1972
Total Sales: $17,220,000 (e)
Alcohol Sales: 2%
Number of Employees: 510
Average Check: Lunch(18); Dinner(24)
Internet Order Processing: Yes
Internet Sales: 1.00%
Total Units: 14
Trade Names: Pizza Hut (14)
Units Franchised From: 14
Preferred Square Footage: 4,200
Preferred Location Types: Freestanding
Alcohol Served: Beer, Wine
Primary Menu: Pizza (14)
Areas of Operation: IL
Type of Foodservice: Fast Casual (14)
Foodservice Management Venues: Schools
Catering Services: Yes
Franchise Affiliation: Pizza Hut Inc., PLANO, TX
Primary Distributors: (Full Line) McLane/Sturtevant, STURTEVANT, WI

Key Personnel
JOHN ADDIS - President; Director Operations, Facility/Maintenance, Supply Chain, Design; Buyer Beverages, Foodservice Equip/Supplies
TRINO GOMEZ - General Manager
MARY JO BURRIS - General Manager
DEA KEITH - General Manager
RANDY ADDIS - Director Information Systems

Antioch Pizza Shop
994 Il Route 59
Antioch, IL 60002

Telephone: (847) 395-6777
Internet Homepage: antiochpizzashop.com
Type of Business: Chain Restaurant Operator
Year Founded: 1977
Total Sales: $4,481,000 (e)
Total Units: 7
Trade Names: Antioch Pizza Shop (7)
Company-Owned Units: 1
Units Franchised To: 6
Primary Menu: Pizza (7)
Type of Foodservice: Casual Dining (7)

Key Personnel
KAREN WICKLEIN - President; Owner
ART WICKLEIN - Owner
KEITH NIEZE - Director Franchise Development

Harold's Chicken Shacks
3577 E New York St
Aurora, IL 60504

Mailing Address: PO Box 1822, Matterson, IL,
Telephone: (877) 360-9527
Type of Business: Chain Restaurant Operator
Year Founded: 1950
Systemwide Sales: $44,340,000 (e)
Total Sales: $7,329,000 (e)
Number of Employees: 10
Average Check: Lunch(10); Dinner(16)
Total Units: 30
Trade Names: Harold's Chicken Shack (30)
Company-Owned Units: 3
Units Franchised To: 27
Preferred Square Footage: 2,200
Preferred Location Types: Downtown; Freestanding
Primary Menu: Chicken (30)
Projected Openings: 1
Areas of Operation: GA, IA, IL, IN
Type of Foodservice: Quick Serve (30)
Catering Services: Yes

Key Personnel
KRISTEN PIERCE - CEO; President

Schmitt Management Corporation
1975 W Downer Pl Ste 302
Aurora, IL 60506-4481

Telephone: (630) 892-4552
Fax Number: (630) 892-4670
Type of Business: Chain Restaurant Operator

Year Founded: 1987
Total Sales: $81,350,000 (e)
Number of Employees: 600
Average Check: Breakfast(8); Lunch(8); Dinner(10)
Total Units: 17
Trade Names: McDonald's (17)
Units Franchised From: 17
Preferred Square Footage: 3,300
Preferred Location Types: Convenience Store/Gas Station; Freestanding; Regional Mall
Primary Menu: Hamburger (17)
Areas of Operation: IL
Type of Foodservice: Quick Serve (17)
Franchise Affiliation: McDonald's Corporation, CHICAGO, IL

Key Personnel
RICHARD SCHMITT - Partner; Manager Operations, Purchasing, Supply Chain; General Buyer

Lujac Inc.
1313 N State St
Belvidere, IL 61008-2002

Telephone: (815) 544-0141
Type of Business: Chain Restaurant Operator
Total Sales: $10,291,000 (e)
Total Units: 2
Trade Names: McDonald's (2)
Units Franchised From: 2
Primary Menu: Hamburger (2)
Areas of Operation: IL
Type of Foodservice: Quick Serve (2)
Franchise Affiliation: McDonald's Corporation, CHICAGO, IL

Key Personnel
MAUREEN KOTELES - President; General Buyer

Preferred Meal Systems
5240 Saint Charles Rd
Berkeley, IL 60163-1341

Telephone: (708) 318-2500
Fax Number: (708) 493-2690
Internet Homepage: preferredmeals.com
Company Email: sales@preferredmeals.com
Type of Business: Foodservice Management Operator
Year Founded: 1967
Total Sales: $121,205,000 (e)
Number of Employees: 700
Number of Locations Served: 160
Total Foodservice Mgmt Accounts: 160
Areas of Operation: IL
Type of Foodservice: Cafeteria (160)
Foodservice Management Venues: Health Care; Schools; Transportation
Primary Distributors: (Full Line) US Foods New York Metro, PERTH AMBOY, NJ

Key Personnel
DAVID GOLDFARB - Senior VP Purchasing
JIM DRUGG - VP Marketing, Sales

Mr. Submarine, Inc.
6341 26th St
Berwyn, IL 60402-2607

Telephone: (708) 795-0800
Fax Number: (708) 461-9384
Internet Homepage: mrsubchicago.com
Type of Business: Chain Restaurant Operator
Year Founded: 1975
Systemwide Sales: $12,225,000 (e)
Total Sales: $2,148,000 (e)
Number of Employees: 240
Total Units: 25
Trade Names: Mr. Submarine (25)
Units Franchised To: 25
Preferred Square Footage: 3,000
Preferred Location Types: Community Mall; Freestanding
Primary Menu: Sandwiches/Deli (25)
Areas of Operation: IL
Type of Foodservice: Quick Serve (25)
Catering Services: Yes

Key Personnel
JOHN KALADIS - VP Purchasing; Controller; General Manager
DENISE TZOUMAS - Treasurer; Manager Human Resources

Paisans Pizza
6226 Ogden Ave
Berwyn, IL 60402

Telephone: (708) 484-5325
Internet Homepage: paisanspizza.com
Company Email: INFO@PAISANSPIZZA.COM
Type of Business: Chain Restaurant Operator
Year Founded: 1985
Total Units: 7
Trade Names: Paisans Pizza (7)
Company-Owned Units: 7
Primary Menu: Pizza (7)
Type of Foodservice: Casual Dining (7)

Key Personnel
PETE FEJZULOSKI - Owner

Slice Factory
6900 Ogden Ave
Berwyn, IL 60402

Telephone: (708) 788-1700
Internet Homepage: theslicefactory.com
Type of Business: Chain Restaurant Operator
Year Founded: 1998
Systemwide Sales: $9,932,000 (e)
Total Sales: $5,716,000 (e)
Total Units: 9
Trade Names: Slice Factory (9)
Company-Owned Units: 1
Units Franchised To: 8
Primary Menu: Pizza (9)
Projected Openings: 2
Type of Foodservice: Fast Casual (9)

Key Personnel
DOMENICO DIDIANA - Founder; President
SILVANA DI DIANA - Owner

The Buona Companies
6801 Roosevelt Rd
Berwyn, IL 60402-1019

Telephone: (708) 749-5424
Fax Number: (708) 749-5429
Internet Homepage: buona.com
Company Email: buona@buona.com
Type of Business: Chain Restaurant Operator
Year Founded: 1986
Total Sales: $60,870,000 (e)
Alcohol Sales: 7%
Number of Employees: 1,118
Average Check: Lunch(14); Dinner(20)
Internet Order Processing: Yes
Internet Sales: 3.00%
Total Units: 26
Trade Names: Barbakoa (1); Brett Favre's Steakhouse (1); Buona (24)
Company-Owned Units: 26
Preferred Square Footage: 5,500; 6,000
Preferred Location Types: Freestanding
Alcohol Served: Beer, Wine
Primary Menu: Latin American/Cuban (1); Sandwiches/Deli (24); Steak (1)
Areas of Operation: IL
Type of Foodservice: Casual Dining (2); Fast Casual (24)
Catering Services: Yes
Distribution Centers: BERWYN, IL
On-site Distribution Center: Yes
Primary Distributors: (Full Line) US Foods, STREATOR, IL

Key Personnel
CARLO BUONAVOLANTO - Owner
NICK ARAUJO - CFO
JOE BUONAVOLANTO SR - Director Real Estate, Menu Development

JOSEPH BUONAVOLANTO JR - Director Purchasing
DOMINIC FALLARA - Director Operations
MIKE IOVINELLI - Director Catering
MARK KEARINS - Director Information Technology
JOHN KERNS - Director Accounting

Canteen Vending Services
171 Covington Dr
Bloomingdale, IL 60108-3107

Telephone: (630) 833-3666
Fax Number: (630) 832-3927
Listing Type: Divisional Office
Type of Business: Foodservice Management Operator
Year Founded: 1928
Number of Employees: 180
Number of Locations Served: 200
Total Foodservice Mgmt Accounts: 200
Areas of Operation: IL
Type of Foodservice: Cafeteria (200)
Foodservice Management Venues: Business & Industry
Primary Distributors: (Equipment) Edward Don & Co., WOODRIDGE, IL; (Food) Gordon Food Service Inc., WYOMING, MI; (Supplies) Edward Don & Co., WOODRIDGE, IL
Parent Company: Compass Group PLC, LONDON, ENG
Headquarters: Compass Group The Americas, CHARLOTTE, NC

Key Personnel
ROGER SWEENEY - General Manager
CARON AIKEN - Director Field Marketing
ANDREW BITTLEMANN - Regional Director
CHRIS MCCARTEY - Manager Region

Biaggi's
1705 Clearwater Ave
Bloomington, IL 61704-2200

Telephone: (309) 664-2148
Fax Number: (309) 664-2149
Internet Homepage: biaggis.com
Company Email: info@biaggis.com
Type of Business: Chain Restaurant Operator
Year Founded: 1998
Total Sales: $75,900,000 (e)
Alcohol Sales: 25%
Number of Employees: 1,836
Average Check: Lunch(20); Dinner(34)
Internet Order Processing: Yes
Internet Sales: 4.00%
Total Units: 17
Trade Names: Biaggi's Ristorante Italiano (17)
Company-Owned Units: 17
Preferred Square Footage: 8,300; 9,400
Preferred Location Types: Freestanding; Other
Alcohol Served: Beer, Wine, Liquor
Primary Menu: Italian (17)
Projected Openings: 1
Areas of Operation: CO, IA, IL, IN, MN, MS, NE, NY, OH, WI
Type of Foodservice: Casual Dining (17)
Catering Services: Yes
Primary Distributors: (Full Line) TPC Cash & Carry, DAVENPORT, IA

Key Personnel
TODD HOVENDEN - Founder; CEO
JOHN BUESCHER - Partner
MONICA GADIENT - Partner
CRAIG GAREISS - Partner
JIM JACKSON - VP Operations; Director Facility/Maintenance, Real Estate, Region
KEVIN REED - VP Operations
PAM VALENTA - VP Construction, Design
PAUL KATZ - Executive Chef
JON LUCKMAN - Director Information Technology
MARK MCCAIN - Director Purchasing
DAVID MORRIS - Director Human Resources
BRIAN POE - Director Operations
AMY GODDARD - Director Marketing
CLAY BAXTER - Director Operations, Facility/Maintenance, Real Estate, Region
ADRIAN T - Director
ROBYN JONES - Director Human Resources
DEREK ROETZER - Manager Restaurant Operations

Canteen Vending Services
208 S Robinson St
Bloomington, IL 61701-5432

Telephone: (309) 821-9501
Fax Number: (309) 821-0116
Listing Type: Branch Office
Type of Business: Foodservice Management Operator
Year Founded: 1929
Number of Employees: 42
Number of Locations Served: 800
Total Foodservice Mgmt Accounts: 125
Areas of Operation: IL
Type of Foodservice: Vending machines (125)
Foodservice Management Venues: Business & Industry; College & University
Primary Distributors: (Food) Vistar Illinois, BOLINGBROOK, IL
Parent Company: Compass Group The Americas, CHARLOTTE, NC
Headquarters: Canteen Vending Services, CHARLOTTE, NC

Key Personnel
TAMMY HALL - General Manager; General Buyer

Miller Group
206 N Williamsburg Dr
Bloomington, IL 61704-3571

Mailing Address: PO Box 1526, BLOOMINGTON, IL, 61702-1526
Telephone: (309) 662-8428
Fax Number: (309) 663-6492
Internet Homepage: mgarbys.com
Type of Business: Chain Restaurant Operator
Year Founded: 1997
Total Sales: $30,040,000 (e)
Number of Employees: 547
Average Check: Lunch(12); Dinner(14)
Total Units: 16
Trade Names: Arby's (16)
Units Franchised From: 16
Preferred Square Footage: 2,600
Preferred Location Types: Convenience Store/Gas Station; Freestanding; Strip Mall
Primary Menu: Sandwiches/Deli (16)
Areas of Operation: IL, VA
Type of Foodservice: Quick Serve (16)
Franchise Affiliation: Arby's Restaurant Group, ATLANTA, GA
Primary Distributors: (Full Line) McLane/Rocky Mount, ROCKY MOUNT, NC

Key Personnel
GLENN MILLER - CEO; Partner
IAN MILLER - President; Partner; Director Finance, Real Estate, Human Resources
EVAN JACOBS - Director Acquisitions

A.P.G. Enterprise Inc.
12660 Western Ave
Blue Island, IL 60406-1725

Telephone: (708) 239-1323
Fax Number: (708) 389-3655
Internet Homepage: beggarspizza.com
Company Email: info@beggarspizza.com
Type of Business: Chain Restaurant Operator
Year Founded: 1976
Systemwide Sales: $36,947,000 (e)
Total Sales: $37,260,000 (e)
Alcohol Sales: 5%
Number of Employees: 500
Average Check: Lunch(14); Dinner(16)
Internet Order Processing: Yes
Total Units: 25
Trade Names: Beggars Pizza (25)
Company-Owned Units: 16
Units Franchised To: 9
Preferred Square Footage: 3,000
Preferred Location Types: Freestanding; Strip Mall
Alcohol Served: Beer
Primary Menu: Pizza (25)
Areas of Operation: IL, IN
Type of Foodservice: Casual Dining (25)

Catering Services: Yes
On-site Distribution Center: Yes
Primary Distributors: (Full Line) Gordon Food Service Inc., WYOMING, MI

Key Personnel
PETER A. GARETTO - President; Executive Chef; Director Information Systems, Catering; General Buyer
BRET ALLEN - Owner
AL GERDES - Owner
LARRY H. GARETTO - Partner; VP Finance, Operations, Purchasing, Facility/Maintenance, Marketing, Advertising, Real Estate, Design, Human Resources, Store Fixtures; Controller
CHERYL GARETTO - Partner; Director Human Resources
AMANDA GARETTO - Partner; Director Accounting

All Star Management
389 William R Latham Sr Dr Ste 2
Bourbonnais, IL 60914-2084

Telephone: (815) 929-9726
Fax Number: (815) 929-9737
Type of Business: Chain Restaurant Operator
Year Founded: 1989
Total Sales: $96,650,000 (e)
Number of Employees: 1,295
Average Check: Breakfast(8); Lunch(10); Dinner(10)
Total Units: 36
Trade Names: Wendy's Old Fashioned Hamburgers (36)
Units Franchised From: 36
Preferred Square Footage: 3,000
Preferred Location Types: Freestanding
Primary Menu: Hamburger (36)
Projected Openings: 1
Areas of Operation: IL
Type of Foodservice: Quick Serve (36)
Franchise Affiliation: The Wendy's Company, DUBLIN, OH
Primary Distributors: (Full Line) Maines Paper & Food Service Chicago, HANOVER PARK, IL

Key Personnel
MIKE ALLEGRO - President; CFO; General Manager Purchasing, Real Estate, Human Resources; Manager Information Technology; General Buyer

G.K.A.M.A.
9 Briarcliff Prof Ctr Ste A
Bourbonnais, IL 60914-2429

Telephone: (815) 932-8012
Fax Number: (815) 937-7994
Type of Business: Chain Restaurant Operator
Year Founded: 1955
Total Sales: $37,980,000 (e)
Number of Employees: 465
Average Check: Breakfast(8); Lunch(8); Dinner(8)
Total Units: 8
Trade Names: McDonald's (8)
Units Franchised From: 8
Preferred Square Footage: 3,000
Preferred Location Types: Freestanding
Primary Menu: Hamburger (8)
Areas of Operation: IL
Type of Foodservice: Quick Serve (8)
Franchise Affiliation: McDonald's Corporation, CHICAGO, IL

Key Personnel
JUDITH LINMAN - President
LAWRENCE LINMAN - Owner; General Buyer
JIM KHALILI - Director Operations

Monical Pizza Corporation
530 N Kinzie Ave
Bradley, IL 60915-1225

Telephone: (815) 937-1890
Fax Number: (815) 937-9828
Internet Homepage: monicals.com
Company Email: comments@monicals.com
Type of Business: Chain Restaurant Operator
Year Founded: 1959
Systemwide Sales: $65,907,000 (e)
Total Sales: $47,406,000 (e)
Alcohol Sales: 8%
Number of Employees: 1,071
Average Check: Lunch(10); Dinner(14)
Internet Order Processing: Yes
Internet Sales: 2.00%
Total Units: 63
Trade Names: Monical's Pizza (63)
Company-Owned Units: 30
Units Franchised To: 33
Preferred Square Footage: 4,000
Preferred Location Types: Freestanding; Strip Mall
Alcohol Served: Beer, Wine
Primary Menu: Pizza (63)
Areas of Operation: IL, IN, MO, WI
Type of Foodservice: Fast Casual (63)
Foodservice Management Venues: Schools

Key Personnel
HARRY BOND - Chairman
JANELLE REENTS - President; CFO; Director Finance, Real Estate
DONNA JAKOB - COO
DOUG DAVIS - Coordinator Information Systems
TERRY PAPPAS - Coordinator Training
CHIP ROREM - Coordinator Architecture
JULIE DEYOUNG - Coordinator

R & B 421, Inc.
422 N Kennedy Dr
Bradley, IL 60915-1536

Telephone: (815) 933-8734
Company Email: arbys2003@yahoo.com
Type of Business: Chain Restaurant Operator
Total Sales: $4,015,000 (e)
Average Check: Dinner(12)
Total Units: 2
Trade Names: Arby's (2)
Units Franchised From: 2
Primary Menu: Sandwiches/Deli (2)
Areas of Operation: IL
Type of Foodservice: Quick Serve (2)
Franchise Affiliation: Arby's Restaurant Group, ATLANTA, GA

Key Personnel
GAIL SANDERS - Manager Administration; General Buyer

The Patio Restaurants Inc.
7216 W 91st St
Bridgeview, IL 60455-2174

Telephone: (708) 430-1313
Fax Number: (708) 430-1325
Internet Homepage: patioribs.com
Company Email: office@patiofoodgroup.com
Type of Business: Chain Restaurant Operator
Total Sales: $10,520,000 (e)
Alcohol Sales: 10%
Number of Employees: 300
Average Check: Lunch(14); Dinner(16)
Internet Order Processing: Yes
Internet Sales: 0.50%
Total Units: 6
Trade Names: The Patio Restaurant (6)
Company-Owned Units: 6
Preferred Location Types: Freestanding; Strip Mall
Alcohol Served: Beer, Wine
Primary Menu: Bar-B-Q (6)
Areas of Operation: IL
Type of Foodservice: Casual Dining (6)
Catering Services: Yes
Primary Distributors: (Full Line) US Foods, BENSENVILLE, IL

Key Personnel
JOHN KOLIOPOULOS - President; Partner; General Manager; Executive Chef; General Buyer
JANET KOLIOPOULOS - Partner; Manager Human Resources
MARIA TAGLER - Director Operations

Domino's Franchisee
133 N Arlington Heights Rd
Buffalo Grove, IL 60089-1781

Telephone: (847) 459-1803
Type of Business: Chain Restaurant Operator
Total Sales: $26,163,000 (e)
Total Units: 13
Trade Names: Domino's (13)
Units Franchised From: 13
Primary Menu: Pizza (13)
Areas of Operation: IL
Type of Foodservice: Quick Serve (13)
Franchise Affiliation: Domino's Pizza Inc, ANN ARBOR, MI

Key Personnel
JAMES W. GRONEMANN - Owner; General Buyer

Lindy Gertie Enterprises, Inc.
8437 S Park Ave
Burr Ridge, IL 60527-6343

Telephone: (630) 308-3759
Fax Number: (630) 323-5449
Internet Homepage: lindyschili.com
Company Email: info@lindyschili.com
Type of Business: Chain Restaurant Operator
Year Founded: 1985
Systemwide Sales: $10,010,000 (e)
Total Sales: $3,429,000 (e)
Alcohol Sales: 10%
Number of Employees: 265
Average Check: Lunch(14); Dinner(16)
Total Units: 7
Trade Names: Lindy's Chili & Gertie's Ice Cream (7)
Units Franchised To: 7
Preferred Square Footage: 10,000
Preferred Location Types: Downtown; Office Complex; Regional Mall; Strip Mall
Primary Menu: American (7)
Areas of Operation: IL
Type of Foodservice: Casual Dining (7)
Primary Distributors: (Food) Pancho Food Products, TINLEY PARK, IL

Key Personnel
JOSEPH YESUTIS - President; Partner; Director Purchasing, Menu Development
LYNN YESUTIS - Partner; Controller; Manager Operations; General Buyer

Nando Corporation
943 River Oaks Dr
Calumet City, IL 60409-5150

Telephone: (708) 891-2393
Fax Number: (708) 891-1238
Internet Homepage: pepes.com
Type of Business: Chain Restaurant Operator
Total Sales: $4,695,000 (e)
Total Units: 3
Trade Names: Pepe's Mexican Restaurant (3)
Units Franchised From: 3
Primary Menu: Mexican (3)
Areas of Operation: IL
Type of Foodservice: Casual Dining (3)
Franchise Affiliation: Pepe's Inc., CHICAGO, IL

Key Personnel
SANTIAGO VACA - Owner; General Buyer
PETER WINKLER - Senior Manager Digital Marketing

C-Mac
18010 William Rd
Carlyle, IL 62231-1265

Telephone: (618) 594-4474
Fax Number: (618) 594-4645
Type of Business: Chain Restaurant Operator
Total Sales: $24,110,000 (e)
Number of Employees: 200
Total Units: 5
Trade Names: McDonald's (5)
Units Franchised From: 5
Preferred Square Footage: 2,500
Preferred Location Types: Convenience Store/Gas Station; Freestanding
Primary Menu: Hamburger (5)
Areas of Operation: IL
Type of Foodservice: Quick Serve (5)
Franchise Affiliation: McDonald's Corporation, CHICAGO, IL

Key Personnel
DAVE EMBRY - President; General Buyer

Cjdq Inc
104 E Plaza Dr
Carterville, IL 62918-1973

Mailing Address: PO Box 327, CARTERVILLE, IL, 62918-0327
Telephone: (618) 985-3362
Fax Number: (618) 985-3860
Company Email: dairyqueen11246@gmail.com
Type of Business: Chain Restaurant Operator
Total Sales: $4,429,000 (e)
Average Check: Dinner(14)
Total Units: 3
Trade Names: Dairy Queen (3)
Units Franchised From: 3
Primary Menu: Snacks (3)
Areas of Operation: IL
Type of Foodservice: Quick Serve (3)
Franchise Affiliation: International Dairy Queen Inc., BLOOMINGTON, MN

Key Personnel
CHARLES E. STEVENS - President; General Buyer

Domino's Franchisee
701 S Greenbriar Rd
Carterville, IL 62918-1694

Telephone: (618) 985-3030
Type of Business: Chain Restaurant Operator
Total Sales: $8,121,000 (e)
Total Units: 4
Trade Names: Domino's (4)
Units Franchised From: 4
Primary Menu: Pizza (4)
Areas of Operation: IL
Type of Foodservice: Quick Serve (4)
Franchise Affiliation: Domino's Pizza Inc, ANN ARBOR, MI

Key Personnel
EARL D. BARWIG - Owner; General Buyer

Franchise Management Systems Inc.
4102 Fieldstone Rd Ste A
Champaign, IL 61822

Telephone: (217) 356-1359
Fax Number: (217) 356-4051
Internet Homepage: arbystogo.com
Type of Business: Chain Restaurant Operator
Year Founded: 1966
Total Sales: $30,400,000 (e)
Number of Employees: 502
Average Check: Lunch(8); Dinner(8)
Total Units: 16
Trade Names: Arby's (16)
Units Franchised From: 16
Preferred Square Footage: 2,300
Preferred Location Types: Freestanding
Primary Menu: Sandwiches/Deli (16)
Areas of Operation: IA, IL
Type of Foodservice: Quick Serve (16)
Franchise Affiliation: Arby's Restaurant Group, ATLANTA, GA

Key Personnel
RANDY G. TUCKER - President; Owner; Director Operations; General Buyer
BOB MCQUEEN - CFO; VP; Director Finance
DAVID TORBECK - Director Information Systems, Marketing, Advertising

Jimmy John's Franchise LLC
2212 Fox Dr
Champaign, IL 61820-7532

Telephone: (217) 356-9900
Fax Number: (217) 359-2956
Internet Homepage: jimmyjohns.com
Company Email: feedback@jimmyjohns.com
Listing Type: Subsidiary
Type of Business: Chain Restaurant Operator
Year Founded: 1983
Systemwide Sales: $3,015,447,000 (e)
Total Sales: $195,980,000 (e)
Number of Employees: 1,300
Average Check: Lunch(10); Dinner(10)
Internet Order Processing: Yes
Internet Sales: 2.00%
Total Units: 2,671
Trade Names: Jimmy John's Gourmet Sandwich Shop (2,671)
Company-Owned Units: 55
Units Franchised To: 2,616
Preferred Square Footage: 800; 1,600
Preferred Location Types: Convenience Store/Gas Station; Downtown; Freestanding; Regional Mall; Strip Mall
Primary Menu: Sandwiches/Deli (2,671)
Projected Openings: 50
Areas of Operation: AL, AR, AZ, CA, CO, DC, FL, GA, IA, ID, IL, IN, KS, KY, LA, MD, MI, MN, MO, MS, MT, NC, ND, NE, NJ, NV, NY, OH, OK, OR, PA, SC, SD, TN, TX, UT, VA, WA, WI, WV, WY
Type of Foodservice: Quick Serve (2,671)
Catering Services: Yes
Parent Company: Inspire Brands, ATLANTA, GA

Key Personnel
JAMES "JIMMY" J. LIAUTAUD - Chairman; Founder
JAMES NORTH - President
DARIN DUGAN - Chief Marketing Officer
TIM ASIRE - Chief Compliance Officer
MARK FONGER - VP
ANDY MIES - VP Operations
JASON NIELSEN - VP Payroll
PAM HIRSCH - Controller
LISA GARBER - Director Logistics
STEPHEN RUTLEDGE - Director Operations, Marketing
KEVIN SHORT - Director Construction, Design, Store Fixtures
KIMBERLY SMITH - Director Training
WILL THOMAS - Director Information Technology
JEFFREY VAUGHAN - Director Finance

La Bamba Mexican Restaurants Group
1905 Glenn Park Dr
Champaign, IL 61821-2458

Telephone: (217) 355-2888
Fax Number: (217) 355-0613
Internet Homepage: labambaburritos.com
Company Email: info@labambaburritos.com
Type of Business: Chain Restaurant Operator
Year Founded: 1987
Total Sales: $10,250,000 (e)
Number of Employees: 100
Average Check: Lunch(10); Dinner(14)
Internet Order Processing: Yes
Total Units: 8
Trade Names: La Bamba (8)
Company-Owned Units: 8
Preferred Square Footage: 2,200
Preferred Location Types: Community Mall; Downtown; Freestanding
Primary Menu: Mexican (8)
Areas of Operation: IL, IN, KY, WI
Type of Foodservice: Fast Casual (8)
Primary Distributors: (Full Line) Sorce Enterprises, EAST PEORIA, IL

Key Personnel
ANTONIO AGUAS - Partner; Controller; General Manager; Executive Chef; Director Marketing; General Buyer
RAMIRO AGUAS - Partner; Controller; General Manager; Executive Chef; General Buyer

Charleston Foods Inc.
683 Castle Dr
Charleston, IL 61920-7471

Telephone: (217) 345-2909
Fax Number: (217) 345-2986
Type of Business: Chain Restaurant Operator
Year Founded: 1972
Total Sales: $33,000,000 (e)
Alcohol Sales: 6%
Number of Employees: 320
Average Check: Breakfast(6); Lunch(20); Dinner(26)
Total Units: 8
Trade Names: Arby's (7); Cheddar's Casual Cafe (1)
Units Franchised From: 8
Preferred Square Footage: 2,800; 3,000
Preferred Location Types: Freestanding
Alcohol Served: Beer, Wine, Liquor
Primary Menu: American (1); Sandwiches/Deli (7)
Areas of Operation: IL
Type of Foodservice: Casual Dining (1); Quick Serve (7)
Franchise Affiliation: Arby's Restaurant Group, ATLANTA, GA; Cheddar's Restaurant Holding Corp., ORLANDO, FL
Primary Distributors: (Food) McLane/Rocky Mount, ROCKY MOUNT, NC; (Supplies) Gordon Food Service Inc., WYOMING, MI

Key Personnel
JERRY MYERSCOUGH - President; Controller; Director Finance, Purchasing, Facility/Maintenance, Information Systems, Real Estate, Design, Store Fixtures
JOHN KEENER - Owner
CAROL MYERSCOUGH - VP Operations, Human Resources; General Buyer
CYNTHIA MYERSCOUGH - Director Operations
DEB BEEVER - Manager Accounting

Domino's Franchisee
806 Lehmen Dr
Chester, IL 62233-1262

Telephone: (618) 826-2020
Type of Business: Chain Restaurant Operator
Total Sales: $7,946,000 (e)
Total Units: 4
Trade Names: Domino's (4)
Units Franchised From: 4
Primary Menu: Pizza (4)
Areas of Operation: IL
Type of Foodservice: Quick Serve (2)
Franchise Affiliation: Domino's Pizza Inc, ANN ARBOR, MI

Key Personnel
NICHOLAS M. BURCH - Owner; General Buyer

4 Star Restaurant Group
1804 W Division St
Chicago, IL 60622-6810

Telephone: (773) 278-1177
Internet Homepage: 4starrestaurantgroup.com
Company Email: info@4srg.com
Type of Business: Chain Restaurant Operator
Year Founded: 2003
Total Units: 9
Trade Names: Crosby's Kitchen (1); D.O.C Wine Bar (2); Ella Elli (1); Frasca (1); Remington's (1); Smoke Daddy (1); The Windsor (1); Tuco and Blondie (1)
Company-Owned Units: 9
Primary Menu: American (6); Bar-B-Q (1); Mexican (1); Pizza (1)
Projected Openings: 2
Areas of Operation: IL
Type of Foodservice: Casual Dining (9)

Key Personnel
DOUG DUNLAY - Partner
MICHAEL DUNLAY - Partner
DEREK RETTELL - Partner

JOSH RUTHERFORD - Partner
KELLY HOXIE - VP Operations
PETER BLAKE - Director Information Technology
JAMES MILLER - Director Operations
ANNI MCNULTY - Director Operations, Event Planning, Catering

Aloha Poke LLC
843 W Belmont Ave
Chicago, IL 60657-4401

Telephone: (872) 817-7300
Internet Homepage: alohapokeco.com
Company Email: info@alohapokeco.com
Type of Business: Chain Restaurant Operator
Year Founded: 2016
Total Sales: $38,720,000 (e)
Total Units: 20
Trade Names: Aloha Poke Co (20)
Company-Owned Units: 20
Primary Menu: American (20)
Projected Openings: 8
Areas of Operation: CA, CO, IL, MN
Type of Foodservice: Fast Casual (20)

Key Personnel
CHRIS BIRKINSHAW - CEO
MAXWELL POWELL - General Manager

America's Dog & Burger
2847 W Catalpa Ave
Chicago, IL 60625

Telephone: (773) 234-9622
Internet Homepage: adbfranchise.com; adbfresh.com
Company Email: FranchiseInfo@ADBFranchise.com
Type of Business: Chain Restaurant Operator
Year Founded: 1996
Total Units: 3
Trade Names: America's Dog & Burger (3)
Company-Owned Units: 3
Primary Menu: Hot Dogs (3)
Projected Openings: 1
Areas of Operation: IL
Type of Foodservice: Quick Serve (3)

Key Personnel
MANOLIS ALPOGIANIS - Co-Founder; Partner; General Buyer
GEORGE ALPLGIANIS - Co-Founder; Partner

Ampler Restaurant Group
833 W Washington Blvd Third Floor
Chicago, IL 60607

Telephone: (402) 882-0112
Internet Homepage: ampler.co
Company Email: ir@agmanpartners.com
Type of Business: Chain Restaurant Operator
Year Founded: 2017
Total Sales: $414,870,000 (e)
Total Units: 231
Trade Names: Burger King (81); Church's Chicken (70); Taco Bell (80)
Units Franchised From: 231
Primary Menu: Chicken (70); Hamburger (81); Taco (80)
Areas of Operation: IL, KY, NM, OH, TX
Type of Foodservice: Quick Serve (231)
Subsidiaries: Ag Bells LLC, RIVERWOODS, IL
Franchise Affiliation: Burger King Worldwide Inc., MIAMI, FL; Church's Chicken, ATLANTA, GA
Parent Company: Agman Partners, OMAHA, NE

Key Personnel
HANS PUSCH - CEO
KEVIN FERNANDEZ - President
MIKE A. COLLINS - President Division
MATTHEW BARS - President
NICK BOYLE - President Real Estate Development
ROGER MENCHACA - Director Operations
AARON CAMPOS - Director Human Resources
CHRISTOPHER COX - Director Operations
JENNIFER JONES - Director Operations
JOE LABRADO - Director Operations
NANCY GERSTENFELD - Director Development, Real Estate

Andies Restaurant
5253 N Clark St
Chicago, IL 60640-2122

Telephone: (773) 784-8616
Fax Number: (773) 561-8030
Internet Homepage: andieschicago.com
Company Email: andieschicago@gmail.com
Type of Business: Chain Restaurant Operator
Year Founded: 1991
Total Sales: $3,861,000 (e)
Alcohol Sales: 10%
Number of Employees: 30
Average Check: Lunch(14); Dinner(18)
Internet Order Processing: Yes
Total Units: 2
Trade Names: Andies Restaurant (2)
Company-Owned Units: 2
Preferred Location Types: Freestanding
Alcohol Served: Beer, Wine, Liquor
Primary Menu: Greek/Mediterranean (2)
Areas of Operation: IL
Type of Foodservice: Casual Dining (2)
Catering Services: Yes
Primary Distributors: (Food) Battaglia Distributing Co. Inc., CHICAGO, IL

Key Personnel
ANDY TAMRAS - President; Owner; Executive Chef; General Buyer
GIL TAMRAS - General Manager
SHANA TAMRAS - Manager Administration
ANDIE TAMRAS JR - Manager Human Resources

Argo Tea Inc.
16 W Randolph St
Chicago, IL 60601-3501

Telephone: (312) 553-1550
Fax Number: (312) 283-0063
Internet Homepage: argotea.com
Company Email: info@argotea.com
Type of Business: Chain Restaurant Operator
Year Founded: 2003
Total Sales: $40,310,000 (e)
Average Check: Breakfast(8); Lunch(8); Dinner(10)
Internet Order Processing: Yes
Total Units: 43
Trade Names: Argo Tea (43)
Company-Owned Units: 43
Primary Menu: Miscellaneous (43)
Projected Openings: 3
Areas of Operation: DC, GA, IL, MA, MD, MI, MN, MO, NC, NY, VA
Foreign Countries: LEBANON; UNITED ARAB EMIRATES
Type of Foodservice: Fast Casual (43)

Key Personnel
CANDACE MACLEOD - Director Retail Operations

Associated Hotels LLC
1 N La Salle St Ste 1015
Chicago, IL 60602-3983

Telephone: (312) 782-6008
Fax Number: (312) 782-2356
Internet Homepage: associatedhotelsllc.com
Type of Business: Foodservice Operations - Hotel/Motels
Year Founded: 2006
Total Sales: $97,980,000 (e)
Alcohol Sales: 23%
Number of Employees: 1,000
Total Units: 8
Restaurants in Hotels: 4
Trade Names: Holiday Inn (2); Holiday Inn Express & Suites (5); Hooters Casino Hotel (1)
Company-Owned Units: 4
Alcohol Served: Beer, Wine, Liquor
Areas of Operation: IL, MO, NC, NV, WI
Type of Foodservice: Casual Dining (4)
Primary Distributors: (Food) SYSCO Food Services of Chicago Inc., DES PLAINES, IL
Notes: The company derives approximately

75% of its revenue from hotel operations.

Key Personnel
DON SZUBERSKI - VP Accounting; Controller Accounting
CRYSTAL PAYTON - Director Human Resources

Axion Corporation
141 W Jackson Blvd Lbby A-12
Chicago, IL 60604-2956

Telephone: (312) 427-9833
Fax Number: (312) 435-5447
Internet Homepage: cellarsmarketchicago.com; cerescafechicago.com
Type of Business: Chain Restaurant Operator
Year Founded: 1937
Total Sales: $5,725,000 (e)
Alcohol Sales: 10%
Number of Employees: 100
Average Check: Breakfast(8); Lunch(14); Dinner(28)
Total Units: 2
Trade Names: Cellar's Market (1); Ceres Cafe (1)
Company-Owned Units: 2
Preferred Location Types: Mixed-use Center; Office Complex
Alcohol Served: Beer, Wine, Liquor
Primary Menu: American (2)
Areas of Operation: IL
Type of Foodservice: Casual Dining (2)
Primary Distributors: (Full Line) SYSCO Food Services of Chicago Inc., DES PLAINES, IL

Key Personnel
LOUIS BOURNAKIS - President
PETER BOURNAKIS - Exec VP; Treasurer; General Manager; General Buyer
JAVIER ESTRADA - Executive Chef; General Buyer
ARIC MER - Manager Restaurant Operations

Bacci Pizza Group
2301 W Taylor St
Chicago, IL 60612-4235

Telephone: (312) 455-1301
Fax Number: (312) 455-9005
Internet Homepage: baccipizza.com
Type of Business: Chain Restaurant Operator
Year Founded: 1996
Total Sales: $7,714,000 (e)
Number of Employees: 138
Average Check: Dinner(16)
Internet Order Processing: Yes
Internet Sales: 1.00%
Total Units: 11
Trade Names: Bacci Pizza (11)
Company-Owned Units: 11
Preferred Location Types: Downtown; Office Complex
Primary Menu: Pizza (11)
Areas of Operation: IL
Type of Foodservice: Fast Casual (11)

Key Personnel
ROBERT DI DIANA - CEO; Owner; Director Menu Development; General Buyer
LISA DIDIANA - President
GIANCARLO DIDIANA - General Manager

BB Cinnamon
414 N Orleans St Ste 402
Chicago, IL 60654-4461

Telephone: (312) 645-9898
Internet Homepage: burritobeach.com
Type of Business: Chain Restaurant Operator
Total Sales: $6,518,000 (e)
Internet Order Processing: Yes
Total Units: 7
Trade Names: Burrito Beach (6); Cinnabon (1)
Company-Owned Units: 6
Units Franchised From: 1
Primary Menu: Mexican (6); Snacks (1)
Areas of Operation: IL
Type of Foodservice: Fast Casual (6); Quick Serve (1)
Franchise Affiliation: Cinnabon Inc., ATLANTA, GA

Key Personnel
GREG SCHULSON - Owner; General Buyer

Billy Goat Tavern
430 N Michigan Ave Lowr 1
Chicago, IL 60611-4080

Telephone: (312) 222-1525
Internet Homepage: billygoattavern.com
Type of Business: Chain Restaurant Operator
Year Founded: 1934
Total Sales: $9,462,000 (e)
Alcohol Sales: 40%
Number of Employees: 79
Average Check: Breakfast(6); Lunch(6); Dinner(6)
Internet Order Processing: Yes
Total Units: 9
Trade Names: Billy Goat Tavern (9)
Company-Owned Units: 9
Preferred Square Footage: 1,500; 2,000; 3,000
Preferred Location Types: Airports; Downtown; Freestanding; Office Complex; Strip Mall
Alcohol Served: Beer, Wine, Liquor
Primary Menu: American (9)
Areas of Operation: DC, IL
Type of Foodservice: Casual Dining (9)
Primary Distributors: (Full Line) Edward Don & Co., WOODRIDGE, IL

Key Personnel
PATTY SIANIS - President
PAUL SIANIS - Owner
BILL SIANIS - General Manager; Director Operations, Information Systems; General Buyer
SAM SIANIS - Executive Chef; Manager Finance, Purchasing, Facility/Maintenance, Supply Chain, Real Estate, Design, Human Resources; Buyer Food, Foodservice Equip/Supplies

Boka Restaurant Group
820 W Lake St
Chicago, IL 60607

Telephone: (312) 238-9896
Fax Number: (312) 337-5820
Internet Homepage: bokagrp.com
Company Email: info@bokagrp.com
Type of Business: Chain Restaurant Operator
Total Sales: $22,150,000 (e)
Alcohol Sales: 5%
Average Check: Dinner(66)
Total Units: 19
Trade Names: Bellemore (1); Boka (1); Boka Catering Group (1); Cold Storage (1); Devereaux (1); Duck Duck Goat (1); Dutch & Doc's (1); Elaine's Coffee Call (1); Girl & The Goat (1); Goat Group Catering (1); GT Fish & Oyster (1); GT Prime (1); Little Goat (1); Momotaro (1); Somerset (1); Swift & Sons (1); The Izakaya (1); the J. Parker (1); The Kennison (1)
Company-Owned Units: 19
Alcohol Served: Beer, Wine, Liquor
Primary Menu: American (8); Chinese (1); Japanese (2); Miscellaneous (2); Seafood (2); Snacks (2); Steak (2)
Areas of Operation: IL
Type of Foodservice: Casual Dining (3); Fast Casual (2); Fine Dining (14)

Key Personnel
KEVIN BOEHM - Co-Founder; Co-CEO
ROB KATZ - Co-Founder; Co-CEO
JAMI MADONIA - CFO
IAN GOLDBERG - COO
TAYLOR CROWLEY - Chief Marketing Officer
GABE GARZA - Chief Development Officer
MATT GRAHAM - VP Operations
EMILY FINKELSTEIN - VP Human Resources
JULIE RHEW - VP Strategy, Business Development
ABBY KRITZLER - Chief Culture Officer; Executive Director
ALICIA ZYBURT - Creative Director
ASHLEY SANTORO - Director Operations, Development

TESSA VOEGELI - Director Event Planning
NICOLE WILLIS - Director Beverages, Food
TIM ZIEGLER - Director Strategy, Business Development
SARAH KRATHEN - Director Operations
DANIEL MILLSTEIN - Director Operations
KYLE PEPPERELL - Director Development, Training
RONDA CULVER - Director Operations
MICHELLE HERNDON - Director Diversity, Community Relations
RACHEL BECKER - Director Communications
KEVIN CARAVELLI - Director Operations
MISSY CLARIN - Director Event Planning
WESLEY CONGER - Director Operations
BRIAN CRAWFORD - Director Sales
JOEY CAPUL - Senior Manager Human Resources
COLLEEN DALY - Senior Manager Social Media
ELIZABETH RIVERA - Senior Manager Human Resources
HYUN SONG - Senior Manager Accounting
MIGUEL TAMURA - Manager Operations
KATHLEEN KONWINSKI - Manager Catering
JOHN GANTZ - Manager Operations, Administration
GUSTAVO AVINA - Manager Accounting
MANIJEH BONSHAHI - Account Executive

Bonci USA
161 N Sangamon St
Chicago, IL 60607

Telephone: (312) 243-4016
Internet Homepage: bonciusa.com
Company Email: INFO@BONCIUSA.COM
Type of Business: Chain Restaurant Operator
Year Founded: 2003
Total Sales: $3,006,000 (e)
Total Units: 2
Trade Names: Bonci USA (2)
Company-Owned Units: 2
Primary Menu: Pizza (2)
Projected Openings: 2
Areas of Operation: IL
Type of Foodservice: Fast Casual (2)
Notes: Bonci was founded in Rome, Italy in 2003. Bonci USA has the exclusive rights to expand the brand in the U.S. and globally excluding locations in Italy and countries bordering Italy.

Key Personnel
GABRIELE BONCI - Founder
RICK TASMAN - President
CHAKIB TOUHAMI - Director Operations

Bottleneck Management
2211 N Elston Ave
Chicago, IL 60614

Telephone: (312) 212-8878
Internet Homepage: bottleneckmgmt.com
Type of Business: Chain Restaurant Operator
Year Founded: 2001
Total Sales: $14,150,000 (e)
Total Units: 15
Trade Names: City Works (9); Old Town Pour House (4); South Branch Tavern & Grille (1); Sweetwater Tavern + Grille (1)
Company-Owned Units: 15
Preferred Location Types: Downtown; Freestanding
Primary Menu: American (15)
Projected Openings: 2
Areas of Operation: IL, MD, MN, OH, PA, TX, VA
Type of Foodservice: Casual Dining (15)

Key Personnel
NATHAN HILDING - Co-Founder; Partner
JASON AKEMANN - Co-Founder; Partner
CHRIS BASAILLON - Partner
MARK GRAY - COO
ANGELA ZOISS - VP Marketing
ZACH VAN GAASBEEK - Corporate Chef Region
CORY HOEKSTRA - Executive Chef
CHRISTINA BLANCO - Director Recruitment
ERIN CARROLL - Director Business Development
JORDAN GIBRICK - Director Restaurant Operations
HUGH CONDON - Director Finance
KEVIN O'BRIEN - Director Information Technology
PAUL WILLIAMS - Director Operations
SARAH JONES - Director Operations
TIMOTHY BENEDICT - Director Facility/Maintenance
JES RODRIGUEZ - Manager Payroll
JULES RICE - Manager Marketing
ALEXANDRA CHANDLER - Manager Training
COLTER POTTS - Administrator Systems
JULIE SCHOENFELDER - Senior Coordinator Event Planning
CHRISTINA C. SOUTER - Coordinator Event Planning
ERIN WHITE - Coordinator Event Planning
CHRISTINE PARO - Coordinator Training

Bravo Restaurants Inc.
201 E Ohio St Ste 300
Chicago, IL 60611-3677

Telephone: (312) 463-1210
Fax Number: (312) 798-6761
Internet Homepage: featuredfoods.com
Company Email: info@featuredfoods.com
Type of Business: Chain Restaurant Operator
Year Founded: 1994
Total Sales: $12,666,000 (e)
Alcohol Sales: 10%
Number of Employees: 825
Average Check: Lunch(10); Dinner(16)
Internet Order Processing: Yes
Internet Sales: 1.00%
Total Units: 17
Trade Names: Eduardos Enoteca (1); Edwardo's Natural Pizza Restaurant (3); Mitchell's Ice Cream (1); Original Gino's East (12)
Company-Owned Units: 17
Preferred Square Footage: 5,000
Preferred Location Types: Freestanding
Alcohol Served: Beer, Wine, Liquor
Primary Menu: Italian (1); Pizza (15); Snacks (1)
Projected Openings: 3
Areas of Operation: IL, IN, TX, WI, FC
Type of Foodservice: Casual Dining (16); Quick Serve (1)
Catering Services: Yes
Primary Distributors: (Full Line) Greco & Sons Inc., BARTLETT, IL

Key Personnel
JEFFERY HIMMEL - CEO; President
JON ELLIS - COO; Director Purchasing, Facility/Maintenance, Real Estate, Construction, Design, Store Fixtures, Menu Development
JORDAN HIMMEL - CIO
DAN MURPHY - Director Finance

Brown Bag Seafood Co.
340 E Randolph St
Chicago, IL 60601

Telephone: (312) 496-3999
Internet Homepage: brownbagseafood.com
Company Email: chatterbox@brownbagseafood.com
Type of Business: Chain Restaurant Operator
Year Founded: 2014
Total Units: 5
Trade Names: Brown Bag Seafood Co. (5)
Company-Owned Units: 5
Primary Menu: Seafood (5)
Projected Openings: 1
Areas of Operation: IL
Type of Foodservice: Fast Casual (5)

Key Personnel
DONNA LEE - Founder; CEO
ZACH FLANZMAN - Chief Strategy Officer
DAANGELA SHEPHERD - Executive Chef
SIDNEY JANKAUSKAS - Director Finance
MELISSA POWELL - Coordinator Catering

Byron's Hot Dogs
1701 W Lawrence Ave
Chicago, IL 60640-4411

Telephone: (773) 271-0900
Fax Number: (773) 271-0979
Internet Homepage: byronschicago.com
Type of Business: Chain Restaurant Operator
Total Sales: $2,287,000 (e)
Average Check: Lunch(8); Dinner(10)
Internet Order Processing: Yes
Total Units: 2
Trade Names: Byron's (2)
Company-Owned Units: 2
Preferred Location Types: Freestanding
Primary Menu: American (2)
Areas of Operation: IL
Type of Foodservice: Quick Serve (2)
Primary Distributors: (Supplies) Edward Don & Co., WOODRIDGE, IL

Key Personnel
ANN PAYNE - Partner
MIKE PAYNE - Partner; General Manager; Executive Chef; General Buyer

Canady Enterprises, Inc.
1700 E 56th St Apt 3609
Chicago, IL 60637-5800

Telephone: (773) 493-5708
Fax Number: (773) 493-7660
Company Email: abooker@btiiinc.com
Type of Business: Chain Restaurant Operator
Total Sales: $15,268,000 (e)
Total Units: 3
Trade Names: McDonald's (3)
Units Franchised From: 3
Preferred Location Types: Office Complex
Primary Menu: Hamburger (3)
Areas of Operation: IL
Type of Foodservice: Quick Serve (3)
Franchise Affiliation: McDonald's Corporation, CHICAGO, IL

Key Personnel
BLANTON CANADY - President; General Buyer

Carson's the Place For Ribs
465 E Illinois St
Chicago, IL 60611-4305

Telephone: (312) 280-9200
Internet Homepage: ribs.com
Company Email: info@ribs.com
Type of Business: Chain Restaurant Operator
Year Founded: 1976
Total Sales: $10,780,000 (e)
Alcohol Sales: 20%
Number of Employees: 325
Average Check: Lunch(16); Dinner(30)
Internet Order Processing: Yes
Internet Sales: 5.00%
Total Units: 3
Trade Names: Carson's the Place For Ribs (3)
Company-Owned Units: 3
Preferred Square Footage: 14,000
Preferred Location Types: Freestanding
Alcohol Served: Beer, Wine, Liquor
Primary Menu: Bar-B-Q (3)
Areas of Operation: IL, WI
Type of Foodservice: Casual Dining (3)
Catering Services: Yes
Primary Distributors: (Full Line) SYSCO Food Services of Chicago Inc., DES PLAINES, IL

Key Personnel
DEAN CARSON - Owner; Director Menu Development; General Buyer

Chicagoland Commissary
1519 W Madison St
Chicago, IL 60607-1840

Telephone: (312) 226-8800
Internet Homepage: clcdd.com
Type of Business: Chain Restaurant Operator
Year Founded: 2005
Total Sales: $45,050,000 (e)
Number of Employees: 330
Average Check: Breakfast(8); Lunch(8); Dinner(8)
Internet Order Processing: Yes
Total Units: 28
Trade Names: Dunkin' Donuts (28)
Units Franchised From: 28
Preferred Square Footage: 1,500; 2,200
Preferred Location Types: Convenience Store/Gas Station
Primary Menu: Snacks (28)
Areas of Operation: IL, IN
Type of Foodservice: Quick Serve (28)
Franchise Affiliation: DD IP Holder, CANTON, MA

Key Personnel
JOHN LUXEM - COO; General Buyer
JENNIFER ODESKY - Controller
STEVE AKERS - Manager Facility/Maintenance

Chipati Inc.
205 E Ohio St
Chicago, IL 60611-3238

Telephone: (877) 818-5211
Internet Homepage: pocketsonline.com
Company Email: contactus@pocketsonline.com
Type of Business: Chain Restaurant Operator
Year Founded: 1989
Total Sales: $3,015,000 (e)
Number of Employees: 44
Average Check: Lunch(22); Dinner(22)
Internet Order Processing: Yes
Internet Sales: 1.00%
Total Units: 5
Trade Names: Pockets (5)
Units Franchised To: 7
Preferred Square Footage: 1,000; 2,000
Preferred Location Types: Freestanding; Office Complex; Strip Mall
Primary Menu: American (5)
Areas of Operation: IL
Type of Foodservice: Quick Serve (5)
Catering Services: Yes
On-site Distribution Center: Yes
Primary Distributors: (Food) SYSCO Food Services of Chicago Inc., DES PLAINES, IL

Key Personnel
DAVID LITCHMAN - President; Manager Finance, Purchasing, Facility/Maintenance, Supply Chain, Real Estate, Design, Menu Development, Catering; General Buyer

Coffee & Tea Bar Holdings, LLC
1620 N Milwaukee Ave
Chicago, IL 60647

Telephone: (608) 469-5657
Internet Homepage: fairgrounds.cafe
Company Email: hello@fairgrounds.cafe
Type of Business: Chain Restaurant Operator
Year Founded: 2017
Total Units: 8
Trade Names: Fairgrounds Craft Coffee and Tea (8)
Company-Owned Units: 8
Preferred Square Footage: 800; 2,200
Preferred Location Types: Downtown; Hotel/Motel
Primary Menu: Coffee (8)
Areas of Operation: CA, IL, MN, WI
Type of Foodservice: Quick Serve (8)

Key Personnel
MICHAEL SHULTZ - Founder; CEO
KATHIE RUBINO - Controller

Connie's Pizza Inc.
2373 S Archer Ave
Chicago, IL 60616-1857

Telephone: (312) 326-3443
Internet Homepage: conniespizza.com
Company Email: info@conniespizza.com
Type of Business: Chain Restaurant Operator
Year Founded: 1963
Total Sales: $4,711,000 (e)

Alcohol Sales: 10%
Number of Employees: 260
Average Check: Lunch(12); Dinner(18)
Internet Order Processing: Yes
Total Units: 2
Trade Names: Connie's Pizza (2)
Company-Owned Units: 2
Preferred Square Footage: 4,000
Preferred Location Types: Freestanding; Strip Mall
Alcohol Served: Beer, Wine, Liquor
Primary Menu: Pizza (2)
Areas of Operation: IL
Type of Foodservice: Casual Dining (2)
Catering Services: Yes
On-site Distribution Center: Yes
Primary Distributors: (Full Line) Edward Don & Co., WOODRIDGE, IL

Key Personnel
MICHAEL STOLFE - President; General Buyer
ROBERT PARSONS - Director
SUSAN HUERTA - Manager Supply Chain

Cornerstone Restaurant Group
1647 W Fulton St
Chicago, IL 60612-2507

Telephone: (312) 455-8626
Fax Number: (312) 455-8376
Internet Homepage:
 cornerstonerestaurants.com
Company Email:
 mail@cornerstonerestaurants.com
Type of Business: Chain Restaurant Operator
Year Founded: 1997
Total Sales: $65,020,000 (e)
Alcohol Sales: 10%
Number of Employees: 780
Average Check: Dinner(72)
Total Units: 11
Trade Names: Belly Shack (1); Eno (2); Michael Jordan's 23 Sportcafe (1); Michael Jordan's Restaurant (1); Michael Jordan's Steakhouse (3); SolToro Tequila Grille (1); The Table at Crate (1); Urban Belly (1)
Company-Owned Units: 11
Preferred Square Footage: 2,500; 4,000
Preferred Location Types: Freestanding; Hotel/Motel
Alcohol Served: Beer, Wine, Liquor
Primary Menu: American (1); Asian (2); Greek/Mediterranean (1); Italian (4); Mexican (1); Steak/Seafood (3)
Areas of Operation: CT, IL, NJ, NY, FC
Foreign Countries: HUNGARY
Type of Foodservice: Casual Dining (12); Fine Dining (1)
Primary Distributors: (Food) SYSCO Food Services of Chicago Inc., DES PLAINES, IL
Notes: The Burger King locations are in Budapest, Hungary and Mexico.

Key Personnel
DAVID ZADIKOFF - Chairman; CEO
JOSH ZADIKOFF - President
MATT GOLDSTICK - CFO
DANNY MCGOWAN - COO
JEFFERY MCLELLAN - VP Real Estate; Director Design
BILL KIM - Executive Chef

da Vinci Group
1732 N Halsted St Ste 1
Chicago, IL 60614-5533

Telephone: (312) 266-1199
Fax Number: (312) 266-8143
Internet Homepage: adobogrill.com; pikkstavern.davinci-group.com; vincichicago.com
Type of Business: Chain Restaurant Operator
Year Founded: 1993
Total Sales: $4,042,000 (e)
Alcohol Sales: 40%
Number of Employees: 80
Average Check: Lunch(16); Dinner(30)
Total Units: 3
Trade Names: Adobo Grill (1); Pikk's Tavern (1); Vinci (1)
Company-Owned Units: 3
Preferred Location Types: Freestanding
Alcohol Served: Beer, Wine, Liquor
Primary Menu: Italian (1); Mexican (1); Steak (1)
Areas of Operation: IL, IN
Type of Foodservice: Casual Dining (1); Fast Casual (1); Fine Dining (1)
Primary Distributors: (Full Line) SYSCO Food Services of Chicago Inc., DES PLAINES, IL

Key Personnel
KATHY LO DUCA - Partner; General Buyer
PAUL LO DUCA - Partner; Executive Chef

Doc B's Restaurant + Bar
100 E Walton St
Chicago, IL 60611

Telephone: (312) 999-9300
Internet Homepage: docbsrestaurant.com
Company Email: info@docbsfreshkitchen.com
Type of Business: Chain Restaurant Operator
Year Founded: 2013
Total Units: 8
Trade Names: Doc B's Fresh Kitchen (8)
Company-Owned Units: 8
Preferred Location Types: Community Mall; Downtown; Freestanding
Primary Menu: American (8)
Areas of Operation: FL, IL, TX
Type of Foodservice: Casual Dining (8)

Key Personnel
CRAIG BERNSTEIN - Founder; President
NICOLE WEINMEIER - Director Human Resources
JANEEN CHAVARRY - Specialist Human Resources

Double P Corporation
5724 N Pulaski Rd
Chicago, IL 60646-6820

Telephone: (773) 539-0500
Type of Business: Chain Restaurant Operator
Total Sales: $53,990,000 (e)
Total Units: 73
Trade Names: Auntie Anne's Hand-Rolled Soft Pretzels (73)
Units Franchised From: 73
Primary Menu: Snacks (73)
Areas of Operation: IL
Type of Foodservice: Quick Serve (73)
Franchise Affiliation: Auntie Anne's Inc., LANCASTER, PA

Key Personnel
PHILLIP PATINKIN - Partner; General Buyer
ADAM LEVY - Partner
MATTHEW PATINKIN - Partner
DANA RAKVICA - Regional Director Operations

DTCT, Inc
PO Box 438425
Chicago, IL 60643-8425

Telephone: (773) 468-3338
Type of Business: Chain Restaurant Operator
Total Sales: $38,560,000 (e)
Number of Employees: 325
Total Units: 8
Trade Names: McDonald's (8)
Units Franchised From: 8
Preferred Square Footage: 2,500
Primary Menu: Hamburger (8)
Areas of Operation: IL
Type of Foodservice: Quick Serve (8)
Franchise Affiliation: McDonald's Corporation, CHICAGO, IL

Key Personnel
DERRICK TAYLOR - President; General Buyer

Elly's Brunch & Cafe
5310 N Milwaukee Ave
Chicago, IL 60630

Telephone: (773) 775-1333
Internet Homepage: ellyspancakehouse.com

Company Email: kellyellys101@gmail.com
Type of Business: Chain Restaurant Operator
Year Founded: 1997
Total Sales: $14,470,000 (e)
Average Check: Breakfast(16);
Total Units: 8
Trade Names: Elly's Brunch & Cafe (8)
Company-Owned Units: 8
Preferred Location Types: Strip Mall
Primary Menu: American (8)
Areas of Operation: AZ, IL, MO
Type of Foodservice: Family Restaurant (8)
Catering Services: Yes

Key Personnel
CHRIS GEORGES - President; Owner; General Buyer

Entertainment Cruises
455 N Cityfront Plaza Dr Ste 2600
Chicago, IL 60611-5506

Telephone: (312) 321-7600
Fax Number: (312) 321-7610
Internet Homepage: entertainmentcruises.com; odyssey.com; odysseycruises.com; odysseywedding.com; spiritcruises.com
Company Email: corporate@entertainmentcruises.com
Type of Business: Chain Restaurant Operator
Year Founded: 1990
Total Sales: $72,810,000 (e)
Alcohol Sales: 18%
Number of Employees: 450
Average Check: Breakfast(10); Lunch(66); Dinner(130)
Internet Order Processing: Yes
Internet Sales: 3.00%
Total Units: 23
Trade Names: Atlantica (2); Bateaux (1); Capital Elite (1); Freedom Elite (1); Mystic Blue (1); Odyssey (3); Seadog (2); Seaport Elite (3); Spirit of Baltimore (1); Spirit of Boston (1); Spirit of Chicago (1); Spirit of New Jersey (1); Spirit of New York (1); Spirit of Norfolk (1); Spirit of Philadelphia (1); Spirit of Washington (1); Windridge Yacht (1)
Company-Owned Units: 23
Preferred Square Footage: 5,500; 6,000
Preferred Location Types: Other
Alcohol Served: Beer, Wine, Liquor
Primary Menu: American (23)
Areas of Operation: FL, IL, MA, MD, NJ, NY, PA, VA, WA
Type of Foodservice: Casual Dining (17); Fine Dining (5); Quick Serve (1)
Primary Distributors: (Food) US Foods, PITTSTON, PA

Key Personnel
MARY MARANG - Director Marketing, Sales
KEVIN OBRIEN - Director Information Technology
TINA SWAN - Director Sales
MELISSA BARR - Manager Sales
BERNARD BELTRAN - Manager Sales
MONICA ALLEN - Representative Sales

Epic Burger, Inc.
1016 W Jackson Blvd
Chicago, IL 60607-2914

Telephone: (312) 243-3605
Internet Homepage: epicburger.com
Company Email: marketing@epicburger.com
Type of Business: Chain Restaurant Operator
Year Founded: 2008
Total Sales: $11,740,000 (e)
Total Units: 8
Trade Names: Epic Burger (8)
Company-Owned Units: 8
Primary Menu: Hamburger (8)
Areas of Operation: IL
Type of Foodservice: Fast Casual (8)

Key Personnel
RICARDO HERRERA - Director Finance

†
Flying Food Group Inc.
212 N Sangamon St Ste 1A
Chicago, IL 60607-1722

Telephone: (312) 243-2122
Fax Number: (312) 243-5088
Internet Homepage: flyingfood.com
Company Email: gambo@flyingfood.com
Type of Business: Foodservice Management Operator
Year Founded: 1983
Total Sales: $2,876,000 (e)
Number of Employees: 2,800
Number of Locations Served: 90
Total Foodservice Mgmt Accounts: 90
Areas of Operation: CA, CO, CT, DC, FL, GA, HI, IL, NY
Type of Foodservice: Quick Serve (90)
Foodservice Management Venues: Transportation
Primary Distributors: (Full Line) SYSCO Food Services of Chicago Inc., DES PLAINES, IL

Key Personnel
DAVID COTTON - CEO; CFO
TOM BILAND - President; COO
WOLFGANG HOENLE - CFO
HENRI ALCADE - VP Research & Development; Executive Chef
GERARD CURRY - Senior Director Marketing, Sales
ABBAS HOSSEINI - Director
CHRIS KIZARIC - Director Finance
RICHARD KOZLOWSKI - Director Sales
DOTTIE SCHOENIG - Director Purchasing
RICARDO VASQUEZ - Director Sales

Gene & Georgetti
500 N Franklin St
Chicago, IL 60654-4604

Telephone: (312) 527-3718
Fax Number: (312) 527-2039
Internet Homepage: geneandgeorgetti.com
Type of Business: Chain Restaurant Operator
Year Founded: 1941
Average Check: Lunch(30); Dinner(66)
Total Units: 2
Trade Names: Gene & Georgetti (2)
Company-Owned Units: 2
Alcohol Served: Beer, Wine, Liquor
Primary Menu: Steak (2)
Areas of Operation: IL
Type of Foodservice: Casual Dining (2)

Key Personnel
TONY DURPETTI - Owner; General Buyer
MARION DURPETTI - VP
RICH CIOTA - General Manager
ARTURO AUCAQUIZHPI - Executive Chef; Manager Purchasing; Buyer Food
GUS MANTAS - Buyer Beverages

●▲
Gianny Corp
1563 N Wells St
Chicago, IL 60610

Telephone: (312) 266-2633
Type of Business: Chain Restaurant Operator
Total Sales: $28,350,000 (e)
Total Units: 6
Trade Names: McDonald's (6)
Units Franchised From: 6
Preferred Location Types: Convenience Store/Gas Station; Freestanding
Primary Menu: Hamburger (6)
Areas of Operation: IL
Type of Foodservice: Quick Serve (6)
Franchise Affiliation: McDonald's Corporation, CHICAGO, IL

Key Personnel
STEVEN FUNKHOUSER - President; General Buyer

Gibson Restaurant Group
1050 N State St
Chicago, IL 60610-7829

Telephone: (312) 587-0575
Fax Number: (312) 787-5649
Internet Homepage: gibsonsrestaurantgroup.com; GibsonsSteakhouse.com; hugosfrogbar.com;

quartinochicago.com
Company Email: info@grgmc.com
Type of Business: Chain Restaurant Operator
Year Founded: 1989
Total Sales: $106,370,000 (e)
Alcohol Sales: 20%
Number of Employees: 1,200
Average Check: Breakfast(18); Lunch(26); Dinner(58)
Internet Order Processing: Yes
Internet Sales: 2.00%
Total Units: 12
Trade Names: Chi Sox Bar & Grill (1); Gibsons Bar & Steakhouse (3); Gibsons Italia (1); Hugo's Frog Bar and Fish House (4); Luxbar (1); Quartino Ristorante, Pizzeria, Wine Bar (1); The Boathouse (1)
Company-Owned Units: 12
Preferred Square Footage: 5,500; 6,000
Preferred Location Types: Downtown; Freestanding; Other
Alcohol Served: Beer, Wine, Liquor
Primary Menu: American (3); Italian (2); Seafood (4); Steak (2); Steak/Seafood (1)
Areas of Operation: IL
Type of Foodservice: Casual Dining (8); Family Restaurant (1); Fine Dining (3)
Primary Distributors: (Full Line) US Foods, BENSENVILLE, IL

Key Personnel
STEVE LOMBARDO - Chairman; President; Partner; General Counsel
HUGO RALLI - Partner; VP Operations
JOHN COLLETTI - Partner; General Manager
REBECCA BRZECZEK - VP Human Resources
JEFF HARRIS - Controller
AUDREY TRIPLETT - Executive Chef; Buyer Beverages
CASSANDRA E. SAKAI - Director Alcoholic Beverages
GREG HORAN - Director Operations; General Buyer
ELIZABETH LOMBARDO STARK - Director Marketing
SHAINA NESTOR - Manager Operations
JAZMIN RODRIGUEZ - Manager Restaurant Operations
JARED BROWN - Manager Restaurant Operations

Giordano's Enterprises Inc.
60 E Superior St Ste 300
Chicago, IL 60611

Telephone: (312) 641-6500
Fax Number: (312) 641-1505
Internet Homepage: giordanos.com
Company Email: giordano@giordanos.com
Type of Business: Chain Restaurant Operator
Year Founded: 1974
Systemwide Sales: $153,685,000 (e)
Total Sales: $58,487,000 (e)
Alcohol Sales: 1%
Number of Employees: 1,240
Average Check: Lunch(24); Dinner(30)
Internet Order Processing: Yes
Internet Sales: 1.00%
Total Units: 61
Trade Names: Giordano's Restaurant & Pizza (61)
Company-Owned Units: 10
Units Franchised To: 50
Preferred Square Footage: 5,000
Preferred Location Types: Downtown; Freestanding; Mobile Unit; Strip Mall
Alcohol Served: Beer, Wine, Liquor
Primary Menu: Pizza (61)
Projected Openings: 2
Areas of Operation: AZ, FL, IL, IN, MI, MN, NV, OH
Type of Foodservice: Casual Dining (61)
Catering Services: Yes
Distribution Centers: CHICAGO, IL
Primary Distributors: (Full Line) Edward Don & Co., WOODRIDGE, IL
Parent Company: Victory Park Capital Advisors, CHICAGO, IL

Key Personnel
YORGO KOUTSOGIORGAS - CEO; President
DAVID POOLE - CFO
SANG LEE - VP Technology
MARTHA SPEZIA-LASHLEY - VP Purchasing
MEGHAN PARRA - Director Marketing, Public Relations
DAN GILLAND - Director E-Commerce
BUFFY BERNARDO - Director Development, Training

Gold Coast Dogs Inc.
3525 W Peterson Ave Ste 505
Chicago, IL 60659-3317

Telephone: (773) 267-8180
Fax Number: (773) 267-8185
Internet Homepage: goldcoastdogs.net
Company Email: goldcoastdogs@goldcoastdogs.net
Type of Business: Chain Restaurant Operator
Year Founded: 1985
Systemwide Sales: $15,072,000 (e)
Total Sales: $1,255,000 (e)
Number of Employees: 88
Average Check: Breakfast(8); Lunch(8); Dinner(8)
Total Units: 4
Trade Names: Gold Coast Dogs (4)
Units Franchised To: 4
Preferred Square Footage: 2,500
Preferred Location Types: Airports; Community Mall; Downtown; Freestanding; Regional Mall; Strip Mall
Primary Menu: Hot Dogs (4)
Areas of Operation: IL
Type of Foodservice: Quick Serve (4)
Catering Services: Yes
Primary Distributors: (Full Line) Gordon Food Service Inc., WYOMING, MI

Key Personnel
NIZARALI LADHANI - President; Partner
SULAIMAN RAHIM - Partner; Director Operations, Supply Chain, Marketing, Franchising
HAMID HUSSAIN - VP Operations, Human Resources; General Buyer
DELOPME T. JAFFERBHIMANI - Director Information Systems, Business Development, Menu Development

Golden Nugget Pancake House
1765 W Lawrence Ave
Chicago, IL 60640-4403

Telephone: (773) 769-6700
Fax Number: (773) 769-1341
Internet Homepage: goldennuggetpancake.com
Company Email: lawrence@goldennuggetpancake.com
Type of Business: Chain Restaurant Operator
Year Founded: 1961
Total Sales: $24,200,000 (e)
Number of Employees: 171
Average Check: Breakfast(6); Lunch(10); Dinner(14)
Total Units: 6
Trade Names: Golden Nugget Pancake House (6)
Company-Owned Units: 6
Preferred Square Footage: 3,500
Preferred Location Types: Freestanding
Primary Menu: American (6)
Areas of Operation: IL
Type of Foodservice: Family Restaurant (6)
Primary Distributors: (Full Line) SYSCO Food Services of Chicago Inc., DES PLAINES, IL

Key Personnel
CATHY GUZMAN - General Manager; Executive Chef; Director Finance, Operations, Facility/Maintenance, Information Systems, Human Resources, Store Fixtures; General Buyer

Goose Island Beer Co.
1800 W Fulton St
Chicago, IL 60612-2512

Telephone: (312) 226-1119
Fax Number: (312) 733-1692
Internet Homepage: gooseisland.com
Company Email: info@gooseisland.com
Type of Business: Chain Restaurant Operator

Year Founded: 1988
Total Sales: $32,610,000 (e)
Alcohol Sales: 25%
Number of Employees: 133
Average Check: Lunch(12); Dinner(18)
Total Units: 8
Trade Names: Goose Island Brew Pub (8)
Company-Owned Units: 8
Preferred Location Types: Freestanding
Alcohol Served: Beer, Wine, Liquor
Primary Menu: American (8)
Areas of Operation: IL, FC
Type of Foodservice: Casual Dining (8)
Primary Distributors: (Food) US Foods, BENSENVILLE, IL

Key Personnel
JOHN HALL - Founder; General Buyer
TODD AHSMANN - President

Greek Islands
200 S Halsted St
Chicago, IL 60661-5404

Telephone: (312) 782-9855
Fax Number: (312) 454-0937
Internet Homepage: greekislands.net
Type of Business: Chain Restaurant Operator
Year Founded: 1971
Total Sales: $4,801,000 (e)
Alcohol Sales: 20%
Number of Employees: 80
Average Check: Lunch(16); Dinner(28)
Total Units: 2
Trade Names: Greek Islands (1); Greek Islands West (1)
Company-Owned Units: 2
Preferred Square Footage: 1,500; 2,000
Preferred Location Types: Freestanding; Office Complex
Alcohol Served: Beer, Wine, Liquor
Primary Menu: Greek/Mediterranean (2)
Areas of Operation: IL
Type of Foodservice: Casual Dining (2)
Primary Distributors: (Food) SYSCO Food Services of Chicago Inc., DES PLAINES, IL

Key Personnel
GUS COUCHELL - President; General Buyer
ANGELO PETRATOS - General Manager

GRK Greek Kitchen
219 W Washington St
Chicago, IL 60606-3405

Telephone: (312) 606-0633
Internet Homepage: greekkitchen.com
Company Email: info@eatgrk.com
Type of Business: Chain Restaurant Operator
Year Founded: 1976
Total Units: 7
Trade Names: Greek Kitchen Bar (1); GRK Greek Kitchen (5); Hub's Restaurant (1)
Company-Owned Units: 7
Primary Menu: Greek/Mediterranean (7)
Projected Openings: 2
Areas of Operation: IL
Type of Foodservice: Casual Dining (1); Fast Casual (6)

Key Personnel
BILL THANOUKOS - Partner
PETER THANOUKOS - Partner
CARLOS CEBALLOS - General Manager

Hannah's Bretzel
116 N Aberdeen St
Chicago, IL 60607

Telephone: (312) 621-1111
Internet Homepage: hannahsbretzel.com
Company Email: info@hannahsbretzel.com
Type of Business: Chain Restaurant Operator
Year Founded: 2004
Total Sales: $6,268,000 (e)
Total Units: 7
Trade Names: Hannah's Bretzel (7)
Company-Owned Units: 7
Preferred Location Types: Office Complex; Other
Primary Menu: Sandwiches/Deli (7)
Areas of Operation: IL
Type of Foodservice: Quick Serve (7)

Key Personnel
FLORIAN PFAHLER - CEO; President; General Buyer
WESLEY FRIEDMAN - Manager Operations

HC Restaurant Group Inc.
33 W Kinzie St
Chicago, IL 60654-4613

Telephone: (312) 828-0966
Fax Number: (312) 828-0962
Internet Homepage: harrycarays.com
Company Email: holycow@harrycarays.com
Type of Business: Chain Restaurant Operator
Year Founded: 1987
Total Sales: $23,960,000 (e)
Alcohol Sales: 30%
Number of Employees: 350
Average Check: Lunch(20); Dinner(46)
Internet Order Processing: Yes
Total Units: 7
Trade Names: Harry Caray's - Midway (1); Harry Caray's 7th Inning Stretch (1); Harry Caray's Italian Steakhouse & Bar (3); Harry Caray's Tavern (1); Holy Mackerel! (1)
Company-Owned Units: 7
Preferred Location Types: Downtown; Office Complex
Alcohol Served: Beer, Wine, Liquor
Primary Menu: American (3); Italian (3); Seafood (1)
Areas of Operation: IL
Type of Foodservice: Casual Dining (4); Fine Dining (3)
Catering Services: Yes
Primary Distributors: (Food) US Foods, BENSENVILLE, IL
Notes: HC Restaurant Group has signed on as a franchisee of Trader Vic's in the Chicago area.

Key Personnel
GRANT DEPORTER - CEO; President; Director Real Estate, Design; General Buyer
PET KRUBECK - CFO; Controller

Hogsalt Hospitality
230 W Kinzie St
Chicago, IL 60654-4908

Telephone: (312) 464-9544
Internet Homepage: giltbarchicago.com; hogsalt.com
Company Email: contact@giltbarchicago.com
Type of Business: Chain Restaurant Operator
Total Sales: $21,290,000 (e)
Total Units: 15
Trade Names: 4 Charlie's Prime Rib (1); Aster Hall (1); Au Cheval (2); Bavette's Bar & Boeuf (2); Ciccio Mio (1); Doughnut Vault (1); Gilt Bar (1); Green Street Smoked Meats (1); High Five Ramen (1); Sawada Coffee (2); Small Cheval (1); Trivoli Tavern (1)
Company-Owned Units: 15
Primary Menu: American (6); Bar-B-Q (1); French/Continental (0); Italian (1); Japanese (1); Snacks (3); Steak (3)
Areas of Operation: IL
Type of Foodservice: Casual Dining (5); Fast Casual (6); Fine Dining (3); Quick Serve (1)

Key Personnel
BRENDAN SODIKOFF - Founder; CEO
JEAN TOMARO - Executive Director Beverages
DIDIER ELENA - Executive Director Quality Assurance
KIMBERLY GALBAN - Executive Director Operations
CARMEN MIRON - Controller
MICHELLE FEDERSCHMIDT - Director Beverages
RYAN NILSON - Director Culinary Development
DUSTIN TRIPP - Director Culinary Development
KAZ MITSUI - Director Food
LEIBIS CAMARENA - Director Safety
RYAN DAILEY - Director Coffee/Tea
BECKI SCHOLL - Director Alcoholic Beverages
RACHEL CARLIN - Manager Development-Training
GAVIN JOHNSON - Manager Restaurant Operations

RACHEL NIEMAN - Administrator Human Resources
DYLAN LERCH - Specialist Operations

Huck Finn Restaurants
6650 S Pulaski Rd
Chicago, IL 60629-5138

Telephone: (773) 581-4285
Fax Number: (773) 581-9108
Internet Homepage: huckfinnrestaurant.com
Type of Business: Chain Restaurant Operator
Year Founded: 1971
Total Sales: $4,915,000 (e)
Number of Employees: 105
Average Check: Breakfast(8); Lunch(8); Dinner(8)
Total Units: 3
Trade Names: Huck Finn Restaurants (3)
Company-Owned Units: 3
Preferred Location Types: Freestanding; Strip Mall
Primary Menu: American (3)
Areas of Operation: IL
Type of Foodservice: Family Restaurant (3)
Primary Distributors: (Full Line) US Foods Holding Corp., ROSEMONT, IL

Key Personnel
GEORGE HIOTIS - President; General Manager; Executive Chef; General Buyer
PAUL HIOTIS - VP Operations
JIM HIOTIS - General Buyer

Hyatt Hotels Corporation
150 N Riverside Plz Floor 8
Chicago, IL 60606-4716

Telephone: (312) 750-1234
Fax Number: (312) 780-5790
Internet Homepage: hyatt.com
Company Email: info@hyatt.com
Type of Business: Foodservice Operations - Hotel/Motels
Year Founded: 1957
Publicly Held: Yes
Total Sales: $3,359,400,000 (e)
Alcohol Sales: 20%
Number of Employees: 60,000
Total Units: 974
Restaurants in Hotels: 657
Trade Names: Hyatt Hotels (974)
Company-Owned Units: 657
Alcohol Served: Beer, Wine, Liquor
Areas of Operation: AL, AZ, CA, CO, CT, DC, FL, GA, HI, ID, IL, IN, KY, LA, MA, MD, MI, MN, NC, NJ, NM, NV, NY, OH, OK, PA, SC, TN, TX, VA, WA, WI, BC, ON
Foreign Countries: ARGENTINA; ARMENIA; ARUBA; AUSTRALIA; AZERBAIJAN; BRAZIL; CANADA; EGYPT; ENGLAND; FRANCE; GERMANY; GREECE; INDIA; INDONESIA; ITALY; JAPAN; MEXICO; NEPAL; OMAN; PANAMA; QATAR; SAUDI ARABIA; SOUTH AFRICA; SOUTH KOREA; SWITZERLAND;THAILAND; UNITED ARAB EMIRATES
Primary Distributors: (Food) SYSCO Food Services of Chicago Inc., DES PLAINES, IL
Notes: Total number of locations include all owned, managed and franchised hotels but excludes vacation ownership and residential properties. Not all hotels have on-site foodservice. The company derives approximately 88% of its revenue from hotel operations.

Key Personnel
THOMAS J. PRITZKER - Executive Chairman
MARK S. HOPLAMAZIAN - CEO; President
PETE SEARS - President Group
LARRY TCHOU - President Group, International Division; Exec VP
PETER FULTON - President Group, International Division; Exec VP
DAVID UDELL - President Group
SUSAN SANTIAGO - President United States, Canada
DAN LOMBARDI - Owner
AJAY THAKUR - Owner
JOAN BOTTARINI - CFO
MALAIKA MYERS - Chief Human Resources Officer
TYRONNE STOUDEMIRE - Chief Diversity Officer; VP
MARK VONDRASEK - Chief Commercial Officer
TONY SANTORO - Chief Engineering Officer
BENJAMIN VAUGHN - Chief Information Security Officer; VP
ERIC CHARLSON - Area Director Human Resources
CARLOS CABRERA - Senior VP Operations
DAVID TARR - Senior VP Real Estate Development, Business Development
BRIAN KARABA - Senior VP Investor Relations; Treasurer
DAVID LEWIN - Senior VP Marketing, Sales
JAMES FRANCQUE - Senior VP; General Counsel
JIM CHU - Senior VP Franchise Operations
GREG CROSS - Senior VP Operations
CHRISTY SINNOTT - Senior VP Talent
SARA KEARNEY - VP Marketing, Sales
ANNE HANCH - VP Procurement
WENDY PARKER - VP Region
JEFFREY HANSEN - VP Construction, Design
SHERRY BATEMAN - VP Sales; Executive Assistant Marketing, Sales
CHAD REPPY - VP Finance, Strategy
PAUL DALY - VP Beverages, Food
STEVE ENSELEIN - VP Catering
JONATHAN MEISTER - VP Design
LAUREN BROWN - VP Employee Compensation
LIZ BAKER-BAUER - VP Finance
GEORGE VIZER - VP Franchise Operations
PHIL LABELLE - VP Information Technology
DEJAN DASIC - VP Licensing
JEFF FLATER - VP Marketing
MICHAEL KOFFLER - VP Operations
MARY TURILLI - VP Real Estate
MATT GINTER - VP Research & Development
TRISTAN DOWELL - VP Retail Operations
MARK BAKER - VP Risk Management
GUS VONDERHEIDE - VP Sales
MICHAEL SEGALL - VP
MALCOLM TURNER - VP
SCOTT RICHER - Regional VP Real Estate Development, Business Development, Franchise Development, Canada
MATT SCHALK - Regional VP Marketing, Sales
DANIEL KUPERSCHMID - Regional VP Operations
EMILY KEIP - Regional VP
MARGARET C. EGAN - Corporate Secretary; General Counsel
DAN MCMENAMY - Controller
MICHELE HAYNES - General Counsel
STEPHANIE JEAN-JACQUES - General Counsel
ANALISA PADILLA - General Counsel
MIRSAD BASIC - General Manager
SILVIYA NIKOLOVA - General Manager
MOLLY CLAYTON - General Manager
JERAMY WOOLDRIDGE - Executive Chef
DESIKAN RAMASWAMY - Senior Director Information Technology; Senior Manager Technology
MICHAEL HALLORAN - Director Food and Beverage
BARBARA NOTTKE - Director Human Resources
FRANK WONG - Director Digital Media
PHILLIP TYLER - Director Marketing
REBECCA PALOMINO - Director Global sales
THOMAS PASCARELLA - Director Finance
MARY STEVENS - Director Human Resources
NOAH HOPPE - Director Development
PAUL STINSA - Director Procurement
GINA FARALLI - Director Tax
SUE CONATSER - Director Tax
SHANE MOORE - Director Marketing, E-Commerce
CORY BAUM - Director Marketing, Sales
MARISOL FISHER - Director Design, Store Planning
ALVARO MONTOYA MORA - Director Design, Store Planning
NICO SCHERMAN - Director Beverages, Food
KATHLEEN LEHAN - Director Accounting
SHANNAN HARRIGAN - Director Branding
MICHAEL COHEN - Director Communications
ZAJIM MARKICIC CSI, CDT - Director Design
MICHELLE ROMEIN - Director Event Planning
DEVIN GRIFFITH - Director Finance
STACEY HICKMAN - Director Finance
KATHRYN PARKER - Director Finance
ERIN VORHIES - Director Global Marketing
PAUL MUMBERGER - Director Global sales
ALFONSO DIEGO - Director Information Technology

ROHAN JANI - Director Information Technology
ALEX SHVARTSMAN - Director Information Technology
DAVID WILSON - Director Information Technology
LESLIE GIRSCH - Director Internal Audit
MARY SCOTT - Director Legal
ROBERT FRAZIER - Director Operations
BILLY BATS - Director Research & Development
GERRY CLARK - Director Sales
PEGGY WOOD - Director Sales
JOHN CZARNECKI - Director Store Development
ADAM ROHMAN - Director Store Development
SASHA MEROLA - Director Strategic Planning
DONNA BONGIOVANNI - Director Strategic Services
BRAD MILLER - Director Strategic Services
CHRISTINE THOMPSON - Director Strategic Services
ELIZABETH BRANNING-SCHULTZ - Director Strategy
NIKKI OCCHINO-MASSEY - Director Talent
RICK SEGAL - Director
HELEN MEI - Assistant Director Finance
MILAGROS CARTER - Senior Manager Branding
SARAH PFOUTS SULLIVAN - Senior Manager Marketing
SHARON LUNDIN - Senior Manager Sales
NORIKO ITO - Senior Manager Tax
KELLY HAYNES - Senior Manager Operations, Information Technology
EILEEN RAINEY - Senior Manager Compliance
MIRIAM BLACKSTONE - Senior Manager Customer Service
RENEE SCHULTZ - Senior Manager Design
DANIEL BJURSTROM - Senior Manager Finance
MEGAN HAYES - Senior Manager Finance
ROSHANDA WALKER - Senior Manager Real Estate Development
ALVINA AYALA - Manager Human Resources
ASHLEY MOHR - Manager Digital Media
FARZANA CHOWDHURY - Manager Tax
JOHN ALLEN - Manager Operations
LAURA PALID - Manager Global sales
LINDSAY O'CONNOR - Manager Sales
MICHELE FRIERI - Manager Sales
SHIVAM MANN - Manager Customer Service
THERESA BAUER - Manager Benefits
DANIELLE BANKS - Manager Accounting
MARIKO GODFREY - Manager Accounting
JUSTIN SMITH - Manager Accounting
KRISTIN SCHROEDER SCHMIDT - Manager Design
ALEKSANDR PAVLENKO - Manager Development
JUSTEN TIMMERMAN - Manager Development
DANIEL MCRAE - Manager Digital
JULIAN TORRES - Manager Information Technology
YING L FREY - Manager Legal
STEPHANIE NEWMARK - Manager Marketing
JOE BONTARUSAY - Manager Operations
DON MIDDLEBROOK - Manager Product Development
MARY GWEN CURRY - Manager Tax
DEMI BARBOS - Manager Accounting, Human Resources
ROBERT BUCKLEY - Manager POS/Scanning, Applications
ERIN PETRUZZELLO - Manager Finance, Information Technology
SHAKIRA MONTGOMERY - Manager Accounting
MIRANDA ROSS - Manager Accounting
RONNIE ALERTA - Manager Applications
MARTHA TAPPLER - Manager Communications
SHEILA CARLSON - Manager Compliance
ASHLEY EHLERS - Manager Employee Compensation
TOM CHAMBERS - Manager Facility/Maintenance
STEPHEN AHRENS - Manager Finance
DENISE DEBOER - Manager Finance
STEPHANIE HARRAH - Manager Finance
RYAN NUCKOLS - Manager Finance
JOSH SIEBERT - Manager Finance
KIM KUJAWA - Manager HRIS
LESLEY GORE - Manager Human Resources
MAHMOUD MOHAMMAD - Manager Human Resources
CHRISTINE SHAUGHNESSY - Manager Information Systems
JORDAN BLEIBTREY CPA - Manager Information Technology
ABNER SAL PADILLA - Manager Information Technology
MEL THOMAS - Manager Information Technology
VELLERA HEARD - Manager Legal
EDUARDO GARZA NORIEGA - Manager Quality Assurance
ANN HARRIS PMP,ITILV3 - Manager Real Estate
ADINA WOLF - Manager Recruitment
KATHERINE GEAR-GANCARZ - Manager Social Media
NICOLE CASEY - Manager Talent
CARLY WALSH - Manager Talent
GINA HENRICKSON - Associate Manager Communications
SIAN MARTIN - Associate Manager Communications
JENNY HARROD - Associate Manager
HANNAH KIM - Associate Manager
NINA GARRISON - Brand Manager
BEN FAJARDO - Supervisor
JACQUELINE PETERSON - Supervisor Customer Service
MIKE VELEZ - Supervisor Customer Service
PETER NAHRSTEDT - Senior Project Manager
TINA LONGAWA WORK - Senior Project Manager
NICOLE MARTINI - Senior Project Manager
TODD FELLERER - Senior Project Manager
AHMED ELAYAN - Project Manager Information Technology
MATHIEU BRUCE - Project Manager Information Systems
DAVID JEFFERY - Project Manager Information Systems
DEBBIE ANNERINO - Project Manager
STEPHANIE HSIEH - Project Manager
MARK MEEKER - Principal
DENA STAMATOUKOS - Specialist Human Resources
CHRIS ORTIZ - Specialist Information Technology
DAN HYATT - Specialist Social Media
HEIDI BRAZIER - Coordinator Human Resources
JAIME SMYTH - Coordinator
REBECCA BYRNE - Coordinator Digital
JENNIFER FORD - Coordinator Branding
JILL LEAHY - Coordinator Facility/Maintenance
IAN WILSON - Agent Customer Service
KATIE GREGORY - Designer
KRISTEN HARDING - Systems Analyst
DEBBIE SCHWIND - Systems Analyst
PAUL JOHNSON - Senior Analyst
ANDREW ULMAN - Senior Analyst
EVE YANAKI - Senior Analyst Development
RENEA GOOD - Senior Analyst HRIS
CHRISSY O'BRIEN - Senior Analyst Tax
YASH PATEL - Senior Analyst Tax
BRIAN OLSZEWSKI - Senior Analyst Applications
CARL PETERSON - Senior Analyst Applications
JENNIFER MILLER - Senior Analyst Employee Compensation
MIKE CLIFTON - Senior Analyst Finance
ERIC EVERT - Senior Analyst Finance
KELLY ROWE - Senior Analyst Operations
JOANNA PAREDES - Analyst HRIS
MIDHAD JAKUPOVIC - Analyst Network
EDITH PACHECO - Analyst Benefits
CHRISTINA WELLS - Analyst Development
MICHAEL MAUNDU - Analyst Information/Data Security
JASON LEWIS - Analyst Sales
TREVOR EVENSON - Analyst Finance
HEATHER WHITMAN - Analyst HRIS
ERIN MCLEAN - Analyst Human Resources
BRYAN SUREK - Architect Information Systems
JYOTHI A. - Developer Software
RAHUL NAGENDRA YELLAPRAGADA - Developer Software
BILL SMITH - Developer Software
SCOTT NEMEC - Developer Software
JAMES WRIGHT - Developer
SHYAM PATEL - Senior Engineer Quality Assurance
GREGORY JACKSON - Engineer Software
JOSEPH BIANCHI - Engineer
BRIAN WALKER - Engineer Quality Assurance
SANYUKTA PODURI - Engineer E-Commerce
FAISAL ABIDI - Engineer
JEFF ATTEN ITIL - Engineer

I Dream of Falafel
851 W Belmont Ave
Chicago, IL 60657-4401

Telephone: (773) 672-2780
Fax Number: (773) 697-4093
Internet Homepage: idreamoffalafel.com
Type of Business: Chain Restaurant Operator
Total Sales: $17,500,000 (e)
Average Check: Dinner(14)
Internet Order Processing: Yes
Total Units: 9
Trade Names: I Dream of Falafel (9)
Company-Owned Units: 9
Primary Menu: Middle Eastern (9)
Areas of Operation: IL
Type of Foodservice: Fast Casual (9)
Catering Services: Yes
Primary Distributors: (Full Line) SYSCO Food Services of Chicago Inc., DES PLAINES, IL; (Supplies) TriMark Marlinn, BEDFORD PARK, IL

Key Personnel
IMRAN KASBATI - Partner; General Buyer
MUNAF KASBATI - Partner; General Buyer
SHOAIB AZIZ - Partner; General Buyer
HENRY NUGUID - Partner; General Buyer
HASSAN NASEEM - Partner
ANA ISABEL - Manager Catering

Intelligentsia Coffee, Inc.
1850 W Fulton St
Chicago, IL 60612

Telephone: (312) 563-0023
Internet Homepage: intelligentsiacoffee.com
Company Email: customersupport@intelligentsiacoffee.com
Type of Business: Chain Restaurant Operator
Year Founded: 1995
Total Units: 11
Trade Names: Intelligentsia (11)
Company-Owned Units: 11
Primary Menu: Coffee (11)
Projected Openings: 2
Areas of Operation: CA, IL, MA, NY
Type of Foodservice: Quick Serve (11)
Parent Company: Peet's Coffee & Tea Inc., EMERYVILLE, CA

Key Personnel
JAMES MCLAUGHLIN - CEO; President; General Buyer
CAMILLE MCLEOD - CFO

Italian Village Restaurants Inc.
71 W Monroe St
Chicago, IL 60603-4910

Telephone: (312) 332-7005
Fax Number: (312) 332-2656
Internet Homepage: italianvillage-chicago.com
Company Email: ivcatering1927@gmail.com
Type of Business: Chain Restaurant Operator
Year Founded: 1927
Total Sales: $9,428,000 (e)
Alcohol Sales: 25%
Number of Employees: 130
Average Check: Lunch(30); Dinner(60)
Total Units: 3
Trade Names: La Cantina Enoteca (1); The Village (1); Vivere (1)
Company-Owned Units: 3
Preferred Location Types: Office Complex
Alcohol Served: Beer, Wine, Liquor
Primary Menu: Italian (3)
Areas of Operation: IL
Type of Foodservice: Casual Dining (1); Fine Dining (2)
Primary Distributors: (Full Line) SYSCO Corporation, HOUSTON, TX

Key Personnel
GINA CAPITANINI - CEO; President
RAY CAPITANINI - VP

Kanela Breakfast Club
3231 N Clark St
Chicago, IL 60657-2172

Telephone: (773) 355-4070
Internet Homepage: kanelabreakfastclub.com
Company Email: events@kanelachicago.com
Type of Business: Chain Restaurant Operator
Total Sales: $12,330,000 (e)
Average Check: Breakfast(20);
Total Units: 6
Trade Names: Kanela Breakfast Club (6)
Company-Owned Units: 6
Primary Menu: American (6)
Areas of Operation: IL
Type of Foodservice: Casual Dining (6)
Catering Services: Yes
Notes: Lardakis also owns the Municipal Bar + Dining Co. (Chicago)

Key Personnel
CHRIS LARDAKIS - Co-Founder; CEO; Partner
ALEXI GIANNOULIAS - Co-Founder; Partner
KAYLA LARDAKIS - Director Operations

Kuma's Corner
2900 W Belmont Ave
Chicago, IL 60618-5804

Telephone: (773) 604-8769
Internet Homepage: kumascorner.com
Type of Business: Chain Restaurant Operator
Total Units: 5
Trade Names: Kuma's Corner (5)
Company-Owned Units: 5
Primary Menu: Hamburger (5)
Areas of Operation: IL, IN
Type of Foodservice: Casual Dining (5)

Key Personnel
MIKE CAIN - Founder
RON CAIN - President; Owner; Director Operations; General Buyer
MIKE KOSIAK - Director Operations

L3 Hospitality Group
100 W Kinzie St Ste 275
Chicago, IL 60654

Telephone: (312) 836-5903
Internet Homepage: l3hg.com
Company Email: epaulsen@L3HG.com
Type of Business: Chain Restaurant Operator
Year Founded: 2013
Total Units: 5
Trade Names: Kinship (1); LYFE Kitchen (3); Next of Kin (1)
Company-Owned Units: 5
Primary Menu: American (5)
Areas of Operation: IL
Type of Foodservice: Casual Dining (4); Fast Casual (1)
Headquarter Offices: Lyfe Kitchen, CHICAGO, IL

Key Personnel
CAREY COOPER - Co-Founder; CEO
GAIL TAGGART - Co-Founder; President

Le Bouchon
1958 N Damen Ave
Chicago, IL 60647-4570

Telephone: (773) 862-6600
Internet Homepage: lasardine.com; lebouchonofchicago.com
Company Email: LeBouchonOfChicago@gmail.com
Type of Business: Chain Restaurant Operator
Year Founded: 1993
Total Sales: $6,227,000 (e)
Alcohol Sales: 35%
Number of Employees: 15
Average Check: Lunch(26); Dinner(54)

Total Units: 2
Trade Names: La Sardine (1); Le Bouchon (1)
Company-Owned Units: 2
Preferred Location Types: Freestanding
Alcohol Served: Beer, Wine, Liquor
Primary Menu: French/Continental (2)
Areas of Operation: IL
Type of Foodservice: Fine Dining (2)

Key Personnel
SUSANNE POILEVEY - Owner; General Manager; General Buyer

Leona's Restaurants Inc.
9156 S Stony Island Ave
Chicago, IL 60617-3511

Telephone: (773) 881-7700
Internet Homepage: leonas.com
Company Email: info@leonas.com
Type of Business: Chain Restaurant Operator
Year Founded: 1950
Total Sales: $13,531,000 (e)
Alcohol Sales: 10%
Number of Employees: 579
Average Check: Lunch(18); Dinner(24)
Internet Order Processing: Yes
Total Units: 3
Trade Names: Leona's Neighborhood Restaurant (3)
Company-Owned Units: 3
Preferred Square Footage: 4,000
Preferred Location Types: Freestanding
Alcohol Served: Beer, Wine, Liquor
Primary Menu: Italian (3)
Areas of Operation: IL
Type of Foodservice: Casual Dining (3)
Catering Services: Yes
On-site Distribution Center: Yes
Primary Distributors: (Equipment) Edward Don & Co., WOODRIDGE, IL; (Food) Food & Paper Supply Co., CHICAGO, IL; (Supplies) Edward Don & Co., WOODRIDGE, IL

Key Personnel
TED MAVRAKIS - President; Partner; General Buyer

Leonidas Cafe
1964 North Halsted Street
Chicago, IL 60614

Telephone: (312) 224-0002
Internet Homepage: leonidas-cafe.com
Company Email: info@leonidas-usa.com
Type of Business: Chain Restaurant Operator
Year Founded: 1913
Total Sales: $6,949,000 (e)
Total Units: 4
Trade Names: Leonidas Cafe (4)
Company-Owned Units: 4
Primary Menu: Miscellaneous (4)
Areas of Operation: IL
Type of Foodservice: Casual Dining (0); Fast Casual (4)

Key Personnel
MARIE DOUAILLY - Owner

Lettuce Entertain You Enterprises Inc.
5419 N Sheridan Rd Ste 116
Chicago, IL 60640-1918

Telephone: (773) 878-7340
Fax Number: (773) 878-7667
Internet Homepage: leye.com
Type of Business: Chain Restaurant Operator
Year Founded: 1971
Total Sales: $1,088,600,000 (e)
Alcohol Sales: 20%
Number of Employees: 7,400
Internet Order Processing: Yes
Total Units: 125
Trade Names: aba (2); Antico Posto (1); B Square Pizza (2); Bar Ramone (1); BARILLA ITALIAN PASTERIA (1); Beatrix (4); Beatrix Market (5); BEN PAO (1); Big Bowl Chinese and Thai (7); Big Bowl Chinese Express (14); BILL'S ORIGINAL TAVERN PIZZA (2); Bub City (2); Cafe Ba-Ba-Reeba! (1); Community Canteen (1); Crab Cellar (1); Di Pescara (1); Eiffel Tower Restaurant (1); El Segundo Sol Taqueria & Margarita Bar (1); Ema (1); Foodease (1); Hub 51 (1); Il Porcellino (1); Joe's Seafood, Prime Steak, and Stone Crab (3); L. Woods Tap & Pine Lodge (1); M Burger (5); Maggiano's Little Italy (7); Mon Ami Gabi (5); Naoki Sushi (1); Osteria Via Stato (1); PADMA'S CURRY LEAF® (1); PAPAGUS (1); Petterino's (1); Pizzera Via Stato (1); Pizzeria Portofino (1); Quality Craband Oyster Bah (1); R.J. Grunts (1); Ramen-san (3); Rotisserie Ema (1); RPM Italian (2); RPM Seafood (1); RPM Steak (1); Saranello's Ristorante Italiano (1); Seasides's Fried Chicken, Slow-Cooked Ribs & Lobster Too (1); Shaw's Crab House (2); Stella Barra Pizzeria (4); Strip Burger and Chicken (1); SUB 51® (1); Summer House Santa Monica (2); Sushi-San (1); Tallboy Taco (1); Three Dots and a Dash (1); Tokio Asian Fusion (1); Tucci Italian (2); Twin City Grill (1); VONG'S THAI KITCHEN (1); Wildfire (7); Wow Bao (8)
Company-Owned Units: 118
Units Franchised From: 7
Preferred Location Types: Community Mall; Downtown; Freestanding; Grocery Stores; Hotel/Motel; Regional Mall
Alcohol Served: Beer, Wine, Liquor
Primary Menu: American (26); Asian (33); Bar-B-Q (3); Chinese (1); French/Continental (6); Greek/Mediterranean (4); Hamburger (6); Italian (16); Japanese(4); Latin American/Cuban (1); Mexican (1); Miscellaneous (1); Pizza (10); Seafood (5); Spanish (1); Steak (1); Steak/Seafood (6); Taco (1)
Projected Openings: 3
Areas of Operation: AZ, CA, IL, MD, MN, NV, VA
Type of Foodservice: Casual Dining (78); Family Restaurant (1); Fast Casual (14); Fine Dining (5); Quick Serve (22)
Catering Services: Yes
Franchise Affiliation: Maggiano's Little Italy, DALLAS, TX
Primary Distributors: (Food) SYSCO Food Services of Chicago Inc., DES PLAINES, IL; (Food) Stock Yards Packing Co., CHICAGO, IL
Headquarter Offices: Wow Bao LLC, CHICAGO, IL

Key Personnel
RICHARD MELMAN - Chairman; Founder
R. J. MELMAN - CEO; President; Partner
HOWARD KATZ - President Group; Partner
JOHN BUCHANAN - President Group; Senior VP
DON CARSON - President Division; Partner
YVES ROUBAUD - President Division; Partner; Executive Chef Division
JEAN JOHO - President; Partner; Executive Chef Group
SCOTT BARTON - President Division; Partner
CHRISTOPHER MEERS - President Group; Partner
MARC JACOBS - President Division; Partner; Exec VP Group
MARK TORMEY - President Group; Partner
MICHAEL CUNNINGHAM - President Division; Partner
DAVE QUILLEN - President Division
KEVIN REYNOLDS - President Division
FRED JOAST - Partner
SUSIE SOUTHGATE-FOX - Partner; Exec VP Operations, Human Resources
JAY STIEBER - Partner; Exec VP; General Counsel
GABINO SOTELINO - Partner; Executive Chef Group
STEVE LAHAIE - Partner; Senior VP Division
JOE DECKER - Partner; VP Group; Executive Chef Group
BOB LOESCHORN - Partner; VP Group
CHRIS FAVERO - Partner; VP Group
MARK DORIAN - Partner; VP Purchasing
ROSS BUTER - Partner; VP Group
PERRY H. FUSELIER JR - Partner; VP Group
RANDY BRAND - Partner; VP Group
JERROD MELMAN - Partner
MYCHAEL BONNER - Partner; Executive Chef Division
DAVID DIGREGORIO - Partner; Executive Chef Group
TIM HOCKETT - Partner; Executive Chef Division
MATT MULVIHILL - Partner

WILLIE NEAL - Partner
RON THOMPSON - Partner
SUSAN WEAVER - Partner; Executive Chef Division
MICHAEL BELLOVICH - Partner; Executive Chef Group
TERRY LYNCH - Partner Division; Executive Chef Division
MOLLY MELMAN - Partner; VP Training
ROSALYN GIBBS DAWSON - Partner
JEFF MAHIN - Partner; Executive Chef Division
ADAM ROCHMAN - Partner
GERARD CENTIOLI - Partner; Senior VP
CHARLES HASKELL - Partner
KIRAN PINTO - Partner
JOHN SIMMONS - Chief Human Resources Officer
MICHAEL HALEY - CIO
JENNIFER BELL - Chief Marketing Officer
THOMAS MUNO - Senior VP Accounting, Strategic Planning; Controller
STEVE DONAHUE - Senior VP Accounting
CARROL SYMANK - VP Risk Management, Training, Food Safety
BILL NEVRUZ - VP
ROBERTA FRIERSON - VP Information Technology
ETHAN SAMSON - VP; General Counsel
ADMIR IBISEVIC - General Manager Food
ASHLEY HAIGHT - General Manager; Assistant
CJ JACOBSON - Executive Chef
CHRISTOPHER GUMPRECHT - Director Marketing
ALLISON GALLESE - Director Marketing, Sales
JERI BLOCK - Director Catering
CHRISTINE HILL - Director
MICHELE FUNK - Director Social Media
KEVIN KOSIEWICZ - Director Operations, Strategy
JULIE FINDLAY - Director Marketing, Public Relations
ELISSA TRAINOR - Director Technology
ALLISON CURATOLO - Director
MARGARET KOSIROG - Director Employee Benefits
BETH CUMMINGS - Director Engineering
SAMANTHA LEVY - Director Human Resources
JAROD DIXON - Director Information Technology, Applications
JOSHUA HAUER - Director Operations
JACOB SCHWIMMER - Director Operations
TOM LAMSON - Director Operations
ALLIE DRAZIN - Director Event Planning
LAUREN SOKOL - Director Employee Development, Division-Training
JORDAN JOHNSON - Director Marketing
ISABEL SHAINDLIN - Director Marketing; Project Manager Logistics
MICHAEL SIMONEAU - Art Director
ERIN KAVANAGH JUACHE - Senior Manager Marketing, Sales
SEAN THOMAS - Manager Operations, Network
BERTHA PETERS - Manager Payroll
MICHELLE MAXSON - Manager Finance
RACHEL QUINTANA - Manager Operations, Information Technology
CARA YAFFE - Manager Marketing
ANDREW HEISLER - Manager Digital Marketing
EMILY SMOKER - Manager Marketing
ELYSE KORT - Manager Marketing

✝ Levy Restaurants

980 N Michigan Ave Ste 400
Chicago, IL 60611-4518

Telephone: (312) 664-8200
Fax Number: (312) 280-2739
Internet Homepage: levyrestaurants.com
Type of Business: Foodservice Management Operator
Year Founded: 1978
Total Sales: $2,742,286,000 (e)
Number of Employees: 16,000
Number of Locations Served: 75
Total Foodservice Mgmt Accounts: 75
Trade Names: American Girl Place (2); Bourbon Pub (1); Bourbon Steak (1); Cafe Spiaggia (1); Jake Melnick's Corner Tap (1); Line + Lure (1); Maddon's Post (1); Michael Jordan's Steak House (1); MOTOR (1); Paddlefish (1); River Roast (1); Spiaggia (1); Terralina Crafted Italian (1)
Areas of Operation: CA, FL, GA, HI, IL, MA, NE, NV, OH, PA, TX, UT, WI
Type of Foodservice: Fast Casual; Full-service sit-down dining; Mobile units/kiosks; Quick Serve
Foodservice Management Venues: Other; Sports Venues
Primary Distributors: (Full Line) SYSCO Food Services of Chicago Inc., DES PLAINES, IL
Parent Company: Compass Group PLC, LONDON, ENG
Headquarters: Compass Group The Americas, CHARLOTTE, NC
Divisional Offices: Levy Restaurants, ATLANTA, GA
Notes: In addition to providing on-site food management services, the company operates a number of restaurants; sales from these restaurants generate approximately 20% of corporate revenue.

Key Personnel
LARRY LEVY - Chairman
ANDREW LANSING - CEO; President
ROBERT WOOD - President Division
ROB ELLIS - CFO Group
BRIAN BRITTON - COO; Exec VP
ALISON WEBER - Chief Creative Officer
JEFF WINEMAN - Exec VP Business Development
SHAUNA GILHOOLY - Exec VP People
DENISE GAFFNEY - Senior VP Construction, Design
EDWARD GILATY - Senior VP Risk Management
DENISE GAFFNEY-NAWROCKI - Senior VP
ED GILATY - VP Risk Management, Quality Assurance, Food Safety
RUSSELL BRY - VP Culinary Operations
ROBIN KUZNETSKY - VP Group
JEFFREY ZOELLER - VP Purchasing
JENNIFER COX - Regional VP; Executive Chef
BILL BARTH - General Manager
RAY FARRIES - General Manager
MARY ANN HADAC - General Manager
JON ZISKAL - General Manager
ROBIN ROSENBERG - Executive Chef Group
NILAM PATEL - Senior Director Internal Audit
CRYSTAL MACLEAN - Director Human Resources
UBERT BERRUM - Director Operations
JEAN GREENWAY - Director Operations
MIKE IACOBELLI - Director Operations
JASON MAXEY - Director Operations
JEUNE N. NAZON - Director Operations
MARC ZUCKERT - Director Operations
DEAN LEBER - Director Purchasing
JORGE PEREZ - Director Purchasing
DAVID HEFFNER - Director Special Projects
NORI BONAVENTURA - Director Talent
KRISTIN CHIPMAN - Director Tax
JENNIFER MORGAN - Director
LISA SIRAGUSA - Director
ALEX KADUSHIN - Assistant Director Operations
MICHAEL SPEREKAS - Assistant Director Operations
BENITO SUERO JR - Assistant Director Operations
DREW SCOTT - Senior Manager Purchasing
SOCORRO PEREZ - Senior Manager
ASHLEY SOCORRO - Senior Manager
TOM KRUK - Regional Manager Information Systems
GUS ANAGNOSTOPOULOS - Regional Manager
CARLIE MCLEAN - Manager Training, Talent
EDWIN QUINONES - Manager Accounting
ASHLEY BAY - Manager Catering
KELCEY LEMKE - Manager Catering
VICTOR RAMIREZ - Manager Catering
ANDREA BERG - Manager Customer Service
ERIKKA BRITTEN - Manager Finance
JENNIFER CALLAHAN - Manager Finance
KHARI ANNES - Manager Purchasing
LENNY PRASCZEWICZ - Manager Purchasing
JOSE SOSA - Manager Purchasing
IMELDA TORRES - Manager Purchasing
COURTNEY CAWLEY - Manager Sales
GEOFF LARA - Manager Alcoholic Beverages
TONY STENTA - Manager Alcoholic Beverages
PAULO DURAN - Manager
HEATHER MULCHRONE - Manager
JESSE ROTHE - Manager
NORMAN SCHNEPF - Manager

Lunan Corporation
414 N Orleans St Ste 402
Chicago, IL 60610

Telephone: (312) 645-9898
Fax Number: (312) 645-0654
Internet Homepage: burritobeach.com; lunancorparbys.com
Company Email: parens@lunancorp.com
Type of Business: Chain Restaurant Operator
Year Founded: 1966
Total Sales: $52,050,000 (e)
Number of Employees: 1,200
Average Check: Lunch(8); Dinner(8)
Total Units: 27
Trade Names: Arby's (21); Burrito Beach (6)
Company-Owned Units: 6
Units Franchised From: 21
Preferred Square Footage: 2,700
Preferred Location Types: Freestanding; Regional Mall
Primary Menu: Mexican (6); Sandwiches/Deli (21)
Areas of Operation: CA, IL, NV
Type of Foodservice: Quick Serve (27)
Foodservice Management Venues: Schools
Franchise Affiliation: Arby's Restaurant Group, ATLANTA, GA
Primary Distributors: (Full Line) McLane/Elkhorn, ELKHORN, WI

Key Personnel
MICHAEL SCHULSON - Chairman; Director Real Estate
GREG SCHULSON - President
HARRY SAX - VP
TONY STELLA - Controller
JANET BROLINE - Manager Marketing

Lyfe Kitchen
100 W Kinzie St Ste 275
Chicago, IL 60654

Telephone: (312) 836-5903
Internet Homepage: lyfekitchen.com
Company Email: guestrelations@lyfekitchen.com
Type of Business: Chain Restaurant Operator
Total Sales: $4,629,000 (e)
Alcohol Sales: 5%
Average Check: Breakfast(5); Lunch(12); Dinner(16)
Total Units: 3
Trade Names: LYFE Kitchen (3)
Company-Owned Units: 3
Alcohol Served: Beer, Wine
Primary Menu: American (3)
Areas of Operation: IL
Type of Foodservice: Casual Dining (3)
Catering Services: Yes
Parent Company: L3 Hospitality Group, CHICAGO, IL
Notes: See parent company L3 Hospitality Group for additional information.

Key Personnel
CAREY COOPER - Co-Founder; CEO
GAIL TAGGART - Co-Founder; President

Marcello's Father & Son Restaurant
2475 N Milwaukee Ave
Chicago, IL 60647-2661

Telephone: (773) 252-2620
Fax Number: (773) 252-3995
Internet Homepage: marcellos.com
Type of Business: Chain Restaurant Operator
Year Founded: 1947
Total Sales: $8,252,000 (e)
Alcohol Sales: 10%
Number of Employees: 100
Average Check: Lunch(10); Dinner(14)
Internet Order Processing: Yes
Total Units: 2
Trade Names: Marcello's Father & Son Pizza (2)
Company-Owned Units: 2
Preferred Location Types: Freestanding; Strip Mall
Alcohol Served: Beer, Wine, Liquor
Primary Menu: Italian (2)
Areas of Operation: IL
Type of Foodservice: Casual Dining (2)
Catering Services: Yes
Primary Distributors: (Food) SYSCO Food Services of Chicago Inc., DES PLAINES, IL; (Supplies) Edward Don & Co., WOODRIDGE, IL
Parent Company: Nation Pizza, CHICAGO, IL

Key Personnel
MARSHALL BAUER - Chairman; Partner
JODY BAUER - Partner
JAY BAUER - VP Purchasing; General Buyer
RAPHAEL GARCIA - Executive Chef; Manager Catering

Mca Chicago Inc
4608 W Fullerton Ave
Chicago, IL 60639-1816

Telephone: (773) 772-9000
Type of Business: Chain Restaurant Operator
Total Sales: $13,916,000 (e)
Total Units: 7
Trade Names: Domino's (7)
Units Franchised From: 7
Primary Menu: Pizza (7)
Areas of Operation: IL
Type of Foodservice: Quick Serve (7)
Franchise Affiliation: Domino's Pizza Inc, ANN ARBOR, MI

Key Personnel
ROBERT PALMIOTTO - Owner; General Buyer

McDonald's Corporation
110 N Carpenter St
Chicago, IL 60607

Telephone: (630) 623-3000
Fax Number: (630) 623-6942
Internet Homepage: mcdonalds.com/us/en-us.html
Type of Business: Chain Restaurant Operator
Year Founded: 1955
Systemwide Sales: $133,677,667,000 (e)
Publicly Held: Yes
Total Sales: $26,316,436,000 (e)
Number of Employees: 205,000
Average Check: Breakfast(6); Lunch(8); Dinner(8)
Total Units: 43,477
Trade Names: CosMc's (2); McCafe (1); McDonald's (43,473); The Corner (1)
Company-Owned Units: 2,770
Units Franchised To: 40,707
Preferred Square Footage: 2,400; 2,500; 3,000
Preferred Location Types: Airports; Community Mall; Convenience Store/Gas Station; Discount Dept. Stores; Downtown; Freestanding; Grocery Stores; Hotel/Motel; Institution (college/hospital); Lifestyle Center; Office Complex; Outlet Mall; Parks; Regional Mall; Stadiums; Strip Mall; Travel Plazas
Primary Menu: Hamburger (43,473); Miscellaneous (2); Snacks (2)
Projected Openings: 50
Projected Remodelings: 2,000
Areas of Operation: AK, AL, AR, AZ, CA, CO, CT, DC, DE, FL, GA, GU, HI, IA, ID, IL, IN, KS, KY, LA, MA, MD, ME, MI, MN, MO, MS, MT, NC, ND, NE, NH, NJ, NM, NV, NY, OH, OK, OR, PA, PR, RI, SC, SD, TN, TX, UT, VA, VI, VT, WA, WI, WV, WY, AB, BC, MB, NB, NL, NS, NT, ON, PE, QC, SK, YT
Foreign Countries: AMERICAN SAMOA; ARGENTINA; AUSTRALIA; AUSTRIA; BAHAMAS; BAHRAIN; BELARUS; BELGIUM; BRAZIL; BULGARIA; CANADA; CHILE; CHINA; COLOMBIA; COSTA RICA; CROATIA; CYPRUS; CZECH REPUBLIC; DENMARK; DOMINICAN REPUBLIC; ECUADOR; EGYPT; EL SALVADOR; ENGLAND; FIJI; FINLAND; FRANCE; GERMANY; GREECE; GUADELOUPE; GUATEMALA; GUYANA; HONDURAS; HONG KONG;HUNGARY; INDIA; INDONESIA; IRELAND; ISRAEL; ITALY; JAPAN; JORDAN; KUWAIT; LATVIA; LEBANON; LIECHTENSTEIN; LITHUANIA;LUXEMBOURG; MACAO; MALAYSIA; MALTA; MARTINIQUE;

MAURITIUS; MEXICO; MONACO; MOROCCO; NEW ZEALAND; NICARAGUA; NORTHERNIRELAND; NORWAY; OMAN; PAKISTAN; PANAMA; PARAGUAY; PERU; POLAND; PORTUGAL; QATAR; ROMANIA; RUSSIA; SAINT MAARTEN; SANMARINO; SAUDI ARABIA; SCOTLAND; SINGAPORE; SLOVAKIA; SLOVENIA; SOUTH AFRICA; SOUTH KOREA; SPAIN; SURINAME; SWEDEN; SWITZERLAND; TAIWAN; THAILAND; THE NETHERLANDS; THE PHILIPPINES; TRINIDAD & TOBAGO; TURKEY; UKRAINE; UNITED ARAB EMIRATES; URUGUAY; VENEZUELA; WALES; WESTERN SAMOA

Type of Foodservice: Quick Serve (43,477)
Foodservice Management Venues: Business & Industry; Schools
Subsidiaries: McDonald's Restaurants of Canada Ltd., TORONTO, ON CANADA
Divisional Offices: McDonald's Central Division, WARRENVILLE, IL
Regional Offices: McDonald's Restaurants of Hawaii, HONOLULU, HI; McDonald's USA LLC, ATLANTA, GA; McDonald's USA LLC, HOUSTON, TX; McDonald's USA LLC, WALNUT CREEK, CA

Key Personnel

CHRIS KEMPCZINSKI - Executive Chairman; CEO; President
GEORGE A. COHON - Founder International Division
JOHN BETTS - CEO Canada; President Canada
KHAMZAT KHASBULATOV - President International Division
CHARLIE STRONG - President West Region
JOSEPH ERLINGER - President United States
MARIO BARBOSA - President East Region
BRIAN MULLENS - CFO International
IAN BORDEN - CFO
TIFFANIE BOYD - Chief People Officer Global
BRIAN RICE - CIO Global
WHITNEY MCGINNIS - CIO
TOM GERGETS - CTO; VP
MORGAN FLATLEY - Chief Marketing Officer Global
ANTOINETTE BENOIT - Chief Marketing Officer Canada
ALSTAIR MACROW - Chief Marketing Officer
TARIQ HASSAN - Chief Marketing Officer United States; Chief Customer Officer Digital
BETHANY T. CORNELL - Chief Development Officer; Chief Learning Officer
TABASSUM ZALOTRAWALA - Chief Development Officer United States; Senior VP
SANDY RODRIQUEZ - Chief Communications Officer Global
MANU STEIJAERT - Chief Customer Officer
MARION GROSS - Chief Supply Chain Officer United States; Senior VP
SHAMMARA HOWELL - Chief Talent Officer; VP
JERRY KRULEWITCH - Exec VP; Corporate Secretary; General Counsel
MIKE RICHARD - Senior VP; Treasurer
PIOTR JUCHA - Senior VP Global Development
MICHAEL GONDA - Senior VP; Chief Learning Officer
CATHY GRIFFIN - VP
JOSEPH ENDRESS - VP Facility/Maintenance
ROB LIDDLE - VP Labor Relations
DAVID TOVAR - VP Communications
ERWIN DITO - VP Global
HASHIM AMIN - VP Engineering, Global
JAMI GUTHRIE - VP Strategic Sourcing
JON GOODBRAND - VP Innovation; Global Operations
CESAR PINA - VP Supply Chain, Strategic Sourcing, Global
CATHY MARTIN - Regional VP
DESIREE RALLS-MORRISON - Corporate Secretary; General Counsel
BRUCE NEUMANN - General Counsel
JOSEPH YOUSSEF - Senior Director Information Technology
SIMONE ALLEYNE - Senior Director Strategic Planning
MYRNA BELL - Senior Director Diversity
JENNIFER FELDMAN - Senior Director Media
DARCI FORREST - Senior Director Menu Development
SHERI MALEC - Senior Director Human Resources
KATHY PYLE - Senior Director Marketing
CHERYL RIDDELL - Senior Director Human Resources
ELIZABETH CAMPBELL - Senior Director Marketing
MICHAEL KOTYNEK - Senior Director Finance
DAVE SEXTON - Senior Director Finance
DARCY GILBERT - Senior Director Sourcing, Supply Chain
CHRISTIAN BRYZINSKI - Senior Director Finance
BOB O'CONNELL - Director Development
MAX GALLEGOS JR - Director Marketing, United States
NATASHA B. LOVE - Director Menu Development
STEVE CREER - Director Real Estate
DIANA DRAM - Director Sourcing, Supply Chain
TINA JOHNSON - Director Training
DORIS SCOTT - Director Human Resources
BILL WICKLUND - Director Operations
AMY WILCOX - Director Information Systems
ROBERT HOLM - Director Security, Safety
TONY ALFAIA - Director Operations, Innovation
ANDREW BRAZIER - Director Supply Chain-Meat & Poultry
DANIELLE DRZAYICH - Director Marketing, Communications
CHRIS HEPPE - Director Menu Development
DENNIS QUILES - Director Security
GEORGE MAROPAKIS - Director Security
STEVE MCCARTHY - Director Information Technology
ANNA ENGEL - Director Content Marketing
SHANNON HAIGH - Director Human Resources
BRIAN HILLEGAS - Director
BRITTANY MCDONOUGH - Director Strategy, Global
AKSHAY SAHNI - Director Global
BRYCE BOOTHBY - Director Global Technology
HELEN SINGER - Director Development
SANA MOHAMMED - Director Field Marketing
SARAH GRADY - Director Supply Chain, Global
COURTNEY MCBURNEY - Director Employee Development
ALEXA MORSE - Director People
DIONNE GOMEZ - Director Communications
JENA HESS - Director Global
KARA SCHMIDT - Director Technology
LAURA GRANGER - Regional Director Human Resources
TODD PRUITT - Regional Director Finance
JOHN ROCKWELL - Senior Manager Sustainability
MIKE DEGLEFFETTI - Senior Manager Information Technology
SCOTT FARNUM - Senior Manager Information Technology
CHRIS GUNDERSEN - Senior Manager Digital Solutions
PRITHWI BARMAN - Senior Manager Technology
KAITLIN LABRUZZO - Senior Manager Marketing
FERN PIAZZA - Area Manager Real Estate
JUDY REYES - Area Manager Real Estate
PATTY ANDREWS - Manager Operations
WILLIAM BALL - Manager Security, Region
ERIC HALFEN - Manager Finance
KRISTYN PUZEN - Manager Finance
KYLE SCHOTT - Manager Sustainability
MOOSA ZUBERI - Manager Finance, Strategic Planning
JEFF KORNAK - Manager Internal Audit
JENNY MARQUEZ - Manager Branch
SHIRLEY CHAPMAN - Manager Design
DAVID BRYAN - Manager Restaurant Operations, Technology
TODD LANGELAND - Manager Digital Solutions
HARIANTI MOHD KHALID - Manager Direct Store Delivery
LIPPOLDT SUE - Manager Employee Benefits
GREG FEYLO - Manager Financial Planning
MATT SAWEIKIS - Manager Menu Development
ALISE FLORES - Manager Media
ERIC MOORE - Manager Digital
LINDSEY MEYER - Manager Real Estate
PAULINE NESWOLD - Supervisor Supply Chain, Construction
CAROL MARTINO - Supervisor Menu Development
PAUL RUGINIS - Supervisor Finance
KATELYNN CUPELLO - Supervisor Human Resources
KAREN NOVAK - Senior Product Manager
SHARON ROURKE - Senior Project Manager Information Systems
RAY GARZA - Project Manager
ROMMEL BENYAMIN - Project Manager Information Technology
STEVE DAVIDS - Specialist Payroll

ZARIN KARANJIA - Specialist Mobility
ROSE GUARINI - Specialist Event Planning
BOKE CONNIE - Coordinator Franchising
TERESA MAGLIO - Coordinator Real Estate; Analyst Finance
VANESSA BEHRENS - Consultant Construction
SANAYA JIJINA - Senior Analyst
NINA CHOKSI - Senior Analyst Sustainability, Information Technology, Supply Chain
ALEEM RAJA - Senior Analyst Business Development

Mendez Enterprises
7105 W Higgins Ave
Chicago, IL 60656-1903

Telephone: (773) 467-1290
Fax Number: (773) 467-1294
Type of Business: Chain Restaurant Operator
Total Sales: $19,624,000 (e)
Number of Employees: 300
Total Units: 4
Trade Names: McDonald's (4)
Units Franchised From: 4
Preferred Square Footage: 2,500
Primary Menu: Hamburger (4)
Areas of Operation: IL
Type of Foodservice: Quick Serve (4)
Franchise Affiliation: McDonald's Corporation, CHICAGO, IL

Key Personnel
JUAN MENDEZ - President; General Buyer

Midan Organization
4338 W North Ave
Chicago, IL 60639-4855

Telephone: (773) 384-8165
Internet Homepage: midanmarketing.com
Type of Business: Chain Restaurant Operator
Total Sales: $15,493,000 (e)
Total Units: 3
Trade Names: McDonald's (3)
Units Franchised From: 3
Preferred Location Types: Freestanding
Primary Menu: Hamburger (3)
Areas of Operation: IL
Type of Foodservice: Quick Serve (3)
Franchise Affiliation: McDonald's Corporation, CHICAGO, IL

Key Personnel
VIRGINIA OVIEDO - President; General Buyer

Naf Naf
720 N Franklin St Ste 401
Chicago, IL 60654

Telephone: (773) 293-6120
Internet Homepage: nafnafgrill.com
Type of Business: Chain Restaurant Operator
Year Founded: 2010
Total Sales: $27,270,000 (e)
Average Check: Lunch(8); Dinner(8)
Total Units: 35
Trade Names: Naf Naf Grill (35)
Company-Owned Units: 35
Preferred Square Footage: 2,000
Primary Menu: Middle Eastern (35)
Projected Openings: 35
Areas of Operation: DC, IL, MI, MN, NJ, OH, PA, WI
Type of Foodservice: Fast Casual (35)
Catering Services: Yes
Parent Company: Roark Capital Group, ATLANTA, GA

Key Personnel
ELAN BURGER - Co-Founder; VP Facility/Maintenance
GREG WILLMAN - CEO
NICO NIETO - Chief Marketing Officer
LISA MCBETH - VP Operations
JORDAN DAVIS - General Manager Training
EDWIN ZETINA - Director Operations, Culinary Development
CHAD CHMIELOWICZ - Director Training
RICK ADAMSKI - District Manager

Nookies
1746 N Wells St
Chicago, IL 60614-5807

Telephone: (312) 337-2454
Internet Homepage: nookieschicago.com
Type of Business: Chain Restaurant Operator
Year Founded: 1973
Total Sales: $9,654,000 (e)
Average Check: Breakfast(16);
Total Units: 4
Trade Names: Nookies (4)
Company-Owned Units: 4
Primary Menu: American (4)
Areas of Operation: IL
Type of Foodservice: Casual Dining (4)
Catering Services: Yes

Key Personnel
NICK ALEXOPOULOS - Partner
PETER ALEXOPOULOS - Partner
NICK KOURTELIS - General Manager

One Off Hospitality Group
808 W Lake St
Chicago, IL 60607

Telephone: (312) 496-0012
Internet Homepage: oneoffhospitality.com
Company Email: maggiep@oneoffhospitality.com
Type of Business: Chain Restaurant Operator
Year Founded: 2011
Total Sales: $9,897,000 (e)
Total Units: 8
Trade Names: Avec (2); Bar Avec (1); Big Star (2); Publican Quality Meats (1); The Publican (1); The Violet Hour (1)
Company-Owned Units: 8
Primary Menu: American (3); Californian (0); French/Continental (0); Greek/Mediterranean (3); Mexican (2); Snacks (0)
Areas of Operation: IL
Type of Foodservice: Casual Dining (8); Fine Dining (0); Quick Serve (0)

Key Personnel
KAREN BROWNE - CEO
DONNIE MADIA - Partner
PAUL KAHAN - Partner; Executive Chef
TERRY ALEXANDER - Partner
EDWARD SEITAN - Partner
PETER GARFIELD - Partner
SARAH IRVINE - CFO
LAURENT YEN - Director Information Technology

Orange Contemporary Brunch
2011 W Roscoe St
Chicago, IL 60618

Telephone: (773) 248-0999
Internet Homepage: orangerestaurantchicago.com
Type of Business: Chain Restaurant Operator
Total Sales: $4,754,000 (e)
Average Check: Breakfast(18);
Total Units: 2
Trade Names: Orange Contemporary Brunch (1)
Company-Owned Units: 1
Primary Menu: American (1)
Areas of Operation: IL
Type of Foodservice: Casual Dining (1)
Catering Services: Yes

Key Personnel
ANDREW KLEMEN - Owner; General Buyer

PB Restaurants LLC
235 S Franklin St
Chicago, IL 60606-4629

Telephone: (312) 346-7300
Internet Homepage: theproteinbar.com
Company Email: info@theproteinbar.com
Type of Business: Chain Restaurant Operator
Year Founded: 2009
Average Check: Lunch(12); Dinner(12)
Total Units: 19
Trade Names: Protein Bar (19)
Company-Owned Units: 19
Primary Menu: Health Foods (19)
Areas of Operation: CO, DC, IL
Type of Foodservice: Quick Serve (19)
Catering Services: Yes

Key Personnel
JEFF DRAKE - CEO; President
DAISY WEST - Manager Human Resources

Pepe's Inc.
1325 W 15th St
Chicago, IL 60608-2107

Telephone: (312) 733-2500
Fax Number: (312) 733-2564
Internet Homepage: pepes.com
Company Email: eat@pepes.com
Type of Business: Chain Restaurant Operator
Year Founded: 1967
Systemwide Sales: $32,205,000 (e)
Total Sales: $9,801,000 (e)
Alcohol Sales: 10%
Number of Employees: 345
Average Check: Breakfast(8); Lunch(10); Dinner(14)
Internet Order Processing: Yes
Total Units: 47
Trade Names: Pepe's Mexican Restaurant (47)
Units Franchised To: 47
Preferred Square Footage: 5,500; 6,000
Preferred Location Types: Community Mall; Downtown; Freestanding; Regional Mall; Strip Mall
Alcohol Served: Beer, Wine, Liquor
Primary Menu: Mexican (47)
Areas of Operation: IL, IN
Type of Foodservice: Casual Dining (47)
Foodservice Management Venues: Business & Industry; College & University; Military Feeding; Schools
Catering Services: Yes
On-site Distribution Center: Yes
Primary Distributors: (Food) SYSCO Food Services of Chicago Inc., DES PLAINES, IL

Key Personnel
ROBERT PTAK - President; Partner; Controller; Manager Menu Development; General Buyer
BARBARA JUSTUS - Partner; Director Information Systems, Ethnic Marketing, Real Estate, Human Resources; Supervisor Training
ROGER FONSECA - General Manager
JOE ESCARENO - Manager Catering

Phil Stefani Signature Restaurants
1033 W Van Buren St
Chicago, IL 60607-2956

Telephone: (312) 275-9000
Fax Number: (312) 275-9012
Internet Homepage: stefanirestaurants.com
Company Email: info@stefanirestaurants.com
Type of Business: Chain Restaurant Operator
Year Founded: 1980
Total Sales: $25,550,000 (e)
Alcohol Sales: 20%
Number of Employees: 380
Average Check: Lunch(26); Dinner(48)
Internet Order Processing: Yes
Total Units: 12
Trade Names: Bar Cargo (1); Broken English Taco Pub (3); Castaways Bar & Grill (1); Mad Social (1); Miller Lite Beer Garden (1); Riva Crab House (1); Stefani Prime (1); Tavern on Rush (1); Tuscany (2)
Company-Owned Units: 12
Preferred Square Footage: 20,000
Preferred Location Types: Freestanding; Office Complex
Alcohol Served: Beer, Wine, Liquor
Primary Menu: American (5); Italian (3); Pizza (1); Seafood (1); Steak (1); Taco (1)
Areas of Operation: IL
Type of Foodservice: Casual Dining (11); Fine Dining (1)
Catering Services: Yes
Primary Distributors: (Full Line) SYSCO Food Services of Chicago Inc., DES PLAINES, IL

Key Personnel
EPI PEREZ - Controller
MASSIMO MORESI - Executive Chef
FRANK VALDEZ - Executive Chef
BOLLA LOZA - Executive Chef
ENRIQUE LOZA - Executive Chef
ALEXA VAICAITIS - Manager Marketing

Pizano's Pizza & Pasta LLC
67 E Madison St Ste 265
Chicago, IL 60603-3014

Telephone: (312) 236-2888
Fax Number: (312) 236-3078
Internet Homepage: pizanoschicago.com; rudysbarandgrillechicago.com
Company Email: info@pizanoschicago.com
Type of Business: Chain Restaurant Operator
Year Founded: 1991
Total Sales: $9,998,000 (e)
Alcohol Sales: 10%
Average Check: Lunch(14); Dinner(24)
Internet Order Processing: Yes
Total Units: 7
Trade Names: Pizano's Pizza & Pasta (6); Rudy's Bar & Grille (1)
Company-Owned Units: 7
Alcohol Served: Beer, Wine, Liquor
Primary Menu: Italian (7)
Areas of Operation: IL
Type of Foodservice: Casual Dining (7)
Catering Services: Yes
Primary Distributors: (Full Line) SYSCO Food Services of Chicago Inc., DES PLAINES, IL

Key Personnel
RUDY MALNATI JR - Owner; Executive Chef; General Buyer
PAUL ROGERS - General Manager

Potbelly Corporation
111 N Canal St Ste 850
Chicago, IL 60606-7204

Telephone: (312) 951-0600
Fax Number: (312) 951-0300
Internet Homepage: potbelly.com
Company Email: info@potbelly.com
Type of Business: Chain Restaurant Operator
Year Founded: 1977
Systemwide Sales: $807,012,000 (e)
Publicly Held: Yes
Total Sales: $503,905,000 (e)
Number of Employees: 5,500
Average Check: Breakfast(8); Lunch(10); Dinner(12)
Internet Sales: 1.00%
Total Units: 424
Trade Names: Potbelly Sandwich Shop (424)
Company-Owned Units: 345
Units Franchised To: 79
Preferred Square Footage: 1,800; 2,200
Preferred Location Types: Airports; Community Mall; Downtown; Freestanding; Regional Mall; Strip Mall
Primary Menu: Sandwiches/Deli (424)
Projected Openings: 49
Areas of Operation: AR, AZ, CO, CT, DC, IL, IN, KS, KY, MA, MD, MI, MN, MO, NC, ND, NE, NJ, NY, OH, OR, PA, SD, TN, TX, UT, VA, WA, WI
Foreign Countries: BAHRAIN; KUWAIT; UNITED ARAB EMIRATES
Type of Foodservice: Quick Serve (424)
Primary Distributors: (Full Line) Reinhart FoodService LLC, CHICAGO, IL

Key Personnel
ROBERT D. WRIGHT - CEO; President
STEVEN CIRULIS - CFO; Chief Strategy Officer
JEFFREY DOUGLAS - CIO; Senior VP

DAVID DANIELS - Chief Marketing Officer
WILL ATKINS - VP; Controller
JEFF BROMWICH - VP Procurement
ANGELA CLAYBROOKS - Senior Director Payroll, Human Resources, HRIS
MIKE NARRAMORE - Senior Director Human Resources
JOE PANOZZO - Senior Director Loss Prevention, Risk Management
KATIE SNYDER - Director Franchising
ROWENA V - Senior Manager Payroll, HRIS
MAUREEN KIRK - Senior Manager Facility/Maintenance
SAM MARTINEZ - Manager

Premier Restaurant Group
215 W Ohio St Ste 1W
Chicago, IL 60654-4415

Telephone: (773) 696-0091
Fax Number: (312) 628-7657
Internet Homepage: foreveryogurt.com; premierrestaurantgroup.com
Company Email: info@foreveryogurt.com
Type of Business: Chain Restaurant Operator
Year Founded: 2011
Systemwide Sales: $3,417,000 (e)
Total Sales: $14,970,000 (e)
Total Units: 48
Trade Names: Cheeburger Cheeburger (22); Forever Yogurt (26)
Company-Owned Units: 3
Units Franchised To: 45
Primary Menu: Hamburger (22); Snacks (26)
Areas of Operation: AL, DE, FL, IL, MD, MN, MO, NJ, NY, PA, SC, TX, UT, VA, WI
Foreign Countries: CHINA
Type of Foodservice: Casual Dining (26); Quick Serve (22)

Key Personnel
ANTHONY WEDO - CEO; Owner

Puttshack
303 W Erie St #600
Chicago, IL 60654

Telephone: (312) 620-7888
Internet Homepage: puttshack.com
Type of Business: Chain Restaurant Operator
Year Founded: 2018
Total Sales: $209,673,000 (e)
Foodservice Sales: $31,450,000 (e)
Total Units: 17
Trade Names: Puttshack (17)
Company-Owned Units: 17
Primary Menu: American (17)
Areas of Operation: AZ, CO, FL, GA, IL, KY, MA, MD, MN, MO, OH, PA, TN, TX, VA
Type of Foodservice: Casual Dining (17)

Key Personnel
STEVEN JOLLIFFE - Founder
DAVE JOLLIFFE - Founder
ADAM BREEDEN - Founder
JOE VRANKIN - CEO
BEN SHEPHERD - CIO; CTO
RYAN NOWICKI - VP Operations
MARK BOYTON - VP Global, Food and Beverage
DAN DAWSON - VP Development, Real Estate
DOMINIC CRESPO - VP Design
KATIE BELL - Director Talent Acquisitions
ALAIN NATAKI - Director Beverages
ROCIO DEJESUS - Director Talent, People
BRYAN MUSGROVE - Director Construction
BRAD BORON - Director Digital Advertising

Rainbow Cone LLC
9233 S. Western Avenue
Chicago, IL 60643

Telephone: (773) 238-9833
Internet Homepage: rainbowcone.com
Company Email: info@rainbowcone.com
Type of Business: Chain Restaurant Operator
Year Founded: 1926
Total Units: 18
Trade Names: The Original Rainbow Cone (18)
Units Franchised To: 18
Primary Menu: Snacks (18)
Projected Openings: 5
Areas of Operation: FL, IL
Type of Foodservice: Quick Serve (18)

Key Personnel
LYNN SAPP - CEO; Owner
ANTHONY GRANDE - Director Operations
MICHAEL BUONAVOLANTO - Director Real Estate Development

Rick Bayless Restaurants
445 N Clark St
Chicago, IL 60654-4682

Telephone: (312) 661-1434
Internet Homepage: fronterafresco.com; fronterakitchens.com; rickbayless.com
Company Email: info@fronterakitchens.com
Type of Business: Chain Restaurant Operator
Year Founded: 1988
Total Sales: $22,560,000 (e)
Alcohol Sales: 20%
Number of Employees: 121
Average Check: Lunch(18); Dinner(32)
Internet Order Processing: Yes
Total Units: 11
Trade Names: Cruz Blanca (1); Frontera Concina (1); Frontera Fresco (2); Frontera Grill (1); Lena Brava (1); Topolobampo (1); Tortas Frontera (3); XOCO (1)
Company-Owned Units: 11
Preferred Location Types: Airports; Downtown; Freestanding; Mixed-use Center
Alcohol Served: Beer, Wine, Liquor
Primary Menu: Mexican (11)
Areas of Operation: CA, FL, IL
Type of Foodservice: Casual Dining (4); Fast Casual (1); Fine Dining (1); Quick Serve (5)
Primary Distributors: (Food) SYSCO Food Services of Chicago Inc., DES PLAINES, IL
Notes: The Frontera Fresco locations are inside Macy's department stores in CA and IL.

Key Personnel
DEANN BAYLESS - Partner; General Manager; General Buyer
RICK BAYLESS - Partner; Executive Chef
WHITNEY BERKE - General Manager
ANDRES PADILLA - Director Culinary Operations

Rockit Ranch Productions
57 W Grand Ave Ste 600
Chicago, IL 60654-4765

Telephone: (312) 943-7600
Fax Number: (312) 943-7603
Internet Homepage: rockitbarandgrill.com; rockitranch.com
Company Email: info@rockitranch.com
Type of Business: Chain Restaurant Operator
Year Founded: 2004
Total Sales: $11,720,000 (e)
Alcohol Sales: 15%
Number of Employees: 500
Total Units: 5
Trade Names: Rocket Burger Bar (1); Rockit Bar & Grill (1); Sunda (2); Underground (1)
Company-Owned Units: 5
Alcohol Served: Beer, Wine, Liquor
Primary Menu: American (2); Asian (2); Hamburger (1)
Areas of Operation: IL
Type of Foodservice: Casual Dining (5)
Primary Distributors: (Food) SYSCO Food Services of Chicago Inc., DES PLAINES, IL
Notes: Rockit Ranch also operates a nightclub named The Underground (www.theundergroundchicago.com)

Key Personnel
BILLY DEC - CEO; Partner
MICHAEL MORALES - Partner; Executive Chef
JAMES GOTTWALD - Corporate Chef
JEREMY STOLBERG - Director Development
MEGHAN TEELA - Director Design
LEILANI CASTRO - Director Finance
KOURTNEY HODGES - Assistant Director Operations
CHOON LAI - Senior Manager Operations
LINDSAY BELTRAME - Manager Operations
OLIVER GAMEZ MANCILLA - Manager

Operations

Ron of Japan
230 E Ontario St Ste B
Chicago, IL 60611-7263

Telephone: (312) 644-6500
Fax Number: (312) 644-8613
Internet Homepage: rojfordinner.com
Type of Business: Chain Restaurant Operator
Year Founded: 1970
Total Sales: $7,781,000 (e)
Alcohol Sales: 10%
Number of Employees: 40
Average Check: Dinner(38)
Total Units: 2
Trade Names: Ron of Japan (2)
Company-Owned Units: 2
Preferred Location Types: Freestanding
Alcohol Served: Beer, Wine, Liquor
Primary Menu: Japanese (2)
Areas of Operation: IL
Type of Foodservice: Fine Dining (2)
Catering Services: Yes
Primary Distributors: (Food) SYSCO Food Services of Chicago Inc., DES PLAINES, IL

Key Personnel
VIVIAN ZAHNG - General Manager; General Buyer
CHEF JUAN - Executive Chef
HANNAH KIM - Coordinator Event Planning

Rosebud Restaurants
1419 W Diversey Pkwy
Chicago, IL 60614-1111

Telephone: (773) 325-9700
Fax Number: (773) 325-9708
Internet Homepage: rosebudrestaurants.com
Company Email: social@rosebud-restaurants.com
Type of Business: Chain Restaurant Operator
Year Founded: 1977
Total Sales: $19,790,000 (e)
Alcohol Sales: 25%
Number of Employees: 345
Average Check: Lunch(22); Dinner(42)
Internet Sales: 1.00%
Total Units: 8
Trade Names: Carmine's (1); Mama's Boy (1); Rosebud of Naperville (1); Rosebud on Rush (1); Rosebud Prime (1); Rosebud Steakhouse (1); Rosebud Theater District (1); The Rosebud of Deerfield (1)
Company-Owned Units: 8
Preferred Square Footage: 8,000
Preferred Location Types: Downtown; Freestanding; Office Complex; Strip Mall
Alcohol Served: Beer, Wine, Liquor
Primary Menu: Italian (5); Steak (3)
Areas of Operation: IL
Type of Foodservice: Casual Dining (1); Fine Dining (7)
Catering Services: Yes
Primary Distributors: (Full Line) US Foods Holding Corp., ROSEMONT, IL

Key Personnel
ALEX DANA - President; Executive Chef; Director Finance, Purchasing, Information Systems, Design; Manager Real Estate, Store Planning; General Buyer
NICK LOMBARDO - General Manager; Director Operations

Roti Mediterranean Grill
600 W Fulton St Lbby 101
Chicago, IL 60661-1231

Telephone: (312) 605-9090
Fax Number: (312) 775-7005
Internet Homepage: roti.com
Company Email: info@roti.com
Type of Business: Chain Restaurant Operator
Year Founded: 2007
Total Sales: $71,139,000 (e)
Alcohol Sales: 5%
Average Check: Dinner(16)
Internet Order Processing: Yes
Total Units: 19
Trade Names: Roti Modern Mediterranean (19)
Company-Owned Units: 19
Preferred Square Footage: 5,000
Preferred Location Types: Downtown; Strip Mall
Alcohol Served: Beer, Wine
Primary Menu: Greek/Mediterranean (19)
Areas of Operation: DC, IL, MD, MN, NY, TX, VA
Type of Foodservice: Fast Casual (19)
Catering Services: Yes
Primary Distributors: (Full Line) SYSCO Food Services of Chicago Inc., DES PLAINES, IL

Key Personnel
JUSTIN SEAMONDS - CEO
VALERIE CALISE - General Manager
WILL JANSSEN - General Manager
SARAH ENLOW - Manager Human Resources
DIANE SIKO - Manager Catering
ANTOINETTE WHISLER - Manager Catering
KAY ELLEN STEIN - Manager Marketing
ANGIE LEWANDOWSKI - Manager Sales, Catering
ROZALYN LAWRENCE - Coordinator Catering

Round The Table Hospitality
1362 W Fulton St
Chicago, IL 60607

Telephone: (312) 421-6666
Fax Number: (312) 421-6669
Internet Homepage: blueplatechicago.com; rtthospitality.com
Company Email: info@blueplatechicago.com
Type of Business: Chain Restaurant Operator
Year Founded: 2016
Total Units: 3
Trade Names: Park Cafe (1); Park Grill (1); Tesori trattoria & bar (1)
Company-Owned Units: 3
Primary Menu: American (2); Italian (1)
Areas of Operation: IL
Type of Foodservice: Casual Dining (3)
Catering Services: Yes
Notes: In addition to its restaurants, Round The Table Hospitality also includes Blue Plate Catering.

Key Personnel
JIM HORAN - Founder; CEO

‡ Strategic Hotels & Resorts Inc.
150 N Riverside Plz Ste 4100
Chicago, IL 60606-3538

Telephone: (312) 658-5000
Fax Number: (312) 658-5799
Internet Homepage: strategichotels.com
Company Email: info@strategichotels.com
Type of Business: Foodservice Operations - Hotel/Motels
Total Sales: $1,652,670,000 (e)
Alcohol Sales: 10%
Number of Employees: 22
Total Units: 17
Restaurants in Hotels: 17
Trade Names: Fairmont Chicago (1); Fairmont Scottsdale Princess (1); Four Seasons Jackson Hole (1); Four Seasons Punta Mita Resort (1); Four Seasons Resort Scottsdale (1); Four Seasons Silicon Valley (1); Four Seasons Washington (1); Hotel del Coronado (1); InterContinental Hotel Chicago (1); InterContinental Miami (1); JW Marriott Essex House (1); Loews Santa Monica Beach Hotel (1); Marriott Hamburg (1); Marriott Lincolnshire Resort (1); Ritz-Carlton Half Moon Bay (1); Ritz-Carlton Laguna Niguel (1); Westin St. Francis (1)
Company-Owned Units: 17
Alcohol Served: Beer, Wine, Liquor
Areas of Operation: AZ, CA, DC, FL, IL, NY, WY
Foreign Countries: GERMANY
Type of Foodservice: Casual Dining; Fine Dining
Primary Distributors: (Food) SYSCO Food Services of Chicago Inc., DES PLAINES, IL
Notes: The company derives approximately 65% of its revenue from hotel/motel operations

& other activities.

Key Personnel
CARLY EDGAR - VP Asset Protection
BRYCE WHITE - VP Information Technology

Suparossa Restaurant Group
4242 N Central Ave
Chicago, IL 60634-1810

Telephone: (773) 736-9009
Fax Number: (773) 736-1372
Internet Homepage: legnochicago.com; suparossa.com; biagioevents.com; realtimesportsbar.com
Company Email: dine@suparossa.com
Type of Business: Chain Restaurant Operator
Year Founded: 1977
Total Sales: $36,970,000 (e)
Alcohol Sales: 22%
Number of Employees: 275
Average Check: Lunch(18); Dinner(28)
Total Units: 8
Trade Names: Cucina Biagio (1); Legno (1); Pete's Pizza (2); Realtime Sports (1); Suparossa Italiania Ristorante & Pizzeria (3)
Company-Owned Units: 8
Preferred Square Footage: 5,500; 6,000
Preferred Location Types: Downtown; Freestanding; Office Complex
Alcohol Served: Beer, Wine, Liquor
Primary Menu: American (1); Italian (5); Pizza (2)
Areas of Operation: FL, IL
Type of Foodservice: Casual Dining (5); Fine Dining (3)
Catering Services: Yes
Primary Distributors: (Equipment) SYSCO Food Services of Chicago Inc., DES PLAINES, IL; (Supplies) SYSCO Food Services of Chicago Inc., DES PLAINES, IL

Key Personnel
SAM CIRRINCIONE - Partner; Director Purchasing, Facility/Maintenance, Real Estate, Design, Store Fixtures
KRISTINA RILEY - General Manager
PETER LESNIAK - Manager Accounting

Swissotel Hotels Inc.
323 E Wacker Dr
Chicago, IL 60601-5282

Telephone: (312) 565-0565
Fax Number: (312) 565-0540
Internet Homepage: swissotel.com
Company Email: reservations.chicago@swissotel.com
Type of Business: Foodservice Operations - Hotel/Motels
Year Founded: 1981
Total Sales: $429,540,000 (e)
Alcohol Sales: 20%
Number of Employees: 4,000
Total Units: 29
Restaurants in Hotels: 29
Trade Names: Merchant Court Hotel (1); Nailert Park (1); Raffles Fairmont Hotels (12); Swissotel (15)
Company-Owned Units: 29
Alcohol Served: Beer, Wine, Liquor
Areas of Operation: IL
Foreign Countries: AUSTRALIA; ECUADOR; ENGLAND; GERMANY; INDONESIA; JAPAN; PERU; RUSSIA; SINGAPORE; SWITZERLAND; THAILAND; THE NETHERLANDS; TURKEY
Type of Foodservice: Casual Dining; Fine Dining
Parent Company: Fairmont Raffles Hotels International, TORONTO, ON CANADA
Notes: The company derives approximately 75% of its revenue from hotel operations.

Key Personnel
RADE PILJA - Director Purchasing

Taco Burrito King
5413 W Belmont Ave
Chicago, IL 60641-4127

Telephone: (773) 777-6200
Fax Number: (773) 777-6201
Internet Homepage: tacoburritoking.com
Company Email: info@tacoburritoking.com
Type of Business: Chain Restaurant Operator
Year Founded: 1992
Total Sales: $7,830,000 (e)
Number of Employees: 152
Average Check: Lunch(10); Dinner(10)
Total Units: 13
Trade Names: Taco Burrito King (13)
Company-Owned Units: 13
Preferred Square Footage: 1,200
Preferred Location Types: Freestanding; Strip Mall
Alcohol Served: Beer, Wine, Liquor
Primary Menu: Mexican (13)
Projected Openings: 1
Areas of Operation: IL
Type of Foodservice: Casual Dining (13)
Catering Services: Yes
Primary Distributors: (Full Line) SYSCO Food Services of Chicago Inc., DES PLAINES, IL

Key Personnel
SALVADOR LAMAS - President; Partner; General Manager; Executive Chef; General Buyer
CARLOS LAMAS - Partner; Director Operations; Manager Purchasing, Supply Chain, Marketing, Human Resources, Catering

Taste America Restaurant Group
35 W Wacker Dr
Chicago, IL 60601-1723

Telephone: (312) 346-3500
Fax Number: (312) 644-9101
Internet Homepage: catch35.com; lloydschicago.com
Company Email: chicago@catch35.com
Type of Business: Chain Restaurant Operator
Year Founded: 1984
Total Sales: $26,406,000 (e)
Alcohol Sales: 25%
Number of Employees: 450
Average Check: Lunch(42); Dinner(90)
Total Units: 3
Trade Names: Catch 35 (2); Lloyd's Chicago (1)
Company-Owned Units: 3
Preferred Location Types: Office Complex
Alcohol Served: Beer, Wine, Liquor
Primary Menu: American (1); Steak/Seafood (2)
Areas of Operation: IL
Type of Foodservice: Casual Dining (1); Fine Dining (2)
Catering Services: Yes
Primary Distributors: (Full Line) SYSCO Food Services of Chicago Inc., DES PLAINES, IL

Key Personnel
BILL LECOMPTE - Partner; Controller
SAM BERNGARD - Partner; Manager Purchasing, Menu Development
CINDY HOFF - Manager Accounting
MELANIE YOECKEL - Manager; Coordinator
CARL JENSEN - Project Manager

Tempo Restaurant
6 E Chestnut St
Chicago, IL 60611-2664

Telephone: (312) 943-4373
Fax Number: (312) 943-4425
Internet Homepage: tempochicago.com; santorinichicago.com
Type of Business: Chain Restaurant Operator
Year Founded: 1983
Total Sales: $4,190,000 (e)
Alcohol Sales: 10%
Number of Employees: 50
Average Check: Breakfast(10); Lunch(18); Dinner(30)
Total Units: 2
Trade Names: Santorini (1); Tempo Restaurant (1)
Company-Owned Units: 2
Preferred Location Types: Freestanding
Alcohol Served: Beer, Wine, Liquor
Primary Menu: American (1); Greek/Mediterranean (1)

Areas of Operation: IL
Type of Foodservice: Casual Dining (1); Fine Dining (1)

Key Personnel
STEFANOS KONTOS - Partner; General Buyer
STELLIOS KONTOS - Partner

The Bacin Group
75 E Wacker Dr Lbby 1
Chicago, IL 60601-3708

Telephone: (312) 263-2350
Fax Number: (312) 263-4965
Internet Homepage: bacinos.com/DIVERSEY; bellabacinos.com; bacinos.com/#!home
Company Email: info@bacinos.com
Type of Business: Chain Restaurant Operator
Year Founded: 1978
Total Sales: $7,551,000 (e)
Alcohol Sales: 15.38%
Number of Employees: 225
Average Check: Breakfast(10); Lunch(12); Dinner(16)
Total Units: 3
Trade Names: Bacino's (1); Bacino's Italian Grill (1); bella! Bacino's (1)
Company-Owned Units: 3
Preferred Square Footage: 4,000
Preferred Location Types: Freestanding; Office Complex; Strip Mall
Alcohol Served: Beer, Wine, Liquor
Primary Menu: Italian (2); Pizza (1)
Areas of Operation: IL
Type of Foodservice: Casual Dining (3)
Catering Services: Yes
Primary Distributors: (Food) Food & Paper Supply Co., CHICAGO, IL

Key Personnel
DAN BACIN - President; Partner; General Manager; Executive Chef; Director Menu Development, Catering; General Buyer
LINDA BACIN - Partner; VP Operations; Controller

The Bagel Restaurant & Deli
3107 N Broadway St
Chicago, IL 60657-4522

Telephone: (773) 477-0300
Fax Number: (773) 477-9895
Internet Homepage: bagelrestaurant.com
Company Email: thebagel@ameritech.net
Type of Business: Chain Restaurant Operator
Year Founded: 1992
Total Sales: $3,906,000 (e)
Alcohol Sales: 30%
Number of Employees: 40
Average Check: Breakfast(8); Lunch(8); Dinner(10)

Internet Order Processing: Yes
Total Units: 2
Trade Names: The Bagel Restaurant & Deli (2)
Company-Owned Units: 2
Preferred Location Types: Freestanding; Strip Mall
Alcohol Served: Beer, Wine, Liquor
Primary Menu: Bagels (2)
Areas of Operation: IL
Type of Foodservice: Casual Dining (2)
Catering Services: Yes
Primary Distributors: (Full Line) US Foods, BENSENVILLE, IL

Key Personnel
RICHARD BRANTNER - General Manager

The Fifty/50 Restaurant Group
1916 W Chicago Ave
Chicago, IL 60622

Telephone: (773) 904-1120
Internet Homepage: thefifty50group.com
Company Email: info@thefifty50restaurantgroup.com
Type of Business: Chain Restaurant Operator
Year Founded: 2008
Total Sales: $197,350,000 (e)
Total Units: 14
Trade Names: 90th Meridian (1); Berkshire Room (1); Bodega (1); Bunny Slope (1); Homestead on the Roof (1); Roots Pizza (1); Ruth's Panmade Pizza (1); Steadfast (1); The Fifty/50 (1); The Second City (1); The Sixth (1); Utopian Tailgate (1); Vu Skyward (1); West Town Bakery (1)
Company-Owned Units: 14
Primary Menu: American (12); Pizza (2)
Type of Foodservice: Casual Dining (13); Fine Dining (1)

Key Personnel
SCOTT WEINER - Co-Founder; Principal
GREG MOHR - Co-Founder; Principal
MARTIN ARELLANO - Partner; Director Culinary Operations
MARK BRAVER - Partner; Director Operations
CHRIS TEIXEIRA - Partner; Director Culinary Operations
JOHN ALDAPE - Partner; Director Development
LYNN YUAN - Corporate Controller
KASSIE BARR - Director Finance, Administration
JENA CHERRY - Director Sales, Catering

The Goddess Restaurant Group
1649 N Damen Ave
Chicago, IL 60647

Telephone: (773) 342-3200
Internet Homepage: goddessandgrocer.com; goddessandthebaker.com
Company Email: info@goddessandgrocer.com
Type of Business: Chain Restaurant Operator
Year Founded: 2004
Total Units: 9
Trade Names: Goddess and the Baker (5); The Goddess and Grocer (4)
Company-Owned Units: 9
Preferred Location Types: Airports; Community Mall; Downtown
Primary Menu: Sandwiches/Deli (9)
Areas of Operation: IL, WI
Type of Foodservice: Fast Casual (9)

Key Personnel
DEBBIE SHARPE - Founder; Owner
JAMES GRAY - Director Operations
LUCY ROBINS - Manager Accounting

The Rosenthal Group Inc.
445 W Erie St Ste 209
Chicago, IL 60654-5733

Telephone: (312) 787-1096
Fax Number: (312) 787-5453
Internet Homepage: trattorianten.com; sopraffina.com
Company Email: info@sopraffina.com
Type of Business: Chain Restaurant Operator
Year Founded: 1986
Total Sales: $18,610,000 (e)
Alcohol Sales: 15%
Number of Employees: 190
Average Check: Breakfast(6); Lunch(16); Dinner(36)
Total Units: 6
Trade Names: Sopraffina Marketcaffe (5); Trattoria No. 10 (1)
Company-Owned Units: 6
Preferred Square Footage: 2,500; 5,500; 6,000
Preferred Location Types: Downtown; Lifestyle Center; Office Complex
Alcohol Served: Beer, Wine, Liquor
Primary Menu: Italian (6)
Areas of Operation: IL
Type of Foodservice: Casual Dining (1); Quick Serve (5)
Catering Services: Yes
Primary Distributors: (Food) SYSCO Food Services of Chicago Inc., DES PLAINES, IL

Key Personnel
DAN ROSENTHAL - President; Executive Chef;

Director Information Systems, Supply Chain, Real Estate; General Buyer
LIN ROSENTHAL - Partner; VP Advertising; Director Marketing, Design
TARYN ROSENTHAL - Partner; Manager Marketing
VALERIE RODGERS - Manager Human Resources

Toast
746 W Webster Ave
Chicago, IL 60614-3747

Telephone: (773) 935-5600
Internet Homepage: chicago-toast.com
Type of Business: Chain Restaurant Operator
Total Sales: $4,826,000 (e)
Number of Employees: 60
Average Check: Breakfast(10); Lunch(14);
Total Units: 2
Trade Names: Toast (2)
Company-Owned Units: 2
Preferred Location Types: Freestanding
Alcohol Served: Beer, Wine, Liquor
Primary Menu: American (2)
Areas of Operation: IL
Type of Foodservice: Casual Dining (2)
Primary Distributors: (Food) Testa Produce Inc., CHICAGO, IL

Key Personnel
JONATHAN STOLTER - Regional VP; District Manager Sales
JEFFREY MILLER - Regional Manager Sales
CHRISTINA PELTIER - Regional Manager Sales

VOLO Restaurant
2008 W Roscoe St
Chicago, IL 60618-6202

Telephone: (773) 348-4600
Internet Homepage: paramountroom.com; kitschn.com; volorestaurant.com
Company Email: volo@dineanddrinkinc.com
Type of Business: Chain Restaurant Operator
Year Founded: 1998
Total Sales: $6,080,000 (e)
Alcohol Sales: 15%
Number of Employees: 65
Average Check: Lunch(12); Dinner(36)
Internet Order Processing: Yes
Total Units: 3
Trade Names: Kitsch'n on Roscoe (1); Paramount Room (1); Volo Restaurant (1)
Company-Owned Units: 3
Preferred Location Types: Freestanding
Alcohol Served: Beer, Wine, Liquor
Primary Menu: American (3)
Areas of Operation: IL
Type of Foodservice: Fast Casual (1); Fine Dining (2)

Catering Services: Yes
Primary Distributors: (Full Line) SYSCO Food Services of Indianapolis LLC, INDIANAPOLIS, IN

Key Personnel
STEPHEN DUNNE - Partner; Executive Chef; General Buyer
JON YOUNG - Partner

Yolk.
1120 S Michigan Ave
Chicago, IL 60605-2301

Telephone: (312) 789-9655
Fax Number: (312) 789-9705
Internet Homepage: eatyolk.com
Company Email: chicago@eatyolk.com
Type of Business: Chain Restaurant Operator
Year Founded: 2006
Total Sales: $28,090,000 (e)
Average Check: Breakfast(16);
Internet Order Processing: Yes
Total Units: 14
Trade Names: Yolk. (14)
Company-Owned Units: 14
Preferred Location Types: Office Complex; Other
Primary Menu: American (14)
Projected Openings: 2
Areas of Operation: IL, IN, TX
Type of Foodservice: Family Restaurant (14)
Catering Services: Yes

Key Personnel
TAKI KASTANIS - Founder; President; Owner; General Buyer
FILISA K. MANTAS - Director Operations

Carr Restaurant Group
5831 W 26th St
Cicero, IL 60804-3254

Telephone: (708) 652-5522
Internet Homepage: steaknegger.com
Type of Business: Chain Restaurant Operator
Year Founded: 1955
Total Units: 7
Trade Names: Steak N Egger (7)
Company-Owned Units: 7
Primary Menu: American (7)
Areas of Operation: IL
Type of Foodservice: Casual Dining (7)

Key Personnel
TERRY CARR SR - Owner

Cocula
4836 W Cermak Rd
Cicero, IL 60804-2531

Telephone: (708) 652-0500
Fax Number: (708) 652-0526
Internet Homepage: cocularestaurant.com
Type of Business: Chain Restaurant Operator
Year Founded: 1978
Total Sales: $12,920,000 (e)
Alcohol Sales: 25%
Number of Employees: 90
Average Check: Lunch(18); Dinner(36)
Total Units: 6
Trade Names: Cocula (6)
Company-Owned Units: 6
Preferred Location Types: Freestanding
Alcohol Served: Beer, Wine, Liquor
Primary Menu: Mexican (6)
Areas of Operation: IL
Type of Foodservice: Casual Dining (6)
Primary Distributors: (Full Line) SYSCO Food Services of Chicago Inc., DES PLAINES, IL

Key Personnel
ROMULDO CAMARENA - President; Controller; General Manager; Executive Chef; Director Quality Assurance, Menu Development, Food Safety; General Buyer

McDonald's Franchise
2827 S Cicero Ave
Cicero, IL 60804-3645

Telephone: (708) 863-6227
Type of Business: Chain Restaurant Operator
Total Sales: $20,351,000 (e)
Total Units: 4
Trade Names: McDonald's (4)
Units Franchised From: 4
Preferred Square Footage: 2,500
Primary Menu: Hamburger (4)
Areas of Operation: IL
Type of Foodservice: Quick Serve (4)
Franchise Affiliation: McDonald's Corporation, CHICAGO, IL

Key Personnel
PHILIP FUENTES - President; General Buyer

Steak -N- Egger
5831 W 26th St
Cicero, IL 60804-3254

Telephone: (708) 652-5522
Fax Number: (708) 652-9355
Internet Homepage: steaknegger.com
Company Email: contact@steaknegger.com
Type of Business: Chain Restaurant Operator

Year Founded: 1965
Systemwide Sales: $10,404,000 (e)
Total Sales: $3,468,000 (e)
Number of Employees: 35
Average Check: Breakfast(8); Lunch(18); Dinner(30)
Total Units: 7
Trade Names: Steak -N- Egger (7)
Company-Owned Units: 1
Units Franchised To: 6
Preferred Square Footage: 2,500
Preferred Location Types: Freestanding
Primary Menu: American (7)
Areas of Operation: IL
Type of Foodservice: Family Restaurant (7)
Primary Distributors: (Full Line) US Foods, STREATOR, IL

Key Personnel
TERRANCE CARR - President; Director Real Estate
CINDY CARR - VP Operations, Supply Chain, Menu Development; Director Finance; General Buyer

Zoey & Yummy Inc
2 S Broadway St
Coal City, IL 60416-1531

Telephone: (815) 634-4412
Fax Number: (815) 634-4495
Type of Business: Chain Restaurant Operator
Total Sales: $33,730,000 (e)
Number of Employees: 100
Total Units: 7
Trade Names: McDonald's (7)
Units Franchised From: 7
Preferred Square Footage: 2,500
Primary Menu: Hamburger (7)
Areas of Operation: IL
Type of Foodservice: Quick Serve (7)
Franchise Affiliation: McDonald's Corporation, CHICAGO, IL

Key Personnel
MARVIN SPENCE - Owner; General Buyer
DONNA SLICK - General Manager

Peoria Ice Cream Company
624 S Main St
Creve Coeur, IL 61610-3974

Telephone: (309) 699-8079
Type of Business: Chain Restaurant Operator
Total Sales: $6,838,000 (e)
Total Units: 5
Trade Names: Dairy Queen Store (5)
Units Franchised From: 5
Primary Menu: Snacks (5)
Areas of Operation: IL
Type of Foodservice: Quick Serve (5)
Franchise Affiliation: International Dairy Queen Inc., BLOOMINGTON, MN

Key Personnel
MIKE KEPPLE - Owner; General Buyer

Nick's Pizza & Pub
856 Pyott Rd
Crystal Lake, IL 60014-8722

Telephone: (815) 356-5559
Fax Number: (815) 356-5551
Internet Homepage: nickspizzapub.com
Company Email: specialevents@nickspizzapub.com
Type of Business: Chain Restaurant Operator
Year Founded: 1995
Total Sales: $12,007,000 (e)
Alcohol Sales: 20%
Number of Employees: 50
Average Check: Lunch(10); Dinner(16)
Internet Order Processing: Yes
Internet Sales: 10.00%
Total Units: 2
Trade Names: Nick's Pizza & Pub (2)
Company-Owned Units: 2
Preferred Location Types: Freestanding
Alcohol Served: Beer, Wine, Liquor
Primary Menu: Pizza (2)
Areas of Operation: IL
Type of Foodservice: Casual Dining (2)
Primary Distributors: (Full Line) Battaglia Distributing Co. Inc., CHICAGO, IL

Key Personnel
NICK SARILLO - Owner; General Manager; Executive Chef; General Buyer
MONICA GARAPOLO - General Manager

McDonald's of Vermilion County
109 S Gilbert St
Danville, IL 61832-6229

Mailing Address: PO Box 2507, DANVILLE, IL, 61834-2507
Telephone: (217) 446-5456
Fax Number: (217) 446-5463
Type of Business: Chain Restaurant Operator
Year Founded: 1992
Total Sales: $27,910,000 (e)
Number of Employees: 265
Average Check: Breakfast(8); Lunch(8); Dinner(10)
Total Units: 6
Trade Names: McDonald's (6)
Units Franchised From: 6
Preferred Square Footage: 2,500; 3,000
Preferred Location Types: Freestanding
Primary Menu: Hamburger (6)
Areas of Operation: IL
Type of Foodservice: Quick Serve (6)
Franchise Affiliation: McDonald's Corporation, CHICAGO, IL
Primary Distributors: (Full Line) PFG - Customized Support Services, LEBANON, TN

Key Personnel
DEANNA WITZEL - Partner; General Buyer
DON WITZEL - Partner; Director Real Estate; Manager Information Systems, Human Resources; General Buyer

Bradley Investments Inc.
3120 N Kandy Ln
Decatur, IL 62526-2806

Telephone: (217) 875-1422
Fax Number: (217) 875-1428
Company Email: decdq@aol.com
Type of Business: Chain Restaurant Operator
Year Founded: 1948
Total Sales: $8,439,000 (e)
Number of Employees: 200
Average Check: Breakfast(8); Lunch(10); Dinner(12)
Total Units: 6
Trade Names: Dairy Queen (6)
Units Franchised From: 6
Preferred Square Footage: 2,500
Preferred Location Types: Freestanding
Primary Menu: American (6)
Areas of Operation: IL
Type of Foodservice: Quick Serve (6)
Franchise Affiliation: International Dairy Queen Inc., BLOOMINGTON, MN
Primary Distributors: (Full Line) Gateway Distribution, LEBANON, IL

Key Personnel
WENDELL R. BRADLEY - President; Director Operations, Facility/Maintenance, Real Estate, Design, Human Resources; General Buyer
PAT ZANNI - Controller; Director Information Systems

Kold Kreations, LLC
20330 N Deer Park Blvd Ste 106
Deer Park, IL 60010-7222

Telephone: (847) 726-2663
Type of Business: Chain Restaurant Operator
Total Sales: $1,203,000 (e)
Total Units: 2
Trade Names: Cold Stone Creamery (2)
Units Franchised From: 2
Primary Menu: Snacks (2)
Areas of Operation: IL
Type of Foodservice: Quick Serve (2)
Franchise Affiliation: Kahala Brands,

SCOTTSDALE, AZ

Key Personnel
UDAYAN SHAH - Partner
BELA SHAH - Partner

BAB Inc.
500 Lake Cook Rd Ste 475
Deerfield, IL 60015-5240

Telephone: (847) 948-7520
Fax Number: (847) 405-8140
Internet Homepage: babcorp.com
Company Email: bab@babcorp.com
Type of Business: Chain Restaurant Operator
Year Founded: 1993
Systemwide Sales: $52,151,000 (e)
Publicly Held: Yes
Total Sales: $4,248,000 (e)
Number of Employees: 15
Average Check: Breakfast(5); Lunch(5); Dinner(5)
Internet Order Processing: Yes
Internet Sales: 2.00%
Total Units: 68
Trade Names: Big Apple Bagels; My Favorite Muffin; Sweet Duet
Units Franchised To: 68
Preferred Square Footage: 600; 800; 1,000; 1,600; 1,800; 2,000
Preferred Location Types: Freestanding; Lifestyle Center; Regional Mall; Strip Mall
Projected Openings: 3
Areas of Operation: AL, CA, CO, FL, GA, IA, IL, IN, KY, MD, MI, MN, MO, NE, NJ, NV, NY, OH, OR, PA, RI, TX, UT, VA, WA, WI
Foreign Countries: EGYPT; UNITED ARAB EMIRATES
Type of Foodservice: Quick Serve (80)
Primary Distributors: (Food) US Foods, CORALVILLE, IA; (Food) Dawn Food Products Inc., PISCATAWAY, NJ

Key Personnel
MICHAEL W. EVANS - Chairman; CEO; President
GERALDINE CONN - CFO
MICHAEL K. MURTAUGH - VP; Corporate Secretary; General Counsel
LESLIE WALTERS - Director Marketing

Shawkins, Inc.
103 N Annie Glidden Rd
Dekalb, IL 60115-2701

Telephone: (815) 517-1009
Type of Business: Chain Restaurant Operator
Total Sales: $5,894,000 (e)
Total Units: 4
Trade Names: Jersey Mike's Subs (4)
Units Franchised From: 4
Primary Menu: Sandwiches/Deli (4)
Areas of Operation: IL
Type of Foodservice: Quick Serve (4)
Franchise Affiliation: Jersey Mike's Franchise Systems, MANASQUAN, NJ

Key Personnel
TODD SHAW - Owner

Antler Management
2860 S River Rd Ste 390
Des Plaines, IL 60018-6008

Telephone: (847) 824-2525
Fax Number: (847) 824-2233
Internet Homepage: antlermgt.com
Type of Business: Chain Restaurant Operator
Year Founded: 1981
Total Sales: $20,990,000 (e)
Number of Employees: 380
Average Check: Lunch(8); Dinner(12)
Total Units: 8
Trade Names: Popeyes Louisiana Kitchen (8)
Units Franchised From: 8
Preferred Square Footage: 2,000
Preferred Location Types: Freestanding; Strip Mall
Primary Menu: Chicken (8)
Areas of Operation: IL, IN
Type of Foodservice: Quick Serve (8)
Franchise Affiliation: Popeyes Louisiana Kitchen Inc., ATLANTA, GA

Key Personnel
ROSLYN JIN - Founder; Director
DAVID ANTLER - President; Director Real Estate; General Buyer
LOUISE JINKINS - Director Risk Management, Food Safety

Francesca Restaurants LLC
2200 E Devon Ave Ste 250
Des Plaines, IL 60018-4591

Telephone: (773) 334-8368
Fax Number: (773) 506-9587
Internet Homepage: miafrancesca.com
Company Email: corpcontact@miafrancesca.com
Type of Business: Chain Restaurant Operator
Year Founded: 1992
Total Sales: $59,950,000 (e)
Alcohol Sales: 40%
Number of Employees: 1,737
Average Check: Lunch(20); Dinner(42)
Internet Order Processing: Yes
Total Units: 17
Trade Names: Davanti Enoteca (4); Disotto (1); Fat Rosie's (2); Francesca's (18)
Company-Owned Units: 25
Preferred Square Footage: 5,500; 6,000
Preferred Location Types: Freestanding; Strip Mall
Alcohol Served: Beer, Wine, Liquor
Primary Menu: Italian (23); Mexican (2)
Areas of Operation: AZ, IL, NC, WI
Type of Foodservice: Casual Dining (25)
Catering Services: Yes

Key Personnel
SCOTT HARRIS - Partner
DAN MYER - Partner; Director Purchasing
HELMUT SCHADINGER - CFO; Controller

Karis Management
960 Rand Rd Ste 222
Des Plaines, IL 60016-2355

Telephone: (847) 297-5220
Fax Number: (847) 297-5233
Type of Business: Chain Restaurant Operator
Total Sales: $61,520,000 (e)
Number of Employees: 320
Average Check: Breakfast(8); Lunch(8); Dinner(8)
Total Units: 13
Trade Names: McDonald's (13)
Units Franchised From: 13
Preferred Square Footage: 2,500
Preferred Location Types: Freestanding
Primary Menu: Hamburger (13)
Areas of Operation: IL
Type of Foodservice: Quick Serve (13)
Franchise Affiliation: McDonald's Corporation, CHICAGO, IL
Primary Distributors: (Food) The Martin-Brower Co. LLC, ROSEMONT, IL

Key Personnel
COLIN NIEBUHR - President Compliance; Manager
CHRISTINE SCHENK - President; Director Finance, Operations, Facility/Maintenance, Real Estate, Design; General Buyer
VICKIE WALLACE - Manager Human Resources

BOZ Hot Dogs
901 California Ave
Dolton, IL 60419-2203

Telephone: (708) 717-3870
Internet Homepage: bozhotdogs.com
Company Email: comments@bozhotdogs.com
Type of Business: Chain Restaurant Operator
Year Founded: 1969
Systemwide Sales: $3,618,000 (e)
Total Sales: $1,833,000 (e)
Number of Employees: 45
Average Check: Dinner(8)
Total Units: 9
Trade Names: BOZ Hot Dogs (9)

Company-Owned Units: 2
Units Franchised To: 7
Preferred Location Types: Freestanding
Primary Menu: Hot Dogs (9)
Areas of Operation: IL, IN
Type of Foodservice: Quick Serve (9)

Key Personnel
CAROL BOLLACKER - Owner
ROBERTA HART - Owner; General Buyer

ARAMARK
2300 Warrenville Rd
Downers Grove, IL 60515-1765

Telephone: (630) 271-2000
Fax Number: (630) 271-2710
Listing Type: Regional Office
Type of Business: Foodservice Management Operator
Year Founded: 1959
Number of Employees: 150
Number of Locations Served: 150
Total Foodservice Mgmt Accounts: 150
Areas of Operation: IL
Type of Foodservice: Cafeteria (150)
Foodservice Management Venues: Schools
Primary Distributors: (Full Line) SYSCO Food Services of Chicago Inc., DES PLAINES, IL
Parent Company: Aramark, PHILADELPHIA, PA
Headquarters: ARAMARK School Support Services, PHILADELPHIA, PA

Key Personnel
TOM ORDROF - CFO; Exec VP

Classic Cinemas
603 Rogers St Fl 1
Downers Grove, IL 60515-3774

Telephone: (630) 968-1600
Fax Number: (630) 968-1626
Internet Homepage: classiccinemas.com
Company Email: yourinput@classiccinemas.com
Type of Business: Foodservice Operations - Movie Theatre
Year Founded: 1978
Total Sales: $15,380,000 (e)
Alcohol Sales: 0.10%
Number of Employees: 484
Average Check: Breakfast(8); Lunch(8); Dinner(8)
Internet Order Processing: Yes
Internet Sales: 0.50%
Total Units: 14
Trade Names: Classic Cinemas (14)
Company-Owned Units: 14
Preferred Location Types: Freestanding; Regional Mall
Alcohol Served: Beer, Wine, Liquor
Primary Menu: Snacks (14)
Projected Remodelings: 2
Areas of Operation: IL
Type of Foodservice: In-Store Feeder (14)
Primary Distributors: (Full Line) Royal Supply Distribution Center, NEW BERLIN, WI
Notes: The company derives approximately 72% of its revenue from movie theater operations.

Key Personnel
CHRIS JOHNSON - CEO; VP Operations
WILLIS JOHNSON - President; Director Real Estate, Menu Development; General Buyer

Cooper's Hawk Holding Inc.
3500 Lacey Rd Suite 1000
Downers Grove, IL 60515

Telephone: (708) 215-5674
Fax Number: (708) 839-2920
Internet Homepage: coopershawkwinery.com
Company Email: info@chwinery.com
Type of Business: Chain Restaurant Operator
Year Founded: 2005
Total Sales: $226,910,000 (e)
Alcohol Sales: 25%
Internet Order Processing: Yes
Total Units: 46
Trade Names: Cooper's Hawk Winery & Restaurant (46)
Company-Owned Units: 46
Preferred Location Types: Freestanding
Primary Menu: Miscellaneous (46)
Projected Openings: 3
Areas of Operation: AZ, FL, IL, IN, MD, MI, MO, OH, VA, WI
Type of Foodservice: Casual Dining (46)
Notes: Sales estimates exclude retail wine sales.

Key Personnel
TIM MCENERY - Founder; CEO
MICHAEL COYNE - CFO
FLORENCE HO - Senior VP Marketing
KRISTEN ZAGOZDON - VP Human Resources
MATT MCMILLIN - VP Culinary Operations
SUSAN LUCAS - VP Information Technology
RANDALL SABADO - Executive Chef Research & Development
MELANIE ROMNIAK - Senior Director Marketing
MELANIE PIERCE - Director Marketing

Mr Submarine
1322 Ogden Ave
Downers Grove, IL 60515-2772

Telephone: (815) 773-6100
Internet Homepage: mrsubchicago.com
Company Email: admin@mrsubmarine.com
Type of Business: Chain Restaurant Operator
Total Sales: $16,020,000 (e)
Total Units: 25
Trade Names: Mr. Submarine (25)
Units Franchised From: 25
Primary Menu: Sandwiches/Deli (25)
Areas of Operation: IL
Type of Foodservice: Quick Serve (25)
Franchise Affiliation: Mr. Submarine, Inc., BERWYN, IL

Key Personnel
GUSS TZOUMAS - President; Partner; General Buyer
NICK TZOUMAS - Partner; VP Operations
MOHAMMAD ALRAMAHE - Manager

Tri City Foods, Inc
1400 Opus Pl Ste 900
Downers Grove, IL 60515-5762

Telephone: (630) 598-3300
Fax Number: (630) 598-2211
Internet Homepage: 3cityfoods.com
Company Email: customerrelations@heartlandfoodcorp.com
Type of Business: Chain Restaurant Operator
Year Founded: 2003
Total Sales: $913,790,000 (e)
Number of Employees: 10,300
Average Check: Breakfast(8); Lunch(8); Dinner(8)
Total Units: 492
Trade Names: Burger King (492)
Units Franchised From: 492
Preferred Square Footage: 3,000; 4,000
Preferred Location Types: Airports; Community Mall; Convenience Store/Gas Station; Downtown; Freestanding; Office Complex; Outlet Mall; Regional Mall; Strip Mall
Primary Menu: Hamburger (492)
Areas of Operation: IA, IL, IN, MI, MN, NE, TN, WI
Type of Foodservice: Quick Serve (492)
Franchise Affiliation: Burger King Worldwide Inc., MIAMI, FL
Primary Distributors: (Food) Reinhart FoodService LLC, CHICAGO, IL
Parent Company: Dhanani Group, ,

Key Personnel
SHOUKAT DHANANI - CEO
ASHRAF MEGHANI - CFO
BILL STEGMEIER - Controller
VICKIE WESTPHAL - Director Marketing
DONNA FAGET - Manager Payroll
CORY BEYER - Manager District

Mary Murray
102 Niagara St
East Alton, IL 62024-1032

Telephone: (618) 259-1075
Fax Number: (618) 551-2813
Type of Business: Chain Restaurant Operator
Total Sales: $20,681,000 (e)
Total Units: 4
Trade Names: McDonald's (4)
Units Franchised From: 4
Primary Menu: Hamburger (4)
Areas of Operation: IL
Type of Foodservice: Quick Serve (4)
Franchise Affiliation: McDonald's Corporation, CHICAGO, IL

Key Personnel
MARY MURRAY - President; General Buyer

Canteen Vending Services
3612 N Main St
East Peoria, IL 61611-1445

Telephone: (309) 699-3971
Fax Number: (309) 699-3976
Listing Type: Branch Office
Type of Business: Foodservice Management Operator
Year Founded: 1929
Number of Employees: 65
Number of Locations Served: 200
Total Foodservice Mgmt Accounts: 200
Areas of Operation: IL
Type of Foodservice: Vending machines (200)
Foodservice Management Venues: Business & Industry; College & University; Health Care; Prison Feeding
Primary Distributors: (Food) Vistar Illinois, BOLINGBROOK, IL
Parent Company: Compass Group The Americas, CHARLOTTE, NC
Headquarters: Canteen Vending Services, CHARLOTTE, NC

Key Personnel
BOB HALL - General Manager Operations, Human Resources, District

L & R Industries Inc.
100 N Main St Ste 200
East Peoria, IL 61611

Telephone: (309) 699-7198
Type of Business: Chain Restaurant Operator
Year Founded: 1976
Total Sales: $3,259,000 (e)
Number of Employees: 50
Average Check: Lunch(12); Dinner(12)
Total Units: 3
Trade Names: Taco John's (3)
Units Franchised From: 3
Preferred Square Footage: 2,000
Preferred Location Types: Freestanding; Regional Mall
Primary Menu: Taco (3)
Areas of Operation: IL
Type of Foodservice: Quick Serve (3)
Franchise Affiliation: Taco John's International Inc., CHEYENNE, WY
Primary Distributors: (Full Line) US Foods, BENSENVILLE, IL

Key Personnel
LARRY ALTRINGER - President; General Manager; General Buyer
JERRY KILDUSKI - CFO; General Manager; Director Operations; General Buyer
CHRIS ORAVEC - COO
ROB SMITH - Treasurer; General Manager

H and H Restaurants Inc
PO Box 429
Effingham, IL 62401-0429

Telephone: (217) 994-9272
Type of Business: Chain Restaurant Operator
Total Sales: $23,640,000 (e)
Total Units: 35
Trade Names: Subway (35)
Units Franchised From: 35
Primary Menu: Sandwiches/Deli (35)
Areas of Operation: IL
Type of Foodservice: Quick Serve (35)
Franchise Affiliation: Doctor's Associates Inc., MILFORD, CT

Key Personnel
MARK DUST - President; General Buyer
HANNAH DUST - Manager Operations

Sub Central
104 S 4th St
Effingham, IL 62401-3639

Telephone: (217) 347-2693
Fax Number: (217) 342-9397
Type of Business: Chain Restaurant Operator
Total Sales: $15,070,000 (e)
Total Units: 22
Trade Names: Subway (22)
Units Franchised From: 22
Primary Menu: Sandwiches/Deli (22)
Areas of Operation: IL
Type of Foodservice: Quick Serve (22)
Franchise Affiliation: Doctor's Associates Inc., MILFORD, CT

Key Personnel
RACHEL WALLACE - Partner; General Buyer
SHAWN WALLACE - Partner; General Buyer

Rosati's Franchising Inc.
2250 Point Blvd Ste 335
Elgin, IL 60123-7824

Telephone: (847) 426-8899
Fax Number: (847) 426-7733
Internet Homepage: myrosatis.com
Company Email: info@myrosatis.com
Type of Business: Chain Restaurant Operator
Systemwide Sales: $128,629,000 (e)
Total Sales: $36,160,000 (e)
Total Units: 154
Trade Names: Rosati's Authentic Italian Pizza (154)
Company-Owned Units: 15
Units Franchised To: 139
Alcohol Served: Beer, Wine, Liquor
Primary Menu: Italian (154)
Projected Openings: 9
Areas of Operation: AZ, CA, CO, FL, GA, IL, IN, KS, NC, NV, PA, TX, WI
Type of Foodservice: Family Restaurant (154)

Key Personnel
MARLA TOPLIFF - President; Corporate Secretary
DAVID M. ROSATI - VP
ANTHONY M. ROSATI - VP
TIM MCCARTHY - VP Franchise Development
NOEL CATARINA - VP Operations
ALEXANDER FABINO - General Manager

Schaffer Enterprises
579 W North Ave Ste 202
Elmhurst, IL 60126-2144

Telephone: (630) 834-9393
Fax Number: (630) 834-9396
Type of Business: Chain Restaurant Operator
Year Founded: 1976
Total Sales: $2,652,000 (e)
Number of Employees: 180
Total Units: 9
Trade Names: Circle Burger (1); Franks & Fries (1); Sbarro (7)
Company-Owned Units: 2
Units Franchised From: 7
Preferred Square Footage: 1,500; 3,000; 4,000
Preferred Location Types: Community Mall; Freestanding; Regional Mall
Primary Menu: Hamburger (1); Hot Dogs (1); Italian (7)
Areas of Operation: IL, IN, TN
Type of Foodservice: Quick Serve (9)
Franchise Affiliation: Sbarro Holdings LLC, COLUMBUS, OH

Primary Distributors: (Full Line) SYSCO Food Services of Chicago Inc., DES PLAINES, IL
Notes: Sbarro locations operate as F&S Foods Inc.

Key Personnel
ROBERT SCHAFFER - Partner; VP; Treasurer; Controller; Manager Accounting, Purchasing, Supply Chain, Menu Development
MARY SCHAFFER - Partner

Auntie Anne's Franchise
266 Saint Clair Sq
Fairview Heights, IL 62208-2134

Telephone: (618) 624-2540
Type of Business: Chain Restaurant Operator
Total Sales: $3,649,000 (e)
Total Units: 5
Trade Names: Auntie Anne's Hand-Rolled Soft Pretzels (5)
Units Franchised From: 5
Primary Menu: Snacks (5)
Areas of Operation: IL
Type of Foodservice: Quick Serve (5)
Franchise Affiliation: Auntie Anne's Inc., LANCASTER, PA

Key Personnel
DONALD PACE - Owner; General Buyer

Kel's Foods Inc./King Enterprises
50 W Douglas St Ste 1101
Freeport, IL 61032-4142

Telephone: (815) 235-7515
Fax Number: (815) 235-8621
Internet Homepage: kingenterprisesjobs.com
Company Email: Contact@kingenterprisesjobs.com
Type of Business: Chain Restaurant Operator
Year Founded: 1976
Total Sales: $76,060,000 (e)
Number of Employees: 25
Average Check: Lunch(12); Dinner(14)
Total Units: 30
Trade Names: KFC (5); KFC/Taco Bell (1); Wendy's Old Fashioned Hamburgers (24)
Units Franchised From: 30
Preferred Square Footage: 3,500
Preferred Location Types: Freestanding
Primary Menu: Chicken (5); Hamburger (24); Taco (1)
Projected Openings: 3
Areas of Operation: IA, IL, NE
Type of Foodservice: Quick Serve (30)
Catering Services: Yes
Franchise Affiliation: KFC Corporation, LOUISVILLE, KY; Taco Bell Corp., IRVINE, CA; The Wendy's Company, DUBLIN, OH
Primary Distributors: (Full Line) McLane/Midwest, DANVILLE, IL

Key Personnel
SCOTT M. KING - President; COO; General Manager; Director Operations, Purchasing, Marketing; General Buyer
JODI TOWNSEND - Manager Finance, Facility/Maintenance, Information Systems, Risk Management, Supply Chain, Real Estate, Design, Human Resources

Vinny Vannucchi's
201 S Main St
Galena, IL 61036-2284

Telephone: (815) 777-8100
Fax Number: (815) 777-8116
Internet Homepage: oneelevenmain.com; theirishcottageboutiquehotel.com; vinnysdubuque.com; vinnysgalena.com; vinnyvanucchis.com
Type of Business: Chain Restaurant Operator
Year Founded: 1992
Total Sales: $6,028,000 (e)
Alcohol Sales: 15%
Number of Employees: 150
Average Check: Lunch(14); Dinner(18)
Internet Order Processing: Yes
Internet Sales: 1.00%
Total Units: 4
Trade Names: Frank O'Dowd's (1); One Eleven Main (1); Vinny Vanucchis (2)
Company-Owned Units: 4
Preferred Location Types: Freestanding; Hotel/Motel
Alcohol Served: Beer, Wine, Liquor
Primary Menu: Italian (2); Miscellaneous (1); Seafood (1)
Areas of Operation: IA, IL
Type of Foodservice: Casual Dining (1); Fine Dining (3)
Primary Distributors: (Food) Reinhart FoodService, SHAWANO, WI

Key Personnel
DEB COULTER - Partner

JS2, Inc.
1770 S Randall Rd Ste C
Geneva, IL 60134-4646

Telephone: (630) 845-9000
Fax Number: (630) 845-9001
Type of Business: Chain Restaurant Operator
Total Sales: $12,350,000 (e)
Total Units: 9
Trade Names: Jersey Mike's Subs (9)
Units Franchised From: 9
Primary Menu: Sandwiches/Deli (9)
Areas of Operation: IL
Type of Foodservice: Quick Serve (9)
Franchise Affiliation: Jersey Mike's Franchise Systems, MANASQUAN, NJ

Key Personnel
JAMES SHIPMAN - Partner; General Buyer
PETER SHIPMAN - Partner
NICK SHIPMAN - Manager Operations

Hackney's on Lake Inc.
1514 E Lake Ave
Glenview, IL 60025-2113

Telephone: (847) 724-7171
Fax Number: (847) 724-7302
Internet Homepage: hackneys.net
Type of Business: Chain Restaurant Operator
Year Founded: 1939
Total Sales: $5,981,000 (e)
Alcohol Sales: 20%
Number of Employees: 265
Average Check: Lunch(14); Dinner(20)
Total Units: 2
Trade Names: Hackney's (2)
Company-Owned Units: 2
Preferred Square Footage: 4,000
Preferred Location Types: Freestanding
Alcohol Served: Beer, Wine, Liquor
Primary Menu: American (2)
Areas of Operation: IL
Type of Foodservice: Casual Dining (2)
Primary Distributors: (Equipment) Edward Don & Co., WOODRIDGE, IL; (Food) SYSCO Food Services of Chicago Inc., DES PLAINES, IL; (Supplies) Edward Don & Co., WOODRIDGE, IL

Key Personnel
ELIZABETH HEBSON - President; Owner; Controller; General Buyer
MIKE MASTERSON - VP; General Manager

Restaurants-America
1840 Pickwick Ln
Glenview, IL 60026-1307

Telephone: (847) 510-2500
Fax Number: (847) 510-2525
Internet Homepage: parktavernchicago.com; primebarchicago.com; townhousewinebar.com
Company Email: gm@primebarchicago.com
Type of Business: Chain Restaurant Operator
Year Founded: 1991
Systemwide Sales: $27,269,000 (e)
Total Sales: $25,267,000 (e)
Alcohol Sales: 35%
Number of Employees: 214
Average Check: Lunch(16); Dinner(34)
Internet Order Processing: Yes
Internet Sales: 2.00%

Total Units: 4
Trade Names: Park Tavern (1); Primebar (1); The Grillroom (1); Townhouse Restaurant & Wine Bar (1)
Company-Owned Units: 4
Preferred Square Footage: 7,000; 8,000
Preferred Location Types: Downtown; Freestanding; Lifestyle Center; Regional Mall; Strip Mall
Alcohol Served: Beer, Wine, Liquor
Primary Menu: American (4)
Projected Openings: 2
Areas of Operation: FL, IL, MN
Type of Foodservice: Casual Dining (4)
Catering Services: Yes

Key Personnel
TED KASEMIR - Co-President; Partner; Director Finance, Information Systems, Research & Development, Store Fixtures, Store Planning
RODD GOLDMAN - Director Marketing
JANE BETTERIDGE - Manager Accounting

Estel Foods Inc
1506 Johnson Rd Ste 115
Granite City, IL 62040-3800

Telephone: (618) 876-3289
Fax Number: (618) 876-3445
Type of Business: Chain Restaurant Operator
Total Sales: $85,260,000 (e)
Number of Employees: 1,170
Total Units: 18
Trade Names: McDonald's (18)
Units Franchised From: 18
Preferred Square Footage: 2,500
Primary Menu: Hamburger (18)
Areas of Operation: IL
Type of Foodservice: Quick Serve (18)
Franchise Affiliation: McDonald's Corporation, CHICAGO, IL

Key Personnel
JAMES ESTEL WILLIAMS JR - President; General Buyer
MARION GROSS - Chief Supply Chain Officer; Senior VP
MICHAEL HANSEN - Director Technology, Global
PRIYANKA CHATTERJEE - Director Technology, Development, Innovation

Pizza World USA Franchise Corp.
1535 Johnson Rd
Granite City, IL 62040-3831

Telephone: (618) 451-1111
Fax Number: (618) 345-4554
Internet Homepage: pizzaworldonline.com
Company Email: contactus@pizzaworldonline.com
Type of Business: Chain Restaurant Operator
Total Sales: $5,202,000 (e)
Number of Employees: 102
Average Check: Lunch(14); Dinner(16)
Internet Order Processing: Yes
Total Units: 8
Trade Names: Pizza World (8)
Company-Owned Units: 8
Preferred Location Types: Freestanding; Strip Mall
Primary Menu: Pizza (8)
Areas of Operation: IL, MO
Type of Foodservice: Quick Serve (8)

Key Personnel
ERICK WORTHAM - CEO; Owner; General Buyer
RYAN WORTHAM - President; General Manager

Jimano's Pizzeria
7010 Grand Ave Ste C
Gurnee, IL 60031-6601

Telephone: (847) 856-8696
Fax Number: (847) 599-2809
Internet Homepage: jimanos.com
Company Email: sales@jimanos.com
Type of Business: Chain Restaurant Operator
Year Founded: 1997
Total Sales: $1,806,000 (e)
Average Check: Dinner(12)
Internet Order Processing: Yes
Total Units: 8
Trade Names: Jimano's Pizzeria (8)
Company-Owned Units: 5
Units Franchised To: 3
Primary Menu: Italian (8)
Areas of Operation: CO, IL
Type of Foodservice: Family Restaurant (8)

Key Personnel
ROD SEALE - Owner; General Buyer
ADAM SCHIFF - VP Operations

Domino's Franchisee
820 S Park Ave
Herrin, IL 62948-4111

Telephone: (618) 988-1686
Type of Business: Chain Restaurant Operator
Total Sales: $4,162,000 (e)
Total Units: 2
Trade Names: Domino's (2)
Units Franchised From: 2
Primary Menu: Pizza (2)
Areas of Operation: IL
Type of Foodservice: Quick Serve (2)
Franchise Affiliation: Domino's Pizza Inc, ANN ARBOR, MI

Key Personnel
DANNY J. DAUGHERTY - Owner; General Buyer

Nayana
8615 W 95th St
Hickory Hills, IL 60457-2704

Telephone: (708) 599-0460
Type of Business: Chain Restaurant Operator
Total Sales: $4,374,000 (e)
Total Units: 7
Trade Names: Subway (7)
Units Franchised From: 7
Primary Menu: Sandwiches/Deli (7)
Areas of Operation: IL
Type of Foodservice: Quick Serve (7)
Franchise Affiliation: Doctor's Associates Inc., MILFORD, CT

Key Personnel
APY PATEL - Owner; General Buyer

Emilio's Tapas Restaurant
4100 Roosevelt Rd
Hillside, IL 60162-1824

Telephone: (708) 547-7177
Fax Number: (708) 547-1935
Internet Homepage: emiliostapas.com
Company Email: contactus@emiliostapas.com
Type of Business: Chain Restaurant Operator
Year Founded: 1988
Total Sales: $9,174,000 (e)
Alcohol Sales: 5%
Number of Employees: 180
Average Check: Lunch(14); Dinner(20)
Total Units: 2
Trade Names: Emilios Tapas (2)
Company-Owned Units: 2
Preferred Location Types: Freestanding
Alcohol Served: Beer, Wine, Liquor
Primary Menu: Spanish (2)
Areas of Operation: IL
Type of Foodservice: Casual Dining (2)
Catering Services: Yes

Key Personnel
EMILIO GERVILLA - President; General Buyer

Shamrock Company
15 Spinning Wheel Rd Ste 110
Hinsdale, IL 60521-2983

Telephone: (630) 655-8274
Fax Number: (630) 655-8275
Type of Business: Chain Restaurant Operator

Year Founded: 1994
Total Sales: $61,860,000 (e)
Number of Employees: 950
Average Check: Lunch(8); Dinner(10)
Total Units: 40
Trade Names: KFC (11); KFC/Taco Bell (6); Taco Bell (23)
Units Franchised From: 40
Preferred Square Footage: 2,500
Preferred Location Types: Freestanding
Primary Menu: Chicken (17); Taco (29)
Areas of Operation: IL, IN
Type of Foodservice: Quick Serve (40)
Franchise Affiliation: KFC Corporation, LOUISVILLE, KY; Taco Bell Corp., IRVINE, CA
Primary Distributors: (Full Line) McLane/Sturtevant, STURTEVANT, WI

Key Personnel
STEPHEN C. MCGUE - President; Director Supply Chain, Real Estate; General Buyer
DICK REDIEHS - CFO
ROBERT RUSS - VP Operations
KEVIN WALLACE - VP Operations
KEN PULLUM - Director Information Technology
JAIME DATA - Manager Information Systems, Human Resources
STEVE KAPPA - Manager Distribution
KRISTINA SILINIS - Coordinator Accounting

Garibaldi's Inc.
2346 W Higgins Rd
Hoffman Estates, IL 60169-2413

Telephone: (847) 884-8663
Fax Number: (847) 884-8064
Internet Homepage: garibaldis.com
Company Email: info@garibaldis.com
Type of Business: Chain Restaurant Operator
Year Founded: 1975
Total Sales: $4,007,000 (e)
Alcohol Sales: 5%
Number of Employees: 200
Average Check: Lunch(14); Dinner(20)
Total Units: 2
Trade Names: Garibaldi's Italian Eatery (2)
Company-Owned Units: 2
Preferred Location Types: Regional Mall; Strip Mall
Alcohol Served: Beer, Wine
Primary Menu: Italian (2)
Areas of Operation: IL
Type of Foodservice: Casual Dining (2)
Catering Services: Yes

Key Personnel
MICHAEL BAGAN - Owner; General Buyer

Blueberry Hill
14355 S Bell Rd
Homer Glen, IL 60491-7876

Telephone: (708) 645-0766
Fax Number: (708) 645-0844
Internet Homepage: blueberrybreakfastcafe.com
Company Email: bluehillthrill@yahoo.com
Type of Business: Chain Restaurant Operator
Total Sales: $9,835,000 (e)
Number of Employees: 225
Average Check: Breakfast(10); Lunch(12);
Total Units: 9
Trade Names: Blueberry Hill Breakfast Cafe (9)
Company-Owned Units: 9
Primary Menu: American (9)
Areas of Operation: IL
Type of Foodservice: Family Restaurant (9)
Catering Services: Yes

Key Personnel
GEORGE NIKOLOPOULOS - President; General Buyer

Heisner Enterprises Partnership
14007 S Bell Rd Ste 314
Homer Glen, IL 60491-8463

Telephone: (815) 603-9721
Type of Business: Chain Restaurant Operator
Total Sales: $66,090,000 (e)
Number of Employees: 687
Total Units: 14
Trade Names: McDonald's (14)
Units Franchised From: 14
Preferred Square Footage: 2,500
Primary Menu: Hamburger (14)
Areas of Operation: FL
Type of Foodservice: Quick Serve (14)
Franchise Affiliation: McDonald's Corporation, CHICAGO, IL

Key Personnel
MICHELE HEISNER - President; General Buyer

Aurelio's Pizza Inc.
18162 Harwood Ave
Homewood, IL 60430-2102

Telephone: (708) 798-8050
Fax Number: (708) 798-6692
Internet Homepage: aureliospizza.com
Type of Business: Chain Restaurant Operator
Year Founded: 1959
Systemwide Sales: $54,037,000 (e)
Total Sales: $5,548,000 (e)
Alcohol Sales: 10%
Number of Employees: 148
Average Check: Lunch(8); Dinner(12)
Internet Order Processing: Yes
Total Units: 39
Trade Names: Aurelio's Pizza (39)
Company-Owned Units: 2
Units Franchised To: 37
Preferred Square Footage: 3,000; 4,000
Preferred Location Types: Community Mall; Freestanding; Strip Mall
Alcohol Served: Beer, Wine, Liquor
Primary Menu: Pizza (39)
Projected Remodelings: 20
Areas of Operation: FL, GA, IL, IN, MN, NV
Type of Foodservice: Casual Dining (39)
Catering Services: Yes
Primary Distributors: (Food) Wilkens Food Service, UNIVERSITY PARK, IL

Key Personnel
JOHN ROMANS - General Manager; Director Operations, Purchasing, Food Safety

Coldwater Investments, Inc
17627 Halsted St
Homewood, IL 60430-2007

Telephone: (708) 922-0900
Fax Number: (708) 922-0903
Type of Business: Chain Restaurant Operator
Total Sales: $5,901,000 (e)
Total Units: 10
Trade Names: Subway (10)
Units Franchised From: 10
Primary Menu: Sandwiches/Deli (10)
Areas of Operation: IL
Type of Foodservice: Quick Serve (10)
Franchise Affiliation: Doctor's Associates Inc., MILFORD, CT

Key Personnel
KATHY BENTZ - President; General Buyer

JDD Investment Co.
300 Park Blvd Ste 300
Itasca, IL 60143-2664

Telephone: (630) 654-9100
Fax Number: (630) 654-1055
Type of Business: Chain Restaurant Operator
Year Founded: 1989
Total Sales: $32,770,000 (e)
Number of Employees: 300
Average Check: Breakfast(8); Lunch(10); Dinner(12)
Total Units: 7
Trade Names: McDonald's (7)
Units Franchised From: 7
Preferred Square Footage: 2,500; 3,000
Preferred Location Types: Community Mall; Convenience Store/Gas Station; Freestanding

Primary Menu: Hamburger (7)
Areas of Operation: IL
Type of Foodservice: Quick Serve (7)
Franchise Affiliation: McDonald's Corporation, CHICAGO, IL

Key Personnel
JOHN DAKAJOS - President; Director Finance, Purchasing, Information Systems, Real Estate

Himalaya Holdings LLC
2100 W Jefferson St
Joliet, IL 60435-6622

Telephone: (815) 725-8989
Fax Number: (815) 725-5391
Internet Homepage: goldencorral.com
Type of Business: Chain Restaurant Operator
Year Founded: 1999
Total Sales: $28,370,000 (e)
Number of Employees: 340
Average Check: Lunch(10); Dinner(14)
Total Units: 7
Trade Names: Golden Corral Buffet & Grill (7)
Units Franchised From: 7
Preferred Square Footage: 7,800; 11,000; 14,000
Preferred Location Types: Freestanding
Primary Menu: American (7)
Areas of Operation: IL, WI
Type of Foodservice: Family Restaurant (7)
Franchise Affiliation: Golden Corral Corp., RALEIGH, NC

Key Personnel
SURESH TUMNALA - Owner; General Buyer

Lawndale Meadows
743 Knox Hwy 10
Knoxville, IL 61448

Telephone: (309) 289-9351
Type of Business: Chain Restaurant Operator
Total Sales: $14,724,000 (e)
Number of Employees: 180
Total Units: 3
Trade Names: McDonald's (3)
Units Franchised From: 3
Preferred Square Footage: 2,500
Preferred Location Types: Freestanding
Primary Menu: Hamburger (3)
Areas of Operation: IL
Type of Foodservice: Quick Serve (3)
Franchise Affiliation: McDonald's Corporation, CHICAGO, IL

Key Personnel
CAROL KIRKENMEIER - President; General Buyer
NANCY HUFF - Supervisor District; Administrator

Q-BBQ
70 S La Grange Rd
La Grange, IL 60525

Telephone: (708) 482-8700
Internet Homepage: q-bbq.com
Company Email: eat@q-bbq.com
Type of Business: Chain Restaurant Operator
Total Units: 4
Trade Names: Q-BBQ (4)
Company-Owned Units: 4
Primary Menu: Bar-B-Q (4)
Areas of Operation: IL, IN
Type of Foodservice: Casual Dining (4)

Key Personnel
KELLIE SIPICH - Director Operations; General Buyer

McEssy Investment Company
1025 W Everett Rd Ste 3
Lake Forest, IL 60045-2668

Telephone: (847) 234-3427
Fax Number: (847) 234-6478
Type of Business: Chain Restaurant Operator
Year Founded: 1979
Total Sales: $103,640,000 (e)
Number of Employees: 550
Average Check: Breakfast(8); Lunch(8); Dinner(10)
Total Units: 22
Trade Names: McDonald's (22)
Units Franchised From: 22
Preferred Square Footage: 1,500
Preferred Location Types: Freestanding
Primary Menu: Hamburger (22)
Areas of Operation: IL, WI
Type of Foodservice: Quick Serve (22)
Franchise Affiliation: McDonald's Corporation, CHICAGO, IL
Primary Distributors: (Food) The Martin-Brower Co. LLC, ROSEMONT, IL

Key Personnel
JOHN HALL - President
JEFF WHITTEN - President; Director Information Systems; General Buyer
BILL MCESSY - Owner; Director Finance, Real Estate
DON BELL - Director Facility/Maintenance
PAT BELL - Manager Accounting
CRAIG CROHN - Manager Facility/Maintenance

Nornet Management
17835 Torrence Ave
Lansing, IL 60438-1835

Telephone: (708) 895-9244
Fax Number: (708) 895-9258
Company Email: nornet2002@yahoo.com
Type of Business: Chain Restaurant Operator
Total Sales: $80,080,000 (e)
Total Units: 17
Trade Names: McDonald's (17)
Units Franchised From: 17
Preferred Square Footage: 2,500
Primary Menu: Hamburger (17)
Areas of Operation: IL, IN
Type of Foodservice: Quick Serve (17)
Franchise Affiliation: McDonald's Corporation, CHICAGO, IL

Key Personnel
OSCAR PERRETTA - Owner; General Buyer
DELIA LOPEZ - Manager Payroll

Subway Development Agent Advisory Corporation
16800 Chicago Ave Rear
Lansing, IL 60438-1171

Telephone: (708) 474-4300
Type of Business: Chain Restaurant Operator
Total Sales: $4,996,000 (e)
Total Units: 8
Trade Names: Subway (8)
Units Franchised From: 8
Primary Menu: Sandwiches/Deli (8)
Areas of Operation: IL
Type of Foodservice: Quick Serve (9)
Franchise Affiliation: Doctor's Associates Inc., MILFORD, CT

Key Personnel
TOM MCSWIGGAN - President

Hamco Inc.
300 Village Grn Ste 200
Lincolnshire, IL 60069-3083

Telephone: (847) 478-5100
Fax Number: (847) 478-5005
Internet Homepage: eggharborcafe.com
Company Email: HAMCO@eggharborcafe.com
Type of Business: Chain Restaurant Operator
Year Founded: 1985
Total Sales: $31,770,000 (e)
Number of Employees: 670
Average Check: Breakfast(10); Lunch(14);
Internet Order Processing: Yes
Total Units: 20

Trade Names: Egg Harbor Cafe (20)
Company-Owned Units: 20
Preferred Square Footage: 4,000
Preferred Location Types: Regional Mall; Strip Mall
Primary Menu: American (20)
Projected Openings: 1
Areas of Operation: GA, IL, WI
Type of Foodservice: Family Restaurant (20)
Primary Distributors: (Equipment) Alliance Paper & Foodservice Equipment, ADDISON, IL; (Supplies) Alliance Paper & Foodservice Equipment, ADDISON, IL

Key Personnel
MICHAEL FARRELL - President; Director Finance, Purchasing, Information Systems, Supply Chain, Human Resources

Sarpino's USA Inc.
200 Tri State Intl Ste 500
Lincolnshire, IL 60069-4431

Telephone: (847) 374-6300
Fax Number: (847) 374-8110
Internet Homepage: gosarpinos.com
Company Email: us@gosarpinos.com
Type of Business: Chain Restaurant Operator
Year Founded: 2000
Systemwide Sales: $19,342,000 (e)
Total Sales: $2,978,000 (e)
Alcohol Sales: 5%
Number of Employees: 157
Average Check: Lunch(36); Dinner(48)
Internet Order Processing: Yes
Total Units: 49
Trade Names: Sarpino's Pizzeria (49)
Units Franchised To: 49
Preferred Square Footage: 250; 1,000; 1,500
Preferred Location Types: Freestanding
Alcohol Served: Beer, Wine, Liquor
Primary Menu: Italian (49)
Projected Openings: 21
Areas of Operation: FL, IA, IL, KS, MN, MO, TX
Type of Foodservice: Fast Casual (49)
Catering Services: Yes
Primary Distributors: (Full Line) SYSCO Food Services of Edmonton, ACHESON, AB
Notes: Total store count reflects U.S. operations only.

Key Personnel
DMITRY SHAPIRO - President
TED BEDNARSKI - VP Real Estate, Design, Franchise Development
DAVID GORDON CHATKIN - VP
DAVID DIOGO - Senior Director Franchise Development
REBECCA KROUPA - Director Research & Development
BRUCE MALAIKO - Manager Operations

NATALLIA DANILOVICH - Manager Marketing

Allgauer's Grill
3003 Corporate West Dr
Lisle, IL 60532-3603

Telephone: (630) 245-7650
Fax Number: (630) 505-8948
Internet Homepage: lislenaperville.hilton.com
Type of Business: Chain Restaurant Operator
Year Founded: 1981
Total Sales: $6,773,000 (e)
Alcohol Sales: 20%
Number of Employees: 70
Average Check: Breakfast(10); Lunch(14); Dinner(26)
Total Units: 3
Trade Names: Allgauer's Grill (3)
Company-Owned Units: 3
Preferred Location Types: Hotel/Motel
Alcohol Served: Beer, Wine, Liquor
Primary Menu: American (3)
Areas of Operation: IL, WI
Type of Foodservice: Casual Dining (3)
Primary Distributors: (Food) SYSCO Food Services of Chicago Inc., DES PLAINES, IL

Key Personnel
FRANK ALLGAUER - Owner; General Buyer
NICK LANDEWEER - Executive Chef; Buyer Beverages

Chicago Diversified Foods Corp.
400 E 22nd St Ste E
Lombard, IL 60148-6104

Telephone: (630) 889-1818
Fax Number: (630) 889-1919
Type of Business: Chain Restaurant Operator
Year Founded: 1987
Total Sales: $3,785,000 (e)
Number of Employees: 800
Average Check: Lunch(12); Dinner(12)
Total Units: 2
Trade Names: KFC (2)
Units Franchised From: 2
Preferred Square Footage: 1,200
Preferred Location Types: Freestanding
Primary Menu: Chicken (2)
Areas of Operation: MI
Type of Foodservice: Quick Serve (2)
Franchise Affiliation: KFC Corporation, LOUISVILLE, KY
Primary Distributors: (Equipment) McLane Foodservice, CARROLLTON, TX; (Food) McLane/Midwest, DANVILLE, IL; (Supplies) McLane Foodservice, CARROLLTON, TX

Key Personnel
ANTHONY BASILE - President; General Buyer

Quest Food Management Services Inc.
2500 S Highland Ave Ste 250
Lombard, IL 60148-7100

Telephone: (630) 627-7708
Fax Number: (630) 627-7768
Internet Homepage: questfms.com
Company Email: Quest@Questfms.com
Type of Business: Foodservice Management Operator
Year Founded: 1985
Total Sales: $29,772,000 (e)
Number of Employees: 370
Number of Locations Served: 54
Total Foodservice Mgmt Accounts: 54
Areas of Operation: IL
Type of Foodservice: Cafeteria (54)
Foodservice Management Venues: Business & Industry; Other; Schools
Primary Distributors: (Full Line) US Foods Holding Corp., ROSEMONT, IL

Key Personnel
MICHAEL MCTAGGART - CEO; Owner
NICK SACCARO - President; General Buyer
JAMES PETERS - CFO
SANDRA KASPRZAK - Exec VP
JIM PETERS - VP Finance
ARDELLA BURKES - VP Human Resources
ANTHONY FERRAZZUOLO - Director Business Development
PHIL MIRITELLO - Director Foodservice
ALICIA CULVERSON - Director Foodservice
PATRICK CARNATHAN - Director Information Technology
CHRISTINA MALHAM - Director Marketing
ROSE CARLSON - Director Compliance
ROBIN GARCIA - Director Foodservice

Beef-A-Roo Inc.
9934 N Alpine Rd Ste 101
Machesney Park, IL 61115-8240

Telephone: (815) 637-1008
Fax Number: (815) 637-1412
Internet Homepage: beefaroo.com
Company Email: info@beefaroo.com
Type of Business: Chain Restaurant Operator
Year Founded: 1967
Systemwide Sales: $1,330,000 (e)
Total Sales: $14,310,000 (e)
Number of Employees: 335
Average Check: Lunch(10); Dinner(10)
Total Units: 7
Trade Names: Beef-A-Roo (7)
Company-Owned Units: 7
Preferred Square Footage: 3,000

Preferred Location Types: Freestanding; Travel Plazas
Primary Menu: American (7)
Areas of Operation: IL
Type of Foodservice: Fast Casual (7)
Catering Services: Yes
On-site Distribution Center: Yes
Primary Distributors: (Full Line) A.D.E. Restaurant Services Inc., ADDISON, IL

Key Personnel
NICK DEBRULER - Partner; Director Operations, Purchasing, Store Fixtures
SHANNON DIEHL - Controller

Mabes Enterprises Inc.
123 W Calhoun St
Macomb, IL 61455-2121

Telephone: (309) 836-3030
Fax Number: (309) 837-6488
Type of Business: Chain Restaurant Operator
Total Sales: $8,260,000 (e)
Total Units: 4
Trade Names: Domino's (4)
Units Franchised From: 4
Preferred Square Footage: 1,200
Preferred Location Types: Freestanding; Strip Mall
Primary Menu: Pizza (4)
Areas of Operation: IA, IL, MO
Type of Foodservice: Quick Serve (4)
Franchise Affiliation: Domino's Pizza Inc, ANN ARBOR, MI

Key Personnel
JEFF MABREY - Owner; General Manager; General Buyer

Bentz Subway
122 Town Center Rd Ste 103
Matteson, IL 60443-2275

Telephone: (708) 747-7370
Fax Number: (708) 747-7371
Company Email: subwayjay@aol.com
Type of Business: Chain Restaurant Operator
Year Founded: 1989
Total Sales: $17,820,000 (e)
Number of Employees: 385
Average Check: Lunch(12); Dinner(12)
Total Units: 24
Trade Names: Subway (24)
Units Franchised From: 24
Preferred Square Footage: 300; 1,200; 2,000
Preferred Location Types: Freestanding
Primary Menu: Sandwiches/Deli (24)
Areas of Operation: IL
Type of Foodservice: Quick Serve (24)
Franchise Affiliation: Doctor's Associates Inc., MILFORD, CT

Key Personnel
JAY BENTZ - Partner; Director Information Systems, Real Estate; General Buyer
KATHY T. BENTZ - Partner; General Buyer
MOLLY SIPLES - Manager Finance

Carnagio Enterprises
121 Mondamin St
Minooka, IL 60447

Telephone: (815) 467-6646
Fax Number: (815) 467-7996
Company Email: jan.martin@jjcrest.com
Type of Business: Chain Restaurant Operator
Total Sales: $61,880,000 (e)
Number of Employees: 690
Total Units: 13
Trade Names: McDonald's (13)
Units Franchised From: 13
Preferred Square Footage: 2,500
Primary Menu: Hamburger (13)
Areas of Operation: IL
Type of Foodservice: Quick Serve (13)
Franchise Affiliation: McDonald's Corporation, CHICAGO, IL

Key Personnel
JOHN CARNAGIO - President; Owner; General Buyer

Chicago Franchise Systems Inc.
18861 90th Ave Ste H
Mokena, IL 60448-8467

Telephone: (708) 478-8440
Fax Number: (708) 478-8499
Internet Homepage: alsbeef.com; nancyspizza.com
Type of Business: Chain Restaurant Operator
Year Founded: 1974
Systemwide Sales: $49,222,000 (e)
Total Sales: $5,219,000 (e)
Alcohol Sales: 3%
Number of Employees: 50
Average Check: Lunch(16); Dinner(28)
Total Units: 36
Trade Names: Al's Italian Beef (8); Nancy's Pizza (28)
Company-Owned Units: 1
Units Franchised To: 35
Preferred Square Footage: 2,500
Preferred Location Types: Freestanding; Strip Mall
Alcohol Served: Beer, Wine
Primary Menu: Pizza (28); Sandwiches/Deli (8)
Projected Openings: 1
Areas of Operation: GA, IL, IN
Type of Foodservice: Quick Serve (36)
Catering Services: Yes

Key Personnel
DAVID HOWEY JR - CEO; President; COO; Executive Chef; Director Facility/Maintenance, Information Systems, Real Estate, Design, Research & Development; General Buyer
GLORIA MEYER - Director Marketing

Barrel House
1321 5th Ave
Moline, IL 61265

Telephone: (309) 517-1973
Internet Homepage: barrelhouse211.com
Company Email: BarrelHouseMoline@gmail.com
Type of Business: Chain Restaurant Operator
Year Founded: 2011
Total Units: 6
Trade Names: Barrel House (5); The Foundry Food + Tap (1)
Company-Owned Units: 6
Preferred Location Types: Downtown; Strip Mall
Primary Menu: American (6)
Areas of Operation: IA, IL
Type of Foodservice: Casual Dining (6)

Key Personnel
MICHAEL DEWITTE - Co-Founder; Partner
JIMMY HOLT - Co-Founder; Partner
BRIANNA MARTINEZ - Director Event Planning
DAVID SERRANO - Director Operations
PAUL MARTINEZ - Director Operations

Heart of America Group
1501 River Dr
Moline, IL 61265-1307

Telephone: (309) 797-9300
Fax Number: (309) 797-8700
Internet Homepage: heartofamericagroup.com
Type of Business: Chain Restaurant Operator
Year Founded: 1978
Total Sales: $133,360,000 (e)
Alcohol Sales: 7%
Number of Employees: 3,675
Internet Order Processing: Yes
Internet Sales: 1.00%
Total Units: 28
Trade Names: Burger Shed (2); Fifth Avenue Syndicate (1); Grammas Kitchen/Checkered Flag (1); Johnny's Italian Steakhouse (13); Machine Shed (6); The J Bar (1); The Republic on Grand (1); Thunder Bay Grille (3)
Company-Owned Units: 28
Preferred Square Footage: 8,000; 13,000; 22,000
Preferred Location Types: Downtown;

Freestanding; Hotel/Motel; Lifestyle Center; Office Complex; Parks
Alcohol Served: Beer, Wine, Liquor
Primary Menu: American (13); Steak (13)
Areas of Operation: IA, IL, KS, MI, MN, NE, OH, TX, WI
Type of Foodservice: Casual Dining (28)
Foodservice Management Venues: Business & Industry
Catering Services: Yes
Primary Distributors: (Full Line) SYSCO Food Services of Chicago Inc., DES PLAINES, IL
Notes: The company derives approximately 33% of its revenue from hotel/motel operations.

Key Personnel
MICHAEL L. WHALEN - Founder; CEO; President
KIM WHALEN - Founder; Exec VP
CHARLES H. ULLRICH - CFO; VP Risk Management
DONTREZ PARRISH - COO
JENNIFER DRAKE - Chief Legal Officer; VP
JENNY DRAKE - Chief Legal Officer
RON SPRINGER - Chief Talent Officer; VP
KATIE TIEGREEN - Area Director Catering
DAN OLIVER - Exec VP Design
ROB WILLIAMS - VP Operations
TERRY WAITE - VP Operations
JASON NASH - VP Operations
KURT STEINER - Controller; Manager Information Systems
MICHELLE SPARKMAN - Director Marketing
BOB PRICE - Director Information Technology
TRUDY MCLAUGHLIN - Director Human Resources
KATIE PFITZENMAIER - Director Training
LESLEY VON TERSCH - Director Marketing
NEIL SKELLY - Director Operations
JOHN LEIENDECKER - Director Food
KRYSIA HANNAM - Director Real Estate
JULIE SHOOPMAN - Regional Director Sales
KATHY STAUDT - Regional Director Sales
MICHELLE KINTZ - Assistant Director Risk Management
TERESA BAILEY - Associate Director

Parochetti Enterprises Inc.
4123 24th Ave
Moline, IL 61265-5010

Telephone: (563) 322-3220
Fax Number: (563) 888-6497
Type of Business: Chain Restaurant Operator
Year Founded: 1983
Total Sales: $36,520,000 (e)
Number of Employees: 325
Average Check: Lunch(8); Dinner(8)
Total Units: 13
Trade Names: Taco Bell (13)
Units Franchised From: 13
Preferred Square Footage: 1,500; 3,000
Preferred Location Types: Freestanding
Primary Menu: Taco (13)
Areas of Operation: IA, IL
Type of Foodservice: Quick Serve (13)
Franchise Affiliation: Taco Bell Corp., IRVINE, CA
Primary Distributors: (Food) McLane/Shawnee, SHAWNEE, KS

Key Personnel
DAVE PAROCHETTI - President; Manager Operations, Facility/Maintenance, Information Systems, Supply Chain, Real Estate, Design, Human Resources; General Buyer
SHELLY ZACHERT - Manager Accounting

Whitey's Ice Cream Inc.
2525 41st St
Moline, IL 61265-5017

Telephone: (309) 762-2175
Fax Number: (309) 762-0053
Internet Homepage: whiteysicecream.com
Company Email: whiteys@whiteysicecream.com
Type of Business: Chain Restaurant Operator
Year Founded: 1933
Total Sales: $11,990,000 (e)
Number of Employees: 250
Average Check: Lunch(8); Dinner(8)
Internet Order Processing: Yes
Internet Sales: 1.00%
Total Units: 10
Trade Names: Whitey's Ice Cream (10)
Company-Owned Units: 10
Preferred Square Footage: 1,200; 3,000
Preferred Location Types: Freestanding; Regional Mall; Strip Mall
Primary Menu: Snacks (10)
Areas of Operation: IA, IL
Type of Foodservice: Quick Serve (10)
On-site Distribution Center: Yes
Primary Distributors: (Food) Elgin Dairy Foods Inc., CHICAGO, IL
Notes: The company derives approximately 25% of its revenue from wholesale operations.

Key Personnel
JEFF TUNBERG - Partner; Director Facility/Maintenance, Real Estate, Design
JON TUNBERG - Partner; Director Operations, Facility/Maintenance, Information Systems, Real Estate, Design
ANNIKA TUNBERG - VP
JASON MEYER - Controller; Director Finance

McDonald's Franchise
1134 N Main St
Monmouth, IL 61462

Telephone: (309) 734-6701
Type of Business: Chain Restaurant Operator
Total Sales: $10,029,000 (e)
Total Units: 2
Trade Names: McDonald's (2)
Units Franchised From: 2
Preferred Location Types: Freestanding
Primary Menu: Hamburger (2)
Areas of Operation: IL
Type of Foodservice: Quick Serve (2)
Franchise Affiliation: McDonald's Corporation, CHICAGO, IL

Key Personnel
DENNIS GENDRON - Owner; General Buyer

La Gondola Spaghetti House
1917 S Main St
Morton, IL 61550-2913

Telephone: (309) 263-7716
Internet Homepage: lagondolaspaghettihouse.com
Type of Business: Chain Restaurant Operator
Year Founded: 1980
Total Sales: $11,400,000 (e)
Number of Employees: 118
Average Check: Lunch(8); Dinner(10)
Total Units: 11
Trade Names: LaGondola Spaghetti House (11)
Company-Owned Units: 13
Preferred Square Footage: 3,000
Preferred Location Types: Freestanding
Alcohol Served: Beer, Wine
Primary Menu: Italian (11)
Areas of Operation: IL
Type of Foodservice: Family Restaurant (11)
Catering Services: Yes
Primary Distributors: (Full Line) SYSCO Food Services of Chicago Inc., DES PLAINES, IL

Key Personnel
DICK LAHOOD - President; Controller; Executive Chef; Manager Finance, Human Resources, Catering
TIRZA LAHOOD - General Manager; Director Purchasing; General Buyer

TDS Services, Inc.
PO Box 985
Mount Vernon, IL 62864-0020

Telephone: (618) 241-9469
Type of Business: Chain Restaurant Operator
Total Sales: $38,330,000 (e)
Number of Employees: 300
Total Units: 8
Trade Names: McDonald's (8)
Units Franchised From: 8
Preferred Square Footage: 2,500
Preferred Location Types: Convenience Store/Gas Station; Freestanding

Primary Menu: Hamburger (8)
Areas of Operation: IL
Type of Foodservice: Quick Serve (8)
Franchise Affiliation: McDonald's Corporation, CHICAGO, IL

Key Personnel
TINA SHORT - President; General Buyer

Dairy Queen of Nokomis
100 S Oak St
Nokomis, IL 62075-1336

Telephone: (217) 563-2815
Company Email: tjfood@consolidated.net
Type of Business: Chain Restaurant Operator
Total Sales: $4,357,000 (e)
Average Check: Dinner(12)
Total Units: 3
Trade Names: Dairy Queen (3)
Units Franchised From: 3
Primary Menu: American (3)
Areas of Operation: IL
Type of Foodservice: Quick Serve (3)
Franchise Affiliation: International Dairy Queen Inc., BLOOMINGTON, MN

Key Personnel
THOMAS SPAINHOUR - President; General Buyer
MARK SPAINHOUR - General Manager
SARAH COLLINS - Store Manager

Eurest Dining Services
211 Landmark Dr Ste B5
Normal, IL 61761-6165

Telephone: (309) 808-2452
Fax Number: (309) 585-0319
Listing Type: Regional Office
Type of Business: Foodservice Management Operator
Year Founded: 1929
Number of Employees: 200
Number of Locations Served: 300
Total Foodservice Mgmt Accounts: 300
Areas of Operation: IL
Type of Foodservice: Cafeteria (300)
Foodservice Management Venues: Business & Industry; College & University; Health Care; Lodging; Military Feeding; Prison Feeding; Schools; Transportation
Primary Distributors: (Full Line) Performance Food Group, RICHMOND, VA
Parent Company: Compass Group The Americas, CHARLOTTE, NC
Headquarters: Eurest Dining Services, CHESTERBROOK, PA

Key Personnel
BETH CASH - VP Region; Director Finance, Operations, Purchasing
DAN HANLEY - Director Region

Malnati Organization Inc.
3685 Woodhead Dr
Northbrook, IL 60062-1816

Telephone: (847) 562-1814
Fax Number: (847) 562-1950
Internet Homepage: loumalnatis.com
Company Email: heylou@loumalnatis.com
Type of Business: Chain Restaurant Operator
Year Founded: 1971
Total Sales: $59,580,000 (e)
Alcohol Sales: 15%
Number of Employees: 2,128
Average Check: Lunch(12); Dinner(12)
Internet Order Processing: Yes
Internet Sales: 5.00%
Total Units: 71
Trade Names: Lou Malnati's Pizzeria (71)
Company-Owned Units: 71
Preferred Square Footage: 1,500; 6,000
Preferred Location Types: Downtown; Freestanding; Strip Mall
Alcohol Served: Beer, Wine, Liquor
Primary Menu: Pizza (71)
Projected Openings: 2
Areas of Operation: IL
Type of Foodservice: Casual Dining (71)
Catering Services: Yes
On-site Distribution Center: Yes
Primary Distributors: (Full Line) Battaglia Distributing Co. Inc., CHICAGO, IL

Key Personnel
MARC MALNATI - CEO; Owner; Director Information Systems, Real Estate
JAMES D'ANGELO - COO
GABRIELLA STREICHER - Director Employee Development
BETH GROSS - Manager Payroll

Pinstripes Inc.
1150 Willow Rd
Northbrook, IL 60062-6819

Telephone: (847) 480-2323
Internet Homepage: pinstripes.com
Company Email: info@pinstripes.com
Type of Business: Foodservice Operations - Bowling Alley
Total Sales: $73,680,000 (e)
Alcohol Sales: 20%
Internet Order Processing: Yes
Total Units: 13
Trade Names: Pinstripes (13)
Company-Owned Units: 13
Preferred Location Types: Downtown; Power Center
Alcohol Served: Beer, Wine, Liquor
Primary Menu: Italian (10)
Projected Openings: 8
Areas of Operation: DC, IL, KS, MD, MN, TX
Type of Foodservice: Casual Dining (10)
Catering Services: Yes
Notes: The company derives approximately 50% of total revenue from bowling and bocce gaming.

Key Personnel
DALE SCHWARTZ - Founder; CEO
DON HOFFMAN - Chief Marketing Officer
CHRIS SOUKUP - Director Operations
CESAR GUTIERREZ - Director Culinary Development
LIDA AHN - Director Training
STEPHEN TYSON - Director Technology

Spire Hospitality
1200 Shermer Rd Ste 400
Northbrook, IL 60062-4566

Mailing Address: 111 Pfingsten Rd, Ste 425, DEERFIELD, IL, 60015
Telephone: (847) 498-6650
Fax Number: (847) 498-6808
Internet Homepage: spirehotels.com
Type of Business: Foodservice Operations - Hotel/Motels
Year Founded: 1980
Total Sales: $452,720,000 (e)
Alcohol Sales: 20%
Number of Employees: 1,250
Total Units: 25
Restaurants in Hotels: 20
Trade Names: Crowne Plaza (1); DoubleTree by Hilton (3); Embassy Suites (7); High Peaks (1); Hilton (1); Holiday Inn (4); Lake House (1); Marriott (3); Renaissance (1); Staybridge Suites (1); Topnotch Resort (1); Waterstone (1)
Company-Owned Units: 20
Alcohol Served: Beer, Wine, Liquor
Areas of Operation: CO, FL, IL, LA, MD, MI, MN, MS, NC, NJ, NY, OH, OR, TX, WA, WI
Type of Foodservice: Casual Dining; Fine Dining
Primary Distributors: (Food) SYSCO Food Services of Chicago Inc., DES PLAINES, IL
Parent Company: AWH Partners, LLC, NEW YORK CITY, NY
Notes: Store count and trade names include some properties that do not provide on-site foodservice. The company derives approximately 70% of its revenue from hotel operations. Menu development is property specific.

Key Personnel
BILL DEFORREST - CEO; President
BILL KEATING - CFO; Exec VP
GREGORY HORETH - COO

GINNY MORRISON - VP Marketing, Sales
GEORGE NORTH - VP Accounting
DAN BENDA - Director Construction

Love's Group
1 Northfield Plz Ste 214
Northfield, IL 60093-1213

Telephone: (847) 784-8700
Fax Number: (847) 784-8790
Internet Homepage: lovesyogurt.com
Company Email: info@lovescatering.com
Type of Business: Chain Restaurant Operator
Year Founded: 1987
Systemwide Sales: $4,028,000 (e)
Total Sales: $434,000 (e)
Number of Employees: 3
Average Check: Lunch(10); Dinner(12)
Total Units: 6
Trade Names: Love's Yogurt & More (6)
Units Franchised To: 6
Preferred Square Footage: 1,800; 2,000
Preferred Location Types: Regional Mall; Strip Mall
Primary Menu: Miscellaneous (6)
Areas of Operation: IL
Type of Foodservice: Quick Serve (6)
Catering Services: Yes
Primary Distributors: (Equipment) Taylor Freezers & Equipment Co., SANDWICH, IL; (Food) Elgin Dairy Foods Inc., CHICAGO, IL; (Supplies) Taylor Freezers & Equipment Co., SANDWICH, IL

Key Personnel
JAMIE BAY - President; Controller; Director Finance, Facility/Maintenance, Supply Chain, Ethnic Marketing, Real Estate, Design, Human Resources, Research & Development, Product Development, Franchising, Store Fixtures, Menu Development
KAREN DONATO - VP Operations, Purchasing; Director Information Systems; General Buyer
JOANN MALMQUIST - Director Marketing, Advertising

The Happ Inn
305 Happ Rd
Northfield, IL 60093

Telephone: (847) 784-9200
Internet Homepage: thehappinn.com; cafecentral.net; taconano.com
Company Email: acarlos1st@aol.com
Listing Type: Subsidiary
Type of Business: Chain Restaurant Operator
Year Founded: 1981
Total Sales: $4,388,000 (e)
Alcohol Sales: 30%
Number of Employees: 25
Average Check: Lunch(32); Dinner(120)
Total Units: 3
Trade Names: Cafe Central (1); Taco Nano (1); The Happ Inn (1)
Company-Owned Units: 3
Preferred Location Types: Freestanding
Alcohol Served: Beer, Wine, Liquor
Primary Menu: American (1); French/Continental (1); Taco (1)
Areas of Operation: IL
Type of Foodservice: Casual Dining (3)
Primary Distributors: (Food) The Seafood Merchants Ltd., VERNON HILLS, IL

Key Personnel
CARLOS NIETO - President; Partner; General Manager; Buyer Beverages
DEBORAH NIETO - Partner; VP Operations; General Manager
DAN MEYERS - General Manager

J&J Sweet Tooth, LLC
3228 Green Mount Crossing Dr
O Fallon, IL 62269-7284

Telephone: (618) 622-0044
Type of Business: Chain Restaurant Operator
Total Sales: $1,226,000 (e)
Total Units: 2
Trade Names: Cold Stone Creamery (2)
Units Franchised From: 2
Primary Menu: Snacks (2)
Areas of Operation: IL
Type of Foodservice: Quick Serve (2)
Franchise Affiliation: Kahala Brands, SCOTTSDALE, AZ

Key Personnel
JOYCE PECINA - Partner
KAREN BECKER - Partner; General Buyer

The Portillo Restaurant Group
2001 Spring Rd Ste 500
Oak Brook, IL 60523-3930

Telephone: (630) 954-3773
Fax Number: (630) 954-5851
Internet Homepage: honeyjamcafe.com; portillos.com
Company Email: info@portillos.com
Type of Business: Chain Restaurant Operator
Year Founded: 1963
Total Sales: $960,190,000 (e)
Alcohol Sales: 3%
Number of Employees: 6,300
Average Check: Lunch(16); Dinner(22)
Internet Order Processing: Yes
Internet Sales: 10.00%
Total Units: 76
Trade Names: Honey Jam Cafe (7); Portillo's Hot Dogs (60); Portillo's Hot Dogs/Barnelli's Pasta Bowl (9)
Company-Owned Units: 76
Preferred Square Footage: 7,995
Preferred Location Types: Freestanding
Alcohol Served: Beer, Wine, Liquor
Primary Menu: American (7); Hot Dogs (69)
Projected Openings: 2
Areas of Operation: AZ, CA, FL, IA, IL, IN, MN, WI
Type of Foodservice: Family Restaurant (7); Fast Casual (69)
Catering Services: Yes
Distribution Centers: ADDISON, IL; AURORA, IL
Parent Company: Berkshire Partners, BOSTON, MA
Notes: All Barnelli's Pasta Bowl locations are located inside Portillo's Hot Dogs restaurants.

Key Personnel
MICHAEL OSANLOO - CEO
MICHELLE HOOK - CFO
TONY DARDEN - COO
JILL WAITE - Chief Human Resources Officer
KEITH CORREIA - CIO
NICK SCARPINO - Chief Marketing Officer
RICK COOK - Senior VP Technology
MICHAEL PORTILLO - VP Training, Employee Development
JOHN HOLMES - VP Information Technology
RANDY GUSE - VP Real Estate
MIKE ROMAN - VP Operations
ERIC BEVINS - Director Operations
JOHN FREEMAN - Director Information Technology
TIM BENSON - Director Finance
MICHAEL DUDZIK - Director Information Technology
DENNIS RIVERA - Senior Manager
CHRISTOPHER BERARDI - Area Manager
REBECCA MACDONALD - Manager Branding, Design
JOSEPH BRIESTANSKY - Manager Purchasing
CASSIE CHYTRACEK - Manager Strategic Sourcing
CHRISTINE DECICCO - Manager Accounting
MATT HARRISON - Manager Information Technology-Help Desk
TREN REED - Manager Development
DAVID PESENKO - Manager Marketing
SHARON MALONEY - Supervisor Food Safety
ERICA SALTSMAN - Specialist Field Marketing

Legendary Baking
16425 Kilbourne Ave
Oak Forest, IL 60452-4602

Telephone: (708) 687-7650
Fax Number: (708) 687-7671
Listing Type: Distribution Center
Type of Business: Foodservice Operations - Bowling Alley

Number of Employees: 150
Areas of Operation: IL, IN, MI, OH
Headquarters: Restaurant Growth Services, LLC, NASHVILLE, TN

Key Personnel
RANDY STONE - General Manager
PAUL MROZINSKI - Manager Distribution, Warehouse, Transportation

A.C. Fox Inc.
9240 S Cicero Ave
Oak Lawn, IL 60453-1807

Telephone: (708) 499-2233
Fax Number: (708) 424-4040
Internet Homepage: foxsrestaurant.com; tailgatersgrill.com
Type of Business: Chain Restaurant Operator
Year Founded: 1959
Total Sales: $12,843,000 (e)
Alcohol Sales: 25%
Number of Employees: 220
Average Check: Lunch(12); Dinner(18)
Internet Order Processing: Yes
Total Units: 4
Trade Names: Fox's Restaurant & Pub (3); Tailgaters Sports Bar (1)
Company-Owned Units: 4
Preferred Location Types: Freestanding
Alcohol Served: Beer, Wine, Liquor
Primary Menu: American (4)
Areas of Operation: IL
Type of Foodservice: Casual Dining (4)
Catering Services: Yes
Primary Distributors: (Full Line) Food & Paper Supply Co., CHICAGO, IL; (Specialty Foods) Meats by Linz, CALUMET CITY, IL

Key Personnel
THERESE FOX - President; Partner; General Manager; General Buyer
THOMAS FOX JR - Partner; VP; Controller; Executive Chef; Manager Store Planning, Menu Development, Catering
FRANK FOX - Partner; VP Operations, Food Safety

Butterfield's Pancake House & Restaurant
1 S 616 Midwest Rd
Oakbrook Terrace, IL 60181

Telephone: (630) 495-2291
Internet Homepage: butterfieldsrestaurant.com; butterfieldsrestaurants.com
Company Email: butterfieldspancakehouse@gmail.com
Type of Business: Chain Restaurant Operator
Year Founded: 2000
Total Sales: $7,191,000 (e)
Average Check: Breakfast(16);
Total Units: 4
Trade Names: Butterfield's Pancake House & Restaurant (4)
Company-Owned Units: 4
Primary Menu: American (4)
Areas of Operation: AZ, IL
Type of Foodservice: Casual Dining (4)
Catering Services: Yes
Notes: Owned by members of multiple families.

Key Personnel
TONY PANAGAKOS - Partner
CHRIS SYREGELAS - Partner
NICK SYREGELAS - Partner

McDonald's Franchise
11241 W 159th St
Orland Park, IL 60467-4416

Telephone: (708) 481-1606
Fax Number: (708) 301-2398
Type of Business: Chain Restaurant Operator
Total Sales: $23,390,000 (e)
Number of Employees: 180
Total Units: 5
Trade Names: McDonald's (5)
Units Franchised From: 5
Preferred Square Footage: 2,500
Primary Menu: Hamburger (5)
Areas of Operation: IL
Type of Foodservice: Quick Serve (5)
Franchise Affiliation: McDonald's Corporation, CHICAGO, IL

Key Personnel
ROBERT FREEMAN - President; General Buyer

Tap House Management Group
56 W Wilson St
Palatine, IL 60067-5018

Telephone: (847) 934-3000
Internet Homepage: taphousegrills.com
Type of Business: Chain Restaurant Operator
Total Units: 8
Trade Names: Tap House Grill (8)
Company-Owned Units: 6
Units Franchised To: 2
Primary Menu: American (8)
Areas of Operation: IL
Type of Foodservice: Casual Dining (8)

Key Personnel
SCOTT WARD - Partner
MARK ZYCH - Partner

TOMS King LLC
220 N Smith St STE 305
Palatine, IL 60067

Telephone: (815) 356-9770
Fax Number: (815) 356-9781
Internet Homepage: TOMSKing.com
Company Email: frontdesk@tomsking.com
Type of Business: Chain Restaurant Operator
Year Founded: 1963
Total Sales: $305,810,000 (e)
Number of Employees: 5,119
Average Check: Breakfast(8); Lunch(8); Dinner(12)
Total Units: 136
Trade Names: Burger King (136)
Units Franchised From: 136
Preferred Square Footage: 2,500
Preferred Location Types: Freestanding
Primary Menu: Hamburger (136)
Areas of Operation: IL, OH, PA, VA
Type of Foodservice: Quick Serve (136)
Franchise Affiliation: Burger King Worldwide Inc., MIAMI, FL
Primary Distributors: (Full Line) Reinhart FoodService, OAK CREEK, WI

Key Personnel
MATT CARPENTER - CEO
ERIN HASSELGREN - COO
DA'MON WARDLOW - VP People
EMELY SOTO - Director Human Resources
DENNIS GREVE - Director Operations
MO EBRAHIM - Director Operations, Region
KIMBERLY NESSEL - Regional Director Operations
STEVEN HAMILTON - District Manager
TODD GEORGE - District Manager
NANCY CAVALERO - Manager Human Resources

Y&S Food Partnership
45 N Northwest Hwy
Palatine, IL 60067-5322

Telephone: (847) 358-1700
Fax Number: (847) 358-1700
Type of Business: Chain Restaurant Operator
Year Founded: 2000
Total Sales: $5,539,000 (e)
Number of Employees: 45
Average Check: Lunch(10); Dinner(12)
Total Units: 2
Trade Names: Popeyes Louisiana Kitchen (2)
Units Franchised From: 2
Preferred Square Footage: 1,200
Preferred Location Types: Freestanding
Primary Menu: Chicken (2)
Areas of Operation: IL, IN
Type of Foodservice: Quick Serve (2)
Franchise Affiliation: Popeyes Louisiana

Kitchen Inc., ATLANTA, GA
Primary Distributors: (Full Line) Reinhart FoodService LLC, CHICAGO, IL

Key Personnel
DEAN FIDAI - President; General Buyer
SHAMA FIDAI - General Manager

S & K Management
10135 S Roberts Rd Ste 201
Palos Hills, IL 60465-1500

Telephone: (708) 430-5404
Type of Business: Chain Restaurant Operator
Total Sales: $19,867,000 (e)
Total Units: 4
Trade Names: McDonald's (4)
Units Franchised From: 4
Preferred Location Types: Freestanding
Primary Menu: Hamburger (4)
Areas of Operation: IL
Type of Foodservice: Quick Serve (4)
Franchise Affiliation: McDonald's Corporation, CHICAGO, IL

Key Personnel
STANLEY STEVENS - President; General Buyer

Avanti's Italian Restaurant Inc.
4711 N Rockwood Dr
Peoria, IL 61615-3628

Telephone: (309) 685-2409
Fax Number: (309) 688-9053
Internet Homepage: avantispeoria.com
Company Email: comments@avantispeoria.com
Type of Business: Chain Restaurant Operator
Year Founded: 1966
Total Sales: $10,950,000 (e)
Alcohol Sales: 1%
Number of Employees: 300
Average Check: Lunch(8); Dinner(12)
Internet Order Processing: Yes
Total Units: 5
Trade Names: Avanti's Italian Restaurant (5)
Company-Owned Units: 5
Preferred Location Types: Freestanding
Alcohol Served: Beer, Wine
Primary Menu: Italian (5)
Areas of Operation: IL
Type of Foodservice: Casual Dining (5)
Catering Services: Yes
Primary Distributors: (Food) Waugh Foods Inc., EAST PEORIA, IL

Key Personnel
STEFAN ZELLER - CEO; General Buyer
JAMIE GENDRON - Controller

RICH HUBBLE - General Manager
NANCY WRAIGHT - Director Human Resources

Lucwork Enterprises Inc.
7211 N Knoxville Ave
Peoria, IL 61614-2077

Telephone: (309) 689-1886
Fax Number: (309) 689-1889
Type of Business: Chain Restaurant Operator
Year Founded: 1982
Total Sales: $38,950,000 (e)
Number of Employees: 380
Average Check: Lunch(8); Dinner(10)
Total Units: 14
Trade Names: Taco Bell (14)
Units Franchised From: 14
Preferred Square Footage: 2,500
Preferred Location Types: Freestanding
Primary Menu: Taco (14)
Areas of Operation: IL
Type of Foodservice: Quick Serve (14)
Franchise Affiliation: Taco Bell Corp., IRVINE, CA
Primary Distributors: (Full Line) McLane/Midwest, DANVILLE, IL

Key Personnel
BUD JENKINS - Partner; General Manager; Director Operations, Information Systems, Real Estate; General Buyer
JANET JENKINS - Partner; Director Finance
MELANIE ROWLEY - Controller

Mercedes Restaurants, Inc
2402 W Nebraska Ave
Peoria, IL 61604-3112

Telephone: (309) 676-6443
Fax Number: (309) 676-7242
Internet Homepage: mercedesrestaurants.com
Company Email: mrirestaurants@comcast.net
Type of Business: Chain Restaurant Operator
Total Sales: $22,700,000 (e)
Average Check: Dinner(14)
Internet Order Processing: Yes
Total Units: 6
Trade Names: Alexander's Steakhouse (4); Famous Dave's (2)
Units Franchised From: 6
Primary Menu: Bar-B-Q (2); Steak (4)
Areas of Operation: IA, IL
Type of Foodservice: Casual Dining (4); Fast Casual (3)
Franchise Affiliation: BBQ Holdings, Inc., MINNETONKA, MN

Key Personnel
STEPHEN R. SHAW - President; General Buyer
DESTINY BUCKLEY - Coordinator Catering

TJM Foods, Inc.
3023 N Sterling Ave
Peoria, IL 61604-2259

Telephone: (309) 688-0235
Type of Business: Chain Restaurant Operator
Total Sales: $3,504,000 (e)
Total Units: 6
Trade Names: Little Caesars Pizza (6)
Units Franchised From: 6
Primary Menu: Pizza (6)
Areas of Operation: IL
Type of Foodservice: Quick Serve (6)
Franchise Affiliation: Little Caesar Enterprises Inc., DETROIT, MI

Key Personnel
TIM MCSHANE - President; General Buyer
CHRIS FULLER - General Manager

Donald Trager
1517 36th St
Peru, IL 61354-1272

Telephone: (815) 223-0300
Type of Business: Chain Restaurant Operator
Total Sales: $5,121,000 (e)
Total Units: 7
Trade Names: Subway (7)
Units Franchised From: 7
Preferred Location Types: Convenience Store/Gas Station; Freestanding; Strip Mall
Primary Menu: Sandwiches/Deli (7)
Projected Openings: 1
Areas of Operation: IL
Type of Foodservice: Quick Serve (7)
Franchise Affiliation: Doctor's Associates Inc., MILFORD, CT

Key Personnel
DONALD TRAGER - Owner; General Buyer

Peru 1 LLC.
3947 Frontage Rd
Peru, IL 61354-1113

Telephone: (815) 224-2386
Fax Number: (815) 224-2389
Type of Business: Chain Restaurant Operator
Total Sales: $20,696,000 (e)
Total Units: 4
Trade Names: McDonald's (4)
Units Franchised From: 4
Preferred Square Footage: 2,500
Primary Menu: Hamburger (4)
Areas of Operation: IL
Type of Foodservice: Quick Serve (4)
Franchise Affiliation: McDonald's Corporation,

CHICAGO, IL

Key Personnel
NATHAN PAPPAS - Owner; General Buyer

Saren Restaurants Inc.
4221 E Ed Urban Dr
Peru, IL 61354-9359

Telephone: (815) 223-2032
Fax Number: (815) 223-6761
Internet Homepage: saren.workatw.com
Type of Business: Chain Restaurant Operator
Year Founded: 1987
Total Sales: $24,490,000 (e)
Number of Employees: 260
Average Check: Lunch(8); Dinner(8)
Total Units: 9
Trade Names: Wendy's Old Fashioned Hamburgers (9)
Units Franchised From: 9
Preferred Square Footage: 3,300
Preferred Location Types: Freestanding
Primary Menu: Hamburger (9)
Areas of Operation: IL
Type of Foodservice: Quick Serve (9)
Franchise Affiliation: The Wendy's Company, DUBLIN, OH
Primary Distributors: (Equipment) The Wasserstrom Co., COLUMBUS, OH; (Supplies) The Wasserstrom Co., COLUMBUS, OH

Key Personnel
STEVEN JOHNSON - Director Operations
PATRICK SAUBER - Coordinator Marketing

Kory Management
15810 S Route 59
Plainfield, IL 60544-2692

Telephone: (815) 436-1623
Type of Business: Chain Restaurant Operator
Total Sales: $42,940,000 (e)
Total Units: 9
Trade Names: McDonald's (9)
Units Franchised From: 9
Preferred Location Types: Freestanding
Primary Menu: Hamburger (9)
Projected Openings: 1
Areas of Operation: IL
Type of Foodservice: Quick Serve (9)
Franchise Affiliation: McDonald's Corporation, CHICAGO, IL

Key Personnel
GARY KORY - President; General Buyer

Lad Corp.
421 N 36th St
Quincy, IL 62301-4601

Telephone: (217) 223-8000
Fax Number: (217) 223-8652
Type of Business: Chain Restaurant Operator
Total Sales: $17,840,000 (e)
Number of Employees: 250
Total Units: 8
Trade Names: Burger King (8)
Units Franchised From: 8
Preferred Square Footage: 2,500
Primary Menu: Hamburger (8)
Areas of Operation: IA, IL
Type of Foodservice: Quick Serve (8)
Franchise Affiliation: Burger King Worldwide Inc., MIAMI, FL

Key Personnel
AL EILERS - President; Owner; General Buyer

Arthur's Garden Delicatessen Inc.
1108 Avenue A
Rock Falls, IL 61071

Telephone: (815) 625-0011
Internet Homepage: arthursdeli.com
Company Email: agddistributing@gmail.com
Type of Business: Chain Restaurant Operator
Year Founded: 1977
Total Sales: $5,293,000 (e)
Number of Employees: 48
Average Check: Lunch(8); Dinner(10)
Total Units: 4
Trade Names: Arthur's Garden Deli (4)
Company-Owned Units: 4
Preferred Square Footage: 2,000
Preferred Location Types: Office Complex; Strip Mall
Primary Menu: Sandwiches/Deli (4)
Areas of Operation: IL
Type of Foodservice: Quick Serve (4)
Catering Services: Yes
On-site Distribution Center: Yes
Primary Distributors: (Full Line) SYSCO Food Services of Chicago Inc., DES PLAINES, IL

Key Personnel
SCOTT WOLBER - President; Controller; Executive Chef; Director Operations, Facility/Maintenance, Information Systems, Real Estate, Human Resources; General Buyer
ANNE FRIEL - General Manager; General Buyer

Sagemark Ltd.
2322 3rd Ave
Rock Island, IL 61201-8808

Telephone: (309) 283-0137
Fax Number: (309) 283-0144
Internet Homepage: hungryhobo.com
Company Email: webmaster@hungryhobo.com
Type of Business: Chain Restaurant Operator
Year Founded: 1968
Systemwide Sales: $11,618,000 (e)
Total Sales: $8,306,000 (e)
Number of Employees: 150
Average Check: Lunch(12); Dinner(12)
Internet Order Processing: Yes
Internet Sales: 1.00%
Total Units: 13
Trade Names: Hungry Hobo (13)
Company-Owned Units: 13
Preferred Square Footage: 1,200
Preferred Location Types: Strip Mall
Primary Menu: Sandwiches/Deli (13)
Areas of Operation: IA, IL
Type of Foodservice: Quick Serve (13)
Catering Services: Yes

Key Personnel
PRYCE T. BOEYE - CEO; President
EARL SMITH - Director Logistics
KAREN ZABLOUDIL - Manager Accounting

Mary's Market Cafe & Bakery LLC
4431 E State St
Rockford, IL 61108-2114

Telephone: (815) 397-7272
Fax Number: (815) 229-6818
Internet Homepage: marysmarket.com
Company Email: peter@marysmarket.com
Type of Business: Chain Restaurant Operator
Year Founded: 1968
Total Sales: $9,033,000 (e)
Alcohol Sales: 5%
Number of Employees: 150
Average Check: Breakfast(6); Lunch(8); Dinner(12)
Total Units: 3
Trade Names: Mary's Market Cafe & Bakery (3)
Company-Owned Units: 3
Preferred Location Types: Other; Strip Mall
Alcohol Served: Beer, Wine
Primary Menu: Sandwiches/Deli (3)
Areas of Operation: IL
Type of Foodservice: Casual Dining (3)
Catering Services: Yes
Primary Distributors: (Food) SYSCO Food Services of Chicago Inc., DES PLAINES, IL

Key Personnel
LISA BEARDSWORTH - President; General Manager
STEPHANIE KOCH - Partner
AARON KOCH - Partner; General Buyer

A.H. Management Group
1151 Rohlwing Rd
Rolling Meadows, IL 60008-1030

Telephone: (847) 253-2070
Fax Number: (847) 394-4285
Internet Homepage: ah-inc.com
Company Email: info@ah-inc.com
Type of Business: Foodservice Management Operator
Year Founded: 1939
Total Sales: $43,256,000 (e)
Number of Employees: 280
Number of Locations Served: 45
Total Foodservice Mgmt Accounts: 45
Trade Names: A.H. Management Group
Areas of Operation: IL, WI
Type of Foodservice: Cafeteria (45)
Foodservice Management Venues: Business & Industry
Primary Distributors: (Full Line) Gordon Food Service Inc., WYOMING, MI

Key Personnel
MARK HESCH - Owner; VP Operations, Risk Management
STEVE HOGLE - Director Information Systems, Information Technology, Human Resources
MARC ELATKIN - Manager Warehouse

Weber Grill Restaurant
1685 Winnetka Cir
Rolling Meadows, IL 60008-1372

Telephone: (224) 764-4500
Fax Number: (224) 764-4529
Internet Homepage: webergrillrestaurant.com
Type of Business: Chain Restaurant Operator
Year Founded: 1989
Total Sales: $9,282,000 (e)
Alcohol Sales: 10%
Number of Employees: 75
Average Check: Lunch(12); Dinner(24)
Internet Order Processing: Yes
Total Units: 5
Trade Names: Weber Grill Restaurant (5)
Company-Owned Units: 5
Preferred Location Types: Freestanding; Hotel/Motel
Alcohol Served: Beer, Wine, Liquor
Primary Menu: American (5)
Areas of Operation: IL, IN, MO
Type of Foodservice: Casual Dining (5)
Primary Distributors: (Food) SYSCO Food Services of Chicago Inc., DES PLAINES, IL
Parent Company: Weber-Stephen Products Co., PALATINE, IL

Key Personnel
BRYAN GERRISH - President
KATHY ESPOSITO - Controller
BRADLEY RITZ - Director Purchasing

NRJM Inc.
1413 Sherman Rd Ste 30
Romeoville, IL 60446-4092

Telephone: (630) 783-0300
Fax Number: (630) 783-8365
Type of Business: Chain Restaurant Operator
Year Founded: 1991
Total Sales: $30,578,000 (e)
Number of Employees: 320
Average Check: Lunch(12); Dinner(20)
Total Units: 15
Trade Names: Domino's (15)
Units Franchised From: 15
Preferred Square Footage: 1,000; 1,300
Preferred Location Types: Strip Mall
Primary Menu: Pizza (15)
Areas of Operation: IL
Type of Foodservice: Quick Serve (15)
Franchise Affiliation: Domino's Pizza Inc, ANN ARBOR, MI
Primary Distributors: (Full Line) Progressive Foods Solutions, WOODRIDGE, IL

Key Personnel
RAY MONTEZ - President; Director Operations, Purchasing, Information Systems, Supply Chain, Real Estate
LYNNE BRADLEY - VP; Director Finance

Bulldog Ale House
394 E Irving Park Rd
Roselle, IL 60172

Telephone: (630) 529-0333
Internet Homepage: bulldogalehouse.com
Type of Business: Chain Restaurant Operator
Year Founded: 2011
Total Sales: $10,590,000 (e)
Total Units: 12
Trade Names: Bulldog Ale House (12)
Company-Owned Units: 12
Primary Menu: American (12)
Areas of Operation: IL
Type of Foodservice: Casual Dining (12)

Key Personnel
MATT AHMETI - Owner
RANDY BOND - General Manager
RANDY SCHOBERT - Director Operations

Colonial Cafe and Ice Cream Inc.
333 N Randall Rd Ste 22
Saint Charles, IL 60174-1500

Telephone: (630) 584-0088
Fax Number: (630) 584-1711
Internet Homepage: colonialcafe.com
Company Email: admin@colonialcafe.com
Type of Business: Chain Restaurant Operator
Year Founded: 1901
Total Sales: $7,687,000 (e)
Number of Employees: 215
Average Check: Breakfast(8); Lunch(10); Dinner(14)
Total Units: 5
Trade Names: Colonial Cafe (5)
Company-Owned Units: 5
Preferred Square Footage: 5,000
Preferred Location Types: Freestanding; Strip Mall
Primary Menu: American (5)
Areas of Operation: IL
Type of Foodservice: Family Restaurant (5)
On-site Distribution Center: Yes
Primary Distributors: (Full Line) Performance Foodservice - Fox River, MONTGOMERY, IL

Key Personnel
DEBBY DIECKMAN - Manager Finance, Human Resources
KATELYN PIETRAZSAK - Coordinator Marketing

Ala Carte Entertainment Inc.
2330 Hammond Dr Ste G
Schaumburg, IL 60173-3869

Telephone: (847) 303-4400
Fax Number: (847) 303-0112
Internet Homepage: rosiesriversedge.com; aceplaces.com; chandlerschophouse.com; finnmccoolschicago.com; lionheadpub.com; morettischicago.com; snuggerychicago.com; sweetcarolinescrabnque.com
Type of Business: Chain Restaurant Operator
Year Founded: 1971
Total Sales: $56,590,000 (e)
Alcohol Sales: 45%
Number of Employees: 1,400
Average Check: Breakfast(6); Lunch(18); Dinner(24)
Internet Order Processing: Yes
Internet Sales: 1.00%
Total Units: 20
Trade Names: Chandler's Chophouse (1); Drink (1); Famous Freddie's Roadhouse (1); Fin McCool's (3); Lucky Star Bartlett (1); Moretti's (9); Snuggery (1); The Alumni Club (1); The Apartment Lounge (1); The Lion Head Pub (1)
Company-Owned Units: 20

Preferred Square Footage: 6,000; 30,000
Preferred Location Types: Downtown; Freestanding; Strip Mall
Alcohol Served: Beer, Wine, Liquor
Primary Menu: American (19); Bar-B-Q (1)
Projected Openings: 1
Areas of Operation: IL
Type of Foodservice: Casual Dining (19); Fast Casual (1)
Catering Services: Yes
Primary Distributors: (Equipment) TriMark Marlinn, BEDFORD PARK, IL; (Food) US Foods, BENSENVILLE, IL; (Supplies) TriMark Marlinn, BEDFORD PARK, IL

Key Personnel
FRED HOFFMANN - CEO; Director Marketing
MARK HOFFMAN - President
MIKE ABBATE - VP Operations, Security, Inventory, Loss Prevention, Quality Assurance
JOHN MCKENDRICK - Controller
JIM EARLEY - General Manager Facility/Maintenance; General Buyer
JAMES ROSATO - Director Operations
ED KUKULSKI - Director Technology
LISA TOMATO - Web Developer

Hostmark Hospitality Group
1300 E Woodfield Rd Ste 400
Schaumburg, IL 60173-5444

Telephone: (847) 517-9100
Fax Number: (847) 517-9797
Internet Homepage: hostmark.com
Company Email: info@hostmark.com
Type of Business: Foodservice Operations - Hotel/Motels
Year Founded: 1974
Total Sales: $601,250,000 (e)
Alcohol Sales: 10%
Number of Employees: 7,049
Total Units: 53
Restaurants in Hotels: 53
Trade Names: Abbey Resort (1); Aspen Club Lodge Sky Hotel (1); Best Western (2); Carnivale (1); Clarion Hotel and Casino (1); Crowne Plaza (2); Danfords Resort, Marina & Conference Center (1); Days Inn (1); DoubleTree by Hilton (2); Gaia Hotel And Spa (1); Grand Seas Resort (2); Hacienda Del Sol Resort (1); Hampton Inn and Suites Chicago West Loop (1); Harrison Hot Springs Resort (1); Hilton College Station And Conference Center (1); Holiday Inn (4); Homewood Suites Chicago West Loop (1); Hostmark (2); Howard Johnson (1); King David Spa and Resort (1); Lake Eve Resort (1); Lake Lawn Lodge (1); Lavers Tennis Resort (1); Marriott Salt Lake City University Park (1); Mount Airy Lodge (1); Perry Hotel Key West (1); Pheasant Run Resort (1); President Abraham Lincoln (1); Queen Mary (5); Radisson Hotel Milwaukee NW (2); Ramada Grand Dakota Lodge (1); Ramada Inn (1); Stretch Run (1); University Plaza (1); Victoria Palms Inn And Suites (1); Wyndham (5)
Company-Owned Units: 53
Alcohol Served: Beer, Wine, Liquor
Projected Openings: 1
Areas of Operation: AZ, CA, FL, GA, IA, IL, IN, MA, MI, NJ, NY, SC, TX, WI
Foreign Countries: EGYPT
Type of Foodservice: Casual Dining (30)
Primary Distributors: (Food) SYSCO Food Services of Chicago Inc., DES PLAINES, IL
Notes: The company derives approximately 85% of its revenue from hotel operations.

Key Personnel
C. A. CATALDO - Chairman
ROBERT J. CATALDO - Vice Chairman; COO; Director Risk Management, Quality Assurance
JEROME F. CATALDO - CEO; President
WILLIAM D. GINGRICH II - CFO; Exec VP
L. W. "BIFF" HAWKEY JR - Senior VP Real Estate
CHRISTINE ANDREWS - VP Human Resources
SHARON MITCHELL - Controller
JAMES GIGLIO - Director Purchasing
NANCY MAZZOCCHETTI - Director Accounting
STEVE FENILI - Director Construction
ANN NASSIRI - Supervisor Accounting

The Melting Pot Franchise
255 W Golf Rd
Schaumburg, IL 60195-3605

Telephone: (847) 843-8970
Fax Number: (312) 640-9610
Internet Homepage: meltingpot.com/schaumburg-il
Type of Business: Chain Restaurant Operator
Total Sales: $12,391,000 (e)
Alcohol Sales: 5%
Average Check: Dinner(42)
Total Units: 4
Trade Names: The Melting Pot (4)
Units Franchised From: 4
Preferred Square Footage: 5,000; 6,000
Alcohol Served: Beer, Wine, Liquor
Primary Menu: Miscellaneous (4)
Areas of Operation: IL
Type of Foodservice: Casual Dining (4)
Franchise Affiliation: The Melting Pot Restaurants Inc., TAMPA, FL

Key Personnel
ERV EMERY - President; Partner; General Buyer
MIKE RUFFOLO - Partner
STEVEN HUEBNER - General Manager

Wildberry Pancakes & Cafe, Inc.
1383 N Meacham Rd
Schaumburg, IL 60173-4805

Telephone: (847) 517-4000
Internet Homepage: wildberrycafe.com
Type of Business: Chain Restaurant Operator
Year Founded: 2004
Total Sales: $8,155,000 (e)
Average Check: Breakfast(16);
Internet Order Processing: Yes
Total Units: 4
Trade Names: Wildberry Pancakes & Cafe (4)
Company-Owned Units: 4
Primary Menu: American (4)
Projected Openings: 1
Areas of Operation: IL
Type of Foodservice: Casual Dining (4)
Catering Services: Yes

Key Personnel
GEORGE ARCHOS - Partner
ANTONINO GARITI - Partner

Huddlestun Creamery, Inc.
1153 Brookforest Ave
Shorewood, IL 60404-8845

Telephone: (815) 609-1893
Type of Business: Chain Restaurant Operator
Total Sales: $1,175,000 (e)
Total Units: 2
Trade Names: Cold Stone Creamery (2)
Units Franchised From: 2
Primary Menu: Snacks (2)
Areas of Operation: IL
Type of Foodservice: Quick Serve (2)
Franchise Affiliation: Kahala Brands, SCOTTSDALE, AZ

Key Personnel
WILLIAM HUDDLESTUN - Partner
RUTH HUDDLESTUN - Partner

T Q M Inc
3 Morgan Ln
South Barrington, IL 60010-6164

Telephone: (847) 844-8051
Fax Number: (847) 844-8052
Type of Business: Chain Restaurant Operator
Total Sales: $5,899,000 (e)
Total Units: 3
Trade Names: Arby's (3)
Units Franchised From: 3
Primary Menu: Sandwiches/Deli (3)
Areas of Operation: IL
Type of Foodservice: Quick Serve (3)

Franchise Affiliation: Arby's Restaurant Group, ATLANTA, GA

Key Personnel
USHA GUGNANI - President; General Buyer
MIKE GUGNANI - VP

Bearco Management Co. Inc.
888 N La Fox St Ste 1
South Elgin, IL 60177-1627

Telephone: (847) 429-6900
Fax Number: (847) 429-6929
Internet Homepage: bearcomgmt.com
Type of Business: Chain Restaurant Operator
Year Founded: 1967
Total Sales: $109,400,000 (e)
Number of Employees: 1,350
Average Check: Breakfast(8); Lunch(8); Dinner(10)
Total Units: 23
Trade Names: McDonald's (23)
Units Franchised From: 23
Preferred Square Footage: 2,500
Preferred Location Types: Community Mall; Convenience Store/Gas Station; Freestanding
Primary Menu: Hamburger (23)
Areas of Operation: IL
Type of Foodservice: Quick Serve (23)
Franchise Affiliation: McDonald's Corporation, CHICAGO, IL
Primary Distributors: (Full Line) The Martin-Brower Co. LLC, ROSEMONT, IL

Key Personnel
DAVID BEAR - President; Partner; General Buyer
JERRY BEAR - Partner; Director Facility/Maintenance
MARC BEAR - Partner; Director Operations, Information Systems
MARCELLE BEAR - Partner; Director Finance, Real Estate
ALICIA YAEGER - Controller Finance
BRANDON GUY - General Manager
GLENN HARRINGTON - Manager Operations, Purchasing, Facility/Maintenance
MIKE NEWMAN - Supervisor Facility/Maintenance
JOHN FALLON - Supervisor

Craveworthy Brands
755 Schneider Drive
South Elgin, IL 60177

Telephone: (847) 608-8500
Internet Homepage: craveworthybrands.com
Type of Business: Chain Restaurant Operator
Year Founded: 2022
Systemwide Sales: $91,800,000 (e)
Total Sales: $82,640,000 (e)
Total Units: 189
Trade Names: BD's Mongolian Grill (26); Dirty Dough (61); Flat Top Grill (4); Ghengis Grill (51); Hot Chicken Takeover (7); Krafted Burger Bar (2); Sigri (2); Soom Soom (18); The Budlong (5); Wing It On (13)
Company-Owned Units: 95
Units Franchised To: 94
Primary Menu: American (2); Asian (81); Chicken (25); Greek/Mediterranean (18); Indian (2); Snacks (61)
Projected Openings: 25
Areas of Operation: AL, AR, AZ, CA, CO, DE, FL, GA, IL, IN, KY, LA, MI, MN, MO, NJ, NM, NY, OH, OK, OR, PA, SC, TX, VA
Type of Foodservice: Fast Casual (171); Quick Serve (18)

Key Personnel
GREGG MAJEWSKI - Founder; CEO
NEIL QUINN - CFO
JEREMY THEISEN - Chief Development Officer; Chief Growth Officer
KIM DECAROLIS - Senior VP Strategy
BECCA MCINTYRE - VP Culinary Operations, Supply Chain
JASON LEVINSON - VP Technology, Information Technology
ROBERT KABAKOFF - Executive Chef
CASSIE MILLER - Senior Director Operations, Training
KRISTIN ALBERT - Director Operations

McGraw Enterprises Inc.
3501 South 6th Ste D
Springfield, IL 62703

Telephone: (217) 698-9103
Fax Number: (217) 698-9105
Internet Homepage: mcgrawmcdonalds.com
Type of Business: Chain Restaurant Operator
Year Founded: 1992
Total Sales: $37,130,000 (e)
Number of Employees: 385
Average Check: Breakfast(8); Lunch(10); Dinner(12)
Total Units: 8
Trade Names: McDonald's (8)
Units Franchised From: 8
Preferred Square Footage: 2,400; 3,000
Preferred Location Types: Freestanding
Primary Menu: Hamburger (8)
Areas of Operation: IL
Type of Foodservice: Quick Serve (8)
Franchise Affiliation: McDonald's Corporation, CHICAGO, IL

Key Personnel
MIKE MCGRAW - Partner; General Manager
RICHARD MCGRAW - Partner; Director Information Systems, Real Estate; General Buyer
LYNN POLIS - Director Human Resources
DONNA MCGRAW - Director Advertising, Promotion
CHARLENE BALINSKI - Coordinator Accounting

O and O Enterprises Inc
232 S Dirksen Pkwy
Springfield, IL 62703-2101

Telephone: (217) 789-9121
Type of Business: Chain Restaurant Operator
Total Sales: $3,649,000 (e)
Total Units: 6
Trade Names: Subway (6)
Units Franchised From: 6
Primary Menu: Sandwiches/Deli (6)
Areas of Operation: IL
Type of Foodservice: Quick Serve (6)
Franchise Affiliation: Doctor's Associates Inc., MILFORD, CT

Key Personnel
MIKE ORLANDO - President; General Buyer

Wali Enterprises, LLC
2951 Montvale Dr Ste A
Springfield, IL 62704-5342

Telephone: (217) 726-6522
Fax Number: (217) 793-9610
Company Email: sjwali@digitalgroup.net
Type of Business: Chain Restaurant Operator
Year Founded: 1989
Total Sales: $22,970,000 (e)
Number of Employees: 320
Average Check: Lunch(8); Dinner(8)
Total Units: 9
Trade Names: Popeyes Louisiana Kitchen (9)
Units Franchised From: 9
Preferred Square Footage: 1,500
Preferred Location Types: Freestanding
Primary Menu: Chicken (9)
Areas of Operation: IL
Type of Foodservice: Quick Serve (9)
Franchise Affiliation: Popeyes Louisiana Kitchen Inc., ATLANTA, GA
Primary Distributors: (Full Line) McLane/Midwest, DANVILLE, IL
Notes: The company also operates as Wail Enterprise LLC.

Key Personnel
RICK WALIMOHAMMAD - Partner; General Manager; General Buyer
SUSAN WALIMOHAMMAD - Partner

Cilantro Taco Grill
1500 N Mannheim Rd
Stone Park, IL 60165-1117

Telephone: (708) 223-8443
Internet Homepage: cilantrotacogrill.com
Type of Business: Chain Restaurant Operator
Year Founded: 2013
Total Units: 8
Trade Names: Cilantro Taco Grill (8)
Company-Owned Units: 8
Primary Menu: Taco (8)
Projected Openings: 1
Areas of Operation: IL
Type of Foodservice: Fast Casual (8)

Key Personnel
CUAHUTEMOC MORFIN - Owner
IVAN ROJAS - General Manager; Manager Marketing
AARON MORFIN - Manager Sales

J & P Enterprises
11 W Jackson St
Sullivan, IL 61951-1420

Telephone: (217) 728-2341
Type of Business: Chain Restaurant Operator
Total Sales: $10,327,000 (e)
Total Units: 2
Trade Names: McDonald's (2)
Units Franchised From: 2
Preferred Location Types: Freestanding; Strip Mall
Primary Menu: Hamburger (2)
Areas of Operation: IL
Type of Foodservice: Quick Serve (2)
Franchise Affiliation: McDonald's Corporation, CHICAGO, IL

Key Personnel
ANGIE DESMOND-MATLOCK - President; General Buyer

Rodebrad of Taylorville
401 W Spresser St
Taylorville, IL 62568-1853

Telephone: (217) 824-4976
Fax Number: (217) 824-4986
Type of Business: Chain Restaurant Operator
Total Sales: $10,032,000 (e)
Number of Employees: 60
Average Check: Breakfast(5); Lunch(8); Dinner(8)
Total Units: 2
Trade Names: McDonald's (2)
Units Franchised From: 2
Preferred Square Footage: 2,500; 3,000
Preferred Location Types: Freestanding
Primary Menu: Hamburger (2)
Areas of Operation: IL
Type of Foodservice: Quick Serve (2)
Franchise Affiliation: McDonald's Corporation, CHICAGO, IL

Key Personnel
MARTIN DAVIS - President; General Buyer
KENNY STEWART - General Manager

McDonald's Franchise
15920 Harlem Ave
Tinley Park, IL 60477-1610

Telephone: (708) 614-0843
Type of Business: Chain Restaurant Operator
Year Founded: 1989
Total Sales: $32,540,000 (e)
Number of Employees: 385
Average Check: Breakfast(8); Lunch(8); Dinner(10)
Total Units: 7
Trade Names: McDonald's (7)
Units Franchised From: 7
Preferred Square Footage: 2,500; 3,000
Preferred Location Types: Freestanding
Primary Menu: Hamburger (7)
Areas of Operation: IL
Type of Foodservice: Quick Serve (7)
Franchise Affiliation: McDonald's Corporation, CHICAGO, IL

Key Personnel
DARREN FREIHAGE - President; General Manager; Director Operations, Facility/Maintenance, Information Systems, Real Estate; General Buyer

McDonald's Central Division
4320 Winfield Rd Ste 400
Warrenville, IL 60555-4038

Telephone: (630) 836-1200
Fax Number: (630) 836-9191
Company Email: info@mcdonalds.com
Listing Type: Divisional Office
Type of Business: Chain Restaurant Operator
Year Founded: 1955
Average Check: Breakfast(8); Lunch(8); Dinner(10)
Total Units: 4,400
Areas of Operation: IL, IN, KS, LA, MI, MN, OH
Type of Foodservice: Quick Serve (4,400)
Parent Company: McDonald's Corporation, CHICAGO, IL

Key Personnel
LEE RENZ - President Central Division
KEITH PERRYEA - Senior Director Real Estate, Central Division; Director Development

Rosati's Franchise and Development LLC
28381 Davis Pkwy Ste 701
Warrenville, IL 60555-3033

Telephone: (630) 393-2280
Fax Number: (630) 393-2281
Internet Homepage: rosatispizza.com
Type of Business: Chain Restaurant Operator
Year Founded: 1964
Systemwide Sales: $65,386,000 (e)
Total Sales: $25,400,000 (e)
Alcohol Sales: 5%
Number of Employees: 1,152
Average Check: Lunch(12); Dinner(14)
Internet Order Processing: Yes
Total Units: 70
Trade Names: Rosati's Pizza (72)
Company-Owned Units: 24
Units Franchised To: 48
Preferred Square Footage: 1,200; 1,800
Preferred Location Types: Freestanding; Strip Mall
Alcohol Served: Beer, Wine
Primary Menu: Pizza (72)
Projected Openings: 2
Areas of Operation: AR, AZ, IL, IN, TX, WI
Type of Foodservice: Quick Serve (72)
Catering Services: Yes
Primary Distributors: (Full Line) Greco & Sons Inc., BARTLETT, IL

Key Personnel
RICK ROSATI - CEO; Partner
MARLA TOPLIFF - President
MICHAEL ROSATI - VP
ANNA MARIE BENFIELD - Corporate Secretary

Bre Mid America
1258 Sun Rd
Washburn, IL 61570-9666

Telephone: (309) 246-4777
Fax Number: (309) 246-4781
Company Email: mkamp@hughes.net
Type of Business: Chain Restaurant Operator
Total Sales: $62,280,000 (e)
Total Units: 13
Trade Names: McDonald's (13)
Units Franchised From: 13
Preferred Square Footage: 2,500
Primary Menu: Hamburger (13)
Areas of Operation: IL
Type of Foodservice: Quick Serve (13)
Franchise Affiliation: McDonald's Corporation, CHICAGO, IL

Key Personnel
PAUL BREZNAY - President; General Buyer

Pizza Resources Corporation
1540 E Walnut St
Watseka, IL 60970-1807

Telephone: (815) 432-3714
Internet Homepage:
 monicals.com/locations/monicals-pizza-of-watseka
Type of Business: Chain Restaurant Operator
Total Sales: $6,550,000 (e)
Average Check: Dinner(16)
Total Units: 4
Trade Names: Monical's Pizza (4)
Units Franchised From: 4
Primary Menu: Pizza (4)
Areas of Operation: IL
Type of Foodservice: Quick Serve (4)
Franchise Affiliation: Monical Pizza Corporation, BRADLEY, IL

Key Personnel
NATHAN HORCHEM - VP

Las Palmas
311 W Ogden Ave
Westmont, IL 60559

Telephone: (630) 963-9999
Internet Homepage: laspalmasofillinois.com
Type of Business: Chain Restaurant Operator
Year Founded: 1984
Total Sales: $9,887,000 (e)
Alcohol Sales: 20%
Number of Employees: 54
Average Check: Lunch(10); Dinner(14)
Internet Order Processing: Yes
Total Units: 4
Trade Names: Las Palmas (4)
Company-Owned Units: 4
Preferred Square Footage: 4,000; 6,000
Preferred Location Types: Freestanding; Strip Mall
Alcohol Served: Beer, Wine, Liquor
Primary Menu: Mexican (4)
Areas of Operation: IL
Type of Foodservice: Casual Dining (4)
Primary Distributors: (Equipment) Edward Don & Co., WOODRIDGE, IL; (Food) Edward Don & Co., WOODRIDGE, IL

Key Personnel
EFRAIN LOPEZ - Founder; VP Operations, Facility/Maintenance
PLACIDO QUINTERO - General Manager; Director Information Systems, Human Resources

The Great American Bagel
353 W Ogden Ave
Westmont, IL 60559-1419

Telephone: (630) 963-3393
Fax Number: (630) 963-7799
Internet Homepage: greatamericanbagel.com
Company Email:
 info@greatamericanbagel.com
Type of Business: Chain Restaurant Operator
Year Founded: 1987
Systemwide Sales: $39,213,000 (e)
Total Sales: $7,418,000 (e)
Number of Employees: 66
Average Check: Breakfast(12); Lunch(12); Dinner(12)
Internet Order Processing: Yes
Total Units: 59
Trade Names: The Great American Bagel (59)
Company-Owned Units: 2
Units Franchised To: 57
Preferred Square Footage: 2,500
Preferred Location Types: Freestanding; Strip Mall
Primary Menu: Bagels (59)
Areas of Operation: AL, AR, DC, FL, ID, IL, IN, KS, MA, MD, MI, MO, MT, NC, NH, NJ, NV, NY, OH, OK, SC, TX, VA, WA, AB, ON
Foreign Countries: BAHRAIN; CANADA; QATAR
Type of Foodservice: Quick Serve (59)
Foodservice Management Venues: Schools
Catering Services: Yes
Primary Distributors: (Full Line) Gordon Food Service Inc., WYOMING, MI

Key Personnel
CHRIS LETTIERI - President
PAUL LETTIERI - Manager Franchise Operations

Domino's Pizza Chicago
PO Box 429
Wheaton, IL 60187-0429

Telephone: (630) 215-4555
Type of Business: Chain Restaurant Operator
Total Sales: $24,977,000 (e)
Total Units: 12
Trade Names: Domino's (12)
Units Franchised From: 12
Preferred Square Footage: 1,200
Primary Menu: Pizza (12)
Areas of Operation: IL, MI
Type of Foodservice: Quick Serve (12)
Franchise Affiliation: Domino's Pizza Inc, ANN ARBOR, MI

Key Personnel
KEN LINDEMAN - President; General Manager

Rammy's International Inc.
834 Wheeling Rd
Wheeling, IL 60090-5711

Telephone: (847) 215-7330
Fax Number: (847) 215-7339
Internet Homepage: rammyssubs.com
Type of Business: Chain Restaurant Operator
Year Founded: 1998
Total Sales: $3,435,000 (e)
Number of Employees: 45
Average Check: Lunch(6); Dinner(12)
Total Units: 2
Trade Names: Rammy's Sub Contractors (2)
Company-Owned Units: 2
Preferred Location Types: Strip Mall
Primary Menu: Sandwiches/Deli (2)
Areas of Operation: IL
Type of Foodservice: Fast Casual (2)
Primary Distributors: (Full Line) SYSCO Food Services of Chicago Inc., DES PLAINES, IL

Key Personnel
MICHAEL HRAMETZ - President; Executive Chef; General Buyer

D L G Management Inc
625 Plainfield Rd Ste 120
Willowbrook, IL 60527-5356

Telephone: (630) 455-6100
Fax Number: (630) 455-6503
Company Email: dlgmgmt@sbcglobal.net
Type of Business: Chain Restaurant Operator
Total Sales: $11,110,000 (e)
Total Units: 5
Trade Names: Burger King (5)
Units Franchised From: 5
Primary Menu: Hamburger (5)
Areas of Operation: IL
Type of Foodservice: Quick Serve (5)
Franchise Affiliation: Burger King Worldwide Inc., MIAMI, FL

Key Personnel
GLENN GLASS - President; General Buyer

Avli
566 Chestnut St
Winnetka, IL 60093

Telephone: (847) 446-9300
Internet Homepage: avli.us
Company Email: events@avli.us
Type of Business: Chain Restaurant Operator
Year Founded: 2009
Total Sales: $5,592,000 (e)
Total Units: 5
Trade Names: Avli (5)

Company-Owned Units: 5
Primary Menu: Greek/Mediterranean (5)
Areas of Operation: IL
Type of Foodservice: Casual Dining (5)

Key Personnel
LOUIE ALEXAKIS - CEO

Little Ricky's Rib Joint
540 Lincoln Ave
Winnetka, IL 60093-2327

Telephone: (847) 784-1444
Internet Homepage: littlerickysrestaurant.com; oneilswinnetka.com; trifectagrillwinnetka.com
Type of Business: Chain Restaurant Operator
Year Founded: 1997
Total Sales: $3,160,000 (e)
Alcohol Sales: 5%
Number of Employees: 25
Average Check: Breakfast(12); Lunch(16); Dinner(22)
Total Units: 3
Trade Names: Little Ricky's (1); O'Neil's Restaurant (1); Trifecta Grill (1)
Company-Owned Units: 3
Preferred Square Footage: 1,500
Preferred Location Types: Community Mall; Downtown; Freestanding
Alcohol Served: Beer, Wine, Liquor
Primary Menu: American (2); Bar-B-Q (1)
Areas of Operation: IL
Type of Foodservice: Casual Dining (3)
Primary Distributors: (Full Line) US Foods, STREATOR, IL

Key Personnel
PATRICK O'NEIL - President; General Manager; General Buyer

Home Run Inn Inc.
1300 Internationale Pkwy
Woodridge, IL 60517-4928

Telephone: (630) 783-9696
Fax Number: (630) 783-0069
Internet Homepage: homeruninn.com
Type of Business: Chain Restaurant Operator
Year Founded: 1947
Total Sales: $39,950,000 (e)
Alcohol Sales: 2%
Number of Employees: 457
Average Check: Lunch(8); Dinner(8)
Internet Order Processing: Yes
Internet Sales: 1.00%
Total Units: 8
Trade Names: Home Run Inn Pizza (8)
Company-Owned Units: 9
Preferred Square Footage: 4,700
Preferred Location Types: Community Mall; Freestanding

Alcohol Served: Beer, Wine, Liquor
Primary Menu: Pizza (8)
Areas of Operation: IL
Type of Foodservice: Casual Dining (8)
Foodservice Management Venues: Parks & Recreation; Schools
Catering Services: Yes
Primary Distributors: (Food) US Foods, BENSENVILLE, IL
Notes: The company derives approximately 60% of its revenue from wholesale distribution.

Key Personnel
DAN COSTELLO - President
KEVIN COSTELLO - Exec VP Finance, Sales
JOHN CARLSON - Exec VP
GINA BOLGER - Senior VP Branding
EDYTA MOWRER - Senior VP Human Resources
NICK PERINO - VP Sales
RENEE PERRINO-STORIE - Director People
JAMIE KAMYKOWSKI-WAGNER - Director Marketing
KATIE MCGINN - Director Finance, Accounting
PAUL BRILL - Director Information Technology
GERI YARKA - Director Restaurant Operations
NICOLETTE REYNOLDS - Manager Marketing

INDIANA

Smokin Subs, Inc. Bigger Better Subs, Inc.
10726 E US Highway 36
Avon, IN 46123-7982

Telephone: (219) 742-1569
Type of Business: Chain Restaurant Operator
Total Sales: $3,653,000 (e)
Total Units: 3
Trade Names: Firehouse Subs (3)
Units Franchised From: 3
Primary Menu: Sandwiches/Deli (3)
Areas of Operation: IN
Type of Foodservice: Fast Casual (3)
Franchise Affiliation: Firehouse Restaurant Group Inc., JACKSONVILLE, FL

Key Personnel
MICHAEL JOHNSON - President; General Buyer

Aver's Pizza Inc.
112 N Walnut St Ste 100
Bloomington, IN 47404-4914

Telephone: (812) 333-1443
Internet Homepage: averspizza.com
Company Email: averspizza@msn.com
Type of Business: Chain Restaurant Operator
Year Founded: 1995

Systemwide Sales: $6,688,000 (e)
Total Sales: $4,256,000 (e)
Number of Employees: 40
Average Check: Lunch(8); Dinner(16)
Internet Order Processing: Yes
Total Units: 4
Trade Names: Aver's Gourmet Pizza (4)
Company-Owned Units: 4
Alcohol Served: Beer
Primary Menu: Pizza (4)
Areas of Operation: IN
Type of Foodservice: Casual Dining (1); Quick Serve (3)
Primary Distributors: (Full Line) Gordon Food Service, SPRINGFIELD, OH

Key Personnel
BRAD RANDALL - Partner; Director Finance, Purchasing, Human Resources
CHRIS WOLF - Director Operations

Gill Guys Group LLC
4653 S Hawks Way
Bloomington, IN 47401-7869

Telephone: (812) 345-2966
Type of Business: Chain Restaurant Operator
Total Sales: $2,852,000 (e)
Total Units: 2
Trade Names: Five Guys Burgers and Fries (1); Subway (1)
Units Franchised From: 2
Primary Menu: Hamburger (1); Sandwiches/Deli (1)
Areas of Operation: IN
Type of Foodservice: Fast Casual (1); Quick Serve (1)
Franchise Affiliation: Doctor's Associates Inc., MILFORD, CT; Five Guys Holdings Inc., LORTON, VA

Key Personnel
PAUL GILLARD - Partner; General Buyer
CAROL GILLARD - Partner

Heartland Beef
1703 N College Ave
Bloomington, IN 47404-2420

Mailing Address: PO Box 98, BLOOMINGTON, IN, 47402-0098
Telephone: (812) 332-4838
Fax Number: (812) 332-0607
Internet Homepage: heartlandbeefarbys.com
Type of Business: Chain Restaurant Operator
Year Founded: 1967
Total Sales: $48,990,000 (e)
Number of Employees: 1,400
Average Check: Breakfast(6); Lunch(8); Dinner(10)
Internet Order Processing: Yes

Total Units: 40
Trade Names: Arby's (36); Harry & Izzy's Steakhouse (3); St Elmo's Steak House (1)
Company-Owned Units: 4
Units Franchised From: 36
Preferred Square Footage: 2,000; 3,000
Preferred Location Types: Freestanding
Primary Menu: Sandwiches/Deli (36); Steak (4)
Projected Openings: 1
Areas of Operation: IA, IL, IN, OH
Type of Foodservice: Fine Dining (4); Quick Serve (36)
Franchise Affiliation: Arby's Restaurant Group, ATLANTA, GA

Key Personnel
TOM BROWNE - CEO
CRAIG TRUELOCK - COO
MICHAEL TODD - Senior VP Development, Construction
JENNIFER FLYNN - VP Human Resources
CHRIS HUNT - Director Finance

One World Enterprises
2361 W Rappel Ave
Bloomington, IN 47404-1769

Mailing Address: PO Box 6955, BLOOMINGTON, IN, 47407-6955
Telephone: (812) 339-2256
Fax Number: (812) 333-3200
Internet Homepage: bloomington.com; lenniesgourmetpizza.com; pizzaxbloomington.com
Type of Business: Chain Restaurant Operator
Year Founded: 1982
Total Sales: $10,120,000 (e)
Alcohol Sales: 16%
Number of Employees: 270
Average Check: Lunch(10); Dinner(14)
Internet Order Processing: Yes
Internet Sales: 5.00%
Total Units: 6
Trade Names: Lennie's (1); Pizza X (5)
Company-Owned Units: 6
Preferred Square Footage: 1,400
Preferred Location Types: Freestanding; Strip Mall
Alcohol Served: Beer, Wine
Primary Menu: Miscellaneous (1); Pizza (5)
Areas of Operation: IN
Type of Foodservice: Casual Dining (1); Quick Serve (5)
Catering Services: Yes
Primary Distributors: (Full Line) SYSCO Food Services of Indianapolis LLC, INDIANAPOLIS, IN

Key Personnel
JEFF MEASE - CEO; Partner; Director Operations, Facility/Maintenance, Real Estate, Design; General Buyer
LENNIE BUSCH - Partner; CFO

CORBIN MORWICK - Executive Chef
DAVE SCHWANDT - Director Finance
PAM THRASH - Director; Community Relations
LYNN SCHWARTZBERG - Manager Catering
OLIVIA DAVIDSON - Specialist Digital Marketing, Design

Upland Brewing Company
4060 W Profile Pkwy
Bloomington, IN 47404-2554

Telephone: (812) 336-2337
Internet Homepage: uplandbeer.com
Company Email: info@uplandbeer.com
Type of Business: Chain Restaurant Operator
Total Units: 6
Trade Names: Upland Brewing Company (6)
Company-Owned Units: 6
Primary Menu: American (6)
Areas of Operation: IN
Type of Foodservice: Casual Dining (6)

Key Personnel
CALEB STATON - Director Operations
ALLI MEDLEY - Manager Human Resources

Wendy's of Bloomington Inc
3900 W Industrial Blvd Ste 3
Bloomington, IN 47403-5150

Mailing Address: PO Box 1289, BLOOMINGTON, IN, 47402-1289
Telephone: (812) 339-3639
Company Email: admin@empire4.com
Type of Business: Chain Restaurant Operator
Total Sales: $40,740,000 (e)
Total Units: 15
Trade Names: Wendy's Old Fashioned Hamburgers (15)
Units Franchised From: 15
Primary Menu: Hamburger (15)
Areas of Operation: IN
Type of Foodservice: Quick Serve (15)
Franchise Affiliation: The Wendy's Company, DUBLIN, OH

Key Personnel
BILL PARKS - Owner; General Buyer
PATRICK MCNAMARA - Director Finance

Richards Restaurants Inc.
8341 N 400 E
Bryant, IN 47326-9003

Telephone: (260) 997-6823
Fax Number: (260) 997-6331
Internet Homepage: richardsrestaurants.com
Company Email: customerservice@richardsrestaurants.com

Type of Business: Chain Restaurant Operator
Year Founded: 1968
Total Sales: $24,650,000 (e)
Number of Employees: 482
Average Check: Breakfast(6); Lunch(8); Dinner(8)
Internet Order Processing: Yes
Total Units: 9
Trade Names: Richards Restaurant (9)
Company-Owned Units: 9
Preferred Square Footage: 5,500
Preferred Location Types: Freestanding
Alcohol Served: Beer, Wine
Primary Menu: American (9)
Areas of Operation: IN
Type of Foodservice: Family Restaurant (9)
Catering Services: Yes
On-site Distribution Center: Yes
Primary Distributors: (Full Line) Dilgard Frozen Food Inc., FORT WAYNE, IN
Headquarter Offices: Richards Restaurants Inc., BRYANT, IN

Key Personnel
DON STRONG - President; Director Facility/Maintenance, Real Estate, Design, Menu Development
JODIE BALES - CFO; Controller
MONA JEAN STRONG - Treasurer

Bubs Franchise Company LLC
210 W Main St
Carmel, IN 46032-1760

Telephone: (317) 706-2827
Internet Homepage: bubsburgersandicecream.com; bubscafe.com
Company Email: info@bubsburgersandicecream.com
Type of Business: Chain Restaurant Operator
Year Founded: 2003
Total Units: 4
Trade Names: Bub's Burgers and Ice Cream (3); Bub's Cafe (1)
Company-Owned Units: 4
Primary Menu: American (1); Hamburger (3)
Areas of Operation: IN
Type of Foodservice: Casual Dining (4)

Key Personnel
MATT FREY - Owner; General Buyer

Smith Foods of Corydon Inc
2350 Landmark Ave NE
Corydon, IN 47112-2018

Telephone: (812) 738-3400
Fax Number: (812) 738-0698
Type of Business: Chain Restaurant Operator

Total Sales: $2,769,000 (e)
Average Check: Dinner(12)
Total Units: 2
Trade Names: Lee's Famous Recipe Chicken (2)
Units Franchised From: 2
Primary Menu: Chicken (2)
Areas of Operation: IN
Type of Foodservice: Quick Serve (2)
Franchise Affiliation: Lee's Famous Recipes Inc., FORT WALTON BEACH, FL

Key Personnel
MARK A. SMITH - President; General Buyer
RANDY YARBROUGH - General Manager

Barney Enterprises
617 Merrillville Rd
Crown Point, IN 46307-3207

Telephone: (219) 663-7770
Fax Number: (219) 663-7772
Type of Business: Chain Restaurant Operator
Year Founded: 1967
Total Sales: $29,450,000 (e)
Number of Employees: 150
Average Check: Lunch(8); Dinner(12)
Total Units: 11
Trade Names: Wendy's Old Fashioned Hamburgers (11)
Units Franchised From: 11
Preferred Square Footage: 2,100; 2,900
Preferred Location Types: Freestanding
Primary Menu: Hamburger (11)
Areas of Operation: IN
Type of Foodservice: Quick Serve (11)
Franchise Affiliation: The Wendy's Company, DUBLIN, OH
Primary Distributors: (Full Line) Maines Paper & Food Service Chicago, HANOVER PARK, IL

Key Personnel
JOHN BARNEY - Chairman; CEO

Great Lakes Creamery LLC
11 W 112th Ave
Crown Point, IN 46307-7844

Telephone: (219) 663-9010
Type of Business: Chain Restaurant Operator
Total Sales: $1,172,000 (e)
Total Units: 2
Trade Names: Cold Stone Creamery (2)
Units Franchised From: 2
Primary Menu: Snacks (2)
Areas of Operation: IN
Type of Foodservice: Quick Serve (2)
Franchise Affiliation: Kahala Brands, SCOTTSDALE, AZ

Key Personnel
JOSEPH MOOS - Partner
FLORENCE MOOS - Partner

T.R. Foods Inc.
1290 Arrowhead Ct Ste B
Crown Point, IN 46307-7766

Telephone: (219) 769-6850
Fax Number: (219) 769-2549
Type of Business: Chain Restaurant Operator
Year Founded: 1978
Total Sales: $10,920,000 (e)
Number of Employees: 300
Average Check: Lunch(14); Dinner(14)
Total Units: 6
Trade Names: KFC (6)
Units Franchised From: 6
Preferred Square Footage: 2,000; 2,500
Preferred Location Types: Freestanding
Primary Menu: Chicken (6); Seafood (6)
Areas of Operation: IN
Type of Foodservice: Quick Serve (6)
Catering Services: Yes
Franchise Affiliation: KFC Corporation, LOUISVILLE, KY

Key Personnel
TERRY ROBINSON - President; Controller; General Manager; Director Finance, Operations, Purchasing, Information Systems, Real Estate
MIKE WILLIAMS - Manager Facility/Maintenance

Greg's Volcano Pizza Inc.
126 Easy Shopping Pl
Elkhart, IN 46516-3535

Telephone: (574) 295-8606
Fax Number: (574) 262-4758
Internet Homepage: volcanopizzaelkhart.com
Company Email: ztirf13@aol.com
Type of Business: Chain Restaurant Operator
Year Founded: 1957
Total Sales: $3,167,000 (e)
Number of Employees: 60
Average Check: Lunch(12); Dinner(16)
Total Units: 3
Trade Names: Greg's Volcano Pizza (3)
Company-Owned Units: 3
Preferred Location Types: Strip Mall
Primary Menu: Pizza (3)
Areas of Operation: IN
Type of Foodservice: Quick Serve (3)

Key Personnel
GREGORY F. CAMPANELLO - Partner; Executive Chef; Director Information Systems, Construction; General Buyer
MICHELLE CAMPANELLO - Partner; VP;
Director Advertising
JUSTIN EYMAR - Store Manager

Azzip Pizza
312 NW M L King Blvd
Evansville, IN 47708

Telephone: (812) 909-4144
Internet Homepage: azzippizza.com
Type of Business: Chain Restaurant Operator
Year Founded: 2014
Total Units: 8
Trade Names: Azzip Pizza (8)
Company-Owned Units: 8
Primary Menu: Pizza (8)
Areas of Operation: IN, KY
Type of Foodservice: Fast Casual (8)

Key Personnel
BRAD NIEMEIER - Founder; Co-CEO
ANDY NIEMEIER - Co-CEO
CRAIG MELVIN - General Manager
BLAKE KOLLKER - Director Purchasing
DAN NIEMEIER - Director Facility/Maintenance
ZACK MATHIS - Director Marketing
KENZIE CAMPBELL - Manager Administration
MARK FELDKAMP - Manager North Region
JOSH BOZE - Manager South Region
MARC WEINZAPFEL - Manager Training

Lloyd's Ice Cream Inc.
11 NW 5th St
Evansville, IN 47708-1601

Telephone: (812) 424-3066
Fax Number: (812) 424-3055
Internet Homepage: licsdeliandicecream.com
Type of Business: Chain Restaurant Operator
Year Founded: 1950
Systemwide Sales: $13,319,000 (e)
Total Sales: $5,966,000 (e)
Number of Employees: 80
Average Check: Lunch(10); Dinner(12)
Total Units: 8
Trade Names: Lic's Deli & Ice Cream (8)
Company-Owned Units: 7
Units Franchised To: 1
Preferred Square Footage: 1,800
Preferred Location Types: Freestanding
Primary Menu: Snacks (8)
Areas of Operation: IN, KY
Type of Foodservice: Quick Serve (8)
Foodservice Management Venues: Schools
On-site Distribution Center: Yes
Primary Distributors: (Full Line) SYSCO Food Services of Louisville, LOUISVILLE, KY

Key Personnel
KARA COMBS - Director Advertising
JAMIA BROWN - Director Purchasing, Information Systems, Loss Prevention, Risk

Management, Human Resources, Menu Development, Food Safety

Ne Ro Inc
6801 Highway 41 N
Evansville, IN 47711-1956

Telephone: (812) 425-6107
Type of Business: Chain Restaurant Operator
Total Sales: $5,894,000 (e)
Average Check: Dinner(14)
Total Units: 4
Trade Names: Dairy Queen Store (4)
Units Franchised From: 4
Primary Menu: American (4)
Areas of Operation: IN
Type of Foodservice: Quick Serve (4)
Franchise Affiliation: International Dairy Queen Inc., BLOOMINGTON, MN

Key Personnel
MICHAEL SCHLOSS - President; General Buyer

Paul Snyder
909 N Saint Joseph Ave
Evansville, IN 47720-6734

Mailing Address: PO Box 6109, EVANSVILLE, IN, 47719-0109
Telephone: (812) 422-8717
Type of Business: Chain Restaurant Operator
Total Sales: $23,820,000 (e)
Total Units: 5
Trade Names: McDonald's (5)
Units Franchised From: 5
Primary Menu: Hamburger (5)
Areas of Operation: IN
Type of Foodservice: Quick Serve (5)
Franchise Affiliation: McDonald's Corporation, CHICAGO, IL

Key Personnel
PAUL SNYDER - President; Owner

Sandy's Associates Inc.
1503 N Boeke Rd
Evansville, IN 47711-4976

Telephone: (812) 477-5569
Fax Number: (812) 474-1653
Type of Business: Chain Restaurant Operator
Year Founded: 1963
Total Sales: $19,170,000 (e)
Number of Employees: 325
Average Check: Breakfast(6); Lunch(8); Dinner(8)
Total Units: 10
Trade Names: Hardee's (10)

Units Franchised From: 10
Preferred Square Footage: 2,500
Preferred Location Types: Freestanding
Primary Menu: Hamburger (10)
Areas of Operation: IN, KY
Type of Foodservice: Quick Serve (10)
Franchise Affiliation: Hardee's Food Systems Inc., FRANKLIN, TN
Primary Distributors: (Food) McLane/Rocky Mount, ROCKY MOUNT, NC

Key Personnel
JAMES W. REYNOLDS - President; Director Information Systems, Real Estate; General Buyer
ROB HILL - Manager Operations, Facility/Maintenance, Human Resources

WKAB Investments, LLC
5435 Pearl Dr Ste 5
Evansville, IN 47712-8103

Telephone: (812) 461-0100
Company Email: coldstonewest@coldstoneamerica.com
Type of Business: Chain Restaurant Operator
Total Sales: $1,211,000 (e)
Total Units: 2
Trade Names: Cold Stone Creamery (2)
Units Franchised From: 2
Primary Menu: Snacks (2)
Areas of Operation: IN
Type of Foodservice: Quick Serve (2)
Franchise Affiliation: Kahala Brands, SCOTTSDALE, AZ

Key Personnel
C. WAYNE KINNEY - Partner
JIM JOHNSON - Partner

CMR Partners, LLP/CMR Associates, LLC
9715 Kincaid Dr Ste 1280
Fishers, IN 46037-9459

Telephone: (317) 845-1250
Fax Number: (317) 845-1252
Internet Homepage: cmr-restaurants.com
Company Email: feedback@cmr-restaurants.com
Type of Business: Chain Restaurant Operator
Year Founded: 1985
Total Sales: $10,790,000 (e)
Alcohol Sales: 2%
Number of Employees: 355
Average Check: Lunch(16); Dinner(20)
Total Units: 6
Trade Names: Ponderosa Steakhouse (4); Qdoba (2)
Units Franchised From: 6

Preferred Square Footage: 6,000; 8,000
Preferred Location Types: Freestanding
Primary Menu: Mexican (2); Steak (4)
Areas of Operation: IN
Type of Foodservice: Family Restaurant (4); Quick Serve (2)
Franchise Affiliation: Fat Brands, Inc., BEVERLY HILLS, CA
Primary Distributors: (Equipment) The Wasserstrom Co., COLUMBUS, OH; (Food) Gordon Food Service Inc., WYOMING, MI; (Supplies) The Wasserstrom Co., COLUMBUS, OH

Key Personnel
MARK BALLARD - Senior VP
RYAN BARTON - Director Operations
SHERRY TAULBEE - Manager Administration

Golden Plate, LLC
8235 E 116th St Ste 201
Fishers, IN 46038-1548

Telephone: (317) 849-6637
Type of Business: Chain Restaurant Operator
Total Sales: $5,207,000 (e)
Total Units: 3
Trade Names: Moe's Southwest Grill (3)
Units Franchised From: 3
Primary Menu: Southwest/Tex-Mex (3)
Areas of Operation: IN
Type of Foodservice: Fast Casual (3)
Franchise Affiliation: Moe's Southwest Grill LLC, ATLANTA, GA

Key Personnel
TOBY NUNLEY - President; General Buyer

Greek's Pizzeria-Pizza Forum
8800 E 116th St
Fishers, IN 46038-2820

Telephone: (317) 915-9111
Internet Homepage: greekspizzeria.com
Type of Business: Chain Restaurant Operator
Year Founded: 1968
Systemwide Sales: $21,852,000 (e)
Total Sales: $3,460,000 (e)
Alcohol Sales: 6%
Number of Employees: 65
Average Check: Lunch(10); Dinner(16)
Total Units: 26
Trade Names: Greek's Pizzeria (26)
Units Franchised To: 26
Preferred Square Footage: 8,000
Preferred Location Types: Freestanding; Strip Mall
Alcohol Served: Beer, Wine, Liquor
Primary Menu: Italian (26)
Areas of Operation: IN
Type of Foodservice: Casual Dining (26)

Catering Services: Yes
Primary Distributors: (Food) Delco Foods, INDIANAPOLIS, IN

Key Personnel
CHRIS KARAMESINES - President; CFO; Director Finance, Loss Prevention, Marketing, Product Development, Menu Development; General Buyer
JASON TAPP - Owner

Sahm's
11530 Fishers Dr
Fishers, IN 46038-1859

Telephone: (317) 705-2062
Internet Homepage: rockstonepizzapub.com; sahms.com
Company Email: eclub@sahms.com
Type of Business: Chain Restaurant Operator
Year Founded: 1986
Total Sales: $19,520,000 (e)
Alcohol Sales: 10%
Number of Employees: 221
Average Check: Lunch(14); Dinner(24)
Internet Order Processing: Yes
Internet Sales: 10.00%
Total Units: 18
Trade Names: Bug Lug (3); Half Liter (1); Liter House (1); Rockstone Pizzeria & Pub (1); Sahm's Ale House (2); Sahm's at Parkwood (1); Sahm's at Pendleton(1); Sahm's At The Tower (1); Sahm's Bar and Grill (1); Sahm's Place (1); Sahm's Restaurant (1); Sahm's Smoke house (1); Sahms Tavern (1); Sahms TowerCafe (1); The Roost (1)
Company-Owned Units: 18
Preferred Location Types: Freestanding; Strip Mall
Alcohol Served: Beer, Wine, Liquor
Primary Menu: American (15); Pizza (1)
Areas of Operation: IN
Type of Foodservice: Casual Dining (16)
Catering Services: Yes
Primary Distributors: (Food) Ben E. Keith Foods, NORTH LITTLE ROCK, AR

Key Personnel
ED SAHM - President; General Manager; Executive Chef; Director Catering; General Buyer

Azar's Inc.
3400 E Coliseum Blvd Ste 100
Fort Wayne, IN 46805-1665

Telephone: (260) 424-1972
Fax Number: (260) 424-1573
Internet Homepage: worldfamousback40junction.com
Company Email: gazar@prodigy.net
Type of Business: Chain Restaurant Operator
Year Founded: 1954
Total Sales: $9,714,000 (e)
Alcohol Sales: 20%
Number of Employees: 750
Average Check: Breakfast(10); Lunch(18); Dinner(26)
Total Units: 2
Trade Names: Azar's Big Boy (1); Back 40 Junction (1)
Company-Owned Units: 1
Units Franchised From: 1
Preferred Square Footage: 8,000
Preferred Location Types: Freestanding; Hotel/Motel
Alcohol Served: Beer, Wine, Liquor
Primary Menu: American (2)
Areas of Operation: AL, IN
Type of Foodservice: Casual Dining (2)
Catering Services: Yes
Franchise Affiliation: Big Boy Restaurants International LLC, WARREN, MI
Primary Distributors: (Full Line) SYSCO Food Services of Indianapolis LLC, INDIANAPOLIS, IN

Key Personnel
ALEXANDER AZAR - Chairman
GEORGE AZAR - CEO; Executive Chef; Director Facility/Maintenance, Real Estate, Menu Development, Catering; Manager Franchising; General Buyer
YOGESH PARIKH - President; CFO; Director Finance, Operations, Supply Chain
DONNA PARIKH - Controller; Director Purchasing, Facility/Maintenance, Information Systems, Design, Store Fixtures; Manager Risk Management, Human Resources

Bandido's Inc.
6060 E State Blvd
Fort Wayne, IN 46815-7639

Telephone: (260) 493-0607
Fax Number: (260) 493-0806
Internet Homepage: bandidos.com
Company Email: corporate@bandidos.com
Type of Business: Chain Restaurant Operator
Year Founded: 1980
Total Sales: $11,480,000 (e)
Alcohol Sales: 12%
Number of Employees: 295
Average Check: Lunch(8); Dinner(14)
Internet Order Processing: Yes
Total Units: 5
Trade Names: Bandido's Mexican Restaurante (5)
Company-Owned Units: 5
Preferred Square Footage: 5,500; 6,000
Preferred Location Types: Freestanding; Strip Mall
Alcohol Served: Beer, Wine, Liquor
Primary Menu: Mexican (5)
Areas of Operation: IN, OH
Type of Foodservice: Casual Dining (5)
Catering Services: Yes
Primary Distributors: (Full Line) US Foods, FISHERS, IN

Key Personnel
CHAD CAMPBELL - Founder
HOLLY TAPP - CFO
TIM MAHER - Director Marketing

Brilliant Blondes
4201 Coldwater Rd
Fort Wayne, IN 46805-1113

Telephone: (260) 482-7601
Type of Business: Chain Restaurant Operator
Total Sales: $2,347,000 (e)
Total Units: 3
Trade Names: Auntie Anne's Hand-Rolled Soft Pretzels (3)
Units Franchised From: 3
Primary Menu: Snacks (3)
Areas of Operation: IN
Type of Foodservice: Quick Serve (3)
Franchise Affiliation: Auntie Anne's Inc., LANCASTER, PA

Key Personnel
CHRIS FORBES - President; General Buyer

Casa Restaurant Group
7539 W Jefferson Blvd
Fort Wayne, IN 46804-4131

Telephone: (260) 399-2455
Fax Number: (260) 745-5503
Internet Homepage: casarestaurants.net
Company Email: office@casarestaurants.net
Type of Business: Chain Restaurant Operator
Year Founded: 1977
Total Sales: $16,638,000 (e)
Alcohol Sales: 20%
Number of Employees: 350
Average Check: Lunch(24), Dinner(42)
Total Units: 4
Trade Names: Casa Grille (2); Casa! Ristorante (2)
Company-Owned Units: 4
Preferred Square Footage: 5,500; 6,000
Preferred Location Types: Freestanding
Alcohol Served: Beer, Wine, Liquor
Primary Menu: Italian (4)
Areas of Operation: IN
Type of Foodservice: Casual Dining (4)
Catering Services: Yes
Primary Distributors: (Food) US Foods, WIXOM, MI

Key Personnel
THOMAS J. CASABURO - President Real Estate, Design; Partner; General Buyer
THOMAS A. CASABURO JR - Partner; General Manager
LOU MESPELL - General Manager
AL THOLEN - Executive Chef

●▲
JMA Enterprises
120 Chambeau Rd
Fort Wayne, IN 46805-1702

Telephone: (260) 482-4626
Fax Number: (260) 482-4627
Type of Business: Chain Restaurant Operator
Year Founded: 1975
Total Sales: $8,528,000 (e)
Number of Employees: 390
Average Check: Breakfast(6); Lunch(8); Dinner(8)
Total Units: 15
Trade Names: Subway (15)
Units Franchised From: 15
Preferred Square Footage: 1,800
Preferred Location Types: Freestanding; Strip Mall
Primary Menu: Sandwiches/Deli (15)
Areas of Operation: IN
Type of Foodservice: Quick Serve (15)
Franchise Affiliation: Doctor's Associates Inc., MILFORD, CT
Primary Distributors: (Food) US Foods, STREATOR, IL

Key Personnel
LARRY PUTT - Partner; Director Supply Chain, Real Estate, Design
JIM AMSTUTZ - Partner; Director Finance, Facility/Maintenance
JOHN GOY - Manager District

●▲
PetePeg, LLC
6408 W Jefferson Blvd Ste A
Fort Wayne, IN 46804-6204

Telephone: (260) 434-9300
Type of Business: Chain Restaurant Operator
Total Sales: $2,942,000 (e)
Total Units: 2
Trade Names: Jersey Mike's Subs (2)
Units Franchised From: 2
Primary Menu: Sandwiches/Deli (2)
Areas of Operation: IN
Type of Foodservice: Quick Serve (2)
Franchise Affiliation: Jersey Mike's Franchise Systems, MANASQUAN, NJ

Key Personnel
TONY LACHOWICV - Partner

●▲
Pizza Hut of Fort Wayne Inc.
7100 W Jefferson Blvd
Fort Wayne, IN 46804-6236

Telephone: (260) 436-7100
Fax Number: (260) 436-0762
Internet Homepage: pizzahutfwi.com
Type of Business: Chain Restaurant Operator
Year Founded: 1972
Total Sales: $59,500,000 (e)
Alcohol Sales: 2%
Number of Employees: 1,575
Average Check: Lunch(12); Dinner(16)
Internet Order Processing: Yes
Internet Sales: 1.00%
Total Units: 49
Trade Names: Pizza Hut (49)
Units Franchised From: 49
Preferred Square Footage: 4,200
Preferred Location Types: Freestanding
Alcohol Served: Beer, Wine
Primary Menu: Pizza (49)
Areas of Operation: IN, OH
Type of Foodservice: Quick Serve (49)
Franchise Affiliation: Pizza Hut Inc., PLANO, TX
Primary Distributors: (Full Line) Gordon Food Service Inc., WYOMING, MI

Key Personnel
TODD HOLLMAN - COO; VP; Director Operations, Purchasing, Loss Prevention, Food Safety; General Buyer
KEVIN ESPY - Director Information Technology
JEFF PALERMO - Regional Director Operations
DAVE RITENOUR - Manager Facility/Maintenance

●▲
Subway Systems Inc
5654 Coventry Ln
Fort Wayne, IN 46804-7140

Telephone: (260) 459-7740
Fax Number: (260) 459-7749
Internet Homepage: subwaysystemsllc.com
Company Email: Office@subwaysystemsllc.com
Type of Business: Chain Restaurant Operator
Total Sales: $25,900,000 (e)
Total Units: 46
Trade Names: Subway (46)
Units Franchised From: 46
Primary Menu: Sandwiches/Deli (46)
Areas of Operation: IN, OH
Type of Foodservice: Quick Serve (46)
Franchise Affiliation: Doctor's Associates Inc., MILFORD, CT

Key Personnel
MARK MINNICK - CEO
CHRISTINE GEORGE - CFO
JAKE MILLER - COO; General Buyer

Wings Etc. Inc.
7337 W Jefferson Blvd Ste 200
Fort Wayne, IN 46804-6283

Telephone: (260) 432-6001
Fax Number: (260) 818-2034
Internet Homepage: wingsetc.net
Company Email: switte@wingsetc.net
Type of Business: Chain Restaurant Operator
Systemwide Sales: $85,502,000 (e)
Total Sales: $28,870,000 (e)
Alcohol Sales: 10%
Number of Employees: 1,016
Internet Order Processing: Yes
Total Units: 74
Trade Names: Wings Etc (74)
Company-Owned Units: 12
Units Franchised To: 62
Primary Menu: American (74)
Areas of Operation: AL, IL, IN, KY, MI, MO, NC, OH, SC
Type of Foodservice: Fast Casual (74)

Key Personnel
ROB HENSMANN - CEO; Partner; COO; VP Purchasing, Marketing, Research & Development
ERIC STUCZYNSKI - Partner; VP Real Estate
CHUCK MOORE - COO
DAVID PONCE - Chief Marketing Officer
MICAH BIGLER - VP Information Technology
GEORGE PASICK - Director Franchise Development
DAVE PONCE - Director Marketing
TIFFANY ARNETT - Director Finance, Administration
JOSHUA LUNDVALL - Director Procurement
MARY HICKS - Director Research & Development
NICHOLAS RADECKI - Director Human Resources-Training
DAN SPARLING - Director Media
MIKE HENSMANN - Manager Information Technology
DOUG NELSON - Manager Human Resources
SHELLY WITTE - Executive Assistant

Ben's Soft Pretzels
1202 W Pike St
Goshen, IN 46526

Telephone: (574) 970-2188
Fax Number: (888) 893-4638
Internet Homepage: benspretzels.com; benspretzelsfranchising.com
Company Email: info@benspretzels.com
Type of Business: Chain Restaurant Operator
Year Founded: 2008
Total Units: 85

Trade Names: Ben's Soft Pretzels (85)
Company-Owned Units: 20
Units Franchised To: 65
Primary Menu: Snacks (85)
Areas of Operation: FL, IL, IN, MI, OH, WI
Type of Foodservice: Quick Serve (85)

Key Personnel
BEN MILLER - Co-Founder; Partner; Executive Chef
SCOTT JONES - Co-Founder; Partner; General Buyer
BRIAN KRIDER - Co-Founder; Partner
LIZ MILLER - Co-Founder

Mozzi's Pizza Inc.
2221 W Main St
Greenfield, IN 46140-2718

Telephone: (317) 462-2999
Fax Number: (317) 467-2645
Internet Homepage: mozzispizza.com
Company Email: mozzispizza@gmail.com
Type of Business: Chain Restaurant Operator
Year Founded: 1982
Total Sales: $3,898,000 (e)
Alcohol Sales: 1%
Number of Employees: 120
Average Check: Lunch(10); Dinner(10)
Internet Order Processing: Yes
Internet Sales: 5.00%
Total Units: 5
Trade Names: Mozzi's Pizza (5)
Company-Owned Units: 5
Preferred Square Footage: 1,200; 5,000
Preferred Location Types: Freestanding; Strip Mall
Alcohol Served: Beer, Wine
Primary Menu: Pizza (5)
Areas of Operation: IN
Type of Foodservice: Casual Dining (5)
Primary Distributors: (Full Line) Delco Foods, INDIANAPOLIS, IN

Key Personnel
CHRIS LEE - Owner; General Buyer
ROB SMITH - VP Operations, Facility/Maintenance

CCreations, LLC
315 US Highway 31 S
Greenwood, IN 46142-3127

Telephone: (317) 497-5480
Fax Number: (317) 534-3097
Internet Homepage: ccreations.co
Type of Business: Chain Restaurant Operator
Year Founded: 2001
Total Sales: $36,660,000 (e)
Total Units: 43
Trade Names: Dunkin' Donuts (1); Subway (37); Wingstop (5)
Units Franchised From: 43
Primary Menu: Chicken (5); Sandwiches/Deli (37); Snacks (1)
Projected Openings: 24
Areas of Operation: FL, GA, IL, IN, KY, TN
Type of Foodservice: Fast Casual; Quick Serve
Franchise Affiliation: DD IP Holder, CANTON, MA; Doctor's Associates Inc., MILFORD, CT; Orange Leaf Holdings LLC, OKLAHOMA CITY, OK; Wingstop Restaurants Inc., DALLAS, TX

Key Personnel
CHINTU PATEL - CEO; President
JIGNA PATEL - Director Group
VIPUL PATEL - Director Group

Luca Pizza Di Roma
107 N State Road 135 Ste 104
Greenwood, IN 46142-1352

Telephone: (317) 882-4125
Fax Number: (317) 889-6209
Internet Homepage: pizzadiroma.com
Type of Business: Chain Restaurant Operator
Year Founded: 1966
Total Sales: $2,637,000 (e)
Average Check: Dinner(10)
Total Units: 10
Trade Names: Luca Pizza di Roma (10)
Company-Owned Units: 10
Preferred Location Types: Community Mall; Outlet Mall; Regional Mall; Strip Mall
Alcohol Served: Beer, Wine
Primary Menu: Pizza (10)
Areas of Operation: IN, OH
Type of Foodservice: Casual Dining (10)

Key Personnel
GIANCARLO DIMIZIO - CEO
ANTONIO DIMIZIO - Owner; General Manager; General Buyer
MIKE WRIGHT - General Manager

Round the Clock Family Restaurants
9010 Indianapolis Blvd
Highland, IN 46322-2501

Telephone: (219) 923-4546
Fax Number: (219) 923-4570
Internet Homepage: roundtheclock.com
Type of Business: Chain Restaurant Operator
Year Founded: 1963
Total Sales: $13,955,000 (e)
Number of Employees: 1,000
Average Check: Breakfast(10); Lunch(10); Dinner(10)
Total Units: 3
Trade Names: Round the Clock Restaurant (3)
Company-Owned Units: 3
Preferred Square Footage: 2,500
Preferred Location Types: Freestanding
Primary Menu: American (3)
Projected Openings: 1
Areas of Operation: IN
Type of Foodservice: Family Restaurant (3)
Catering Services: Yes

Key Personnel
MINAS LITOS - President; Director Finance, Menu Development

Schoop's Hamburgers Inc.
3905 45th St
Highland, IN 46322-3010

Telephone: (219) 924-6012
Internet Homepage: schoophamburgers.com
Company Email: comments@schoophamburgers.com
Type of Business: Chain Restaurant Operator
Year Founded: 1948
Systemwide Sales: $12,470,000 (e)
Total Sales: $2,395,000 (e)
Number of Employees: 24
Average Check: Lunch(12); Dinner(12)
Total Units: 17
Trade Names: Schoop's Hamburgers (17)
Units Franchised To: 17
Preferred Square Footage: 2,500
Preferred Location Types: Freestanding; Regional Mall
Primary Menu: Hamburger (17)
Areas of Operation: IL, IN
Type of Foodservice: Quick Serve (17)
Primary Distributors: (Full Line) US Foods, FISHERS, IN

Key Personnel
MARK SCHOOP - President; Partner; Executive Chef; Director Supply Chain, Real Estate, Design; General Buyer
RICK NEWELL - Partner; VP Operations, Human Resources; Controller; Director Real Estate, Design

SME Inc.
9200 Indianapolis Blvd
Highland, IN 46322-2506

Telephone: (219) 923-9170
Internet Homepage: amarillo-roadhouse.com; texascorral.net
Type of Business: Chain Restaurant Operator
Total Sales: $46,240,000 (e)
Alcohol Sales: 18%
Total Units: 11
Trade Names: Amarillo Roadhouse (1); Houlihans (1); Texas Corral (9)

Company-Owned Units: 10
Units Franchised From: 1
Alcohol Served: Beer, Wine, Liquor
Primary Menu: American (1); Steak (10)
Areas of Operation: IN, MI
Type of Foodservice: Casual Dining (11)
Notes: The company also operates as Chicago Roadhouse Concepts LLC.

Key Personnel
PAUL SWITZER - President; General Buyer
CHRIS HEADLEY - Director Technology
HELENA KNOX - Senior Manager Marketing
REBECCA ROUX - District Manager
RUSSELL HOWELL - District Manager
JACOB SAYLOR - Manager Software Development, Human Resources

Sather Management Corp
287 Home St
Huntington, IN 46750-1348

Telephone: (260) 356-1686
Type of Business: Chain Restaurant Operator
Year Founded: 1998
Total Sales: $33,420,000 (e)
Number of Employees: 210
Average Check: Breakfast(8); Lunch(8); Dinner(8)
Total Units: 7
Trade Names: McDonald's (7)
Units Franchised From: 7
Preferred Location Types: Freestanding
Primary Menu: Hamburger (7)
Areas of Operation: IN
Type of Foodservice: Quick Serve (7)
Franchise Affiliation: McDonald's Corporation, CHICAGO, IL

Key Personnel
BRITT G. SATHER - President; Director Operations, Real Estate, Human Resources
BRITTANY FELTNER - General Manager

Arby's Restaurant Group
2411 Directors Row Ste E
Indianapolis, IN 46241

Telephone: (317) 705-3000
Fax Number: (317) 705-3003
Company Email: info@arbys.com
Listing Type: Divisional Office
Type of Business: Chain Restaurant Operator
Year Founded: 1964
Number of Employees: 15,000
Average Check: Breakfast(8); Lunch(8); Dinner(10)
Total Units: 600
Trade Names: Arby's (367)
Company-Owned Units: 367
Preferred Location Types: Convenience Store/Gas Station; Freestanding; Regional Mall
Primary Menu: Sandwiches/Deli (367)
Projected Openings: 75
Areas of Operation: CT, DC, DE, IL, IN, KY, MA, MD, ME, NH, NJ, NY, OH, PA, RI, VA, VT
Type of Foodservice: Quick Serve (367)
Parent Company: Inspire Brands, ATLANTA, GA
Headquarters: Arby's Restaurant Group, ATLANTA, GA

Key Personnel
DAVE EMBERTON - VP Human Resources
LINDSAY ROBERTSON - Senior Director Human Resources

Auntie Anne's Franchise
10617 E Washington St
Indianapolis, IN 46229-2611

Telephone: (317) 890-7655
Internet Homepage: auntieannes.com
Type of Business: Chain Restaurant Operator
Total Sales: $1,532,000 (e)
Total Units: 2
Trade Names: Auntie Anne's Hand-Rolled Soft Pretzels (2)
Units Franchised From: 2
Primary Menu: Snacks (2)
Areas of Operation: IN
Type of Foodservice: Quick Serve (2)
Franchise Affiliation: Auntie Anne's Inc., LANCASTER, PA

Key Personnel
AMRITPAL PANNU - Owner; General Buyer

Bar-B-Q Heaven Inc.
717 W 26th St
Indianapolis, IN 46208-5505

Telephone: (317) 925-6311
Fax Number: (317) 924-4624
Internet Homepage: barbqheaven1952.com
Company Email: barbqheaven1952@gmail.com
Type of Business: Chain Restaurant Operator
Year Founded: 1952
Total Sales: $2,765,000 (e)
Number of Employees: 20
Average Check: Lunch(12); Dinner(14)
Total Units: 2
Trade Names: Bar-B-Q Heaven (2)
Company-Owned Units: 2
Preferred Location Types: Freestanding
Primary Menu: Bar-B-Q (2)
Areas of Operation: IN
Type of Foodservice: Quick Serve (2)
Catering Services: Yes
Primary Distributors: (Equipment) Zesco Products Inc., INDIANAPOLIS, IN

Key Personnel
RONALD JONES - President; General Manager; Executive Chef; General Buyer

Bazbeaux
811 E Westfield Blvd
Indianapolis, IN 46220-1715

Telephone: (317) 255-5711
Internet Homepage: bazbeaux.com
Company Email: info@bazbeaux.com
Type of Business: Chain Restaurant Operator
Year Founded: 1986
Total Units: 3
Trade Names: Bazbeaux (3)
Company-Owned Units: 3
Primary Menu: Pizza (3)
Areas of Operation: IN
Type of Foodservice: Casual Dining (3)

Key Personnel
JEFFREY BERMAN - Owner; General Buyer
JEREMIAH DALTON - General Manager
MATTHEW SPENCE - General Manager
JOE BEHRINGER - General Manager

Brozinni Pizzeria
8810 S Emerson Ave
Indianapolis, IN 46237-8581

Telephone: (317) 865-0911
Internet Homepage: brozinni.net
Company Email: info@brozinni.net
Type of Business: Chain Restaurant Operator
Total Units: 3
Trade Names: Brozinni Pizzeria (3)
Company-Owned Units: 3
Primary Menu: Pizza (3)
Areas of Operation: FL, IN
Type of Foodservice: Fast Casual (3)

Key Personnel
JAMES CROSS - Owner; Executive Chef; General Buyer

Company Kitchen
2120 S Meridian St
Indianapolis, IN 46225-1923

Telephone: (317) 899-1234
Fax Number: (317) 791-0719
Internet Homepage: companykitchen.com; treatamerica.com
Company Email: sales@calderonbrothers.com
Listing Type: Regional Office
Type of Business: Foodservice Management Operator

Year Founded: 1949
Total Sales: $41,350,000 (e)
Number of Employees: 50
Number of Locations Served: 6,000
Total Foodservice Mgmt Accounts: 1,700
Areas of Operation: IA, IN, KS, NE
Type of Foodservice: Cafeteria (30); Vending machines (1,700)
Foodservice Management Venues: Business & Industry; Health Care; Lodging; Prison Feeding; Schools
Primary Distributors: (Full Line) SYSCO Food Services of Indianapolis LLC, INDIANAPOLIS, IN
Parent Company: Company Kitchen, MISSION, KS

Key Personnel
WILLIAM PELLIEN - Chief Customer Officer
JOHN PROCTOR - Manager Purchasing, Foodservice
MATT HARRIS - Manager Sales
YAZMIN ESTEVEZ - Manager Operations

Cunningham Restaurant Group
530 Fulton St
Indianapolis, IN 46202-3511

Telephone: (317) 378-7274
Internet Homepage: bouldercreekdining.com; bruburgerbar.com; cafe251.com; charbonos.com; crgdining.com; meshrestaurants.com; moerleinlagerhouse.com; provision-restaurant.com; stonecreekdining.com; union-50.com; vida-restaurant.com
Company Email: bouldercreek@crgdining.com
Type of Business: Chain Restaurant Operator
Year Founded: 1997
Total Sales: $24,680,000 (e)
Total Units: 31
Trade Names: Boulder Creek Dining Company (1); BRU Burger Bar (10); Cafe 251 (1); Charbonos (1); Livery (2); Marquee at the Landing (1); Mesh (2); Modita (1); Nesso Coastal Italia (1); Provision (1); Rize (1); Stone Creek Dining Company (6); Tavern At The Point (1); Union 50 (1); Vida (1)
Company-Owned Units: 31
Primary Menu: American (17); Hamburger (10); Sandwiches/Deli (1)
Areas of Operation: IN, KY, OH
Type of Foodservice: Casual Dining (29); Fine Dining (1)

Key Personnel
MIKE CUNNINGHAM - CEO; President; Partner
MICHAEL O'DONNELL - COO
CRAIG A. MORRIS - General Manager
CHRIS FARNEY-PROVISION - General Manager

CARL CHAMBERS - Executive Chef
KIM WOODWARD - Director Human Resources
MICHAEL BROWN - Director Operations
CARISSA NEWTON - Director Marketing
ROBERT GANNAWAY - Director Operations
DAN MAZZIO - Manager Information Technology
MEREDITH GRONOTTE - Manager Training
ELIZABETH AMADOR - Manager Marketing
KATIE WEFLER - Manager Payroll
DOUGLAS HENDREN - Manager Restaurant Operations

Daddy Jack's Inc.
9419 N Meridian St
Indianapolis, IN 46260-1308

Telephone: (317) 843-1609
Fax Number: (317) 571-6987
Internet Homepage: jacksarebetter.net; konajacksindy.com
Company Email: info@konajacksindy.com
Type of Business: Chain Restaurant Operator
Total Sales: $9,294,000 (e)
Alcohol Sales: 30%
Number of Employees: 85
Average Check: Lunch(10); Dinner(24)
Total Units: 3
Trade Names: Apres Jack's (1); Daddy Jack's (1); Kona Jack's Fish Market and Sushi Bar (1)
Company-Owned Units: 3
Preferred Location Types: Strip Mall
Alcohol Served: Beer, Wine, Liquor
Primary Menu: American (2); Seafood (1)
Areas of Operation: IN
Type of Foodservice: Casual Dining (3)
Primary Distributors: (Full Line) SYSCO Food Services of Indianapolis LLC, INDIANAPOLIS, IN

Key Personnel
JIM THOMPSON - President; Owner
LARRY FINE - General Manager; Director Operations
JAMIE CARTER - Corporate Chef; General Buyer
DONNA JOHNSON - Director Finance

Eckceed Eckspectations, LLC
1030 E 86th St Ste 34H
Indianapolis, IN 46240-1854

Telephone: (317) 566-9298
Fax Number: (317) 566-9299
Internet Homepage: lepeepindy.com
Type of Business: Chain Restaurant Operator
Total Units: 6
Trade Names: Le Peep Restaurant (6)
Units Franchised From: 6
Primary Menu: American (6)

Areas of Operation: IN
Type of Foodservice: Casual Dining (6)
Franchise Affiliation: H.W. Holdings Corporation, LITTLETON, CO

Key Personnel
MIKE MARTIN - President; Owner; General Buyer

General Hotels Corporation
2501 S High School Rd
Indianapolis, IN 46241-4919

Telephone: (317) 556-1500
Fax Number: (317) 243-1077
Internet Homepage: genhotels.com
Company Email: info@genhotels.com
Type of Business: Foodservice Operations - Hotel/Motels
Year Founded: 1979
Total Sales: $118,890,000 (e)
Alcohol Sales: 25%
Number of Employees: 1,650
Total Units: 33
Restaurants in Hotels: 9
Trade Names: Best Western Plus (1); Candlewood Suites (1); Comfort Suites (1); Courtyard (2); Crowne Plaza (1); Fairfield Inn & Suites (3); Hampton Inn (6); Holiday Inn (2); Holiday Inn Express (6); Homewood Suites (4); Hyatt (2); La Quinta Inn & Suites (1); Springhill Suites (1); TownePlace Suites (1); Wingate (1)
Company-Owned Units: 9
Alcohol Served: Beer, Wine, Liquor
Projected Remodelings: 6
Areas of Operation: IN
Type of Foodservice: Casual Dining (9)
Primary Distributors: (Food) SYSCO Food Services of Indianapolis LLC, INDIANAPOLIS, IN
Notes: The company derives approximately 70% of its revenue from hotel operations.

Key Personnel
JAMES E. DORA - Chairman
RICHARD A. JETT - CFO; Exec VP Finance
RICK JETT - CFO; Exec VP
GLENN BROOKS - Exec VP Marketing, Sales
CHUCK SUMMERS - Exec VP Operations
AMY SPRINGER - VP Finance
TRINA BLACK - VP Sales
CINDY KURTZ - VP Operations
RIA MCDANIEL - General Manager
MATTHEW GINDHART - Executive Chef
RANDY BUSSY - Executive Chef
KRISTINE WESTON - Director Human Resources, Training, HRMS
ELIZABETH HARRY - Director Operations
CHRIS HIST - Director Information Technology
GREG HOVIS - Director Business Development
CHAD BURYANEK - Director Catering
SUE MILLER - Director Human Resources

MICHELLE LAIRD - Director Marketing, Advertising, Promotion
KIM LYONS-DARDING - Manager Finance
MELISSA PERRY - Manager Sales
ARIANNA FETTINGER - Manager Finance
KEVIN ARNOLD - Manager Accounting
AMANDA TAYLOR - Manager Sales
ROBERT WEBB - Manager Operations

Gerrie N Eddie's Restaurants Inc
2524 E County Line Rd
Indianapolis, IN 46227-6317

Telephone: (317) 888-0112
Type of Business: Chain Restaurant Operator
Total Sales: $36,860,000 (e)
Total Units: 8
Trade Names: McDonald's (8)
Units Franchised From: 8
Primary Menu: Hamburger (8)
Areas of Operation: IN
Type of Foodservice: Quick Serve (8)
Franchise Affiliation: McDonald's Corporation, CHICAGO, IL

Key Personnel
PETE WOJTOWICZ - President; General Buyer

HotBox Pizza
6551 Carrollton Ave
Indianapolis, IN 46220-1664

Telephone: (317) 252-2775
Internet Homepage: hotboxpizza.com
Type of Business: Chain Restaurant Operator
Year Founded: 2005
Internet Order Processing: Yes
Total Units: 22
Trade Names: HotBox Pizza (22)
Company-Owned Units: 22
Primary Menu: Pizza (22)
Areas of Operation: IN
Type of Foodservice: Quick Serve (22)

Key Personnel
GABE CONNELL - Owner; Executive Chef; General Buyer
CASLON SMITH - Director Marketing
SAMANTHA PETERSON - Director Marketing; Community Relations

Hubbard & Cravens Coffee
1114 E 52nd St
Indianapolis, IN 46205-1213

Telephone: (800) 545-2009
Internet Homepage: hubbardandcravens.com
Company Email: info@hubbardandcravens.com
Type of Business: Chain Restaurant Operator
Year Founded: 1991
Total Units: 4
Trade Names: Hubbard & Cravens Coffee (4)
Company-Owned Units: 4
Primary Menu: Snacks (4)
Areas of Operation: IN
Type of Foodservice: Fast Casual (4)

Key Personnel
RICK HUBBARD - Partner; General Buyer
JERRY CRAVENS - Partner; General Buyer

Huse Culinary, Inc
101 W Washington St Suite 1250E
Indianapolis, IN 46204

Telephone: (317) 637-1811
Internet Homepage: burgerstudy.com; harryandizzys.com; huseculinary.com; stelmos.com; stelmos.com/1933-lounge
Type of Business: Chain Restaurant Operator
Year Founded: 1997
Total Sales: $5,870,000 (e)
Total Units: 6
Trade Names: 1933 Lounge (1); Burger Study (1); Harry & Izzy's (3); St. Elmo Steak House (1)
Company-Owned Units: 6
Preferred Location Types: Airports; Downtown; Freestanding
Primary Menu: American (1); Hamburger (1); Steak (1); Steak/Seafood (3)
Areas of Operation: IN
Type of Foodservice: Casual Dining (2); Fine Dining (4)

Key Personnel
CRAIG HUSE - CEO; Partner
STEVE HUSE - Partner
JAMIE BLAKE - CFO
BRYN JONES - VP Retail Operations, Marketing
JASON BENISH - VP Operations
CHRIS CLIFFORD - VP Purchasing, Business Development
LEANNA CHROMAN - VP Employee Development
JEFFERY PERKINS - General Manager
WENDY VAN VELZEN - General Manager
EMILY TUDOR - General Manager
NATHAN WHITE - Executive Chef
ELLIOTT DIXON - Director Business Development
MICHAEL CHRISTENSEN - Director Culinary Operations
CHRISTINA PAYTON - Director Information Technology
BRYNN GESSNER - Director Customer Care
RACHEL FITRZYK - Manager Accounting
LISA METTERT - Administrator Payroll
ASHLY KOTASKA - Coordinator Marketing
JEAN GRAHAM - Assistant Information Technology
GINA GILGE - Generalist Human Resources

Jockamo Upper Crust Pizza
5646 E Washington St
Indianapolis, IN 46219-6428

Telephone: (317) 356-6612
Internet Homepage: jockamopizza.com
Company Email: jockamo@jockamopizza.com
Type of Business: Chain Restaurant Operator
Total Units: 3
Trade Names: Jockamo Upper Crust Pizza (3)
Company-Owned Units: 3
Primary Menu: Pizza (3)
Areas of Operation: IN
Type of Foodservice: Casual Dining (3)

Key Personnel
MICK MCGRATH - Partner
JOSEPH EHRGOTT - Manager Social Media

K and JK Enterprises
2611 Waterfront Parkway East Dr Ste 250
Indianapolis, IN 46214-2028

Mailing Address: PO Box 429, BROWNSBURG, IN, 46112
Telephone: (317) 280-6000
Fax Number: (317) 280-6999
Type of Business: Chain Restaurant Operator
Year Founded: 1986
Total Sales: $20,260,000 (e)
Number of Employees: 252
Average Check: Breakfast(8); Lunch(10); Dinner(10)
Total Units: 9
Trade Names: Burger King (9)
Units Franchised From: 9
Preferred Square Footage: 2,800; 3,200; 4,000
Preferred Location Types: Freestanding
Primary Menu: Hamburger (9)
Areas of Operation: IN
Type of Foodservice: Quick Serve (9)
Franchise Affiliation: Burger King Worldwide Inc., MIAMI, FL
Primary Distributors: (Full Line) Reinhart FoodService, AUSTELL, GA

Key Personnel
KATHLENE HAAS - President; Director Real Estate; General Buyer
KEVIN HAAS - VP; Manager Finance, Purchasing
PHIL VENTURA - Director Operations, Facility/Maintenance; Manager Information Systems
LORI SPIEGEL - Manager Administration,

Kilroy's Indy
201 S Meridian St
Indianapolis, IN 46225-1018

Telephone: (317) 638-9464
Internet Homepage: kilroysindy.com
Company Email: info@kilroysindy.com
Type of Business: Chain Restaurant Operator
Total Units: 2
Trade Names: Kilroy's Broadripple (1); Kilroy's Downtown (1)
Company-Owned Units: 2
Primary Menu: American (2)
Areas of Operation: IN
Type of Foodservice: Casual Dining (2)

Key Personnel
PAUL MURZYN - Partner; General Buyer
STEPHAN KELLY - Regional Manager

La Raza Pizza Inc.
6654 W Washington St
Indianapolis, IN 46241-3002

Mailing Address: PO Box 8008, AMARILLO, TX, 79114-8008
Telephone: (317) 248-0434
Fax Number: (317) 248-0492
Internet Homepage: larazapizza.com
Company Email: cservice@larazapizza.com
Type of Business: Chain Restaurant Operator
Year Founded: 1992
Total Sales: $71,830,000 (e)
Alcohol Sales: 5%
Number of Employees: 1,440
Average Check: Lunch(16); Dinner(34)
Total Units: 58
Trade Names: Pizza Hut (58)
Units Franchised From: 58
Preferred Square Footage: 2,500
Preferred Location Types: Freestanding
Alcohol Served: Beer, Wine
Primary Menu: Pizza (58)
Projected Openings: 3
Areas of Operation: IN, NM, TX
Type of Foodservice: Quick Serve (58)
Franchise Affiliation: Pizza Hut Inc., PLANO, TX
Primary Distributors: (Full Line) McLane/Arlington, ARLINGTON, TX; (Full Line) McLane/Hebron, HEBRON, KY

Key Personnel
GENE CAMARENA - President; General Manager; Director Purchasing, Facility/Maintenance, Real Estate; General Buyer
TRACY STAHL - CFO; Manager Marketing
BOB SWEITZER - Director Information Technology, Loss Prevention; Manager Communications
ROBERT SWEITZER - Director Information Technology, Security
DONNA BRIDGEWATER - Director Human Resources
ANN BROWDER - Director Training
BRAD DAVIS - Director Operations
STEPHANIE GRANADO - Director Marketing
MARCOS RENTERIA - Director Facility/Maintenance

Late Harvest Kitchen
8605 River Crossing Blvd
Indianapolis, IN 46240-2168

Telephone: (317) 663-8063
Internet Homepage: lateharvestkitchen.com; thenorthendbbq.com
Company Email: info@lateharvestkitchen.com/
Type of Business: Chain Restaurant Operator
Year Founded: 2011
Total Units: 2
Trade Names: Late Harvest Kitchen (1); North End Barbecue & Moonshine (1)
Company-Owned Units: 2
Primary Menu: American (1); Bar-B-Q (1)
Areas of Operation: IN
Type of Foodservice: Casual Dining (2)

Key Personnel
RYAN NELSON - Partner; Executive Chef; General Buyer
LAURIE NELSON - Partner
ASHLEY LINE - Manager Customer Service

Lux Restaurants
156 E Market St Ste Mezz
Indianapolis, IN 46204-3290

Telephone: (317) 635-3333
Internet Homepage: binkleyskitchenandbar.com; blindowlbrewery.com; broadrippletavern.com; luxrestaurants.com; meridianonmeridian.com; nickelplatebarandgrill.com
Type of Business: Chain Restaurant Operator
Total Units: 6
Trade Names: Binkley's Kitchen & Bar (1); Blind Owl Brewery (1); Broad Ripple Tavern (1); Elbow Room (1); Meridian Restaurant & Bar (1); Nickel Plate Bar & Grill (1)
Company-Owned Units: 6
Primary Menu: American (6)
Areas of Operation: IN
Type of Foodservice: Casual Dining (6)

Key Personnel
RICK LUX - Owner
BETH LUX - Manager Human Resources

MCL Restaurant & Bakery
2730 E 62nd St
Indianapolis, IN 46220-2958

Telephone: (317) 257-5425
Fax Number: (317) 254-5410
Internet Homepage: mclhomemade.com
Company Email: comments@mclhomemade.com
Type of Business: Chain Restaurant Operator
Year Founded: 1950
Total Sales: $56,738,000 (e)
Number of Employees: 1,040
Average Check: Lunch(8); Dinner(10)
Internet Order Processing: Yes
Total Units: 16
Trade Names: MCL Cafeteria (16)
Company-Owned Units: 16
Preferred Square Footage: 8,000; 12,000
Preferred Location Types: Community Mall; Freestanding; Regional Mall; Strip Mall
Primary Menu: American (16)
Areas of Operation: IL, IN, OH
Type of Foodservice: Cafeteria (16)
Catering Services: Yes
Primary Distributors: (Full Line) US Foods, FISHERS, IN

Key Personnel
TONY HAMLIN - Treasurer; Controller
IAN KILLE - Corporate Chef
SHAYNA WYATT - Manager Payroll, Human Resources
KELLY AILES - Assistant Help Desk

Naked Tchopstix
3855 E 96th St
Indianapolis, IN 46240

Telephone: (317) 569-6444
Internet Homepage: nakedtchopstix96.com
Type of Business: Chain Restaurant Operator
Total Units: 1
Trade Names: Naked Tchopstix (1)
Company-Owned Units: 1
Preferred Location Types: Airports; Freestanding
Primary Menu: Asian (1)
Areas of Operation: IN, KY
Type of Foodservice: Casual Dining (1)

Key Personnel
PAUL LEE - Owner
ERIC VOLL - Store Manager

Neal Brown Hospitality
608 Massachusetts Ave
Indianapolis, IN 46204-1607

Telephone: (317) 685-2550
Internet Homepage: nealbrownhospitality.com
Company Email: info@pizzologyindy.com
Type of Business: Chain Restaurant Operator
Year Founded: 2009
Total Units: 4
Trade Names: Libertine Liquor Bar (1); Midtown (1); Pizzology Craft Pizza & Pub (1); Ukiyo (1)
Company-Owned Units: 4
Primary Menu: American (2); Japanese (1); Pizza (1)
Areas of Operation: IN
Type of Foodservice: Casual Dining (4)

Key Personnel
NEAL BROWN - Founder; Owner; Executive Chef
HARRY THOMPSON - CEO

Noble Roman's Inc.
6612 E 75th St Ste 450
Indianapolis, IN 46250

Telephone: (317) 634-3377
Fax Number: (317) 636-3207
Internet Homepage: nobleromans.com
Company Email: franchise@nobleromans.com
Type of Business: Chain Restaurant Operator
Year Founded: 1972
Systemwide Sales: $134,886,000 (e)
Publicly Held: Yes
Total Sales: $19,050,000 (e)
Number of Employees: 36
Average Check: Lunch(10); Dinner(14)
Total Units: 3,079
Trade Names: Noble Roman's Craft Pizza & Pub (10); Noble Roman's Pizza (3,069)
Company-Owned Units: 9
Units Franchised To: 3,069
Preferred Square Footage: 750; 2,000
Preferred Location Types: Airports; Convenience Store/Gas Station; Downtown; Freestanding; Grocery Stores; Hotel/Motel; Institution (college/hospital); Kiosk; Mobile Unit; Office Complex; Other; Parks; Regional Mall; Strip Mall; Travel Plazas
Primary Menu: Pizza (3,079)
Areas of Operation: AK, AL, AR, AZ, CA, CO, CT, DC, DE, FL, GA, GU, HI, IA, ID, IL, IN, KS, KY, LA, MA, MD, ME, MI, MN, MO, MS, NC, ND, NH, NJ, NM, NV, NY, OH, OK, OR, PA, PR, RI, SC, TN, TX, UT, VA, VT, WA, WI, WV, AB, BC, MB, NB, NS, NT, ON, PE, QC, SK, YT
Foreign Countries: CANADA; ITALY
Type of Foodservice: Casual Dining (10); Quick Serve (3,069)
Foodservice Management Venues: Business & Industry; College & University; Health Care; Military Feeding; Parks & Recreation; Recreational; Schools
Catering Services: Yes
Primary Distributors: (Full Line) SYSCO Central Texas Inc., NEW BRAUNFELS, TX
Notes: Systemwide sales reflect Noble Roman's Pizza operations only. The company has entered into a co-branding alliance with TCBY Enterprises & Subway.

Key Personnel
PAUL W. MOBLEY - Chairman; CFO
A. SCOTT MOBLEY - CEO; President
TROY BRANSON - Exec VP Franchising

Patachou Inc.
4923 N College Ave Ste 25
Indianapolis, IN 46205-1183

Telephone: (317) 202-0765
Internet Homepage: cafepatachou.com; napolesepizzeria.com; patachouinc.com; petitechoubistro.com; publicgreensurbankitchen.com
Company Email: office@cafepatachou.com
Type of Business: Chain Restaurant Operator
Year Founded: 1989
Total Sales: $12,740,000 (e)
Total Units: 14
Trade Names: Apocalypse Burger (1); Bar One Fourteen (1); Cafe Patachou (6); Napolese (2); Petite Chou (1); Public Greens (3)
Company-Owned Units: 12
Units Franchised To: 2
Primary Menu: American (5); French/Continental (1); Pizza (2); Sandwiches/Deli (7)
Projected Openings: 1
Areas of Operation: IN
Type of Foodservice: Casual Dining (7); Fast Casual (7)

Key Personnel
MARTHA HOOVER - President; Owner
MADDY BARNAS - Director Marketing
KIM LEWANDOWSKI MBA, HRM - Director Human Resources

Puccini's Smiling Teeth
1508 W 86th St
Indianapolis, IN 46260-2156

Telephone: (317) 875-9223
Internet Homepage: puccinissmilingteeth.com
Type of Business: Chain Restaurant Operator
Year Founded: 1991
Total Sales: $7,241,000 (e)
Alcohol Sales: 5%
Average Check: Dinner(14)
Total Units: 10
Trade Names: Puccini's Smiling Teeth (10)
Company-Owned Units: 10
Preferred Location Types: Freestanding
Alcohol Served: Beer, Wine
Primary Menu: Italian (10)
Areas of Operation: IN, KY
Type of Foodservice: Family Restaurant (10)
Catering Services: Yes

Key Personnel
DEVEN WILLIS - CEO
DON MAIN - Owner; Executive Chef; General Buyer

Punch Burger
137 E Ohio St
Indianapolis, IN 46204-2128

Telephone: (317) 426-5280
Internet Homepage: punchburger.com
Type of Business: Chain Restaurant Operator
Year Founded: 2012
Total Units: 2
Trade Names: Punch Burger (2)
Company-Owned Units: 1
Units Franchised To: 1
Primary Menu: Hamburger (2)
Areas of Operation: IN
Type of Foodservice: Fast Casual (2)
Notes: Owner of Carmel, Indiana franchise location is Matt McGraw (317.564.0637).

Key Personnel
TRAVIS SEALLS - Owner; General Buyer

Royal Pin Leisure Centers Corporate Offices
8463 Castlewood Dr Ste 103
Indianapolis, IN 46250-5558

Telephone: (317) 576-5174
Fax Number: (317) 576-5173
Internet Homepage: royalpin.com
Company Email: Info@royalpin.com
Type of Business: Foodservice Operations - Bowling Alley
Year Founded: 1968
Total Sales: $13,655,000 (e)
Alcohol Sales: 3%
Number of Employees: 250
Average Check: Lunch(6); Dinner(6)
Total Units: 4
Trade Names: Expo Bowl and Laser Storm (1); Southern Bowl (1); Western Bowl (1); Woodland Bowl (1)
Company-Owned Units: 4
Preferred Location Types: Freestanding
Alcohol Served: Beer, Wine, Liquor
Primary Menu: American (4)
Areas of Operation: IN

Type of Foodservice: In-Store Feeder (4)
Primary Distributors: (Full Line) US Foods, FISHERS, IN
Notes: The company derives approximately 80% of its revenue from bowling center operations.

Key Personnel
CRAIG MAY - President; VP
BRAD FROST - Controller
CASEY RAWLEY - Director Promotions

Shapiro's Delicatessen
808 S Meridian St
Indianapolis, IN 46225-1335

Telephone: (317) 631-4041
Fax Number: (317) 631-3958
Internet Homepage: shapiros.com
Company Email: deli@shapiros.com
Type of Business: Chain Restaurant Operator
Year Founded: 1905
Internet Order Processing: Yes
Total Units: 4
Trade Names: Shapiro's Delicatessen (3); Shapiro's Twisted Traditions (1)
Company-Owned Units: 4
Primary Menu: Sandwiches/Deli (4)
Areas of Operation: IN, OH
Type of Foodservice: Casual Dining (1); Fast Casual (3)

Key Personnel
BRIAN SHAPIRO - President; Owner; General Buyer
MARK TOTEDO - General Manager
RONDA GUDE - General Manager
SALLY SHAPIRO - Director Marketing, Branding, Customer Service
KYLE MCBRIDE - Manager Catering
JOHN PITTS - Manager Foodservice
JAY SLAVIN - Manager Marketing

Some Guys Pizza Pasta Grill
6235 Allisonville Rd
Indianapolis, IN 46220-1543

Telephone: (317) 257-1364
Internet Homepage: someguyspizza.com
Type of Business: Chain Restaurant Operator
Total Units: 2
Trade Names: Some Guys Pizza Pasta Grill (2)
Company-Owned Units: 2
Primary Menu: Italian (2)
Areas of Operation: IN
Type of Foodservice: Casual Dining (2)

Key Personnel
KEITH CAREY - Partner
NANCY CAREY - Partner; General Manager; General Buyer

Tap Ventures LLC
719 Massachusetts Ave
Indianapolis, IN 46204-1608

Telephone: (317) 917-8425
Internet Homepage: chathamtap.com; ralstonsdrafthouse.com; saintjoseph.beer
Type of Business: Chain Restaurant Operator
Year Founded: 2010
Total Units: 4
Trade Names: Chatham Tap (2); Ralston's Draft House (1); St Joseph Brewery & Public House (1)
Company-Owned Units: 4
Primary Menu: American (4)
Areas of Operation: IN
Type of Foodservice: Casual Dining (4)

Key Personnel
DAVID PENTZIEN - Partner
DANIEL JONES - Partner
JIM AILES - Partner
SCOTT REIFENBERGER - Partner; Executive Chef
KARL MANN - General Manager Branch

The Steak n Shake Operations Inc.
107 S Pennsylvania St Ste 400
Indianapolis, IN 46204-3663

Telephone: (317) 633-4100
Fax Number: (317) 633-4105
Internet Homepage: steaknshake.com
Type of Business: Chain Restaurant Operator
Year Founded: 1934
Systemwide Sales: $1,456,656,000 (e)
Total Sales: $399,870,000 (e)
Number of Employees: 21,000
Average Check: Lunch(8); Dinner(8)
Internet Order Processing: Yes
Total Units: 493
Trade Names: Steak 'n Shake (493)
Company-Owned Units: 172
Units Franchised To: 321
Preferred Square Footage: 500; 800; 3,200; 4,000
Preferred Location Types: Community Mall; Downtown; Freestanding; Institution (college/hospital); Lifestyle Center; Mobile Unit; Outlet Mall; Regional Mall; Strip Mall; Travel Plazas
Primary Menu: Hamburger (493)
Areas of Operation: AL, AR, AZ, CA, CO, FL, GA, IA, IL, IN, KS, KY, LA, MD, MI, MO, MS, NC, NJ, NV, NY, OH, OK, PA, SC, TN, TX, VA, WV, FC
Foreign Countries: UNITED ARAB EMIRATES
Type of Foodservice: Family Restaurant (493)
Distribution Centers: BLOOMINGTON, IL
Primary Distributors: (Food) The SYGMA Network Inc. - Oklahoma, PRYOR, OK; (Food) The SYGMA Network Inc.- Florida, ORLANDO, FL
Parent Company: Biglari Holdings Inc., SAN ANTONIO, TX

Key Personnel
SARDAR BIGLARI - Chairman; CEO; President
JILL KELM - President Division
STEVE MAY - CFO
KEITH CORREIA - CIO
RONALD DORSTEN - Chief Transformation Officer
SUSAN SUMMERS - VP Training
DAVID MILNE - VP; General Counsel
PAUL LEDGARD - VP Transformation
BRIAN BOVEY - VP
BRUCE LEWIS - Controller
DAMIEN FRAZIER - General Manager Operations
ANTOINE KIEFER - Senior Director Supply Chain, International
LARRY OFFUTT - Director Safety, Risk Management
STEVEN MINCIN - Director Human Resources
JEFF GOEHRING - Director Information Technology, Infrastructure
JAY KAMMEYER - Director Construction
JEFF LAHMAN - Regional Director Operations
MARK DOERR - Senior Manager Software
SARASWATHI RAVIKUMAR - Manager Systems
HEATHER J YOUNG - Manager Benefits

Toucan, Inc
3830 W Morris St
Indianapolis, IN 46241-2612

Telephone: (317) 248-1097
Fax Number: (317) 243-0199
Company Email: macling@sbcglobal.net
Type of Business: Chain Restaurant Operator
Total Sales: $23,300,000 (e)
Number of Employees: 170
Average Check: Breakfast(5); Lunch(8); Dinner(8)
Total Units: 5
Trade Names: McDonald's (5)
Units Franchised From: 5
Preferred Square Footage: 2,500; 3,000
Preferred Location Types: Convenience Store/Gas Station; Freestanding
Primary Menu: Hamburger (5)
Areas of Operation: IN
Type of Foodservice: Quick Serve (5)
Franchise Affiliation: McDonald's Corporation, CHICAGO, IL

Key Personnel
RANDY SHIELDS - President; General Buyer

Yats Cajun Creole
5363 N College Ave
Indianapolis, IN 46220-3141

Telephone: (317) 253-8817
Internet Homepage: yatscajuncreole.com
Type of Business: Chain Restaurant Operator
Total Sales: $8,064,000 (e)
Total Units: 15
Trade Names: Yats (15)
Company-Owned Units: 15
Primary Menu: Cajun/Creole (15)
Areas of Operation: IN, OH, TN
Type of Foodservice: Fast Casual (15)

Key Personnel
JOE VUSKOVICH - Partner; General Buyer
GINA VUSKOVICH - Partner; General Buyer

SERVUS!
4201 Mannheim Rd Ste A
Jasper, IN 47546-9617

Telephone: (812) 482-3212
Fax Number: (812) 634-5415
Internet Homepage: greatservus.com
Type of Business: Chain Restaurant Operator
Year Founded: 1964
Total Sales: $92,150,000 (e)
Number of Employees: 3,100
Average Check: Breakfast(12); Lunch(12); Dinner(12)
Total Units: 34
Trade Names: Wendy's Old Fashioned Hamburgers (34)
Units Franchised From: 34
Preferred Square Footage: 2,500; 20,000
Preferred Location Types: Community Mall; Convenience Store/Gas Station; Downtown; Freestanding; Regional Mall; Strip Mall
Primary Menu: Hamburger (34)
Areas of Operation: IL, IN, KY, MI
Type of Foodservice: Quick Serve (34)
Catering Services: Yes
Franchise Affiliation: Denny's Corporation, SPARTANBURG, SC; Papa Johns International Inc., LOUISVILLE, KY; The Wendy's Company, DUBLIN, OH
Primary Distributors: (Full Line) McLane/Midwest, DANVILLE, IL

Key Personnel
ROBERT RUCKRIEGEL - Chairman
KRISTI MEHRINGER - CFO
LOVELLA RUCKRIEGEL - VP; Treasurer
CAROL MEYER - Director Real Estate

Boldt Enterprises Inc
8 N Shield St
Knox, IN 46534-1143

Mailing Address: PO Box 39, KNOX, IN, 46534-0039
Telephone: (574) 772-2729
Fax Number: (574) 772-0767
Type of Business: Chain Restaurant Operator
Total Sales: $38,510,000 (e)
Total Units: 8
Trade Names: McDonald's (8)
Units Franchised From: 8
Primary Menu: Hamburger (8)
Areas of Operation: IN
Type of Foodservice: Quick Serve (8)
Franchise Affiliation: McDonald's Corporation, CHICAGO, IL

Key Personnel
WILLIAM BOLDT - President; General Buyer
SANDY MECHLING - Office Manager

Bruno Enterprises Inc
410 Pine Lake Ave Ste A
La Porte, IN 46350-2304

Mailing Address: P.O Box 178, La Porte, IN, 46352
Telephone: (219) 324-0773
Fax Number: (219) 362-0081
Company Email: brunoadministrator@comcast.net
Type of Business: Chain Restaurant Operator
Total Sales: $66,540,000 (e)
Number of Employees: 200
Average Check: Lunch(8); Dinner(10)
Total Units: 21
Trade Names: Arby's (12); Buffalo Wild Wings (9)
Units Franchised From: 21
Preferred Square Footage: 1,400; 3,200
Preferred Location Types: Freestanding
Primary Menu: Chicken (9); Sandwiches/Deli (12)
Areas of Operation: IN, MI
Type of Foodservice: Fast Casual (9); Quick Serve (12)
Franchise Affiliation: Arby's Restaurant Group, ATLANTA, GA; Buffalo Wild Wings Inc., ATLANTA, GA

Key Personnel
JAMES BRUNO - President; General Buyer
SHELLIE STOUT - General Manager
NANCY BRUNO - Director Finance
MISSY MILLER - Manager Payroll

Arni's Inc.
2200 Elmwood Ave Ste D10
Lafayette, IN 47904-2347

Telephone: (765) 838-2985
Fax Number: (765) 838-2235
Internet Homepage: meetyouatarnis.com
Company Email: info@meetyouatarnis.com
Type of Business: Chain Restaurant Operator
Year Founded: 1965
Systemwide Sales: $26,201,000 (e)
Total Sales: $18,435,000 (e)
Alcohol Sales: 3%
Number of Employees: 323
Average Check: Lunch(10); Dinner(12)
Internet Order Processing: Yes
Total Units: 18
Trade Names: Arni's (18)
Company-Owned Units: 14
Units Franchised To: 4
Preferred Square Footage: 5,500; 6,000
Preferred Location Types: Freestanding; Grocery Stores; Strip Mall
Alcohol Served: Beer, Wine, Liquor
Primary Menu: American (18)
Areas of Operation: IN
Type of Foodservice: Casual Dining (18)
Catering Services: Yes
Distribution Centers: LAFAYETTE, IN
Primary Distributors: (Equipment) SYSCO Food Services of Indianapolis LLC, INDIANAPOLIS, IN; (Food) Gordon Food Service Inc., WYOMING, MI;(Supplies) Gordon Food Service Inc., WYOMING, MI

Key Personnel
KURT COHEN - President; Partner; Manager Operations, Marketing, Human Resources, Menu Development; General Buyer
BRIAN NELSON - Manager Purchasing
ED MOSKOVITZ - Manager Franchising
LIZ MITCHELL - Manager Marketing

Bauer Inc
325 N 9th St Ste A
Lafayette, IN 47904-2588

Telephone: (765) 463-0080
Fax Number: (765) 463-6457
Company Email: office@bauersubway.com
Type of Business: Chain Restaurant Operator
Total Sales: $8,795,000 (e)
Total Units: 15
Trade Names: Subway (15)
Units Franchised From: 15
Primary Menu: Sandwiches/Deli (15)
Areas of Operation: IN
Type of Foodservice: Quick Serve (15)
Franchise Affiliation: Doctor's Associates Inc., MILFORD, CT

Key Personnel
CATHY BAUER - President; Partner; General Buyer
ROGER BAUER - Partner
ROBERT MERWIN - Director Sales

Linar Co. Distribution Center/Arni's
2415 N 18th St
Lafayette, IN 47904-1109

Telephone: (765) 742-7455
Fax Number: (765) 742-6123
Listing Type: Distribution Center
Type of Business: Chain Restaurant Operator
Number of Employees: 16
Areas of Operation: IN
Parent Company: Arni's Inc., LAFAYETTE, IN

Key Personnel
BRIAN NELSON - Director Operations; Manager Warehouse

The Pizza King Inc.
221 Farabee Dr S
Lafayette, IN 47905-4706

Telephone: (765) 447-2172
Fax Number: (765) 447-5491
Internet Homepage: pizzakingindiana.com; theoriginalpizzaking.com
Type of Business: Chain Restaurant Operator
Year Founded: 1955
Systemwide Sales: $42,303,000 (e)
Total Sales: $4,882,000 (e)
Alcohol Sales: 5%
Number of Employees: 230
Average Check: Lunch(12); Dinner(14)
Total Units: 48
Trade Names: Pizza King (48)
Company-Owned Units: 4
Units Franchised To: 44
Preferred Square Footage: 1,700
Preferred Location Types: Freestanding; Strip Mall
Alcohol Served: Beer, Wine
Primary Menu: Pizza (48)
Areas of Operation: IN
Type of Foodservice: Quick Serve (48)
On-site Distribution Center: Yes
Primary Distributors: (Full Line) US Foods, FISHERS, IN

Key Personnel
SCOT SCHUTZ - CEO; President; General Buyer
BETTY BENJAMIN - Exec VP Purchasing, Information Systems, Human Resources; Treasurer; Manager Operations, Risk Management, Training, Menu Development

Marion Restaurants Inc.
106 E 4th St
Marion, IN 46952-4000

Telephone: (765) 662-0956
Fax Number: (765) 573-4940
Type of Business: Chain Restaurant Operator
Year Founded: 2001
Total Sales: $13,900,000 (e)
Number of Employees: 140
Average Check: Lunch(8); Dinner(10)
Total Units: 5
Trade Names: Wendy's Old Fashioned Hamburgers (5)
Units Franchised From: 5
Preferred Square Footage: 2,100; 2,900
Preferred Location Types: Freestanding
Primary Menu: Hamburger (5)
Areas of Operation: IN
Type of Foodservice: Quick Serve (5)
Franchise Affiliation: The Wendy's Company, DUBLIN, OH
Primary Distributors: (Full Line) US Foods, FISHERS, IN

Key Personnel
RANDY H. CHEKOURAS - President; Director Finance, Purchasing, Supply Chain, Real Estate; General Buyer
CHRIS CHEKOURAS - Director Operations, Facility/Maintenance, Information Technology
LORI WARNOCK - Director Human Resources
JERRY MILFORD - Manager Area

Ron-Rick Inc.
1225 N Baldwin Ave
Marion, IN 46952-2533

Telephone: (765) 664-5149
Fax Number: (765) 662-0048
Type of Business: Chain Restaurant Operator
Total Sales: $32,620,000 (e)
Total Units: 7
Trade Names: McDonald's (7)
Units Franchised From: 7
Primary Menu: Hamburger (7)
Areas of Operation: IN
Type of Foodservice: Quick Serve (7)
Franchise Affiliation: McDonald's Corporation, CHICAGO, IL

Key Personnel
RICK REICHENBACH - President; General Buyer

S&S Franchise Development, Inc
816 N Baldwin Ave
Marion, IN 46952

Telephone: (765) 573-4942
Type of Business: Chain Restaurant Operator
Total Sales: $3,587,000 (e)
Total Units: 2
Trade Names: Moe's Southwest Grill (2)
Units Franchised From: 2
Primary Menu: Southwest/Tex-Mex (2)
Areas of Operation: IN
Type of Foodservice: Fast Casual (2)
Franchise Affiliation: Moe's Southwest Grill LLC, ATLANTA, GA

Key Personnel
CAROLYN SWAN - Owner; General Buyer

Modrak Group
8868 Louisiana St
Merrillville, IN 46410-7153

Telephone: (219) 738-1889
Type of Business: Chain Restaurant Operator
Year Founded: 1958
Total Sales: $15,475,000 (e)
Number of Employees: 150
Average Check: Breakfast(8); Lunch(8); Dinner(10)
Total Units: 3
Trade Names: McDonald's (3)
Units Franchised From: 3
Preferred Square Footage: 2,400; 3,000
Preferred Location Types: Freestanding
Primary Menu: Hamburger (3)
Areas of Operation: IN
Type of Foodservice: Quick Serve (3)
Franchise Affiliation: McDonald's Corporation, CHICAGO, IL

Key Personnel
CHERI MODRAK - Partner; VP
ERIC WALKER - General Manager; Director Operations

White Lodging Services Corp.
701 E 83rd Ave Ste 7
Merrillville, IN 46410-9202

Telephone: (219) 472-2900
Internet Homepage: whitelodging.com
Company Email: info@whitelodging.com
Type of Business: Foodservice Operations - Hotel/Motels
Year Founded: 1986

Total Sales: $233,980,000 (e)
Alcohol Sales: 18%
Number of Employees: 6,000
Total Units: 59
Restaurants in Hotels: 43
Trade Names: French Creek Sportmans Club (1); Hilton (26); Holiday Inn (1); Hyatt (9); Magee Homestead (1); Marriott (19); Purdue Union Club Hotel (1); The Lodge & Spa (1)
Company-Owned Units: 41
Units Franchised From: 2
Alcohol Served: Beer, Wine, Liquor
Areas of Operation: CO, FL, IL, IN, MI, NE, TX, UT
Type of Foodservice: Casual Dining (41); Fine Dining (2)
Franchise Affiliation: T.G.I. Friday's Inc., DALLAS, TX
Primary Distributors: (Food) SYSCO Food Services of Indianapolis LLC, INDIANAPOLIS, IN
Notes: The company derives approximately 80% of its revenue from hotel operations.

Key Personnel
BRUCE W. WHITE - Chairman; CEO
BRUCE HOFFMANN - CFO; Senior VP
CHRIS ANDERSON - Chief Accounting Officer; Senior VP
DAVE SIBLEY - COO
LAURA BROUK - Senior VP Sales, Business Development, E-Commerce
CAROLYN COCHRAN - Senior VP Accounting
JASON DRUSO - VP Restaurant Operations
STEVE HANDLER - VP Finance
PETER REARDON - VP Procurement-Beverages, Procurement-Food, Purchasing-Beverages, Purchasing-Food
MEHDI SPADAVECCHIA - Director Food and Beverage

Glenhaven Management Company
823 Franklin St
Michigan City, IN 46360-3507

Telephone: (219) 879-4200
Fax Number: (219) 879-2933
Type of Business: Chain Restaurant Operator
Total Sales: $24,120,000 (e)
Number of Employees: 400
Average Check: Breakfast(8); Lunch(8); Dinner(10)
Total Units: 5
Trade Names: McDonald's (5)
Units Franchised From: 5
Preferred Square Footage: 2,400; 3,000
Preferred Location Types: Freestanding
Primary Menu: Hamburger (5)
Areas of Operation: IN
Type of Foodservice: Quick Serve (5)
Franchise Affiliation: McDonald's Corporation, CHICAGO, IL

Primary Distributors: (Full Line) The Martin-Brower Co. LLC, ROSEMONT, IL

Key Personnel
GLENN LUBEZNIK - President; Partner; Director Finance, Real Estate; General Buyer
KATHY LUBEZNIK - Partner; Director Human Resources
SAM LUBEZNIK - Partner; Director Operations, Facility/Maintenance, Information Systems
LOIS WARD - Director Accounting

Kada Partnership
118 S Mill St
Mishawaka, IN 46544-2005

Telephone: (574) 255-1933
Fax Number: (574) 255-2376
Company Email: kada118@aol.com
Type of Business: Chain Restaurant Operator
Year Founded: 1990
Total Sales: $32,540,000 (e)
Number of Employees: 550
Average Check: Breakfast(8); Lunch(10); Dinner(12)
Total Units: 7
Trade Names: McDonald's (7)
Units Franchised From: 7
Preferred Square Footage: 2,500
Preferred Location Types: Freestanding; Regional Mall
Primary Menu: Hamburger (7)
Areas of Operation: IN
Type of Foodservice: Quick Serve (7)
Franchise Affiliation: McDonald's Corporation, CHICAGO, IL

Key Personnel
KATHLEEN SPARKS - Partner; Director Real Estate, Design
LISA HODGES - Director Operations, Facility/Maintenance

Quality Dining Inc.
4220 Edison Lakes Pkwy Ste 300
Mishawaka, IN 46545-1440

Telephone: (574) 271-4600
Fax Number: (574) 243-6904
Internet Homepage: qdi.com
Company Email: corpquestions@qdi.com
Type of Business: Chain Restaurant Operator
Year Founded: 1981
Total Sales: $567,250,000 (e)
Alcohol Sales: 5%
Number of Employees: 9,086
Average Check: Breakfast(6); Lunch(10); Dinner(16)
Total Units: 196
Trade Names: Burger King (155); Chili's Grill & Bar (39); Papa Vino's Italian Kitchen (2)

Company-Owned Units: 3
Units Franchised From: 211
Preferred Square Footage: 2,400; 4,000; 6,200
Preferred Location Types: Community Mall; Convenience Store/Gas Station; Downtown; Freestanding; Outlet Mall; Regional Mall; Strip Mall
Alcohol Served: Beer, Wine, Liquor
Primary Menu: Hamburger (155); Italian (2); Southwest/Tex-Mex (39)
Areas of Operation: DE, FL, IN, MI, NJ, OH, PA
Type of Foodservice: Casual Dining (41); Quick Serve (155)
Franchise Affiliation: Burger King Worldwide Inc., MIAMI, FL; Chili's Grill & Bar, DALLAS, TX
Primary Distributors: (Food) Reinhart FoodService, OAK CREEK, WI

Key Personnel
DANIEL B. FITZPATRICK - Chairman; CEO
JOHN C. FIRTH - President
CHRISTOPHER L. COLLIER - CFO
JOSEPH E. OLIN - VP Division
JEANNE M. YODER - VP; Controller
STEVEN C. HUNTER - VP Division
CHRISTOPHER J. FITZPATRICK - VP Division
JENNIFER TYLER - VP Real Estate Development
SHARON BOREK - Director Risk Management
KELLI STOPCZYNSKI - Director Marketing
DARREN HESTAD - Director Information Technology
DAVID KENNEDY - Director People
TIM MURDOCK - Director Facility/Maintenance, Construction
JAMES CAMPBELL - Director Security, Safety
CAROL SIKORSKI - Director Accounting, Systems
ANDRÉ GOLDSON - District Manager
KIRT PRCHLIK - Manager Information Technology
JOHN MARQUETTE - Manager Database; Administrator
BETTY WILLIAMS - Manager Human Resources
AMANDA WEBBER - Manager Marketing
CINDI CLAWSON - Manager Marketing
TREVOR GREGORY - Manager Store Design
CHAD WILSON - Project Manager

Squealers Barbeque
390 E High St
Mooresville, IN 46158-1671

Telephone: (317) 834-8888
Fax Number: (317) 834-8389
Internet Homepage: squealersbarbeque.com
Type of Business: Chain Restaurant Operator
Year Founded: 2001
Internet Order Processing: Yes

Total Units: 3
Trade Names: Squealers Barbeque (3)
Company-Owned Units: 3
Primary Menu: Bar-B-Q (3)
Areas of Operation: IN
Type of Foodservice: Casual Dining (3)

Key Personnel
JEFF YATER - President; Owner; General Buyer
MEGAN BECKWITH - Manager

Amazing Joe's Grill
909 N Wheeling Ave
Muncie, IN 47303-2866

Telephone: (765) 288-9470
Internet Homepage: amazingjoes.com
Type of Business: Chain Restaurant Operator
Year Founded: 2008
Total Units: 2
Trade Names: Amazing Joe's Grill (2)
Company-Owned Units: 2
Primary Menu: American (2)
Areas of Operation: IN
Type of Foodservice: Casual Dining (2)

Key Personnel
NICK GRAMS - Partner; General Buyer
CHAD MASSOTH - Partner
MIKE ROBINSON - Partner; Director Customer Service

Terhune's Inc.
4707 N Wheeling Ave
Muncie, IN 47304-1222

Telephone: (765) 284-8708
Fax Number: (765) 284-8738
Type of Business: Chain Restaurant Operator
Year Founded: 1914
Total Sales: $64,577,000 (e)
Number of Employees: 935
Average Check: Breakfast(5); Lunch(8); Dinner(8)
Total Units: 13
Trade Names: McDonald's (13)
Units Franchised From: 13
Preferred Square Footage: 3,000
Preferred Location Types: Freestanding
Primary Menu: Hamburger (13)
Areas of Operation: IN
Type of Foodservice: Quick Serve (13)
Franchise Affiliation: McDonald's Corporation, CHICAGO, IL
Primary Distributors: (Food) Golden State Foods Corporation, IRVINE, CA

Key Personnel
KIM HICKS - Manager Human Resources

C & M Smith Restaurants Inc.
5140 Charlestown Rd Ste 4
New Albany, IN 47150

Telephone: (812) 945-9810
Fax Number: (812) 945-7776
Internet Homepage: cmstacobell.com
Company Email: dmorrison@cmstacobell.com
Type of Business: Chain Restaurant Operator
Year Founded: 1988
Total Sales: $55,030,000 (e)
Number of Employees: 555
Average Check: Lunch(10); Dinner(10)
Total Units: 23
Trade Names: Taco Bell (20); Taco Bell/KFC (3)
Units Franchised From: 23
Preferred Square Footage: 1,800
Preferred Location Types: Freestanding
Primary Menu: Chicken (3); Taco (20)
Areas of Operation: IN, KY
Type of Foodservice: Quick Serve (23)
Franchise Affiliation: KFC Corporation, LOUISVILLE, KY; Taco Bell Corp., IRVINE, CA
Primary Distributors: (Full Line) McLane/Hebron, HEBRON, KY

Key Personnel
STACEY CRANMER - Director Accounting
CLINTON SMITH - Director Operations
DANNY JONES - District Manager
DEBBIE MORRISON - Administrative Assistant

Jack's Donuts
2410 S 14th St
New Castle, IN 47362-2107

Telephone: (765) 529-2956
Internet Homepage: jacksdonuts.com
Company Email: info@jacksdonuts.com
Type of Business: Chain Restaurant Operator
Year Founded: 1961
Total Units: 23
Trade Names: Jack's Donuts (23)
Company-Owned Units: 1
Units Franchised To: 22
Primary Menu: Snacks (23)
Areas of Operation: IN
Type of Foodservice: Quick Serve (23)

Key Personnel
LEE MARCUM - Owner; General Buyer

Hall Drive Ins Inc.
216 State Road 930 W
New Haven, IN 46774-2148

Telephone: (260) 493-3522
Fax Number: (260) 493-6064

Internet Homepage: donhalls.com
Company Email: info@donhalls.com
Type of Business: Chain Restaurant Operator
Year Founded: 1946
Total Sales: $28,510,000 (e)
Alcohol Sales: 15%
Number of Employees: 931
Average Check: Breakfast(14); Lunch(16); Dinner(36)
Internet Order Processing: Yes
Internet Sales: 2.00%
Total Units: 16
Trade Names: Commissary (1); Don Halls Guesthouse Grill (1); Don Halls Tavern at Coventry (1); Guest House Bar & Grill (1); Hall Drive In North (1); Hall's Catering Service (1); Hall's Orginal (1); Hall's Takes the Cake (1); Halls Factory (1); Halls Gas House (1); Halls Takaoka (1); Halls Triangle Park (1); Prime Rib (1); Tap Haus (1); The Deck (1); The Philmore on Broadway (1)
Company-Owned Units: 16
Preferred Square Footage: 4,000
Preferred Location Types: Downtown; Freestanding; Hotel/Motel
Alcohol Served: Beer, Wine, Liquor
Primary Menu: American (12); Japanese (1)
Areas of Operation: IN
Type of Foodservice: Casual Dining (8); Fine Dining (4); Quick Serve (1)
Catering Services: Yes
On-site Distribution Center: Yes
Primary Distributors: (Full Line) SYSCO Food Services of Indianapolis LLC, INDIANAPOLIS, IN

Key Personnel
DON D. HALL II - President; Partner; General Manager
JEFF HALL - Partner; General Buyer; Buyer Food

Clancy's Inc.
120 Carey Dr
Noblesville, IN 46060-1301

Telephone: (317) 773-3284
Fax Number: (317) 776-6869
Internet Homepage: clancyshamburgers.com; michaelangelosbistro.com; grindstonecharleys.com
Type of Business: Chain Restaurant Operator
Year Founded: 1965
Total Sales: $13,560,000 (e)
Alcohol Sales: 10%
Number of Employees: 770
Average Check: Breakfast(6); Lunch(16); Dinner(28)
Internet Order Processing: Yes
Total Units: 6
Trade Names: Clancy's (1); Grindstone Charley's (4); Michaelangelo's (1)
Company-Owned Units: 6

Preferred Square Footage: 3,000; 4,500; 6,500
Preferred Location Types: Community Mall; Freestanding
Alcohol Served: Beer, Wine, Liquor
Primary Menu: American (5); Italian (1)
Areas of Operation: IN, OH
Type of Foodservice: Casual Dining (4); Quick Serve (2)
Catering Services: Yes
Franchise Affiliation: Fat Brands, Inc., BEVERLY HILLS, CA; HRI Inc., LEAWOOD, KS
Primary Distributors: (Full Line) Gordon Food Service Inc., WYOMING, MI

Key Personnel
PERRY FOGELSONG - President; VP Operations, Loss Prevention, Supply Chain, Ethnic Marketing; Executive Chef; Director Facility/Maintenance, Risk Management, Marketing, Advertising, Real Estate, Design, Human Resources, Product Development, Store Fixtures, Food Safety, Catering

Carlisle Restaurants Inc.
1877 Center St
Portage, IN 46368-1644

Telephone: (219) 762-2105
Fax Number: (219) 762-7852
Type of Business: Chain Restaurant Operator
Year Founded: 1979
Total Sales: $25,350,000 (e)
Number of Employees: 350
Average Check: Lunch(8); Dinner(8)
Total Units: 15
Trade Names: A&W All American Food (2); KFC (12); Taco Bell (1)
Units Franchised From: 15
Preferred Square Footage: 2,200
Preferred Location Types: Convenience Store/Gas Station; Freestanding
Primary Menu: American (3); Chicken (12); Taco (1)
Areas of Operation: IN
Type of Foodservice: Quick Serve (15)
Franchise Affiliation: A&W Restaurants Inc., LEXINGTON, KY; KFC Corporation, LOUISVILLE, KY; Taco Bell Corp., IRVINE, CA
Primary Distributors: (Full Line) McLane/Midwest, DANVILLE, IL

Key Personnel
ORYN CARLISLE JR - President; Controller; Manager Purchasing, Facility/Maintenance, Marketing, Store Planning
ERIC CARLISLE - VP Operations, Risk Management; Director Information Systems, Real Estate

W.W. Pizza Inc.
927 S Main St
Princeton, IN 47670-2653

Mailing Address: PO Box 1268, PRINCETON, IN, 47670-0968
Telephone: (812) 385-8747
Fax Number: (812) 385-4213
Internet Homepage: godfathers.com
Type of Business: Chain Restaurant Operator
Year Founded: 1981
Total Sales: $6,481,000 (e)
Alcohol Sales: 5%
Number of Employees: 250
Average Check: Lunch(10); Dinner(14)
Internet Order Processing: Yes
Total Units: 4
Trade Names: Godfather's Pizza (4)
Units Franchised From: 4
Preferred Location Types: Strip Mall
Alcohol Served: Beer
Primary Menu: Pizza (4)
Areas of Operation: IN, OH
Type of Foodservice: Fast Casual (4)
Franchise Affiliation: Godfather's Pizza, Inc., OMAHA, NE
Primary Distributors: (Full Line) I Supply Co., FAIRBORN, OH

Key Personnel
CHARLES WHEELER - Partner; Executive Chef; General Buyer
CHARLES WINTERS - Partner; VP Purchasing, Advertising; General Manager; General Buyer
JEFF JACOBS - Manager District; General Buyer

Kosmo Inc
8834 W State Road 114
Rensselaer, IN 47978-8812

Telephone: (219) 866-4408
Type of Business: Chain Restaurant Operator
Total Sales: $15,137,000 (e)
Total Units: 3
Trade Names: McDonald's (3)
Units Franchised From: 3
Preferred Location Types: Freestanding
Primary Menu: Hamburger (3)
Areas of Operation: IN
Type of Foodservice: Quick Serve (3)
Franchise Affiliation: McDonald's Corporation, CHICAGO, IL

Key Personnel
LARRY KOSANOVICH - President; General Buyer
MAUREEN KOSANOVICH - VP; General Buyer

Famous Foods of Richmond Inc
2819 E Main St
Richmond, IN 47374-3543

Telephone: (765) 966-7615
Type of Business: Chain Restaurant Operator
Total Sales: $4,882,000 (e)
Total Units: 4
Trade Names: Lee's Famous Recipe Chicken (4)
Units Franchised From: 4
Primary Menu: Chicken (4)
Areas of Operation: IN
Type of Foodservice: Quick Serve (4)
Franchise Affiliation: Lee's Famous Recipes Inc., FORT WALTON BEACH, FL

Key Personnel
JERRY (VAN) BELL - President; General Buyer

House of Kobe
1951 US Highway 41
Schererville, IN 46375-1603

Telephone: (219) 322-1919
Fax Number: (219) 322-1960
Internet Homepage: houseofkobe.com
Type of Business: Chain Restaurant Operator
Year Founded: 1979
Total Sales: $3,017,000 (e)
Alcohol Sales: 5%
Number of Employees: 13
Average Check: Lunch(12); Dinner(18)
Total Units: 2
Trade Names: House of Kobe (2)
Company-Owned Units: 2
Preferred Location Types: Freestanding
Alcohol Served: Beer, Wine, Liquor
Primary Menu: Japanese (2)
Areas of Operation: IN
Type of Foodservice: Casual Dining (2)
Primary Distributors: (Full Line) Gordon Food Service Inc., WYOMING, MI

Key Personnel
BILLY CHIANG - Owner; General Manager; Executive Chef; General Buyer
ERIC CHIANG - Owner; General Manager

Subway Franchisee
5500 US Highway 30
Schererville, IN 46375-3422

Telephone: (219) 865-8782
Type of Business: Chain Restaurant Operator
Total Sales: $2,264,000 (e)
Total Units: 7
Trade Names: Subway (7)

Units Franchised From: 7
Areas of Operation: IN
Franchise Affiliation: Doctor's Associates Inc., MILFORD, CT

Key Personnel
JEFFREY OWCZARZAK - Owner; General Buyer

AJS Inc.
7604 Old State Road 60
Sellersburg, IN 47172-1837

Telephone: (800) 505-8449
Fax Number: (812) 246-4270
Internet Homepage: ajskfc.com
Type of Business: Chain Restaurant Operator
Year Founded: 1977
Total Sales: $49,090,000 (e)
Number of Employees: 935
Average Check: Lunch(10); Dinner(12)
Total Units: 29
Trade Names: A&W All American Food (2); KFC (26); Long John Silver's (1)
Units Franchised From: 29
Preferred Square Footage: 3,000
Preferred Location Types: Freestanding
Primary Menu: American (2); Chicken (26); Seafood (1)
Areas of Operation: IN, KY, TN
Type of Foodservice: Quick Serve (29)
Franchise Affiliation: A&W Restaurants Inc., LEXINGTON, KY; KFC Corporation, LOUISVILLE, KY; Long John Silver's Inc., LOUISVILLE, KY
Primary Distributors: (Full Line) McLane Foodservice, CARROLLTON, TX

Key Personnel
ALICE J. SCHLEICHER - President; Partner
RICHARD SCHLEICHER - Partner
JOHN REVIS - Director Operations
KANDI SCHLEICHER - Manager Payroll
KANDICE MCMILLAN - Manager Payroll

Alice J Schliecher, Inc
7604 Old State Road 60
Sellersburg, IN 47172

Telephone: (800) 505-8449
Type of Business: Chain Restaurant Operator
Total Sales: $27,630,000 (e)
Total Units: 15
Trade Names: KFC (15)
Units Franchised From: 15
Primary Menu: Chicken (15)
Areas of Operation: IN, KY, TN
Type of Foodservice: Fast Casual (15)
Franchise Affiliation: KFC Corporation, LOUISVILLE, KY

Key Personnel
ALICE J. SCHLIECHER - Owner; General Buyer
JOHN REVIS - Director Operations
NICK POTTER - Supervisor Area

The Pines Restaurant Inc.
4289 N US Highway 31
Seymour, IN 47274-8432

Telephone: (812) 522-4955
Internet Homepage: thepinesonline.com
Type of Business: Chain Restaurant Operator
Year Founded: 1950
Total Sales: $3,125,000 (e)
Alcohol Sales: 5%
Number of Employees: 60
Average Check: Lunch(14); Dinner(18)
Total Units: 3
Trade Names: KFC (1); Pines Restaurant (2)
Company-Owned Units: 2
Units Franchised From: 1
Preferred Location Types: Freestanding
Alcohol Served: Beer, Wine, Liquor
Primary Menu: American (2); Chicken (1)
Areas of Operation: IN
Type of Foodservice: Cafeteria (2); Quick Serve (1)
Catering Services: Yes
Franchise Affiliation: KFC Corporation, LOUISVILLE, KY
Primary Distributors: (Food) Gordon Food Service Inc., WYOMING, MI; (Food) US Foods Holding Corp., ROSEMONT, IL

Key Personnel
MIKE HALL - President; General Manager; Director Information Systems, Risk Management, Marketing, Advertising, Human Resources; General Buyer

Hacienda Mexican Restaurants
1501 N Ironwood Dr
South Bend, IN 46635-1841

Telephone: (574) 272-5922
Fax Number: (574) 272-6055
Internet Homepage: mybarbici.com; haciendafiesta.com; lasenorita.com
Company Email: haciendahq@haciendafiesta.com
Type of Business: Chain Restaurant Operator
Year Founded: 1978
Total Sales: $48,520,000 (e)
Alcohol Sales: 27%
Number of Employees: 2,020
Average Check: Lunch(8); Dinner(12)
Internet Order Processing: Yes
Internet Sales: 1.00%
Total Units: 17
Trade Names: BarBici Italian Street Food (1); Hacienda Mexican Restaurant (15); La Senorita (1)
Company-Owned Units: 17
Preferred Square Footage: 5,000
Preferred Location Types: Freestanding; Regional Mall; Strip Mall
Alcohol Served: Beer, Wine, Liquor
Primary Menu: Italian (1); Mexican (16)
Areas of Operation: IN, MI
Type of Foodservice: Casual Dining (16); Fast Casual (1)
Primary Distributors: (Full Line) Gordon Food Service Inc., WYOMING, MI

Key Personnel
TAMMY BOETSMA - CEO
JEFF LESLIE - VP Marketing, Advertising, Design
GLORIA MARIETTA - General Manager
JESUS LUGO - General Manager
JODI WADE - General Manager
LAURIE SHAFFER - General Manager
LEE ANN PALUZZI - General Manager
LORELEI WILHITE - General Manager
PAUL PHILLIPS - General Manager
PAUL VEEN - General Manager
WILLIAM TURNER - General Manager
ALEX FISHER - General Manager
ALICIA DEUTSCHER - General Manager
BARBARA FUNNELL - General Manager
BECKY THOMPSON - General Manager
ALLAN OLLIS - General Manager
MATT DUNIVAN - General Manager
STEVE NEBUS - General Manager
GARY WHITE - Director Product Development, Menu Development, Food Safety
JAMES MORRISON - Director Finance, Accounting
DANACA PALUZZI - Director Training
CAREY SEALS - Manager
MADELEINE SIGUENZA - Manager Marketing
HEATHER MORSE - Manager Restaurant Operations

McDonald's of Spencer
480 E Morgan St
Spencer, IN 47460-1542

Telephone: (812) 829-2630
Fax Number: (812) 829-2630
Type of Business: Chain Restaurant Operator
Total Sales: $9,940,000 (e)
Average Check: Breakfast(8); Lunch(8); Dinner(8)
Total Units: 2
Trade Names: McDonald's (2)
Units Franchised From: 2
Preferred Square Footage: 2,500; 3,000
Preferred Location Types: Freestanding
Primary Menu: Hamburger (2)
Areas of Operation: IN
Type of Foodservice: Quick Serve (2)
Franchise Affiliation: McDonald's Corporation,

CHICAGO, IL
Primary Distributors: (Full Line) Golden State Foods Corporation, IRVINE, CA

Key Personnel
MARCEL COMTE - Partner; General Buyer
MATTHEW COMTE - Partner; General Buyer

Domino's Franchisee
527 N Section St
Sullivan, IN 47882-1245

Telephone: (812) 268-3300
Type of Business: Chain Restaurant Operator
Total Sales: $27,973,000 (e)
Total Units: 14
Trade Names: Domino's (14)
Units Franchised From: 14
Primary Menu: Pizza (14)
Areas of Operation: IN
Type of Foodservice: Quick Serve (14)
Franchise Affiliation: Domino's Pizza Inc, ANN ARBOR, MI

Key Personnel
SCOTT S. WILSON - Owner; General Buyer

Domino's Franchisee
955 Wabash Ave
Terre Haute, IN 47807-3229

Telephone: (812) 232-8133
Type of Business: Chain Restaurant Operator
Total Sales: $4,092,000 (e)
Total Units: 2
Trade Names: Domino's (2)
Units Franchised From: 2
Primary Menu: Pizza (2)
Areas of Operation: IN
Type of Foodservice: Quick Serve (2)
Franchise Affiliation: Domino's Pizza Inc, ANN ARBOR, MI

Key Personnel
SHAWN J. SPINNEY - Owner; General Buyer

Burgerhaus
3304 Calumet Ave
Valparaiso, IN 46383-2644

Telephone: (219) 286-3296
Internet Homepage: visitburgerhaus.com
Company Email: valpo@visitburgerhaus.com
Type of Business: Chain Restaurant Operator
Internet Order Processing: Yes
Total Units: 4
Trade Names: Burgerhaus (4)
Company-Owned Units: 4
Primary Menu: Hamburger (4)
Areas of Operation: IN
Type of Foodservice: Casual Dining (4)

Key Personnel
EVAN COSTAS - Owner

Sage Management
37 S 100 W
Valparaiso, IN 46385

Telephone: (219) 477-5046
Fax Number: (219) 477-5147
Type of Business: Chain Restaurant Operator
Year Founded: 2000
Total Sales: $15,430,000 (e)
Number of Employees: 75
Total Units: 13
Trade Names: Little Caesars Pizza (13)
Units Franchised From: 13
Preferred Square Footage: 1,200
Preferred Location Types: Strip Mall
Primary Menu: Pizza (13)
Areas of Operation: IN, MI
Type of Foodservice: Quick Serve (13)
Franchise Affiliation: Little Caesar Enterprises Inc., DETROIT, MI

Key Personnel
BRIAN SAVAGE - Founder; CEO
PATRICK LOWELL - CEO
DAN HANCOCK - President; Owner; Controller; Director Purchasing
LINDA CROSS - Director Customer Analytics

Jhn Corporation Inc
2807 Adams Meyer Ln
Vincennes, IN 47591-3600

Telephone: (812) 886-5511
Fax Number: (812) 886-9067
Company Email: dwnmanagement@att.net
Type of Business: Chain Restaurant Operator
Total Sales: $37,050,000 (e)
Total Units: 8
Trade Names: McDonald's (8)
Units Franchised From: 8
Primary Menu: Hamburger (8)
Areas of Operation: IL, IN
Type of Foodservice: Quick Serve (8)
Franchise Affiliation: McDonald's Corporation, CHICAGO, IL

Key Personnel
WALTER NOWAKOWSKI - President; General Buyer

Gregory Enterprises, Inc
1671 W Lake St
Warsaw, IN 46580-2490

Telephone: (574) 267-3900
Fax Number: (574) 267-3800
Type of Business: Chain Restaurant Operator
Total Sales: $5,878,000 (e)
Total Units: 9
Trade Names: Subway (9)
Units Franchised From: 9
Primary Menu: Sandwiches/Deli (9)
Areas of Operation: IN
Type of Foodservice: Quick Serve (9)
Franchise Affiliation: Doctor's Associates Inc., MILFORD, CT

Key Personnel
DANNY GREGORY - President; General Buyer

O'Bryan's Nine Irish Brothers, LLC
119 Howard Ave
West Lafayette, IN 47906-6327

Telephone: (765) 746-4782
Internet Homepage: nineirishbrothers.com
Company Email: contact@nineirishbrothers.com
Type of Business: Chain Restaurant Operator
Total Units: 3
Company-Owned Units: 3
Primary Menu: Irish (3)
Areas of Operation: IN
Type of Foodservice: Casual Dining (3)

Key Personnel
JERRY O'BRYAN - Owner; General Buyer
JAN O'BRYAN - Owner

CBDM Inc.
14655 N Gray Rd
Westfield, IN 46062-9274

Telephone: (317) 218-3786
Internet Homepage: thelocaleateryandpub.com
Company Email: info@localeateryandpub.com
Type of Business: Chain Restaurant Operator
Total Units: 1
Trade Names: The Local Eatery & Pub (1)
Company-Owned Units: 1
Primary Menu: American (1)
Areas of Operation: IN
Type of Foodservice: Casual Dining (1)

Key Personnel
DEREK MEANS - Partner; General Buyer

Pasto Itiliano Restaurant & Bar
3150 E State Road 32
Westfield, IN 46074

Telephone: (317) 804-2051
Internet Homepage: pastoitilianowestfield.com
Type of Business: Chain Restaurant Operator
Total Units: 1
Trade Names: Pasto Itiliano (1)
Company-Owned Units: 1
Primary Menu: Italian (1)
Areas of Operation: IN
Type of Foodservice: Casual Dining (1)

Key Personnel
KENT MCNALL - Partner; General Buyer
PATSY MCNALL - Partner

KANSAS

Sonic Drive-In of Kansas Inc.
1717 S Santa Fe Ave
Chanute, KS 66720-3224

Telephone: (620) 431-4410
Fax Number: (620) 431-4457
Internet Homepage: sonicdrivein.com
Type of Business: Chain Restaurant Operator
Year Founded: 1987
Total Sales: $6,822,000 (e)
Number of Employees: 100
Average Check: Breakfast(8); Lunch(8); Dinner(8)
Total Units: 3
Trade Names: Sonic America's Drive-In (3)
Units Franchised From: 3
Preferred Square Footage: 1,100; 1,200; 1,350
Preferred Location Types: Freestanding
Primary Menu: Hamburger (3)
Areas of Operation: KS
Type of Foodservice: Quick Serve (3)
Franchise Affiliation: Sonic Corp., OKLAHOMA CITY, OK
Primary Distributors: (Full Line) US Foods, OKLAHOMA CITY, OK

Key Personnel
JEFF PORTS - Owner; General Manager; General Buyer

Goodcents Fresh Deli Subs
8997 Commerce Dr
De Soto, KS 66018-8428

Telephone: (913) 583-8400
Fax Number: (913) 583-3500
Internet Homepage: goodcentssubs.com
Type of Business: Chain Restaurant Operator
Year Founded: 1989
Systemwide Sales: $54,151,000 (e)
Total Sales: $991,000 (e)
Number of Employees: 30
Average Check: Lunch(12); Dinner(12)
Internet Order Processing: Yes
Internet Sales: 1.00%
Total Units: 66
Trade Names: Goodcents Deli Fresh Subs (85)
Company-Owned Units: 4
Units Franchised To: 81
Preferred Square Footage: 1,800; 2,000
Preferred Location Types: Freestanding; Strip Mall
Primary Menu: Sandwiches/Deli (85)
Areas of Operation: AR, AZ, CO, KS, MN, MO, NE, OH, OK, SD, TX
Type of Foodservice: Quick Serve (85)
Catering Services: Yes
Primary Distributors: (Food) SYSCO Food Services of Kansas City Inc., OLATHE, KS; (Supplies) SYSCO Food Services of Kansas City Inc., OLATHE, KS

Key Personnel
JOSEPH J. BISOGNO - Chairman
FARRELLYNN WOLF - CFO; COO
DANNY CHAFFIN - Director Real Estate, Construction, Design
RICK FREDERICK - Manager Information Systems
AMANDA ROBERTSON - Manager Human Resources

DSC
330 E Madison Ave Ste B10
Derby, KS 67037-1738

Telephone: (316) 788-4883
Fax Number: (316) 788-4873
Type of Business: Chain Restaurant Operator
Year Founded: 1986
Total Sales: $2,640,000 (e)
Alcohol Sales: 10%
Number of Employees: 275
Average Check: Lunch(10); Dinner(14)
Total Units: 2
Trade Names: Pizza Hut (2)
Units Franchised From: 2
Preferred Square Footage: 2,500
Preferred Location Types: Freestanding
Alcohol Served: Beer, Wine
Primary Menu: Pizza (2)
Areas of Operation: AR, KS, OK
Type of Foodservice: Casual Dining (2)
Catering Services: Yes
Franchise Affiliation: Pizza Hut Inc., PLANO, TX

Key Personnel
STEVEN CHAMBERS - President; Partner
VINCENT COLLIER - Partner; VP
RUTHIE NUGEN - Manager Finance, Operations, Information Systems, Supply Chain, Human Resources

Lane Enterprises
115 W Olive Ave
El Dorado, KS 67042-3416

Telephone: (316) 321-3310
Fax Number: (316) 321-3345
Type of Business: Chain Restaurant Operator
Year Founded: 1975
Total Sales: $131,780,000 (e)
Number of Employees: 1,245
Average Check: Breakfast(6); Lunch(8); Dinner(8)
Total Units: 38
Trade Names: McDonald's (38)
Units Franchised From: 38
Preferred Square Footage: 2,500; 3,000
Preferred Location Types: Freestanding
Primary Menu: Hamburger (38)
Areas of Operation: KS
Type of Foodservice: Quick Serve (38)
Franchise Affiliation: McDonald's Corporation, CHICAGO, IL
Primary Distributors: (Food) Earp Distribution, EDWARDSVILLE, KS

Key Personnel
JANICE BUFFINGTON - President; Controller
ROBERT LANE - President; Partner; Director Finance, Operations, Facility/Maintenance, Information Systems, Real Estate; General Buyer
JEN LANE - Partner
ANNETTE BLISS - Senior VP East Region
BRIAN BRIGGS - VP Plant; Manager
MARK DICK - VP Division
MICHAEL MCCAULEY - VP Strategy
KEVIN MILLER - Director Product Development
KIMBERLY PHILLIPS - Manager Human Resources
GENE ANDERSON - Manager Sales

Stroud's Restaurant & Bar
4200 Shawnee Mission Pkwy
Fairway, KS 66205-2506

Telephone: (913) 262-8500
Fax Number: (913) 262-8509
Internet Homepage: stroudsrestaurant.com
Type of Business: Chain Restaurant Operator
Year Founded: 1993
Systemwide Sales: $5,878,000 (e)
Total Sales: $4,703,000 (e)
Alcohol Sales: 10%
Number of Employees: 50
Average Check: Dinner(24)
Total Units: 3

Trade Names: Stroud's Restaurant & Bar (3)
Company-Owned Units: 3
Alcohol Served: Beer, Wine, Liquor
Primary Menu: American (3)
Areas of Operation: KS, MO
Type of Foodservice: Casual Dining (3)
Catering Services: Yes

Key Personnel
MIKE DONAGAN - President; Owner; General Buyer

Milligan Enterprises Inc
4245 Chambers Dr
Garden City, KS 67846-9621

Telephone: (620) 275-7139
Type of Business: Chain Restaurant Operator
Total Sales: $27,740,000 (e)
Total Units: 6
Trade Names: McDonald's (6)
Units Franchised From: 6
Primary Menu: Hamburger (6)
Areas of Operation: KS
Type of Foodservice: Quick Serve (6)
Franchise Affiliation: McDonald's Corporation, CHICAGO, IL

Key Personnel
OVETA MILLIGAN - Owner; General Buyer

Domino's Franchisee
2505 Vine St
Hays, KS 67601-2404

Telephone: (785) 625-2311
Type of Business: Chain Restaurant Operator
Total Sales: $9,907,000 (e)
Total Units: 5
Trade Names: Domino's (5)
Units Franchised From: 5
Primary Menu: Pizza (5)
Areas of Operation: KS
Type of Foodservice: Quick Serve (5)
Franchise Affiliation: Domino's Pizza Inc, ANN ARBOR, MI

Key Personnel
JEFFREY W. MADDOX - Owner; General Buyer
ANDREW GIESE - General Manager

Northhays, Inc
2705 Vine St Ste 6
Hays, KS 67601-1900

Telephone: (785) 625-4144
Type of Business: Chain Restaurant Operator
Total Sales: $23,880,000 (e)
Total Units: 5

Trade Names: McDonald's (5)
Units Franchised From: 5
Primary Menu: Hamburger (5)
Areas of Operation: KS
Type of Foodservice: Quick Serve (5)
Franchise Affiliation: McDonald's Corporation, CHICAGO, IL

Key Personnel
RICHARD D. KUEHL - President; Partner; General Buyer
JAMIE KUEHL - Partner

Domino's Franchisee
8055 State Ave
Kansas City, KS 66112-2454

Telephone: (913) 766-2333
Company Email: dominos9633gm@hotmail.com
Type of Business: Chain Restaurant Operator
Total Sales: $6,070,000 (e)
Total Units: 3
Trade Names: Domino's (3)
Units Franchised From: 3
Primary Menu: Pizza (3)
Areas of Operation: KS
Type of Foodservice: Quick Serve (3)
Franchise Affiliation: Domino's Pizza Inc, ANN ARBOR, MI

Key Personnel
ROBERT W. JONES - Owner; General Buyer

Joe's Kansas City BBQ
3002 W 47th Ave
Kansas City, KS 66103

Telephone: (913) 722-3366
Internet Homepage: joeskc.com
Type of Business: Chain Restaurant Operator
Year Founded: 1996
Total Units: 3
Trade Names: Joe's Kansas City Bar-B-Que (3)
Company-Owned Units: 3
Preferred Location Types: Convenience Store/Gas Station; Freestanding; Strip Mall
Primary Menu: Bar-B-Q (3)
Areas of Operation: KS
Type of Foodservice: Casual Dining (3)

Key Personnel
JOY STEHNEY - Partner
JEFF STEHNEY - Partner
JERRY TAYLOR - General Manager
RYAN BARROWS - Director Operations
STEVE QUERREY - Director Operations
DARCY KARLEN - Director Human Resources, Training
NATALIE SHACKLETON - Manager

PACO MARTIN - Manager Facility/Maintenance
JENNIFER CARL - Manager Sales, Catering

Wyandot Barbeque
8441 State Ave
Kansas City, KS 66112-1860

Telephone: (913) 788-7554
Internet Homepage: wyandotbbq.com
Type of Business: Chain Restaurant Operator
Year Founded: 1977
Total Sales: $2,346,000 (e)
Alcohol Sales: 5%
Number of Employees: 50
Average Check: Lunch(6); Dinner(10)
Total Units: 2
Trade Names: Wyandot Barbeque (2)
Company-Owned Units: 2
Preferred Location Types: Freestanding
Alcohol Served: Beer
Primary Menu: American (2)
Areas of Operation: KS
Type of Foodservice: Casual Dining (2)
Catering Services: Yes
Primary Distributors: (Food) US Foods, TOPEKA, KS

Key Personnel
RON WILLIAMS - President; Executive Chef; General Buyer

Dobski & Associates Inc.
1313 W 6th St
Lawrence, KS 66044-2220

Telephone: (785) 832-1444
Fax Number: (785) 832-8804
Internet Homepage: archpowered.com/kansmcd
Type of Business: Chain Restaurant Operator
Year Founded: 1981
Total Sales: $87,500,000 (e)
Number of Employees: 1,030
Average Check: Breakfast(5); Lunch(8); Dinner(8)
Total Units: 18
Trade Names: McDonald's (18)
Units Franchised From: 18
Preferred Square Footage: 2,500; 3,000
Preferred Location Types: Freestanding
Primary Menu: Hamburger (18)
Areas of Operation: KS
Type of Foodservice: Quick Serve (18)
Franchise Affiliation: McDonald's Corporation, CHICAGO, IL
Primary Distributors: (Food) Earp Distribution, EDWARDSVILLE, KS

Key Personnel
TOM DOBSKI - President; Partner; Director Finance, Purchasing, Facility/Maintenance,

Real Estate, Design, Store Fixtures
MARILYN DOBSKI - Partner; VP
SHANNON ABRAHAMSON - Director Finance
JEFF MCDANIEL - Director Operations,
  Information Systems, Ethnic Marketing
ALETIA VAUGHN - Manager Human Resources
WESLEY JOHNSON - Manager
HEIDI GOWEN - Administrator Finance, Human
  Resources

RWT LLC
2040 W 31st St Ste G
Lawrence, KS 66046-5164

Telephone: (785) 840-5797
Type of Business: Chain Restaurant Operator
Total Sales: $14,100,000 (e)
Total Units: 7
Trade Names: Five Guys Burgers and Fries (7)
Units Franchised From: 7
Primary Menu: Hamburger (7)
Areas of Operation: KS, MO
Type of Foodservice: Fast Casual (7)
Franchise Affiliation: Five Guys Holdings Inc., LORTON, VA

Key Personnel
HOLLY RICHEY - Partner; General Buyer
MIKE RICHEY - Partner; General Buyer

Sodak Tacos Inc
3500 Westridge Dr
Lawrence, KS 66049-2258

Telephone: (785) 749-1388
Type of Business: Chain Restaurant Operator
Total Sales: $4,510,000 (e)
Total Units: 4
Trade Names: Taco John's (4)
Units Franchised From: 4
Primary Menu: Taco (4)
Areas of Operation: KS
Type of Foodservice: Quick Serve (4)
Franchise Affiliation: Taco John's International Inc., CHEYENNE, WY

Key Personnel
KENNETH CREASEY - President; General Buyer

801 Restaurant Group
11616 Ash St
Leawood, KS 66211-7800

Telephone: (913) 322-1801
Internet Homepage: 801restaurantgroup.com
Company Email: 801chophouseLEA@801restaurants.com
Type of Business: Chain Restaurant Operator
Year Founded: 1993
Total Sales: $14,500,000 (e)
Average Check: Dinner(96)
Total Units: 9
Trade Names: 801 Chophouse (6); 801 Fish (1); Pig & Finch (2)
Company-Owned Units: 9
Primary Menu: American (1); Seafood (1); Steak (7)
Areas of Operation: CO, IA, KS, MO, NE
Type of Foodservice: Fine Dining (9)
Catering Services: Yes

Key Personnel
JAMES LYNCH - Executive Director East Region
HUGO XOLO - Executive Chef
BRIAN DENNIS - Executive Chef

AMC Entertainment Holdings Inc.
11500 Ash St
Leawood, KS 66211-7804

Telephone: (913) 213-2000
Internet Homepage: amctheatres.com
Type of Business: Foodservice Operations - Movie Theatre
Year Founded: 1968
Publicly Held: Yes
Total Sales: $2,128,725,000 (e)
Alcohol Sales: 1%
Number of Employees: 38,872
Foodservice Sales: $651,390,000 (e)
Total Units: 898
Trade Names: AMC Theatre (898)
Company-Owned Units: 898
Preferred Square Footage: 50,000
Preferred Location Types: Community Mall; Freestanding; Lifestyle Center
Alcohol Served: Beer, Wine, Liquor
Primary Menu: Snacks (898)
Areas of Operation: AL, AR, AZ, CA, CO, CT, DC, FL, GA, IA, IL, IN, KS, KY, LA, MA, MD, MI, MN, MO, NC, NE, NJ, NV, NY, OH, OK, PA, SC, TX, UT, VA, WA, WI, ON
Foreign Countries: CANADA; DENMARK; ENGLAND; FINLAND; GERMANY; HONG KONG; IRELAND; ITALY; LATVIA; LITHUANIA; NORWAY; PORTUGAL; SPAIN; SWEDEN
Type of Foodservice: In-Store Feeder (898)
Primary Distributors: (Full Line) Vistar Rocky Mountain, DENVER, CO
Parent Company: Dalian Wanda Group Co., Ltd., , CHN
Notes: AMC derives approximately 70% of its revenue from AMC Movie Theater admissions, on-screen advertising, & other sales.

Key Personnel
ADAM M. ARON - CEO; President
JENNIFER DOUGLASS - President Food
PETER LIEU - President Operations
CYNTHIA PIERCE - President
SEAN GOODMAN - CFO
CHRIS A. COX - Chief Accounting Officer; Senior VP
CARLA CHAVARRIA - Chief Human Resources Officer; Senior VP Human Resources
MARK PEARSON - Chief Strategy Officer
KEVIN M. CONNOR - Senior VP; Corporate Secretary; General Counsel
JASON COLE - VP Acquisitions, Procurement, International Division
DERRICK LEGGETT - VP Strategy, Enterprise Solutions
JOHN GREINER - VP
MIKE HAINES - VP Finance
JOHN MERRIWETHER - VP Investor Relations
NIKKOLE DENSON-RANDOLPH - VP Strategy
TIM ANDERSON - VP Sales
PAMELA SANDLER - VP Social Media
MICHAEL HANS - VP Real Estate
DEBBI WEBBER - VP Finance
HANK GREEN - VP Operations
ROB BRUCHMAN - VP Government Affairs
JONATHAN GREER - VP Operations
WALTER JENNINGS - VP Procurement
BRADLEY MCCAFFREY - Senior Director Information Technology
NELS STORM - Senior Director
SCOTT STIPSITS - Director Food and Beverage; General Buyer
SCOTT LANDES - Director Content Development
IAN JOYCE - Director E-Commerce
KEVIN GRAY - Director Information Technology
TRAVIS MADDOX - Director Applications
FRANCO HANDLIN - Director Facility/Maintenance
AMANDA KELLY DENNIS - Director Marketing
NATALIE MARTINEZ - Director Human Resources
RAVI TERALA - Director Finance
RYAN NOONAN - Director Communications
WENDY HANS - Director Loss Prevention
ELIZABETH BLASDEL - Director Administration, Sales
MARK GARCIA - Director Operations
KATE GUSKE - Director Construction
SUSAN NAVARRO - Director Operations
THERESE O'DONNELL - Director; Community Relations
JANA SALQUERO - Director Construction
ROB TOLENTINO - Director Operations
BRIAN DOUGLASS - Director Real Estate, Global
JOE ORPIN - Manager Quality Assurance
DAN MCCOY - Manager Applications
CAITLIN BALLARD - Manager Logistics
BRYCE BURROWS - Manager Internal Audit
MARK CROUSE - Manager Information Technology; Environment
JESSICA DAVIS - Manager Group
THOMAS G FRAME, JR - Manager Talent
ROBERTA LAGREGA - Manager

VANESSA MCNAIR - Manager Administration
SATISH RAMABHOTLA - Manager
JEFFREY A SIMPSON - Manager Operations
SUMIT SHARMA - Manager
KATHLEEN LOFTUS - Manager Sales
WAYNE MORGAN - Manager Food
NATHALI DUBE - Project Manager Operations

TNT Pizza Partners Inc.
2641 W 139th Ter
Leawood, KS 66224-3925

Mailing Address: PO Box 480043, Kansas City, MO, 64148
Telephone: (913) 948-8350
Fax Number: (913) 948-8354
Company Email: tntpizza@kc.rr.com
Type of Business: Chain Restaurant Operator
Year Founded: 2007
Total Sales: $28,030,000 (e)
Alcohol Sales: 4%
Number of Employees: 471
Average Check: Lunch(10); Dinner(16)
Total Units: 23
Trade Names: Pizza Hut (23)
Units Franchised From: 23
Preferred Square Footage: 1,400; 4,500
Preferred Location Types: Freestanding; Strip Mall
Alcohol Served: Beer
Primary Menu: Pizza (23)
Projected Openings: 1
Areas of Operation: PA
Type of Foodservice: Quick Serve (23)
Franchise Affiliation: Pizza Hut Inc., PLANO, TX
Notes: The company also operates as Keystone Pizza Partners LLC.

Key Personnel
BRYAN NEUENDORF - President; Partner; Director Facility/Maintenance, Real Estate, Store Fixtures; General Buyer
DEIDRE NEUENDORF - Owner
MICHAEL BAIRD - Partner; COO
TONY BURCH - General Manager

Genesh, Inc.
8831 Long St
Lenexa, KS 66215-3586

Telephone: (913) 492-0007
Fax Number: (913) 492-1112
Internet Homepage: geneshinc.com
Type of Business: Chain Restaurant Operator
Year Founded: 1998
Total Sales: $120,440,000 (e)
Number of Employees: 2,914
Average Check: Breakfast(8); Lunch(10); Dinner(12)
Total Units: 53
Trade Names: Burger King (53)
Units Franchised From: 53
Preferred Square Footage: 1,900; 4,300
Preferred Location Types: Freestanding; Institution (college/hospital)
Primary Menu: Hamburger (53)
Areas of Operation: KS, MO
Type of Foodservice: Quick Serve (53)
Franchise Affiliation: Burger King Worldwide Inc., MIAMI, FL
Primary Distributors: (Full Line) Reinhart FoodService, OMAHA, NE

Key Personnel
ANTHONY ROBINSON - COO
TONY ROBINSON - COO
TOMMY FIEDS - General Manager

Side Pockets Inc.
13320 W 87th Street Pkwy
Lenexa, KS 66215-4536

Mailing Address: P O Box 14545, Lenexa, KS, 66285
Telephone: (800) 490-9809
Internet Homepage: sidepockets.com
Type of Business: Chain Restaurant Operator
Year Founded: 1994
Total Sales: $9,721,000 (e)
Average Check: Dinner(18)
Total Units: 5
Trade Names: Side Pockets (5)
Units Franchised To: 5
Preferred Location Types: Freestanding
Alcohol Served: Beer, Wine, Liquor
Primary Menu: American (5)
Areas of Operation: KS, MO
Type of Foodservice: Casual Dining (5)

Key Personnel
KEITH ROBINSON - President; Partner

Peabody Peabody Inc.
1150 Westloop Pl
Manhattan, KS 66502-2838

Telephone: (785) 539-3333
Type of Business: Chain Restaurant Operator
Total Sales: $1,648,000 (e)
Total Units: 2
Trade Names: Little Caesars Pizza (2)
Units Franchised From: 2
Primary Menu: Pizza (2)
Areas of Operation: KS
Type of Foodservice: Quick Serve (2)
Franchise Affiliation: Little Caesar Enterprises Inc., DETROIT, MI

Key Personnel
DAN PEABODY - President; General Buyer
JASON PEABODY - General Manager

P & S of Kansas Inc.
2101 E Kansas Ave
Mcpherson, KS 67460-4007

Mailing Address: PO Box 986, MCPHERSON, KS, 67460-0986
Telephone: (620) 241-2076
Fax Number: (620) 241-2076
Type of Business: Chain Restaurant Operator
Year Founded: 1977
Total Sales: $15,203,000 (e)
Number of Employees: 160
Average Check: Breakfast(5); Lunch(8); Dinner(8)
Total Units: 3
Trade Names: McDonald's (3)
Units Franchised From: 3
Preferred Square Footage: 2,500; 3,000
Preferred Location Types: Discount Dept. Stores; Freestanding
Primary Menu: Hamburger (3)
Areas of Operation: KS
Type of Foodservice: Quick Serve (3)
Franchise Affiliation: McDonald's Corporation, CHICAGO, IL
Primary Distributors: (Food) Earp Distribution, EDWARDSVILLE, KS

Key Personnel
DAVID JENNINGS - President; General Manager; Director Purchasing
TINA SNYDER - Manager Administration

Sunset Equities
1321 E 1st St
Mcpherson, KS 67460-3601

Mailing Address: PO Box 1303, MCPHERSON, KS, 67460-1303
Telephone: (620) 241-1061
Fax Number: (620) 241-6157
Type of Business: Chain Restaurant Operator
Year Founded: 1976
Total Sales: $24,570,000 (e)
Number of Employees: 300
Average Check: Breakfast(8); Lunch(8); Dinner(8)
Total Units: 9
Trade Names: Wendy's Old Fashioned Hamburgers (9)
Units Franchised From: 9
Preferred Square Footage: 2,500
Preferred Location Types: Freestanding
Primary Menu: Hamburger (9)
Areas of Operation: IA, IL
Type of Foodservice: Quick Serve (9)
Franchise Affiliation: The Wendy's Company, DUBLIN, OH
Primary Distributors: (Supplies) The

Wasserstrom Co., COLUMBUS, OH

Key Personnel
TED MORRIS - President; Partner; General Manager; Director Operations, Facility/Maintenance, Information Systems, Real Estate, Design; General Buyer
GARY REIMAN - Partner; Controller; Director Finance, Supply Chain, Human Resources

Sunset Equities, Inc.
1032 W Kansas Ave
Mcpherson, KS 67460-4111

Telephone: (620) 241-5600
Fax Number: (620) 241-5638
Type of Business: Chain Restaurant Operator
Total Sales: $35,050,000 (e)
Total Units: 13
Trade Names: Wendy's Old Fashioned Hamburgers (13)
Units Franchised From: 13
Primary Menu: Hamburger (13)
Areas of Operation: KS
Type of Foodservice: Quick Serve (13)
Franchise Affiliation: The Wendy's Company, DUBLIN, OH

Key Personnel
GARY REIMAN - President; General Buyer
WARREN NELSON - General Manager

Kings Management
5800 Foxridge Dr Ste 408
Mission, KS 66202-2335

Telephone: (913) 281-9800
Type of Business: Chain Restaurant Operator
Year Founded: 1993
Total Sales: $28,500,000 (e)
Number of Employees: 300
Average Check: Breakfast(8); Lunch(8); Dinner(10)
Total Units: 6
Trade Names: McDonald's (6)
Units Franchised From: 6
Preferred Square Footage: 2,500; 3,000
Preferred Location Types: Freestanding; Regional Mall
Primary Menu: Hamburger (6)
Areas of Operation: KS, MO
Type of Foodservice: Quick Serve (6)
Franchise Affiliation: McDonald's Corporation, CHICAGO, IL

Key Personnel
RALPH KING - President; General Manager; Director Operations; General Buyer
TAMMY ENGEL - Director Facility/Maintenance, Information Systems, Human Resources;
General Buyer

BCT&G, Inc.
12221 S Strang Line Rd
Olathe, KS 66062-5224

Telephone: (913) 782-2867
Type of Business: Chain Restaurant Operator
Total Sales: $2,306,000 (e)
Total Units: 3
Trade Names: Schlotzsky's (3)
Units Franchised From: 3
Primary Menu: Sandwiches/Deli (3)
Areas of Operation: KS
Type of Foodservice: Quick Serve (3)
Franchise Affiliation: Schlotzsky's Ltd., ATLANTA, GA

Key Personnel
STEVE JONES - Owner; General Buyer
BART HASTERT - Owner

Pioneer College Caterers Inc.
25055 W Valley Pkwy Ste 120
Olathe, KS 66061-8449

Telephone: (913) 492-1004
Fax Number: (888) 432-0329
Internet Homepage: pcconline.com
Type of Business: Foodservice Management Operator
Year Founded: 1973
Total Sales: $42,606,000 (e)
Number of Employees: 520
Number of Locations Served: 46
Total Foodservice Mgmt Accounts: 46
Areas of Operation: KS
Type of Foodservice: Cafeteria (46)
Foodservice Management Venues: College & University
Primary Distributors: (Full Line) SYSCO Atlanta LLC, COLLEGE PARK, GA

Key Personnel
STANLEY KASAKEVICS - CFO
CARL HOBI - Manager Information Systems

Devera Management
8100 Marty St Ste 103
Overland Park, KS 66204-3737

Telephone: (913) 642-0577
Fax Number: (913) 642-0576
Type of Business: Chain Restaurant Operator
Total Sales: $37,360,000 (e)
Number of Employees: 345
Total Units: 8
Trade Names: McDonald's (8)
Units Franchised From: 8
Preferred Square Footage: 2,500
Primary Menu: Hamburger (8)
Areas of Operation: KS, MO
Type of Foodservice: Quick Serve (8)
Franchise Affiliation: McDonald's Corporation, CHICAGO, IL

Key Personnel
JOHN DEVERA - President; General Buyer

Garozzo's Ristorante
9950 College Blvd
Overland Park, KS 66210-1756

Telephone: (913) 491-8300
Fax Number: (913) 491-9797
Internet Homepage: garozzos.com
Type of Business: Chain Restaurant Operator
Year Founded: 1989
Total Sales: $3,925,000 (e)
Alcohol Sales: 35%
Number of Employees: 500
Average Check: Dinner(54)
Total Units: 2
Trade Names: Garozzo's Ristorante (2)
Company-Owned Units: 2
Preferred Location Types: Freestanding
Alcohol Served: Beer, Wine, Liquor
Primary Menu: Italian (2)
Areas of Operation: KS, MO
Type of Foodservice: Fine Dining (2)
Catering Services: Yes
Primary Distributors: (Food) FreshPoint Dallas, DALLAS, TX

Key Personnel
MICHAEL GAROZZO - Owner; General Manager; General Buyer
KIMBERLY KEITH - Manager
AMANDA MCCOY - Manager
TONYA ROUND - Manager Catering; General Buyer

Johnny's Tavern
6765 W 119th St
Overland Park, KS 66209-2013

Telephone: (913) 451-4542
Fax Number: (913) 451-8959
Internet Homepage: johnnystavern.com
Company Email: overlandpark@johnnystavern.com
Type of Business: Chain Restaurant Operator
Year Founded: 1953
Total Sales: $13,100,000 (e)
Alcohol Sales: 50%
Number of Employees: 200
Average Check: Lunch(12); Dinner(18)
Total Units: 10
Trade Names: Johnny's Tavern (10)
Company-Owned Units: 10

Preferred Square Footage: 5,000
Preferred Location Types: Freestanding
Alcohol Served: Beer, Wine, Liquor
Primary Menu: American (10)
Areas of Operation: KS
Type of Foodservice: Casual Dining (10)
Catering Services: Yes
Primary Distributors: (Full Line) SYSCO Food Services of Kansas City Inc., OLATHE, KS

Key Personnel
LOUIE RIEDERER - Partner
PATRICK ROBERTS - Partner; Executive Chef; Director Operations, Facility/Maintenance, Information Systems, Real Estate, Design, Human Resources, Catering; General Buyer
KYLE WITHERSPOON - Partner; General Manager; Director Finance, Purchasing, Supply Chain

Jose Pepper's Restaurant Group
8400 W 110th St
Overland Park, KS 66210-2331

Telephone: (913) 341-5060
Fax Number: (913) 341-6061
Internet Homepage: cactusgrill.com; josepeppers.com
Company Email: wecare@josepeppers.com
Type of Business: Chain Restaurant Operator
Year Founded: 1988
Total Sales: $12,780,000 (e)
Alcohol Sales: 15%
Number of Employees: 250
Average Check: Lunch(8); Dinner(12)
Internet Order Processing: Yes
Total Units: 14
Trade Names: Cactus Grill (1); Jose Pepper's (13)
Company-Owned Units: 14
Preferred Location Types: Freestanding
Alcohol Served: Beer, Wine, Liquor
Primary Menu: Mexican (14)
Areas of Operation: KS, MO
Type of Foodservice: Casual Dining (14)
Primary Distributors: (Food) SYSCO Food Services of Kansas City Inc., OLATHE, KS

Key Personnel
EDWARD J. GIESELMAN - CEO; President; Owner; Manager Finance, Operations, Facility/Maintenance, Information Systems, Supply Chain, Real Estate, Design, Human Resources; General Buyer
JODY SIGHT - Director Human Resources
BRENT SULLIVAN - Director Food and Beverage; Manager Marketing

KBP Foods LLC
10950 Grandview Dr Ste 300
Overland Park, KS 66210

Telephone: (913) 356-6300
Internet Homepage: kbp-foods.com
Type of Business: Chain Restaurant Operator
Year Founded: 1990
Total Sales: $1,722,414,000 (e)
Number of Employees: 7,000
Average Check: Lunch(12); Dinner(14)
Total Units: 816
Trade Names: A&W All American Food/ KFC (6); KFC (663); Long John Silver's/ KFC (32); Taco Bell/ KFC (115)
Units Franchised From: 816
Preferred Square Footage: 2,400
Preferred Location Types: Community Mall; Freestanding; Regional Mall; Strip Mall
Primary Menu: American (6); Seafood (32); Taco (115)
Areas of Operation: AL, AR, FL, GA, IA, IL, IN, KS, LA, MD, MI, MO, NC, NE, NJ, NY, OH, OK, PA, TN, TX, VA, WV
Type of Foodservice: Quick Serve (816)
Catering Services: Yes
Franchise Affiliation: KFC Corporation, LOUISVILLE, KY; Long John Silver's Inc., LOUISVILLE, KY; Pizza Hut Inc., PLANO, TX; Taco Bell Corp., IRVINE, CA
Primary Distributors: (Full Line) McLane/Sturtevant, STURTEVANT, WI

Key Personnel
MICHAEL G. KULP - CEO; President
BOB HYNICK - Owner; Regional VP
MATT DRUTEN - CFO
MATT HANSEN - COO
MATTHEW HANSEN - COO
NANCY FOX - Chief People Officer
BARRY W. DUBIN - Chief Strategy Officer
AKIL JEMMOTT - Area Director
DERRIUS BAUGH - Area Director
TONY BUFORD - Senior VP Operations
JIM STANTON - Senior VP Operations
CHRISTIE HUGHES - Senior VP Development
ANTHONY GIANINO - VP Marketing
MARK EVERETT - VP Division
KRISTIN MANA - VP Finance, Accounting
SCOTT DUKE - Regional VP
RUSTY HOWARD - Regional VP
JESSE AVILA - Regional VP
BRIAN GENTILE - Regional VP
DWAYNE MCINTYRE - Regional VP
LORI SMELT - Regional VP
JOE SCHMIDT - Regional VP Operations
TIM VICKREY - Regional VP Operations
KRISTEN DELADURANTAYE - Executive Director; Community Relations
BEN JOHNSON - General Counsel
MAGDALENA WYKO - Senior Director Talent
MIKE VALENTI - Director Operations
RHONDA HOHL - Director Talent Acquisitions
LORI BYERS - Director
MAT OVERBAUGH - Director Financial Planning
BEN CHWASTIAK - Director Operations
ANGELO PICCONE - Director Operations
KEITH ROBINSON - Director Operations
MITCHELL LEVENS - Director Operations
SCOTT SYLVERA - Director Operations
LUCIA TINOCO - Director Operations
THERESA THOMAS - Director Operations
SHEILA DINAPOLI - Director Operations
DANA LIKELY - Regional Director Catering
BRITT DAHLSTROM - Manager
MINDY MULLER - Manager Benefits
DENISSE E PEREZ - Manager Talent
CARLY SLATTERY - Administrator Finance

KC Hopps Ltd.
9401 Reeds Rd Ste 101
Overland Park, KS 66207-2532

Telephone: (913) 322-2440
Fax Number: (913) 322-2448
Internet Homepage: kchopps.com
Company Email: binman@kchopps.com
Type of Business: Chain Restaurant Operator
Year Founded: 1993
Total Sales: $24,280,000 (e)
Alcohol Sales: 30%
Number of Employees: 690
Average Check: Lunch(18); Dinner(24)
Total Units: 11
Trade Names: Barley's Kitchen + Tap (2); O'Dowd's Little Dublin (1); Stroud's (2); The Blue Moose Bar & Grill (6)
Company-Owned Units: 11
Preferred Square Footage: 5,500; 6,000
Preferred Location Types: Community Mall; Freestanding
Alcohol Served: Beer, Wine, Liquor
Primary Menu: American (11)
Areas of Operation: KS, MO
Type of Foodservice: Casual Dining (11)
Catering Services: Yes
Primary Distributors: (Full Line) US Foods, TOPEKA, KS

Key Personnel
EDWARD E. NELSON - President
LAURA DEKAM - Controller
TIM GRIFFIN - General Manager
SHAWN GRUBER - Director Operations
BETHANY NIEL - Manager Marketing

PB&J Restaurants Inc.
10220 W 87th St
Overland Park, KS 66212-4674

Telephone: (913) 648-6033
Fax Number: (913) 648-6065
Internet Homepage: eatpbj.com
Company Email: comments@eatpbj.com

Type of Business: Chain Restaurant Operator
Year Founded: 1987
Total Sales: $53,570,000 (e)
Alcohol Sales: 25%
Number of Employees: 938
Average Check: Lunch(12); Dinner(30)
Total Units: 16
Trade Names: Burnt End BBQ (1); Dunn Cafe (1); Newport Grill (2); Paradise Diner (1); Red Robin Gourmet Burgers & Spirits (7); YaYa's Euro Bistro (4)
Company-Owned Units: 9
Units Franchised From: 7
Preferred Square Footage: 6,000
Preferred Location Types: Freestanding; Office Complex; Strip Mall
Alcohol Served: Beer, Wine, Liquor
Primary Menu: American (2); Bar-B-Q (1); Hamburger (6); Italian (4); Seafood (2)
Areas of Operation: AR, CO, KS, MO
Type of Foodservice: Casual Dining (11); Fast Casual (1); Fine Dining (4)
Catering Services: Yes
Franchise Affiliation: Red Robin Gourmet Burgers Inc., ENGLEWOOD, CO
Primary Distributors: (Equipment) Edward Don & Co., WOODRIDGE, IL; (Food) SYSCO Food Services of Kansas City Inc., OLATHE, KS; (Supplies) Edward Don & Co., WOODRIDGE, IL

Key Personnel
PAUL KHOURY - President
TOM PETERSEN - CFO; VP Finance, Facility/Maintenance, Real Estate; Controller
NATE LAWRENCE - VP Sales
MARTIN WOODS - Executive Chef
BRIAN FLAVIN - Director Information Technology; Manager Administration
MARCO MUNOZ - Director Operations
JACOB SCHNOEBELEN - Director Information Technology

Smallcakes: A Cupcakery
14383 Metcalf Ave
Overland Park, KS 66223-2988

Telephone: (850) 213-4037
Internet Homepage: smallcakescupcakery.com
Company Email: info@smallcakescupcakery.com
Type of Business: Chain Restaurant Operator
Average Check: Lunch(20); Dinner(20)
Total Units: 146
Trade Names: Smallcakes A Cupcakery (188)
Units Franchised To: 188
Primary Menu: Snacks (188)
Projected Openings: 15
Areas of Operation: AL, AZ, CA, CO, FL, GA, IA, ID, IL, IN, KS, MN, MO, MS, NC, NE, NM, NY, OK, SC, SD, TN, TX, VA, WA, PR
Foreign Countries: SAUDI ARABIA; UNITED ARAB EMIRATES

Type of Foodservice: Quick Serve (188)
Notes: Total locations includes only stand-alone units and excludes those co-branded with FreshBerry.

Key Personnel
BRANDY MARTIN - Partner

T.B. & G. Inc.
10146 W 119th St
Overland Park, KS 66213-1461

Telephone: (913) 345-1217
Fax Number: (913) 451-3147
Internet Homepage: tannersbarandgrill.com
Type of Business: Chain Restaurant Operator
Year Founded: 1981
Total Sales: $15,820,000 (e)
Alcohol Sales: 55%
Number of Employees: 546
Average Check: Lunch(36); Dinner(36)
Internet Order Processing: Yes
Total Units: 14
Trade Names: Tanner's Bar & Grill (14)
Company-Owned Units: 5
Units Franchised To: 9
Preferred Square Footage: 4,500
Preferred Location Types: Freestanding; Strip Mall
Alcohol Served: Beer, Wine, Liquor
Primary Menu: American (14)
Areas of Operation: IA, KS, MO, NE, WI
Type of Foodservice: Casual Dining (14)
Primary Distributors: (Full Line) US Foods, TOPEKA, KS

Key Personnel
MARK BRENTANO - General Manager; Executive Chef; Manager Finance, Operations, Real Estate, Human Resources, Food Safety; General Buyer

WKRP Management LLC
10880 Benson Dr Ste 2320
Overland Park, KS 66210-1525

Telephone: (913) 383-8177
Fax Number: (913) 383-8094
Type of Business: Chain Restaurant Operator
Year Founded: 1993
Total Sales: $36,290,000 (e)
Alcohol Sales: 1%
Number of Employees: 765
Average Check: Lunch(22); Dinner(28)
Total Units: 35
Trade Names: Pizza Hut (35)
Units Franchised From: 35
Preferred Square Footage: 2,500; 3,200
Preferred Location Types: Freestanding
Alcohol Served: Beer
Primary Menu: Pizza (35)

Areas of Operation: CO, KS, MO, NM
Type of Foodservice: Quick Serve (35)
Franchise Affiliation: GC Pizza Hut, LLC, MT KISCO, NY
Primary Distributors: (Food) McLane/Shawnee, SHAWNEE, KS

Key Personnel
TERRY RUDER - President; Director Purchasing; General Buyer
STEVE PATTON - Director Finance, Operations, Facility/Maintenance, Information Systems, Real Estate, Human Resources

Bates Enterprises
1610 E Peoria St
Paola, KS 66071-1893

Telephone: (913) 294-9395
Type of Business: Chain Restaurant Operator
Total Sales: $27,900,000 (e)
Number of Employees: 327
Total Units: 6
Trade Names: McDonald's (6)
Units Franchised From: 6
Preferred Square Footage: 2,500; 3,000
Primary Menu: Hamburger (6)
Areas of Operation: KS
Type of Foodservice: Quick Serve (6)
Franchise Affiliation: McDonald's Corporation, CHICAGO, IL

Key Personnel
DAVE BATES - President; General Buyer

Briley Sonics
1101 Industrial Park Dr
Paola, KS 66071-9174

Telephone: (913) 294-4810
Fax Number: (913) 294-4835
Internet Homepage: brileysonics.com
Company Email: MBF1957@aol.com
Type of Business: Chain Restaurant Operator
Year Founded: 1986
Total Sales: $71,920,000 (e)
Number of Employees: 555
Average Check: Breakfast(8); Lunch(8); Dinner(8)
Total Units: 34
Trade Names: Sonic America's Drive-In (34)
Units Franchised From: 34
Preferred Square Footage: 1,200
Preferred Location Types: Freestanding
Primary Menu: Hamburger (34)
Areas of Operation: IA, KS, MO
Type of Foodservice: Quick Serve (34)
Franchise Affiliation: Sonic Corp., OKLAHOMA CITY, OK
Primary Distributors: (Full Line) Reinhart

FoodService, LEES SUMMIT, MO

Key Personnel
LYLE BRILEY - President; CFO; Director Real Estate; General Buyer
CLAUDIA SAN PEDRO - President
ROBERTA BRILEY - VP Human Resources; Director Finance
KIM LEWIS - VP Digital
LEON BRILEY - Director Operations, Business Development

Salty Iguana
8228 Mission Rd
Prairie Village, KS 66208-5211

Telephone: (913) 381-3888
Fax Number: (913) 381-4604
Internet Homepage: saltyiguana.net
Type of Business: Chain Restaurant Operator
Year Founded: 1992
Total Sales: $4,547,000 (e)
Alcohol Sales: 12%
Number of Employees: 100
Average Check: Lunch(10); Dinner(16)
Total Units: 5
Trade Names: Salty Iguana (5)
Company-Owned Units: 5
Preferred Location Types: Freestanding; Strip Mall
Alcohol Served: Beer, Wine, Liquor
Primary Menu: Mexican (5)
Areas of Operation: KS, MO
Type of Foodservice: Casual Dining (5)
Primary Distributors: (Food) US Foods, SALEM, MO

Key Personnel
DAN CHANDLER - Partner
STEPHEN CONRAD - Partner
MATT ZYCH - Partner
LEANN BROCK - General Manager; General Buyer

Summitt Ventures Inc
1940 S Ohio St
Salina, KS 67401-6643

Telephone: (785) 827-7255
Type of Business: Chain Restaurant Operator
Total Sales: $5,765,000 (e)
Average Check: Dinner(12)
Total Units: 2
Trade Names: Wendy's Old Fashioned Hamburgers (2)
Units Franchised From: 2
Primary Menu: Hamburger (2)
Areas of Operation: KS
Type of Foodservice: Quick Serve (2)
Franchise Affiliation: The Wendy's Company, DUBLIN, OH

Key Personnel
TOD ELAND - President; General Buyer

Kmg Enterprises, Inc.
17619 W 66th Ter
Shawnee Mission, KS 66217-9101

Telephone: (913) 962-1816
Type of Business: Chain Restaurant Operator
Total Sales: $18,850,000 (e)
Total Units: 6
Trade Names: IHOP (6)
Units Franchised From: 6
Primary Menu: American (6)
Areas of Operation: AL, GA, KS, MS
Type of Foodservice: Family Restaurant (6)
Franchise Affiliation: IHOP Restaurant System, GLENDALE, CA

Key Personnel
KAREN GARRETT - Owner; General Buyer
STAN PELL - CFO

Sheridan's Franchise Systems
16012 Metcalf Ave Ste 2
Stilwell, KS 66085-8960

Telephone: (913) 341-5339
Fax Number: (866) 635-5065
Internet Homepage: sheridansfrozencustard.com; unforked.com
Type of Business: Chain Restaurant Operator
Year Founded: 1998
Systemwide Sales: $43,074,000 (e)
Total Sales: $2,102,000 (e)
Number of Employees: 2
Average Check: Lunch(8); Dinner(8)
Internet Order Processing: Yes
Total Units: 12
Trade Names: Sheridan's Frozen Custard (10); Unforked Eats and Sweets (2)
Company-Owned Units: 2
Units Franchised To: 10
Preferred Square Footage: 1,000
Preferred Location Types: Freestanding; Regional Mall; Strip Mall
Primary Menu: American (2); Snacks (10)
Areas of Operation: IL, KS, MO, TN, TX, WA
Type of Foodservice: Quick Serve (12)

Key Personnel
JIM SHERIDAN - President; General Manager; Director Menu Development; General Buyer

Legacy Restaurant Group LLC
4100 SW Southgate Dr
Topeka, KS 66609-1228

Telephone: (785) 266-5533
Fax Number: (785) 266-5529
Company Email: legacy.office@legacywendys.com
Type of Business: Chain Restaurant Operator
Total Sales: $38,600,000 (e)
Number of Employees: 384
Total Units: 48
Trade Names: Wendy's Old Fashioned Hamburgers (48)
Units Franchised From: 48
Preferred Location Types: Freestanding; Other; Strip Mall
Primary Menu: Hamburger (48)
Areas of Operation: KS, MO
Type of Foodservice: Quick Serve (48)
Franchise Affiliation: The Wendy's Company, DUBLIN, OH
Notes: Acquired 35 Wendy's locations from NPC International.

Key Personnel
KIRK WILLIAMS - President; General Buyer
FELIX TOLLINCHE - CFO
MO YEGANEH - VP Operations
RUFUS FREEMAN - Director Culinary Operations, Area
ANDREW SEEMILLER - Director Facility/Maintenance, Construction
JOHN GADDIS - Director Operations

Mechtley Enterprises, Inc.
2019 SW Gage Blvd
Topeka, KS 66604-3339

Telephone: (785) 272-8227
Type of Business: Chain Restaurant Operator
Total Sales: $1,504,000 (e)
Total Units: 4
Trade Names: Cinnabon
Units Franchised From: 4
Areas of Operation: KS
Type of Foodservice: Quick Serve
Franchise Affiliation: Cinnabon Inc., ATLANTA, GA

Key Personnel
KEN MECHTLEY - Owner; General Buyer

RSI
5877 SW 29th St
Topeka, KS 66614-2465

Telephone: (785) 273-1805

Fax Number: (785) 273-4852
Type of Business: Chain Restaurant Operator
Year Founded: 1978
Total Sales: $33,180,000 (e)
Alcohol Sales: 10%
Number of Employees: 875
Average Check: Lunch(12); Dinner(12)
Total Units: 28
Trade Names: Pizza Hut (28)
Units Franchised From: 28
Preferred Square Footage: 2,500; 4,000
Preferred Location Types: Freestanding; Strip Mall
Alcohol Served: Beer
Primary Menu: Pizza (28)
Areas of Operation: KS, MO, NE
Type of Foodservice: Fast Casual (28)
Foodservice Management Venues: College & University; Schools
Franchise Affiliation: Pizza Hut Inc., PLANO, TX
Primary Distributors: (Full Line) McLane/Shawnee, SHAWNEE, KS

Key Personnel
DAVE CLARK - CFO; COO
SHELDON HOCHULI - CFO; Director Finance, Human Resources
JOE CRAWFORD - COO; Exec VP Operations, Purchasing

Apple Corps, LP
1877 N Rock Rd
Wichita, KS 67206-1260

Telephone: (316) 683-2611
Fax Number: (316) 681-2481
Type of Business: Chain Restaurant Operator
Year Founded: 1998
Total Sales: $95,440,000 (e)
Average Check: Dinner(24)
Total Units: 24
Trade Names: Applebee's Neighborhood Grill & Bar (24)
Units Franchised From: 24
Preferred Square Footage: 3,600; 5,000
Preferred Location Types: Downtown; Freestanding; Strip Mall
Alcohol Served: Beer, Wine, Liquor
Primary Menu: American (24)
Areas of Operation: IA, IL
Type of Foodservice: Fast Casual (24)
Franchise Affiliation: Applebee's Services Inc., KANSAS CITY, MO

Key Personnel
DAVID ROLPH - Chairman; President; CIO
REID LESLIE - VP Brand Marketing
DAVE PHILLIPS - Director Marketing

Atlantic Development Corporation of Pennsylvania
1445 N Rock Rd Ste 200
Wichita, KS 67206-1292

Telephone: (316) 634-2213
Fax Number: (316) 634-2413
Type of Business: Chain Restaurant Operator
Total Sales: $26,910,000 (e)
Number of Employees: 475
Total Units: 22
Trade Names: Pizza Hut (22)
Units Franchised From: 22
Preferred Square Footage: 1,400; 4,500
Preferred Location Types: Freestanding; Strip Mall
Alcohol Served: Beer
Primary Menu: Pizza (22)
Areas of Operation: PA
Type of Foodservice: Quick Serve (22)
Franchise Affiliation: Pizza Hut Inc., PLANO, TX

Key Personnel
LARRY ARBUCKLE - Co-Founder; Partner
ROBERT CADWELL - Co-Founder; Partner
GREGORY DAVIS - President; Partner
STACEY BYRUM - Chief Administrative Officer
TAYLOR BEAMAN - Administrative Assistant

Bionic Burger
660 N Ridge Rd Ste 101
Wichita, KS 67212-3578

Telephone: (316) 945-3838
Internet Homepage: bionic-burger.com
Company Email: bionicburger1@yahoo.com
Type of Business: Chain Restaurant Operator
Total Sales: $4,549,000 (e)
Number of Employees: 36
Average Check: Lunch(8); Dinner(12)
Total Units: 4
Trade Names: Bionic Burger (4)
Company-Owned Units: 4
Preferred Location Types: Freestanding
Primary Menu: Hamburger (5)
Areas of Operation: KS
Type of Foodservice: Quick Serve (4)
Primary Distributors: (Food) SYSCO Food Services of Kansas City Inc., OLATHE, KS

Key Personnel
RAQUEL CHAVEZ - President; General Buyer

Chisholm Enterprises Inc.
8100 E 22nd St N Bldg 200
Wichita, KS 67226-2302

Mailing Address: PO Box 780538, WICHITA, KS, 67278-0538
Telephone: (316) 685-9278
Fax Number: (316) 685-8051
Type of Business: Chain Restaurant Operator
Year Founded: 1969
Total Sales: $61,670,000 (e)
Alcohol Sales: 15%
Number of Employees: 890
Average Check: Lunch(10); Dinner(14)
Total Units: 51
Trade Names: Pizza Hut (51)
Units Franchised From: 51
Preferred Square Footage: 3,500
Preferred Location Types: Freestanding; Strip Mall
Alcohol Served: Beer, Wine
Primary Menu: Pizza (51)
Areas of Operation: KS, OH, OK
Type of Foodservice: Quick Serve (51)
Franchise Affiliation: Pizza Hut Inc., PLANO, TX
Primary Distributors: (Full Line) McLane/Shawnee, SHAWNEE, KS

Key Personnel
JACK SHELTON - Chairman; CEO; Owner; General Buyer
DOUG O'CONNOR - CFO

Cinnamon's Deli Inc.
209 S West St
Wichita, KS 67213

Telephone: (316) 945-8770
Internet Homepage: cinnamonsdeli.com
Type of Business: Chain Restaurant Operator
Year Founded: 1985
Total Sales: $2,858,000 (e)
Number of Employees: 80
Average Check: Breakfast(8); Lunch(8); Dinner(8)
Total Units: 1
Trade Names: Cinnamon's (1)
Company-Owned Units: 1
Preferred Location Types: Freestanding; Strip Mall
Primary Menu: Sandwiches/Deli (1)
Areas of Operation: KS
Type of Foodservice: Quick Serve (1)
Primary Distributors: (Full Line) SYSCO Food Services of St. Louis LLC, SAINT CHARLES, MO

Key Personnel
LARRY WILSON - President; General Manager; Executive Chef; General Buyer

Daland Corporation
9313 E 34th St N Ste 100
Wichita, KS 67226-2638

Telephone: (316) 681-1081
Fax Number: (316) 681-1780
Internet Homepage: dalandcorp.com
Type of Business: Chain Restaurant Operator
Year Founded: 1976
Total Sales: $112,850,000 (e)
Alcohol Sales: 10%
Number of Employees: 1,802
Average Check: Lunch(12); Dinner(14)
Internet Order Processing: Yes
Total Units: 94
Trade Names: Pizza Hut (94)
Units Franchised From: 94
Preferred Square Footage: 2,500; 3,200; 4,480
Preferred Location Types: Freestanding; Stadiums
Alcohol Served: Beer, Wine
Primary Menu: Pizza (106)
Areas of Operation: FL, GA, IN, KY, MD, MI, NC, NY, OH, PA, VA, WI
Type of Foodservice: Casual Dining (103); Quick Serve (3)
Franchise Affiliation: Pizza Hut Inc., PLANO, TX
Primary Distributors: (Food) McLane/Shawnee, SHAWNEE, KS

Key Personnel
WILLIAM J. WALSH JR - President; Partner; Director Real Estate; General Buyer
DALE WIGGINS - Partner; General Buyer
ROGER KAROLICK - COO; VP Operations; Director Information Systems
ROBERT RODIER - VP Operations
MARK RUCAS - Senior Director Information Systems
DARCI SMITH - Senior Director Administration
JESSICA FONGEMIE - Director Communications

Freddy's LLC
260 N Rock Rd Ste 200
Wichita, KS 67206-2285

Telephone: (316) 719-7800
Internet Homepage: freddysusa.com
Listing Type: Corporate Office
Type of Business: Chain Restaurant Operator
Year Founded: 2002
Systemwide Sales: $673,523,000 (e)
Total Sales: $31,680,000 (e)
Alcohol Sales: 2%
Number of Employees: 1,077
Average Check: Lunch(10); Dinner(10)
Total Units: 512
Trade Names: Freddy's Frozen Custard & Steakburgers (512)
Company-Owned Units: 15
Units Franchised To: 497
Preferred Square Footage: 2,500; 5,500; 6,000
Preferred Location Types: Freestanding
Primary Menu: American (512)
Projected Openings: 50
Areas of Operation: AR, AZ, CA, CO, FL, GA, IA, ID, IL, IN, KS, KY, MN, MO, MS, NC, NE, NM, NV, OK, PA, SC, TX, UT, VA
Type of Foodservice: Quick Serve (512)
Catering Services: Yes
Primary Distributors: (Full Line) Dairyland, The Chefs' Warehouse, BRONX, NY
Parent Company: Thompson Street Capital Partners, ST. LOUIS, MO

Key Personnel
CHRIS DULL - CEO; President
BILL SIMON - President
BILL VALENTAS - CFO
BRIAN WISE - COO
LAURA RUECKEL - Chief Marketing Officer
ANDREW P. THENGVALL - Chief Development Officer; Chief Legal Officer
ERIN WALTER - VP Brand Marketing
SHELLEY YOUNG - VP Marketing
MARY COOTS - VP Franchise Development
BEN J. SIMON - VP Operations
JON SIMON - Director Purchasing
JOHN GILROY - Director Real Estate
TODD PHELPS - Director Franchise Operations, Real Estate
ZACH WOODBURN - Director Operations
SEAN THOMPSON - Director Information Technology
PATRICIA RUSSEY - Regional Director Operations

Fugate Enterprises
208 S Maize Rd
Wichita, KS 67209-3110

Telephone: (316) 722-5670
Fax Number: (316) 722-2437
Company Email: info@fugate-ent.com
Type of Business: Chain Restaurant Operator
Year Founded: 1974
Total Sales: $431,700,000 (e)
Alcohol Sales: 3%
Number of Employees: 2,500
Average Check: Lunch(10); Dinner(20)
Total Units: 257
Trade Names: Pizza Hut (169); Sonic America's Drive-In (13); Taco Bell (75)
Units Franchised From: 257
Preferred Square Footage: 4,500
Preferred Location Types: Freestanding; Strip Mall
Alcohol Served: Beer
Primary Menu: Hamburger (13); Pizza (169); Taco (75)
Areas of Operation: CA, CO, KS, KY, MO, NE, NY, OK, OR, TN, TX
Type of Foodservice: Quick Serve (257)
Catering Services: Yes
Franchise Affiliation: Pizza Hut Inc., PLANO, TX; Taco Bell Corp., IRVINE, CA
Primary Distributors: (Food) McLane/Shawnee, SHAWNEE, KS
Notes: Taco Bell restaurants operate as TB of America Inc.

Key Personnel
LARRY FUGATE - President
RON BAZZELLE - CFO; Director Accounting
BRETT JACKSON - Controller Payroll; Director Payroll
ANTHONY PIZZUTI - General Manager
RYAN WASINGER - Director Development, Real Estate
LINDSEY WASINGER - Director; Community Relations
VIVIAN LAFEVER - Director Operations
PATRICIA TURPIN - District Manager
JEFF STUTEY - Manager Information Technology
MELISSA HENNEN - Manager Marketing
SHELLEY MOREHEAD - Coordinator Development
LEXI LONGACRE - Coordinator Accounting

Hog Wild Pit Bar-B-Q
1445 N Brock Rd
Wichita, KS 67206

Telephone: (316) 613-2444
Fax Number: (316) 613-3555
Internet Homepage: gohogwild.com
Type of Business: Chain Restaurant Operator
Year Founded: 1997
Total Sales: $9,883,000 (e)
Average Check: Lunch(10); Dinner(14)
Total Units: 17
Trade Names: Hog Wild Pit Bar-B-Q (17)
Company-Owned Units: 17
Preferred Location Types: Freestanding; Strip Mall
Primary Menu: Bar-B-Q (17)
Projected Openings: 1
Areas of Operation: AZ, IA, KS, NE
Type of Foodservice: Family Restaurant (17)
Catering Services: Yes
Primary Distributors: (Food) SYSCO Food Services of Kansas City Inc., OLATHE, KS

Key Personnel
T.D. O'CONNELL - President; General Buyer
BRENT BAHNER - CFO
BOB WILSON - General Manager
DEVIN ANDERSON - Director Information Technology

IFGB, LLC / OPFGB, LLC
8100 E 22nd St N Bldg 900
Wichita, KS 67226-2309

Telephone: (316) 682-3300
Fax Number: (316) 682-3304
Type of Business: Chain Restaurant Operator
Total Sales: $13,830,000 (e)
Total Units: 7
Trade Names: Five Guys Burgers and Fries (7)
Units Franchised From: 7
Preferred Square Footage: 3,000
Primary Menu: Hamburger (7)
Areas of Operation: IN, KS, MO
Type of Foodservice: Fast Casual (7)
Franchise Affiliation: Five Guys Holdings Inc., LORTON, VA

Key Personnel
LARRY COOLEY - President; Manager Real Estate; General Buyer
JOHN MCKENZIE - Controller

In The Sauce Brands Inc.
101 N Ridge Rd Ste 8
Wichita, KS 67212-3367

Telephone: (316) 945-2277
Fax Number: (316) 945-2494
Internet Homepage: gambinospizza.com
Company Email: info@gambinospizza.com
Type of Business: Chain Restaurant Operator
Year Founded: 1980
Systemwide Sales: $14,830,000 (e)
Total Sales: $4,113,000 (e)
Alcohol Sales: 1%
Number of Employees: 455
Average Check: Lunch(6); Dinner(10)
Internet Order Processing: Yes
Total Units: 47
Trade Names: Gambino's Pizza (47)
Units Franchised To: 47
Preferred Square Footage: 5,500; 6,000
Preferred Location Types: Freestanding; Strip Mall
Alcohol Served: Beer
Primary Menu: Pizza (47)
Projected Openings: 3
Areas of Operation: KS, MO, NE, OK, TX
Type of Foodservice: Casual Dining (47)
Foodservice Management Venues: Schools
Catering Services: Yes
Primary Distributors: (Food) Performance Foodservice, SPRINGFIELD, MO

Key Personnel
GENE SUELLENTROP - CEO; President; Director Purchasing, Marketing, Real Estate, Design, Franchising, Menu Development; General Buyer
BARB MILLER - Controller; Director Finance, Information Systems, Human Resources
TONY SUELLENTROP - Director Advertising
TIM WAGNER - Manager District
KEVIN HULETT - Manager Operations

J.S. Ventures Inc.
2400 N Woodlawn Blvd Ste 230
Wichita, KS 67220-3956

Telephone: (316) 683-7799
Fax Number: (316) 683-3969
Type of Business: Chain Restaurant Operator
Year Founded: 1986
Total Sales: $92,690,000 (e)
Alcohol Sales: 5%
Number of Employees: 2,300
Total Units: 23
Trade Names: Applebee's Neighborhood Grill & Bar (23)
Units Franchised From: 23
Preferred Square Footage: 3,600; 5,000
Preferred Location Types: Freestanding
Alcohol Served: Beer, Wine, Liquor
Primary Menu: American (23)
Areas of Operation: IA, KS, MO, NE
Type of Foodservice: Casual Dining (23)
Franchise Affiliation: Applebee's Services Inc., KANSAS CITY, MO; Deli Management Inc., BEAUMONT, TX

Key Personnel
JAMES H. STEVENS - President; Director Finance
JESSICA LETO - Owner
RICH CHANDLER - VP Operations, Purchasing, Supply Chain, Human Resources

Lodging Enterprises Inc.
8080 E Central Ave Ste 180
Wichita, KS 67206-2371

Telephone: (316) 634-6100
Fax Number: (316) 634-6552
Internet Homepage: lodgingenterprisesllc.com; oaktreeinn.net
Type of Business: Foodservice Operations - Hotel/Motels
Year Founded: 1986
Total Sales: $62,000,000 (e)
Alcohol Sales: 3%
Number of Employees: 1,000
Total Units: 31
Restaurants in Hotels: 31
Trade Names: Econolodge (1); Oak Tree Inn (29); Super 8 (1)
Company-Owned Units: 31
Areas of Operation: AZ, CA, CO, IA, KS, LA, MO, NE, NM, NV, NY, OR, TX, UT, WY
Type of Foodservice: Family Restaurant (31)
Primary Distributors: (Food) SYSCO Food Services of Kansas City Inc., OLATHE, KS

Notes: The company derives approximately 80% of its revenue from hotel operations.

Key Personnel
LURIE JACKLE - CFO; VP Finance, Information Systems; Controller
KAYLA HEDGES - Director Human Resources

Raper Organizaton
550 N 159th St E Ste 303
Wichita, KS 67230-7523

Telephone: (316) 218-1177
Internet Homepage: mcwichita.com
Type of Business: Chain Restaurant Operator
Total Sales: $33,200,000 (e)
Total Units: 7
Trade Names: McDonald's (7)
Units Franchised From: 7
Primary Menu: Hamburger (7)
Areas of Operation: KS
Type of Foodservice: Quick Serve (7)
Franchise Affiliation: McDonald's Corporation, CHICAGO, IL

Key Personnel
ELIZABETH RAPER - Partner
WILLIAM M. RAPER - Partner; General Buyer

Red Letter J, Inc.
2929 N Rock Rd
Wichita, KS 67226-1190

Telephone: (719) 229-4299
Type of Business: Chain Restaurant Operator
Total Sales: $6,340,000 (e)
Total Units: 3
Trade Names: Five Guys Burgers and Fries (3)
Units Franchised From: 3
Preferred Location Types: Freestanding; Strip Mall
Primary Menu: Hamburger (3)
Type of Foodservice: Fast Casual (3)
Franchise Affiliation: Five Guys Holdings Inc., LORTON, VA

Key Personnel
JEFF MILLER - Owner; General Buyer

Restaurant Management Company
7700 E Polo Dr
Wichita, KS 67206-3000

Telephone: (316) 634-1190
Fax Number: (316) 634-1662
Type of Business: Chain Restaurant Operator
Year Founded: 1974

Total Sales: $189,520,000 (e)
Alcohol Sales: 1%
Number of Employees: 3,016
Average Check: Breakfast(12); Lunch(12); Dinner(12)
Total Units: 169
Trade Names: KFC (7); Long John Silver's/A&W All American Food (1); Pizza Hut (161)
Units Franchised From: 169
Preferred Square Footage: 2,400; 2,500
Preferred Location Types: Freestanding; Strip Mall
Alcohol Served: Beer, Wine
Primary Menu: American (1); Chicken (6); Pizza (161); Seafood (1)
Areas of Operation: CO, KS, LA, MT, NJ, OK, TX, WY
Type of Foodservice: Quick Serve (169)
Foodservice Management Venues: Schools
Franchise Affiliation: A&W Restaurants Inc., LEXINGTON, KY; KFC Corporation, LOUISVILLE, KY; Long John Silver's Inc., LOUISVILLE, KY; Pizza Hut Inc., PLANO, TX
Primary Distributors: (Food) McLane/Shawnee, SHAWNEE, KS

Key Personnel
LYNDA CARRIER-METZ - Chief Marketing Officer
REG REDDING - Controller
BOB LANSKA - General Manager Area
MIKE KOCHER - General Manager
HEATHER MATTHEWS - Director Risk Management, Human Resources
JACK K. JONES - Director Construction
THOMAS HUNT - Area Manager
DELANEY STOUT - Manager Marketing
DEBBIE PAGANO - Administrative Assistant

Spangles Inc.
437 N Hillside St
Wichita, KS 67214-4917

Telephone: (316) 685-8817
Fax Number: (316) 685-1671
Internet Homepage: spanglesinc.com
Type of Business: Chain Restaurant Operator
Year Founded: 1978
Total Sales: $34,970,000 (e)
Number of Employees: 745
Average Check: Breakfast(8); Lunch(12); Dinner(12)
Total Units: 27
Trade Names: Spangles (27)
Company-Owned Units: 27
Preferred Square Footage: 2,500
Preferred Location Types: Freestanding
Primary Menu: Hamburger (27)
Areas of Operation: KS
Type of Foodservice: Quick Serve (27)
Primary Distributors: (Full Line) F & A Food Sales Inc., CONCORDIA, KS

Key Personnel
CRAIG STEVEN SR - President; Partner
DALE STEVEN - Partner; VP; Director Marketing, Menu Development; General Buyer
DAVE DOOMAN - CFO; Director Finance, Purchasing, Real Estate, Design

Thrive Restaurant Group
1877 N Rock Rd
Wichita, KS 67206-1260

Telephone: (316) 683-2611
Fax Number: (316) 681-2481
Internet Homepage: carlosokellys.com
Company Email: comments@carlosokellys.com
Type of Business: Chain Restaurant Operator
Year Founded: 1983
Total Sales: $51,900,000 (e)
Alcohol Sales: 15%
Number of Employees: 4,400
Average Check: Lunch(6); Dinner(10)
Total Units: 14
Trade Names: Carlos O'Kelly's (14)
Company-Owned Units: 14
Preferred Square Footage: 6,300
Preferred Location Types: Freestanding; Regional Mall; Strip Mall
Alcohol Served: Beer, Wine, Liquor
Primary Menu: Mexican (14)
Areas of Operation: IA, IL, IN, KS, MI, MN, MO, NE, SD, VA, WI
Type of Foodservice: Casual Dining (14)
Catering Services: Yes
Primary Distributors: (Food) US Foods, CORALVILLE, IA; (Food) US Foods, OKLAHOMA CITY, OK
Notes: The Applebee's restaurants operate as Apple Corps LP.

Key Personnel
DAVID ROLPH - Chairman; Partner; VP Operations
JON ROLPH - President
DARREL ROLPH - Partner
GREG STROUD - CFO; VP
JOE WILLIAMS - COO Division
MIKE COFFEY - COO; VP
RYAN BOND - Chief People Officer
BRIAN HOUCHIN - Director Information Technology
BRIAN DONNELLY - Director Operations
RYAN ENTZ - Director Branding
PAUL LAVENDER - Director Special Projects
DAVID EDLESTON - Director Facility/Maintenance, Construction
BETH TULLY - Director Branding, Innovation
RENEE CHALOUPA - Director People
DARREN SCHUMACHER - Director Operations
TODD SCHRIEVER - Director Operations
DAVID CRAIG - Regional Manager
GREGG BOLINGER - Manager POS/Scanning
KIRA CROSS - Manager
TINA KRITENBRINK - Manager Operations

Wil-Ken Enterprises Inc
224 N Ohio Ave
Wichita, KS 67214-3934

Telephone: (316) 262-2725
Fax Number: (316) 262-2762
Company Email: office@popeyes.kscoxmail.com
Type of Business: Chain Restaurant Operator
Total Sales: $12,880,000 (e)
Average Check: Dinner(12)
Total Units: 5
Trade Names: Popeyes Louisiana Kitchen (5)
Units Franchised From: 5
Preferred Location Types: Downtown; Freestanding
Primary Menu: Chicken (5)
Areas of Operation: KS
Type of Foodservice: Quick Serve (5)
Franchise Affiliation: Popeyes Louisiana Kitchen Inc., ATLANTA, GA

Key Personnel
WILLIE KENDRICK - President; General Buyer

KENTUCKY

Giovanni's Pizza
715 Greenup Avenue
Ashland, KY 41101

Telephone: (180) 095-59055
Internet Homepage: giovannispizzapower.com
Type of Business: Chain Restaurant Operator
Total Sales: $3,291,000 (e)
Average Check: Dinner(12)
Total Units: 5
Trade Names: Giovanni's Pizza (5)
Company-Owned Units: 5
Primary Menu: Pizza (5)
Areas of Operation: OH
Type of Foodservice: Fast Casual (5)

Key Personnel
JOHN BURNS - Owner

Giovanni's Pizza Inc.
715 Greenup Ave
Ashland, KY 41101-7434

Telephone: (606) 325-9743
Fax Number: (606) 325-3017
Internet Homepage: giovannispizzapower.com

Company Email:
    comments@giovannispizzapower.com
Type of Business: Chain Restaurant Operator
Year Founded: 1965
Systemwide Sales: $95,392,000 (e)
Total Sales: $20,100,000 (e)
Alcohol Sales: 1%
Number of Employees: 202
Average Check: Lunch(6); Dinner(6)
Total Units: 101
Trade Names: Giovanni's Pizza (101)
Units Franchised To: 101
Preferred Square Footage: 1,800
Preferred Location Types: Freestanding; Strip Mall
Alcohol Served: Beer, Wine, Liquor
Primary Menu: Italian (101)
Projected Openings: 2
Areas of Operation: KY, OH, WV
Type of Foodservice: Casual Dining (101)
Primary Distributors: (Full Line) SYSCO Food Services of Louisville, LOUISVILLE, KY

Key Personnel
TOM LEMASTER - President; Director Operations, Marketing, Franchising, Menu Development; General Buyer

Greater Kentucky Corporation
6926 US Route 60
Ashland, KY 41102-9519

Telephone: (606) 928-6459
Fax Number: (606) 928-6459
Type of Business: Chain Restaurant Operator
Total Units: 5
Trade Names: Giovanni's Pizza (5)
Units Franchised From: 5
Primary Menu: Pizza (5)
Areas of Operation: KY
Type of Foodservice: Casual Dining (5)

Key Personnel
WILLIAM WAGGONER - President; General Buyer
BRENT CORDIAL - VP Operations

●▲
KSK Management
1905 13th St
Ashland, KY 41101-3515

Mailing Address: PO Box 1879, ASHLAND, KY, 41105-1879
Telephone: (606) 324-5421
Fax Number: (606) 329-2927
Type of Business: Chain Restaurant Operator
Year Founded: 1966
Total Sales: $40,280,000 (e)
Number of Employees: 370
Average Check: Lunch(12); Dinner(12)
Total Units: 21
Trade Names: KFC (17); Steak N Shake (4)
Units Franchised From: 21
Preferred Square Footage: 3,000
Preferred Location Types: Convenience Store/Gas Station; Freestanding
Primary Menu: American (4); Chicken (17); Taco (2)
Areas of Operation: KY, OH, WV
Type of Foodservice: Family Restaurant (4); Quick Serve (17)
Franchise Affiliation: KFC Corporation, LOUISVILLE, KY; Taco Bell Corp., IRVINE, CA; The Steak n Shake Operations Inc., INDIANAPOLIS, IN
Primary Distributors: (Food) McLane/Midwest, DANVILLE, IL

Key Personnel
C. DOUGLAS KNIPP - President; Director Finance, Operations, Purchasing, Real Estate; General Buyer
BARRY KNIPP - CFO
ARGUEST KNIPP - VP Human Resources
TRACY STEPHENS - Manager Information Technology

●▲
Garland Restaurants
76 Old 25 E
Barbourville, KY 40906-7282

Telephone: (606) 546-3909
Fax Number: (606) 546-4044
Type of Business: Chain Restaurant Operator
Total Sales: $7,953,000 (e)
Number of Employees: 80
Average Check: Dinner(10)
Total Units: 4
Trade Names: Arby's (4)
Units Franchised From: 4
Preferred Square Footage: 2,500
Primary Menu: Sandwiches/Deli (4)
Areas of Operation: KY, TN
Type of Foodservice: Quick Serve (4)
Franchise Affiliation: Arby's Restaurant Group, ATLANTA, GA

Key Personnel
JERRY W. GARLAND II - CEO; President; General Buyer

●▲
Lavco Food Services Inc.
110 Knox St Ste B
Barbourville, KY 40906-1426

Telephone: (606) 546-2504
Type of Business: Chain Restaurant Operator
Year Founded: 1985
Total Sales: $25,810,000 (e)
Number of Employees: 450
Average Check: Lunch(10); Dinner(10)
Total Units: 14
Trade Names: Arby's (14)
Units Franchised From: 14
Preferred Square Footage: 2,500
Preferred Location Types: Freestanding
Primary Menu: Sandwiches/Deli (14)
Areas of Operation: IN, KY
Type of Foodservice: Quick Serve (14)
Franchise Affiliation: Arby's Restaurant Group, ATLANTA, GA
Primary Distributors: (Full Line) McLane/Frankfort, FRANKFORT, KY

Key Personnel
JOHN BOWLING - President; Director Human Resources; General Buyer
LYNN TAYLOR - VP Operations, Purchasing; Director Facility/Maintenance, Information Systems

●▲
Tanner Management Company L.L.C.
316 N Broadway St
Beaverdam, KY 42320

Mailing Address: PO Box 129, HARTFORD, KY, 42347-0129
Telephone: (270) 298-4646
Type of Business: Chain Restaurant Operator
Total Sales: $10,160,000 (e)
Total Units: 2
Trade Names: McDonald's (2)
Units Franchised From: 2
Primary Menu: Hamburger (2)
Areas of Operation: KY
Type of Foodservice: Quick Serve (2)
Franchise Affiliation: McDonald's Corporation, CHICAGO, IL

Key Personnel
VINCE TANNER - President; General Buyer
TERESA BALL - Director Business Development

●▲
Brandicorp
45 Fairfield Ave Ste 4
Bellevue, KY 41073-1149

Telephone: (859) 292-8040
Fax Number: (859) 292-8050
Internet Homepage: brandicorp.com
Company Email: info@brandicorp.com
Type of Business: Chain Restaurant Operator
Year Founded: 1983
Total Sales: $9,640,000 (e)
Number of Employees: 155
Average Check: Breakfast(8); Lunch(12); Dinner(12)
Total Units: 8
Trade Names: Arby's (3); Guthries Chicken (2);

Hot Head Burritos (2); Subway (1)
Units Franchised From: 8
Preferred Square Footage: 1,800; 2,300; 2,500
Preferred Location Types: Freestanding; Strip Mall
Primary Menu: Chicken (2); Mexican (2); Sandwiches/Deli (4)
Areas of Operation: IN, KY, OH
Type of Foodservice: Quick Serve (8)
Franchise Affiliation: Arby's Restaurant Group, ATLANTA, GA
Primary Distributors: (Food) I Supply Co., FAIRBORN, OH

Key Personnel
MICHAEL BRANDY JR - President; General Manager; Director Human Resources, Franchising; General Buyer
MATTHEW GREVER - COO
GREG COZZART - VP Operations, Purchasing, Supply Chain, Real Estate
MATT KRAMER - VP Finance, Accounting
MIKE DOTY - Director Construction

Carney Inc
339 Paint Lick Rd
Berea, KY 40403

Mailing Address: PO Box 88, BEREA, KY, 40403-0088
Telephone: (859) 986-4522
Type of Business: Chain Restaurant Operator
Total Sales: $2,771,000 (e)
Total Units: 1
Trade Names: Lee's Famous Recipe Chicken (1)
Units Franchised From: 1
Primary Menu: Chicken (1)
Areas of Operation: KY
Type of Foodservice: Quick Serve (1)
Franchise Affiliation: Lee's Famous Recipes Inc., FORT WALTON BEACH, FL

Key Personnel
STEVE CARTER - Partner; General Buyer
PHYLLIS CARTER - Partner; General Buyer
ALLEN PRICE - VP Business Development
ELIZABETH EVERSOLE - General Manager
ANDRE T - Manager

Auntie Anne's Franchise
2625 Scottsville Rd
Bowling Green, KY 42104-4477

Telephone: (207) 418-2625
Type of Business: Chain Restaurant Operator
Total Sales: $1,533,000 (e)
Total Units: 2
Trade Names: Auntie Anne's Hand-Rolled Soft Pretzels (2)
Units Franchised From: 2
Primary Menu: Snacks (2)
Areas of Operation: KY
Type of Foodservice: Quick Serve (2)
Franchise Affiliation: Auntie Anne's Inc., LANCASTER, PA

Key Personnel
KIMBERLY PAYNE - Owner; General Buyer

Bluegrass Specialty Foods Inc
1945 Scottsville Rd Ste B2
Bowling Green, KY 42104-5836

Telephone: (270) 846-1361
Type of Business: Chain Restaurant Operator
Total Sales: $35,820,000 (e)
Number of Employees: 100
Average Check: Lunch(8); Dinner(10)
Total Units: 10
Trade Names: Zaxby's (10)
Units Franchised From: 10
Preferred Square Footage: 3,500
Primary Menu: Chicken (10)
Areas of Operation: KY, TN
Type of Foodservice: Fast Casual (10)
Franchise Affiliation: Zaxby's Franchising Inc., ATHENS, GA
Primary Distributors: (Full Line) Performance Foodservice - Lester, LEBANON, TN

Key Personnel
M. KEVIN MADDOX - President
BRIAN RAWELL - Owner
MIKE CARR - Manager Operations; General Buyer
STACEY MADDOX - Manager Marketing

Houchens Food Group, Inc.
700 Church St
Bowling Green, KY 42101-1816

Telephone: (270) 780-2900
Type of Business: Chain Restaurant Operator
Total Sales: $12,440,000 (e)
Total Units: 10
Trade Names: Schlotzsky's (10)
Units Franchised From: 10
Primary Menu: Sandwiches/Deli (10)
Areas of Operation: KY
Type of Foodservice: Quick Serve (10)
Franchise Affiliation: Schlotzsky's Deli, LOUISVILLE, KY

Key Personnel
JIMMIE GIPSON - CEO; General Buyer
GREG RUSH - Chief Marketing Officer; VP Merchandising
MICHAEL WADE - Area Director
SHANNON CLARK - Director Brand Marketing

Rafferty's Inc.
1750 Scottsville Rd Ste 2
Bowling Green, KY 42104-3375

Telephone: (270) 781-2857
Fax Number: (270) 781-2860
Internet Homepage: raffertys.com; montanagrille.com
Type of Business: Chain Restaurant Operator
Year Founded: 1981
Total Sales: $78,120,000 (e)
Alcohol Sales: 10%
Number of Employees: 1,248
Average Check: Breakfast(5); Lunch(10); Dinner(14)
Internet Order Processing: Yes
Internet Sales: 5.00%
Total Units: 15
Trade Names: Montana Grille (1); Rafferty's Restaurant & Bar (14)
Company-Owned Units: 15
Preferred Square Footage: 5,500; 6,500
Preferred Location Types: Freestanding; Strip Mall
Alcohol Served: Beer, Wine, Liquor
Primary Menu: American (16)
Areas of Operation: GA, IN, KY, NC, OH, SC, TN
Type of Foodservice: Casual Dining (16)

Key Personnel
JOHN RENFROW - Partner
DOUG TAULBEE - CFO; Controller; Manager Finance
TONY FERNANDEZ - Exec VP
WAYNE WILKINSON - Director Real Estate, Construction, Store Planning
CHERYL MCCHESNEY - Director Human Resources
TERENCE HILTON - Director Human Resources-Training
MELISSA GRIMES - Specialist Marketing

Rogman Corporation
855 Lovers Ln Ste 111
Bowling Green, KY 42103-7989

Telephone: (270) 783-8880
Fax Number: (270) 783-9373
Type of Business: Chain Restaurant Operator
Year Founded: 1998
Total Sales: $12,710,000 (e)
Number of Employees: 180
Average Check: Lunch(10); Dinner(12)
Total Units: 7
Trade Names: KFC (7)
Units Franchised From: 7
Preferred Square Footage: 2,500; 3,200
Preferred Location Types: Freestanding

Primary Menu: Chicken (7)
Areas of Operation: KY, TN
Type of Foodservice: Quick Serve (7)
Franchise Affiliation: KFC Corporation, LOUISVILLE, KY; Taco Bell Corp., IRVINE, CA
Primary Distributors: (Full Line) McLane/Hebron, HEBRON, KY

Key Personnel
TERRY ROGERS - President; Partner; Director Finance, Operations, Information Systems, Human Resources; General Buyer
CHRIS ROGERS - Partner; VP; Director Operations, Facility/Maintenance
JULIE MANTLOW - Director Marketing
TERESA ROGERS - Manager Accounting

Seagle Pizza Inc
1021 Broadway Ave
Bowling Green, KY 42104-2445

Telephone: (270) 782-0271
Fax Number: (270) 782-5706
Type of Business: Chain Restaurant Operator
Total Sales: $43,119,000 (e)
Total Units: 21
Trade Names: Domino's (21)
Units Franchised From: 21
Primary Menu: Pizza (21)
Areas of Operation: IN, KY
Type of Foodservice: Quick Serve (21)
Franchise Affiliation: Domino's Pizza Inc, ANN ARBOR, MI

Key Personnel
JOSEPH SEAGLE - President; Partner; General Buyer
KIETH BROWN - Partner

Wendy's of Bowling Green
2501 Crossings Blvd Ste 300
Bowling Green, KY 42104-5459

Telephone: (270) 782-6124
Type of Business: Chain Restaurant Operator
Total Sales: $148,530,000 (e)
Number of Employees: 2,741
Average Check: Lunch(8); Dinner(8)
Total Units: 55
Trade Names: Wendy's Old Fashioned Hamburgers (55)
Units Franchised From: 55
Preferred Square Footage: 2,100; 2,900
Preferred Location Types: Freestanding
Primary Menu: Hamburger (55)
Projected Openings: 30
Areas of Operation: AL, IN, KY, TN
Type of Foodservice: Quick Serve (55)
Franchise Affiliation: The Wendy's Company, DUBLIN, OH

Key Personnel
JOHN HUGHES - President; Partner; General Buyer
MIKE O'MALLEY - Partner; Director Real Estate
JEREMIAH HUSSUNG - CFO
BAYNE MILLION - VP
RICH SUTTON - VP Operations
LARIE VERNON - Director Human Resources, Talent
DERRICK GARCIA - Director Operations, Area
NICOLE SIMPSON - Manager Finance

Snappy Tomato Pizza Co.
6111 Burgundy Hill Dr Unit A
Burlington, KY 41005-8941

Telephone: (859) 525-4680
Fax Number: (859) 525-4686
Internet Homepage: snappytomato.com
Company Email: snappytomato@earthlink.net
Type of Business: Chain Restaurant Operator
Year Founded: 1978
Systemwide Sales: $48,568,000 (e)
Total Sales: $10,210,000 (e)
Alcohol Sales: 2%
Number of Employees: 75
Average Check: Lunch(10); Dinner(12)
Internet Order Processing: Yes
Internet Sales: 1.00%
Total Units: 43
Trade Names: Snappy Tomato Pizza (47)
Company-Owned Units: 2
Units Franchised To: 45
Preferred Square Footage: 1,500; 1,800
Preferred Location Types: Convenience Store/Gas Station; Downtown; Freestanding; Institution (college/hospital); Strip Mall
Alcohol Served: Beer
Primary Menu: Pizza (53)
Areas of Operation: AL, FL, IN, KY, MO, OH, TN
Type of Foodservice: Quick Serve (47)
Catering Services: Yes

Key Personnel
CHARLES DETERS - President; Manager Finance, Facility/Maintenance, Loss Prevention, Real Estate, Design, Human Resources; General Buyer
ANDY RITTER - Director Marketing
VITO LACORTE - Director Operations, Catering; Manager Product Development, Menu Development, Food Safety; General Buyer
BILL TEPE - Director Information Technology

Barleycorn's Inc.
1073 Industrial Rd
Cold Spring, KY 41076-8797

Telephone: (859) 442-3400
Fax Number: (859) 442-3419
Internet Homepage: barleycorns.com
Type of Business: Chain Restaurant Operator
Year Founded: 1976
Total Sales: $8,571,000 (e)
Alcohol Sales: 40%
Number of Employees: 250
Average Check: Lunch(14); Dinner(22)
Total Units: 3
Trade Names: Barleycorn's (3)
Company-Owned Units: 3
Preferred Location Types: Freestanding
Alcohol Served: Beer, Wine, Liquor
Primary Menu: American (3)
Areas of Operation: KY
Type of Foodservice: Casual Dining (3)
Catering Services: Yes
Primary Distributors: (Equipment) Trendco Supply Inc., BATAVIA, OH; (Food) The Chefs' Warehouse, CINCINNATI, OH; (Supplies) The Chefs' Warehouse, CINCINNATI, OH

Key Personnel
KEN HEIL - President; Partner; Director Marketing, Catering; Manager Menu Development; General Buyer
JOE HEIL - Partner; Manager Operations; General Buyer

Agave & Rye
635 Madison Ave
Covington, KY 41011

Telephone: (859) 360-1060
Internet Homepage: agaveandrye.com
Company Email: agaveandrye@rmdadvertising.com
Type of Business: Chain Restaurant Operator
Year Founded: 2018
Total Units: 3
Trade Names: Agave & Rye (3)
Company-Owned Units: 3
Preferred Square Footage: 2,500; 4,300; 5,100
Primary Menu: Taco (3)
Areas of Operation: KY, OH
Type of Foodservice: Casual Dining (3)

Key Personnel
YVONNE SARBER - Partner
WADE SARBER - Partner
GAVIN MULLEN - Director Training

Columbia Sussex Corporation
740 Centre View Blvd
Crestview Hills, KY 41017-5434

Telephone: (859) 578-1100
Fax Number: (859) 578-1154
Internet Homepage: columbiasussex.com

Company Email: info@columbiasussex.com
Type of Business: Foodservice Operations - Hotel/Motels
Year Founded: 1972
Total Sales: $1,169,700,000 (e)
Alcohol Sales: 20%
Number of Employees: 8,234
Total Units: 46
Restaurants in Hotels: 22
Trade Names: Courtyard by Marriott (1); DoubleTree by Hilton (1); Hampton Inn (1); Hilton (4); Homewood Suites (1); Marriott (35); Renaissance Philadelphia(3)
Company-Owned Units: 39
Alcohol Served: Beer, Wine, Liquor
Projected Remodelings: 6
Areas of Operation: AK, AL, AZ, CA, CT, FL, GA, IN, KY, LA, MA, MI, MN, MO, MS, NC, NJ, NM, NV, NY, OH, OK, PA, SC, TN, TX, VA
Foreign Countries: CAYMAN ISLANDS; SAINT MAARTEN
Type of Foodservice: Casual Dining; Fine Dining; Quick Serve
Primary Distributors: (Food) SYSCO Food Services of Louisville, LOUISVILLE, KY
Notes: The company derives approximately 70% of its revenue from hotel operations & also operates in the British West Indies.

Key Personnel
WILLIAM J. YUNG III - CEO; President
CHRIS BALLAD - CFO
ASSAAD KARAM - Senior VP Operations
HENRY MICHAUD - VP Risk Management, Quality Assurance, Menu Development, Food Safety, Food and Beverage; Executive Chef
TOM DAY - Controller Division; Manager Accounting

Domino's Franchisee
135 E Main St
Danville, KY 40422-1662

Telephone: (859) 236-2900
Type of Business: Chain Restaurant Operator
Total Sales: $8,271,000 (e)
Total Units: 4
Trade Names: Domino's (4)
Units Franchised From: 4
Primary Menu: Pizza (4)
Areas of Operation: KY
Type of Foodservice: Quick Serve (4)
Franchise Affiliation: Domino's Pizza Inc, ANN ARBOR, MI

Key Personnel
JOSEPH M. WILLIAMS - Owner; General Buyer

Subway Franchise
125 1/2 N 4th St
Danville, KY 40422

Telephone: (859) 236-7964
Internet Homepage: subway.com
Type of Business: Chain Restaurant Operator
Total Sales: $1,357,000 (e)
Total Units: 2
Trade Names: Subway (2)
Units Franchised From: 2
Primary Menu: Sandwiches/Deli (2)
Areas of Operation: KY
Type of Foodservice: Quick Serve (2)
Franchise Affiliation: Doctor's Associates Inc., MILFORD, CT

Key Personnel
BOBBIE MURPHY - President

Sinkula Investments Ltd. Co.
3005 Dixie Hwy Ste 150
Edgewood, KY 41017-2380

Telephone: (859) 578-8880
Fax Number: (859) 578-6222
Internet Homepage: sinkula.com
Company Email: comments@sinkula.com
Type of Business: Chain Restaurant Operator
Year Founded: 1995
Total Sales: $27,370,000 (e)
Number of Employees: 335
Average Check: Lunch(10); Dinner(12)
Total Units: 10
Trade Names: Wendy's Old Fashioned Hamburgers (10)
Units Franchised From: 10
Preferred Square Footage: 2,100; 2,900
Preferred Location Types: Freestanding
Primary Menu: Hamburger (10)
Areas of Operation: KY
Type of Foodservice: Quick Serve (10)
Franchise Affiliation: The Wendy's Company, DUBLIN, OH
Primary Distributors: (Food) The SYGMA Network Inc. - Columbus, COLUMBUS, OH

Key Personnel
CINDY SINKULA - Partner
TRACY HURD - VP Operations
MICHELLE HUELSMAN - Manager Human Resources

Burrell Management
226 Peterson Dr Ste 122
Elizabethtown, KY 42701-4319

Telephone: (270) 765-5300
Fax Number: (270) 769-3596
Type of Business: Chain Restaurant Operator
Year Founded: 1981
Total Sales: $72,130,000 (e)
Number of Employees: 600
Average Check: Breakfast(8); Lunch(8); Dinner(8)
Total Units: 15
Trade Names: McDonald's (15)
Units Franchised From: 15
Preferred Square Footage: 2,500; 3,000
Preferred Location Types: Discount Dept. Stores; Freestanding
Primary Menu: Hamburger (15)
Areas of Operation: KY
Type of Foodservice: Quick Serve (15)
Franchise Affiliation: McDonald's Corporation, CHICAGO, IL

Key Personnel
THOMAS BURRELL - President; Director Real Estate, Design; General Buyer
KEVIN MATHERLY - Director Operations
STEPHANIE BOWLES - Director Operations
DARLENE MOORE - Manager Human Resources

JPL Management, Inc.
430 Commerce Dr
Elizabethtown, KY 42701-1293

Telephone: (270) 769-2248
Fax Number: (270) 769-2031
Company Email: info@jplmgt.com
Type of Business: Chain Restaurant Operator
Total Sales: $31,610,000 (e)
Number of Employees: 435
Total Units: 14
Trade Names: Burger King (14)
Units Franchised From: 14
Preferred Square Footage: 2,500
Primary Menu: Hamburger (14)
Areas of Operation: KY
Type of Foodservice: Quick Serve (14)
Franchise Affiliation: Burger King Worldwide Inc., MIAMI, FL

Key Personnel
ANDREW SCHORY - Owner; General Buyer
MIKE TOLLE - Director Operations

Archways
10063 Dixie Hwy
Florence, KY 41042-3311

Telephone: (859) 371-8614
Fax Number: (859) 371-8736
Internet Homepage: archwaysmcd.com
Type of Business: Chain Restaurant Operator
Year Founded: 1985
Total Sales: $90,250,000 (e)
Number of Employees: 1,150

Average Check: Breakfast(8); Lunch(10); Dinner(10)
Total Units: 23
Trade Names: McDonald's (23)
Units Franchised From: 23
Preferred Square Footage: 2,500
Preferred Location Types: Community Mall; Freestanding
Primary Menu: Hamburger (23)
Areas of Operation: KY
Type of Foodservice: Quick Serve (23)
Franchise Affiliation: McDonald's Corporation, CHICAGO, IL

Key Personnel
PAUL GROEN - President; Partner; Director Finance, Real Estate
ERICA GROEN - Partner; VP
GRANT GROEN - Partner; VP
FRED LEPORT - Director Operations
TIM OEHLER - Director Operations
JAMIE CALDWELL - Manager Facility/Maintenance

Copeland Investments
73 Cavalier Blvd Ste 105
Florence, KY 41042-5172

Telephone: (859) 746-8760
Fax Number: (859) 746-0203
Company Email: mcdonalds@fuse.net
Type of Business: Chain Restaurant Operator
Total Sales: $19,794,000 (e)
Total Units: 4
Trade Names: McDonald's (4)
Units Franchised From: 4
Primary Menu: Hamburger (4)
Areas of Operation: KY
Type of Foodservice: Quick Serve (4)
Franchise Affiliation: McDonald's Corporation, CHICAGO, IL

Key Personnel
JETHRO COPELAND - President; General Buyer

Team Goliath Inc
15 Grandview Dr
Frankfort, KY 40601-3235

Telephone: (502) 695-1558
Type of Business: Chain Restaurant Operator
Total Sales: $16,256,000 (e)
Total Units: 8
Trade Names: Domino's (8)
Units Franchised From: 8
Primary Menu: Pizza (8)
Areas of Operation: KY
Type of Foodservice: Quick Serve (8)
Franchise Affiliation: Domino's Pizza Inc, ANN ARBOR, MI

Key Personnel
CHRISTIAN J. REISCH - Owner; General Buyer

BMT of Kentucky
1131 Lexington Rd
Georgetown, KY 40324-9321

Mailing Address: P O Box 398, Georgetown, KY, 40324
Telephone: (502) 863-4612
Fax Number: (502) 863-4612
Internet Homepage: bmtofkentucky.com
Company Email: customerfeedback@bmtofkentucky.com
Type of Business: Chain Restaurant Operator
Total Sales: $32,840,000 (e)
Total Units: 15
Trade Names: Burger King (15)
Units Franchised From: 15
Primary Menu: Hamburger (15)
Areas of Operation: KY
Type of Foodservice: Quick Serve (15)
Franchise Affiliation: Burger King Worldwide Inc., MIAMI, FL

Key Personnel
BILL KELLER - Owner
TOM KELLER - Director Operations

Gaunce Management INC
113 W Public Sq Ste 200
Glasgow, KY 42141-2438

Telephone: (270) 651-9302
Fax Number: (270) 651-2880
Type of Business: Chain Restaurant Operator
Total Sales: $4,427,000 (e)
Average Check: Dinner(8)
Total Units: 4
Trade Names: Long John Silver's (4)
Units Franchised From: 4
Preferred Location Types: Freestanding
Primary Menu: Seafood (4)
Areas of Operation: KY
Type of Foodservice: Quick Serve (4)
Franchise Affiliation: Long John Silver's Inc., LOUISVILLE, KY

Key Personnel
WAYNE GAUNCE - Owner; General Buyer

Mc Donald's of Harrodsburg
127 Beaumont Plz
Harrodsburg, KY 40330

Telephone: (859) 734-9000
Fax Number: (859) 734-4147
Type of Business: Chain Restaurant Operator
Total Sales: $32,600,000 (e)
Total Units: 7
Trade Names: McDonald's (7)
Units Franchised From: 7
Primary Menu: Hamburger (7)
Areas of Operation: KY
Type of Foodservice: Quick Serve (7)
Franchise Affiliation: McDonald's Corporation, CHICAGO, IL

Key Personnel
MARK PRATER - Owner; General Buyer

Neighborhood Hospitality, Inc
601 Main St Ste 102
Hazard, KY 41701-1382

Telephone: (606) 436-0736
Fax Number: (606) 439-2969
Type of Business: Chain Restaurant Operator
Year Founded: 1998
Total Sales: $115,940,000 (e)
Alcohol Sales: 10%
Number of Employees: 750
Average Check: Lunch(12); Dinner(18)
Total Units: 30
Trade Names: Applebee's Neighborhood Grill & Bar (30)
Units Franchised From: 30
Preferred Square Footage: 3,600; 5,000
Preferred Location Types: Freestanding; Regional Mall
Alcohol Served: Beer, Wine, Liquor
Primary Menu: American (30)
Areas of Operation: KY, OH, TN, VA
Type of Foodservice: Casual Dining (30)
Franchise Affiliation: Applebee's Services Inc., KANSAS CITY, MO
Primary Distributors: (Full Line) Performance Foodservice - Lester, LEBANON, TN

Key Personnel
BRANDON MAKHANI - Co-Founder
MARTY JOHNSON - President; Partner
THERESA JOHNSON - Partner; VP
MELISSA STAMPER - CFO
CHARLES GREEN - General Manager Training
AROMA BATES - Director Finance, Strategic Planning
DAVID BATES - Director Human Resources

Neighborhood Restaurant Group
601 Main St Ste 102
Hazard, KY 41701-1382

Telephone: (606) 436-0736
Fax Number: (606) 435-1838

Type of Business: Chain Restaurant Operator
Year Founded: 2005
Total Sales: $27,600,000 (e)
Alcohol Sales: 10%
Number of Employees: 590
Average Check: Lunch(10); Dinner(12)
Total Units: 10
Trade Names: Wendy's Old Fashioned Hamburgers (10)
Units Franchised From: 10
Preferred Square Footage: 6,300
Preferred Location Types: Freestanding
Primary Menu: Hamburger (10)
Areas of Operation: KY, WV
Type of Foodservice: Quick Serve (10)
Franchise Affiliation: The Wendy's Company, DUBLIN, OH

Key Personnel
MICHAEL BABIN - Founder; Partner
MARTY JOHNSON - President; Partner; Director Purchasing, Facility/Maintenance, Real Estate, Design, Store Fixtures; General Buyer
THERESA JOHNSON - Partner; VP
MELISSA STAMPER - CFO
KEITH VEDRAL - Director Operations
KEVIN VERMILLION - Director Information Technology
DAVID BATES - Director Human Resources

Sam Patel
2925 Fort Campbell Blvd
Hopkinsville, KY 42240-4901

Telephone: (270) 885-2867
Fax Number: (270) 885-2867
Type of Business: Chain Restaurant Operator
Total Sales: $2,121,000 (e)
Total Units: 3
Trade Names: Subway (3)
Units Franchised From: 3
Primary Menu: Sandwiches/Deli (3)
Areas of Operation: KY
Type of Foodservice: Quick Serve (3)
Franchise Affiliation: Doctor's Associates Inc., MILFORD, CT

Key Personnel
SAM PATEL - President; General Buyer

Hometown Pizza
111 E Adams St
La Grange, KY 40031-1229

Telephone: (502) 222-5541
Fax Number: (502) 222-5526
Internet Homepage: hometownpizza.com
Company Email: info@hometownpizza.com
Type of Business: Chain Restaurant Operator
Year Founded: 1982
Total Sales: $27,430,000 (e)
Alcohol Sales: 8%
Number of Employees: 450
Average Check: Lunch(12); Dinner(18)
Internet Order Processing: Yes
Total Units: 18
Trade Names: Hometown Pizza (18)
Company-Owned Units: 18
Preferred Square Footage: 5,500; 6,000
Preferred Location Types: Freestanding; Strip Mall
Alcohol Served: Beer
Primary Menu: Pizza (18)
Areas of Operation: KY
Type of Foodservice: Casual Dining (18)
Primary Distributors: (Food) Presto Foods, MONROE, OH

Key Personnel
MIKE FOSTER - Founder
THOMAS BROWN - Owner; Director Operations, Security, Inventory, Loss Prevention, Risk Management, Quality Assurance, Supply Chain, Real Estate, Design, Menu Development, Food Safety; General Buyer
JENNIFER PIPES - Controller
BRYAN MORRISON - General Manager
RENEE STIVERS - Manager Human Resources

Lawson's Restaurant
846 W Main St
Lebanon, KY 40033-1804

Telephone: (270) 692-2169
Fax Number: (270) 692-3075
Company Email: lawsonsrestaurant@gmail.com
Type of Business: Chain Restaurant Operator
Total Sales: $13,260,000 (e)
Total Units: 6
Trade Names: Captain D's Seafood Kitchen (1); Wendy's Old Fashioned Hamburgers (5)
Units Franchised From: 6
Primary Menu: Hamburger (5); Seafood (1)
Areas of Operation: KY
Type of Foodservice: Quick Serve (6)
Franchise Affiliation: The Wendy's Company, DUBLIN, OH

Key Personnel
RANDALL LAWSON - President; General Buyer

A&W Restaurants Inc.
1648 McGrathiana Pkwy Ste 380
Lexington, KY 40511-1339

Telephone: (859) 219-0019
Fax Number: (859) 219-0029
Internet Homepage: awrestaurants.com
Type of Business: Chain Restaurant Operator
Year Founded: 1919
Systemwide Sales: $379,934,000 (e)
Total Sales: $44,500,000 (e)
Number of Employees: 100
Average Check: Lunch(8); Dinner(10)
Total Units: 969
Trade Names: A&W All American Food (969)
Company-Owned Units: 4
Units Franchised To: 965
Preferred Square Footage: 2,500; 3,200
Preferred Location Types: Airports; Community Mall; Convenience Store/Gas Station; Downtown; Freestanding; Grocery Stores; Hotel/Motel; Institution(college/hospital); Office Complex; Outlet Mall; Parks; Regional Mall; Stadiums; Strip Mall; Travel Plazas
Primary Menu: American (969)
Areas of Operation: AK, AL, AR, AZ, CA, CO, FL, GA, IA, ID, IL, IN, KS, KY, MA, MD, MI, MN, MO, NC, ND, NE, NM, NV, NY, OH, OK, OR, PA, RI, SC, SD, TN, TX, UT, VA, VT, WA, WI, WV, WY, FC
Foreign Countries: BAHRAIN; BANGLADESH; INDONESIA; ITALY; JAPAN; MALAYSIA; QATAR; THAILAND
Type of Foodservice: Quick Serve (969)
Primary Distributors: (Full Line) McLane Foodservice, CARROLLTON, TX
Parent Company: A Great American Brand LLC, LEXINGTON, KY

Key Personnel
E. DALE MULDER - Chairman
KEVIN M. BAZNER - CEO
PAUL MARTINO - President; COO
WILLIAM S. FRY - Senior VP Operations
RON LEWIS - Director Construction, Design
DAVE CROWLEY - Director Franchise Sales
RANDY CORDRAY - Director Operations
LIZ BAZNER - Senior Manager Digital
BEN LABORIO - Manager Accounting

Barton Restaurant Group, LLC
2467 Nicholasville Rd
Lexington, KY 40503-3166

Telephone: (859) 260-1471
Company Email: fiveguyslex@gmail.com
Type of Business: Chain Restaurant Operator
Total Sales: $4,327,000 (e)
Total Units: 2
Trade Names: Five Guys Burgers and Fries (2)
Units Franchised From: 2
Primary Menu: Hamburger (2)
Areas of Operation: GA
Type of Foodservice: Fast Casual (2)
Franchise Affiliation: Five Guys Holdings Inc., LORTON, VA

Bluegrass Hospitality Group
3347 Tates Creek Rd
Lexington, KY 40502-3407

Telephone: (859) 335-6500
Internet Homepage: bluegrasshospitality.com
Company Email: acook@bhglx.com
Type of Business: Chain Restaurant Operator
Total Sales: $21,590,000 (e)
Internet Order Processing: Yes
Total Units: 25
Trade Names: Aqua Sushi (1); Drake's (18); Harry's (2); Malone's (3); OBC Kitchen (1)
Company-Owned Units: 25
Primary Menu: American (24); Asian (1)
Areas of Operation: KY
Type of Foodservice: Casual Dining (24); Fast Casual (1)

Key Personnel
BRIAN MCCARTY - Partner; General Buyer
BRUCE DRAKE - Partner; General Buyer
RON RAGER - COO
MARK THORNBURG - COO
JOHN MCNAMARA - Chief Business Officer
RACHEL WOELLHOF - General Manager
RYAN SCHERER - General Manager
JOHN JONES - Corporate Chef
MATT COMBS - Executive Chef
WAI LIN - Executive Chef
KYAW OO - Executive Chef
TIN OO - Executive Chef
PABLO DIAZ - Executive Chef
DAVE CUPOLO - Executive Chef
ALEX ALVAREZ - Executive Chef
JESSICA BLACKBURN - Executive Chef
JAVIER MENDOSA - Executive Chef
MIKE HILLARD - Director Information Technology
JOSHUA MORRIS - Director Quality Assurance
EMILY WINZER - Director Employee Development-Training
KATE COUGHLIN - Manager Customer Service
THOMAS DREEDING - Manager Alcoholic Beverages

Canteen Vending Services
808 Newtown Cir
Lexington, KY 40511

Telephone: (859) 254-2737
Fax Number: (859) 226-0374
Listing Type: Branch Office
Type of Business: Foodservice Management Operator
Year Founded: 1929
Number of Employees: 75
Number of Locations Served: 250
Total Foodservice Mgmt Accounts: 250
Areas of Operation: KY
Type of Foodservice: Vending machines (250)
Foodservice Management Venues: Business & Industry; College & University; Health Care; Schools
Parent Company: Compass Group The Americas, CHARLOTTE, NC
Headquarters: Canteen Vending Services, CHARLOTTE, NC

Key Personnel
BRAD GILES - General Manager; General Buyer

Domino's Franchisee
3101 Clays Mill Rd
Lexington, KY 40503-2772

Telephone: (859) 223-1540
Type of Business: Chain Restaurant Operator
Total Sales: $6,032,000 (e)
Total Units: 3
Trade Names: Domino's (3)
Units Franchised From: 3
Primary Menu: Pizza (3)
Areas of Operation: KY
Type of Foodservice: Quick Serve (3)
Franchise Affiliation: Domino's Pizza Inc, ANN ARBOR, MI

Key Personnel
CAREY J. BOUVIN - Owner; General Buyer

Domino's Franchisee
801 Euclid Ave
Lexington, KY 40502-1741

Telephone: (859) 269-3030
Type of Business: Chain Restaurant Operator
Total Sales: $17,899,000 (e)
Total Units: 9
Trade Names: Domino's (9)
Units Franchised From: 9
Primary Menu: Pizza (9)
Areas of Operation: KY
Type of Foodservice: Quick Serve (9)
Franchise Affiliation: Domino's Pizza Inc, ANN ARBOR, MI

Key Personnel
CHRIS REISCH - Owner; General Buyer

Fazoli's Restaurant LLC
2470 Palumbo Dr
Lexington, KY 40509-1117

Telephone: (859) 268-1668
Fax Number: (859) 268-2263
Internet Homepage: fazolis.com
Type of Business: Chain Restaurant Operator
Year Founded: 1989
Systemwide Sales: $543,650,000 (e)
Total Sales: $256,243,000 (e)
Alcohol Sales: 0.50%
Number of Employees: 5,976
Average Check: Lunch(8); Dinner(8)
Total Units: 213
Trade Names: Fazoli's (213)
Company-Owned Units: 111
Units Franchised To: 102
Preferred Square Footage: 2,100; 2,300; 2,900; 3,200
Preferred Location Types: Freestanding; Institution (college/hospital); Travel Plazas
Alcohol Served: Beer, Wine, Liquor
Primary Menu: Italian (213)
Projected Openings: 16
Areas of Operation: AL, AR, CA, CO, CT, FL, GA, IA, ID, IL, IN, KS, KY, LA, MD, MI, MN, MO, MS, NC, NE, NV, OH, OK, OR, PA, SC, SD, TN, TX, UT, VA, WI, WV
Foreign Countries: THE PHILIPPINES
Type of Foodservice: Fast Casual (213)
Catering Services: Yes
Parent Company: Sentinel Capital Holdings, NEW YORK, NY

Key Personnel
DOUG BOSTICK - President
TRACY HASKINS - VP Finance; Controller
WALTER G. ROMP JR - VP Training
TIM KIMMEL - VP Company Operations, Training
SPENCER HOULIHAN - VP Finance
WAYNE WRIGHT - VP Franchise Operations, Franchise Development
TERESA BROADDUS - Senior Director Quality Assurance, Supply Chain
CHRIS BYARS - Director Facility/Maintenance, Construction
KEVIN KARNES - Director Training
JAMES SANTOS - Director Construction
TISH CHISM - Senior Manager Customer Service
HAROLD D. IKARD II - Senior Manager Supply Chain
STEPHANIE LOVICH - Senior Manager Marketing
VICKIE WHITE - Manager Human Resources
GARY EVERETT - Manager Facility/Maintenance
BECKY LOUDEN - Manager Real Estate
CONNIE HILLIARD - Manager Supply Chain
JAYNIE MCINTYRE - Manager Marketing

Goodfellas Pizzeria
110 N Mill St
Lexington, KY 40507-1207

Telephone: (859) 281-1101

Key Personnel
TYLER BARTON - Partner; General Buyer
SHARRON BARTON - Partner; General Buyer

Internet Homepage: goodfellaspizzeria.com
Company Email: office@goodfellaspizzeria.com
Type of Business: Chain Restaurant Operator
Year Founded: 2005
Internet Order Processing: Yes
Total Units: 4
Trade Names: Goodfellas Pizzeria (4)
Company-Owned Units: 4
Primary Menu: Pizza (4)
Areas of Operation: IN, KY, OH
Type of Foodservice: Casual Dining (4)

Key Personnel
ALEX COATS - Co-Founder; Partner
ERIC BOGGS - Co-Founder; Partner
ELVIN HARKINS - Manager Recruitment

K & S Silvers Inc.
811 Corporate Dr Ste 303
Lexington, KY 40503-5410

Telephone: (859) 223-5353
Fax Number: (859) 223-5394
Company Email: npate@smcpa.com
Type of Business: Chain Restaurant Operator
Year Founded: 1970
Total Sales: $5,296,000 (e)
Number of Employees: 180
Average Check: Lunch(12); Dinner(14)
Total Units: 5
Trade Names: Long John Silver's (5)
Units Franchised From: 5
Preferred Square Footage: 2,400
Preferred Location Types: Freestanding
Primary Menu: Seafood (5)
Areas of Operation: IN, KY, OH
Type of Foodservice: Quick Serve (5)
Franchise Affiliation: Long John Silver's Inc., LOUISVILLE, KY
Primary Distributors: (Food) McLane/Hebron, HEBRON, KY

Key Personnel
RONALD SWITZER - President; Partner; Director Real Estate
BUD SILVERTHORNE - Partner; CFO; Director Operations, Supply Chain, Human Resources; General Buyer
CLAUDETTE SWITZER - Partner
NANINE PATE - Manager Accounting, Information Systems

K.I.D. of Lexington, L.L.C.
3735 Palomar Centre Dr Ste 70
Lexington, KY 40513-1169

Telephone: (859) 224-8280
Fax Number: (859) 224-4286
Type of Business: Chain Restaurant Operator
Total Sales: $7,033,000 (e)
Average Check: Dinner(16)
Total Units: 6
Trade Names: Little Caesars Pizza (6)
Units Franchised From: 6
Preferred Square Footage: 1,600
Preferred Location Types: Freestanding; Strip Mall
Primary Menu: Pizza (6)
Areas of Operation: KY
Type of Foodservice: Quick Serve (6)
Franchise Affiliation: Little Caesar Enterprises Inc., DETROIT, MI

Key Personnel
JULIAN GORHAM - Owner; General Buyer

Lexarb Inc
3391 Tates Creek Rd
Lexington, KY 40502-3407

Telephone: (859) 266-0112
Fax Number: (859) 266-0112
Company Email: lexarb5426@yahoo.com
Type of Business: Chain Restaurant Operator
Total Sales: $5,877,000 (e)
Number of Employees: 80
Average Check: Dinner(8)
Total Units: 3
Trade Names: Arby's (3)
Units Franchised From: 3
Preferred Square Footage: 2,500
Preferred Location Types: Freestanding; Regional Mall
Primary Menu: Sandwiches/Deli (3)
Areas of Operation: KY
Type of Foodservice: Quick Serve (3)
Franchise Affiliation: Arby's Restaurant Group, ATLANTA, GA

Key Personnel
REZA TIMAJI - CEO; President; General Buyer
JOEY MANN - General Manager

M and S Restaurants
501 Darby Creek Rd Ste 43
Lexington, KY 40509-1671

Telephone: (859) 225-7124
Fax Number: (859) 225-8160
Company Email: lexmcmac@aol.com
Type of Business: Chain Restaurant Operator
Total Sales: $19,979,000 (e)
Total Units: 4
Trade Names: McDonald's (4)
Units Franchised From: 4
Preferred Location Types: Freestanding
Primary Menu: Hamburger (4)
Areas of Operation: KY
Type of Foodservice: Quick Serve (4)
Franchise Affiliation: McDonald's Corporation, CHICAGO, IL

Key Personnel
WILLIAM NELSON MCMAKIN - President; Partner; General Buyer
MARY LONG - Partner; General Buyer

Penn Brothers Enterprises
201 N Limestone
Lexington, KY 40507-1014

Telephone: (859) 263-4040
Fax Number: (859) 263-4949
Internet Homepage: columbiassteakhouse.com
Type of Business: Chain Restaurant Operator
Year Founded: 1984
Total Sales: $3,045,000 (e)
Alcohol Sales: 25%
Number of Employees: 150
Average Check: Lunch(10); Dinner(20)
Total Units: 3
Trade Names: Columbia Steak Express (1); Columbia Steak House (2)
Company-Owned Units: 3
Preferred Square Footage: 5,000
Preferred Location Types: Freestanding
Alcohol Served: Beer, Wine, Liquor
Primary Menu: Steak (3)
Areas of Operation: KY
Type of Foodservice: Casual Dining (2); Quick Serve (1)
Catering Services: Yes
On-site Distribution Center: Yes

Key Personnel
GREG PENN - President; Controller
SCOTTIE BROCKMAN - Owner; General Buyer
TIM BLAIR - General Manager; Manager Operations; General Buyer
FLO COWLEY - General Manager; Director Menu Development, Catering; General Buyer

PJ Operations LLC
1999 Richmond Rd
Lexington, KY 40502-1210

Telephone: (859) 335-8363
Fax Number: (859) 335-0110
Type of Business: Chain Restaurant Operator
Total Sales: $72,110,000 (e)
Total Units: 54
Trade Names: Papa John's Pizza (54)
Units Franchised From: 54
Primary Menu: Pizza (54)
Areas of Operation: CO, ID, IL, KS, KY, LA, MN, MS, ND, TN, VA
Type of Foodservice: Quick Serve (54)
Franchise Affiliation: Papa Johns International Inc., LOUISVILLE, KY

Key Personnel
TOM WYLIE - President
ERICKA BAKER - Manager Human Resources
JENNIFER DUNCAN - Office Manager

Portofino
249 E Main St Ste 102
Lexington, KY 40507-1330

Telephone: (859) 253-9300
Fax Number: (859) 258-2488
Internet Homepage: grillfishlexington.com; portofinolexington.com; serafinifrankfort.com; gooseandgandermidway.com
Company Email: info@portofinolexington.com
Type of Business: Chain Restaurant Operator
Year Founded: 1999
Total Sales: $6,131,000 (e)
Alcohol Sales: 10%
Number of Employees: 40
Average Check: Lunch(20); Dinner(60)
Total Units: 4
Trade Names: Goose & Gander (1); Grillfish (1); Portofino (1); Serafini (1)
Company-Owned Units: 4
Preferred Location Types: Downtown; Office Complex
Alcohol Served: Beer, Wine, Liquor
Primary Menu: American (1); Italian (2); Seafood (1)
Areas of Operation: KY
Type of Foodservice: Casual Dining (2); Fine Dining (2)
Primary Distributors: (Food) SYSCO Food Services of Louisville, LOUISVILLE, KY

Key Personnel
WAYNE MASTERMAN - President
SUSAN MASTERMAN - Partner

Rallco Inc.
121 Prosperous Pl Ste 5A
Lexington, KY 40509-1828

Telephone: (859) 263-5704
Fax Number: (859) 263-2854
Type of Business: Chain Restaurant Operator
Total Sales: $1,763,000 (e)
Total Units: 6
Trade Names: Rally's Hamburgers (6)
Units Franchised From: 6
Primary Menu: Hamburger (6)
Areas of Operation: FL, KY, OH, WV
Type of Foodservice: Quick Serve (6)
Franchise Affiliation: Checkers Drive-In Restaurants Inc., TAMPA, FL

Key Personnel
WILL DARRAGH - President; Partner; General Buyer
DAWNE EHRLER - Partner; Manager Finance

Sir Pizza of Kentucky Inc.
2604 Richmond Rd
Lexington, KY 40509-1501

Telephone: (859) 266-5979
Fax Number: (859) 269-1747
Internet Homepage: sirpizzaky.com
Type of Business: Chain Restaurant Operator
Year Founded: 1963
Total Sales: $5,647,000 (e)
Alcohol Sales: 1%
Number of Employees: 50
Average Check: Lunch(12); Dinner(18)
Total Units: 5
Trade Names: Sir Pizza (5)
Units Franchised From: 5
Preferred Square Footage: 4,000
Preferred Location Types: Freestanding; Travel Plazas
Primary Menu: Pizza (5)
Areas of Operation: KY
Type of Foodservice: Casual Dining (5)
Franchise Affiliation: Fortner Foods, MURFREESBORO, TN

Key Personnel
HOSSEIN DELSHAD - President; General Manager; Director Finance, Operations, Purchasing, Facility/Maintenance, Information Systems, Real Estate, Design, Human Resources

The Zenith Company
427 S Mill St
Lexington, KY 40508

Telephone: (859) 226-9001
Type of Business: Chain Restaurant Operator
Year Founded: 1987
Total Sales: $25,270,000 (e)
Alcohol Sales: 15%
Number of Employees: 235
Average Check: Lunch(10); Dinner(14)
Total Units: 7
Trade Names: Carino's Italian (6); Taziki's Mediterranean Cafe (1)
Units Franchised From: 7
Preferred Square Footage: 5,400
Preferred Location Types: Community Mall; Freestanding
Alcohol Served: Beer, Wine, Liquor
Primary Menu: Greek/Mediterranean (1); Italian (6)
Areas of Operation: IN, KY, OH
Type of Foodservice: Casual Dining (7)
Franchise Affiliation: Fired Up Inc., AUSTIN, TX

Key Personnel
MIKE SCANLON - CEO; President
BILL SIMMS - VP Operations
MELODY AFZALIRAD - Director Marketing
ROBERT HENRY - Director Operations
AMY KEMKER - Director Operations

Tomato Express, Inc.
426 Codell Dr Ste B
Lexington, KY 40509

Telephone: (859) 309-0885
Fax Number: (859) 317-9255
Internet Homepage: bellanotte.com; smashingtomato.com; tomatoexpress.net
Company Email: tomatoexpress@insightbb.com
Type of Business: Chain Restaurant Operator
Total Sales: $9,488,000 (e)
Internet Order Processing: Yes
Total Units: 4
Trade Names: Bella Notte (1); Crust (1); Smashing Tomato (2)
Company-Owned Units: 4
Primary Menu: Italian (1); Pizza (3)
Areas of Operation: KY
Type of Foodservice: Casual Dining (4)

Key Personnel
KUNI TOYODA - President; Executive Chef; General Buyer
CAROL TOYODA - VP

McDonald's of London
1804 N Main St
London, KY 40741-4015

Telephone: (606) 878-8255
Fax Number: (606) 878-8255
Type of Business: Chain Restaurant Operator
Total Sales: $110,510,000 (e)
Total Units: 23
Trade Names: McDonald's (23)
Units Franchised From: 23
Primary Menu: Hamburger (23)
Areas of Operation: KY
Type of Foodservice: Quick Serve (23)
Franchise Affiliation: McDonald's Corporation, CHICAGO, IL

Key Personnel
REAGAN HEINRICH - Owner; General Buyer
MARK BROWNING - Director Operations
KAREN LEONARD - Director Development, Talent-Training
HEATHER KEPHART - Manager Human Resources

Trinity Corporation
90 Thompson Poynter Rd
London, KY 40741-7238

Telephone: (606) 878-6879
Fax Number: (606) 878-2323
Type of Business: Chain Restaurant Operator
Year Founded: 1986
Total Sales: $16,100,000 (e)
Number of Employees: 285
Average Check: Breakfast(8); Lunch(8); Dinner(8)
Total Units: 7
Trade Names: Burger King (7)
Units Franchised From: 7
Preferred Square Footage: 2,500; 4,000
Preferred Location Types: Freestanding
Primary Menu: Hamburger (7)
Areas of Operation: KY
Type of Foodservice: Quick Serve (7)
Franchise Affiliation: Burger King Worldwide Inc., MIAMI, FL
Primary Distributors: (Full Line) Reinhart FoodService, CEDAR RAPIDS, IA

Key Personnel
RICHARD CONLEY - President
STEVE MILLS - Director Operations, Purchasing, Information Systems, Supply Chain, Human Resources; General Buyer
WENDALL SMITH - Manager Facility/Maintenance, Real Estate, Design, Store Fixtures

2JR Pizza Enterprises LLC
305 Townepark Cir Ste 101
Louisville, KY 40243-2329

Telephone: (502) 254-0422
Fax Number: (502) 254-0428
Type of Business: Chain Restaurant Operator
Year Founded: 2000
Total Sales: $35,410,000 (e)
Alcohol Sales: 3%
Number of Employees: 710
Average Check: Lunch(10); Dinner(12)
Total Units: 29
Trade Names: Pizza Hut (29)
Units Franchised From: 29
Preferred Square Footage: 2,500; 3,200
Preferred Location Types: Freestanding; Strip Mall
Alcohol Served: Beer
Primary Menu: Pizza (29)
Areas of Operation: IN, KY
Type of Foodservice: Quick Serve (29)
Franchise Affiliation: Pizza Hut Inc., PLANO, TX
Primary Distributors: (Full Line) McLane/Hebron, HEBRON, KY

Key Personnel
JEFF REETZ - President; Director Operations, Purchasing, Supply Chain

Bearno's Inc.
2900 Taylorsville Rd
Louisville, KY 40205-3162

Telephone: (502) 458-8605
Fax Number: (502) 614-5441
Internet Homepage: bearnos.com
Company Email: gtimmering@aol.com
Type of Business: Chain Restaurant Operator
Year Founded: 1977
Systemwide Sales: $24,534,000 (e)
Total Sales: $9,077,000 (e)
Alcohol Sales: 3%
Number of Employees: 150
Average Check: Lunch(14); Dinner(24)
Internet Order Processing: Yes
Total Units: 15
Trade Names: Bearno's Little Sicily Pizza (15)
Company-Owned Units: 4
Units Franchised To: 11
Preferred Square Footage: 5,500; 6,000
Preferred Location Types: Downtown; Freestanding; Strip Mall
Primary Menu: Pizza (15)
Areas of Operation: FL, IN, KY
Foreign Countries: CHINA
Type of Foodservice: Casual Dining (15)
Primary Distributors: (Full Line) SYSCO Food Services of Louisville, LOUISVILLE, KY

Key Personnel
E. JOSEPH STEIER III - Chairman
JOE STEIER - Chairman
ROB MOONEY - President; Partner; COO; General Buyer
GEORGE TIMMERING JR - Partner; General Manager; Director Marketing; Manager Purchasing, Supply Chain

BoomBozz Craft Pizza & Taphouse
1448 Bardstown Rd
Louisville, KY 40204

Telephone: (502) 458-8889
Internet Homepage: boombozz.com
Type of Business: Chain Restaurant Operator
Year Founded: 1998
Total Sales: $7,217,000 (e)
Total Units: 9
Trade Names: BoomBozz Craft Pizza & Taphouse (9)
Company-Owned Units: 9
Preferred Location Types: Freestanding; Strip Mall
Primary Menu: Pizza (9)
Areas of Operation: IN, KY, TN
Type of Foodservice: Casual Dining (9)

Key Personnel
TONY PALOMBINO - Founder; CEO
JORDAN ROOF - CFO
HANNAH DERRINGER - Director Marketing-Training

Buckhead Management Inc.
106 Bauer Ave Ste 4
Louisville, KY 40207-2564

Telephone: (502) 899-3030
Fax Number: (502) 899-3036
Internet Homepage: buckheadmanagement.com; eatatbuckheads.com
Company Email: comments@eatatbuckheads.com
Type of Business: Chain Restaurant Operator
Year Founded: 1980
Total Sales: $17,721,000 (e)
Alcohol Sales: 20%
Number of Employees: 450
Average Check: Lunch(14); Dinner(22)
Total Units: 3
Trade Names: Buckhead Mountain Grill (3)
Company-Owned Units: 3
Preferred Square Footage: 9,000
Preferred Location Types: Freestanding
Alcohol Served: Beer, Wine, Liquor
Primary Menu: American (3)
Areas of Operation: IN, KY
Type of Foodservice: Casual Dining (4)

Key Personnel
WES JOHNSON JR - CEO; President; Director Facility/Maintenance, Supply Chain, Real Estate, Design
SHARON CURRY - Controller
AMBER TERRY - General Manager
TONJA LOGSDON - Manager Information Systems, Human Resources
ANGELA JIMENEZ - Supervisor Area

Cakes and Cones, Inc.
10521 Fischer Park Dr
Louisville, KY 40241-4139

Telephone: (502) 425-1025
Type of Business: Chain Restaurant Operator
Total Sales: $4,301,000 (e)
Total Units: 3
Trade Names: Jersey Mike's Subs (3)
Units Franchised From: 3
Primary Menu: Sandwiches/Deli (3)
Areas of Operation: KY
Type of Foodservice: Quick Serve (3)
Franchise Affiliation: Jersey Mike's Franchise Systems, MANASQUAN, NJ

Key Personnel
DEBORAH B. THOMPSON - Owner; General Buyer
MIKE RUCKER - Owner; General Manager
MARCUSE WIGGINS - General Manager

Churchill Downs Inc.
600 N Hurstbourne Pkwy Ste 400
Louisville, KY 40222-5389

Telephone: (502) 636-4400
Fax Number: (502) 638-3907
Internet Homepage: arlingtonpark.com; calderracecourse.com; churchilldowns.com; churchilldownsincorporated.com; fairgroundsracecourse.com; harlowscasino.com
Type of Business: Foodservice Operations - Casinos
Publicly Held: Yes
Total Sales: $1,694,200,000 (e)
Number of Employees: 122
Average Check: Dinner(26)
Foodservice Sales: $84,710,000 (e)
Total Units: 12
Trade Names: Arlington Park (1); Calder Casino (1); Churchill Downs (1); Fair Grounds (1); Harlow's Casino & Resort (1); Lady Luck Casino (1); Miami Valley Gaming (1); Ocean Downs (1); Oxford Casino (1); Presque Isle Downs (1); Rivers Casino (1); Turfway Park (1)
Company-Owned Units: 12
Preferred Square Footage: 2,500; 5,500; 6,000
Preferred Location Types: Other
Alcohol Served: Beer
Primary Menu: American (9)
Projected Remodelings: 2
Areas of Operation: FL, IL, KY, LA, ME, MS, WA
Type of Foodservice: Casual Dining (9)
Notes: The company derives approximately 95% of its revenue from pari-mutuel operations, admissions fees, sales of programs, online wagering, and other activities.

Key Personnel
WILLIAM C. CARSTANJEN - CEO
JAMES E. GAY - President E-Commerce, Internet Development
WILLIAM E. MUDD - President; COO
TIM BRYANT - President Division; Senior VP
PAUL THELEN - President Division
MARCIA A. DALL - CFO; Exec VP
BEN MURR - CTO; Senior VP
TONY PETRILLO - Senior VP; General Manager Division
REBECCA C. REED - Senior VP; Corporate Secretary; General Counsel
CHUCK KENYON - Senior VP Human Resources
KATHERINE ARMSTRONG - Senior VP Human Resources
BRAD BLACKWELL - Senior VP; General Counsel
MIKE ANDERSON - VP Finance; Treasurer
MIKE ZIEGLER - Executive Director Division
RYAN JORDAN - General Manager
BABAK ABBASCHIAN - Senior Director Strategy
JOHN WESTBROOK - Director Information Technology

Eggheadz LLC
1211 Herr Ln Ste 290
Louisville, KY 40222-4387

Telephone: (502) 409-7848
Internet Homepage: wildeggs.com
Type of Business: Chain Restaurant Operator
Total Sales: $12,170,000 (e)
Total Units: 14
Trade Names: Wild Eggs (14)
Company-Owned Units: 14
Primary Menu: American (14)
Projected Openings: 2
Areas of Operation: IN, KY, OH, TN
Type of Foodservice: Casual Dining (14)

Key Personnel
SHANE HALL - Co-Founder; Partner; COO

Feast BBQ
909 E Market St Ste 100
Louisville, KY 40206-1670

Telephone: (502) 749-9900
Internet Homepage: feastbbq.com; hicottonhospitality.com; barvetti.com; royalshotchicken.com
Type of Business: Chain Restaurant Operator
Year Founded: 2012
Total Sales: $3,033,000 (e)
Average Check: Dinner(14)
Internet Order Processing: Yes
Total Units: 4
Trade Names: Bar Vetti (1); Feast BBQ (2); Royals Hot Chicken (1)
Company-Owned Units: 4
Primary Menu: Bar-B-Q (2); Chicken (1); Italian (1)
Areas of Operation: KY
Type of Foodservice: Casual Dining (4)
Catering Services: Yes

Key Personnel
RYAN ROGERS - Owner; Executive Chef; General Buyer

Heine Brothers
1250 Bardstown Rd
Louisville, KY 40204-1303

Telephone: (502) 456-5108
Internet Homepage: heinebroscoffee.com
Type of Business: Chain Restaurant Operator
Year Founded: 1994
Total Sales: $14,950,000 (e)
Number of Employees: 215
Total Units: 17
Trade Names: Heine Brothers' (17)
Company-Owned Units: 17
Preferred Location Types: Downtown; Freestanding; Mobile Unit
Alcohol Served: Beer, Wine
Primary Menu: Coffee (17)
Projected Openings: 3
Areas of Operation: IN, KY
Type of Foodservice: Quick Serve (17)

Key Personnel
MIKE MAYS - President; General Buyer
TONI LAVERNSON - Manager Operations
ANDREA TRIMMER - Manager Operations

Indi's Fast Food Restaurant
1033 W Broadway
Louisville, KY 40203-2030

Telephone: (502) 589-7985
Fax Number: (502) 589-7986
Internet Homepage: indischicken.com
Type of Business: Chain Restaurant Operator
Year Founded: 1981
Total Sales: $8,658,000 (e)
Alcohol Sales: 2%
Number of Employees: 100
Average Check: Lunch(8); Dinner(8)
Total Units: 9
Trade Names: Indi's Fast Food Restaurant (9)
Company-Owned Units: 9
Preferred Square Footage: 2,500
Preferred Location Types: Freestanding
Primary Menu: Chicken (9)
Areas of Operation: KY
Type of Foodservice: Quick Serve (9)

Key Personnel
MURCHISON THOMAS - President; Executive Chef; Director Advertising, Real Estate; General Buyer
RUSSELL MUHAMMED - General Manager; Director Food Safety; Buyer Beverages
DILLON EVANCZYK - Manager Finance

Kap Enterprises Inc.
12405 Taylorsville Rd
Louisville, KY 40299-4430

Telephone: (502) 261-8002
Fax Number: (502) 261-8050
Type of Business: Chain Restaurant Operator
Year Founded: 1975
Total Sales: $8,555,000 (e)
Number of Employees: 200
Average Check: Lunch(10); Dinner(12)
Total Units: 9
Trade Names: A&W All American Food (2); Long John Silver's (7)
Units Franchised From: 9
Preferred Square Footage: 2,400
Preferred Location Types: Freestanding
Primary Menu: American (2); Seafood (7)
Areas of Operation: KY
Type of Foodservice: Quick Serve (9)
Franchise Affiliation: A&W Restaurants Inc., LEXINGTON, KY; Long John Silver's Inc., LOUISVILLE, KY
Primary Distributors: (Full Line) McLane/Hebron, HEBRON, KY

Key Personnel
FRANK KAPFHAMMER JR - President; VP Operations; Director Finance, Purchasing, Facility/Maintenance, Supply Chain, Ethnic Marketing, Real Estate; General Buyer
STEVEN STERNBERG - General Manager; General Buyer

KFC Corporation
1441 Gardiner Ln
Louisville, KY 40213-1914

Mailing Address: PO Box 34550, LOUISVILLE, KY, 40232-4550
Telephone: (502) 874-8300
Fax Number: (502) 874-8792
Internet Homepage: kfc.ca; kfc.com
Type of Business: Chain Restaurant Operator
Year Founded: 1952
Systemwide Sales: $34,608,656,000 (e)
Publicly Held: Yes
Total Sales: $2,892,316,000 (e)
Number of Employees: 21,000
Average Check: Lunch(8); Dinner(10)
Total Units: 29,900
Trade Names: KFC (29,900)
Company-Owned Units: 299
Units Franchised To: 29,601
Preferred Square Footage: 2,500; 3,200
Preferred Location Types: Airports; Community Mall; Downtown; Freestanding; Regional Mall; Strip Mall
Primary Menu: Chicken (29,900)
Areas of Operation: AK, AL, AR, AZ, CA, CO, CT, DC, DE, FL, GA, GU, HI, IA, ID, IL, IN, KS, KY, LA, MA, MD, ME, MI, MN, MO, MS, MT, NC, ND, NE, NH, NJ, NM, NV, NY, OH, OK, OR, PA, PR, RI, SC, SD, TN, TX, UT, VA, VI, VT, WA, WI, WV, WY, AB, BC, MB, NB, NL, NS, NT, ON, PE, QC, SK, YT
Foreign Countries: AMERICAN SAMOA; ANDORRA; ANTIGUA; ARUBA; AUSTRALIA; AUSTRIA; BAHAMAS; BAHRAIN; BANGLADESH; BARBADOS; BERMUDA; BOLIVIA; BONAIRE; BOTSWANA; BRAZIL; BRUNEI; BULGARIA; BURMA; CAMBODIA; CANADA; CAYMAN ISLANDS; CHILE; CHINA; COLOMBIA; COSTA RICA; CYPRUS; CZECH REPUBLIC; DENMARK; DOMINICA; DOMINICAN REPUBLIC; ECUADOR; EGYPT; EL SALVADOR;ENGLAND; FIJI; FRANCE; GERMANY; GREECE; GRENADA; GUADELOUPE; GUATEMALA; GUYANA; HONDURAS; HONG KONG; HUNGARY; ICELAND; INDIA; INDONESIA; IRAN; IRELAND; ISRAEL; JAMAICA; JAPAN; JORDAN; KENYA; KUWAIT; LEBANON; LESOTHO; LITHUANIA; MALAYSIA; MALTA;MARTINIQUE; MAURITIUS; MEXICO; MONGOLIA; MOROCCO; MOZAMBIQUE; NAMIBIA; NEPAL; NEW ZEALAND; NIGERIA; NORTHERN IRELAND;OMAN; PAKISTAN; PANAMA; PERU; POLAND; PORTUGAL; QATAR; ROMANIA; RUSSIA; SAINT KITTS AND NEVIS; SAINT MAARTEN; SAINT MARTIN; SAUDI ARABIA; SCOTLAND; SINGAPORE; SLOVAKIA; SOUTH AFRICA; SOUTH KOREA; SPAIN; SRI LANKA; ST. LUCIA; ST. VINCENT; SURINAME;SWAZILAND; TAIWAN; THAILAND; THE NETHERLANDS; THE PHILIPPINES; TRINIDAD & TOBAGO; TURKEY; UNITED ARAB EMIRATES; VENEZUELA; VIETNAM; WALES; YEMEN ARAB REPUBLIC; ZAMBIA; ZIMBABWE
Type of Foodservice: Quick Serve (29,900)
Catering Services: Yes
Primary Distributors: (Full Line) McLane Foodservice, CARROLLTON, TX
Parent Company: YUM! Brands Inc., LOUISVILLE, KY

Key Personnel
JOEY WAT - CEO International Division
SABIR SAMI - CEO Global
TARUN LAL - President Operations, United States
NIVERA WALLANI - President Canada
DALE BLACK - President
CATHERINE TAN-GILLESPIE - President; Chief Marketing Officer United States; Chief Development Officer United States
ALEX BARSK - CFO
BRIAN GOLDSTEIN - COO United States
MONICA ROTHGERY - COO United States
DYKE SHIPP - Chief People Officer International Division; Chief Development Officer International Division
NEIL PIPER - Chief People Officer Region
HEATHER MCCOY - Chief People Officer
DHRUV KAUL - Chief Marketing Officer Region
NICK CHAVEZ - Chief Marketing Officer
RYAN KOON - Chief Development Officer
STACI RAWLS - Chief Communications Officer
MATTHEW PRESTON - Chief Legal Officer
JONATHAN BLUM - Chief Ethics Officer; Senior VP Communications
TERESA CRAWFORD - VP Engineering
THOMAS PETRECCA - VP Operations
JIM MCKELVIE - VP Franchising
HOLLY GOODE - Treasurer; Director Marketing
SCOTT MEZVINSKY - General Manager Region
SHELISA GAUTREAUX - Senior Director Human Resources
MIKE WESLEY - Senior Director Marketing
JOSEPH CALL - Senior Director Global Development
JOSHUA FUNK - Director Quality Assurance, Food Safety
DAVID GRAVES - Director Strategy, Branding, Innovation
PATRICK COTY - Director Technology
CHERYL VANALLEN - Director Training, Employee Development
NEVILLE BARRETT - Director Operations
DONUALE DEAN - Director Development, Digital
SAM ULLRICH - Director Financial Planning
GREG TRAUPMAN - Director Strategy, Development, Construction
BRIAN ROSS - Director Operations
ANDREAS BOMMES - Manager Information Technology, Applications, Software
STEVEN BROCK - Manager Help Desk
CLAIRE MAYNARD - Manager Innovation
DMITRY PERLIN - Manager Information Technology
DUANE PETERSON - Manager Information Technology
MANDY PHUA - Manager Operations
JOSHUA BOVA - Manager Development

Le Moo
2300 Lexington Rd
Louisville, KY 40206-2821

Telephone: (502) 458-8888
Internet Homepage: lemoorestaurant.com; villageanchor.com
Type of Business: Chain Restaurant Operator
Year Founded: 1987
Total Sales: $11,157,000 (e)
Alcohol Sales: 20%
Number of Employees: 160
Average Check: Lunch(10); Dinner(20)
Total Units: 3
Trade Names: Grassa Gramma. (1); Le Moo Steak (1); The Village Anchor (1)
Company-Owned Units: 3
Preferred Location Types: Freestanding
Alcohol Served: Beer, Wine, Liquor
Primary Menu: Italian (1); Southern (1); Steak (1)

Areas of Operation: KY
Type of Foodservice: Casual Dining (1); Fine Dining (2)

Key Personnel
CATHY KRUER - VP Operations; General Buyer
RICHARD FLOYD - General Manager
CHIP LAWRENCE - Executive Chef; General Buyer

Long John Silver's Inc.
13050 Ormsby Park Place
Louisville, KY 40222-5090

Telephone: (502) 815-6100
Internet Homepage: longjohnsilvers.com
Company Email: info@ljsilvers.com
Type of Business: Chain Restaurant Operator
Year Founded: 1946
Systemwide Sales: $618,075,000 (e)
Total Sales: $27,180,000 (e)
Number of Employees: 8,725
Average Check: Lunch(8); Dinner(12)
Total Units: 695
Trade Names: Long John Silver's (695)
Company-Owned Units: 200
Units Franchised To: 495
Preferred Square Footage: 2,500; 3,200
Preferred Location Types: Community Mall; Convenience Store/Gas Station; Downtown; Freestanding; Institution (college/hospital); Kiosk; Regional Mall; Strip Mall
Primary Menu: Seafood (695)
Areas of Operation: AL, AR, AZ, CA, CO, CT, FL, GA, HI, IA, IL, IN, KS, KY, LA, MA, MD, MI, MN, MO, MS, NC, ND, NE, NH, NJ, NM, NV, NY, OH, OK, OR, PA, SC, SD, TN, TX, UT, VA, WI, WV, WY
Foreign Countries: JAPAN; MALAYSIA; SINGAPORE; TAIWAN
Type of Foodservice: Quick Serve (695)
Parent Company: LJS Partners LLC, LOUISVILLE, KY

Key Personnel
CRAIG DANIEL - CFO; VP; Treasurer
ANGELA SANDERS - Chief Marketing Officer
PAULA ASHLEY ROGNESS - VP Marketing, Communications
KRISTA FOSTER - VP Human Resources
SHERRY BLISSETT - Director Operations-Training
DUANE BURTON - Manager Construction

Main Street Management
1308 Bardstown Rd
Louisville, KY 40204-1320

Mailing Address: PO Box 4607, LOUISVILLE, KY, 40204-0607
Telephone: (502) 456-6762
Fax Number: (502) 456-6784
Internet Homepage: bristolbarandgrille.com
Company Email: info@bristolbarandgrill.com
Type of Business: Chain Restaurant Operator
Year Founded: 1977
Total Sales: $5,660,000 (e)
Alcohol Sales: 20%
Number of Employees: 200
Average Check: Lunch(12); Dinner(18)
Total Units: 3
Trade Names: Bristol Bar & Grille (3)
Company-Owned Units: 3
Preferred Location Types: Freestanding; Strip Mall
Alcohol Served: Beer, Wine, Liquor
Primary Menu: American (3)
Areas of Operation: KY
Type of Foodservice: Casual Dining (3)
Catering Services: Yes
Primary Distributors: (Full Line) SYSCO Food Services of Louisville, LOUISVILLE, KY

Key Personnel
DOUGLAS K. GOSSMANN - President; Executive Chef; Director Catering; Buyer Food, Foodservice Equip/Supplies
SCOTT HARPER - VP; Director Marketing
EMILIE PFEIFFER - Director Catering
TJ OAKLEY - Manager Operations

Manna Inc.
3309 Collins Ln
Louisville, KY 40245-1629

Telephone: (502) 254-7130
Fax Number: (502) 254-7031
Internet Homepage: bfcompanies.com
Company Email: info@bfcompanies.com
Type of Business: Chain Restaurant Operator
Year Founded: 1987
Total Sales: $898,260,000 (e)
Alcohol Sales: 9%
Number of Employees: 17,359
Average Check: Lunch(12); Dinner(16)
Total Units: 268
Trade Names: Blaze Pizza (11); Fazoli's (83); Golden Corral Buffet & Grill (28); Mark's Feed Store (6); Napa River Grill (1); Wendy's Old Fashioned Hamburgers (139)
Company-Owned Units: 7
Units Franchised From: 261
Preferred Square Footage: 2,500; 3,000; 6,000
Preferred Location Types: Community Mall; Freestanding
Alcohol Served: Beer, Wine, Liquor
Primary Menu: American (28); Bar-B-Q (6); Californian (1); Hamburger (139); Italian (83); Pizza (11)
Areas of Operation: FL, IA, IL, IN, KY, MI, MN, MO, ND, OH, SD, TN, WI
Type of Foodservice: Casual Dining (-181); Family Restaurant (89); Quick Serve (139)
Franchise Affiliation: Blaze Pizza LLC, PASADENA, CA; Chili's Grill & Bar, DALLAS, TX; Fazoli's Restaurant LLC, LEXINGTON, KY; Golden Corral Corp., RALEIGH, NC; Perkins Restaurant & Bakery, MEMPHIS, TN; The Wendy's Company, DUBLIN, OH
Primary Distributors: (Food) The SYGMA Network, Inc., DUBLIN, OH; (Food) Maines Paper & Food Service Chicago, HANOVER PARK, IL; (Supplies) Maines Paper & Food Service Chicago, HANOVER PARK, IL
Divisional Offices: BF Fort Myers Inc, PUNTA GORDA, FL

Key Personnel
AMY HOOVER - CIO; VP Information Technology
DALE BRUNER - VP Loss Prevention
ANDRE BYNUM - VP Marketing
MARY LAZZARONI - VP Development, People
MARSHA LITTLEJOHN - Controller
SHANNON BUCKINGHAM - Controller
GLADYS BARCLAY - Controller
RHONDA KNIGHT - Director Recruitment
TED OWEN - Director Construction
MONICA PEASE - Director Training
GINA SISK - Director Media
STACY HETTICH - Director Marketing
ANN WATSON - Regional Manager Marketing
TORI POWELL - Regional Manager Marketing
MICHELLE MCCURDY - Regional Manager Marketing
BRUCE KNUTSON - District Manager
STEPHANIE THOMAS - District Manager
CHRISTINA SHELDON - Manager Human Resources
MONICA POLCHERT - Manager Training
RYAN MOORE - Manager Operations
BLAYKE HERMAN - Manager Tax
KATHERINE HUSS - Supervisor Area
CECE HENDERSON - Administrator Benefits
DANIEL HENDERSON - Administrator Network, Systems
MINERVA VALLEZ - Coordinator Human Resources
CHERYL JENKINS - Administrative Assistant

Mark's Feed Store Bar B Q
11422 Shelbyville Rd
Louisville, KY 40243-1306

Telephone: (502) 244-0140
Internet Homepage: marksfeedstore.com
Type of Business: Chain Restaurant Operator
Year Founded: 1988
Total Sales: $3,845,000 (e)
Alcohol Sales: 5%
Average Check: Dinner(12)
Total Units: 6
Trade Names: Mark's Feed Store (6)
Company-Owned Units: 6
Alcohol Served: Beer, Wine
Primary Menu: Bar-B-Q (6)

Areas of Operation: IN, KY
Type of Foodservice: Fast Casual (6)

Key Personnel
GARY DANE - General Manager; Executive Chef; General Buyer

Moby Dick Seafood Restaurant Inc.
530 Terry Blvd
Louisville, KY 40229-4053

Telephone: (502) 385-0877
Internet Homepage: mobydickwinkler.com
Company Email: mobydickwinkler@insightbb.com
Type of Business: Chain Restaurant Operator
Year Founded: 1968
Systemwide Sales: $22,779,000 (e)
Total Sales: $14,570,000 (e)
Number of Employees: 145
Average Check: Breakfast(8); Lunch(8); Dinner(8)
Total Units: 17
Trade Names: Moby Dick Seafood Restaurant (17)
Company-Owned Units: 2
Units Franchised To: 15
Preferred Square Footage: 2,500
Preferred Location Types: Freestanding
Primary Menu: Seafood (17)
Areas of Operation: IN, KY
Type of Foodservice: Quick Serve (17)
On-site Distribution Center: Yes
Primary Distributors: (Food) SYSCO Food Services of Louisville, LOUISVILLE, KY

Key Personnel
BRIAN DEELEY - President; Director Operations, Risk Management, Marketing, Advertising

Molly Malone's Irish Pub and Restaurant
933 Baxter Ave
Louisville, KY 40204-2046

Telephone: (502) 473-1222
Fax Number: (502) 473-1206
Internet Homepage: mollymalonesirishpub.com
Company Email: morgan@mollymalonesirishpub.com
Type of Business: Chain Restaurant Operator
Year Founded: 1998
Total Sales: $4,074,000 (e)
Alcohol Sales: 5%
Average Check: Dinner(18)
Internet Order Processing: Yes
Total Units: 4
Trade Names: Molly Malone's Irish Pub and Restaurant (4)
Company-Owned Units: 4
Preferred Location Types: Freestanding; Office Complex
Alcohol Served: Beer, Wine, Liquor
Primary Menu: Miscellaneous (4)
Areas of Operation: KY, OH
Type of Foodservice: Casual Dining (4)

Key Personnel
DONAL RYAN - President; Partner; General Buyer
JOSH RHODES - Partner

▲
Papa Johns International Inc.
2002 Papa Johns Blvd
Louisville, KY 40299-3393

Mailing Address: PO Box 99900, LOUISVILLE, KY, 40269-0900
Telephone: (502) 261-7272
Fax Number: (502) 261-4731
Internet Homepage: papajohns.com
Type of Business: Chain Restaurant Operator
Year Founded: 1984
Systemwide Sales: $5,515,351,000 (e)
Publicly Held: Yes
Total Sales: $3,036,074,000 (e)
Number of Employees: 16,500
Average Check: Lunch(8); Dinner(12)
Foodservice Sales: $1,821,644,000 (e)
Internet Order Processing: Yes
Internet Sales: 50.00%
Total Units: 5,906
Trade Names: Papa Johns Pizza (5,906)
Company-Owned Units: 648
Units Franchised To: 5,258
Preferred Square Footage: 1,100; 1,500
Preferred Location Types: Airports; Downtown; Freestanding; Regional Mall; Stadiums; Strip Mall
Primary Menu: Pizza (5,906)
Projected Openings: 150
Areas of Operation: AK, AL, AR, AZ, CA, CO, CT, DC, DE, FL, GA, GU, HI, IA, ID, IL, IN, KS, KY, LA, MA, MD, ME, MI, MN, MO, MS, MT, NC, ND, NE, NH, NJ, NM, NV, NY, OH, OK, OR, PA, PR, RI, SC, SD, TN, TX, UT, VA, VT, WA, WI, WV, WY, FC, AB, BC, MB, NB, ON, SK
Foreign Countries: AZERBAIJAN; BAHAMAS; BAHRAIN; BELARUS; BOLIVIA; CANADA; CAYMAN ISLANDS; CHILE; CHINA; COLOMBIA; COSTA RICA; CYPRUS; DOMINICAN REPUBLIC; ECUADOR; EGYPT; EL SALVADOR; ENGLAND; FRANCE; GUATEMALA; IRAQ; IRELAND; ISRAEL; KAZAKHSTAN; KUWAIT; KYRGYZSTAN; MEXICO; MOROCCO; NICARAGUA; OMAN; PANAMA; PERU; POLAND; PORTUGAL; QATAR; RUSSIA; SAUDI ARABIA; SOUTHKOREA; SPAIN; THE PHILIPPINES; TRINIDAD & TOBAGO; TUNISIA; TURKEY; UNITED ARAB EMIRATES; VENEZUELA
Type of Foodservice: Quick Serve (5,906)
Foodservice Management Venues: Schools
Distribution Centers: GILBERT, AZ; AURORA, CO; ORLANDO, FL; DES MOINES, IA; GARNER, NC; PORTLAND, OR; FREEDOM, PA; GRAND PRAIRIE, TX
On-site Distribution Center: Yes
Notes: The company derives approximately 40% of its revenue from commissary & equipment sales & other sales.

Key Personnel
RAVI THANAWALA - CEO Interim; CFO
TODD PENEGOR - CEO; President
JULIE LARNER - President Food
ANDREY KLYCHEV - CFO
CHRIS COLLINS - CFO Interim; VP Tax
KEVIN VASCONTI - CTO; Chief Digital Officer
JOE SIEVE - Chief Development Officer International
CAROLINE OYLER - Chief Legal Officer; Chief Risk Officer; Senior VP
SHANE HUTCHINS - Chief Supply Chain Officer
MADELINE CHADWICK - Senior VP Communications, Corporate Affairs
PATRICK COELHO - Senior VP Development
BRIAN REED - VP Transportation, Logistics, Foodservice
JOE MAIN - VP Procurement
ERNESTO CLAUTIER - Regional VP
BRAD CUNNINGHAM - General Counsel
CARLOS PINEDA - General Counsel
DANITA GARCIA - General Manager
SACHIN SINGH - General Manager Training
WESLEY GREEN - General Manager Training
SARIKA ATTAL - Senior Director Architecture
MICHAEL WYANT - Senior Director
JAMES YOUNGBLOOD - Senior Director Internal Audit
TYE RUTLEDGE - Senior Director Operations
ROB PEPPER - Senior Director Strategy; Transformation
JAMES HARRIS - Director Tax
CHAD JONES - Director Development
JJ FUQUA - Director Risk Management, Global
ADAM WILCOCK - Director Development
VALARIE GIOVENCO - Director North America
ANGELA JORGENSEN - Director Talent
BOB RICHWINE - Director
ERIN SNYDER - Director Business Development, Global
RAY TURNER - Director
HIREN PATEL - Director Operations
REBECCA DURICA - Director
ELENA BELYANSKAYA - Director International
TIM VESSELS - Director Development
GREG POTTS - Director
DON CECCARELLI - Director
JEFF SURRAN - Director
VIVIEN LEONG - Director
DAVID KIMINKI - Director Operations
KARINA MARTYNOVA - Director Purchasing
CHRISTOPHER LATHAM - Director Operations

CHRISTOPHER ARAGON - Director Operations
LAURE SPRINGS - Director Marketing
LEE FARMER - Director Training
MICHAEL BACHTEL - Director Operations
WILLIAM BARNETT - Director Digital, Digital Developer
SHASTA TRUMBO MHRIR - Director Human Resources
CARLOS HERRERA MS - Director Quality Assurance
CHARLES POFF - Director Operations
BELICIA PARGA - Senior Manager Quality Assurance
CRAIG JONES - Senior Manager Security, Safety, Loss Prevention
MARIA DANIEL - Senior Manager Development
DANA YURKANIN - Manager Facility/Maintenance
TIM BELLIS - Manager Transportation, Fleet
BRAD ROSEN - Specialist Operations

Radcliff Co.
4218 Shelbyville Rd
Louisville, KY 40207-3956

Telephone: (502) 895-4265
Fax Number: (502) 896-1930
Company Email: info@radcliffco.com
Type of Business: Chain Restaurant Operator
Year Founded: 1954
Total Sales: $9,204,000 (e)
Number of Employees: 615
Average Check: Lunch(10); Dinner(12)
Total Units: 31
Trade Names: Rally's Hamburgers (31)
Units Franchised From: 31
Preferred Square Footage: 2,400
Preferred Location Types: Freestanding
Primary Menu: Hamburger (31)
Areas of Operation: IN, KY
Type of Foodservice: Quick Serve (31)
Franchise Affiliation: Checkers Drive-In Restaurants Inc., TAMPA, FL
Primary Distributors: (Full Line) McLane/Hebron, HEBRON, KY

Key Personnel
JOE HERTZMAN - President; Partner; General Manager; Director Facility/Maintenance, Real Estate, Design; General Buyer
DARREN HAGGARD - Partner
ALLEN HERTZMAN - Partner
SUZANNE SCHULER - CFO

Subway Franchise
4417 Cane Run Rd
Louisville, KY 40216-4501

Telephone: (502) 448-6872
Internet Homepage: subway.com
Type of Business: Chain Restaurant Operator
Total Sales: $2,058,000 (e)
Total Units: 3
Trade Names: Subway (3)
Units Franchised From: 3
Primary Menu: Sandwiches/Deli (3)
Areas of Operation: KY
Type of Foodservice: Quick Serve (3)
Franchise Affiliation: Doctor's Associates Inc., MILFORD, CT

Key Personnel
A K KANJI - President

Texas Roadhouse Inc.
6040 Dutchmans Ln Ste 100
Louisville, KY 40205-3305

Telephone: (502) 426-9984
Fax Number: (502) 426-3274
Internet Homepage: bubbas33.com; eatjaggers.com; texasroadhouse.com
Company Email: info@texasroadhouse.com
Type of Business: Chain Restaurant Operator
Year Founded: 1993
Systemwide Sales: $4,340,450,000 (e)
Publicly Held: Yes
Total Sales: $4,858,716,000 (e)
Alcohol Sales: 10.70%
Number of Employees: 91,000
Average Check: Lunch(16); Dinner(20)
Internet Order Processing: Yes
Internet Sales: 1.00%
Total Units: 741
Trade Names: Bubba's 33 (45); Jaggers (8); Texas Roadhouse (688)
Company-Owned Units: 635
Units Franchised To: 106
Preferred Square Footage: 6,679; 7,079
Preferred Location Types: Community Mall; Freestanding; Regional Mall
Alcohol Served: Beer, Wine, Liquor
Primary Menu: American (53); Steak (688)
Projected Openings: 25
Projected Remodelings: 4
Areas of Operation: AK, AL, AR, AZ, CA, CO, CT, DE, FL, GA, IA, ID, IL, IN, KS, KY, LA, MA, MD, ME, MI, MN, MO, MS, MT, NC, ND, NE, NH, NJ, NM, NV, NY, OH, OK, OR, PA, RI, SC, SD, TN, TX, UT, VA, VT, WA, WI, WV, WY
Foreign Countries: BAHRAIN; CHINA; KUWAIT; MEXICO; SAUDI ARABIA; SOUTH KOREA; TAIWAN; THE PHILIPPINES; UNITED ARAB EMIRATES
Type of Foodservice: Casual Dining (733); Quick Serve (8)
Primary Distributors: (Food) SYSCO Food Services of Louisville, LOUISVILLE, KY; (Supplies) SYSCO Food Services of Louisville, LOUISVILLE, KY

Key Personnel
JERRY MORGAN - CEO; President
REGINA TOBIN - President
NEAL NIKLAUS - Owner
CHRIS MONROE - CFO
HERNAN MUJICA - CIO; VP Information Technology
CHRIS JACOBSEN - Chief Marketing Officer
TRAVIS DOSTER - Chief Communications Officer
RACHAEL LOONEY - VP Employee Development
SEAN RENFROE - General Counsel; Senior Director
BRAD SCHEINER - Senior Director Information Systems, Information Technology
JORDAN TROUT - Senior Director Purchasing
PATRICK STERLING - Senior Director Risk Management, People
JASON MENNIE - Senior Director Food
RUSSELL ARBUCKLE - Senior Director Real Estate
CLAUDETTE GELB - Senior Director People
TIM GETTY - Director Operations, International Division
VICKIE ELDER - Director Payroll
MICHAEL HENRY - Director
REBECCA HOOPER - Director Procurement
MICHAEL BAILEN - Director Finance
KRISTAL BAIRD - Director Accounting
MICHELE BISHOP - Director Marketing
CHRIS COOPER - Director Information Technology
MARY NEWELL - Director Digital, Brand Marketing
MIKE PARKER - Director Information Technology, Digital Solutions
ERIC MARTIN - Director Food Safety
JOE DOREN - Director
AMANDA KREUTZER - Director Employee Benefits
LAINIE YARMUTH - Director Procurement
LISA TWOHEY - Director Benefits, Compensation
ALVIN VARUGHESE - Director; Architect
CASSIE WALL - Director Training
JAMES WOOD - Director Operations, Systems-Training
MANDY SCHNURR - Director Internal Audit
SCOTT RUDERMAN - Director Global
GAYLE SHUFF - Director Design
MELISSA PRICE - Director Purchasing
MINDY STAYTON - Director Accounting, Payroll
KIRSTEN SANDS - Regional Director Marketing
JAMES WORKMAN - Regional Director
DOUG DRUEN - Regional Director Real Estate
KARYN COLLINS - Regional Director People
JUSTIN GRANT - Senior Manager Marketing
RYAN HECK - Senior Manager Marketing, Customer Analytics
KELLY MASDEN - Senior Manager Marketing
ADAM PIKE - Senior Manager Procurement
MATT MCMAHAN - Senior Manager Strategy; Manager
JOE PFALZGRAF - Manager Graphic Design
ALEC MCAFEE - Manager Digital Marketing
ASHLEY MCCULLOUGH - Manager; Merchant
EMMA JARDINES - Manager Marketing

BETH FRANKLIN - Manager Digital Marketing
BRANDON DRURY - Manager Procurement
JOSH SELL - Manager Procurement
MEGAN SMITH - Manager Marketing
KATIE DETERS - Supervisor Facility/Maintenance

The Wells Co.
130 Saint Matthews Ave Ste 301
Louisville, KY 40207-3113

Telephone: (502) 896-8881
Type of Business: Chain Restaurant Operator
Year Founded: 1983
Total Sales: $10,370,000 (e)
Alcohol Sales: 10%
Number of Employees: 250
Average Check: Lunch(12); Dinner(22)
Total Units: 7
Trade Names: Captain D's Seafood (6); WW Cousins (1)
Company-Owned Units: 1
Units Franchised From: 6
Preferred Square Footage: 2,500; 10,000
Preferred Location Types: Freestanding
Alcohol Served: Beer
Primary Menu: American (1); Seafood (6)
Areas of Operation: IN, KY
Type of Foodservice: Casual Dining (1); Fast Casual (6)
Franchise Affiliation: Captain D's LLC, NASHVILLE, TN

Key Personnel
MARTY JOHNSON - President; General Buyer
EARL SMITH - VP
CHERYL KORFHAGE - Controller; Manager Accounting, Human Resources

Tumbleweed Inc.
2301 River Rd Ste 200
Louisville, KY 40206-3004

Telephone: (502) 893-0323
Fax Number: (502) 897-0237
Internet Homepage: tumbleweedrestaurants.com
Type of Business: Chain Restaurant Operator
Year Founded: 1970
Systemwide Sales: $32,158,000 (e)
Total Sales: $28,750,000 (e)
Alcohol Sales: 20%
Number of Employees: 1,460
Average Check: Lunch(16); Dinner(22)
Internet Order Processing: Yes
Internet Sales: 2.00%
Total Units: 19
Trade Names: Tumbleweed Tex Mex Grill & Margarita (19)
Company-Owned Units: 19
Preferred Square Footage: 5,200
Preferred Location Types: Freestanding; Regional Mall; Strip Mall
Alcohol Served: Beer, Wine, Liquor
Primary Menu: Southwest/Tex-Mex (19)
Areas of Operation: IN, KY, OH
Type of Foodservice: Casual Dining (19)
Primary Distributors: (Equipment) The Wasserstrom Co., COLUMBUS, OH; (Supplies) The Wasserstrom Co., COLUMBUS, OH

Key Personnel
MATT HIGGINS - CEO; President; CFO; Treasurer; Director Finance
BUDDY MATTINGLY - CFO
JOHN BUTORAC - COO
JEREMY SONS - Director Operations
BRIAN NIEMANN - Director Franchise Operations, Menu Development, Development-Beverages
KATHY CORUM - Director Payroll, Human Resources
HELEN TAYLOR - Manager Accounting

UP Inc.
3309 Collins Ln
Louisville, KY 40245-1629

Telephone: (502) 254-7130
Fax Number: (502) 254-7031
Type of Business: Chain Restaurant Operator
Year Founded: 1978
Total Sales: $30,890,000 (e)
Number of Employees: 300
Average Check: Lunch(16); Dinner(26)
Total Units: 21
Trade Names: Fazoli's (21)
Units Franchised From: 21
Preferred Square Footage: 2,900
Preferred Location Types: Office Complex; Regional Mall
Primary Menu: Italian (21)
Areas of Operation: IN, KY, TN, WI
Type of Foodservice: Fast Casual (21)
Franchise Affiliation: Fazoli's Restaurant LLC, LEXINGTON, KY
Primary Distributors: (Food) US Foods, MENOMONEE FALLS, WI
Notes: Operates as UP Inc., UP Properties of Kentucky LLC and UP Properties of Tennessee LLC.

Key Personnel
PAUL THOMPSON - President; General Manager Finance, Real Estate, Human Resources, Store Fixtures; General Buyer
GREG STEVENS - Manager Operations, Facility/Maintenance, Information Systems, Supply Chain

White Castle System Inc.
4730 Allmond Ave
Louisville, KY 40209-1405

Telephone: (502) 361-2317
Fax Number: (502) 368-2685
Listing Type: Regional Office
Type of Business: Chain Restaurant Operator
Number of Employees: 900
Total Units: 40
Areas of Operation: IN, KY, TN
On-site Distribution Center: Yes
Parent Company: White Castle Management Co., COLUMBUS, OH

Key Personnel
ROBERT LILIENSTERN - CFO
NINA MARATTO - Senior Director Employee Benefits, Business Development
TOBY REEL - Director Accounting
SUSAN CARROLL-BOSER - Director Information Technology
AUDRA MAZZEO - Director National Accounts
LORA SCHOEFFEL - Regional Director Operations
MIKE COY - Manager Facility/Maintenance; Supervisor Construction

Wick's P&P LLC
2301 River Rd Ste 102
Louisville, KY 40206-3003

Telephone: (502) 259-9113
Fax Number: (502) 259-9114
Internet Homepage: wickspizza.com
Company Email: comments@wickspizza.com
Type of Business: Chain Restaurant Operator
Total Sales: $6,185,000 (e)
Alcohol Sales: 8%
Number of Employees: 52
Average Check: Lunch(10); Dinner(16)
Internet Order Processing: Yes
Total Units: 4
Trade Names: Wick's Pizza Parlor and Pub (4)
Company-Owned Units: 4
Preferred Location Types: Freestanding
Alcohol Served: Beer, Wine, Liquor
Primary Menu: Pizza (4)
Areas of Operation: KY
Type of Foodservice: Casual Dining (4)

Key Personnel
MIKE WICKLIFFE - President; Partner; Director Real Estate, Menu Development
MEREDITH WICKLIFFE - Partner; Director Finance, Operations, Purchasing, Human Resources
JERI PUTMAN - Manager Payroll

YUM! Brands Inc.
1441 Gardiner Ln
Louisville, KY 40213-1914

Mailing Address: PO Box 34550, LOUISVILLE, KY, 40232-4550
Telephone: (502) 874-8300
Fax Number: (502) 874-8306
Internet Homepage: yum.com
Company Email: comments@yum.com
Listing Type: Corporate Office
Type of Business: Chain Restaurant Operator
Year Founded: 1997
Systemwide Sales: $67,840,872,000 (e)
Publicly Held: Yes
Total Sales: $7,525,467,000 (e)
Alcohol Sales: 0.50%
Number of Employees: 550,000
Internet Order Processing: Yes
Total Units: 58,708
Trade Names: KFC (29,900); Pizza Hut (19,866); Taco Bell (8,548); Taco Bell Cantina (16); The Habit Burger Grill (378)
Company-Owned Units: 1,174
Units Franchised To: 57,534
Preferred Location Types: Airports; Community Mall; Convenience Store/Gas Station; Discount Dept. Stores; Downtown; Freestanding; Grocery Stores; Hotel/Motel; Institution (college/hospital); Kiosk; Mobile Unit; Office Complex; Other; Outlet Mall; Parks; Regional Mall; Stadiums; Strip Mall; Travel Plazas
Alcohol Served: Beer, Wine
Primary Menu: Chicken (29,900); Hamburger (378); Pizza (19,866); Taco (8,564)
Areas of Operation: AK, AL, AR, AZ, CA, CO, CT, DC, DE, FL, GA, GU, HI, IA, ID, IL, IN, KS, KY, LA, MA, MD, ME, MI, MN, MO, MS, MT, NC, ND, NE, NH, NJ, NM, NV, NY, OH, OK, OR, PA, PR, RI, SC, SD, TN, TX, UT, VA, VI, VT, WA, WI, WV, WY
Type of Foodservice: Fast Casual (394); Quick Serve (58,314)
Primary Distributors: (Full Line) McLane Foodservice, CARROLLTON, TX
Headquarter Offices: KFC Corporation, LOUISVILLE, KY; Pizza Hut Inc., PLANO, TX; Taco Bell Corp., IRVINE, CA; The Habit Restaurants Inc, IRVINE, CA; Yum! Restaurants International (Canada) Co., VAUGHAN, ON CANADA

Key Personnel
BRIAN CORNELL - Chairman
DAVID W. GIBBS - CEO; President
JOEY WAT - CEO Group, International Division
AARON POWELL - CEO
SHANNON HENNESSY - CEO Division
VIPUL CHAWLA - President International Division, Division
SCOTT MEZVINSKY - President International, Division
CHRIS TURNER - CFO
LYNNE BROAD - CFO Division
JONATHAN OJANY - CFO Division
TRACY SKEANS - COO; Chief People Officer
ROB SAVAGE - COO
KELLY ANTUSH - Chief People Officer
CLAY JOHNSON - CTO; Chief Digital Officer
JOE PARK - CTO; Chief Digital Officer
KEN MUENCH - Chief Marketing Officer
NICK CHAVEZ - Chief Marketing Officer Division
JAMES FRIPP - Chief Diversity Officer; Chief Inclusion Officer
ERIKA BURKHARDT - Chief Legal Officer; Corporate Secretary
LAWRENCE KIM - Chief Innovation Officer
CAMERON DAVIES - Chief Data Officer
MARK LAGESTEE - VP Loyalty Program
GREG DZURIK - VP Marketing, Innovation
PAT ROXWORTHY - VP Tax
PHILLIP STUECKER - VP Internal Audit
ERIC NEWTON - Controller; Director Division
CARSON STEWART - General Counsel; Director Legal
JENNIFER GREEN - General Counsel; Director
JOSEPH CALL - Senior Director Global Development, Division
JEFF BELCHER - Senior Director Employee Compensation
JASON GRAF - Senior Director Information Technology
DAVID MINDELL - Senior Director Legal, Compliance
CHARLIE TEWELL - Senior Director Information Technology
MICHAEL WESLEY - Senior Director Marketing
MARYBETH BOEHNLEIN - Director Talent Acquisitions; Senior Manager Talent
JOSHUA FUNK - Director Quality Assurance, Food Safety
DAVE LOWE - Director Accounting
TIM SAWYER - Director Infrastructure
TED MARKS - Director Applications, Integration
DONUALE DEAN - Director Applications, Digital
MIKE MAYER - Director Acquisitions, Mergers, International Division
TIMOTHY VOGEL - Director Architecture
LINDA NESTOR - Director Promotion, Division
LISA JACKSON - Director Employee Development
VIRGINIA F. CHEATHAM - Director Public Relations
MOHIT KHURANA - Director Human Resources
AMAN LAL - Director Human Resources
MATTHEW LATHROP - Director
JAMES LI - Director Information Technology
REBECCA POE OHLEMACHER - Director Finance
ROB SKEETERS - Director Information Technology
ANDY STEINBACH - Director Finance
GARLAND STRAUB - Director Information Technology
LEO SUN - Director Information Technology
MICKI THOMAS - Director Information Technology
AARON THOMAS - Director Engineering
JASON TRIAIL - Director Culinary Development
WILL BORTZ - Senior Manager Branding, Division
ANN GRAPPIN - Senior Manager Compliance
DANIEL TEW - Senior Manager Compliance, Food Safety
MAUREEN CROWLEY - Senior Manager Communications
CHRIS PERRY - Senior Manager Network, Engineering
STEPHANUS STEVE VOORMOLEN - Senior Manager Applications, Infrastructure
BEN WILDER - Senior Manager Information Technology
JULIE LLOYD - Senior Manager Human Resources
ANTHONY MICHELI - Senior Manager Corporate Development
JENIFER CONKLING - Manager Accounting, Payroll
KEVIN JONES - Manager Finance, Information Technology
JENNIFER HAGAN - Manager Operations, Promotion
JIM BENNETT - Manager Information Technology
DUDLEY BOOTH - Manager Operations
DAISY HAN - Manager Information Technology
ESTHER LIU - Manager HRIS
SHARON PERKINS - Manager Technology
LEKSI STERRITT - Manager Information Technology
ZHENGYIN WU - Manager HRIS
LEONARDO PESSOA - Manager Development
RAVEN HARRIS - Project Manager Technology
SUSAN SCHROEDER - Specialist Human Resources
SUSAN BURTON - Specialist Recruitment
DIANE MATTINGLY - Senior Coordinator Recruitment
MEGHAN BIELSKI - Coordinator Training

Joella's Hot Chicken
3400 Frankfort Ave
Lousiville, KY 40207

Telephone: (502) 895-2235
Internet Homepage: joellas.com
Company Email: comments@joellas.com
Type of Business: Chain Restaurant Operator
Year Founded: 2015
Total Sales: $14,340,000 (e)
Total Units: 18
Trade Names: Joella's Hot Chicken (18)
Company-Owned Units: 18
Primary Menu: Chicken (18)
Projected Openings: 2
Areas of Operation: FL, GA, IN, KY, OH
Type of Foodservice: Fast Casual (18)
Parent Company: Schulte Restaurant Group, LOUISVILLE, KY

Key Personnel
DARRYL SCHULTE - CEO

JRS Restaurant Group
1910 Cumberland Ave
Middlesboro, KY 40965-1231

Mailing Address: P. O. Box 218, MIDDLESBORO, KY, 40965
Telephone: (606) 248-8352
Internet Homepage: jrskfc.com
Company Email: info@jrskfc.com
Type of Business: Chain Restaurant Operator
Year Founded: 1964
Total Sales: $55,310,000 (e)
Number of Employees: 299
Average Check: Lunch(12); Dinner(16)
Total Units: 31
Trade Names: KFC (31)
Units Franchised From: 31
Preferred Square Footage: 2,400
Preferred Location Types: Freestanding
Primary Menu: Chicken (31)
Areas of Operation: IN, KY, TN
Type of Foodservice: Quick Serve (31)
Franchise Affiliation: Long John Silver's Inc., LOUISVILLE, KY
Primary Distributors: (Food) McLane/Hebron, HEBRON, KY

Key Personnel
JAY SHOFFNER - CEO; President; CFO; Manager Supply Chain, Real Estate, Design, Human Resources; General Buyer

Janbakhsh Inc.
1215 N Main St Ste 15
Monticello, KY 42633-2900

Telephone: (606) 348-3377
Type of Business: Chain Restaurant Operator
Total Sales: $16,046,000 (e)
Total Units: 8
Trade Names: Domino's (8)
Units Franchised From: 8
Primary Menu: Pizza (8)
Areas of Operation: KY
Type of Foodservice: Quick Serve (8)
Franchise Affiliation: Domino's Pizza Inc, ANN ARBOR, MI

Key Personnel
HASSAN JANBAKHSH - Owner; General Buyer

Domino's Franchisee
155 Pine Crest Rd
Morehead, KY 40351-8835

Telephone: (606) 783-0030
Type of Business: Chain Restaurant Operator
Total Sales: $22,945,000 (e)
Total Units: 11
Trade Names: Domino's (11)
Units Franchised From: 11
Primary Menu: Pizza (11)
Areas of Operation: KY
Type of Foodservice: Quick Serve (11)
Franchise Affiliation: Domino's Pizza Inc, ANN ARBOR, MI

Key Personnel
CHRISTOPHER J. SHORT - Owner; General Buyer

BB Riverboats
101 Riverboat Row
Newport, KY 41071-1069

Telephone: (859) 261-8500
Fax Number: (859) 292-2452
Internet Homepage: bbriverboats.com
Company Email: info@bbriverboats.com
Type of Business: Chain Restaurant Operator
Year Founded: 1968
Total Sales: $24,024,000 (e)
Alcohol Sales: 25%
Number of Employees: 600
Average Check: Lunch(12); Dinner(36)
Internet Order Processing: Yes
Total Units: 2
Trade Names: Belle of Cincinnati (1); River Queen (1)
Company-Owned Units: 2
Preferred Square Footage: 5,000; 8,000
Preferred Location Types: Freestanding
Alcohol Served: Beer, Wine, Liquor
Primary Menu: American (2)
Areas of Operation: KY
Type of Foodservice: Casual Dining (2)
Catering Services: Yes
Primary Distributors: (Equipment) Atlanta Fixture & Sales Co., ATLANTA, GA; (Food) SYSCO Food Services of Louisville, LOUISVILLE, KY; (Supplies) xpedx, LOVELAND, OH

Key Personnel
TERRI BERNSTEIN - CEO; General Buyer
BEN BERNSTEIN - CFO
NANCY WILLHOITE - Director Business Development
GARY BRYANT - Manager Human Resources

Cincinnati Subs, LLC
86 Carothers Rd Ste B
Newport, KY 41071-2457

Telephone: (859) 581-5551
Type of Business: Chain Restaurant Operator
Total Sales: $6,941,000 (e)
Total Units: 5
Trade Names: Jersey Mike's Subs (5)
Units Franchised From: 5
Primary Menu: Sandwiches/Deli (5)
Areas of Operation: KY
Type of Foodservice: Quick Serve (5)
Franchise Affiliation: Jersey Mike's Franchise Systems, MANASQUAN, NJ

Key Personnel
MICHAEL OUIMET - Owner

Dixie Chili Inc.
733 Monmouth St
Newport, KY 41071-1812

Telephone: (859) 291-5337
Fax Number: (859) 291-5547
Internet Homepage: dixiechili.com
Company Email: info@dixiechili.com
Type of Business: Chain Restaurant Operator
Year Founded: 1929
Total Sales: $4,523,000 (e)
Number of Employees: 55
Average Check: Lunch(12); Dinner(14)
Internet Order Processing: Yes
Internet Sales: 20.00%
Total Units: 3
Trade Names: Dixie Chili (3)
Company-Owned Units: 3
Preferred Location Types: Freestanding
Primary Menu: American (3)
Areas of Operation: KY
Type of Foodservice: Quick Serve (3)
On-site Distribution Center: Yes
Primary Distributors: (Full Line) Gordon Food Service, SPRINGFIELD, OH
Notes: The company derives approximately 20% of its revenue from the manufacture and sale of chili.

Key Personnel
JIM KRUMME - CFO; VP Operations; Controller

McMaflah, Inc
607 N Main St
Nicholasville, KY 40356-1025

Telephone: (859) 885-5698
Type of Business: Chain Restaurant Operator
Year Founded: 1976
Total Sales: $32,720,000 (e)
Number of Employees: 400
Average Check: Breakfast(8); Lunch(8); Dinner(8)
Total Units: 7
Trade Names: McDonald's (7)
Units Franchised From: 7
Preferred Square Footage: 2,500; 3,000
Preferred Location Types: Freestanding
Primary Menu: Hamburger (7)

Areas of Operation: KY
Type of Foodservice: Quick Serve (7)
Franchise Affiliation: McDonald's Corporation, CHICAGO, IL

Key Personnel
ALLAN NAHRA - President; General Manager; Director Finance, Operations, Real Estate, Human Resources; General Buyer
DAN SETTLES - General Manager; Director Purchasing, Information Systems, Supply Chain; Supervisor Area

De Max Inc
1001 Burlew Blvd
Owensboro, KY 42303-1736

Telephone: (270) 685-4542
Internet Homepage: leesfamousrecipe.com/locations/kentucky/owensbor
Type of Business: Chain Restaurant Operator
Total Sales: $2,799,000 (e)
Total Units: 3
Trade Names: Lee's Famous Recipe Chicken (3)
Units Franchised From: 3
Primary Menu: Chicken (3)
Areas of Operation: IN, KY
Type of Foodservice: Quick Serve (3)
Franchise Affiliation: Lee's Famous Recipes Inc., FORT WALTON BEACH, FL

Key Personnel
BILL WATHEN - President; General Buyer

D G W Investment, Inc
5250 US Highway 60 W
Paducah, KY 42001-9331

Telephone: (270) 443-4364
Fax Number: (270) 477-0656
Type of Business: Chain Restaurant Operator
Total Sales: $16,930,000 (e)
Total Units: 8
Trade Names: Sonic America's Drive-In (8)
Units Franchised From: 8
Primary Menu: Hamburger (8)
Areas of Operation: IN, KY, MO, TN
Type of Foodservice: Quick Serve (8)
Franchise Affiliation: Sonic Corp., OKLAHOMA CITY, OK

Key Personnel
MICHAEL MCDORMAN - CEO
HEATHER BUCHANAN - Manager Payroll

Dippin' Dots Franchising Co.
2775 W Park Dr
Paducah, KY 42001

Mailing Address: PO Box 9207, PADUCAH, KY, 42002-9207
Telephone: (270) 575-6990
Fax Number: (270) 443-8997
Internet Homepage: dippindots.com; docpopcorn.com/contact-us
Company Email: email@dippindots.com
Type of Business: Chain Restaurant Operator
Year Founded: 1988
Systemwide Sales: $41,783,000 (e)
Total Sales: $4,664,000 (e)
Number of Employees: 225
Average Check: Breakfast(8); Lunch(8); Dinner(8)
Internet Order Processing: Yes
Internet Sales: 3.00%
Total Units: 172
Trade Names: Dippin' Dots (105); Doc Popcorn (67)
Units Franchised To: 172
Preferred Square Footage: 2,500
Preferred Location Types: Community Mall; Institution (college/hospital); Kiosk; Mobile Unit; Outlet Mall; Parks; Regional Mall; Stadiums
Primary Menu: Snacks (172)
Projected Openings: 10
Areas of Operation: AK, AL, AR, AZ, CA, CO, CT, DE, FL, GA, HI, IL, IN, KY, LA, MD, MN, MO, MS, NC, ND, NE, NM, NV, NY, OH, OK, OR, PA, PR, SC, SD, TN, TX, UT, VA, WV, WY, FC
Foreign Countries: AUSTRALIA; CANADA; ENGLAND; GREECE; JAPAN; SOUTH KOREA; THE PHILIPPINES
Type of Foodservice: Quick Serve (172)
Distribution Centers: LANCASTER, CA; PADUCAH, KY
On-site Distribution Center: Yes
Subsidiaries: Doc Popcorn Franchising Inc., PADUCAH, KY
Parent Company: Dippin' Dots LLC, OKLAHOMA CITY, OK

Key Personnel
MICHAEL G. BARRETTE - Chief Marketing Officer; Chief Sales Officer
MIKE MILNER - VP Finance
STEPHEN C. HEISNER - VP Administration, Information Systems, Customer Service, Human Resources
STEVE HEISNER - VP Administration, Human Resources
ADAM GROSS - Senior Director Sales
DANA KNUDSEN - Senior Director Marketing
BLAIRE LIPERT - Senior Director Business Development, International
JAMES MCCLELLAN - Director Information Systems
KIMBERLY MILITE - Director Sales
NATE HEIDER - Director Marketing
RICK NOBLE - Director Operations
HOLLY BLAKE - Division Manager
ALPHONSO CLARK - Manager Region
BILLIE STUBER - Manager Communications
JEFF VANCLEVE - Manager Transportation
JOHN WRIGHT - Manager Facility/Maintenance
TERESA JARRETT - Manager Franchise Development

Doc Popcorn Franchising Inc.
2775 W Park Dr
Paducah, KY 42001

Telephone: (270) 575-6990
Fax Number: (270) 575-6997
Internet Homepage: docpopcorn.com
Company Email: doc@docpopcorn.com
Listing Type: Subsidiary
Type of Business: Chain Restaurant Operator
Year Founded: 2003
Total Sales: $3,742,000 (e)
Internet Order Processing: Yes
Total Units: 100
Trade Names: Doc Popcorn (100); Doc Popcorn/Dippin' Dots (1)
Company-Owned Units: 1
Units Franchised To: 100
Preferred Location Types: Kiosk; Mobile Unit; Regional Mall; Stadiums
Primary Menu: Snacks (101)
Areas of Operation: AZ, CA, CO, CT, DC, FL, GA, HI, IL, IN, KY, MA, MD, MI, MN, MO, NC, NH, NJ, NV, NY, OH, OK, PA, PR, SC, TN, TX, VA, WI, FC
Foreign Countries: JAPAN
Type of Foodservice: Quick Serve (101)
Parent Company: Dippin' Dots Franchising Co., PADUCAH, KY

Key Personnel
SCOTT FISCHER - President
STEVE ROTHENSTEIN - Senior Director Franchising

Kentucky Bell Incorporated
3120 James Sanders Blvd
Paducah, KY 42001-9481

Mailing Address: PO Box 9225, PADUCAH, KY, 42002-9225
Telephone: (270) 442-8226
Fax Number: (270) 442-8226
Type of Business: Chain Restaurant Operator
Total Sales: $8,786,000 (e)
Total Units: 3
Trade Names: Taco Bell (3)
Units Franchised From: 3
Primary Menu: Taco (3)

Areas of Operation: KY
Type of Foodservice: Quick Serve (3)
Franchise Affiliation: Taco Bell Corp., IRVINE, CA

Key Personnel
STEVE SMITH - President; General Buyer

MCL Corp.
240 Berger Rd Ste 2
Paducah, KY 42003-4574

Mailing Address: PO Box 7809, PADUCAH, KY, 42002-7809
Telephone: (270) 554-4002
Fax Number: (270) 554-4279
Type of Business: Chain Restaurant Operator
Year Founded: 1975
Total Sales: $47,360,000 (e)
Number of Employees: 450
Average Check: Breakfast(8); Lunch(8); Dinner(10)
Total Units: 10
Trade Names: McDonald's (10)
Units Franchised From: 10
Preferred Square Footage: 2,500; 3,000
Preferred Location Types: Freestanding
Primary Menu: Hamburger (10)
Projected Remodelings: 2
Areas of Operation: IL, KY
Type of Foodservice: Quick Serve (10)
Franchise Affiliation: McDonald's Corporation, CHICAGO, IL
Primary Distributors: (Full Line) Gateway Distribution, LEBANON, IL

Key Personnel
MICHAEL LOVE - President; Director Real Estate; General Buyer
CATHY ELLIOT - Director Marketing
TED GALVIN - Director Operations
PHYLLIS BALL - Manager Accounting
TRENT SNEAD - Store Manager
STONEY SAMONS - Supervisor Area

Tug Valley Arch
1104 3rd St
Paintsville, KY 41240-1822

Telephone: (606) 297-7000
Fax Number: (606) 297-7010
Type of Business: Chain Restaurant Operator
Year Founded: 1979
Total Sales: $61,110,000 (e)
Number of Employees: 600
Average Check: Breakfast(8); Lunch(8); Dinner(10)
Total Units: 13
Trade Names: McDonald's (13)
Units Franchised From: 13
Preferred Square Footage: 2,500
Preferred Location Types: Freestanding
Primary Menu: Hamburger (13)
Areas of Operation: KY
Type of Foodservice: Quick Serve (13)
Franchise Affiliation: McDonald's Corporation, CHICAGO, IL

Key Personnel
BOB HUTCHISON - Partner; Director Finance, Operations, Facility/Maintenance, Information Systems, Real Estate, Human Resources; General Buyer
TOM HUTCHISON - Partner; Director Operations, Facility/Maintenance, Information Systems, Supply Chain, Marketing, Real Estate, Design, Human Resources, Store Fixtures; General Buyer

Subway Franchise
2204 Martin Luther King Jr Blvd
Paris, KY 40361-1281

Telephone: (859) 987-7827
Internet Homepage: subway.com
Type of Business: Chain Restaurant Operator
Total Sales: $1,540,000 (e)
Total Units: 2
Trade Names: Subway (2)
Units Franchised From: 2
Primary Menu: Sandwiches/Deli (2)
Areas of Operation: KY
Type of Foodservice: Quick Serve (2)
Franchise Affiliation: Doctor's Associates Inc., MILFORD, CT

Key Personnel
DANIEL BIDDLE - President

Domino's Franchisee
115 Pike St
Pikeville, KY 41501-1119

Telephone: (606) 432-1133
Type of Business: Chain Restaurant Operator
Total Sales: $29,147,000 (e)
Total Units: 14
Trade Names: Domino's (14)
Units Franchised From: 14
Primary Menu: Pizza (14)
Areas of Operation: KY
Type of Foodservice: Quick Serve (14)
Franchise Affiliation: Domino's Pizza Inc, ANN ARBOR, MI

Key Personnel
TIMOTHY A. HURD - Owner; General Buyer

McEnaney Enterprises
618 Marion Rd
Princeton, KY 42445-6289

Telephone: (270) 365-6224
Fax Number: (270) 365-6225
Company Email: mcenaneyent@yahoo.com
Type of Business: Chain Restaurant Operator
Total Sales: $33,140,000 (e)
Total Units: 7
Trade Names: McDonald's (7)
Units Franchised From: 7
Preferred Square Footage: 2,500
Primary Menu: Hamburger (7)
Areas of Operation: KY
Type of Foodservice: Quick Serve (7)
Franchise Affiliation: McDonald's Corporation, CHICAGO, IL

Key Personnel
JOSEPH MCENANEY - President; General Buyer
KATHY MCENANEY - Owner

McKenzie Enterprise Associates LLC
1613 Diederich Blvd
Russell, KY 41169-1627

Telephone: (606) 836-6969
Fax Number: (606) 836-6999
Company Email: mck_enterprises@yahoo.com
Type of Business: Chain Restaurant Operator
Total Sales: $9,057,000 (e)
Number of Employees: 100
Average Check: Lunch(14); Dinner(24)
Total Units: 4
Trade Names: Fazoli's (4)
Units Franchised From: 4
Preferred Square Footage: 2,900
Preferred Location Types: Freestanding; Strip Mall
Primary Menu: Italian (4)
Areas of Operation: KY, WV
Type of Foodservice: Fast Casual (4)
Franchise Affiliation: Fazoli's Restaurant LLC, LEXINGTON, KY

Key Personnel
NANCY MCKENZIE - President; General Manager; General Buyer

Domino's Franchisee
213 E Main St
Scottsville, KY 42164-1415

Telephone: (270) 237-5555
Type of Business: Chain Restaurant Operator
Total Sales: $6,210,000 (e)

Total Units: 3
Trade Names: Domino's (3)
Units Franchised From: 3
Primary Menu: Pizza (3)
Areas of Operation: KY
Type of Foodservice: Quick Serve (3)
Franchise Affiliation: Domino's Pizza Inc, ANN ARBOR, MI

Key Personnel
ROBERT D. LAWSON - Owner; General Buyer

John T. McGinnis Inc.
111 Midland Blvd
Shelbyville, KY 40065-9732

Telephone: (502) 633-5100
Fax Number: (502) 633-5105
Company Email: mcginnis@dcr.net
Type of Business: Chain Restaurant Operator
Year Founded: 1983
Total Sales: $13,641,000 (e)
Number of Employees: 650
Average Check: Breakfast(10); Lunch(10); Dinner(10)
Total Units: 7
Trade Names: Hardee's (7)
Units Franchised From: 7
Preferred Square Footage: 2,500
Preferred Location Types: Freestanding
Primary Menu: Hamburger (7)
Areas of Operation: IN, KY
Type of Foodservice: Quick Serve (7)
Franchise Affiliation: Hardee's Food Systems Inc., FRANKLIN, TN
Primary Distributors: (Food) McLane/Rocky Mount, ROCKY MOUNT, NC

Key Personnel
JOHN MCGINNIS - President; Owner; General Buyer

Dairy Queen of Somerset
205 N Main St
Somerset, KY 42501-1404

Mailing Address: PO Box 401, SOMERSET, KY, 42502-0401
Telephone: (606) 678-8563
Fax Number: (606) 561-6209
Type of Business: Chain Restaurant Operator
Year Founded: 1969
Total Sales: $12,310,000 (e)
Number of Employees: 72
Average Check: Breakfast(8); Lunch(8); Dinner(8)
Total Units: 9
Trade Names: Dairy Queen (9)
Units Franchised From: 9
Preferred Location Types: Freestanding
Primary Menu: American (9)
Areas of Operation: KY
Type of Foodservice: Quick Serve (9)
Foodservice Management Venues: Schools
Franchise Affiliation: International Dairy Queen Inc., BLOOMINGTON, MN
Primary Distributors: (Full Line) SYSCO Food Services of Louisville, LOUISVILLE, KY

Key Personnel
GENE CHESHIRE - Chairman
DAN CHESHIRE - President; General Buyer

Shellmark Corp
4412 S Highway 27
Somerset, KY 42501-6177

Telephone: (606) 679-2266
Type of Business: Chain Restaurant Operator
Total Sales: $9,591,000 (e)
Total Units: 4
Trade Names: Burger King (4)
Units Franchised From: 4
Preferred Location Types: Freestanding
Primary Menu: Hamburger (4)
Areas of Operation: KY
Type of Foodservice: Quick Serve (4)
Franchise Affiliation: Burger King Worldwide Inc., MIAMI, FL

Key Personnel
MARK MERRICK - Owner; General Buyer

Graviss McDonald's Restaurants
100 United Dr Ste 4C
Versailles, KY 40383-1497

Telephone: (859) 873-2394
Fax Number: (859) 879-8989
Type of Business: Chain Restaurant Operator
Year Founded: 1967
Total Sales: $41,960,000 (e)
Number of Employees: 405
Average Check: Breakfast(8); Lunch(8); Dinner(10)
Total Units: 9
Trade Names: McDonald's (9)
Units Franchised From: 9
Preferred Square Footage: 2,500
Preferred Location Types: Freestanding
Primary Menu: Hamburger (9)
Areas of Operation: KY
Type of Foodservice: Quick Serve (9)
Franchise Affiliation: McDonald's Corporation, CHICAGO, IL

Key Personnel
JOE GRAVISS - President; Director Information Systems, Real Estate; General Buyer
BOB WAITKUS - Director Operations, Facility/Maintenance, Marketing

McDonald's of Winchester
1324 Fulton Rd
Winchester, KY 40391-1009

Telephone: (859) 744-7160
Fax Number: (859) 744-7161
Internet Homepage: mcdonaldsofkentucky.com
Type of Business: Chain Restaurant Operator
Year Founded: 1973
Total Sales: $55,950,000 (e)
Number of Employees: 580
Average Check: Breakfast(8); Lunch(8); Dinner(8)
Total Units: 12
Trade Names: McDonald's (12)
Units Franchised From: 12
Preferred Square Footage: 2,500
Preferred Location Types: Convenience Store/Gas Station; Freestanding
Primary Menu: Hamburger (12)
Areas of Operation: KY
Type of Foodservice: Quick Serve (12)
Franchise Affiliation: McDonald's Corporation, CHICAGO, IL
Primary Distributors: (Food) The Anderson-DuBose, ROCHESTER, NY

Key Personnel
GERALD HEALY III - President; Director Finance, Information Systems, Real Estate, Human Resources; General Buyer
JIM BENNETT - Director Operations, Facility/Maintenance

Cartee Land Development Inc.
201 Stewart Ave
Worthington, KY 41183-9331

Telephone: (606) 836-1196
Fax Number: (606) 836-9617
Internet Homepage: carteeland.com
Company Email: carteeland@carteeland.com
Type of Business: Chain Restaurant Operator
Year Founded: 1990
Total Sales: $35,840,000 (e)
Number of Employees: 480
Average Check: Lunch(10); Dinner(10)
Total Units: 19
Trade Names: Arby's (19)
Units Franchised From: 19
Preferred Square Footage: 2,500; 3,000
Preferred Location Types: Freestanding
Primary Menu: Sandwiches/Deli (19)
Areas of Operation: KY, OH, WV
Type of Foodservice: Quick Serve (19)
Franchise Affiliation: Arby's Restaurant Group, ATLANTA, GA
Primary Distributors: (Full Line) I Supply Co.,

FAIRBORN, OH

Key Personnel
RON CARTEE SR - President; Director Operations, Purchasing, Supply Chain; General Buyer
DIANA CARTEE - Partner; VP
RON CARTEE JR - Partner; Director Facility/Maintenance, Real Estate, Design, Store Fixtures
BEN R. COOKSEY - CFO; Director Finance, Human Resources

LOUISIANA

Pam Miller, Inc.
2761 Rodeo Rd
Abbeville, LA 70510-4054

Mailing Address: PO Box 760, ABBEVILLE, LA, 70511-0760
Telephone: (337) 893-1455
Fax Number: (337) 893-1484
Type of Business: Chain Restaurant Operator
Total Sales: $43,720,000 (e)
Number of Employees: 500
Total Units: 9
Trade Names: McDonald's (9)
Units Franchised From: 9
Preferred Square Footage: 2,500
Preferred Location Types: Discount Dept. Stores; Freestanding
Primary Menu: Hamburger (9)
Areas of Operation: LA
Type of Foodservice: Quick Serve (9)
Franchise Affiliation: McDonald's Corporation, CHICAGO, IL

Key Personnel
LAWRENCE MILLER - President; General Buyer

Krispy Krunchy Foods LLC
1826 Sterkx Road
Alexandria, LA 71301

Telephone: (188) 871-51950
Internet Homepage: krispykrunchy.com
Type of Business: Chain Restaurant Operator
Year Founded: 1989
Total Sales: $3,136,826,000 (e)
Total Units: 2,800
Trade Names: Krispy Krunchy Chicken (2,800)
Units Franchised To: 2,800
Primary Menu: Chicken (2,800)
Areas of Operation: AL, AR, AZ, CA, CO, CT, DC, FL, GA, IA, ID, IL, IN, KS, KY, LA, MA, MD, ME, MI, MN, MO, MS, NC, NE, NH, NJ, NM, NV, NY, OH, OK, OR, PA, RI, SC, SD, TN, TX, UT, VA, VT, WA, WI, WV, WY
Type of Foodservice: Quick Serve (2,800)

Key Personnel
JIM NORBERG - CEO
JIM ZIELKE - CFO
JOE GORDON - Chief Administrative Officer
ALICE CROWDER - Chief Marketing Officer
ALBERT PONT - Senior Director Operations
KYLE FRANZEN - Senior Director Supply Chain
ALAN DEMPSEY - Director Quality Assurance, Food Safety
RAY KEES - Director Culinary Development, Menu Development

Shelton Restaurant Group LLC
1439 Centre Ct Ste 600
Alexandria, LA 71301-3468

Telephone: (318) 443-3163
Fax Number: (318) 443-3170
Company Email: mikeshelto@aol.com
Type of Business: Chain Restaurant Operator
Total Sales: $168,460,000 (e)
Number of Employees: 450
Average Check: Dinner(8)
Total Units: 65
Trade Names: Popeyes Louisiana Kitchen (65)
Units Franchised From: 65
Preferred Location Types: Freestanding
Primary Menu: Chicken (65)
Areas of Operation: AR, LA, TX
Type of Foodservice: Quick Serve (65)
Franchise Affiliation: Popeyes Louisiana Kitchen Inc., ATLANTA, GA

Key Personnel
MIKE SHELTON - President; General Buyer

Subway Franchise
3748 S MacArthur Dr Ste 4418
Alexandria, LA 71302-3338

Telephone: (318) 442-8018
Internet Homepage: subway.com
Type of Business: Chain Restaurant Operator
Total Units: 3
Trade Names: Subway (3)
Units Franchised From: 3
Primary Menu: Sandwiches/Deli (3)
Areas of Operation: LA
Type of Foodservice: Quick Serve (3)
Franchise Affiliation: Doctor's Associates Inc., MILFORD, CT

Key Personnel
PARESHKUMAR PATEL - Owner

Wilburn Enterprises
1458 Peterman Dr
Alexandria, LA 71301-3432

Telephone: (318) 619-9567
Fax Number: (318) 619-9568
Type of Business: Chain Restaurant Operator
Year Founded: 1987
Total Sales: $28,230,000 (e)
Number of Employees: 300
Average Check: Breakfast(8); Lunch(10); Dinner(10)
Total Units: 6
Trade Names: McDonald's (6)
Units Franchised From: 6
Preferred Square Footage: 2,500; 3,000
Preferred Location Types: Freestanding; Institution (college/hospital)
Primary Menu: Hamburger (6)
Areas of Operation: LA
Type of Foodservice: Quick Serve (6)
Franchise Affiliation: McDonald's Corporation, CHICAGO, IL
Primary Distributors: (Full Line) SYSCO Food Services of New Orleans LLC, HARAHAN, LA

Key Personnel
TERRY WILBURN - President; General Buyer
JASON LAMBERT - Director Operations, Facility/Maintenance, Store Fixtures
ANITA CARLINO - Manager Human Resources, Branch
NIKIA DENSON - Supervisor Payroll

CCs Coffee House
9131 Amber Dr
Baton Rouge, LA 70809

Mailing Address: P.O. Box 77910, BATON ROUGE, LA, 70817
Telephone: (225) 930-4630
Fax Number: (225) 368-4564
Internet Homepage: ccscoffee.com; communitycoffee.com
Company Email: customerservice@ccscoffee.com
Type of Business: Chain Restaurant Operator
Year Founded: 1910
Total Sales: $279,120,000 (e)
Number of Employees: 600
Average Check: Breakfast(8); Lunch(10); Dinner(10)
Internet Order Processing: Yes
Internet Sales: 2.00%
Total Units: 45
Trade Names: CC's Coffee House (45)
Company-Owned Units: 45
Preferred Square Footage: 2,500
Preferred Location Types: Community Mall; Downtown; Strip Mall
Primary Menu: Coffee (45)

Areas of Operation: LA, MS
Type of Foodservice: Quick Serve (45)
Catering Services: Yes
Distribution Centers: BATON ROUGE, LA; PORT ALLEN, LA
On-site Distribution Center: Yes
Primary Distributors: (Full Line) SYSCO Food Services of New Orleans LLC, HARAHAN, LA
Notes: The company derives approximately 78% of its revenue from wholesale operations.

Key Personnel
CELTON HAYDEN - President; General Buyer

Chicken Shacks
725 Lettsworth St
Baton Rouge, LA 70802-7138

Telephone: (225) 343-1687
Fax Number: (225) 383-3973
Internet Homepage: chickenshack.org
Type of Business: Chain Restaurant Operator
Year Founded: 1937
Total Sales: $3,127,000 (e)
Number of Employees: 28
Average Check: Lunch(8); Dinner(8)
Total Units: 3
Trade Names: Chicken Shack (3)
Company-Owned Units: 3
Preferred Location Types: Freestanding
Primary Menu: Chicken (3)
Areas of Operation: LA
Type of Foodservice: Family Restaurant (3)
On-site Distribution Center: Yes
Primary Distributors: (Full Line) Cayard's Inc., BATON ROUGE, LA

Key Personnel
JOSEPH A. DELPIT - President; Partner; Controller; Executive Chef
HENRY BAPTISTE - Partner; General Manager; General Buyer
JHAUNE DELPIT - VP Finance; Manager Accounting
DERRICK DELPIT - VP Operations

Clements Management
3003 Old Forge Dr Ste B
Baton Rouge, LA 70808-3150

Mailing Address: PO Box 14477, BATON ROUGE, LA, 70898-4477
Telephone: (225) 926-9495
Fax Number: (225) 926-8976
Type of Business: Chain Restaurant Operator
Year Founded: 1999
Total Sales: $29,750,000 (e)
Number of Employees: 397
Average Check: Breakfast(8); Lunch(10); Dinner(10)
Total Units: 13
Trade Names: Burger King (13)
Units Franchised From: 13
Preferred Square Footage: 2,500; 4,000
Preferred Location Types: Freestanding
Primary Menu: Hamburger (13)
Areas of Operation: LA
Type of Foodservice: Quick Serve (13)
Franchise Affiliation: Burger King Worldwide Inc., MIAMI, FL
Primary Distributors: (Full Line) Performance Food Group, RICHMOND, VA

Key Personnel
CINDI MCDANIEL - Manager Operations, Facility/Maintenance, District

Jackiana, LLC
2431 S Acadian Thruway
Baton Rouge, LA 70808-2300

Telephone: (225) 456-7313
Type of Business: Chain Restaurant Operator
Total Sales: $40,960,000 (e)
Total Units: 16
Trade Names: Jack in the Box (16)
Units Franchised From: 16
Primary Menu: Hamburger (16)
Areas of Operation: LA
Type of Foodservice: Quick Serve (16)
Franchise Affiliation: Jack in the Box Restaurants, SAN DIEGO, CA

Key Personnel
TODD KELLER - Owner; General Buyer

McDonald's of Baton Rouge
7077 S Choctaw Dr
Baton Rouge, LA 70806-1353

Telephone: (225) 927-2453
Fax Number: (225) 927-2472
Type of Business: Chain Restaurant Operator
Year Founded: 1963
Total Sales: $186,960,000 (e)
Number of Employees: 3,500
Average Check: Breakfast(5); Lunch(8); Dinner(8)
Total Units: 63
Trade Names: McDonald's (63)
Units Franchised From: 63
Preferred Square Footage: 2,500; 3,000
Preferred Location Types: Discount Dept. Stores; Freestanding; Strip Mall
Primary Menu: Hamburger (63)
Areas of Operation: LA
Type of Foodservice: Quick Serve (63)
On-site Distribution Center: Yes
Franchise Affiliation: McDonald's Corporation, CHICAGO, IL
Primary Distributors: (Full Line) The Martin-Brower Co., PORT ALLEN, LA

Key Personnel
CHARLES L. VALLUZZO - CEO; President
JODY RYAN - General Manager
BRIAN GEHRLS - Director Operations
BRIAN SMALLWOOD - Area Manager Construction
NICOLE TRACY - Manager
LORI CASE - Manager Franchising
CHRISTINA DUPRE - Manager Sales
BENJAMIN MYERS - Manager
NIGEL ORRIS - Manager Finance
NIELESH PATEL - Manager
ARTHUR PEYTON - Manager

Mike Anderson's Seafood Restaurants
1031 W Lee Dr
Baton Rouge, LA 70820-4918

Telephone: (225) 766-7823
Fax Number: (225) 761-0707
Internet Homepage: mikeandersons.com
Company Email: gonzales@mikeandersons.com
Type of Business: Chain Restaurant Operator
Year Founded: 1975
Total Sales: $7,657,000 (e)
Alcohol Sales: 20%
Number of Employees: 150
Average Check: Lunch(18); Dinner(42)
Internet Order Processing: Yes
Total Units: 2
Trade Names: Mike Anderson's Seafood (2)
Company-Owned Units: 2
Preferred Square Footage: 5,500; 6,000
Preferred Location Types: Downtown; Freestanding; Mixed-use Center
Alcohol Served: Beer, Wine, Liquor
Primary Menu: Seafood (2)
Areas of Operation: LA
Type of Foodservice: Casual Dining (2)

Key Personnel
MIKE ANDERSON SR - Founder; Partner
MIKE ANDERSON JR - Partner; General Buyer

Piccadilly Restaurants LLC
4150 S Sherwood Forest Blvd Ste 100
Baton Rouge, LA 70816-4691

Telephone: (225) 293-9440
Fax Number: (225) 296-8370
Internet Homepage: piccadilly.com
Company Email: guestservices@piccadilly.com
Type of Business: Chain Restaurant Operator
Year Founded: 1944
Systemwide Sales: $368,609,000 (e)
Total Sales: $319,600,000 (e)

Number of Employees: 7,000
Average Check: Breakfast(8); Lunch(8); Dinner(10)
Internet Order Processing: Yes
Total Units: 33
Trade Names: Piccadilly Cafeteria (33)
Company-Owned Units: 33
Preferred Square Footage: 7,500; 10,000
Preferred Location Types: Freestanding; Regional Mall; Strip Mall
Primary Menu: American (33)
Projected Openings: 1
Areas of Operation: AL, FL, GA, LA, MS, TN, VA
Type of Foodservice: Cafeteria (33)
Foodservice Management Venues: Business & Industry; College & University; Health Care; Schools
Catering Services: Yes
Parent Company: Piccadilly Investments LLC, WEST HOLLYWOOD, CA

Key Personnel
CHRIS SANCHEZ - COO; VP Operations
FRED OTILLIO - VP Information Technology
PATRICK PRUDHOMME - VP
KEITH BROWN - VP Foodservice
DAVID STIDHAM - VP Marketing
DAVE TYNER - General Counsel
JEFF MILLER - Director Culinary Operations
CALLIE TUCKER - Director Marketing, Sales
DAVID JONES - Regional Manager
MORGAN BECK - Manager Region

Raising Cane's LLC
100 North St Ste 802
Baton Rouge, LA 70802

Telephone: (225) 383-7400
Fax Number: (225) 383-7404
Internet Homepage: raisingcanes.com
Company Email: info@raisingcanes.com
Type of Business: Chain Restaurant Operator
Year Founded: 1996
Systemwide Sales: $2,274,941,000 (e)
Total Sales: $2,044,150,000 (e)
Number of Employees: 4,950
Average Check: Lunch(10); Dinner(12)
Total Units: 788
Trade Names: Raising Cane's Chicken Fingers (788)
Company-Owned Units: 348
Units Franchised To: 440
Preferred Square Footage: 3,500
Preferred Location Types: Freestanding; Strip Mall
Primary Menu: Chicken (788)
Projected Openings: 5
Areas of Operation: AL, AR, AZ, CA, CO, GA, HI, IA, IL, KS, KY, LA, MA, MN, MO, MS, NE, NM, NV, OH, OK, SC, TN, TX, VA
Foreign Countries: BAHRAIN; KUWAIT; LEBANON; SAUDI ARABIA; UNITED ARAB EMIRATES
Type of Foodservice: Quick Serve (788)
Primary Distributors: (Full Line) SYSCO Food Services of New Orleans LLC, HARAHAN, LA

Key Personnel
TODD B. GRAVES - Chairman; Founder; CEO
MIKE ANDREWS - CFO
CHRISTINA CLARKE - Chief Marketing Officer
BRYAN L. BROWN - Chief Development Officer
KELBY LEUTHOLD - Senior VP Supply Chain
VINCE SEVERNS - VP Information Technology
DOMINIQUE VITRY - VP Research & Development
JD CUMMINGS - VP Recruitment
RICK FUCHS - VP Real Estate
DALE GOSS - VP Real Estate
JULIE A. JUVERA - VP Employee Development
ED LINK - Senior Director Restaurant Operations, Information Systems
DAVID A. ROGERS - Senior Director Business Development
KEVIN RIPLEY - Director Information Technology, Infrastructure
JORGE RODRIGUEZ - Director Asset Management
ROBERT MONTGOMERY - Director Real Estate Development
BRUCE SMITH - Director Facility/Maintenance
BEN HALBERT - Director
JOHN FINDLEY - Director Purchasing
CHERIE BEASLEY - Director Consumer Insights, Research & Development
JEREMY HUDSON - Regional Director Real Estate
DEVIN BUNDICK BONNER - Senior Manager
DAVID ROUSE MBA - Senior Manager Real Estate
JANELLE LEAKE - Area Manager Recruitment
MADELYN JARREAU - Manager Operations
MELANIE CORNELL - Manager Social Media
CHRIS PARK - Manager
MARI S. MARTINEZ - Manager Leasing
JOSHUA TERRITO - Manager Operations
BRITTNY THOMPSON MBA - Manager Field Marketing
CHRISTOPHER WALKER - Manager Real Estate

Rotolo's Pizzeria
2985 Millerville Rd
Baton Rouge, LA 70816-2828

Telephone: (225) 367-6400
Fax Number: (225) 400-9680
Internet Homepage: rotolos.com
Company Email: rotolosllc@rotolos.com
Type of Business: Chain Restaurant Operator
Year Founded: 1994
Total Sales: $25,760,000 (e)
Average Check: Dinner(12)
Total Units: 37
Trade Names: Rotolo's Pizzeria (37)
Company-Owned Units: 10
Units Franchised To: 27
Preferred Square Footage: 1,200; 2,500
Preferred Location Types: Freestanding; Strip Mall
Alcohol Served: Beer, Wine, Liquor
Primary Menu: Pizza (30)
Areas of Operation: AL, FL, LA, TX
Type of Foodservice: Casual Dining (30)
Catering Services: Yes

Key Personnel
MITCH ROTOLO - Partner; Executive Chef; Director Operations; General Buyer
TODD TROSCLAIR - Partner; General Buyer
RYAN BRACH - COO
ERIC MESSA - Regional Manager

Santa Fe Cattle Co.
16851 Jefferson Hwy Ste 9A
Baton Rouge, LA 70817-6988

Telephone: (225) 615-7191
Fax Number: (225) 757-9769
Internet Homepage: santafecattleco.com
Company Email: info@santafecattleco.com
Type of Business: Chain Restaurant Operator
Year Founded: 1996
Total Sales: $32,590,000 (e)
Alcohol Sales: 10%
Number of Employees: 692
Average Check: Lunch(14); Dinner(14)
Internet Order Processing: Yes
Total Units: 14
Trade Names: Santa Fe Cattle Co. (14)
Company-Owned Units: 1
Units Franchised To: 13
Preferred Square Footage: 6,000
Preferred Location Types: Downtown; Freestanding
Alcohol Served: Beer, Wine, Liquor
Primary Menu: Steak (14)
Areas of Operation: AL, LA, OK, TN
Type of Foodservice: Casual Dining (14)
Primary Distributors: (Full Line) Reinhart FoodService, AUSTELL, GA
Parent Company: Morrison Companies, BATON ROUGE, LA

Key Personnel
SHANE MORRISON - President; General Buyer
MIGUEL CRESPO - General Manager
MICHAEL SWANN - Manager

Walk-On's Enterprises
3960 Burbank Dr
Baton Rouge, LA 70808

Telephone: (225) 330-4533
Fax Number: (225) 330-4487
Internet Homepage: walk-ons.com;

walkonsenterprises.com
Company Email: contact@walkonsenterprises.com
Type of Business: Chain Restaurant Operator
Year Founded: 2003
Systemwide Sales: $191,709,000 (e)
Total Sales: $58,220,000 (e)
Internet Order Processing: Yes
Total Units: 64
Trade Names: Walk-On's (64)
Company-Owned Units: 4
Units Franchised To: 60
Preferred Square Footage: 7,000; 8,000; 8,400
Alcohol Served: Beer, Wine, Liquor
Primary Menu: American (64)
Projected Openings: 33
Areas of Operation: AL, FL, LA, MS, NC, TX
Type of Foodservice: Casual Dining (64)
Catering Services: Yes
Parent Company: Morrison Companies, BATON ROUGE, LA

Key Personnel
BRANDON LANDRY - Chairman; Co-Founder; Partner
SCOTT TAYLOR - CEO
CHRIS PORCELLI - CEO
DREW BREES - Partner
CHRIS OLIVIER - Partner
LAURIE CURTIS - Chief Marketing Officer
JENNIFER PECORARO-STRIEPLING - Chief Development Officer
TONY CABALLERO - VP Operations, Training
MICHAEL TURNER - VP Supply Chain, Culinary Development
JAMIE DAVIS - VP Procurement, Supply Chain
TYLER SCHACK - VP Technology
ANDY IZQUIERDO - VP Communications
BOBBY FRADELLA - Director Franchise Operations
JEANNE STUART HUNT - Manager Franchise Development
KELLY PARKER - Manager Marketing, Franchise Sales
ADAM COLE - Manager Culinary Operations, Region
JESSICA COMEAUX - Manager Kitchen Equipment
JODIE SUMMERS - Manager Catering

Yogurtland Franchisee
7474 Corporate Blvd Ste 104
Baton Rouge, LA 70809-1182

Telephone: (225) 636-5551
Type of Business: Chain Restaurant Operator
Total Sales: $4,249,000 (e)
Total Units: 4
Trade Names: Yogurtland (4)
Units Franchised From: 4
Primary Menu: Snacks (4)
Areas of Operation: LA
Type of Foodservice: Quick Serve (4)
Franchise Affiliation: Yogurtland Franchising Inc., FARMERS BRANCH, TX

Key Personnel
CHRIS PUCKETT - Owner; General Buyer

Domino's Franchisee
201 Superior Ave
Bogalusa, LA 70427-2622

Telephone: (985) 732-5551
Type of Business: Chain Restaurant Operator
Total Sales: $10,383,000 (e)
Total Units: 5
Trade Names: Domino's (5)
Units Franchised From: 5
Primary Menu: Pizza (5)
Areas of Operation: LA
Type of Foodservice: Quick Serve (5)
Franchise Affiliation: Domino's Pizza Inc, ANN ARBOR, MI

Key Personnel
GREGORY S. MAGEE - Owner; General Buyer

FWC Enterprises
688 Boardwalk Blvd
Bossier City, LA 71111-4385

Telephone: (318) 549-0636
Fax Number: (318) 741-5531
Internet Homepage: fwcfoods.com
Type of Business: Chain Restaurant Operator
Year Founded: 1997
Total Units: 12
Trade Names: IHOP (12)
Units Franchised From: 12
Primary Menu: American (12)
Areas of Operation: AL, LA, TX
Type of Foodservice: Family Restaurant (12)

Key Personnel
WAYNE COURT - CEO; President; Owner
LANCE WITT - Owner; Director Operations; General Buyer
JOHN CHILDERS - VP Operations

SHRI Modheswari Corp., Inc
420 Boardwalk Blvd
Bossier City, LA 71111-4383

Telephone: (318) 746-5055
Type of Business: Chain Restaurant Operator
Total Sales: $1,276,000 (e)
Total Units: 2
Trade Names: Cold Stone Creamery (2)
Units Franchised From: 2
Primary Menu: Snacks (2)
Areas of Operation: LA
Type of Foodservice: Quick Serve (2)
Franchise Affiliation: Kahala Brands, SCOTTSDALE, AZ

Key Personnel
KAMLESH KIRALAL MODI - Partner
JAGRUTI KAMLESH MODI - Partner

Bayou's Best Burgers, LLC
324 E Lockwood St
Covington, LA 70433-2914

Telephone: (985) 327-5717
Fax Number: (888) 371-9041
Internet Homepage: bayousbestburgers.com
Company Email: info@bayousbestburgers.com
Type of Business: Chain Restaurant Operator
Total Sales: $15,790,000 (e)
Total Units: 8
Trade Names: Five Guys Burgers and Fries (8)
Units Franchised From: 8
Preferred Location Types: Freestanding; Strip Mall
Primary Menu: Hamburger (8)
Projected Openings: 2
Areas of Operation: LA
Type of Foodservice: Fast Casual (8)
Franchise Affiliation: Five Guys Holdings Inc., LORTON, VA

Key Personnel
ANDY MITTS - CEO; Partner
WILLIAM JACOB - President; Partner; General Buyer
SANDRA C. BLANCHARD - Manager Administration

PJ's Coffee of New Orleans LLC
180 New Camellia Blvd Ste 100
Covington, LA 70433-7835

Telephone: (985) 792-5899
Fax Number: (985) 792-1201
Internet Homepage: pjscoffee.com
Company Email: information@pjscoffee.com
Type of Business: Chain Restaurant Operator
Year Founded: 1979
Total Sales: $17,120,000 (e)
Alcohol Sales: 2%
Number of Employees: 813
Average Check: Dinner(14)
Internet Order Processing: Yes
Total Units: 92
Trade Names: PJ's Coffee of New Orleans (100)
Company-Owned Units: 12
Units Franchised To: 79
Preferred Location Types: Freestanding

Primary Menu: Coffee (100)
Areas of Operation: AR, GA, LA, MS, NJ, TX
Type of Foodservice: Quick Serve (100)
Parent Company: Ballard Brands, COVINGTON, LA

Key Personnel
SCOTT BALLARD - CEO
CORRADO GIACONA - VP Distribution
RYAN STANSBURY - Director Franchise Development
JEFF D. GIAVOTELLA - Manager Finance

Ott & Ballard Enterprises, LLC
1701 W Laurel Ave Ste C
Eunice, LA 70535-4055

Telephone: (318) 348-0147
Fax Number: (318) 644-0200
Company Email: mballard1967@yahoo.com
Type of Business: Chain Restaurant Operator
Total Sales: $2,420,000 (e)
Total Units: 3
Trade Names: Little Caesars Pizza (3)
Units Franchised From: 3
Primary Menu: Pizza (3)
Areas of Operation: LA
Type of Foodservice: Quick Serve (3)
Franchise Affiliation: Little Caesar Enterprises Inc., DETROIT, MI

Key Personnel
MARTY BALLARD - Partner; General Buyer
TONYA BALLARD - Partner; General Buyer

Hoot Owl Corporation
113 W Thomas St
Hammond, LA 70401-3250

Mailing Address: PO Box 2785, HAMMOND, LA, 70404-2785
Telephone: (985) 542-9210
Fax Number: (985) 542-9211
Internet Homepage: bradysdowntown.com; jacmelinn.com; nuvolaris.com
Company Email: hootowlcorp@bellsouth.net
Type of Business: Chain Restaurant Operator
Year Founded: 1977
Total Sales: $7,760,000 (e)
Alcohol Sales: 25%
Number of Employees: 65
Average Check: Breakfast(10); Lunch(16); Dinner(30)
Total Units: 3
Trade Names: Brady's (1); Jacmel Inn (1); Nuvolari's Ristorante (1)
Company-Owned Units: 3
Preferred Location Types: Freestanding
Alcohol Served: Beer, Wine, Liquor

Primary Menu: American (1); Italian (1); Sandwiches/Deli (1)
Areas of Operation: LA
Type of Foodservice: Casual Dining (1); Fine Dining (2)
Catering Services: Yes
Primary Distributors: (Full Line) SYSCO Food Services of New Orleans LLC, HARAHAN, LA

Key Personnel
PAUL MURPHY - President; Partner; Executive Chef; Director Loss Prevention, Advertising, Real Estate, Product Development, Food Safety; General Buyer
RICK COLUCCI - Partner; VP
WALLY SIMMONS - General Manager
MICHELLE BARNUM - Manager Administration

S&D Spicy Kitchens
110 W Robert St
Hammond, LA 70401-3227

Telephone: (985) 542-4780
Fax Number: (985) 542-4892
Internet Homepage: sd-kitchens.com
Company Email: customerservice@spicykitchens.com
Type of Business: Chain Restaurant Operator
Year Founded: 1991
Total Sales: $17,870,000 (e)
Number of Employees: 155
Average Check: Lunch(8); Dinner(8)
Total Units: 11
Trade Names: Popeyes Chicken (11)
Units Franchised From: 11
Preferred Square Footage: 2,200; 2,500
Preferred Location Types: Freestanding
Primary Menu: Chicken (11)
Areas of Operation: AR, LA
Type of Foodservice: Quick Serve (11)
Primary Distributors: (Full Line) Reinhart FoodService, SHREVEPORT, LA

Key Personnel
MATHEW HUNT - President; General Manager; Director Food Safety; General Buyer
SHIRLEY HUNT - VP; Director Finance, Operations, Information Systems, Human Resources; General Buyer

The Salad Station
2520 W Church St
Hammond, LA 70401

Telephone: (985) 345-7253
Internet Homepage: thesaladstation.com
Type of Business: Chain Restaurant Operator
Year Founded: 2012
Total Units: 28
Trade Names: The Salad Station (28)
Company-Owned Units: 28

Primary Menu: Health Foods (28)
Projected Openings: 8
Areas of Operation: AR, FL, LA, MS, TN
Type of Foodservice: Fast Casual (28)

Key Personnel
SCOTT HENDERSON - Founder; President; Partner
CINDY HENDERSON - Partner

DEROCHE GRILLS OF HOUMA, L.L.C.
1826 Martin Luther King Jr Blvd
Houma, LA 70360-2499

Telephone: (985) 262-1012
Type of Business: Chain Restaurant Operator
Total Sales: $7,079,000 (e)
Total Units: 4
Trade Names: Moe's Southwest Grill (4)
Units Franchised From: 4
Primary Menu: Southwest/Tex-Mex (4)
Areas of Operation: LA
Type of Foodservice: Fast Casual (4)
Franchise Affiliation: Moe's Southwest Grill LLC, ATLANTA, GA

Key Personnel
BRADLEY DEROCHE - Owner; General Buyer

Abnar Corp
414 Hospital Dr
Jennings, LA 70546-3636

Telephone: (337) 824-7847
Fax Number: (337) 824-7849
Type of Business: Chain Restaurant Operator
Year Founded: 1995
Total Sales: $74,890,000 (e)
Number of Employees: 1,800
Average Check: Breakfast(8); Lunch(8); Dinner(10)
Total Units: 16
Trade Names: McDonald's (16)
Units Franchised From: 16
Preferred Square Footage: 2,500; 3,000
Preferred Location Types: Freestanding
Primary Menu: Hamburger (16)
Areas of Operation: LA
Type of Foodservice: Quick Serve (16)
Franchise Affiliation: McDonald's Corporation, CHICAGO, IL
Primary Distributors: (Full Line) The Martin-Brower Co., PORT ALLEN, LA

Key Personnel
AJAY PATEL - Owner; General Buyer
RENEE PETTERSEN - Director Operations; General Buyer
JULEE CHIASSON - Manager

MISTY LEGROS - Administrative Assistant

Bud's Broiler Inc.
2309 Salem St
Kenner, LA 70062-7945

Telephone: (504) 467-0610
Fax Number: (504) 467-0609
Internet Homepage: budsbroiler.com
Company Email: info@budsbroiler.com
Type of Business: Chain Restaurant Operator
Year Founded: 1952
Systemwide Sales: $6,701,000 (e)
Total Sales: $2,504,000 (e)
Alcohol Sales: 2%
Number of Employees: 96
Total Units: 6
Trade Names: Bud's Broiler (6)
Company-Owned Units: 1
Units Franchised To: 5
Preferred Square Footage: 2,000
Preferred Location Types: Community Mall; Freestanding; Strip Mall
Alcohol Served: Beer
Primary Menu: Hamburger (6)
Areas of Operation: LA
Type of Foodservice: Quick Serve (6)
On-site Distribution Center: Yes

Key Personnel
JOSEPH CATALANO - President; Controller; Executive Chef; Manager Operations, Facility/Maintenance, Information Systems, Marketing, Real Estate, Design, Human Resources

Ground Pat'i Inc.
130 Rue Beauregard Ste D
Lafayette, LA 70508-3130

Telephone: (337) 984-7779
Fax Number: (337) 984-7769
Internet Homepage: groundpati.com
Company Email: racambre@aol.com
Type of Business: Chain Restaurant Operator
Year Founded: 1971
Systemwide Sales: $6,032,000 (e)
Total Sales: $2,400,000 (e)
Alcohol Sales: 30%
Number of Employees: 65
Average Check: Lunch(10); Dinner(16)
Total Units: 5
Trade Names: Ground Pat'i (5)
Company-Owned Units: 2
Units Franchised To: 3
Preferred Square Footage: 4,000
Preferred Location Types: Freestanding
Alcohol Served: Beer, Wine, Liquor
Primary Menu: American (5)
Areas of Operation: LA
Type of Foodservice: Casual Dining (5)

On-site Distribution Center: Yes
Primary Distributors: (Full Line) Reinhart FoodService, SHREVEPORT, LA

Key Personnel
RICK CAMBRE - President; CFO; Executive Chef; Manager Operations, Facility/Maintenance, Information Systems, Real Estate, Design, Human Resources, Menu Development; General Buyer

Kergan Bros.
3 Flagg Pl
Lafayette, LA 70508

Mailing Address: PO Box 80154, LAFAYETTE, LA, 70598-0154
Telephone: (337) 988-5301
Internet Homepage: sonic-blast.com
Type of Business: Chain Restaurant Operator
Total Sales: $118,930,000 (e)
Number of Employees: 1,555
Total Units: 56
Trade Names: Sonic America's Drive-In (56)
Units Franchised From: 56
Primary Menu: Hamburger (56)
Areas of Operation: LA
Type of Foodservice: Quick Serve (56)
Franchise Affiliation: Sonic Corp., OKLAHOMA CITY, OK

Key Personnel
TED KERGAN - President; General Buyer
JANET HEBERT - VP Finance
RHONDA GERHARD - Manager

MacLaff Inc
106 Oak Way Ln
Lafayette, LA 70506-3900

Telephone: (337) 981-4800
Fax Number: (337) 981-2826
Type of Business: Chain Restaurant Operator
Year Founded: 1987
Total Sales: $51,860,000 (e)
Number of Employees: 1,636
Average Check: Breakfast(8); Lunch(8); Dinner(10)
Total Units: 11
Trade Names: McDonald's (11)
Units Franchised From: 11
Preferred Square Footage: 2,500; 3,000
Preferred Location Types: Convenience Store/Gas Station; Discount Dept. Stores; Freestanding; Regional Mall
Primary Menu: Hamburger (11)
Projected Openings: 30
Areas of Operation: LA
Type of Foodservice: Quick Serve (11)
Franchise Affiliation: McDonald's Corporation, CHICAGO, IL

Primary Distributors: (Full Line) The Martin-Brower Co., PORT ALLEN, LA

Key Personnel
CHRIS KRAMPE - Partner; General Manager
E J. KRAMPE III - Partner; General Manager; Manager Facility/Maintenance
KEN KASTNER - VP Operations

RIV Corporation
3755 Ambassador Caffery Pkwy
Lafayette, LA 70503-5233

Mailing Address: PO Box 2907, LAFAYETTE, LA, 70502-2907
Telephone: (337) 981-1818
Fax Number: (337) 981-9085
Internet Homepage: chrispoboys.com
Type of Business: Chain Restaurant Operator
Year Founded: 1981
Total Sales: $1,920,000 (e)
Alcohol Sales: 15%
Number of Employees: 60
Average Check: Lunch(8); Dinner(8)
Total Units: 3
Trade Names: Chris' Poboys (3)
Company-Owned Units: 3
Preferred Location Types: Freestanding
Alcohol Served: Beer
Primary Menu: American (3)
Areas of Operation: LA
Type of Foodservice: Casual Dining (3)

Key Personnel
RICHARD RIVET - President; Executive Chef; Manager Operations, Purchasing, Marketing, Menu Development; General Buyer

TMJ Group
91 Settlers Trace Blvd Ste 2
Lafayette, LA 70508-6090

Telephone: (504) 302-2918
Internet Homepage: margaritavillebossiercity.com; thetmjgroup.com; willieschickenshack.com
Type of Business: Chain Restaurant Operator
Total Units: 9
Trade Names: Margaritaville Resort and Casino (1); The Halal Guys (1); Willie's Chicken Shack (7)
Company-Owned Units: 7
Units Franchised From: 2
Primary Menu: American (1); Chicken (7); Middle Eastern (1)
Projected Openings: 2
Areas of Operation: LA
Type of Foodservice: Quick Serve (9)
Franchise Affiliation: The Halal Guys Inc., ASTORIA, NY

Key Personnel
LOGAN TROTTER - Partner
AARON MOTWANI - Partner
TARUN JOLLY - Partner

Yobe Acquisition, LLC
3909 Ambassador Caffery Pkwy Ste I
Lafayette, LA 70503-5280

Telephone: (803) 701-9623
Internet Homepage: myyobe.com
Company Email: myyobe@myyobe.com
Type of Business: Chain Restaurant Operator
Total Units: 34
Trade Names: Yobe Frozen Yogurt (34)
Units Franchised To: 34
Preferred Location Types: Community Mall; Convenience Store/Gas Station; Freestanding; Kiosk; Strip Mall
Primary Menu: Snacks (34)
Areas of Operation: FL, GA, LA, NJ
Type of Foodservice: Quick Serve (34)

Key Personnel
SEENU G. KASTURI - Owner

Gehrig Enterprises
3414 Common St
Lake Charles, LA 70607-1729

Telephone: (337) 436-3368
Fax Number: (337) 436-3361
Type of Business: Chain Restaurant Operator
Year Founded: 1979
Total Sales: $38,240,000 (e)
Number of Employees: 275
Average Check: Breakfast(8); Lunch(8); Dinner(10)
Total Units: 8
Trade Names: McDonald's (8)
Units Franchised From: 8
Preferred Square Footage: 2,500
Preferred Location Types: Discount Dept. Stores; Freestanding
Primary Menu: Hamburger (8)
Areas of Operation: LA
Type of Foodservice: Quick Serve (8)
Franchise Affiliation: McDonald's Corporation, CHICAGO, IL
Primary Distributors: (Food) The Martin-Brower Co., PORT ALLEN, LA

Key Personnel
DOUG GEHRIG - President; Director Operations, Facility/Maintenance, Real Estate, Design; General Buyer
GERARD MACK - Director Operations
DUSTIN SMITH - Supervisor
MELANIE LONG - Supervisor

Ballard Brands LLC
4480 La 22 Suite 2
Mandeville, LA 70471

Telephone: (985) 792-5776
Fax Number: (985) 792-1201
Internet Homepage: ballardbrandsllc.com; wowcafe.com
Company Email: admin@wingery.com
Type of Business: Chain Restaurant Operator
Year Founded: 2001
Systemwide Sales: $98,362,000 (e)
Total Sales: $18,320,000 (e)
Alcohol Sales: 20%
Number of Employees: 122
Average Check: Lunch(14); Dinner(18)
Internet Order Processing: Yes
Internet Sales: 1.00%
Total Units: 243
Trade Names: Ideation Hospitality (11); PJ's Coffee of New Orleans (190); WOW American Eats (42)
Company-Owned Units: 3
Units Franchised To: 240
Preferred Square Footage: 3,000; 4,500
Preferred Location Types: Airports; Freestanding; Institution (college/hospital); Stadiums; Strip Mall
Alcohol Served: Beer, Wine, Liquor
Primary Menu: American (42); Coffee (190); Latin American/Cuban (11)
Projected Openings: 30
Areas of Operation: AL, CA, CO, DC, GA, IL, LA, MD, MI, MN, MO, MS, MT, NC, NJ, NM, NY, PA, TN, TX, VA, VT, WI
Type of Foodservice: Casual Dining (11); Family Restaurant (0); Fast Casual (42); Quick Serve (190)
Catering Services: Yes
Primary Distributors: (Full Line) SYSCO Food Services of New Orleans LLC, HARAHAN, LA
Parent Company: Ballard Brands, COVINGTON, LA
Headquarter Offices: Garces Restaurant Group Inc. LLC, PHILADELPHIA, PA

Key Personnel
PAUL BALLARD - Founder; Owner
STEVEN BALLARD - CEO; Owner
PETER BOYLAN - President
JEFF GIAVOTELLA - CFO
WILLIAM DIPAOLA - COO
DAVID MESA - Chief Development Officer; Exec VP
ALAN GUILBEAU - Exec VP Business Development
BRAD GRAHAM - VP Supply Chain
REID NOLTE - VP Brand Marketing
PATRICK SHAHEEN - VP Operations
RYAN STANSBURY - VP Franchise Development; Director Franchise Development
CORRADO GIACONA III - VP Branding

NORMAN ALBRIGHT - VP Operations
MELISSA DEBARBIERIS - General Counsel
NICHOLAS RENZI - Director Sales
TORI JONES BERMOND - Manager Franchise Development
SEAN CRONIN - Manager Operations

Miracle Restaurant Group, LLC
100 Mariners Blvd Ste 8
Mandeville, LA 70448-6896

Telephone: (985) 674-5840
Fax Number: (985) 674-9710
Internet Homepage: miraclerestaurantgroup.com
Type of Business: Chain Restaurant Operator
Year Founded: 1997
Total Sales: $52,570,000 (e)
Number of Employees: 588
Average Check: Lunch(10); Dinner(10)
Internet Order Processing: Yes
Total Units: 25
Trade Names: Arby's (25)
Units Franchised From: 25
Preferred Square Footage: 2,300
Preferred Location Types: Freestanding
Primary Menu: Sandwiches/Deli (25)
Areas of Operation: IL, IN, LA, MS, TX
Type of Foodservice: Quick Serve (25)
Franchise Affiliation: Arby's Restaurant Group, ATLANTA, GA
Primary Distributors: (Full Line) McLane/Lagrange, LAGRANGE, GA

Key Personnel
DON MOORE - CEO; President; General Manager; Director Finance, Operations, Purchasing, Information Systems, Real Estate
PATRICK GERNON - CFO
RICK O'HARA - Controller
JEREMY MOORE - Director Area

Acme Oyster House
110 Veterans Memorial Blvd Ste 203A
Metairie, LA 70005-4914

Telephone: (504) 835-6410
Fax Number: (504) 835-6414
Internet Homepage: acmeoyster.com
Type of Business: Chain Restaurant Operator
Year Founded: 1910
Total Sales: $7,247,000 (e)
Total Units: 7
Trade Names: Acme Oyster (7)
Company-Owned Units: 7
Preferred Location Types: Freestanding
Alcohol Served: Beer, Wine, Liquor
Primary Menu: Seafood (7)
Areas of Operation: AL, FL, LA

Type of Foodservice: Casual Dining (7)

Key Personnel
PAUL ROTNER - CEO; Director Operations; General Buyer
MIKE RODRIGUE - Owner
MONIQUE RICCI - Manager Marketing

Atomic Burger
3934 Veterans Boulevard
Metairie, LA 70002

Internet Homepage: theatomicburger.com
Type of Business: Chain Restaurant Operator
Year Founded: 2013
Number of Employees: 30
Total Units: 2
Company-Owned Units: 2
Primary Menu: Hamburger (2)
Projected Openings: 1
Areas of Operation: LA
Type of Foodservice: Quick Serve (2)

Key Personnel
JOSEPH SPITALE - Co-Founder
NICK SPITALE - Co-Founder

Copeland's of New Orleans Inc.
2601 Severn Ave Fl 17
Metairie, LA 70002-5934

Telephone: (504) 830-1000
Fax Number: (504) 620-2016
Internet Homepage: alcopeland.com; copelandscheesecakebistro.com; copelandsofneworleans.com
Company Email: comments@alcopeland.com
Type of Business: Chain Restaurant Operator
Year Founded: 1983
Systemwide Sales: $54,111,000 (e)
Total Sales: $19,720,000 (e)
Alcohol Sales: 20%
Number of Employees: 1,062
Average Check: Lunch(14); Dinner(30)
Total Units: 17
Trade Names: Copeland's Cheesecake Bistro (2); Copeland's of New Orleans (15)
Company-Owned Units: 12
Units Franchised To: 5
Preferred Square Footage: 1,500; 6,100; 6,500; 8,000
Preferred Location Types: Community Mall; Freestanding
Alcohol Served: Beer, Wine, Liquor
Primary Menu: American (2); Cajun/Creole (15)
Projected Openings: 3
Areas of Operation: AR, FL, GA, LA, TX
Type of Foodservice: Casual Dining (17)
Catering Services: Yes
Primary Distributors: (Food) SYSCO Food Services of New Orleans LLC, HARAHAN, LA
Parent Company: Al Copeland Investments Inc., METAIRIE, LA
Notes: Systemwide sales reflect operations of Copeland's of New Orleans restaurants only.

Key Personnel
WILLIAM H. MARVIN - Senior VP Purchasing
ALLISON COPELAND - VP
GLEN A. SLAVICH - Director Franchise Operations

David Briggs Enterprises Inc.
641 Papworth Ave
Metairie, LA 70005-3112

Telephone: (504) 831-9415
Fax Number: (504) 831-9763
Internet Homepage: fat-tuesday.com
Company Email: info@fat-tuesday.com
Type of Business: Chain Restaurant Operator
Year Founded: 1983
Systemwide Sales: $87,535,000 (e)
Total Sales: $47,640,000 (e)
Alcohol Sales: 70%
Number of Employees: 1,050
Average Check: Breakfast(10); Lunch(14); Dinner(26)
Internet Order Processing: Yes
Internet Sales: 1.00%
Total Units: 70
Trade Names: Fat Tuesday's (29); New Orleans Original Daiquiris (41)
Company-Owned Units: 22
Units Franchised To: 48
Preferred Square Footage: 3,000
Preferred Location Types: Freestanding; Lifestyle Center; Regional Mall; Strip Mall
Alcohol Served: Beer, Wine, Liquor
Primary Menu: Miscellaneous (70)
Areas of Operation: AZ, FL, LA, MN, NM, NV, PA, FC
Type of Foodservice: Fast Casual (70)
Primary Distributors: (Food) SYSCO Food Services of New Orleans LLC, HARAHAN, LA

Key Personnel
DAVID BRIGGS - Chairman
TRAVIS BRIGGS - President; General Buyer
DANNY DRAGO - CFO; Exec VP; Director Finance, Purchasing, Menu Development
ARCHIE DION - VP Information Technology
CAREY HOLLE - Director Real Estate, Design
MARLO CHRISTENSEN - Director Marketing

Deanie's Seafood Restaurant
1713 Lake Ave
Metairie, LA 70005-1313

Telephone: (504) 831-4141
Fax Number: (504) 833-3524
Internet Homepage: deanies.com
Company Email: customerservice@deanies.com
Type of Business: Chain Restaurant Operator
Year Founded: 1982
Total Sales: $9,573,000 (e)
Alcohol Sales: 15%
Number of Employees: 104
Average Check: Lunch(12); Dinner(18)
Internet Order Processing: Yes
Total Units: 3
Trade Names: Deanie's Seafood Restaurant (3)
Company-Owned Units: 3
Preferred Location Types: Freestanding
Alcohol Served: Beer, Wine, Liquor
Primary Menu: Seafood (3)
Areas of Operation: LA
Type of Foodservice: Casual Dining (3)
Catering Services: Yes
Primary Distributors: (Food) Reinhart Foodservice, HARAHAN, LA

Key Personnel
BARBARA A. CHIFICI - President; Partner; Executive Chef
DARREN CHIFICI - Partner; General Buyer
CHANDRA CHIFICI - Director Catering; General Buyer

Don's Seafood
4801 Veterans Memorial Blvd
Metairie, LA 70006-5209

Telephone: (504) 889-1550
Fax Number: (504) 889-1811
Internet Homepage: donsseafoodonline.com
Company Email: donsseafoodhut@bellsouth.net
Type of Business: Chain Restaurant Operator
Year Founded: 1934
Total Sales: $2,490,000 (e)
Alcohol Sales: 10%
Number of Employees: 115
Average Check: Lunch(14); Dinner(24)
Total Units: 6
Trade Names: Don's Seafood (6)
Company-Owned Units: 6
Preferred Location Types: Freestanding
Alcohol Served: Beer, Wine, Liquor
Primary Menu: Seafood (6)
Areas of Operation: LA
Type of Foodservice: Casual Dining (6)

Key Personnel
JULIE LANDRY - President

Duke Unlimited Inc.
3817 Edenborn Ave
Metairie, LA 70002-1521

Telephone: (504) 888-3985
Fax Number: (504) 888-3984
Type of Business: Chain Restaurant Operator
Year Founded: 1975
Total Sales: $37,310,000 (e)
Alcohol Sales: 15%
Number of Employees: 20
Total Units: 5
Trade Names: Ruth's Chris Steak House (5)
Units Franchised From: 5
Preferred Location Types: Hotel/Motel; Office Complex
Alcohol Served: Beer, Wine, Liquor
Primary Menu: Steak (5)
Projected Openings: 2
Areas of Operation: TX, ON
Foreign Countries: CANADA
Type of Foodservice: Fine Dining (5)
Catering Services: Yes
Franchise Affiliation: Ruth's Hospitality Group Inc., WINTER PARK, FL

Key Personnel
LANA DUKE - CEO; President

Fat Boy's Pizza
2565 Metairie Rd.
Metairie, LA 70001

Internet Homepage: eatfatboyspizza.com
Type of Business: Chain Restaurant Operator
Year Founded: 2019
Number of Employees: 100
Total Units: 9
Trade Names: Fat Boy's Pizza (9)
Company-Owned Units: 9
Primary Menu: Pizza (9)
Areas of Operation: LA, MS, TX
Type of Foodservice: Fast Casual (9)

Key Personnel
GABE CORCHIANI - Owner
CASEY BIEHL - VP Operations
PETE LEWIS - VP Finance, Human Resources
GEORGE MALEK - Director Operations
FAITH HILES - Manager Marketing

NOHSC Restaurant Group
6920 Veterans Memorial Blvd
Metairie, LA 70003-4419

Telephone: (504) 837-3382
Fax Number: (504) 835-3384
Internet Homepage: legacykitchen.com; nocbc.com; nohsc.com; nohsc.com
Company Email: info@nohsc.com
Type of Business: Chain Restaurant Operator
Year Founded: 1985
Total Sales: $11,050,000 (e)
Alcohol Sales: 1%
Number of Employees: 117
Average Check: Lunch(10); Dinner(14)
Internet Order Processing: Yes
Internet Sales: 1.00%
Total Units: 13
Trade Names: Legacy Kitchen (4); New Orleans Coffee & Beignet Company (1); New Orleans Hamburger & Seafood (8)
Company-Owned Units: 12
Preferred Location Types: Freestanding
Alcohol Served: Beer
Primary Menu: American (12); Coffee (1)
Projected Openings: 2
Areas of Operation: LA
Type of Foodservice: Casual Dining (12); Quick Serve (1)
Primary Distributors: (Full Line) SYSCO Food Services of New Orleans LLC, HARAHAN, LA

Key Personnel
NORRIS GREMILLION - Chairman; Partner
GARY S. WIENER - Partner; General Manager; Executive Chef; General Buyer
JERRY MARCIANTE - General Manager

B&G Food Enterprises LLC
1430 Sandra St
Morgan City, LA 70380-2136

Mailing Address: PO Drawer 3608, MORGAN CITY, LA, 70381-3608
Telephone: (985) 384-3333
Fax Number: (985) 384-4951
Internet Homepage: bgfood.com
Company Email: jleblanc@bgfood.com
Type of Business: Chain Restaurant Operator
Year Founded: 1982
Total Sales: $412,930,000 (e)
Number of Employees: 1,088
Average Check: Lunch(16); Dinner(16)
Total Units: 151
Trade Names: Taco Bell (151)
Units Franchised From: 151
Preferred Square Footage: 2,500
Preferred Location Types: Downtown; Freestanding; Strip Mall
Primary Menu: Chicken (4); Taco (132)
Areas of Operation: LA, MS, TX
Type of Foodservice: Quick Serve (136)
Franchise Affiliation: KFC Corporation, LOUISVILLE, KY; Taco Bell Corp., IRVINE, CA
Primary Distributors: (Full Line) McLane Foodservice, CARROLLTON, TX
Notes: B & G Food Enterprises of Texas and B & G Diversified Concepts also operate under the same management at this address; store counts & revenue include units operated by all three companies.

Key Personnel
ELLEN PENNISON - CFO; VP
TAMMIE TRAHAN - COO Group
JOHN HOVER - Exec VP Operations; VP Operations
GREGORY J. HAMER JR - Exec VP Administration
VALERIE LEBLANC - VP Operations; Director Marketing; Buyer Foodservice Equip/Supplies
TIM MCCONNELL - VP East Region
JAY LEBLANC - VP Human Resources
JOLENE BROWN - VP Marketing
GREG THEILE - VP Logistics
LARRY POORE - VP West Region
BRENDA C. HAMER - Treasurer; Corporate Secretary
MARY AUCOIN - Controller
ANDY WILKERSON - Director Operations
KRISTY LEBLANC - Director Marketing
TOMMY GEGENHEIMER - Director Facility/Maintenance
DENNIS TURNER - Director Information Systems
DAVIS MENDOZA - Director Human Resources, Training
SABRINA MERCHANT - Director Purchasing
WENDI ARCHAMBAULT - Director Sales
BRYAN LITTLETON - Director Operations
LISA REFUGE - Manager Finance
TODD BROWN - Manager Operations, District
JASON LONG - Manager Operations, District
MICHELLE MATHERNE - Manager Operations, District
CAROLINA WILKERSON - Manager Operations, District
JENNIFER TATE - Analyst Supply Chain

Tampico Restaurant Inc.
1025 N Victor II Blvd Ste I
Morgan City, LA 70380-1349

Telephone: (985) 385-6059
Fax Number: (985) 385-2302
Internet Homepage: tampicos.com
Type of Business: Chain Restaurant Operator
Year Founded: 1971
Total Sales: $7,244,000 (e)
Alcohol Sales: 40%
Number of Employees: 200
Average Check: Lunch(14); Dinner(20)
Total Units: 3
Trade Names: Acapulco Mexican Restaurant (1); Tampico's Restaurant (2)
Company-Owned Units: 3
Preferred Location Types: Freestanding; Strip Mall
Alcohol Served: Beer, Wine, Liquor
Primary Menu: Mexican (3)
Areas of Operation: LA

Type of Foodservice: Casual Dining (3)
Primary Distributors: (Full Line) US Foods, BENSENVILLE, IL

Key Personnel
JOE ARIAS - CEO; President; Controller; Executive Chef; Director Operations, Food Safety; General Buyer
PASCUAL IZAGUIRRE - Exec VP
KAREN DELAUNE - Manager Accounting

Moffett Foodservice
1424A Texas St
Natchitoches, LA 71457-3844

Telephone: (318) 352-4033
Fax Number: (318) 357-8122
Internet Homepage: moffettoil.com
Company Email: info@moffettoil.com
Type of Business: Chain Restaurant Operator
Total Sales: $4,839,000 (e)
Total Units: 3
Trade Names: Checkers (3)
Units Franchised From: 3
Primary Menu: Hamburger (3)
Areas of Operation: LA
Type of Foodservice: Quick Serve (3)
Franchise Affiliation: Checkers Drive-In Restaurants Inc., TAMPA, FL

Key Personnel
HENRY MOFFETT - President; General Buyer

Arnaud's
813 Bienville St
New Orleans, LA 70112-3121

Telephone: (504) 523-5433
Fax Number: (504) 355-5730
Internet Homepage: arnauds.com; remoulade.com
Company Email: info@arnauds.com
Type of Business: Chain Restaurant Operator
Year Founded: 1918
Total Sales: $11,301,000 (c)
Alcohol Sales: 30%
Number of Employees: 160
Average Check: Lunch(24); Dinner(66)
Total Units: 2
Trade Names: Arnaud's (1); Remoulade (1)
Company-Owned Units: 2
Preferred Location Types: Downtown
Alcohol Served: Beer, Wine, Liquor
Primary Menu: Cajun/Creole (1); French/Continental (1)
Areas of Operation: LA
Type of Foodservice: Casual Dining (1); Fine Dining (1)
Primary Distributors: (Full Line) SYSCO Food Services of New Orleans LLC, HARAHAN, LA

Key Personnel
ARCHIE CASBARIAN - Partner
JANE CASBARIAN - Partner; Director Menu Development; Manager Operations; General Buyer
KATY CASBARIAN - Partner; Director Operations; General Buyer
TOMMY DIGIOVANNI - Executive Chef; General Buyer

BRG Hospitality
426 Gravier St
New Orleans, LA 70130

Telephone: (504) 323-7707
Internet Homepage: brg-hospitality.com
Company Email: press@brg-hospitality.com
Type of Business: Chain Restaurant Operator
Total Sales: $12,530,000 (e)
Total Units: 9
Trade Names: August (1); Borgne (1); CHO THAI (1); Domenica (1); Eunice (1); Luke (1); Pizza Domenica (1); Shaya (1); Willa Jean (1)
Company-Owned Units: 9
Primary Menu: American (2); Asian (1); Cajun/Creole (1); Greek/Mediterranean (1); Italian (1); Mexican (0); Pizza (1); Seafood (1); Southern (1)
Areas of Operation: LA
Type of Foodservice: Casual Dining (8); Fine Dining (1)

Key Personnel
SHANNON WHITE - CEO
OCTAVIO MANTILLA - Owner
DAWN HAZEN - Director Human Resources
CAROL RIPLEY - Director Finance
MELISSA JOYCE - Director Operations, Catering
BROOKE BARNETT - Manager Marketing, Communications

Brooks Restaurants Inc.
PO Box 6577
New Orleans, LA 70174-6577

Telephone: (504) 363-0210
Fax Number: (504) 363-0224
Internet Homepage: brooksrestaurants.com; brooksrestaurants.com
Type of Business: Chain Restaurant Operator
Year Founded: 1989
Total Sales: $64,670,000 (e)
Number of Employees: 865
Average Check: Breakfast(8); Lunch(10); Dinner(10)
Total Units: 28
Trade Names: Burger King (28)
Units Franchised From: 28
Preferred Square Footage: 2,500; 4,000
Preferred Location Types: Freestanding
Primary Menu: Hamburger (28)
Areas of Operation: LA, MS, TN
Type of Foodservice: Quick Serve (28)
Franchise Affiliation: Burger King Worldwide Inc., MIAMI, FL

Key Personnel
EUGENE BROOKS - President; Director Information Systems, Real Estate
ANDREW BROOKS - Director Operations, Purchasing, Facility/Maintenance
COLIN BROOKS - Director Finance, Human Resources
CHALEA MARTIN - Manager Accounting

Creole Cuisine Restaurant Concepts
311 Decatur St
New Orleans, LA 70130

Telephone: (504) 586-2074
Internet Homepage: creolecuisine.com
Type of Business: Chain Restaurant Operator
Year Founded: 1989
Total Sales: $17,370,000 (e)
Total Units: 19
Trade Names: Boulevard American Bistro (1); Broussard's Restaurant & Courtyard (1); Cafe Maspero (1); Chartres House (1); Creole House Restaurant & Oyster Bar (1); Crescent City Pizza Works (1); Curio (1); Ernst Cafe (1); Flamingo A-Go-Go (1); Gumbo Ya-Ya (1); Kingfish Kitchen & Cocktails (1); Le BayouRestaurant & Oyster Bar (1); New Orleans Social House (1); Pier 424 Seafood Market (1); Royal House Oyster Bar (1); The Bombay Club (1); The Governor Restaurant (1); The Original Pierre Maspero's (1); Tommy's Cuisine (1)
Company-Owned Units: 19
Preferred Location Types: Downtown; Strip Mall
Primary Menu: American (3); Cajun/Creole (13); Italian (1); Pizza (1); Seafood (1)
Areas of Operation: LA
Type of Foodservice: Casual Dining (12); Fine Dining (6); Quick Serve (1)
Notes: The company also owns a variety of Daiquiri bars that do not serve food.

Key Personnel
MARV AMMARI - CEO
TRENT ANDERSON - COO
THOMAS BURNS - Area Director
ZEID AMMARI - VP
RICHY AMMARI - VP
JERMAINE STEVENSON - Executive Chef
MONA DEROUSSELLE - Executive Chef
CRISTINA QUACKENBUSH - Executive Chef
CAROL K. MILLER - Director Training
ROB IRWIN - Director Area
ART ARNOLD - Director Development

CAROL KELTZ MILLER - Director Training
REBECCA SCHATTMAN - Area Manager
STEPHANIE BAKER - Manager Catering
CAROLYN BUTLER - Manager Area
BRENT LEDET - Manager Marketing
ANGELLE V. JEANSONNE - Coordinator Development, Training

Dat Dog
3336 Magazine St
New Orleans, LA 70115-2411

Telephone: (504) 418-5456
Internet Homepage: datdog.com
Company Email: catering@datdog.com
Type of Business: Chain Restaurant Operator
Total Units: 5
Trade Names: Dat Dog (5)
Company-Owned Units: 5
Primary Menu: American (5)
Projected Openings: 5
Type of Foodservice: Fast Casual (5)

Key Personnel
LAURIE FISHER - Director Marketing

Dickie Brennan & Co.
605 Canal St
New Orleans, LA 70130-2307

Telephone: (504) 521-8313
Fax Number: (504) 523-1633
Internet Homepage: bourbonhouse.com; dickiebrennanssteakhouse.com; frenchquarter-dining.com; palacecafe.com; tableaufrenchquarter.com
Company Email: feedback@dickiebrennansssteakhouse.com
Type of Business: Chain Restaurant Operator
Year Founded: 1997
Total Sales: $30,814,000 (e)
Alcohol Sales: 12.50%
Number of Employees: 300
Average Check: Dinner(30)
Total Units: 4
Trade Names: Bourbon House (1); Dickie Brennan's Steakhouse (1); Palace Cafe (1); Tableau (1)
Company-Owned Units: 4
Preferred Location Types: Downtown; Hotel/Motel
Alcohol Served: Beer, Wine, Liquor
Primary Menu: Cajun/Creole (2); Seafood (1); Steak/Seafood (1)
Projected Remodelings: 1
Areas of Operation: LA
Type of Foodservice: Fine Dining (4)
Catering Services: Yes
Primary Distributors: (Full Line) SYSCO Food Services of New Orleans LLC, HARAHAN, LA

Key Personnel
DICKIE BRENNAN - President; Partner; General Buyer
LAUREN BRENNAN BROWER - Partner; General Buyer
STEVE PETTUS - Partner; Director Operations, Human Resources; General Buyer
MICHAEL MUNOZ - General Manager

H.N. Fernandez Inc.
813 Decatur St
New Orleans, LA 70116-3305

Telephone: (504) 581-2914
Fax Number: (504) 587-0847
Internet Homepage: cafedumonde.com
Company Email: office@cafedumonde.com
Type of Business: Chain Restaurant Operator
Year Founded: 1942
Total Sales: $4,810,000 (e)
Number of Employees: 236
Average Check: Breakfast(6); Lunch(6); Dinner(6)
Internet Order Processing: Yes
Internet Sales: 5.00%
Total Units: 9
Trade Names: Cafe Du Monde (9)
Company-Owned Units: 9
Preferred Square Footage: 2,000
Preferred Location Types: Downtown; Regional Mall
Primary Menu: Coffee (9)
Areas of Operation: LA
Type of Foodservice: Quick Serve (9)
On-site Distribution Center: Yes

Key Personnel
JAY ROMAN - President; Treasurer; Controller; Manager Finance; General Buyer
JOE MESA - Manager Purchasing, Supply Chain, Menu Development, Food Safety

Home on the Range: Folse Tramonto Restaurant Devel
777 Bienville St
New Orleans, LA 70130-2210

Telephone: (504) 553-2277
Internet Homepage: revolutionnola.com
Type of Business: Chain Restaurant Operator
Year Founded: 2010
Total Units: 2
Trade Names: Restaurant R'evolution (1); Seafood R'evolution (1)
Company-Owned Units: 2
Primary Menu: Cajun/Creole (1); Seafood (1)
Areas of Operation: LA, MS
Type of Foodservice: Fine Dining (2)

Key Personnel
JOHN FOLSE - Partner; Executive Chef
RICK TRAMONTO - Partner; Executive Chef
LUIS OCHOA - General Manager
BRIGETTE FOLSE - Director Marketing

Movie Tavern LLC
935 Gravier St Ste 1200
New Orleans, LA 70112

Telephone: (504) 297-1133
Fax Number: (214) 271-4134
Internet Homepage: movietavern.com
Type of Business: Foodservice Operations - Movie Theatre
Year Founded: 1998
Total Sales: $44,410,000 (e)
Alcohol Sales: 5%
Number of Employees: 1,107
Average Check: Lunch(14); Dinner(14)
Internet Order Processing: Yes
Internet Sales: 10.00%
Total Units: 60
Trade Names: Marcus Theatres (38); Movie Tavern (22)
Company-Owned Units: 60
Preferred Square Footage: 2,500
Preferred Location Types: Freestanding; Strip Mall
Alcohol Served: Beer, Wine, Liquor
Primary Menu: American (24)
Areas of Operation: CO, GA, KY, OH, PA, TX, VA
Type of Foodservice: In-Store Feeder (60)
Notes: The company derives approximately 80% of its revenue from theatre operations.

Key Personnel
DON WATSON - COO
HERLENE LAUX - Controller

Pat O'Brien's Bar Inc.
718 Saint Peter St
New Orleans, LA 70116-3119

Telephone: (504) 525-4823
Fax Number: (504) 588-2752
Internet Homepage: patobriens.com
Company Email: corporate@patobriens.com
Type of Business: Chain Restaurant Operator
Year Founded: 1933
Systemwide Sales: $23,433,000 (e)
Total Sales: $8,592,000 (e)
Alcohol Sales: 40%
Number of Employees: 250
Average Check: Lunch(18); Dinner(28)
Internet Order Processing: Yes
Internet Sales: 1.00%
Total Units: 3
Trade Names: Pat O'Brien's (3)
Company-Owned Units: 3

Alcohol Served: Beer, Wine, Liquor
Primary Menu: Cajun/Creole (3)
Areas of Operation: FL, LA, TX
Type of Foodservice: Casual Dining (3)
Catering Services: Yes
Primary Distributors: (Full Line) Sirocco Enterprises Inc., JEFFERSON, LA

Key Personnel
SHELLY OECHSNER WAGUESPACK - President; Owner
CHARLIE BATEMAN - VP Operations; General Buyer
SHELLEY WAGUESPACK - VP Administration
KENNY NEREIM - General Manager Operations
CHERYL SNOW - General Manager
HEATHER VARISH - Manager Human Resources
LYNN ARCENEAUX - Manager Event Planning
JENNIFER GREEN - Manager Event Planning, Sales
DONALD LANDRY - Manager Restaurant Operations
JESSICA MARTINO - Supervisor Human Resources
ROBERT COSTANTINI - Consultant

Shell Square Subway
701 Poydras St Ste 135
New Orleans, LA 70139-7723

Mailing Address: PO Box 27, NEW ORLEANS, LA, 70139
Telephone: (504) 524-5008
Type of Business: Chain Restaurant Operator
Total Sales: $2,402,000 (e)
Total Units: 4
Trade Names: Subway (4)
Units Franchised From: 4
Primary Menu: Sandwiches/Deli (4)
Areas of Operation: LA
Type of Foodservice: Quick Serve (4)
Franchise Affiliation: Doctor's Associates Inc., MILFORD, CT

Key Personnel
SHAHID QAYUM - President; General Buyer

Sizzling Steak Concepts, Inc.
812 Hillary St
New Orleans, LA 70118

Telephone: (504) 861-3377
Internet Homepage: sizzlingsteakconcepts.com
Type of Business: Chain Restaurant Operator
Total Sales: $94,280,000 (e)
Alcohol Sales: 5%
Number of Employees: 55
Average Check: Lunch(26); Dinner(70)
Total Units: 13
Trade Names: Ruth's Chris Steak House (12); Up On The Roof (1)
Company-Owned Units: 1
Units Franchised From: 12
Alcohol Served: Beer, Wine, Liquor
Primary Menu: American (1); Steak (12)
Areas of Operation: AL, GA, SC, TN
Type of Foodservice: Casual Dining (1); Fine Dining (12)
Catering Services: Yes
Franchise Affiliation: Ruth's Hospitality Group Inc., WINTER PARK, FL
Notes: Former franchisee has apparently sold most restaurants back. Contact info is for Ruth's HQ.

Key Personnel
MARK OSWALD - CEO; Partner
NANCY OSWALD - Partner
JOHN HAROF - CIO
MEGAN CROMWELL - General Manager
GINNY MASSEY - Creative Director
TISH MORRIS - Director Human Resources
CARLIE FLORENCE - Director Sales
WILSON OSWALD - Director Beverages
STEPHANIE TOBBEN - Director Marketing, Communications
NIKI REECE - Manager Payroll, Human Resources

Southeast Restaurant Group
1201 Canal St Ste C-2
New Orleans, LA 70112

Telephone: (504) 585-1535
Fax Number: (504) 585-1536
Internet Homepage: kfkgroup.com
Company Email: info@kfkgroup.com
Type of Business: Chain Restaurant Operator
Total Sales: $160,900,000 (e)
Total Units: 50
Trade Names: Chevys Fresh Mex (1); Marigny Brasserie (1); Mazza (1); NOLA Brasserie (1); Taco Bell (26); TGI Fridays (20)
Company-Owned Units: 3
Units Franchised From: 47
Primary Menu: American (22); Greek/Mediterranean (1); Mexican (1); Taco (26)
Areas of Operation: AL, AR, FL, LA, MS, TN, TX
Type of Foodservice: Casual Dining (24); Quick Serve (26)
Franchise Affiliation: Newk's Franchise Company, JACKSON, MS; T.G.I. Friday's Inc., DALLAS, TX; Taco Bell Corp., IRVINE, CA; Xperience Restaurant Group, CYPRESS, CA
Notes: Southeast Restaurant Group is part of KFK Group, a real estate development firm.

Key Personnel
ELIE KHOURY - CEO; President; Owner
LINDSEY LEE - CEO; Executive Assistant
PETE LEWIS - VP Administration
LEE CUICCHI - VP Development, Asset Management
ALLIE MCBRIDE - Director Human Resources
MO AL-HABASHNEH - Director Operations
NICHOLAS MORET - Director Operations
TIM LUPIN - Director Operations, Design
GARY POTTER - Director Facility/Maintenance
HEIDI ALLEN - Administrator Accounting

Taste Buds Inc.
8301 Oak St
New Orleans, LA 70118-2043

Telephone: (504) 486-4570
Fax Number: (504) 486-5563
Internet Homepage: mizadococina.com; semolina.com; tastebudsmgmt.com; zearestaurants.com
Type of Business: Chain Restaurant Operator
Systemwide Sales: $29,028,000 (e)
Total Sales: $13,820,000 (e)
Alcohol Sales: 20%
Number of Employees: 339
Average Check: Dinner(30)
Internet Order Processing: Yes
Internet Sales: 15.00%
Total Units: 11
Trade Names: Semolina (1); Zea Rotisserie & Grill (10)
Company-Owned Units: 11
Preferred Square Footage: 5,500; 6,000
Preferred Location Types: Freestanding
Alcohol Served: Beer, Wine, Liquor
Primary Menu: American (9); Italian (1)
Areas of Operation: AL, FL, LA, NM, TX
Type of Foodservice: Casual Dining (11)
Catering Services: Yes
Primary Distributors: (Full Line) SYSCO Food Services of New Orleans LLC, HARAHAN, LA

Key Personnel
GARY DARLING - Partner; Executive Chef; Manager Menu Development
HANS LIMBURG - Partner
GREG REGGIO - Partner
PAUL HUTSON - COO
FRANK LANGENBACKER - Senior VP Purchasing
KEVIN GUIDROZ - VP Restaurant Operations
JAMIE USEY - Director Accounting
MICHELLE BREATH - Director Human Resources, Training

The Commander's Palace Family Of Restaurants
1427 Washington Ave
New Orleans, LA 70130-5751

Telephone: (504) 891-4466
Fax Number: (504) 896-7606

Internet Homepage: brennanshouston.com; cafeadelaide.com; commanderspalace.com; reginellis.com; sobounola.com
Company Email: sam@commanderspalace.com
Type of Business: Chain Restaurant Operator
Year Founded: 1945
Total Sales: $30,040,000 (e)
Alcohol Sales: 9.50%
Number of Employees: 689
Average Check: Breakfast(30); Lunch(44); Dinner(58)
Internet Order Processing: Yes
Total Units: 13
Trade Names: Brennan's of Houston (1); Cafe Adelaide (1); Commander's Palace (1); Reginelli's Pizzaria (9); So Bou (1)
Company-Owned Units: 13
Preferred Location Types: Freestanding; Hotel/Motel
Alcohol Served: Beer, Wine, Liquor
Primary Menu: Cajun/Creole (4); Italian (9)
Areas of Operation: LA, TX
Type of Foodservice: Casual Dining (10); Fine Dining (3)
Catering Services: Yes
Primary Distributors: (Full Line) SYSCO Corporation, HOUSTON, TX

Key Personnel
TI MARTIN - President; Partner
ALEX BRENNAN-MARTIN - Partner; Director Operations; General Buyer
BRADFORD BRENNAN - Partner
LALLY BRENNAN - Partner; Manager Marketing
DOTTY BRENNAN - Partner
ARLENE NESSER - CFO; Treasurer
LAUREN S. KAPLAN - General Manager
DON STRUNK - General Manager
MEG BICKFORD - Executive Chef
STEPHEN WOODRUFF - Manager Operations

The Ralph Brennan Restaurant Group
550 Bienville St
New Orleans, LA 70130-2207

Telephone: (504) 539-5520
Fax Number: (504) 539-5538
Internet Homepage: brennansneworleans.com; neworleans-food.com
Company Email: info@neworleans-food.com
Type of Business: Chain Restaurant Operator
Year Founded: 1991
Total Sales: $10,820,000 (e)
Alcohol Sales: 15%
Number of Employees: 115
Average Check: Lunch(24); Dinner(36)
Internet Order Processing: Yes
Total Units: 6
Trade Names: Brennan's (1); Cafe NOMA (1); Jazz Kitchen (1); Ralph's On The Park (1); Red Fish Grill (1); The Napoleon House (1)
Company-Owned Units: 6
Preferred Location Types: Freestanding
Alcohol Served: Beer, Wine, Liquor
Primary Menu: Cajun/Creole (3); French/Continental (2); Italian (1)
Areas of Operation: CA, LA
Type of Foodservice: Casual Dining (1); Fine Dining (5)
Catering Services: Yes
Primary Distributors: (Food) SYSCO Food Services of New Orleans LLC, HARAHAN, LA; (Supplies) SYSCO Food Services of New Orleans LLC, HARAHAN, LA

Key Personnel
RALPH BRENNAN - President
CHARLEE WILLIAMSON - Exec VP Marketing, Business Development, Strategic Planning
ROY BARRE - General Manager
HALEY BITTERMANN - Corporate Chef; Director Operations, Menu Development; General Buyer
HALEY GABEL - Director Operations
JULIE JACOB - Director Human Resources
ANITA MONTERO - Manager Sales
TITUS PERKINS - Manager
CHRISTINA PERSAND - Manager Marketing, Promotions
KITTY POLK - Manager Purchasing
SHARON SALISBURY - Manager Sales
CALLIE STRICKLAND - Manager Marketing
CALLIE FOLSE - Manager Advertising

The Ruby Slipper Cafe
200 Magazine St
New Orleans, LA 70130-2423

Telephone: (504) 525-9355
Internet Homepage: therubyslippercafe.net
Type of Business: Chain Restaurant Operator
Year Founded: 2008
Total Units: 10
Trade Names: The Ruby Slipper Cafe (10)
Company-Owned Units: 10
Primary Menu: American (10)
Projected Openings: 2
Areas of Operation: AL, FL, LA
Type of Foodservice: Casual Dining (10)

Key Personnel
JENNIFER WEISHAUPT - CEO; Partner
JENNIFER BEOUGHER - CFO
JENNIFER MARTINDALE - Director Marketing
JEFF VINSON - Director Training
FREDRIC WOODS - Regional Director Operations
EDWIN VEGA - Senior Manager
MADELYN SAROLA - Manager Corporate Affairs

Checkerboard Restaurants, Inc.
2811 S Union St
Opelousas, LA 70570-5738

Telephone: (337) 942-3041
Fax Number: (337) 942-7112
Internet Homepage: goingcpa.com
Company Email: scott@goingcpa.com
Type of Business: Chain Restaurant Operator
Total Sales: $9,091,000 (e)
Total Units: 6
Trade Names: Checkers (6)
Units Franchised From: 6
Primary Menu: Hamburger (6)
Areas of Operation: LA, TX
Type of Foodservice: Quick Serve (6)
Franchise Affiliation: Checkers Drive-In Restaurants Inc., TAMPA, FL

Key Personnel
M SCOTT SEBASTIEN - CEO; President

VooDoo BBQ Franchising
40306 Highway 42 Ste 202
Prairieville, LA 70769-5286

Telephone: (225) 926-8780
Fax Number: (225) 924-6553
Internet Homepage: voodoobbq.com
Company Email: franchiseinfo@voodoobbq.com
Type of Business: Chain Restaurant Operator
Internet Order Processing: Yes
Total Units: 8
Trade Names: VooDoo BBQ & Grill (8)
Units Franchised To: 8
Alcohol Served: Beer, Wine, Liquor
Primary Menu: Bar-B-Q (8)
Areas of Operation: FL, IN, LA, TX
Type of Foodservice: Casual Dining (8)
Notes: Alternate phone (franchising): 877-902-4BBQ

Key Personnel
RICK JONES - Executive Director Culinary Operations
JOHNATHAN LINDSEY - General Manager

Domino's Franchisee
995 Tech Dr
Ruston, LA 71270-0701

Telephone: (318) 251-3030
Type of Business: Chain Restaurant Operator
Total Sales: $10,163,000 (e)
Total Units: 5
Trade Names: Domino's (5)
Units Franchised From: 5

Primary Menu: Pizza (5)
Areas of Operation: LA
Type of Foodservice: Quick Serve (5)
Franchise Affiliation: Domino's Pizza Inc, ANN ARBOR, MI

Key Personnel
CALVIN E. BARCOMB - Owner; General Buyer

BBQ Management, Inc.
9030 Mansfield Rd
Shreveport, LA 71118-2608

Telephone: (318) 688-1712
Fax Number: (318) 688-1199
Internet Homepage: podnuhs.com
Type of Business: Chain Restaurant Operator
Year Founded: 1977
Total Sales: $21,560,000 (e)
Number of Employees: 166
Average Check: Lunch(10); Dinner(14)
Total Units: 5
Trade Names: Podnuh's BBQ (5)
Company-Owned Units: 4
Units Franchised To: 1
Preferred Square Footage: 3,000
Preferred Location Types: Freestanding
Primary Menu: Bar-B-Q (5)
Areas of Operation: LA
Type of Foodservice: Quick Serve (5)
Catering Services: Yes
Primary Distributors: (Full Line) Reinhart FoodService, SHREVEPORT, LA

Key Personnel
SAM TALKINGTON - CEO; President; Executive Chef; Director Finance, Operations, Supply Chain, Real Estate, Design
SUZANNE TALKINGTON - Director Human Resources

Chick-A-Dilly
1029 Ilawn Ave
Shreveport, LA 71107-7036

Mailing Address: PO Box 78448, SHREVEPORT, LA, 71137-8448
Telephone: (318) 424-1369
Fax Number: (318) 424-1368
Type of Business: Chain Restaurant Operator
Year Founded: 1976
Total Sales: $6,555,000 (e)
Number of Employees: 50
Average Check: Lunch(8); Dinner(8)
Total Units: 5
Trade Names: Chick-A-Dilly (5)
Company-Owned Units: 5
Preferred Square Footage: 2,000
Preferred Location Types: Freestanding
Primary Menu: Chicken (5)
Areas of Operation: AR, LA
Type of Foodservice: Quick Serve (5)
Primary Distributors: (Food) Ben E. Keith Foods, NORTH LITTLE ROCK, AR

Key Personnel
GAIL FANNING - President; Director Information Systems, Real Estate, Design, Human Resources, Menu Development; Manager Operations; General Buyer

Classic Restaurants LLC
9415 Mansfield Rd
Shreveport, LA 71118

Telephone: (318) 686-7200
Internet Homepage: southernclassicchicken.com
Type of Business: Chain Restaurant Operator
Year Founded: 1989
Total Sales: $3,216,000 (e)
Total Units: 17
Trade Names: Southern Classic Chicken (17)
Company-Owned Units: 13
Units Franchised To: 4
Preferred Location Types: Freestanding
Primary Menu: Chicken (17)
Areas of Operation: AR, LA, TX
Type of Foodservice: Quick Serve (17)

Key Personnel
LEON FANNING - Founder; Partner
AVON FANNING - Partner

Fire Marshall's, LLC
7230 Youree Dr Ste 113
Shreveport, LA 71105-5119

Telephone: (318) 798-6547
Type of Business: Chain Restaurant Operator
Total Sales: $2,524,000 (e)
Total Units: 2
Trade Names: Firehouse Subs (2)
Units Franchised From: 2
Preferred Location Types: Strip Mall
Primary Menu: Sandwiches/Deli (2)
Areas of Operation: LA
Type of Foodservice: Fast Casual (2)
Franchise Affiliation: Firehouse Restaurant Group Inc., JACKSONVILLE, FL

Key Personnel
GREG BURKE - President; General Buyer

Griggs Enterprises Inc.
330 Marshall St Ste 711
Shreveport, LA 71101-3016

Telephone: (318) 424-9748
Fax Number: (318) 425-2526
Type of Business: Chain Restaurant Operator
Year Founded: 1989
Total Sales: $66,000,000 (e)
Number of Employees: 950
Average Check: Breakfast(8); Lunch(8); Dinner(10)
Total Units: 14
Trade Names: McDonald's (14)
Units Franchised From: 14
Preferred Square Footage: 2,500; 3,000
Preferred Location Types: Freestanding
Primary Menu: Hamburger (14)
Areas of Operation: LA, TX
Type of Foodservice: Quick Serve (14)
Franchise Affiliation: McDonald's Corporation, CHICAGO, IL
Primary Distributors: (Food) The Martin-Brower Co., PORT ALLEN, LA

Key Personnel
ROY GRIGGS - CEO; President; Director Finance, Operations, Facility/Maintenance, Information Systems, Real Estate, Design; General Buyer

Helm Restaurants
1520 N Hearne Ave Ste 122
Shreveport, LA 71107-7155

Mailing Address: PO Box 7157, SHREVEPORT, LA, 71137-7157
Telephone: (318) 226-8500
Fax Number: (318) 226-4500
Type of Business: Chain Restaurant Operator
Year Founded: 1969
Total Sales: $40,830,000 (e)
Number of Employees: 750
Average Check: Lunch(8); Dinner(8)
Total Units: 15
Trade Names: Taco Bell (15)
Units Franchised From: 15
Preferred Square Footage: 2,500
Preferred Location Types: Freestanding
Primary Menu: Taco (15)
Areas of Operation: LA
Type of Foodservice: Quick Serve (15)
Franchise Affiliation: Taco Bell Corp., IRVINE, CA
Primary Distributors: (Food) McLane/Arlington, ARLINGTON, TX

Key Personnel
STEVE HELM - President; Director Facility/Maintenance, Real Estate, Design, Franchising
KATHY BAKER - Controller
CATHY REMEDIES - Manager Operations, Marketing; General Buyer

Monjunis
1315 Louisiana Ave
Shreveport, LA 71101-4623

Telephone: (318) 227-0847
Fax Number: (318) 227-9499
Internet Homepage: monjunis.com
Type of Business: Chain Restaurant Operator
Total Sales: $4,999,000 (e)
Alcohol Sales: 15%
Number of Employees: 16
Average Check: Lunch(14); Dinner(24)
Internet Order Processing: Yes
Internet Sales: 1.00%
Total Units: 4
Trade Names: Monjunis (4)
Company-Owned Units: 4
Preferred Square Footage: 3,000
Preferred Location Types: Freestanding; Strip Mall
Alcohol Served: Beer, Wine, Liquor
Primary Menu: Italian (4)
Areas of Operation: LA
Type of Foodservice: Casual Dining (4)
Catering Services: Yes
Primary Distributors: (Full Line) Doerle Food Services, SHREVEPORT, LA

Key Personnel
JIMMY ROSSO - Partner; Executive Chef; Director Catering; General Buyer
JUDY ROSSO - Partner; General Manager
LISA SUSANO - Partner
RICHARD TAYLOR - Partner

Superior Bar & Grill
6123 Line Ave
Shreveport, LA 71106-2052

Telephone: (318) 869-3243
Fax Number: (318) 869-4879
Internet Homepage: shreveport.superiorgrill.com
Type of Business: Chain Restaurant Operator
Year Founded: 1983
Total Sales: $23,290,000 (e)
Alcohol Sales: 35%
Number of Employees: 150
Average Check: Lunch(14); Dinner(22)
Total Units: 5
Trade Names: Superior Bar & Grill (5)
Company-Owned Units: 5
Preferred Location Types: Freestanding
Alcohol Served: Beer, Wine, Liquor
Primary Menu: Mexican (5)
Areas of Operation: AL, LA
Type of Foodservice: Casual Dining (5)
Catering Services: Yes
Primary Distributors: (Food) Reinhart Foodservice, LAFAYETTE, LA

Key Personnel
PHILIP BARBAREE - Partner; General Buyer
ROBERT L. KIRCHOFF - Partner; General Buyer
BRIAN WHITLEY - General Manager
CARLOS BROWN - General Manager; Executive Chef; General Buyer; Buyer Food
MARK BRYAN - Manager

El Paso Mexican Grill
602 N Canal Blvd
Thibodaux, LA 70301-8070

Telephone: (985) 447-3833
Internet Homepage: elpasomex.com
Type of Business: Chain Restaurant Operator
Year Founded: 2009
Total Units: 26
Trade Names: El Paso Mexican Grill (26)
Company-Owned Units: 26
Primary Menu: Mexican (26)
Projected Openings: 2
Areas of Operation: FL, LA, MS
Type of Foodservice: Casual Dining (26)

Key Personnel
RUBEN CHAVEZ - Owner; General Buyer

Premier Hospitality Inc.
1600 Richfield Rd
Thibodaux, LA 70301

Telephone: (985) 446-0075
Fax Number: (985) 446-0707
Internet Homepage: pepperspizzeria.com
Company Email: info@pepperspizzeria.com
Type of Business: Chain Restaurant Operator
Year Founded: 1999
Total Sales: $6,572,000 (e)
Number of Employees: 150
Total Units: 2
Trade Names: Peppers Pizzeria (2)
Company-Owned Units: 2
Preferred Location Types: Freestanding
Alcohol Served: Beer, Wine, Liquor
Primary Menu: Pizza (2)
Areas of Operation: LA
Type of Foodservice: Casual Dining (2)
Notes: Premier Hospitality also operates a catering service and full-service mobile kitchen.

Key Personnel
GRADY VERRET - Owner; General Buyer

Gilley Enterprises
455 Industrial Pkwy
West Monroe, LA 71291-9185

Telephone: (318) 396-4846
Fax Number: (318) 396-5180
Type of Business: Chain Restaurant Operator
Year Founded: 1999
Total Sales: $115,230,000 (e)
Number of Employees: 750
Average Check: Breakfast(8); Lunch(8); Dinner(10)
Total Units: 24
Trade Names: McDonald's (24)
Units Franchised From: 24
Preferred Square Footage: 2,500; 3,000
Preferred Location Types: Discount Dept. Stores; Freestanding
Primary Menu: Hamburger (24)
Projected Openings: 10
Areas of Operation: AR, LA
Type of Foodservice: Quick Serve (24)
Franchise Affiliation: McDonald's Corporation, CHICAGO, IL
Primary Distributors: (Full Line) McLane/Fort Worth, FORT WORTH, TX

Key Personnel
TONY GILLEY - President; Partner; General Manager Real Estate, Design, Store Fixtures; General Buyer
DEBI GILLEY - Partner; VP; Director Finance
AUSTIN ORBECK - General Manager
BRAD BURCH - Director Operations, Facility/Maintenance

Imperial Associates LLC
106 Ozone St
West Monroe, LA 71291-5220

Telephone: (318) 324-9000
Fax Number: (318) 324-9031
Company Email: tacotio@bayou.com
Type of Business: Chain Restaurant Operator
Year Founded: 1984
Total Sales: $16,580,000 (e)
Number of Employees: 150
Average Check: Lunch(8); Dinner(8)
Total Units: 6
Trade Names: Taco Bell (6)
Units Franchised From: 6
Preferred Square Footage: 1,800
Preferred Location Types: Freestanding; Strip Mall
Primary Menu: Taco (6)
Areas of Operation: LA
Type of Foodservice: Quick Serve (6)
Franchise Affiliation: Taco Bell Corp., IRVINE, CA
Primary Distributors: (Full Line)

McLane/Memphis, MEMPHIS, TN

Key Personnel
JIM DOULL - Owner; Manager Supply Chain, Real Estate, Design
DON TAYLOR - Controller; Manager Information Systems, Human Resources
DARRELL WHALEY - Manager Operations; General Buyer

Johnny's Pizza House Inc.
100 Arkansas Rd
West Monroe, LA 71291-2302

Mailing Address: PO Box 2757, WEST MONROE, LA, 71294-2757
Telephone: (318) 323-0518
Fax Number: (318) 322-3191
Internet Homepage: johnnysph.com
Company Email: johnny@johnnys-pizza.com
Type of Business: Chain Restaurant Operator
Year Founded: 1966
Total Sales: $38,440,000 (e)
Alcohol Sales: 3%
Number of Employees: 946
Average Check: Lunch(10); Dinner(10)
Total Units: 48
Trade Names: Johnny's Pizza House (48)
Company-Owned Units: 30
Units Franchised To: 18
Preferred Square Footage: 3,000
Preferred Location Types: Freestanding; Strip Mall
Alcohol Served: Beer
Primary Menu: Pizza (48)
Projected Openings: 3
Areas of Operation: LA
Type of Foodservice: Quick Serve (48)
Primary Distributors: (Full Line) US Foods, FLOWOOD, MS

Key Personnel
MELVIN DELACERDA - President; Executive Chef; Director Finance, Operations, Advertising, Real Estate, Design, Training
JAMES SPARKS - Manager Information Technology

MASSACHUSETTS

Barrett Restaurants Inc.
1235 Bedford St
Abington, MA 02351-1273

Telephone: (781) 871-3025
Fax Number: (781) 871-6524
Internet Homepage: abingtonalehouse.com; barrettrestaurantgroup.com; thecharliehorse.net
Company Email: info@barrettrestaruantgroup.com
Type of Business: Chain Restaurant Operator
Year Founded: 1973
Total Sales: $15,716,000 (e)
Alcohol Sales: 25%
Number of Employees: 100
Average Check: Lunch(14); Dinner(22)
Internet Order Processing: Yes
Total Units: 2
Trade Names: Abington Ale House & Grill (1); Charlie Horse (1)
Company-Owned Units: 2
Preferred Square Footage: 13,000
Preferred Location Types: Freestanding
Alcohol Served: Beer, Wine, Liquor
Primary Menu: American (2)
Areas of Operation: MA
Type of Foodservice: Casual Dining (2)
Catering Services: Yes
Primary Distributors: (Full Line) Reinhart Agar Supply Inc., TAUNTON, MA

Key Personnel
CAREY BARRETT-ALLAN - Owner; VP
STEVE SCHEPICI - Executive Chef; General Buyer
RALPH ALLEN - Manager Facility/Maintenance

Domino's Franchisee
75 Great Rd
Acton, MA 01720-5678

Telephone: (978) 264-4141
Type of Business: Chain Restaurant Operator
Total Sales: $3,960,000 (e)
Total Units: 2
Trade Names: Domino's (2)
Units Franchised From: 2
Primary Menu: Pizza (2)
Areas of Operation: MA
Type of Foodservice: Quick Serve (2)
Franchise Affiliation: Domino's Pizza Inc, ANN ARBOR, MI

Key Personnel
WALTER A. WYLAND - Owner; General Buyer

Spike's Junkyard Dogs, USA LLC
108 Brighton Ave
Allston, MA 02134

Telephone: (617) 254-7700
Internet Homepage: spikesjunkyarddogs.com
Type of Business: Chain Restaurant Operator
Year Founded: 1991
Systemwide Sales: $5,664,000 (e)
Total Sales: $4,681,000 (e)
Number of Employees: 54
Average Check: Breakfast(6); Lunch(8); Dinner(8)
Total Units: 3
Trade Names: Spike's Junkyard Dogs (3)
Units Franchised To: 3
Preferred Square Footage: 2,000
Preferred Location Types: Community Mall; Freestanding; Strip Mall
Primary Menu: Hot Dogs (3)
Areas of Operation: MA, RI
Type of Foodservice: Fast Casual (3)
Catering Services: Yes
Primary Distributors: (Full Line) Reinhart Agar Supply Inc., TAUNTON, MA

Key Personnel
DAVID DRAKE - President; Director Operations, Menu Development, Catering; General Buyer
BOB ANDREOLI - Owner

Burtons Grill LLC
300 Brickstone Sq Ste 103
Andover, MA 01810-1450

Telephone: (978) 664-5520
Fax Number: (978) 409-1764
Internet Homepage: burtonsgrill.com
Company Email: info@burtonsgrill.com
Type of Business: Chain Restaurant Operator
Total Sales: $78,340,000 (e)
Alcohol Sales: 15%
Number of Employees: 1,190
Average Check: Dinner(72)
Total Units: 16
Trade Names: Burtons Grill (16)
Company-Owned Units: 16
Preferred Location Types: Freestanding; Strip Mall
Alcohol Served: Beer, Wine, Liquor
Primary Menu: American (16)
Projected Openings: 1
Areas of Operation: CT, FL, MA, MD, NC, NH, SC, VA
Type of Foodservice: Fine Dining (16)

Key Personnel
FRANK PARZYCH - Area Director Operations
DENISE BARON HERRERA VP Operations; Executive Chef
BRIAN WHALEN - General Manager
JENNIFER QUIRK - Director Training

The Upper Crust Pizzeria
60 Massachusetts Ave
Arlington, MA 02474-8621

Telephone: (781) 646-1060
Fax Number: (781) 646-1062
Type of Business: Chain Restaurant Operator
Year Founded: 2001
Total Sales: $6,054,000 (e)
Total Units: 7

Trade Names: Upper Crust Pizzeria (7)
Company-Owned Units: 7
Primary Menu: Pizza (7)
Areas of Operation: MA, FC
Type of Foodservice: Casual Dining (7)

Key Personnel
DEB SUDIPBRATA - CFO
RAMI KHATATBA - Director Operations

Karl S. Vucich LLC
254 Hartford Ave
Bellingham, MA 02019-3000

Telephone: (508) 966-3769
Company Email: moesbellingham@gmail.com
Type of Business: Chain Restaurant Operator
Total Sales: $7,154,000 (e)
Total Units: 4
Trade Names: Moe's Southwest Grill (4)
Units Franchised From: 4
Primary Menu: Southwest/Tex-Mex (4)
Areas of Operation: MA
Type of Foodservice: Fast Casual (4)
Franchise Affiliation: Moe's Southwest Grill LLC, ATLANTA, GA

Key Personnel
KARL VUCICH - Owner; General Buyer

Grade Inc
411 Cabot St
Beverly, MA 01915-3158

Telephone: (978) 922-9727
Type of Business: Chain Restaurant Operator
Year Founded: 1986
Total Sales: $71,360,000 (e)
Total Units: 44
Trade Names: Dunkin' Donuts (44)
Units Franchised From: 44
Preferred Square Footage: 1,500; 2,200
Primary Menu: Snacks (44)
Areas of Operation: MA
Type of Foodservice: Quick Serve (44)
Franchise Affiliation: DD IP Holder, CANTON, MA

Key Personnel
DINART SERPA - President; General Buyer
GLENDA MATKINS - Controller; Office Manager

Aquitaine Group
584 Tremont St
Boston, MA 02118-1603

Telephone: (617) 247-1102
Fax Number: (617) 247-1107
Internet Homepage: aquitaineboston.com; aquitainechestnuthill.com; aquitainededham.com; aquitainegroup.com; gaslight560.com; gaslightlynnfield.com; unionrestaurant.com
Type of Business: Chain Restaurant Operator
Year Founded: 1998
Total Sales: $32,030,000 (e)
Alcohol Sales: 20%
Number of Employees: 505
Average Check: Breakfast(18); Lunch(30); Dinner(60)
Total Units: 8
Trade Names: Aquataine Boston (1); Aquataine Chestnut Hill (1); Aquataine Dedham (1); Cinquecento (1); Gaslight (2); Gaslight Lynnfield (1); Metropolis Cafe (1)
Company-Owned Units: 8
Preferred Square Footage: 2,000
Preferred Location Types: Downtown; Freestanding; Strip Mall
Alcohol Served: Beer, Wine, Liquor
Primary Menu: French/Continental (5); Italian (1); Steak/Seafood (2)
Areas of Operation: MA
Type of Foodservice: Fine Dining (8)
Primary Distributors: (Food) SYSCO Food Services of Albany, HALFMOON, NY; (Food) Specialty Foods, CHELSEA, MA

Key Personnel
SETH WOODS - Partner; Executive Chef; General Buyer
MATHEW BURNS - Partner; Director Human Resources
CHRISTOPHER GLIONNA - Director Operations
HUNT LATHAM - Manager Restaurant Operations

b.good LLC
2 Park Plz Ste 216
Boston, MA 02116-3985

Telephone: (617) 927-8333
Fax Number: (617) 424-5222
Internet Homepage: bgood.com
Type of Business: Chain Restaurant Operator
Year Founded: 2003
Total Sales: $69,330,000 (e)
Average Check: Lunch(10); Dinner(12)
Internet Order Processing: Yes
Total Units: 47
Trade Names: b.good (77)
Company-Owned Units: 61
Units Franchised To: 16
Preferred Square Footage: 2,000; 2,500
Primary Menu: Hamburger (77)
Areas of Operation: CT, IL, MA, ME, NC, NH, NJ, NY, PA, RI, TX, VA, VT, FC, ON
Foreign Countries: CANADA; GERMANY; SWITZERLAND
Type of Foodservice: Fast Casual (77)
Primary Distributors: (Full Line) US Foods, SEABROOK, NH

Parent Company: Stellar Restaurant Group, BOSTON, MA

Key Personnel
JON OLINTO - Co-Founder; President
J J. SMITH - COO
TONY ROSENFELD - VP Food; Executive Chef
JUDY LARKEE - VP; Controller

Barbara Lynch Gruppo
550 Tremont St Ste 2
Boston, MA 02116-6314

Telephone: (617) 399-8513
Fax Number: (661) 749-9991
Internet Homepage: barbaralynch.com
Company Email: info@barbaralynch.com
Type of Business: Chain Restaurant Operator
Total Sales: $32,070,000 (e)
Alcohol Sales: 25%
Number of Employees: 249
Average Check: Lunch(48); Dinner(90)
Total Units: 6
Trade Names: B&G Oysters Ltd. (1); Drink (1); Menton (1); No. 9 Park (1); Sportello (1); The Butcher Shop (1)
Company-Owned Units: 6
Preferred Location Types: Freestanding
Alcohol Served: Beer, Wine, Liquor
Primary Menu: American (1); French/Continental (3); Italian (1); Seafood (1)
Areas of Operation: MA
Type of Foodservice: Casual Dining (2); Fine Dining (4)
Catering Services: Yes

Key Personnel
BARBARA LYNCH - Owner; Executive Chef; General Buyer
MICHELE CARTER - Executive Chef
CAT SILIRIE - Director Alcoholic Beverages

Big Night Entertainment Group
186 Tremont St
Boston, MA 02116

Telephone: (617) 338-4343
Fax Number: (857) 753-4709
Internet Homepage: bneg.com
Company Email: info@bneg.com
Type of Business: Chain Restaurant Operator
Year Founded: 2006
Total Sales: $21,020,000 (e)
Foodservice Sales: $19,969,000 (e)
Total Units: 18
Trade Names: CBS Sporting Club (1); Empire (1); Explorateur (1); Foxwoods (1); Guy Fieri's Foxwoods (1); Guy Fieri's Tequila Cocina (1); High Rollers (1); Mémoire (1); Mystique (1);

Red Lantern (2); Shrine (1); Studio B (1); The Grand (1); The Scorpion Bar (3); VERSUS (1)
Company-Owned Units: 18
Preferred Location Types: Downtown
Alcohol Served: Beer, Wine, Liquor
Primary Menu: American (8); Asian (5); French/Continental (1); Mexican (4)
Areas of Operation: CT, MA
Type of Foodservice: Casual Dining (10); Fine Dining (8)

Key Personnel
ED KANE - Partner
JOE KANE - Partner
RANDY GREENSTEIN - Partner
JASON NICHOLS - VP Operations
KALI FOBERT - Controller Finance
JAMIE POLLOCK - Director Restaurant Operations
CHRISTINA NAJM - Director Marketing
KERRY LYNCH - Director Sales
MATT NEWTON - Director Talent

Bombolotti, Inc. / FFC, Inc.
250 Hanover St
Boston, MA 02113

Telephone: (617) 371-1176
Fax Number: (617) 371-1129
Internet Homepage: cantinaitaliana.com; ristorantefiore.com
Company Email: mgr@ristorantefiore.com
Type of Business: Chain Restaurant Operator
Total Sales: $3,161,000 (e)
Alcohol Sales: 15%
Number of Employees: 100
Average Check: Lunch(18); Dinner(36)
Internet Order Processing: Yes
Total Units: 2
Trade Names: Cantina Italiana (1); Ristorante Fiore (1)
Company-Owned Units: 2
Preferred Square Footage: 5,000
Preferred Location Types: Freestanding
Alcohol Served: Beer, Wine, Liquor
Primary Menu: Italian (2)
Areas of Operation: MA
Type of Foodservice: Fine Dining (2)
Primary Distributors: (Full Line) SYSCO of Boston, PLYMPTON, MA

Key Personnel
FIORE COLELLA - President; General Manager; Executive Chef; General Buyer

Boston Harbor Hotel
70 Rowes Wharf
Boston, MA 02110-3300

Telephone: (617) 439-7000
Fax Number: (617) 330-9450
Internet Homepage: bhh.com; meritagetherestaurant.com
Company Email: meritagetherestaurant@bhh.com
Type of Business: Foodservice Operations - Hotel/Motels
Total Sales: $10,288,000 (e)
Alcohol Sales: 20%
Number of Employees: 200
Total Units: 1
Restaurants in Hotels: 2
Trade Names: Boston Harbor Hotel (1)
Company-Owned Units: 2
Alcohol Served: Beer, Wine, Liquor
Areas of Operation: MA
Type of Foodservice: Casual Dining (2)
Primary Distributors: (Food) US Foods, SEABROOK, NH

Key Personnel
JOHN NOLEN - CEO
PAUL JACQUES - General Manager
STEPHEN JOHNSTON - General Manager
DANIEL BRUCE - Executive Chef; General Buyer
NORMA AYALA LEONG - Director Security
JENNIFER HARRIS - Director Sales
GARY SLOPER - Director
RACHEL STINGLETS - Director Catering
JENNIFER MCMAHON - Regional Director Marketing, Sales
REBECCA GUSTIN - Regional Director
JONATHAN MARTINEZ - Manager Security
MIKE MISILO - Manager Food and Beverage
WILLIAM KELLEY - Supervisor Security
ALISSA VIEIRA - Coordinator Sales
MARK GRADY - Engineer

Chin Management
150 Staniford St Ste 3
Boston, MA 02114-2557

Telephone: (617) 391-0038
Type of Business: Chain Restaurant Operator
Year Founded: 1988
Total Sales: $32,830,000 (e)
Number of Employees: 200
Average Check: Breakfast(8); Lunch(10); Dinner(12)
Total Units: 7
Trade Names: McDonald's (7)
Units Franchised From: 7
Preferred Square Footage: 2,500; 3,000
Preferred Location Types: Downtown; Freestanding
Primary Menu: Hamburger (7)
Areas of Operation: MA
Type of Foodservice: Quick Serve (7)
Franchise Affiliation: McDonald's Corporation, CHICAGO, IL

Key Personnel
VERN CHIN - President; Partner; Director Information Systems, Real Estate; General Buyer
CAROL CHIN - Partner; Director Finance, Human Resources; General Buyer

Classic Restaurant Concepts LLC
15 Court Sq Ste 230
Boston, MA 02108-2514

Telephone: (617) 371-0901
Fax Number: (617) 371-0903
Internet Homepage: classicirish.com
Type of Business: Chain Restaurant Operator
Year Founded: 1997
Total Sales: $14,125,000 (e)
Alcohol Sales: 10%
Number of Employees: 150
Average Check: Lunch(14); Dinner(20)
Total Units: 2
Trade Names: The Asgard (1); The Kinsale (1)
Company-Owned Units: 2
Preferred Location Types: Other
Alcohol Served: Beer, Wine, Liquor
Primary Menu: Miscellaneous (2)
Areas of Operation: MA
Type of Foodservice: Casual Dining (2)
Primary Distributors: (Food) SYSCO of Boston, PLYMPTON, MA

Key Personnel
BURTON SACK - Owner; General Manager; Executive Chef; General Buyer

Clover Food Lab
160 Federal St
Boston, MA 02110-1700

Mailing Address: 1075 Cambridge St, Cambridge, MA, 02139
Telephone: (617) 299-1284
Internet Homepage: cloverfoodlab.com
Company Email: info@cloverfoodlab.com
Type of Business: Chain Restaurant Operator
Year Founded: 2008
Total Sales: $12,700,000 (c)
Total Units: 14
Trade Names: Clover Food Lab (14)
Company-Owned Units: 14
Primary Menu: Health Foods (14)
Projected Openings: 2
Areas of Operation: MA
Type of Foodservice: Fast Casual (14)

Key Personnel
AYR MUIR - Founder; CEO
KIERNAN SCHMITT - Chief Marketing Officer
LUCIA JAZAYERI - Director Communications
MICHELE ZYLA - Director Finance
CHRISTOPHER SIMARD - Director Store

Cosi Inc.
294 Washington St Ste 510
Boston, MA 02108

Telephone: (857) 415-5000
Fax Number: (847) 597-8884
Internet Homepage: getcosi.com
Company Email: contactus@getcosi.com
Type of Business: Chain Restaurant Operator
Year Founded: 1998
Systemwide Sales: $32,428,000 (e)
Total Sales: $41,490,000 (e)
Alcohol Sales: 5%
Number of Employees: 1,213
Average Check: Breakfast(8); Lunch(10); Dinner(14)
Internet Order Processing: Yes
Total Units: 26
Trade Names: Cosi Sandwich Bar (26)
Company-Owned Units: 18
Units Franchised To: 8
Preferred Square Footage: 2,600
Preferred Location Types: Community Mall; Discount Dept. Stores; Downtown; Freestanding; Institution (college/hospital); Lifestyle Center; Regional Mall; Strip Mall
Alcohol Served: Beer, Wine
Primary Menu: Sandwiches/Deli (26)
Areas of Operation: CT, DC, DE, IL, IN, MA, MD, MN, NJ, NY, OH, PA, VA
Foreign Countries: COSTA RICA
Type of Foodservice: Fast Casual (26)
Catering Services: Yes
Primary Distributors: (Food) McLane/Rocky Mount, ROCKY MOUNT, NC; (Supplies) Maines Paper & Food Service Inc., CONKLIN, NY

Key Personnel
CONNIE HANSEN - Founder; CEO
WILLIAM BESSETTE - COO Operations; VP
DAVID POLONITZA - Exec VP

Davio's Restaurants Inc.
75 Arlington St
Boston, MA 02116-3936

Telephone: (617) 357-4810
Fax Number: (617) 357-1997
Internet Homepage: davios.com
Company Email: info@davios.com
Type of Business: Chain Restaurant Operator
Year Founded: 1977
Total Sales: $14,210,000 (e)
Alcohol Sales: 30%
Number of Employees: 300
Average Check: Breakfast(12); Lunch(24); Dinner(42)
Total Units: 12
Trade Names: Davio's (12)
Company-Owned Units: 12
Preferred Location Types: Freestanding
Alcohol Served: Beer, Wine, Liquor
Primary Menu: Italian (12)
Projected Openings: 1
Areas of Operation: GA, MA, NY, PA
Type of Foodservice: Fine Dining (12)
Catering Services: Yes
Primary Distributors: (Food) US Foods, SEABROOK, NH

Key Personnel
STEVE DIFILIPPO - Owner; General Buyer
ARMANDO DIAS - General Manager
ERIC SWARTZ - Executive Chef; General Buyer
ANNY DEIRMENJIAN - Director Marketing, Public Relations
KRISTINE WACKES - Manager Sales

East Coast Tavern Group
6 Beacon St Ste 205
Boston, MA 02108-3830

Telephone: (617) 742-3800
Internet Homepage: 6bloungeandrestaurant.com; emmetsirishpubandrestaurant.com; scholarsbostonbistro.com; carrienationcocktailclub.com; ectgboston.com
Company Email: contact@scholarsboston.com
Type of Business: Chain Restaurant Operator
Total Units: 6
Trade Names: 6B Lounge (1); Carrie Nation Restaurant (1); Emmets Pub & Restaurant (2); Magnolia Smokehouse (1); Scholars American Bistro (1)
Company-Owned Units: 6
Primary Menu: American (4); Bar-B-Q (1); Steak/Seafood (1)
Areas of Operation: MA
Type of Foodservice: Casual Dining (6)

Key Personnel
THOMAS (SAM) CARLYLE - President
ORAN MCGONAGLE - Manager Operations
FRANK LUNARDI - Manager Restaurant Operations

Frank DePasquale Ventures
241 Hanover St
Boston, MA 21113

Telephone: (617) 248-6800
Internet Homepage: bricco.com; depasqualeventures.com; mareoysterbar.com; quattro-boston.com; trattoriailpanino.com
Type of Business: Chain Restaurant Operator
Year Founded: 1983
Total Sales: $18,160,000 (e)
Alcohol Sales: 35%
Number of Employees: 146
Average Check: Lunch(36); Dinner(78)
Total Units: 8
Trade Names: AquaPazza (1); Assaggio (1); Mare Oyster Bar (1); Quattro (1); Ristorante Bricco (3); Trattoria Il Panino (1)
Company-Owned Units: 8
Preferred Location Types: Downtown; Freestanding
Alcohol Served: Beer, Wine, Liquor
Primary Menu: Italian (7); Seafood (1)
Areas of Operation: MA
Type of Foodservice: Casual Dining (5); Fine Dining (3)
Primary Distributors: (Supplies) SYSCO of Boston, PLYMPTON, MA

Key Personnel
FRANK DEPASQUALE - President; Treasurer; Executive Chef; General Buyer

Giacomo's Ristorante
355 Hanover St
Boston, MA 02113-1910

Telephone: (617) 523-9026
Type of Business: Chain Restaurant Operator
Year Founded: 1987
Total Sales: $5,546,000 (e)
Alcohol Sales: 25%
Number of Employees: 7
Average Check: Dinner(22)
Total Units: 3
Trade Names: Giacomo's (3)
Company-Owned Units: 3
Preferred Location Types: Freestanding
Alcohol Served: Beer, Wine
Primary Menu: Italian (3)
Areas of Operation: MA
Type of Foodservice: Casual Dining (3)
Primary Distributors: (Food) Accardi Foods, MEDFORD, MA

Key Personnel
JACK TAGLIERI - President; General Manager
ROSEMARIE TAGLIERI - General Manager; General Buyer
RICH TAGLIERI - Executive Chef; Director Menu Development; General Buyer

Hampshire House Corp
84 Beacon St
Boston, MA 02108-3421

Telephone: (617) 227-9600
Fax Number: (617) 854-7662
Internet Homepage: 75chestnut.com; 75onlibertywharf.com; cheersboston.com; hampshirehouse.com
Company Email: restaurantmanage@75chestnut.com

Type of Business: Chain Restaurant Operator
Year Founded: 1969
Total Sales: $22,269,000 (e)
Alcohol Sales: 40%
Number of Employees: 80
Average Check: Breakfast(18); Lunch(24); Dinner(36)
Total Units: 4
Trade Names: 75 Chestnut (1); 75 on the Liberty Wharf (1); Cheers Beacon Hill (1); Cheers Faneuil Hall (1)
Company-Owned Units: 4
Preferred Square Footage: 5,500; 6,000
Preferred Location Types: Freestanding
Alcohol Served: Beer, Wine, Liquor
Primary Menu: American (4)
Areas of Operation: MA
Type of Foodservice: Casual Dining (3); Fine Dining (1)
Primary Distributors: (Food) Cambridge Packing Co. Inc., BOSTON, MA

Key Personnel
THOMAS A. KERSHAW - Chairman; General Manager; Director Finance, Supply Chain, Real Estate, Design; General Buyer
MARKUS RIPPERGER - President; Executive Chef; Director Operations, Facility/Maintenance, Menu Development
TERRI CANNADY - VP Information Technology
MICHELE GIACOMOZZI - Director Operations, Catering
MICHELLE GIACOMOZZI - Director Sales, Catering
KARIM LAMECHATT - Director Operations, Information Systems, Human Resources
KARIM ALMECHATT - Director Operations
GAIL RICHMAN - Director Procurement, Distribution, Logistics, Marketing
BETSY TOCZKO - Manager Restaurant Operations
SARA O'MALLEY - Coordinator Marketing

Himmel Hospitality Group
20 Park Plz Ste 1102
Boston, MA 02116-4310

Telephone: (617) 868-2255
Fax Number: (617) 896-1072
Internet Homepage: grill23.com; harvestcambridge.com; post390restaurant.com; bistrodumidi.com
Company Email: info@harvestcambridge.com
Type of Business: Chain Restaurant Operator
Year Founded: 1975
Total Sales: $53,616,000 (e)
Alcohol Sales: 30%
Number of Employees: 85
Average Check: Lunch(36); Dinner(96)
Internet Sales: 1.00%
Total Units: 4
Trade Names: Bistro du Midi (1); Grill 23 & Bar (1); Harvest (1); Post 390 (1)
Company-Owned Units: 4
Preferred Location Types: Downtown
Alcohol Served: Beer, Wine, Liquor
Primary Menu: American (3); French/Continental (1)
Areas of Operation: MA
Type of Foodservice: Fine Dining (4)
Primary Distributors: (Equipment) United Restaurant Equipment Co. Inc., BILLERICA, MA; (Food) SYSCO of Boston, PLYMPTON, MA; (Supplies) SYSCO of Boston, PLYMPTON, MA

Key Personnel
KENNETH A. HIMMEL - Partner; General Manager
BRIAN SOMMERS - CFO; Exec VP; General Manager; General Buyer
MICHAEL A. SEZNEC - Senior VP Operations
TYLER KINNETT - Executive Chef

Legal Sea Foods Inc.
1 Seafood Way
Boston, MA 02210-2702

Telephone: (617) 530-9000
Fax Number: (617) 530-9021
Internet Homepage: legalseafoods.com
Company Email: support@legalseafoods.com
Type of Business: Chain Restaurant Operator
Year Founded: 1967
Systemwide Sales: $382,765,000 (e)
Total Sales: $404,670,000 (e)
Alcohol Sales: 20%
Number of Employees: 3,750
Average Check: Lunch(30); Dinner(48)
Internet Order Processing: Yes
Internet Sales: 15.00%
Total Units: 36
Trade Names: Legal C Bar (4); Legal Crossing (1); Legal Fish Bowl (2); Legal Harborside (1); Legal on the Mystic (1); Legal Oysteria (1); Legal Sea Bar (2); Legal Sea Foods (23); Legal Test Kitchen LTK (2)
Company-Owned Units: 36
Preferred Square Footage: 5,000; 8,000
Preferred Location Types: Airports; Community Mall; Hotel/Motel; Regional Mall
Alcohol Served: Beer, Wine, Liquor
Primary Menu: Seafood (37)
Areas of Operation: DC, MA, NJ, PA, RI, VA
Type of Foodservice: Casual Dining (35); Fast Casual (2)
Catering Services: Yes
On-site Distribution Center: Yes
Primary Distributors: (Food) SYSCO of Boston, PLYMPTON, MA
Parent Company: PPX Hospitality Brands, ,

Key Personnel
ANN MARIE LAGROTTERIA ESCOBAR - COO
MATT KING - COO
KIM LAPINE - Chief Marketing Officer
SANDY BLOCK - VP Operations-Alcoholic Beverages, Operations-Beverages
KEN NOGUEIRA - VP Finance
TOM MATHEWS - VP Operations-Seafood, Purchasing-Seafood
PATRICK SCULLY - VP Construction
CHRISTINE MCCARTHY - Executive Director Human Resources
GABRIELLE GREEN - General Manager; Assistant
ANN FLANNERY - Director Communications
MARNEY WHITTAKER - Director Risk Management
LEO LEITE - Director Operations
TOM CLANCY - Director Operations
SUSAN BUTLER - Director Payroll
JOANNE O'NEILL - Manager Customer Service
ELISE ERWIN - Manager Payroll
CHIP NESTOR - Manager Information Technology, Systems
LEAH HAMILTON - Manager
CHRISTINE COCCE - Manager Strategy, Marketing

Lyons Group Ltd
334 Boylston St Ste 500
Boston, MA 02116

Telephone: (617) 262-2605
Fax Number: (617) 262-3943
Internet Homepage: gameonboston.com; kingsbowlamerica.com; scampoboston.com; sweetwatercafeboston.com; backbaysocialclub.com; harvardgardens.com; lorettaslastcall.com; luckyslounge.com; sonsieboston.com; summershackrestaurant.com; towneboston.com; lyonsgroup.com
Type of Business: Chain Restaurant Operator
Year Founded: 1978
Total Sales: $88,680,000 (e)
Alcohol Sales: 20%
Number of Employees: 1,207
Average Check: Breakfast(14); Lunch(30); Dinner(60)
Internet Order Processing: Yes
Internet Sales: 2.00%
Total Units: 22
Trade Names: Alibi (1); Backbay Social Club (1); Five Roses (1); Game On (1); Harvard Gardens (1); Kings Bowl (11); Lorettas (1); Lucky's (2); Scampo (1); Sonsie (1); Sweetwater Cafe (1)
Company-Owned Units: 22
Preferred Square Footage: 5,500; 6,000
Preferred Location Types: Downtown; Freestanding; Institution (college/hospital); Lifestyle Center; Office Complex
Alcohol Served: Beer, Wine, Liquor
Primary Menu: American (20); Bar-B-Q (1); Italian (1)
Areas of Operation: CT, FL, IL, MA, NJ
Type of Foodservice: Casual Dining (11); In-

Store Feeder (10)
Primary Distributors: (Food) SYSCO of Boston, PLYMPTON, MA

Key Personnel
MARCUS LYONS - Owner; Principal
PATRICK LYONS - Partner; General Manager; Director Facility/Maintenance, Real Estate
ED SPARKS - Partner
DAVID JOAQUIN - CFO
MYLES KOPKA - Director Training
KATINA KOURIPINES - Manager Risk Management

Pyramid Hotel Group LLC
1 Post Office Sq Ste 1950
Boston, MA 02109-2120

Telephone: (617) 412-2800
Fax Number: (617) 946-2040
Internet Homepage: pyramidadvisors.com
Company Email: phginfo@pyramidhotelgroup.com
Type of Business: Foodservice Operations - Hotel/Motels
Total Sales: $1,960,800,000 (e)
Alcohol Sales: 5%
Number of Employees: 2,500
Total Units: 53
Restaurants in Hotels: 53
Trade Names: Candlewood Suites (1); Crowne Plaza (1); DoubleTree by Hilton (6); Hilton (5); Hilton Garden Inn (1); Holiday Inn (1); Hotel Indigo (1); Hyatt (2); Independent Resort (13); JW Marriott (2); Marriott (5); Renaissance (1); Residence Inn (3); Ritz-Carlton (2); Sheraton (3); Westin (5); Wyndham (1)
Company-Owned Units: 53
Alcohol Served: Beer, Wine, Liquor
Projected Remodelings: 2
Areas of Operation: AZ, CA, CO, CT, DC, FL, GA, HI, IL, IN, MA, ME, MI, MO, NC, NH, NJ, NV, PA, TN, TX, VA
Type of Foodservice: Casual Dining; Fine Dining
Primary Distributors: (Food) SYSCO Central Florida Inc., OCOEE, FL
Notes: The company derives approximately 70% of its revenue from hotel operations, including a large number of limited-service & extended-stay hotels.

Key Personnel
RICHARD M. KELLEHER - CEO; Partner
JAMES R. DINA - Partner; COO
WARREN Q. FIELDS - Partner; Chief Investment Officer
CHRISTOPHER DEVINE - CFO
CAROLINE WARREN - Chief Human Resources Officer; Exec VP
JIM MERRILL - Exec VP Operations
ALAN BEDNOWITZ - Senior VP Marketing, Sales
ROBERT BEVIER - Senior VP Business Development
CHUCK FREIJE - Senior VP Operations
JOHN GREEN - Senior VP Loss Prevention, Business Development
JOHN S. HAMILTON - Senior VP Business Development
JEFF WEGGEMAN - Senior VP Marketing, Sales, E-Commerce
DOUG COLE - VP Food and Beverage

Smith & Wollensky Restaurant Group
260 Franklin St Ste 240
Boston, MA 02110-3143

Telephone: (617) 600-3500
Fax Number: (857) 239-9219
Internet Homepage: smithandwollensky.com
Type of Business: Chain Restaurant Operator
Year Founded: 1977
Total Sales: $6,513,000 (e)
Alcohol Sales: 20%
Internet Order Processing: Yes
Total Units: 10
Trade Names: Smith & Wollensky (9); Wollensky's Grill (1)
Company-Owned Units: 10
Preferred Location Types: Downtown; Hotel/Motel; Regional Mall
Alcohol Served: Beer, Wine, Liquor
Primary Menu: Steak (10)
Areas of Operation: DC, FL, IL, MA, NV, NY, OH, PA, TX, FC
Foreign Countries: ENGLAND
Type of Foodservice: Casual Dining (1); Fine Dining (9)
Notes: The Smith & Wollensky restaurant in New York City is owned and operated by Fourth Wall Restaurant Group.

Key Personnel
MICHAEL FEIGHERY - CEO; President
CATHY TSOUKALAS - Exec VP Finance
MATT KING - VP Culinary Operations; Corporate Chef; Director Culinary Development

Somers Pubs Inc.
11 Marshall St
Boston, MA 02108-2404

Telephone: (617) 367-2114
Fax Number: (617) 321-4999
Internet Homepage: somerspubs.com
Type of Business: Chain Restaurant Operator
Year Founded: 1986
Total Sales: $10,190,000 (e)
Alcohol Sales: 36%
Number of Employees: 115
Average Check: Lunch(14); Dinner(16)
Total Units: 7
Trade Names: Durty Nelly's (1); Green Dragon Tavern (1); Hennessy's of Boston (2); Mr. Dooley's Boston Tavern (2); Paddy O's (1)
Company-Owned Units: 7
Preferred Square Footage: 5,500; 6,000
Preferred Location Types: Downtown; Freestanding
Alcohol Served: Beer, Wine, Liquor
Primary Menu: American (7)
Areas of Operation: MA
Type of Foodservice: Casual Dining (7)
Primary Distributors: (Full Line) Performance Foodservice - Springfield, SPRINGFIELD, MA

Key Personnel
NOELLE SOMERS - COO
STUART ABBOTT - General Manager
CHRISTINE HIGGINS - Manager Accounting, Customer Service, Training

Stellar Restaurant Group
1080 Boylston St
Boston, MA 02115

Telephone: (617) 369-9087
Internet Homepage: boloco.com
Company Email: hello@boloco.com
Type of Business: Chain Restaurant Operator
Year Founded: 1997
Total Sales: $14,540,000 (e)
Alcohol Sales: 0.50%
Number of Employees: 242
Average Check: Breakfast(8); Lunch(10); Dinner(10)
Internet Order Processing: Yes
Internet Sales: 0.50%
Total Units: 9
Trade Names: Boloco (9)
Company-Owned Units: 9
Preferred Square Footage: 1,500
Preferred Location Types: Downtown; Office Complex; Strip Mall
Alcohol Served: Beer, Wine
Primary Menu: Miscellaneous (9)
Projected Openings: 5
Areas of Operation: MA, NH, RI
Type of Foodservice: Fast Casual (9)
Catering Services: Yes
Primary Distributors: (Full Line) Reinhart Agar Supply Inc., TAUNTON, MA
Headquarter Offices: b.good LLC, BOSTON, MA
Notes: The company's franchising operations are located at 188 N Brookwood Ave., Ste 100, Hamilton OH 45013; the phone number is 513-896-9695, fax number is 513-896-3750

Key Personnel
JOHN S. PEPPER - Founder
MATT TAYLOR - COO
FRANK DENNISTON - Senior VP
BARBARA FREITAS - Manager Human

Resources

The Franklin Restaurant Group
278 Shawmut Ave
Boston, MA 02118-2125

Telephone: (617) 303-0410
Internet Homepage: citizenpub.com; franklincafe.com
Type of Business: Chain Restaurant Operator
Year Founded: 1996
Total Sales: $8,977,000 (e)
Alcohol Sales: 40%
Number of Employees: 25
Average Check: Lunch(18); Dinner(30)
Total Units: 5
Trade Names: Citizen Public House and Oyster Bar (1); Feathers (1); Taasty Burger (1); The Franklin Cafe (1); The Franklin Cape Ann (1)
Company-Owned Units: 4
Units Franchised To: 1
Preferred Location Types: Downtown; Office Complex
Alcohol Served: Beer, Wine, Liquor
Primary Menu: American (4); Hamburger (1)
Areas of Operation: MA
Type of Foodservice: Casual Dining (5)
Primary Distributors: (Food) SYSCO Food Services of Baltimore, JESSUP, MD; (Supplies) Eastern B&G Restaurant Supply, WESTWOOD, MA
Headquarter Offices: Tasty Burger Corp., ROXBURY, MA

Key Personnel
DAVID DUBOIS - Co-Founder; CEO; Partner
MAUREEN MCLAUGHLIN - Co-Founder; Partner
PHIL AUDINO - Partner; CFO

The Glynn Hospitality Group
03 Central St
Boston, MA 02109-3413

Telephone: (617) 451-7400
Fax Number: (617) 451-7414
Internet Homepage: irishconnection.com; bostonsportsgrille.com
Company Email: info@irishconnection.com
Type of Business: Chain Restaurant Operator
Year Founded: 1983
Total Sales: $25,280,000 (e)
Alcohol Sales: 40%
Number of Employees: 290
Average Check: Breakfast(14); Lunch(16); Dinner(22)
Internet Order Processing: Yes
Internet Sales: 2.00%
Total Units: 9
Trade Names: Boston Sports Grill (1); Brownstone (1); Central Wharf (1); Clery's (1); Coogan's (1); Dillon's (1); Granery Tavern (1); Sterling (1); The Black Rose (1)
Company-Owned Units: 9
Preferred Square Footage: 2,500
Preferred Location Types: Downtown; Freestanding
Alcohol Served: Beer, Wine, Liquor
Primary Menu: American (9)
Areas of Operation: MA
Type of Foodservice: Casual Dining (9)
Primary Distributors: (Full Line) SYSCO Corporation, HOUSTON, TX

Key Personnel
P. J. GLYNN - CEO; President; Partner
MICHAEL GLYNN - Partner; Exec VP Facility/Maintenance, Real Estate, Training, Store Planning
NEIL GLYNN - Partner; Controller
CHRISTINE FREEMAN - CFO
PAUL WILSON - Director Foodservice, Menu Development

Tico Boston
222 Berkeley St
Boston, MA 02116

Telephone: (617) 351-0400
Fax Number: (617) 422-0014
Internet Homepage: theriggsby.com; ticoboston.com; altastradarestaurant.com
Company Email: info@ticoboston.com
Type of Business: Chain Restaurant Operator
Year Founded: 2002
Total Sales: $10,230,000 (e)
Alcohol Sales: 12%
Number of Employees: 125
Average Check: Lunch(18); Dinner(36)
Total Units: 10
Trade Names: Alta Strada (4); Casolare (1); Cavatina (1); Nama Sushi Bar (1); Riggsby (1); Tico (2)
Company-Owned Units: 10
Preferred Location Types: Community Mall; Downtown
Alcohol Served: Beer, Wine, Liquor
Primary Menu: American (2); Asian (1); Italian (5); Latin American/Cuban (2)
Areas of Operation: DC, MA, NH, VA
Type of Foodservice: Casual Dining (10)
Primary Distributors: (Full Line) SYSCO of Boston, PLYMPTON, MA

Key Personnel
MICHAEL SCHLOW - President; Executive Chef; General Buyer

Todd English Enterprises
89 Commercial Wharf Fl 1
Boston, MA 02110-3816

Telephone: (617) 242-9715
Fax Number: (617) 242-1333
Internet Homepage: cheftoddenglish.com
Company Email: contact@toddenglish.com
Type of Business: Chain Restaurant Operator
Year Founded: 1987
Total Sales: $137,750,000 (e)
Alcohol Sales: 20%
Number of Employees: 555
Average Check: Lunch(14); Dinner(36)
Internet Order Processing: Yes
Total Units: 18
Trade Names: BlueZoo (1); Ca Va Brasserie (1); Figs (7); MXDC (1); Olives (4); The Stinger (1); Todd English Food Hall (1); Todd English P.U.B (1); Todd English Tuscany (1)
Company-Owned Units: 18
Preferred Square Footage: 4,000; 10,000
Preferred Location Types: Downtown
Alcohol Served: Beer, Wine, Liquor
Primary Menu: American (2); French/Continental (1); Greek/Mediterranean (2); Italian (11); Mexican (1); Miscellaneous (1)
Areas of Operation: AL, CT, DC, FL, MA, NV, NY, FC
Foreign Countries: BAHAMAS; KUWAIT; THE PHILIPPINES; UNITED ARAB EMIRATES
Type of Foodservice: Casual Dining (2); Fast Casual (1); Fine Dining (16)
Primary Distributors: (Equipment) TriMark USA Inc., MANSFIELD, MA; (Supplies) TriMark USA Inc., MANSFIELD, MA

Key Personnel
TODD ENGLISH - CEO; President; Executive Chef; Director Finance, Real Estate, Menu Development
JULIE FOX - VP Communications
AARON GRINNELL - Director Operations
MICHAEL REPUCCI - Manager Food and Beverage

Wagamama US
745 Atlantic Ave
Boston, MA 02111-2735

Telephone: (617) 778-2440
Fax Number: (617) 778-2441
Internet Homepage: wagamama.us
Type of Business: Chain Restaurant Operator
Total Sales: $15,950,000 (e)
Alcohol Sales: 10%
Number of Employees: 135
Average Check: Lunch(14); Dinner(26)
Total Units: 5
Trade Names: Wagamama (5)
Company-Owned Units: 5

Alcohol Served: Beer, Wine
Primary Menu: Asian (5)
Areas of Operation: MA, NY
Type of Foodservice: Casual Dining (5)
Primary Distributors: (Full Line) SYSCO of Boston, PLYMPTON, MA
Parent Company: Wagamama Ltd, LONDON, ENG
Notes: Parent company Wagamama Ltd. operates restaurants in the United Kingdom, as well as Australia, Belgium, Cyprus, Denmark, Dubai, Egypt, Ireland, Netherlands, New Zealand, Switzerland and Turkey.

Key Personnel
RICHARD FLAHERTY - Owner
MEREDITH CLANCY - Coordinator Marketing

Hogan Management Company
12 Pearl St
Braintree, MA 02184-6522

Telephone: (781) 849-8311
Fax Number: (781) 848-7506
Type of Business: Chain Restaurant Operator
Total Sales: $104,970,000 (e)
Number of Employees: 950
Total Units: 22
Trade Names: McDonald's (22)
Units Franchised From: 22
Preferred Square Footage: 2,500
Primary Menu: Hamburger (22)
Areas of Operation: MA, ME, NH
Type of Foodservice: Quick Serve (22)
Franchise Affiliation: McDonald's Corporation, CHICAGO, IL

Key Personnel
ROBERT HOGAN - President; General Buyer
CHRISTINA JENKINS - CFO
MICHAEL JACKSON - Chief Accounting Officer
MARTIN MEADOR - Chief People Officer Human Resources; VP
KEVIN REINHARDT - Senior Director
PAUL KOMADINA - Senior Director Logistics, Sales
MICHAEL LEDONNE - Director
JOSEPH MCVEY - Director Human Resources
KASANDRA FERNANDEZ - Director Development, Sales
LINDSEY FLICK - Director
RALPH SAMPLES - Director Development, Sales, Midwest Region
JOSEPH THORNTON - Director
TREY HOGAN - Director Marketing
NICK INCROCCI - Director Quality Assurance
CYNTHIA OVERBY - Director Development, Sales, South Region
MARK WYATT - Senior Manager
BRENNAN OBRAY - Regional Manager
JULIE CROSSLEY - Area Manager

THOMAS BAYER - Manager Promotion

The Briar Group
311 Washington St
Brighton, MA 02135-3303

Telephone: (617) 789-4111
Fax Number: (617) 789-4110
Internet Homepage: briar-group.com
Company Email: info@briar-group.com
Type of Business: Chain Restaurant Operator
Year Founded: 1975
Total Sales: $33,560,000 (e)
Alcohol Sales: 20%
Number of Employees: 802
Average Check: Lunch(30); Dinner(42)
Total Units: 11
Trade Names: Anthem (1); City Bar (1); City Table (1); District Hall (1); Gather (1); Glass House (1); M.J. O'Connor's (1); Ned Devine's (1); Solas (1); The Green Briar (1); The Harp (1)
Company-Owned Units: 11
Preferred Square Footage: 5,500; 6,000
Preferred Location Types: Freestanding; Hotel/Motel
Alcohol Served: Beer, Wine, Liquor
Primary Menu: American (11)
Areas of Operation: MA
Type of Foodservice: Casual Dining (11)
Primary Distributors: (Full Line) SYSCO of Boston, PLYMPTON, MA

Key Personnel
AUSTIN O'CONNOR - CEO; President; General Manager Menu Development; General Buyer
TOM SHEA - Director Operations
TODD BENNETT - Director Operations
DESSIE KERINS - Director Operations, Purchasing
TIM MCGEE - Director Human Resources-Training

Owen O'Leary's
1280 Belmont St Ste 8
Brockton, MA 02301-4441

Telephone: (508) 584-2221
Fax Number: (508) 587-7729
Internet Homepage: owenolearys.com
Type of Business: Chain Restaurant Operator
Year Founded: 1989
Total Sales: $4,546,000 (e)
Alcohol Sales: 20%
Number of Employees: 45
Average Check: Lunch(14); Dinner(18)
Total Units: 3
Trade Names: Owen O'Leary's (3)
Company-Owned Units: 3
Preferred Location Types: Community Mall; Freestanding

Alcohol Served: Beer, Wine, Liquor
Primary Menu: American (3)
Projected Remodelings: 1
Areas of Operation: MA
Type of Foodservice: Casual Dining (3)

Key Personnel
KEVIN GILL - Owner; General Buyer
JIM DEANGELO - Executive Chef; General Buyer

American Food Systems
30 B St
Burlington, MA 01803

Telephone: (781) 273-3230
Internet Homepage: jimmysarlington.com
Type of Business: Chain Restaurant Operator
Total Units: 7
Trade Names: Grassfields (2); Jimmy's Steer House (2); Jimmy's Tavern and Grill (1); Mario's (1); Prime 131 Grill (1)
Company-Owned Units: 7
Primary Menu: American (1); Italian (1); Steak (2); Steak/Seafood (3)
Areas of Operation: MA
Type of Foodservice: Casual Dining (7)

Key Personnel
TONY KARAPATSAS - President; Owner; General Buyer

Chicago Scoops LLC
2 Wayside Rd
Burlington, MA 01803-4605

Telephone: (781) 270-2621
Type of Business: Chain Restaurant Operator
Total Sales: $25,650,000 (e)
Total Units: 43
Trade Names: Cold Stone Creamery (43)
Units Franchised From: 43
Primary Menu: Snacks (43)
Areas of Operation: MA, MD, UT, WI
Type of Foodservice: Quick Serve (43)
Franchise Affiliation: Kahala Brands, SCOTTSDALE, AZ

Key Personnel
KYLE WELCH - Partner
JON SHULKIN - Partner
RICARDO HERRERA - Director Finance
JASON BOCK - Manager

Healthy Acquisitions Corp
22 A St
Burlington, MA 01803-3418

Telephone: (617) 787-6000

Fax Number: (781) 750-3044
Internet Homepage: ufoodgrill.com
Company Email: info@ufoodgrill.com
Type of Business: Chain Restaurant Operator
Systemwide Sales: $4,370,000 (e)
Total Sales: $2,750,000 (e)
Average Check: Lunch(10); Dinner(10)
Internet Order Processing: Yes
Total Units: 5
Trade Names: UFood Grill (5)
Company-Owned Units: 1
Units Franchised To: 4
Preferred Square Footage: 800; 1,000; 1,500; 2,500
Preferred Location Types: Airports; Downtown; Lifestyle Center; Office Complex; Regional Mall
Primary Menu: Health Foods (5)
Areas of Operation: CA, DE, FL, IL, LA, MA, MD, ND, NY, SD, TX, UT, VA, WY
Foreign Countries: CANADA
Type of Foodservice: Fast Casual (5)
Catering Services: Yes

Key Personnel
RICHARD "RICK" GOLDEN - Chairman
IRMA NORTON - CFO
WALTER POMERLEAU - VP Real Estate, Construction
PHILIP KAFKA - Corporate Chef
STEPHANIE HUNTER - Director Training

Boca Grande
1728 Massachusetts Ave
Cambridge, MA 02138-1804

Telephone: (617) 354-7400
Internet Homepage: bocagranderestaurant.com
Type of Business: Chain Restaurant Operator
Year Founded: 1986
Total Units: 2
Trade Names: Boca Grande Taqueria (2)
Company-Owned Units: 2
Primary Menu: Taco (2)
Areas of Operation: MA
Type of Foodservice: Fast Casual (2)

Key Personnel
SILVIA WHITMAN - Owner

Cambridge School of Culinary Arts
2020 Massachusetts Ave
Cambridge, MA 02140-2104

Telephone: (617) 354-2020
Fax Number: (617) 576-1963
Internet Homepage: cambridgeculinary.com
Company Email: info@cambridgeculinary.com
Type of Business: Culinary Schools
Areas of Operation: MA

Key Personnel
RANDALL FREIDUS - Owner; Executive Director Operations
JOHN HANNON - Director Operations, Marketing
SEAN LEONARD - Director Culinary Operations
TED VILLA - Director Purchasing
ALDA SHARXHI - Manager Finance

Domino's Franchisee
1033 Massachusetts Ave
Cambridge, MA 02138-5319

Telephone: (617) 441-2101
Type of Business: Chain Restaurant Operator
Total Sales: $3,977,000 (e)
Total Units: 2
Trade Names: Domino's (2)
Units Franchised From: 2
Primary Menu: Pizza (2)
Areas of Operation: MA
Type of Foodservice: Quick Serve (2)
Franchise Affiliation: Domino's Pizza Inc, ANN ARBOR, MI

Key Personnel
MOHAMMAD A. EL-SIBAI - Owner; General Buyer

Le's Vietnamese Restaurant
35 Dunster St
Cambridge, MA 02138

Telephone: (617) 864-4100
Fax Number: (617) 864-4471
Internet Homepage: lescambridge.com
Type of Business: Chain Restaurant Operator
Total Sales: $4,938,000 (e)
Alcohol Sales: 10%
Number of Employees: 40
Average Check: Lunch(8); Dinner(16)
Total Units: 3
Trade Names: Le's Vietnamese Restaurant (3)
Company-Owned Units: 3
Preferred Location Types: Freestanding
Alcohol Served: Beer, Wine
Primary Menu: Asian (3)
Areas of Operation: MA
Type of Foodservice: Casual Dining (3)

Key Personnel
DUYEN LE - Owner; General Manager; Executive Chef; General Buyer

One World Cuisine
575 Massachusetts Ave
Cambridge, MA 02139-4088

Mailing Address: 575 Massachusetts Ave, CAMBRIDGE, MA, 02139
Telephone: (617) 262-4770
Fax Number: (617) 661-6301
Internet Homepage: oneworldcuisine.com
Company Email: drashti@oneworldcuisine.com
Type of Business: Chain Restaurant Operator
Total Sales: $14,240,000 (e)
Alcohol Sales: 12%
Number of Employees: 80
Average Check: Lunch(18); Dinner(24)
Internet Order Processing: Yes
Internet Sales: 10.00%
Total Units: 6
Trade Names: Bao Nation (1); Bukhara (1); Diva Indian Bistro (1); Dosa Factory (2); Mela Modern Indian Cuisine (1)
Company-Owned Units: 6
Preferred Square Footage: 5,500; 6,000
Preferred Location Types: Freestanding; Strip Mall
Alcohol Served: Beer, Wine, Liquor
Primary Menu: Chinese (1); Indian (5)
Areas of Operation: MA
Type of Foodservice: Casual Dining (6)
Catering Services: Yes
Primary Distributors: (Full Line) Shaheen Brothers Inc., AMESBURY, MA

Key Personnel
AMRIK PABLA - President; Executive Chef; Director Real Estate, Store Fixtures, Menu Development; General Buyer

RJK & Company
200 Monsignor Obrien Hwy
Cambridge, MA 02141-1254

Telephone: (617) 354-9027
Fax Number: (617) 354-0235
Company Email: rjk@rjkcompany.com
Type of Business: Chain Restaurant Operator
Year Founded: 1999
Total Sales: $86,470,000 (e)
Number of Employees: 1,660
Average Check: Breakfast(8); Lunch(10); Dinner(10)
Total Units: 18
Trade Names: McDonald's (18)
Units Franchised From: 18
Preferred Square Footage: 2,500; 3,000
Preferred Location Types: Freestanding
Primary Menu: Hamburger (18)
Projected Openings: 1
Areas of Operation: MA
Type of Foodservice: Quick Serve (18)

Franchise Affiliation: McDonald's Corporation, CHICAGO, IL
Primary Distributors: (Full Line) The Martin-Brower Co., ENFIELD, CT

Key Personnel
ROBERT KING - President; Partner; Director Supply Chain, Real Estate; General Buyer
VIJAY SELHI - Partner; Director Operations, Facility/Maintenance, Design, Store Fixtures; General Buyer
AMITA WADHWA - Director Human Resources
ED POIRIER - Director Finance, Information Systems

Tremont 647
1 Kendall Sq
Cambridge, MA 02139

Telephone: (617) 577-7427
Internet Homepage: thesmokeshopbbq.com
Company Email: office@tremont647
Type of Business: Chain Restaurant Operator
Year Founded: 1996
Total Sales: $10,523,000 (e)
Alcohol Sales: 30%
Number of Employees: 2
Average Check: Lunch(22); Dinner(42)
Total Units: 3
Trade Names: The Smoke Shop BBQ (3)
Company-Owned Units: 3
Preferred Location Types: Downtown; Freestanding
Alcohol Served: Beer, Wine, Liquor
Primary Menu: Bar-B-Q (3)
Areas of Operation: MA
Type of Foodservice: Casual Dining (3)
Catering Services: Yes

Key Personnel
JORGE RUIZ - General Manager
MICHAEL BOUGHTON - Director Food and Beverage
IAN GROSSMAN - Director Operations

BR IP Holder LLC
130 Royall St
Canton, MA 02021-1010

Telephone: (781) 737-3000
Fax Number: (781) 737-4000
Internet Homepage: baskinrobbins.com; dunkinbrands.com
Company Email: customerservice@dunkinbrands.com
Type of Business: Chain Restaurant Operator
Year Founded: 1946
Systemwide Sales: $2,929,305,000 (e)
Total Sales: $251,180,000 (e)
Number of Employees: 1,100
Average Check: Breakfast(8); Lunch(8); Dinner(8)
Internet Order Processing: Yes
Total Units: 10,078
Trade Names: Baskin-Robbins (10,078)
Units Franchised To: 10,078
Preferred Square Footage: 1,500; 2,200
Preferred Location Types: Airports; Community Mall; Convenience Store/Gas Station; Discount Dept. Stores; Downtown; Freestanding; Institution (college/hospital); Mobile Unit; Regional Mall; Strip Mall; Travel Plazas
Primary Menu: Snacks (10,078)
Projected Openings: 50
Areas of Operation: AK, AL, AR, AZ, CA, CO, CT, DC, DE, FL, GA, HI, IA, ID, IL, IN, KS, KY, LA, MA, MD, ME, MI, MN, MO, MS, MT, NC, NE, NJ, NM, NV, NY, OH, OK, OR, PA, RI, SC, TN, TX, UT, VA, WA, WI, WV, WY, AB, BC, MB, ON, QC
Foreign Countries: ARUBA; AUSTRALIA; BAHRAIN; CANADA; CHINA; COLOMBIA; CURACAO; DOMINICAN REPUBLIC; ECUADOR; EGYPT; ENGLAND; HONDURAS; INDIA; INDONESIA; JAPAN; KUWAIT; LEBANON; MALAYSIA; MEXICO; OMAN; PANAMA; PORTUGAL; QATAR; RUSSIA; SAINT MAARTEN; SAUDI ARABIA; SCOTLAND; SINGAPORE; SOUTH KOREA; SPAIN; TAIWAN; THAILAND; UNITED ARAB EMIRATES; VIETNAM; WALES; YEMEN ARABREPUBLIC
Type of Foodservice: Quick Serve (10,078)
Catering Services: Yes
Parent Company: Inspire Brands, ATLANTA, GA
Notes: Store counts represent points of distribution, which consist of traditional end-cap, in-line and stand-alone restaurants, many with drive thrus, and gas and convenience locations, as well as alternative points of distribution ("APODs"), such as full- or self-service kiosks in grocery stores, hospitals, airports, offices, colleges and other smaller-footprint properties. Sales of ice cream products to franchisees account for more than 65% of total revenues.

Key Personnel
DAVID HOFFMANN - CEO
WILLIAM M. MITCHELL - President
JONATHAN BIGGS - Senior VP Operations, United States, Canada
LOU BECCARELLI - Regional VP
EVERETT GASBARRO - Senior Director Operations

DD IP Holder
130 Royall St
Canton, MA 02021-1010

Telephone: (781) 737-3000
Fax Number: (781) 737-4000
Internet Homepage: baskinrobbins.com; dunkinbrands.com; dunkindonuts.com; dunkinfranchising.com
Company Email: customerservice@dunkinbrands.com
Type of Business: Chain Restaurant Operator
Year Founded: 1950
Systemwide Sales: $13,390,236,000 (e)
Total Sales: $979,820,000 (e)
Number of Employees: 1,100
Average Check: Breakfast(8); Lunch(8); Dinner(8)
Internet Order Processing: Yes
Total Units: 12,478
Trade Names: Dunkin' Donuts (12,478)
Units Franchised To: 12,478
Preferred Square Footage: 800; 1,500; 2,000; 2,400
Preferred Location Types: Airports; Community Mall; Convenience Store/Gas Station; Downtown; Freestanding; Grocery Stores; Institution (college/hospital); Kiosk; Lifestyle Center; Regional Mall; Stadiums; Strip Mall; Travel Plazas
Primary Menu: Snacks (12,478)
Areas of Operation: AL, AR, AZ, CA, CO, CT, DC, DE, FL, GA, IA, IL, IN, KS, KY, LA, MA, MD, ME, MI, MO, MS, NC, NH, NJ, NM, NV, NY, OH, OK, PA, PR, RI, SC, TN, TX, VA, VT, WI, WV, QC
Foreign Countries: ARUBA; BAHAMAS; BULGARIA; CANADA; CHILE; CHINA; COLOMBIA; DENMARK; ECUADOR; GERMANY; HONDURAS; ICELAND; INDIA; INDONESIA; JAPAN; KUWAIT; LEBANON; LUXEMBOURG; MALAYSIA; NEW ZEALAND; OMAN; PAKISTAN; PANAMA; PERU; QATAR; RUSSIA; SAUDI ARABIA; SINGAPORE; SOUTH KOREA; SPAIN; SWITZERLAND; TAIWAN; THAILAND; THE PHILIPPINES; UNITED ARAB EMIRATES
Type of Foodservice: Quick Serve (12,478)
Distribution Centers: GROVELAND, FL; MOKENA, IL; BELLINGHAM, MA
Primary Distributors: (Food) S&D Coffee & Tea Inc., CONCORD, NC; (Food) CSM Bakery Products, SANDY SPRINGS, GA; (Food) Keurig Dr Pepper Inc., BURLINGTON, MA; (Food) Rich Products Corp., NILES, IL
Parent Company: Inspire Brands, ATLANTA, GA
Notes: Store counts represent points of distribution, which consist of traditional end-cap, in-line and stand-alone restaurants, many with drive thrus, and gas and convenience locations, as well as alternative points of distribution ("APODs"), such as full- or self-service kiosks in grocery stores, hospitals, airports, offices, colleges and other smaller-footprint properties.

Key Personnel
KATE JASPON - CFO
RICK COLON - Senior VP Operations, Development

JOHN VARUGHESE - Senior VP International Division
JASON MACEDA - Senior VP Division
BOB WIGGINS - VP Operations, Northeast Region
MARTIN STRUDWICK - Director Quality Assurance, Manufacturing, Food Safety
ROBERT GERSTENFELD - Director Business Development
PAUL RACICOT - Director Culinary Development
BRUCE KATZ - Director Real Estate
MELANIE RABINO - Director Branding
KATIE LECLAIR - Director Innovation
KRISTENA HART - Director Operations
COLLEEN KRYGIEL - Manager Marketing
JEFF ZAVORAL - Manager Real Estate

Froio Management
960 Turnpike St Ste 3B
Canton, MA 02021-2818

Telephone: (781) 828-4111
Fax Number: (781) 828-4149
Company Email: froiofoods@att.net
Type of Business: Chain Restaurant Operator
Total Sales: $11,240,000 (e)
Number of Employees: 100
Average Check: Breakfast(8); Lunch(8); Dinner(8)
Total Units: 5
Trade Names: Burger King (5)
Units Franchised From: 5
Preferred Square Footage: 2,500; 4,000
Preferred Location Types: Freestanding
Primary Menu: Hamburger (5)
Areas of Operation: MA
Type of Foodservice: Quick Serve (5)
Franchise Affiliation: Burger King Worldwide Inc., MIAMI, FL
Primary Distributors: (Food) Maines Paper & Food Service Inc., CONKLIN, NY

Key Personnel
JAMES FROIO - President; General Buyer
STANLEY KAKLEAS - District Manager

Domino's Franchisee
118 Chelmsford St
Chelmsford, MA 01824-2732

Telephone: (978) 250-1555
Type of Business: Chain Restaurant Operator
Total Sales: $13,996,000 (e)
Total Units: 7
Trade Names: Domino's (7)
Units Franchised From: 7
Primary Menu: Pizza (7)
Areas of Operation: MA
Type of Foodservice: Quick Serve (7)
Franchise Affiliation: Domino's Pizza Inc, ANN ARBOR, MI

Key Personnel
GEOFFREY D. SCHEMBECHLER - Owner; General Buyer

McCoy Associates
10 Jean Ave Ste 2
Chelmsford, MA 01824-1740

Telephone: (978) 458-5780
Fax Number: (978) 458-5782
Type of Business: Chain Restaurant Operator
Year Founded: 2000
Total Sales: $61,440,000 (e)
Number of Employees: 550
Average Check: Breakfast(8); Lunch(10); Dinner(12)
Total Units: 13
Trade Names: McDonald's (13)
Units Franchised From: 13
Preferred Square Footage: 2,500
Preferred Location Types: Freestanding
Primary Menu: Hamburger (13)
Areas of Operation: MA
Type of Foodservice: Quick Serve (13)
Franchise Affiliation: McDonald's Corporation, CHICAGO, IL
Primary Distributors: (Food) The Martin-Brower Co., ENFIELD, CT

Key Personnel
TIMOTHY MCCOY - President; Director Supply Chain, Real Estate, Design, Store Fixtures; General Buyer
JANE CHERNEY - Owner; Principal
ROBERT BROUGHTON - Director Operations
APRIL MENDIS - Administrator

T & W Subway
1525 Memorial Dr
Chicopee, MA 01020-3900

Telephone: (413) 538-5129
Type of Business: Chain Restaurant Operator
Total Sales: $1,882,000 (e)
Total Units: 3
Trade Names: Subway (3)
Units Franchised From: 3
Preferred Location Types: Strip Mall
Primary Menu: Sandwiches/Deli (3)
Areas of Operation: MA
Type of Foodservice: Quick Serve (3)
Franchise Affiliation: Doctor's Associates Inc., MILFORD, CT

Key Personnel
WAYNE YVON - President; General Buyer

Merchants Row Restaurant
48 Monument Sq
Concord, MA 01742-1875

Telephone: (978) 369-2373
Fax Number: (978) 371-1533
Internet Homepage: concordscolonialinn.com
Company Email: colonial@concordscolonialinn.com
Type of Business: Chain Restaurant Operator
Total Sales: $5,769,000 (e)
Alcohol Sales: 10%
Number of Employees: 40
Average Check: Breakfast(6); Lunch(10); Dinner(24)
Internet Order Processing: Yes
Total Units: 4
Trade Names: Forge Tavern (1); Merchants Row Restaurant (1); Tap Room (1); The Liberty Restaurant (1)
Company-Owned Units: 4
Preferred Location Types: Hotel/Motel
Alcohol Served: Beer, Wine, Liquor
Primary Menu: American (4)
Areas of Operation: MA
Type of Foodservice: Casual Dining (4)
Primary Distributors: (Food) US Foods, SEABROOK, NH; (Supplies) TriMark USA Inc., MANSFIELD, MA

Key Personnel
ERIN GABAREE - Director Food and Beverage

Barnsider Management Corporation
15 Newbury St Ste A
Danvers, MA 01923-1014

Telephone: (978) 777-3885
Fax Number: (978) 777-5038
Internet Homepage: barnsiderrestaurants.com
Company Email: info@barnsiderrestaurants.com
Type of Business: Chain Restaurant Operator
Year Founded: 1967
Total Sales: $15,647,000 (e)
Alcohol Sales: 25%
Number of Employees: 305
Average Check: Dinner(54)
Internet Order Processing: Yes
Internet Sales: 1.00%
Total Units: 3
Trade Names: Barnsider (1); Beverly Depot (1); Hardcover (1)
Company-Owned Units: 3
Preferred Square Footage: 5,000
Preferred Location Types: Freestanding
Alcohol Served: Beer, Wine, Liquor
Primary Menu: American (3)
Areas of Operation: MA, NY
Type of Foodservice: Fine Dining (3)

Primary Distributors: (Equipment) United Restaurant Equipment Co. Inc., BILLERICA, MA; (Food) US Foods, SEABROOK, NH; (Supplies) US Foods, SEABROOK, NH

Key Personnel
JOHN DESY - President; Owner; Director Advertising, Real Estate
LORI DALTON - VP Finance; Controller; Director Information Systems, Human Resources

Boston Pie Inc.
100 Conifer Hill Dr Ste 401
Danvers, MA 01923-1171

Telephone: (978) 777-8044
Fax Number: (978) 777-8045
Type of Business: Chain Restaurant Operator
Year Founded: 1998
Total Sales: $71,413,000 (e)
Number of Employees: 566
Average Check: Lunch(14); Dinner(22)
Total Units: 35
Trade Names: Domino's (35)
Units Franchised From: 35
Preferred Square Footage: 1,000; 1,300
Preferred Location Types: Strip Mall
Primary Menu: Pizza (35)
Areas of Operation: MA, ME, NH
Type of Foodservice: Quick Serve (35)
Franchise Affiliation: Domino's Pizza Inc, ANN ARBOR, MI
Primary Distributors: (Full Line) Progressive Foods Solutions, WOODRIDGE, IL

Key Personnel
DAVID JENKS - President; Director Finance; General Buyer
DOMINIC BENVENUTI - Owner; VP Operations; Manager Facility/Maintenance, Information Systems, Real Estate, Design
REYES JONATHAN - General Manager
EILEEN LEBLANC - Specialist Human Resources

Domino's Franchisee
628 Washington St Ste A
Dedham, MA 02026-4453

Telephone: (781) 329-7999
Type of Business: Chain Restaurant Operator
Total Sales: $5,946,000 (e)
Total Units: 3
Trade Names: Domino's (3)
Units Franchised From: 3
Primary Menu: Pizza (3)
Areas of Operation: MA
Type of Foodservice: Quick Serve (3)
Franchise Affiliation: Domino's Pizza Inc, ANN ARBOR, MI

Key Personnel
ANDREW L. POLVAY - Owner; General Buyer

Papa Gino's Holdings Corp.
600 Providence Hwy
Dedham, MA 02026-6804

Telephone: (781) 461-1200
Fax Number: (781) 461-1896
Internet Homepage: dangelos.com; papaginos.com; papaginos.com/corporate
Type of Business: Chain Restaurant Operator
Year Founded: 1961
Total Sales: $246,773,000 (e)
Number of Employees: 4,300
Average Check: Lunch(12); Dinner(16)
Total Units: 165
Trade Names: D'Angelo Grilled Sandwiches (84); Papa Gino's Pizzeria (81)
Company-Owned Units: 165
Preferred Location Types: Community Mall; Convenience Store/Gas Station; Downtown; Freestanding; Institution (college/hospital); Stadiums; Travel Plazas
Primary Menu: Italian (81); Sandwiches/Deli (84)
Areas of Operation: CT, MA, ME, NH, RI
Type of Foodservice: Fast Casual (84); Quick Serve (81)
Catering Services: Yes
Primary Distributors: (Food) Reinhart Agar Supply Inc., TAUNTON, MA

Key Personnel
DEENA MCKINLEY - Chief Experience Officer
JILL GROGAN - VP Marketing
DON M. CLARK - VP Finance; Controller
DEBBIE KULKA - Senior Director Information Technology
ELLIE ABLEMAN - Director Risk Management
LISA TREMBLAY - Director Marketing
KATHY MURPHY - Director Customer Service
BRIDGET CASSIDY - Director Real Estate
MAUREEN PIRONE - Director Training

Ebb Tide Beach Club
94 Chase Ave
Dennis Port, MA 02639-2610

Mailing Address: P.O BOX 69, Dennis Port, MA, 02639
Telephone: (508) 398-8733
Fax Number: (508) 398-5069
Internet Homepage: seaviewcapecod.com; ebbtiderestaurant.com
Type of Business: Chain Restaurant Operator
Year Founded: 1959
Total Sales: $3,821,000 (e)
Number of Employees: 80
Average Check: Dinner(30)
Total Units: 2
Trade Names: Ebb Tide Beach Club (1); The Seaview (1)
Company-Owned Units: 2
Preferred Location Types: Freestanding
Alcohol Served: Beer, Wine, Liquor
Primary Menu: American (1); Seafood (1)
Areas of Operation: MA
Type of Foodservice: Casual Dining (1); Fine Dining (1)
Catering Services: Yes

Key Personnel
GAIL MCCORMICK - General Manager; General Buyer
ANDRE PASCAL - Executive Chef; Manager Catering

Domino's Franchisee
11 Union St
Easthampton, MA 01027-1417

Telephone: (413) 527-0821
Type of Business: Chain Restaurant Operator
Total Sales: $10,347,000 (e)
Total Units: 5
Trade Names: Domino's (5)
Units Franchised From: 5
Primary Menu: Pizza (5)
Areas of Operation: MA
Type of Foodservice: Quick Serve (5)
Franchise Affiliation: Domino's Pizza Inc, ANN ARBOR, MI

Key Personnel
ANTHONY P. PATALANO - Owner; General Buyer

Piezoni
25 Robert Dr
Easton, MA 02375

Internet Homepage: piezonis.com
Type of Business: Chain Restaurant Operator
Systemwide Sales: $21,534,000 (e)
Total Sales: $20,000,000 (e)
Total Units: 18
Trade Names: Piezoni (18)
Company-Owned Units: 1
Units Franchised To: 17
Primary Menu: Pizza (18)
Type of Foodservice: Fast Casual (18)

Key Personnel
JOE FERREIRA - CEO
VICTOR MARTINEZ - COO

Domino's Franchisee
390 Rhode Island Ave
Fall River, MA 02721-2369

Telephone: (508) 677-3030
Type of Business: Chain Restaurant Operator
Total Sales: $6,145,000 (e)
Total Units: 3
Trade Names: Domino's (3)
Units Franchised From: 3
Primary Menu: Pizza (3)
Areas of Operation: MA
Type of Foodservice: Quick Serve (3)
Franchise Affiliation: Domino's Pizza Inc, ANN ARBOR, MI

Key Personnel
CARLOS H. FERREIRA - Owner; General Buyer

Domino's Franchisee
407 S Main St
Fall River, MA 02721-5345

Telephone: (508) 676-3030
Type of Business: Chain Restaurant Operator
Total Sales: $4,044,000 (e)
Total Units: 2
Trade Names: Domino's (2)
Units Franchised From: 2
Primary Menu: Pizza (2)
Areas of Operation: MA
Type of Foodservice: Quick Serve (2)
Franchise Affiliation: Domino's Pizza Inc, ANN ARBOR, MI

Key Personnel
SETH HOCKERT-LOTZ - Owner; General Buyer

PR Management Corp.
550 Cchituate Road
Farmingham, MA 10701

Telephone: (617) 581-6160
Internet Homepage: prmanagementcorp.com; panerabread.com/en-us/home.html
Company Email: supportcenter@prrestaurants.com
Type of Business: Chain Restaurant Operator
Year Founded: 1997
Total Sales: $192,860,000 (e)
Total Units: 59
Trade Names: Panera Bread (59)
Units Franchised From: 59
Primary Menu: Sandwiches/Deli (59)
Areas of Operation: MA, ME, NH
Type of Foodservice: Fast Casual (59)
Franchise Affiliation: Panera Bread Company, SAINT LOUIS, MO

Key Personnel
MITCHELL ROBERTS - Co-Founder; CEO; Owner
DAVID PETERMAN - Co-Founder
DEAN CARMAN - CFO
CHARLIE HECHT - VP Information Technology
BRYAN OGLESBY - VP Human Resources
STEFANO NETO - General Manager
JOHN ROSENFIELD - Director Human Resources
JOHN HALL - District Manager
JOE RODRIGUES - District Manager
ROBERT ZAHARA - District Manager

Domino's Franchisee
141 Water St
Fitchburg, MA 01420

Telephone: (978) 342-0050
Type of Business: Chain Restaurant Operator
Total Sales: $5,946,000 (e)
Total Units: 3
Trade Names: Domino's (3)
Units Franchised From: 3
Primary Menu: Pizza (3)
Areas of Operation: MA
Type of Foodservice: Quick Serve (3)
Franchise Affiliation: Domino's Pizza Inc, ANN ARBOR, MI

Key Personnel
SHAWN LAING - Owner; General Buyer

Dufficy Enterprises, Inc
2 Mill St
Franklin, MA 02038-1225

Telephone: (508) 520-1000
Internet Homepage: massbaycapital.com
Type of Business: Chain Restaurant Operator
Total Sales: $37,556,000 (e)
Total Units: 18
Trade Names: Domino's (18)
Units Franchised From: 18
Primary Menu: Pizza (18)
Areas of Operation: MA
Type of Foodservice: Quick Serve (18)
Franchise Affiliation: Domino's Pizza Inc, ANN ARBOR, MI

Key Personnel
JEFFREY P. DUFFICY - Owner; General Buyer
CHRIS COURTEMANCHE - VP

Braga Management Team LLC
132 Washington St
Gloucester, MA 01930-3545

Telephone: (978) 283-4339
Fax Number: (978) 283-5496
Internet Homepage: bragamanagement.com
Company Email: dbraga7827@aol.com
Type of Business: Chain Restaurant Operator
Total Sales: $17,400,000 (e)
Number of Employees: 207
Average Check: Dinner(6)
Total Units: 11
Trade Names: Azorean (1); Dunkin' Donuts (10)
Company-Owned Units: 1
Units Franchised From: 10
Preferred Square Footage: 1,500; 2,200
Preferred Location Types: Freestanding
Primary Menu: Greek/Mediterranean (1); Snacks (10)
Areas of Operation: MA
Type of Foodservice: Casual Dining (1); Quick Serve (10)
Franchise Affiliation: DD IP Holder, CANTON, MA

Key Personnel
DEODATO BRAGA - President; General Buyer

Webber Restaurant Group
61 Lowell Rd
Groton, MA 01450

Internet Homepage: webberrestaurantgroup.com
Type of Business: Chain Restaurant Operator
Number of Employees: 50
Total Units: 3
Trade Names: Gibbett Hill Grill (1); Scarlet Oak Tavern (1); The Bancroft (1)
Company-Owned Units: 3
Primary Menu: American (2); Steak (1)
Areas of Operation: MA
Type of Foodservice: Casual Dining (2); Fine Dining (1)

Key Personnel
DEIRDRE CLARK - CFO
TOM TOTMAN - COO; General Manager
LISA HANEY-COWLES - General Manager
MARTHA LISIO - General Manager
KEN ROBICHEAU - General Manager
SHEENA LAKE - General Manager
BRENDAN PELLEY - Executive Chef
STEPHEN SHERMAN - Executive Chef
MARCELO PINEDA - Executive Chef
BREE OATES - Director Sales
MARIO CAPONE - Director Culinary Operations
DEIRDRE GONSALVES - Director Sales
DAVE WERTHMAN - Director; Manager

AMY SEVERINO - Manager Marketing

Glg Corp.
455 Russell St
Hadley, MA 01035-9432

Telephone: (413) 253-7640
Type of Business: Chain Restaurant Operator
Total Sales: $3,519,000 (e)
Total Units: 2
Trade Names: Friendly's (2)
Units Franchised From: 2
Primary Menu: American (2)
Areas of Operation: MA
Type of Foodservice: Family Restaurant (2)
Franchise Affiliation: FIC Restaurants, WILBRAHAM, MA

Key Personnel
GARY L. GLENN - President; General Buyer

D.E. Foods Inc.
170 Olde Forge Rd
Hanover, MA 02339-2438

Telephone: (781) 982-0755
Fax Number: (781) 982-9904
Type of Business: Chain Restaurant Operator
Total Sales: $111,950,000 (e)
Number of Employees: 620
Total Units: 61
Trade Names: KFC (48); Taco Bell (13)
Units Franchised From: 61
Preferred Location Types: Freestanding
Primary Menu: Chicken (48); Taco (13)
Areas of Operation: MA, RI
Type of Foodservice: Quick Serve (61)
Franchise Affiliation: KFC Corporation, LOUISVILLE, KY; Taco Bell Corp., IRVINE, CA

Key Personnel
DAVE EVANS - President; Partner; General Buyer
MARYANN EVANS - Partner; General Buyer

Linchris Hotel Corp.
269 Hanover St Ste 2
Hanover, MA 02339-2245

Telephone: (781) 826-8824
Fax Number: (781) 826-2411
Internet Homepage: linchris.com
Company Email: reception@linchris.com
Type of Business: Foodservice Operations - Hotel/Motels
Year Founded: 1985
Total Sales: $164,670,000 (e)
Alcohol Sales: 25%
Number of Employees: 210
Total Units: 30
Trade Names: Anchorage At The Lake (1); Ashworth By The Sea (1); Beach Retreat & Lodge At Tahoe (1); Best Western (2); Comfort Inn (1); DoubleTree by Hilton (2); Hampton (1); Harbor Hotel (1); Hilton (1); Holiday Inn (4); Holiday Inn Express (4); Hotel 1620 (1); Hotel Providence (1); Hotel Tybee (1); Hyatt Place (3); Inn at Middletown (1); Marriott (2); Pleasant View Inn (1); Surfside Hotel (1)
Company-Owned Units: 30
Alcohol Served: Beer, Wine, Liquor
Areas of Operation: CT, DE, FL, GA, MA, NH, NY, PA, RI, TX, VT, WV
Primary Distributors: (Food) SYSCO Food Services of Pittsburgh Inc., HARMONY, PA
Notes: The company derives approximately 80% of its revenue from hotel operations.

Key Personnel
CHRISTOPHER GISTIS - CEO
MICHAEL SULLIVAN - President; VP Finance, Information Systems
GLENN GISTIS - CFO
BOB ANDERSON - Senior VP Operations
NICK PANCOAST - VP Operations
JANINE HODGE - Controller

FJ Catalano Company
188 Ayer Rd
Harvard, MA 01451-1101

Telephone: (978) 456-2300
Fax Number: (978) 456-9955
Type of Business: Chain Restaurant Operator
Total Sales: $33,100,000 (e)
Number of Employees: 407
Average Check: Dinner(8)
Total Units: 21
Trade Names: Dunkin' Donuts (21)
Units Franchised From: 21
Preferred Square Footage: 1,500; 2,200
Preferred Location Types: Downtown; Freestanding
Primary Menu: Snacks (21)
Areas of Operation: MA, TN
Type of Foodservice: Quick Serve (21)
Franchise Affiliation: DD IP Holder, CANTON, MA

Key Personnel
FRANK CATALANO - Partner; Director Operations
STEVE CATALANO - Partner; Director Operations; General Buyer
JESSICA HALLORAN - Director Marketing

Wequassett Inn Resort and Golf Club
2173 Route 28 Head of the Bay Rd
Harwich, MA 02645

Telephone: (508) 469-0378
Fax Number: (508) 432-5032
Internet Homepage: wequassett.com
Company Email: info@wequassett.com
Type of Business: Foodservice Operations - Hotel/Motels
Total Sales: $7,225,000 (e)
Alcohol Sales: 8%
Number of Employees: 300
Total Units: 1
Restaurants in Hotels: 5
Trade Names: Wequassett Resort (1)
Company-Owned Units: 5
Alcohol Served: Beer, Wine, Liquor
Areas of Operation: MA
Type of Foodservice: Casual Dining (5)
Primary Distributors: (Food) SYSCO of Boston, PLYMPTON, MA

Key Personnel
TIM VICKERS - Controller
JAMES HACKNEY - Executive Chef; General Buyer
AMY FARRELL - Director Catering
RENE VOTTELER - Director Food and Beverage

Corporate Chefs
22 Parkridge Rd Ste 1
Haverhill, MA 01835-7279

Telephone: (978) 372-7400
Fax Number: (978) 372-0150
Internet Homepage: corporatechefs.com
Type of Business: Foodservice Management Operator
Year Founded: 1987
Total Sales: $51,413,000 (e)
Number of Employees: 550
Number of Locations Served: 100
Total Foodservice Mgmt Accounts: 100
Trade Names: Corporate Chefs
Areas of Operation: MA
Type of Foodservice: Cafeteria (100)
Foodservice Management Venues: Business & Industry; College & University; Schools
Primary Distributors: (Food) Performance Foodservice - Springfield, SPRINGFIELD, MA

Key Personnel
DAVID DESROSIERS - President; Director Operations
SEAN BRAMBLES - VP Operations
SHAWN BRAMBLE - VP Operations
SALVATORE ZOTOLLA - Regional Director Finance

LYNN DEINNOCENTIS - Manager Quality Assurance, Human Resources, Food Safety
JENNIFER TAFT - Manager Accounting

Eat Well Inc.
19 North St
Hingham, MA 02043-2232

Telephone: (781) 741-5100
Fax Number: (781) 740-0440
Internet Homepage: eatwellinc.com
Type of Business: Chain Restaurant Operator
Year Founded: 1989
Total Sales: $14,947,000 (e)
Alcohol Sales: 25%
Number of Employees: 350
Average Check: Breakfast(12); Lunch(16); Dinner(20)
Internet Order Processing: Yes
Total Units: 3
Trade Names: Cafe Tosca (1); Stars on Hingham Harbor (1); Tosca (1)
Company-Owned Units: 3
Preferred Square Footage: 12,000; 16,000
Preferred Location Types: Freestanding
Alcohol Served: Beer, Wine, Liquor
Primary Menu: American (1); Italian (2)
Areas of Operation: MA
Type of Foodservice: Casual Dining (2); Fine Dining (1)
Catering Services: Yes
Primary Distributors: (Equipment) Paramount Restaurant Supply Corp., FARMINGDALE, NY; (Food) SYSCO of Boston, PLYMPTON, MA; (Supplies) SYSCO of Boston, PLYMPTON, MA

Key Personnel
CHRIS JULE - General Manager
KEVIN LONG - Executive Chef
JIM HODGSON - Manager Operations, Facility/Maintenance, Information Systems, Store Fixtures

Wahlburgers
350 Lincoln St Ste 2501
Hingham, MA 02043-1579

Telephone: (781) 749-4972
Internet Homepage: wahlburgersrestaurant.com
Company Email: contact@wahlburgerscorp.com
Type of Business: Chain Restaurant Operator
Systemwide Sales: $82,284,000 (e)
Total Sales: $57,410,000 (e)
Average Check: Lunch(16); Dinner(18)
Total Units: 40
Trade Names: Wahlburgers (40)
Company-Owned Units: 16
Units Franchised To: 24
Primary Menu: American (40)
Projected Openings: 3
Areas of Operation: AL, CA, CT, FL, GA, MA, MI, NV, NY, OH, PA, SC, ON
Foreign Countries: CANADA
Type of Foodservice: Casual Dining (40)

Key Personnel
MARK WAHLBERG - Co-Founder; Partner
PAUL WAHLBERG - Co-Founder; Partner; Executive Chef
DONNIE WAHLBERG - Co-Founder; Partner
JOHN FULLER - CEO; President
CHRIS SNYDER - VP Purchasing
SARAH DOTCHIN - Senior Director Human Resources
LISA CORRADO - Director Marketing
HOLLY ROOP - Director Marketing

Karmichael Holdings, LLC
33 Main St
Hudson, MA 01749

Telephone: (978) 293-3552
Internet Homepage: lessthangreaterthan.com; newcitymicrocreamery.com; railtrailflatbread.com
Company Email: eat@rtfbco.com
Type of Business: Chain Restaurant Operator
Year Founded: 2012
Total Units: 4
Trade Names: Less Than Greater Than (1); New City Microcreamery (2); The Rail Trail Flatbread Co. (1)
Company-Owned Units: 4
Preferred Location Types: Downtown; Strip Mall
Primary Menu: American (2); Snacks (2)
Areas of Operation: MA
Type of Foodservice: Casual Dining (2); Quick Serve (2)

Key Personnel
KARIM EL-GAMAL - Co-Founder; Partner
MICHAEL KASSERIS - Co-Founder; Partner

Sal's Group
354 Merrimack St
Lawrence, MA 01843-1755

Telephone: (978) 291-0220
Fax Number: (978) 687-6764
Internet Homepage: sals-pizza.com; salvatoresrestaurants.com
Company Email: marketing@sals-pizza.com
Type of Business: Chain Restaurant Operator
Year Founded: 1990
Total Sales: $11,240,000 (e)
Alcohol Sales: 5%
Number of Employees: 856
Average Check: Dinner(26)
Internet Order Processing: Yes
Total Units: 11
Trade Names: Sal's Pizza (12); Salvatore's (5)
Company-Owned Units: 12
Units Franchised To: 5
Alcohol Served: Beer, Wine, Liquor
Primary Menu: Italian (5); Pizza (12)
Areas of Operation: MA, NH
Foreign Countries: INDIA
Type of Foodservice: Casual Dining (17)
Catering Services: Yes

Key Personnel
SALVATORE LUPOLI - President; Partner; Executive Chef; General Buyer
NICK LUPOLI - Partner; VP Quality Control

Dunkin' Donuts Franchise
456 Main St
Leominster, MA 01453-2939

Telephone: (978) 534-9754
Fax Number: (978) 534-6159
Internet Homepage: dunkindonuts.com
Type of Business: Chain Restaurant Operator
Total Sales: $13,860,000 (e)
Number of Employees: 100
Average Check: Dinner(8)
Total Units: 9
Trade Names: Dunkin' Donuts (9)
Units Franchised From: 9
Preferred Square Footage: 1,500; 2,200
Preferred Location Types: Convenience Store/Gas Station; Freestanding; Strip Mall
Primary Menu: Snacks (9)
Areas of Operation: MA
Type of Foodservice: Quick Serve (9)
Franchise Affiliation: DD IP Holder, CANTON, MA

Key Personnel
JOHN NADREAU - President; General Buyer

Happy Jack's
785 N Main St
Leominster, MA 01453-1413

Telephone: (978) 466-3433
Fax Number: (978) 466-5788
Internet Homepage: happyjacksrestaurant.com; southsidemargaritafactory.com
Company Email: happyjacks@verizon.net
Type of Business: Chain Restaurant Operator
Year Founded: 1993
Total Sales: $3,016,000 (e)
Alcohol Sales: 10%
Number of Employees: 35
Average Check: Lunch(12); Dinner(16)
Internet Order Processing: Yes
Total Units: 2

Trade Names: Happy Jack's (1); The Southside Grille & Margarita Factory (1)
Company-Owned Units: 2
Preferred Location Types: Freestanding
Alcohol Served: Beer, Wine, Liquor
Primary Menu: Caribbean (1); Southwest/Tex-Mex (1)
Areas of Operation: MA
Type of Foodservice: Casual Dining (2)
Catering Services: Yes
Primary Distributors: (Food) SYSCO Food Services of Albany, HALFMOON, NY

Key Personnel
CHRIS KNIGHT - Partner; Executive Chef; Director Catering

B E Donuts, Inc.
4 Harding Ave
Ludlow, MA 01056-2370

Telephone: (413) 589-1761
Fax Number: (413) 589-8791
Type of Business: Chain Restaurant Operator
Year Founded: 2002
Total Sales: $17,340,000 (e)
Number of Employees: 163
Average Check: Breakfast(8); Lunch(8); Dinner(8)
Total Units: 11
Trade Names: Dunkin' Donuts (11)
Units Franchised From: 11
Preferred Square Footage: 1,500; 2,200
Preferred Location Types: Convenience Store/Gas Station; Freestanding
Primary Menu: Snacks (11)
Areas of Operation: MA
Type of Foodservice: Quick Serve (11)
Franchise Affiliation: DD IP Holder, CANTON, MA

Key Personnel
LORI MARTINS - President; General Buyer
DEREK SALEMA - Partner; Manager Information Systems
JESSICA SALEMA - Partner; Director Finance; Manager Human Resources
JOHN SALEMA - Partner; Manager Real Estate

Gomez Enterprises LLC
420 Center St
Ludlow, MA 01056-2728

Telephone: (413) 532-0229
Type of Business: Chain Restaurant Operator
Total Sales: $142,520,000 (e)
Total Units: 30
Trade Names: McDonald's (30)
Units Franchised From: 30
Primary Menu: Hamburger (30)
Areas of Operation: MA
Type of Foodservice: Quick Serve (30)
Franchise Affiliation: McDonald's Corporation, CHICAGO, IL

Key Personnel
JORGE GOMEZ - Owner; General Buyer

Salema Management
4 Harding Ave
Ludlow, MA 01056-2370

Telephone: (413) 589-1761
Fax Number: (413) 589-8791
Type of Business: Chain Restaurant Operator
Total Sales: $95,010,000 (e)
Average Check: Dinner(8)
Total Units: 60
Trade Names: Dunkin' Donuts (60)
Units Franchised From: 60
Preferred Square Footage: 1,500; 2,200
Preferred Location Types: Convenience Store/Gas Station; Freestanding
Primary Menu: Snacks (60)
Areas of Operation: MA, NH, VT
Type of Foodservice: Quick Serve (60)
Franchise Affiliation: DD IP Holder, CANTON, MA

Key Personnel
JOHN SALEMA - President; Partner; General Buyer
ANTONIO SALEMA - Partner
DEREK SALEMA - VP
JESSICA SALEMA - Manager Human Resources
KELSEY SALEMA - Analyst Financial Planning

Domino's Franchisee
707 Western Ave
Lynn, MA 01905-2226

Telephone: (781) 581-8080
Type of Business: Chain Restaurant Operator
Total Sales: $8,065,000 (e)
Total Units: 4
Trade Names: Domino's (4)
Units Franchised From: 4
Primary Menu: Pizza (4)
Areas of Operation: MA
Type of Foodservice: Quick Serve (4)
Franchise Affiliation: Domino's Pizza Inc, ANN ARBOR, MI

Key Personnel
YOUSSEF ABOURJAILI - Owner; General Buyer

Lockwood McKinnon Taco Ventures Inc.
79 N Main St
Mansfield, MA 02048-2229

Telephone: (508) 339-6150
Fax Number: (508) 339-6159
Internet Homepage: lockwoodmckinnon.com
Type of Business: Chain Restaurant Operator
Year Founded: 1995
Total Sales: $77,190,000 (e)
Number of Employees: 630
Average Check: Lunch(8); Dinner(12)
Total Units: 28
Trade Names: Taco Bell (28)
Units Franchised From: 28
Preferred Square Footage: 3,000
Preferred Location Types: Community Mall; Freestanding
Primary Menu: Taco (28)
Areas of Operation: MA, RI
Type of Foodservice: Quick Serve (28)
Franchise Affiliation: Taco Bell Corp., IRVINE, CA

Key Personnel
ROGER LOCKWOOD - Chairman; Partner
DAVID LOCKWOOD - President; Partner; Manager Information Systems; General Buyer
STEVE PERRONE - VP Operations
LISA BRISSETTE - Director Human Resources

Domino's Franchisee
54 Main St
Marlborough, MA 01752-3864

Telephone: (508) 481-5335
Type of Business: Chain Restaurant Operator
Total Sales: $11,958,000 (e)
Total Units: 6
Trade Names: Domino's (6)
Units Franchised From: 6
Primary Menu: Pizza (6)
Areas of Operation: MA
Type of Foodservice: Quick Serve (6)
Franchise Affiliation: Domino's Pizza Inc, ANN ARBOR, MI

Key Personnel
JEFF ZADEH - Owner; General Buyer

5 & Diner North America
24 Main St
Maynard, MA 01754-2506

Telephone: (877) 951-1951
Internet Homepage: 5anddiner.com; lpmhci.com
Company Email: info@5anddiner.com

Type of Business: Chain Restaurant Operator
Year Founded: 1989
Systemwide Sales: $7,444,000 (e)
Total Sales: $637,000 (e)
Number of Employees: 129
Average Check: Breakfast(8); Lunch(8); Dinner(12)
Total Units: 3
Trade Names: 5 & Diner (3)
Company-Owned Units: 1
Units Franchised To: 2
Preferred Square Footage: 3,000
Preferred Location Types: Freestanding
Primary Menu: Hamburger (3)
Areas of Operation: AZ, FL
Type of Foodservice: Family Restaurant (3)
Primary Distributors: (Full Line) US Foods, PHOENIX, AZ

Key Personnel
CHRISTINE ARNOLD - General Manager

D'Alelio Management Company
430 Salem St
Medford, MA 02155-3344

Telephone: (781) 391-7590
Fax Number: (781) 395-1881
Internet Homepage: dalelco.com
Company Email: mwest@dalelco.com
Type of Business: Chain Restaurant Operator
Total Sales: $30,550,000 (e)
Number of Employees: 475
Average Check: Dinner(8)
Total Units: 19
Trade Names: Dunkin' Donuts (19)
Units Franchised From: 19
Preferred Square Footage: 1,400
Preferred Location Types: Downtown; Freestanding; Strip Mall
Primary Menu: Snacks (19)
Areas of Operation: MA
Type of Foodservice: Quick Serve (19)
Franchise Affiliation: DD IP Holder, CANTON, MA

Key Personnel
MITZI D'ALELIO LAWLOR - CEO; President
GARY D'ALELIO - President
DAWN KELSEY - Manager Human Resources

Five Olsons LLC
163 Main St Unit 102
Medway, MA 02053-1533

Telephone: (508) 533-3030
Internet Homepage: fiveolsons.com
Type of Business: Chain Restaurant Operator
Total Sales: $14,090,000 (e)
Number of Employees: 115
Total Units: 7
Trade Names: Five Guys Burgers and Fries (7)
Units Franchised From: 7
Preferred Square Footage: 3,000
Preferred Location Types: Strip Mall
Primary Menu: Hamburger (7)
Areas of Operation: MA
Type of Foodservice: Fast Casual (7)
Franchise Affiliation: Five Guys Holdings Inc., LORTON, VA

Key Personnel
NELS OLSON - Owner; General Buyer
ROBYN EMERSON - Director Finance

Cafua Management Company LLC
280 Merrimack St
Methuen, MA 01844-6435

Telephone: (978) 682-2382
Fax Number: (978) 683-2634
Internet Homepage: cafuamanagement.com
Type of Business: Chain Restaurant Operator
Total Sales: $396,120,000 (e)
Number of Employees: 5,000
Total Units: 247
Trade Names: Dunkin' Donuts (240); Dunkin' Donuts/Baskin-Robbins (7)
Units Franchised From: 247
Preferred Square Footage: 1,500; 2,200
Primary Menu: Snacks (247)
Areas of Operation: FL, MA, ME, NH, NY, PA, VT
Type of Foodservice: Quick Serve (247)
Franchise Affiliation: BR IP Holder LLC, CANTON, MA; DD IP Holder, CANTON, MA

Key Personnel
MARK CAFUA - CEO; Partner
DAVID CAFUA - President; Partner
GREGORY CAFUA - Partner; Chief Business Officer
SCOTT ZEITLAN - CFO
FRANK SERVIDIO - COO
CHRISTOPHER COOK - Chief People Officer
GABE COGLEY - Area Director
FELICIA CAFUA - VP Operations
LUIS FILIPE MARQUES - VP Talent, People
JENNIFER MILLER - General Manager
CRAIG PATTERSON - Director Operations
CHRISTOPHER PIERCE - Director Operations
REBECCA SCHWEIGARD - Director Development, People-Training
JERONIMO SILVA - Director
DOUG SPOLYAR - Director Operations
GREG TATARIAN - Director Operations
VANCE WHITE - Director Technology, Information Systems
DAIANA YOUNG - Director Operations
KEVIN MARTIN - Director Employee Development
ANDREW FISHLEY - Director Operations
KIM KEYS - Director Talent, People
RICHARD KOSTON - Director Operations
DAVID ECKHART - Director Operations
MANNY FERREIRA - Director Operations
KIM CASALE - Director Human Resources
PATTY COLLINS - Director Accounting
REBECCA MANIKIAN - Regional Director Operations
SANDY LUCIA - Manager Accounting
MICHELE COSTELLO - Manager

Newcomb Farms Family Restaurant
1139 Randolph Ave
Milton, MA 02186-5264

Telephone: (617) 698-9547
Fax Number: (617) 770-4180
Internet Homepage: newcombfarmsrestaurant.com
Type of Business: Chain Restaurant Operator
Year Founded: 1965
Total Sales: $2,885,000 (e)
Number of Employees: 35
Average Check: Breakfast(8); Lunch(10); Dinner(12)
Total Units: 2
Trade Names: Newcomb Farms Family Restaurant (2)
Company-Owned Units: 2
Preferred Square Footage: 3,500
Preferred Location Types: Freestanding; Outlet Mall
Primary Menu: American (2)
Areas of Operation: MA
Type of Foodservice: Family Restaurant (2)

Key Personnel
DAVE NEWCOMB - Owner; General Manager; General Buyer
STEVEN KNOWLES - Executive Chef; General Buyer

Not Your Average Joe's Inc.
2 Granite Ave Ste 300
Milton, MA 02186-4377

Telephone: (774) 213-2800
Fax Number: (774) 213-2899
Internet Homepage: notyouraveragejoes.com; nyajoes.com
Company Email: info@nyajoes.com
Type of Business: Chain Restaurant Operator
Year Founded: 1994
Total Sales: $69,800,000 (e)
Alcohol Sales: 20%
Number of Employees: 1,090
Average Check: Breakfast(12); Lunch(16); Dinner(26)

Internet Order Processing: Yes
Internet Sales: 1.00%
Total Units: 19
Trade Names: Not Your Average Joe's (19)
Company-Owned Units: 19
Preferred Square Footage: 3,200; 6,000
Preferred Location Types: Freestanding; Strip Mall
Alcohol Served: Beer, Wine, Liquor
Primary Menu: American (23)
Areas of Operation: MA, MD, NH, PA, RI, VA
Type of Foodservice: Casual Dining (23)
Primary Distributors: (Full Line) SYSCO of Boston, PLYMPTON, MA

Key Personnel
PETER D'AMELIO - CEO; President
JOSEPH MCGUIRE - CFO; Controller
DENNIS MAHER - VP Development, Real Estate
MAUREEN DUTRA - VP Purchasing
JOE GARTLAND - Regional VP Operations
KELLY KELLEY - Controller
MARLO MCFADDEN - Manager Restaurant Operations

Auntie Anne's Franchise
1245 Worcester St Ste 1114
Natick, MA 01760-1529

Telephone: (508) 318-5609
Type of Business: Chain Restaurant Operator
Total Sales: $4,993,000 (e)
Total Units: 7
Trade Names: Auntie Anne's Hand-Rolled Soft Pretzels (7)
Units Franchised From: 7
Primary Menu: Snacks (7)
Areas of Operation: MA
Type of Foodservice: Quick Serve (7)
Franchise Affiliation: Auntie Anne's Inc., LANCASTER, PA

Key Personnel
ROBERT BURNESS - Owner; General Buyer

Fresh City
1400 Worchester Road
Natick, MA 01760

Telephone: (508) 875-5750
Internet Homepage: freshcity.com
Company Email: info@freshcity.com
Type of Business: Chain Restaurant Operator
Year Founded: 1996
Total Units: 10
Trade Names: Fresh City (10)
Company-Owned Units: 10
Preferred Location Types: Airports; Freestanding; Institution (college/hospital); Travel Plazas

Primary Menu: Health Foods (10)
Areas of Operation: CT, MA, NJ
Type of Foodservice: Fast Casual (10)

Key Personnel
PETE MINICH - Owner

Kimbaman Corp.
1274 Worcester St
Natick, MA 01760-1511

Telephone: (508) 653-4700
Type of Business: Chain Restaurant Operator
Total Sales: $3,563,000 (e)
Total Units: 2
Trade Names: Moe's Southwest Grill (2)
Units Franchised From: 2
Primary Menu: Southwest/Tex-Mex (2)
Areas of Operation: MA
Type of Foodservice: Fast Casual (2)
Franchise Affiliation: Moe's Southwest Grill LLC, ATLANTA, GA

Key Personnel
STEVE HIXSON - Owner; General Buyer

Daly-Kenney Group
PO Box 51147
New Bedford, MA 02745-0039

Telephone: (508) 995-0513
Company Email: dunkindonuts@dalykenney.com
Type of Business: Chain Restaurant Operator
Total Sales: $16,060,000 (e)
Number of Employees: 275
Total Units: 10
Trade Names: Dunkin' Donuts (10)
Units Franchised From: 10
Preferred Square Footage: 1,500; 2,200
Primary Menu: Snacks (10)
Areas of Operation: MA
Type of Foodservice: Quick Serve (10)
Franchise Affiliation: DD IP Holder, CANTON, MA

Key Personnel
WILLIAM DALY - President; General Buyer

Domino's Pizza New Bedford
821 Rockdale Ave
New Bedford, MA 02740-2701

Telephone: (508) 999-2911
Company Email: teamnewbedford@hotmail.com
Type of Business: Chain Restaurant Operator
Total Sales: $3,994,000 (e)
Number of Employees: 50
Average Check: Lunch(16); Dinner(16)
Total Units: 2
Trade Names: Domino's (2)
Units Franchised From: 2
Preferred Square Footage: 1,000; 1,300
Preferred Location Types: Freestanding; Other
Primary Menu: Pizza (2)
Areas of Operation: MA
Type of Foodservice: Quick Serve (2)
Franchise Affiliation: Domino's Pizza Inc, ANN ARBOR, MI
Primary Distributors: (Full Line) SYSCO of Boston, PLYMPTON, MA

Key Personnel
NELSON HOCKERT-LOTZ - President; General Manager; General Buyer

Anna's Taqueria
27 Lincoln St
Newton, MA 02461

Telephone: (617) 850-2933
Internet Homepage: annastaqueria.com
Company Email: orders@shopannas.net
Type of Business: Chain Restaurant Operator
Year Founded: 1995
Internet Order Processing: Yes
Total Units: 8
Trade Names: Anna's Taqueria (8)
Company-Owned Units: 8
Primary Menu: Taco (8)
Projected Openings: 1
Areas of Operation: MA
Type of Foodservice: Fast Casual (8)

Key Personnel
BETSY KAMIO - Owner; General Buyer

Cafe Sol Azteca
75 Union St
Newton, MA 02459-2224

Telephone: (617) 964-0920
Fax Number: (617) 964-0258
Internet Homepage: solaztecaboston.com; cafesolazteca.com
Type of Business: Chain Restaurant Operator
Year Founded: 1990
Total Sales: $1,868,000 (e)
Alcohol Sales: 12%
Number of Employees: 12
Average Check: Lunch(14); Dinner(24)
Total Units: 2
Trade Names: Cafe Sol Azteca (1); Sol Azteca (1)
Company-Owned Units: 2
Preferred Location Types: Freestanding
Alcohol Served: Beer, Wine, Liquor
Primary Menu: Mexican (2)

Areas of Operation: MA
Type of Foodservice: Casual Dining (2)
Catering Services: Yes
Primary Distributors: (Food) S.M. Sneider Co., BOSTON, MA

Key Personnel
HERMAN AGUILAR - President; General Manager; Director Menu Development
RIMA OSORNIO - General Manager; Director Food and Beverage; General Buyer
GABRIEL AGUILAR - General Manager

Finagle A Bagel
77 Rowe St Ste 100
Newton, MA 02466-1511

Telephone: (617) 213-8400
Fax Number: (617) 213-8428
Internet Homepage: finagleabagel.com; finagleonline.com
Company Email: guestrelations@finagleonline.com
Type of Business: Chain Restaurant Operator
Year Founded: 1982
Total Sales: $8,672,000 (e)
Alcohol Sales: 1%
Number of Employees: 240
Average Check: Breakfast(8); Lunch(12); Dinner(12)
Total Units: 4
Trade Names: Finagle Bakery & Cafe (4)
Company-Owned Units: 4
Preferred Square Footage: 3,000
Preferred Location Types: Freestanding; Regional Mall; Strip Mall
Primary Menu: Bagels (4)
Areas of Operation: MA
Type of Foodservice: Quick Serve (4)
Catering Services: Yes
Distribution Centers: AUBURNDALE, MA
On-site Distribution Center: Yes
Primary Distributors: (Full Line) SYSCO Food Services of Albany, HALFMOON, NY

Key Personnel
ALAN LITCHMAN - Partner; Director Finance, Menu Development, Catering; General Buyer
LAURA TRUST - Partner; General Buyer
RANDY MOORE - Controller
SUSAN GOULD - Director Marketing, Human Resources; Developer Production
JEFF MALICH - Director Sales

Sonesta International Hotels Corp.
255 Washington St Ste 270
Newton, MA 02458-1634

Telephone: (617) 421-5400
Fax Number: (617) 421-5402
Internet Homepage: sonesta.com
Company Email: info@sonesta.com
Type of Business: Foodservice Operations - Hotel/Motels
Year Founded: 1950
Total Sales: $460,480,000 (e)
Alcohol Sales: 5%
Number of Employees: 11,600
Total Units: 58
Restaurants in Hotels: 58
Trade Names: Sonesta Hotels and Resorts (58)
Company-Owned Units: 58
Alcohol Served: Beer, Wine, Liquor
Areas of Operation: AZ, FL, GA, IL, LA, MA, MD, MI, MO, NC, NJ, OH, PA, SC, TX
Foreign Countries: BRAZIL; EGYPT; PERU; SAINT MAARTEN
Type of Foodservice: Casual Dining; Fine Dining
Subsidiaries: Red Lion Hotels Corporation, DENVER, CO
Primary Distributors: (Food) SYSCO Food Services of Virginia LLC, HARRISONBURG, VA
Notes: Sonesta also has management agreements for six hotels in Egypt, five Nile River cruise vessels and has granted licenses for the use of its name to six hotels in Peru, two hotels in St. Maarten and two hotels in Brazil. The company derives approximately 79% of its revenue from hotel operations.

Key Personnel
CARLOS FLORES - CEO; President
DAVID RAKOUSKAS - Controller
BETTY YUEN - Director Purchasing; General Buyer

Auntie Anne's Franchise
332 Emerald Sq
North Attleboro, MA 02760-3647

Telephone: (508) 643-0856
Type of Business: Chain Restaurant Operator
Total Sales: $3,666,000 (e)
Total Units: 5
Trade Names: Auntie Anne's Hand-Rolled Soft Pretzels (5)
Units Franchised From: 5
Primary Menu: Snacks (5)
Areas of Operation: MA
Type of Foodservice: Quick Serve (5)
Franchise Affiliation: Auntie Anne's Inc., LANCASTER, PA

Key Personnel
CHRISTOPHER WOOD - Owner; General Buyer

McDonald's Franchise
50 Oliver St
North Easton, MA 02356-1446

Telephone: (508) 230-2190
Type of Business: Chain Restaurant Operator
Total Sales: $47,880,000 (e)
Total Units: 10
Trade Names: McDonald's (10)
Units Franchised From: 10
Preferred Square Footage: 2,500
Primary Menu: Hamburger (10)
Areas of Operation: MA
Type of Foodservice: Quick Serve (10)
Franchise Affiliation: McDonald's Corporation, CHICAGO, IL

Key Personnel
JANISE JARAMILLO-MCBEE - President; General Buyer

N.G.P Management LLC
3 Pluff Ave
North Reading, MA 01864-1342

Telephone: (978) 898-1200
Fax Number: (978) 664-4160
Type of Business: Chain Restaurant Operator
Year Founded: 1965
Total Sales: $170,430,000 (e)
Average Check: Dinner(10)
Total Units: 109
Trade Names: Dunkin' Donuts (109)
Units Franchised From: 109
Preferred Square Footage: 1,500; 2,200
Primary Menu: Snacks (109)
Areas of Operation: MA, ME, NH, VT
Type of Foodservice: Quick Serve (109)
Franchise Affiliation: DD IP Holder, CANTON, MA

Key Personnel
CONSTANTINE SCRIVANOS - CEO; President; General Buyer
JUNE LEI - CFO
PATRICIA LINCOLN - VP Operations
SUZANNE WILSON - Director Development, Human Resources, People
JIM CLIFFORD - Director Real Estate
ANNE GILDEA - Director Operations
JIM PIRAINO - Director Tax
CHRISTOPHER MCCARTHY - District Manager
JOHN MEOLA - Manager Plant
JEFF LEBLANC - Manager Information Technology

Domino's Franchisee
241 King St Ste 115
Northampton, MA 01060-2344

Telephone: (413) 584-2111
Type of Business: Chain Restaurant Operator
Total Sales: $3,973,000 (e)
Total Units: 2
Trade Names: Domino's (2)
Units Franchised From: 2
Primary Menu: Pizza (2)
Areas of Operation: MA
Type of Foodservice: Quick Serve (2)
Franchise Affiliation: Domino's Pizza Inc, ANN ARBOR, MI

Key Personnel
SCOTT D. AKERS - Owner; General Buyer

Herrell's Developement Corporation
8 Old South St
Northampton, MA 01060-3847

Telephone: (413) 586-9700
Internet Homepage: herrells.com
Type of Business: Chain Restaurant Operator
Year Founded: 1973
Systemwide Sales: $5,332,000 (e)
Total Sales: $1,827,000 (e)
Number of Employees: 150
Average Check: Lunch(6); Dinner(6)
Internet Order Processing: Yes
Internet Sales: 5.00%
Total Units: 2
Trade Names: Herrell's (2)
Company-Owned Units: 1
Units Franchised To: 1
Preferred Square Footage: 2,500
Preferred Location Types: Freestanding; Regional Mall
Primary Menu: Snacks (2)
Areas of Operation: MA, NY
Type of Foodservice: Quick Serve (2)
Catering Services: Yes
Primary Distributors: (Full Line) Gordon Food Service, TAUNTON, MA; (Supplies) Mansfield Paper Co. Inc., WEST SPRINGFIELD, MA

Key Personnel
JUDITH HARRELL - President; General Buyer
STEPHAN WURMBRAND - COO

Bertucci's Corporation
155 Otis St
Northborough, MA 01532-2456

Telephone: (508) 351-2500
Fax Number: (508) 393-8046
Internet Homepage: bertuccis.com
Type of Business: Chain Restaurant Operator
Year Founded: 1981
Systemwide Sales: $316,443,000 (e)
Total Sales: $202,066,000 (e)
Alcohol Sales: 10%
Number of Employees: 4,845
Average Check: Lunch(14); Dinner(18)
Internet Order Processing: Yes
Total Units: 50
Trade Names: Bertucci's Italian Restaurant (50)
Company-Owned Units: 50
Preferred Square Footage: 6,000
Preferred Location Types: Freestanding; Regional Mall; Strip Mall
Alcohol Served: Beer, Wine, Liquor
Primary Menu: Italian (50)
Areas of Operation: CT, DC, DE, MA, MD, NH, NJ, NY, PA, RI, VA
Type of Foodservice: Casual Dining (50)
Catering Services: Yes
Primary Distributors: (Full Line) Maines Paper & Food Service New England, WESTBOROUGH, MA
Parent Company: Jacobson Partners, NEW YORK, NY

Key Personnel
BRIAN CONNELL - CFO; Senior VP
KEVIN BAKAS - VP Real Estate, Construction
JOE ENOS - VP
SEAN CAMPBELL - VP Division
DONNA PLACE - Controller
CHRISTINE MOREIRA - General Manager
BOBBY BURNS - Senior Manager Financial Planning
JESSICA MOREY - Manager
PAUL RICHARDS - Manager Operations
CHRISTOPHER MARRONE - Manager

Foley Food & Vending Company Inc.
180 Kerry Pl Ste B
Norwood, MA 02062-4735

Telephone: (781) 551-0711
Fax Number: (781) 762-6088
Internet Homepage: foleyfoodservice.com
Company Email: service@FoleyFoodService.com
Type of Business: Foodservice Management Operator
Year Founded: 1973
Total Sales: $7,289,000 (e)
Number of Employees: 16
Number of Locations Served: 300
Total Foodservice Mgmt Accounts: 300
Areas of Operation: MA
Type of Foodservice: Vending machines (300)
Foodservice Management Venues: Business & Industry; College & University; Health Care; Other; Schools

Key Personnel
STEVE FOLEY - President
KEN FOLEY - VP Purchasing, Facility/Maintenance
BRIAN FOLEY - VP; Treasurer; Manager Finance, Human Resources

National Amusements Inc.
846 University Ave
Norwood, MA 02062-2631

Mailing Address: PO Box 9108, NORWOOD, Ma, 02062-9108
Telephone: (781) 461-1600
Fax Number: (781) 407-0052
Internet Homepage: nationalamusements.com; showcasecinemas.com
Company Email: customer_service@national-amusements.com
Type of Business: Foodservice Operations - Movie Theatre
Year Founded: 1936
Total Sales: $133,180,000 (e)
Alcohol Sales: 1%
Number of Employees: 1,181
Average Check: Breakfast(8); Lunch(8); Dinner(8)
Total Units: 25
Trade Names: Imax (1); Showcase Cinemas (24)
Company-Owned Units: 27
Preferred Square Footage: 2,500
Preferred Location Types: Community Mall; Freestanding; Strip Mall
Alcohol Served: Beer, Wine, Liquor
Primary Menu: Snacks (27)
Projected Openings: 1
Areas of Operation: CT, MA, NJ, NY, OH, RI, FC
Type of Foodservice: In-Store Feeder (27)
Franchise Affiliation: Nathan's Famous Inc., JERICHO, NY; Sbarro Holdings LLC, COLUMBUS, OH
Primary Distributors: (Full Line) SYSCO Food Services of Northern New England Inc., WESTBROOK, ME
Notes: Total store count excludes international units. The company derives approximately 74% of its revenue from movie theatre operations.

Key Personnel
SUMNER REDSTONE - Chairman
SHARI REDSTONE - CEO; President
JOE MOLLO - CIO; Senior VP Information Technology
TED JANKOWSKI - Exec VP; General Counsel
MARK MALINOWSKI - VP Global Marketing
VIK JOSHI - Assistant VP Technology
JULIE HEINZELMAN - General Counsel
RACHEL LULAY - Senior Director Marketing

DEBI HELLER - Director Communications
DAN HERRLE - Director Business Development
JOSEPH DECHRISTOPHER - Director Internal Audit, Asset Protection
JERRY FORMAN - Director Foodservice
MICHELLE NORMAN - Director Employee Development-Training
TONY PUNGITORE - Director Operations
MIA BECKMAN - Manager Purchasing; General Buyer

Uno Restaurants, LLC
44 Industrial Way
Norwood, MA 02062

Telephone: (781) 551-0574
Fax Number: (617) 323-6906
Internet Homepage: unoduego.com; unofoods.com; unos.com
Company Email: mail@unos.com
Type of Business: Chain Restaurant Operator
Year Founded: 1978
Systemwide Sales: $254,363,000 (e)
Total Sales: $187,160,000 (e)
Alcohol Sales: 5%
Number of Employees: 8,000
Average Check: Lunch(16); Dinner(20)
Internet Order Processing: Yes
Internet Sales: 1.00%
Total Units: 78
Trade Names: Uno Due Go (1); Uno Pizzeria & Grill (77)
Company-Owned Units: 75
Units Franchised To: 3
Preferred Square Footage: 150; 1,000; 4,800; 5,300; 6,000
Preferred Location Types: Airports; Community Mall; Downtown; Freestanding; Hotel/Motel; Kiosk; Outlet Mall; Regional Mall; Strip Mall
Alcohol Served: Beer, Wine, Liquor
Primary Menu: American (78); Mexican (0)
Areas of Operation: CA, CO, DC, FL, IL, IN, MA, MD, ME, MI, NH, NJ, NM, NY, OH, PA, RI, SC, TX, VA, VT, WI, WV
Foreign Countries: SAUDI ARABIA; SOUTH KOREA; UNITED ARAB EMIRATES
Type of Foodservice: Casual Dining (77); Fast Casual (1)
Parent Company: Twin Haven Capital Partners, LLC, LOS ANGELES, CA
Notes: The company derives approximately 15% of its revenue from sales of its consumer products division & other operations. Store counts exclude Uno Express locations which operate primarily as carts and kiosks. Systemwide sales reflect Uno Chicago Grill operations only.

Key Personnel
ERIK FREDERICK - CEO
GEORGE W. HERZ II - Chief Administrative Officer; Senior VP; General Counsel
REGINA JEROME - Senior VP Information Technology
MARY ISBERG - VP Operations, Quality Control
PAUL RANKIN - VP
JEFF MCNALLY - VP Supply Chain
ADAM HOLZHAUER - VP Finance, Administration
BRUCE HOFFMAN - Director Franchise Operations
KIMBERLY BOYNTON - Director Marketing
STEPHEN BRENNAN - Regional Director Operations
DINO GRAVANIS - Regional Director
EDGAR CRUZ - Regional Director
GARY MCCAULEY - Regional Director Operations
KYLA CASEY - Regional Director Operations

IMC Management
1465 N Main St
Palmer, MA 01069-1226

Telephone: (413) 284-0422
Fax Number: (413) 289-1538
Type of Business: Chain Restaurant Operator
Year Founded: 1991
Total Sales: $18,810,000 (e)
Average Check: Breakfast(8); Lunch(8); Dinner(8)
Total Units: 12
Trade Names: Dunkin' Donuts (12)
Units Franchised From: 12
Preferred Square Footage: 1,500; 2,200
Primary Menu: Snacks (12)
Areas of Operation: MA
Type of Foodservice: Quick Serve (12)
Franchise Affiliation: DD IP Holder, CANTON, MA

Key Personnel
KRIS VENTURA - President; General Buyer

Essen Foods
12 Sylvan St
Peabody, MA 01960-1607

Telephone: (978) 774-1724
Fax Number: (978) 750-6707
Internet Homepage: sylvanstreetgrille.com
Company Email: etremblay@sylvanstreetgrille.com
Type of Business: Chain Restaurant Operator
Year Founded: 1989
Total Sales: $10,757,000 (e)
Alcohol Sales: 27%
Number of Employees: 185
Average Check: Lunch(10); Dinner(14)
Internet Order Processing: Yes
Total Units: 2
Trade Names: Sylvan Street Grille (2)
Company-Owned Units: 2
Preferred Location Types: Freestanding
Alcohol Served: Beer, Wine, Liquor
Primary Menu: American (2)
Areas of Operation: MA
Type of Foodservice: Casual Dining (2)
Primary Distributors: (Full Line) US Foods, SEABROOK, NH

Key Personnel
CODY TREMBLAY - VP Operations
TRICIA OLIVAL - General Manager
RHONDA GAGNON - Manager Administration

Cadete Enterprises Inc.
12 Riverside Dr Ste 1
Pembroke, MA 02359-4986

Telephone: (781) 829-1156
Fax Number: (781) 829-9468
Internet Homepage: cadeteenterprises.com
Type of Business: Chain Restaurant Operator
Year Founded: 1980
Total Sales: $77,380,000 (e)
Number of Employees: 1,400
Average Check: Breakfast(12); Lunch(8); Dinner(8)
Total Units: 50
Trade Names: Dunkin' Donuts (50)
Units Franchised From: 50
Preferred Square Footage: 1,500; 2,200
Preferred Location Types: Convenience Store/Gas Station; Freestanding; Regional Mall
Primary Menu: Snacks (50)
Areas of Operation: MA
Type of Foodservice: Quick Serve (50)
Franchise Affiliation: DD IP Holder, CANTON, MA

Key Personnel
JOHN CADETE - President; Partner; General Buyer
CARLOS RESENDES - Partner; COO
JASON CADETE - CFO
SUSAN BRODIL - VP Operations
NELIA RESENDES - Manager Human Resources

Domino's Franchisee
1229 North St
Pittsfield, MA 01201-1525

Telephone: (413) 499-7979
Type of Business: Chain Restaurant Operator
Total Sales: $18,009,000 (e)
Total Units: 9
Trade Names: Domino's (9)
Units Franchised From: 9
Primary Menu: Pizza (9)
Areas of Operation: MA
Type of Foodservice: Quick Serve (9)

Franchise Affiliation: Domino's Pizza Inc, ANN ARBOR, MI

Key Personnel
JOSEPH V. ZONFRILLI - Owner; General Buyer

Hot Harry's Fresh Burritos, Inc.
37 North St
Pittsfield, MA 01201-5105

Telephone: (413) 448-6155
Internet Homepage: hotharrysburritos.com
Type of Business: Chain Restaurant Operator
Total Units: 5
Trade Names: Hot Harry's Fresh Burritos (5)
Company-Owned Units: 5
Primary Menu: Mexican (5)
Areas of Operation: CT, IA, MA, NY
Type of Foodservice: Fast Casual (5)

Key Personnel
SAMIR ABDALLAH - Founder; President; General Buyer

Honey Dew Associates Inc.
2 Taunton St Unit 3
Plainville, MA 02762-2137

Telephone: (508) 699-3900
Fax Number: (508) 699-3949
Internet Homepage: honeydewdonuts.com
Company Email: customersupport@honeydewdonuts.com
Type of Business: Chain Restaurant Operator
Year Founded: 1973
Systemwide Sales: $70,933,000 (e)
Total Sales: $7,755,000 (e)
Number of Employees: 17
Average Check: Breakfast(8); Lunch(8); Dinner(8)
Total Units: 129
Trade Names: Honey Dew Donuts (130)
Company-Owned Units: 1
Units Franchised To: 129
Preferred Square Footage: 1,200; 1,600
Preferred Location Types: Convenience Store/Gas Station; Freestanding; Strip Mall
Primary Menu: Snacks (130)
Areas of Operation: MA, NH, RI
Type of Foodservice: Quick Serve (130)
Primary Distributors: (Full Line) SYSCO of Boston, PLYMPTON, MA

Key Personnel
RICHARD BOWEN - President; Director Finance, Supply Chain, Real Estate, Design
KATHY PATROVANIE - Controller; Director Marketing, Human Resources; Manager Accounting
DARLENE GUENETTE - Director Product Development; Manager Loss Prevention, Food Safety
DON LEAVITT - Director Information Systems, Real Estate, Construction
CHERYL ZANNINO - Director Franchise Development
JEANNE QUINN - Manager Marketing

British Beer Company
11 Resnik Rd Unit 3
Plymouth, MA 02360-4892

Telephone: (508) 888-6610
Fax Number: (774) 773-9680
Internet Homepage: britishbeer.com
Type of Business: Chain Restaurant Operator
Year Founded: 1997
Total Sales: $32,550,000 (e)
Alcohol Sales: 45%
Number of Employees: 580
Average Check: Lunch(8); Dinner(18)
Internet Order Processing: Yes
Total Units: 10
Trade Names: British Beer Company (10)
Company-Owned Units: 10
Preferred Location Types: Freestanding
Alcohol Served: Beer, Wine, Liquor
Primary Menu: American (10)
Projected Openings: 2
Areas of Operation: MA, ME, NH
Type of Foodservice: Casual Dining (10)
Primary Distributors: (Full Line) SYSCO of Boston, PLYMPTON, MA

Key Personnel
HARRY GNONG - Founder; Partner
GARY SIMON - President; Partner
DOUGLAS FREEMAN - Partner; Director Real Estate
JOHN DAWES - Controller
MICHAEL VALITSKY - General Manager
SEAN SUGDEN - Director Information Technology

Domino's Franchisee
100 Market St
Rockland, MA 02370-2604

Telephone: (781) 871-3030
Type of Business: Chain Restaurant Operator
Total Sales: $4,139,000 (e)
Total Units: 2
Trade Names: Domino's (2)
Units Franchised From: 2
Primary Menu: Pizza (2)
Areas of Operation: MA
Type of Foodservice: Quick Serve (2)
Franchise Affiliation: Domino's Pizza Inc, ANN ARBOR, MI

Key Personnel
ROBERT E. BENSON - Owner; General Buyer

Napoli Management
100 Weymouth St Ste G1
Rockland, MA 02370-1146

Telephone: (781) 347-4644
Fax Number: (781) 347-4643
Internet Homepage: mcdsnapoli.com
Type of Business: Chain Restaurant Operator
Total Sales: $87,780,000 (e)
Number of Employees: 408
Total Units: 18
Trade Names: McDonald's (18)
Units Franchised From: 18
Preferred Square Footage: 2,500
Primary Menu: Hamburger (18)
Areas of Operation: MA, RI
Type of Foodservice: Quick Serve (18)
Franchise Affiliation: McDonald's Corporation, CHICAGO, IL

Key Personnel
JOE NAPOLI - President; General Buyer
ANNA MACHADO - Controller

Tasty Burger Corp.
2306 Washington St
Roxbury, MA 02119-3213

Telephone: (617) 303-0410
Internet Homepage: tastyburger.com
Type of Business: Chain Restaurant Operator
Total Units: 4
Trade Names: Tasty Burger (4)
Company-Owned Units: 4
Preferred Location Types: Freestanding; Stadiums
Primary Menu: Hamburger (4)
Projected Openings: 2
Areas of Operation: MA
Type of Foodservice: Quick Serve (4)
Parent Company: The Franklin Restaurant Group, BOSTON, MA

Key Personnel
DAVID DUBOIS - CEO; General Buyer

The Waldwin Group Inc
15 Allerton St Ste 3
Roxbury, MA 02119-2901

Telephone: (617) 541-1911
Fax Number: (617) 541-1919
Internet Homepage: thewaldwingroup.com
Company Email: info@thewaldwingroup.com
Type of Business: Chain Restaurant Operator
Year Founded: 1992

Total Sales: $21,920,000 (e)
Number of Employees: 298
Total Units: 14
Trade Names: Dunkin' Donuts (14)
Units Franchised From: 14
Preferred Square Footage: 1,500; 2,200
Preferred Location Types: Freestanding; Strip Mall
Primary Menu: Snacks (14)
Areas of Operation: MA
Type of Foodservice: Quick Serve (14)
Franchise Affiliation: DD IP Holder, CANTON, MA

Key Personnel
CLAYTON H. TURNBULL - CEO; President; Partner; Manager Real Estate
LINDA TURNBULL - Partner; Director Human Resources; Manager Information Systems
JIM MCCREADY - Controller
KEVIN REYNOLDS - Director Operations; General Buyer

Bobby Byrne's Management Corp.
65 Route 6A
Sandwich, MA 02563-1893

Mailing Address: PO Box 1659, SANDWICH, MA, 02563-1659
Telephone: (508) 833-1155
Fax Number: (508) 833-1614
Internet Homepage: bobbybyrnes.com
Type of Business: Chain Restaurant Operator
Year Founded: 1973
Total Sales: $5,487,000 (e)
Alcohol Sales: 35%
Number of Employees: 100
Average Check: Lunch(10); Dinner(16)
Total Units: 3
Trade Names: Bobby Byrne's Pub (3)
Company-Owned Units: 3
Preferred Location Types: Freestanding
Alcohol Served: Beer, Wine, Liquor
Primary Menu: Steak/Seafood (3)
Areas of Operation: MA
Type of Foodservice: Casual Dining (3)
Primary Distributors: (Full Line) SYSCO of Boston, PLYMPTON, MA

Key Personnel
ROBERT V. BYRNE - CEO; Director Purchasing, Real Estate, Research & Development, Store Planning
JEFFREY MOORE - President; Owner; Controller; Director Operations, Marketing
ELLEN GILMORE - Controller
DAVE GRADY - Director
ELISE PERRY - Director Human Resources

KRB Management Inc.
605 Broadway Ste 300
Saugus, MA 01906-3200

Telephone: (781) 233-5700
Fax Number: (781) 233-9788
Internet Homepage: kellysroastbeef.com
Company Email: info@kellysroastbeef.com
Type of Business: Chain Restaurant Operator
Year Founded: 1951
Total Sales: $5,008,000 (e)
Number of Employees: 100
Average Check: Lunch(12); Dinner(16)
Internet Order Processing: Yes
Total Units: 4
Trade Names: Kelly's Roast Beef (4)
Company-Owned Units: 4
Preferred Location Types: Office Complex; Strip Mall
Primary Menu: Sandwiches/Deli (4)
Areas of Operation: MA
Type of Foodservice: Quick Serve (4)
Primary Distributors: (Food) SYSCO of Boston, PLYMPTON, MA

Key Personnel
BOB FLOT - General Manager
DAN DOHERTY - Director Operations; General Buyer

Hartford Pike Donuts
866 Hartford Tpke
Shrewsbury, MA 01545-4107

Telephone: (508) 845-3911
Fax Number: (508) 845-3914
Type of Business: Chain Restaurant Operator
Total Sales: $17,270,000 (e)
Average Check: Dinner(8)
Total Units: 11
Trade Names: Dunkin' Donuts (11)
Units Franchised From: 11
Preferred Square Footage: 1,500; 2,200
Preferred Location Types: Freestanding; Strip Mall
Primary Menu: Snacks (11)
Areas of Operation: MA
Type of Foodservice: Quick Serve (11)
Franchise Affiliation: DD IP Holder, CANTON, MA

Key Personnel
GEORGE CADETTE - President; Director Franchise Development; General Buyer
GLAULIANA SOARES - General Manager
ANDREW CADETTE - Manager Human Resources

Watermark Donut Co.
370 Dorchester Ave
South Boston, MA 02127-2407

Telephone: (617) 464-3796
Fax Number: (617) 464-3880
Type of Business: Chain Restaurant Operator
Year Founded: 1990
Total Sales: $15,500,000 (e)
Number of Employees: 640
Average Check: Breakfast(6); Lunch(6); Dinner(6)
Total Units: 10
Trade Names: Dunkin' Donuts (10)
Units Franchised From: 10
Preferred Square Footage: 1,200; 2,000
Preferred Location Types: Downtown; Freestanding; Strip Mall
Primary Menu: Snacks (10)
Projected Openings: 10
Areas of Operation: MA
Type of Foodservice: Quick Serve (10)
Franchise Affiliation: DD IP Holder, CANTON, MA

Key Personnel
SHUJIE CHEN - General Manager
ERIK LANIA - Director Manufacturing
LILLIAN LAROSA - Director Loss Prevention, Risk Management, Quality Assurance, Human Resources, Training, Recruitment, Food Safety

F B Enterprises Inc.
606 Washington St
South Easton, MA 02375-1167

Telephone: (508) 230-8737
Type of Business: Chain Restaurant Operator
Total Sales: $8,039,000 (e)
Average Check: Dinner(8)
Total Units: 5
Trade Names: Dunkin' Donuts (5)
Units Franchised From: 5
Preferred Square Footage: 1,500; 2,200
Preferred Location Types: Downtown; Freestanding
Primary Menu: Snacks (5)
Areas of Operation: MA
Type of Foodservice: Quick Serve (5)
Franchise Affiliation: DD IP Holder, CANTON, MA

Key Personnel
FRANK BAROUNIS - President; General Buyer

Domino's Franchisee
484 Station Ave Unit E
South Yarmouth, MA 02664-1220

Telephone: (508) 394-6688
Type of Business: Chain Restaurant Operator
Total Sales: $12,083,000 (e)
Total Units: 6
Trade Names: Domino's (6)
Units Franchised From: 6
Primary Menu: Pizza (6)
Areas of Operation: MA
Type of Foodservice: Quick Serve (6)
Franchise Affiliation: Domino's Pizza Inc, ANN ARBOR, MI

Key Personnel
CHRIS JONES - Owner; General Buyer

FPS Inc.
158 College Hwy
Southampton, MA 01073-9401

Mailing Address: PO Box 357, SOUTHAMPTON, MA, 01073-0357
Telephone: (413) 527-7474
Fax Number: (413) 527-7654
Type of Business: Chain Restaurant Operator
Year Founded: 1981
Total Sales: $24,250,000 (e)
Number of Employees: 450
Average Check: Breakfast(8); Lunch(8); Dinner(8)
Total Units: 11
Trade Names: Burger King (11)
Units Franchised From: 11
Preferred Square Footage: 3,000
Preferred Location Types: Freestanding
Primary Menu: Hamburger (11)
Areas of Operation: CT, MA
Type of Foodservice: Quick Serve (11)
Franchise Affiliation: Burger King Worldwide Inc., MIAMI, FL
Primary Distributors: (Full Line) Maines Paper & Food Service New England, WESTBOROUGH, MA

Key Personnel
STAN PAULAUSKAS - President; COO; Director Purchasing, Supply Chain, Marketing, Advertising, Real Estate
JOHN J. WILLIAMS - Director Operations, Facility/Maintenance, Information Systems, Loss Prevention, Store Fixtures, Food Safety; General Buyer
JOHN JOE WILLIAMS - Director
CINDY TURNER - Manager Accounting, Human Resources

Domino's Franchisee
21 Turnpike Rd Ste C
Southborough, MA 01772-2117

Telephone: (508) 481-3939
Type of Business: Chain Restaurant Operator
Total Sales: $26,423,000 (e)
Total Units: 13
Trade Names: Domino's (13)
Units Franchised From: 13
Primary Menu: Pizza (13)
Areas of Operation: MA
Type of Foodservice: Quick Serve (13)
Franchise Affiliation: Domino's Pizza Inc, ANN ARBOR, MI

Key Personnel
HENRY G. ASKEW - Owner; General Buyer

Sellia Corporation
8 Lake St
Spencer, MA 01562-1802

Telephone: (508) 885-9011
Type of Business: Chain Restaurant Operator
Total Sales: $70,730,000 (e)
Total Units: 15
Trade Names: McDonald's (15)
Units Franchised From: 15
Preferred Square Footage: 2,500
Primary Menu: Hamburger (15)
Areas of Operation: MA, RI
Type of Foodservice: Quick Serve (15)
Franchise Affiliation: McDonald's Corporation, CHICAGO, IL

Key Personnel
JOSEPH SPADEA - President; General Buyer

BTA Group, Inc.
1070 Saint James Ave
Springfield, MA 01104-1453

Telephone: (413) 788-8880
Type of Business: Chain Restaurant Operator
Total Sales: $1,940,000 (e)
Total Units: 2
Trade Names: Little Caesars Pizza (2)
Units Franchised From: 2
Primary Menu: Pizza (2)
Areas of Operation: MA
Type of Foodservice: Quick Serve (2)
Franchise Affiliation: Little Caesar Enterprises Inc., DETROIT, MI

Key Personnel
ALI AWADA - Partner; General Buyer
SAM BERRY - Partner; Executive Director

Kodiak Creamery, Inc.
1000 W Columbus Ave
Springfield, MA 01105-2518

Telephone: (413) 736-6060
Type of Business: Chain Restaurant Operator
Total Sales: $1,211,000 (e)
Total Units: 2
Trade Names: Cold Stone Creamery (2)
Units Franchised From: 2
Primary Menu: Snacks (2)
Areas of Operation: MA
Type of Foodservice: Quick Serve (2)
Franchise Affiliation: Kahala Brands, SCOTTSDALE, AZ

Key Personnel
DAVID WHITE - Partner
BRIAN WHITE - Partner

McDonald's Franchise
660 Liberty St
Springfield, MA 01104-2420

Telephone: (413) 731-1529
Type of Business: Chain Restaurant Operator
Total Sales: $42,580,000 (e)
Total Units: 9
Trade Names: McDonald's (9)
Units Franchised From: 9
Preferred Square Footage: 2,500
Primary Menu: Hamburger (9)
Areas of Operation: MA
Type of Foodservice: Quick Serve (9)
Franchise Affiliation: McDonald's Corporation, CHICAGO, IL

Key Personnel
DANIEL ASHBURN - President; Partner; General Buyer
KAREN ASHBURN - Partner; General Buyer

Michael's Restaurant
5 Elm St
Stockbridge, MA 01262

Telephone: (413) 298-3530
Internet Homepage: luckysicecream.com; michaelsofstockbridge.com
Company Email: Michael@MichaelsofStockbridge.com
Type of Business: Chain Restaurant Operator
Year Founded: 1981
Total Sales: $5,403,000 (e)
Alcohol Sales: 35%
Number of Employees: 40
Average Check: Lunch(14); Dinner(16)
Total Units: 3
Trade Names: Bogies (1); Luckys Ice Cream &

Grill (1); Michael's Restaurant (1)
Company-Owned Units: 3
Preferred Square Footage: 200; 250
Preferred Location Types: Freestanding
Alcohol Served: Beer, Wine, Liquor
Primary Menu: American (2); Steak (1)
Areas of Operation: MA
Type of Foodservice: Casual Dining (2); Quick Serve (1)
Catering Services: Yes
Primary Distributors: (Supplies) SYSCO Food Services of Albany, HALFMOON, NY

Key Personnel
MICHAEL ABDALLA JR - President; Owner; General Manager; General Buyer
RICK ABDALLA - President Group
JOHN ROGERS JR - Executive Chef; Manager Catering; General Buyer

The Red Lion Inn
30 Main St
Stockbridge, MA 01262-9701

Telephone: (413) 298-5545
Fax Number: (413) 298-5130
Internet Homepage: redlioninn.com
Company Email: info@redlioninn.com
Type of Business: Chain Restaurant Operator
Year Founded: 1773
Total Sales: $9,775,000 (e)
Alcohol Sales: 25%
Number of Employees: 200
Average Check: Breakfast(18); Lunch(30); Dinner(60)
Total Units: 3
Trade Names: Lion's Den Pub (1); The Red Lion Restaurant (1); Widow Bingham's Tavern (1)
Company-Owned Units: 3
Preferred Location Types: Hotel/Motel
Alcohol Served: Beer, Wine, Liquor
Primary Menu: American (3)
Areas of Operation: MA
Type of Foodservice: Casual Dining (2); Fine Dining (1)
Catering Services: Yes
Primary Distributors: (Equipment) B & G Restaurant Supply Inc., PITTSFIELD, MA; (Food) SYSCO Food Services of Albany, HALFMOON, NY; (Supplies) B & G Restaurant Supply Inc., PITTSFIELD, MA

Key Personnel
TIMOTHY EUSTIS - Director
GRETA KIPP - Director Development
JANET BOYER - Executive Assistant

Couto Management Group, LLC
169 Main St
Stoneham, MA 02180-1613

Telephone: (781) 279-0290
Fax Number: (781) 279-0360
Internet Homepage: coutomanagement.com
Company Email: office@coutomanagement.com
Type of Business: Chain Restaurant Operator
Total Sales: $126,880,000 (e)
Average Check: Dinner(8)
Total Units: 79
Trade Names: Dunkin' Donuts (79)
Units Franchised From: 79
Preferred Square Footage: 1,500; 2,200
Preferred Location Types: Freestanding
Primary Menu: Snacks (79)
Areas of Operation: MA, NH, VT
Type of Foodservice: Quick Serve (79)
Franchise Affiliation: DD IP Holder, CANTON, MA

Key Personnel
SALVI COUTO - CEO; President; General Buyer
KEN AMIOTT - VP Operations
STEPHANIE SOUSA ANDRADE - Director Operations

D & P Associates
281 Willis Rd
Sudbury, MA 01776-1333

Telephone: (978) 440-7251
Fax Number: (978) 443-3650
Company Email: pearson.k@verizon.net
Type of Business: Chain Restaurant Operator
Year Founded: 1984
Total Sales: $41,530,000 (e)
Number of Employees: 400
Average Check: Breakfast(8); Lunch(10); Dinner(12)
Total Units: 9
Trade Names: McDonald's (9)
Units Franchised From: 9
Preferred Square Footage: 2,400; 3,000
Preferred Location Types: Downtown; Freestanding
Primary Menu: Hamburger (9)
Areas of Operation: MA
Type of Foodservice: Quick Serve (9)
Franchise Affiliation: McDonald's Corporation, CHICAGO, IL

Key Personnel
PAULA WRIGHT - President; Director Marketing, Real Estate; General Buyer
DIANE CASACELI - Controller
RICHARD LOPEZ - Director Operations

KIM PEARSON - Manager Branch

Anthony's Pier 4 Inc.
299 Salem St
Swampscott, MA 01907-1322

Telephone: (781) 599-0240
Fax Number: (781) 598-9321
Type of Business: Chain Restaurant Operator
Year Founded: 1937
Total Sales: $10,807,000 (e)
Alcohol Sales: 25%
Number of Employees: 160
Average Check: Lunch(30); Dinner(48)
Internet Sales: 1.00%
Total Units: 1
Trade Names: Hawthorne by the Sea Tavern (1)
Company-Owned Units: 1
Preferred Square Footage: 6,000
Preferred Location Types: Freestanding
Alcohol Served: Beer, Wine, Liquor
Primary Menu: Seafood (1)
Areas of Operation: MA
Type of Foodservice: Fine Dining (1)

Key Personnel
ANTHONY ATHANAS JR - President; Partner; Executive Chef; Director Operations, Menu Development

Sarah L. Teck, Inc.
16 Preston Ct
Swampscott, MA 01907-1650

Telephone: (781) 598-0036
Type of Business: Chain Restaurant Operator
Total Sales: $15,465,000 (e)
Total Units: 3
Trade Names: McDonald's (3)
Units Franchised From: 3
Preferred Location Types: Airports; Freestanding
Primary Menu: Hamburger (3)
Areas of Operation: MA
Type of Foodservice: Quick Serve (3)
Franchise Affiliation: McDonald's Corporation, CHICAGO, IL

Key Personnel
SARAH L. TECK - President; General Buyer

Wade Enterprises
20 Cape Rd
Taunton, MA 02780-2704

Telephone: (508) 822-2006
Type of Business: Chain Restaurant Operator
Year Founded: 1967

Total Sales: $10,780,000 (e)
Number of Employees: 230
Average Check: Lunch(8); Dinner(12)
Total Units: 6
Trade Names: KFC (6)
Units Franchised From: 6
Preferred Square Footage: 3,000
Preferred Location Types: Freestanding
Primary Menu: Chicken (6)
Areas of Operation: MA
Type of Foodservice: Quick Serve (6)
Foodservice Management Venues: Schools
Franchise Affiliation: KFC Corporation, LOUISVILLE, KY
Primary Distributors: (Full Line) McLane/Guilderland Center, GUILDERLAND CENTER, NY

Key Personnel
MILTON DAHLENE - President; Partner; Manager Facility/Maintenance, Real Estate
LARRY STARKEY - Partner; VP Purchasing; Manager Finance, Operations; General Buyer
STEVE LEPAGE - General Manager
DIANE COMIER - Manager Human Resources, Training

The Black Dog Tavern Co. Inc.
21 Beach Street Ext
Vineyard Haven, MA 02568

Mailing Address: PO Box 2219, VINEYARD HAVEN, MA, 02568-0917
Telephone: (508) 693-9223
Fax Number: (508) 693-1131
Internet Homepage: theblackdog.com
Company Email: info@theblackdog.com
Type of Business: Chain Restaurant Operator
Year Founded: 1971
Total Sales: $11,640,000 (e)
Number of Employees: 150
Average Check: Breakfast(12); Lunch(16); Dinner(34)
Internet Order Processing: Yes
Internet Sales: 1.00%
Total Units: 5
Trade Names: Dockside Cafe at Oak Bluffs (1); Heights Cafe (1); The Black Dog Bakery and Cafe (1); The Black Dog Tavern (1); The Black Dog Water St. Bakery and General Store (1)
Company-Owned Units: 5
Preferred Location Types: Freestanding
Alcohol Served: Beer, Wine
Primary Menu: American (2); Sandwiches/Deli (3)
Areas of Operation: MA
Type of Foodservice: Casual Dining (2); Quick Serve (3)
Primary Distributors: (Food) SYSCO Food Services of Baltimore, JESSUP, MD
Notes: Pet supplies and cafe operations account for 40% of the company's business.

Key Personnel
DAN PUCILLO - COO
DONNY GLASS - Executive Chef; General Buyer

ARAMARK Campus Services(HIGHER EDUCATION)
2 Pleasure Island Rd
Wakefield, MA 01880-1242

Telephone: (781) 246-8465
Fax Number: (781) 246-8482
Listing Type: Regional Office
Type of Business: Foodservice Management Operator
Year Founded: 1959
Number of Employees: 15
Number of Locations Served: 42
Total Foodservice Mgmt Accounts: 42
Areas of Operation: MA
Type of Foodservice: Cafeteria (42)
Foodservice Management Venues: College & University
Primary Distributors: (Full Line) SYSCO Food Services of Albany, HALFMOON, NY
Parent Company: Aramark, PHILADELPHIA, PA
Headquarters: ARAMARK Higher Education, PHILADELPHIA, PA

Key Personnel
JEN RADICE - Director Human Resources

Mastoran Corp.
822 Lexington St Fl 2
Waltham, MA 02452-4848

Telephone: (781) 893-0990
Fax Number: (781) 891-0668
Internet Homepage: mastoran.com
Type of Business: Chain Restaurant Operator
Year Founded: 1985
Total Sales: $91,360,000 (e)
Number of Employees: 1,200
Average Check: Breakfast(8); Lunch(8); Dinner(10)
Total Units: 40
Trade Names: Burger King (40)
Units Franchised From: 40
Preferred Square Footage: 2,500; 3,200; 4,000
Preferred Location Types: Freestanding
Primary Menu: Hamburger (40)
Areas of Operation: MA, ME, NH
Type of Foodservice: Quick Serve (40)
Franchise Affiliation: Burger King Worldwide Inc., MIAMI, FL
Primary Distributors: (Full Line) Maines Paper & Food Service New England, WESTBOROUGH, MA

Key Personnel
LARRY KOHLER - President; Partner; Director Finance, Information Systems; General Buyer
BREK KOHLER - Partner; Director Operations, Facility/Maintenance, Information Technology, Real Estate
MARC ROCHON - Senior Manager Construction
KAREN MURPHY - Coordinator Payroll, Benefits

Sodexo
309 Waverly Oaks Road
Waltham, MA 02451

Telephone: (781) 902-7500
Fax Number: (781) 902-7513
Listing Type: Divisional Office
Type of Business: Foodservice Management Operator
Number of Employees: 140
Number of Locations Served: 300
Total Foodservice Mgmt Accounts: 300
Areas of Operation: MA
Type of Foodservice: Cafeteria (300)
Foodservice Management Venues: Business & Industry
Parent Company: Sodexo, MONTIGNY-LE-BRETONNEUX, FRA
Headquarters: Sodexo Inc., GAITHERSBURG, MD

Key Personnel
JOHNNY BRUE - President Finance
JOE FRASER - CFO
DREW NANNIS - Senior VP Communications, Digital Marketing
EDOUARD LYON - VP Operations
CINDY SCOTT - VP Finance
STEPHEN DELANEY - VP Operations
MIKE BAKER - VP Finance
JULIAN BENNETT - Executive Director Facility/Maintenance
TADD STONE - General Manager
NILZETE TREFRY - General Manager
GARY SANTORE - General Manager Area
COURTNEY HOLDMAN - Executive Chef
JOHN WHITE - Senior Director Operations
KATELYN WHITTENBURG - Director Marketing
ROBERT DAVIDSON - Director Operations
DAVID TROTTER - Director Division
MARCY SPAULDING - Director Business Development
CLIFF ROY - Senior Manager Marketing, Culinary Development
LINDA DESPRES - Manager Human Resources

The Chateau of Waltham
195 School St
Waltham, MA 02451-4545

Telephone: (781) 894-3339
Fax Number: (781) 894-5291
Internet Homepage: chateaurestaurant.com
Type of Business: Chain Restaurant Operator
Year Founded: 1987
Total Sales: $3,395,000 (e)
Alcohol Sales: 15%
Number of Employees: 300
Average Check: Lunch(24); Dinner(36)
Internet Order Processing: Yes
Internet Sales: 2.00%
Total Units: 8
Trade Names: The Chateau Italian Restaurant (8)
Company-Owned Units: 8
Preferred Location Types: Freestanding
Alcohol Served: Beer, Wine, Liquor
Primary Menu: Italian (8)
Areas of Operation: MA
Type of Foodservice: Fine Dining (8)
Primary Distributors: (Equipment) TriMark USA Inc., MANSFIELD, MA

Key Personnel
JAMES NOCERA - Partner; Executive Chef; General Buyer
JEFFREY NOCERA - Partner
CHRIS BELLA - General Manager
GREG HAMM - Director Human Resources

Alta Strada LLC
92 Central St
Wellesley, MA 02482-5714

Telephone: (781) 237-6100
Fax Number: (781) 489-2002
Internet Homepage: altastrada-wellesley.com
Company Email: info@altastrada-wellesley.com
Type of Business: Chain Restaurant Operator
Year Founded: 2008
Total Sales: $11,910,000 (e)
Average Check: Dinner(26)
Total Units: 8
Trade Names: Altastrada (4); Casolare (1); The Riggsby (1); Tico Boston (2)
Company-Owned Units: 8
Preferred Location Types: Freestanding
Alcohol Served: Beer, Wine, Liquor
Primary Menu: American (3); Italian (5)
Areas of Operation: CT, DC, VA
Type of Foodservice: Casual Dining (4); Fine Dining (4)

Key Personnel
MICHAEL SCHLOW - Owner; Executive Chef; General Buyer
GUY NEIL - Manager

Sandwich Specialists, Inc.
50 Briar Ln
Wellfleet, MA 02667-7210

Telephone: (508) 349-3509
Internet Homepage: boxlunchcapecod.com
Company Email: info@boxlunch.com
Type of Business: Chain Restaurant Operator
Year Founded: 1977
Systemwide Sales: $2,925,000 (e)
Total Sales: $586,000 (e)
Number of Employees: 10
Average Check: Breakfast(8); Lunch(10);
Total Units: 4
Trade Names: The Box Lunch of Cape Cod (4)
Company-Owned Units: 2
Units Franchised To: 2
Preferred Square Footage: 1,200; 2,000
Preferred Location Types: Community Mall; Freestanding; Strip Mall
Primary Menu: Sandwiches/Deli (4)
Areas of Operation: MA
Type of Foodservice: Quick Serve (4)
Catering Services: Yes

Key Personnel
OWEN MACNUTT - Founder; President; Director Finance, Operations, Purchasing, Facility/Maintenance, Information Systems, Real Estate, Design, Human Resources, Menu Development, Food Safety; General Buyer

MHC Inc.
201 Park Ave Ste 8
West Springfield, MA 01089-3366

Telephone: (413) 734-2148
Fax Number: (413) 731-7639
Company Email: mhcquikdoc@aol.com
Type of Business: Chain Restaurant Operator
Year Founded: 1981
Total Sales: $18,250,000 (e)
Number of Employees: 650
Average Check: Breakfast(5); Lunch(8); Dinner(8)
Total Units: 10
Trade Names: Burger King (7); KFC (3)
Units Franchised From: 10
Preferred Square Footage: 2,500; 3,000
Preferred Location Types: Freestanding; Strip Mall
Primary Menu: Chicken (3); Hamburger (7)
Areas of Operation: MA
Type of Foodservice: Quick Serve (10)
Franchise Affiliation: Burger King Worldwide Inc., MIAMI, FL; KFC Corporation, LOUISVILLE, KY
Primary Distributors: (Food) Maines Paper & Food Service Inc., CONKLIN, NY; (Supplies) Maines Paper & Food Service Inc., CONKLIN, NY

Key Personnel
HAROLD CROMWELL - President; General Buyer
MARIE CROMWELL - VP; Director Finance
DAVID O'CONNELL - VP Operations, Purchasing, Risk Management, Human Resources; Director Facility/Maintenance, Information Systems, Real Estate
ERIC CROMWELL - VP

Onset Donuts Inc.
2360
West Wareham, MA 02576

Telephone: (508) 291-2214
Type of Business: Chain Restaurant Operator
Total Sales: $9,401,000 (e)
Number of Employees: 230
Average Check: Dinner(8)
Total Units: 6
Trade Names: Dunkin' Donuts (6)
Units Franchised From: 6
Preferred Square Footage: 1,500; 2,200
Preferred Location Types: Freestanding; Strip Mall
Primary Menu: Snacks (6)
Areas of Operation: MA
Type of Foodservice: Quick Serve (6)
Franchise Affiliation: DD IP Holder, CANTON, MA

Key Personnel
DINARTE PIMENTAL - President; General Buyer

Domino's Franchisee
26 Main St
Westfield, MA 01085-3121

Telephone: (413) 562-4411
Type of Business: Chain Restaurant Operator
Total Sales: $4,090,000 (e)
Total Units: 2
Trade Names: Domino's (2)
Units Franchised From: 2
Primary Menu: Pizza (2)
Areas of Operation: MA
Type of Foodservice: Quick Serve (2)
Franchise Affiliation: Domino's Pizza Inc, ANN ARBOR, MI

Key Personnel
PAULO R. NAVES - Owner; General Buyer

Dunkin' Donuts Franchise
127 N Elm St
Westfield, MA 01085-1612

Telephone: (413) 562-9820
Internet Homepage: dunkindonuts.com
Type of Business: Chain Restaurant Operator
Total Sales: $94,460,000 (e)
Average Check: Dinner(8)
Total Units: 60
Trade Names: Dunkin' Donuts (60)
Units Franchised From: 60
Preferred Square Footage: 1,500; 2,200
Preferred Location Types: Freestanding
Primary Menu: Snacks (60)
Areas of Operation: MA
Type of Foodservice: Quick Serve (60)
Franchise Affiliation: DD IP Holder, CANTON, MA

Key Personnel
JOAO SARDINHA - President; General Buyer

110 Grill
4 Lan Dr
Westford, MA 01886

Telephone: (978) 496-1867
Internet Homepage: 110grill.com
Type of Business: Chain Restaurant Operator
Year Founded: 2014
Total Sales: $95,070,000 (e)
Total Units: 30
Trade Names: 110 Grill (30)
Company-Owned Units: 30
Primary Menu: American (30)
Projected Openings: 8
Areas of Operation: MA, NH, NY
Type of Foodservice: Casual Dining (30)

Key Personnel
ROBERT WALKER - Partner
RYAN DION - Partner
DOUG STADTMAN - Area Director
BERNIE LONTINE - Area Director
KIM WALLACE - Director Operations

FIC Restaurants
1855 Boston Rd Ste 200
Wilbraham, MA 01095-1002

Telephone: (413) 543-2400
Fax Number: (413) 731-4472
Internet Homepage: friendlys.com
Company Email: franchising@friendlys.com
Type of Business: Chain Restaurant Operator
Year Founded: 1935
Systemwide Sales: $227,486,000 (e)
Total Sales: $113,240,000 (e)
Number of Employees: 14,000
Average Check: Breakfast(8); Lunch(10); Dinner(10)
Internet Order Processing: Yes
Total Units: 130
Trade Names: Friendly's (130)
Company-Owned Units: 77
Units Franchised To: 53
Preferred Square Footage: 2,200; 2,400; 3,500; 4,500; 5,000
Preferred Location Types: Community Mall; Downtown; Freestanding; Hotel/Motel; Institution (college/hospital); Outlet Mall; Regional Mall; Stadiums; Strip Mall
Primary Menu: American (174)
Areas of Operation: CT, DE, FL, MA, MD, ME, NH, NJ, NY, OH, PA, RI, SC, VA, VT
Type of Foodservice: Family Restaurant (174)
Distribution Centers: CHICOPEE, MA
Subsidiaries: The Johnny Rockets Group Inc., LAKE FOREST, CA
Parent Company: BRIX Holdings LLC, DALLAS, TX

Key Personnel
JOHN CAMPION - Director Operations

Bickford's Grille
331 Montvale Ave Ste 330
Woburn, MA 01801

Telephone: (800) 969-5653
Fax Number: (508) 583-2120
Internet Homepage: bickfords.com
Type of Business: Chain Restaurant Operator
Year Founded: 1920
Total Sales: $5,359,000 (e)
Alcohol Sales: 10%
Number of Employees: 125
Average Check: Breakfast(10); Lunch(14); Dinner(18)
Internet Order Processing: Yes
Internet Sales: 1.00%
Total Units: 3
Trade Names: Bickford's Family Restaurant (1); Bickford's Grille (2)
Company-Owned Units: 3
Preferred Square Footage: 2,700; 7,400
Preferred Location Types: Freestanding; Strip Mall
Alcohol Served: Beer, Wine, Liquor
Primary Menu: American (3)
Areas of Operation: MA
Type of Foodservice: Casual Dining (3)
Primary Distributors: (Full Line) Performance Foodservice - Springfield, SPRINGFIELD, MA
Parent Company: ELXSI Corp., ORLANDO, FL

Key Personnel
DAVID M. DOOLITTLE - CFO; VP; Treasurer; Corporate Secretary; Executive Chef; Director Operations, Purchasing, Facility/Maintenance, Supply Chain, Real Estate, Design, Store Fixtures
BERNIE DRISCOLL - Controller; Manager Information Systems
LINDA BAILEY - Manager Human Resources

Boston Restaurant Associates
48 Cummings Park
Woburn, MA 01801-2123

Telephone: (781) 305-4474
Fax Number: (781) 305-3292
Internet Homepage: pizzeriaregina.com
Type of Business: Chain Restaurant Operator
Year Founded: 1946
Total Sales: $32,655,000 (e)
Alcohol Sales: 15%
Number of Employees: 400
Average Check: Lunch(14); Dinner(18)
Internet Order Processing: Yes
Internet Sales: 2.00%
Total Units: 16
Trade Names: Polcari's Authenic Italian Restaurant (2); Regina Pizza (14)
Company-Owned Units: 16
Preferred Square Footage: 1,000; 4,000
Preferred Location Types: Community Mall; Downtown; Freestanding; Office Complex; Regional Mall; Strip Mall
Alcohol Served: Beer, Wine, Liquor
Primary Menu: Italian (2); Pizza (14)
Areas of Operation: CT, MA, NH
Type of Foodservice: Casual Dining (2); Fast Casual (14)
Distribution Centers: WOBURN, MA
On-site Distribution Center: Yes
Primary Distributors: (Food) Costa Fruit & Produce Co., BOSTON, MA
Parent Company: Dolphin Direct Equity, NEW YORK, NY

Key Personnel
PETER SALAS - CEO
FRAN V. ROSS - CFO
ANTHONY BUCCIERI - COO; VP Operations; Director Loss Prevention, Quality Assurance, Supply Chain
ROBERT FABRIZIO - Chief Administrative Officer; Controller
MARIO SUSI - General Manager; Director Facility/Maintenance, Distribution, Warehouse, Transportation, Store Fixtures
DONNA DEVLIN - Director Human Resources

Boston Restaurant Associates
48 Cummings Park
Woburn, MA 01801-2123

Telephone: (781) 305-4474

Fax Number: (781) 305-3292
Internet Homepage: pizzeriaregina.com
Type of Business: Chain Restaurant Operator
Year Founded: 1926
Total Sales: $20,550,000 (e)
Alcohol Sales: 2%
Number of Employees: 230
Average Check: Dinner(14)
Total Units: 16
Trade Names: Polcari's Pizza (2); Regina Pizzeria (14)
Company-Owned Units: 16
Preferred Location Types: Downtown; Freestanding; Strip Mall
Alcohol Served: Beer, Wine
Primary Menu: Pizza (16)
Areas of Operation: MA
Type of Foodservice: Family Restaurant (16)

Key Personnel
PETER SALAS - Owner; General Manager; Executive Chef; General Buyer
MICHAEL GOGGIN - Manager
ANTONE HAZARD - Manager

Jaton Management Co.
10 State St
Woburn, MA 01801-6804

Telephone: (781) 939-3156
Fax Number: (781) 939-3159
Type of Business: Chain Restaurant Operator
Total Sales: $18,900,000 (e)
Average Check: Dinner(8)
Total Units: 12
Trade Names: Dunkin' Donuts (12)
Units Franchised From: 12
Preferred Square Footage: 1,500; 2,200
Preferred Location Types: Freestanding
Primary Menu: Snacks (12)
Areas of Operation: MA
Type of Foodservice: Quick Serve (12)
Franchise Affiliation: DD IP Holder, CANTON, MA

Key Personnel
FRANK PINO - President; General Buyer
JASON PINO - COO

Wocester Restaurant Group
118 Highland St
Worcester, MA 01609-2731

Telephone: (508) 798-3477
Fax Number: (508) 798-3474
Internet Homepage: 111chophouse.com; thesole.com; viaitaliantable.com; worcesterrestaurantgroup.com
Company Email: cfood@thesole.com
Type of Business: Chain Restaurant Operator
Year Founded: 1979
Total Sales: $10,798,000 (e)
Alcohol Sales: 25%
Number of Employees: 75
Average Check: Lunch(14); Dinner(24)
Internet Order Processing: Yes
Total Units: 3
Trade Names: 111 Chop House (1); The Sole Proprietor (1); Via Italian Table (1)
Company-Owned Units: 3
Preferred Location Types: Freestanding
Alcohol Served: Beer, Wine, Liquor
Primary Menu: Italian (1); Seafood (1); Steak (1)
Areas of Operation: MA
Type of Foodservice: Casual Dining (3)
Primary Distributors: (Food) SYSCO of Boston, PLYMPTON, MA

Key Personnel
MADELEINE AHLQUIST - Co-Founder; Partner
ROBBIN AHLQUIST - President; Partner; General Buyer
CAITLYN CAROLAN - COO
AARON FRANCISCO - General Manager; General Buyer
ERIC ANDREOLI - General Manager; Buyer Beverages
JOSEPH WONG - Executive Chef

MARYLAND

Fantastic Foods Inc
1952 West St
Annapolis, MD 21401-3931

Telephone: (410) 643-8695
Type of Business: Chain Restaurant Operator
Total Sales: $4,731,000 (e)
Total Units: 2
Trade Names: Burger King (2)
Units Franchised From: 2
Primary Menu: Hamburger (2)
Areas of Operation: MD
Type of Foodservice: Quick Serve (2)
Franchise Affiliation: Burger King Worldwide Inc., MIAMI, FL

Key Personnel
CARL DELP III - President; General Buyer

Gold Hat
1610 West St Ste 207
Annapolis, MD 21401-4054

Telephone: (410) 626-2002
Fax Number: (410) 626-9898
Type of Business: Chain Restaurant Operator
Total Sales: $28,400,000 (e)
Number of Employees: 267
Total Units: 6
Trade Names: McDonald's (6)
Units Franchised From: 6
Preferred Square Footage: 2,500
Primary Menu: Hamburger (6)
Areas of Operation: MD
Type of Foodservice: Quick Serve (6)
Franchise Affiliation: McDonald's Corporation, CHICAGO, IL

Key Personnel
GERALD GIMELSTOB - President; General Buyer
CAROL O'BRIEN - Manager Accounting

Land & Sea Group
100 Main St Ste 2
Annapolis, MD 21401-2013

Telephone: (410) 626-1100
Fax Number: (410) 263-0933
Internet Homepage: buddysonline.com; redskylaurel.com; thebigfishgrille.com; yellowfinrestaurant.com
Company Email: info@buddysonline.com
Type of Business: Chain Restaurant Operator
Year Founded: 1985
Total Sales: $23,130,000 (e)
Alcohol Sales: 30%
Number of Employees: 220
Average Check: Lunch(14); Dinner(22)
Internet Order Processing: Yes
Total Units: 7
Trade Names: Buddy's Crabs & Ribs (2); Crab House (1); Fatboys (1); Market House (1); The Big Fish Grille (1); Yellowfin Steak & Fish House (1)
Company-Owned Units: 8
Preferred Location Types: Freestanding; Strip Mall
Alcohol Served: Beer, Wine, Liquor
Primary Menu: American (1); Seafood (5); Steak/Seafood (1)
Areas of Operation: MD
Type of Foodservice: Casual Dining (5); Fine Dining (2)
Catering Services: Yes
Primary Distributors: (Equipment) Adams-Burch Inc., LANDOVER, MD; (Food) US Foods, SEVERN, MD; (Supplies) PJP, ROSEDALE, MD

Key Personnel
KEVIN BLONDER - General Manager; Director Menu Development; General Buyer

Ledo Pizza System Inc.
41 Old Solomons Island Rd unit 201
Annapolis, MD 21401-3860

Telephone: (410) 721-6887
Fax Number: (410) 571-8395

Internet Homepage: ledopizza.com; iloveubq.com
Company Email: ledo@aol.com
Type of Business: Chain Restaurant Operator
Year Founded: 1955
Systemwide Sales: $136,769,000 (e)
Total Sales: $19,870,000 (e)
Alcohol Sales: 15%
Number of Employees: 15
Average Check: Lunch(12); Dinner(20)
Internet Order Processing: Yes
Internet Sales: 2.00%
Total Units: 107
Trade Names: Ledo Pizza (104); Urban B B Q (3)
Units Franchised To: 107
Preferred Square Footage: 2,500
Preferred Location Types: Downtown; Freestanding; Strip Mall
Alcohol Served: Beer, Wine
Primary Menu: Bar-B-Q (3); Pizza (104)
Areas of Operation: DC, DE, FL, GA, MD, NC, VA, WV
Type of Foodservice: Casual Dining (104); Fast Casual (3)
Primary Distributors: (Full Line) US Foods, MANASSAS, VA

Key Personnel
ROBERT G. BEALL - CEO; CFO; General Buyer
JAMES M. BEALL - President; COO; Director Franchise Development, Franchising
MIKE CONWAY - VP Operations; Director Security, Inventory, Loss Prevention, Risk Management, Quality Assurance, Design, Store Fixtures, Food Safety
WILLIAM ROBINSON - VP Marketing; Director Information Systems
AARON WEEDY - VP Finance
JUSTIN BARNES - Director Franchise Development

Mezeh Mediterranean Grill
1054 Annapolis Mall
Annapolis, MD 21401

Telephone: (410) 571-0600
Internet Homepage: mezeh.com
Type of Business: Chain Restaurant Operator
Total Sales: $33,956,000 (e)
Trade Names: Mezeh Mediterranean Grill (32)
Company-Owned Units: 32
Primary Menu: Pizza (32)
Areas of Operation: MD, NC, VA
Type of Foodservice: Fast Casual (32)

Key Personnel
SALEH MOHAMADI - Founder; Owner

MONTE Restaurant Development Group
1919 West St Stw 202
Annapolis, MD 21401

Telephone: (410) 421-9555
Internet Homepage: meatballsetcfranchise.com; monterdg.com; squisitofranchise.com; squisitopizzaandpasta.com
Company Email: info@squisitofranchise.com
Type of Business: Chain Restaurant Operator
Total Sales: $10,830,000 (e)
Total Units: 11
Trade Names: Squisito (10); Tuscan Prime (1)
Company-Owned Units: 2
Units Franchised To: 9
Primary Menu: Italian (11)
Projected Openings: 2
Areas of Operation: MD, VA
Type of Foodservice: Casual Dining (10); Fine Dining (1)

Key Personnel
GENNARO DIMEO - Founder; Owner; Director Development
MICHELE DIMEO - President; COO
TODD KOSAKOWSKI - Manager

OTAC Inc.
528 College Pkwy Ste I
Annapolis, MD 21409-4694

Telephone: (410) 757-0446
Fax Number: (410) 757-6531
Internet Homepage: otacinc.net
Company Email: comments@otacinc.net
Type of Business: Chain Restaurant Operator
Year Founded: 1991
Total Sales: $40,610,000 (e)
Number of Employees: 500
Average Check: Breakfast(8); Lunch(12); Dinner(12)
Total Units: 22
Trade Names: Hardees/Red Burrito (22)
Units Franchised From: 22
Preferred Square Footage: 2,000
Preferred Location Types: Convenience Store/Gas Station; Freestanding; Strip Mall
Primary Menu: Hamburger (22); Mexican (22)
Areas of Operation: DE, MD
Type of Foodservice: Quick Serve (22)
Franchise Affiliation: Hardee's Food Systems Inc., FRANKLIN, TN
Primary Distributors: (Food) McLane/Rocky Mount, ROCKY MOUNT, NC

Key Personnel
PAUL CATO - President; Director Information Systems, Real Estate; General Buyer
MICHAEL CATO - VP Operations
FRED MATTES - Director Information Technology
SUE PIERSON - Director Operations
SUSAN WARD - Manager District
LINDSEY BERRY - Manager Human Resources

R & R Ventures Inc.
2530 Riva Rd Ste 400
Annapolis, MD 21401-7486

Telephone: (410) 573-0220
Fax Number: (410) 573-0288
Type of Business: Chain Restaurant Operator
Total Sales: $229,810,000 (e)
Number of Employees: 1,056
Average Check: Dinner(8)
Total Units: 86
Trade Names: KFC (10); Taco Bell (76)
Units Franchised From: 86
Preferred Square Footage: 1,400; 2,500; 3,200; 4,500
Preferred Location Types: Downtown; Freestanding; Regional Mall
Primary Menu: Chicken (10); Taco (76)
Areas of Operation: DE, GA, MD, VA
Type of Foodservice: Quick Serve (86)
Franchise Affiliation: KFC Corporation, LOUISVILLE, KY; Long John Silver's Inc., LOUISVILLE, KY; Pizza Hut Inc., PLANO, TX; Taco Bell Corp., IRVINE, CA

Key Personnel
ROBERT CARLUCCI - President; General Buyer
PETER DE ANGELO - CFO
JEFFREY KATZ - CFO
BILL RETZ - VP Operations
AMY RICE - Controller
RICHARD RILEY - Director Loss Prevention, Training
JESSE MORELAND - Director Operations
TREVOR NEASE - Director Operations
SHERRIE CASTER - Supervisor Human Resources
DOMINIC CARLUCCI - Specialist Loss Prevention

Atlas Restaurant Group
650 S Exeter St Suite 1095
Baltimore, MD 21202

Telephone: (410) 244-5830
Internet Homepage: atlasrestaurantgroup.com
Type of Business: Chain Restaurant Operator
Year Founded: 2010
Total Sales: $1,590,129,000 (e)
Total Units: 51
Trade Names: Armada (1); Atlas Farms (1); Atlas Fish Market (1); Azumi Baltimore (1); Azumi Houston (1); Big Fish Grill (3); Crab House (1); Cross Street Cocktails (1);

Cunningham's Cafe (1); Dockside (1); Harbor East Deli (1); Italian Disco (1); James Joyce (1); Loch Bar (4); Market Ale House (1); Marmo (2);Maximon (1); Mikimotos (1); Monarque (1); Obie's By the Sea (1); Order of the Ace (1); Ouzo (2); Perennial (1); Salt Air (1); Sazio (1); Stingray (1); Striper Bites(1); Taco Grande (1); Tagliata (1); The Admiral's Cup (1); The Bygone (1); The Choptank (2); The Elk Room (1); The Market at Big Fish (1); The Oregon Grille(1); The Ruxton (1); The Undefeated (1); The Valley Inn (1); Torbert Street Social (1); Trolley Square Oyster House (1); Washington Street Ale House (1); Waterfront Hotel (1); Watershed (1)
Company-Owned Units: 51
Primary Menu: American (31); Mexican (1); Seafood (19)
Type of Foodservice: Casual Dining (7); Fine Dining (44)

Key Personnel
ALEXANDER SMITH - Founder; President
BRIAN MCCORMACK - COO
TRACEY ENGLISH - VP Finance
ERIN BLACK - VP Marketing, Design
STEPHEN LONDON - Director Operations
GABBY LOWMAN - Director Human Resources
JONATHAN LI - Director Operations
BRIAN BAGLEY - Director Operations
JOE SWEENEY - Director Marketing, Public Relations
RITA LYMPEROP - Director Operations
CHRIS MCKENNA - Director Training
DAVID GOODMAN - Regional Director Operations

Auntie Anne's Franchise
6901 Security Blvd
Baltimore, MD 21244-2412

Telephone: (410) 298-5242
Internet Homepage: auntieannesfranchising.com
Type of Business: Chain Restaurant Operator
Total Sales: $6,400,000 (e)
Total Units: 9
Trade Names: Auntie Anne's Hand-Rolled Soft Pretzels (9)
Units Franchised From: 9
Primary Menu: Snacks (9)
Areas of Operation: MD
Type of Foodservice: Quick Serve (9)
Franchise Affiliation: Auntie Anne's Inc., LANCASTER, PA

Key Personnel
MICHAEL TANNER - Owner; General Buyer

Double T Diner
6300 Baltimore National Pike
Baltimore, MD 21228-3901

Telephone: (410) 744-4151
Fax Number: (410) 744-4128
Internet Homepage: doubletdiner.com
Type of Business: Chain Restaurant Operator
Year Founded: 1958
Total Sales: $3,589,000 (e)
Alcohol Sales: 10%
Number of Employees: 437
Average Check: Lunch(10); Dinner(12)
Internet Order Processing: Yes
Total Units: 7
Trade Names: Double T Diner (7)
Company-Owned Units: 7
Preferred Square Footage: 4,000
Preferred Location Types: Freestanding
Alcohol Served: Beer, Wine, Liquor
Primary Menu: American (7)
Areas of Operation: MD
Type of Foodservice: Casual Dining (7)
Primary Distributors: (Full Line) US Foods Holding Corp., ROSEMONT, IL

Key Personnel
JOHN KOROS - Partner; Director Facility/Maintenance, Supply Chain, Real Estate, Design
LOUIS KOROS - Partner; Director Information Systems
TOMMY KOROS - Partner; Executive Chef; General Buyer

DuClaw Brew Co.
8901 Yellow Brick Rd Ste B
Baltimore, MD 21237-2349

Telephone: (443) 559-9900
Fax Number: (443) 559-9906
Internet Homepage: duclaw.com
Company Email: feedback@duclaw.com
Type of Business: Chain Restaurant Operator
Year Founded: 1996
Total Sales: $4,520,000 (e)
Alcohol Sales: 30%
Number of Employees: 125
Average Check: Lunch(12); Dinner(30)
Total Units: 1
Trade Names: DuClaw Brewing Co. (1)
Units Franchised To: 1
Preferred Location Types: Strip Mall
Alcohol Served: Beer, Wine, Liquor
Primary Menu: American (1)
Areas of Operation: MD
Type of Foodservice: Casual Dining (1)
Catering Services: Yes
Primary Distributors: (Food) SYSCO Food Services of Baltimore, JESSUP, MD

Key Personnel
DAVID BENFIELD - President; Executive Chef; General Buyer

Foreman Wolf Restaurant Group
1000 Lancaster St Ste 150
Baltimore, MD 21202-4770

Telephone: (410) 332-7373
Fax Number: (410) 332-8425
Internet Homepage: johnnysdownstairs.com; petitlouis.com; charlestonrestaurant.com; cgeno.com; barvasquez.com
Company Email: info@charlestonrestaurant.com
Type of Business: Chain Restaurant Operator
Year Founded: 1997
Total Sales: $26,070,000 (e)
Alcohol Sales: 25%
Number of Employees: 85
Average Check: Lunch(30); Dinner(48)
Internet Order Processing: Yes
Total Units: 5
Trade Names: Bar Vasquez (1); Charleston Restaurant (1); Cinghiale (1); Johnny's (1); Petit Louis Bistro (1)
Company-Owned Units: 5
Preferred Location Types: Downtown; Freestanding
Alcohol Served: Beer, Wine, Liquor
Primary Menu: American (2); French/Continental (1); Italian (1); Steak (1)
Areas of Operation: MD
Type of Foodservice: Casual Dining (3); Fine Dining (2)
Primary Distributors: (Food) Keany Produce Co., LANDOVER, MD; (Full Line) SYSCO Food Services of Baltimore, JESSUP, MD

Key Personnel
TONY FOREMAN - Partner; General Manager; General Buyer
CINDY WOLF - Partner; Executive Chef; General Buyer
MARIO CANO CATALAN - Executive Chef
CHUCK KRATZ - Executive Chef

Guy Fieri Signature Restaurants
1525 Russell St
Baltimore, MD 21230

Telephone: (844) 777-7463
Internet Homepage: guyfieri.com; texwasabis.com
Type of Business: Chain Restaurant Operator
Year Founded: 1996
Total Sales: $32,860,000 (e)
Alcohol Sales: 15%

Number of Employees: 457
Average Check: Lunch(26); Dinner(28)
Total Units: 17
Trade Names: Guy Fieri's (17)
Company-Owned Units: 17
Preferred Location Types: Freestanding; Strip Mall
Alcohol Served: Beer, Wine, Liquor
Primary Menu: Miscellaneous (17)
Type of Foodservice: Casual Dining (17)

Key Personnel
AMY SOLUS - CFO
JEFF POETZEL - COO; Corporate Chef

Hip Hop Fish & Chicken
Baltimore National Pike
Baltimore, MD 21229

Telephone: (410) 744-0440
Internet Homepage: hiphopfc.com
Type of Business: Chain Restaurant Operator
Total Sales: $37,100,000 (e)
Total Units: 29
Trade Names: Hip Hop Fish & Chicken (29)
Company-Owned Units: 29
Primary Menu: Chicken (29)
Areas of Operation: MD
Type of Foodservice: Quick Serve (29)

Key Personnel
RAMADAN ZABLAH - Owner

Mo's Seafood Factory
219 President St
Baltimore, MD 21202-4421

Telephone: (410) 837-8600
Internet Homepage: mosseafood.com
Type of Business: Chain Restaurant Operator
Year Founded: 1983
Total Sales: $13,546,000 (e)
Alcohol Sales: 25%
Number of Employees: 220
Average Check: Lunch(14); Dinner(30)
Total Units: 4
Trade Names: Mo's Inner Harbour (1); Mo's Neighborhood Bar & Grill (1); Mo's Towson (1); Mo's White Marsh (1)
Company-Owned Units: 4
Preferred Square Footage: 3,500
Preferred Location Types: Freestanding
Alcohol Served: Beer, Wine, Liquor
Primary Menu: Seafood (4)
Areas of Operation: MD
Type of Foodservice: Casual Dining (4)
Catering Services: Yes
Primary Distributors: (Equipment) Halperns' Steak and Seafood Inc, ATLANTA, GA; (Food) SYSCO Food Services of Baltimore, JESSUP, MD

Key Personnel
MO MANOCHEH - President; Controller; General Manager; Executive Chef; Director Purchasing, Information Systems, Real Estate, Franchise Development, Catering; General Buyer
DIANE JANNEY - Executive Director Risk Management, Human Resources
TERRIE BILLINGS - Manager Operations

Phillips Foods Inc.
3761 Commerce Dr Ste 413
Baltimore, MD 21227-1644

Telephone: (443) 263-1200
Fax Number: (410) 837-8526
Internet Homepage: phillipsfoods.com; phillipsseafood.com
Company Email: comments@phillipsfoods.com
Type of Business: Chain Restaurant Operator
Year Founded: 1956
Total Sales: $354,770,000 (e)
Alcohol Sales: 25%
Number of Employees: 935
Average Check: Lunch(26); Dinner(40)
Internet Order Processing: Yes
Internet Sales: 2.00%
Total Units: 11
Trade Names: Phillip's Seafood (1); Phillips Crab Deck (1); Phillips Seafood - Airports and Travel (7); Phillips Seafood - Foxwoods (1); Seneca Buffalo Creek Casino (1)
Company-Owned Units: 11
Preferred Square Footage: 10,000; 40,000
Preferred Location Types: Freestanding; Hotel/Motel; Regional Mall
Alcohol Served: Beer, Wine, Liquor
Primary Menu: Seafood (11); Steak/Seafood (0)
Areas of Operation: DC, GA, MD, NJ, NV, PA
Type of Foodservice: Casual Dining (4); Quick Serve (7)
On-site Distribution Center: Yes
Primary Distributors: (Full Line) SYSCO Food Services of Baltimore, JESSUP, MD
Notes: The company derives approximately 72% of its revenue from its seafood processing and wholesale operations.

Key Personnel
STEPHEN PHILLIPS - CEO
PAUL OPITZ - President International Division
JOHN KNORR - Senior VP Sales
JAMES R. KING - VP Finance
SARAH PALMER - VP Foodservice
WAYNE CANAPP - VP Restaurant Operations
SARAH LANGELER - VP Sales, Foodservice
JOHN BAXTER - VP Marketing
MAX PHILLIPS - VP Business Development, International
BOB BANKS - Controller
MANOJ PARAMANANDAM - Controller
WILLIAM SEXTON - General Manager
JIM KNUDSON - Director Human Resources
BRAD GRANT - Director Information Systems
BOBBY LOVE - Director Quality Assurance, Food Safety
DONALD MANNING - Director Training
KEELY DZIUBAN - Director Marketing, Foodservice
BRICE PHILLIPS - Director Sales
STEVE WONSER - Regional Manager Sales, South Region
NICK HANCOCK - Regional Manager Sales, Southwest Region
BRIAN MUSHRUSH - District Manager
JOANNA PHILLIPS - Manager Marketing
DAVID EHLY - Manager Logistics
WESLEY MILLER - Manager Supply Chain
ANDREW PREVATT - Coordinator Information Technology

The Prime Rib
1101 N Calvert St Ste 102
Baltimore, MD 21202-3809

Telephone: (410) 539-1804
Fax Number: (410) 837-0244
Internet Homepage: theprimerib.com
Company Email: prime1101@aol.com
Type of Business: Chain Restaurant Operator
Year Founded: 1964
Total Sales: $18,538,000 (e)
Alcohol Sales: 15%
Number of Employees: 75
Average Check: Lunch(24); Dinner(48)
Internet Order Processing: Yes
Total Units: 3
Trade Names: The Prime Rib (3)
Company-Owned Units: 3
Preferred Location Types: Freestanding
Alcohol Served: Beer, Wine, Liquor
Primary Menu: Steak/Seafood (3)
Projected Openings: 1
Areas of Operation: DC, MD, PA
Type of Foodservice: Fine Dining (3)
Primary Distributors: (Food) SYSCO Food Services of Baltimore, JESSUP, MD

Key Personnel
GABRIEL HADDAD - General Manager
JAMES MINARIK - Executive Chef; General Buyer
JOHN KLAUS - General Buyer; Buyer Alcoholic Beverages

Harloe Management
260 Gateway Dr Ste 9-10B
Bel Air, MD 21014-4268

Telephone: (410) 879-4703
Fax Number: (410) 893-9142

Type of Business: Chain Restaurant Operator
Year Founded: 1979
Total Sales: $11,480,000 (e)
Number of Employees: 280
Average Check: Breakfast(8); Lunch(8); Dinner(10)
Total Units: 5
Trade Names: Burger King (5)
Units Franchised From: 5
Preferred Square Footage: 3,000
Preferred Location Types: Freestanding
Primary Menu: Hamburger (5)
Areas of Operation: MD
Type of Foodservice: Quick Serve (5)
Franchise Affiliation: Burger King Worldwide Inc., MIAMI, FL
Primary Distributors: (Full Line) Maines Paper & Food Service Maryland, SAVAGE, MD

Key Personnel
DIANA HARLOE - President; Director Finance, Operations, Information Systems, Real Estate, Human Resources; General Buyer
KATHY BITTINGER - Manager Accounting, Branch

B.F. Saul Co.
7501 Wisconsin Ave Ste 1500
Bethesda, MD 20814-6522

Telephone: (301) 986-6000
Fax Number: (301) 986-6066
Internet Homepage: bfsaulhotels.com
Type of Business: Foodservice Operations - Hotel/Motels
Year Founded: 1896
Total Sales: $81,330,000 (e)
Alcohol Sales: 20%
Number of Employees: 1,470
Total Units: 21
Restaurants in Hotels: 8
Trade Names: Best Western (1); Courtyard by Marriott (1); Crowne Plaza (2); DoubleTree (1); Fairfield Inn (1); Hampton Inn Dulles Airport (3); Holiday Inn (3); Holiday Inn Express & Suites (1); SpringHill Suites By Marriott (2); The Hay-Adams (1); TownePlace Suites By Marriott (5)
Company-Owned Units: 8
Alcohol Served: Beer, Wine, Liquor
Areas of Operation: MD, MI, VA
Type of Foodservice: Casual Dining (8)
Primary Distributors: (Food) SYSCO Food Services of Baltimore, JESSUP, MD
Notes: The company derives approximately 77% of its revenue from hotel operations.

Key Personnel
MARK CARRIER - Senior VP Division
KEN KOVACH - Senior VP Human Resources, Personnel

Black Restaurant Group LLC
7752 Woodmont Ave Ste 210
Bethesda, MD 20814-6031

Telephone: (301) 215-6397
Fax Number: (301) 215-6398
Internet Homepage: blackjackdc.com; blackmarketrestaurant.com; blackrestaurantgroup.com; blacksbarandkitchen.com; pearldivedc.com; republictakoma.com; tiltdc.com
Company Email: info@blackrestaurantgroup.com
Type of Business: Chain Restaurant Operator
Year Founded: 1999
Total Sales: $11,790,000 (e)
Alcohol Sales: 30%
Number of Employees: 105
Average Check: Lunch(30); Dinner(42)
Total Units: 8
Trade Names: Addie's (1); Black Jack Restaurant (1); Black Market Bistro (1); Black Salt (1); Black's Bar & Kitchen (1); Pearl Dive Oyster Bar (1); Republic (1); Tilt Side Bar (1)
Company-Owned Units: 8
Preferred Location Types: Downtown; Freestanding
Alcohol Served: Beer, Wine, Liquor
Primary Menu: American (7); Seafood (1)
Areas of Operation: MD
Type of Foodservice: Casual Dining (8)
Primary Distributors: (Food) Congressional Seafood Inc., JESSUP, MD

Key Personnel
BARBARA BLACK - Partner; Director Food and Beverage
JEFF BLACK - Partner; Executive Chef; Director Finance, Menu Development; General Buyer
JENNIFER LARKIN - Partner Administration; Manager Administration
JON LINCK - Partner; Director Operations
BRIAN CONSIDINE - Controller
DOUG DOYLE - General Manager

Clover Restaurant Group
5272 River Rd Ste 650
Bethesda, MD 20816-1448

Telephone: (202) 362-9842
Internet Homepage: cafedeluxe.com; tortillacoast.com
Company Email: info@cafedeluxe.com
Type of Business: Chain Restaurant Operator
Year Founded: 1988
Total Sales: $11,381,000 (e)
Alcohol Sales: 25%
Number of Employees: 420
Average Check: Lunch(14); Dinner(36)
Total Units: 6
Trade Names: Cafe Deluxe (3); Chef Geoff's (1); Lia's (1); Tortilla Coast (1)
Company-Owned Units: 6
Preferred Location Types: Freestanding
Alcohol Served: Beer, Wine, Liquor
Primary Menu: American (5); Southwest/Tex-Mex (1)
Areas of Operation: DC, MD, VA
Type of Foodservice: Casual Dining (6)
Primary Distributors: (Food) SYSCO Food Services of Baltimore, JESSUP, MD

Key Personnel
DAWN DALY - Manager Administration; Specialist Payroll

DiamondRock Hospitality Company
3 Bethesda Metro Ctr Ste 1500
Bethesda, MD 20814-6352

Telephone: (240) 744-1150
Fax Number: (240) 744-1199
Internet Homepage: drhc.com
Company Email: info@drhc.com
Type of Business: Foodservice Operations - Hotel/Motels
Year Founded: 2004
Publicly Held: Yes
Total Sales: $481,420,000 (e)
Alcohol Sales: 15%
Number of Employees: 31
Total Units: 31
Restaurants in Hotels: 31
Trade Names: Cavallo Point, The Lodge at theGolden Gate (1); Chicago Marriott (1); Courtyard by Marriott (3); Frenchman's Reef (1); Havana Cabana Key West (1); Hilton (2); Hilton Garden Inn (1); Hotel Emblem (1); JW Marriott Cherry Creek (1); L'Auberge de Sedona (1); Lexington Hotel (1); Marriott (3); MarriottSuites (1); Orchards Inn (1); Renaissance (2); Sheraton Suites Key West (1); Shorebreak Hotel (1); The Gwen Chicago (1); The Landing Resort & Spa (1); TheLodge at Sonoma (1); Vail Marriott Mountain Resort & Spa (1); Westin (4)
Company-Owned Units: 31
Alcohol Served: Beer, Wine, Liquor
Areas of Operation: CA, CO, DC, FL, GA, IL, MA, MD, MN, NY, SC, TX, UT, VI, VT
Type of Foodservice: Casual Dining; Fine Dining
Notes: The company derives approximately 77% of its revenue from hotel & resort operations.

Key Personnel
WILLIAM W. MCCARTEN - Chairman
MARK W. BRUGGER - CEO; President
SEAN M. MAHONEY - CFO; Exec VP; Treasurer
BRIONY R. QUINN - Chief Accounting Officer;

Controller
TROY FURBAY - Chief Investment Officer; Exec VP
WILLIAM J. TENNIS - Exec VP; Corporate Secretary; General Counsel

Gusto Farm to Street
7101 Democracy Blvd Suite FC17
Bethesda, MD 20817

Telephone: (301) 312-6509
Internet Homepage: eatgusto.com
Company Email: info@eatgusto.com
Type of Business: Chain Restaurant Operator
Year Founded: 2015
Total Units: 6
Trade Names: Gusto Farm to Street (6)
Company-Owned Units: 6
Primary Menu: Pizza (6)
Projected Openings: 1
Areas of Operation: MD, NC, VA
Type of Foodservice: Fast Casual (6)

Key Personnel
RUSS BEHRMAN - Director Operations
BRENT PROTHEROE - Director Operations
JOI GREEN - Coordinator Marketing, Sales

†•▲
HMSHost Corporation
6905 Rockledge Dr Fl 1
Bethesda, MD 20817-7826

Telephone: (866) 467-4672
Fax Number: (240) 694-4695
Internet Homepage: hmshost.com
Company Email: comments@hmshost.com
Type of Business: Foodservice Management Operator
Year Founded: 1897
Total Sales: $5,202,240,000 (e)
Number of Employees: 41,000
Number of Locations Served: 4,400
Total Foodservice Mgmt Accounts: 375
Trade Names: 96th Street Steakburgers; Au Bon Pain; Auntie Anne's Hand-Rolled Soft Pretzels; Baja Fresh; Baskin-Robbins; Big Apple Bagels; Blue Burrito; Bruegger's Bagel Bakery; Burger King; Cafe Chocolat; Cafe Patachou; California Pizza Kitchen ASAP; Carvel Ice Cream; Casa Bacardi; Cheers; Chick-fil-A;Chili's too; Ciao; Cigar City Brewing; Cinnabon; Cold Stone Creamery; Columbia Cafe; Corner Bakery Cafe; Denver ChopHouse; Dewar's Clubhouse; Dick Clark's AB Grill; Dunkin' Donuts; Famous Famiglia; FOX Sports Sky Box; Freshens; Gordon Biersch Brewing Co.; Great American Bagel; Gustav's Pub & Grill; Haagen-Dazs; Hudson Valley Wine Bar; Jamba Juice; Java City; Johnny Rockets; Jose Cuervo Tequileria; KFC; King David Dog's; Krispy Kreme; La Salsa; LaTapenade; Legal Sea Foods; LongHorn Steakhouse; Maggiano's Little Italy; MaggieMoo's; mamma ilardo's pizzeria; Mrs. Field's Cookies; Nathan's Famous Hot Dogs; On The Border Mexican Grill & Cantina; Outback Steakhouse; Panda Express; Panera Bread; Pei Wei Asian Diner; Phillips Famous Seafood; Pinkberry;Pizza Hut; Popeyes Famous Chicken & Biscuits; Quiznos; Rising Roll Gourmet; Romano's Macaroni Grill; Roy Rogers Family Restaurant; Rubio's FreshMexican Grill; Ruby's Dinette; Sammy's Beach Bar & Grill; Samuel Adams; Sbarro; Silks Saratoga Bistro; Starbucks Coffee; Starbucks Reserve Evenings; T.G.I. Friday's; Taco Bell; Talie; Taste; TCBY; The Cheesecake Factory Bakery Cafe; The Counter; Wendy's Old Fashioned Hamburgers; WHOPPER Bar; Wolfgang Puck Express
Units Franchised From: 900
Areas of Operation: MD
Type of Foodservice: Cafeteria (375); Fast Casual (375); Full-service sit-down dining (375); Quick Serve (375)
Foodservice Management Venues: Transportation; Travel Plazas
Franchise Affiliation: ABP Corporation, BOSTON, MA; Auntie Anne's Inc., LANCASTER, PA; BAB Inc., DEERFIELD, IL; BR IP Holder LLC, CANTON, MA; Bruegger's Enterprises Inc., DALLAS, TX; Burger King Worldwide Inc., MIAMI, FL; California Pizza Kitchen Inc., COSTA MESA, CA; Carvel Corporation, ATLANTA, GA; CB Franchise Systems LLC, SCOTTSDALE, AZ; CBC Restaurant Corp., DALLAS, TX; Chick-fil-A Inc., ATLANTA, GA; Chili's Grill & Bar,DALLAS, TX; Cinnabon Inc., ATLANTA, GA; Cold Stone Creamery Inc., SCOTTSDALE, AZ; DD IP Holder, CANTON, MA; Dividend Restaurant Group, DENVER, CO; Famiglia - DeBartolo, LLC, WHITE PLAINS, NY; Famous Brands International, BROOMFIELD, CO; Fresh Enterprises, LLC, SCOTTSDALE, AZ; Global Franchise Group, ATLANTA, GA; Gordon Biersch Brewery Restaurant Group, CHATTANOOGA, TN; Jamba Inc., FRISCO, TX; Java City Inc.,SACRAMENTO, CA; KFC Corporation, LOUISVILLE, KY; Krispy Kreme Doughnut Corporation, CHARLOTTE, NC; Maggiano's Little Italy, DALLAS, TX; Nathan's Famous Inc., JERICHO, NY; On The Border LLC, IRVING, TX; Outback Steakhouse Restaurants, TAMPA, FL; Panda Restaurant Group Inc., ROSEMEAD, CA; Phillips Foods Inc., BALTIMORE, MD; Piezzetta, TOWSON, MD; Pizza Hut Inc., PLANO, TX; Plamondon Companies Inc., FREDERICK, MD; Popeyes Louisiana Kitchen Inc., ATLANTA, GA; Rising Roll Gourmet Co., ATLANTA, GA; Rubio's Restaurants Inc., CARLSBAD, CA; Sbarro Holdings LLC, COLUMBUS, OH; Starbucks Corporation, SEATTLE, WA; T.G.I. Friday's Inc., DALLAS, TX; Taco Bell Corp., IRVINE, CA; TCBY Systems LLC, BROOMFIELD, CO; The Cheesecake Factory Incorporated, CALABASAS HILLS, CA; The Great American Bagel, WESTMONT, IL; The Haagen-Dazs Shoppe Company Inc., MINNEAPOLIS, MN; The Johnny Rockets Group Inc., LAKE FOREST, CA; The Quiznos Master LLC, DENVER, CO; The Ruby Restaurant Group, NEWPORT BEACH, CA; The Wendy's Company, DUBLIN, OH; Wolfgang Puck Inc., LAS VEGAS, NV
Primary Distributors: (Full Line) US Foods Holding Corp., ROSEMONT, IL
Parent Company: Autogrill SpA, MILAN, ITA
Notes: HMSHost operates in 120 airports around the globe and in 80 motorway travel plazas throughout the U.S. and Canada. HMSHost also operates in specialty destinations and shopping and entertainment locations. The company derives approximately 4% of its revenue from retail operations.

Key Personnel
STEVEN JOHNSON - CEO; President
MARK RATYCH - CFO; Exec VP
LAURA FITZRANDOLPH - Chief Human Resources Officer; Exec VP
SARAH NAQVI - CIO; Exec VP
PAUL MAMALIAN - Exec VP; General Counsel
STEPHANIE HAVARD - Exec VP Business Development
DERRYL BENTON - Exec VP Business Development
RON GOMES - VP Strategic Planning
JIM DAINO - Senior Director Operations
KIRK CHRISTIAN - Senior Director Operations
SPARTACO CICERCHIA - Senior Director Security, Compliance
TYLER PITMAN - Director Restaurant Operations
JODI STANLEY - Director Operations
NOELLE SPAFFORD - Director Operations
ADRIAN SEDANO - Regional Director Operations

‡
Hospitality Partners
3 Bethesda Metro Ctr Ste 1500
Bethesda, MD 20814-6352

Telephone: (301) 718-6161
Fax Number: (301) 913-9596
Internet Homepage: hospart.com
Company Email: hpinfo@hospitalitypartners.com
Type of Business: Foodservice Operations - Hotel/Motels
Year Founded: 1986
Total Sales: $86,180,000 (e)
Alcohol Sales: 15%
Number of Employees: 975
Total Units: 13
Restaurants in Hotels: 13

Trade Names: Atlantic Oceanfront Hotel & Suites (1); Bonita Beach Oceanblock Hotel (1); Carousel Beachfront Hotel (1); Cayman Suites Beach Hotel (1); Coastal Palms Beach Hotel (1); Courtyard by Marriott (1); Crossroads Inn (1); Crystal Beach Oceanfront Hotel (1); Fairfield Inn & Suites by Marriott Chincoteague Island (1); The English Inn of Charlottesville (1); Thornburg Inn & Suites (1); Tidelands Caribbean Hotel 7 Suites (1); Town Place Suites (1)
Company-Owned Units: 13
Alcohol Served: Beer, Wine, Liquor
Areas of Operation: MD, VA
Type of Foodservice: Casual Dining (13)
Primary Distributors: (Food) US Foods, MANASSAS, VA
Notes: Hospitality Partners also operates several limited-service hotels. The company derives approximately 70% of its revenue from hotel operations.

Key Personnel
MICHAEL JAMES - CEO; President; Partner
FRED PALLONI - Partner; CFO; VP Finance, Accounting; Director Information Systems
JOHN VERNON - Exec VP Operations, Human Resources, Foodservice, Food Safety; General Buyer
DEBBIE REINDOLLAR - Controller
RAY SMITH - Director Information Technology
GREG WEST - Director Administration, Risk Management

Host Hotels & Resorts Inc.
4747 Bethesda Ave Ste 1300
Bethesda, MD 20814

Telephone: (240) 744-1000
Fax Number: (240) 744-5125
Internet Homepage: hosthotels.com
Company Email: info@hosthotels.com
Type of Business: Foodservice Operations - Hotel/Motels
Year Founded: 1993
Publicly Held: Yes
Total Sales: $2,610,500,000 (e)
Alcohol Sales: 15%
Number of Employees: 184
Total Units: 80
Trade Names: AC Hotels (1); Autograph Collection (1); Fairmont (1); Hilllton Collection (3); Hyatt Collection (11); Ibis (1); Independent Hotel Collection (4); Jw Marriott (4); Luxury Collection (2); Marriott (29); Novotel (1); Sheraton Hotel (3); St. Regis (1); Swissotel (1); The Ritz-Carlton (5); W (2); Westin (10)
Company-Owned Units: 80
Alcohol Served: Beer, Wine, Liquor
Areas of Operation: AZ, CA, CO, DC, FL, GA, HI, IL, IN, LA, MA, MD, MN, MO, NC, NJ, NY, OH, OR, PA, TX, VA, WA, AB, ON
Foreign Countries: AUSTRALIA; BELGIUM; BRAZIL; CANADA; CHILE; ENGLAND; FRANCE; GERMANY; ITALY; MEXICO; POLAND; SPAIN; SWEDEN; THE NETHERLANDS
Type of Foodservice: Casual Dining; Family Restaurant; Fast Casual; Fine Dining; Quick Serve
Primary Distributors: (Food) SYSCO Food Services of Baltimore, JESSUP, MD
Notes: The company derives approximately 74% of its revenue from hotel & other operations.

Key Personnel
RICHARD E. MARRIOTT - Chairman
JAMES F. RISOLEO - CEO; President
NATHAN S. TYRRELL - Chief Investment Officer; Exec VP
MINAZ ABJI - Exec VP Finance
JULIE ASLAKSEN - Exec VP; Corporate Secretary; General Counsel
JAY L. JOHNSON - Senior VP; Treasurer
BRIAN G. MACNAMARA - Senior VP; Controller
SUKHVINDER SINGH - Senior VP Internet Development

Marriott International Inc.
10400 Fernwood Rd
Bethesda, MD 20817-1102

Telephone: (301) 380-3000
Fax Number: (301) 380-7837
Internet Homepage: marriott.com; ritzcarlton.com
Type of Business: Foodservice Operations - Hotel/Motels
Year Founded: 1927
Publicly Held: Yes
Total Sales: $17,100,800,000 (e)
Alcohol Sales: 10%
Number of Employees: 176,000
Total Units: 7,642
Restaurants in Hotels: 7642
Trade Names: AC Hotel by Marriott (145); Aloft (159); Autograph Collection (166); Bulgari Hotel & Resort (6); Courtyard By Marriott (1,199); Delta Hotel & Resorts (63); Design Hotels (141); EDITION (8); Element by Westin (39); Fairfield Inn (979); Four Points by Sheraton (271); Gaylord Resorts (6); JW Marriott (84); Le Meridien (107); Luxury Collection (110); Marriott Executive Apartments (30); Marriott Hotels & Resorts (567); Moxy (37); Protea Hotel (80); Renaissance Hotels & Resorts (175); Residence Inn (803); Sheraton Hotels & Resorts (441); SpringHill Suites (414); St. Regis (41); The Ritz-Carlton (101); The Ritz-Carlton Residental (19); The Ritz-Carlton Serviced Apartments (5); TownePlace Suites (388); Tribute (31); W Hotels (55); W Residences (13); Westin Hotels & Resorts (223)
Company-Owned Units: 7,642
Alcohol Served: Beer, Wine, Liquor
Projected Openings: 250
Areas of Operation: AK, AL, AR, AZ, CA, CO, CT, DC, DE, FL, GA, GU, HI, IA, ID, IL, IN, KS, KY, LA, MA, MD, ME, MI, MN, MO, MS, MT, NC, ND, NE, NH, NJ, NM, NV, NY, OH, OK, OR, PA, PR, RI, SC, SD, TN, TX, UT, VA, VI, VT, WA, WI, WV, WY, AB, BC, NS, ON, QC
Foreign Countries: ALGERIA; ARGENTINA; ARMENIA; ARUBA; AUSTRALIA; AUSTRIA; AZERBAIJAN; BAHAMAS; BAHRAIN; BARBADOS; BELGIUM; BRAZIL; CANADA; CAYMAN ISLANDS; CHILE; CHINA; COLOMBIA; COSTA RICA; CZECH REPUBLIC; DENMARK; DOMINICAN REPUBLIC; ECUADOR; EGYPT; EL SALVADOR; ENGLAND; FRANCE; GERMANY; GREECE; GUATEMALA; HAITI; HONDURAS; HUNGARY; INDIA; INDONESIA; IRELAND; ISRAEL; ITALY; JAMAICA; JAPAN; JORDAN; KUWAIT; MALAYSIA; MEXICO; OMAN; PAKISTAN; PANAMA; PERU; POLAND; PORTUGAL; QATAR;ROMANIA; RUSSIA; SAINT KITTS AND NEVIS; SAUDI ARABIA; SCOTLAND; SINGAPORE; SOUTH KOREA; SPAIN; SURINAME; SWEDEN;SWITZERLAND; TAIWAN; THAILAND; THE NETHERLANDS; THE PHILIPPINES; TRINIDAD & TOBAGO; TURKEY; UNITED ARAB EMIRATES;VENEZUELA; VIETNAM; WALES
Type of Foodservice: Casual Dining; Family Restaurant; Fine Dining
Primary Distributors: (Food) SYSCO Food Services of Baltimore, JESSUP, MD

Key Personnel
J. W. MARRIOTT JR - Executive Chairman
AMY C. MCPHERSON - President International Division
CRAIG S. SMITH - President Division
DON CLEARY - President Canada
DAVID J. GRISSEN - President Division
LEENY OBERG - CFO
VAL BAUDUIN - Chief Accounting Officer; Controller
ANTHONY G. CAPUANO - Chief Development Officer; Exec VP
TRICIA PRIMROSE - Chief Communications Officer; Senior Exec VP Public Relations
RON HARRISON - Chief Design Officer
CAROLYN B. HANDLON - Exec VP Finance; Treasurer
PAUL FOSKEY - Exec VP Business Development
RENA H. REISS - Exec VP; General Counsel
DAVID A. RODRIGUEZ - Exec VP Human Resources
NANCY C. LEE - Senior VP; General Counsel
DEBORAH MARRIOTT HARRISON - Senior VP Government Affairs
KENNETH RYAN - VP Operations
BRAD NELSON - VP Operations
CALLETTE NIELSEN - VP Division; Manager

Branding
STEPHANE C. MASSON - VP Purchasing
ANNE MARIE WEMMLINGER - VP Operations, Franchising
JENNIFER KELLOGG CMP - Senior Director Event Planning
KELLY COOPER CMP - Senior Director Development, Design
OLIVER LAU - Director Operations
DANIEL HOFFMAN - Director Operations-Beverages
CARMESHA YOUNG - Senior Manager
CARLETON BENNETT - Business Manager
DREW BOOTH CMP - Manager Event Planning
GLENN BROWN - Manager Operations
GREG BASALLA - Manager Food and Beverage

Pebblebrook Hotel Trust
4747 Bethesda Ave Ste 1100
Bethesda, MD 20814-5422

Telephone: (240) 507-1300
Internet Homepage: pebblebrookhotels.com
Company Email: info@pebblebrookhotels.com
Type of Business: Foodservice Operations - Hotel/Motels
Year Founded: 2010
Publicly Held: Yes
Total Sales: $722,760,000 (e)
Number of Employees: 50
Total Units: 57
Restaurants in Hotels: 28
Trade Names: Argonaut Hotel (1); Chamberlain West Hollywood Hotel (1); Chaminade Resort & Spa (1); Donovan Hotel (1); Embassy Suites San Diego Bay - Downtown (1); George Hotel (1); Grafton on Sunset (1); Harbor Court Hotel San Francisco (1); Hilton San Diego Gaslamp Quarter (1); Hotel Chicago Downtown(1); Hotel Colonnade (1); Hotel Monaco (1); Hotel Monaco Seattle (1); Hotel Palomar Los Angeles (1); Hotel Spero (1); Hotel Vintage Park (1); Hotel VintagePlaza (1); Hotel Vitale (1); Hotel Zelos (1); Hotel Zena Washington DC (1); Hotel Zephyr (1); Hotel Zeppelin (1); Hotel Zetta (1); Hotel Zoe Fishermans Wharf (1); Hyatt Regency Boston Harbor (1); InterContinental Buckhead (1); Jekyll Island Club Resort (1); L'Auberge Del Mar (1); LaPlaya Beach Resort & Club (1); LeMeridien Delfina (1); Le Parc Suite Hotel (1); Mondrian Hotel Los Angeles (1); Montrose West Hollywood (1); Paradise Point Resort & Spa (1); Revere Hotel Boston Common (1); San Diego Mission Bay Resort (1); Skamania Lodge (1); Sofitel Philadelphia (1); Solamar Hotel (1); Southernmost Beach Resort (1); TheHeathman Hotel (1); The Hotel Zags (1); The Liberty (1); The Marker Key West (1); The Marker San Francisco (1); The Nines Portland (1); The Tuscan Fisherman's Wharf (1); The Westin Colonnade Coral Gables (1); The Westin Copley Place, Boston (1); The Westin Gaslamp Quarter (1); Topaz Hotel (1); UnionStation Hotel (1); Viceroy (2); Villa Florence (1); W Boston (1); W Los Angeles - Westwood (1)
Company-Owned Units: 28
Alcohol Served: Beer, Wine, Liquor
Areas of Operation: CA, DC, FL, GA, MA, MD, MN, NY, OR, PA, TN, WA
Type of Foodservice: Casual Dining; Fine Dining
Notes: The company derives approximately 79% of total revenue from hotel and other operations.

Key Personnel
JON E. BORTZ - Chairman; CEO; President
RAYMOND D. MARTZ - CFO; Exec VP; Treasurer; Corporate Secretary
THOMAS C. FISHER - Chief Investment Officer; Exec VP

RLJ Lodging Trust
3 Bethesda Metro Ctr Ste 1000
Bethesda, MD 20814-6347

Telephone: (301) 280-7777
Fax Number: (301) 280-7750
Internet Homepage: rljlodgingtrust.com
Company Email: info@rljlodgingtrust.com
Type of Business: Foodservice Operations - Hotel/Motels
Publicly Held: Yes
Total Sales: $766,800,000 (e)
Alcohol Sales: 10%
Number of Employees: 84
Total Units: 103
Restaurants in Hotels: 103
Trade Names: Courtyard by Marriott (14); Doubletree (4); Embassy Suites (21); Fairfield Inn & Suites by Marriott (5); Hampton Inn/Hampton Inn & Suites (2); Hilton (1); Hilton Garden Inn (5); Homewood Suites (2); Hyatt Centric (2); Hyatt House (7); Hyatt/Hyatt Place (3); Marriott (5); Other (5); Renaissance (3); Residence Inn by Marriott (13); SpringHill Suites by Marriott (3); Wyndham (8)
Company-Owned Units: 103
Projected Remodelings: 6
Areas of Operation: CA, CO, CT, DC, FL, GA, HI, IL, IN, KY, LA, MA, MD, MI, NC, NV, NY, OH, OR, PA, SC, TX, UT
Type of Foodservice: Casual Dining; Family Restaurant
Notes: Total stores and trade names include limited-service hotels/motels that do not provide on-site foodservice.

Key Personnel
ROBERT L. JOHNSON - Chairman; Founder
ROSS H. BIERKAN - CEO; President
LESLIE D. HALE - CFO; COO; Exec VP; Treasurer
CHRISTOPHER A. GORMSEN - Chief Accounting Officer
FREDERICK D. MCKALIP - Senior VP; General Counsel
JEFF DURAY - Senior VP Acquisitions
CARL MAYFIELD - Senior VP Construction, Design
SUSAN SLOAN - VP; Controller
NIKHIL BHALLA - VP Finance
DEMOND HICKS - Manager Payroll

Three Brothers Pizza
4521 Kenilworth Ave
Bladensburg, MD 20710-1217

Telephone: (301) 864-1570
Fax Number: (301) 699-8233
Internet Homepage: threebrotherspizza.com
Type of Business: Chain Restaurant Operator
Year Founded: 1976
Total Sales: $17,190,000 (e)
Average Check: Dinner(22)
Total Units: 12
Trade Names: Three Brothers Pizza (12)
Company-Owned Units: 12
Preferred Location Types: Downtown; Freestanding; Strip Mall
Alcohol Served: Beer, Wine, Liquor
Primary Menu: Italian (12)
Areas of Operation: MD
Type of Foodservice: Family Restaurant (12)

Key Personnel
PETER REPOLE - CEO; President
RAVI REPOLE - Owner; Director Training, Franchise Development
GREGG REPOLE - General Manager; Director Operations, Franchising
MELISSA REPOLE - General Manager; Director Catering

Malamis Holdings, LLC
6844 Race Track Rd
Bowie, MD 20715-3011

Telephone: (301) 262-0505
Type of Business: Chain Restaurant Operator
Total Sales: $19,230,000 (e)
Total Units: 14
Trade Names: Jersey Mike's Subs (14)
Units Franchised From: 14
Primary Menu: Sandwiches/Deli (14)
Areas of Operation: MD
Type of Foodservice: Quick Serve (14)
Franchise Affiliation: Jersey Mike's Franchise Systems, MANASQUAN, NJ

Key Personnel
DANNY MALAMIS - Owner; General Buyer

Rip's Country Inn
3809 Crain Hwy
Bowie, MD 20716-3605

Telephone: (301) 805-5900
Internet Homepage: annapolisseafoodmarket.com; ripscountryinn.com
Company Email: bill@ripscountryinn.com
Type of Business: Chain Restaurant Operator
Year Founded: 1952
Total Sales: $5,851,000 (e)
Alcohol Sales: 12%
Number of Employees: 130
Average Check: Breakfast(8); Lunch(8); Dinner(24)
Total Units: 2
Trade Names: Annapolis Seafood Market (1); Rip's Country Inn (1)
Company-Owned Units: 2
Preferred Location Types: Freestanding
Alcohol Served: Beer, Wine, Liquor
Primary Menu: Seafood (1); Steak/Seafood (1)
Areas of Operation: MD
Type of Foodservice: Casual Dining (2)

Key Personnel
MARSHELE BURGESS - President; Director Menu Development

Sonshine Creamery, LLC
15754 Annapolis Rd
Bowie, MD 20715-3006

Telephone: (301) 464-9790
Type of Business: Chain Restaurant Operator
Total Sales: $1,220,000 (e)
Total Units: 3
Trade Names: Cold Stone Creamery (3)
Units Franchised From: 3
Primary Menu: Snacks (3)
Areas of Operation: MD
Type of Foodservice: Quick Serve (3)
Franchise Affiliation: Kahala Brands, SCOTTSDALE, AZ

Key Personnel
CHRIS BLAZEVICH - Partner
KELLI BLAZEVICH - Partner

Crofton Drive Thru, Inc.
45370 Alton Ln Ste 202A
California, MD 20619-3125

Telephone: (301) 737-2301
Fax Number: (301) 737-1101
Company Email: dmccheck@aol.com
Type of Business: Chain Restaurant Operator
Total Sales: $14,860,000 (e)
Total Units: 10
Trade Names: Checkers (10)
Units Franchised From: 10
Primary Menu: Hamburger (10)
Areas of Operation: MD, VA
Type of Foodservice: Quick Serve (10)
Franchise Affiliation: Checkers Drive-In Restaurants Inc., TAMPA, FL

Key Personnel
PHIL DORSEY - Owner; General Buyer

GCGC Fair
10850 Town Center Blvd
California, MD 20754

Telephone: (301) 855-7561
Type of Business: Chain Restaurant Operator
Total Sales: $46,650,000 (e)
Total Units: 10
Trade Names: McDonald's (10)
Units Franchised From: 10
Preferred Square Footage: 2,500
Primary Menu: Hamburger (10)
Areas of Operation: MD
Type of Foodservice: Quick Serve (10)
Franchise Affiliation: McDonald's Corporation, CHICAGO, IL

Key Personnel
GERALD FAIR - President; Partner; General Buyer
CHARLENE LEWIS-FAIR - Partner; Manager Accounting

FEC Management
1701 Ritchie Station Ct
Capitol Heights, MD 20743

Telephone: (301) 808-0033
Internet Homepage: mcdmateos.com
Type of Business: Chain Restaurant Operator
Total Sales: $85,840,000 (c)
Number of Employees: 466
Total Units: 18
Trade Names: McDonald's (18)
Units Franchised From: 18
Preferred Square Footage: 2,500
Primary Menu: Hamburger (18)
Projected Openings: 2
Areas of Operation: DC, MD, VA
Type of Foodservice: Quick Serve (18)
Franchise Affiliation: McDonald's Corporation, CHICAGO, IL

Key Personnel
LUIS MATEOS - President; General Buyer

Rod-N-Reel
4165 Mears Ave
Chesapeake Beach, MD 20732-5116

Mailing Address: PO Box 99, CHESAPEAKE BEACH, MD, 20732-0099
Telephone: (410) 257-2735
Fax Number: (301) 855-1119
Internet Homepage: cbresortspa.com
Company Email: marketing@cbresortspa.com
Type of Business: Chain Restaurant Operator
Year Founded: 1946
Total Sales: $4,178,000 (e)
Alcohol Sales: 10%
Number of Employees: 85
Average Check: Breakfast(14); Lunch(18); Dinner(30)
Total Units: 2
Trade Names: Boardwalk Cafe (1); Rod-N-Reel (1)
Company-Owned Units: 2
Preferred Location Types: Hotel/Motel
Alcohol Served: Beer, Wine, Liquor
Primary Menu: American (1); Seafood (1)
Areas of Operation: MD
Type of Foodservice: Casual Dining (2)
Catering Services: Yes
Primary Distributors: (Food) US Foods, SEVERN, MD

Key Personnel
MARY DONOVAN - Partner

Pyramid Enterprises, LLC
1 E Lenox St
Chevy Chase, MD 20815-4210

Telephone: (301) 526-2025
Type of Business: Chain Restaurant Operator
Total Sales: $21,670,000 (e)
Total Units: 11
Trade Names: Five Guys Burgers and Fries (11)
Units Franchised From: 11
Preferred Square Footage: 3,000
Primary Menu: Hamburger (11)
Areas of Operation: MD
Type of Foodservice: Fast Casual (11)
Franchise Affiliation: Five Guys Holdings Inc., LORTON, VA

Key Personnel
MANUEL BRAMAO - CEO; CFO
STEPHEN PERKINS - President; Manager Real Estate; General Buyer

Cluck-U-Corporate
7305 Baltimore Ave Ste 301
College Park, MD 20740

Telephone: (301) 604-2535
Fax Number: (301) 604-2536
Internet Homepage: cluckuchicken.com
Company Email: info@cluckuchicken.com
Type of Business: Chain Restaurant Operator
Year Founded: 1985
Systemwide Sales: $16,448,000 (e)
Total Sales: $3,063,000 (e)
Number of Employees: 381
Average Check: Lunch(8); Dinner(12)
Internet Order Processing: Yes
Total Units: 17
Trade Names: Cluck-U-Chicken (17)
Units Franchised To: 17
Preferred Square Footage: 800; 1,600
Preferred Location Types: Freestanding; Strip Mall
Primary Menu: Chicken (17)
Areas of Operation: MD, NC, NJ, PA
Foreign Countries: LEBANON
Type of Foodservice: Quick Serve (17)
Foodservice Management Venues: Recreational
Catering Services: Yes
Primary Distributors: (Food) US Foods, SWEDESBORO, NJ

Key Personnel
J.P. HADDAD - CEO; President; VP Operations, Menu Development; Director Facility/Maintenance
ROULA ZOGHBY - VP Site Selection
JUSTIN HUERTAS - General Manager
BEATRICE MAGGIO - Director Purchasing

Blue Ridge Restaurant Group LLC
10500 Little Patuxent Pkwy Ste 770
Columbia, MD 21044-3544

Telephone: (410) 997-3600
Fax Number: (301) 596-5471
Internet Homepage: blueridgerestaurantgroup.com; ccgrill.com
Type of Business: Chain Restaurant Operator
Year Founded: 1999
Total Sales: $8,474,000 (e)
Alcohol Sales: 5%
Average Check: Dinner(26)
Total Units: 6
Trade Names: Copper Canyon Grill (4); Stanford Grill (1); Stanford Kitchen (1)
Company-Owned Units: 6
Preferred Location Types: Freestanding; Strip Mall
Alcohol Served: Wine
Primary Menu: American (6)
Projected Openings: 1
Areas of Operation: FL, MD
Type of Foodservice: Casual Dining (6)

Key Personnel
ZANIA PATTERSON - VP Marketing, Sales
ERICK COOPER - Director Operations

Brdancat Enterprises
9017 Mendenhall Ct Ste B
Columbia, MD 21045-4732

Telephone: (410) 884-5351
Fax Number: (410) 884-5450
Type of Business: Chain Restaurant Operator
Year Founded: 1999
Total Sales: $70,250,000 (e)
Number of Employees: 430
Average Check: Breakfast(8); Lunch(10); Dinner(12)
Total Units: 15
Trade Names: McDonald's (15)
Units Franchised From: 15
Preferred Square Footage: 2,400; 3,000
Preferred Location Types: Discount Dept. Stores; Freestanding
Primary Menu: Hamburger (15)
Areas of Operation: MD
Type of Foodservice: Quick Serve (15)
Franchise Affiliation: McDonald's Corporation, CHICAGO, IL
Primary Distributors: (Full Line) The Martin-Brower Co. LLC, ROSEMONT, IL

Key Personnel
DANITRA BELL - Partner; Director Operations, Human Resources
DANNY BELL - Partner; General Buyer
GLORIA OTEY - Manager Customer Service

Kings Contrivance
10150 Shaker Dr
Columbia, MD 21046-1304

Telephone: (410) 995-0500
Fax Number: (410) 730-8063
Internet Homepage: miltoninn.com; thekingscontrivance.com
Company Email: info@thekingscontrivance.com
Type of Business: Chain Restaurant Operator
Year Founded: 1974
Total Sales: $12,302,000 (e)
Alcohol Sales: 25%
Number of Employees: 480
Average Check: Lunch(30); Dinner(58)
Total Units: 2
Trade Names: King's Contrivance Restaurant (1); Milton Inn (1)
Company-Owned Units: 2
Preferred Square Footage: 6,000
Preferred Location Types: Freestanding
Alcohol Served: Beer, Wine, Liquor
Primary Menu: American (2)
Areas of Operation: MD
Type of Foodservice: Fine Dining (2)
Catering Services: Yes
Primary Distributors: (Full Line) SYSCO Food Services of Baltimore, JESSUP, MD

Key Personnel
STUART TEPER - President; Partner; CFO; Treasurer; Executive Chef; General Buyer
BRIAN BOSTON - Partner; Executive Chef
RICHARD ACKMAN - VP; General Buyer

Maiwand Kabob
5467 Harpers Farm Road
Columbia, MD 21044

Telephone: (410) 992-7754
Internet Homepage: maiwandkabob.com/index.html
Type of Business: Chain Restaurant Operator
Year Founded: 1999
Total Sales: $5,433,000 (e)
Total Units: 6
Trade Names: Maiwand Kabob (6)
Company-Owned Units: 6
Primary Menu: Greek/Mediterranean (6)
Areas of Operation: MD
Type of Foodservice: Fast Casual (6)

Key Personnel
RUKHSHANA RAFIQ - Founder; Owner

Milabon, LLC
10300 Little Patuxent Pkwy
Columbia, MD 21044-3341

Telephone: (410) 202-2611
Type of Business: Chain Restaurant Operator
Total Sales: $766,000 (e)
Total Units: 2
Trade Names: Cinnabon (2)
Units Franchised From: 2
Primary Menu: Snacks (2)
Areas of Operation: MD
Type of Foodservice: Quick Serve (2)
Franchise Affiliation: Cinnabon Inc., ATLANTA, GA

Key Personnel
DHARMESH SHAH - Owner; General Buyer

Pizza Hut of Maryland Inc.
7070 Oakland Mills Rd
Columbia, MD 21046-1692

Telephone: (410) 720-6336

Fax Number: (410) 720-5740
Internet Homepage: pizzahutpizza.com
Company Email: feedback@pizzahutofmd.com
Type of Business: Chain Restaurant Operator
Year Founded: 1970
Total Sales: $56,040,000 (e)
Alcohol Sales: 3%
Number of Employees: 1,370
Average Check: Lunch(8); Dinner(16)
Internet Order Processing: Yes
Total Units: 42
Trade Names: Pizza Hut (42)
Units Franchised From: 42
Preferred Square Footage: 4,000
Preferred Location Types: Freestanding; Strip Mall
Alcohol Served: Beer, Wine
Primary Menu: Pizza (42)
Areas of Operation: MD
Type of Foodservice: Casual Dining (27); Quick Serve (15)
Franchise Affiliation: Pizza Hut Inc., PLANO, TX
Primary Distributors: (Full Line) McLane/Manassas, MANASSAS, VA

Key Personnel
JOHN F. SCHULZE - VP Purchasing, Facility/Maintenance, Loss Prevention, Risk Management, Marketing, Real Estate, Design, Store Fixtures, Store Planning, Food Safety
ROSS HUEBNER - Controller; Director Finance
TRICIA MORRISON - Director Information Systems

The Greene Turtle Franchising Corporation
6990 Columbia Gateway Dr Ste 120
Columbia, MD 21046-2989

Telephone: (443) 661-4298
Fax Number: (443) 661-4395
Internet Homepage: thegreeneturtle.com
Company Email: franchicing@thegreenturtle.com
Type of Business: Chain Restaurant Operator
Year Founded: 1976
Systemwide Sales: $15,327,000 (e)
Total Sales: $9,082,000 (e)
Alcohol Sales: 35%
Number of Employees: 400
Average Check: Lunch(10); Dinner(18)
Internet Order Processing: Yes
Total Units: 37
Trade Names: the Greene Turtle (44)
Company-Owned Units: 14
Units Franchised To: 30
Preferred Square Footage: 5,500; 6,000; 7,400
Preferred Location Types: Airports; Downtown; Freestanding; Strip Mall
Alcohol Served: Beer, Wine, Liquor
Primary Menu: American (44)
Areas of Operation: DE, MD, NJ, NY, PA, VA, WV
Type of Foodservice: Casual Dining (44)
Primary Distributors: (Full Line) Sysco Eastern Maryland Inc., POCOMOKE CITY, MD
Parent Company: Stone-Goff Partners, NEW YORK, NY
Notes: Stone-Goff Partner, a New York private equity firm, has acquired a majority stake the Greene Turtle Sports Bar & Grille.

Key Personnel
GEOVANNIE CONCEPCION - CEO; President
TOM FINN - VP Franchise Development

Domino's Franchisee
10518 Greensboro Rd
Denton, MD 21629-3307

Telephone: (410) 479-5600
Type of Business: Chain Restaurant Operator
Total Sales: $7,938,000 (e)
Total Units: 4
Trade Names: Domino's (4)
Units Franchised From: 4
Primary Menu: Pizza (4)
Areas of Operation: MD
Type of Foodservice: Quick Serve (4)
Franchise Affiliation: Domino's Pizza Inc, ANN ARBOR, MI

Key Personnel
ANDREW KENT - Partner; General Buyer
AMBER BEAR - Partner; General Buyer

Domino's Franchisee
10367 Southern Maryland Blvd
Dunkirk, MD 20754-9500

Telephone: (410) 286-0700
Type of Business: Chain Restaurant Operator
Total Sales: $14,019,000 (e)
Total Units: 7
Trade Names: Domino's (7)
Units Franchised From: 7
Primary Menu: Pizza (7)
Areas of Operation: MD
Type of Foodservice: Quick Serve (7)
Franchise Affiliation: Domino's Pizza Inc, ANN ARBOR, MI

Key Personnel
MALCOLM CARTER - Owner; General Buyer

Adam's Taphouse and Grille
169 Mayo Rd
Edgewater, MD 21037-1804

Telephone: (410) 956-2995
Fax Number: (410) 956-2970
Internet Homepage: adamsribs.com
Company Email: info@adamsribs.com
Type of Business: Chain Restaurant Operator
Year Founded: 1981
Total Sales: $9,508,000 (e)
Alcohol Sales: 12%
Number of Employees: 240
Average Check: Lunch(14); Dinner(14)
Total Units: 6
Trade Names: Adam's Ribs East (1); Adam's Ribs North (1); Adam's The Place For Ribs (4)
Company-Owned Units: 6
Preferred Square Footage: 5,500; 6,000
Preferred Location Types: Freestanding; Strip Mall
Alcohol Served: Beer, Wine, Liquor
Primary Menu: Bar-B-Q (6)
Projected Openings: 1
Areas of Operation: MD
Type of Foodservice: Casual Dining (6)
Catering Services: Yes
Primary Distributors: (Full Line) US Foods Philadelphia Metro, BRIDGEPORT, NJ

Key Personnel
BILL BAGDASIAN - President; Partner; Director Finance, Purchasing, Facility/Maintenance, Supply Chain, Real Estate, Design, Franchise Development
JOE LEFAVOR - Partner; General Buyer

Cuzino's Pizza
801 E Pulaski Hwy Ste 15
Elkton, MD 21921-6665

Telephone: (410) 392-3030
Fax Number: (410) 392-4985
Internet Homepage: ninospizza.net
Company Email: ninospizza@comcast.net
Type of Business: Chain Restaurant Operator
Year Founded: 1980
Total Sales: $2,861,000 (e)
Alcohol Sales: 10%
Number of Employees: 140
Average Check: Lunch(10); Dinner(18)
Internet Order Processing: Yes
Internet Sales: 1.00%
Total Units: 9
Trade Names: Nino's Pizza (9)
Company-Owned Units: 8
Preferred Square Footage: 5,500; 6,000
Preferred Location Types: Freestanding; Strip Mall
Alcohol Served: Beer, Wine, Liquor
Primary Menu: Pizza (9)
Areas of Operation: DE, MD
Type of Foodservice: Casual Dining (9)
Foodservice Management Venues: Schools
Catering Services: Yes
Primary Distributors: (Food) US Foods, SWEDESBORO, NJ

Key Personnel
NICK DIOMEDE - Owner; General Manager; Executive Chef; Director Finance, Operations, Information Systems, Real Estate, Design, Human Resources; General Buyer
DOMINIC DIOMEDE - General Manager; Director Catering; General Buyer

Domino's Franchisee
1 Wormans Mill Ct Ste 2
Frederick, MD 21701-3022

Telephone: (301) 696-1600
Type of Business: Chain Restaurant Operator
Total Sales: $3,985,000 (e)
Total Units: 2
Trade Names: Domino's (2)
Units Franchised From: 2
Primary Menu: Pizza (2)
Areas of Operation: MD
Type of Foodservice: Quick Serve (2)
Franchise Affiliation: Domino's Pizza Inc, ANN ARBOR, MI

Key Personnel
BENNET Z. KAUFMAN - Owner; General Buyer

Plamondon Companies Inc.
4991 New Design Rd Ste 109
Frederick, MD 21703-7342

Telephone: (301) 695-5051
Fax Number: (301) 695-5066
Internet Homepage: royrogersrestaurants.com
Company Email: katrinaw@plamondon-cos.com
Type of Business: Chain Restaurant Operator
Year Founded: 1980
Systemwide Sales: $115,768,000 (e)
Total Sales: $28,150,000 (e)
Number of Employees: 377
Average Check: Breakfast(14); Lunch(16); Dinner(16)
Total Units: 48
Trade Names: Roy Rogers Restaurant (48)
Company-Owned Units: 24
Units Franchised To: 24
Preferred Square Footage: 2,500
Preferred Location Types: Freestanding
Primary Menu: American (48)
Areas of Operation: MD, NJ, NY, PA, VA, WV
Type of Foodservice: Quick Serve (48)
Primary Distributors: (Food) McLane/Rocky Mount, ROCKY MOUNT, NC

Key Personnel
PETER PLAMONDON SR - Chairman
PETER PLAMONDON JR - Co-President; Partner
ED PRENSKY - CFO
JEREMY BISER - Exec VP
MIKE HENNINGSEN - Exec VP Operations
RICK JENKINS - Senior Director Marketing
AL JONES - Director Operations
GARY FENNELL - Director Facility/Maintenance
JOSEPH BRIGLIA - Director Real Estate Development, Franchise Development

Roy Rogers Restaurants
4991 New Design Rd Suite 109
Frederick, MD 21703

Telephone: (130) 169-55051
Fax Number: (410) 859-8665
Internet Homepage: royrogersrestaurants.com
Type of Business: Chain Restaurant Operator
Year Founded: 1968
Total Sales: $60,890,000 (e)
Total Units: 46
Trade Names: Roy Rogers (46)
Company-Owned Units: 22
Units Franchised To: 24
Primary Menu: American (46)
Areas of Operation: DC, MD, VA
Type of Foodservice: Quick Serve (46)
Parent Company: Imasco Ltd., MONTREAL, QC CANADA
Headquarters: Imasco Ltd., MONTREAL, QC CANADA

Key Personnel
AL JONES - Director Operations
JOE BRIGLIA - Director Real Estate, Franchise Development
JOHN GRIFFIN - Manager Customer Care

The Jeffrey Corp.
5295 Westview Dr Suite 250
Frederick, MD 21703

Telephone: (301) 663-3511
Fax Number: (301) 663-5205
Internet Homepage: jeffreycorp.net
Type of Business: Chain Restaurant Operator
Total Sales: $29,100,000 (e)
Number of Employees: 286
Total Units: 13
Trade Names: Burger King (13)
Units Franchised From: 13
Preferred Square Footage: 2,500
Primary Menu: Hamburger (13)
Areas of Operation: MD, PA
Type of Foodservice: Quick Serve (13)
Franchise Affiliation: Burger King Worldwide Inc., MIAMI, FL

Key Personnel
GARY GIANGRANDE - President; General Buyer
CRAIG GIANGRANDE - VP

Auntie Anne's Franchise
701 Russell Ave Ste E155
Gaithersburg, MD 20877-6602

Telephone: (301) 987-0345
Type of Business: Chain Restaurant Operator
Total Sales: $3,650,000 (e)
Total Units: 5
Trade Names: Auntie Anne's Hand-Rolled Soft Pretzels (5)
Units Franchised From: 5
Primary Menu: Snacks (5)
Areas of Operation: MD
Type of Foodservice: Quick Serve (5)
Franchise Affiliation: Auntie Anne's Inc., LANCASTER, PA

Key Personnel
ALYSSA TANNER - Owner; General Buyer

Coal Fire
116 Main St
Gaithersburg, MD 20878-5573

Telephone: (301) 519-2625
Internet Homepage: coalfireonline.com
Type of Business: Chain Restaurant Operator
Year Founded: 2009
Average Check: Lunch(20); Dinner(30)
Total Units: 7
Trade Names: Coal Fire (7)
Company-Owned Units: 7
Preferred Location Types: Strip Mall
Alcohol Served: Beer, Wine, Liquor
Primary Menu: Pizza (7)
Projected Openings: 1
Areas of Operation: MD, VA
Type of Foodservice: Casual Dining (7)
Catering Services: Yes

Key Personnel
DENNIS SHAROKY - Founder; President
MARK LUCAS - Chief Information Security Officer; VP
ADAM SHNIDER - VP
MARK CARNEY - VP Security
CHRISTOPHER BEIRO - VP
MICHAEL EISENBERG - VP Strategy, Risk Management
RON KONRATH - Director Infrastructure
MICAH RAMSEY - Director Business Development
STEVEN KRIZ - Director Business Development
MICHAEL MCKENNA - Director Business Development
RJ WIDMAN - Director Systems
TIMOTHY P. O'BRIEN - Director Infrastructure
KARL STEINKAMP - Director Midwest Region; Transformation
BAIG NAJIB - Senior Manager Engineering; Manager Engineering

DIANA PITT - Manager Operations
ASIM BHATTI - Product Manager

Glory Days Inc.
9426 Stewartown Rd Ste 2E
Gaithersburg, MD 20879-1601

Telephone: (703) 778-5200
Fax Number: (301) 330-0993
Internet Homepage: glorydaysgrill.com
Company Email: info@glorydaysgrill.com
Type of Business: Chain Restaurant Operator
Year Founded: 1996
Systemwide Sales: $98,246,000 (e)
Total Sales: $107,440,000 (e)
Alcohol Sales: 25%
Number of Employees: 1,375
Average Check: Lunch(18); Dinner(28)
Internet Order Processing: Yes
Internet Sales: 1.00%
Total Units: 42
Trade Names: Glory Days Grill (42)
Company-Owned Units: 26
Units Franchised To: 16
Preferred Square Footage: 5,000; 6,500
Preferred Location Types: Community Mall; Freestanding; Strip Mall
Alcohol Served: Beer, Wine, Liquor
Primary Menu: American (42)
Projected Openings: 8
Areas of Operation: MD, VA, WV
Type of Foodservice: Casual Dining (42)
Catering Services: Yes
Primary Distributors: (Food) US Foods, MANASSAS, VA

Key Personnel
RICHARD DANKER - Partner; Director Design
BOB GARNER - Partner
JEFF NEWMAN - Partner; Director Real Estate, Design, Franchising
TONY COCHONES - Exec VP Culinary Operations
GARY COHEN - Exec VP
BEN ELDRIDGE - VP Operations
MICHELLE MCCURDY - Director Sales, Business Development
CARLY DUNN - Director Training
JIM KLAVIS - Manager Franchise Development

Sodexo Inc.
9801 Washingtonian Blvd Fl 1
Gaithersburg, MD 20878-5355

Telephone: (301) 987-4000
Fax Number: (301) 987-4438
Internet Homepage: sodexo.com; sodexoca.com; sodexousa.com
Company Email: sdxcommunications@sodexousa.com
Type of Business: Foodservice Management Operator
Year Founded: 1998
Publicly Held: Yes
Total Sales: $39,459,007,000 (e)
Number of Employees: 419,000
Number of Locations Served: 10,000
Total Foodservice Mgmt Accounts: 6,000
Trade Names: A&W All American Food; AFC Sushi; Blimpies; Burger King; Carvel; Chick-Fil-A; Cinnabon; Currito; Damon's Grill; Einstein Bros. Bagels; Freshens Smoothie Company; Jamba Juice; Jazzman's Cafe; KFC; Mein Bowl; Panda Express; Pandini's; Pizza Hut; Pollo Campero; Popeyes Chicken &Biscuits; Qdoba Mexican Grill; Quiznos; Salsa Rico; Sandella's; Sbarro; SodexoMAGIC; Starbucks Coffee; Subconnection; Sunset Strips; Surf City Squeeze; Taco Bell; Wendy's Old Fashioned Hamburgers; Zyng Asian Grill
Projected Openings: 100
Areas of Operation: AK, AL, AR, AZ, CA, CO, CT, DC, DE, FL, GA, GU, HI, IA, ID, IL, IN, KS, KY, LA, MA, MD, ME, MI, MN, MO, MS, MT, NC, ND, NE, NH, NJ, NM, NV, NY, OH, OK, OR, PA, PR, RI, SC, SD, TN, TX, UT, VA, VI, VT, WA, WI, WV, WY, FC, AB, BC, MB, NB, NL, NS, NT, NU, ON, PE, QC, SK, YT
Type of Foodservice: Cafeteria; Quick Serve
Foodservice Management Venues: Business & Industry; College & University; Health Care; Military Feeding; Other; Schools
Franchise Affiliation: A&W Restaurants Inc., LEXINGTON, KY; Blimpie International Inc., SCOTTSDALE, AZ; Burger King Worldwide Inc., MIAMI, FL; Carvel Corporation, ATLANTA, GA; Chick-fil-A Inc., ATLANTA, GA; Cinnabon Inc., ATLANTA, GA; Coffee & Bagel Brands, LAKEWOOD, CO; Cold Stone Creamery Inc., SCOTTSDALE, AZ; Damon's of North America LLC, HAZLETON, PA; Freshens Quality Brands, ATLANTA, GA; Jamba Inc., FRISCO, TX; Kahala Brands, SCOTTSDALE, AZ; KFC Corporation, LOUISVILLE, KY; McDonald's Corporation, CHICAGO, IL; MTY Food Group Inc., SAINT-LAURENT, QC; Panda Restaurant Group Inc., ROSEMEAD, CA; Pizza Hut Inc., PLANO, TX; Qdoba Mexican Eats, SAN DIEGO, CA; Sandella's LLC, WEST REDDING, CT; Sbarro Holdings LLC, COLUMBUS, OH; Starbucks Corporation, SEATTLE, WA; Taco Bell Corp., IRVINE, CA; The Quiznos Master LLC, DENVER, CO
Primary Distributors: (Full Line) SYSCO Food Services of Jackson, JACKSON, MS
Parent Company: Sodexo, MONTIGNY-LE-BRETONNEUX, FRA
Divisional Offices: Sodexo, WALTHAM, MA; Sodexo (Campus Services Division), ALTAMONTE SPRINGS, FL; Sodexo (Health Care Services Division), WEATOGUE, CT
Regional Offices: Sodexo, ALLENTOWN, PA; Sodexo Dining Service, ALLENTOWN, PA
Notes: Total sales include North American food & management services operations only. The company derives approximately 15% of its revenue from facility maintenance & other operations.

Key Personnel
BRETT LADD - CEO Government Affairs
STEPHEN DUNMORE - President Division
SIAN HERBERT-JONES - CFO
ELISABETH CARPENTIER - Chief Human Resources Officer
NASIM SALIMI - Senior VP Operations
DREW NANNIS - Director Marketing

Zolman Systems, Inc.
7415 Ritchie Hwy
Gen Burnie, MD 21061

Telephone: (410) 760-6230
Type of Business: Chain Restaurant Operator
Total Sales: $28,100,000 (e)
Total Units: 6
Trade Names: McDonald's (6)
Units Franchised From: 6
Preferred Location Types: Freestanding
Primary Menu: Hamburger (6)
Areas of Operation: MD
Type of Foodservice: Quick Serve (6)
Franchise Affiliation: McDonald's Corporation, CHICAGO, IL

Key Personnel
KEITH ZOLMAN - Partner
NANCY ZOLMAN - Partner; VP

Malament Enterprises Inc
13050 Middlebrook Rd
Germantown, MD 20874-2617

Telephone: (301) 540-8342
Company Email: dominosgt@hotmail.com
Type of Business: Chain Restaurant Operator
Total Sales: $10,222,000 (e)
Total Units: 5
Trade Names: Domino's (5)
Units Franchised From: 5
Primary Menu: Pizza (5)
Areas of Operation: MD
Type of Foodservice: Quick Serve (5)
Franchise Affiliation: Domino's Pizza Inc, ANN ARBOR, MI

Key Personnel
CHARLIE MALAMENT - President; General Buyer

Mission BBQ
7750 Governor Ritchie Hwy
Glen Burnie, MD 21060

Telephone: (855) 552-7300
Internet Homepage: mission-bbq.com
Type of Business: Chain Restaurant Operator
Year Founded: 2011
Total Units: 91
Trade Names: Mission BBQ (65)
Company-Owned Units: 65
Primary Menu: Bar-B-Q (65)
Projected Openings: 5
Areas of Operation: DE, FL, IL, IN, KY, MD, NC, NJ, OH, PA, SC, TN, VA
Type of Foodservice: Cafeteria (65)

Key Personnel
BILL KRAUS - Co-Founder; Partner
STEPHEN NEWTON - Co-Founder; Partner; General Buyer
JERRY COOLEY - Area Director Operations
RANDY RINIKER - VP Operations, Catering
PAUL SATTLER - VP Operations
GREG LYNN - Director Operations
DOUG BRUSER - Regional Director Operations

Taco Bill of Baltimore, Inc.
1414 Crain Hwy N Ste 1B
Glen Burnie, MD 21061-7002

Telephone: (530) 885-2455
Fax Number: (410) 787-1966
Type of Business: Chain Restaurant Operator
Total Sales: $59,210,000 (e)
Total Units: 22
Trade Names: Taco Bell (22)
Units Franchised From: 22
Primary Menu: Taco (22)
Areas of Operation: MD
Type of Foodservice: Quick Serve (22)
Franchise Affiliation: Taco Bell Corp., IRVINE, CA

Key Personnel
CHRISTOPHER WALSH - President; General Buyer

Chesapeake Hospitality
6404 Ivy Ln Ste 510
Greenbelt, MD 20770-1405

Telephone: (301) 474-3307
Fax Number: (301) 474-0807
Internet Homepage: Chesapeakehospitality.com
Company Email: inquiry@chesapeakehospitality.com
Type of Business: Foodservice Operations - Hotel/Motels
Year Founded: 1985
Total Sales: $213,110,000 (e)
Alcohol Sales: 20%
Number of Employees: 1,200
Total Units: 24
Restaurants in Hotels: 41
Trade Names: Crowne Plaza (5); Days Inn (1); Doubletree by Hilton (2); Fenwick Inn (1); Hampton Inn (1); Hilton (3); Holiday Inn (5); Homewood Suites (1); Indigo Hotel (1); Riverview Suites (1); Shell Island Resort (1); Sheraton (1); The Georgian Terrace Hotel (1)
Company-Owned Units: 38
Units Franchised From: 3
Alcohol Served: Beer, Wine, Liquor
Areas of Operation: DE, FL, GA, IN, MD, NC, OK, PA, TX, VA, WI
Franchise Affiliation: Ruth's Hospitality Group Inc., WINTER PARK, FL
Primary Distributors: (Food) SYSCO Food Services of Baltimore, JESSUP, MD; (Specialty Foods) Spectrum Foods, LANDOVER, MD
Notes: The company derives approximately 80% of its revenue from hotel operations.

Key Personnel
KIM SIMS - Chairman
W. CHRIS GREEN - CEO; President
LOUIS SCHAAB - CFO
STEVE SMITH - Exec VP; Principal
CHRIS SIMS - Exec VP; Principal
CLIFFORD FERRARA - Exec VP Sales
LISA CARLSON - Senior VP Operations
BRENDA MCGREGOR - VP Human Resources
SARAH TURNER - Supervisor Operations, Development

Coakley & Williams Hotel Management Co.
6404 Ivy Ln Ste 720
Greenbelt, MD 20770-1425

Telephone: (301) 474-6200
Fax Number: (301) 614-8836
Internet Homepage: cwhotels.com
Company Email: mail@cwhotels.com
Type of Business: Foodservice Operations - Hotel/Motels
Year Founded: 1961
Total Sales: $117,740,000 (e)
Alcohol Sales: 10%
Number of Employees: 1,700
Total Units: 31
Restaurants in Hotels: 30
Trade Names: Best Western (1); Candlewood Suites (2); Country Inn & Suites (1); Days Inn (4); Daytona Beach Resort (1); Double Tree Baltimore (1); Hampton Inn (3); Hilton (3); Historic Kent Manor Inn (1); Holiday Inn (9); Houlihans Restaurants (1); LaQuinta Inn (1); Quality Inn (1); Royal Mansions Resort (1); The Red Coach Inn (1)
Company-Owned Units: 31
Alcohol Served: Beer, Wine, Liquor
Areas of Operation: CA, CT, DC, DE, FL, KY, MA, MD, MO, NC, NJ, NY, PA, TN, UT, VA, VT
Type of Foodservice: Casual Dining (30)
Primary Distributors: (Food) SYSCO Food Services of Baltimore, JESSUP, MD
Notes: The company derives approximately 80% of its revenue from hotel operations.

Key Personnel
MARK WILLIAMS - CEO
GARY S. WILLIAMS - President
MARTIN FLAHERTY - Director Facility/Maintenance
JUNE TAYLOR-WATTS - Director Human Resources

Stanley Neal
13 N Edgewood Dr
Hagerstown, MD 21740-6501

Telephone: (301) 766-4557
Company Email: L.bennett.mcd@myactv.net
Type of Business: Chain Restaurant Operator
Total Sales: $102,410,000 (e)
Total Units: 22
Trade Names: McDonald's (22)
Units Franchised From: 22
Primary Menu: Hamburger (22)
Projected Remodelings: 3
Areas of Operation: MD, WV
Type of Foodservice: Quick Serve (22)
Franchise Affiliation: McDonald's Corporation, CHICAGO, IL

Key Personnel
STANLEY R. NEAL - President; General Buyer

The Golden M Company
1101 Opal Ct Ste 315
Hagerstown, MD 21740-5943

Telephone: (301) 766-7100
Type of Business: Chain Restaurant Operator
Total Sales: $19,982,000 (e)
Total Units: 4
Trade Names: McDonald's (4)
Units Franchised From: 4
Preferred Location Types: Freestanding
Primary Menu: Hamburger (4)
Areas of Operation: MD
Type of Foodservice: Quick Serve (4)
Franchise Affiliation: McDonald's Corporation, CHICAGO, IL

Key Personnel
MARK LEVINE - President; General Buyer
MICHELLE WINTERMOYER - General Manager

JEFF SPRING - Director Operations

Western Maryland Fast Foods
11949 Robinwood Dr
Hagerstown, MD 21742-4455

Telephone: (301) 790-7474
Fax Number: (301) 790-7499
Type of Business: Chain Restaurant Operator
Year Founded: 1995
Total Sales: $29,010,000 (e)
Number of Employees: 190
Average Check: Breakfast(6); Lunch(8); Dinner(10)
Total Units: 13
Trade Names: Burger King (13)
Units Franchised From: 13
Preferred Square Footage: 2,500; 4,000
Preferred Location Types: Freestanding
Primary Menu: Hamburger (13)
Areas of Operation: MD, PA, WV
Type of Foodservice: Quick Serve (13)
Franchise Affiliation: Burger King Worldwide Inc., MIAMI, FL
Primary Distributors: (Equipment) Franke Foodservice Systems, SMYRNA, TN; (Food) Maines Paper & Food Service Maryland, SAVAGE, MD

Key Personnel
HOWARD BOWEN - Owner; Director Facility/Maintenance, Real Estate, Design
MIKE BROCKWAY - Controller
ROSE WOOD - General Manager

Moby Dick House of Kabob
3329 75th Ave
Hyattsville, MD 20785-1509

Telephone: (202) 544-1500
Fax Number: (202) 544-1558
Internet Homepage: mobyskabob.com
Company Email: mobys@mobyskabob.com
Type of Business: Chain Restaurant Operator
Systemwide Sales: $31,605,000 (e)
Total Sales: $20,892,000 (e)
Number of Employees: 448
Average Check: Lunch(12); Dinner(18)
Internet Order Processing: Yes
Total Units: 23
Trade Names: Moby Dick's House of Kabobs (23)
Company-Owned Units: 15
Units Franchised To: 8
Preferred Location Types: Freestanding; Strip Mall
Primary Menu: Middle Eastern (23)
Projected Openings: 1
Areas of Operation: DC, MD, VA

Type of Foodservice: Fast Casual (23)

Key Personnel
SARAH KIAN - Area Director
NED DARYOUSH - VP
FARHAD KAMRANI - Manager Catering

Farmers Restaurant Group
10605 Concord St Ste 201
Kensington, MD 20895-2527

Telephone: (301) 340-8783
Fax Number: (301) 340-6133
Internet Homepage: farmersrestaurantgroup.com; wearefoundingfarmers.com
Type of Business: Chain Restaurant Operator
Systemwide Sales: $93,234,000 (e)
Total Sales: $5,568,000 (e)
Average Check: Dinner(38)
Internet Order Processing: Yes
Total Units: 8
Trade Names: Farmers & Distillers (1); Farmers Fishers Bakers (1); First Bake Cafe & Creamery (1); Founding Farmers (5)
Company-Owned Units: 8
Alcohol Served: Beer, Wine, Liquor
Primary Menu: American (6); Sandwiches/Deli (1); Seafood (1)
Areas of Operation: DC, MD, PA, VA
Type of Foodservice: Casual Dining (8)
Catering Services: Yes

Key Personnel
DAN SIMONS - Partner; General Buyer
JOSEPH GOETZE - Partner; Senior VP; Corporate Chef
MICHAEL VUCUREVICH - Partner
NATHAN FEGELY - CFO
JILLIAN HELTZEL - VP Human Resources
HILLARY MIKO - Director Operations, Event Planning, Catering
DAWN VILENO - Director Operations

Rashid CSC Inc.
13600 Baltimore Ave Ste 304
Laurel, MD 20707-9496

Telephone: (301) 776-6770
Type of Business: Chain Restaurant Operator
Total Sales: $1,222,000 (e)
Total Units: 2
Trade Names: Cold Stone Creamery (2)
Units Franchised From: 2
Primary Menu: Snacks (2)
Areas of Operation: MD
Type of Foodservice: Quick Serve (2)
Franchise Affiliation: Kahala Brands, SCOTTSDALE, AZ

Key Personnel
MOHAMMAD RASHID - Owner

Wings To Go Inc.
8305 Cherry Ln
Laurel, MD 20707-4830

Telephone: (410) 846-5598
Fax Number: (410) 846-5947
Internet Homepage: wingstogo.com
Company Email: wingsinfo@wingstogo.com
Type of Business: Chain Restaurant Operator
Year Founded: 1985
Systemwide Sales: $46,601,000 (e)
Total Sales: $1,708,000 (e)
Alcohol Sales: 3%
Number of Employees: 9
Average Check: Lunch(14); Dinner(14)
Internet Order Processing: Yes
Total Units: 34
Trade Names: Wings To Go (34)
Units Franchised To: 34
Preferred Square Footage: 1,600
Preferred Location Types: Freestanding; Strip Mall
Alcohol Served: Beer
Primary Menu: Chicken (34)
Projected Openings: 10
Areas of Operation: AL, AR, DC, DE, MD, MS, NC, NJ, OH, OK, PA, RI, TX, VA
Type of Foodservice: Casual Dining (64)
Catering Services: Yes
Primary Distributors: (Full Line) US Foods, SWEDESBORO, NJ

Key Personnel
JOHN MARTINO - Chairman; President
JOHN BRINTON - CIO; VP Operations; Director Finance, Operations, Purchasing, Information Systems, Information Technology, Risk Management, Marketing, Design, Human Resources, Franchising, Menu Development, Food Safety, Food and Beverage; Buyer Foodservice Equip/Supplies

Domino's Inc.
785 Elkridge Landing Rd Ste 120
Linthicum Heights, MD 21090-2956

Telephone: (410) 859-3030
Fax Number: (410) 850-4436
Listing Type: Regional Office
Type of Business: Chain Restaurant Operator
Total Units: 50
Areas of Operation: MD, VA
Parent Company: Domino's Pizza Inc, ANN ARBOR, MI

Key Personnel
MICHAEL GRICE - CIO
ROSS PATRICK BEHRMAN - Senior VP

Operations; VP Operations
DEBBIE SWEENEY - VP Franchise Development
MICHAEL HOLSER - VP Human Resources, Talent
MIKE DAVIS - VP Technology, International
ROB CECERE - Director Operations
ESTEBAN HERNANDEZ - Director Operations
DUSTIN OPIELA - Director Finance
JOHN PREVOST - Director Supply Chain
RYON RESNER - Director Supply Chain
SHANNON YUEN - Director
CHRIS JAQUAY-WILLIAMS - Director Information Technology; Manager Supply Chain
MIKE JOHNS - Director Product Development; Manager Software
KRISTEN FINNERTY - Director Marketing, Franchising
GREG GAYLOR - Senior Manager Information/Data Security, Security
JOSE AYVAZIAN - Manager Training
LARRY HOOKER - Manager Information Technology

Mar-Chek, Inc.
6895 Baltimore Annapolis Blvd
Linthicum Heights, MD 21090-1601

Telephone: (410) 787-1175
Fax Number: (410) 768-4494
Type of Business: Chain Restaurant Operator
Total Sales: $12,100,000 (e)
Total Units: 8
Trade Names: Checkers (8)
Units Franchised From: 8
Preferred Location Types: Freestanding
Primary Menu: Hamburger (8)
Areas of Operation: MD, VA
Type of Foodservice: Quick Serve (8)
Franchise Affiliation: Checkers Drive-In Restaurants Inc., TAMPA, FL

Key Personnel
KEITH A. MARTIN - Owner; General Buyer

Bill Bateman's
63 E Padonia Rd
Lutherville, MD 21093-2306

Mailing Address: PO Box 98, Perry Hall, MD, 21128
Telephone: (410) 667-0650
Fax Number: (410) 667-0660
Internet Homepage: billbateman.com
Type of Business: Chain Restaurant Operator
Year Founded: 1986
Systemwide Sales: $27,479,000 (e)
Total Sales: $11,598,000 (e)
Alcohol Sales: 30%
Number of Employees: 216
Average Check: Lunch(14); Dinner(20)
Internet Order Processing: Yes
Total Units: 6
Trade Names: Bill Bateman's Bistro (4); Bill Bateman's Express (2)
Company-Owned Units: 3
Units Franchised To: 3
Preferred Square Footage: 7,000
Preferred Location Types: Downtown; Freestanding; Strip Mall
Alcohol Served: Beer, Wine, Liquor
Primary Menu: American (6)
Areas of Operation: MD, PA
Type of Foodservice: Casual Dining (4); Quick Serve (2)
Catering Services: Yes
Primary Distributors: (Full Line) SYSCO Food Services of Baltimore, JESSUP, MD

Key Personnel
BILL BATEMAN - CEO; Partner; General Manager; Director Supply Chain, Real Estate, Design, Menu Development; General Buyer
MARC LOUNDAS - President Franchising; Partner; General Manager; General Buyer
MARY WATTS - Director Finance, Facility/Maintenance, Information Systems, Human Resources

Sage Dining Services Inc.
1402 York Rd Ste 100
Lutherville, MD 21093-6018

Telephone: (410) 339-3950
Fax Number: (410) 339-3955
Internet Homepage: sagedining.com
Company Email: info@sagedining.com
Type of Business: Foodservice Management Operator
Year Founded: 1990
Number of Employees: 2,000
Total Foodservice Mgmt Accounts: 200
Areas of Operation: DC, FL, MD, ME, NJ, PA, TX, VA
Foodservice Management Venues: Business & Industry; College & University; Schools
Primary Distributors: (Full Line) SYSCO Food Services of Baltimore, JESSUP, MD

Key Personnel
PACO RODRIGUEZ - Co-Founder; President; General Buyer
TINA RODRIGUEZ - Co-Founder; CFO; General Counsel
MARCEL GALLO - COO
JON HESS - VP Operations, Southeast Region
LYLE KAN - VP Marketing, Sales
MARK BENFIELD - VP Operations, Midwest Region
THERESA DITOMO - General Manager Foodservice; Director
STEPHEN FREAS - Director Purchasing
KIMBERLY CHEN - Director Foodservice
LISA CHERTOK - Director Supply Chain
AUBREE CHORBA - Director Foodservice

Triangle Restaurant Management
108 Solomons Ridge Ct
Millersville, MD 21108-1265

Telephone: (443) 618-9044
Type of Business: Chain Restaurant Operator
Total Sales: $15,770,000 (e)
Number of Employees: 3
Total Units: 8
Trade Names: Five Guys Burgers and Fries (8)
Units Franchised From: 8
Preferred Square Footage: 3,000
Preferred Location Types: Freestanding; Strip Mall
Primary Menu: Hamburger (8)
Areas of Operation: MD
Type of Foodservice: Fast Casual (8)
Franchise Affiliation: Five Guys Holdings Inc., LORTON, VA

Key Personnel
MICHAEL MCLAUGHLIN - President; General Buyer

Sefmo, Inc.
18314 Contour Rd
Montgomery Village, MD 20877-2614

Telephone: (301) 990-3900
Type of Business: Chain Restaurant Operator
Total Sales: $3,429,000 (e)
Total Units: 6
Trade Names: Little Caesars Pizza (6)
Units Franchised From: 6
Primary Menu: Pizza (6)
Areas of Operation: MD
Type of Foodservice: Quick Serve (6)
Franchise Affiliation: Little Caesar Enterprises Inc., DETROIT, MI

Key Personnel
ELLIE DANESHKHAH - Partner; General Buyer
MORY GHOLAMI - Partner; General Buyer

Team Maryland Inc.
11717 Old National Pike Ste 18
New Market, MD 21774-6153

Telephone: (301) 865-1208
Type of Business: Chain Restaurant Operator
Total Sales: $38,321,000 (e)
Number of Employees: 394
Total Units: 19
Trade Names: Domino's (19)
Units Franchised From: 19

Preferred Square Footage: 1,000
Preferred Location Types: Strip Mall
Primary Menu: Pizza (19)
Areas of Operation: MD, PA
Type of Foodservice: Quick Serve (19)
Franchise Affiliation: Domino's Pizza Inc, ANN ARBOR, MI

Key Personnel
ED TREACY III - President; General Manager; General Buyer
DONNA BOWNE - Manager Branch

Bull on the Beach
12507 Sunset Ave Ste 8
Ocean City, MD 21842-9295

Telephone: (410) 213-2555
Fax Number: (410) 213-2594
Internet Homepage: craballeyoc.com; bullonthebeachoc.com
Company Email: info@bullonthebeachoc.com/
Type of Business: Chain Restaurant Operator
Year Founded: 1979
Total Sales: $4,732,000 (e)
Alcohol Sales: 25%
Number of Employees: 75
Average Check: Lunch(14); Dinner(20)
Internet Order Processing: Yes
Total Units: 3
Trade Names: Bull on the Beach (2); Crab Alley (1)
Company-Owned Units: 3
Preferred Square Footage: 10,000
Preferred Location Types: Freestanding
Alcohol Served: Beer, Wine, Liquor
Primary Menu: American (2); Seafood (1)
Areas of Operation: MD
Type of Foodservice: Casual Dining (3)
Primary Distributors: (Full Line) SYSCO Food Services of Virginia LLC, HARRISONBURG, VA

Key Personnel
PHIL HOUCK - President; CFO; Executive Chef; General Buyer
MARIE HOUCK - VP
MICHELLE KNOPP - General Manager; General Buyer
THERESE GOLDBERG - Office Manager

Dumser's Restaurants
501 S Philadelphia Ave
Ocean City, MD 21842-4218

Telephone: (410) 289-1192
Fax Number: (410) 250-0047
Internet Homepage: dumsersdairyland.com
Company Email: dumsersicecream@aol.com
Type of Business: Chain Restaurant Operator
Year Founded: 1939
Total Sales: $14,629,000 (e)
Number of Employees: 200
Average Check: Breakfast(10); Lunch(12); Dinner(14)
Total Units: 7
Trade Names: Dumser's Dairyland (5); Dumser's Restaurant (2)
Company-Owned Units: 7
Preferred Square Footage: 900; 2,000
Preferred Location Types: Freestanding
Primary Menu: American (2); Snacks (5)
Areas of Operation: MD
Type of Foodservice: Family Restaurant (2); Quick Serve (5)
Primary Distributors: (Full Line) SYSCO Corporation, HOUSTON, TX

Key Personnel
DON TIMMONS - President; General Manager; Executive Chef; Director Facility/Maintenance, Real Estate, Design, Menu Development
TOM COUTU - VP; Manager Operations, Purchasing, Loss Prevention, Risk Management, Supply Chain

Domino's Distribution Center
8271 Anderson Ct
Odenton, MD 21113-1681

Telephone: (410) 305-0535
Fax Number: (410) 305-5242
Internet Homepage: dominos.com
Listing Type: Distribution Center
Type of Business: Chain Restaurant Operator
Number of Employees: 65
Areas of Operation: DE, MD, NJ, PA, VA, WV
Parent Company: Domino's Pizza Inc, ANN ARBOR, MI

Key Personnel
RUSSELL GIBSON - General Manager

TGC Foods Inc.
11447 Cronhill Dr Ste K
Owings Mills, MD 21117-2286

Telephone: (410) 363-7701
Fax Number: (410) 363-7703
Internet Homepage: thegreatcookie.com
Company Email: info@thegreatcookie.com
Type of Business: Chain Restaurant Operator
Year Founded: 2008
Total Sales: $8,748,000 (e)
Number of Employees: 60
Average Check: Breakfast(6); Lunch(6); Dinner(6)
Internet Order Processing: Yes
Total Units: 8
Trade Names: The Great Cookie (8)
Company-Owned Units: 8
Preferred Location Types: Institution (college/hospital); Regional Mall
Primary Menu: Snacks (8)
Areas of Operation: MD
Type of Foodservice: Quick Serve (8)
Primary Distributors: (Full Line) US Foods Holding Corp., ROSEMONT, IL

Key Personnel
JASON FRUMAN - President; Director Finance; General Buyer

SRG Concepts
152 Waterfront St
Oxon Hill, MD 20745-1137

Telephone: (301) 567-6100
Internet Homepage: starrestaurantgroup.com
Company Email: stars@starrestaurantgroup.com
Type of Business: Chain Restaurant Operator
Total Units: 3
Trade Names: Chicken and Whiskey (1); The Walrus Oysters & Ale House (2)
Company-Owned Units: 3
Primary Menu: Chicken (1); Seafood (2)
Areas of Operation: DC, MD
Type of Foodservice: Casual Dining (2); Fast Casual (1)

Key Personnel
KRISTOPHER CARR - Partner Real Estate Development, Store Development
DESMOND REILLY - Partner Marketing, Branding
STU DAMON - Partner Finance, Human Resources

Don's Crabs Inc.
1764 E Joppa Rd
Parkville, MD 21234-3620

Telephone: (410) 661-1232
Fax Number: (410) 661-1952
Internet Homepage: donscrabsandseafood.com
Company Email: donscrabs@prodigy.net
Type of Business: Chain Restaurant Operator
Year Founded: 1973
Total Sales: $3,136,000 (e)
Number of Employees: 15
Average Check: Lunch(12); Dinner(12)
Total Units: 2
Trade Names: Don's Crabs (2)
Company-Owned Units: 2
Preferred Location Types: Freestanding
Primary Menu: Seafood (2)
Areas of Operation: MD
Type of Foodservice: Quick Serve (2)
Catering Services: Yes
Primary Distributors: (Full Line) PFG - Customized Distribution Maryland, ELKTON,

MD

Key Personnel
CHRIS HUBBARD - Partner; General Manager
JEFF HUBBARD - Partner; General Manager; Executive Chef; General Buyer

Big Steaks Management LLC
1777 Reisterstown Rd Lbby
Pikesville, MD 21208-1500

Telephone: (410) 653-2133
Fax Number: (410) 602-3152
Internet Homepage: serioussteaks.com
Company Email: info@serioussteaks.com
Type of Business: Chain Restaurant Operator
Year Founded: 2000
Total Sales: $36,160,000 (e)
Alcohol Sales: 20%
Number of Employees: 540
Average Check: Dinner(54)
Total Units: 9
Trade Names: Ruth's Chris Steak House (9)
Units Franchised From: 9
Preferred Square Footage: 8,000
Preferred Location Types: Freestanding
Alcohol Served: Beer, Wine, Liquor
Primary Menu: Steak (9)
Projected Openings: 1
Areas of Operation: MD, NC, NJ
Type of Foodservice: Fine Dining (9)
Franchise Affiliation: Ruth's Hospitality Group Inc., WINTER PARK, FL
Primary Distributors: (Full Line) SYSCO Food Services of Baltimore, JESSUP, MD

Key Personnel
STEVE F. DE CASTRO - CEO; Owner
ELY HURWITZ - President
JAMES MITICH - President; COO
CRAIG ROBERTS - VP
BARBARA ESSLINGER - Controller Beverages, Food
NICKI KERN - General Manager
MARIO VIDICH - General Manager
CHRIS JEWEL - Executive Chef
BEAU IZAD - Director Human Resources, Training
RENEE SAKELL - Director Human Resources
CARLY TORTORELLO-DAVIS - Manager Event Planning, Sales
DEANNA FAID - Manager Design
REBECCA YATES - Manager Customer Service
LISA LOTSEY - Manager Human Resources

Prosperity Systems Inc.
3 Greenwood Pl Ste 208
Pikesville, MD 21208-3639

Telephone: (800) 234-2654
Fax Number: (443) 544-1505

Internet Homepage: pizzabolis.com
Company Email: info@pizzabolis.com
Type of Business: Chain Restaurant Operator
Year Founded: 1984
Systemwide Sales: $66,996,000 (e)
Total Sales: $8,574,000 (e)
Number of Employees: 10
Average Check: Lunch(10); Dinner(14)
Internet Order Processing: Yes
Internet Sales: 3.00%
Total Units: 81
Trade Names: Pizza Boli's (80)
Units Franchised To: 80
Preferred Square Footage: 1,400
Preferred Location Types: Freestanding; Office Complex; Strip Mall
Primary Menu: Pizza (80)
Projected Openings: 1
Areas of Operation: CT, DC, MD, VA
Type of Foodservice: Quick Serve (80)
Primary Distributors: (Food) US Foods, SEVERN, MD; (Supplies) US Foods, SEVERN, MD

Key Personnel
JOHN NASIR - President; Partner; Director Facility/Maintenance, Information Systems, Real Estate, Design, Store Fixtures; General Buyer
SYED SHAH - Partner; Director Marketing, Menu Development
IKE SYED - Director Operations, Marketing

California Tortilla Group Inc.
7825 Tuckerman Ln Ste 214
Potomac, MD 20854

Telephone: (301) 545-0035
Fax Number: (301) 545-0051
Internet Homepage: californiatortilla.com
Type of Business: Chain Restaurant Operator
Year Founded: 1995
Systemwide Sales: $22,801,000 (e)
Total Sales: $5,922,000 (e)
Alcohol Sales: 2%
Number of Employees: 178
Average Check: Lunch(8); Dinner(10)
Total Units: 38
Trade Names: California Tortilla (38)
Company-Owned Units: 5
Units Franchised To: 33
Preferred Square Footage: 2,500
Preferred Location Types: Airports; Freestanding; Regional Mall; Strip Mall
Alcohol Served: Beer
Primary Menu: Mexican (38)
Projected Openings: 5
Areas of Operation: DC, DE, MD, NJ, PA, VA, WV
Foreign Countries: QATAR
Type of Foodservice: Fast Casual (38)
Catering Services: Yes
Primary Distributors: (Full Line) Saval Foods

Corp., ELKRIDGE, MD

Key Personnel
BOB PHILLIPS - CEO; President; Director Finance, Facility/Maintenance, Real Estate, Store Fixtures; General Buyer
KEITH GOLDMAN - COO
TIM SCOTT - Director Human Resources

Restaurant Zone, Inc
10220 River Rd Ste 1
Potomac, MD 20854-4916

Mailing Address: P O Box 59160, POTOMAC, MD, 20859-9160
Telephone: (301) 983-9700
Internet Homepage: bagelsngrinds.com; potomacpizza.com
Company Email: info@potomacpizza.com
Type of Business: Chain Restaurant Operator
Year Founded: 1994
Total Units: 6
Trade Names: Bagels n Grinds (2); Potomac Pizza (4)
Company-Owned Units: 6
Primary Menu: Bagels (2); Pizza (4)
Projected Openings: 1
Areas of Operation: MD
Type of Foodservice: Casual Dining (4); Quick Serve (2)

Key Personnel
ADAM GREENBERG - Founder; President; Partner; General Buyer
REA PYLE - Partner
ANDREW GOLDSTEIN - General Manager
JIM HARDING - General Manager
STEVE LEVY - General Manager
BRAD BARR - Executive Chef
CHRIS MARTIN - Manager Communications

R/C Theatres Management Corp.
231 W Cherry Hill Ct
Reisterstown, MD 21136-6203

Mailing Address: PO Box 1056, REISTERSTOWN, MD, 21136-7056
Telephone: (410) 526-4774
Fax Number: (410) 526-6871
Internet Homepage: rctheatres.com
Company Email: rctheatres@rctheatres.com
Type of Business: Foodservice Operations - Movie Theatre
Year Founded: 1932
Total Sales: $57,100,000 (e)
Number of Employees: 600
Average Check: Lunch(6); Dinner(6)
Total Units: 11
Trade Names: R/C Theatres (11)

Company-Owned Units: 11
Preferred Square Footage: 53,000; 60,000; 65,000
Preferred Location Types: Community Mall; Freestanding; Regional Mall
Primary Menu: Snacks (11)
Areas of Operation: MD, NC, PA, VA
Type of Foodservice: In-Store Feeder (11)
Notes: The company derives approximately 72% of its revenue from theater admissions, on-screen advertising, and other sales.

Key Personnel
SCOTT COHEN - CEO; President; Director Real Estate, Construction, Site Selection, Design, Menu Development
DAVID PHILLIPS - CFO; COO; VP; Director Finance, Operations, Purchasing, Facility/Maintenance, Information Systems, Human Resources, Store Fixtures; General Buyer
LAURA CAMPBELL - General Manager
SHARON GUTSCHICK - Director Marketing

Auntie Anne's Franchise
6 Monterra Ct
Rockville, MD 20850-3471

Telephone: (347) 229-9030
Type of Business: Chain Restaurant Operator
Total Sales: $4,297,000 (e)
Total Units: 6
Trade Names: Auntie Anne's Hand-Rolled Soft Pretzels (6)
Units Franchised From: 6
Primary Menu: Snacks (6)
Areas of Operation: MD
Type of Foodservice: Quick Serve (6)
Franchise Affiliation: Auntie Anne's Inc., LANCASTER, PA

Key Personnel
KARYN SIMON - President; Owner; General Buyer

El Mariachi
765 Rockville Pike Ste C
Rockville, MD 20852-1148

Telephone: (301) 738-7177
Fax Number: (301) 738-1603
Internet Homepage: mexicalicantina.com; caciquefrederick.com; elmariachirockville.com
Company Email: Eat@elmariachirockville.com
Type of Business: Chain Restaurant Operator
Year Founded: 1991
Total Sales: $6,412,000 (e)
Alcohol Sales: 5%
Number of Employees: 125
Average Check: Dinner(26)
Total Units: 4
Trade Names: Cacique (1); El Mariachi (2); Mexacali Cantina (1)
Company-Owned Units: 4
Preferred Location Types: Freestanding; Strip Mall
Alcohol Served: Beer, Wine, Liquor
Primary Menu: Mexican (4)
Areas of Operation: DE, MD
Type of Foodservice: Casual Dining (2); Fine Dining (2)

Key Personnel
JOSE PEREZ - Owner; Executive Director; General Manager; General Buyer

Jerry's Systems Inc.
1201 Seven Locks Rd Ste 360
Rockville, MD 20854

Telephone: (888) 684-6670
Fax Number: (301) 948-3508
Internet Homepage: jerrysusa.com
Company Email: support@jerrysusa.com
Type of Business: Chain Restaurant Operator
Year Founded: 1954
Systemwide Sales: $31,823,000 (e)
Total Sales: $3,588,000 (e)
Alcohol Sales: 4%
Number of Employees: 54
Average Check: Lunch(10); Dinner(12)
Internet Order Processing: Yes
Internet Sales: 1.00%
Total Units: 24
Trade Names: Jerry's Subs & Pizza (24)
Company-Owned Units: 1
Units Franchised To: 23
Preferred Square Footage: 1,800; 2,500; 3,600
Preferred Location Types: Airports; Community Mall; Convenience Store/Gas Station; Downtown; Freestanding; Kiosk; Office Complex; Outlet Mall; Parks; Regional Mall; Strip Mall
Alcohol Served: Beer, Wine
Primary Menu: Sandwiches/Deli (24)
Areas of Operation: DE, MD, VA, WV
Type of Foodservice: Fast Casual (24)
Primary Distributors: (Full Line) SYSCO Food Services of Baltimore, JESSUP, MD
Parent Company: Blackstreet Capital Management LLC, CHEVY CHASE, MD

Key Personnel
ELI CHEDIAK - CEO; President
HELEN SISLER - Controller

Silver Diner Development Inc.
12276 Rockville Pike
Rockville, MD 20852-1664

Telephone: (301) 770-0333
Fax Number: (301) 770-2832
Internet Homepage: silverdiner.com
Company Email: customerrelations@silverdiner.com
Type of Business: Chain Restaurant Operator
Year Founded: 1989
Total Sales: $64,030,000 (e)
Alcohol Sales: 10%
Number of Employees: 1,280
Average Check: Breakfast(10); Lunch(14); Dinner(14)
Internet Order Processing: Yes
Internet Sales: 2.00%
Total Units: 16
Trade Names: Silver Diner (16)
Company-Owned Units: 16
Preferred Square Footage: 4,000; 6,000
Preferred Location Types: Airports; Freestanding; Regional Mall
Alcohol Served: Beer, Wine, Liquor
Primary Menu: American (16)
Areas of Operation: MD, NJ, VA
Type of Foodservice: Casual Dining (16)
Catering Services: Yes
Primary Distributors: (Full Line) SYSCO Food Services of Baltimore, JESSUP, MD

Key Personnel
ROBERT GIAIMO - CEO; President; Partner; Director Real Estate
YPE VON HENGST - Partner; COO; VP Culinary Operations; Executive Chef; General Buyer
ERIC FORWARD - CFO
JOHN HUDDLE - VP Information Technology
GLENN D'AMORE - VP Operations; Director Region
MARK RUSSELL - VP Development, Real Estate
MATILDE OTT - VP Strategy, Brand Marketing
CHRIS SHAND - Director Human Resources, Recruitment
VICKI BENDURE - Manager Media Relations
BRIAN HALL - Manager Restaurant Operations

Baxter Enterprises
2424 Northgate Dr Ste 500
Salisbury, MD 21801-7889

Telephone: (410) 572-6031
Fax Number: (410) 572-6032
Internet Homepage: baxterent.com
Type of Business: Chain Restaurant Operator
Year Founded: 1993
Total Sales: $70,610,000 (e)

Number of Employees: 455
Average Check: Breakfast(8); Lunch(8); Dinner(8)
Total Units: 15
Trade Names: McDonald's (15)
Units Franchised From: 15
Preferred Square Footage: 2,500; 3,000
Preferred Location Types: Community Mall; Freestanding
Primary Menu: Hamburger (15)
Areas of Operation: DE, MD, VA
Type of Foodservice: Quick Serve (15)
Franchise Affiliation: McDonald's Corporation, CHICAGO, IL
Primary Distributors: (Food) The Martin-Brower Co., MANASSAS, VA

Key Personnel
THOMAS BAXTER - President; Director Finance, Operations, Purchasing, Facility/Maintenance, Supply Chain, Real Estate, Store Fixtures
TOM LIBERATI - VP Business Development
DAOUDA OUATTARA - VP Operations
JOHN DANYLUK - Director

Delmarby Inc.
114 Ward St
Salisbury, MD 21804-5031

Telephone: (410) 742-1854
Fax Number: (410) 749-4832
Type of Business: Chain Restaurant Operator
Year Founded: 1970
Total Sales: $5,872,000 (e)
Number of Employees: 125
Average Check: Lunch(10); Dinner(12)
Total Units: 3
Trade Names: Arby's (3)
Units Franchised From: 3
Preferred Square Footage: 2,500; 3,000
Preferred Location Types: Freestanding
Primary Menu: Sandwiches/Deli (3)
Areas of Operation: MD
Type of Foodservice: Quick Serve (3)
Franchise Affiliation: Arby's Restaurant Group, ATLANTA, GA
Primary Distributors: (Full Line) Willow Run Foods Inc., KIRKWOOD, NY

Key Personnel
TODD HERSHEY - President; Controller; General Manager; Manager Marketing; General Buyer
REGINA TRADER - VP; Manager Operations, Business Development; General Buyer
STEVE HOUREY - Manager Operations, Facility/Maintenance

Marshall Hotels & Resorts Inc.
1315 S Division St
Salisbury, MD 21804-6920

Telephone: (410) 749-8464
Fax Number: (410) 749-0679
Internet Homepage: marshallhotels.com
Type of Business: Foodservice Operations - Hotel/Motels
Year Founded: 1980
Total Sales: $130,300,000 (e)
Alcohol Sales: 6%
Number of Employees: 1,736
Total Units: 49
Restaurants in Hotels: 50
Trade Names: Best Western (2); Chip Factory Hotel an Ascend Collection (1); Crowne Plaza Grand Rapids (1); Fairfield Inn (1); Fenwick Inn (1); Four Points(2); Hampton Inn (13); Hilton (2); Hilton Garden Inn (3); Holiday Inn (4); Holiday Inn Express (1); La Quinta (2); Microtel Inn (2); Quality Inn & Suites (1); Radisson (1); SpringHill Suites (2); Staybridge Suites (1); TownePlace Suites (1); Wingate Inn (2); Wyndham Hotel (6)
Company-Owned Units: 49
Alcohol Served: Beer, Wine, Liquor
Areas of Operation: FL, GA, KY, MD, MI, NC, NJ, NY, OH, PA, VA
Type of Foodservice: Casual Dining (49)
Primary Distributors: (Food) SYSCO Food Services of Baltimore, JESSUP, MD
Notes: The company derives approximately 75% of its revenue from hotel operations; not all concepts have on-site foodservice.

Key Personnel
MICHAEL P. MARSHALL - CEO; President
MIKE GETZEY - COO
RANDY GRIFFIN - Exec VP Marketing, Sales
ROBERT BRUNING - Regional VP Operations
PAT WALLS - Director Human Resources
DAVID CAVALARRO - Regional Director Operations

Janjer Enterprises Inc.
12150 Tech Rd
Silver Spring, MD 20904-1914

Telephone: (301) 625-5920
Fax Number: (301) 625-0045
Type of Business: Chain Restaurant Operator
Year Founded: 1980
Total Sales: $86,570,000 (e)
Number of Employees: 870
Average Check: Lunch(8); Dinner(8)
Total Units: 34
Trade Names: Popeyes Louisiana Kitchen (34)
Units Franchised From: 34
Preferred Square Footage: 2,500
Preferred Location Types: Community Mall; Freestanding; Regional Mall
Primary Menu: Chicken (34)
Areas of Operation: DC, MD, VA
Type of Foodservice: Quick Serve (34)
Catering Services: Yes
Franchise Affiliation: Popeyes Louisiana Kitchen Inc., ATLANTA, GA
Primary Distributors: (Full Line) Willow Run Foods Inc., KIRKWOOD, NY

Key Personnel
JEROME FRIEDLANDER - President
MIKE BURKE - COO
JAN STROMPF - VP
LISA WYATT - Director Human Resources
MIKE BYRNE - Director Operations
ROBERT FRIEDLANDER - Director Catering
DAVID BURDETTE - Director Information Technology
JOHN GRMISLEY - Regional Manager

K & K Fast Foods, Inc.
15434 New Hampshire Ave
Silver Spring, MD 20905-4163

Telephone: (301) 236-9000
Fax Number: (301) 384-9148
Internet Homepage: iccsmiles.com
Type of Business: Chain Restaurant Operator
Total Sales: $4,703,000 (e)
Average Check: Lunch(12); Dinner(12)
Total Units: 3
Trade Names: Checkers (3)
Units Franchised From: 3
Primary Menu: Hamburger (3)
Areas of Operation: MD
Type of Foodservice: Quick Serve (3)
Franchise Affiliation: Checkers Drive-In Restaurants Inc., TAMPA, FL
Notes: Phone Number is to Partner David Keith's dental practice.

Key Personnel
STEFAN M. KUEHNERT - President; Partner
DANA D. KEITH - Partner
BRYAN DECIENTIO - Director Operations

Auntie Anne's Franchise
825 Dulaney Valley Rd Spc 469-A
Towson, MD 21204-1010

Telephone: (410) 821-7688
Type of Business: Chain Restaurant Operator
Total Sales: $3,156,000 (e)
Total Units: 4
Trade Names: Auntie Anne's Hand-Rolled Soft Pretzels (4)
Units Franchised From: 4
Primary Menu: Snacks (4)
Areas of Operation: MD

Type of Foodservice: Quick Serve (4)
Franchise Affiliation: Auntie Anne's Inc., LANCASTER, PA

Key Personnel
GILAD ARIE - Owner; General Buyer

Piezzetta
28 Allegheny Ave Ste 1207
Towson, MD 21204-3919

Telephone: (443) 931-4265
Fax Number: (410) 296-9156
Internet Homepage: piezzetta.com
Type of Business: Chain Restaurant Operator
Year Founded: 2015
Systemwide Sales: $43,871,000 (e)
Total Sales: $884,000 (e)
Alcohol Sales: 9%
Number of Employees: 35
Average Check: Lunch(12); Dinner(16)
Total Units: 2
Trade Names: Piezzetta (2)
Company-Owned Units: 2
Preferred Square Footage: 400; 1,000; 1,900
Preferred Location Types: Downtown; Lifestyle Center; Regional Mall; Strip Mall
Alcohol Served: Beer, Wine
Primary Menu: Pizza (2)
Areas of Operation: MD, NV
Type of Foodservice: Quick Serve (2)
Foodservice Management Venues: Health Care; Recreational; Schools; Transportation
Primary Distributors: (Food) Roma Food Enterprises Inc., RICHMOND, VA

Key Personnel
CHRIS ILARDO - Director Operations, Facility/Maintenance, Security, Inventory, Loss Prevention, Quality Assurance, Human Resources, Training, Menu Development, Food Safety

KBJN, Inc.
4 Industrial Park Dr Ste B
Waldorf, MD 20602-2757

Telephone: (301) 645-7878
Fax Number: (301) 645-7441
Type of Business: Chain Restaurant Operator
Total Sales: $15,950,000 (e)
Number of Employees: 230
Total Units: 7
Trade Names: Burger King (7)
Units Franchised From: 7
Preferred Square Footage: 2,500
Primary Menu: Hamburger (7)
Areas of Operation: MD
Type of Foodservice: Quick Serve (7)
Franchise Affiliation: Burger King Worldwide Inc., MIAMI, FL

Key Personnel
BILL NEBLETT - President; General Buyer

Moore Hospitality, Inc.
2526 University Blvd W
Wheaton, MD 20902-1911

Telephone: (301) 942-2323
Type of Business: Chain Restaurant Operator
Year Founded: 2000
Total Sales: $1,350,000 (e)
Total Units: 2
Trade Names: IHOP (2)
Units Franchised From: 2
Primary Menu: American (2)
Areas of Operation: MD
Type of Foodservice: Family Restaurant (2)

Key Personnel
WILLIAM MOORE - President; Owner; General Buyer

MAINE

Domino's Franchisee
62 School St
Auburn, ME 04210-5440

Telephone: (207) 783-2200
Type of Business: Chain Restaurant Operator
Total Sales: $12,011,000 (e)
Total Units: 6
Trade Names: Domino's (6)
Units Franchised From: 6
Primary Menu: Pizza (6)
Areas of Operation: ME
Type of Foodservice: Quick Serve (6)
Franchise Affiliation: Domino's Pizza Inc, ANN ARBOR, MI

Key Personnel
FERNANDO J. STELSER - Owner; General Buyer

Restwend LLC
36 Anthony Ave Ste 201
Augusta, ME 04330-7891

Telephone: (207) 622-6253
Fax Number: (207) 622-9162
Internet Homepage: wendysmaine.com
Company Email: wendys@jrgall.com
Type of Business: Chain Restaurant Operator
Year Founded: 1963
Total Sales: $27,950,000 (e)
Number of Employees: 377
Average Check: Lunch(8); Dinner(8)
Total Units: 10
Trade Names: Wendy's Old Fashioned Hamburgers (10)
Units Franchised From: 10
Preferred Square Footage: 2,000
Preferred Location Types: Freestanding
Primary Menu: Hamburger (10)
Areas of Operation: ME
Type of Foodservice: Quick Serve (10)
Franchise Affiliation: The Wendy's Company, DUBLIN, OH
Primary Distributors: (Equipment) The Wasserstrom Co., COLUMBUS, OH; (Food) Willow Run Foods Inc., KIRKWOOD, NY; (Supplies) The Wasserstrom Co., COLUMBUS, OH

Key Personnel
DICK STOWELL - Controller; Director Finance, Information Systems
COREY RICKARD - Manager District
TREVOR TARDIFF - Manager District

Bega Inc.
304 Hancock St Ste 3F
Bangor, ME 04401-6573

Telephone: (207) 990-2763
Type of Business: Chain Restaurant Operator
Year Founded: 1986
Total Sales: $14,821,000 (e)
Number of Employees: 150
Average Check: Breakfast(8); Lunch(8); Dinner(8)
Total Units: 3
Trade Names: McDonald's (3)
Units Franchised From: 3
Preferred Square Footage: 2,500; 3,000
Preferred Location Types: Freestanding
Primary Menu: Hamburger (3)
Areas of Operation: ME
Type of Foodservice: Quick Serve (3)
Franchise Affiliation: McDonald's Corporation, CHICAGO, IL
Primary Distributors: (Food) The Martin-Brower Co., ENFIELD, CT

Key Personnel
GARY ECKMANN - President; General Manager; General Buyer

J J Myers LLC
305 Odlin Rd
Bangor, ME 04401-6703

Telephone: (207) 942-0400
Type of Business: Chain Restaurant Operator
Total Sales: $3,556,000 (e)
Total Units: 2
Trade Names: Tim Hortons (2)

Units Franchised From: 2
Primary Menu: Snacks (2)
Areas of Operation: ME
Type of Foodservice: Quick Serve (2)
Franchise Affiliation: Tim Hortons Inc., OAKVILLE, ON

Key Personnel
JAMIE MYERS - General Buyer

North Country Management Group
24 Spruce St
Bangor, ME 04401-5518

Telephone: (207) 942-0060
Type of Business: Chain Restaurant Operator
Year Founded: 1982
Total Sales: $11,230,000 (e)
Number of Employees: 220
Average Check: Breakfast(5); Lunch(8); Dinner(8)
Total Units: 5
Trade Names: Burger King (5)
Units Franchised From: 5
Preferred Square Footage: 1,500
Preferred Location Types: Freestanding
Primary Menu: Hamburger (5)
Areas of Operation: ME
Type of Foodservice: Quick Serve (5)
Franchise Affiliation: Burger King Worldwide Inc., MIAMI, FL
Primary Distributors: (Food) Maines Paper & Food Service Inc., CONKLIN, NY

Key Personnel
STEVE WEGNER - President; Director Real Estate; General Buyer
MELANIE MENEES - VP Finance; Treasurer
KAREN GIFFORD - Controller; Director Operations, Purchasing, Information Systems, Human Resources

Dunkin' Donuts Franchise
476 Alfred St
Biddeford, ME 04005-9479

Telephone: (207) 282-2002
Type of Business: Chain Restaurant Operator
Total Sales: $17,110,000 (e)
Number of Employees: 100
Average Check: Dinner(10)
Total Units: 11
Trade Names: Dunkin' Donuts (11)
Units Franchised From: 11
Preferred Square Footage: 1,500; 2,200
Preferred Location Types: Freestanding
Primary Menu: Snacks (11)
Areas of Operation: ME
Type of Foodservice: Quick Serve (11)

Franchise Affiliation: DD IP Holder, CANTON, MA

Key Personnel
DIONISIOS BOUZIANIS - President; General Buyer

Sanweco Inc.
2 Main St Ste 17-227
Biddeford, ME 04005-2070

Mailing Address: PO Box 506, SACO, ME, 04072-0506
Telephone: (207) 283-4046
Fax Number: (207) 283-3138
Type of Business: Chain Restaurant Operator
Year Founded: 1980
Total Sales: $14,410,000 (e)
Number of Employees: 132
Average Check: Lunch(8); Dinner(8)
Total Units: 8
Trade Names: KFC/Taco Bell (8)
Units Franchised From: 8
Preferred Square Footage: 2,500
Preferred Location Types: Freestanding; Strip Mall
Primary Menu: Chicken (8); Taco (8)
Areas of Operation: ME, NH
Type of Foodservice: Quick Serve (8)
Franchise Affiliation: KFC Corporation, LOUISVILLE, KY; Taco Bell Corp., IRVINE, CA
Primary Distributors: (Food) McLane/Guilderland Center, GUILDERLAND CENTER, NY

Key Personnel
RON GILES - CEO; Manager Purchasing, Loss Prevention, Supply Chain, Marketing, Real Estate, Design, Business Development, Store Planning; General Buyer
STACEY DION - President; Director Finance, Accounting, Information Systems
LINDA GILES - VP Operations, Store Planning; Director Facility/Maintenance
SUE JOHNSTON - Manager Human Resources

Subco Enterprises Inc
292 Main St
Bridgton, ME 04009-1343

Telephone: (207) 893-0645
Fax Number: (207) 647-5375
Type of Business: Chain Restaurant Operator
Total Sales: $6,868,000 (e)
Total Units: 14
Trade Names: Subway (14)
Units Franchised From: 14
Primary Menu: Sandwiches/Deli (14)
Areas of Operation: ME
Type of Foodservice: Quick Serve (14)
Franchise Affiliation: Doctor's Associates Inc., MILFORD, CT

Key Personnel
MARVIN MAYBERRY - Owner

Substantial Investments
42 Gray Rd
Cumberland Center, ME 04021-3117

Telephone: (207) 829-3668
Type of Business: Chain Restaurant Operator
Year Founded: 1984
Total Sales: $4,404,000 (e)
Number of Employees: 67
Average Check: Lunch(8); Dinner(12)
Total Units: 5
Trade Names: D'Angelo's Sandwich Shop (5)
Units Franchised From: 5
Preferred Square Footage: 5,000
Preferred Location Types: Downtown; Freestanding
Primary Menu: Sandwiches/Deli (5)
Areas of Operation: ME
Type of Foodservice: Quick Serve (5)
Franchise Affiliation: Papa Gino's Holdings Corp., DEDHAM, MA

Key Personnel
JERRY HOWLAND - President; CFO; Director Real Estate
JEFF HOWLAND - VP; Treasurer; Director Operations, Facility/Maintenance, Information Systems, Real Estate; General Buyer

The Wolak Group
65 Gray Rd Unit 4
Falmouth, ME 04105-2057

Mailing Address: 65 Gray Road, Box 4, FALMOUTH, ME, 04105
Telephone: (207) 797-7600
Fax Number: (207) 797-4300
Internet Homepage: wolakgroup.com
Company Email: info@wolakgroup,com
Type of Business: Chain Restaurant Operator
Total Sales: $127,680,000 (e)
Average Check: Dinner(8)
Total Units: 80
Trade Names: Dunkin' Donuts (80)
Units Franchised From: 80
Preferred Square Footage: 1,500; 2,200
Primary Menu: Snacks (80)
Areas of Operation: ME, NH, NY
Type of Foodservice: Quick Serve (80)
Franchise Affiliation: DD IP Holder, CANTON, MA

Key Personnel
EDWARD WOLAK - CEO; President; General Buyer

KIMBERLY WOLAK - Owner; COO
KIMBERLY GARRETT - COO
BOB ALBERTI - Chief of Staff
DAN ROBERTS - VP; General Counsel
THOMAS SANTURRI - VP Operations
GUY RUFFO - Executive Director Operations
GREG CONSTANTINO - Director Operations

Harraseeket Inn
162 Main St
Freeport, ME 04032-1311

Telephone: (207) 865-9377
Fax Number: (207) 865-1684
Internet Homepage: harraseeketinn.com
Company Email: harraseeke@aol.com
Type of Business: Chain Restaurant Operator
Year Founded: 1984
Total Sales: $7,381,000 (e)
Alcohol Sales: 20%
Number of Employees: 100
Average Check: Lunch(20); Dinner(30)
Total Units: 2
Trade Names: The Broad Arrow Tavern (1); The Maine Harvest Dining Room (1)
Company-Owned Units: 2
Preferred Location Types: Freestanding
Alcohol Served: Beer, Wine, Liquor
Primary Menu: American (2)
Areas of Operation: ME
Type of Foodservice: Casual Dining (1); Fine Dining (1)
Primary Distributors: (Food) SYSCO of Boston, PLYMPTON, MA

Key Personnel
CHIP GRAY - General Manager
TROY MAINS - Executive Chef; General Buyer
MARSHA AURIEMMA - Director Operations

Domino's Franchisee
621 Main St
Gorham, ME 04038-2623

Telephone: (207) 854-2500
Type of Business: Chain Restaurant Operator
Total Sales: $21,974,000 (e)
Total Units: 11
Trade Names: Domino's (11)
Units Franchised From: 11
Primary Menu: Pizza (11)
Areas of Operation: ME
Type of Foodservice: Quick Serve (11)
Franchise Affiliation: Domino's Pizza Inc, ANN ARBOR, MI

Key Personnel
LEE PRIOR - Owner; General Buyer

Sparetime Recreation
215 Whitten Rd
Hallowell, ME 04347

Telephone: (207) 623-6000
Fax Number: (207) 621-0250
Internet Homepage: sparetimerec.com
Type of Business: Foodservice Operations - Bowling Alley
Total Sales: $3,019,000 (e)
Average Check: Dinner(8)
Total Units: 2
Trade Names: Ground Round Sports Grille (1); SpareTime Bowling (1)
Company-Owned Units: 1
Units Franchised From: 1
Preferred Location Types: Freestanding
Alcohol Served: Beer, Wine, Liquor
Primary Menu: American (2)
Areas of Operation: ME
Type of Foodservice: In-Store Feeder (2)
Franchise Affiliation: Ground Round I.O.C. LLC, FREEPORT, ME

Key Personnel
ANDY COUTURE - Owner; General Buyer

The White Barn Inn
37 Beach Ave
Kennebunk, ME 04043-7614

Mailing Address: PO Box 5600, KENNEBUNKPORT, ME, 04046
Telephone: (207) 967-2321
Fax Number: (207) 967-1100
Internet Homepage: whitebarninn.com; gracehotels.com
Company Email: innkeeper.wbi@gracehotels.com
Type of Business: Chain Restaurant Operator
Year Founded: 1988
Total Sales: $4,173,000 (e)
Alcohol Sales: 15%
Number of Employees: 45
Average Check: Dinner(90)
Internet Order Processing: Yes
Internet Sales: 20.00%
Total Units: 2
Trade Names: The Bistro (1); The White Barn Inn (1)
Company-Owned Units: 2
Preferred Location Types: Freestanding
Alcohol Served: Beer, Wine, Liquor
Primary Menu: American (1); Seafood (1)
Areas of Operation: ME
Type of Foodservice: Casual Dining (1); Fine Dining (1)
Primary Distributors: (Full Line) TriMark USA Inc., MANSFIELD, MA
Notes: The White Barn Inn is owned by US Hotels.

Key Personnel
MATTHEW PADILLA - Executive Chef; General Buyer

Weathervane Seafood Restaurants
306 US Route 1 Ste O
Kittery, ME 03904-5504

Telephone: (207) 439-0335
Fax Number: (207) 439-7754
Internet Homepage: weathervaneseafoods.com
Type of Business: Chain Restaurant Operator
Year Founded: 1969
Total Sales: $21,850,000 (e)
Alcohol Sales: 8%
Number of Employees: 500
Average Check: Lunch(10); Dinner(16)
Internet Order Processing: Yes
Internet Sales: 1.00%
Total Units: 5
Trade Names: Weathervane Lobster in the Rough (1); Weathervane Seafood Restaurant (4)
Company-Owned Units: 5
Preferred Square Footage: 6,000
Preferred Location Types: Freestanding
Alcohol Served: Beer, Wine, Liquor
Primary Menu: Seafood (5)
Areas of Operation: ME, NH
Type of Foodservice: Casual Dining (5)
On-site Distribution Center: Yes
Primary Distributors: (Full Line) SYSCO of Boston, PLYMPTON, MA

Key Personnel
BILL KURKUL - CFO
JEREMY GAGNER - COO; VP Operations, Purchasing, Real Estate, Site Selection, Food Safety; Director Facility/Maintenance, Site Selection, Design, Human Resources
MEG CLOUD - Director Marketing

Sam's Italian Foods
268 Main St
Lewiston, ME 04240-7024

Telephone: (207) 782-2550
Fax Number: (207) 782-3827
Internet Homepage: samsitalian.com
Company Email: info@samsitalian.com
Type of Business: Chain Restaurant Operator
Year Founded: 1969
Systemwide Sales: $8,816,000 (e)
Total Sales: $6,009,000 (e)
Alcohol Sales: 3%
Number of Employees: 185

Average Check: Lunch(18); Dinner(30)
Total Units: 13
Trade Names: Sam's Italian Restaurant (13)
Company-Owned Units: 13
Preferred Square Footage: 2,200
Preferred Location Types: Freestanding
Alcohol Served: Beer, Wine
Primary Menu: Italian (13)
Areas of Operation: ME
Type of Foodservice: Fast Casual (13)
Catering Services: Yes
On-site Distribution Center: Yes
Primary Distributors: (Full Line) SYSCO Food Services of Northern New England Inc., WESTBROOK, ME

Key Personnel
RICK MICHAUD - Owner; Controller; Manager Operations, Marketing, Real Estate, Design; General Buyer
STEPHANIE LAW - VP

Conifer Industries Inc.
633 Intervale Rd
New Gloucester, ME 04260

Mailing Address: PO Box 500, NEW GLOUCESTER, ME, 04260-0500
Telephone: (207) 926-4147
Fax Number: (207) 926-4470
Type of Business: Chain Restaurant Operator
Year Founded: 1971
Total Sales: $42,270,000 (e)
Number of Employees: 495
Average Check: Lunch(10); Dinner(10)
Total Units: 23
Trade Names: KFC (23)
Units Franchised From: 23
Preferred Square Footage: 2,500
Preferred Location Types: Freestanding
Primary Menu: Chicken (23)
Areas of Operation: ME, NH
Type of Foodservice: Quick Serve (23)
Franchise Affiliation: KFC Corporation, LOUISVILLE, KY; Taco Bell Corp., IRVINE, CA
Primary Distributors: (Food) McLane/Guilderland Center, GUILDERLAND CENTER, NY

Key Personnel
FRED THURSTON - CEO; Owner; Controller; General Buyer
MATTHEW THURSTON - President; Director Operations, Purchasing, Facility/Maintenance, Supply Chain, Design, Store Fixtures

Barnacle Billy's Etc.
70 Perkins Cove Rd
Ogunquit, ME 03907

Mailing Address: PO Box 837, OGUNQUIT, ME, 03907-0837
Telephone: (207) 646-5575
Fax Number: (207) 646-1219
Internet Homepage: barnbilly.com
Company Email: info@barnbilly.com
Type of Business: Chain Restaurant Operator
Year Founded: 1962
Total Sales: $5,419,000 (e)
Alcohol Sales: 20%
Number of Employees: 130
Average Check: Lunch(12); Dinner(18)
Total Units: 2
Trade Names: Barnacle Billy's (1); Barnacle Billy's Etc. (1)
Company-Owned Units: 2
Preferred Square Footage: 350
Preferred Location Types: Freestanding
Alcohol Served: Beer, Wine, Liquor
Primary Menu: Seafood (2)
Areas of Operation: ME
Type of Foodservice: Casual Dining (2)
Primary Distributors: (Food) SYSCO Food Services of Northern New England Inc., WESTBROOK, ME

Key Personnel
WILLIAM "TIM" TOWER III - President; General Manager; General Buyer
COURTLAND TOWER - VP
MARGARET TOWER - VP

Governor's Restaurant
963 Stillwater Ave
Old Town, ME 04468-2166

Telephone: (207) 827-4277
Fax Number: (207) 827-6118
Internet Homepage: governorsrestaurant.com
Company Email: info@governorsrestaurant.com.
Type of Business: Chain Restaurant Operator
Year Founded: 1985
Total Sales: $13,440,000 (e)
Alcohol Sales: 2%
Number of Employees: 340
Average Check: Lunch(8); Dinner(12)
Total Units: 6
Trade Names: Governor's Restaurant (6)
Company-Owned Units: 6
Preferred Square Footage: 5,000
Preferred Location Types: Freestanding; Hotel/Motel
Alcohol Served: Beer, Wine
Primary Menu: American (6)
Areas of Operation: ME
Type of Foodservice: Casual Dining (6)
Primary Distributors: (Equipment) R.M. Flagg Co. Inc., VEAZIE, ME; (Food) SYSCO Food Services of Northern New England Inc., WESTBROOK, ME

Key Personnel
RANDY WADLEIGH - President; General Manager; Executive Chef; Director Finance, Operations, Facility/Maintenance, Information Systems, Supply Chain, Ethnic Marketing, Real Estate, Design, Human Resources; General Buyer
JASON CLAY - Director Marketing

Farnsworth Enterprises
11 Mill St
Orono, ME 04473-4034

Telephone: (207) 866-2111
Fax Number: (207) 866-3304
Internet Homepage: patspizzaorono.com
Company Email: oronopatspizza@aol.com
Type of Business: Chain Restaurant Operator
Year Founded: 1931
Systemwide Sales: $20,048,000 (e)
Total Sales: $2,552,000 (e)
Alcohol Sales: 15%
Number of Employees: 40
Average Check: Breakfast(8); Lunch(10); Dinner(14)
Internet Order Processing: Yes
Total Units: 17
Trade Names: Pat's Pizza (17)
Company-Owned Units: 1
Units Franchised To: 16
Preferred Square Footage: 2,500
Preferred Location Types: Freestanding
Alcohol Served: Beer, Wine, Liquor
Primary Menu: Pizza (17)
Areas of Operation: ME
Type of Foodservice: Casual Dining (17)
Primary Distributors: (Food) Performance Foodservice - Springfield, SPRINGFIELD, MA

Key Personnel
BRUCE FARNSWORTH - President; Partner; CFO; Controller; Director Purchasing, Risk Management, Marketing, Human Resources
CAROLYN FARNSWORTH - Partner; General Manager; Executive Chef; Director Facility/Maintenance

Amato Enterprises Inc
312 Saint John St 2nd Floor
Portland, ME 04102

Telephone: (207) 828-5978
Fax Number: (207) 761-0977
Internet Homepage: amatos.com
Company Email: CustomerService@amatos.com
Type of Business: Chain Restaurant Operator
Average Check: Dinner(14)
Total Units: 40
Trade Names: Amato's Sandwich Shop (40)
Units Franchised From: 40
Primary Menu: Sandwiches/Deli (40)
Areas of Operation: ME, NH, NY, VT

Type of Foodservice: Casual Dining (40)
Franchise Affiliation: Amato Sandwich Shops Inc., PORTLAND, ME

Key Personnel
DOMINIC REALI - President

Amato Sandwich Shops Inc.
312 Saint John St Fl 2
Portland, ME 04102-3020

Telephone: (207) 828-5981
Fax Number: (207) 761-0977
Internet Homepage: amatos.com
Company Email: customerservice@amatos.com
Type of Business: Chain Restaurant Operator
Year Founded: 1902
Total Sales: $32,570,000 (e)
Alcohol Sales: 18%
Number of Employees: 324
Average Check: Lunch(8); Dinner(10)
Total Units: 44
Trade Names: Amato's Sandwich Shop (44)
Company-Owned Units: 44
Preferred Square Footage: 4,000
Preferred Location Types: Convenience Store/Gas Station; Freestanding
Alcohol Served: Beer, Wine
Primary Menu: Sandwiches/Deli (44)
Areas of Operation: ME, NH, NY, VT
Type of Foodservice: Casual Dining (44)
Catering Services: Yes
Primary Distributors: (Food) Micucci Wholesale Foods Inc., PORTLAND, ME; (Supplies) Gordon Food Service, TAUNTON, MA

Key Personnel
DAN GORE - Executive Chef; Manager Operations, Purchasing, Marketing, Research & Development
PATSY TROIANO - Buyer Beverages

Aroma Joe's Franchising, LLC
352 Warren Ave Suite 8
Portland, ME 04103

Telephone: (207) 553-2975
Internet Homepage: aromajoes.com
Type of Business: Chain Restaurant Operator
Year Founded: 2000
Total Units: 67
Trade Names: Aroma Joe's Coffee (67)
Company-Owned Units: 1
Units Franchised To: 66
Preferred Location Types: Freestanding
Primary Menu: Coffee (67)
Areas of Operation: MA, ME, NH

Type of Foodservice: Quick Serve (67)

Key Personnel
MARTY MCKENNA - Co-Founder
TIM MCKENNA - Co-Founder
MIKE SILLON - Co-Founder
BRIAN SILLON - Co-Founder
LOREN GOODRIDGE - CEO
JAIMIE L - Area Director
CAROLINE M. RILEY - Director Marketing
DAVID TUCCI - Director Operations, Franchise Development
ERICA TARNOWSKI - Director Franchise Development
ALLISON GOODRIDGE - Manager Design
JORY POTTLE - Manager Operations
ASHLEY SIDNEY - Coordinator Development
MEGAN GOODRIDGE - Consultant

Hartread, Inc.
599 Forest Ave
Portland, ME 04101-1514

Telephone: (207) 775-0718
Internet Homepage: misterbagel.com
Company Email: mebagelmaster@gmail.com
Type of Business: Chain Restaurant Operator
Year Founded: 1977
Total Sales: $2,762,000 (e)
Total Units: 10
Trade Names: Mister Bagel (10)
Units Franchised To: 10
Primary Menu: Bagels (10)
Areas of Operation: ME
Type of Foodservice: Quick Serve (10)

Key Personnel
GAIL HARTGLASS - President
JOEL BAKER - General Manager; General Buyer
JANE BAKER - Store Manager
ROBIN TAYLOR - Store Manager
RASH SANDHU - Store Manager
TERRI TYSON - Store Manager
JOHN LANCASTER - Store Manager
ADAM SHAPIRO - Store Manager
RALPH CURRY - Store Manager

Olympia Hotel Management
7 Custom House St Ste 5
Portland, ME 04101-4185

Mailing Address: P O Box 508, Portland, ME, 04112-0508
Telephone: (207) 874-9990
Fax Number: (207) 874-9993
Internet Homepage: theolympiacompanies.com
Company Email: info@olympiacompanies.com
Type of Business: Foodservice Operations - Hotel/Motels

Year Founded: 1969
Total Sales: $76,620,000 (e)
Alcohol Sales: 13%
Number of Employees: 1,500
Total Units: 26
Restaurants in Hotels: 9
Trade Names: America's Best Inn (1); Clarion Hotel (1); Courtyard Jacksonville (1); Hampton Inn & Suites (5); Hilton Garden Inn (2); Holiday Inn (2); Howard Johnson (1); Hyatt Place (4); Inn by the Sea (1); Microtel Inn & Suites (1); Residence Inn (1); Sophy (1); The Alfond Inn (1); The Brunswick Hotel & Tavern (1); The Glen House (1); The Hotel at Oberlin (1); The Inn at Swarthmore (1)
Company-Owned Units: 9
Alcohol Served: Beer, Wine, Liquor
Areas of Operation: CT, FL, IL, ME, NC, NH, OH, VA
Type of Foodservice: Casual Dining (9)
Primary Distributors: (Food) SYSCO Food Services of Virginia LLC, HARRISONBURG, VA
Notes: The company derives approximately 80% of its revenue from hotel operations.

Key Personnel
DAN FLAHERTY - President Group; CFO; Controller
JOHN SCHULTZEL - VP Purchasing, Food and Beverage; Executive Chef; Director Operations, Menu Development
MIKE ZIMMERMAN - VP Business Development
TOM SPAULDING - General Manager
GREG MACLEAN - Director Operations

Raffel Brothers
500 Forest Ave Ste 4
Portland, ME 04101-1520

Telephone: (207) 773-1501
Fax Number: (207) 773-4257
Type of Business: Chain Restaurant Operator
Year Founded: 1978
Total Sales: $5,941,000 (e)
Number of Employees: 70
Average Check: Lunch(8); Dinner(10)
Total Units: 3
Trade Names: Arby's (3)
Units Franchised From: 3
Preferred Square Footage: 2,500; 3,000
Preferred Location Types: Freestanding
Primary Menu: Sandwiches/Deli (3)
Areas of Operation: ME
Type of Foodservice: Quick Serve (3)
Franchise Affiliation: Arby's Restaurant Group, ATLANTA, GA
Primary Distributors: (Food) Willow Run Foods Inc., KIRKWOOD, NY

Key Personnel
JAMES RAFFEL - President; Controller; Director

Operations, Purchasing, Information Systems, Real Estate, Franchising

The Shipyard Brewing Company
86 Newbury St
Portland, ME 04101-4219

Telephone: (207) 761-0807
Fax Number: (207) 775-5567
Internet Homepage: seadogbrewing.com; shipyard.com
Company Email: info@SHIPYARD.com
Type of Business: Chain Restaurant Operator
Year Founded: 1993
Total Sales: $43,580,000 (e)
Internet Order Processing: Yes
Total Units: 15
Trade Names: Cody's Road House (1); Federal Jacks Restaurant & Brewpub (1); Sea Dog Brewing Co. (9); The Inn on Peaks Island (1); The Shipyard Brew Haus (2); The Shipyard Brewpub (1)
Company-Owned Units: 14
Units Franchised From: 1
Primary Menu: American (15)
Projected Openings: 1
Areas of Operation: FL, MA, ME, NH
Type of Foodservice: Casual Dining (15)

Key Personnel
BRUCE FORSLEY - President
FRED FORSLEY - Owner
BEN KELLER - Director E-Commerce

Domino's Franchisee
212 Park St
Rockland, ME 04841-2126

Telephone: (207) 593-8307
Type of Business: Chain Restaurant Operator
Total Sales: $8,171,000 (e)
Total Units: 4
Trade Names: Domino's (4)
Units Franchised From: 4
Primary Menu: Pizza (4)
Areas of Operation: ME
Type of Foodservice: Quick Serve (4)
Franchise Affiliation: Domino's Pizza Inc, ANN ARBOR, MI

Key Personnel
LEE S. PRIOR - Owner; General Buyer
DALE PRIOR - VP

Domino's Franchisee
58 Ossipee Trl E
Standish, ME 04084

Telephone: (207) 642-5200
Type of Business: Chain Restaurant Operator
Total Sales: $26,548,000 (e)
Total Units: 13
Trade Names: Domino's (13)
Units Franchised From: 13
Primary Menu: Pizza (13)
Areas of Operation: ME
Type of Foodservice: Quick Serve (13)
Franchise Affiliation: Domino's Pizza Inc, ANN ARBOR, MI

Key Personnel
LEE PRIOR - Owner; General Buyer

Romad Company
59 Nelson St
Waterville, ME 04901-5018

Mailing Address: PO Box 400, WATERVILLE, ME, 04903-0400
Telephone: (207) 872-6260
Fax Number: (207) 873-5669
Company Email: romad@myfairpoint.net
Type of Business: Chain Restaurant Operator
Year Founded: 1986
Total Sales: $33,350,000 (e)
Number of Employees: 350
Average Check: Breakfast(8); Lunch(8); Dinner(10)
Total Units: 7
Trade Names: McDonald's (7)
Units Franchised From: 7
Preferred Square Footage: 2,500; 3,000
Preferred Location Types: Freestanding
Primary Menu: Hamburger (7)
Areas of Operation: ME
Type of Foodservice: Quick Serve (7)
Franchise Affiliation: McDonald's Corporation, CHICAGO, IL
Primary Distributors: (Full Line) The Martin-Brower Co., ENFIELD, CT

Key Personnel
ARTHUR ORTINS - President; Partner; Manager Information Systems
LARAINE ORTINS - Partner; VP Finance
MICHAEL ORTINS - Partner; Director Operations; General Buyer
LANA ORTINS - Manager Accounting
PAM MAYHEW - Manager Human Resources

Wadleigh Food Services, Inc.
741 Roosevelt Trl
Windham, ME 04062-5269

Telephone: (207) 893-0023
Type of Business: Chain Restaurant Operator
Total Sales: $3,979,000 (e)
Total Units: 3
Trade Names: Little Caesars Pizza (3)
Units Franchised From: 3
Primary Menu: Pizza (3)
Areas of Operation: ME
Type of Foodservice: Quick Serve (3)
Franchise Affiliation: Little Caesar Enterprises Inc., DETROIT, MI

Key Personnel
JOE GIOVANNI - Owner; General Buyer
ANDRE MAGANA - General Manager
CHRISTOPHER POWERS - Supervisor

Wild Willy's Burgers
765 US Route 1
York, ME 03909-5834

Telephone: (207) 363-9924
Internet Homepage: wildwillysburgers.com
Company Email: info@wildwillysburgers.com
Type of Business: Chain Restaurant Operator
Year Founded: 2001
Total Sales: $6,117,000 (e)
Number of Employees: 40
Average Check: Dinner(14)
Total Units: 4
Trade Names: Wild Willy's Burgers (4)
Company-Owned Units: 3
Units Franchised To: 1
Preferred Square Footage: 3,200; 3,600
Preferred Location Types: Freestanding; Strip Mall
Alcohol Served: Beer, Wine
Primary Menu: Hamburger (4)
Areas of Operation: MA, ME, NH
Type of Foodservice: Quick Serve (4)

Key Personnel
MIKE TOTTLE - General Manager; Executive Chef; General Buyer
JIM WILLIAMS JR - General Manager

MICHIGAN

T W Management
5750 US 31 N
Acme, MI 49610

Telephone: (231) 938-5908
Type of Business: Chain Restaurant Operator

Total Sales: $4,601,000 (e)
Total Units: 8
Trade Names: Subway (8)
Units Franchised From: 8
Primary Menu: Sandwiches/Deli (8)
Areas of Operation: MI
Type of Foodservice: Quick Serve (8)
Franchise Affiliation: Doctor's Associates Inc., MILFORD, CT

Key Personnel
WENDY WILLIAMS - Owner; General Buyer

Jennell Corporation
1960 Sand Creek Hwy
Adrian, MI 49221-9213

Mailing Address: PO Box 3007, ADRIAN, MI, 49221-6307
Telephone: (517) 265-2221
Fax Number: (517) 264-2844
Company Email: jennellcorp@comcast.net
Type of Business: Chain Restaurant Operator
Total Sales: $14,799,000 (e)
Number of Employees: 150
Total Units: 3
Trade Names: McDonald's (3)
Units Franchised From: 3
Preferred Square Footage: 2,500
Preferred Location Types: Freestanding
Primary Menu: Hamburger (3)
Areas of Operation: MI
Type of Foodservice: Quick Serve (3)
Franchise Affiliation: McDonald's Corporation, CHICAGO, IL

Key Personnel
RALPH BODMAN - President; General Buyer

Peppino's Pizzeria
4647 Lake Michigan Dr
Allendale, MI 49401-8842

Telephone: (616) 895-4308
Internet Homepage: peppinospizza.com
Type of Business: Chain Restaurant Operator
Year Founded: 1976
Total Sales: $7,774,000 (e)
Average Check: Dinner(14)
Total Units: 10
Trade Names: Peppino's Pizzeria (7); Peppino's Pizzeria & Sports Grille (3)
Company-Owned Units: 5
Units Franchised To: 5
Preferred Location Types: Freestanding
Alcohol Served: Beer, Wine, Liquor
Primary Menu: Pizza (10)
Areas of Operation: MI
Type of Foodservice: Casual Dining (3); Quick Serve (7)

Catering Services: Yes

Key Personnel
JOE DILEONARDO - Director Franchise Development

Ludlow Enterprises
319 E Parson St
Alpena, MI 49707-3652

Telephone: (989) 356-2699
Fax Number: (989) 356-2811
Internet Homepage: ludlowenterprises.com
Type of Business: Chain Restaurant Operator
Total Sales: $4,642,000 (e)
Average Check: Dinner(16)
Total Units: 2
Trade Names: Big Boy (1); Mancino's Pizza (1)
Company-Owned Units: 1
Units Franchised From: 1
Primary Menu: American (1); Pizza (1)
Areas of Operation: MI
Type of Foodservice: Family Restaurant (1); Quick Serve (1)
Franchise Affiliation: Big Boy Restaurants International LLC, WARREN, MI

Key Personnel
BRIAN LUDLOW - President; General Buyer
ANDREA LUDLOW - Owner

WMCR Corporation
234 W Chisholm St
Alpena, MI 49707-2419

Mailing Address: PO Box 456, ALPENA, MI, 49707-0456
Telephone: (989) 356-3048
Fax Number: (989) 356-3854
Internet Homepage: wmcrco.com
Type of Business: Chain Restaurant Operator
Year Founded: 1986
Total Sales: $37,040,000 (e)
Number of Employees: 635
Average Check: Lunch(8); Dinner(8)
Total Units: 21
Trade Names: KFC (20); Long John Silvers (1)
Units Franchised From: 21
Preferred Square Footage: 3,800
Preferred Location Types: Freestanding
Primary Menu: Chicken (20); Seafood (1)
Areas of Operation: IN, MI, WI
Type of Foodservice: Quick Serve (20)
Franchise Affiliation: KFC Corporation, LOUISVILLE, KY; Long John Silver's Inc., LOUISVILLE, KY
Primary Distributors: (Full Line) McLane/Sturtevant, STURTEVANT, WI

Key Personnel
TIM FITZPATRICK - President; Director Real Estate
DOUGLAS HORNE - CFO; VP Finance, Facility/Maintenance, Information Systems; Manager Operations, Purchasing

Cottage Inn Pizza Inc.
4390 Concourse Dr
Ann Arbor, MI 48108-9687

Telephone: (734) 663-2470
Fax Number: (734) 747-7177
Internet Homepage: cottageinn.com
Company Email: info@cottageinn.com
Type of Business: Chain Restaurant Operator
Year Founded: 1948
Systemwide Sales: $17,788,000 (e)
Total Sales: $7,662,000 (e)
Number of Employees: 125
Average Check: Lunch(12); Dinner(12)
Internet Order Processing: Yes
Total Units: 52
Trade Names: Cottage Inn Pizza (52)
Company-Owned Units: 10
Units Franchised To: 42
Preferred Square Footage: 1,300
Preferred Location Types: Freestanding; Regional Mall; Strip Mall
Primary Menu: Pizza (52)
Areas of Operation: MI, NC, OH
Type of Foodservice: Quick Serve (52)
Catering Services: Yes
On-site Distribution Center: Yes
Primary Distributors: (Full Line) SYSCO Detroit LLC, CANTON, MI

Key Personnel
THEO MICHOS - CFO; Director Finance, Supply Chain
TOM CARRAS - Senior Director Store Operations
OLIVIA O'CONNOR - Manager Communications

Domino's Pizza Inc
30 Frank Lloyd Wright Dr
Ann Arbor, MI 48105-9757

Mailing Address: PO Box 485, ANN ARBOR, MI, 48106
Telephone: (734) 930-3030
Fax Number: (734) 930-4346
Internet Homepage: dominos.com; dominosbiz.com
Type of Business: Chain Restaurant Operator
Year Founded: 1960
Systemwide Sales: $33,971,649,000 (e)
Publicly Held: Yes
Total Sales: $6,414,560,000 (e)
Number of Employees: 14,500
Average Check: Lunch(12); Dinner(16)

Internet Order Processing: Yes
Internet Sales: 50.00%
Total Units: 20,500
Trade Names: Domino's (20,500)
Company-Owned Units: 288
Units Franchised To: 20,212
Preferred Square Footage: 1,000; 1,200; 1,300
Preferred Location Types: Airports; Community Mall; Convenience Store/Gas Station; Downtown; Freestanding; Institution (college/hospital); Regional Mall; Stadiums; Strip Mall
Primary Menu: Pizza (20,500)
Projected Openings: 300
Areas of Operation: AK, AL, AR, AZ, CA, CO, CT, DC, DE, FL, GA, GU, HI, IA, ID, IL, IN, KS, KY, LA, MA, MD, ME, MI, MN, MO, MS, MT, NC, ND, NE, NH, NJ, NM, NV, NY, OH, OK, OR, PA, PR, RI, SC, SD, TN, TX, UT, VA, VI, VT, WA, WI, WV, WY, AB, BC, MB, NB, NL, NS, NT, ON, PE, QC, SK, YT
Foreign Countries: AUSTRALIA; AZERBAIJAN; BAHAMAS; BAHRAIN; BELARUS; BELGIUM; BRAZIL; BULGARIA; CAMBODIA; CANADA; CAYMAN ISLANDS; CHILE; CHINA; COLOMBIA; COSTA RICA; CYPRUS; DENMARK; DOMINICAN REPUBLIC; ECUADOR; EGYPT; ENGLAND; FRANCE; GEORGIA;GERMANY; GREECE; GUATEMALA; HAITI; HONDURAS; ICELAND; INDIA; INDONESIA; IRELAND; ISRAEL; ITALY; JAPAN; JORDAN; KENYA; KUWAIT; LEBANON; MACEDONIA; MALAYSIA; MEXICO; MOROCCO; NEW ZEALAND; NIGERIA; NORWAY; OMAN; PAKISTAN; PANAMA; PARAGUAY; PERU; POLAND; PORTUGAL; QATAR; ROMANIA; RUSSIA; SAINT KITTS AND NEVIS; SAINT MAARTEN; SAUDI ARABIA; SCOTLAND; SINGAPORE; SOUTHAFRICA; SOUTH KOREA; SPAIN; ST. LUCIA; SWITZERLAND; TAIWAN; THAILAND; THE NETHERLANDS; TURKEY; UKRAINE; VENEZUELA; VIETNAM; WALES
Type of Foodservice: Quick Serve (20,500)
Distribution Centers: CALGARY, AB; ANCHORAGE, AK; PHOENIX, AZ; LANGLEY, BC; HAYWARD, CA; ONTARIO, CA; DENVER, CO; EAST GRANBY, CT; GROVELAND, FL; KENNESAW, GA; AIEA, HI; ERLANGER, KY; BATON ROUGE, LA; WINNEPEG, MB; ODENTON, MD; NEW BOSTON, MI; EAGAN, MN; SAINT PETERS, MO; GARNER, NC; GRAND PRAIRIE, TX; KENT, WA
On-site Distribution Center: Yes
Parent Company: Bain Capital Partners LLC., BOSTON, MA
Regional Offices: Domino's Inc., LINTHICUM HEIGHTS, MD
Notes: Online sales percentage reflects domestic operations only. The company derives approximately 63% of its revenue from distribution of food & supplies to its franchisees.

Key Personnel
DAVID A. BRANDON - Chairman
RUSSELL J. WEINER - CEO
JOE JORDAN - President United States; COO
SANDEEP REDDY - CFO
KELLY GARCIA - CTO; Exec VP
KATE TRUMBULL - Chief Marketing Officer Global; Exec VP
KEVIN MORRIS - Exec VP; Corporate Secretary; General Counsel
CINDY HEADEN - Exec VP Supply Chain
WEIKING NG - Exec VP International
RYAN MULALLY - Exec VP; Corporate Secretary; General Counsel
CRISTOPHER THOMAS-MOORE - Senior VP Store Systems, Customer Care
JUAN JOACHIN - Senior VP Finance
MIKE DAVIS - VP Information Technology
DEBBIE SWEENEY - VP Franchise Development
VICTORIA PETRELLA - VP Marketing, International Division
FRANK GARRIDO - VP Operations
TODD SARGENT - VP Supply Chain
HOVIG AYVAZIAN - VP Operations
ANDREW BIRCH - VP
ROSS PATRICK BEHRMAN - VP Operations
CORY WILSON - VP Engineering
DIANE PORTER - VP Franchise Operations
RYAN GOERS - VP Financial Planning, Global
SAM JACKSON - VP Human Resources
ULLIC YOUNG - VP; Transformation
JOHN KUJAN - Director Information Technology
JENNY FOURACRE-PETKO - Director Public Relations
MICHAEL GRANGE - Director Digital Experience
JASON MCMANN - Director E-Commerce
JUNE ESPINOSA - Director Construction
CRAIG TOMCAL - Director Development
COREY PETTYJOHN - Director Development, West Region
MARK MESSING - Director Digital Marketing
MARCUS JACKSON - Director Logistics
ZACHARY BUGOSH - Director Strategy, Consumer Insights
KELLY ELDRACHER - Director Franchise Development
JESSICA PARISH - Director Financial Planning
MIKE HARDIN - Director Operations, Innovation
KRIS HOLLEY - Director Field Marketing
TOBIN NORTHWAY - Director Finance
JON RICHARDS - Director Finance, International
KUTSAL BERBEROGLU - Director Architecture
LAUREN FARRANT - Director Human Resources
AURELIUS SUMPTER - Director Operations
SCOTT DOWLER - Director
TIM CHIPMAN - Director Engineering
DUSTIN OPIELA - Director Finance
SCOTT KNAPP - Director Supply Chain
JOHN PEOPLES - Director Supply Chain
RADEK WILK - Regional Director
DAN CARDEN - Manager Purchasing
BRIAN LEIPOLD - Manager Communications
ERIC MEERSCHAERT - Manager Franchise Development
TODD BOS - Manager
ANTONIOS SAAD - Manager Information Technology
PETER ECHTINAW - Administrator Network
LANA CHUMACHENKO - Consultant Franchise Development
BRANT LANCE - Analyst Finance
TANYA SPRY - Analyst Marketing, Advertising

Lefty's Famous Cheesesteaks, Hoagies & Grill
3157 Ann Arbor Saline Rd
Ann Arbor, MI 48108

Telephone: (734) 929-2122
Internet Homepage: eatleftys.com
Type of Business: Chain Restaurant Operator
Year Founded: 2012
Systemwide Sales: $30,546,000 (e)
Total Sales: $6,965,000 (e)
Total Units: 29
Trade Names: Lefty's Famous Cheesesteaks, Hoagies & Grill (29)
Company-Owned Units: 1
Units Franchised To: 28
Primary Menu: American (29)
Type of Foodservice: Fast Casual (29)

Key Personnel
SAM BERRY - Founder; President

Mainstreet Ventures Inc.
15 Research Dr
Ann Arbor, MI 48103-2974

Telephone: (734) 668-6062
Fax Number: (734) 668-7261
Internet Homepage: msventures.com
Company Email: info@msventures.com
Type of Business: Chain Restaurant Operator
Year Founded: 1980
Total Sales: $25,290,000 (e)
Alcohol Sales: 10%
Number of Employees: 865
Average Check: Lunch(24); Dinner(36)
Total Units: 23
Trade Names: Blue Pointe Oyster Bar & Seafood Grill (1); Carson's American Bistro (1); Ciao (1); EO Burgers (1); Gratzi Restauant (2); Palio (3); Real Seafood (4); Stillwater Grill (2); The Chop House (6); Tidewater Grill (1); Zia's (1)
Company-Owned Units: 23
Preferred Square Footage: 5,000; 20,000

Preferred Location Types: Freestanding; Regional Mall
Alcohol Served: Beer, Wine, Liquor
Primary Menu: American (1); Hamburger (1); Italian (7); Seafood (6); Steak (6); Steak/Seafood (2)
Areas of Operation: FL, MD, MI, OH, WV
Type of Foodservice: Casual Dining (3); Fine Dining (20)
Primary Distributors: (Full Line) SYSCO Detroit LLC, CANTON, MI

Key Personnel
MICHAEL C. GIBBONS - CEO; President
BRENT COURSON - Executive Chef
KEVIN GUDEJKO - Director Operations
PAM TALCOTT - Director Finance
TODD WINTERS - Director Marketing
KIMBERLY SHELDON - Director Marketing

Noble Food Group
1000 Frank Lloyd Wright Dr
Ann Arbor, MI 48106

Telephone: (314) 435-6714
Type of Business: Chain Restaurant Operator
Total Sales: $89,516,000 (e)
Total Units: 44
Trade Names: Domino's (44)
Units Franchised From: 44
Primary Menu: Pizza (44)
Areas of Operation: MI
Type of Foodservice: Quick Serve (44)
Franchise Affiliation: Domino's Pizza Inc, ANN ARBOR, MI

Key Personnel
BRUCE VANDENBERG - Chairman
JOSEPH E. SIEVE - President
MICHAEL BERG - General Manager
DAVID JOY - Manager Operations

Sweetwaters Group LLC
123 W Washington St
Ann Arbor, MI 48104

Telephone: (734) 769-2331
Internet Homepage: sweetwaterscafe.com
Type of Business: Chain Restaurant Operator
Year Founded: 1993
Total Sales: $38,767,000 (e)
Total Units: 27
Trade Names: Sweetwaters Coffee & Tea (27)
Company-Owned Units: 1
Units Franchised To: 26
Primary Menu: Coffee (27)
Projected Openings: 13
Type of Foodservice: Fast Casual (27)

Key Personnel
WEI BEE - Co-Founder; Co-President
LISA BEE - Co-Founder; Co-President

Zingerman's Community of Business
422 Detroit St
Ann Arbor, MI 48104-1118

Telephone: (734) 663-3354
Fax Number: (734) 913-5383
Internet Homepage: zingermans.com; zingermanscommunity.com
Company Email: service@zingermans.com
Type of Business: Chain Restaurant Operator
Year Founded: 1982
Total Sales: $10,880,000 (e)
Alcohol Sales: 10%
Number of Employees: 550
Average Check: Breakfast(12); Lunch(20); Dinner(20)
Internet Order Processing: Yes
Internet Sales: 10.00%
Total Units: 6
Trade Names: Miss Kim (1); Zingerman's Bakehouse (1); Zingerman's Coffee Co. (1); Zingerman's Creamery (1); Zingerman's Delicatessen (1); Zingerman's Roadhouse (1)
Company-Owned Units: 6
Preferred Location Types: Downtown; Freestanding
Alcohol Served: Beer, Wine, Liquor
Primary Menu: American (1); Asian (1); Coffee (1); Sandwiches/Deli (1); Snacks (2)
Projected Openings: 1
Areas of Operation: MI
Type of Foodservice: Family Restaurant (5); Quick Serve (1)
Catering Services: Yes
Notes: The company also operates Zingerman's mail order.

Key Personnel
PAUL SAGINAW - Co-Founder; VP Menu Development
ARI WEINZWEIG - CEO
JILL CLOKE - VP Development
RON MAURER - VP Finance, Operations

Thumb Big Boy Restaurants, Inc.
900 N Van Dyke Rd
Bad Axe, MI 48413-9174

Telephone: (989) 269-9515
Type of Business: Chain Restaurant Operator
Total Sales: $3,400,000 (e)
Total Units: 2
Trade Names: Big Boy (2)
Units Franchised From: 2
Primary Menu: American (2)
Areas of Operation: MI, OH
Type of Foodservice: Family Restaurant (2)
Franchise Affiliation: Big Boy Restaurants International LLC, WARREN, MI

Key Personnel
DARCY HUMPHREY-PHILLIPS - President; General Buyer

Kitchen Enterprises Inc
241 Latimer Ln
Battle Creek, MI 49015-3565

Telephone: (269) 962-8478
Type of Business: Chain Restaurant Operator
Total Sales: $4,816,000 (e)
Total Units: 4
Trade Names: Schlotzsky's Deli (4)
Units Franchised From: 4
Primary Menu: Sandwiches/Deli (4)
Areas of Operation: MI
Type of Foodservice: Fast Casual (4)
Franchise Affiliation: Schlotzsky's Ltd., ATLANTA, GA

Key Personnel
ERIC KITCHEN - Owner; General Buyer

McDonald's Franchise
806 Columbia Ave W
Battle Creek, MI 49015-3030

Telephone: (269) 965-1402
Type of Business: Chain Restaurant Operator
Total Sales: $33,090,000 (e)
Total Units: 7
Trade Names: McDonald's (7)
Units Franchised From: 7
Preferred Square Footage: 2,500
Preferred Location Types: Freestanding
Primary Menu: Hamburger (7)
Areas of Operation: MI
Type of Foodservice: Quick Serve (7)
Franchise Affiliation: McDonald's Corporation, CHICAGO, IL

Key Personnel
BILL MRAK - Owner; General Buyer

Novo Operations, Inc.
950 Territorial Rd W
Battle Creek, MI 49015-2930

Telephone: (269) 962-6808
Fax Number: (269) 962-1117
Type of Business: Chain Restaurant Operator
Total Sales: $11,320,000 (e)
Number of Employees: 250

Total Units: 5
Trade Names: Burger King (5)
Units Franchised From: 5
Preferred Square Footage: 2,500
Primary Menu: Hamburger (5)
Areas of Operation: MI
Type of Foodservice: Quick Serve (5)
Franchise Affiliation: Burger King Worldwide Inc., MIAMI, FL

Key Personnel
BRUCE GALEN - President; General Buyer
CLIFFORD GALEN - VP

Arches Up North Inc
3323 Fairway Dr
Bay City, MI 48706-3373

Telephone: (989) 684-1214
Type of Business: Chain Restaurant Operator
Total Sales: $14,963,000 (e)
Total Units: 3
Trade Names: McDonald's (3)
Units Franchised From: 3
Primary Menu: Hamburger (3)
Areas of Operation: MI
Type of Foodservice: Quick Serve (3)
Franchise Affiliation: McDonald's Corporation, CHICAGO, IL

Key Personnel
PAUL DRZEWICKI - President; General Buyer
MARY LOU DRZEWICKI - VP

Domino's Franchisee
1213 Kosciuszko Ave
Bay City, MI 48708-7903

Telephone: (989) 892-2520
Type of Business: Chain Restaurant Operator
Total Sales: $6,125,000 (e)
Total Units: 3
Trade Names: Domino's (3)
Units Franchised From: 3
Primary Menu: Pizza (3)
Areas of Operation: MI
Type of Foodservice: Quick Serve (3)
Franchise Affiliation: Domino's Pizza Inc, ANN ARBOR, MI

Key Personnel
CHRIS A. SCHLOEMANN - Owner; General Buyer

Inn At Bay Harbor
3600 Village Harbor Dr
Bay Harbor, MI 49770-8577

Telephone: (231) 439-4000
Fax Number: (231) 439-4094
Internet Homepage: innatbayharbor.com
Company Email: info@boyne.com
Type of Business: Chain Restaurant Operator
Year Founded: 1999
Total Sales: $9,026,000 (e)
Alcohol Sales: 8%
Number of Employees: 45
Average Check: Breakfast(14); Lunch(20); Dinner(28)
Total Units: 4
Trade Names: The Inn Cafe (1); The Links Grill (1); The Sagamore Room (1); Vintage Chophouse (1)
Company-Owned Units: 4
Preferred Location Types: Hotel/Motel
Alcohol Served: Beer, Wine, Liquor
Primary Menu: American (3); Steak (1)
Areas of Operation: MI
Type of Foodservice: Casual Dining (2); Fine Dining (1); Quick Serve (1)
Primary Distributors: (Food) SYSCO Food Services of Grand Rapids LLC, GRAND RAPIDS, MI

Key Personnel
MIKE COSTELLO - President; General Manager; General Buyer
KENT KREHEL - Director Food and Beverage
CHRISTOPHER EWING - Manager Restaurant Operations

Benito's Pizza
565 Main St
Belleville, MI 48111-2649

Telephone: (734) 697-9128
Internet Homepage: benitospizza.com
Type of Business: Chain Restaurant Operator
Systemwide Sales: $20,066,000 (e)
Total Sales: $7,855,000 (e)
Number of Employees: 242
Average Check: Dinner(6)
Internet Order Processing: Yes
Total Units: 23
Trade Names: Benito's Pizza (23)
Company-Owned Units: 8
Units Franchised To: 18
Primary Menu: Pizza (23)
Projected Openings: 1
Areas of Operation: AZ, CA, MI
Type of Foodservice: Fast Casual (23)

Key Personnel
BENITO MAUTONE - Partner; General Buyer
JASON MAUTONE - Partner

Sobeck Enterprises
1755 Rosemont Rd
Berkley, MI 48072-2174

Telephone: (248) 563-3563
Fax Number: (248) 542-9832
Internet Homepage: chickenshack.com
Company Email: comments@chickenshack.com
Type of Business: Chain Restaurant Operator
Year Founded: 1956
Total Sales: $13,480,000 (e)
Number of Employees: 65
Average Check: Lunch(8); Dinner(8)
Total Units: 21
Trade Names: Chicken Shack (21)
Company-Owned Units: 21
Preferred Square Footage: 3,000
Preferred Location Types: Freestanding; Outlet Mall; Regional Mall; Strip Mall
Primary Menu: Chicken (21)
Areas of Operation: MI
Type of Foodservice: Family Restaurant (21)

Key Personnel
MARK SOBECK - President; Director Menu Development; General Buyer
PHILIP SOBECK - Owner
NEIL SOBECK - VP
IOLA SOBECK - Treasurer

FJH Investment Co
33703 Woodward Ave
Birmingham, MI 48009-0913

Mailing Address: PO Box 1809, BIRMINGHAM, MI, 48012-1809
Telephone: (248) 644-3090
Fax Number: (248) 644-3895
Internet Homepage: oph-mi.com
Company Email: office@oph-mi.com
Type of Business: Chain Restaurant Operator
Year Founded: 1962
Total Sales: $10,680,000 (e)
Number of Employees: 100
Average Check: Breakfast(12); Lunch(14); Dinner(14)
Total Units: 3
Trade Names: The Original Pancake House (3)
Units Franchised From: 3
Preferred Location Types: Downtown; Freestanding
Primary Menu: American (3)
Areas of Operation: MI
Type of Foodservice: Family Restaurant (3)
Franchise Affiliation: The Original Pancake House Franchising Inc., PORTLAND, OR
Primary Distributors: (Full Line) SYSCO Detroit LLC, CANTON, MI

Key Personnel
FRANK HAMILTON - President; General Manager; General Buyer
JOHANNA HAMILTON - Manager Accounting, Human Resources

G & S Restaurants
33900 Woodward Ave
Birmingham, MI 48009-0916

Telephone: (248) 646-1375
Type of Business: Chain Restaurant Operator
Year Founded: 1974
Total Sales: $9,085,000 (e)
Number of Employees: 125
Average Check: Lunch(10); Dinner(12)
Total Units: 5
Trade Names: KFC (4); KFC/Taco Bell (1)
Units Franchised From: 5
Preferred Square Footage: 3,000
Preferred Location Types: Freestanding
Primary Menu: Chicken (5); Taco (1)
Areas of Operation: MI
Type of Foodservice: Quick Serve (5)
Franchise Affiliation: KFC Corporation, LOUISVILLE, KY; Taco Bell Corp., IRVINE, CA
Primary Distributors: (Full Line) Caramagno Foods Co. Inc., DETROIT, MI

Key Personnel
JAMES MIKULA SR - President; Owner; General Manager; Director Operations, Facility/Maintenance, Information Systems, Real Estate, Design, Training, Food Safety; General Buyer

Heirloom Hospitality Group, LLC
217 Pierce St Ste 207
Birmingham, MI 48009

Telephone: (248) 294-0700
Internet Homepage: eatattownhouse.com; heirloomhospitality.com; primeandproperdetroit.com; http:clementinadetroit.com
Company Email: info@heirloomhospitality.com
Type of Business: Chain Restaurant Operator
Total Units: 4
Trade Names: Clementina (1); Prime + Proper (1); Townhouse (2)
Company-Owned Units: 4
Primary Menu: American (2); Mexican (1); Steak (1)
Areas of Operation: MI
Type of Foodservice: Casual Dining (4)

Key Personnel
JEREMY SASSON - President
KRIS VELASQUEZ - Executive Director

Benefits-Beverages
SHARYN HARDING - Executive Chef
JUSTIN JONES - Manager Restaurant Operations

Leo's Coney Island
154 S Old Woodward Ave Ste 100
Birmingham, MI 48009-6104

Telephone: (248) 540-3173
Internet Homepage: leosconeyisland.com
Company Email: contact@leosconeyisland.com
Type of Business: Chain Restaurant Operator
Year Founded: 1972
Internet Order Processing: Yes
Total Units: 61
Trade Names: Leo's Coney Island (61)
Company-Owned Units: 61
Primary Menu: Greek/Mediterranean (61)
Areas of Operation: MI
Type of Foodservice: Quick Serve (61)

Key Personnel
LEO STASSINOPOULOS - Partner; VP Purchasing, Marketing, Menu Development
KELLY ROY - CFO

BC Pizza Inc.
1191 S M 75
Boyne City, MI 49712-9726

Mailing Address: PO Box 244, BOYNE CITY, MI, 49712-0244
Telephone: (231) 582-2288
Fax Number: (231) 582-3478
Internet Homepage: bcpizza.net; bclanes.com
Company Email: contactcorporate@bcpizza.net
Type of Business: Chain Restaurant Operator
Year Founded: 1988
Systemwide Sales: $25,158,000 (e)
Total Sales: $4,127,000 (e)
Number of Employees: 68
Average Check: Lunch(10); Dinner(16)
Internet Order Processing: Yes
Total Units: 31
Trade Names: BC Lanes (1); BC Pizza (30)
Company-Owned Units: 6
Units Franchised To: 25
Preferred Square Footage: 1,500; 2,500; 3,500; 4,000
Preferred Location Types: Freestanding; Regional Mall; Strip Mall
Primary Menu: American (1); Pizza (30)
Areas of Operation: MI
Type of Foodservice: Casual Dining (1); Fast Casual (31)
Catering Services: Yes

Key Personnel
CHRIS NELSON - Partner; Director Operations, Facility/Maintenance, Information Systems, Supply Chain, Marketing, Real Estate, Design; General Buyer
SANDRA NELSON - Partner; Executive Chef; Director Catering
WAYNE NELSON - Partner; Director Operations, Purchasing, Facility/Maintenance, Information Systems, Real Estate, Design, Franchising, Store Fixtures

Team Lyders
7915 Kensington Ct
Brighton, MI 48116-8597

Telephone: (248) 446-0100
Fax Number: (248) 446-0300
Internet Homepage: teamlyders.com
Type of Business: Chain Restaurant Operator
Year Founded: 1983
Total Sales: $299,890,000 (e)
Number of Employees: 3,900
Average Check: Lunch(10); Dinner(10)
Total Units: 174
Trade Names: KFC; Taco Bell; Taco Bell/KFC; Taco Bell/Pizza Hut
Units Franchised From: 174
Preferred Square Footage: 2,500
Preferred Location Types: Freestanding; Strip Mall
Areas of Operation: IL, MI, OH, WI
Type of Foodservice: Quick Serve (174)
Franchise Affiliation: KFC Corporation, LOUISVILLE, KY; Pizza Hut Inc., PLANO, TX; Taco Bell Corp., IRVINE, CA
Primary Distributors: (Food) McLane/Hebron, HEBRON, KY

Key Personnel
PETE LYDERS - President; Director Finance, Real Estate
JINI FOUST - COO
DON CLARK - CIO
BRANDON TYLER - General Manager Restaurant Operations
TIM KRAUSE - Director Construction
CLINT LYDERS-PETERSEN - Director Development
SCOTT JORDAN-WHEELER - Director Operations
CHRISTOPHER HENRY - Director Operations
DANE MAMULA - Regional Director
MARTY KIRBY - Manager Accounting, Human Resources
JENNIFER CRAWFORD - Manager Development
KATELYN LYDERS-PETERSEN - Specialist Human Resources

Nevaeh
306 S Main St
Brooklyn, MI 49230-9307

Telephone: (517) 592-6134
Type of Business: Chain Restaurant Operator
Total Sales: $47,860,000 (e)
Total Units: 10
Trade Names: McDonald's (10)
Units Franchised From: 10
Preferred Square Footage: 2,500
Preferred Location Types: Freestanding
Primary Menu: Hamburger (10)
Areas of Operation: MI
Type of Foodservice: Quick Serve (10)
Franchise Affiliation: McDonald's Corporation, CHICAGO, IL

Key Personnel
STEVEN HOGWOOD - President; General Buyer

Halo Country LLC
5161 E Court St N
Burton, MI 48509

Telephone: (800) 293-4256
Fax Number: (810) 771-4493
Internet Homepage: haloburger.com
Company Email:
   customercare@haloburger.com
Type of Business: Chain Restaurant Operator
Year Founded: 1923
Total Sales: $36,030,000 (e)
Number of Employees: 1,350
Average Check: Lunch(8); Dinner(8)
Total Units: 8
Trade Names: Halo Burger (8)
Company-Owned Units: 8
Preferred Square Footage: 1,700
Preferred Location Types: Downtown; Freestanding
Primary Menu: Hamburger (8)
Areas of Operation: MI
Type of Foodservice: Quick Serve (8)

Key Personnel
CHANCE RICHIE - CEO; Partner
DANIEL STERN - Partner
ROB KULZA - Director Information Technology

Bradley Investments Ltd
1445 N Mitchell St
Cadillac, MI 49601-1128

Telephone: (231) 775-1782
Type of Business: Chain Restaurant Operator
Total Sales: $12,830,000 (e)
Total Units: 21

Trade Names: Subway (21)
Units Franchised From: 21
Primary Menu: Sandwiches/Deli (21)
Areas of Operation: MI
Type of Foodservice: Quick Serve (21)
Franchise Affiliation: Doctor's Associates Inc., MILFORD, CT

Key Personnel
BRAD LAPOE - President; General Buyer
STEVEN MACDONALD - President

May Van Corp
47665 Gratiot Ave
Chesterfield, MI 48051-2719

Telephone: (586) 949-8570
Type of Business: Chain Restaurant Operator
Total Sales: $2,473,000 (e)
Number of Employees: 18
Total Units: 4
Trade Names: Subway (4)
Units Franchised From: 4
Primary Menu: Sandwiches/Deli (4)
Areas of Operation: MI
Type of Foodservice: Quick Serve (4)
Franchise Affiliation: Doctor's Associates Inc., MILFORD, CT

Key Personnel
MARYJANE MAY - President

Union Joints LLC
90 N Main St
Clarkston, MI 48346-1516

Telephone: (248) 537-0300
Internet Homepage: unionjoints.com
Company Email: info@unionjoints.com
Type of Business: Chain Restaurant Operator
Total Units: 7
Trade Names: Clarkston Union (1); Fenton Firehall (1); Honcho (1); Pumphouse Custard (1); Union General (1); Union Woodshop (1); Vinsetta Garage (1)
Company-Owned Units: 7
Primary Menu: American (4); Bar-B-Q (1); Snacks (2)
Areas of Operation: MI
Type of Foodservice: Casual Dining (5); Quick Serve (2)

Key Personnel
CURT CATALLO - Owner; General Buyer

Angona Pizza, Inc.
5318 Lancaster Ln
Commerce Township, MI 48382-2882

Telephone: (248) 515-2185
Internet Homepage: teamangona.com
Type of Business: Chain Restaurant Operator
Total Sales: $11,130,000 (e)
Total Units: 9
Trade Names: Little Caesars Pizza (9)
Units Franchised From: 9
Primary Menu: Pizza (9)
Areas of Operation: MI
Type of Foodservice: Quick Serve (9)
Franchise Affiliation: Little Caesar Enterprises Inc., DETROIT, MI

Key Personnel
ROBERT ANGONA - President; General Buyer

Askar Brands
8101 Richardson Rd Ste 101
Commerce Township, MI 48390-4115

Telephone: (248) 363-4580
Fax Number: (248) 888-0011
Internet Homepage: askarbrands.com; cjsbrewery.com; mrpita.com; papaspizzatogo.com; stucchisicecream.com; blackjackpizza.com; breadeauxpizza.com
Company Email: comments@askarbrands.com
Type of Business: Chain Restaurant Operator
Year Founded: 1985
Systemwide Sales: $49,095,000 (e)
Total Sales: $4,753,000 (e)
Alcohol Sales: 3%
Number of Employees: 20
Average Check: Dinner(20)
Total Units: 142
Trade Names: Blackjack Pizza (45); Breadeaux Pizza (15); CJs Brewery (2); Mr. Pita (23); Papa Romano's (27); Papa's Pizza To Go (28); Stucchi's Ice Cream (2)
Units Franchised To: 142
Preferred Square Footage: 1,000; 1,500; 2,200; 3,000; 5,000
Preferred Location Types: Community Mall; Freestanding; Strip Mall
Alcohol Served: Beer, Wine
Primary Menu: American (2); Health Foods (23); Pizza (115); Snacks (2)
Projected Openings: 10
Areas of Operation: CO, FL, IL, MI, MO, TN
Type of Foodservice: Casual Dining (2); Quick Serve (140)
Foodservice Management Venues: Schools
Catering Services: Yes
Primary Distributors: (Food) Performance Foodservice, SPRINGFIELD, MO

Key Personnel
CASEY ASKAR - Chairman; President
SAM ASKAR - CEO
MIKE GASTON - VP Division
SCOTT MOSER - Director Operations, Branding
MIKE MATCZAK - Director Administration, Training, Business Development
MITCHELL REUTER - Director Business Development

Pfau Properties
8086 Flagstaff St
Commerce Township, MI 48382-2329

Telephone: (248) 366-7601
Type of Business: Chain Restaurant Operator
Total Sales: $55,700,000 (e)
Total Units: 12
Trade Names: McDonald's (12)
Units Franchised From: 12
Preferred Square Footage: 2,500
Primary Menu: Hamburger (12)
Areas of Operation: MI
Type of Foodservice: Quick Serve (12)
Franchise Affiliation: McDonald's Corporation, CHICAGO, IL

Key Personnel
F. MARK PFAU - President; General Buyer

MAC Pizza LLC
1081 S State Rd
Davison, MI 48423-1903

Mailing Address: P.O. Box 479, DAVISON, MI, 48423
Telephone: (810) 653-8165
Type of Business: Chain Restaurant Operator
Total Sales: $26,310,000 (e)
Number of Employees: 465
Average Check: Dinner(16)
Total Units: 21
Trade Names: Little Caesars Pizza (21)
Units Franchised From: 21
Preferred Square Footage: 1,600; 3,000
Preferred Location Types: Freestanding; Strip Mall
Primary Menu: Pizza (21)
Areas of Operation: MI
Type of Foodservice: Quick Serve (21)
Franchise Affiliation: Little Caesar Enterprises Inc., DETROIT, MI

Key Personnel
MIKE CAIN - Owner; Controller
DAN SHEROSKI - VP
DENISE SHEROSKI - Director Restaurant Operations
SHARON SHEROSKI - Director Accounting

Joe Kowal
400 N Telegraph Rd
Dearborn, MI 48128-1619

Telephone: (313) 730-7918
Type of Business: Chain Restaurant Operator
Total Sales: $2,511,000 (e)
Total Units: 4
Trade Names: Subway (4)
Units Franchised From: 4
Primary Menu: Sandwiches/Deli (4)
Areas of Operation: MI
Type of Foodservice: Quick Serve (4)
Franchise Affiliation: Doctor's Associates Inc., MILFORD, CT

Key Personnel
JOE KOWAL - President; General Buyer

Leon's
23830 Michigan Ave
Dearborn, MI 48124-1829

Telephone: (313) 563-3713
Fax Number: (313) 563-2341
Internet Homepage: thehouseofleon.com
Type of Business: Chain Restaurant Operator
Year Founded: 1983
Total Sales: $9,061,000 (e)
Number of Employees: 280
Average Check: Breakfast(6); Lunch(8); Dinner(8)
Total Units: 7
Trade Names: Leon's (7)
Company-Owned Units: 7
Preferred Square Footage: 5,500; 6,000
Preferred Location Types: Freestanding
Primary Menu: American (7)
Areas of Operation: MI
Type of Foodservice: Family Restaurant (7)
Primary Distributors: (Food) US Foods, WIXOM, MI

Key Personnel
SAM LEON - President; Executive Chef; Director Finance, Operations, Facility/Maintenance, Design, Store Fixtures; General Buyer
WALLY LEON - Partner; Director Real Estate, Human Resources
ABE LEON - Partner; General Manager; General Buyer
LENA LEON - Partner; General Manager; General Buyer
MOE LEON - Partner; Director Supply Chain, Ethnic Marketing
TOM LEWIS - General Manager; Director Purchasing, Information Systems

The Henry Ford Museum
20900 Oakwood Blvd
Dearborn, MI 48124-5029

Mailing Address: PO Box 1970, DEARBORN, MI, 48121-1970
Telephone: (313) 271-1620
Internet Homepage: thehenryford.org
Company Email: sales@thehenryford.org
Type of Business: Chain Restaurant Operator
Year Founded: 1929
Total Sales: $23,860,000 (e)
Alcohol Sales: 7%
Number of Employees: 1,320
Average Check: Lunch(16); Dinner(16)
Internet Order Processing: Yes
Internet Sales: 1.00%
Total Units: 12
Trade Names: A Taste Of History (1); American Dog House (1); Eagle Tavern (1); Frozen Custard (1); Lamy's Diner (1); Michigan Cafe (1); Mrs. Fisher's Southern Cooking (1); Sir John Bennett Sweet Shop (1); State Street Lunch Stand (1); Tea At The Cotwald Cottage (1); The Carousel (1); The Guild Beer Hall(1)
Company-Owned Units: 12
Preferred Square Footage: 4,000
Preferred Location Types: Freestanding; Kiosk; Mobile Unit; Parks
Alcohol Served: Beer, Wine, Liquor
Primary Menu: American (7); Bar-B-Q (1); Hot Dogs (1); Snacks (3)
Areas of Operation: MI
Type of Foodservice: Cafeteria (2); Casual Dining (4); Family Restaurant (1); Quick Serve (5)
On-site Distribution Center: Yes
Primary Distributors: (Full Line) SYSCO Detroit LLC, CANTON, MI

Key Personnel
PATRICIA K. MOORADIAN - President; Corporate Secretary
BRENT OTT - CFO; VP
SPENCE MEDFORD - VP
LISA A. PAYNE - Treasurer
CYNTHIA JONES - General Manager
AMY COX - Director Operations
CAROLYN WARD - Director Marketing
LEE WARD - Director Food and Beverage
WENDY METROS - Director Media
KEVIN CUBBERLY - Director Information Technology
CHRISTIAN CULLEN - Director Operations
CINDY BARAN - Coordinator Food and Beverage

Toarmina's Pizza Inc.
23922 Cherry Hill
Dearborn, MI 48124

Telephone: (313) 274-6116
Fax Number: (734) 729-1882
Internet Homepage: toarminas.com
Type of Business: Chain Restaurant Operator
Year Founded: 1986
Systemwide Sales: $17,250,000 (e)
Total Sales: $6,185,000 (e)
Number of Employees: 10
Average Check: Dinner(36)
Total Units: 23
Trade Names: Toarmina's Pizza (23)
Units Franchised To: 23
Preferred Square Footage: 1,000
Preferred Location Types: Airports; Downtown; Freestanding; Regional Mall; Strip Mall
Primary Menu: Pizza (14)
Areas of Operation: MI
Type of Foodservice: Quick Serve (14)
Catering Services: Yes

Key Personnel
LOU TOARMINA - Owner; Executive Chef; Director Loss Prevention, Risk Management, Quality Assurance, Research & Development, Product Development, Menu Development, Food Safety; General Buyer

Greektown Holdings LLC
555 E Lafayette Blvd
Detroit, MI 48226-2924

Telephone: (313) 223-2999
Internet Homepage: greektowncasino.com
Company Email: contactus@greektowncasino.com
Type of Business: Foodservice Operations - Casinos
Year Founded: 2005
Total Sales: $481,290,000 (e)
Alcohol Sales: 10%
Total Units: 10
Trade Names: American Burger Bar (1); Basil Leaf Pizza (1); Bistro 555 (1); Josephine Bakery (1); Noodle Art (1); Pit Boss (1); Prism (1); Southern Fry (1); Stack'd (1); Tia Loca (1)
Company-Owned Units: 10
Alcohol Served: Beer, Wine, Liquor
Primary Menu: American (1); Asian (1); Bar-B-Q (1); Chicken (1); Hamburger (1); Mexican (1); Miscellaneous (1); Snacks (1); Steak/Seafood (1)
Areas of Operation: MI
Type of Foodservice: Casual Dining (4); Fast Casual (1); Fine Dining (1); Quick Serve (4)

Key Personnel
MARVIN BEATTY - Owner
CLIFFORD J. VALLIER - CFO
NATHAN WELLMAN - Director
BRAD BALDWIN - Director Operations
MARIELA MYFTARI - Director Internal Audit
JOSEPH LOPEZ - Assistant Director Food and Beverage
SEAN MATSON - Manager

Janjomar Inc.
1000 Mack Ave
Detroit, MI 48207

Mailing Address: PO Box 07518, DETROIT, MI, 48207
Telephone: (313) 394-0436
Internet Homepage: jamjomar.mybigcommerce.com
Type of Business: Chain Restaurant Operator
Year Founded: 1989
Total Sales: $80,910,000 (e)
Total Units: 17
Trade Names: McDonald's (17)
Units Franchised From: 17
Preferred Square Footage: 2,500
Primary Menu: Hamburger (17)
Areas of Operation: LA, MI
Type of Foodservice: Quick Serve (17)
Franchise Affiliation: McDonald's Corporation, CHICAGO, IL

Key Personnel
JAMES THROWER - President; Partner; General Buyer
JAMES THROWER JR - Partner
JONI THROWER - Partner; General Counsel
MARLA THROWER - Partner
JAMAR THROWER - Partner

Little Caesar Enterprises Inc.
2125 Woodward Ave
Detroit, MI 48201-3400

Telephone: (313) 471-6000
Fax Number: (313) 471-6399
Internet Homepage: franchise.littlecaesars.com; littlecaesars.ca; littlecaesars.com
Company Email: customerservice@lcecorp.com
Type of Business: Chain Restaurant Operator
Year Founded: 1959
Systemwide Sales: $5,566,731,000 (e)
Total Sales: $783,700,000 (e)
Average Check: Lunch(12); Dinner(12)
Total Units: 4,237
Trade Names: Little Caesars Pizza (4,237)
Company-Owned Units: 567
Units Franchised To: 3,670
Preferred Square Footage: 1,600; 3,000
Preferred Location Types: Airports; Community Mall; Freestanding; Institution (college/hospital); Stadiums; Strip Mall; Travel Plazas
Primary Menu: Pizza (4,237)
Projected Openings: 195
Areas of Operation: AK, AL, AR, AZ, CA, CO, CT, DE, FL, GA, GU, HI, IA, ID, IL, IN, KS, KY, LA, MA, MD, ME, MI, MN, MO, MS, MT, NC, ND, NE, NH, NJ, NM, NV, NY, OH, OK, OR, PA, PR, RI, SC, SD, TN, TX, UT, VA, VI, VT, WA, WI, WV, WY, AB, BC, MB, NB, NS, ON, QC, SK
Foreign Countries: ARUBA; AUSTRALIA; BAHRAIN; CANADA; COSTA RICA; CZECH REPUBLIC; ECUADOR; EGYPT; EL SALVADOR; GUATEMALA; HONDURAS; INDIA; IRELAND; JORDAN; KUWAIT; MEXICO; PANAMA; SAUDI ARABIA; SINGAPORE; SLOVAKIA; THE PHILIPPINES; TURKEY; UNITED ARAB EMIRATES
Type of Foodservice: Quick Serve (4,237)
Primary Distributors: (Full Line) Blue Line Foodservice Distribution, SAN ANTONIO, TX
Parent Company: Ilitch Holdings Inc., DETROIT, MI
Regional Offices: Little Caesar's of Canada Inc., MISSISSAUGA, ON CANADA
Notes: Total units and sales reflect US operations only.

Key Personnel
DAVID SCRIVANO - CEO; President
CHRISTOPHER ILITCH - CEO Division; President Division
EDWARD GLEICH - President Global
PAULA VISSING - President Retail Operations
KEITH FAIGIN - CIO
ANITA KLOPHENSTEIN - CIO
LANCE SHINABARGER - CIO Technology
GREG HAMILTON - Chief Marketing Officer
AFIA PHILLIPS - Chief Information Security Officer
RUSSELL PAGAN - Global VP Operations
DARRELL SNYGG - Senior VP Finance, Accounting, Administration
ERIN MARTIN - VP; General Counsel
SCOTT HAVEMAN - VP Compliance
ALISON BIERI - VP Accounting
TRACY SHUMAN - VP Operations
JAMES DAMLE - VP Financial Planning
ROBERT "BOB" KARWAN - Senior Director Real Estate
WALT FREDERIKSEN - Senior Director Advertising
BOB LAFEVER - Director Construction
BILL OCHADLEUS - Director Loss Prevention
CHRISTINE SNYDER - Director Brand Marketing
MIKE FLAHERTY - Director Finance
ROBERT VERIATO - Director Real Estate, West Region
HIBA KAKISH - Director Product Development
COURTNEY HODARE - Director Recruitment; Developer Talent Acquisitions

JODI GENRICH - Director Finance, Franchise Operations
DEAN BAGNASCO - Director Field Marketing
BRYAN KETELHUT - Director Strategic Planning
SCOTT RICHARDS - Director Accounting
BILL KNEIFEL - Director Innovation
JEFF LANG - Director E-Commerce
LINDA ZAZISKI - Director Safety
SCOTT FLECK - Director Applications, Digital
MINIMOL MATHEW - Director Software Engineering
JULIE BLUE AIA - Director Architecture, Design
THOMAS T. SCHOENBERGER - Director Real Estate
KEVIN BURRIS - Director Franchise Operations
LUIS MENENDEZ - Regional Manager Loss Prevention
CHRISTINE MASSA - Manager Purchasing
BRADLEY PUCKETT - Manager Information Systems, Real Estate
LAURIE MEGUIAR-LISISCKI - Manager Human Resources
JORGE CONCHA - Manager Marketing
MICHELLE KING BARKOFF - Coordinator Construction
KAYLA GERBER - Coordinator Event Planning

Mexican Village Restaurant
2600 Bagley St
Detroit, MI 48216-1722

Telephone: (313) 237-0333
Fax Number: (313) 237-0203
Internet Homepage: mexicanvillagefood.com
Company Email: mexicanvillage@comcast.net
Type of Business: Chain Restaurant Operator
Total Sales: $4,457,000 (e)
Alcohol Sales: 5%
Average Check: Dinner(12)
Total Units: 2
Trade Names: Mexican Village Restaurant (2)
Company-Owned Units: 2
Preferred Location Types: Freestanding
Alcohol Served: Beer, Wine, Liquor
Primary Menu: Mexican (2)
Areas of Operation: MI
Type of Foodservice: Casual Dining (2)
Catering Services: Yes

Key Personnel
SEVERO GONZALEZ - Partner; Director Menu Development

MotorCity Casino
2901 Grand River Ave
Detroit, MI 48201-2907

Telephone: (866) 752-9622
Internet Homepage: motorcitycasino.com
Type of Business: Chain Restaurant Operator
Total Sales: $1,031,300,000 (e)
Foodservice Sales: $257,825,000 (e)
Total Units: 6
Trade Names: Assembly Line (1); Grand River Deli (1); Iridescence (1); Little Caesars (1); Sweet Ride Coffee (1); The Lodge Diner (1)
Company-Owned Units: 5
Units Franchised From: 1
Preferred Location Types: Hotel/Motel
Alcohol Served: Beer, Wine, Liquor
Primary Menu: American (2); Bar-B-Q (1); Pizza (1); Sandwiches/Deli (1); Snacks (1)
Areas of Operation: MI
Type of Foodservice: Cafeteria (1); Casual Dining (1); Family Restaurant (1); Fine Dining (1); Quick Serve (2)

Key Personnel
BRUCE DALL - CFO; Senior VP
DAVID NEHRA - CIO; VP
PHILIP TROFIBIO - Senior VP Operations
RANDALL VILLAREAL - VP Operations, Food and Beverage
JOHN POLICICCHIO - VP Marketing
BRAD BAILEY - VP Finance
MICHELLE DUFFY - Director Sales
SHAWN BAUER - Director
JAMES FLYNN - Director Purchasing
ALAN GALANTY - Director Development- Training
JOEL DOEHRING - Director Operations
JOANN TAYLOR - Director Human Resources
KEVIN WHITE - Manager Production

The Epicurean Group
1380 E Jefferson Ave
Detroit, MI 48207-3104

Telephone: (248) 646-0370
Fax Number: (313) 259-3474
Internet Homepage: theepicureangroup.com; thenomadgrill.com
Type of Business: Chain Restaurant Operator
Year Founded: 1980
Total Sales: $59,700,000 (e)
Alcohol Sales: 11%
Number of Employees: 440
Average Check: Breakfast(14); Lunch(26); Dinner(40)
Internet Order Processing: Yes
Internet Sales: 4.00%
Total Units: 5
Trade Names: Epic Cafe by Design (1); Green Space Cafe (1); Nomad Grill (1); Novi Chophouse (1); Plaza Deli (1)
Company-Owned Units: 5
Preferred Location Types: Freestanding; Hotel/Motel; Strip Mall
Alcohol Served: Beer, Wine, Liquor
Primary Menu: American (3); Sandwiches/Deli (1); Steak/Seafood (1)
Areas of Operation: MI
Type of Foodservice: Casual Dining (3); Fine Dining (1); Quick Serve (1)
Catering Services: Yes
Primary Distributors: (Full Line) US Foods, WIXOM, MI
Notes: Formerly Matt Prentice Restaurant Group.

Key Personnel
PIERRE VERBEKE - Owner
HAN EPICUREAN - Owner
JONATHAN HORESKI - General Manager

Conrad's Grill
1219 E Grand River Ave
East Lansing, MI 48823

Telephone: (517) 333-7104
Internet Homepage: conradsgrill.com
Type of Business: Chain Restaurant Operator
Year Founded: 2007
Total Units: 5
Trade Names: Conrad's Grill (5)
Company-Owned Units: 5
Primary Menu: American (5)
Areas of Operation: MI
Type of Foodservice: Fast Casual (5)
Parent Company: Pivotal Growth Partners, CHICAGO, IL

Key Personnel
JOSEPH CONRAD - President
CAITLIN YOST - General Manager

Domino's Franchisee
143 N Harrison Rd Ste 200
East Lansing, MI 48823-4153

Telephone: (517) 351-7100
Type of Business: Chain Restaurant Operator
Total Sales: $7,955,000 (e)
Total Units: 4
Trade Names: Domino's (4)
Units Franchised From: 4
Primary Menu: Pizza (4)
Areas of Operation: MI
Type of Foodservice: Quick Serve (4)
Franchise Affiliation: Domino's Pizza Inc, ANN ARBOR, MI

Key Personnel
DAVID L. CESARINI - Owner; General Buyer

Global Orange Development
2501 Coolidge Rd
East Lansing, MI 48823-6352

Mailing Address: PO Box 710, EAST LANSING, MI, 48826-0710
Telephone: (517) 482-8145

Fax Number: (517) 482-8625
Internet Homepage: biggby.com
Company Email: info@biggby.com
Type of Business: Chain Restaurant Operator
Year Founded: 1995
Systemwide Sales: $175,435,000 (e)
Total Sales: $32,830,000 (e)
Number of Employees: 54
Average Check: Breakfast(10); Lunch(12); Dinner(12)
Internet Order Processing: Yes
Internet Sales: 3.00%
Total Units: 240
Trade Names: Biggby Coffee (277)
Units Franchised To: 277
Preferred Square Footage: 2,500
Preferred Location Types: Community Mall; Downtown; Freestanding; Kiosk; Office Complex; Regional Mall; Strip Mall
Primary Menu: Coffee (277)
Projected Openings: 25
Areas of Operation: FL, IL, IN, KY, MI, NJ, OH, SC, TX, WI
Type of Foodservice: Quick Serve (277)
Catering Services: Yes
Primary Distributors: (Full Line) SYSCO Detroit LLC, CANTON, MI

Key Personnel
ROBERT FISH - Co-CEO; Co-President
MICHAEL MCFALL - Co-CEO; Co-President
STEPHANIE SCHLICHTER - Director Operations
JEREMY DERUITER - Director Branding
ANTONIO DIPIETRO - Director Franchise Development
CAITLIN CARPENTER - Manager Branding
JESSICA PIPER - Specialist Internet Development-Coffee/Tea
ABBY BARTSHE - Coordinator Franchise Development

Ansara Restaurant Group
23925 Industrial Park Dr
Farmington Hills, MI 48335-2862

Telephone: (248) 848-9099
Fax Number: (248) 848-1864
Internet Homepage: ansararestaurantgroup.com
Company Email: info@ansararestaurantgroup.com
Type of Business: Chain Restaurant Operator
Year Founded: 2000
Total Sales: $49,490,000 (e)
Alcohol Sales: 10%
Number of Employees: 884
Average Check: Breakfast(8); Lunch(10); Dinner(12)
Total Units: 26
Trade Names: 2Booli (2); Burgrz (1); Portofino (1); Red Robin Gourmet Burgers & Spirits (22)
Company-Owned Units: 2
Units Franchised From: 24
Preferred Square Footage: 5,000; 7,000
Preferred Location Types: Freestanding
Alcohol Served: Beer, Wine, Liquor
Primary Menu: American (23); Greek/Mediterranean (2); Italian (1)
Areas of Operation: MI, OH
Type of Foodservice: Casual Dining (26)
Franchise Affiliation: Red Robin Gourmet Burgers Inc., ENGLEWOOD, CO
Primary Distributors: (Full Line) US Foods, WIXOM, MI

Key Personnel
VICTOR ANSARA - President; General Buyer
NADIA KHALYLEH - CFO
BRIAN COOKE - COO
ERIKA SMITH - Director Information Technology

Buddy's Pizza
31800 Northwestern Hwy Ste 206
Farmington Hills, MI 48334-1664

Telephone: (248) 855-6222
Fax Number: (248) 855-6329
Internet Homepage: buddyspizza.com
Company Email: info@buddyspizza.com
Type of Business: Chain Restaurant Operator
Year Founded: 1946
Total Sales: $23,830,000 (e)
Alcohol Sales: 20%
Number of Employees: 469
Average Check: Lunch(10); Dinner(14)
Internet Order Processing: Yes
Total Units: 12
Trade Names: Buddy's Pizzeria (12)
Company-Owned Units: 12
Preferred Square Footage: 5,000; 6,000
Preferred Location Types: Freestanding; Strip Mall
Alcohol Served: Beer, Wine, Liquor
Primary Menu: Pizza (12)
Projected Openings: 2
Areas of Operation: MI
Type of Foodservice: Casual Dining (6); Quick Serve (5)
Primary Distributors: (Full Line) US Foods, WIXOM, MI

Key Personnel
FARHAN J. - CFO
WESLEY PIKULA - VP Operations, Purchasing, Loss Prevention, Quality Assurance, Marketing, Research & Development, Menu Development, Food Safety; Executive Chef
RENEE TUCKER - Director Finance, Information Systems, Supply Chain, Human Resources

Culinary Studies Institute Oakland
27055 Orchard Lake Rd
Farmington Hills, MI 48334-4556

Telephone: (248) 522-3700
Fax Number: (248) 522-3706
Internet Homepage: oaklandcc.edu
Type of Business: Culinary Schools
Areas of Operation: MI

Key Personnel
DOUG GANHS - Executive Chef Training

Happy's Pizza LLC
30201 Orchard Lake Rd Ste 200
Farmington Hills, MI 48334-2278

Telephone: (248) 538-0000
Fax Number: (248) 539-1684
Internet Homepage: happyspizza.com
Company Email: info@happyspizza.com
Type of Business: Chain Restaurant Operator
Year Founded: 1994
Systemwide Sales: $80,313,000 (e)
Total Sales: $37,070,000 (e)
Alcohol Sales: 0.50%
Number of Employees: 470
Average Check: Dinner(14)
Internet Order Processing: Yes
Total Units: 100
Trade Names: Happy's Pizza (100)
Company-Owned Units: 24
Units Franchised To: 76
Preferred Square Footage: 1,800; 4,000
Preferred Location Types: Regional Mall; Strip Mall
Alcohol Served: Beer, Wine
Primary Menu: Pizza (100)
Areas of Operation: CA, IL, IN, MI, NV, OH
Type of Foodservice: Fast Casual (100)
Catering Services: Yes

Key Personnel
JOHN MORAN - CFO
MUSTAFA TATE - General Manager

King Dining, Inc.
32825 Northwestern Hwy
Farmington Hills, MI 48334-1453

Telephone: (248) 539-3333
Fax Number: (248) 932-4050
Internet Homepage: asmarcapital.com
Type of Business: Chain Restaurant Operator
Total Sales: $9,308,000 (e)
Total Units: 5
Trade Names: Arby's (5)
Units Franchised From: 5

Preferred Square Footage: 2,500
Primary Menu: Sandwiches/Deli (5)
Areas of Operation: MI
Type of Foodservice: Quick Serve (5)
Franchise Affiliation: Arby's Restaurant Group, ATLANTA, GA

Key Personnel
ROBERT ASMAR - President; Owner; General Buyer
JIMMY ASMAR - VP

Natron Corp.
29375 W 10 Mile Rd
Farmington Hills, MI 48336-2819

Telephone: (248) 426-9841
Fax Number: (248) 426-9849
Type of Business: Chain Restaurant Operator
Year Founded: 1985
Total Sales: $29,880,000 (e)
Number of Employees: 275
Average Check: Lunch(8); Dinner(10)
Total Units: 11
Trade Names: Taco Bell (11)
Units Franchised From: 11
Preferred Square Footage: 3,000
Preferred Location Types: Freestanding
Primary Menu: Taco (11)
Areas of Operation: IL, IN, MI
Type of Foodservice: Quick Serve (11)
Franchise Affiliation: Pizza Hut Inc., PLANO, TX; Taco Bell Corp., IRVINE, CA
Primary Distributors: (Food) McLane/Houston, HOUSTON, TX

Key Personnel
JIM SATA - President; Director Operations; General Buyer
MELISSA MCNALLY - Manager Customer Service
STEPHANIE BLEVINS - Administrator Payroll

Zoup! Fresh Soup Company LLC
28555 Orchard Lake Rd Unit 200
Farmington Hills, MI 48334

Telephone: (248) 663-1111
Fax Number: (248) 663-9880
Internet Homepage: zoup.com; zoupfranchise.com
Company Email: info@zoup.com
Type of Business: Chain Restaurant Operator
Year Founded: 1998
Systemwide Sales: $140,688,000 (e)
Total Sales: $57,630,000 (e)
Number of Employees: 792
Average Check: Lunch(10); Dinner(10)
Internet Order Processing: Yes

Total Units: 88
Trade Names: Zoup! (88)
Company-Owned Units: 3
Units Franchised To: 85
Preferred Location Types: Freestanding; Strip Mall
Primary Menu: American (88)
Areas of Operation: CO, DC, DE, IL, IN, KY, MA, MI, MO, NE, NJ, NY, OH, OR, PA, SD, VA, WA, WI, ON
Foreign Countries: CANADA
Type of Foodservice: Fast Casual (88)
Primary Distributors: (Full Line) US Foods, WIXOM, MI

Key Personnel
ERIC ERSHER - Co-Founder; CEO; Manager Menu Development; General Buyer
RICHARD SIMTOB - Co-Founder; President
ROBERT KIRMA - Director Construction, Design
SCOTT DAY - Director Finance, Administration
MOLLY VANASSCHE - Manager Human Resources

C.H.E.W., Inc.
3253 Owen Rd
Fenton, MI 48430-1755

Telephone: (810) 750-3423
Fax Number: (810) 750-2346
Company Email: hjbeef@aol.com
Type of Business: Chain Restaurant Operator
Total Sales: $22,620,000 (e)
Number of Employees: 285
Average Check: Dinner(12)
Total Units: 12
Trade Names: Arby's (12)
Units Franchised From: 12
Preferred Location Types: Freestanding
Primary Menu: Sandwiches/Deli (12)
Areas of Operation: MI, OH
Type of Foodservice: Quick Serve (12)
Franchise Affiliation: Arby's Restaurant Group, ATLANTA, GA

Key Personnel
JOE CRAWFORD - Partner; General Buyer
JAMES CRAWFORD - Partner

Talbot's On The Water, Inc.
14184 Eastview Dr
Fenton, MI 48430-1304

Telephone: (810) 618-6968
Type of Business: Chain Restaurant Operator
Total Sales: $1,591,000 (e)
Total Units: 2
Trade Names: Little Caesars Pizza (2)
Units Franchised From: 2
Primary Menu: Pizza (2)
Areas of Operation: MI

Type of Foodservice: Quick Serve (2)
Franchise Affiliation: Little Caesar Enterprises Inc., DETROIT, MI

Key Personnel
BILL TALBOT - President; General Buyer
COLLEEN TALBOT - Controller

Auntie Anne's Franchise
3279 S Linden Rd Spc 260
Flint, MI 48507-3005

Telephone: (810) 732-5685
Type of Business: Chain Restaurant Operator
Total Sales: $3,030,000 (e)
Total Units: 4
Trade Names: Auntie Anne's Hand-Rolled Soft Pretzels (4)
Units Franchised From: 4
Primary Menu: Snacks (4)
Areas of Operation: MI
Type of Foodservice: Quick Serve (4)
Franchise Affiliation: Auntie Anne's Inc., LANCASTER, PA

Key Personnel
WILLIAM ETTER - Owner; General Buyer

Big John Steak & Onion Inc.
4184 Pier North Blvd Ste B
Flint, MI 48504-1393

Mailing Address: PO Box 310617, FLINT, MI, 48531-0617
Telephone: (810) 230-9000
Fax Number: (810) 230-1244
Internet Homepage: bigjohnsteakandonion.net
Type of Business: Chain Restaurant Operator
Year Founded: 1972
Total Sales: $13,315,000 (e)
Number of Employees: 320
Average Check: Dinner(12)
Total Units: 16
Trade Names: Big John Steak & Onion (16)
Company-Owned Units: 16
Preferred Square Footage: 1,200
Preferred Location Types: Freestanding
Primary Menu: Sandwiches/Deli (16)
Areas of Operation: MI
Type of Foodservice: Quick Serve (16)
Primary Distributors: (Full Line) Gordon Food Service Inc., WYOMING, MI

Key Personnel
JOE KLOBUCAR - CEO; President; VP Advertising, Real Estate, Design; General Buyer
BILL ADAMS - Executive Chef; Supervisor Food Safety

CSC Inc.
521 S Dort Hwy
Flint, MI 48503-2848

Telephone: (810) 235-6550
Fax Number: (810) 235-5210
Internet Homepage: yayas.com
Company Email: customerservice@yayas.com
Type of Business: Chain Restaurant Operator
Year Founded: 1985
Systemwide Sales: $13,935,000 (e)
Total Sales: $6,122,000 (e)
Number of Employees: 200
Average Check: Lunch(8); Dinner(12)
Total Units: 11
Trade Names: YaYa's Flame Broiled Chicken (11)
Company-Owned Units: 4
Units Franchised To: 8
Preferred Square Footage: 2,500
Preferred Location Types: Freestanding; Regional Mall; Strip Mall
Primary Menu: Chicken (11)
Areas of Operation: FL, MI
Type of Foodservice: Quick Serve (11)
Catering Services: Yes

Key Personnel
JOHN PLOUCHA - President; Owner; CFO; Director Real Estate

Miller Apple L.P.
5084 Exchange Dr
Flint, MI 48507-2906

Telephone: (810) 733-0663
Fax Number: (810) 733-1734
Internet Homepage: millerapple.com
Company Email: Comments@malpmi.com
Type of Business: Chain Restaurant Operator
Year Founded: 1993
Total Sales: $81,930,000 (e)
Alcohol Sales: 20%
Number of Employees: 1,500
Average Check: Lunch(14); Dinner(22)
Total Units: 21
Trade Names: Applebee's Neighborhood Grill & Bar (21)
Units Franchised From: 21
Preferred Square Footage: 3,500
Preferred Location Types: Freestanding
Alcohol Served: Beer, Wine, Liquor
Primary Menu: American (21)
Areas of Operation: MI
Type of Foodservice: Casual Dining (21)
Franchise Affiliation: Applebee's Services Inc., KANSAS CITY, MO
Primary Distributors: (Food) The SYGMA Network Inc. - Detroit, MONROE, MI

Key Personnel
WILLIAM WENTWORTH - President; Director Finance
MARTHA SANFORD - Owner; Director Marketing, Ethnic Marketing, Promotion
WILLIAM WENTWORTH JR - VP; Director Real Estate
JIM PRICE - Director Operations
LIZ ALLEN - Director Human Resources-Training
MICHAEL BROWN - Director Information Technology
DAN PITTENGER - Manager Facility/Maintenance, Store Fixtures

The Coffee Beanery Ltd.
3429 Pierson Pl
Flushing, MI 48433-2413

Telephone: (810) 733-1020
Fax Number: (810) 733-1536
Internet Homepage: coffeebeanery.com
Company Email: info@beanerysupport.com
Type of Business: Nontraditional Foodservice Operator
Year Founded: 1976
Systemwide Sales: $60,801,000 (e)
Total Sales: $21,410,000 (e)
Number of Employees: 100
Internet Order Processing: Yes
Internet Sales: 1.00%
Total Units: 31
Trade Names: The Coffee Beanery (120)
Company-Owned Units: 2
Units Franchised To: 118
Preferred Square Footage: 200; 400; 800; 1,200; 2,200; 3,500
Preferred Location Types: Airports; Freestanding; Kiosk; Mobile Unit; Office Complex; Regional Mall; Strip Mall
Primary Menu: Coffee (120)
Projected Openings: 20
Areas of Operation: AR, AZ, CT, DC, DE, FL, GA, GU, IL, IN, KS, KY, MA, MD, MI, MO, MS, NC, NH, NJ, NY, OH, OK, PA, PR, TN, TX, VA
Foreign Countries: CHINA; CYPRUS; QATAR; UNITED ARAB EMIRATES
Type of Foodservice: Quick Serve (120)
Foodservice Management Venues: College & University; Health Care
Catering Services: Yes
On-site Distribution Center: Yes
Primary Distributors: (Food) US Foods, WIXOM, MI
Notes: Foodservice sales excludes revenues derived from wholesale activity and the sale of product and equipment to franchisees.

Key Personnel
JULIUS SHAW - Chairman
JOANNE SHAW - CEO; President; Director Marketing
LAURIE SHAW - COO
BRITAIN BUTCHER - Director E-Commerce

A & R Hospitality
1006 W Main St
Gaylord, MI 49735

Mailing Address: PO Box 624, GAYLORD, MI, 49734-6024
Telephone: (989) 731-2074
Fax Number: (989) 732-8222
Internet Homepage: spicybobs.com
Company Email: admin@spicybobs.com
Type of Business: Chain Restaurant Operator
Year Founded: 1989
Total Sales: $2,589,000 (e)
Number of Employees: 35
Average Check: Lunch(12); Dinner(12)
Total Units: 5
Trade Names: Spicy Bob's Italian Express (5)
Company-Owned Units: 5
Preferred Square Footage: 2,500
Preferred Location Types: Freestanding; Strip Mall
Primary Menu: Pizza (5)
Areas of Operation: MI
Type of Foodservice: Quick Serve (5)
Catering Services: Yes

Key Personnel
MATTHEW ROOYAKKER - Partner

New Adventure Inc
122 S Illinois Ave
Gaylord, MI 49735-1703

Telephone: (989) 732-7482
Type of Business: Chain Restaurant Operator
Total Sales: $4,027,000 (e)
Average Check: Dinner(12)
Total Units: 2
Trade Names: Arby's (2)
Units Franchised From: 2
Primary Menu: Sandwiches/Deli (2)
Areas of Operation: MI
Type of Foodservice: Quick Serve (2)
Franchise Affiliation: Arby's Restaurant Group, ATLANTA, GA

Key Personnel
KATIE FITZEK - Owner; General Buyer
BATHANY BROWN - Manager Administration; General Buyer

Amway Grand Plaza Hotel
187 Monroe Ave NW
Grand Rapids, MI 49503-2621

Telephone: (616) 774-2000
Fax Number: (616) 776-6489

Internet Homepage: amwaygrand.com
Company Email: info@amwaygrand.com
Type of Business: Foodservice Operations - Hotel/Motels
Year Founded: 1981
Total Sales: $75,319,000 (e)
Alcohol Sales: 25%
Number of Employees: 800
Total Units: 1
Restaurants in Hotels: 7
Trade Names: Amway Grand Plaza (1)
Company-Owned Units: 3
Units Franchised From: 4
Alcohol Served: Beer, Wine, Liquor
Areas of Operation: MI
Type of Foodservice: Casual Dining (5); Fine Dining (2)
Franchise Affiliation: Ruth's Hospitality Group Inc., WINTER PARK, FL; Starbucks Corporation, SEATTLE, WA; Wolfgang Puck Inc., LAS VEGAS, NV
Primary Distributors: (Food) Gordon Food Service Inc., WYOMING, MI; (Specialty Foods) Gordon Food Service Inc., WYOMING, MI
Notes: The company derives approximately 70% of its revenue from hotel operations.

Key Personnel
RICK WINN - CEO; President; COO; General Manager; Director Operations, Risk Management, Quality Assurance, Real Estate, Foodservice, Food Safety
MARK KOSTER - VP Finance
STEVE NAWROCKI - VP; Director Human Resources
RONALD BRONDYKE - VP; Director Sales
CHRIS MADSEN - Executive Chef
TAMARA AUGUSTONI - Director Food and Beverage
KELLY VAN DYKE CMP, CTA - Assistant Director Event Planning
HEATHER BACLE - Manager Sales
NICOLE ROBINSON - Manager Division
CINDY BREU - Manager Sales
SYDNEY SARE - Manager Credit
EFRAIN MELENDEZ - Manager Division
JACKSON PRICHARD - Supervisor Administration
GOSIA MORRIS - Specialist Accounting

Anna's House
2409 E Beltline Ave SE
Grand Rapids, MI 49546-5907

Telephone: (616) 551-0434
Internet Homepage: annashouseus.com
Company Email: info@annashouseus.com
Type of Business: Chain Restaurant Operator
Total Units: 8
Trade Names: Anna's House (8)
Company-Owned Units: 8
Primary Menu: American (8)
Areas of Operation: MI
Type of Foodservice: Family Restaurant (8)

Key Personnel
JOSH BECKETT - CEO; President; Owner
BILL HOGAN - General Manager
COLLEEN CRAWFORD - Director Finance

Arnie's Inc.
815 Leonard St NW
Grand Rapids, MI 49504-4147

Telephone: (616) 458-1107
Fax Number: (616) 458-3085
Internet Homepage: arniesrestaurants.com
Type of Business: Chain Restaurant Operator
Year Founded: 1905
Total Sales: $15,523,000 (e)
Number of Employees: 500
Average Check: Breakfast(10); Lunch(12); Dinner(14)
Total Units: 4
Trade Names: Arnie's Bakery Restaurant (4)
Company-Owned Units: 4
Preferred Location Types: Freestanding
Primary Menu: American (4)
Areas of Operation: MI
Type of Foodservice: Family Restaurant (4)
Primary Distributors: (Full Line) Gordon Food Service Inc., WYOMING, MI

Key Personnel
JIM FAHLEN - Chairman
RICHARD FAHLEN - Director Marketing
NANCY ZINGER - Director Human Resources
JERRY HOOGTERP - Director Food; General Buyer
LUKE GETZ - Director Human Resources

Barfly
1575 Arboretum Drive SE Suite 404
Grand Rapids, MI 49546

Internet Homepage: wearebarfly.com
Type of Business: Chain Restaurant Operator
Total Sales: $19,909,000 (e)
Total Units: 12
Trade Names: Hopcat (11); Stella's Lounge (1)
Company-Owned Units: 12
Primary Menu: American (12)
Type of Foodservice: Casual Dining (12)

Key Personnel
TRAVIS BALDWIN - Executive Chairman
KYLE RITTER - Owner
ELLEN WINTERBURN - VP Human Resources
JESSICA REINSCH - Director Development, Training
ELISE MASTIO - Director Marketing
CAROLINE DEVOS - Director Human Resources

Brann's Inc.
25 Commerce Ave SW Ste 50
Grand Rapids, MI 49503-4100

Telephone: (616) 233-0002
Fax Number: (616) 451-3212
Internet Homepage: branns.com
Type of Business: Chain Restaurant Operator
Year Founded: 1938
Total Sales: $23,230,000 (e)
Alcohol Sales: 20%
Number of Employees: 535
Average Check: Lunch(8); Dinner(12)
Internet Order Processing: Yes
Internet Sales: 1.00%
Total Units: 9
Trade Names: Brann's Steakhouse & Grille (9)
Company-Owned Units: 9
Preferred Square Footage: 7,100
Preferred Location Types: Freestanding
Alcohol Served: Beer, Wine, Liquor
Primary Menu: Steak (9)
Areas of Operation: MI
Type of Foodservice: Casual Dining (9)
Catering Services: Yes
Primary Distributors: (Full Line) Gordon Food Service Inc., WYOMING, MI

Key Personnel
JOHNNY BRANN SR - Partner
MIKE BRANN - Partner; VP Facility/Maintenance

Loeks Theatres, Inc
2121 Celebration Dr NE Ste 425
Grand Rapids, MI 49525-9587

Telephone: (616) 447-4200
Fax Number: (616) 447-4201
Internet Homepage: celebrationcinema.com
Company Email: feedback@bigscreenmovies.com
Type of Business: Foodservice Operations - Movie Theatre
Year Founded: 1944
Total Sales: $26,820,000 (e)
Number of Employees: 250
Average Check: Dinner(6)
Total Units: 11
Trade Names: Celebration! Cinema (8); Cinema Carousel (1); Getty Drive-In (1); Studio C (1)
Company-Owned Units: 11
Preferred Square Footage: 2,500
Preferred Location Types: Freestanding
Primary Menu: Snacks (11)
Areas of Operation: MI
Type of Foodservice: In-Store Feeder (11)
Notes: The company derives approximately

72% of its revenue from theater admissions, on-screen advertising, and other sales.

Key Personnel
JOHN LOEKS - Chairman; CEO; Director Facility/Maintenance, Supply Chain, Internet Development; General Buyer
J.D LOEKS - President
NANCY HAGAN - CFO; Treasurer
STEVE FORSYTHE - VP Information Systems, Human Resources
ROGER LUBS - VP Operations, Facility/Maintenance, Real Estate, Construction, Site Selection, Franchising
KENYON SHANE - VP Operations
DAN BREWSTER - Manager Operations

Meijer Inc.
2350 3 Mile Rd NW
Grand Rapids, MI 49544-1305

Telephone: (616) 453-6711
Internet Homepage: meijer.com
Type of Business: Nontraditional Foodservice Operator
Year Founded: 1934
Total Sales: $21,950,000,000 (e)
Alcohol Sales: 1%
Number of Employees: 96,331
Average Check: Lunch(8); Dinner(8)
Foodservice Sales: $219,500,000 (e)
Total Units: 276
Trade Names: Deli Cafe (276)
Company-Owned Units: 276
Preferred Location Types: Freestanding; Grocery Stores; Strip Mall
Primary Menu: American (276)
Areas of Operation: IL, IN, KY, MI, OH, WI
Type of Foodservice: In-Store Feeder (276)
Primary Distributors: (Food) Van Eerden Foodservice, GRAND RAPIDS, MI
Notes: The company derives more than 99% of its revenue from retail operations.

Key Personnel
HANK MEIJER - Executive Chairman
MARK MURRAY - Vice Chairman
RICK KEYES - CEO; President
TERRY LEDBETTER - CIO; Senior VP
LYNETTE ACKLEY - Group VP Hardlines Division
KRISTEN WILLIAMS - VP Technology, Digital
TODD ANDERSON - VP Region
BRIAN PUGH - Director Digital Experience
JACKIE ADAMS - Director Human Resources
TAREQ SALEH - Manager Engineering, Manufacturing
JOSEPH OPENSHAW - Manager
MIKE DELANGE - Manager Engineering, Security

Meritage Hospitality Group Inc.
45 Ottawa Ave SW Ste 600
Grand Rapids, MI 49503-4011

Telephone: (616) 776-2600
Fax Number: (616) 776-2776
Internet Homepage: committothemitt.com; crookedgoose.com; meritagehospitality.com; twisted-rooster.com
Company Email: meritage@mhgi.net
Type of Business: Chain Restaurant Operator
Year Founded: 1986
Publicly Held: Yes
Total Sales: $897,351,000 (e)
Alcohol Sales: 1.50%
Number of Employees: 10,000
Average Check: Breakfast(14); Lunch(12); Dinner(18)
Total Units: 388
Trade Names: Morning Belle (3); Stan's Tacos (3); Taco John's (6); Wendy's Old Fashioned Hamburgers (376)
Company-Owned Units: 6
Units Franchised From: 382
Preferred Square Footage: 2,700; 3,400; 5,000; 6,800
Preferred Location Types: Convenience Store/Gas Station; Freestanding; Strip Mall
Alcohol Served: Beer, Wine, Liquor
Primary Menu: American (3); Hamburger (376); Mexican (6); Taco (3)
Projected Openings: 50
Areas of Operation: AR, CT, FL, GA, IN, MA, MI, MO, MS, NC, OH, OK, SC, TN, TX, VA
Type of Foodservice: Casual Dining (3); Fast Casual (3); Quick Serve (382)
Franchise Affiliation: The Wendy's Company, DUBLIN, OH
Primary Distributors: (Full Line) The SYGMA Network Inc. - Detroit, MONROE, MI

Key Personnel
ROBERT E. SCHERMER SR - Chairman
ROBERT E. SCHERMER JR - CEO
GARY ROSE - President; COO
TRACEY SMITH - CFO; VP
TAMMY DODDS - Area Director
JUDY GAMBINO - Area Director
GREG CORR - Exec VP Operations
DOUGLAS POLAND - VP Real Estate
JEFF VANHAITSMA - VP Human Resources
DAYNA KRUG - Controller
KRISTEN BUTER - General Counsel
MICHAEL BALDWIN - Director Operations
AARON BESMER - Director Construction, Design
MARIE GLANTZMAN - Director Employee Development
ALEX RUSTICUS - Director Finance
SUSIE SCHULZ - Director Operations
JON SYKES - Director Information Technology
JOHNNY STUBBS - Regional Director Operations
JARED OLSON - Senior Manager
VONETTA HARRIS - Area Manager
ERICA BONNAU - District Manager
KRISTINA BALDWIN - District Manager
RANDY CHENOWETH - Manager Construction
DAVID JACKIEWICZ - Manager Marketing
JAY GARNER - Manager District
KEVIN PARK - Manager District
BRIAN MAXWELL - Manager Compliance
KRIS MILLER - Manager Human Resources
DAVID SUKENIK - Manager Real Estate
JOSHUA SWEM - Manager Talent
VICKI STEWART - Manager Area
GLENN GREEN - Project Manager Facility/Maintenance
TODD VARNAS - Administrator Systems
KENDALL WILTERDINK - Specialist Talent Acquisitions
MITCH NOUSAIN - Specialist Acquisitions
MARY LAUDAZIO - Specialist Talent Acquisitions
EMILY SMITH - Coordinator Risk Management
CRYSTAL KARSTEN - Coordinator Operations
DONALD DUNGU - Coordinator Construction
SHARI BOURGETTE - Coordinator Human Resources
NATHAN RIJFKOGEL - Senior Analyst Finance
LAUREN PEELER - Analyst Finance
JEFFREY HALL - Technician Information Technology

Opi Enterprises Inc
4076 Kings Row Ct NW
Grand Rapids, MI 49534-3405

Telephone: (616) 453-5835
Type of Business: Chain Restaurant Operator
Total Units: 4
Trade Names: Subway (4)
Units Franchised From: 4
Primary Menu: Sandwiches/Deli (4)
Areas of Operation: MI
Type of Foodservice: Quick Serve (4)
Franchise Affiliation: Doctor's Associates Inc., MILFORD, CT

Key Personnel
STAN LISKIEWITZ - President; General Buyer

River City Food Company
3425 Lake Eastbrook Blvd SE
Grand Rapids, MI 49546-5935

Telephone: (616) 776-7600
Fax Number: (616) 451-2900
Internet Homepage: finleysamericangrill.com; rcfc.com; thescore-restaurant.com
Company Email: general@rcfc.com
Type of Business: Chain Restaurant Operator
Year Founded: 1977

Total Sales: $21,440,000 (e)
Alcohol Sales: 7%
Number of Employees: 615
Average Check: Lunch(8); Dinner(14)
Internet Order Processing: Yes
Internet Sales: 1.00%
Total Units: 9
Trade Names: bd's Mongolian Barbeque (2); Finley's Grill and Smokehouse (5); Pietro's Italian Restaurant (1); The Score (1)
Company-Owned Units: 7
Units Franchised From: 2
Preferred Square Footage: 5,000; 7,000
Preferred Location Types: Downtown; Freestanding
Alcohol Served: Beer, Wine, Liquor
Primary Menu: American (6); Asian (2); Italian (1)
Areas of Operation: KS, MI
Type of Foodservice: Casual Dining (9)
Catering Services: Yes
Franchise Affiliation: BD's Mongolian Grill, IRVING, TX
Primary Distributors: (Full Line) Gordon Food Service Inc., WYOMING, MI

Key Personnel
MATTHEW BURN - CFO
DOUG MCKINNON - VP Operations, Supply Chain; General Buyer
JOY RENO - Director Accounting

The Gilmore Collection
20 Monroe Ave NW Ste 400
Grand Rapids, MI 49503-6209

Telephone: (616) 356-2627
Fax Number: (616) 493-2011
Internet Homepage: thebob.com; thegilmorecollection.com
Type of Business: Chain Restaurant Operator
Year Founded: 1989
Total Sales: $22,710,000 (e)
Alcohol Sales: 18%
Number of Employees: 533
Average Check: Breakfast(6); Lunch(12); Dinner(24)
Total Units: 14
Trade Names: B.O.B's Brewery (1); Blue Water Grill (1); Bobarino's (1); Boswick Lake Inn (1); Flat River Grill (1); Gilly's (1); Judson's (1); K2 (1); Kirby House(1); Mangiamo's (1); Nick Finks (1); Rose's (1); The Grill Room (1); The Pub at Paddock (1)
Company-Owned Units: 14
Preferred Square Footage: 3,000; 6,000
Preferred Location Types: Freestanding
Alcohol Served: Beer, Wine, Liquor
Primary Menu: American (11); Italian (1); Pizza (1); Steak (2); Steak/Seafood (1)
Areas of Operation: CO, MI
Type of Foodservice: Casual Dining (14)
Catering Services: Yes

Primary Distributors: (Full Line) SYSCO Food Services of North Texas, LEWISVILLE, TX

Key Personnel
JOHN F. GILMORE - Chairman
GREGORY S. GILMORE - CEO; General Manager Finance; General Buyer
AMBER CRUMBACK - General Manager
MATT DOWDY - Director Information Systems, Marketing, Design
WILLIAM S. KOSKI - Director Region
KIM LEMMEN-BRAAT - Director Promotion, Sales, Food and Beverage, Catering
KIM LEMMEN-GILMORE COLLECTION - Director Operations
JOSH HILL - Manager Security
STEVE BOK - Manager Security
BRANDI SHELLEY - Manager Security
LAURA SCHOLTEN - Manager Social Media

Donald Alan Worst Inc
4375 Chicago Dr SW
Grandville, MI 49418-1546

Telephone: (616) 551-2771
Type of Business: Chain Restaurant Operator
Total Units: 9
Trade Names: Little Caesars Pizza (9)
Units Franchised From: 9
Primary Menu: Pizza (9)
Areas of Operation: MI
Type of Foodservice: Quick Serve (9)
Franchise Affiliation: Little Caesar Enterprises Inc., DETROIT, MI

Key Personnel
DONALD WORST - President; General Buyer

Da Edoardo Restaurants
19767 Mack Ave
Grosse Pointe Woods, MI 48236

Telephone: (313) 471-3500
Fax Number: (313) 881-3813
Internet Homepage: daedoardo.com
Company Email: ahk@daedoardo.com
Type of Business: Chain Restaurant Operator
Year Founded: 2001
Total Sales: $4,647,000 (e)
Alcohol Sales: 15%
Number of Employees: 100
Average Check: Lunch(18); Dinner(24)
Internet Order Processing: Yes
Total Units: 4
Trade Names: Cafe Nini (1); Da Edoardo (2); La Lanterna (1)
Company-Owned Units: 4
Preferred Location Types: Downtown; Freestanding; Strip Mall
Alcohol Served: Beer, Wine, Liquor
Primary Menu: Italian (3); Pizza (1)

Areas of Operation: MI
Type of Foodservice: Casual Dining (1); Fine Dining (3)
Primary Distributors: (Food) Caramagno Foods Co. Inc., DETROIT, MI

Key Personnel
EDDIE BARBIERI - Partner; General Buyer
ANNIE BARBIERI-KOLINSKI - Partner; Director Finance, Menu Development

Black Rock Restaurants
10100 Highland Rd
Hartland, MI 48353

Telephone: (810) 632-5500
Internet Homepage: blackrockrestaurants.com
Type of Business: Chain Restaurant Operator
Year Founded: 2013
Total Sales: $16,060,000 (e)
Total Units: 16
Trade Names: Black Rock (16)
Company-Owned Units: 16
Primary Menu: Steak (16)
Projected Openings: 2
Areas of Operation: FL, IL, MI, OH
Type of Foodservice: Casual Dining (16)

Key Personnel
JANETTE MORGANROTH - President; Partner
LONNY MORGANROTH - Partner; Treasurer; Director

Kabb Management
1215 W State St
Hastings, MI 49058-9712

Telephone: (269) 948-8233
Type of Business: Chain Restaurant Operator
Total Sales: $20,036,000 (e)
Total Units: 4
Trade Names: McDonald's (4)
Units Franchised From: 4
Preferred Location Types: Freestanding
Primary Menu: Hamburger (4)
Areas of Operation: MI
Type of Foodservice: Quick Serve (4)
Franchise Affiliation: McDonald's Corporation, CHICAGO, IL

Key Personnel
KEITH BERG - President; General Buyer
ANNETTE SNYDER - General Manager

Highland House Inc.
2630 E Highland Rd
Highland, MI 48356-2726

Telephone: (248) 887-4161

Fax Number: (248) 889-1662
Internet Homepage: thehighlandhouse.net; barnonebrighton.com; egnicks.net; guscarryout.com; smokestreetmilford.com; tomatobros.com
Type of Business: Chain Restaurant Operator
Year Founded: 1976
Total Sales: $22,340,000 (e)
Alcohol Sales: 10%
Number of Employees: 600
Average Check: Lunch(16); Dinner(22)
Total Units: 10
Trade Names: BAR NONE (1); E.G. Nicks (1); Gus's Carryout (3); Highland House (1); Highland House Cafe (2); Smoke Street (1); Tomato Brothers (1)
Company-Owned Units: 10
Preferred Square Footage: 8,000
Preferred Location Types: Freestanding; Strip Mall
Alcohol Served: Beer, Wine, Liquor
Primary Menu: American (3); Bar-B-Q (1); Italian (5); Steak/Seafood (1)
Areas of Operation: MI
Type of Foodservice: Casual Dining (10)
Foodservice Management Venues: Transportation
Catering Services: Yes
Primary Distributors: (Equipment) SYSCO Food Services of Grand Rapids LLC, GRAND RAPIDS, MI; (Food) Gordon Food Service Inc., WYOMING, MI;(Supplies) SYSCO Food Services of Grand Rapids LLC, GRAND RAPIDS, MI

Key Personnel
GENE REYSON - Partner
CHRIS BURKE - Executive Chef; Director Operations, Quality Assurance, Menu Development, Food Safety; Buyer Food

Metro H&N, Inc.
4100 Chevron Dr
Highland, MI 48356-1118

Telephone: (248) 830-2287
Type of Business: Chain Restaurant Operator
Total Sales: $19,950,000 (e)
Total Units: 13
Trade Names: Checkers (10); Rally's Hamburgers (3)
Units Franchised From: 13
Primary Menu: Hamburger (13)
Areas of Operation: MI
Type of Foodservice: Quick Serve (13)
Franchise Affiliation: Checkers Drive-In Restaurants Inc., TAMPA, FL

Key Personnel
PAUL AMELL - President; General Buyer

R & E Pizza People, Inc.
380 W Carleton Rd
Hillsdale, MI 49242-1048

Telephone: (517) 439-1424
Type of Business: Chain Restaurant Operator
Total Sales: $3,067,000 (e)
Total Units: 5
Trade Names: Little Caesars Pizza (5)
Units Franchised From: 5
Primary Menu: Pizza (5)
Areas of Operation: IN, MI, OH
Type of Foodservice: Quick Serve (5)
Franchise Affiliation: Little Caesar Enterprises Inc., DETROIT, MI

Key Personnel
RICHARD MASSEY - President; General Buyer

Peachwave Frozen Yogurt
6 W 8th St
Holland, MI 49423-3153

Telephone: (616) 403-2327
Fax Number: (405) 607-8215
Internet Homepage: peachwaveyogurt.com
Company Email: info@peachwaveyogurt.com
Type of Business: Chain Restaurant Operator
Year Founded: 2009
Systemwide Sales: $12,351,000 (e)
Total Sales: $3,540,000 (e)
Number of Employees: 16
Average Check: Lunch(8); Dinner(8)
Total Units: 39
Trade Names: Peachwave Self Serve Frozen Yogurt (39)
Company-Owned Units: 2
Units Franchised To: 37
Preferred Square Footage: 1,600; 1,800; 2,000
Preferred Location Types: Community Mall; Strip Mall
Primary Menu: Snacks (39)
Projected Openings: 2
Areas of Operation: AL, CO, CT, FL, GA, IA, IL, KS, MA, MI, MO, NC, NE, NH, NJ, NY, OK, OR, RI, SD, TN, TX
Foreign Countries: CANADA; CAYMAN ISLANDS
Type of Foodservice: Quick Serve (39)
Distribution Centers: EDMOND, OK
On-site Distribution Center: Yes
Notes: The company derives approximately 23% of its total revenue from the sales of branded products to its franchisees.

Key Personnel
BOYD FELTMAN - CEO; Owner; General Buyer
YORK RAGSDALE - Chief Development Officer
KAITLYN JOHNSON - Manager Social Media

Russ' Restaurants Inc.
390 E 8th St
Holland, MI 49423-3743

Telephone: (616) 396-6571
Fax Number: (616) 396-6755
Internet Homepage: russrestaurants.com
Type of Business: Chain Restaurant Operator
Year Founded: 1934
Systemwide Sales: $21,439,000 (e)
Total Sales: $13,540,000 (e)
Number of Employees: 500
Average Check: Breakfast(6); Lunch(10); Dinner(12)
Internet Order Processing: Yes
Total Units: 12
Trade Names: Russ' Restaurant (12)
Company-Owned Units: 11
Units Franchised To: 1
Preferred Square Footage: 7,000
Preferred Location Types: Freestanding
Primary Menu: American (12)
Areas of Operation: MI
Type of Foodservice: Family Restaurant (12)
Distribution Centers: HOLLAND, MI
Primary Distributors: (Full Line) Gordon Food Service Inc., WYOMING, MI

Key Personnel
BRYAN BOUWS - President; General Buyer
RYAN MEYERINK - General Manager
JACK POSTHUMUS - Manager District

Russ's Commissary
3440 128th Ave
Holland, MI 49424-9263

Telephone: (616) 399-7084
Fax Number: (616) 399-7085
Internet Homepage: russrestaurants.com
Listing Type: Distribution Center
Type of Business: Chain Restaurant Operator
Number of Employees: 50
Areas of Operation: MI
Parent Company: Russ' Restaurants Inc., HOLLAND, MI

Key Personnel
ROSS BOERESMA - General Manager Purchasing, Distribution, Warehouse, Transportation, Human Resources

Domino's Franchisee
200 Pearl St Ste 4
Houghton, MI 49931-1341

Telephone: (906) 482-6060
Type of Business: Chain Restaurant Operator
Total Sales: $20,545,000 (e)

Total Units: 10
Trade Names: Domino's (10)
Units Franchised From: 10
Primary Menu: Pizza (10)
Areas of Operation: MI, WI
Type of Foodservice: Quick Serve (10)
Franchise Affiliation: Domino's Pizza Inc, ANN ARBOR, MI

Key Personnel
ADAM K. LAMBERT - Owner; General Buyer

Mariane Inc./Bells & Birds
7870 Knapp Rd
Houghton Lake, MI 48629-9617

Mailing Address: PO Box 250, HOUGHTON LAKE, MI, 48629-0250
Telephone: (989) 422-3534
Fax Number: (989) 422-5440
Internet Homepage: northlandinv.com
Type of Business: Chain Restaurant Operator
Year Founded: 1987
Total Sales: $142,050,000 (e)
Number of Employees: 1,700
Average Check: Lunch(8); Dinner(10)
Total Units: 52
Trade Names: A&W All American Food (1); KFC (5); Taco Bell (46)
Units Franchised From: 52
Preferred Square Footage: 2,500
Preferred Location Types: Convenience Store/Gas Station; Freestanding; Regional Mall
Primary Menu: American (1); Chicken (5); Taco (46)
Areas of Operation: IN, MI, OH
Type of Foodservice: Quick Serve (52)
Franchise Affiliation: A&W Restaurants Inc., LEXINGTON, KY; KFC Corporation, LOUISVILLE, KY; Taco Bell Corp., IRVINE, CA
Primary Distributors: (Full Line) McLane/Midwest, DANVILLE, IL
Parent Company: Northland Investments Inc, HOUGHTON LAKE, MI

Key Personnel
STEVEN STUCK - CEO; Partner
RODNEY WALKER - President; Partner; Director Finance, Real Estate
JIM SUTIKA - CFO; Controller; Director Information Systems
DAVE PIERCE - VP Operations
CHRIS JANASIK - Director Purchasing, Facility/Maintenance, Risk Management

Andy's Pizza Inc.
1208 W Ganson St
Jackson, MI 49202

Telephone: (517) 783-1320
Fax Number: (517) 764-1456
Internet Homepage: andyspizzajackson.com
Company Email: comments@andyspizzajackson.com
Type of Business: Chain Restaurant Operator
Year Founded: 1966
Total Sales: $3,637,000 (e)
Number of Employees: 40
Average Check: Lunch(14); Dinner(16)
Total Units: 3
Trade Names: Andy's Pizza (3)
Company-Owned Units: 3
Preferred Location Types: Freestanding
Primary Menu: Pizza (3)
Areas of Operation: MI
Type of Foodservice: Quick Serve (3)
Distribution Centers: MICHIGAN CENTER, MI

Key Personnel
NICK TODOROFF JR - VP; General Manager
DENNIS NUSBAUM - General Manager

Stanton & Associates Inc.
714 W Michigan Ave
Jackson, MI 49201-1909

Telephone: (517) 784-4094
Fax Number: (517) 784-4355
Internet Homepage: stantonnet.com
Type of Business: Chain Restaurant Operator
Year Founded: 1975
Total Sales: $89,640,000 (e)
Number of Employees: 190
Average Check: Lunch(8); Dinner(8)
Total Units: 72
Trade Names: Bigby Coffee (5); Wendy's (67)
Units Franchised From: 72
Preferred Square Footage: 3,500
Preferred Location Types: Freestanding; Institution (college/hospital)
Primary Menu: Coffee (6); Hamburger (67)
Areas of Operation: MI
Type of Foodservice: Quick Serve (72)
Primary Distributors: (Food) The SYGMA Network, Inc., DUBLIN, OH; (Supplies) SYSCO Food Services of Cleveland Inc., CLEVELAND, OH

Key Personnel
GRACE STANTON - Founder
DAVE WENGLEKOWSKI - VP; Director Marketing

Millennium Restaurant Group
3505 Greenleaf Blvd
Kalamazoo, MI 49008-5616

Telephone: (269) 375-1193
Fax Number: (269) 375-1346
Internet Homepage: millenniumrestaurants.com
Type of Business: Chain Restaurant Operator
Year Founded: 1987
Total Sales: $15,120,000 (e)
Alcohol Sales: 22%
Number of Employees: 342
Average Check: Lunch(30); Dinner(72)
Internet Order Processing: Yes
Total Units: 10
Trade Names: 600 Kitchen & Bar (1); Cove Lakeside Bistro (1); Fieldstone Grill (1); Idler Riverboat (1); Martell's (1); The Tap House (3); The Union (1); Wine Loft (1)
Company-Owned Units: 10
Preferred Square Footage: 5,500; 6,000
Preferred Location Types: Downtown; Freestanding
Alcohol Served: Beer, Wine, Liquor
Primary Menu: American (10)
Projected Openings: 1
Areas of Operation: MI
Type of Foodservice: Casual Dining (8); Fine Dining (2)
Catering Services: Yes
Primary Distributors: (Food) Gordon Food Service Inc., WYOMING, MI

Key Personnel
KEN MILLER - CEO; Partner
SHELLY PASTOR - Partner; Director Operations, Purchasing
BOB LEWIS - Partner; Director Operations, Purchasing
BRETT GULLEY - General Manager
JASON MCCLELLAN - Executive Chef
ERIC GILLISH - Executive Chef
ERIC GRILLISH - Executive Chef
RENEE HRADSKY - Director Event Planning, Sales
SCOTT MOORE - Director Finance
KELLI BLOWERS - Senior Manager
JESSICA ABBOTT - Manager Accounting

Goodrich Quality Theatres Inc.
4417 Broadmoor Ave SE
Kentwood, MI 49512-5367

Telephone: (616) 698-7733
Fax Number: (616) 698-7220
Internet Homepage: gqti.com
Company Email: goodrich@gqti.com
Type of Business: Foodservice Operations - Movie Theatre
Year Founded: 1975
Total Sales: $75,640,000 (e)
Number of Employees: 967
Average Check: Lunch(6); Dinner(6)
Internet Order Processing: Yes
Internet Sales: 1.00%
Total Units: 30
Trade Names: Goodrich Quality Theatres (30)

Company-Owned Units: 30
Preferred Square Footage: 20,000; 45,000
Preferred Location Types: Community Mall; Freestanding; Regional Mall; Strip Mall
Primary Menu: Snacks (30)
Areas of Operation: IL, IN, MI, MO
Type of Foodservice: In-Store Feeder (30)
Primary Distributors: (Full Line) SYSCO Food Services of Grand Rapids LLC, GRAND RAPIDS, MI
Notes: The company derives approximately 72% of its revenue from theater admissions, on-screen advertising, & other sales.

Key Personnel
HEATH THOMAS - VP Facility/Maintenance
SUE HOWARD - Controller; Manager Security, Inventory, Loss Prevention, Risk Management, Quality Assurance
PATRICIA LINTNER - Director Human Resources

Dolly's Pizza Franchising Inc.
1188 S Lapeer Rd
Lake Orion, MI 48360

Telephone: (248) 783-7444
Internet Homepage: dollyspizza.com
Company Email: dollyaccounts@yahoo.com
Type of Business: Chain Restaurant Operator
Year Founded: 1966
Systemwide Sales: $8,039,000 (e)
Total Sales: $345,000 (e)
Number of Employees: 45
Average Check: Dinner(14)
Internet Order Processing: Yes
Internet Sales: 1.00%
Total Units: 17
Trade Names: Dolly's Pizza (17)
Company-Owned Units: 2
Units Franchised To: 15
Preferred Square Footage: 1,200
Preferred Location Types: Freestanding; Strip Mall
Primary Menu: Pizza (17)
Areas of Operation: MI
Type of Foodservice: Family Restaurant (17)
Foodservice Management Venues: Schools
Catering Services: Yes

Key Personnel
DOLLY LEWIS - Director Operations

Southeast Michigan Management Corp
901 Wheatfield Dr
Lake Orion, MI 48362-3496

Telephone: (248) 693-9714
Type of Business: Chain Restaurant Operator
Total Sales: $2,827,000 (e)
Total Units: 4
Trade Names: Subway (4)
Units Franchised From: 4
Primary Menu: Sandwiches/Deli (4)
Areas of Operation: MI
Type of Foodservice: Quick Serve (4)
Franchise Affiliation: Doctor's Associates Inc., MILFORD, CT

Key Personnel
SEAN GRETKIEREWICZ - Partner; General Buyer
KEITH GRETKIEREWICZ - Partner; General Buyer

Subway Franchise
181 N Park Blvd
Lake Orion, MI 48362-3147

Telephone: (248) 693-6868
Internet Homepage: subway.com
Type of Business: Chain Restaurant Operator
Total Units: 5
Trade Names: Subway (5)
Units Franchised From: 5
Primary Menu: Sandwiches/Deli (5)
Areas of Operation: MI
Type of Foodservice: Quick Serve (5)
Franchise Affiliation: Doctor's Associates Inc., MILFORD, CT

Key Personnel
FRANK AGRUSA - Partner; General Buyer
TODD GILDERSLEEVE - Partner

EAT Pizza LLC
4800 W Saginaw Hwy
Lansing, MI 48917-2661

Telephone: (517) 323-7575
Type of Business: Chain Restaurant Operator
Total Sales: $18,008,000 (e)
Total Units: 9
Trade Names: Domino's (9)
Units Franchised From: 9
Primary Menu: Pizza (9)
Areas of Operation: MI
Type of Foodservice: Quick Serve (9)
Franchise Affiliation: Domino's Pizza Inc, ANN ARBOR, MI

Key Personnel
ERIC M. ARNTSON - Owner; General Buyer

SRS Management Inc.
983 S Main St
Lapeer, MI 48446-3044

Telephone: (810) 660-8450
Type of Business: Chain Restaurant Operator
Total Sales: $5,231,000 (e)
Total Units: 2
Trade Names: Sonic America's Drive-In (1); Taco Bell (1)
Units Franchised From: 2
Areas of Operation: MI
Franchise Affiliation: Sonic Corp., OKLAHOMA CITY, OK; Taco Bell Corp., IRVINE, CA

Key Personnel
SEJAL SHAH - Owner; General Buyer

Karns Enterprises
4500 Hull Rd
Leslie, MI 49251-9586

Telephone: (517) 589-8878
Fax Number: (517) 589-9015
Type of Business: Chain Restaurant Operator
Total Sales: $19,881,000 (e)
Total Units: 4
Trade Names: McDonald's (4)
Units Franchised From: 4
Preferred Location Types: Freestanding
Primary Menu: Hamburger (4)
Areas of Operation: MI
Type of Foodservice: Quick Serve (4)
Franchise Affiliation: McDonald's Corporation, CHICAGO, IL

Key Personnel
DARLENE KARNS - Partner; General Buyer
SCOTT KARNS - Partner; General Buyer

Windward Management
717 Southfield Rd
Lincoln Park, MI 48146-2608

Telephone: (313) 389-4700
Fax Number: (313) 389-5247
Company Email: kfcwindward@yahoo.com
Type of Business: Chain Restaurant Operator
Year Founded: 1967
Total Sales: $5,754,000 (e)
Number of Employees: 120
Average Check: Lunch(8); Dinner(12)
Total Units: 3
Trade Names: KFC (3)
Units Franchised From: 3
Preferred Square Footage: 2,000
Preferred Location Types: Freestanding
Primary Menu: Chicken (3)

Areas of Operation: MI
Type of Foodservice: Quick Serve (3)
Franchise Affiliation: KFC Corporation, LOUISVILLE, KY
Primary Distributors: (Full Line) McLane/Plymouth, PLYMOUTH, MI

Key Personnel
KIRK GURNEY - Owner; General Buyer

Hammer Management, Inc.
19311 Farmington Rd
Livonia, MI 48152-1404

Telephone: (248) 478-4691
Fax Number: (248) 478-3037
Company Email: livoniamcd@yahoo.com
Type of Business: Chain Restaurant Operator
Total Sales: $10,320,000 (e)
Total Units: 2
Trade Names: McDonald's (2)
Units Franchised From: 2
Primary Menu: Hamburger (2)
Areas of Operation: MI
Type of Foodservice: Quick Serve (2)
Franchise Affiliation: McDonald's Corporation, CHICAGO, IL

Key Personnel
PAUL W. HAMMER - President; General Buyer

Nehmeh Enterprises, Inc
15574 Middlebelt Rd
Livonia, MI 48154-3808

Telephone: (734) 261-4740
Type of Business: Chain Restaurant Operator
Total Sales: $2,534,000 (e)
Total Units: 2
Trade Names: Little Caesars Pizza (2)
Units Franchised From: 2
Primary Menu: Pizza (2)
Areas of Operation: MI
Type of Foodservice: Quick Serve (2)
Franchise Affiliation: Little Caesar Enterprises Inc., DETROIT, MI

Key Personnel
ALI NEHMEH - President; General Buyer

Olga's Kitchen Inc.
17800 N Laurel Park Dr Ste 200C
Livonia, MI 48152-3985

Telephone: (248) 357-6183
Fax Number: (248) 262-1815
Internet Homepage: teamschostak.com; olgaskitchen.com
Listing Type: Subsidiary
Type of Business: Chain Restaurant Operator
Year Founded: 1970
Systemwide Sales: $49,353,000 (e)
Total Sales: $49,180,000 (e)
Alcohol Sales: 5%
Number of Employees: 1,395
Average Check: Lunch(8); Dinner(18)
Internet Order Processing: Yes
Internet Sales: 1.00%
Total Units: 28
Trade Names: Olga's Kitchen (28)
Company-Owned Units: 28
Preferred Square Footage: 3,500
Preferred Location Types: Freestanding; Regional Mall; Strip Mall
Primary Menu: Greek/Mediterranean (28)
Areas of Operation: IL, MI
Type of Foodservice: Fast Casual (28)
Distribution Centers: CANTON, MI
On-site Distribution Center: Yes
Primary Distributors: (Equipment) SYSCO Detroit LLC, CANTON, MI; (Food) SYSCO Detroit LLC, CANTON, MI; (Supplies) The Wasserstrom Co., COLUMBUS, OH
Parent Company: Team Schostak Family Restaurants, LIVONIA, MI

Key Personnel
WILLIAM AUGOTT - CEO; President
BART OSTROWSKI - Area Director
RICK LOFTUS - Director Facility/Maintenance, Construction

Team Schostak Family Restaurants
17800 N Laurel Park Dr Ste 200C
Livonia, MI 48152-3985

Telephone: (248) 357-6183
Fax Number: (248) 262-1814
Internet Homepage: teamschostak.com
Company Email: tsfrinfo@teamschostak.com
Type of Business: Chain Restaurant Operator
Year Founded: 1980
Total Sales: $527,530,000 (e)
Alcohol Sales: 2%
Number of Employees: 4,080
Average Check: Breakfast(6); Lunch(6); Dinner(8)
Internet Order Processing: Yes
Total Units: 165
Trade Names: Applebee's Neighborhood Grill & Bar (64); Del Taco (8); MOD Pizza (13); Olga's (24); Wendy's (56)
Company-Owned Units: 24
Units Franchised From: 141
Preferred Square Footage: 3,900; 4,600
Preferred Location Types: Freestanding
Alcohol Served: Beer, Wine, Liquor
Primary Menu: American (88); Hamburger (56); Mexican (8); Pizza (13)
Areas of Operation: IL, MI, OH
Type of Foodservice: Casual Dining (88); Fast Casual (69); Quick Serve (8)
Subsidiaries: Olga's Kitchen Inc., LIVONIA, MI
Franchise Affiliation: Applebee's Services Inc., KANSAS CITY, MO; Del Taco Restaurants Inc., LAKE FOREST, CA
Primary Distributors: (Food) Reinhart Foodservice, WARREN, MI

Key Personnel
MARK SCHOSTAK - Executive Chairman; Owner
BILL ANGOTT - CEO; President
KEN STANECKI - CFO
ANGELA DAWSON - Area Director
JEFFERY GARKO - Area Director
LISA HILLER - Area Director
MILES BOOHER - Area Director
KARIM JAFFER - Area Director
ANDREA YKEMA - Area Director
BRYAN WEGRZYN - Area Director
RICHARD SCHOSTAK - Senior VP Operations
JOHN ANDREWS - VP Operations
BARB PASCIAK - VP Operations
TOM GERGICH - VP Development, Real Estate
RYAN JONES - VP Operations
DAN DILLON - VP Marketing
AUSTIN PARVIN - General Manager
BRIAN THOMPSON - Senior Director Facility/Maintenance
BRENT KEYES - Senior Director Operations
MIKE CHERETON - Director Operations
JEREMY BRASWELL - Director Operations
JEFF PITTEL - Director Food and Beverage
BARBARA PASCIAK - Director Operations
CYNDI BARNES - Director Accounting
SUSAN WRIGHT - Director Operations
LAURA SZCZEPANSKI - Director Training
CHRISTOPHER CARPENTER - Senior Manager Security
GREG FUCHS - Manager
LYNN L. BABALA - Manager Administration, Communications

Kentucky Fried Chicken of Ludington Inc
6786 W Timber Ln
Ludington, MI 49431-1068

Mailing Address: PO Box 336, LUDINGTON, MI, 49431-0336
Telephone: (231) 843-4344
Type of Business: Chain Restaurant Operator
Total Sales: $3,864,000 (e)
Total Units: 2
Trade Names: KFC (2)
Units Franchised From: 2
Primary Menu: Chicken (2)
Areas of Operation: MI
Type of Foodservice: Quick Serve (2)
Franchise Affiliation: KFC Corporation, LOUISVILLE, KY

Scotty's
5910 W US Highway 10
Ludington, MI 49431-2448

Mailing Address: PO Box 571, LUDINGTON, MI, 49431-0571
Telephone: (231) 843-4033
Fax Number: (231) 845-5577
Internet Homepage: pmsteamers.com; scottysrestaurant.com
Company Email: scottys@scottysrestaurant.com
Type of Business: Chain Restaurant Operator
Year Founded: 1964
Total Sales: $5,329,000 (e)
Alcohol Sales: 17%
Number of Employees: 100
Average Check: Breakfast(8); Lunch(8); Dinner(18)
Total Units: 2
Trade Names: P.M. Steamer's (1); Scotty's (1)
Company-Owned Units: 2
Preferred Location Types: Freestanding
Alcohol Served: Beer, Wine, Liquor
Primary Menu: American (2)
Areas of Operation: MI
Type of Foodservice: Casual Dining (2)
Catering Services: Yes
Primary Distributors: (Food) Gordon Food Service Inc., WYOMING, MI

Key Personnel
RICHARD D. SCOTT - President; General Buyer
KYLE JENSEN - Executive Chef; Manager Catering; Buyer Food

Hungry Howie's Pizza & Subs Inc.
30300 Stephenson Hwy Ste 200
Madison Heights, MI 48071-1619

Telephone: (248) 414-3300
Fax Number: (248) 414-3301
Internet Homepage: hungryhowies.com
Company Email: hungryhinc@hungryhowies.com
Type of Business: Chain Restaurant Operator
Year Founded: 1973
Systemwide Sales: $556,951,000 (e)
Total Sales: $35,510,000 (e)
Number of Employees: 60
Average Check: Lunch(8); Dinner(8)
Internet Order Processing: Yes
Internet Sales: 1.00%
Total Units: 770
Trade Names: Hungry Howie's Pizza & Subs (770)
Company-Owned Units: 20
Units Franchised To: 750
Preferred Square Footage: 300; 400; 1,000; 1,500
Preferred Location Types: Airports; Community Mall; Convenience Store/Gas Station; Downtown; Freestanding; Regional Mall; Strip Mall
Primary Menu: Pizza (770)
Areas of Operation: AL, AZ, CA, FL, GA, IN, LA, MD, MI, MS, NC, NV, OH, OK, PA, SC, TN, TX, UT
Type of Foodservice: Quick Serve (770)
Distribution Centers: LAKELAND, FL
On-site Distribution Center: Yes
Primary Distributors: (Food) SYSCO Food Services of Grand Rapids LLC, GRAND RAPIDS, MI

Key Personnel
STEVEN E. JACKSON - President
ROBERT ELLIOTT - Exec VP Marketing
JEFFREY RINKE - VP Marketing, Product Development
MOE SHRIKIAN - VP; General Counsel
ROB ELLIOTT - VP Marketing
JEFF RINKE - VP Marketing
DAN MCKAY - Director Information Technology
GEORGE SCHLICKENMAYER - Director Quality Assurance, Construction
ALAN NEWMAN - Director Training
DAVID YEAGER - Director Accounting
AL NEWMAN - Director Training
STEVE CLOUGH - Director Franchise Development
JOHN HEDRICK - Manager Warehouse
KURT GOETZKE - General Buyer; Agent Purchasing

Salvatore Scallopini Inc.
1650 E 12 Mile Rd
Madison Heights, MI 48071-2679

Telephone: (248) 542-3281
Fax Number: (248) 542-7660
Internet Homepage: luxebarandgrill.com; salvatorescallopini.com
Company Email: info@salvatorescallopini.com
Type of Business: Chain Restaurant Operator
Year Founded: 1983
Total Sales: $6,866,000 (e)
Alcohol Sales: 17%
Number of Employees: 100
Average Check: Lunch(12); Dinner(18)
Total Units: 6
Trade Names: Luxe Bar & Grill (2); Salvatore Scallopini (4)
Company-Owned Units: 6
Preferred Square Footage: 3,000
Preferred Location Types: Freestanding
Alcohol Served: Beer, Wine, Liquor
Primary Menu: American (2); Italian (4)
Projected Openings: 1
Areas of Operation: MI
Type of Foodservice: Casual Dining (6)
Catering Services: Yes
Primary Distributors: (Full Line) Caramagno Foods Co. Inc., DETROIT, MI

Key Personnel
LARRY BONGIOVANNI - President; CFO; Executive Chef; Manager Operations, Marketing, Real Estate, Design, Research & Development, Product Development, Store Planning, Menu Development
JASON JOHNSON - General Manager; Executive Chef

T & J Inc.
3100 Gratiot Blvd
Marysville, MI 48040-1488

Telephone: (810) 364-4385
Fax Number: (810) 364-2363
Type of Business: Chain Restaurant Operator
Total Sales: $9,835,000 (e)
Number of Employees: 165
Total Units: 4
Trade Names: Burger King (4)
Units Franchised From: 4
Preferred Square Footage: 2,500
Primary Menu: Hamburger (4)
Areas of Operation: MI
Type of Foodservice: Quick Serve (4)
Franchise Affiliation: Burger King Worldwide Inc., MIAMI, FL

Key Personnel
TIM CLAYTON - President; General Buyer
JANET CLAYTON - Owner

Yes Sir/E Bob, Inc
4000 Page Ave
Michigan Center, MI 49254-1028

Telephone: (517) 748-9240
Fax Number: (517) 990-1257
Company Email: subwaybob@tds.net
Type of Business: Chain Restaurant Operator
Total Sales: $8,008,000 (e)
Total Units: 14
Trade Names: Subway (14)
Units Franchised From: 14
Primary Menu: Sandwiches/Deli (14)
Areas of Operation: MI
Type of Foodservice: Quick Serve (14)
Franchise Affiliation: Doctor's Associates Inc., MILFORD, CT

Key Personnel
BOB RICHARDSON - President; General Buyer

Pete's Garage
930 N Telegraph Rd
Monroe, MI 48162-5131

Telephone: (734) 243-0343
Fax Number: (734) 243-2042
Internet Homepage: michigangrill.com; petesgaragemi.com
Company Email: info@petesgaragemi.com
Type of Business: Chain Restaurant Operator
Year Founded: 1980
Total Sales: $4,380,000 (e)
Alcohol Sales: 20%
Number of Employees: 130
Average Check: Breakfast(10); Lunch(14); Dinner(26)
Total Units: 2
Trade Names: Michigan Bar and Grill (1); Pete's Garage (1)
Company-Owned Units: 2
Preferred Location Types: Freestanding
Alcohol Served: Beer, Wine, Liquor
Primary Menu: American (2)
Areas of Operation: MI
Type of Foodservice: Casual Dining (2)
Primary Distributors: (Full Line) US Foods, WIXOM, MI

Key Personnel
JOHN RENDINA - Owner; Executive Chef; General Buyer
JOEY RENDINA - General Manager

Marino's Pizza Inc.
14 Market St
Mount Clemens, MI 48043-5640

Telephone: (586) 463-8677
Internet Homepage: sorrentopizza.com
Type of Business: Chain Restaurant Operator
Year Founded: 1961
Total Sales: $2,818,000 (e)
Number of Employees: 100
Average Check: Lunch(22); Dinner(22)
Internet Order Processing: Yes
Total Units: 10
Trade Names: Sam's Sorrento Pizza (10)
Company-Owned Units: 10
Preferred Square Footage: 2,000
Preferred Location Types: Freestanding; Strip Mall
Primary Menu: Pizza (10)
Areas of Operation: MI
Type of Foodservice: Quick Serve (10)
Primary Distributors: (Food) Roselli's Wholesale Foods Inc., FRASER, MI

Key Personnel
AL MARINO - President; General Manager; Director Finance, Facility/Maintenance, Information Systems, Real Estate, Design, Human Resources, Menu Development; General Buyer
SAM MARINO - VP Supply Chain; Controller; General Manager

Rudoni Management Inc.
614 E Mosher St Ste 1
Mount Pleasant, MI 48858-1777

Mailing Address: PO Box 637, MOUNT PLEASANT, MI, 48804-0637
Telephone: (989) 772-4981
Fax Number: (989) 772-7333
Type of Business: Chain Restaurant Operator
Year Founded: 1976
Total Sales: $9,132,000 (e)
Number of Employees: 160
Average Check: Lunch(8); Dinner(8)
Total Units: 5
Trade Names: KFC (5)
Units Franchised From: 5
Preferred Square Footage: 3,000
Preferred Location Types: Freestanding
Primary Menu: Chicken (5)
Areas of Operation: MI
Type of Foodservice: Quick Serve (5)
Franchise Affiliation: KFC Corporation, LOUISVILLE, KY
Primary Distributors: (Food) McLane/Plymouth, PLYMOUTH, MI

Key Personnel
STEVE RUDONI - President; Controller; Director Facility/Maintenance, Loss Prevention, Real Estate, Design, Franchising, Catering; General Buyer
DANA RUDONI - VP Finance, Administration; Controller
JOHN COLDWELL - VP Operations; Manager Information Systems, Human Resources

Inspired Concepts
555 S Mission St
Mt. Pleasant, MI 48858

Telephone: (989) 817-4790
Type of Business: Chain Restaurant Operator
Total Sales: $17,680,000 (e)
Total Units: 23
Trade Names: Bennigans (3); Big Apple Bagels (2); Italian Oven (2); Noodles and Company (2); Old Chicago (4); Pixie (1); Ponderosa Steakhouse (6); Smashburger (3)
Company-Owned Units: 9
Units Franchised To: 14
Primary Menu: American (4); Hamburger (3); Italian (4); Miscellaneous (0); Pizza (4); Snacks (2); Steak (6)
Areas of Operation: IN, MI
Type of Foodservice: Casual Dining (11); Family Restaurant (6); Fast Casual (3); Quick Serve (3)
Franchise Affiliation: Fat Brands, Inc., BEVERLY HILLS, CA

Key Personnel
JEFF NEELY - CEO; General Buyer
STEVE MORSE - General Manager

Famous Foods of Muskegon Inc
13 Hartford Ave
Muskegon, MI 49442-3311

Mailing Address: PO Box 869, MUSKEGON, MI, 49443-0869
Telephone: (231) 726-2888
Internet Homepage: muskegonleeschicken.com
Type of Business: Chain Restaurant Operator
Total Sales: $9,670,000 (e)
Total Units: 4
Trade Names: Golden Corral (1); Lee's Famous Recipe Chicken (3)
Units Franchised From: 4
Primary Menu: American (1); Chicken (3)
Areas of Operation: MI
Type of Foodservice: Family Restaurant (1); Quick Serve (3)
Franchise Affiliation: Lee's Famous Recipes Inc., FORT WALTON BEACH, FL

Key Personnel
CURTIS R. PUTHOFF - President; General Buyer
KENNETH JAMES - Chief Diversity Officer
ROSEMARY ZINK - VP Finance, Administration
SARAH LUKER - Director
TINA DEE - Director; Community Relations
VAN MCMULLAN - Director Diversity
KIM SALINAS - Director Human Resources
LESLIE NELSON - Associate Director

The Culinary Institute of Michigan Baker College
1903 Marquette Ave
Muskegon, MI 49442

Telephone: (231) 777-6644
Internet Homepage: culinaryinstitutemi.com
Type of Business: Culinary Schools
Areas of Operation: MI

Key Personnel
CHRIS SOWA - Executive Chef; General Buyer
TOM RECINELLA - Director

Domino's Distribution Center
17605 Commerce Dr
New Boston, MI 48164-1002

Telephone: (734) 551-0220
Fax Number: (734) 551-0240
Listing Type: Distribution Center
Type of Business: Chain Restaurant Operator
Number of Employees: 60
Average Check: Lunch(12); Dinner(18)
Preferred Location Types: Community Mall; Downtown; Freestanding; Lifestyle Center; Other; Outlet Mall; Regional Mall; Strip Mall; Travel Plazas
Areas of Operation: IL, IN, MI, OH, WI
On-site Distribution Center: Yes
Parent Company: Domino's Pizza Inc, ANN ARBOR, MI

Key Personnel
HAROLD WORSHAM - General Manager; General Buyer

Rocky's of Northville
41122 7 Mile Rd
Northville, MI 48167-2648

Telephone: (248) 349-4434
Fax Number: (248) 349-8517
Internet Homepage: steveandrockys.com; rockysnorthville.com
Company Email: dbrady@steveandrockys.com
Type of Business: Chain Restaurant Operator
Year Founded: 1992
Total Sales: $4,127,000 (e)
Alcohol Sales: 25%
Number of Employees: 250
Average Check: Lunch(12); Dinner(20)
Total Units: 2
Trade Names: Rocky's of Northville (1); Steve & Rocky's (1)
Company-Owned Units: 2
Preferred Location Types: Freestanding
Alcohol Served: Beer, Wine, Liquor
Primary Menu: Seafood (2)
Areas of Operation: MI
Type of Foodservice: Casual Dining (2)
Catering Services: Yes
Primary Distributors: (Food) SYSCO Detroit LLC, CANTON, MI

Key Personnel
CHUCK RACHWITZ - President; Executive Chef; General Buyer
JOSEPH GARDNER - Executive Chef

Emagine Entertainment LLC
44425 W 12 Mile Rd
Novi, MI 48377-2503

Mailing Address: PO Box 841, TROY, MI, 48099-0841
Telephone: (248) 468-2990
Fax Number: (248) 468-2994
Internet Homepage: emagine-entertainment.com
Type of Business: Foodservice Operations - Movie Theatre
Total Sales: $41,080,000 (e)
Number of Employees: 2,835
Total Units: 21
Trade Names: Emagine Theater (21)
Company-Owned Units: 21
Preferred Location Types: Freestanding
Alcohol Served: Beer, Wine, Liquor
Primary Menu: Snacks (21)
Areas of Operation: MI
Type of Foodservice: In-Store Feeder (21)
Primary Distributors: (Full Line) SYSCO Detroit LLC, CANTON, MI
Notes: The company derives approximately 72% of its revenue from movie theatre operations.

Key Personnel
PAUL GLANTZ - Chairman
ANTHONY LAVERDE - CEO
SCOTT LARGENT - General Manager

Epoch Hospitality Group
46700 Grand River Ave
Novi, MI 48374

Telephone: (248) 735-6010
Fax Number: (248) 735-6016
Internet Homepage: knotjustabar.com; epochhospitality.com
Company Email: info@epochhospitality.com
Type of Business: Chain Restaurant Operator
Year Founded: 1982
Total Sales: $7,715,000 (e)
Alcohol Sales: 35%
Number of Employees: 290
Average Check: Lunch(18); Dinner(90)
Total Units: 2
Trade Names: Knot Just a Bar (2)
Company-Owned Units: 2
Preferred Location Types: Freestanding
Alcohol Served: Beer, Wine, Liquor
Primary Menu: American (2)
Areas of Operation: MI
Type of Foodservice: Casual Dining (2)
Catering Services: Yes

Key Personnel
STEVE DAVIS - President; Director Menu Development; General Buyer
PAUL HESS - Director Operations
DAVE WASKIEWICZ - Store Manager

Kimchi Box
43170 Grand River Ave
Novi, MI 48375

Internet Homepage: kimchiboxusa.com
Type of Business: Chain Restaurant Operator
Year Founded: 2021
Number of Employees: 150
Total Units: 8
Trade Names: Kimchi Box (8)
Company-Owned Units: 8
Primary Menu: Korean (8)
Areas of Operation: MI
Type of Foodservice: Quick Serve (8)

Key Personnel
MIN KYU KIM - Founder; CEO

Walker Franchises Inc
43432 W Oaks Dr
Novi, MI 48377-3300

Telephone: (248) 347-1020
Fax Number: (248) 347-1020
Type of Business: Chain Restaurant Operator
Total Sales: $2,410,000 (e)
Total Units: 4
Trade Names: Subway (4)
Units Franchised From: 4
Primary Menu: Sandwiches/Deli (4)
Areas of Operation: MI
Type of Foodservice: Quick Serve (4)
Franchise Affiliation: Doctor's Associates Inc., MILFORD, CT

Key Personnel
JOHN WALKER - President; General Buyer

Stewart Systems Inc
1669 Hamilton Rd Ste 210
Okemos, MI 48864-1962

Telephone: (517) 336-9155
Type of Business: Chain Restaurant Operator
Total Sales: $5,241,000 (e)
Total Units: 9
Trade Names: Subway (9)
Units Franchised From: 9
Primary Menu: Sandwiches/Deli (9)
Areas of Operation: MI
Type of Foodservice: Quick Serve (9)
Franchise Affiliation: Doctor's Associates Inc., MILFORD, CT

Key Personnel
WILLIAM STEWART - President; General Buyer

TINA SHEA - Director Administration, Human Resources

Stafford's Hospitality Inc.
118 Lewis St
Petoskey, MI 49770-2449

Mailing Address: PO Box 657, PETOSKEY, MI, 49770-0657
Telephone: (231) 758-3545
Fax Number: (231) 758-3547
Internet Homepage: staffords.com
Company Email: hospitality@staffords.com
Type of Business: Chain Restaurant Operator
Year Founded: 1968
Total Sales: $6,268,000 (e)
Alcohol Sales: 30%
Number of Employees: 87
Average Check: Breakfast(18); Lunch(36); Dinner(48)
Total Units: 3
Trade Names: Stafford's Pier (1); Stafford's Weathervane (1); The Noggin Pub (@ Stafford's Perry Hotel) (1)
Company-Owned Units: 3
Preferred Square Footage: 10,000
Preferred Location Types: Freestanding; Hotel/Motel
Alcohol Served: Beer, Wine, Liquor
Primary Menu: American (3)
Areas of Operation: MI
Type of Foodservice: Casual Dining (3)
Catering Services: Yes
Primary Distributors: (Full Line) Gordon Food Service Inc., WYOMING, MI

Key Personnel
DUDLEY MARVIN - President; Partner; General Manager; Director Quality Assurance, Human Resources, Menu Development
REGINALD SMITH - VP
JUDY HONOR - Director Marketing; Manager Loss Prevention, Risk Management, Advertising

Bearclaw Coffee Co.
2400 Baseview Dr
Pinckney, MI 48169-9516

Telephone: (734) 369-9660
Internet Homepage: bearclawcoffee.com
Company Email: debi@bearclawcoffee.com
Type of Business: Chain Restaurant Operator
Year Founded: 2002
Total Sales: $3,494,000 (e)
Number of Employees: 90
Average Check: Breakfast(6); Lunch(6); Dinner(6)
Internet Order Processing: Yes
Total Units: 5
Trade Names: Bearclaw Coffee Co (5)

Units Franchised To: 5
Preferred Square Footage: 2,500
Preferred Location Types: Community Mall; Freestanding; Strip Mall
Primary Menu: Coffee (5)
Areas of Operation: MI
Type of Foodservice: Quick Serve (5)
Catering Services: Yes
On-site Distribution Center: Yes

Key Personnel
DOUG SCROGGINS - President; Partner; COO; Director Finance, Purchasing
JOSH BARRON - Manager Distribution

Greggco Management Co.
630 Martin Luther King Jr Blvd N
Pontiac, MI 48342-1623

Telephone: (248) 335-9370
Fax Number: (248) 335-9384
Company Email: sgreggco@cs.com
Type of Business: Chain Restaurant Operator
Total Sales: $8,211,000 (e)
Number of Employees: 15
Average Check: Lunch(8); Dinner(8)
Total Units: 3
Trade Names: Popeyes Louisiana Kitchen (3)
Units Franchised From: 3
Preferred Location Types: Freestanding
Primary Menu: Chicken (3)
Areas of Operation: MI
Type of Foodservice: Quick Serve (3)
Franchise Affiliation: Popeyes Louisiana Kitchen Inc., ATLANTA, GA
Primary Distributors: (Full Line) I Supply Co., FAIRBORN, OH

Key Personnel
GREGORY SCOTT - President; General Manager; Executive Chef; General Buyer

Bellacinos, Inc
10096 Shaver Rd
Portage, MI 49024-6738

Telephone: (269) 329-0782
Internet Homepage: bellacinos.com
Type of Business: Chain Restaurant Operator
Year Founded: 1998
Systemwide Sales: $20,118,000 (e)
Total Sales: $1,150,000 (e)
Alcohol Sales: 3%
Number of Employees: 435
Average Check: Lunch(12); Dinner(16)
Total Units: 58
Trade Names: Bellacino's Pizzas and Grinders (58)
Units Franchised To: 58
Preferred Square Footage: 2,500; 3,400
Preferred Location Types: Freestanding; Regional Mall; Strip Mall
Alcohol Served: Beer, Wine, Liquor
Primary Menu: Pizza (58)
Areas of Operation: FL, GA, IA, IL, IN, MI, MO, NC, OH, OK, SC, TN, VA, WV
Type of Foodservice: Quick Serve (58)
Catering Services: Yes
Primary Distributors: (Full Line) Sofo Foods, TOLEDO, OH

Key Personnel
SANDRA MANCINO - President; Director Site Selection, Product Development
DAN WARNAAR - COO; Director Operations
KIM D. LOSIK - Exec VP; VP Training, Product Development, Menu Development, Purchasing-Foodservice Equip/Supplies
MARIA E. LOSIK - Treasurer; Corporate Secretary; Manager Human Resources

HLR Scoopers, LLC
6800 S Westnedge Ave
Portage, MI 49002-3596

Telephone: (269) 327-4674
Type of Business: Chain Restaurant Operator
Total Sales: $1,226,000 (e)
Total Units: 2
Trade Names: Cold Stone Creamery (2)
Units Franchised From: 2
Primary Menu: Snacks (2)
Areas of Operation: MI
Type of Foodservice: Quick Serve (2)
Franchise Affiliation: Kahala Brands, SCOTTSDALE, AZ

Key Personnel
JAMES MELLUISH - Owner

Nu-Ventures Inc.
5228 Lovers Ln Ste 102
Portage, MI 49002-1521

Telephone: (269) 226-4400
Fax Number: (269) 226-4466
Internet Homepage: samuelmancinos.com
Company Email: nuven@samuelmancinos.com
Type of Business: Chain Restaurant Operator
Year Founded: 1994
Systemwide Sales: $18,549,000 (e)
Total Sales: $1,590,000 (e)
Number of Employees: 3
Average Check: Lunch(14); Dinner(20)
Total Units: 18
Trade Names: Samuel Mancino's Italian Eatery (18)
Units Franchised To: 18
Preferred Square Footage: 5,500; 6,000
Preferred Location Types: Freestanding; Strip Mall

Primary Menu: Italian (18)
Areas of Operation: IN, MI, OH
Type of Foodservice: Casual Dining (18)
Catering Services: Yes

Key Personnel
JAMIE KUDARY - Manager Accounting

Suzanne of Richmond, Inc.
67600 S Main St
Richmond, MI 48062-1926

Telephone: (586) 727-2800
Fax Number: (586) 727-2800
Type of Business: Chain Restaurant Operator
Total Sales: $20,009,000 (e)
Total Units: 4
Trade Names: McDonald's (4)
Units Franchised From: 4
Primary Menu: Hamburger (4)
Areas of Operation: MI
Type of Foodservice: Quick Serve (4)
Franchise Affiliation: McDonald's Corporation, CHICAGO, IL

Key Personnel
ERICA SCHULZ-ROGERS - President; General Buyer

Lonigro Enterprises, Inc.
14177 Cranbrook St
Riverview, MI 48193-7527

Telephone: (734) 284-4963
Fax Number: (734) 284-6555
Type of Business: Chain Restaurant Operator
Total Sales: $9,826,000 (e)
Total Units: 4
Trade Names: Burger King (4)
Units Franchised From: 4
Preferred Location Types: Freestanding
Primary Menu: Hamburger (4)
Areas of Operation: MI
Type of Foodservice: Quick Serve (4)
Franchise Affiliation: Burger King Worldwide Inc., MIAMI, FL

Key Personnel
NICK LONIGRO - President; Owner; General Buyer

Kosch Catering & Dining Services
324 East St
Rochester, MI 48307-2013

Telephone: (248) 608-0690
Fax Number: (248) 608-0695
Internet Homepage: koschcatering.com
Company Email: info@koschcatering.com
Type of Business: Foodservice Management Operator
Year Founded: 1982
Total Sales: $14,248,000 (e)
Number of Employees: 200
Number of Locations Served: 50
Total Foodservice Mgmt Accounts: 50
Areas of Operation: MI
Type of Foodservice: Cafeteria (50)
Foodservice Management Venues: Business & Industry
Primary Distributors: (Full Line) Gordon Food Service Inc., WYOMING, MI

Key Personnel
GORDON KOSCH - CEO; President; Partner; Manager Advertising, Business Development; Buyer Foodservice Equip/Supplies
GARY KOSCH - Partner; CFO; VP Accounting, Operations
JERRY MOUTGAHIAS - Manager District

Kruse & Muer Restaurants
100 E 3rd St Ste 105
Rochester, MI 48307-6710

Telephone: (248) 652-3896
Fax Number: (248) 652-2254
Internet Homepage: kruseandmuerrestaurants.com
Company Email: info@kruseandmuerrestaurants.com
Type of Business: Chain Restaurant Operator
Year Founded: 1988
Total Sales: $13,690,000 (e)
Alcohol Sales: 20%
Number of Employees: 400
Average Check: Lunch(16); Dinner(28)
Total Units: 7
Trade Names: Kabin Kruser's Oyster Bar (1); Kruse & Muer (4); Kruse's Deer Lake Inn (1); Rochester Chop House (1)
Company-Owned Units: 7
Preferred Square Footage: 4,000
Preferred Location Types: Downtown; Freestanding; Regional Mall
Alcohol Served: Beer, Wine, Liquor
Primary Menu: Seafood (1); Steak/Seafood (6)
Areas of Operation: MI
Type of Foodservice: Casual Dining (6); Fine Dining (1)
Catering Services: Yes
Primary Distributors: (Full Line) SYSCO Food Services of Grand Rapids LLC, GRAND RAPIDS, MI

Key Personnel
BILL KRUSE - President; CFO; Director Real Estate; General Buyer
CASEY MUER - VP Operations
KELLY LUPU - Director Information Systems, Marketing

Dorsey Culinary Academy
31522 Gratiot Ave
Roseville, MI 48066

Telephone: (586) 296-3225
Internet Homepage: dorsey.edu
Type of Business: Culinary Schools
Areas of Operation: MI

Key Personnel
JOHN O'SULLIVAN - VP Marketing
MATT SCHELLIG - Director Culinary Development

National Coney Island Inc.
27947 Groesbeck Hwy
Roseville, MI 48066-5221

Telephone: (586) 771-7744
Fax Number: (586) 771-9578
Internet Homepage: nationalconeyisland.com
Type of Business: Chain Restaurant Operator
Year Founded: 1965
Total Sales: $10,670,000 (e)
Alcohol Sales: 10%
Number of Employees: 675
Average Check: Lunch(10); Dinner(14)
Internet Order Processing: Yes
Internet Sales: 1.00%
Total Units: 15
Trade Names: National Coney Island (15)
Company-Owned Units: 15
Preferred Square Footage: 6,000
Preferred Location Types: Freestanding; Strip Mall
Alcohol Served: Beer, Wine
Primary Menu: Hot Dogs (15)
Projected Openings: 3
Areas of Operation: MI
Type of Foodservice: Casual Dining (15)
Catering Services: Yes
On-site Distribution Center: Yes
Primary Distributors: (Full Line) Caramagno Foods Co. Inc., DETROIT, MI

Key Personnel
TOM GIFTOS - President; Controller; Director Finance, Supply Chain, Marketing, Real Estate, Research & Development, Store Planning
BOB NICHOLS - VP; Manager Operations, Purchasing, Information Systems, Inventory, Marketing, Product Development, Menu Development, Catering
BRIAN BUCK - Director Information Systems
WILLIAM ZANETTI - Manager Facility/Maintenance, Construction

S B K Inc
423 W 11 Mile Rd
Royal Oak, MI 48067-2240

Telephone: (248) 543-9888
Fax Number: (586) 427-5567
Type of Business: Chain Restaurant Operator
Total Sales: $32,970,000 (e)
Total Units: 8
Trade Names: McDonald's (8)
Units Franchised From: 8
Primary Menu: Hamburger (8)
Areas of Operation: MI
Type of Foodservice: Quick Serve (8)
Franchise Affiliation: McDonald's Corporation, CHICAGO, IL

Key Personnel
ANTHONY J. KOSTECKI - President; General Buyer

Saputo Inc
30807 Woodward Ave
Royal Oak, MI 48073-0921

Telephone: (248) 435-3160
Type of Business: Chain Restaurant Operator
Total Sales: $113,030,000 (e)
Total Units: 24
Trade Names: McDonald's (24)
Units Franchised From: 24
Primary Menu: Hamburger (24)
Areas of Operation: MI
Type of Foodservice: Quick Serve (24)
Franchise Affiliation: McDonald's Corporation, CHICAGO, IL

Key Personnel
WILLIAM SAPUTO - President; Partner; General Buyer
JESSICA SAPUTO - Partner
WILLIAM SAPUTO JR - Partner
BRETT TANTTU - Senior VP Research & Development
STEVE GALBRAITH - VP Procurement, Risk Management
JASON HUSSEY - VP Supply Chain
MICHAEL MURRAY - VP Operations
BRIAN LOCH - VP Sales
LUC ROBERT - VP Human Resources
JEREMY HASTINGS - Director Consumer Insights
NICK SMITH - Director Communications
CHARMAINE BURKE - Director Finance
ANDY MORRIS - Director Operations
AMEY KENNEDY - Director Talent
PIERRE GUITOR - Director Purchasing
JEAN MILLER - Director Customer Service
DENISE DUFRESNE - Director Compliance, Safety-Food
JASON RAWLINS - Director Procurement
VICTORIA VAL - Director Quality Assurance
DOUG BISSING - Director Strategic Planning
JIM BYAM - Director Technology
MICHAEL HUYG - Director Operations
COREY BROWER - Director Research & Development
JIM RUSSELL - Director Sales
MICHELLE COLLINS - Director Human Resources
CONNOR DONOVAN - Director Sales, East Region
PATRICIA BAILEY - Regional Director Human Resources
BRIAN VOLBRIGHT - Regional Director Operations
DANIEL LAMORA - Senior Manager Finance
SAMANTHA BERNARDI - Senior Manager Operations
BRIAN NOBLE - Senior Manager Information Technology
MELISSA LAMEY - Regional Manager Sales
DAVE FRICK - Regional Manager Sales
ALEXUS BERNDT - Manager Quality Assurance
SARTAJ S. NARULA - Manager Quality Assurance, Safety-Food
EMILIE C. MUSSON - Manager Supply Chain
NATALIE MALICOAT - Manager Data Quality
GINA CAMPO - Manager Human Resources
NICOLE AUSTIN - Manager Marketing
NICK PIERSCINSKI - Manager Sales
KAYE BUSHDIECKER - Manager Technology
DAVID CALL - Manager Quality Assurance
DENNIS MCCLUNG - Manager Information Technology
ANTHONY GARCIA - Manager Sales
MILES GROESCHEL - Manager Plant

Sign of The Beefcarver Inc.
1530 Rochester Rd
Royal Oak, MI 48067

Telephone: (248) 645-6444
Fax Number: (248) 645-6694
Internet Homepage: thebeefcarver.com
Company Email: beefcarver@gmail.com
Type of Business: Chain Restaurant Operator
Year Founded: 1957
Total Sales: $4,573,000 (e)
Alcohol Sales: 10%
Number of Employees: 75
Average Check: Lunch(12); Dinner(12)
Total Units: 1
Trade Names: Sign of the Beefcarver (1)
Company-Owned Units: 1
Preferred Square Footage: 6,000
Preferred Location Types: Freestanding; Office Complex
Primary Menu: American (1)
Areas of Operation: MI
Type of Foodservice: Casual Dining (1)
Primary Distributors: (Full Line) SYSCO Food Services of Grand Rapids LLC, GRAND RAPIDS, MI

Key Personnel
CHUCK PELZER - President; Manager Operations

After Tax Dough Inc
1910 Court St
Saginaw, MI 48602-3701

Telephone: (989) 249-7000
Type of Business: Chain Restaurant Operator
Total Sales: $4,333,000 (e)
Total Units: 3
Trade Names: Papa John's Pizza (3)
Units Franchised From: 3
Primary Menu: Pizza (3)
Areas of Operation: MI
Type of Foodservice: Quick Serve (3)
Franchise Affiliation: Papa Johns International Inc., LOUISVILLE, KY

Key Personnel
KIRK W. MOSHER - Owner; General Buyer

Bell's Chicken Villa Inc.
3734 Hess Ave
Saginaw, MI 48601-4043

Mailing Address: PO Box 2216, SAGINAW, MI, 48605-2216
Telephone: (989) 754-6554
Fax Number: (989) 754-6150
Type of Business: Chain Restaurant Operator
Year Founded: 1964
Total Sales: $9,135,000 (e)
Number of Employees: 120
Average Check: Lunch(12); Dinner(12)
Total Units: 5
Trade Names: KFC (5)
Units Franchised From: 5
Preferred Square Footage: 3,000
Preferred Location Types: Freestanding
Primary Menu: Chicken (5)
Areas of Operation: MI
Type of Foodservice: Quick Serve (5)
Franchise Affiliation: KFC Corporation, LOUISVILLE, KY

Key Personnel
BRIAN H. DENMAN - President; Director Finance, Supply Chain, Real Estate, Design; General Buyer
SHANNON HALL - General Manager; Director Purchasing, Facility/Maintenance
CARRIE KLUPF - Manager Human Resources

A S Enterprises Inc
4296 Scott B Dr
Saint Clair, MI 48079-3566

Telephone: (810) 326-0624
Type of Business: Chain Restaurant Operator
Total Sales: $1,510,000 (e)
Total Units: 2
Trade Names: Little Caesars Pizza (2)
Units Franchised From: 2
Primary Menu: Pizza (2)
Areas of Operation: MI
Type of Foodservice: Quick Serve (2)
Franchise Affiliation: Little Caesar Enterprises Inc., DETROIT, MI

Key Personnel
PAT PEARSON - Owner; General Buyer

Popco Inc
920 S US Highway 27
Saint Johns, MI 48879-2436

Telephone: (989) 224-3325
Type of Business: Chain Restaurant Operator
Total Sales: $15,096,000 (e)
Total Units: 3
Trade Names: McDonald's (3)
Units Franchised From: 3
Primary Menu: Hamburger (3)
Areas of Operation: MI
Type of Foodservice: Quick Serve (3)
Franchise Affiliation: McDonald's Corporation, CHICAGO, IL

Key Personnel
ROBERT VAN POPPELEN - President; General Buyer
BRENDA HOLMES - General Manager
ERIC KRAFVE - Director Business Development
MARY KUNTZ - Manager National

Michigan Pizza Hut Inc.
2053 Niles Rd
Saint Joseph, MI 49085-2505

Telephone: (269) 983-3888
Fax Number: (269) 983-2214
Internet Homepage: michiganpizzahut.com
Type of Business: Chain Restaurant Operator
Year Founded: 1972
Total Sales: $48,880,000 (e)
Alcohol Sales: 3%
Number of Employees: 1,216
Average Check: Lunch(14); Dinner(22)
Total Units: 39
Trade Names: Pizza Hut (39)
Units Franchised From: 39
Preferred Square Footage: 4,000
Preferred Location Types: Freestanding; Strip Mall
Alcohol Served: Beer, Wine
Primary Menu: Pizza (39)
Areas of Operation: MI
Type of Foodservice: Quick Serve (39)
Catering Services: Yes
Franchise Affiliation: Pizza Hut Inc., PLANO, TX
Primary Distributors: (Full Line) McLane Foodservice, CARROLLTON, TX

Key Personnel
JEFF WHITE - Chairman; Director Real Estate; General Buyer
GAYLE KIRBY - Director Operations
CHAD WHITE - Manager Marketing

Dickendesher Inc
450 W Sanilac Rd
Sandusky, MI 48471

Telephone: (810) 648-2465
Type of Business: Chain Restaurant Operator
Total Sales: $9,960,000 (e)
Total Units: 2
Trade Names: McDonald's (2)
Units Franchised From: 2
Primary Menu: Hamburger (2)
Areas of Operation: MI
Type of Foodservice: Quick Serve (2)
Franchise Affiliation: McDonald's Corporation, CHICAGO, IL

Key Personnel
MICHAEL DICKENDESHER - President; General Buyer

Sharing The Bread, Inc.
12161 23 Mile Rd
Shelby Township, MI 48315-2615

Telephone: (586) 997-1571
Type of Business: Chain Restaurant Operator
Total Sales: $62,210,000 (e)
Total Units: 42
Trade Names: Del Taco (2); Jersey Mike's Subs (18); Little Caesars (19); Sonic Drive In (3)
Units Franchised From: 42
Primary Menu: Pizza (19); Sandwiches/Deli (21); Taco (2)
Areas of Operation: MI
Type of Foodservice: Quick Serve (42)
Franchise Affiliation: Jersey Mike's Franchise Systems, MANASQUAN, NJ

Key Personnel
ROBERT MIDDLETON - Owner; General Buyer

Clementine's Restaurants Inc.
500 Phoenix St
South Haven, MI 49090-1443

Telephone: (269) 637-4755
Fax Number: (269) 637-2917
Internet Homepage: ohmydarling.com
Company Email: info@ohmydarling.com
Type of Business: Chain Restaurant Operator
Year Founded: 1982
Total Sales: $7,852,000 (e)
Alcohol Sales: 20%
Number of Employees: 90
Average Check: Lunch(10); Dinner(18)
Total Units: 2
Trade Names: Clementine's (1); Clementine's Too (1)
Company-Owned Units: 2
Preferred Location Types: Freestanding
Alcohol Served: Beer, Wine, Liquor
Primary Menu: American (2)
Areas of Operation: MI
Type of Foodservice: Casual Dining (2)
Primary Distributors: (Food) SYSCO Food Services of Grand Rapids LLC, GRAND RAPIDS, MI

Key Personnel
AL RUPPERT - President; Owner
JOHN RUPPERT - General Manager; Executive Chef; General Buyer; Buyer Beverages, Food

Bigalora
29410 Northwestern Hwy
Southfield, MI 48034-5717

Telephone: (248) 356-6600
Internet Homepage: baccoristorante.com; bigalora.com
Company Email: jack@baccoristorante.com
Type of Business: Chain Restaurant Operator
Year Founded: 2002
Total Units: 7
Trade Names: Bacco (1); Bigalora (6)
Company-Owned Units: 7
Preferred Location Types: Airports; Freestanding; Stadiums
Primary Menu: Italian (7)
Areas of Operation: MI
Type of Foodservice: Casual Dining (6); Fine Dining (1)

Key Personnel
LUCIANO DEL SIGNORE - Partner; Executive Chef; General Buyer
MICHAEL COLLINS - Partner
MICHAEL CHETCUTI - Partner
LANDSEY GLASSON - Manager Catering

Diversified Restaurant Holdings Inc.
27680 Franklin Rd
Southfield, MI 48034-8203

Telephone: (833) 374-7282
Fax Number: (866) 737-8689
Internet Homepage: diversifiedrestaurantholdings.com
Listing Type: Subsidiary
Type of Business: Chain Restaurant Operator
Year Founded: 2006
Total Sales: $324,420,000 (e)
Alcohol Sales: 25%
Number of Employees: 2,549
Total Units: 64
Trade Names: Buffalo Wild Wings Grill & Bar (64)
Units Franchised From: 64
Preferred Square Footage: 3,500; 3,800; 6,200; 6,400; 7,500
Alcohol Served: Beer, Wine, Liquor
Primary Menu: Chicken (64)
Areas of Operation: FL, IL, IN, MI, MO
Type of Foodservice: Casual Dining (64)
Parent Company: ICV Partners, LLC, NEW YORK, NY
Notes: Diversified Restaurant Holdings (DRH) operates as AMC Group Inc., a franchisee of Buffalo Wild Wings

Key Personnel
T. MICHAEL ANSLEY - Chairman; Founder; CEO Interim
TONI WERNER - CFO Interim; Controller
JASON T. CURTIS - COO
JAY ALAN DUSENBERRY - Corporate Secretary
MISTY SIRCH - Director Real Estate

Lou's Finer Delicatessen Inc.
22819 Greenfield Rd
Southfield, MI 48075-3711

Telephone: (248) 559-6001
Fax Number: (248) 559-3262
Internet Homepage: lousdeli.net
Company Email: comments@lousdeli.net
Type of Business: Chain Restaurant Operator
Year Founded: 1940
Total Sales: $2,872,000 (e)
Number of Employees: 100
Average Check: Lunch(16); Dinner(16)
Total Units: 3
Trade Names: Lou's Deli (3)
Company-Owned Units: 3
Preferred Location Types: Freestanding
Primary Menu: Sandwiches/Deli (3)
Areas of Operation: MI
Type of Foodservice: Quick Serve (3)
Primary Distributors: (Full Line) SYSCO Detroit LLC, CANTON, MI

Key Personnel
MARTIN GOODMAN - President; Owner; General Manager; Executive Chef; Director Menu Development; General Buyer

Ram's Horn Restaurants Inc.
29777 Telegraph Rd Ste 3050
Southfield, MI 48034-7665

Telephone: (248) 350-3430
Fax Number: (248) 350-1024
Internet Homepage: ramshornrestaurants.com
Company Email: ramshornrestaurants@gmail.com
Type of Business: Chain Restaurant Operator
Year Founded: 1967
Systemwide Sales: $50,149,000 (e)
Total Sales: $22,590,000 (e)
Number of Employees: 280
Average Check: Breakfast(8); Lunch(12); Dinner(14)
Total Units: 16
Trade Names: Ram's Horn Restaurant (16)
Company-Owned Units: 5
Units Franchised To: 11
Preferred Square Footage: 4,000
Preferred Location Types: Freestanding
Primary Menu: American (16)
Areas of Operation: MI
Type of Foodservice: Family Restaurant (16)
Primary Distributors: (Equipment) People's Restaurant Equipment Co., DETROIT, MI; (Food) US Foods, WIXOM, MI; (Supplies) People's Restaurant Equipment Co., DETROIT, MI
Parent Company: Kasapis Brothers Inc., SOUTHFIELD, MI

Key Personnel
EUGENE KASAPIS - President; Director Finance, Information Systems, Supply Chain, Real Estate, Construction, Design, Store Planning, Menu Development
GUS KASAPIS - VP Operations, Purchasing, Marketing; General Manager; Director Facility/Maintenance; General Buyer
JOHNNA LASALA - Manager Human Resources

STA Management, LLC
29850 Northwestern Hwy Ste 200
Southfield, MI 48034-5711

Telephone: (248) 557-5454
Fax Number: (248) 557-5959
Internet Homepage: team-sta.com
Type of Business: Chain Restaurant Operator
Total Sales: $100,110,000 (e)
Total Units: 52
Trade Names: Domino's (52)
Units Franchised From: 52
Primary Menu: Pizza (52)
Areas of Operation: FL, IN, MI
Type of Foodservice: Quick Serve (52)
Franchise Affiliation: Domino's Pizza Inc, ANN ARBOR, MI

Key Personnel
RON ASMAR - CEO; President
RONNIE ASMAR JR - VP Operations
RANDY ASMAR - VP Development
DESIREE FOUMIA - VP Finance
REMY ASMAR - VP Marketing
WADE ROSS - Director Operations
PATRICK FISHER - Director Operations

Van Master Management Inc.
22114 Telegraph Rd
Southfield, MI 48033-4213

Telephone: (248) 353-7600
Fax Number: (248) 353-9807
Internet Homepage: kfcmichigan.com
Type of Business: Chain Restaurant Operator
Year Founded: 1965
Total Sales: $34,210,000 (e)
Number of Employees: 300
Average Check: Lunch(8); Dinner(8)
Internet Order Processing: Yes
Total Units: 19
Trade Names: KFC (19)
Units Franchised From: 19
Preferred Square Footage: 3,500
Preferred Location Types: Freestanding; Strip Mall
Primary Menu: Chicken (19)
Areas of Operation: MI
Type of Foodservice: Quick Serve (19)
Franchise Affiliation: KFC Corporation, LOUISVILLE, KY
Primary Distributors: (Full Line) Caramagno Foods Co. Inc., DETROIT, MI

Key Personnel
SHIRLEY VAN GELOFF - President; General Buyer

Tria Co
4555 W Dickman Rd
Springfield, MI 49037-7328

Telephone: (269) 660-2800
Fax Number: (269) 660-8236
Type of Business: Chain Restaurant Operator
Year Founded: 1982
Total Sales: $67,160,000 (e)
Number of Employees: 940
Average Check: Breakfast(8); Lunch(8); Dinner(8)
Total Units: 30
Trade Names: Arby's (4); Burger King (26)

Units Franchised From: 30
Preferred Square Footage: 2,500; 4,000
Preferred Location Types: Freestanding
Primary Menu: Hamburger (26); Sandwiches/Deli (4)
Areas of Operation: IN, MI
Type of Foodservice: Quick Serve (32)
Franchise Affiliation: Arby's Restaurant Group, ATLANTA, GA; Burger King Worldwide Inc., MIAMI, FL
Primary Distributors: (Full Line) Reinhart Foodservice, WARREN, MI

Key Personnel
PAUL D. GREGORY - CEO; General Buyer
MICHELLE WICKENS - Director Operations
MARK WILLIAMS - Manager District

Jet's America Inc.
37501 Mound Rd
Sterling Heights, MI 48310-4124

Telephone: (586) 268-5870
Fax Number: (586) 268-6762
Internet Homepage: jetspizza.com
Company Email: comments@jetspizza.com
Type of Business: Chain Restaurant Operator
Year Founded: 1978
Systemwide Sales: $319,833,000 (e)
Total Sales: $14,960,000 (e)
Number of Employees: 460
Average Check: Lunch(14); Dinner(20)
Internet Order Processing: Yes
Internet Sales: 10.00%
Total Units: 372
Trade Names: Jet's Pizza (400)
Company-Owned Units: 20
Units Franchised To: 380
Preferred Square Footage: 1,400
Preferred Location Types: Convenience Store/Gas Station; Strip Mall
Primary Menu: Pizza (400)
Projected Openings: 2
Areas of Operation: AL, AZ, CO, FL, GA, IL, IN, KY, MI, MN, MO, NC, OH, PA, SC, TN, TX, VA, WI
Type of Foodservice: Quick Serve (400)
Catering Services: Yes
Primary Distributors: (Full Line) Caramagno Foods Co. Inc., DETROIT, MI

Key Personnel
JOHN JETTS - President; VP Marketing; Director Information Systems
JEFFREY GALLOWAY - VP Operations
MARY KOPIETZ - Manager Human Resources

Trigo Hospitality
3090 Johnson Rd
Stevensville, MI 49127-1270

Telephone: (269) 556-5000
Fax Number: (269) 465-0008
Company Email: admin@trigohospitality.com
Type of Business: Chain Restaurant Operator
Year Founded: 1992
Total Sales: $41,510,000 (e)
Number of Employees: 2,030
Average Check: Lunch(10); Dinner(16)
Total Units: 33
Trade Names: Moe's Southwest Grill (3); Pizza Hut (30)
Units Franchised From: 33
Preferred Square Footage: 1,400; 3,200; 4,500; 4,700
Preferred Location Types: Freestanding; Strip Mall
Primary Menu: Pizza (30); Southwest/Tex-Mex (3)
Areas of Operation: MI
Type of Foodservice: Fast Casual (3); Quick Serve (30)
Catering Services: Yes
Franchise Affiliation: Moe's Southwest Grill LLC, ATLANTA, GA; Pizza Hut Inc., PLANO, TX; Sonic Corp., OKLAHOMA CITY, OK

Key Personnel
GREGORY MOLTER - Partner
GREG COLLINS - VP Operations
BRIAN CRONKRITE - VP Marketing
HEIDI DEJA - Controller
MORGAN VAN DYKE - General Manager Restaurant Operations

STC Inc.
21649 Goddard Rd Ste A
Taylor, MI 48180-4299

Telephone: (734) 374-8080
Fax Number: (734) 374-2160
Type of Business: Chain Restaurant Operator
Year Founded: 1980
Total Sales: $90,170,000 (e)
Number of Employees: 1,000
Average Check: Breakfast(8); Lunch(8); Dinner(10)
Total Units: 19
Trade Names: McDonald's (19)
Units Franchised From: 19
Preferred Square Footage: 2,500; 3,000
Preferred Location Types: Freestanding
Primary Menu: Hamburger (19)
Areas of Operation: MI
Type of Foodservice: Quick Serve (19)
Franchise Affiliation: McDonald's Corporation, CHICAGO, IL

Key Personnel
VASANT CHAPATWALA - President; General Manager; Director Operations, Facility/Maintenance, Supply Chain, Real Estate; General Buyer
BRAD CROSS - President
TERRY FRYAR - Manager Software Development
GAIL MCLACHLIN - Manager Accounting, Information Systems
RHONDA CLANCY - Manager Customer Service, Human Resources

Taylor Restaurants, Inc.
10450 Telegraph Rd
Taylor, MI 48180-3328

Telephone: (313) 291-7700
Type of Business: Chain Restaurant Operator
Total Sales: $3,339,000 (e)
Total Units: 2
Trade Names: Big Boy (2)
Units Franchised From: 2
Primary Menu: American (2)
Areas of Operation: MI
Type of Foodservice: Family Restaurant (2)
Franchise Affiliation: Big Boy Restaurants International LLC, WARREN, MI

Key Personnel
GEORGE DARANY SR - President; Partner; General Buyer
RICH SWOR - Partner

Casciano Traverse City
1800 S Garfield Ave
Traverse City, MI 49686-4380

Telephone: (231) 947-0630
Type of Business: Chain Restaurant Operator
Year Founded: 1988
Total Sales: $15,540,000 (e)
Number of Employees: 233
Average Check: Breakfast(5); Lunch(8); Dinner(8)
Total Units: 7
Trade Names: Burger King (7)
Units Franchised From: 7
Preferred Square Footage: 5,000
Preferred Location Types: Freestanding
Primary Menu: Hamburger (7)
Areas of Operation: MI
Type of Foodservice: Quick Serve (7)
Franchise Affiliation: Burger King Worldwide Inc., MIAMI, FL

Key Personnel
DANIEL CASCIANO JR - President; Manager Finance, Operations, Facility/Maintenance, Supply Chain, Marketing, Real Estate

MIKE CASCIANO - VP; General Buyer

Grand Traverse Pie Co.
525 W Front St Ste A
Traverse City, MI 49684-2002

Telephone: (231) 929-7841
Internet Homepage: gtpie.com
Company Email: info@gtpie.com
Type of Business: Chain Restaurant Operator
Year Founded: 1996
Systemwide Sales: $31,667,000 (e)
Total Sales: $65,170,000 (e)
Number of Employees: 300
Average Check: Dinner(16)
Total Units: 15
Trade Names: Grand Traverse Pie Company (15)
Company-Owned Units: 5
Units Franchised To: 10
Preferred Square Footage: 3,100; 4,800
Preferred Location Types: Downtown; Freestanding; Institution (college/hospital); Strip Mall
Primary Menu: Sandwiches/Deli (15)
Areas of Operation: IN, MI
Type of Foodservice: Fast Casual (15)
Catering Services: Yes
Primary Distributors: (Full Line) Lipari Foods Inc., WARREN, MI

Key Personnel
MIKE BUSLEY - President; Partner
DENISE BUSLEY - Partner; Director Menu Development

Great Lakes Culinary Institute
1701 E Front St
Traverse City, MI 49686-3016

Telephone: (231) 995-1000
Fax Number: (231) 995-1330
Internet Homepage: nmc.edu
Company Email: admissions@nmc.edu
Type of Business: Culinary Schools
Areas of Operation: MI

Key Personnel
LESLIE ECKERT - Director

Resorts Beef Ltd
530 S Union St
Traverse City, MI 49684-3247

Telephone: (231) 941-7774
Type of Business: Chain Restaurant Operator
Total Sales: $18,740,000 (e)
Average Check: Dinner(12)
Total Units: 10
Trade Names: Arby's (10)
Units Franchised From: 10
Primary Menu: Sandwiches/Deli (10)
Areas of Operation: MI
Type of Foodservice: Quick Serve (10)
Franchise Affiliation: Arby's Restaurant Group, ATLANTA, GA

Key Personnel
MICHAEL ZIPSER - President; General Buyer

Saco, Inc.
1221 E Front St
Traverse City, MI 49686-2928

Telephone: (231) 938-1800
Type of Business: Chain Restaurant Operator
Total Sales: $3,992,000 (e)
Total Units: 3
Trade Names: Little Caesars Pizza (3)
Units Franchised From: 3
Primary Menu: Pizza (3)
Areas of Operation: MI
Type of Foodservice: Quick Serve (3)
Franchise Affiliation: Little Caesar Enterprises Inc., DETROIT, MI

Key Personnel
PAT BUCK - President; General Buyer

Michigan Multi-King Corporation
4897 Rochester Rd
Troy, MI 48085-4962

Telephone: (248) 528-2860
Fax Number: (248) 528-1549
Internet Homepage: multiking.com
Type of Business: Chain Restaurant Operator
Year Founded: 1980
Total Sales: $25,220,000 (e)
Number of Employees: 760
Average Check: Breakfast(8); Lunch(8); Dinner(8)
Total Units: 11
Trade Names: Burger King (11)
Units Franchised From: 11
Preferred Square Footage: 4,000
Preferred Location Types: Freestanding
Primary Menu: Hamburger (11)
Areas of Operation: MI
Type of Foodservice: Quick Serve (11)
Franchise Affiliation: Burger King Worldwide Inc., MIAMI, FL
Primary Distributors: (Food) Reinhart Foodservice, WARREN, MI

Key Personnel
ANTHONY VERSACI - CEO
TRAVIS HARTMAN - General Manager
LEE ANN CASE - Director Supply Chain, Training, Food Safety
KEVIN BARNES - Director Operations, Purchasing
TODD WOZNIAK - District Manager

Pizza Papalis
631 E Big Beaver Rd Ste 107
Troy, MI 48083-1400

Telephone: (248) 740-1100
Fax Number: (248) 740-2284
Internet Homepage: pizzapapalis.com; riowraps.com
Company Email: comments@pizzapapalis.com
Type of Business: Chain Restaurant Operator
Year Founded: 1986
Total Sales: $10,440,000 (e)
Alcohol Sales: 9%
Number of Employees: 310
Average Check: Dinner(14)
Internet Order Processing: Yes
Total Units: 10
Trade Names: Pizza Papalis (7); Rio Wraps (3)
Company-Owned Units: 10
Preferred Location Types: Downtown; Freestanding; Strip Mall
Alcohol Served: Beer, Wine, Liquor
Primary Menu: Pizza (7); Sandwiches/Deli (3)
Areas of Operation: MI, OH
Type of Foodservice: Casual Dining (7); Fast Casual (3)
Catering Services: Yes

Key Personnel
JOE SHINA - President
MARK SHINA - Partner; VP; Director Menu Development
TOM STEGMAN - Partner; General Buyer
SEAN BAILEY - Director Marketing
GEORGE KRESEK - Director Accounting

Sheena Management
631 E Big Beaver Rd Ste 107
Troy, MI 48083-1400

Telephone: (248) 740-1100
Fax Number: (248) 740-2284
Internet Homepage: pizzapapalis.com; riowraps.com
Type of Business: Chain Restaurant Operator
Year Founded: 1986
Systemwide Sales: $20,100,000 (e)
Total Sales: $3,671,000 (e)
Alcohol Sales: 5%
Number of Employees: 250
Average Check: Lunch(12); Dinner(16)
Internet Order Processing: Yes
Internet Sales: 1.00%
Total Units: 8

Trade Names: PizzaPapalis (5); PizzaPapalis/Rio Wraps (3)
Company-Owned Units: 8
Preferred Square Footage: 3,000
Preferred Location Types: Freestanding; Strip Mall
Alcohol Served: Beer, Wine, Liquor
Primary Menu: Pizza (8)
Areas of Operation: MI, OH
Type of Foodservice: Casual Dining (7)
Catering Services: Yes
Primary Distributors: (Equipment) People's Restaurant Equipment Co., DETROIT, MI; (Food) Caramagno Foods Co. Inc., DETROIT, MI; (Supplies) People's Restaurant Equipment Co., DETROIT, MI

Key Personnel
MARK SHEENA - Owner; General Manager; Executive Chef; Director Operations, Facility/Maintenance, Quality Assurance, Human Resources, Food Safety, Catering; General Buyer
TOM STEGEMAN - Director Supply Chain, Franchising

Shield's Franchise Restaurants LLC
1476 W Maple Rd
Troy, MI 48084-7101

Telephone: (248) 637-3131
Fax Number: (248) 637-3130
Internet Homepage: shieldspizza.com
Company Email: info@shieldspizza.com
Type of Business: Chain Restaurant Operator
Year Founded: 1946
Systemwide Sales: $6,214,000 (e)
Total Sales: $4,661,000 (e)
Alcohol Sales: 20%
Number of Employees: 30
Average Check: Lunch(10); Dinner(18)
Internet Order Processing: Yes
Internet Sales: 1.00%
Total Units: 3
Trade Names: Shields Restaurant Bar & Pizzeria (3)
Company-Owned Units: 2
Units Franchised To: 1
Preferred Square Footage: 5,500; 6,000
Preferred Location Types: Freestanding; Strip Mall
Alcohol Served: Beer, Wine, Liquor
Primary Menu: Pizza (3)
Areas of Operation: MI
Type of Foodservice: Casual Dining (3)
Catering Services: Yes
Primary Distributors: (Food) Atlas Wholesale Food Co., DETROIT, MI

Key Personnel
PAUL ANDONI - Partner; General Manager; Director Information Systems, Real Estate, Design; General Buyer
PETER ANDONI - Partner; Manager Finance, Supply Chain
JEAN EVANS - General Manager; Manager Human Resources, Catering
JOSE MARTINEZ - Executive Chef; General Buyer

Stage & Company
6873 Orchard Lake Rd
W Bloomfield, MI 48322-3415

Telephone: (248) 855-6622
Fax Number: (248) 855-5163
Internet Homepage: thestagedeli.com
Type of Business: Chain Restaurant Operator
Year Founded: 1982
Total Sales: $2,467,000 (e)
Alcohol Sales: 3%
Number of Employees: 60
Average Check: Breakfast(12); Lunch(16); Dinner(28)
Total Units: 1
Trade Names: Stage & Company (1)
Company-Owned Units: 1
Preferred Location Types: Freestanding
Alcohol Served: Beer, Wine, Liquor
Primary Menu: American (1)
Areas of Operation: MI
Type of Foodservice: Quick Serve (1)
Catering Services: Yes
Primary Distributors: (Food) SYSCO Detroit LLC, CANTON, MI

Key Personnel
STEVE GOLDBERG - President; General Buyer

Andiamo Restaurant Group
7096 E 14 Mile Rd
Warren, MI 48092-1285

Telephone: (586) 268-3200
Fax Number: (586) 268-3224
Internet Homepage: andiamoitalia.com
Company Email: info@andiamoitalia.com
Type of Business: Chain Restaurant Operator
Year Founded: 1990
Total Sales: $17,150,000 (e)
Alcohol Sales: 30%
Number of Employees: 382
Average Check: Lunch(14); Dinner(22)
Internet Order Processing: Yes
Total Units: 8
Trade Names: Andiamo Bloomfield Township (1); Andiamo Dearborn (1); Andiamo Livonia (1); Andiamo Pastry Shop (1); Andiamo Riverfront (1); Andiamo Stering Heights (1); Andiamo Trattoria Clarkson (1); Andiamo Warren (1)
Company-Owned Units: 8
Preferred Square Footage: 5,500; 6,000
Preferred Location Types: Freestanding
Alcohol Served: Beer, Wine, Liquor
Primary Menu: American (1); Italian (7)
Areas of Operation: MI
Type of Foodservice: Fine Dining (7); Quick Serve (1)
Catering Services: Yes
Primary Distributors: (Full Line) US Foods, WIXOM, MI

Key Personnel
JOSEPH P. VICARI - CEO; President; Director Finance, Operations, Real Estate, Design, Human Resources; General Buyer
TOM VITALE - General Manager; Director Facility/Maintenance, Supply Chain, Design, Store Fixtures

Big Boy Restaurants International LLC
4199 Marcy St
Warren, MI 48091-1733

Telephone: (586) 759-6000
Fax Number: (586) 757-4737
Internet Homepage: bigboy.com
Company Email: operations@bigboy.com
Type of Business: Chain Restaurant Operator
Year Founded: 1936
Systemwide Sales: $289,907,000 (e)
Total Sales: $50,550,000 (e)
Number of Employees: 1,326
Average Check: Breakfast(6); Lunch(8); Dinner(12)
Internet Order Processing: Yes
Internet Sales: 0.50%
Total Units: 76
Trade Names: Big Boy (75)
Company-Owned Units: 14
Units Franchised To: 61
Preferred Square Footage: 4,200; 4,450; 5,000; 5,200; 5,400
Preferred Location Types: Community Mall; Downtown; Freestanding; Office Complex; Regional Mall; Stadiums; Strip Mall; Travel Plazas
Primary Menu: American (75)
Projected Openings: 5
Areas of Operation: CA, IL, MI, ND, OH
Type of Foodservice: Family Restaurant (75)
Catering Services: Yes
On-site Distribution Center: Yes
Primary Distributors: (Full Line) Reinhart Foodservice, WARREN, MI
Parent Company: The Liggett Restaurant Enterprises LLC, WARREN, MI
Headquarter Offices: Big Boy Restaurants International, WARREN, MI
Notes: The company derives approximately 6% of its revenue from commissary operations. The company operates 113 franchise

operations in Japan.

Key Personnel
ROBERT G. LIGGETT JR - Chairman
TOM JABLONSKI - VP Development
STEPHEN FACIONE - VP Development
FRANK ALESSANDRINI - VP Operations

ECS Partnership
25300 Mound Rd
Warren, MI 48091-3858

Telephone: (586) 756-5016
Fax Number: (586) 756-5939
Type of Business: Chain Restaurant Operator
Year Founded: 1994
Total Sales: $61,210,000 (e)
Number of Employees: 550
Average Check: Breakfast(8); Lunch(12); Dinner(12)
Total Units: 13
Trade Names: McDonald's (13)
Units Franchised From: 13
Preferred Square Footage: 2,500; 3,000
Preferred Location Types: Freestanding
Primary Menu: Hamburger (13)
Areas of Operation: MI
Type of Foodservice: Quick Serve (13)
Franchise Affiliation: McDonald's Corporation, CHICAGO, IL
Primary Distributors: (Full Line) The Martin-Brower Co. LLC, ROSEMONT, IL

Key Personnel
ERROL SERVICE - President; Director Finance, Information Systems, Real Estate; General Buyer
JOANNE SCHIPINSKI - Manager Human Resources
MARY DARDEN - Administrative Assistant

Lucky Dining Inc
7750 Cooley Lake Rd
Waterford, MI 48327-4182

Telephone: (248) 363-6098
Fax Number: (248) 363-5720
Internet Homepage: tricountykfc.com
Type of Business: Chain Restaurant Operator
Year Founded: 1988
Total Sales: $12,350,000 (e)
Number of Employees: 60
Average Check: Lunch(12); Dinner(12)
Total Units: 7
Trade Names: KFC (7)
Units Franchised From: 7
Preferred Location Types: Freestanding
Primary Menu: Chicken (7)
Areas of Operation: MI
Type of Foodservice: Quick Serve (7)
Catering Services: Yes
Franchise Affiliation: KFC Corporation, LOUISVILLE, KY

Key Personnel
GLEN FLEWELLING - President; General Buyer

Domino's Franchisee
35171 E Michigan Ave
Wayne, MI 48184-1660

Telephone: (734) 722-3030
Type of Business: Chain Restaurant Operator
Total Sales: $16,540,000 (e)
Total Units: 8
Trade Names: Domino's (8)
Units Franchised From: 8
Primary Menu: Pizza (8)
Areas of Operation: MI
Type of Foodservice: Quick Serve (8)
Franchise Affiliation: Domino's Pizza Inc, ANN ARBOR, MI

Key Personnel
AARON DOLKOWSKI - Owner; General Buyer

Bardha Enterprises
3300 Lone Pine Rd
West Bloomfield, MI 48323-3324

Telephone: (248) 851-7310
Fax Number: (248) 851-7343
Type of Business: Chain Restaurant Operator
Total Sales: $20,032,000 (e)
Total Units: 4
Trade Names: McDonald's (4)
Units Franchised From: 4
Preferred Square Footage: 2,500
Preferred Location Types: Freestanding
Primary Menu: Hamburger (4)
Areas of Operation: MI
Type of Foodservice: Quick Serve (4)
Franchise Affiliation: McDonald's Corporation, CHICAGO, IL

Key Personnel
EKREM BARDHA - President; General Buyer

Grand Traverse Resort & Spa
6300 US Highway 31 N
Williamsburg, MI 49690

Mailing Address: PO Box 404, ACME, MI, 49610-0404
Telephone: (231) 534-6000
Fax Number: (231) 534-6304
Internet Homepage: gtresort.com
Company Email: info@grandtraverseresort.com
Type of Business: Foodservice Operations - Hotel/Motels
Year Founded: 1980
Total Sales: $58,969,000 (e)
Alcohol Sales: 20%
Number of Employees: 550
Total Units: 1
Restaurants in Hotels: 5
Trade Names: Grand Traverse Resort and Spa (1)
Company-Owned Units: 5
Alcohol Served: Beer, Wine, Liquor
Areas of Operation: MI
Type of Foodservice: Casual Dining (4); Fine Dining (1)
Primary Distributors: (Food) Gordon Food Service Inc., WYOMING, MI; (Food) SYSCO Food Services of Grand Rapids LLC, GRAND RAPIDS, MI
Notes: The company derives approximately 75% of its revenue from hotel operations. Restaurants within the hotel include: Aerie Restaurant & Lounge, Sweetwater American Bistro and The Grille

Key Personnel
SCOTT CHOUINARD - VP Finance; Assistant Manager Finance
TIM NORMAN - General Manager
NICK CHOUINARD - Manager Foodservice; General Buyer
KAYLA CONDON - Manager Sales
KATIE LEONARD - Manager Sales

Maaks Inc.
200 W Grand River Ave
Williamston, MI 48895-1320

Telephone: (517) 393-5355
Type of Business: Chain Restaurant Operator
Year Founded: 1991
Total Sales: $51,580,000 (e)
Number of Employees: 440
Average Check: Breakfast(8); Lunch(10); Dinner(10)
Total Units: 11
Trade Names: McDonald's (11)
Units Franchised From: 11
Preferred Square Footage: 2,500; 3,000
Preferred Location Types: Freestanding
Primary Menu: Hamburger (11)
Areas of Operation: MI
Type of Foodservice: Quick Serve (11)
Franchise Affiliation: McDonald's Corporation, CHICAGO, IL
Primary Distributors: (Food) The Martin-Brower Co. LLC, ROSEMONT, IL

Key Personnel
MICHAEL DICKERSON - President; General Manager; Manager Information Systems, Real Estate; General Buyer
DEBBIE FILDEY - Manager Accounting,

Administration, Human Resources

Vinckier Foods
115 S Main St
Yale, MI 48097

Telephone: (810) 387-2132
Type of Business: Chain Restaurant Operator
Total Sales: $1,330,000 (e)
Total Units: 2
Trade Names: A&W All American Food (2)
Units Franchised From: 2
Primary Menu: American (2)
Areas of Operation: MI
Type of Foodservice: Quick Serve (2)
Franchise Affiliation: A&W Restaurants Inc., LEXINGTON, KY

Key Personnel
LORI VINCKIER - Owner; General Buyer

Aubree's
39 E Cross St
Ypsilanti, MI 48198-2812

Telephone: (734) 483-8888
Internet Homepage: aubrees.com
Company Email: franchiseinfo@aubrees.com
Type of Business: Chain Restaurant Operator
Year Founded: 1972
Systemwide Sales: $11,147,000 (e)
Total Sales: $6,350,000 (e)
Alcohol Sales: 18%
Total Units: 10
Trade Names: Aubree's Pizzeria & Grill (10)
Company-Owned Units: 4
Units Franchised To: 6
Preferred Location Types: Strip Mall
Alcohol Served: Beer, Wine, Liquor
Primary Menu: Pizza (10)
Areas of Operation: MI
Type of Foodservice: Casual Dining (10)

Key Personnel
ANDREW FRENCH - CEO; President; General Buyer

Domino's Franchisee
2121 S Grove St
Ypsilanti, MI 48198-6829

Telephone: (734) 483-8000
Type of Business: Chain Restaurant Operator
Total Sales: $4,022,000 (e)
Total Units: 2
Trade Names: Domino's (2)
Units Franchised From: 2
Primary Menu: Pizza (2)
Areas of Operation: MI
Type of Foodservice: Quick Serve (2)
Franchise Affiliation: Domino's Pizza Inc, ANN ARBOR, MI

Key Personnel
PAUL YOUNG - Owner; General Buyer

Domino's Franchisee
953 Washtenaw Rd
Ypsilanti, MI 48197-2715

Telephone: (734) 482-5555
Type of Business: Chain Restaurant Operator
Total Sales: $8,225,000 (e)
Total Units: 4
Trade Names: Domino's (4)
Units Franchised From: 4
Primary Menu: Pizza (4)
Areas of Operation: MI
Type of Foodservice: Quick Serve (4)
Franchise Affiliation: Domino's Pizza Inc, ANN ARBOR, MI

Key Personnel
THOMAS D. REDIES - Owner; General Buyer

Creative Dining Services Inc.
1 Royal Park Dr Ste 3
Zeeland, MI 49464-2243

Telephone: (616) 748-1700
Fax Number: (616) 748-1900
Internet Homepage: creativedining.com
Company Email: creative@creativedining.com
Type of Business: Foodservice Management Operator
Year Founded: 1990
Total Sales: $79,664,000 (e)
Number of Employees: 1,100
Number of Locations Served: 70
Total Foodservice Mgmt Accounts: 70
Areas of Operation: MI
Type of Foodservice: Cafeteria (3); Full-service sit-down dining (67)
Foodservice Management Venues: Business & Industry; College & University
Primary Distributors: (Full Line) Gordon Food Service Inc., WYOMING, MI

Key Personnel
JIM EICKHOFF - CEO; President; General Buyer
SHEILA KENNEDY - Director Menu Development
JILL BANCHERI - Manager Human Resources

Lakeshore Partnership
8436 Homestead Dr Ste 200
Zeeland, MI 49464-9091

Telephone: (616) 748-0909
Fax Number: (616) 748-0955
Type of Business: Chain Restaurant Operator
Year Founded: 1991
Total Sales: $70,990,000 (e)
Number of Employees: 700
Average Check: Breakfast(8); Lunch(10); Dinner(10)
Total Units: 15
Trade Names: McDonald's (15)
Units Franchised From: 15
Preferred Square Footage: 3,000
Preferred Location Types: Freestanding
Primary Menu: Hamburger (15)
Areas of Operation: MI
Type of Foodservice: Quick Serve (15)
Franchise Affiliation: McDonald's Corporation, CHICAGO, IL

Key Personnel
RANDELL PRICE - President; Director Finance, Real Estate; General Buyer
BILL SAVICKAS - Director Operations, Facility/Maintenance, Information Systems
SUE BROPHY - Manager Human Resources

MINNESOTA

Acapulco Restaurante Mexicano
13753 Ibis St NW
Andover, MN 55304-7606

Telephone: (763) 323-8772
Internet Homepage: acapulcomn.com
Type of Business: Chain Restaurant Operator
Year Founded: 1996
Total Sales: $5,938,000 (e)
Total Units: 8
Trade Names: Acapulco Restaurante Mexicano (8)
Company-Owned Units: 8
Primary Menu: Mexican (8)
Areas of Operation: MN
Type of Foodservice: Casual Dining (8)
Catering Services: Yes

Key Personnel
JESUS LEON - Partner; General Buyer
MARIA LEON - Partner; Director Menu Development; General Buyer

Chanticlear Franchise Systems
18015 Ulysses St NE Ste 400
Andover, MN 55304-4896

Telephone: (763) 862-2230
Fax Number: (763) 862-7977
Internet Homepage: chanticlearpizza.com
Type of Business: Chain Restaurant Operator
Year Founded: 1964
Systemwide Sales: $20,924,000 (e)
Total Sales: $7,913,000 (e)
Number of Employees: 430
Average Check: Lunch(28); Dinner(28)
Total Units: 16
Trade Names: Chanticlear Pizza (16)
Units Franchised To: 16
Preferred Square Footage: 1,200
Preferred Location Types: Strip Mall
Primary Menu: Pizza (16)
Areas of Operation: MN
Type of Foodservice: Quick Serve (16)

Key Personnel
DALE HEILLE - CEO; President; Executive Chef; Director Real Estate, Design, Franchise Development; General Buyer
BRIAN KELLER - COO

KFC of Anoka
711 W Main St
Anoka, MN 55303-1619

Telephone: (763) 427-1960
Type of Business: Chain Restaurant Operator
Year Founded: 1960
Total Sales: $7,647,000 (e)
Number of Employees: 95
Average Check: Lunch(14); Dinner(14)
Total Units: 4
Trade Names: KFC (4)
Units Franchised From: 4
Preferred Location Types: Freestanding
Primary Menu: Chicken (4)
Areas of Operation: MN
Type of Foodservice: Quick Serve (4)
Franchise Affiliation: KFC Corporation, LOUISVILLE, KY
Primary Distributors: (Food) Sorce Enterprises, EAST PEORIA, IL

Key Personnel
RYAN SMITH - Partner; Director Purchasing
WESTON STEWART - Partner; Director Purchasing

Quality Restaurants Inc
7818 Excelsior Rd
Baxter, MN 56425

Telephone: (218) 828-0629
Internet Homepage: quality-restaurants-inc.localbookmark.it
Type of Business: Chain Restaurant Operator
Total Sales: $13,520,000 (e)
Total Units: 5
Trade Names: Wendy's Old Fashioned Hamburgers (5)
Units Franchised From: 5
Primary Menu: Hamburger (5)
Areas of Operation: MN, ND
Type of Foodservice: Quick Serve (5)
Franchise Affiliation: The Wendy's Company, DUBLIN, OH

Key Personnel
BOB SULLIVAN - President; General Buyer

PMG 56, LLC, MN Series
10340 Baltimore St NE Ste 150
Blaine, MN 55449-5155

Telephone: (763) 786-1411
Type of Business: Chain Restaurant Operator
Total Sales: $6,937,000 (e)
Total Units: 5
Trade Names: Jersey Mike's Subs (5)
Units Franchised From: 5
Primary Menu: Sandwiches/Deli (5)
Areas of Operation: MN
Type of Foodservice: Quick Serve (5)
Franchise Affiliation: Jersey Mike's Franchise Systems, MANASQUAN, NJ

Key Personnel
JOHN GRIPARIS - Owner

International Dairy Queen Inc.
8331 Norman Center Dr 8000 Tower, Ste 700
Bloomington, MN 55437

Telephone: (952) 830-0200
Fax Number: (952) 830-0498
Internet Homepage: dq.com; dqcakes.com; karmelkorn.com; orangejulius.com
Company Email: sanrelations@idq.com
Type of Business: Chain Restaurant Operator
Year Founded: 1940
Total Sales: $261,660,000 (e)
Number of Employees: 324
Average Check: Lunch(10); Dinner(10)
Foodservice Sales: $65,415,000 (e)
Total Units: 7,561
Trade Names: Dairy Queen Brazier (1,040); Dairy Queen/Orange Julius (1,013); DQ Grill & Chill (2,312); Karmelkorn Shoppe (5); Limited Brazier and Other Concepts (2,795); Orange Julius (396)
Company-Owned Units: 2
Units Franchised To: 7,559
Preferred Location Types: Airports; Community Mall; Downtown; Freestanding; Outlet Mall; Regional Mall; Strip Mall; Travel Plazas
Primary Menu: American (7,160); Snacks (401)
Projected Openings: 75
Areas of Operation: AK, AL, AR, AZ, CA, CO, CT, DE, FL, GA, GU, HI, IA, ID, IL, IN, KS, KY, LA, MA, MD, ME, MI, MN, MO, MS, MT, NC, ND, NE, NH, NJ, NM, NV, NY, OH, OK, OR, PA, PR, RI, SC, SD, TN, TX, UT, VA, VI, VT, WA, WI, WV, WY, AB, BC, MB, NB, NL, NS, NT, ON, PE, QC, SK, YT
Foreign Countries: BAHRAIN; CANADA; CHINA; CYPRUS; ICELAND; KUWAIT; MEXICO; PANAMA; POLAND; SINGAPORE; SOUTH KOREA; THAILAND; THE PHILIPPINES; UNITED ARAB EMIRATES
Type of Foodservice: Quick Serve (7,561)
Subsidiaries: Dairy Queen Canada Inc., BURLINGTON, ON CANADA
Primary Distributors: (Food) PFD Supply Corp., ST PETERS, MO; (Full Line) US Foods, PLYMOUTH, MN; (Supplies) PFD Supply Corp., ST PETERS, MO
Parent Company: Berkshire Hathaway Inc., OMAHA, NE
Notes: The company derives approximately 75% of its revenue from the sale of equipment to stores & of product & supplies to wholesale warehouses. The current store count includes Limited Brazier and other concept stores that were not included in recent store counts.

Key Personnel
TROY BADER - CEO; President
JEAN CHAMPAGNE - COO
NICOLAS BOUDET - COO International
ART D'ELIA - COO United States, Canada
DANIEL KRUPP - Chief Development Officer; Chief Supply Chain Officer
MARIA HOKANSON - Exec VP Marketing; VP Marketing
DAVID WHEELER - Exec VP Human Resources
KEVIN BAARTMAN - VP Information Technology
KELLY KENNY - VP Brand Marketing
PETE SCHUMACHER - Director Food and Beverage
DANIEL GRUIS - Director Purchasing, Sourcing
MOHIT BAKHRU - Director Information Technology
SUSIE MOSCHKAU - Director Digital Marketing
JASON MITCHELL - Director Operations, Development
KIRK HILLABRAND - Regional Director Operations
CAROLYN KIDDER - Manager Customer

Service
MICHAEL NIENALTOWSKI - Manager Retail Information Systems
CLAYTON HERSH - Project Manager Marketing

Leeann Chin Inc.
3600 American Blvd W Ste 165
Bloomington, MN 55431-4500

Telephone: (952) 896-3606
Fax Number: (952) 896-3615
Internet Homepage: leeannchin.com
Company Email: info@leeannchin.com
Type of Business: Chain Restaurant Operator
Year Founded: 1980
Total Sales: $50,830,000 (e)
Alcohol Sales: 5%
Number of Employees: 1,333
Average Check: Lunch(8); Dinner(14)
Total Units: 47
Trade Names: Leeann Chin (47)
Company-Owned Units: 47
Preferred Square Footage: 3,500
Preferred Location Types: Freestanding; Grocery Stores; Strip Mall
Primary Menu: Asian (47)
Areas of Operation: IA, MD, MN, ND, SD, WI
Type of Foodservice: Quick Serve (47)
Catering Services: Yes
Distribution Centers: BURNSVILLE, MN
On-site Distribution Center: Yes
Parent Company: West Coast Capital, SHERMAN OAKS, CA

Key Personnel
MIKE LONEY - Chairman; CEO; President; COO; Director Facility/Maintenance, Marketing, Real Estate, Design, Store Fixtures
LORNE GOLDBERG - Owner
CLARK GRANT - Controller
KELLY KEARNEY - Director Operations, Catering
DAWN COHOON - Regional Director Operations
TIMOTHY NOVY - Assistant Director Operations, Catering

Mann Theatres Inc.
900 E 80th St
Bloomington, MN 55420-1322

Telephone: (952) 767-0102
Fax Number: (952) 767-0103
Internet Homepage: manntheatres.com
Type of Business: Foodservice Operations - Movie Theatre
Year Founded: 1935
Total Sales: $1,600,000 (e)
Number of Employees: 310
Average Check: Lunch(12); Dinner(18)
Internet Order Processing: Yes
Total Units: 10
Trade Names: Mann Theatre (10)
Company-Owned Units: 10
Preferred Square Footage: 65,000
Preferred Location Types: Community Mall; Freestanding; Regional Mall; Strip Mall
Primary Menu: Snacks (10)
Areas of Operation: MN
Type of Foodservice: In-Store Feeder (10)
Notes: This company is not affiliated with the Mann Theatres chain in California. Mann Theatres derives approximately 72% of its revenue from theater admissions, on-screen advertising, and other sales.

Key Personnel
STEVE MANN - President; Director Finance; Manager Real Estate, Construction, Site Selection; General Buyer

Nath Companies Inc.
900 American Blvd E Ste 300
Bloomington, MN 55420-1393

Telephone: (952) 853-1400
Fax Number: (952) 853-1410
Internet Homepage: axelsrestaurants.com; bonfirewoodfirecooking.com; nathcompanies.com
Company Email: information@nathcompanies.com
Type of Business: Chain Restaurant Operator
Year Founded: 1991
Total Sales: $16,000,000 (e)
Number of Employees: 1,480
Average Check: Breakfast(6); Lunch(16); Dinner(20)
Total Units: 9
Trade Names: Axel's (3); Bonfire Woodfire Cookingl (5); Burger King (1)
Company-Owned Units: 8
Units Franchised From: 1
Preferred Square Footage: 2,500
Preferred Location Types: Community Mall; Freestanding; Regional Mall
Alcohol Served: Beer, Wine, Liquor
Primary Menu: Hamburger (1); Steak (8)
Areas of Operation: MN, WI
Type of Foodservice: Fine Dining (8); Quick Serve (1)
Franchise Affiliation: Burger King Worldwide Inc., MIAMI, FL
Notes: The company derives approximately 30% of its revenue from hotel operations.

Key Personnel
MAHENDRA NATH - CEO; President; Partner; CFO; Director Real Estate
ASHA NATH - Partner; VP
LIZ MICHKA - VP Human Resources

Tri City Management
8030 Old Cedar Ave S Ste 120
Bloomington, MN 55425-1214

Telephone: (952) 854-7405
Fax Number: (952) 854-7958
Internet Homepage: corkspub.com; woolleysrestaurant.com
Company Email: a-r@tricitymanagement.com
Type of Business: Chain Restaurant Operator
Year Founded: 1980
Total Sales: $8,027,000 (e)
Alcohol Sales: 30%
Number of Employees: 150
Average Check: Lunch(22); Dinner(46)
Total Units: 2
Trade Names: The Cork Irish Pub (1); Woolley's Steak House (1)
Company-Owned Units: 2
Preferred Location Types: Hotel/Motel
Alcohol Served: Beer, Wine, Liquor
Primary Menu: Miscellaneous (1); Steak (1)
Areas of Operation: MN
Type of Foodservice: Casual Dining (1); Fine Dining (1)
Primary Distributors: (Full Line) Reinhart FoodService, MARSHALL, MN

Key Personnel
RAY PETERS - President; General Manager; Director Menu Development
BOB KINSELLA - CFO; Controller; Manager Information Systems, Loss Prevention, Real Estate

Domino's Franchisee
413 W Washington St Ste C
Brainerd, MN 56401-2925

Telephone: (218) 828-5066
Type of Business: Chain Restaurant Operator
Total Sales: $9,894,000 (e)
Total Units: 5
Trade Names: Domino's (5)
Units Franchised From: 5
Primary Menu: Pizza (5)
Areas of Operation: MN
Type of Foodservice: Quick Serve (5)
Franchise Affiliation: Domino's Pizza Inc, ANN ARBOR, MI

Key Personnel
COREY L. JOHNSON - Owner; General Buyer

Guests Inc
601 W Washington St
Brainerd, MN 56401-2934

Telephone: (218) 828-9790

Fax Number: (218) 825-8137
Type of Business: Chain Restaurant Operator
Total Sales: $70,110,000 (e)
Number of Employees: 900
Total Units: 15
Trade Names: McDonald's (15)
Units Franchised From: 15
Preferred Square Footage: 2,500
Preferred Location Types: Convenience Store/Gas Station; Discount Dept. Stores; Freestanding
Primary Menu: Hamburger (15)
Areas of Operation: MN
Type of Foodservice: Quick Serve (15)
Franchise Affiliation: McDonald's Corporation, CHICAGO, IL

Key Personnel
GLEN COOK - President; General Buyer
KEITH STEPHENS - Owner
TERI BUTLER - Director Branch

Madden's on Gull Lake
11266 Pine Beach Peninsula Rd
Brainerd, MN 56401-2080

Telephone: (218) 829-2811
Fax Number: (218) 829-7698
Internet Homepage: maddens.com
Company Email: info@maddens.com
Type of Business: Foodservice Operations - Hotel/Motels
Year Founded: 1942
Total Sales: $46,915,000 (e)
Alcohol Sales: 20%
Number of Employees: 500
Total Units: 1
Restaurants in Hotels: 7
Trade Names: Madden's on Gull Lake (1)
Company-Owned Units: 7
Alcohol Served: Beer, Wine, Liquor
Areas of Operation: MN
Notes: The company derives approximately 70% of its revenue from hotel operations.

Key Personnel
CARL THURINGER - CEO; President
BEN THURINGER - COO
ABBEY PIEPER - Chief Marketing Officer; Chief Sales Officer; Treasurer

Breezy Point Resort
9252 Breezy Point Dr
Breezy Point, MN 56472-3159

Telephone: (218) 562-7811
Fax Number: (218) 562-4510
Internet Homepage: breezypointresort.com
Company Email: info@breezypointresort.com
Type of Business: Chain Restaurant Operator
Year Founded: 1945
Total Sales: $7,172,000 (e)
Alcohol Sales: 20%
Number of Employees: 75
Average Check: Breakfast(10); Lunch(16); Dinner(26)
Total Units: 5
Trade Names: Antler's Bar & Grill (1); Dockside (1); Marina II (1); Palmer's at Deacon's Lodge (1); The Coffee House (1)
Company-Owned Units: 5
Preferred Location Types: Freestanding; Hotel/Motel
Alcohol Served: Beer, Wine, Liquor
Primary Menu: American (4); Coffee (1)
Areas of Operation: MN
Type of Foodservice: Casual Dining (4); Quick Serve (1)
Catering Services: Yes
Primary Distributors: (Full Line) Reinhart FoodService, MARSHALL, MN

Key Personnel
BOB SPIZZO - CEO; Owner
JOYCE BZOSKIE - President
DAVID SPIZZO - VP
BONNIE TWEED - Director Catering
DAVID SOOS - Manager Operations-Food

Caribou Coffee Co.
3900 Lake Breeze Ave
Brooklyn Center, MN 55429-3839

Telephone: (763) 592-2200
Fax Number: (763) 592-2300
Internet Homepage: cariboucoffee.com
Company Email: info@cariboucoffee.com
Type of Business: Chain Restaurant Operator
Year Founded: 1992
Systemwide Sales: $452,364,000 (e)
Total Sales: $199,230,000 (e)
Number of Employees: 5,500
Average Check: Breakfast(8); Lunch(8); Dinner(8)
Internet Order Processing: Yes
Internet Sales: 15.00%
Total Units: 451
Trade Names: Caribou Coffee (451)
Company-Owned Units: 235
Units Franchised To: 216
Preferred Square Footage: 1,600
Preferred Location Types: Airports; Community Mall; Convenience Store/Gas Station; Downtown; Freestanding; Grocery Stores; Hotel/Motel; Institution(college/hospital); Kiosk; Lifestyle Center; Office Complex; Regional Mall; Stadiums; Strip Mall
Primary Menu: Coffee (451)
Projected Openings: 50
Areas of Operation: CO, FL, GA, IA, IL, IN, KS, MI, MN, MO, NC, ND, NE, OH, OK, SD, VA, WI, WY
Foreign Countries: BAHRAIN; EGYPT; INDONESIA; KUWAIT; OMAN; QATAR; SAUDI ARABIA; TURKEY; UNITED ARAB EMIRATES
Type of Foodservice: Quick Serve (451)
On-site Distribution Center: Yes
Parent Company: Panera Brands, SAINT LOUIS, MO
Notes: The company derives approximately 26% of its revenue from wholesale operations; foodservice sales includes some revenue from the sale of whole beans & coffee-related merchandise in the coffee-houses.

Key Personnel
SCOTT KENNEDY - CEO Interim; President Interim; CFO
JOHN WALBRUN - Senior VP Supply Chain
LIVA WOLF - VP Licensing
ERIN NEWKIRK - VP Strategy, Global
MATTHEW REITER - VP Merchandising
STACEY GARRY - VP Human Resources
KENDALL HARRELL - VP People
SHELLY SELBY - Controller; Assistant
TODD SKAUGE - General Counsel; Director
MOLLY O'BRIEN - Senior Director Legal
JON OLSEN - Senior Director Facility/Maintenance
MOHAMED ABDELMAWLA - Senior Director Operations
JANNA BROSS - Senior Director Finance
ERIC CARON - Senior Director Information Technology
CAROLINE LARSON - Senior Director Marketing
DAVID LUETH - Senior Director Applications
LEAH PALMQUIST - Creative Director
DANNY SALAS - Director Operations
CARRIE SAZAMA - Director Product Development
TODD LARAMY - Director Operations
JULIE PRICE - Director Development
MIKE SPEER - Director Warehouse
MATTHEW WALLS - Director Franchise Operations
STEPHANIE WEIMAR - Director Human Resources
MATTHEW MASICA AIA - Director Store Design
RIANNA MATTER - Director Operations
JOLENE LARSON - Director Risk Management
LISA CURSKI - Director Branding
STEVE BRYANT - Director Loss Prevention
KAYLEEN ALEXSON - Director
EMILY HEURING - Director Construction
JONATHAN HOCK - Director Franchise Operations
JENNIFER ESNOUGH - Senior Manager Franchise Operations
MICHELLE LANGKAU - Senior Manager Business Development
MARTHA HROBAK - Manager Facility/Maintenance
ROBERT CANNALTE - Manager Facility/Maintenance
JOSEPH THORSON - Product Manager Information Technology

BARB PEARSON - Executive Assistant

Superior Concepts Inc.
14296 Plymouth Ave
Burnsville, MN 55337-5785

Telephone: (952) 892-7555
Fax Number: (952) 435-3187
Internet Homepage: chiantigrill.com;
 porterhousesteakandseafood.com;
 stoutspub.com
Type of Business: Chain Restaurant Operator
Year Founded: 1997
Total Sales: $11,240,000 (e)
Alcohol Sales: 15%
Total Units: 5
Trade Names: Chianti Grill (2); Porterhouse Steak & Seafood (2); Stout's Pub (1)
Company-Owned Units: 5
Alcohol Served: Beer, Wine, Liquor
Primary Menu: American (1); Italian (2); Steak/Seafood (2)
Areas of Operation: MN
Type of Foodservice: Casual Dining (5)

Key Personnel
KENT TOBIN - CEO; President
KEVIN SCHLEIF - Partner

Chanhassen Dinner Theatres
501 W 78th St
Chanhassen, MN 55317-9677

Mailing Address: PO Box 100, CHANHASSEN, MN, 55317-0100
Telephone: (952) 934-1500
Fax Number: (952) 934-1511
Internet Homepage: chanhassendt.com
Company Email: information@chanhassendt.com
Type of Business: Chain Restaurant Operator
Year Founded: 1968
Total Sales: $26,292,000 (e)
Alcohol Sales: 12%
Number of Employees: 250
Average Check: Lunch(16); Dinner(24)
Internet Order Processing: Yes
Internet Sales: 15.00%
Total Units: 4
Trade Names: Brindisi's Pub (1); Fireside Dinner Theatre (1); Main Dinner Theatre (1); Playhouse Dinner Theatre (1)
Company-Owned Units: 4
Preferred Location Types: Freestanding
Alcohol Served: Beer, Wine, Liquor
Primary Menu: American (4)
Areas of Operation: MN
Type of Foodservice: Casual Dining (1); Fine Dining (3)
Primary Distributors: (Food) US Foods, PLYMOUTH, MN

Key Personnel
MICHAEL BRINDISI - President
SOLVEIG HUSETH - General Manager
KRIS HOWLAND - Director Public Relations
PAULA WEGLER - Business Manager
JOEL RAINVILLE - Manager Marketing
MONICA GRIAK - Specialist Sales

Northcott Hospitality International LLC
250 Lake Dr E
Chanhassen, MN 55317-9364

Telephone: (952) 294-5000
Fax Number: (952) 294-5101
Internet Homepage: americinn.com; northcotthospitatility.com
Company Email: info@northcotthospitality.com
Type of Business: Chain Restaurant Operator
Total Sales: $62,710,000 (e)
Alcohol Sales: 20%
Number of Employees: 60
Total Units: 25
Trade Names: Houlihan's (3); Perkins Restaurant & Bakery (22)
Units Franchised From: 25
Preferred Square Footage: 4,400; 5,500
Preferred Location Types: Freestanding
Alcohol Served: Beer, Wine, Liquor
Primary Menu: American (25)
Projected Openings: 10
Areas of Operation: MN
Type of Foodservice: Casual Dining (3); Family Restaurant (22)
Franchise Affiliation: HRI Inc., LEAWOOD, KS; Perkins Restaurant & Bakery, MEMPHIS, TN
Primary Distributors: (Full Line) US Foods, PLYMOUTH, MN
Notes: The company also operates a number of limited service inns whose operations are not reflected in this directory.

Key Personnel
BRIAN SCHWEN - CFO; Director Purchasing, Supply Chain; General Buyer
GEORGE STALLWOOD - Director Development, Franchise Sales
KRIS VONBUSCH - Manager Operations

Cornelius, Vaughn
915 State Highway 24
Clearwater, MN 55320-1610

Mailing Address: PO Box 355, CLEARWATER, MN, 55320-0355
Telephone: (320) 558-4502
Type of Business: Chain Restaurant Operator
Total Sales: $5,276,000 (e)
Total Units: 9
Trade Names: Subway (9)
Units Franchised From: 9
Primary Menu: Sandwiches/Deli (9)
Areas of Operation: MN
Type of Foodservice: Quick Serve (9)
Franchise Affiliation: Doctor's Associates Inc., MILFORD, CT

Key Personnel
VAUGHN CORNELIUS - Owner; General Buyer

Zorbaz
714 Lake Ave
Detroit Lakes, MN 56501

Telephone: (218) 847-8932
Fax Number: (218) 847-0502
Internet Homepage: zorbaz.com
Company Email: hq@zorbaz.com
Type of Business: Chain Restaurant Operator
Year Founded: 1969
Total Sales: $1,980,000 (e)
Alcohol Sales: 10%
Number of Employees: 600
Total Units: 14
Trade Names: Zorbaz on the Lake (14)
Company-Owned Units: 14
Preferred Location Types: Freestanding
Alcohol Served: Beer, Wine, Liquor
Primary Menu: Miscellaneous (14)
Areas of Operation: MN
Type of Foodservice: Casual Dining (14)

Key Personnel
COLE HANSON - Owner; General Buyer

Grandma's Restaurant Company
525 S Lake Ave
Duluth, MN 55802-2362

Telephone: (218) 727-2250
Fax Number: (218) 727-5604
Internet Homepage: grandmasrestaurants.com
Company Email: info@grccorp.com
Type of Business: Chain Restaurant Operator
Year Founded: 1976
Total Sales: $20,360,000 (e)
Alcohol Sales: 20%
Number of Employees: 600
Average Check: Lunch(30); Dinner(36)
Total Units: 7
Trade Names: Adventure Zone (1); Bellisio's Italian Restaurant and Wine Bar (1); Grandma's Saloon & Grill (3); Little Angie's Cantina (1); The Sports Garden(1)
Company-Owned Units: 7
Preferred Square Footage: 6,500

Preferred Location Types: Freestanding
Alcohol Served: Beer, Wine, Liquor
Primary Menu: American (5); Italian (1); Southwest/Tex-Mex (1)
Areas of Operation: MN
Type of Foodservice: Casual Dining (6); Fine Dining (1)
Catering Services: Yes

Key Personnel
ANDY BORG - CEO
BRIAN DAUGHERTY - President; Director Operations, Facility/Maintenance, Design
MICHAEL MELBY - VP Purchasing
MIKE MELBY - VP Purchasing, Food Safety
AMANDA DEBLOCK - General Manager
SANDY KOLASINSKI - General Manager
TONY BRONSON - Director Business Development
TONY BOEN - Director Operations

Labovitz Enterprises
227 W 1st St Ste 950
Duluth, MN 55802-5051

Telephone: (218) 727-7765
Fax Number: (218) 727-7362
Internet Homepage: lionhotelgroup.com
Type of Business: Foodservice Operations - Hotel/Motels
Year Founded: 1981
Total Sales: $55,830,000 (e)
Alcohol Sales: 20%
Number of Employees: 200
Total Units: 6
Restaurants in Hotels: 6
Trade Names: Courtyard by Marriott Dayton Beavercreek (1); Hilton Garden Inn Palm Coast Town Center (1); Holiday Inn & Suites Duluth (1); Holiday Inn Bozeman (1); Home2 Suites (1); Residence Inn (1)
Company-Owned Units: 6
Alcohol Served: Beer, Wine, Liquor
Areas of Operation: FL, MN, MT, OH
Type of Foodservice: Casual Dining (6)
Primary Distributors: (Food) SYSCO Food Services of Minnesota Inc., MOUNDSVIEW, MN
Notes: The company derives approximately 75% of its revenue from hotel operations.

Key Personnel
MARK LABOVITZ - CEO; President
TOM BOUVINE - CFO
RACHEL STREIT - Controller
AMY FOLDESI - Director Human Resources
BARB PERRELLA - Manager Real Estate

Landfall Development Corp
2502 London Rd
Duluth, MN 55812-2223

Telephone: (218) 728-3619
Type of Business: Chain Restaurant Operator
Total Sales: $10,166,000 (e)
Total Units: 4
Trade Names: Perkins (4)
Units Franchised From: 4
Primary Menu: American (4)
Areas of Operation: MN, WI
Type of Foodservice: Family Restaurant (4)
Franchise Affiliation: Perkins Restaurant & Bakery, MEMPHIS, TN

Key Personnel
SEAN FLAHERTY - Owner; General Buyer
KATIE MILLER - General Manager; General Buyer

New London Corp.
230 E Superior St Ste 200
Duluth, MN 55802-2158

Telephone: (218) 628-0064
Fax Number: (218) 624-8460
Internet Homepage: blackwoods.com
Type of Business: Chain Restaurant Operator
Year Founded: 1998
Total Sales: $17,000,000 (e)
Alcohol Sales: 25%
Number of Employees: 600
Average Check: Breakfast(10); Lunch(10); Dinner(18)
Internet Order Processing: Yes
Total Units: 6
Trade Names: Blackwood's Grill & Bar (3); Perkins (1); Tavern on the Hill (1); The Black Water Lounge (1)
Company-Owned Units: 5
Units Franchised From: 1
Preferred Square Footage: 11,000
Preferred Location Types: Freestanding
Alcohol Served: Beer, Wine, Liquor
Primary Menu: American (6)
Areas of Operation: MN, WI
Type of Foodservice: Casual Dining (5); Family Restaurant (1)
Catering Services: Yes
Primary Distributors: (Full Line) SYSCO Food Services of Minnesota Inc., MOUNDSVIEW, MN

Key Personnel
SEAN STEPHAN - CFO; Controller; General Buyer
BENJAMINE THOEN - Executive Chef
JAX EISENMANN - Manager Catering

Sammy's Pizza Inc.
103 W 1st St
Duluth, MN 55802-2092

Telephone: (218) 727-8551
Internet Homepage: mysammys.com
Type of Business: Chain Restaurant Operator
Year Founded: 1956
Total Sales: $16,500,000 (e)
Alcohol Sales: 1%
Number of Employees: 285
Average Check: Lunch(8); Dinner(10)
Internet Order Processing: Yes
Total Units: 15
Trade Names: Sammy's Pizza (15)
Units Franchised To: 15
Preferred Location Types: Office Complex
Alcohol Served: Beer
Primary Menu: Pizza (15)
Areas of Operation: MN, ND, WI
Type of Foodservice: Casual Dining (15)
Primary Distributors: (Food) Upper Lakes Foods Inc., CLOQUET, MN

Key Personnel
JULIE DALY - Controller; General Manager; General Buyer
TERRY PERRELLA - General Manager; Buyer Beverages

Domino's Distribution Center
3355 Mike Collins Dr
Eagan, MN 55121-2235

Telephone: (651) 688-2929
Fax Number: (651) 688-2585
Internet Homepage: domino.com
Listing Type: Distribution Center
Type of Business: Chain Restaurant Operator
Number of Employees: 50
Areas of Operation: IA, MN, ND, SD, WI
Parent Company: Domino's Pizza Inc, ANN ARBOR, MI

Key Personnel
LUIS FLORES - Manager Production

McDonald's Franchise
2020 Silver Bell Rd Ste 2
Eagan, MN 55122-1050

Telephone: (651) 203-4170
Fax Number: (651) 203-4175
Type of Business: Chain Restaurant Operator
Total Sales: $25,139,000 (e)
Number of Employees: 200
Total Units: 5
Trade Names: McDonald's (5)
Units Franchised From: 5

Preferred Square Footage: 2,500
Preferred Location Types: Freestanding
Primary Menu: Hamburger (5)
Areas of Operation: MN
Type of Foodservice: Quick Serve (5)
Franchise Affiliation: McDonald's Corporation, CHICAGO, IL

Key Personnel
KAY BUTLER - VP

PET Investments, LLC
1550 Highview Ave
Eagan, MN 55121-1108

Telephone: (651) 846-4349
Type of Business: Chain Restaurant Operator
Total Sales: $12,480,000 (e)
Total Units: 21
Trade Names: Little Caesars Pizza (21)
Units Franchised From: 21
Primary Menu: Pizza (21)
Areas of Operation: MN
Type of Foodservice: Quick Serve (21)
Franchise Affiliation: Little Caesar Enterprises Inc., DETROIT, MI

Key Personnel
MIKE MCGUIRE - Partner; General Buyer
JOE NACHTRAB - Partner

Platinum Pizza Holdings
3140 Neil Armstrong Blvd Ste 321
Eagan, MN 55121-2273

Telephone: (651) 289-3000
Fax Number: (651) 289-3002
Internet Homepage: platinumpizza.com
Company Email: mvr.dominos@gmail.com
Type of Business: Chain Restaurant Operator
Total Sales: $55,887,000 (e)
Number of Employees: 540
Total Units: 27
Trade Names: Domino's (27)
Units Franchised From: 27
Preferred Square Footage: 1,000
Primary Menu: Pizza (27)
Areas of Operation: IA, MN, WI
Type of Foodservice: Quick Serve (27)
Franchise Affiliation: Domino's Pizza Inc, ANN ARBOR, MI

Key Personnel
WAYNE PETERSON - Owner; General Manager
YVETTE WETCH - Controller

Crave America
6545 Flying Cloud Dr Ste 101
Eden Praire, MN 55344

Telephone: (952) 562-5600
Fax Number: (952) 854-4458
Internet Homepage: craveamerica.com
Type of Business: Chain Restaurant Operator
Total Sales: $50,800,000 (e)
Alcohol Sales: 10%
Number of Employees: 825
Average Check: Lunch(30); Dinner(30)
Internet Order Processing: Yes
Total Units: 11
Trade Names: CRAVE (10); CRAVE Cafe & Deli (1)
Company-Owned Units: 11
Alcohol Served: Beer, Wine, Liquor
Primary Menu: American (11)
Areas of Operation: FL, MD, MN, NE, NV, OH, TX
Type of Foodservice: Casual Dining (10)

Key Personnel
KAM TALEBI - CEO; Owner
ZACH SUSSMAN - Chief Marketing Officer
CHRIS LESKAUSKAS - Director Operations
SHAYNA NIENOW - Manager Human Resources

Armstrong Subway Inc.
7887 Fuller Rd Ste 113
Eden Prairie, MN 55344-2100

Telephone: (952) 949-6704
Fax Number: (952) 949-2393
Type of Business: Chain Restaurant Operator
Year Founded: 1987
Total Sales: $12,660,000 (e)
Number of Employees: 138
Average Check: Lunch(8); Dinner(12)
Total Units: 22
Trade Names: Subway (22)
Units Franchised From: 22
Preferred Square Footage: 1,200; 1,600
Preferred Location Types: Freestanding; Strip Mall
Primary Menu: Sandwiches/Deli (22)
Projected Openings: 20
Areas of Operation: MN
Type of Foodservice: Quick Serve (22)
Franchise Affiliation: Doctor's Associates Inc., MILFORD, CT
Primary Distributors: (Full Line) Reinhart FoodService, MARSHALL, MN

Key Personnel
JAMES ARMSTRONG JR - President; Controller; Director Finance, Facility/Maintenance, Supply Chain, Advertising, Design; General Buyer

Lucky Seven Bagel Company, LLC
16528 W 78th St
Eden Prairie, MN 55346-4302

Telephone: (952) 238-1388
Company Email: prairie@brueggers.com
Type of Business: Chain Restaurant Operator
Total Sales: $2,194,000 (e)
Total Units: 2
Trade Names: Bruegger's Bagel Bakery (2)
Units Franchised From: 2
Primary Menu: Bagels (2)
Areas of Operation: MN
Type of Foodservice: Fast Casual (2)
Catering Services: Yes
Franchise Affiliation: Bruegger's Enterprises Inc., DALLAS, TX

Key Personnel
COLIN DANIELS - Owner; General Buyer

Redstone American Grill
7636 Executive Dr
Eden Prairie, MN 55344-3677

Telephone: (952) 404-3333
Fax Number: (952) 745-0623
Internet Homepage: redstonegrill.com
Type of Business: Chain Restaurant Operator
Total Sales: $37,200,000 (e)
Alcohol Sales: 15%
Number of Employees: 420
Average Check: Lunch(10); Dinner(18)
Internet Order Processing: Yes
Total Units: 9
Trade Names: Redstone American Grill (8); RS Sports Grill (1)
Company-Owned Units: 9
Preferred Location Types: Freestanding
Alcohol Served: Beer, Wine, Liquor
Primary Menu: American (9)
Projected Openings: 1
Areas of Operation: IL, MA, MD, MN, NJ, PA
Type of Foodservice: Casual Dining (9)
Primary Distributors: (Food) US Foods, PLYMOUTH, MN

Key Personnel
CRAIG OBERLANDER - CFO
KRISTIN KROEGER - Director Operations

Nova Restaurant Group
5151 Edina Industrial Blvd Ste 675
Edina, MN 55439

Telephone: (952) 942-1089

Internet Homepage: chesterskb.com; hazellewoodgrill.com; pescarafresh.com; tavern4and5.com; loroaustin.com; novarestaurantgroup.com
Type of Business: Chain Restaurant Operator
Total Sales: $13,540,000 (e)
Alcohol Sales: 12%
Total Units: 6
Trade Names: Chester's Kitchen & Bar (1); Hazellewood Grill and Tap Room (1); Hazelwood Food and Drink (1); Pescara (1); Tavern 4 and 5 (1); Terza (1)
Company-Owned Units: 6
Preferred Location Types: Regional Mall
Alcohol Served: Beer, Wine, Liquor
Primary Menu: American (4); Italian (1); Seafood (1)
Areas of Operation: MN
Type of Foodservice: Casual Dining (6)

Key Personnel
SCOTT FOSTER - Partner; Executive Chef
PAT WOODRING - Partner; General Buyer
BRUCE NELSON - CFO
FELIPE NAVARRO - Director Operations

Parasole Restaurant Holdings Inc.
5032 France Ave S
Edina, MN 55410-2033

Telephone: (612) 822-0016
Fax Number: (612) 822-0705
Internet Homepage: parasole.com
Company Email: parasole@parasole.com
Type of Business: Chain Restaurant Operator
Year Founded: 1979
Total Sales: $64,830,000 (e)
Alcohol Sales: 30%
Number of Employees: 1,022
Average Check: Breakfast(10); Lunch(12); Dinner(72)
Internet Order Processing: Yes
Internet Sales: 0.50%
Total Units: 11
Trade Names: Field Day by Good Earth (1); Good Earth I (2); Manny's Steakhouse (1); Pittsburgh Blue Steakhouse (3); Prohibition (1); Salut Bar Americain(2); The Living Room (1)
Company-Owned Units: 11
Preferred Square Footage: 5,000
Preferred Location Types: Freestanding; Regional Mall
Alcohol Served: Beer, Wine, Liquor
Primary Menu: American (7); Health Foods (2); Miscellaneous (1); Steak (4)
Areas of Operation: MN
Type of Foodservice: Casual Dining (14)
Primary Distributors: (Food) Upper Lakes Foods Inc., CLOQUET, MN

Key Personnel
PHIL ROBERTS - President; Partner; COO; Director Facility/Maintenance, Real Estate, Design, Menu Development; General Buyer
PETER MIHAJLOV - Partner; Exec VP
BARB MARSHALL - CFO; Manager Loss Prevention
DONNA FAHS - COO
KIP CLAYTON - VP Marketing, Business Development
RANDI GILBERTSON - Manager Food and Beverage

Steen Enterprises
18100 Stockhousen Rd NW
Evansville, MN 56326-8260

Telephone: (320) 876-2120
Type of Business: Chain Restaurant Operator
Year Founded: 1996
Total Sales: $15,106,000 (e)
Number of Employees: 150
Average Check: Breakfast(6); Lunch(8); Dinner(8)
Total Units: 3
Trade Names: McDonald's (3)
Units Franchised From: 3
Preferred Square Footage: 2,500; 3,000
Preferred Location Types: Freestanding
Primary Menu: Hamburger (3)
Areas of Operation: MN, ND
Type of Foodservice: Quick Serve (3)
Franchise Affiliation: McDonald's Corporation, CHICAGO, IL
Primary Distributors: (Full Line) The Martin-Brower Co., FRIDLEY, MN

Key Personnel
MICHAEL J. STEEN - President; Partner; Director Finance, Purchasing
RICK STEEN - President
JOANN STEEN - Partner; General Manager
BRIAN SEMKEN - Manager Sales

Wess Clerc
2217 N State St
Fairmont, MN 56031-3634

Telephone: (507) 238-4832
Type of Business: Chain Restaurant Operator
Total Sales: $23,680,000 (e)
Total Units: 5
Trade Names: McDonald's (5)
Units Franchised From: 5
Primary Menu: Hamburger (5)
Areas of Operation: MN
Type of Foodservice: Quick Serve (5)
Franchise Affiliation: McDonald's Corporation, CHICAGO, IL

Key Personnel
WESS CLERC - President; Partner; General Buyer
RICK CLERC - Partner

Domino's Franchisee
629 4th St NW
Faribault, MN 55021-5034

Telephone: (507) 334-3954
Type of Business: Chain Restaurant Operator
Total Sales: $10,352,000 (e)
Total Units: 5
Trade Names: Domino's (5)
Units Franchised From: 5
Primary Menu: Pizza (5)
Areas of Operation: MN
Type of Foodservice: Quick Serve (5)
Franchise Affiliation: Domino's Pizza Inc, ANN ARBOR, MI

Key Personnel
WILLIAM C. KRUSE - Owner; General Buyer

Keys Cafe & Bakery
1960 W Broadway Ave Ste 206
Forest Lake, MN 55025-1385

Telephone: (651) 982-2929
Fax Number: (651) 982-2842
Internet Homepage: keyscafe.com
Type of Business: Chain Restaurant Operator
Year Founded: 1973
Total Units: 9
Trade Names: Keys Cafe & Bakery (9)
Company-Owned Units: 9
Primary Menu: American (9)
Areas of Operation: MN, WI
Type of Foodservice: Quick Serve (9)

Key Personnel
BARBARA HUNN-MIESEN - Founder
CAROL H. GREGORY - Partner
BRIAN CARLSON - Partner
ROY HUNN - Partner
AMY HUNN - Partner

Domino's Franchisee
1200 S Pokegama Ave Ste 80
Grand Rapids, MN 55744-4292

Telephone: (218) 326-9444
Company Email: extratoppins@hotmail.com
Type of Business: Chain Restaurant Operator
Total Sales: $16,320,000 (e)
Total Units: 8
Trade Names: Domino's (8)
Units Franchised From: 8
Primary Menu: Pizza (8)

Projected Openings: 1
Areas of Operation: MN
Type of Foodservice: Quick Serve (8)
Franchise Affiliation: Domino's Pizza Inc, ANN ARBOR, MI

Key Personnel
DUANE L. CARLSON - Owner; General Buyer

CLK Management Company
1440 E 40th St
Hibbing, MN 55746-3667

Telephone: (218) 262-6618
Fax Number: (218) 262-0694
Type of Business: Chain Restaurant Operator
Year Founded: 1986
Total Sales: $57,290,000 (e)
Number of Employees: 600
Average Check: Breakfast(8); Lunch(8); Dinner(8)
Total Units: 12
Trade Names: McDonald's (12)
Units Franchised From: 12
Preferred Square Footage: 2,500; 3,000
Preferred Location Types: Freestanding
Primary Menu: Hamburger (12)
Areas of Operation: MN
Type of Foodservice: Quick Serve (12)
Franchise Affiliation: McDonald's Corporation, CHICAGO, IL
Primary Distributors: (Full Line) The Martin-Brower Co., FRIDLEY, MN

Key Personnel
COREY KLINEFELTER - President; General Buyer
DON MARCHBANKS - VP Construction
ANDREA BOSCO - VP Area

Ronald & Patty Hendrickson
10950 175th Ct W
Lakeville, MN 55044-5546

Telephone: (952) 892-5001
Type of Business: Chain Restaurant Operator
Total Sales: $5,860,000 (e)
Average Check: Dinner(12)
Total Units: 4
Trade Names: Dairy Queen (4)
Units Franchised From: 4
Primary Menu: American (4)
Areas of Operation: MN
Type of Foodservice: Quick Serve (4)
Franchise Affiliation: International Dairy Queen Inc., BLOOMINGTON, MN

Key Personnel
PATTY HENDRICKSON - Partner; General Buyer

RON HENDRICKSON - Partner; General Buyer

Fresh Concepts, LLC
1924 Adams St
Mankato, MN 56001-6802

Telephone: (507) 625-8454
Type of Business: Chain Restaurant Operator
Total Sales: $2,923,000 (e)
Total Units: 2
Trade Names: Jersey Mike's Subs (2)
Units Franchised From: 2
Primary Menu: Sandwiches/Deli (2)
Areas of Operation: MN
Type of Foodservice: Quick Serve (2)
Franchise Affiliation: Jersey Mike's Franchise Systems, MANASQUAN, NJ

Key Personnel
MICHAEL NOLAN - Owner
TOM BACHAR - VP
JEFF MENDELSOHN - Director Sales
CAITLIN WEBSTER - Director Sales

RedKing Foods LLC
11775 Justen Cir Ste B
Maple Grove, MN 55369-4591

Telephone: (763) 428-0071
Fax Number: (763) 428-0079
Internet Homepage: vikingrestaurants.com
Company Email: info@redkingfoods.com
Type of Business: Chain Restaurant Operator
Year Founded: 1998
Total Sales: $61,810,000 (e)
Number of Employees: 696
Average Check: Breakfast(8); Lunch(8); Dinner(8)
Total Units: 27
Trade Names: Burger King (27)
Units Franchised From: 27
Preferred Square Footage: 2,500
Preferred Location Types: Community Mall; Downtown; Freestanding
Primary Menu: Hamburger (27)
Areas of Operation: MN, ND, SD
Type of Foodservice: Quick Serve (27)
Franchise Affiliation: Burger King Worldwide Inc., MIAMI, FL
Primary Distributors: (Full Line) Reinhart FoodService, MARSHALL, MN

Key Personnel
JOHN KRUCHTEN - President; Director Operations, Loss Prevention, Supply Chain, Food Safety; General Buyer
SANDIY RYAN - Manager
DIANE STENBERG - Manager
MATT CLEUVER - Manager Information Systems

G R N J R Inc
1205 E College Dr
Marshall, MN 56258-2009

Telephone: (507) 537-1120
Type of Business: Chain Restaurant Operator
Total Sales: $5,049,000 (e)
Total Units: 9
Trade Names: Subway (9)
Units Franchised From: 9
Primary Menu: Sandwiches/Deli (9)
Areas of Operation: MN
Type of Foodservice: Quick Serve (9)
Franchise Affiliation: Doctor's Associates Inc., MILFORD, CT

Key Personnel
RANDY WARTNER - President; General Buyer

Har-Mar Foods Inc.
1402 E College Dr
Marshall, MN 56258-2027

Telephone: (507) 532-5027
Fax Number: (507) 532-2230
Type of Business: Chain Restaurant Operator
Year Founded: 1975
Total Sales: $19,640,000 (e)
Number of Employees: 690
Average Check: Breakfast(5); Lunch(8); Dinner(8)
Total Units: 11
Trade Names: Hardee's (11)
Units Franchised From: 11
Preferred Square Footage: 3,000; 3,500
Preferred Location Types: Freestanding
Primary Menu: Hamburger (11)
Areas of Operation: MN, SD
Type of Foodservice: Quick Serve (11)
Franchise Affiliation: Hardee's Food Systems Inc., FRANKLIN, TN
Primary Distributors: (Full Line) McLane/Mason City, MASON CITY, IA

Key Personnel
LIONEL BOLDEN - CEO; Partner; VP; General Manager; General Buyer
JOHN FIGLEWICZ - President; Partner

Bartmann Group
1600 W Lake St
Minneapolis, MN 55408

Telephone: (612) 827-5710
Internet Homepage: bartmanngroup.com
Type of Business: Chain Restaurant Operator
Year Founded: 1991
Systemwide Sales: $23,200,000 (e)
Total Units: 9

Trade Names: Barbette (1); Book Club (1); Bread & Pickle (1); Gigi's Cafe (1); Pat's Tap (1); Red Stag Supperclub (1); The Bird (1); Tiny Diner (1); Trapeze (1)
Company-Owned Units: 9
Preferred Location Types: Downtown; Freestanding
Primary Menu: American (5); Californian (1); French/Continental (1); Health Foods (1); Snacks (1)
Areas of Operation: MN
Type of Foodservice: Casual Dining (8); Quick Serve (1)

Key Personnel
KIM BARTMANN - Founder; CEO
REBECCA SLAPNICHER - Director Food
MAUREEN MOE BEYER - Director Marketing

Blue Plate Restaurant Company
901 N 3rd St Ste 117
Minneapolis, MN 55401

Telephone: (612) 249-5466
Fax Number: (651) 690-1330
Internet Homepage: blueplaterestaurantcompany.com
Type of Business: Chain Restaurant Operator
Total Sales: $16,680,000 (e)
Alcohol Sales: 10%
Number of Employees: 1,142
Total Units: 8
Trade Names: 3 Squares (1); Edina Grill (1); Groveland Tap (1); Highland Grill (1); Longfellow Grill (1); Mercury Dining Room & Rail (1); The Freehouse (1); The Lowry (1)
Company-Owned Units: 8
Alcohol Served: Beer, Wine, Liquor
Primary Menu: American (7); Hamburger (1)
Projected Openings: 1
Areas of Operation: MN
Type of Foodservice: Casual Dining (8)

Key Personnel
DAVID BURLEY - CEO; Partner
JEFF TRENAM - Owner Operations; Director
STEPHANIE SHIMP - Senior VP Marketing
JOE WILKINSON - Controller
PATRICK DOW - General Manager
CASEY SAEGER - Director Human Resources
DANIEL SIPMA - Director Information Technology
PHIL POLING - Director Food

Break Bread Hospitality Group
831 Nicollet Mall
Minneapolis, MN 55402-2506

Telephone: (612) 333-7000
Fax Number: (612) 333-7707
Internet Homepage: ciaobellamn.com; zelomn.com
Type of Business: Chain Restaurant Operator
Year Founded: 1997
Total Sales: $7,623,000 (e)
Alcohol Sales: 25%
Number of Employees: 100
Average Check: Lunch(18); Dinner(30)
Total Units: 1
Trade Names: Zelo (1)
Company-Owned Units: 2
Preferred Location Types: Freestanding; Strip Mall
Alcohol Served: Beer, Wine, Liquor
Primary Menu: Italian (1)
Areas of Operation: MN
Type of Foodservice: Fine Dining (1)

Key Personnel
BOB TINSLEY - Owner; General Buyer

Brinda-Heilicher Inc.
820 Decatur Ave N
Minneapolis, MN 55427-4324

Telephone: (763) 544-0818
Internet Homepage: williamsminneapolis.com
Company Email: contact@vicsminneapolis.com
Type of Business: Chain Restaurant Operator
Total Sales: $4,279,000 (e)
Alcohol Sales: 10%
Number of Employees: 100
Average Check: Lunch(10); Dinner(12)
Total Units: 2
Trade Names: Tuggs River Saloon (1); Williams Uptown Pub & Peanut Bar (1)
Company-Owned Units: 2
Preferred Square Footage: 5,500; 6,000
Preferred Location Types: Freestanding
Alcohol Served: Beer, Wine, Liquor
Primary Menu: American (2)
Areas of Operation: MN
Type of Foodservice: Casual Dining (2)
Primary Distributors: (Full Line) SYSCO Food Services of Minnesota Inc., MOUNDSVIEW, MN

Key Personnel
SCOTT BRINDA - Owner; Executive Chef; Director Information Systems, Menu Development
MARK MELLES - Controller
DOUGLAS PITTMAN - General Manager; Executive Chef
VICTORIA BARLOW - Manager Marketing

Broders' Cucina Italiana
2308 W 50th St
Minneapolis, MN 55410-2202

Telephone: (612) 925-3113
Internet Homepage: broders.com; broderspastabar.com; terzompls.com
Company Email: bci@broders.com
Type of Business: Chain Restaurant Operator
Year Founded: 1982
Total Sales: $5,765,000 (e)
Alcohol Sales: 8%
Number of Employees: 20
Average Check: Lunch(10); Dinner(18)
Total Units: 3
Trade Names: Broders' Cucina Italiana (1); Broders' Pasta Bar (1); Terzo (1)
Company-Owned Units: 3
Preferred Location Types: Freestanding
Alcohol Served: Beer, Wine
Primary Menu: Italian (3)
Areas of Operation: MN
Type of Foodservice: Casual Dining (3)
Catering Services: Yes
Primary Distributors: (Food) US Foods, PLYMOUTH, MN; (Specialty Foods) Fortune Fish & Gourmet, MINNEAPOLIS, MN

Key Personnel
MOLLY BRODER - Owner; General Manager; General Buyer
THOMAS BRODER - Executive Chef; General Buyer
LEE KNUTSOM - Manager Retail Operations
WENDY MERGENS - Manager
ANN RICHARDS - Manager Catering

Cara Irish Pubs
931 Nicollet Mall
Minneapolis, MN 55402-3201

Telephone: (612) 904-1000
Fax Number: (612) 904-1005
Internet Homepage: carairishpubs.com; the-local.com
Company Email: comments@the-local.com
Type of Business: Chain Restaurant Operator
Year Founded: 1998
Total Sales: $12,107,000 (e)
Alcohol Sales: 30%
Number of Employees: 200
Average Check: Lunch(24); Dinner(34)
Total Units: 4
Trade Names: Cooper Irish Pub (1); Kieran's Pub (1); The Liffey (1); The Local Irish Pub (1)
Company-Owned Units: 4
Preferred Location Types: Community Mall; Freestanding

Alcohol Served: Beer, Wine, Liquor
Primary Menu: Miscellaneous (4)
Areas of Operation: MN
Type of Foodservice: Casual Dining (4)

Key Personnel
HENRY COUSINEAU - Partner
JAY JOHNSON - General Manager
KATE LOSCHEIDER - Administrator Information Systems

Christos Greek Restaurant
2632 Nicollet Ave
Minneapolis, MN 55408-1662

Telephone: (612) 871-2111
Fax Number: (612) 871-8129
Internet Homepage: christos.com
Type of Business: Chain Restaurant Operator
Year Founded: 1986
Total Sales: $2,507,000 (e)
Alcohol Sales: 10%
Number of Employees: 45
Average Check: Lunch(12); Dinner(22)
Total Units: 2
Trade Names: Christos Greek Restaurant (2)
Company-Owned Units: 2
Preferred Location Types: Freestanding; Strip Mall
Alcohol Served: Beer, Wine
Primary Menu: Greek/Mediterranean (2)
Areas of Operation: MN
Type of Foodservice: Casual Dining (2)

Key Personnel
CAROL PARPAS - Partner
GUS PARPAS - Partner; General Manager; Executive Chef; General Buyer

D'Amico & Partners Inc.
211 N 1st St Ste 175
Minneapolis, MN 55401-1480

Telephone: (612) 374-1776
Fax Number: (612) 374-1869
Internet Homepage: parma8200.com; cafelurcat.com; campiello.damico.com; continentalnaples.com; damico.com; damicoandsons.com; masa-restaurant.com
Type of Business: Chain Restaurant Operator
Year Founded: 1983
Total Sales: $15,820,000 (e)
Alcohol Sales: 22%
Number of Employees: 985
Internet Order Processing: Yes
Total Units: 11
Trade Names: Cafe Lurcat & Bar (1); Campiello (2); D'Amico & Sons Italian Deli (7); The Continental (1)
Company-Owned Units: 11
Preferred Square Footage: 3,000; 4,000; 11,000
Preferred Location Types: Freestanding; Strip Mall
Alcohol Served: Beer, Wine, Liquor
Primary Menu: American (1); Italian (9); Steak/Seafood (1)
Areas of Operation: FL, MN
Type of Foodservice: Casual Dining (10); Fine Dining (1)
Catering Services: Yes
Primary Distributors: (Full Line) SYSCO Food Services of Minnesota Inc., MOUNDSVIEW, MN

Key Personnel
RICHARD D'AMICO - Founder; CEO; Director Information Systems, Design
LARRY D'AMICO - President; Director Risk Management, Marketing, Real Estate, Menu Development, Food Safety
PAUL SMITH - CFO; Director Finance
AMY BRITTON - Manager Operations

Davanni's Pizza & Hot Hoagies
1100 Xenium Ln N Ste 2
Minneapolis, MN 55441-4440

Telephone: (952) 927-2300
Fax Number: (952) 927-2323
Internet Homepage: coffeebene.com; davannis.com
Company Email: davannis_info@davannis.com
Type of Business: Chain Restaurant Operator
Year Founded: 1975
Total Sales: $48,770,000 (e)
Alcohol Sales: 1%
Number of Employees: 1,150
Average Check: Breakfast(6); Lunch(14); Dinner(24)
Internet Order Processing: Yes
Total Units: 23
Trade Names: Coffee Bene (1); Davanni's Pizza & Hot Hoagies (22)
Company-Owned Units: 23
Preferred Square Footage: 4,200
Preferred Location Types: Freestanding; Strip Mall
Alcohol Served: Beer
Primary Menu: Coffee (1); Pizza (22)
Areas of Operation: MN
Type of Foodservice: Casual Dining (22); Quick Serve (1)
Catering Services: Yes
Primary Distributors: (Food) Sysco Western Minnesota, SAINT CLOUD, MN; (Food) Jerry's Produce Co., SAINT PAUL, MN

Key Personnel
G. M. STENSON - CEO; Director Facility/Maintenance, Design
BOB STUPKA - President; CFO; Manager Finance, Purchasing
LAURA ABBLETT - General Manager
KATHI PROIS - General Manager
CHRISTINA MOLDEN - General Manager
KIRSTEN GOODWALT - Manager Human Resources

Doolittles Restaurants
9201 E Bloomington Fwy Ste Gg
Minneapolis, MN 55420-3472

Telephone: (952) 944-6070
Fax Number: (952) 944-6079
Internet Homepage: doolittles.com; portercreek.com
Company Email: info@portercreek.com
Type of Business: Chain Restaurant Operator
Year Founded: 1989
Total Sales: $24,750,000 (e)
Alcohol Sales: 20%
Number of Employees: 560
Average Check: Lunch(20); Dinner(34)
Internet Order Processing: Yes
Total Units: 7
Trade Names: Doolittles Woodfire Grill (5); Porter Creek Hardwood Grill (2)
Company-Owned Units: 7
Preferred Square Footage: 5,000
Preferred Location Types: Downtown; Freestanding
Alcohol Served: Beer, Wine, Liquor
Primary Menu: American (5); Steak/Seafood (2)
Projected Openings: 1
Areas of Operation: MN, ND, WI
Type of Foodservice: Casual Dining (7)
Catering Services: Yes

Key Personnel
LYNN REIMER - Co-CEO; President; Partner; CFO
JOHN SHEEHAN - Co-CEO; Partner; COO
STEPHEN NORDNESS - Controller; Director Risk Management, Human Resources
BRIAN NEWMAN - General Manager
MELANIE BRUDOS - Director Marketing, Advertising, Business Development

Dunn Bros. Coffee Franchising Inc.
111 3rd Ave S Ste 130
Minneapolis, MN 55401-2551

Telephone: (612) 334-9746
Fax Number: (612) 334-9749
Internet Homepage: dunnbros.com
Company Email: dunnbros6@dunnbros.com
Type of Business: Chain Restaurant Operator
Year Founded: 1987
Systemwide Sales: $33,363,000 (e)

Total Sales: $13,740,000 (e)
Number of Employees: 120
Average Check: Breakfast(8); Lunch(8); Dinner(8)
Internet Order Processing: Yes
Total Units: 74
Trade Names: Dunn Brothers Coffee (74)
Company-Owned Units: 3
Units Franchised To: 71
Preferred Square Footage: 1,200; 1,600; 1,800; 2,000
Preferred Location Types: Downtown; Freestanding; Strip Mall
Primary Menu: Coffee (74)
Areas of Operation: KS, MN, MO, ND, SD, TN, TX, WI
Type of Foodservice: Quick Serve (74)
Primary Distributors: (Full Line) SYSCO Food Services of Minnesota Inc., MOUNDSVIEW, MN
Notes: The company derives approximately 49% of its revenue from retail sale of coffee beans & coffee accessories.

Key Personnel
KIM PLAHN - President; CFO; General Buyer

Fourteen Foods
7101 W 78th St Ste 100
Minneapolis, MN 55439-2527

Telephone: (952) 944-1304
Internet Homepage: fourteenfoods.com
Company Email: information@fourteenfoods.com
Type of Business: Chain Restaurant Operator
Total Sales: $280,160,000 (e)
Number of Employees: 9,000
Average Check: Lunch(8); Dinner(8)
Total Units: 202
Trade Names: Dairy Queen (4); Dairy Queen Brazier (26); DQ Grill & Chill (172)
Units Franchised From: 202
Preferred Square Footage: 2,500; 3,600
Preferred Location Types: Freestanding; Strip Mall
Primary Menu: Snacks (202)
Projected Openings: 17
Areas of Operation: AL, FL, IA, IN, KY, MN, NE, SD, TN, WI
Type of Foodservice: Quick Serve (202)
Franchise Affiliation: International Dairy Queen Inc., BLOOMINGTON, MN
Primary Distributors: (Full Line) SYSCO Food Services of Minnesota Inc., MOUNDSVIEW, MN
Notes: Administrative offices are located at 2341 Crossroads Blvd, ALBERT LEA, MN [PO Box 771] 56007 507-377-9225 (p) 507-377-1612 (f)

Key Personnel
MATT FRAUENSHUH - CEO; President; Director Facility/Maintenance, Real Estate
MIKE ROGERS - COO
JILL WALZ - COO
JUSTIN KRAUS - Chief Investment Officer
ASHLEIGH M - VP Marketing, Human Resources
WAYNE PEDERSON - VP Information Technology
BILL GRANDSTAFF - VP Operations
DAVE CRAIG - VP Human Resources
PATRICK DAVIS - VP Employee Development
HOMER DHOLS - General Manager
DOUG HELLERUD - Senior Director
SEBASTIAN FERRER - Senior Director Operations
JOEY GOODE - Director Operations
AMBER HOLT - Director Employee Benefits
JESSICA KERNS - Director Operations
SHAYANNE KINSLEY - Director Operations
GENE DODGE - Director Information Technology
JONATHAN BERKOFSKY - Director Operations
MAURICE CHANDLER - Director Operations
MARTIN CLARK - Director Operations
JEREMY COOK - Director Operations
JOHN PICKERING - Director Operations
TODD MCGLAMERY - Director Development, Real Estate
STEVE LUNDSTROM - Director Finance
MICHAEL TOLLIVER - Director Operations
JENNIFER RAMEY - Regional Director Recruitment
GABRIEL WHIPPLE - Senior Manager Information Technology
JEFF WIELAND - Manager Human Resources
JORDAN SONAGLIA - Manager Marketing
LESLEY ADAM - Manager Operations
DEANNA FLOYD - Manager Marketing
MIKE SELBITSCHKA - Supervisor Operations
CARMINO LOMBARDI - Coordinator Customer Service

Hemisphere Restaurant Partners LLC
1501 Washington Ave S Ste 300
Minneapolis, MN 55454-6601

Telephone: (612) 238-2166
Fax Number: (612) 338-8126
Internet Homepage: atlasgrill.com; missionamerican.com; thetaverngrill.com; hrprestaurants.com
Company Email: info@hrprestaurants.com
Type of Business: Chain Restaurant Operator
Year Founded: 2003
Total Sales: $5,721,000 (e)
Alcohol Sales: 5%
Total Units: 9
Trade Names: Atlas Grill (1); Good to Go Mediterranean Deli (1); Mission American Kitchen (1); Sphere Kitchen & Bar (1); The Tavern Grill (5)
Company-Owned Units: 9
Alcohol Served: Beer, Wine, Liquor
Primary Menu: American (7); Greek/Mediterranean (1); Steak/Seafood (1)
Areas of Operation: MN
Type of Foodservice: Casual Dining (7); Fine Dining (1); Quick Serve (1)

Key Personnel
HADI ANBAR - Partner; General Buyer
ANUSH ANSARI - Partner; General Buyer

Mandarin Holdings/Leeann Chin Inc
3600 American Blvd W Ste 52
Minneapolis, MN 55431-4513

Telephone: (952) 896-3606
Fax Number: (952) 896-3615
Internet Homepage: leeannchin.com; mandarinexpress.us
Type of Business: Chain Restaurant Operator
Total Sales: $81,420,000 (e)
Average Check: Dinner(16)
Total Units: 87
Trade Names: Leeann Chin (44); Mandarin Express (43)
Company-Owned Units: 87
Preferred Location Types: Freestanding; Regional Mall; Strip Mall
Primary Menu: Asian (44); Chinese (43)
Projected Openings: 2
Areas of Operation: AR, FL, GA, LA, MN, MS, NC, ND, PA, TN, TX, VA
Type of Foodservice: Quick Serve (87)
Catering Services: Yes
Parent Company: West Coast Capital, SHERMAN OAKS, CA

Key Personnel
LORNE GOLDBERG - Owner; General Buyer
MIKE LONEY - COO
JOHN TVEDT - VP Operations
JOE KOHAUT - VP Operations
LONNY CRUSE - Regional Director Operations

My Burger
601 Marquette Ave
Minneapolis, MN 55402

Telephone: (612) 436-0330
Internet Homepage: myburgerusa.com
Type of Business: Chain Restaurant Operator
Total Sales: $6,754,000 (e)
Total Units: 7
Trade Names: My Burger (7)
Company-Owned Units: 7
Primary Menu: Hamburger (7)
Areas of Operation: MN
Type of Foodservice: Fast Casual (7)

Key Personnel
JOHN ABDO - President
PAUL ABDO - VP
JOE SPENCER - District Manager
JASON MARTIN - Manager Facility/Maintenance

New Bohemia
233 E Hennepin Ave
Minneapolis, MN 55414-1013

Telephone: (612) 331-4929
Internet Homepage: newbohemiausa.com
Company Email: info@newbohemiausa.com
Type of Business: Chain Restaurant Operator
Total Units: 8
Trade Names: New Bohemia (8)
Company-Owned Units: 8
Areas of Operation: MN

Key Personnel
BRAD TEARE - CEO; President; Partner
JEFF BORNMANN - Partner

Obresky Enterprises Inc
4900 Highway 169 N Ste 107
Minneapolis, MN 55428-4047

Telephone: (763) 553-9616
Fax Number: (763) 553-2006
Internet Homepage: oeisubway.com
Type of Business: Chain Restaurant Operator
Total Sales: $12,908,000 (e)
Total Units: 16
Trade Names: Subway (16)
Units Franchised From: 16
Primary Menu: Sandwiches/Deli (16)
Areas of Operation: MN
Type of Foodservice: Quick Serve (16)
Franchise Affiliation: Doctor's Associates Inc., MILFORD, CT

Key Personnel
JOY OBRESKY - VP

Pepitos Restaurant
4624 Nicollet Ave
Minneapolis, MN 55419

Telephone: (612) 825-6311
Internet Homepage: pepitosrestaurant.com
Type of Business: Chain Restaurant Operator
Year Founded: 1970
Total Sales: $2,270,000 (e)
Alcohol Sales: 8%
Number of Employees: 17
Average Check: Lunch(8); Dinner(12)
Total Units: 1
Trade Names: Pepito's Mexigo Deli (1)
Company-Owned Units: 1
Preferred Location Types: Freestanding
Alcohol Served: Beer, Wine, Liquor
Primary Menu: Mexican (1)
Areas of Operation: MN
Type of Foodservice: Casual Dining (1)
Catering Services: Yes
Primary Distributors: (Food) SYSCO Food Services of Minnesota Inc., MOUNDSVIEW, MN

Key Personnel
JOE MINJARES - Owner
SUSAN SENKYR - VP
WILLIAM J. SENKYR - General Manager; Executive Chef; General Buyer
PABLO SENKYR - General Manager; General Buyer

Pizza Luce Management
119 N 4th St
Minneapolis, MN 55401

Telephone: (612) 333-7359
Internet Homepage: pizzaluce.com
Type of Business: Chain Restaurant Operator
Year Founded: 1993
Total Sales: $31,300,000 (e)
Alcohol Sales: 1%
Number of Employees: 455
Average Check: Lunch(12); Dinner(18)
Total Units: 10
Trade Names: Pizza Luce (10)
Company-Owned Units: 10
Preferred Location Types: Downtown; Freestanding
Alcohol Served: Beer, Wine, Liquor
Primary Menu: Pizza (10)
Areas of Operation: MN
Type of Foodservice: Casual Dining (10)

Key Personnel
JJ HAYWOOD - CEO; Partner; Director Purchasing, Information Systems, Real Estate, Menu Development
LAURA HENSEN - Partner; Director Operations
BUCKY JASZEWSKI - General Manager
COREY SAX - Manager Marketing

Target Corporation
1000 Nicollet Mall
Minneapolis, MN 55403-2542

Telephone: (612) 304-6073
Fax Number: (612) 696-3682
Internet Homepage: target.com
Company Email: guest.relations@target.com
Type of Business: Nontraditional Foodservice Operator
Year Founded: 1909
Publicly Held: Yes
Total Sales: $161,368,907,000 (e)
Number of Employees: 347,000
Average Check: Breakfast(6); Lunch(6); Dinner(6)
Foodservice Sales: $4,841,067,000 (e)
Internet Order Processing: Yes
Total Units: 1,948
Trade Names: Food Avenue (1,948)
Company-Owned Units: 1,948
Preferred Square Footage: 4,000
Preferred Location Types: Downtown; Freestanding
Primary Menu: American (1,948)
Areas of Operation: AK, AL, AR, AZ, CA, CO, CT, DC, DE, FL, GA, HI, IA, ID, IL, IN, KS, KY, LA, MA, MD, ME, MI, MN, MO, MS, MT, NC, ND, NE, NH, NJ, NM, NV, NY, OH, OK, OR, PA, RI, SC, SD, TN, TX, UT, VA, WA, WI, WV, WY
Type of Foodservice: In-Store Feeder (1,948)
Franchise Affiliation: D'Amico & Partners Inc., MINNEAPOLIS, MN; Pizza Hut Inc., PLANO, TX; Pret A Manger (USA) Ltd, NEW YORK, NY; Starbucks Corporation, SEATTLE, WA; Taco Bell Corp., IRVINE, CA
Primary Distributors: (Food) McLane/Minnesota, NORTHFIELD, MN
Notes: Target derives approximately 97% of its revenue from retail sales.

Key Personnel
BRIAN CORNELL - Chairman; CEO
WILLIAM FOUNDY JR - President Sourcing
JIM LEE - CFO
ROBERT HARRISON - Chief Accounting Officer; Senior VP; Controller
JOHN J. MULLIGAN - COO; Exec VP
MICHAEL FIDDELKE - COO; Exec VP
MELISSA KREMER - Chief Human Resources Officer; Exec VP
LAYSHA L. WARD - Chief Administrative Officer; Chief Compliance Officer; Exec VP
MICHAEL MCNAMARA - CIO; Exec VP
JILL SANDO - Chief Merchandising Officer; Exec VP
KATIE BOYLAN - Chief Communications Officer; Exec VP
DON LIU - Chief Legal Officer; Chief Risk Officer; Exec VP
TODD WATERBURY - Chief Creative Officer
CHRISTINA HENNINGTON - Chief Growth Officer; Exec VP
PRAT VEMANA - Chief Digital Officer; Exec VP
JANNA POTTS - Chief Stores Officer; Exec VP
RICK GOMEZ - Exec VP
COREY L. HAALAND - Senior VP; Treasurer
SAMIR SHAH - Senior VP Store Operations
DAWN BLOCK - Senior VP Digital, E-Commerce, Division
JOHN CONLIN - Senior VP Merchandising-Beverages, Merchandising-Food
JOEL CRABB - VP Real Estate Development
JOHN HULBERT - Director Investor Relations
BRIAN TREBER - Regional Director Real Estate
BOB MEZA - Senior Manager Construction

JON PLEMONS - Buyer

The Haagen-Dazs Shoppe Company Inc.
500 Washington Ave S Ste 2040
Minneapolis, MN 55415-1183

Telephone: (612) 337-3300
Fax Number: (612) 337-3301
Internet Homepage: haagendazs.com
Type of Business: Chain Restaurant Operator
Year Founded: 1960
Systemwide Sales: $191,603,000 (e)
Total Sales: $7,497,000 (e)
Number of Employees: 10
Average Check: Lunch(8); Dinner(8)
Total Units: 175
Trade Names: Haagen-Dazs (249)
Units Franchised To: 249
Preferred Square Footage: 1,000
Preferred Location Types: Community Mall; Downtown; Freestanding; Lifestyle Center; Outlet Mall; Regional Mall; Strip Mall; Travel Plazas
Primary Menu: Snacks (249)
Areas of Operation: AL, AR, AZ, CA, CO, CT, DC, FL, GA, GU, HI, IL, IN, KS, LA, MA, MD, MI, MN, MO, NC, NJ, NM, NV, NY, OH, PA, PR, RI, SC, TX, VA, WA, WI, WY
Foreign Countries: ARUBA; AUSTRIA; BELGIUM; BRAZIL; CAYMAN ISLANDS; CHINA; COSTA RICA; CYPRUS; CZECH REPUBLIC; DOMINICAN REPUBLIC; EGYPT; ENGLAND; FRANCE; GERMANY; GREECE; HONG KONG; HUNGARY; INDIA; INDONESIA; IRELAND; JAMAICA; JAPAN; KUWAIT;LEBANON; LUXEMBOURG; MACAO; MALAYSIA; MEXICO; MONACO; PANAMA; POLAND; PORTUGAL; QATAR; ROMANIA; SAINT MARTIN; SAUDI ARABIA; SINGAPORE; SOUTH KOREA; SPAIN; TAIWAN; THAILAND; THE NETHERLANDS; THE PHILIPPINES; TRINIDAD & TOBAGO; TURKEY; UNITEDARAB EMIRATES
Type of Foodservice: Quick Serve (249)
Catering Services: Yes
Primary Distributors: (Food) SYSCO Food Services of Minnesota Inc., MOUNDSVIEW, MN
Parent Company: Dreyer's Grand Ice Cream, OAKLAND, CA
Notes: Store count reflects only US operations.

Key Personnel
DAWN UREMOVICH - VP
ROB SCHELL - Director Franchise Development
JEN MCLEAN - Manager Marketing

Y.H.D. Foods, Inc
11360 Foley Blvd NW
Minneapolis, MN 55448-3348

Telephone: (763) 767-0902
Internet Homepage: archpowered.com/yhdfoods
Company Email: yhdfoods.mcd@gmail.com
Type of Business: Chain Restaurant Operator
Total Sales: $32,930,000 (e)
Total Units: 7
Trade Names: McDonald's (7)
Units Franchised From: 7
Primary Menu: Hamburger (7)
Areas of Operation: MN
Type of Foodservice: Quick Serve (7)
Franchise Affiliation: McDonald's Corporation, CHICAGO, IL

Key Personnel
JEFF SMITH - President; General Buyer
JEFF LAPKA - Manager Administration

Taher Inc. - Restaurant Division
5570 Smetana Dr Ste 27
Minnetonka, MN 55343-9022

Telephone: (952) 945-0505
Fax Number: (952) 345-0444
Internet Homepage: taher.com; timberlodgesteakhouse.com
Company Email: taher@taher.com
Type of Business: Chain Restaurant Operator
Year Founded: 1989
Systemwide Sales: $30,044,000 (e)
Total Sales: $3,650,000 (e)
Alcohol Sales: 15%
Number of Employees: 960
Average Check: Lunch(12); Dinner(26)
Internet Order Processing: Yes
Internet Sales: 1.00%
Total Units: 1
Trade Names: Timber Lodge Steakhouse (1)
Company-Owned Units: 1
Preferred Square Footage: 7,500
Preferred Location Types: Freestanding; Strip Mall
Alcohol Served: Beer, Wine, Liquor
Primary Menu: Steak (1)
Areas of Operation: MN
Type of Foodservice: Casual Dining (1)
Catering Services: Yes
Primary Distributors: (Full Line) Reinhart FoodService, MARSHALL, MN
Parent Company: Taher Inc., HOPKINS, MN

Key Personnel
BRUCE TAHER - CEO; President
JUDY CAMERON - Senior VP Operations
MARK BRODERSEN - VP Operations
SHAWN TAHER - VP
TRENT TAHER - VP Purchasing
JIM MADDEN - VP Operations; Manager Region
NISSA HUBER - Director Human Resources
SHERRY BERKOWITZ - Manager Finance, Accounting

Village Inn
12701 Whitewater Dr Ste 100
Minnetonka, MN 55343

Telephone: (952) 294-1300
Fax Number: (615) 782-5043
Internet Homepage: villageinnrestaurants.com
Company Email: vicustomerservice@abrholdings.com
Type of Business: Chain Restaurant Operator
Year Founded: 1958
Systemwide Sales: $414,196,000 (e)
Total Sales: $261,360,000 (e)
Number of Employees: 5,100
Average Check: Breakfast(10); Lunch(10); Dinner(14)
Internet Order Processing: Yes
Internet Sales: 1.00%
Total Units: 205
Trade Names: Village Inn (205)
Company-Owned Units: 119
Units Franchised To: 86
Preferred Square Footage: 5,000
Preferred Location Types: Freestanding; Strip Mall
Primary Menu: American (205)
Projected Openings: 3
Areas of Operation: AK, AR, AZ, CO, FL, IA, IL, KS, MN, MO, ND, NE, NM, OK, OR, TX, UT, VA, WA, WY
Type of Foodservice: Family Restaurant (205)
Distribution Centers: OAK FOREST, IL; CHASKA, MN
Primary Distributors: (Full Line) US Foods, CENTENNIAL, CO
Parent Company: Famous Hospitality Inc., MINNETONKA, MN

Key Personnel
KURT SCHNAUBELT - CFO
MIKE MUNIZ - VP Region; Regional VP
DANNY GRESHAM - VP Construction, Design
ASHLEY BERLAND - Senior Director Supply Chain
DAVE BRANSCOMB - Director Operations
STACEY CLAIR - Director Operations
ROBERT CORNNOR - Director Development
TAMMY ALCANTAR - Director Human Resources
LEROY BAKER - Director Operations
FRED RASO - Director Franchise Operations
DEREK RIVERA - Director Operations
TERESA RIVERA - Director Operations
GINGER ROGERS - Director Internal Audit
ANN SMITH - Director Operations

ANGIE LIPPS - Administrator POS/Scanning

Border Foods Inc.
5425 Boone Ave N
New Hope, MN 55428-3614

Telephone: (763) 559-7338
Fax Number: (763) 559-2077
Internet Homepage: borderfoods.com
Type of Business: Chain Restaurant Operator
Year Founded: 1979
Total Sales: $478,660,000 (e)
Number of Employees: 3,170
Average Check: Lunch(10); Dinner(14)
Total Units: 178
Trade Names: Taco Bell (178)
Units Franchised From: 178
Preferred Square Footage: 800
Preferred Location Types: Community Mall; Convenience Store/Gas Station; Freestanding
Primary Menu: Taco (178)
Projected Openings: 10
Areas of Operation: IL, MI, MN, SD, WI, WY
Type of Foodservice: Quick Serve (178)
Franchise Affiliation: ABP Corporation, BOSTON, MA; Taco Bell Corp., IRVINE, CA
Primary Distributors: (Full Line) McLane/Arlington, ARLINGTON, TX
Notes: Border Foods plans to open 3-5 Sonic Drive-In locations per year & expects to open a total of 35 in MN.

Key Personnel
JEFF ENGLER - Chairman; Co-Founder; Partner
LEE ENGLER - Co-Founder; CEO; President; Partner
AARON ENGLER - CFO; Chief Administrative Officer
JEFF WILLIAMS - COO
BARRY ZELICKSON - Senior VP Operations
BRIAN AXNESS - Controller; Director Finance
JACOB PAPKE - General Manager
BRIAN DAVIES - Director Facility/Maintenance
KASEY BAEZA - Director Operations
CHASITY BAILEY - Director Human Resources
VINCENT BOSSCHER - Director Operations
TODD AUSTIN - Director Operations
SHARLA HENNEK - Director Development
KEN LUND - Director Operations
DAVID ZIEMER - Senior Manager Technology
CHRISTOPHER BROWN - Regional Manager Facility/Maintenance
NATE WENGER - Area Manager
JARRET PERSONS - District Manager
TERI STAGGEMEYER - Manager
KATHERINE CRAMER - Manager Training
JENNIFER BANG - Manager Operations
ZACHARY ZELICKSON - Manager Development
ADAM WILSON - Manager Operations
JERRA SWENSON - Specialist Payroll
EVAN HATTON - Analyst

MAX CORRIGAN - Analyst Finance

Subslingers Inc
1 S Minnesota St
New Ulm, MN 56073-3001

Telephone: (507) 354-7827
Fax Number: (507) 354-7820
Internet Homepage: subslingers.com
Type of Business: Chain Restaurant Operator
Total Sales: $3,475,000 (e)
Total Units: 6
Trade Names: Subway (6)
Units Franchised From: 6
Primary Menu: Sandwiches/Deli (6)
Areas of Operation: MN
Type of Foodservice: Quick Serve (6)
Franchise Affiliation: Doctor's Associates Inc., MILFORD, CT

Key Personnel
RANDY WARTNER - President; Owner; General Buyer

Wendy's FourCrown Inc.
434 Hale Ave N Ste 160
Oakdale, MN 55128-7568

Telephone: (651) 714-0030
Internet Homepage: wendysfourcrown.com
Type of Business: Chain Restaurant Operator
Year Founded: 1986
Total Sales: $155,340,000 (e)
Number of Employees: 1,900
Average Check: Lunch(8); Dinner(8)
Total Units: 55
Trade Names: Wendy's Old Fashioned Hamburgers (55)
Units Franchised From: 55
Preferred Square Footage: 2,500
Preferred Location Types: Freestanding
Primary Menu: Hamburger (55)
Projected Remodelings: 2
Areas of Operation: MN, WI
Type of Foodservice: Quick Serve (55)
Franchise Affiliation: The Wendy's Company, DUBLIN, OH
Primary Distributors: (Food) Upper Lakes Foods Inc., CLOQUET, MN

Key Personnel
LINDA GIVENS - CEO
DAN OPITZ - President; General Buyer
MICHAEL R. GIVENS - VP Operations
DON JENSEN - Controller
MEGAN GIVENS - Director Marketing
CAROL BARES - Director Human Resources
PAUL BROTEN - Director Marketing

Domino's Franchisee
221 Mineral Springs Rd
Owatonna, MN 55060-2197

Telephone: (507) 451-3030
Type of Business: Chain Restaurant Operator
Total Sales: $17,798,000 (e)
Total Units: 9
Trade Names: Domino's (9)
Units Franchised From: 9
Primary Menu: Pizza (9)
Areas of Operation: MN
Type of Foodservice: Quick Serve (9)
Franchise Affiliation: Domino's Pizza Inc, ANN ARBOR, MI

Key Personnel
JOEL G. KRUEGER - Owner; General Buyer

Subway Franchise
520 8th Ave SE
Pipestone, MN 56164-2050

Telephone: (507) 825-5951
Fax Number: (507) 825-5951
Internet Homepage: subway.com
Type of Business: Chain Restaurant Operator
Total Sales: $3,037,000 (e)
Total Units: 5
Trade Names: Subway (5)
Units Franchised From: 5
Primary Menu: Sandwiches/Deli (5)
Areas of Operation: MN
Type of Foodservice: Quick Serve (5)
Franchise Affiliation: Doctor's Associates Inc., MILFORD, CT

Key Personnel
MARTY WALLACE - President

Khan's Mongolian Barbeque
500 E 78th St
Richfield, MN 55423-4316

Telephone: (612) 861-7991
Fax Number: (651) 639-8788
Internet Homepage: khansmongolianbarbecue.com
Type of Business: Chain Restaurant Operator
Year Founded: 1988
Total Sales: $5,319,000 (e)
Alcohol Sales: 10%
Number of Employees: 120
Average Check: Lunch(18); Dinner(20)
Total Units: 3
Trade Names: Khan's Mongolian BBQ (3)
Company-Owned Units: 3
Preferred Location Types: Grocery Stores
Alcohol Served: Beer, Wine, Liquor

Primary Menu: Asian (3)
Areas of Operation: MN
Type of Foodservice: Casual Dining (3)
Primary Distributors: (Full Line) US Foods, PLYMOUTH, MN

Key Personnel
MITCH LAW - President; Executive Chef; General Buyer
SHERIE LAW - VP Operations, Marketing

ACL Ice Cream Inc.
3780 Marketplace Dr NW Ste 111
Rochester, MN 55901-3225

Telephone: (507) 424-3374
Type of Business: Chain Restaurant Operator
Total Sales: $1,839,000 (e)
Total Units: 3
Trade Names: Cold Stone Creamery (3)
Units Franchised From: 3
Primary Menu: Snacks (3)
Areas of Operation: MN
Type of Foodservice: Quick Serve (3)
Franchise Affiliation: Kahala Brands, SCOTTSDALE, AZ

Key Personnel
LEYZER TOPEL - Partner
MARIA TOPEL - Partner

JLC Food Systems
2480 Superior Dr NW
Rochester, MN 55901-1799

Telephone: (507) 282-3090
Fax Number: (507) 282-7375
Type of Business: Chain Restaurant Operator
Year Founded: 1982
Total Sales: $21,190,000 (e)
Number of Employees: 210
Average Check: Breakfast(12); Lunch(14); Dinner(14)
Total Units: 6
Trade Names: Perkins Restaurant & Bakery (6)
Units Franchised From: 6
Preferred Square Footage: 4,000
Preferred Location Types: Freestanding
Primary Menu: American (6)
Areas of Operation: MN
Type of Foodservice: Family Restaurant (6)
Franchise Affiliation: Perkins Restaurant & Bakery, MEMPHIS, TN
Primary Distributors: (Full Line) US Foods, PLYMOUTH, MN

Key Personnel
DAVE HANSON - Owner; Director Finance, Operations, Facility/Maintenance, Information Systems, Supply Chain, Real Estate, Design, Human Resources; General Buyer

Domino's Franchisee
8060 State Highway 55
Rockford, MN 55373-9407

Telephone: (763) 477-4443
Type of Business: Chain Restaurant Operator
Total Sales: $3,984,000 (e)
Total Units: 2
Trade Names: Domino's (2)
Units Franchised From: 2
Primary Menu: Pizza (2)
Areas of Operation: MN
Type of Foodservice: Quick Serve (2)
Franchise Affiliation: Domino's Pizza Inc, ANN ARBOR, MI

Key Personnel
SKIP HERDKLOTZ - Owner; General Buyer

Twin Cities TJs
2589 Hamline Ave N Ste A
Roseville, MN 55113-3185

Telephone: (651) 636-8062
Fax Number: (651) 636-6472
Internet Homepage: tacojohnsbonus.com
Type of Business: Chain Restaurant Operator
Year Founded: 1973
Total Sales: $5,387,000 (e)
Number of Employees: 195
Average Check: Lunch(8); Dinner(12)
Total Units: 9
Trade Names: Taco John's (9)
Units Franchised From: 9
Preferred Square Footage: 2,700
Preferred Location Types: Community Mall; Freestanding; Strip Mall
Primary Menu: Taco (9)
Areas of Operation: IA, MN
Type of Foodservice: Quick Serve (9)
Catering Services: Yes
Franchise Affiliation: Taco John's International Inc., CHEYENNE, WY
Primary Distributors: (Food) Performance Foodservice, RICE, MN; (Supplies) Performance Foodservice, RICE, MN
Notes: Camille's Sidewalk Cafe operates as Platinum Restaurant Group.

Key Personnel
TAMRA KENNEDY - CEO; President; CFO; Director Real Estate, Design; General Buyer
JEFF KENNEDY - Director Operations, Facility/Maintenance

Malinen Management, LLC
4517 64th St SE
Saint Cloud, MN 56304-4501

Telephone: (320) 251-8863
Type of Business: Chain Restaurant Operator
Total Sales: $2,655,000 (e)
Total Units: 3
Trade Names: Little Caesars Pizza (3)
Units Franchised From: 3
Primary Menu: Pizza (3)
Areas of Operation: MN
Type of Foodservice: Quick Serve (3)
Franchise Affiliation: Little Caesar Enterprises Inc., DETROIT, MI

Key Personnel
MARTY MALINEN - President; General Buyer

Domino's Franchisee
23168 Saint Francis Blvd NW Ste 800
Saint Francis, MN 55070-8799

Telephone: (763) 753-4300
Type of Business: Chain Restaurant Operator
Total Sales: $8,025,000 (e)
Total Units: 4
Trade Names: Domino's (4)
Units Franchised From: 4
Primary Menu: Pizza (4)
Areas of Operation: MN
Type of Foodservice: Quick Serve (4)
Franchise Affiliation: Domino's Pizza Inc, ANN ARBOR, MI

Key Personnel
DAVID A. GIEFER - Owner; General Buyer

JMMN, LLC
1650 Park Place Blvd Ste 106
Saint Louis Park, MN 55416-1540

Telephone: (952) 512-1600
Type of Business: Chain Restaurant Operator
Total Sales: $4,360,000 (e)
Total Units: 3
Trade Names: Jersey Mike's Subs (3)
Units Franchised From: 3
Primary Menu: Sandwiches/Deli (3)
Areas of Operation: MN
Type of Foodservice: Quick Serve (3)
Franchise Affiliation: Jersey Mike's Franchise Systems, MANASQUAN, NJ

Key Personnel
MICHAEL MCGUIRE - Owner; General Buyer

Carbone's Pizza Inc.
680 7th St E
Saint Paul, MN 55106-5003

Telephone: (651) 771-5553
Internet Homepage: carbonespizzeria.com
Type of Business: Chain Restaurant Operator
Year Founded: 1954
Systemwide Sales: $47,114,000 (e)
Total Sales: $14,057,000 (e)
Alcohol Sales: 5%
Number of Employees: 500
Average Check: Lunch(6); Dinner(10)
Internet Order Processing: Yes
Total Units: 37
Trade Names: Carbone's Pizza (37)
Company-Owned Units: 1
Units Franchised To: 36
Preferred Square Footage: 2,500
Preferred Location Types: Community Mall; Freestanding
Alcohol Served: Beer, Wine, Liquor
Primary Menu: Pizza (37)
Areas of Operation: MN, MT, WI
Type of Foodservice: Casual Dining (37)
Catering Services: Yes
On-site Distribution Center: Yes
Primary Distributors: (Food) Jerry's Produce Co., SAINT PAUL, MN

Key Personnel
TOM M. CARBONE - Owner; Manager Operations, Purchasing, Facility/Maintenance, Design, Human Resources; General Buyer

Dino's The Greek Place
1700 Snelling Ave N
Saint Paul, MN 55113-5726

Telephone: (651) 645-8800
Fax Number: (651) 646-4702
Internet Homepage: dinosgyros.com
Type of Business: Chain Restaurant Operator
Year Founded: 1975
Total Sales: $1,827,000 (e)
Number of Employees: 37
Average Check: Dinner(8)
Total Units: 4
Trade Names: Dino's The Greek Place (4)
Company-Owned Units: 3
Units Franchised To: 1
Primary Menu: Greek/Mediterranean (4)
Areas of Operation: MN
Type of Foodservice: Fast Casual (4)

Key Personnel
JASON ADAMIDIS - President; Partner
VONA ADAMIDIS - Partner; CFO; VP; Treasurer; Corporate Secretary

Franchise Foods Systems, Inc.
260 Aurora Ave
Saint Paul, MN 55103-2301

Telephone: (651) 224-2000
Type of Business: Chain Restaurant Operator
Total Sales: $24,100,000 (e)
Total Units: 5
Trade Names: McDonald's (5)
Units Franchised From: 5
Preferred Location Types: Freestanding
Primary Menu: Hamburger (5)
Areas of Operation: MN
Type of Foodservice: Quick Serve (5)
Franchise Affiliation: McDonald's Corporation, CHICAGO, IL

Key Personnel
LOUIS HENRY JR - President; General Buyer

Green Mill Restaurants Inc.
1342 Grand Ave Ste 200
Saint Paul, MN 55105-3569

Telephone: (651) 203-3100
Fax Number: (651) 203-3101
Internet Homepage: crookedpint.com; greenmill.com
Company Email: info@greenmill.com
Type of Business: Chain Restaurant Operator
Year Founded: 1990
Systemwide Sales: $152,261,000 (e)
Total Sales: $9,872,000 (e)
Alcohol Sales: 25%
Number of Employees: 8
Average Check: Lunch(14); Dinner(24)
Internet Order Processing: Yes
Internet Sales: 1.00%
Total Units: 34
Trade Names: Crooked Pint Ale House (11); Green Mill Restaurant & Bar (23)
Units Franchised To: 34
Preferred Square Footage: 5,500; 6,000
Preferred Location Types: Community Mall; Freestanding; Hotel/Motel; Strip Mall
Alcohol Served: Beer, Wine, Liquor
Primary Menu: American (34)
Areas of Operation: KS, MN, ND, WI
Type of Foodservice: Casual Dining (34)
Catering Services: Yes
Primary Distributors: (Food) SYSCO Food Services of Minnesota Inc., MOUNDSVIEW, MN
Notes: The company derives approximately 5% of its revenue from retail sales of its sauces & pasta.

Key Personnel
MARY JULE ERICKSON - President; CFO
JOHN HINZ - Chief Marketing Officer
PETE WALDON - Executive Chef; Director Purchasing, Security, Inventory, Loss Prevention, Risk Management, Quality Assurance, Food Safety, Catering

M Street Cafe
350 Market St
Saint Paul, MN 55102-1430

Telephone: (651) 292-9292
Fax Number: (651) 228-3810
Internet Homepage: stpaulgrill.com; mstcafe.com; saintpaulhotel.com
Company Email: info@stpaulgrill.com
Type of Business: Chain Restaurant Operator
Year Founded: 1983
Total Sales: $3,163,000 (e)
Alcohol Sales: 12%
Number of Employees: 70
Average Check: Breakfast(14); Lunch(14); Dinner(22)
Total Units: 2
Trade Names: M Street Cafe (1); St. Paul Grill (1)
Company-Owned Units: 2
Preferred Location Types: Hotel/Motel
Alcohol Served: Beer, Wine, Liquor
Primary Menu: American (2)
Areas of Operation: MN
Type of Foodservice: Casual Dining (2)
Catering Services: Yes

Key Personnel
PHIL JUNGWIRTH - CEO; President
BRIAN SCHMECHEL - General Manager
DAVID SOOS - General Manager; General Buyer
LANCE CAPPS - Executive Chef

Punch Pizza
704 Cleveland Ave S
Saint Paul, MN 55116-1319

Telephone: (651) 696-1066
Internet Homepage: punchpizza.com
Type of Business: Chain Restaurant Operator
Year Founded: 1996
Total Sales: $11,430,000 (e)
Total Units: 12
Trade Names: Punch Neapolitan Pizza (12)
Company-Owned Units: 12
Primary Menu: Pizza (12)
Areas of Operation: MN
Type of Foodservice: Family Restaurant (12)

Key Personnel
JOHN SORRANO - Partner
JOHN PUCKETT - Partner
PAIGE CIERNIA - Director Store Operations

J M L M Restaurants Inc.
8646 Eagle Creek Cir Ste 206
Savage, MN 55378-1571

Telephone: (952) 224-8370
Type of Business: Chain Restaurant Operator
Total Units: 9
Trade Names: Subway (9)
Units Franchised From: 9
Primary Menu: Sandwiches/Deli (9)
Areas of Operation: MN
Type of Foodservice: Quick Serve (9)

Key Personnel
MANNY PEREZ - President; General Buyer

Canterbury Park Holding Corporation
1100 Canterbury Rd S
Shakopee, MN 55379-1867

Telephone: (952) 445-7223
Fax Number: (952) 496-6400
Internet Homepage: canterburypark.com
Company Email: cbypark@canterburypark.com
Type of Business: Foodservice Operations - Casinos
Year Founded: 1995
Publicly Held: Yes
Total Sales: $52,630,000 (e)
Alcohol Sales: 8%
Number of Employees: 416
Average Check: Breakfast(10); Lunch(12); Dinner(16)
Foodservice Sales: $6,842,000 (e)
Total Units: 8
Trade Names: Canterbury Cantina (1); HOMESTRETCH (1); Ice Cream Stand (1); Pizza & Pasta (1); Pub Grub (1); Trifecta Cafe (1); Triple Crown Buffet (1); Triple Crown Restaurant (1)
Company-Owned Units: 9
Preferred Square Footage: 3,000; 5,500; 6,000
Preferred Location Types: Freestanding
Alcohol Served: Beer, Wine, Liquor
Primary Menu: American (5); Mexican (1); Miscellaneous (1)
Areas of Operation: MN
Type of Foodservice: Casual Dining (6); Quick Serve (2)
Notes: The company derives approximately 86% of its revenue from pari-mutuel and card club operations.

Key Personnel
MARK A. ERICKSON - President; VP Facility/Maintenance
RANDY DEHMER - CFO Finance; VP
MARY FLEMING - VP Human Resources
JOHN GROEN - VP Marketing
MICHAEL HOCHMAN - VP Gaming/Entertainment
CASEY SHANNON - Director Information Technology
VICKEY WICKENHAUSER - Manager Catering
SHANTI JENSEN - Manager Catering
KERRY LARSON - Manager
JEFF MADAY - Manager Marketing, Communications

Domino's Franchisee
224 1st Ave E
Shakopee, MN 55379-1441

Telephone: (952) 445-9200
Type of Business: Chain Restaurant Operator
Total Sales: $4,012,000 (e)
Total Units: 2
Trade Names: Domino's (2)
Units Franchised From: 2
Primary Menu: Pizza (2)
Areas of Operation: MN
Type of Foodservice: Quick Serve (2)
Franchise Affiliation: Domino's Pizza Inc, ANN ARBOR, MI

Key Personnel
JEFFREY L. PIERSON - Owner; General Buyer

Valleyfair
1 Valleyfair Dr
Shakopee, MN 55379-3012

Telephone: (952) 445-7600
Fax Number: (952) 445-1539
Company Email: info@valleyfair.com
Listing Type: Divisional Office
Type of Business: Foodservice Operations - Theme Parks
Number of Employees: 1,400
Total Units: 40
Company-Owned Units: 40
Areas of Operation: MN
Parent Company: Cedar Fair LLP, SANDUSKY, OH

Key Personnel
PAM AMUNDSON - Director Sales
RON HUBNER - Director Merchandising
MATT LORRECIA - Director Operations
TOM SUEL - Director Construction
BRIAN O'DONNELL - Manager Security, Safety

VJ's Foodservice
1633 County Highway 10 Ste 8
Spring Lake Park, MN 55432-2140

Telephone: (763) 792-4308
Fax Number: (763) 792-4310
Type of Business: Chain Restaurant Operator
Year Founded: 1993
Total Sales: $70,050,000 (e)
Number of Employees: 100
Average Check: Breakfast(8); Lunch(8); Dinner(8)
Total Units: 15
Trade Names: McDonald's (15)
Units Franchised From: 15
Preferred Square Footage: 2,500; 3,000
Preferred Location Types: Freestanding
Primary Menu: Hamburger (15)
Areas of Operation: MN
Type of Foodservice: Quick Serve (15)
Franchise Affiliation: McDonald's Corporation, CHICAGO, IL
Primary Distributors: (Full Line) The Martin-Brower Co., FRIDLEY, MN

Key Personnel
VALERIE NETLAND - President; Partner; General Manager; General Buyer
VALERIE JOHNSON - Partner; General Buyer
NANCY STROMBERG - Representative Human Resources

Tomsec Inc.
3746 Sunset Dr
Spring Park, MN 55384-9630

Telephone: (952) 471-8513
Fax Number: (952) 471-8937
Internet Homepage: lordfletchers.com
Type of Business: Chain Restaurant Operator
Year Founded: 1968
Total Sales: $7,637,000 (e)
Alcohol Sales: 30%
Number of Employees: 270
Average Check: Lunch(20); Dinner(42)
Total Units: 3
Trade Names: Lord Fletcher's Dining Room (1); The Oar House (1); The Wharf (1)
Company-Owned Units: 3
Preferred Location Types: Freestanding
Alcohol Served: Beer, Wine, Liquor
Primary Menu: American (2); Steak/Seafood (1)
Areas of Operation: MN
Type of Foodservice: Casual Dining (2); Fine Dining (1)
Catering Services: Yes
Primary Distributors: (Food) US Foods, PLYMOUTH, MN

Key Personnel
WILLIAM O. NAEGELE - Partner
PETER PEYERL - Partner; CFO
TOM EMER - General Manager
THOMAS PIVEC - Executive Chef; General Buyer

Urban Wok
209 4th St E
St Paul, MN 55101

Telephone: (651) 493-4717
Internet Homepage: urbanwokusa.com
Type of Business: Chain Restaurant Operator
Total Sales: $8,297,000 (e)
Total Units: 3
Trade Names: Urban Wok (3)
Company-Owned Units: 3
Primary Menu: Asian (3)
Type of Foodservice: Fast Casual (3)

Key Personnel
MARK TOTH - Founder; CEO

Steve Erhard
10600 10th St W
Waconia, MN 55387

Telephone: (952) 442-6366
Type of Business: Chain Restaurant Operator
Total Sales: $1,794,000 (e)
Total Units: 3
Trade Names: Subway (3)
Units Franchised From: 3
Primary Menu: Sandwiches/Deli (3)
Projected Openings: 1
Areas of Operation: MN
Type of Foodservice: Quick Serve (3)
Franchise Affiliation: Doctor's Associates Inc., MILFORD, CT

Key Personnel
STEVE ERHARD - President; Owner; General Buyer

Cinema Entertainment Corp
1621 Division St
Waite Park, MN 56387-1811

Telephone: (320) 251-9131
Fax Number: (320) 251-1003
Internet Homepage: cectheatres.com
Company Email: comments@cectheatres.com
Type of Business: Foodservice Operations - Movie Theatre
Total Sales: $50,610,000 (e)
Number of Employees: 158
Average Check: Breakfast(5); Lunch(5); Dinner(5)
Internet Order Processing: Yes
Total Units: 20
Trade Names: Cinema Entertainment Corp (20)
Company-Owned Units: 20
Preferred Location Types: Freestanding; Regional Mall; Strip Mall
Primary Menu: Snacks (20)
Areas of Operation: IA, MN, NE, WI
Type of Foodservice: In-Store Feeder (20)
Primary Distributors: (Full Line) SYSCO Food Services of Iowa Inc., ANKENY, IA

Key Personnel
ROB ROSS - President; General Buyer
TONY ROSS - VP Finance
GREG CARTER - VP Operations
AMBER EISENSCHENK - Director Human Resources
ANDY BERGSTROM - Director Information Systems

Letnes Brothers
137 2nd Ave S
Waite Park, MN 56387-1323

Telephone: (320) 259-0589
Fax Number: (320) 259-6070
Internet Homepage: grizzlysgrill.com
Company Email: info@grizzlysgrill.com
Type of Business: Chain Restaurant Operator
Year Founded: 1995
Total Sales: $18,940,000 (e)
Alcohol Sales: 20%
Number of Employees: 720
Average Check: Lunch(10); Dinner(14)
Internet Order Processing: Yes
Total Units: 8
Trade Names: Grizzly's Grill N' Saloon (8)
Company-Owned Units: 8
Preferred Square Footage: 4,500
Preferred Location Types: Freestanding
Alcohol Served: Beer, Wine, Liquor
Primary Menu: American (8)
Areas of Operation: MN, WI
Type of Foodservice: Casual Dining (8)

Key Personnel
STEVE LETNES - CEO; Partner; Director Facility/Maintenance, Supply Chain, Real Estate, Design, Store Fixtures
CURT LETNES - Partner; CFO
BRANDON GUNDERSON - Director Human Resources

Carisch Inc.
681 Lake St E Ste 262
Wayzata, MN 55391-1757

Telephone: (952) 476-5495
Fax Number: (952) 473-8813
Internet Homepage: carischinc.com
Company Email: marqueeplace@carischinc.com
Type of Business: Chain Restaurant Operator
Year Founded: 1978
Total Sales: $114,910,000 (e)
Number of Employees: 1,755
Average Check: Breakfast(5); Lunch(8); Dinner(12)
Total Units: 62
Trade Names: Arby's (62)
Units Franchised From: 62
Preferred Square Footage: 3,000
Preferred Location Types: Community Mall; Freestanding
Primary Menu: Sandwiches/Deli (62)
Projected Openings: 3
Areas of Operation: FL, IA, MN, MT, ND, NE, WI
Type of Foodservice: Quick Serve (62)
Franchise Affiliation: Arby's Restaurant Group, ATLANTA, GA

Key Personnel
FRED STAUBER - President
KENDRA BAKER KRUGMAN - VP Design, Merchandising
LAURA BAUMGARTNER - VP Merchandising, Licensing
MICHELLE GUTHRIE - VP Allocation
BRANDON CLAWSON - Senior Director Real Estate
PAMELA GORDY - Senior Director Sales
MIKE TIBODEAU - Director Information Technology
LORI LIEBERMAN - Director Marketing
PATRICIA MENDELSOHN RYAN - Art Director Brand Marketing
NANCI GEYER - Regional Manager

Crisp & Green
755 East Lake Street STE #120
Wayzata, MN 55391

Telephone: (952) 476-2591
Internet Homepage: crispandgreen.com
Type of Business: Chain Restaurant Operator
Year Founded: 2016
Systemwide Sales: $26,000,000 (e)
Total Sales: $17,450,000 (e)
Total Units: 35
Trade Names: Crisp & Green (35)
Units Franchised To: 35
Primary Menu: Miscellaneous (35)
Areas of Operation: AR, AZ, CO, FL, IA, IL, KS, MN, MO, MT, NC, ND, NE, NY, SD, TN, TX, UT, WI
Type of Foodservice: Fast Casual (35)

Key Personnel
STEELE SMILEY - Founder; Owner
KELLY C. BALTES - CEO

Dough Management Inc.
1617 Highway 12 E
Willmar, MN 56201-5814

Mailing Address: PO Box 795, WILLMAR, MN, 56201

Telephone: (320) 235-8277
Fax Number: (320) 235-7550
Type of Business: Chain Restaurant Operator
Total Sales: $220,666,000 (e)
Number of Employees: 1,437
Total Units: 108
Trade Names: Domino's (108)
Units Franchised From: 108
Preferred Square Footage: 1,000
Primary Menu: Pizza (108)
Areas of Operation: IA, KY, MN, ND, OH, PA, SD, WI, WV
Type of Foodservice: Quick Serve (108)
Franchise Affiliation: Domino's Pizza Inc, ANN ARBOR, MI

Key Personnel
SUSAN GRAVES - President; General Buyer
TACARIE BERMEJO - General Manager
JORDAN SCHON - Director Operations

Jimmy's Pizza Inc.
PO Box 326
Willmar, MN 56201-0326

Telephone: (320) 444-7502
Fax Number: (888) 905-7085
Internet Homepage: jimmyspizza.com
Company Email: info@jimmyspizza.com
Type of Business: Chain Restaurant Operator
Year Founded: 1986
Systemwide Sales: $25,903,000 (e)
Total Sales: $6,421,000 (e)
Number of Employees: 90
Average Check: Lunch(8); Dinner(8)
Total Units: 28
Trade Names: Jimmy's Pizza (28)
Units Franchised To: 28
Preferred Location Types: Freestanding; Strip Mall
Primary Menu: Pizza (28)
Areas of Operation: IA, MN, ND, SD
Type of Foodservice: Quick Serve (28)
Primary Distributors: (Food) Performance Foodservice, RICE, MN

Key Personnel
JANA GORDON - CFO; Director Operations

Morgan Enterprises
1558 W Service Dr
Winona, MN 55987-2540

Telephone: (507) 452-7719
Type of Business: Chain Restaurant Operator
Year Founded: 1983
Total Sales: $92,090,000 (e)
Number of Employees: 80
Average Check: Lunch(8); Dinner(12)
Total Units: 51
Trade Names: KFC (51)

Units Franchised From: 51
Preferred Location Types: Freestanding
Primary Menu: Chicken (51)
Areas of Operation: MN
Type of Foodservice: Quick Serve (51)
Catering Services: Yes
Franchise Affiliation: KFC Corporation, LOUISVILLE, KY
Primary Distributors: (Food) McLane/Sturtevant, STURTEVANT, WI

Key Personnel
JAMES MORGAN - President; CFO
PAUL BANTA - General Manager
KYLE VAN NORMAN - Director Operations, Purchasing, Marketing, Catering
CHASE MORGAN - Director
LANCE MORGAN - Director

Broadway Station Restaurants Inc.
1818 Wooddale Dr Ste 202
Woodbury, MN 55125-2983

Telephone: (651) 731-0800
Fax Number: (651) 731-9609
Internet Homepage: broadwaypizza.com
Company Email: bpoffice@broadwaypizza.com
Type of Business: Chain Restaurant Operator
Year Founded: 1960
Systemwide Sales: $17,687,000 (e)
Total Sales: $8,402,000 (e)
Alcohol Sales: 20%
Number of Employees: 200
Average Check: Lunch(14); Dinner(34)
Internet Order Processing: Yes
Internet Sales: 1.00%
Total Units: 14
Trade Names: Broadway Bar& Pizza (14)
Company-Owned Units: 3
Units Franchised To: 11
Preferred Square Footage: 4,000
Preferred Location Types: Freestanding; Strip Mall
Alcohol Served: Beer, Wine, Liquor
Primary Menu: Pizza (14)
Areas of Operation: MN
Type of Foodservice: Casual Dining (14)
Primary Distributors: (Full Line) Reinhart FoodService LLC, CHICAGO, IL

Key Personnel
JIM KRUIZENGA - President; Director Facility/Maintenance, Information Systems, Design
RANDALL J. WINGER - CFO; VP Finance, Operations, Purchasing, Supply Chain, Real Estate, Human Resources, Store Fixtures; Executive Chef

Zantigo Franchising Corporation
680 Commerce Dr Ste 170
Woodbury, MN 55125-4503

Telephone: (651) 578-7435
Fax Number: (651) 578-0212
Internet Homepage: zantigo.com
Company Email: feedback@zantigo.com
Type of Business: Chain Restaurant Operator
Year Founded: 2000
Systemwide Sales: $13,030,000 (e)
Total Sales: $4,886,000 (e)
Number of Employees: 56
Average Check: Lunch(6); Dinner(6)
Total Units: 4
Trade Names: Zantigo (4)
Company-Owned Units: 4
Preferred Square Footage: 2,000
Preferred Location Types: Freestanding; Strip Mall
Primary Menu: Mexican (4)
Areas of Operation: MN
Type of Foodservice: Fast Casual (4)
Catering Services: Yes
Primary Distributors: (Full Line) Reinhart FoodService, MARSHALL, MN

Key Personnel
DON KAELBLE - Partner; General Buyer
KEVIN KAELBLE - Partner; Executive Chef
TERRY TUCKER - Controller

MISSOURI

Fortel's Pizza Den
7932 MacKenzie Rd
Affton, MO 63123-2721

Telephone: (314) 353-2360
Fax Number: (314) 353-1522
Internet Homepage: fortelspizzaden.com
Company Email: info@fortelspizzaden.com
Type of Business: Chain Restaurant Operator
Year Founded: 1981
Systemwide Sales: $4,100,000 (e)
Total Sales: $1,229,000 (e)
Alcohol Sales: 3%
Number of Employees: 24
Average Check: Lunch(10); Dinner(14)
Total Units: 2
Trade Names: Fortel's Pizza Den (2)
Company-Owned Units: 2
Preferred Square Footage: 2,000
Preferred Location Types: Freestanding; Strip Mall
Alcohol Served: Beer, Wine
Primary Menu: Pizza (2)
Areas of Operation: MO
Type of Foodservice: Casual Dining (2)

Primary Distributors: (Full Line) US Foods, SALEM, MO

Key Personnel
JAN FORTEL - President
SHELLY FORTEL - VP; Director Operations; Manager Finance, Purchasing, Facility/Maintenance, Information Systems, Supply Chain, Ethnic Marketing, Real Estate, Design, Store Fixtures, Menu Development

Ro Jo Foods LLC
903 NW 12th Ave
Ava, MO 65608

Mailing Address: P O Box 918, ROGERSVILLE, MO, 65742
Telephone: (417) 683-4009
Fax Number: (877) 744-4054
Internet Homepage: rojofoods.com
Company Email: rojofoods@gmail.com
Type of Business: Chain Restaurant Operator
Systemwide Sales: $6,755,000 (e)
Total Sales: $7,546,000 (e)
Average Check: Dinner(12)
Total Units: 4
Trade Names: KFC (1); KFC/Taco Bell (1); Taco Bell (2)
Units Franchised From: 4
Preferred Location Types: Freestanding
Primary Menu: Chicken (2); Mexican (3)
Areas of Operation: MO
Type of Foodservice: Quick Serve (4)
Franchise Affiliation: KFC Corporation, LOUISVILLE, KY; Taco Bell Corp., IRVINE, CA

Key Personnel
ROGER KJAR - Owner; General Buyer

Keyser Enterprises, Inc.
1223 Dunloe Rd
Ballwin, MO 63021-5661

Telephone: (618) 201-1120
Type of Business: Chain Restaurant Operator
Total Sales: $3,117,000 (e)
Total Units: 5
Trade Names: Little Caesars Pizza (5)
Units Franchised From: 5
Primary Menu: Pizza (5)
Projected Openings: 1
Areas of Operation: IL, KY, MO
Type of Foodservice: Quick Serve (5)
Franchise Affiliation: Little Caesar Enterprises Inc., DETROIT, MI

Key Personnel
CHARLES KEYSER - Partner; General Buyer
JESSE KEYSER - Partner; General Buyer

Domino's Franchisee
700 E North Ave
Belton, MO 64012

Telephone: (816) 331-5100
Type of Business: Chain Restaurant Operator
Total Sales: $5,965,000 (e)
Total Units: 3
Trade Names: Domino's (3)
Units Franchised From: 3
Primary Menu: Pizza (3)
Areas of Operation: MO
Type of Foodservice: Quick Serve (3)
Franchise Affiliation: Domino's Pizza Inc, ANN ARBOR, MI

Key Personnel
JAMIE PAULSON - Owner; General Buyer

Hawaiian Bros Island Grill
1112 E North Ave
Belton, MO 64012

Telephone: (816) 425-4437
Internet Homepage: hawaiianbros.com
Type of Business: Chain Restaurant Operator
Total Sales: $13,310,000 (e)
Total Units: 31
Trade Names: Hawaiian Bros Island Grill (31)
Company-Owned Units: 31
Primary Menu: Chicken (31)
Type of Foodservice: Casual Dining (31)

Key Personnel
TYLER MCNIE - Partner
CAMERON MCNIE - Partner
BRECK TEMPLETON - CFO
CAREY MALLOY - Chief Development Officer
LEE PATTERSON - Senior VP Technology, Customer Service
AMY HOWARTER - VP Marketing
JOHN MCDERMOT - Executive Director Information Systems
RANDY WEBB - Executive Director Culinary Operations
AARON BOWEN - Executive Director People
DANIEL HILL - Executive Director Operations
VERNON BLAZEK - Director Facility/Maintenance
MIKE CASTILLA - Director Training
KAYLEA FORD - Senior Manager Field Marketing
TIMOTHY MCGUIRE - Manager Operations

Summit Restaurant Group, LLC
600 NW Mock Ave
Blue Springs, MO 64014-2412

Telephone: (816) 224-3336
Fax Number: (816) 224-2174
Internet Homepage: summitrestaurants.com
Company Email: jburleson@srg.email
Type of Business: Chain Restaurant Operator
Total Sales: $19,530,000 (e)
Average Check: Dinner(12)
Total Units: 123
Trade Names: Long John Silver's (12); Pizza Hut (111)
Units Franchised From: 123
Preferred Square Footage: 2,500; 3,200
Preferred Location Types: Downtown; Freestanding; Strip Mall
Alcohol Served: Beer, Wine
Primary Menu: Pizza (111); Seafood (12)
Areas of Operation: AR, CA, IL, KS, MO, OK, TX
Type of Foodservice: Quick Serve (123)
Franchise Affiliation: Long John Silver's Inc., LOUISVILLE, KY

Key Personnel
JOE LANGTEAU - CEO; President
TOM JORGENSON - President; General Buyer
IAN ALLEN - VP; General Counsel
ROGER GOOS - Director Marketing
RICK ZIEGELBEIN - Director

Zarda Bar-B-Q & Catering Co.
613 SE Central Dr
Blue Springs, MO 64014-3311

Telephone: (816) 229-3670
Internet Homepage: zarda.com
Company Email: info@zarda.com
Type of Business: Chain Restaurant Operator
Year Founded: 1976
Total Sales: $14,062,000 (e)
Alcohol Sales: 10%
Number of Employees: 140
Average Check: Lunch(12); Dinner(12)
Internet Sales: 10.00%
Total Units: 2
Trade Names: Zarda Bar-B-Q & Catering Co. (2)
Company-Owned Units: 2
Preferred Location Types: Freestanding
Alcohol Served: Beer
Primary Menu: Bar-B-Q (2)
Areas of Operation: KS, MO
Type of Foodservice: Casual Dining (2)
Catering Services: Yes
Primary Distributors: (Food) Reinhart

FoodService, LEES SUMMIT, MO

Key Personnel
MIKE ZARDA - Partner; General Manager Catering; Executive Chef Catering; Director Catering
STEVE ZARDA - Partner; General Buyer
TERRY HYER - COO
DAVID DILL - Controller
SUZANNE ZARDA - General Manager
DAVID SCHWIRTZ - Director Business Development

Excel Investments
215 W Chestnut St
Bolivar, MO 65613-1540

Mailing Address: PO Box 333, BOLIVAR, MO, 65613-0333
Telephone: (417) 326-8735
Fax Number: (417) 326-8977
Internet Homepage: excelsdigroup.com
Company Email: info@excelsdigroup.com
Type of Business: Chain Restaurant Operator
Year Founded: 1985
Total Sales: $40,360,000 (e)
Number of Employees: 1,200
Average Check: Breakfast(8); Lunch(10); Dinner(10)
Total Units: 19
Trade Names: Sonic America's Drive-In (19)
Units Franchised From: 19
Preferred Square Footage: 1,200
Preferred Location Types: Freestanding
Primary Menu: Hamburger (19)
Areas of Operation: AR, MO
Type of Foodservice: Quick Serve (19)
Franchise Affiliation: Sonic Corp., OKLAHOMA CITY, OK
Primary Distributors: (Full Line) Reinhart FoodService, LEES SUMMIT, MO

Key Personnel
BRENT JOHNSON - President; Director Finance, Operations, Supply Chain, Real Estate, Food Safety; General Buyer
GERMAN URIBE - President
STACIE JOHNSON - Manager Information Systems, Risk Management, Human Resources
JUDY SAVAGE - Manager

Fogle Enterprises
3460 W 76 Country Blvd
Branson, MO 65616-3546

Telephone: (417) 334-0754
Fax Number: (417) 335-6664
Internet Homepage: bransonsbestrestaurant.com
Company Email: bransonsbestrestaurant@gmail.com
Type of Business: Chain Restaurant Operator
Year Founded: 1992
Total Sales: $8,677,000 (e)
Number of Employees: 80
Average Check: Breakfast(8); Lunch(10); Dinner(16)
Total Units: 6
Trade Names: Burger Shack (1); Ci Ci's Pizza (1); Fall Creek Steak and Catfish House (1); Pasghetti's (1); The Great American Steak & Chicken House (1); WhipperSnappers (1)
Company-Owned Units: 6
Preferred Square Footage: 6,200
Preferred Location Types: Freestanding
Alcohol Served: Beer, Wine, Liquor
Primary Menu: American (1); Hamburger (1); Italian (1); Pizza (1); Seafood (1); Steak/Seafood (1)
Areas of Operation: MO
Type of Foodservice: Casual Dining (5); Family Restaurant (1)
Primary Distributors: (Full Line) SYSCO Food Services of St. Louis LLC, SAINT CHARLES, MO

Key Personnel
NOLAN FOGLE - President; General Manager; Executive Chef; General Buyer
JEFF HURSHMAN - Director Operations
NICOLLE WARNER - Director Marketing

ITEC Attractions Inc.
3562 Shepherd of the Hills Expy
Branson, MO 65616-8107

Telephone: (417) 335-3533
Fax Number: (417) 336-5348
Internet Homepage: bransonimax.com
Type of Business: Foodservice Operations - Movie Theatre
Total Sales: $10,492,000 (e)
Average Check: Breakfast(8); Lunch(8); Dinner(8)
Total Units: 3
Trade Names: Florentina's Ristorante Italiano (1); McFarlain's Family Restaurant (1); Montana Mike's Steakhouse (1)
Company-Owned Units: 3
Preferred Location Types: Freestanding; Other
Alcohol Served: Beer, Wine, Liquor
Primary Menu: American (1); Italian (1); Steak (1)
Areas of Operation: MO
Type of Foodservice: Casual Dining (3)
Notes: The company derives approximately 61% of its revenue from theater, mall and retail operations; foodservice sales do not include revenue from theater concessions.

Key Personnel
PAUL M. BLUTO - Chairman; CEO; CFO; Executive Chef
STEVE BLUTO - VP Administration
DEBBY BLACK - VP Division
GAYLE PITMAN - VP Retail Operations
TOM FORSTER - Director Marketing

Show Me Bread Inc.
PO Box 109
Camdenton, MO 65020-0109

Telephone: (573) 346-1577
Type of Business: Chain Restaurant Operator
Total Sales: $32,400,000 (e)
Number of Employees: 450
Average Check: Lunch(6); Dinner(6)
Total Units: 11
Trade Names: Andy's Frozen Custard (7); Panera Bread (4)
Company-Owned Units: 11
Preferred Square Footage: 3,200
Preferred Location Types: Freestanding
Primary Menu: American (4); Snacks (7)
Areas of Operation: MO, NC
Type of Foodservice: Casual Dining (4); Quick Serve (7)
Franchise Affiliation: Panera Bread Company, SAINT LOUIS, MO
Primary Distributors: (Full Line) US Foods, CHARLOTTE, NC

Key Personnel
GREG ANDERSON - Owner; General Buyer
CHRIS LUCAS - General Manager
DALE SALINAS - Director Operations
CAROLYN HANDTKE - Director Marketing
JOHN BARTLETT - Manager Operations

Fifty Seven Corporation
310 N Kingshighway St
Cape Girardeau, MO 63701-4332

Telephone: (573) 334-8444
Type of Business: Chain Restaurant Operator
Total Sales: $2,880,000 (e)
Total Units: 5
Trade Names: Little Caesars Pizza (5)
Units Franchised From: 5
Preferred Location Types: Freestanding; Strip Mall
Primary Menu: Pizza (5)
Areas of Operation: MO
Type of Foodservice: Quick Serve (5)
Franchise Affiliation: Little Caesar Enterprises Inc., DETROIT, MI

Key Personnel
JORDAN WEISS - Partner; General Buyer
JARED WEISE - Partner; General Buyer

Lynn Enterprises Inc
1028 N Sprigg St Ste 101
Cape Girardeau, MO 63701-4832

Telephone: (573) 651-4275
Fax Number: (573) 651-3763
Type of Business: Chain Restaurant Operator
Total Sales: $6,180,000 (e)
Total Units: 3
Trade Names: Domino's (3)
Units Franchised From: 3
Primary Menu: Pizza (3)
Areas of Operation: MO
Type of Foodservice: Quick Serve (3)
Franchise Affiliation: Domino's Pizza Inc, ANN ARBOR, MI

Key Personnel
DANNY F. LYNN - President; General Buyer

Midamerica Hotels Corporation
105 S Mount Auburn Rd
Cape Girardeau, MO 63703-4915

Telephone: (573) 334-0546
Fax Number: (573) 334-3567
Internet Homepage: midamcorp.com
Company Email: info@midamcorp.com
Type of Business: Chain Restaurant Operator
Total Sales: $89,190,000 (e)
Number of Employees: 1,766
Total Units: 38
Trade Names: Burger King (35); Popeyes (3)
Units Franchised From: 38
Preferred Square Footage: 2,500
Primary Menu: Chicken (3); Hamburger (35)
Areas of Operation: AR, IL, KY, MO, TN
Type of Foodservice: Quick Serve (38)
Franchise Affiliation: Burger King Worldwide Inc., MIAMI, FL

Key Personnel
DAN DRURY - President; General Buyer
DIANE DRURY - VP
LARRY HUBER - VP Finance
MINDY CROWLEY - Director Human Resources
SHAWN LOWERY - Manager Information Technology
JERI HOLCOMB - Manager Design

YPYKA Inc
429 N Broadview St
Cape Girardeau, MO 63701-4309

Telephone: (573) 334-7311
Fax Number: (573) 334-1439
Type of Business: Chain Restaurant Operator
Total Sales: $55,920,000 (e)
Total Units: 12
Trade Names: McDonald's (12)
Units Franchised From: 12
Preferred Location Types: Freestanding
Primary Menu: Hamburger (12)
Areas of Operation: MO
Type of Foodservice: Quick Serve (12)
Franchise Affiliation: McDonald's Corporation, CHICAGO, IL

Key Personnel
SHANNON DAVIS - President; General Buyer

Bandanas MO LLC
16141 Swingley Ridge Rd Ste 205
Chesterfield, MO 63017-1780

Telephone: (636) 537-8200
Fax Number: (636) 537-8444
Internet Homepage: bandanasbbq.com
Company Email: info@bandanasbbq.com
Type of Business: Chain Restaurant Operator
Year Founded: 1996
Systemwide Sales: $36,182,000 (e)
Total Sales: $30,060,000 (e)
Alcohol Sales: 8%
Number of Employees: 750
Average Check: Lunch(10); Dinner(10)
Internet Order Processing: Yes
Internet Sales: 5.00%
Total Units: 28
Trade Names: Bandana's Bar-B-Q (28)
Company-Owned Units: 23
Units Franchised To: 5
Preferred Square Footage: 5,000; 5,500
Preferred Location Types: Freestanding; Strip Mall
Alcohol Served: Beer, Wine, Liquor
Primary Menu: Bar-B-Q (28)
Areas of Operation: IA, IL, IN, MO
Type of Foodservice: Casual Dining (28)
Catering Services: Yes
Primary Distributors: (Food) Kuna Foodservice Co., DUPO, IL
Notes: The company derives approximately 24% of its revenue from catering operations.

Key Personnel
RICK WHITE - CEO; Owner; Director Operations, Facility/Maintenance, Information Systems, Risk Management, Marketing, Human Resources, Menu Development, Food Safety; General Buyer
LYNNETTE LEMKE - CFO
TERRIE SCHOENHOFF - Manager Human Resources

Central Missouri Pizza Inc.
201 Chesterfield Business Pkwy
Chesterfield, MO 63005-1241

Telephone: (636) 537-1120
Fax Number: (636) 537-1265
Type of Business: Chain Restaurant Operator
Year Founded: 1981
Total Sales: $63,632,000 (e)
Number of Employees: 610
Average Check: Lunch(8); Dinner(8)
Total Units: 32
Trade Names: Domino's (32)
Units Franchised From: 32
Preferred Square Footage: 3,000
Preferred Location Types: Freestanding; Strip Mall
Primary Menu: Pizza (32)
Projected Openings: 3
Areas of Operation: KY, MO
Type of Foodservice: Quick Serve (32)
Franchise Affiliation: Domino's Pizza Inc, ANN ARBOR, MI
Primary Distributors: (Full Line) Domino's Distribution Center, DENVER, CO

Key Personnel
GREG NEICHTER - President; Director Facility/Maintenance, Information Systems, Supply Chain, Real Estate; General Buyer
EILEEN SOKOLOWSKI - VP Marketing
JOHN NEICHTER - Director Operations, Purchasing

Opaa Food Management Inc.
16401 Swingley Ridge Rd Ste 600
Chesterfield, MO 63017

Telephone: (636) 812-0777
Fax Number: (636) 812-0100
Internet Homepage: opaafood.com
Company Email: sales@opaafood.com
Type of Business: Foodservice Management Operator
Year Founded: 1978
Total Sales: $21,720,000 (e)
Number of Employees: 750
Number of Locations Served: 155
Total Foodservice Mgmt Accounts: 150
Areas of Operation: KS, MO
Type of Foodservice: Cafeteria (150)
Foodservice Management Venues: Schools
Primary Distributors: (Full Line) US Foods, SALEM, MO

Key Personnel
KEVIN SHORT - CEO; President; General Buyer
ANDREW CONDIE - CEO
BECKY GLIMKA - Area Director Operations

ROBERT VICIN - Regional Director

Crushed Red
8007 Maryland Ave
Clayton, MO 63105-3717

Telephone: (314) 725-8007
Fax Number: (314) 725-0982
Internet Homepage: crushed-red.com
Company Email: info@crushed-red.com
Type of Business: Chain Restaurant Operator
Year Founded: 2012
Average Check: Lunch(8); Dinner(14)
Total Units: 8
Trade Names: Crushed Red Urban Bake and Chop Shop (8)
Company-Owned Units: 3
Units Franchised To: 5
Alcohol Served: Beer, Wine
Primary Menu: Pizza (8)
Projected Openings: 5
Areas of Operation: CO, IL, KS, MO, OK
Type of Foodservice: Fast Casual (8)

Key Personnel
CHRIS LAROCCA - Co-Founder; Partner

Niche Food Group
7734 Forsyth Blvd
Clayton, MO 63105-1810

Telephone: (314) 773-7755
Internet Homepage: pastariastl.com; tastebarstl; brasseriebyniche.com; nichestlouis.com; poranopasta.com
Company Email: info@nichestlouis.com
Type of Business: Chain Restaurant Operator
Total Units: 6
Trade Names: Brasserie By Niche (1); Pastaria (2); Porano by Pastaria (1); Sardella (1); Taste (1)
Company-Owned Units: 6
Primary Menu: American (1), French/Continental (1); Italian (4)
Areas of Operation: MO
Type of Foodservice: Casual Dining (5); Fast Casual (1)

Key Personnel
GERARD CRAFT - Owner

C & W LLC
2000 Forum Blvd Ste 4
Columbia, MO 65203-5460

Telephone: (573) 445-0015
Fax Number: (573) 446-2236
Type of Business: Chain Restaurant Operator
Total Sales: $29,500,000 (e)
Total Units: 35
Trade Names: Five Guys Burgers and Fries (4); Moe's Southwest Grill (2); Subway (29)
Units Franchised From: 35
Primary Menu: Hamburger (4); Mexican (2); Sandwiches/Deli (29)
Areas of Operation: MO
Type of Foodservice: Casual Dining (2); Fast Casual (4); Quick Serve (29)
Franchise Affiliation: Doctor's Associates Inc., MILFORD, CT

Key Personnel
JEFF OFFUTT - Owner

Dunafon Enterprises Inc.
1431 Cinnamon Hill Ln Ste 201
Columbia, MO 65201-7638

Telephone: (573) 442-8373
Fax Number: (573) 875-0019
Type of Business: Chain Restaurant Operator
Year Founded: 1985
Total Sales: $66,190,000 (e)
Number of Employees: 525
Average Check: Lunch(8); Dinner(8)
Total Units: 24
Trade Names: Taco Bell (24)
Units Franchised From: 24
Preferred Square Footage: 2,500
Preferred Location Types: Freestanding; Institution (college/hospital); Regional Mall
Primary Menu: Taco (24)
Projected Openings: 2
Areas of Operation: MN, MO, ND, SD
Type of Foodservice: Quick Serve (24)
Franchise Affiliation: Taco Bell Corp., IRVINE, CA
Primary Distributors: (Full Line) McLane/Hebron, HEBRON, KY

Key Personnel
CAMERON DUNAFON - President; Manager Operations, Facility/Maintenance, Risk Management, Supply Chain, Human Resources, Store Fixtures, Food Safety; General Buyer

Fresh Ideas Food Service Management LLC
1000 W Nifong Blvd Ste 3-220
Columbia, MO 65203-5609

Telephone: (573) 445-4321
Fax Number: (573) 445-2799
Internet Homepage: freshideasfood.com
Company Email: info@freshideasfood.com/
Type of Business: Foodservice Management Operator
Year Founded: 1999
Total Sales: $7,386,000 (e)
Number of Employees: 55
Number of Locations Served: 215
Total Foodservice Mgmt Accounts: 15
Areas of Operation: MO
Type of Foodservice: Cafeteria
Foodservice Management Venues: Business & Industry; College & University; Health Care; Other; Schools

Key Personnel
JOHN ORSCHELN - CEO; Partner
DENNIS OWENS - President; Partner
MATTHEW CLERVI - Partner; VP; Controller; Director Finance, Operations, Purchasing, Information Systems
RACHEL KLOSTERMAN - Director Restaurant Operations
MELISSA STROTHER - Director Human Resources
SHANA WOODY - Manager Catering
TAMMY BURTON - Manager Human Resources
MARIA SCRUGGS - Manager Accounting

Shakespeare's Pizza
225 S 9th St
Columbia, MO 65201-4817

Telephone: (573) 449-2454
Internet Homepage: shakespeares.com
Type of Business: Chain Restaurant Operator
Year Founded: 1973
Total Sales: $3,464,000 (e)
Alcohol Sales: 5%
Number of Employees: 93
Average Check: Lunch(8); Dinner(5)
Internet Order Processing: Yes
Internet Sales: 1.00%
Total Units: 3
Trade Names: Shakespeare's Pizza (3)
Company-Owned Units: 3
Preferred Location Types: Freestanding
Alcohol Served: Beer, Wine, Liquor
Primary Menu: Pizza (3)
Areas of Operation: MO
Type of Foodservice: Casual Dining (3)
Catering Services: Yes
Primary Distributors: (Food) SYSCO Food Services of Kansas City Inc., OLATHE, KS

Key Personnel
NANCY LEWIS - Owner; General Buyer
KURT MIRTSCHING - General Manager
TOBIAS EPSTEIN - General Manager
CLAIRE BUTTICE - Director Sales

Michael Del Pietro Restaurant Group
10419 Clayton Rd
Frontenac, MO 63131-2909

Telephone: (314) 569-0400
Fax Number: (314) 725-6631
Internet Homepage: mdprestaurants.com
Type of Business: Chain Restaurant Operator
Total Sales: $3,069,000 (e)
Alcohol Sales: 5%
Average Check: Dinner(20)
Total Units: 7
Trade Names: Babbo's Spaghetteria (2); Il Palato (1); Sugo's Spaghetteria (2); Tavolo V (1); Via Vino Enoteca (1)
Company-Owned Units: 7
Alcohol Served: Beer, Wine, Liquor
Primary Menu: Italian (7)
Areas of Operation: IL, KS, MO
Type of Foodservice: Casual Dining (7)
Catering Services: Yes

Key Personnel
MICHAEL DEL PIETRO - Owner; Executive Chef; General Buyer

B&B Theatres
2700 NE Kendallwood Pkwy Ste 106
Gladstone, MO 64119-2081

Mailing Address: PO Box 129, LIBERTY, MO, 64069-0129
Telephone: (816) 407-7469
Fax Number: (816) 407-9805
Internet Homepage: bbtheatres.com
Company Email: comments@bbtheatres.com
Type of Business: Foodservice Operations - Movie Theatre
Year Founded: 1924
Total Sales: $127,970,000 (e)
Number of Employees: 1,318
Average Check: Lunch(6); Dinner(6)
Internet Order Processing: Yes
Total Units: 53
Trade Names: B & B Movie Co. (53)
Company-Owned Units: 53
Preferred Square Footage: 25,000
Preferred Location Types: Downtown; Freestanding; Regional Mall; Strip Mall
Primary Menu: Snacks (53)
Areas of Operation: KS, MO, OK
Type of Foodservice: In-Store Feeder (53)
Primary Distributors: (Food) Regal Distributing Co., LENEXA, KS
Notes: The company derives approximately 72% of its revenue from theater admissions, on-screen advertising, & other sales.

Key Personnel
BROCK BAGBY - President Media
BRIDGET BAGBY - Partner
MICHAEL HAGAN - CIO; VP Finance
BOBBIE BAGBY - VP Marketing
PAUL FARNSWORTH - Executive Director
ROBERT SWEARINGIN - Executive Director Technology
DAN VAN ORDEN - General Manager; General Buyer
BRETT ZORNES - General Manager
CHRIS TICKNER - Director Marketing
ANGELA FISHER - Director Media
JESSE BAKER - Director Design
CHAD CHRISTOPHER - Director
GINA LIBERTY - Director Accounting
ALYSSA MCMANUS - Director
HALEIGH OETTING - Director Social Media

Jim Wagy's Management Co.
5950 N Oak Trfy Ste 204
Gladstone, MO 64118-5164

Telephone: (816) 455-0800
Type of Business: Chain Restaurant Operator
Year Founded: 2001
Total Sales: $37,200,000 (e)
Number of Employees: 350
Average Check: Breakfast(8); Lunch(8); Dinner(8)
Total Units: 8
Trade Names: McDonald's (8)
Units Franchised From: 8
Preferred Square Footage: 2,500; 3,000
Preferred Location Types: Freestanding
Primary Menu: Hamburger (8)
Areas of Operation: MO
Type of Foodservice: Quick Serve (8)
Franchise Affiliation: McDonald's Corporation, CHICAGO, IL
Primary Distributors: (Full Line) Earp Distribution, EDWARDSVILLE, KS

Key Personnel
JIM WAGY - Owner; General Manager; Director Finance, Operations, Facility/Maintenance, Supply Chain, Real Estate; General Buyer
JAN BRANSON - Manager Administration, Information Systems, Human Resources

Yano Management
5907 High Grove Rd
Grandview, MO 64030-2670

Telephone: (816) 765-1887
Fax Number: (816) 765-2890
Company Email: mcyanomanagement@hotmail.com
Type of Business: Chain Restaurant Operator
Total Sales: $62,640,000 (e)
Total Units: 13
Trade Names: McDonald's (13)
Units Franchised From: 13
Preferred Square Footage: 2,500
Primary Menu: Hamburger (12)
Areas of Operation: KS, MO
Type of Foodservice: Quick Serve (12)
Franchise Affiliation: McDonald's Corporation, CHICAGO, IL

Key Personnel
TAKASHI YANO - President; General Buyer
JEANETTE STEADMAN - Manager Administration

Tiger Pride LLC
201 N 3rd St Ste 205
Hannibal, MO 63401-3548

Telephone: (573) 406-3106
Type of Business: Chain Restaurant Operator
Total Sales: $24,030,000 (e)
Total Units: 5
Trade Names: McDonald's (5)
Units Franchised From: 5
Preferred Location Types: Convenience Store/Gas Station; Freestanding
Primary Menu: Hamburger (5)
Areas of Operation: MO
Type of Foodservice: Quick Serve (5)
Franchise Affiliation: McDonald's Corporation, CHICAGO, IL

Key Personnel
BOB GILSTRAP - Owner; General Buyer

Pizza Works Inc.
140 W Simon Blvd
Holts Summit, MO 65043

Mailing Address: PO Box 205, HOLTS SUMMIT, MO, 65043-0205
Telephone: (573) 896-5153
Type of Business: Chain Restaurant Operator
Year Founded: 1978
Total Sales: $1,314,000 (e)
Alcohol Sales: 5%
Number of Employees: 40
Average Check: Lunch(10); Dinner(10)
Total Units: 2
Trade Names: Pizza Works (2)
Company-Owned Units: 2
Preferred Square Footage: 2,000
Preferred Location Types: Freestanding
Alcohol Served: Beer
Primary Menu: Pizza (2)
Areas of Operation: MO
Type of Foodservice: Quick Serve (2)
Primary Distributors: (Full Line) SYSCO Food Services of St. Louis LLC, SAINT CHARLES, MO

2025 Chain Restaurant Operators

Key Personnel
KEN CASTAGNO - President; Controller; Executive Chef; Director Operations, Purchasing, Marketing, Human Resources; General Buyer

D & D Pizza Inc
318 E Main St Ste D
Jackson, MO 63755-1462

Telephone: (573) 243-1474
Fax Number: (573) 243-1790
Type of Business: Chain Restaurant Operator
Total Sales: $8,288,000 (e)
Total Units: 4
Trade Names: Domino's (4)
Units Franchised From: 4
Primary Menu: Pizza (4)
Areas of Operation: MO
Type of Foodservice: Quick Serve (4)
Franchise Affiliation: Domino's Pizza Inc, ANN ARBOR, MI

Key Personnel
DAVID BUMPUS - President; General Buyer

B & R Food Service
219 E Dunklin St Ste B
Jefferson City, MO 65101-3167

Telephone: (573) 635-4844
Fax Number: (573) 635-3881
Type of Business: Chain Restaurant Operator
Total Sales: $56,850,000 (e)
Total Units: 12
Trade Names: McDonald's (12)
Units Franchised From: 12
Preferred Location Types: Freestanding
Primary Menu: Hamburger (12)
Areas of Operation: MO
Type of Foodservice: Quick Serve (12)
Franchise Affiliation: McDonald's Corporation, CHICAGO, IL

Key Personnel
DAVID RUPRECHT - President; General Buyer

Roman's Road Pizza Inc.
8120 N Gretlein Rd
Jefferson City, MO 65101-9492

Telephone: (573) 496-5470
Type of Business: Chain Restaurant Operator
Total Sales: $10,096,000 (e)
Number of Employees: 65
Average Check: Lunch(14); Dinner(14)
Total Units: 5
Trade Names: Domino's (5)
Units Franchised From: 5

Preferred Square Footage: 1,000
Primary Menu: Pizza (5)
Areas of Operation: MO
Type of Foodservice: Quick Serve (5)
Franchise Affiliation: Domino's Pizza Inc, ANN ARBOR, MI

Key Personnel
BOB BLACK - President; General Manager; General Buyer

Domino's Franchisee
2316 S Maiden Ln
Joplin, MO 64804-0369

Telephone: (417) 623-5211
Type of Business: Chain Restaurant Operator
Total Sales: $14,066,000 (e)
Total Units: 7
Trade Names: Domino's (7)
Units Franchised From: 7
Primary Menu: Pizza (7)
Areas of Operation: KS, MO, OK
Type of Foodservice: Quick Serve (7)
Franchise Affiliation: Domino's Pizza Inc, ANN ARBOR, MI

Key Personnel
EMILY E. ELWELL - Owner; General Buyer

Nichols Management Inc
5113 Dutch Elm Dr
Joplin, MO 64804-8904

Telephone: (417) 623-1150
Fax Number: (417) 623-6916
Type of Business: Chain Restaurant Operator
Total Sales: $104,870,000 (e)
Total Units: 22
Trade Names: McDonald's (22)
Units Franchised From: 22
Preferred Square Footage: 2,500
Primary Menu: Hamburger (22)
Areas of Operation: MO
Type of Foodservice: Quick Serve (22)
Franchise Affiliation: McDonald's Corporation, CHICAGO, IL

Key Personnel
GLEN NICHOLS - Owner; General Buyer

Anderson Restaurant Group
30 W Pershing Rd Ste 370
Kansas City, MO 64108-2400

Telephone: (816) 842-8718
Fax Number: (816) 221-4478
Internet Homepage: herefordhouse.com; pierponts.com
Company Email: jsmith@herefordhouse.com
Type of Business: Chain Restaurant Operator
Year Founded: 1957
Total Sales: $26,030,000 (e)
Alcohol Sales: 25%
Number of Employees: 400
Average Check: Lunch(24); Dinner(48)
Internet Order Processing: Yes
Internet Sales: 2.00%
Total Units: 5
Trade Names: Hereford House (4); Pierponts (1)
Company-Owned Units: 5
Preferred Square Footage: 2,500; 3,000
Preferred Location Types: Freestanding; Lifestyle Center
Alcohol Served: Beer, Wine, Liquor
Primary Menu: Steak/Seafood (5)
Areas of Operation: KS, MO
Type of Foodservice: Casual Dining (4); Fine Dining (1)
Catering Services: Yes

Key Personnel
CAMELLIA ANDERSON - Owner
CAROL BENJAMIN - Director Human Resources
ROBBIE MCGOWAN - Director Catering
STACI PENA - Manager Payroll
GABRIEL JOBE - Manager Catering

Andre Bollier Ltd.
5018 Main St
Kansas City, MO 64112-2755

Telephone: (816) 561-3440
Fax Number: (816) 561-2922
Internet Homepage: andreschocolates.com
Company Email: customer_service@andreschocolates.com
Type of Business: Chain Restaurant Operator
Year Founded: 1955
Systemwide Sales: $8,583,000 (e)
Total Sales: $2,048,000 (e)
Number of Employees: 50
Average Check: Breakfast(6); Lunch(18);
Internet Order Processing: Yes
Internet Sales: 10.00%
Total Units: 2
Trade Names: Andre's Confiserie Suisse (2)
Company-Owned Units: 1
Units Franchised To: 1
Preferred Location Types: Freestanding; Strip Mall
Primary Menu: Miscellaneous (2)
Areas of Operation: KS, MO
Type of Foodservice: Family Restaurant (2)
Primary Distributors: (Full Line) SYSCO Food Services of St. Louis LLC, SAINT CHARLES, MO

Key Personnel
MARCEL BOLLIER - Chairman; Manager

Information Systems, Loss Prevention, Real Estate
RENE BOLLIER - President; General Buyer
CONNIE BOLLIER - VP

Applebee's Services Inc.
8140 Ward Pkwy
Kansas City, MO 64114-2029

Telephone: (913) 890-0100
Internet Homepage: applebees.com
Company Email: franchise.information@applebees.com
Type of Business: Chain Restaurant Operator
Year Founded: 1986
Systemwide Sales: $6,157,332,000 (e)
Publicly Held: Yes
Total Sales: $200,431,000 (e)
Alcohol Sales: 13%
Number of Employees: 105,000
Average Check: Lunch(12); Dinner(18)
Internet Order Processing: Yes
Internet Sales: 0.50%
Total Units: 1,642
Trade Names: Applebee's Neighborhood Grill & Bar (1,642)
Units Franchised To: 1,642
Preferred Square Footage: 3,600; 4,300; 4,700; 5,000
Preferred Location Types: Airports; Community Mall; Downtown; Freestanding; Mobile Unit; Regional Mall; Strip Mall
Alcohol Served: Beer, Wine, Liquor
Primary Menu: American (1,642)
Projected Openings: 3
Areas of Operation: AK, AL, AR, AZ, CA, CO, CT, DE, FL, GA, HI, IA, ID, IL, IN, KS, KY, LA, MA, MD, ME, MI, MN, MO, MS, MT, NC, ND, NE, NH, NJ, NM, NV, NY, OH, OK, OR, PA, PR, RI, SC, SD, TN, TX, UT, VA, VI, VT, WA, WI, WV, WY, AB, MB, NS, ON, SK
Foreign Countries: BRAZIL; CANADA; CHILE; COSTA RICA; DOMINICAN REPUBLIC; EGYPT; GUATEMALA; INDONESIA; JORDAN; KUWAIT; MEXICO; QATAR; SAUDI ARABIA; THE PHILIPPINES; UNITED ARAB EMIRATES
Type of Foodservice: Casual Dining (1,642)
Primary Distributors: (Food) The SYGMA Network, Inc., DUBLIN, OH
Parent Company: Dine Brands Global, Inc., PASADENA, CA

Key Personnel
RICHARD DAHL - Chairman; Director
TONY MORALEJO - President
KEVIN CARROLL - COO; Senior VP
JOEL YASHINSKY - Chief Marketing Officer
ROBERT MADDEN - Area Director
STEPHEN BULGARELLI - Exec VP Culinary Operations; VP
BRYAN R. ADEL - Senior VP; Corporate Secretary; General Counsel
BRYAN MARKS - VP Division
KEITH VEDRAL - VP Operations
BARRY BEAM - VP Operations
BILL O'KEEFE - Executive Director Development
AIDAN SCULLY - Senior Director Franchising
KENNY KIDD - Director Franchise Operations
HEATHER BOYER - Director Advertising
MIKE BLACKBURN - Director Area
BOB EBERLEY - Senior Manager Facility/Maintenance
DARREN HUNT - Senior Manager Marketing, Branding
SHEFALI PATEL - Senior Manager Marketing, Communications, Digital Media
DANIELLE INGRAM - Senior Manager Brand Marketing
BRETT HINDMAN - Senior Manager
GABE LLOYD - Manager Human Resources, Employee Benefits
STEFANIE ZAMBELLI - Manager Brand Marketing
SONDRA SCHEIB - Specialist Recruitment

Bo Ling's
4701 Jefferson St
Kansas City, MO 64112-1884

Telephone: (816) 753-1718
Internet Homepage: bolings.com
Company Email: info@bolings.com
Type of Business: Chain Restaurant Operator
Year Founded: 1981
Total Sales: $8,412,000 (e)
Alcohol Sales: 3%
Number of Employees: 200
Average Check: Lunch(18); Dinner(26)
Internet Order Processing: Yes
Total Units: 6
Trade Names: Bo Ling's (6)
Company-Owned Units: 6
Preferred Location Types: Strip Mall
Alcohol Served: Beer, Wine, Liquor
Primary Menu: Chinese (6)
Areas of Operation: KS, MO
Type of Foodservice: Fine Dining (6)
Catering Services: Yes

Key Personnel
RICHARD NG - Partner; General Buyer
THERESA NG - Partner; Director Catering
REBECCA NG - Director Marketing

Cascone's
3733 N Oak Trfy
Kansas City, MO 64116-2778

Telephone: (816) 454-7977
Fax Number: (816) 454-8041
Internet Homepage: cascones.com; johnnycascones.com
Company Email: info@cascones.com
Type of Business: Chain Restaurant Operator
Year Founded: 1954
Total Sales: $4,401,000 (e)
Alcohol Sales: 25%
Number of Employees: 120
Average Check: Lunch(22); Dinner(36)
Total Units: 2
Trade Names: Cascone's (1); Johnny Cascone's (1)
Company-Owned Units: 2
Preferred Location Types: Freestanding
Alcohol Served: Beer, Wine, Liquor
Primary Menu: Italian (2)
Areas of Operation: KS, MO
Type of Foodservice: Casual Dining (2)
Catering Services: Yes
Primary Distributors: (Full Line) SYSCO Food Services of Kansas City Inc., OLATHE, KS

Key Personnel
FRANK CASCONE - CEO; Partner
JIM CASCONE - Partner; VP; General Manager; Executive Chef; General Buyer
VICTOR CASCONE - Partner; General Manager; Director Food Safety, Catering
DESMOND NORTHCUTT - General Manager

Fiorella's Jack Stack Barbecue
13441 Holmes Rd
Kansas City, MO 64145-1445

Telephone: (816) 942-9141
Fax Number: (816) 941-8762
Internet Homepage: jackstackbbq.com
Company Email: info@worldclassbbq.com
Type of Business: Chain Restaurant Operator
Year Founded: 1974
Total Sales: $36,270,000 (e)
Alcohol Sales: 15%
Number of Employees: 50
Average Check: Lunch(10); Dinner(22)
Internet Order Processing: Yes
Internet Sales: 1.00%
Total Units: 5
Trade Names: Jack Stack Barbecue (5)
Company-Owned Units: 5
Preferred Location Types: Freestanding
Alcohol Served: Beer, Wine, Liquor
Primary Menu: Bar-B-Q (5)
Areas of Operation: KS, MO
Type of Foodservice: Casual Dining (5)
Catering Services: Yes
Primary Distributors: (Full Line) SYSCO Food Services of Kansas City Inc., OLATHE, KS
Notes: The company derives approximately 10% of its revenue from wholesale operations.

Key Personnel
CASE DORMAN - CEO; President
CRAIG TEIGAN - CFO

ROD TOELKS - VP Restaurant Operations
TIM KEEGAN - Executive Chef Purchasing; Director Purchasing
TRAVIS NAPIER - Senior Manager
KEVIN FIORELLA - Manager Transportation; General Buyer
ALICIA FRIES - Manager Customer Service

Gates Bar-B-Q Inc.
4621 Paseo Blvd
Kansas City, MO 64110-1825

Telephone: (816) 923-0900
Fax Number: (816) 923-3922
Internet Homepage: gatesbbq.com
Company Email: sales@gatesbbq.com
Type of Business: Chain Restaurant Operator
Year Founded: 1946
Total Sales: $4,959,000 (e)
Alcohol Sales: 10%
Number of Employees: 230
Internet Order Processing: Yes
Internet Sales: 1.00%
Total Units: 6
Trade Names: Gates Bar-B-Q (6)
Company-Owned Units: 6
Preferred Square Footage: 2,400
Preferred Location Types: Freestanding
Alcohol Served: Beer, Wine, Liquor
Primary Menu: Bar-B-Q (6)
Areas of Operation: KS, MO
Type of Foodservice: Casual Dining (6)
Catering Services: Yes
Distribution Centers: KANSAS CITY, MO
Primary Distributors: (Full Line) SYSCO Food Services of Kansas City Inc., OLATHE, KS

Key Personnel
OLLIE W. GATES - President; Controller; General Manager; Director Finance; General Buyer
GEORGE GATES - VP Operations; Executive Chef; Director Purchasing, Information Systems, Research & Development, Product Development, Foodservice, Menu Development, Food and Beverage
BIANCA GATES - VP Real Estate
KIVA GATES - Manager Operations, Training, Food Safety

KRM Restaurant Group Inc.
5921 NW Barry Rd Ste 100
Kansas City, MO 64154-2579

Telephone: (816) 455-9008
Fax Number: (816) 455-9024
Internet Homepage: 54thstreetgrill.com
Type of Business: Chain Restaurant Operator
Year Founded: 1994
Total Sales: $69,520,000 (e)
Alcohol Sales: 20%
Number of Employees: 804
Average Check: Lunch(10); Dinner(22)
Total Units: 30
Trade Names: 54th Street Grill and Bar (30)
Company-Owned Units: 30
Preferred Square Footage: 5,000; 5,800; 6,000
Preferred Location Types: Freestanding; Strip Mall
Alcohol Served: Beer, Wine, Liquor
Primary Menu: American (30)
Projected Openings: 2
Areas of Operation: IL, KS, MO, TX
Type of Foodservice: Casual Dining (30)

Key Personnel
TOM NORSWORTHY - Founder; Director Real Estate
MICHAEL NORSWORTHY - President; COO; Director Real Estate; General Buyer
AL STENNER - Director Information Systems

Minsky's
5105 Main St
Kansas City, MO 64112-2742

Telephone: (816) 561-5100
Fax Number: (816) 531-3352
Internet Homepage: minskys.com
Type of Business: Chain Restaurant Operator
Year Founded: 1976
Systemwide Sales: $15,726,000 (e)
Total Sales: $12,260,000 (e)
Alcohol Sales: 20%
Number of Employees: 870
Average Check: Lunch(8); Dinner(10)
Internet Order Processing: Yes
Internet Sales: 1.00%
Total Units: 20
Trade Names: eggtc (2); Minsky's Pizza (17); Osteria IL Centro (1)
Company-Owned Units: 14
Units Franchised To: 6
Preferred Square Footage: 5,500; 6,000
Preferred Location Types: Downtown; Freestanding
Alcohol Served: Beer, Wine, Liquor
Primary Menu: American (2); Italian (1); Pizza (17)
Areas of Operation: KS, MO
Type of Foodservice: Casual Dining (20)
Catering Services: Yes
Primary Distributors: (Full Line) Performance Foodservice, SPRINGFIELD, MO

Key Personnel
GREGG JOHNSON - President; Director Finance, Purchasing, Facility/Maintenance, Information Systems, Real Estate, Design, Human Resources, Store Fixtures, Menu Development
TIM LAMASTERS - General Manager

Pizza Shoppe Franchising Inc.
6121 NW Klamm Rd
Kansas City, MO 64152-4378

Telephone: (816) 587-2800
Fax Number: (816) 587-7171
Internet Homepage: pizzashoppe.com
Type of Business: Chain Restaurant Operator
Year Founded: 1967
Systemwide Sales: $22,084,000 (e)
Total Sales: $4,925,000 (e)
Alcohol Sales: 6%
Number of Employees: 32
Average Check: Lunch(14); Dinner(18)
Total Units: 16
Trade Names: Pizza Shoppe (16)
Company-Owned Units: 1
Units Franchised To: 15
Preferred Square Footage: 2,500
Preferred Location Types: Freestanding; Strip Mall
Alcohol Served: Beer, Wine
Primary Menu: Pizza (16)
Areas of Operation: KS, MO, OK
Type of Foodservice: Casual Dining (16)
Catering Services: Yes
Primary Distributors: (Full Line) Pizza Specialities Inc., SHAWNEE MISSION, KS

Key Personnel
TOM RYAN - President
JOE BUTLER - VP Marketing, Franchising

Planet Sub
4928 Main St
Kansas City, MO 64112-2630

Telephone: (844) 289-7782
Internet Homepage: planetsub.com
Type of Business: Chain Restaurant Operator
Year Founded: 1998
Total Sales: $18,690,000 (e)
Internet Order Processing: Yes
Total Units: 37
Trade Names: Planet Sub (37)
Company-Owned Units: 18
Units Franchised To: 19
Primary Menu: Sandwiches/Deli (37)
Areas of Operation: AZ, IA, KS, MO, NE, OH, OK, SD, TX
Type of Foodservice: Quick Serve (37)

Key Personnel
SEAN KELLY - Partner; VP Purchasing
JEFF KLUSMAN - Partner; VP Marketing, Research & Development
ZACH PARSONS - General Manager

ROBERT COXON - General Manager
BRENT SIEMERS - Director Franchise Operations

SPIN! Concepts Inc
222 W Gregory Blvd Ste 340
Kansas City, MO 64114-1127

Telephone: (816) 621-7746
Internet Homepage: spinpizza.com
Company Email: catering@spinpizza.com
Type of Business: Chain Restaurant Operator
Total Sales: $30,770,000 (e)
Alcohol Sales: 5%
Number of Employees: 312
Total Units: 15
Trade Names: SPIN! Pizza (15)
Company-Owned Units: 11
Units Franchised To: 4
Alcohol Served: Beer, Wine
Primary Menu: Pizza (15)
Areas of Operation: CA, KS, MO, NE, TX
Type of Foodservice: Fast Casual (15)
Catering Services: Yes

Key Personnel
EDWIN BROWNELL - Owner; General Buyer
SARA CARHART - VP Operations
CHUCK GOODALL - General Manager

The Mixx
4855 Main St
Kansas City, MO 64112-2502

Telephone: (816) 756-2300
Fax Number: (816) 756-3002
Internet Homepage: mixxingitup.com
Company Email: plaza@mixxingitup.com
Type of Business: Chain Restaurant Operator
Year Founded: 2005
Total Sales: $5,997,000 (e)
Average Check: Dinner(22)
Internet Order Processing: Yes
Total Units: 2
Trade Names: The Mixx (2)
Company-Owned Units: 2
Preferred Location Types: Downtown; Strip Mall
Alcohol Served: Beer, Wine, Liquor
Primary Menu: American (2)
Projected Openings: 1
Projected Remodelings: 1
Areas of Operation: MO
Type of Foodservice: Fast Casual (2)
Catering Services: Yes

Key Personnel
JO MARIE SCAGLIA - President; Owner; Executive Chef; General Buyer
BOBBI SCHRADER - General Manager; General Buyer

Topsy's International Inc.
221 W 74th Ter
Kansas City, MO 64114-5730

Telephone: (816) 523-5555
Fax Number: (816) 523-4747
Internet Homepage: topsyspopcorn.com
Company Email: info@topsyspopcorn.com
Type of Business: Chain Restaurant Operator
Year Founded: 1948
Systemwide Sales: $6,587,000 (e)
Total Sales: $5,138,000 (e)
Number of Employees: 100
Average Check: Breakfast(6); Lunch(6); Dinner(6)
Internet Order Processing: Yes
Internet Sales: 1.00%
Total Units: 13
Trade Names: Topsy's Popcorn Shoppe (13)
Company-Owned Units: 10
Units Franchised To: 3
Preferred Square Footage: 1,500
Preferred Location Types: Regional Mall; Strip Mall
Primary Menu: Snacks (13)
Areas of Operation: KS, MO
Type of Foodservice: Quick Serve (13)
On-site Distribution Center: Yes
Primary Distributors: (Full Line) VISTAR Specialty, ENGLEWOOD, CO

Key Personnel
ROBERT RAMM - President; Controller; Director Operations, Facility/Maintenance, Information Systems, Real Estate, Design, Menu Development; General Buyer

Worlds of Fun & Oceans of Fun
4545 NE Worlds of Fun Dr
Kansas City, MO 64161-9302

Telephone: (816) 303-5025
Fax Number: (816) 303-5029
Company Email: info@worldsoffun.com
Listing Type: Divisional Office
Type of Business: Foodservice Operations - Theme Parks
Number of Employees: 2,300
Total Units: 25
Company-Owned Units: 25
Areas of Operation: MO
Parent Company: Cedar Fair LLP, SANDUSKY, OH

Key Personnel
CORI DAY - Director Sales
SARA ESTLE - Director Risk Management

DEBBIE MANN - Director Purchasing
MATT STEER - General Buyer

Taco Via
1221 NE Rice Rd
Lees Summit, MO 64086-6789

Telephone: (816) 554-2121
Internet Homepage: taco-via.com
Company Email: Comments@Taco-Via.com
Type of Business: Chain Restaurant Operator
Year Founded: 1968
Systemwide Sales: $4,340,000 (e)
Total Sales: $1,162,000 (e)
Number of Employees: 40
Average Check: Lunch(12); Dinner(16)
Total Units: 3
Trade Names: Taco Via (3)
Units Franchised To: 3
Preferred Square Footage: 1,800
Preferred Location Types: Strip Mall
Primary Menu: Mexican (3)
Areas of Operation: KS, MO
Type of Foodservice: Quick Serve (3)
Primary Distributors: (Food) US Foods, SALEM, MO

Key Personnel
STEVE THORNEBERRY - Partner
MARY THRONEBERRY - Partner; Manager Operations

Tri N Subway, Inc
506 SE State Route 291
Lees Summit, MO 64063-4388

Telephone: (816) 524-7827
Type of Business: Chain Restaurant Operator
Total Sales: $2,892,000 (e)
Total Units: 4
Trade Names: Subway (4)
Units Franchised From: 4
Primary Menu: Sandwiches/Deli (4)
Areas of Operation: MO
Type of Foodservice: Quick Serve (4)
Franchise Affiliation: Doctor's Associates Inc., MILFORD, CT

Key Personnel
WILLIAM SCOTT-NELSON - President; General Buyer

B & B Theatres
PO Box 129
Liberty, MO 64069-0129

Telephone: (816) 407-7469
Fax Number: (816) 407-9805
Internet Homepage: bbtheatres.com

Company Email: contact@bbtheatres.com
Type of Business: Foodservice Operations - Movie Theatre
Year Founded: 1920
Total Sales: $220,290,000 (e)
Number of Employees: 2,000
Average Check: Dinner(8)
Foodservice Sales: $52,870,000 (e)
Internet Order Processing: Yes
Internet Sales: 1.00%
Total Units: 52
Trade Names: B & B Theatre (52)
Company-Owned Units: 52
Preferred Square Footage: 2,500
Preferred Location Types: Community Mall; Freestanding
Primary Menu: Snacks (52)
Areas of Operation: AR, AZ, FL, KS, MO, MS, NE, OK, TX
Type of Foodservice: In-Store Feeder (52)
Primary Distributors: (Full Line) Vistar Kansas City, RIVERSIDE, MO

Key Personnel
BOB BAGBY - CEO; President; General Buyer
BROCK BAGBY - President; Chief Development Officer
BOBBIE BAGBY FORD - Exec VP
MICHAEL HAGAN - VP Finance
DAN VAN ORDEN - General Manager
PAUL FARNSWORTH - Director Public Relations
ANGELA FISHER - Manager

Dream Team Pizza, LLC
244 W Mill St Ste 104
Liberty, MO 64068-2398

Telephone: (806) 407-9079
Type of Business: Chain Restaurant Operator
Total Sales: $74,240,000 (e)
Total Units: 37
Trade Names: Domino's (37)
Units Franchised From: 37
Primary Menu: Pizza (37)
Areas of Operation: MO
Type of Foodservice: Quick Serve (37)
Franchise Affiliation: Domino's Pizza Inc, ANN ARBOR, MI

Key Personnel
JAMIE S. POULSEN - Owner; General Buyer
LESLIE CARDWELL - Manager Customer Service

G & L Simons
1500 N Church Rd Ste B
Liberty, MO 64068-7161

Mailing Address: PO Box 157, LIBERTY, MO, 64069-0157

Telephone: (816) 415-9980
Fax Number: (816) 415-9992
Type of Business: Chain Restaurant Operator
Year Founded: 1989
Total Sales: $67,790,000 (e)
Number of Employees: 565
Average Check: Breakfast(8); Lunch(8); Dinner(8)
Total Units: 32
Trade Names: Sonic America's Drive-In (32)
Units Franchised From: 32
Preferred Square Footage: 1,200
Preferred Location Types: Freestanding
Primary Menu: Hamburger (32)
Areas of Operation: MO
Type of Foodservice: Quick Serve (32)
Franchise Affiliation: Sonic Corp., OKLAHOMA CITY, OK
Primary Distributors: (Food) Reinhart FoodService, LEES SUMMIT, MO

Key Personnel
GARY SIMONS - President; Partner; General Manager; Director Real Estate, Training; General Buyer
LIZ SIMONS - Partner; VP Finance, Purchasing, Information Systems, Marketing, Human Resources

Tucker's Place
14282 Manchester Rd
Manchester, MO 63011-4508

Telephone: (636) 227-0966
Fax Number: (636) 227-0966
Internet Homepage: tuckersplacestl.com
Type of Business: Chain Restaurant Operator
Year Founded: 1982
Total Sales: $12,223,000 (e)
Alcohol Sales: 40%
Number of Employees: 260
Average Check: Lunch(10); Dinner(14)
Internet Order Processing: Yes
Total Units: 3
Trade Names: Tucker's Place (3)
Company-Owned Units: 3
Preferred Location Types: Freestanding
Alcohol Served: Beer, Wine, Liquor
Primary Menu: Steak (3)
Areas of Operation: MO
Type of Foodservice: Casual Dining (3)
Primary Distributors: (Full Line) Kuna Foodservice Co., DUPO, IL

Key Personnel
TOM STRUHARIK - Owner; CFO; General Manager; Executive Chef; General Buyer

Mik-Di Enterprises
2110 S Odell Ave
Marshall, MO 65340-3728

Telephone: (660) 886-5187
Type of Business: Chain Restaurant Operator
Total Sales: $42,670,000 (e)
Number of Employees: 220
Total Units: 9
Trade Names: McDonald's (9)
Units Franchised From: 9
Preferred Square Footage: 2,500
Primary Menu: Hamburger (9)
Areas of Operation: MO
Type of Foodservice: Quick Serve (9)
Franchise Affiliation: McDonald's Corporation, CHICAGO, IL

Key Personnel
MICHAEL GREMAUD - President; General Buyer

Canteen Vending Services
2331 Millpark Dr
Maryland Heights, MO 63043-3529

Telephone: (314) 423-6200
Listing Type: Branch Office
Type of Business: Foodservice Management Operator
Year Founded: 1929
Number of Employees: 50
Number of Locations Served: 116
Total Foodservice Mgmt Accounts: 116
Areas of Operation: MO
Type of Foodservice: Vending machines (116)
Foodservice Management Venues: Business & Industry; College & University; Health Care; Schools; Travel Plazas
Parent Company: Compass Group The Americas, CHARLOTTE, NC
Headquarters: Canteen Vending Services, CHARLOTTE, NC

Key Personnel
KELLY HASTY - General Manager; Director Operations, Purchasing

Hotshots Sports Bar & Grill
12664 Dorsett Rd
Maryland Heights, MO 63043-2130

Telephone: (314) 485-3242
Internet Homepage: hotshotsnet.com
Company Email: CustomerService@HotShotsNet.com
Type of Business: Chain Restaurant Operator
Year Founded: 2000
Total Sales: $16,050,000 (e)

Total Units: 14
Trade Names: Hotshots Sports Bar & Grill (14)
Company-Owned Units: 11
Units Franchised To: 3
Primary Menu: American (14)
Areas of Operation: AR, MO, NC
Type of Foodservice: Casual Dining (14)

Key Personnel
DAN VOLMERT - Founder; Owner
JUSTIN BOYD - Director Marketing

Kramer Management Inc
1820 N Main St
Mountain Grove, MO 65711-1044

Telephone: (417) 926-5004
Type of Business: Chain Restaurant Operator
Total Sales: $20,320,000 (e)
Number of Employees: 150
Total Units: 4
Trade Names: McDonald's (4)
Units Franchised From: 4
Preferred Square Footage: 2,500
Primary Menu: Hamburger (4)
Areas of Operation: MO
Type of Foodservice: Quick Serve (4)
Franchise Affiliation: McDonald's Corporation, CHICAGO, IL

Key Personnel
WILLIAM KRAMER - President; General Buyer

Heavy B, LLC
1669 Kaitlin Cir
Nixa, MO 65714-7906

Telephone: (417) 725-5006
Type of Business: Chain Restaurant Operator
Total Sales: $2,613,000 (e)
Total Units: 4
Trade Names: Little Caesars Pizza (4)
Units Franchised From: 4
Primary Menu: Pizza (4)
Areas of Operation: MO
Type of Foodservice: Quick Serve (4)
Franchise Affiliation: Little Caesar Enterprises Inc., DETROIT, MI

Key Personnel
CARL BIONDO - Partner; General Buyer
ELIZABETH BIONDO - Partner

Domino's Franchisee
307 W Lincoln Ave
Owensville, MO 65066-1332

Telephone: (573) 437-8777
Type of Business: Chain Restaurant Operator

Total Sales: $4,053,000 (e)
Total Units: 2
Trade Names: Domino's (2)
Units Franchised From: 2
Primary Menu: Pizza (2)
Areas of Operation: MO
Type of Foodservice: Quick Serve (2)
Franchise Affiliation: Domino's Pizza Inc, ANN ARBOR, MI

Key Personnel
BENJAMIN MCGOWAN - Owner; General Buyer

K2M Inc.
510 E South St
Ozark, MO 65721-8571

Telephone: (417) 725-4933
Type of Business: Chain Restaurant Operator
Total Sales: $2,221,000 (e)
Number of Employees: 40
Average Check: Lunch(8); Dinner(10)
Total Units: 4
Trade Names: Godfather's Pizza (4)
Units Franchised From: 4
Preferred Location Types: Strip Mall
Primary Menu: Pizza (4)
Areas of Operation: MO
Type of Foodservice: Quick Serve (4)
Franchise Affiliation: Godfather's Pizza, Inc., OMAHA, NE
Primary Distributors: (Full Line) US Foods, SALEM, MO

Key Personnel
RICHARD PELLEGRINO - Senior VP Technology, Development
OMID ABBARIN - Director Operations, Information Technology
T.J. DONELOW - Store Manager

Gilbertson Restaurants L.L.C.
5812 Trailridge Dr
Parkville, MO 64152-6065

Telephone: (816) 505-9344
Fax Number: (816) 505-9345
Type of Business: Chain Restaurant Operator
Year Founded: 2002
Total Sales: $13,490,000 (e)
Number of Employees: 200
Average Check: Breakfast(8); Lunch(8); Dinner(12)
Total Units: 6
Trade Names: Burger King (6)
Units Franchised From: 6
Preferred Square Footage: 1,900; 4,300
Preferred Location Types: Freestanding

Primary Menu: Hamburger (6)
Areas of Operation: MO
Type of Foodservice: Quick Serve (6)
Franchise Affiliation: Burger King Worldwide Inc., MIAMI, FL
Primary Distributors: (Full Line) Reinhart FoodService, AUSTELL, GA

Key Personnel
TODD GILBERTSON - President; Director Finance, Operations, Information Systems, Real Estate; General Buyer

Rancho Grande Cantina
11015 NW Highway 45
Parkville, MO 64152-3990

Telephone: (816) 505-9097
Fax Number: (816) 505-9285
Internet Homepage: ranchograndecantina.com
Type of Business: Chain Restaurant Operator
Total Sales: $3,046,000 (e)
Alcohol Sales: 10%
Average Check: Dinner(12)
Total Units: 3
Trade Names: Rancho Grande Cantina (3)
Company-Owned Units: 3
Preferred Location Types: Freestanding; Strip Mall
Alcohol Served: Beer, Wine, Liquor
Primary Menu: Mexican (3)
Areas of Operation: MO
Type of Foodservice: Casual Dining (3)
Catering Services: Yes

Key Personnel
JOE JENNINGS - President; Executive Chef; General Buyer

Essig Management Co. Inc.
6603CA Royal St Ste C
Pleasant Valley, MO 64068-8707

Mailing Address: PO Box 550, LIBERTY, MO, 64069-0550
Telephone: (816) 792-1124
Fax Number: (816) 903-5101
Internet Homepage: essigmanagement.com
Type of Business: Chain Restaurant Operator
Year Founded: 1977
Total Sales: $66,550,000 (e)
Number of Employees: 678
Average Check: Breakfast(6); Lunch(10); Dinner(12)
Total Units: 14
Trade Names: McDonald's (14)
Units Franchised From: 14
Preferred Square Footage: 2,400; 3,000
Preferred Location Types: Freestanding
Primary Menu: Hamburger (14)
Areas of Operation: MO

Type of Foodservice: Quick Serve (14)
Franchise Affiliation: McDonald's Corporation, CHICAGO, IL
Primary Distributors: (Full Line) The Martin-Brower Co. LLC, ROSEMONT, IL

Key Personnel
DAVID ESSIG - Partner; General Buyer
LISA ESSIG - Partner
KELLEY SCHINDLER - Director Operations

Daniel Blumenstock, Inc. dba McDonald's
935 US Highway 60 E
Republic, MO 65738-1571

Mailing Address: PO Box 331, Republic, Mo, 65738-0331
Telephone: (417) 732-8787
Fax Number: (417) 732-8206
Type of Business: Chain Restaurant Operator
Total Sales: $23,750,000 (e)
Number of Employees: 60
Total Units: 5
Trade Names: McDonald's (5)
Units Franchised From: 5
Preferred Square Footage: 2,500
Primary Menu: Hamburger (4)
Areas of Operation: MO
Type of Foodservice: Quick Serve (5)
Franchise Affiliation: McDonald's Corporation, CHICAGO, IL

Key Personnel
RYAN BLUMENSTOCK - President; General Buyer

Big Cedar Lodge
190 Top of the Rock Rd
Ridgedale, MO 65739-4500

Telephone: (417) 335-2777
Fax Number: (417) 339-5270
Internet Homepage: bigcedar.com
Company Email: bigcedar@big-cedar.com
Type of Business: Chain Restaurant Operator
Year Founded: 1987
Total Sales: $10,990,000 (e)
Alcohol Sales: 20%
Number of Employees: 315
Average Check: Breakfast(12); Lunch(18); Dinner(22)
Total Units: 9
Trade Names: Arnie's Barn (1); Buffalo Bar (1); Buzzard Bar (1); Canteen at Long Creek (1); Devil's Pool (1); Mountain Top Grill (1); Osage Restaurant (1); Truman Cafe (1); Uncle Buck's Fish Bowl & Grill (1)
Company-Owned Units: 9
Preferred Square Footage: 5,500; 6,000

Preferred Location Types: Freestanding
Alcohol Served: Beer, Wine, Liquor
Primary Menu: American (9)
Areas of Operation: MO
Type of Foodservice: Casual Dining (9)
Catering Services: Yes
Primary Distributors: (Food) SYSCO Food Services of St. Louis LLC, SAINT CHARLES, MO

Key Personnel
JOHNNY MORRIS - Owner; Director Facility/Maintenance, Real Estate, Design, Menu Development; General Buyer
MATT PACE - Director Operations
CRISTI PARKER - Director Sales
JASON ROBINSON - Director Marketing, Sales
MARYBETH ZAHNER - Director Operations
MELANIE DELONG - Director Human Resources
LAURA HEAD ELLIOTT - Director Marketing
JARED HENZLIK - Director Retail Operations
JAMIE KEYS - Director Operations; Assistant Manager
TODD LEONARD - Director Food and Beverage, Catering
JESSICA ABERNATHY - Assistant Director Human Resources
GREG THOMAS - Assistant Director Operations
STEVEN PYLE - Assistant Director Security, Safety
JIM CARDENZANA - Manager Information Systems
SYDNEY FRIAR - Manager Design
LYNN LYNCH - Merchandise Manager

Culpepper's
3010 W Clay St
Saint Charles, MO 63301-1067

Telephone: (636) 916-3102
Fax Number: (636) 493-1911
Internet Homepage: culpeppers.com
Company Email: info@culpeppers.com
Type of Business: Chain Restaurant Operator
Year Founded: 1989
Total Sales: $4,204,000 (e)
Alcohol Sales: 15%
Number of Employees: 135
Average Check: Lunch(12); Dinner(20)
Total Units: 2
Trade Names: Culpepper's (2)
Company-Owned Units: 2
Preferred Square Footage: 5,500; 6,000
Preferred Location Types: Freestanding; Strip Mall
Alcohol Served: Beer, Wine, Liquor
Primary Menu: American (2)
Areas of Operation: MO
Type of Foodservice: Casual Dining (2)
Primary Distributors: (Food) Performance Foodservice - Middendorf, SAINT LOUIS, MO

Key Personnel
CHRIS OLSEN - President; Owner; COO; Director Finance, Purchasing, Facility/Maintenance, Information Systems, Supply Chain, Real Estate, Design, Menu Development

MBR Management
201 N Main St Ste 300
Saint Charles, MO 63301-2878

Telephone: (636) 947-4433
Fax Number: (636) 947-6917
Internet Homepage: mbrdominos.com
Company Email: comments@mbrdominos.com
Type of Business: Chain Restaurant Operator
Year Founded: 1982
Total Sales: $162,580,000 (e)
Number of Employees: 1,174
Average Check: Lunch(8); Dinner(8)
Total Units: 81
Trade Names: Domino's (81)
Units Franchised From: 81
Preferred Square Footage: 1,000; 1,300
Preferred Location Types: Freestanding; Strip Mall
Primary Menu: Pizza (81)
Areas of Operation: IL, MO
Type of Foodservice: Quick Serve (81)
Foodservice Management Venues: Schools; Transportation
Distribution Centers: SAINT LOUIS, MO
On-site Distribution Center: Yes
Franchise Affiliation: Domino's Pizza Inc, ANN ARBOR, MI
Primary Distributors: (Food) Domino's Pizza Inc, ANN ARBOR, MI

Key Personnel
MARK RATTERMAN - President; Director Facility/Maintenance, Real Estate, Design, Store Fixtures; General Buyer
JEFFREY TOPE - VP Finance
GARY BUGAJSKI - Director Region
BAMBI HULSEY - Director Finance
KEITH LINKEMAN - Director Region

Domino's Franchisee
940 Plaza Dr Ste A
Saint Clair, MO 63077-1167

Telephone: (636) 629-2929
Type of Business: Chain Restaurant Operator
Total Sales: $10,341,000 (e)
Total Units: 5
Trade Names: Domino's (5)
Units Franchised From: 5
Primary Menu: Pizza (5)
Areas of Operation: MO
Type of Foodservice: Quick Serve (5)
Franchise Affiliation: Domino's Pizza Inc, ANN

ARBOR, MI

Key Personnel
STEPHEN E. WAMPLER - Owner; General Buyer

Domino's Franchisee
2110 Messanie St
Saint Joseph, MO 64507-2418

Telephone: (816) 232-6060
Type of Business: Chain Restaurant Operator
Total Sales: $9,970,000 (e)
Total Units: 5
Trade Names: Domino's (5)
Units Franchised From: 5
Primary Menu: Pizza (5)
Areas of Operation: MO
Type of Foodservice: Quick Serve (5)
Franchise Affiliation: Domino's Pizza Inc, ANN ARBOR, MI

Key Personnel
DARYL M. MILLER - Owner; General Buyer

Habiger Enterprises
3508 N Belt Hwy Ste D
Saint Joseph, MO 64506-1330

Telephone: (816) 232-3399
Fax Number: (816) 232-4293
Type of Business: Chain Restaurant Operator
Total Sales: $32,770,000 (e)
Total Units: 7
Trade Names: McDonald's (7)
Units Franchised From: 7
Preferred Square Footage: 2,500
Preferred Location Types: Freestanding
Primary Menu: Hamburger (7)
Areas of Operation: MO
Type of Foodservice: Quick Serve (7)
Franchise Affiliation: McDonald's Corporation, CHICAGO, IL

Key Personnel
CHRIS HABIGER - Owner; General Buyer

Taco John's of St Joseph Inc
3801 Oakland Ave
Saint Joseph, MO 64506-3622

Telephone: (816) 233-4667
Type of Business: Chain Restaurant Operator
Total Sales: $5,226,000 (e)
Number of Employees: 115
Total Units: 5
Trade Names: Taco John's (5)
Units Franchised From: 5
Preferred Location Types: Freestanding; Regional Mall; Strip Mall
Primary Menu: Taco (5)
Areas of Operation: MO
Type of Foodservice: Quick Serve (5)
Franchise Affiliation: Taco John's International Inc., CHEYENNE, WY

Key Personnel
VIRGIL (FRED) FREDERES - President; General Buyer

Turk Enterprises Inc
3304 Ashland Ave
Saint Joseph, MO 64506

Telephone: (816) 232-3744
Fax Number: (816) 232-5496
Type of Business: Chain Restaurant Operator
Total Sales: $1,577,000 (e)
Total Units: 2
Trade Names: Little Caesars Pizza (2)
Units Franchised From: 2
Preferred Location Types: Strip Mall
Primary Menu: Pizza (2)
Areas of Operation: MO
Type of Foodservice: Quick Serve (2)
Franchise Affiliation: Little Caesar Enterprises Inc., DETROIT, MI

Key Personnel
DUANE TURK - President; General Buyer

Banduccie Enterprises
11521 Olive Blvd
Saint Louis, MO 63141-7110

Telephone: (314) 993-9949
Type of Business: Chain Restaurant Operator
Total Sales: $37,690,000 (e)
Total Units: 8
Trade Names: McDonald's (8)
Units Franchised From: 8
Primary Menu: Hamburger (8)
Areas of Operation: MO
Type of Foodservice: Quick Serve (8)
Franchise Affiliation: McDonald's Corporation, CHICAGO, IL

Key Personnel
JOHN BANDUCCI - Partner; General Buyer
MICHELLE BANDUCCI - Partner; VP
CHRIS SAUL - General Manager

Dominic's Restaurant
5101 Wilson Ave
Saint Louis, MO 63110-3109

Telephone: (314) 771-1632
Internet Homepage: dominicsrestaurant.com/trattoria; giosdowntown.com; dominicsrestaurant.com
Type of Business: Chain Restaurant Operator
Year Founded: 1971
Total Sales: $7,679,000 (e)
Alcohol Sales: 30%
Number of Employees: 40
Average Check: Lunch(22); Dinner(54)
Total Units: 3
Trade Names: Dominic's (1); Dominic's Trattoria (1); Gio's (1)
Company-Owned Units: 3
Preferred Location Types: Downtown; Freestanding; Office Complex
Alcohol Served: Beer, Wine, Liquor
Primary Menu: Italian (3)
Areas of Operation: MO
Type of Foodservice: Casual Dining (1); Fine Dining (2)
Catering Services: Yes
Primary Distributors: (Full Line) SYSCO Food Services of St. Louis LLC, SAINT CHARLES, MO

Key Personnel
JACKIE GALATI - Partner

Domino's Franchisee
1613 S 9th St
Saint Louis, MO 63104-3827

Telephone: (314) 621-2030
Type of Business: Chain Restaurant Operator
Total Sales: $6,080,000 (e)
Total Units: 3
Trade Names: Domino's (3)
Units Franchised From: 3
Primary Menu: Pizza (3)
Areas of Operation: MO
Type of Foodservice: Quick Serve (3)
Franchise Affiliation: Domino's Pizza Inc, ANN ARBOR, MI

Key Personnel
RICHARD W. GALLOWAY - Owner; General Buyer

Gourmet To Go
1865 Craig Rd
Saint Louis, MO 63146-4711

Telephone: (314) 205-1151
Fax Number: (314) 205-1525
Internet Homepage: gourmettogo.com
Company Email: info@gourmet-to-go.com
Type of Business: Foodservice Management Operator
Year Founded: 1982
Total Sales: $11,747,000 (e)
Number of Employees: 200
Number of Locations Served: 15,000

Total Foodservice Mgmt Accounts: 15,000
Internet Order Processing: Yes
Areas of Operation: MO
Type of Foodservice: Fast Casual (15,000)
Foodservice Management Venues: Business & Industry; College & University; Health Care
Primary Distributors: (Full Line) US Foods, SALEM, MO

Key Personnel
SANDI SIERON - Director Marketing, Real Estate, Human Resources, Store Planning

Imo's Pizza
800 N 17th St
Saint Louis, MO 63106-3730

Telephone: (314) 822-7227
Fax Number: (314) 647-7241
Internet Homepage: imospizza.com
Company Email: imos@imospizza.com
Type of Business: Chain Restaurant Operator
Year Founded: 1964
Systemwide Sales: $110,408,000 (e)
Total Sales: $12,180,000 (e)
Alcohol Sales: 3%
Number of Employees: 8
Average Check: Lunch(14); Dinner(30)
Internet Order Processing: Yes
Total Units: 99
Trade Names: Imo's Pizza (99)
Units Franchised To: 99
Preferred Square Footage: 2,000
Preferred Location Types: Freestanding; Strip Mall
Alcohol Served: Beer
Primary Menu: Pizza (99)
Projected Openings: 3
Areas of Operation: IL, KS, MO
Type of Foodservice: Casual Dining (99)
On-site Distribution Center: Yes
Primary Distributors: (Food) Roma Grocery Co., SAINT LOUIS, MO

Key Personnel
EDWARD L. IMO - Founder
VINCE IMO - Owner
MARGE IMO - VP Information Systems, Advertising, Franchising
MARK IMOS - General Manager

Kaldi's Coffee Roasting Company
3983 Gratiot St
Saint Louis, MO 63110-1723

Telephone: (314) 727-9991
Fax Number: (314) 727-9991
Internet Homepage: kaldiscoffee.com
Company Email: roastmaster@kaldiscoffee.com
Type of Business: Chain Restaurant Operator
Year Founded: 1994
Total Sales: $18,590,000 (e)
Number of Employees: 17
Average Check: Dinner(14)
Total Units: 17
Trade Names: Kaldi's Coffeehouse (17)
Company-Owned Units: 17
Preferred Location Types: Freestanding; Institution (college/hospital); Strip Mall
Primary Menu: Coffee (17)
Areas of Operation: GA, KS, MO
Type of Foodservice: Quick Serve (17)

Key Personnel
JOSH FERGUSON - Partner
TRICIA FERGUSON - Partner; General Buyer
KEITH KILDRON - VP Operations
TIM MURRAY - Director Finance

LC Corporate LLC
12977 N 40 Dr Ste 100
Saint Louis, MO 63141-8654

Telephone: (314) 821-8665
Fax Number: (314) 548-6620
Internet Homepage: lionschoice.com
Type of Business: Chain Restaurant Operator
Year Founded: 1967
Systemwide Sales: $34,427,000 (e)
Total Sales: $27,240,000 (e)
Number of Employees: 493
Average Check: Lunch(8); Dinner(10)
Internet Order Processing: Yes
Total Units: 29
Trade Names: Lion's Choice (29)
Company-Owned Units: 20
Units Franchised To: 9
Preferred Square Footage: 2,800
Preferred Location Types: Convenience Store/Gas Station; Freestanding
Primary Menu: American (29)
Areas of Operation: MO
Type of Foodservice: Quick Serve (29)
Primary Distributors: (Food) US Foods, SALEM, MO

Key Personnel
MARK DISPER - Chairman; President
MIKE KUPSTAS - CEO
BECKY FINE - COO
TODD WILSON - Director Operations
DAVE SANNING - District Manager; Manager Operations

Lombardo's Restaurant
10488 Natural Bridge Rd
Saint Louis, MO 63134-3304

Telephone: (314) 429-5151
Fax Number: (314) 429-0851
Internet Homepage: lombardosrestaurants.com
Company Email: LombRestSTL@att.net
Type of Business: Chain Restaurant Operator
Year Founded: 1993
Total Sales: $2,394,000 (e)
Alcohol Sales: 30%
Number of Employees: 40
Average Check: Lunch(12); Dinner(24)
Total Units: 4
Trade Names: Angelo's Taverna (1); Carmines Steak House (1); Lombardo's Restaurant (1); Lombardo's Trattoria (1)
Company-Owned Units: 4
Preferred Square Footage: 6,000
Preferred Location Types: Freestanding; Hotel/Motel
Alcohol Served: Beer, Wine, Liquor
Primary Menu: Italian (4)
Areas of Operation: MO
Type of Foodservice: Casual Dining (4)

Key Personnel
CARMEN LAMBARDO - Owner; General Buyer
MARIO LOMBARDO - Owner
ANGELO LOMBARDO - Executive Chef; General Buyer

Panera Bread Company
3630 S Geyer Rd Ste 100
Saint Louis, MO 63127-1234

Telephone: (314) 984-1000
Fax Number: (314) 909-3300
Internet Homepage: paneracares.org; panerabread.com; paradisebakery.com
Company Email: info@panerabread.com
Type of Business: Chain Restaurant Operator
Year Founded: 1981
Systemwide Sales: $9,817,525,000 (e)
Total Sales: $5,401,142,000 (e)
Number of Employees: 36,300
Average Check: Breakfast(10); Lunch(10); Dinner(10)
Internet Order Processing: Yes
Internet Sales: 3.00%
Total Units: 2,193
Trade Names: Panera Bread (2,193)
Company-Owned Units: 943
Units Franchised To: 1,250
Preferred Square Footage: 3,200; 4,480; 4,600; 4,747
Preferred Location Types: Airports; Community Mall; Downtown; Freestanding; Lifestyle Center; Regional Mall; Strip Mall
Primary Menu: Sandwiches/Deli (2,193)
Projected Openings: 2
Areas of Operation: AL, AR, AZ, CA, CO, CT, DC, DE, FL, GA, IA, IL, IN, KS, KY, LA, MA, MD, ME, MI, MN, MO, MS, NC, ND, NE, NH, NJ, NM, NV, NY, OH, OK, OR, PA, RI, SC, SD, TN, TX, UT, VA, VT, WA, WI, WV, ON

Foreign Countries: CANADA; INDIA; THAILAND
Type of Foodservice: Fast Casual (2,193)
Catering Services: Yes
Primary Distributors: (Equipment) The Wasserstrom Co., COLUMBUS, OH; (Food) The SYGMA Network Inc. - Illinois, DANVILLE, IL
Parent Company: Panera Brands, SAINT LOUIS, MO

Key Personnel
PATRICK GRISMER - Chairman
PAUL CARBONE - CEO Interim; CFO
MARK WOOLDRIDGE - Chief Accounting Officer; VP; Controller
DEBBIE ROBERTS - COO
MARK SHAMBURA - Chief Marketing Officer
BRIAN KRAUSE - Chief Development Officer
GREGG WATERMAN - Chief Supply Chain Officer
WILLIAM H. SIMPSON JR - Senior VP Business Development
RICHARD CRANNICK - Senior VP Operations
ROBERT PASSANISI - Senior VP Strategy
ROBIN SEWARD - Senior VP Brand Marketing
HARRY RAFT - VP Design
TYRELL CHILDS - VP Supply Chain
MICHAEL WOJCIK - VP Technology
SCOTT UEHLEIN - VP Culinary Operations
DAVID GAIDOS - Chief Culinary Officer; Chief Safety Officer
CHRIS BRANDT - Treasurer; Director Finance
BRUCE WALDEN - Controller Development
MARK WELLE - Senior Director Financial Planning, Information Technology
VANESSA GREER - Senior Director Information Systems
CHRIS SKILES - Director Facility/Maintenance, Special Projects
DAN BRUNO - Director Franchise Operations
PETER ODMAN - Director Internal Audit
RALEIGH STENNETT - Director Distribution
COURTNEY HIGGINS - Director Human Resources
MATT SCOBBIE - Director Real Estate
JIM GERLOCK - Director Sales, National Accounts
ELIZABETH WALSH - Director Direct Store Delivery
KATIE COLLINS - Director Software Engineering
BERNADETTE SANTUCCI - Director Marketing
FRANCINE VOSS - Director E-Commerce
DONNA KONIECZNY - Director
SACCHIN LAHOTI - Director Database
BILLY MEYERS - Director Technology
ADIS GUTIC - Senior Manager IT Applications
DENNIS DUNN - Senior Manager Information/Data Security
ADAM FURTWENGLER - Senior Manager Operations, Information Technology, E-Commerce
JEFF KUHLENGEL - Senior Manager Software
JULIE SMITH - Manager POS/Scanning
MICHAEL KELLER - Manager Loss Prevention
SHAWN LOLLIS - Manager Finance, Information Technology
MIKE SALIBA - Manager Information Technology
MARK P DAVIS - Senior Program Manager Information Technology
BIZZY HYDE - Project Manager Operations, Information Technology
GRAYSEN SUMMERS - Project Manager Information Technology

Pi Pizzeria
6144 Delmar Blvd
Saint Louis, MO 63112-1204

Telephone: (314) 727-6633
Fax Number: (314) 727-6655
Internet Homepage: restaurantpi.com
Company Email: info@restaurantpi.com
Type of Business: Chain Restaurant Operator
Total Sales: $4,351,000 (e)
Internet Order Processing: Yes
Total Units: 5
Trade Names: Pi Pizzeria (5)
Company-Owned Units: 5
Primary Menu: Pizza (5)
Areas of Operation: DC, MO
Type of Foodservice: Casual Dining (5)

Key Personnel
CHRIS SOMMERS - Partner; General Buyer
FRANK UIBLE - Partner
ROBYN SCIACCA - Director Finance

Syberg's Family Restaurants
3650 S Lindbergh Blvd
Saint Louis, MO 63127-1204

Telephone: (314) 984-0026
Fax Number: (314) 984-5004
Internet Homepage: helenfitzgeralds.com; sybergs.com; twistedtreesteakhouse.com
Company Email: tracy@sybergs.com
Type of Business: Chain Restaurant Operator
Year Founded: 1992
Total Sales: $13,580,000 (e)
Alcohol Sales: 10%
Number of Employees: 785
Average Check: Lunch(14); Dinner(20)
Internet Order Processing: Yes
Internet Sales: 0.50%
Total Units: 9
Trade Names: Helen Fitzgeralds (1); Sybergs (7); Twisted Tree (1)
Company-Owned Units: 9
Preferred Location Types: Freestanding
Alcohol Served: Beer, Wine, Liquor
Primary Menu: American (9)
Areas of Operation: MO
Type of Foodservice: Casual Dining (9)
Catering Services: Yes

Key Personnel
KIRK SYBERG - President; Partner; General Buyer
BRETT SYBERG - Partner; General Buyer
CONNER SYBERG - General Manager
TRACY STAMPER - Manager Marketing

The Crossing
7823 Forsyth Blvd
Saint Louis, MO 63105-3307

Telephone: (314) 721-7375
Internet Homepage: fialafood.com
Type of Business: Chain Restaurant Operator
Year Founded: 1998
Total Sales: $4,721,000 (e)
Alcohol Sales: 5%
Number of Employees: 30
Average Check: Lunch(12); Dinner(36)
Total Units: 2
Trade Names: Acero (1); The Crossing (1)
Company-Owned Units: 2
Preferred Location Types: Freestanding
Alcohol Served: Beer, Wine, Liquor
Primary Menu: American (1); Italian (1)
Areas of Operation: MO
Type of Foodservice: Fine Dining (2)
Catering Services: Yes
Primary Distributors: (Full Line) Reinhart FoodService, MARSHALL, MN

Key Personnel
JIM FIALA - President; General Manager; Executive Chef; General Buyer

The Pasta House Company
700 N New Ballas Rd
Saint Louis, MO 63141-6716

Telephone: (314) 535-6644
Fax Number: (314) 531-2499
Internet Homepage: pastahouse.com
Type of Business: Chain Restaurant Operator
Year Founded: 1974
Systemwide Sales: $60,721,000 (e)
Total Sales: $11,130,000 (e)
Alcohol Sales: 15%
Number of Employees: 1,710
Average Check: Lunch(32); Dinner(48)
Internet Order Processing: Yes
Internet Sales: 1.00%
Total Units: 19
Trade Names: Pasta House Co. (18); Pasta House Co. Pronto! (1)
Company-Owned Units: 11
Units Franchised To: 8
Preferred Square Footage: 1,700; 3,800; 6,000
Preferred Location Types: Community Mall;

Freestanding; Regional Mall; Strip Mall
Alcohol Served: Beer, Wine, Liquor
Primary Menu: Italian (19)
Areas of Operation: IL, MO
Type of Foodservice: Casual Dining (19)
Catering Services: Yes
Primary Distributors: (Full Line) US Foods, SALEM, MO

Key Personnel
JOSEPH A. FRESTA - Co-Founder; Partner; VP Purchasing, Facility/Maintenance, Quality Assurance, Construction, Design, Franchising, Store Fixtures
ROGER BASTAR - Supervisor Operations

White Castle System Inc.
1111 Macklind Ave
Saint Louis, MO 63110-1429

Telephone: (314) 535-7430
Fax Number: (314) 535-6456
Listing Type: Regional Office
Type of Business: Chain Restaurant Operator
Number of Employees: 39
Total Units: 39
Areas of Operation: IL, MO
On-site Distribution Center: Yes
Parent Company: White Castle Management Co., COLUMBUS, OH

Key Personnel
MIKE KLAESNER - Supervisor Construction
LISA BRAY - Supervisor Warehouse

Christian Foods Foods LLC
9 Stoll Ln
Saint Peters, MO 63376-1650

Telephone: (636) 244-4870
Type of Business: Chain Restaurant Operator
Total Sales: $56,400,000 (e)
Total Units: 12
Trade Names: McDonald's (12)
Units Franchised From: 12
Primary Menu: Hamburger (12)
Areas of Operation: MO
Type of Foodservice: Quick Serve (12)
Franchise Affiliation: McDonald's Corporation, CHICAGO, IL

Key Personnel
CHRIS GIARLA - President; General Buyer

Domino's Distribution Center
1 Cermak Blvd
Saint Peters, MO 63376-1019

Telephone: (636) 970-3030
Fax Number: (636) 279-3037
Internet Homepage: dominos.com
Listing Type: Distribution Center
Type of Business: Chain Restaurant Operator
Number of Employees: 90
Areas of Operation: AR, IA, IL, IN, KS, KY, MO, NE, TN
Parent Company: Domino's Pizza Inc, ANN ARBOR, MI

Key Personnel
A J SUMPTER - General Manager

Lambert's Cafe
2305 E Malone Ave
Sikeston, MO 63801-3801

Telephone: (573) 471-4261
Fax Number: (573) 471-7563
Internet Homepage: throwedrolls.com
Type of Business: Chain Restaurant Operator
Total Sales: $27,849,000 (e)
Number of Employees: 200
Average Check: Lunch(16); Dinner(16)
Total Units: 3
Trade Names: Lambert's Cafe (3)
Company-Owned Units: 3
Preferred Location Types: Freestanding
Primary Menu: American (3)
Areas of Operation: AL, MO
Type of Foodservice: Family Restaurant (3)
Primary Distributors: (Full Line) US Foods, SALEM, MO

Key Personnel
SCOTT LAMBERT - President; Partner
JERRY JOHNSON - General Manager
KELLY BROWN - Manager

A&M Pizza
538 S National Ave
Springfield, MO 65802-3434

Telephone: (417) 865-8443
Fax Number: (417) 865-9043
Internet Homepage: dominos.com
Company Email: dominosteam@aol.com
Type of Business: Chain Restaurant Operator
Total Sales: $46,050,000 (e)
Number of Employees: 174
Internet Order Processing: Yes
Internet Sales: 1.00%
Total Units: 23
Trade Names: Domino's (23)
Units Franchised From: 23
Preferred Square Footage: 1,000
Primary Menu: Pizza (23)
Areas of Operation: MO
Type of Foodservice: Quick Serve (23)
Franchise Affiliation: Domino's Pizza Inc, ANN ARBOR, MI

Key Personnel
ART HURTEAU - President; General Manager; General Buyer

America's Incredible Pizza Company
2522 S Campbell Ave
Springfield, MO 65807-3502

Telephone: (417) 890-1408
Fax Number: (417) 890-1635
Internet Homepage: incrediblepizza.com
Company Email: info@incrediblepizza.com
Type of Business: Chain Restaurant Operator
Year Founded: 2002
Systemwide Sales: $48,574,000 (e)
Total Sales: $11,330,000 (e)
Number of Employees: 522
Average Check: Lunch(8); Dinner(10)
Total Units: 6
Trade Names: America's Incredible Pizza Company (6)
Units Franchised To: 6
Preferred Square Footage: 70,000
Preferred Location Types: Freestanding
Primary Menu: Pizza (6)
Areas of Operation: MO, OK, TN, TX, FC
Foreign Countries: MEXICO
Type of Foodservice: Family Restaurant (6)

Key Personnel
RICK BARSNESS - Chairman; Founder; CEO; Partner
CHERYL BARSNESS - President; Partner
DON HARVEY - Partner
JEFF MADDOCK - Partner
EDUARDO MARTINEZ - COO
TREYSON ABBE - VP Web Development
MONICA GSELL - Senior Director Customer Service
MICHAEL TODD - Director Customer Service
JERRY BARTON - Director
JESSICA BURNS - Director Group
JEREMY KELLAR - Director Marketing
KENDALL LEWIS - Manager Event Planning
SUZANNE JANICK - Manager Sales

Andy's Frozen Custard
211 E Water St
Springfield, MO 65806

Telephone: (417) 881-3500
Fax Number: (417) 881-3571
Internet Homepage: eatandys.com
Company Email: info@eatandys.com
Type of Business: Chain Restaurant Operator
Year Founded: 1986
Number of Employees: 1,350

Total Units: 74
Trade Names: Andy's Frozen Custard (74)
Company-Owned Units: 44
Units Franchised To: 10
Preferred Location Types: Freestanding
Primary Menu: Snacks (74)
Areas of Operation: AR, AZ, CO, IL, KS, MO, NC, OK, TN, TX
Type of Foodservice: Quick Serve (74)

Key Personnel
CAROL KUNTZ - Founder
ANDY KUNTZ - President; Owner
RANDAL SCHULZE - President Operations; General Manager
AVERY KLEIN - Owner; Manager Marketing, Communications
BUDDY COULTER - CFO
TODD ARTH - COO
RICH TURER - VP Marketing
BRANDON CRABTREE - VP Operations
ASHLEY KANEL - Director Accounting
FABIAN VARGAS - Director Operations
ALICIA ARMSTRONG - Director Supply Chain
DILLON VANWINKLE - Director New Store Development
ERIN BARTEL - Regional Manager Marketing
KATIE STERLING - Manager Human Resources
KRISTIE DAINS - Manager Customer Service
BECKIE REIDLE - Manager Branch
ANN BURGE - Manager Operations

Bass Pro Shops
2500 E Kearney St
Springfield, MO 65807

Telephone: (417) 873-5000
Fax Number: (417) 869-5993
Internet Homepage: restaurants.basspro.com; basspro.com
Type of Business: Chain Restaurant Operator
Year Founded: 1972
Total Sales: $38,440,000 (e)
Total Units: 12
Trade Names: Hemingway's Blue Water Cafe (1); Islamorada Fish Company (5); Uncle Buck's Fishbowl and Grill (5); White River Fish House (1)
Company-Owned Units: 12
Preferred Location Types: Freestanding
Alcohol Served: Beer, Wine, Liquor
Primary Menu: American (6); Sandwiches/Deli (0); Seafood (6); Steak (0)
Areas of Operation: AL, AZ, CA, CO, FL, IA, IL, IN, LA, MO, SC, TN, TX, VA, WA
Type of Foodservice: Casual Dining (12)

Key Personnel
JOHN L. MORRIS - Founder; CEO
GARY EHLERS - Chief Human Resources Officer; Chief Diversity Officer
M J JOBE - General Manager
DANIEL SALAZAR - General Manager

STEVE WELLMAN - Director Digital Marketing
TOM PILE - Director Architecture, Information Technology
NICOLE MEYERS - Director Marketing
CHARLES DIECKER - Director Information Technology, Security
JIM GOFF - Regional Director
JIM OSBORNE - Regional Director
HEATHER EBERLE - Manager Integration
KIM BLOK - Manager Human Resources
AMANDA PETERSON - Program Manager Retail Operations
JENNIFER GOSNEY - Category Manager Procurement

Big Whiskeys Concepts LLC
315 Park Central E
Springfield, MO 65806-2206

Telephone: (417) 869-2449
Internet Homepage: bigwhiskeys.com
Company Email: info@bigwhiskeys.com
Type of Business: Chain Restaurant Operator
Total Units: 11
Trade Names: Big Whiskey's American Restaurant & Bar (11)
Company-Owned Units: 9
Units Franchised To: 2
Primary Menu: American (11)
Projected Openings: 2
Areas of Operation: AR, MO
Type of Foodservice: Casual Dining (11)

Key Personnel
AUSTIN HERSCHEND - President; Partner
PAUL SUNDY - Senior VP Operations
LAURA ELLIOTT - Director Marketing

FazWest Group, Inc.
2137 N Glenstone Ave Ste R
Springfield, MO 65803-4645

Mailing Address: PO Box 10726, SPRINGFIELD, MO, 65808-0726
Telephone: (417) 831-8299
Company Email: fazolis@fazwest.com
Type of Business: Chain Restaurant Operator
Total Sales: $8,255,000 (e)
Number of Employees: 150
Average Check: Lunch(16); Dinner(20)
Total Units: 3
Trade Names: Fazoli's (3)
Units Franchised From: 3
Preferred Square Footage: 2,900
Preferred Location Types: Freestanding
Primary Menu: Italian (3)
Areas of Operation: MO
Type of Foodservice: Fast Casual (3)
Catering Services: Yes
Franchise Affiliation: Fazoli's Restaurant LLC,

LEXINGTON, KY

Key Personnel
JAMES JACOBSEN - President; Partner
LARRY GRAHAM - Partner; General Buyer
DONNA JACOBSEN - Manager Human Resources

Gilbert & Sons Inc.
1722 S Glenstone Ave Ste T
Springfield, MO 65804-1516

Telephone: (417) 887-9817
Fax Number: (417) 887-9819
Internet Homepage: arbysspringfield.com
Company Email: arbysspringfield@sbcglobal.net
Type of Business: Chain Restaurant Operator
Year Founded: 1968
Total Sales: $9,351,000 (e)
Number of Employees: 105
Average Check: Lunch(8); Dinner(8)
Total Units: 5
Trade Names: Arby's (5)
Units Franchised From: 5
Preferred Square Footage: 2,500; 3,000
Preferred Location Types: Freestanding
Primary Menu: Sandwiches/Deli (5)
Areas of Operation: MO
Type of Foodservice: Quick Serve (5)
Franchise Affiliation: Arby's Restaurant Group, ATLANTA, GA
Primary Distributors: (Full Line) The SYGMA Network Inc. - Oklahoma, PRYOR, OK

Key Personnel
WILLIAM GILBERT JR - President; Controller; General Buyer
BILLY GILBERT - VP; General Manager; Manager Operations

Hamra Enterprises
1855 S Ingram Mill Rd Ste 100
Springfield, MO 65804-2100

Telephone: (417) 887-7677
Fax Number: (417) 890-5397
Internet Homepage: hamraenterprises.com
Type of Business: Chain Restaurant Operator
Year Founded: 1975
Total Sales: $276,030,000 (e)
Number of Employees: 7,000
Average Check: Lunch(8); Dinner(8)
Total Units: 169
Trade Names: Noodles and Company (8); Panera Bread (68); Wendy's Old Fashioned Hamburgers (93)
Units Franchised From: 169
Preferred Square Footage: 2,100; 2,900; 4,480
Preferred Location Types: Freestanding

Primary Menu: Hamburger (93); Miscellaneous (8); Sandwiches/Deli (68)
Areas of Operation: AR, IL, KS, MA, MO, MS, NH, TN, TX
Type of Foodservice: Fast Casual (68); Quick Serve (101)
Franchise Affiliation: Noodles & Company, BROOMFIELD, CO; Panera Bread Company, SAINT LOUIS, MO; The Wendy's Company, DUBLIN, OH
Primary Distributors: (Full Line) The SYGMA Network Inc. - Oklahoma, PRYOR, OK
Notes: The Wendy's restaurants operate as Wendy's of Missouri; the Panera restaurants operate as Boston Bread LLC & Chicago Bread LLC.

Key Personnel
JUNE HAMRA - Chairman; CEO
MIKE HAMRA - CEO; President; COO; Director Real Estate; General Buyer
SIMEON SHELTON - CFO
AKSHIT SHAH - CIO
JOHN ADDELIA - VP Operations
BEN KAPLAN - VP Real Estate
LORI JOHNSON - Treasurer
KRISTA KRON - General Counsel
EVE METHENY - Director Brand Marketing
ANTHONY MONTANARO - Director Loss Prevention, Asset Protection
VALERIE ROOT - Director Information Technology
WM KERRIGAN - Director Human Resources
WM SCOTT KERRIGAN - Director Human Resources
KRISTI DYKSTRA - Director
GRAHAM THEODORE - Director Operations
BONNIE SIMON - Regional Director Operations
JOEL ALDRICH - Regional Director Operations
BOB MARCUM - Regional Director Operations
ABIGAIL CRIMMINS - Regional Manager Training
CHASE GRUBB - Manager Procurement
CODY KNIGHT - Manager Real Estate
JAMES WORMINGTON - Manager Human Resources
JANELLE HEATH - Specialist Accounting

Leonard's Steak-N-Shake
1550 S Glenstone Ave
Springfield, MO 65804-1408

Telephone: (417) 887-0906
Type of Business: Chain Restaurant Operator
Year Founded: 1972
Total Sales: $9,035,000 (e)
Number of Employees: 240
Average Check: Lunch(6); Dinner(6)
Total Units: 6
Trade Names: Steak 'n Shake (6)
Units Franchised From: 6
Preferred Square Footage: 3,900
Preferred Location Types: Freestanding
Primary Menu: Hamburger (6)
Areas of Operation: MO
Type of Foodservice: Family Restaurant (6)
Franchise Affiliation: The Steak n Shake Operations Inc., INDIANAPOLIS, IN
Primary Distributors: (Food) The SYGMA Network Inc. - Oklahoma, PRYOR, OK

Key Personnel
GARY L. LEONARD - President; Controller; Director Operations, Purchasing, Facility/Maintenance, Information Systems, Real Estate, Design, Store Fixtures

Mexican Villa Resaurants, LLC
1100 W Sunshine St
Springfield, MO 65807-2448

Telephone: (417) 869-5300
Fax Number: (417) 869-5373
Internet Homepage: mexicanvilla.net
Company Email: info@mexicanvilla.net
Type of Business: Chain Restaurant Operator
Year Founded: 1951
Total Sales: $6,798,000 (e)
Alcohol Sales: 1%
Number of Employees: 250
Average Check: Lunch(14); Dinner(18)
Internet Order Processing: Yes
Total Units: 7
Trade Names: Mexican Villa (7)
Company-Owned Units: 7
Preferred Square Footage: 2,500; 4,000
Preferred Location Types: Freestanding
Alcohol Served: Beer
Primary Menu: Mexican (7)
Areas of Operation: MO
Type of Foodservice: Casual Dining (7)
On-site Distribution Center: Yes
Primary Distributors: (Full Line) US Foods, SALEM, MO

Key Personnel
THOMAS H. FERGUSON - Chairman; CEO; President; Director Risk Management, Menu Development, Food Safety
MARK R. FERGUSON - Executive Chef; Director Risk Management, Menu Development, Food Safety; General Buyer

Phillip Stocker Co.
2728 E Chestnut Expy
Springfield, MO 65802-2555

Telephone: (417) 865-7877
Fax Number: (471) 865-8925
Type of Business: Chain Restaurant Operator
Total Sales: $28,490,000 (e)
Number of Employees: 100
Total Units: 6
Trade Names: McDonald's (6)
Units Franchised From: 6
Preferred Square Footage: 2,500
Primary Menu: Hamburger (6)
Areas of Operation: MO
Type of Foodservice: Quick Serve (6)
Franchise Affiliation: McDonald's Corporation, CHICAGO, IL

Key Personnel
PHILLIP STOCKER - President; General Buyer
SAM STEPHENS - Director Operations

Village Inn Pancake House of Springfield Inc.
909 E Republic Rd Ste B100
Springfield, MO 65807-6010

Telephone: (417) 881-2752
Fax Number: (417) 887-2113
Company Email: viphoffice@aol.com
Type of Business: Chain Restaurant Operator
Year Founded: 1964
Total Sales: $6,168,000 (e)
Number of Employees: 160
Average Check: Breakfast(10); Lunch(10); Dinner(10)
Total Units: 4
Trade Names: Village Inn (4)
Units Franchised From: 4
Preferred Square Footage: 5,000
Preferred Location Types: Freestanding
Primary Menu: American (4)
Areas of Operation: MO
Type of Foodservice: Family Restaurant (4)
Franchise Affiliation: Village Inn, MINNETONKA, MN

Key Personnel
ROBERT J. GREENE JR - President; Partner
BILL GREENE - Partner; VP Purchasing; Director Finance, Risk Management, Food Safety
DEBRA BORDEN - General Manager

So Hospitality Group
612 N 2nd St Ste 400
St Louis, MO 63102

Telephone: (314) 241-3474
Internet Homepage: sohospitalitygroup.com
Company Email: info@sohospitalitygroup.com
Type of Business: Chain Restaurant Operator
Year Founded: 2003
Total Units: 6
Trade Names: Drunken Fish Sushi Restaurant & Lounge (4); Kimchi Guys Casual Eatery + Korean Fried Chicken (1); Miss Java (1)
Company-Owned Units: 6

Preferred Location Types: Downtown; Strip Mall
Primary Menu: Asian (5); Coffee (1)
Areas of Operation: MO
Type of Foodservice: Casual Dining (5); Quick Serve (1)

Key Personnel
MUNSOK SO - CEO; President
JIHYE BAEK - Manager Marketing
TASHAUN EWING - Coordinator Event Planning

Sugarfire Smokehouse
5 Maryview Ln
St Louis, MO 63124

Telephone: (314) 619-5407
Internet Homepage: cyranos.com; hipointedrivein.com; sugarfirepie.com; sugarfiresmokehouse.com
Company Email: hi@hipointedrivein.com
Type of Business: Chain Restaurant Operator
Systemwide Sales: $38,761,000 (e)
Total Sales: $28,610,000 (e)
Total Units: 17
Trade Names: Boathouse at Forest Park (1); Cyrano's Cafe & Wine Bar (1); Hi-Pointe Drive-In (1); Sugarfire Pie (1); Sugarfire Smokehouse (15)
Company-Owned Units: 13
Units Franchised To: 6
Primary Menu: American (3); Bar-B-Q (15); Snacks (1)
Areas of Operation: MO
Type of Foodservice: Casual Dining (2); Fast Casual (17)

Key Personnel
CAROLYN DOWNS - Partner
MIKE JOHNSON - Partner; Executive Chef
KATE WALLACE - Executive Chef
HEATHER DOUGHERTY - Director Operations
VERONICA SCHUSTER - Director Customer Service
JOSE ROMO - Director Facility/Maintenance

Native Foods Cafe LLC
7733 Forsyth Blvd Ste 1525
St. Louis, MO 63105

Telephone: (314) 450-7799
Internet Homepage: nativefoods.com
Company Email: onlinesupport@nativefoods.com
Type of Business: Chain Restaurant Operator
Year Founded: 1994
Total Sales: $11,610,000 (e)
Alcohol Sales: 5%
Average Check: Lunch(16); Dinner(16)
Internet Order Processing: Yes
Total Units: 13
Trade Names: Native Foods (13)
Company-Owned Units: 13
Preferred Location Types: Downtown; Freestanding; Lifestyle Center
Alcohol Served: Beer, Wine, Liquor
Primary Menu: Health Foods (13)
Areas of Operation: CA, CO, IL, OR
Type of Foodservice: Casual Dining (13)
Primary Distributors: (Full Line) US Foods, CORONA, CA
Parent Company: Millstone Capital Group, ,

Key Personnel
FRED SHAFI - General Manager

Seoul Taco
571 Melville Ave
St. Louis, MO 63130

Internet Homepage: seoultaco.com
Type of Business: Chain Restaurant Operator
Total Sales: $7,050,000 (e)
Total Units: 7
Trade Names: Seoul Taco (7)
Company-Owned Units: 7
Primary Menu: Asian (7)
Areas of Operation: IL, MO
Type of Foodservice: Fast Casual (7)

Key Personnel
DAVID CHOI - Owner; Executive Chef
CHEVALA DAVENPORT - Director Catering

Tilford Restaurant Group
6233 Delmar Blvd Unit 204
St. Louis, MO 63130

Telephone: (314) 480-5129
Internet Homepage: cateralfresco.com; milagromodernmexican.com; missiontacojoint.com
Company Email: info@CateralFresco.com
Type of Business: Chain Restaurant Operator
Total Units: 7
Trade Names: Milagro Modern Mexican (1); Mission Taco Joint (6)
Company-Owned Units: 7
Primary Menu: Mexican (1); Taco (6)
Areas of Operation: MO
Type of Foodservice: Casual Dining (7)

Key Personnel
ADAM TILFORD - Partner
JASON TILFORD - Partner
MARK TILFORD - Director Facility/Maintenance
COURTNEY KNIERIM - Manager Human Resources

Domino's Franchisee
121 N Service Rd W
Sullivan, MO 63080-1234

Telephone: (573) 468-3030
Type of Business: Chain Restaurant Operator
Total Sales: $12,070,000 (e)
Total Units: 6
Trade Names: Domino's (6)
Units Franchised From: 6
Primary Menu: Pizza (6)
Areas of Operation: MO
Type of Foodservice: Quick Serve (6)
Franchise Affiliation: Domino's Pizza Inc, ANN ARBOR, MI

Key Personnel
LEONARD J. NAUGLE - Owner; General Buyer

W & M Restaurants, Inc
405 US Highway 50 W Ste 700
Union, MO 63084-1967

Telephone: (636) 583-4052
Fax Number: (636) 583-4154
Type of Business: Chain Restaurant Operator
Total Sales: $35,620,000 (e)
Total Units: 13
Trade Names: Taco Bell (13)
Units Franchised From: 13
Primary Menu: Taco (13)
Areas of Operation: AZ, IL, MO
Type of Foodservice: Quick Serve (13)
Franchise Affiliation: Taco Bell Corp., IRVINE, CA

Key Personnel
JOHN W. WALLER - President; General Buyer
MICHAEL GOMAS - Director Operations

Great Restaurants
47 S Old Orchard Ave
Webster Groves, MO 63119-3202

Telephone: (314) 962-5757
Fax Number: (314) 962-6478
Internet Homepage: bigskycafe.net
Company Email: kelly@allgreatrestaurants.com
Type of Business: Chain Restaurant Operator
Year Founded: 1995
Total Sales: $3,638,000 (e)
Alcohol Sales: 30%
Number of Employees: 110
Average Check: Lunch(34); Dinner(44)
Internet Order Processing: Yes
Internet Sales: 1.00%
Total Units: 1
Trade Names: Big Sky Cafe (1)

Company-Owned Units: 1
Preferred Location Types: Downtown; Freestanding
Alcohol Served: Beer, Wine, Liquor
Primary Menu: Greek/Mediterranean (1)
Projected Remodelings: 1
Areas of Operation: MO
Type of Foodservice: Casual Dining (1)
Catering Services: Yes

Key Personnel
TIM MALLETT - President; Director Operations; General Buyer
KELLY DONOVAN - Director Marketing, Communications
SHELLY GIUALLANNI - Manager Finance

Erbe Pizza I, Inc.
1700 Gratree Ln
Wentzville, MO 63385-4934

Telephone: (314) 223-8963
Type of Business: Chain Restaurant Operator
Total Sales: $1,409,000 (e)
Total Units: 2
Trade Names: Little Caesars Pizza (2)
Units Franchised From: 2
Preferred Location Types: Strip Mall
Primary Menu: Pizza (2)
Areas of Operation: MO
Type of Foodservice: Quick Serve (2)
Franchise Affiliation: Little Caesar Enterprises Inc., DETROIT, MI

Key Personnel
STEPHEN ERBE - President; General Buyer

Peak Resorts Inc.
17409 Hidden Valley Dr
Wildwood, MO 63025-2213

Telephone: (636) 938-7474
Fax Number: (636) 549-0064
Internet Homepage: peakresorts.com
Type of Business: Nontraditional Foodservice Operator
Year Founded: 1997
Total Sales: $267,785,000 (e)
Number of Employees: 70
Total Units: 12
Trade Names: Alpine Valley (1); Attitash (1); Boston Mills Brandywine (1); Crotched Mountain (1); Hidden Valley (1); Hunter Mountain (1); Jack Frost Big Boulder (1); Mad River (1); Mount Snow (1); Paoli Peaks (1); Snow Creek (1); Wildcat (1)
Company-Owned Units: 12
Alcohol Served: Beer, Wine, Liquor
Areas of Operation: IN, MO, NH, OH, PA, VT
Type of Foodservice: Casual Dining (12)

Key Personnel
TIMOTHY D. BOYD - Chairman; CEO; President
RICHARD K. DEUTSCH - VP Real Estate, Business Development
SHAWN MUNZ - Manager Inventory

MISSISSIPPI

Domino's Franchisee
700A Main St N
Amory, MS 38821-2335

Telephone: (662) 256-3663
Type of Business: Chain Restaurant Operator
Total Sales: $16,115,000 (e)
Total Units: 8
Trade Names: Domino's (8)
Units Franchised From: 8
Primary Menu: Pizza (8)
Areas of Operation: MS
Type of Foodservice: Quick Serve (8)
Franchise Affiliation: Domino's Pizza Inc, ANN ARBOR, MI

Key Personnel
TIMOTHY B. BROWN - Owner; General Buyer

Domino's Franchisee
460 Highway 6 E
Batesville, MS 38606-3000

Telephone: (662) 563-5600
Type of Business: Chain Restaurant Operator
Total Sales: $3,960,000 (e)
Total Units: 2
Trade Names: Domino's (2)
Units Franchised From: 2
Primary Menu: Pizza (2)
Areas of Operation: MS
Type of Foodservice: Quick Serve (2)
Franchise Affiliation: Domino's Pizza Inc, ANN ARBOR, MI

Key Personnel
RICHARD A. DAVIS - Owner; General Buyer

Auntie Anne's Franchise
842 Eagle Eyrie Dr
Biloxi, MS 39531

Telephone: (228) 388-3805
Type of Business: Chain Restaurant Operator
Total Sales: $2,392,000 (e)
Total Units: 3
Trade Names: Auntie Anne's Hand-Rolled Soft Pretzels (3)
Units Franchised From: 3
Primary Menu: Snacks (3)
Areas of Operation: MS
Type of Foodservice: Quick Serve (3)
Franchise Affiliation: Auntie Anne's Inc., LANCASTER, PA

Key Personnel
RICHARD REAVES - Owner; General Buyer

Domino's Franchisee
975 Brookway Blvd
Brookhaven, MS 39601-2643

Telephone: (601) 835-3278
Type of Business: Chain Restaurant Operator
Total Sales: $5,972,000 (e)
Total Units: 3
Trade Names: Domino's (3)
Units Franchised From: 3
Primary Menu: Pizza (3)
Areas of Operation: MS
Type of Foodservice: Quick Serve (3)
Franchise Affiliation: Domino's Pizza Inc, ANN ARBOR, MI

Key Personnel
MATTHEW MAGEE - Owner; General Buyer

Jackie's International Inc.
1554 W Peace St
Canton, MS 39046-5325

Telephone: (601) 855-0146
Fax Number: (601) 855-9305
Internet Homepage: bumpersdrivein.com; jackiesinternational.com
Company Email: comments@bumpersdrivein.com
Type of Business: Chain Restaurant Operator
Year Founded: 1984
Systemwide Sales: $58,229,000 (e)
Total Sales: $56,820,000 (e)
Number of Employees: 1,050
Average Check: Lunch(14); Dinner(20)
Total Units: 35
Trade Names: Bumpers Drive-In (30); Fresh Market Cafe (2); Simply Southern Grill & Buffet (3)
Company-Owned Units: 35
Preferred Square Footage: 1,500
Preferred Location Types: Freestanding
Alcohol Served: Beer, Wine, Liquor
Primary Menu: American (30); Southern (5)
Areas of Operation: MS, TN
Type of Foodservice: Family Restaurant (5); Quick Serve (30)
Primary Distributors: (Full Line) Merchants Distributors Inc., HICKORY, NC

Key Personnel
S. L. SETHI - CEO; President; Director Finance, Real Estate, Menu Development
JERRY BECKWITH - CFO
SUNNY SETHI - VP

Domino's Franchisee
425C N Davis Ave
Cleveland, MS 38732-2351

Telephone: (662) 843-3663
Type of Business: Chain Restaurant Operator
Total Sales: $4,131,000 (e)
Total Units: 2
Trade Names: Domino's (2)
Units Franchised From: 2
Primary Menu: Pizza (2)
Areas of Operation: MS
Type of Foodservice: Quick Serve (2)
Franchise Affiliation: Domino's Pizza Inc, ANN ARBOR, MI

Key Personnel
NEAL W. ANDERSON - Owner; General Buyer

Eat With Us Group
104 1/2 3rd St S
Columbus, MS 39701-5628

Mailing Address: PO Box 1368, COLUMBUS, MS, 39703-1368
Telephone: (662) 327-6982
Fax Number: (662) 327-1672
Internet Homepage: eatwithus.com
Company Email: info@eatwithus.com
Type of Business: Chain Restaurant Operator
Year Founded: 1981
Total Sales: $19,270,000 (e)
Alcohol Sales: 20%
Number of Employees: 409
Average Check: Lunch(10); Dinner(16)
Internet Order Processing: Yes
Total Units: 17
Trade Names: Bull Dog Burger Co (1); Grill (3); Harvey's (3); Smacker (1); Sweet Peppers Deli (9)
Company-Owned Units: 8
Units Franchised To: 8
Preferred Square Footage: 10,000
Preferred Location Types: Community Mall; Freestanding
Alcohol Served: Beer, Wine, Liquor
Primary Menu: American (6); Hamburger (1); Sandwiches/Deli (9); Snacks (1)
Areas of Operation: MS
Type of Foodservice: Casual Dining (16); Quick Serve (1)
Catering Services: Yes
Primary Distributors: (Equipment) Hotel & Restaurant Supply, MERIDIAN, MS; (Food) US Foods, MEMPHIS, TN; (Supplies) Hotel & Restaurant Supply, MERIDIAN, MS

Key Personnel
JOHN BEAN - CEO; President
BRYANT BEAN - Partner
PAT CAMPEAU - Partner
ROBERT FORT - CFO
BERNARD BEAN - COO
ROBIN FANT - CTO; VP
ASHLEY WILSON - VP People
CHARLOTTE PHILLIPS - Controller
MATT BRONSKI - Corporate Chef
DUSTON PRICE - Director Beverages
JORDAN TARTER - Director Marketing, Sales
MEREDITH FRASER - Office Manager

Eat With Us Group
104 1/2 3rd St S
Columbus, MS 39701-5628

Mailing Address: PO Box 1368, COLUMBUS, MS, 39703-1368
Telephone: (662) 327-6982
Fax Number: (662) 327-1672
Internet Homepage: eatwithpeppers.com
Type of Business: Chain Restaurant Operator
Year Founded: 1997
Systemwide Sales: $25,887,000 (e)
Total Sales: $26,110,000 (e)
Number of Employees: 665
Average Check: Lunch(10); Dinner(10)
Total Units: 16
Trade Names: Bull Dog Burgers (1); Harveys (3); Sweet Peppers Deli (9); The Grill (3)
Company-Owned Units: 10
Units Franchised To: 6
Preferred Location Types: Community Mall; Freestanding; Lifestyle Center; Strip Mall
Alcohol Served: Beer, Wine
Primary Menu: American (6); Hamburger (1); Sandwiches/Deli (9)
Areas of Operation: AL, FL, GA, MS, TN
Type of Foodservice: Casual Dining (6); Fast Casual (10)
Catering Services: Yes
Primary Distributors: (Full Line) US Foods, FLOWOOD, MS; (Supplies) Hotel & Restaurant Supply, MERIDIAN, MS

Key Personnel
JOHN BEAN - President
ROBERT FORT - CFO
BERNARD BEAN - COO
ROBIN FANT - VP Operations, Training
CHARLOTTE PHILLIPS - Controller
MATT BRONSKI - Corporate Chef
ASHLEY DODSON - Director Human Resources

JACO Foods
111 Maxwell Ln
Columbus, MS 39702-5243

Telephone: (662) 328-5009
Fax Number: (662) 328-5154
Type of Business: Chain Restaurant Operator
Year Founded: 1975
Total Sales: $14,720,000 (e)
Number of Employees: 200
Average Check: Breakfast(8); Lunch(10); Dinner(12)
Total Units: 7
Trade Names: Sonic America's Drive-In (7)
Units Franchised From: 7
Preferred Square Footage: 1,100; 1,200; 1,350
Preferred Location Types: Freestanding
Primary Menu: Hamburger (7)
Areas of Operation: MS
Type of Foodservice: Quick Serve (7)
Franchise Affiliation: Sonic Corp., OKLAHOMA CITY, OK
Primary Distributors: (Full Line) US Foods, NORCROSS, GA

Key Personnel
ERNIE JACOBSEN - President; Partner; General Buyer
DONNA JACOBSEN - Partner; VP Supply Chain; Director Real Estate
PAUL DORN - COO; Director Operations
CINDY HALL - Manager Accounting

Joe Asadi
1907 Highway 45 N Ste 1
Columbus, MS 39705-1950

Telephone: (662) 327-5508
Type of Business: Chain Restaurant Operator
Total Units: 2
Trade Names: Subway (2)
Units Franchised From: 2
Primary Menu: Sandwiches/Deli (2)
Areas of Operation: MS
Type of Foodservice: Quick Serve (2)
Franchise Affiliation: Doctor's Associates Inc., MILFORD, CT

Key Personnel
JOE ASADI - President; General Buyer

Little Foods Inc.
610 E Waldron St
Corinth, MS 38834-4863

Mailing Address: PO Box 1150, CORINTH, MS, 38835-1150
Telephone: (662) 287-0959

Fax Number: (662) 287-0970
Type of Business: Chain Restaurant Operator
Year Founded: 1987
Total Sales: $16,170,000 (e)
Number of Employees: 110
Average Check: Lunch(8); Dinner(12)
Total Units: 6
Trade Names: Taco Bell (6)
Units Franchised From: 6
Preferred Location Types: Freestanding
Primary Menu: Taco (6)
Areas of Operation: MS
Type of Foodservice: Quick Serve (6)
Franchise Affiliation: Taco Bell Corp., IRVINE, CA
Primary Distributors: (Full Line) McLane Foodservice, CARROLLTON, TX

Key Personnel
PHIL LITTLE - President; Partner; General Manager; General Buyer
VICKI LITTLE - Partner
KEITH SAYLORS - Director Operations

Perimeter Foods Inc
517 Keywood Cir Ste 1B
Flowood, MS 39232-3054

Telephone: (601) 936-6027
Fax Number: (601) 936-9633
Type of Business: Chain Restaurant Operator
Total Sales: $27,330,000 (e)
Total Units: 10
Trade Names: Wendy's Old Fashioned Hamburgers (10)
Units Franchised From: 10
Primary Menu: Hamburger (10)
Areas of Operation: MS
Type of Foodservice: Quick Serve (10)
Franchise Affiliation: The Wendy's Company, DUBLIN, OH

Key Personnel
JAN COLLINS - President; General Buyer

Valley Services Inc.
10 Canebrake Blvd Ste 120
Flowood, MS 39232

Mailing Address: PO Box 5454, JACKSON, MS, 39288-5454
Telephone: (601) 664-3100
Fax Number: (601) 664-3399
Internet Homepage: valleyinc.com
Company Email: sales@valleyinc.com
Type of Business: Foodservice Management Operator
Year Founded: 1960
Total Sales: $305,086,000 (e)
Number of Employees: 2,200
Number of Locations Served: 475
Total Foodservice Mgmt Accounts: 250
Areas of Operation: FL, GA, LA, MS
Type of Foodservice: Quick Serve (250)
Foodservice Management Venues: College & University; Health Care; Parks & Recreation; Prison Feeding
Primary Distributors: (Food) SYSCO Food Services of Jackson, JACKSON, MS
Parent Company: TrustHouse Services Group, CHARLOTTE, NC

Key Personnel
SCOTT BALL - Exec VP

Doe's Inc
502 Nelson St
Greenville, MS 38701-2937

Telephone: (662) 334-3315
Fax Number: (662) 334-1872
Internet Homepage: doeseatplace.com
Type of Business: Chain Restaurant Operator
Year Founded: 1941
Systemwide Sales: $17,218,000 (e)
Total Sales: $7,459,000 (e)
Alcohol Sales: 3%
Number of Employees: 91
Average Check: Dinner(42)
Total Units: 15
Trade Names: Doe's Eat Place (15)
Company-Owned Units: 2
Units Franchised To: 13
Preferred Square Footage: 2,000
Preferred Location Types: Freestanding
Alcohol Served: Beer, Wine, Liquor
Primary Menu: American (15)
Areas of Operation: AL, AR, KY, LA, MS, OK
Type of Foodservice: Casual Dining (15)
Primary Distributors: (Full Line) SYSCO Food Services of Jackson, JACKSON, MS

Key Personnel
CHARLES SIGNA JR - President; General Manager; Manager Information Systems; General Buyer
DOE SIGNA III - VP; Manager Real Estate, Franchise Development; General Buyer

Retzer Resources
1215 S Main St
Greenville, MS 38701-6342

Telephone: (662) 335-7138
Fax Number: (662) 332-3519
Type of Business: Chain Restaurant Operator
Year Founded: 1973
Total Sales: $326,678,000 (e)
Number of Employees: 15,510
Average Check: Breakfast(8); Lunch(8); Dinner(8)
Total Units: 92
Trade Names: McDonald's (92)
Units Franchised From: 92
Preferred Square Footage: 2,500
Preferred Location Types: Freestanding
Primary Menu: Hamburger (92)
Areas of Operation: AR, MS
Type of Foodservice: Quick Serve (92)
Franchise Affiliation: McDonald's Corporation, CHICAGO, IL
Primary Distributors: (Food) The Martin-Brower Co., PORT ALLEN, LA

Key Personnel
DANIELLE MEERHOLZ - Director
TERRI MUREL - Manager Accounting

Southern Partners LLC
1404 Highway 82 E
Greenville, MS 38703-5907

Mailing Address: PO Box 6041, GREENVILLE, MS, 38704-6041
Telephone: (662) 335-9120
Fax Number: (662) 335-9436
Type of Business: Chain Restaurant Operator
Total Sales: $32,970,000 (e)
Total Units: 15
Trade Names: Sonic America's Drive-In (15)
Units Franchised From: 15
Primary Menu: Hamburger (15)
Areas of Operation: MS
Type of Foodservice: Quick Serve (15)
Franchise Affiliation: Sonic Corp., OKLAHOMA CITY, OK

Key Personnel
RICKY BAGWELL - President; General Buyer
CHAZ WESTER - Director Operations

Domino's Franchisee
919 Highway 82 W
Greenwood, MS 38930-2727

Telephone: (662) 455-3030
Type of Business: Chain Restaurant Operator
Total Sales: $6,162,000 (e)
Total Units: 3
Trade Names: Domino's (3)
Units Franchised From: 3
Primary Menu: Pizza (3)
Areas of Operation: MS
Type of Foodservice: Quick Serve (3)
Franchise Affiliation: Domino's Pizza Inc, ANN ARBOR, MI

Key Personnel
MARIO VARELA - Owner; General Buyer

Southern Pizza Co.
110 Professional Pl
Greenwood, MS 38930-9633

Mailing Address: PO Box 9382,
 GREENWOOD, MS, 38930-8982
Telephone: (662) 455-1616
Fax Number: (662) 455-3431
Type of Business: Chain Restaurant Operator
Year Founded: 1982
Total Sales: $5,499,000 (e)
Alcohol Sales: 2%
Number of Employees: 140
Average Check: Lunch(12); Dinner(12)
Total Units: 4
Trade Names: Pizza Inn (4)
Units Franchised From: 4
Preferred Square Footage: 1,600
Preferred Location Types: Freestanding
Alcohol Served: Beer
Primary Menu: Pizza (4)
Areas of Operation: AL, MS
Type of Foodservice: Casual Dining (4)
Franchise Affiliation: RAVE Restaurant Group
 Inc., THE COLONY, TX

Key Personnel
BOB SINGH - President; Manager Operations,
 Information Systems, Marketing, Real Estate;
 General Buyer
ANITA WILLIAMS - Manager Human Resources

RPM Pizza Inc.
15384 5th St
Gulfport, MS 39503-3184

Telephone: (228) 832-4000
Fax Number: (228) 832-1092
Internet Homepage: rpmpizza.com
Company Email: help@rpmpizza.com
Type of Business: Chain Restaurant Operator
Year Founded: 1981
Total Sales: $356,998,000 (e)
Number of Employees: 5,670
Average Check: Lunch(14); Dinner(14)
Total Units: 180
Trade Names: Domino's (180)
Units Franchised From: 180
Preferred Square Footage: 1,000; 1,200
Preferred Location Types: Convenience
 Store/Gas Station; Freestanding; Strip Mall
Primary Menu: Pizza (180)
Areas of Operation: AL, IN, LA, MI, MS
Type of Foodservice: Quick Serve (180)
Franchise Affiliation: Domino's Pizza Inc, ANN
 ARBOR, MI

Key Personnel
RICHARD MUELLER - Chairman
GLENN MUELLER - VP Marketing
ALAN LOVELACE - VP Strategy, Technology,
 Development
STEVE CONNELL - Senior Director Operations
MARGARET JACKSON - Director Development-
 Training
ROGERS MUELLER - Director Security, Safety,
 Construction
DANIEL DISHMAN - Director Operations
CHRIS BRADLEY - Director Operations
WANDA LAURENT - Director Operations
FRED COOK - Director Operations
SARA SMOOT - Director Talent
PEYTON WHITTY - Director Quality Assurance
TIMOTHY FIKES - Manager Information
 Technology

Chers Restaurant Group, LLC
100 Titus Blvd
Hattiesburg, MS 39402-6500

Telephone: (601) 602-4020
Fax Number: (601) 602-4022
Internet Homepage: mugshotsgrillandbar.com
Type of Business: Chain Restaurant Operator
Year Founded: 2004
Total Sales: $8,685,000 (e)
Alcohol Sales: 15%
Total Units: 16
Trade Names: MugShots Grill & Bar (16)
Company-Owned Units: 4
Units Franchised To: 12
Alcohol Served: Beer, Wine, Liquor
Primary Menu: American (16)
Projected Openings: 2
Areas of Operation: AL, LA, MS
Type of Foodservice: Casual Dining (16)

Key Personnel
RON SAVELL - Owner; General Buyer
EDDIE HALL - COO
BROCK BIESINGER - General Manager
CRYSTAL ROGERS - Manager

New South Restaurant Group
3904 Hardy St
Hattiesburg, MS 39402-1541

Telephone: (601) 264-0672
Fax Number: (601) 264-0681
Internet Homepage: nsrg.com
Type of Business: Chain Restaurant Operator
Total Sales: $7,211,000 (e)
Alcohol Sales: 10%
Number of Employees: 240
Total Units: 8
Trade Names: Branch (1); Crescent City Grill
 (1); Ed's Burger Joint (1); Mahogany Bar and
 Courtyard (1); Midtown Donut (1); Midtowner
 (1); Purple Parrot Cafe (1); Tabella (1)
Company-Owned Units: 5
Preferred Location Types: Freestanding; Strip
 Mall
Alcohol Served: Beer, Wine, Liquor
Primary Menu: American (2); Cajun/Creole (3);
 Hamburger (1); Italian (1); Snacks (1)
Areas of Operation: MS
Type of Foodservice: Casual Dining (5); Fine
 Dining (2); Quick Serve (1)
Primary Distributors: (Full Line) SYSCO Food
 Services of Jackson, JACKSON, MS

Key Personnel
ROBERT ST. JOHN - Owner; Executive Chef;
 General Buyer
MARIA KEYES - CFO
STACEY ANDREWS - Director Marketing,
 Advertising; Manager Branch

PAP, LLC
2056 Oak Grove Rd
Hattiesburg, MS 39402-1475

Telephone: (601) 584-7877
Fax Number: (601) 584-7824
Type of Business: Chain Restaurant Operator
Year Founded: 1995
Total Sales: $20,610,000 (e)
Number of Employees: 460
Average Check: Lunch(12); Dinner(12)
Total Units: 8
Trade Names: Popeyes Louisiana Kitchen (8)
Units Franchised From: 8
Preferred Square Footage: 2,000
Preferred Location Types: Freestanding
Primary Menu: Chicken (8)
Projected Openings: 1
Areas of Operation: AL, MS
Type of Foodservice: Quick Serve (8)
Franchise Affiliation: Popeyes Louisiana
 Kitchen Inc., ATLANTA, GA

Key Personnel
DAVID CHUNN - President; Owner; Director
 Finance, Operations, Purchasing, Information
 Systems, Real Estate; General Buyer
GEORGE HOLLOWELL - VP
BECKY ANDERSON - Manager Accounting,
 Administration

Sherman Foods, LLC
6106 U S Highway 98
Hattiesburg, MS 39402-8530

Telephone: (601) 261-9433
Type of Business: Chain Restaurant Operator
Total Sales: $2,484,000 (e)
Total Units: 2
Trade Names: Firehouse Subs (2)
Units Franchised From: 2
Preferred Location Types: Strip Mall

Primary Menu: Sandwiches/Deli (2)
Areas of Operation: AL, MS
Type of Foodservice: Fast Casual (2)
Franchise Affiliation: Firehouse Restaurant Group Inc., JACKSONVILLE, FL

Key Personnel
JUSTIN GREEN - President; General Buyer

Ward's Food Systems Inc.
5133 Lincoln Road Ext
Hattiesburg, MS 39402-8071

Telephone: (601) 268-9273
Fax Number: (601) 268-9283
Internet Homepage: wardsrestaurants.com
Company Email: wardsfranchise@bellsouth.net
Type of Business: Chain Restaurant Operator
Year Founded: 1984
Systemwide Sales: $20,575,000 (e)
Total Sales: $8,793,000 (e)
Number of Employees: 407
Average Check: Breakfast(8); Lunch(10); Dinner(12)
Internet Order Processing: Yes
Total Units: 37
Trade Names: Ward's Restaurant (37)
Company-Owned Units: 15
Units Franchised To: 22
Preferred Square Footage: 2,000
Preferred Location Types: Convenience Store/Gas Station; Freestanding
Primary Menu: American (37)
Areas of Operation: MS
Type of Foodservice: Quick Serve (37)
Primary Distributors: (Full Line) SYSCO Food Services of Jackson, JACKSON, MS

Key Personnel
SHELLEY SULLIVAN - CEO; President; Partner; Director Finance, Purchasing, Advertising, Product Development, Menu Development; Manager Information Technology
GLEN SULLIVAN - Partner; Director Operations, Loss Prevention, Food Safety; Manager Real Estate

Oxford Foods Inc.
761 Goodman Rd W
Horn Lake, MS 38637-1434

Telephone: (662) 349-8585
Type of Business: Chain Restaurant Operator
Total Sales: $69,640,000 (e)
Total Units: 20
Trade Names: Zaxby's (20)
Units Franchised From: 20
Primary Menu: Chicken (20)
Areas of Operation: MS
Type of Foodservice: Fast Casual (20)

Franchise Affiliation: Zaxby's Franchising Inc., ATHENS, GA

Key Personnel
TOM SCOTT - President
JENNIFER COBB - Director Operations

The Lost Pizza Co Inc.
807 Highway 82 W
Indianola, MS 38751-2038

Telephone: (662) 887-1555
Internet Homepage: lostpizza.com
Company Email: Eat@lostpizza.com
Type of Business: Chain Restaurant Operator
Year Founded: 2007
Average Check: Lunch(20); Dinner(26)
Total Units: 15
Trade Names: Lost Pizza (15)
Company-Owned Units: 4
Units Franchised To: 11
Primary Menu: Pizza (15)
Projected Openings: 2
Areas of Operation: AR, MS
Type of Foodservice: Fast Casual (15)

Key Personnel
BROOKS ROBERTS - Co-Founder; Partner
PRESTON LOTT - Co-Founder; Partner

Eat Here Brands
4500 I 55 N Ste 221
Jackson, MS 39211-5931

Telephone: (601) 956-7419
Fax Number: (601) 956-8484
Internet Homepage: eathere.com
Type of Business: Chain Restaurant Operator
Total Sales: $8,236,000 (e)
Total Units: 7
Trade Names: Babalu Tacos & Tapas (6); Table 100 (1)
Company-Owned Units: 7
Primary Menu: American (1); Spanish (6)
Areas of Operation: AL, GA, MS, TN
Type of Foodservice: Casual Dining (7)

Key Personnel
WILLIAM LATHAM - Partner; General Buyer
Al ROBERTS - Partner; VP; General Buyer
STEVEN ROCKWELL - General Manager
KATHY DIAMOND-ULEPIC - Director Branding
LULU INTAN - Consultant Digital

Mangia Bene, Inc.
3317 N State St
Jackson, MS 39216-3130

Telephone: (601) 982-4443

Fax Number: (601) 982-4301
Internet Homepage: bravobuzz.com; broadstbakery.com; salandmookies.com
Company Email: jeffg@bravobuzz.com
Type of Business: Chain Restaurant Operator
Year Founded: 1993
Total Sales: $15,384,000 (e)
Alcohol Sales: 30%
Number of Employees: 189
Average Check: Lunch(18); Dinner(42)
Internet Order Processing: Yes
Total Units: 4
Trade Names: Bravo! Italian Restaurant and Bar (1); Broad Street Baking Company & Cafe (1); Sal & Mookie's New York Style Pizza & Ice Cream Joint (2)
Company-Owned Units: 4
Preferred Location Types: Freestanding
Alcohol Served: Beer, Wine, Liquor
Primary Menu: Italian (1); Pizza (2); Sandwiches/Deli (1)
Areas of Operation: MS
Type of Foodservice: Casual Dining (4)
Catering Services: Yes
Primary Distributors: (Food) SYSCO Atlanta LLC, COLLEGE PARK, GA

Key Personnel
DAN BLUMENTHAL - Partner; Executive Chef; General Buyer
JEFF GOOD - Partner; General Manager
TERRY MUELLER - Manager

Newk's Franchise Company
2680 Crane Ridge Dr
Jackson, MS 39216-4905

Telephone: (601) 982-1160
Fax Number: (601) 982-1161
Internet Homepage: newks.com
Type of Business: Chain Restaurant Operator
Year Founded: 2004
Systemwide Sales: $359,286,000 (e)
Total Sales: $71,260,000 (e)
Average Check: Lunch(12); Dinner(14)
Total Units: 106
Trade Names: Newk's Eatery (106)
Company-Owned Units: 10
Units Franchised To: 96
Alcohol Served: Beer, Wine
Primary Menu: American (106)
Projected Openings: 18
Areas of Operation: AL, AR, FL, GA, KY, LA, MD, MO, MS, NC, SC, TN, TX
Type of Foodservice: Fast Casual (106)
Catering Services: Yes
Parent Company: FSC Franchise Co., LLC, TAMPA, FL

Key Personnel
DON NEWCOMB - Chairman; Co-Founder
DEBRA BRYSON - Co-Founder
CHRIS NEWCOMB - Co-Founder; CEO

JOE PATE - COO
MARK REEDY - VP Franchise Operations
ADAM KARVELLER - VP Information Technology
KEITH MOODY - VP Franchise Operations
SCOTT STINSON - VP Human Resources
CODY GARDNER - Director Operations
EDNA FUENTES-BELOU - Manager Sales
JARON SMITH - Manager Technology
MATT WILSON - Consultant Franchise Operations

Penn's Fish House Inc.
2085 Lakeland Dr
Jackson, MS 39216-5010

Telephone: (601) 982-0805
Fax Number: (601) 982-0910
Internet Homepage: pennsrestaurant.com
Company Email: pennsrestaurant@aol.com
Type of Business: Chain Restaurant Operator
Year Founded: 1967
Total Sales: $13,040,000 (e)
Alcohol Sales: 1%
Number of Employees: 85
Average Check: Lunch(14); Dinner(20)
Total Units: 11
Trade Names: Penn's Fish House (10); Penn's To-Go (1)
Company-Owned Units: 11
Units Franchised To: 11
Preferred Square Footage: 6,000
Preferred Location Types: Convenience Store/Gas Station; Freestanding
Primary Menu: Seafood (11)
Areas of Operation: MS
Type of Foodservice: Casual Dining (10); Quick Serve (1)
Catering Services: Yes
Primary Distributors: (Full Line) US Foods, MONTGOMERY, AL

Key Personnel
MICHAEL PENN - President; Manager Finance

West Quality Food Service
220 N 16th Ave
Laurel, MS 39440-4134

Mailing Address: PO Box 2906, LAUREL, MS, 39442-2906
Telephone: (601) 649-2522
Fax Number: (601) 649-9307
Company Email: info@westquality.com
Type of Business: Chain Restaurant Operator
Year Founded: 1967
Total Sales: $142,150,000 (e)
Number of Employees: 1,943
Average Check: Lunch(10); Dinner(10)
Total Units: 69
Trade Names: Checkers (1); KFC (45); KFC/Long John Silver's (3); KFC/Taco Bell (15); Rally's Hamburgers (4); Vic's Biscuits and Burgers (1)
Units Franchised From: 69
Preferred Square Footage: 1,000; 3,000
Preferred Location Types: Convenience Store/Gas Station; Freestanding
Primary Menu: Chicken (42); Hamburger (6); Seafood (3); Taco (15)
Areas of Operation: AL, LA, MS, TN
Type of Foodservice: Quick Serve (69)
Franchise Affiliation: Checkers Drive-In Restaurants Inc., TAMPA, FL; KFC Corporation, LOUISVILLE, KY; Long John Silver's Inc., LOUISVILLE, KY; Taco Bell Corp., IRVINE, CA
Primary Distributors: (Full Line) McLane/Memphis, MEMPHIS, TN

Key Personnel
RICHARD WEST - President; Director Operations, Construction
WILLIAM WEST - Senior VP; Director Real Estate, Construction
CHARLES T. WEST - VP Operations, Purchasing, Supply Chain; General Manager
MIKE SERVOLINI - VP Operations, Human Resources
STEVE WEST - VP Facility/Maintenance
RACHEL SCHOEN - Director Marketing, Catering
HILLARY BLACK - Director Human Resources, Training, South Region
MIKE WEST - Director Facility/Maintenance, Construction

What A Combo Inc.
202 3rd St
Mccomb, MS 39648-4102

Telephone: (601) 249-0403
Fax Number: (601) 684-3689
Internet Homepage: blueskycstores.com
Type of Business: Chain Restaurant Operator
Year Founded: 1995
Total Sales: $20,500,000 (e)
Number of Employees: 208
Average Check: Lunch(12); Dinner(12)
Total Units: 16
Trade Names: Chester's Chicken (1); Church's Chicken (1); Krystal (4); Penn's (1); Subway (9)
Units Franchised From: 16
Preferred Square Footage: 3,000
Preferred Location Types: Freestanding
Primary Menu: Chicken (2); Hamburger (4); Sandwiches/Deli (9); Seafood (1)
Areas of Operation: MS
Type of Foodservice: Quick Serve (16)
Franchise Affiliation: Church's Chicken, ATLANTA, GA; Doctor's Associates Inc., MILFORD, CT; Penn's Fish House Inc., JACKSON, MS; The Krystal Co., DUNWOODY, GA
Primary Distributors: (Full Line) US Foods, FLOWOOD, MS

Key Personnel
DAVID CRADDOCK - Chairman; Partner
BEN CRADDOCK - President; Partner; CFO; VP Purchasing; Treasurer; Director Finance, Supply Chain
BEVERLY LITTLE - CFO; Manager Accounting, Information Systems, Human Resources
CHRIS LITTLE - VP Operations

Paradise Companies LLC
296 Highland Blvd
Natchez, MS 39120-4609

Mailing Address: PO Box 18939, NATCHEZ, MS, 39122-8939
Telephone: (601) 445-9710
Fax Number: (601) 445-4397
Internet Homepage: natchezoffice.com
Type of Business: Chain Restaurant Operator
Year Founded: 1988
Total Sales: $62,790,000 (e)
Alcohol Sales: 9%
Number of Employees: 1,700
Average Check: Breakfast(14); Lunch(16); Dinner(20)
Total Units: 83
Trade Names: Applebee's Neighborhood Grill & Bar (45); IHOP Restaurant (14); Pizza Hut (15); Taco Bell (9)
Units Franchised From: 83
Preferred Square Footage: 3,000
Preferred Location Types: Freestanding; Regional Mall
Alcohol Served: Beer, Wine, Liquor
Primary Menu: American (59); Pizza (15); Taco (9)
Projected Openings: 3
Areas of Operation: IL, IN, KY, LA, MS, OH
Type of Foodservice: Casual Dining (74); Quick Serve (9)
Franchise Affiliation: Applebee's Services Inc., KANSAS CITY, MO; IHOP Restaurant System, GLENDALE, CA; Taco Bell Corp., IRVINE, CA
Primary Distributors: (Food) McLane/Southern, BROOKHAVEN, MS

Key Personnel
DAVID PARADISE - President; Partner; Director Facility/Maintenance, Real Estate, Design
DAN CAMPBELL - Partner
FRANCK HEATH - Partner
ROBERT PARADISE - VP Information Systems, Human Resources; Director Purchasing; Manager Operations
LARRY KERNS - VP Operations
LAURIE MORGAN - Controller
MICHAEL PETTUS - Director Operations, Division
ROBERT HILL - Director Transportation

JACKIE GETER - Manager Accounting

Ten D Enterprises
6520 Sunplex Dr
Ocean Springs, MS 39564-8691

Telephone: (228) 875-0232
Fax Number: (228) 875-0935
Company Email: mcdonaldsoffice@hotmail.com
Type of Business: Chain Restaurant Operator
Year Founded: 1991
Total Sales: $81,520,000 (e)
Number of Employees: 750
Average Check: Breakfast(8); Lunch(10); Dinner(10)
Total Units: 17
Trade Names: McDonald's (17)
Units Franchised From: 17
Preferred Square Footage: 2,500; 3,000
Preferred Location Types: Freestanding
Primary Menu: Hamburger (17)
Areas of Operation: MS
Type of Foodservice: Quick Serve (17)
Franchise Affiliation: McDonald's Corporation, CHICAGO, IL
Primary Distributors: (Full Line) SYSCO Food Services of Jackson, JACKSON, MS

Key Personnel
WILLIAM DESCHER - President; Partner; General Manager; General Buyer
BILL DESCHER - Partner
GREG DESCHER - Partner; Director Information Systems, Real Estate
JEFF DESCHER - Director Operations, Facility/Maintenance
MARY ASHBAKER - Coordinator Accounting

Davis Pizza Enterprises, Inc
1603 Jackson Ave W
Oxford, MS 38655-4252

Telephone: (662) 236-3840
Type of Business: Chain Restaurant Operator
Total Sales: $26,298,000 (e)
Average Check: Dinner(16)
Total Units: 13
Trade Names: Domino's (13)
Units Franchised From: 13
Primary Menu: Pizza (13)
Areas of Operation: MS
Type of Foodservice: Quick Serve (13)
Franchise Affiliation: Domino's Pizza Inc, ANN ARBOR, MI

Key Personnel
DIANE BARRENTINE - President; Partner; General Buyer
BRETT BROWN - Partner

Vasco Properties
1204 Office Park Dr Ste A
Oxford, MS 38655-3597

Mailing Address: PO Box 1610, OXFORD, MS, 38655-1610
Telephone: (662) 236-3026
Fax Number: (632) 236-0031
Type of Business: Chain Restaurant Operator
Year Founded: 1987
Total Sales: $22,230,000 (e)
Number of Employees: 240
Average Check: Lunch(8); Dinner(8)
Total Units: 8
Trade Names: Taco Bell (8)
Units Franchised From: 8
Preferred Square Footage: 2,500; 3,200
Preferred Location Types: Freestanding
Primary Menu: Taco (8)
Areas of Operation: MS
Type of Foodservice: Quick Serve (8)
Franchise Affiliation: Taco Bell Corp., IRVINE, CA
Primary Distributors: (Food) McLane/Southern, BROOKHAVEN, MS

Key Personnel
BOB VASILYEV - President; Director Finance, Purchasing, Real Estate
NAPOLEON BOYD - General Manager; Director Operations; General Buyer
JOEY VASILYEV - Director Facility/Maintenance, Supply Chain
SCOTT VASILYEV - Director Information Systems, Human Resources

Choctaw Resort Development Enterprise
13541 Highway 16 W
Philadelphia, MS 39350-6510

Mailing Address: PO Box 6048, CHOCTAW, MS, 39350-6048
Telephone: (601) 663-0066
Fax Number: (601) 663-0076
Internet Homepage: pearlriverresort.com
Company Email: guest.services@pearlriverresort.com
Type of Business: Foodservice Operations - Casinos
Year Founded: 1994
Total Sales: $360,440,000 (e)
Alcohol Sales: 10%
Number of Employees: 2,720
Average Check: Breakfast(10); Lunch(14); Dinner(32)
Total Units: 10
Trade Names: Beach Club Restaurant (1); Bistro 24 (1); Chef's Pavillion Buffet (1); Club House Restaurant (1); Phillip M's (1); Rally Alley (1); Staatz Bar and Grill (1); The Bakery (1); Time Out Lounge (1); Whiskey Bean (1)
Company-Owned Units: 10
Preferred Square Footage: 5,500; 6,000
Preferred Location Types: Freestanding; Hotel/Motel
Alcohol Served: Beer, Wine, Liquor
Primary Menu: American (4); Caribbean (1); Coffee (1); Miscellaneous (1); Sandwiches/Deli (2); Steak/Seafood (1)
Areas of Operation: MS
Type of Foodservice: Casual Dining (7); Family Restaurant (1); Fast Casual (1); Quick Serve (1)
Primary Distributors: (Food) SYSCO Food Services of Jackson, JACKSON, MS
Notes: Restaurants operate at the Silver Star Hotel & Casino and the Golden Moon Hotel & Casino at the Pearl River Resort. The company derives approximately 87% of its revenue from casino and hotel operations.

Key Personnel
PHYLISS ANDERSON - Chairman
CONNIE DEON - Executive Director Finance
ERICA CLEMONS MOORE - Director Communications

Vaughn Brothers Inc.
1019 W Beacon St
Philadelphia, MS 39350

Mailing Address: PO Box 3312, MERDIAN, MS, 39303-3312
Telephone: (601) 485-6358
Fax Number: (601) 483-5933
Type of Business: Chain Restaurant Operator
Total Sales: $20,540,000 (e)
Number of Employees: 2
Average Check: Lunch(10); Dinner(12)
Total Units: 8
Trade Names: Popeyes Louisiana Kitchen (8)
Units Franchised From: 8
Preferred Location Types: Freestanding
Primary Menu: Chicken (8)
Areas of Operation: MS
Type of Foodservice: Quick Serve (8)
Franchise Affiliation: Popeyes Louisiana Kitchen Inc., ATLANTA, GA

Key Personnel
SCOTT VAUGHN - President; General Buyer

Keelboat Concepts, Inc.
141 Madison Landing Cir
Ridgeland, MS 39157-9243

Telephone: (601) 856-5500
Fax Number: (601) 856-5502
Internet Homepage: cockofthewalkrestaurant.com
Company Email: billprisock@icloud.com

Type of Business: Chain Restaurant Operator
Year Founded: 1977
Systemwide Sales: $9,195,000 (e)
Total Sales: $1,532,000 (e)
Alcohol Sales: 5%
Number of Employees: 30
Average Check: Lunch(14); Dinner(14)
Total Units: 3
Trade Names: Cock of the Walk (3)
Company-Owned Units: 3
Preferred Square Footage: 1,000; 5,000
Preferred Location Types: Convenience Store/Gas Station; Freestanding
Alcohol Served: Beer, Wine, Liquor
Primary Menu: American (3)
Areas of Operation: MS, TN
Type of Foodservice: Casual Dining (3)

Key Personnel
MIKE RICKELS - CEO; President; Executive Chef; General Buyer

MVP Sonic Group
425 Christine Dr
Ridgeland, MS 39157-3437

Mailing Address: PO Box 2128, RIDGELAND, MS, 39158-2128
Telephone: (601) 914-3401
Fax Number: (601) 914-3405
Internet Homepage: mcclainsonics.com
Type of Business: Chain Restaurant Operator
Total Sales: $219,000,000 (e)
Number of Employees: 1,904
Average Check: Breakfast(10); Lunch(10); Dinner(12)
Total Units: 102
Trade Names: Sonic America's Drive-In (102)
Units Franchised From: 102
Preferred Square Footage: 1,100; 1,200; 1,350
Preferred Location Types: Freestanding
Primary Menu: Hamburger (102)
Projected Openings: 3
Areas of Operation: AL, FL, MS
Type of Foodservice: Quick Serve (102)
Franchise Affiliation: Sonic Corp., OKLAHOMA CITY, OK
Primary Distributors: (Full Line) SYSCO Food Services of Jackson, JACKSON, MS

Key Personnel
BUDDY MCCLAIN - CEO; General Buyer
STEFANIE MCCLAIN NEELY - CEO
BRUCE VAUGHN - President
CLARK SPENCER - CFO
OLIVIA VAUGHN WEBB - VP
STEFANIE MCCLAIN FAIRLY - VP; Director Marketing
MIKE BEACHAM - Regional VP Operations
CHRIS RANSOM - Supervisor District

Pinnacle Restaurant Corp.
203 Park Ct
Ridgeland, MS 39157-2229

Telephone: (601) 853-0650
Fax Number: (601) 853-0659
Internet Homepage: olivetobistro.com; pinnaclerestaurantcorp.com
Type of Business: Chain Restaurant Operator
Year Founded: 1982
Total Sales: $20,570,000 (e)
Alcohol Sales: 1%
Number of Employees: 425
Average Check: Lunch(20); Dinner(22)
Total Units: 22
Trade Names: Ken's Pizza (2); Mazzio's Italian Eatery (16); McAlister's Deli (3); Oliveto (1)
Company-Owned Units: 18
Units Franchised From: 4
Preferred Square Footage: 3,600
Preferred Location Types: Freestanding; Strip Mall
Primary Menu: Italian (20); Pizza (2)
Areas of Operation: MS, TX
Type of Foodservice: Fast Casual (22)
Catering Services: Yes

Key Personnel
TOMMY JOHNSEY - President; General Buyer
LISA RICE - Director Marketing

Hudson Management Corporation
144 S Thomas St Ste 208
Tupelo, MS 38801-5337

Telephone: (662) 841-7770
Type of Business: Chain Restaurant Operator
Total Sales: $15,407,000 (e)
Total Units: 3
Trade Names: McDonald's (3)
Units Franchised From: 3
Primary Menu: Hamburger (3)
Areas of Operation: MS
Type of Foodservice: Quick Serve (3)
Franchise Affiliation: McDonald's Corporation, CHICAGO, IL

Key Personnel
ROB HUDSON - President; General Buyer

M and M Investments Inc
707 S Gloster St
Tupelo, MS 38801-4902

Telephone: (662) 842-4767
Fax Number: (662) 840-4656
Type of Business: Chain Restaurant Operator
Total Sales: $7,996,000 (e)
Total Units: 13
Trade Names: Subway (13)
Units Franchised From: 13
Primary Menu: Sandwiches/Deli (13)
Areas of Operation: MS
Type of Foodservice: Quick Serve (13)
Franchise Affiliation: Doctor's Associates Inc., MILFORD, CT

Key Personnel
PETE MALONE - Owner; General Buyer

Sweetwater Franchise Group
221 Ball Ave
Tylertown, MS 39667-2103

Telephone: (601) 876-3374
Fax Number: (601) 876-4186
Company Email: v_baskins@aol.com
Type of Business: Chain Restaurant Operator
Total Sales: $65,460,000 (e)
Total Units: 30
Trade Names: Sonic America's Drive-In (30)
Units Franchised From: 30
Primary Menu: Hamburger (30)
Areas of Operation: FL, MS
Type of Foodservice: Quick Serve (30)
Franchise Affiliation: Sonic Corp., OKLAHOMA CITY, OK

Key Personnel
BRAD YOUNG - Director Operations
VICKY BASKINS - Office Manager

Hannon's Food Service
3144 Indiana Ave
Vicksburg, MS 39180-5154

Telephone: (601) 638-2115
Fax Number: (601) 638-2191
Type of Business: Chain Restaurant Operator
Total Sales: $8,940,000 (e)
Total Units: 5
Trade Names: KFC (4); KFC/Taco Bell (1)
Units Franchised From: 5
Primary Menu: Chicken (4); Taco (1)
Areas of Operation: MS
Type of Foodservice: Quick Serve (5)
Franchise Affiliation: KFC Corporation, LOUISVILLE, KY; Taco Bell Corp., IRVINE, CA

Key Personnel
ROBERT RIALS - President; General Buyer

Taco Casa Franchise
3404 Pemberton Square Blvd
Vicksburg, MS 39180-5573

Telephone: (601) 638-4026

Type of Business: Chain Restaurant Operator
Total Sales: $2,297,000 (e)
Total Units: 3
Trade Names: Taco Casa (3)
Units Franchised From: 3
Primary Menu: Taco (3)
Areas of Operation: MS
Type of Foodservice: Quick Serve (3)

Key Personnel
REGAN NOSSER - Owner

C & C Food Systems
903 Azalea Dr
Waynesboro, MS 39367-2720

Mailing Address: PO Box 599, WAYNESBORO, MS, 39367-0599
Telephone: (601) 735-1192
Fax Number: (601) 735-4028
Type of Business: Chain Restaurant Operator
Year Founded: 1983
Total Sales: $25,310,000 (e)
Number of Employees: 430
Average Check: Breakfast(8); Lunch(8); Dinner(12)
Total Units: 14
Trade Names: Hardee's (14)
Units Franchised From: 14
Preferred Square Footage: 3,000
Preferred Location Types: Freestanding
Primary Menu: Hamburger (14)
Areas of Operation: LA, MS
Type of Foodservice: Quick Serve (14)
Franchise Affiliation: Hardee's Food Systems Inc., FRANKLIN, TN
Primary Distributors: (Full Line) McLane/Lagrange, LAGRANGE, GA

Key Personnel
JOHN CLARK - President; Director Operations, Real Estate; General Buyer
ROY CRAVEY - VP; Controller; Director Information Systems, Human Resources
MARK LELLI - Director Operations, Marketing

MONTANA

City Brew Coffee
PO Box 22209
Billings, MT 59104-2209

Telephone: (866) 880-2489
Fax Number: (406) 294-4622
Internet Homepage: citybrew.com
Type of Business: Chain Restaurant Operator
Year Founded: 1998
Total Sales: $18,570,000 (e)
Number of Employees: 182
Total Units: 26
Trade Names: City Brew Coffee (22); City Brew Coffee Kiosk (4)
Company-Owned Units: 26
Preferred Location Types: Kiosk; Lifestyle Center; Mixed-use Center
Primary Menu: Coffee (26)
Areas of Operation: MT, ND, WY
Type of Foodservice: Quick Serve (26)

Key Personnel
BECKY RENO - CEO; President
CHRISSY O'MALLEY - Director Retail Operations
JEREMY WELCH - Director Human Resources
JACE WIDDICOMBE - Manager Operations; Project Manager
CHAYLA JONES - Manager

Domino's Franchisee
904 Main St Ste 1
Billings, MT 59105-3360

Telephone: (406) 245-6633
Type of Business: Chain Restaurant Operator
Total Sales: $16,249,000 (e)
Total Units: 8
Trade Names: Domino's (8)
Units Franchised From: 8
Primary Menu: Pizza (8)
Areas of Operation: MT
Type of Foodservice: Quick Serve (8)
Franchise Affiliation: Domino's Pizza Inc, ANN ARBOR, MI

Key Personnel
RHETT D. HIGHTOWER - Owner; General Buyer

P.J.J. Inc.
2222 Broadwater Ave Ste 100
Billings, MT 59102-4762

Telephone: (406) 248-9913
Fax Number: (406) 245-6625
Internet Homepage: jakers.com
Type of Business: Chain Restaurant Operator
Year Founded: 1982
Total Sales: $23,530,000 (e)
Alcohol Sales: 25%
Number of Employees: 400
Average Check: Lunch(12); Dinner(24)
Internet Order Processing: Yes
Total Units: 8
Trade Names: Jaker's (6); Red Robin Gourmet Burgers & Spirits (2)
Company-Owned Units: 6
Units Franchised From: 2
Preferred Square Footage: 8,000; 20,000
Preferred Location Types: Community Mall; Freestanding
Alcohol Served: Beer, Wine, Liquor
Primary Menu: American (2); Steak/Seafood (6)
Projected Openings: 1
Areas of Operation: ID, MT
Type of Foodservice: Casual Dining (2); Fine Dining (6)
Franchise Affiliation: Red Robin Gourmet Burgers Inc., ENGLEWOOD, CO
Primary Distributors: (Full Line) SYSCO Food Services of Montana Inc., BILLINGS, MT

Key Personnel
JAKE JONES - President; Partner; CFO; General Manager; Director Supply Chain, Real Estate, Design; General Buyer
TYNA SMITH - Controller; Director Finance, Purchasing, Human Resources
DOUG COLLIER - General Manager; Executive Chef
JOE DEBOARD - General Manager; Executive Chef
LUKE HADLEY - Supervisor Region

Ryan Restaurant Corporation
2038 Overland Ave
Billings, MT 59102-6453

Telephone: (406) 656-6858
Fax Number: (406) 656-3485
Company Email: info@ryansrestaurantcorp.com
Type of Business: Chain Restaurant Operator
Total Sales: $58,080,000 (e)
Alcohol Sales: 18%
Number of Employees: 900
Average Check: Lunch(12); Dinner(14)
Total Units: 15
Trade Names: Applebee's Neighborhood Grill & Bar (6); Denny's (2); Famous Dave's (7)
Units Franchised From: 15
Preferred Square Footage: 3,600; 5,000
Preferred Location Types: Freestanding
Alcohol Served: Beer, Wine, Liquor
Primary Menu: American (15)
Areas of Operation: ID, MT, SD
Type of Foodservice: Casual Dining (15)
Franchise Affiliation: Applebee's Services Inc., KANSAS CITY, MO; BBQ Holdings, Inc., MINNETONKA, MN; Denny's Corporation, SPARTANBURG, SC

Key Personnel
WILLIAM RYAN - President
TIM BALLOU - VP Finance, Facility/Maintenance, Real Estate
JARED GAGE - Director Finance, Tax
STEPHEN PUTMAN - Director Information Technology
ERIC WHIRLEY - Director Operations; General Buyer

Stageline Pizza Co.
57 Antelope Trl
Billings, MT 59105-3013

Telephone: (406) 245-6062
Fax Number: (406) 245-6062
Internet Homepage:
  stagelinepizzacompany.com
Company Email: stevensonr@bresnan.net
Type of Business: Chain Restaurant Operator
Year Founded: 1981
Systemwide Sales: $4,520,000 (e)
Total Sales: $4,520,000 (e)
Number of Employees: 74
Average Check: Dinner(18)
Total Units: 13
Trade Names: Stageline Pizza (13)
Units Franchised To: 13
Preferred Location Types: Freestanding
Primary Menu: Pizza (13)
Areas of Operation: MT
Type of Foodservice: Quick Serve (13)
On-site Distribution Center: Yes

Key Personnel
RON STEVENSON - Treasurer; Corporate Secretary

Finally, Inc.
1232 N 15th Ave Ste 2
Bozeman, MT 59715-3299

Telephone: (406) 551-4982
Internet Homepage: ribandchophouse.com
Company Email:
  HR@RIBANDCHOPHOUSE.COM
Type of Business: Chain Restaurant Operator
Year Founded: 2001
Total Sales: $20,670,000 (e)
Total Units: 16
Trade Names: Accomplice (2); Rib & Chop House (11); Rio Sabinas (1); TJ Ribs (2)
Company-Owned Units: 14
Primary Menu: American (13); Bar-B-Q (2); Mexican (1)
Areas of Operation: LA, MT, PA, UT, WY
Type of Foodservice: Casual Dining (16)

Key Personnel
BURKE MORAN - Co-Founder; CEO; Partner; General Buyer
MELISSA MORAN - Co-Founder; Partner; VP; General Buyer

Happy People Pizza Inc
203 N 7th Ave
Bozeman, MT 59715-3305

Telephone: (406) 586-5431
Type of Business: Chain Restaurant Operator
Total Sales: $59,337,000 (e)
Total Units: 29
Trade Names: Domino's (29)
Units Franchised From: 29
Primary Menu: Pizza (29)
Areas of Operation: MT
Type of Foodservice: Quick Serve (29)
Franchise Affiliation: Domino's Pizza Inc, ANN ARBOR, MI

Key Personnel
ALLAN F. ERWIN - Owner; General Buyer

John's Sandwich Shop Inc.
8 W Mercury St
Butte, MT 59701-2020

Telephone: (406) 782-0812
Fax Number: (406) 782-6645
Internet Homepage: porkchopjohns.com
Company Email: info@porkchopjohns.com
Type of Business: Chain Restaurant Operator
Year Founded: 1928
Total Sales: $3,560,000 (e)
Number of Employees: 45
Average Check: Lunch(8); Dinner(8)
Internet Order Processing: Yes
Internet Sales: 3.00%
Total Units: 2
Trade Names: Pork Chop John's Sandwich Shop (2)
Company-Owned Units: 2
Preferred Location Types: Freestanding; Strip Mall
Primary Menu: Sandwiches/Deli (2)
Areas of Operation: MT
Type of Foodservice: Quick Serve (2)
On-site Distribution Center: Yes
Primary Distributors: (Full Line) SYSCO Food Services of Montana Inc., BILLINGS, MT

Key Personnel
ED ORIZOTTI - President; Executive Chef; Director Purchasing, Information Systems
THOMAS V. ORIZOTTI - VP; General Buyer

Great Harvest Bread Co.
28 S Montana St
Dillon, MT 59725-2434

Telephone: (406) 683-6842
Fax Number: (406) 683-5537
Internet Homepage: greatharvest.com
Company Email: diannep@greatharvest.com
Type of Business: Chain Restaurant Operator
Year Founded: 1976
Systemwide Sales: $139,356,000 (e)
Total Sales: $6,463,000 (e)
Number of Employees: 1,900
Total Units: 184
Trade Names: Great Harvest Bread (184)
Units Franchised To: 184
Preferred Square Footage: 2,000
Preferred Location Types: Freestanding; Lifestyle Center; Power Center; Strip Mall
Primary Menu: Sandwiches/Deli (184)
Areas of Operation: AK, AZ, CA, CO, CT, DE, FL, GA, HI, ID, IL, IN, KS, KY, LA, MA, MD, MI, MN, MO, MS, MT, NC, ND, NE, NH, NM, NV, OH, OK, OR, PA, RI, SC, SD, TN, TX, UT, VA, VT, WA, WI, WY
Type of Foodservice: Casual Dining (184)

Key Personnel
NIDO QUBEIN - Chairman
J. MICHAEL FERRETTI - CEO; Director Marketing, Real Estate; General Buyer
ERIC KESHIN - President; Chief Marketing Officer
AINLEY DOYLE-JEWELL - President
JENNIFER B. GIEM - Controller
PAUL TIKALSKY - Senior Director Training
BEN GREEN - Director Franchise Sales
MARK PETERSON - Director Restaurant Operations
T.J. NELSON - Director Site Selection
JANET TATARKA - Director Training
KAYLEE ZITO - Art Director
JASSEN FERRIS - Manager Operations
AMBER GARRETT - Manager Human Resources
CHRISTY STAUFFENBERG - Manager Graphic Design
MOLLY LARICCIA - Manager Marketing
JASON FILDES - Manager Production
MARGARET CARR - Manager Social Media
GREG BASTEK - Specialist Franchise Development

Himco, Inc.
101 River Dr N Ste 102
Great Falls, MT 59401-4200

Telephone: (406) 761-0624
Fax Number: (406) 761-0629
Type of Business: Chain Restaurant Operator
Total Sales: $15,471,000 (e)
Total Units: 3
Trade Names: McDonald's (3)
Units Franchised From: 3
Primary Menu: Hamburger (3)
Areas of Operation: MT
Type of Foodservice: Quick Serve (3)
Franchise Affiliation: McDonald's Corporation, CHICAGO, IL

Key Personnel
WILLIAM HIMMELBERG - President; General Buyer
ANNE BURWOOD - Senior Manager Finance; Manager Finance

Northwest Pizza Company, Inc.
2118 10th Ave S
Great Falls, MT 59405-2867

Telephone: (406) 770-3251
Internet Homepage: littlecaesarsmontana.com
Type of Business: Chain Restaurant Operator
Total Sales: $8,598,000 (e)
Average Check: Lunch(22); Dinner(22)
Total Units: 7
Trade Names: Little Caesars Pizza (7)
Units Franchised From: 7
Primary Menu: Pizza (7)
Areas of Operation: MT
Type of Foodservice: Quick Serve (7)
Franchise Affiliation: Little Caesar Enterprises Inc., DETROIT, MI

Key Personnel
LARRY JOLLY - President; General Buyer
LINDA JOLLY - Treasurer; Corporate Secretary

Subs Inc.
1601 Fox Farm Rd
Great Falls, MT 59404-3338

Telephone: (406) 459-3006
Company Email: davidn@subsincmontana.com
Type of Business: Chain Restaurant Operator
Total Sales: $5,233,000 (e)
Total Units: 9
Trade Names: Subway (9)
Units Franchised From: 9
Primary Menu: Sandwiches/Deli (9)
Areas of Operation: MT
Type of Foodservice: Quick Serve (9)
Franchise Affiliation: Doctor's Associates Inc., MILFORD, CT

Key Personnel
MISTY DAVISON - District Manager
DINA JONES - Manager District

Taco Treat of Great Falls
2517 10th Ave S
Great Falls, MT 59405-3236

Telephone: (406) 727-7582
Fax Number: (406) 727-7583
Internet Homepage: tacotreat.net
Type of Business: Chain Restaurant Operator
Year Founded: 1956
Systemwide Sales: $4,834,000 (e)
Total Sales: $3,812,000 (e)
Alcohol Sales: 15%
Number of Employees: 70
Average Check: Lunch(6); Dinner(8)
Internet Order Processing: Yes
Total Units: 7
Trade Names: Taco Treat (7)
Company-Owned Units: 7
Preferred Square Footage: 2,200
Preferred Location Types: Freestanding
Alcohol Served: Beer
Primary Menu: Taco (7)
Areas of Operation: MT
Type of Foodservice: Quick Serve (7)
Primary Distributors: (Full Line) SYSCO Food Services of Montana Inc., BILLINGS, MT

Key Personnel
JOHN ENOTT - CEO; Owner; Director Operations; General Buyer

AmHeath, Inc.
3385 Colton Dr Ste B
Helena, MT 59602-0252

Mailing Address: PO Box 4939, HELENA, MT, 59604-4939
Telephone: (406) 449-6227
Type of Business: Chain Restaurant Operator
Total Sales: $10,318,000 (e)
Total Units: 2
Trade Names: McDonald's (2)
Units Franchised From: 2
Preferred Location Types: Freestanding
Primary Menu: Hamburger (2)
Areas of Operation: MT
Type of Foodservice: Quick Serve (2)
Franchise Affiliation: McDonald's Corporation, CHICAGO, IL

Key Personnel
TERRY GAUTHIER - President; General Buyer

Icicle Creek Inc
1110 US Highway 2 W
Kalispell, MT 59901-1620

Mailing Address: PO Box 7803, KALISPELL, MT, 59904-0803
Telephone: (406) 752-0505
Type of Business: Chain Restaurant Operator
Total Sales: $23,280,000 (e)
Number of Employees: 200
Total Units: 5
Trade Names: McDonald's (5)
Units Franchised From: 5
Preferred Square Footage: 2,500
Primary Menu: Hamburger (5)
Areas of Operation: MT
Type of Foodservice: Quick Serve (5)
Franchise Affiliation: McDonald's Corporation, CHICAGO, IL

Key Personnel
KATHY KILLMAN - President Engineering; Principal
MICHELLE HADWIN - Partner
SCOTT HADWIN - Partner; General Buyer

Bridge Pizza
600 S Higgins Ave
Missoula, MT 59801-2734

Telephone: (406) 542-7787
Internet Homepage: bridgepizza.com
Type of Business: Chain Restaurant Operator
Year Founded: 1978
Total Sales: $4,087,000 (e)
Total Units: 2
Company-Owned Units: 2
Primary Menu: Pizza (2)
Type of Foodservice: Casual Dining (2)

Key Personnel
SHIRLEY JUHL - Partner
DAVID MCEWEN - Partner; Executive Chef; General Buyer

CLC Restaurants, Inc
218 E Front St Ste 300
Missoula, MT 59802

Telephone: (406) 543-6458
Fax Number: (406) 543-6284
Type of Business: Chain Restaurant Operator
Total Sales: $99,530,000 (e)
Number of Employees: 894
Total Units: 58
Trade Names: KFC (58); Taco Bell (58)
Units Franchised From: 58
Preferred Location Types: Freestanding
Primary Menu: Chicken (58); Taco (58)
Projected Openings: 1
Projected Remodelings: 2
Areas of Operation: CA, ID, MT, WA
Type of Foodservice: Quick Serve (50)
Franchise Affiliation: Taco Bell Corp., IRVINE, CA

Key Personnel
CRAIG LANGEL - President; Owner; General Buyer
CYD HOBLITT - VP Operations

Five on Black
3850 S Reserve St Ste 59801
Missoula, MT 59801

Telephone: (406) 926-1305
Internet Homepage: fiveonblack.com
Type of Business: Chain Restaurant Operator
Total Units: 6

Trade Names: Five on Black (6)
Company-Owned Units: 6
Areas of Operation: MT

Key Personnel
TOM SNYDER - Founder; President; Executive Chef

HuHot Mongolian Grills LLC
223 E Main St
Missoula, MT 59802-4423

Telephone: (406) 251-4303
Fax Number: (406) 327-1232
Internet Homepage: huhot.com
Company Email: contact@huhot.com
Type of Business: Chain Restaurant Operator
Year Founded: 1999
Systemwide Sales: $24,955,000 (e)
Total Sales: $9,291,000 (e)
Alcohol Sales: 5%
Number of Employees: 7
Average Check: Lunch(10); Dinner(14)
Total Units: 66
Trade Names: HuHot Mongolian Grill (66)
Company-Owned Units: 11
Units Franchised To: 55
Preferred Square Footage: 5,500; 6,000
Preferred Location Types: Freestanding; Strip Mall
Alcohol Served: Beer, Wine, Liquor
Primary Menu: Asian (66)
Areas of Operation: CO, IA, IN, KS, MN, MO, MT, NC, ND, NE, OK, SC, SD, TX, WA, WI
Type of Foodservice: Casual Dining (66)

Key Personnel
ANDREW W. VAP - CEO; Partner; Director Menu Development
LINDA E. VAP - President; Partner; General Manager; General Buyer
MOLLY VAP O'SHEA - Chief Merchandising Officer
CASSIE GRUEBELE - Controller
ERIC KNIGHT - Director Franchise Operations
MONICA MINFORD - Director Social Media, Internet Development
PAUL DULLARD - Director Operations

Montana Pizza Inc.
223 E Main St
Missoula, MT 59802-4423

Telephone: (406) 251-3461
Fax Number: (406) 327-1232
Internet Homepage: montana-pizza-inc.placestars.us
Type of Business: Chain Restaurant Operator
Year Founded: 1979
Total Sales: $2,723,000 (e)
Alcohol Sales: 5%

Number of Employees: 150
Average Check: Lunch(10); Dinner(14)
Total Units: 2
Trade Names: Godfather's Pizza (2)
Units Franchised From: 2
Preferred Square Footage: 3,200
Preferred Location Types: Strip Mall
Alcohol Served: Beer
Primary Menu: Pizza (2)
Areas of Operation: MT
Type of Foodservice: Fast Casual (2)
Franchise Affiliation: Godfather's Pizza, Inc., OMAHA, NE
Primary Distributors: (Full Line) US Foods, BILLINGS, MT

Key Personnel
ANDREW VAP - CEO; Controller; Manager Food and Beverage

MTB Management Inc.
1515 E Broadway St Ste A
Missoula, MT 59802-4931

Telephone: (406) 728-3233
Fax Number: (406) 728-3428
Type of Business: Chain Restaurant Operator
Year Founded: 1990
Total Sales: $22,020,000 (e)
Number of Employees: 230
Average Check: Lunch(12); Dinner(12)
Total Units: 8
Trade Names: Taco Bell (8)
Units Franchised From: 8
Preferred Square Footage: 3,500
Preferred Location Types: Freestanding
Primary Menu: Taco (8)
Areas of Operation: MT
Type of Foodservice: Quick Serve (8)
Franchise Affiliation: Taco Bell Corp., IRVINE, CA
Primary Distributors: (Food) McLane/Northwest, LAKEWOOD, WA

Key Personnel
JOSEPH SAMPLE - President; General Buyer
EMILY AGINIGA - General Manager

Tri-Star Pizza Enterprises
1916 Brooks St
Missoula, MT 59801-6664

Telephone: (406) 549-9992
Company Email: doug@centric.net
Type of Business: Chain Restaurant Operator
Total Sales: $5,141,000 (e)
Total Units: 4
Trade Names: Little Caesars Pizza (4)
Units Franchised From: 4
Primary Menu: Pizza (4)
Areas of Operation: MT

Type of Foodservice: Quick Serve (4)
Franchise Affiliation: Little Caesar Enterprises Inc., DETROIT, MI

Key Personnel
DOUG LUNDELL - President; General Buyer

Dodson Enterprises Inc
3909 US Highway 93 N Ste 1
Stevensville, MT 59870-6490

Telephone: (406) 961-3945
Type of Business: Chain Restaurant Operator
Total Sales: $1,546,000 (e)
Total Units: 2
Trade Names: Subway (2)
Units Franchised From: 2
Primary Menu: Sandwiches/Deli (2)
Areas of Operation: MT
Type of Foodservice: Quick Serve (2)
Franchise Affiliation: Doctor's Associates Inc., MILFORD, CT

Key Personnel
JUNE DODSON - Owner; General Buyer

Wheat Montana Farms & Bakery
10778 US Highway 287
Three Forks, MT 59752-9518

Telephone: (406) 285-3614
Fax Number: (406) 285-3749
Internet Homepage: wheatmontana.com
Company Email: info@wheatmontana.com
Type of Business: Chain Restaurant Operator
Systemwide Sales: $3,058,000 (e)
Total Sales: $420,000 (e)
Total Units: 4
Trade Names: Wheat Montana Deli (4)
Units Franchised To: 4
Preferred Location Types: Freestanding; Travel Plazas
Primary Menu: Sandwiches/Deli (4)
Areas of Operation: MT
Type of Foodservice: Fast Casual (4)
On-site Distribution Center: Yes
Notes: Total sales information reflects deli operations only, not production or wholesale operations.

Key Personnel
DEAN FOLKVORD - CEO; General Buyer
NANCY TODD - Manager Human Resources

Glacier Restaurant Group LLC
284 Flathead Ave Ste 200
Whitefish, MT 59937-2672

Telephone: (406) 862-5245
Fax Number: (406) 862-5228
Internet Homepage: ciaomambo.com; grgfood.com; latitude48bistro.com; mackenzieriverpizza.com; thecraggyrange.com
Company Email: grg@grgfood.com
Type of Business: Chain Restaurant Operator
Year Founded: 2007
Total Sales: $44,310,000 (e)
Alcohol Sales: 5%
Number of Employees: 1,618
Average Check: Lunch(12); Dinner(12)
Total Units: 60
Trade Names: Chalkboard (1); Ciao Mambo (3); Latitude 48 Bistro (1); MacKenzie River Pizza and Grill (29); Max & Erma's (10); The Brass Rabbit (1); The Craggy Range Bar & Grill (1)
Company-Owned Units: 49
Units Franchised To: 11
Preferred Location Types: Downtown; Freestanding; Regional Mall; Strip Mall
Alcohol Served: Beer, Wine, Liquor
Primary Menu: American (13); Italian (3); Miscellaneous (1); Pizza (29)
Areas of Operation: ID, IN, KY, MI, MO, MS, MT, ND, OH, PA, SC, VA, WA, WV
Type of Foodservice: Casual Dining (46)
Subsidiaries: Max & Erma's Restaurants Inc., WHITEFISH, MT
Primary Distributors: (Food) US Foods, BILLINGS, MT

Key Personnel
BRAD RIDGEWAY - President
RYAN FULLER - COO
WILL HAGIN - Exec VP; General Counsel
BRAD TOWNSEND - VP Supply Chain
JAMES BLYSTONE - VP Communications, Franchising
KRISTIN BODEEN - Controller
KARY FEELEY - Controller Group
CORY UTTERBACK - Senior Director Human Resources
KEVIN O'MEARA - Director Operations
DAVE TURK - Director Information Technology
BRIGETTA SCHWAIGER - Director Marketing
NINA STEFANI - Director Human Resources
CLARE GABLE - Director Training
JENNIFER BRAZINSKY - Director Human Resources
ERICA COFFMAN- TERRELL - Director Marketing
JASON ANDERSON - Regional Manager
CANDICE KLOBUCHAR - Manager Training

Max & Erma's Restaurants Inc.
284 Flathead Ave Ste 200
Whitefish, MT 59937-2672

Telephone: (303) 296-2121
Fax Number: (406) 862-5228
Internet Homepage: maxandermas.com
Listing Type: Subsidiary
Type of Business: Chain Restaurant Operator
Year Founded: 1972
Systemwide Sales: $74,835,000 (e)
Total Sales: $78,450,000 (e)
Alcohol Sales: 10%
Number of Employees: 943
Average Check: Lunch(16); Dinner(20)
Internet Order Processing: Yes
Internet Sales: 1.00%
Total Units: 10
Trade Names: Max & Erma's (10)
Company-Owned Units: 10
Preferred Square Footage: 5,500; 6,700
Preferred Location Types: Airports; Downtown; Freestanding; Hotel/Motel; Lifestyle Center; Regional Mall; Strip Mall
Alcohol Served: Beer, Wine, Liquor
Primary Menu: American (10)
Areas of Operation: IN, KY, MI, MO, OH, PA, VA
Type of Foodservice: Casual Dining (10)
Distribution Centers: COLUMBUS, OH
On-site Distribution Center: Yes
Primary Distributors: (Full Line) The SYGMA Network, Inc., DUBLIN, OH
Parent Company: Glacier Restaurant Group LLC, WHITEFISH, MT

Key Personnel
KARY FEELEY - Controller
KEVIN O'MEARA - Director Operations
SUSAN CZUPRYNSKI - Director Development, Training
LORELY LAVILLA - Coordinator Human Resources

NORTH CAROLINA

Frank Butler
270 Magnolia Square Ct
Aberdeen, NC 28315-2226

Mailing Address: PO Box 98, ABERDEEN, NC, 28315-0098
Telephone: (910) 944-7118
Type of Business: Chain Restaurant Operator
Total Sales: $15,175,000 (e)
Total Units: 3
Trade Names: McDonald's (3)
Units Franchised From: 3
Primary Menu: Hamburger (3)
Areas of Operation: NC
Type of Foodservice: Quick Serve (3)
Franchise Affiliation: McDonald's Corporation, CHICAGO, IL

Key Personnel
FRANK BUTLER - President; General Buyer

Mid-South Food Service Inc.
203 W South St
Aberdeen, NC 28315-2709

Mailing Address: PO Box 518, ABERDEEN, NC, 28315-0518
Telephone: (910) 944-2305
Fax Number: (910) 944-9398
Type of Business: Foodservice Management Operator
Year Founded: 1963
Total Sales: $8,372,000 (e)
Number of Employees: 100
Number of Locations Served: 57
Total Foodservice Mgmt Accounts: 57
Total Units: 40
Trade Names: Mid-South Food Service (40)
Company-Owned Units: 40
Projected Remodelings: 3
Areas of Operation: NC
Type of Foodservice: Cafeteria (57); Vending machines (57)
Foodservice Management Venues: Business & Industry; College & University
Primary Distributors: (Food) SYSCO Food Services of Charlotte LLC, CONCORD, NC

Key Personnel
G. ALAN MOON - President
JIMMY LOFTON - General Manager; Manager Operations; General Buyer

Domino's Franchisee
250 NC Highway 801 N
Advance, NC 27006-7944

Telephone: (336) 998-2000
Type of Business: Chain Restaurant Operator
Total Sales: $6,022,000 (e)
Total Units: 3
Trade Names: Domino's (3)
Units Franchised From: 3
Primary Menu: Pizza (3)
Areas of Operation: NC
Type of Foodservice: Quick Serve (3)
Franchise Affiliation: Domino's Pizza Inc, ANN ARBOR, MI

Key Personnel
PAUL G. MEHAFFEY - Owner; General Buyer

Florida Success Management Group LLC
1071 Pemberton Hill Rd Ste 202
Apex, NC 27502-4268

Telephone: (919) 303-3300
Fax Number: (919) 303-3308
Internet Homepage: densuccess.com
Company Email: comments@densuccess.com
Type of Business: Chain Restaurant Operator
Year Founded: 1994
Total Sales: $12,052,000 (e)
Alcohol Sales: 1%
Number of Employees: 95
Average Check: Breakfast(10); Lunch(10); Dinner(18)
Total Units: 4
Trade Names: Denny's (4)
Units Franchised From: 4
Preferred Square Footage: 4,000
Preferred Location Types: Freestanding; Hotel/Motel
Primary Menu: American (4)
Areas of Operation: FL, TN
Type of Foodservice: Casual Dining (4)
Franchise Affiliation: Denny's Corporation, SPARTANBURG, SC
Primary Distributors: (Food) McLane/Rocky Mount, ROCKY MOUNT, NC

Key Personnel
CARL FERLAND - President; Director Real Estate; General Buyer

Patronies, Inc.
1761 Highway 55
Apex, NC 27523

Telephone: (919) 363-6453
Type of Business: Chain Restaurant Operator
Total Sales: $2,974,000 (e)
Total Units: 2
Trade Names: Jersey Mike's Subs (2)
Units Franchised From: 2
Primary Menu: Sandwiches/Deli (2)
Areas of Operation: NC
Type of Foodservice: Quick Serve (2)
Franchise Affiliation: Jersey Mike's Franchise Systems, MANASQUAN, NJ

Key Personnel
JOHN PATRONE - Owner; General Buyer

Renaissance Restaurant Group, LLC
1047 Beaver Creek Commons Dr
Apex, NC 27502-3918

Telephone: (919) 367-0111
Type of Business: Chain Restaurant Operator
Total Sales: $6,881,000 (e)
Total Units: 6
Trade Names: Firehouse Subs (6)
Units Franchised From: 6
Preferred Location Types: Strip Mall
Primary Menu: Sandwiches/Deli (6)
Areas of Operation: NC
Type of Foodservice: Fast Casual (6)
Franchise Affiliation: Firehouse Restaurant Group Inc., JACKSONVILLE, FL

Key Personnel
MOHAMMAD ASAD - President; General Buyer

Rogers Family Investments Inc
2050 Creekside Landing Dr
Apex, NC 27502-3982

Telephone: (919) 387-1888
Type of Business: Chain Restaurant Operator
Total Sales: $1,192,000 (e)
Total Units: 2
Trade Names: Cold Stone Creamery (2)
Units Franchised From: 2
Areas of Operation: NC
Type of Foodservice: Quick Serve
Franchise Affiliation: Kahala Brands, SCOTTSDALE, AZ

Key Personnel
JANE ROGERS - Partner
DANIEL ROGERS - Partner

BOJ of WNC LLC
131 Glenn Bridge Rd
Arden, NC 28704

Mailing Address: P.O. Box 15748, ASHEVILLE, NC, 28813
Telephone: (877) 265-9621
Fax Number: (828) 684-1862
Internet Homepage: bocountry.com
Type of Business: Chain Restaurant Operator
Total Sales: $166,980,000 (e)
Total Units: 59
Trade Names: Bojangles' Famous Chicken 'n Biscuits (59)
Units Franchised From: 59
Primary Menu: Chicken (59)
Areas of Operation: GA, KY, NC, SC, TN
Type of Foodservice: Quick Serve (59)
Franchise Affiliation: Bojangles Restaurants Inc., CHARLOTTE, NC

Key Personnel
JEFF RIGSBY SR - CEO; President; General Manager; General Buyer
RANDY ODOM - CFO; VP Business Development
JOHNNY CALDWELL - COO; VP
MELISSA NAYSMITH - Area Director
JC HOFMEISTER - Area Director
MARIO DRUMMOND - Area Director
SCOTT SANDRIDGE - Area Director
DONNIE HINSON - Area Director
STEPHANIE KNAPP - Controller
LINDSAY HANSON - Director Human Resources
PATRICK SHELINE - Director Operations
JEFFREY RIGSBY JR - Director Operations, Development, Business Development
STEVE REX - Director District
KEN SCOTT - Director Operations
CHRIS BAILEY - Director Development
ALLYSON CAMPBELL - Director Marketing, Social Media
LISA ESSEX - Director Training
GARY KANE - Director Financial Planning
TONY BIRCH - Director Special Projects, Development
MEAGAN CALDWELL - Director Branding
DAVID MINNICK - Art Director Region
ANTHONY WILSON - Assistant Director
KAMI DEEL - Assistant Director
KATHY LARK - Area Manager
CRAIG BARTON - Manager Technology
KEVIN ISBELL - Manager
ELIZIA RIVERA - Assistant Manager
BONNIE SULLIVAN - Assistant Manager
RAJAH CORBITT - Assistant Manager
JESSICA MELTON - Administrator Payroll
BELINDA RUSSELL - Administrator Payroll
DEBBIE PETERSON - Specialist Information Systems; Coordinator Information Technology
DONNIE CATES - Coordinator Training
JONDA CHAPMAN - Coordinator Training
MEGAN LUNSFORD - Assistant Human Resources

Asheville Investment Partners
900 Hendersonville Rd Ste 304
Asheville, NC 28803-1762

Telephone: (828) 274-3694
Fax Number: (828) 274-3696
Company Email: ashevilleip@aol.com
Type of Business: Chain Restaurant Operator
Total Sales: $2,577,000 (e)
Total Units: 4
Trade Names: Little Caesars Pizza (4)
Units Franchised From: 4
Primary Menu: Pizza (4)

Areas of Operation: NC
Type of Foodservice: Quick Serve (4)
Franchise Affiliation: Little Caesar Enterprises Inc., DETROIT, MI

Key Personnel
MICHAEL FREEMAN - Owner

Brumit Restaurant Group
40 Seminole St
Asheville, NC 28803-1713

Mailing Address: PO Box 15726, ASHEVILLE, NC, 28813-0726
Telephone: (828) 274-5835
Fax Number: (828) 274-9555
Internet Homepage: ncarbys.com
Type of Business: Chain Restaurant Operator
Year Founded: 1988
Total Sales: $100,740,000 (e)
Number of Employees: 685
Average Check: Breakfast(8); Lunch(8); Dinner(8)
Total Units: 53
Trade Names: Arby's (53)
Units Franchised From: 53
Preferred Square Footage: 2,300
Preferred Location Types: Freestanding
Primary Menu: Sandwiches/Deli (53)
Projected Openings: 10
Areas of Operation: NC, SC
Type of Foodservice: Quick Serve (53)
Franchise Affiliation: Arby's Restaurant Group, ATLANTA, GA
Primary Distributors: (Full Line) McLane/Rocky Mount, ROCKY MOUNT, NC

Key Personnel
JOE BRUMIT - CEO; Partner
JOANN YODER - President; Partner; VP Operations, Marketing
GREG CATEVENIS - Partner; CFO; Senior VP; Controller; Director Real Estate
BRENDA SCOTT - General Manager
HEIDI HANG - General Manager Restaurant Operations
TYLER LANCE - Director Facility/Maintenance
JASON MCCAMMON - Manager Information Technology

Burgerworx
1 Page Ave
Asheville, NC 28801

Telephone: (828) 253-2333
Fax Number: (828) 254-2300
Internet Homepage: burgerworxavl.com
Type of Business: Chain Restaurant Operator
Total Sales: $3,119,000 (e)
Total Units: 2
Trade Names: Burgerworx (2)

Company-Owned Units: 2
Primary Menu: Hamburger (2)
Areas of Operation: NC
Type of Foodservice: Fast Casual (2)

Key Personnel
MELISSA LAUSCH - General Manager

Cooler South Enterprises, LLC
30 Town Square Blvd
Asheville, NC 28803-5066

Telephone: (828) 650-3013
Type of Business: Chain Restaurant Operator
Total Sales: $2,416,000 (e)
Total Units: 4
Trade Names: Cold Stone Creamery (4)
Units Franchised From: 4
Primary Menu: Snacks (4)
Areas of Operation: NC
Type of Foodservice: Quick Serve (4)
Franchise Affiliation: Kahala Brands, SCOTTSDALE, AZ

Key Personnel
CHAD EADS - Owner

McDonald's Franchise
51 Tunnel Rd
Asheville, NC 28805-1229

Telephone: (828) 254-6715
Type of Business: Chain Restaurant Operator
Total Sales: $19,976,000 (e)
Number of Employees: 337
Total Units: 4
Trade Names: McDonald's (4)
Units Franchised From: 4
Primary Menu: Hamburger (4)
Areas of Operation: NC
Type of Foodservice: Quick Serve (4)
Franchise Affiliation: McDonald's Corporation, CHICAGO, IL

Key Personnel
DON RASNICK - President; General Buyer

The Biltmore Co.
1 N Pack Sq Ste 401
Asheville, NC 28801-3409

Telephone: (828) 225-6776
Fax Number: (828) 225-6139
Internet Homepage: biltmore.com
Type of Business: Chain Restaurant Operator
Year Founded: 1979
Total Sales: $31,320,000 (e)
Alcohol Sales: 10%
Number of Employees: 240
Average Check: Breakfast(20); Lunch(24); Dinner(24)
Internet Order Processing: Yes
Internet Sales: 1.00%
Total Units: 12
Trade Names: Bistro (1); Cedric's Tavern (1); Deerpark Restaurant (1); Dining Room (1); Library Lounge (1); Stable Cafe (1); The Bake Shop (1); The Conservatory Cafe (1); The Courtyard Market (1); The Kitchen Cafe (1); The Smokehouse (1); Village Social (1)
Company-Owned Units: 10
Preferred Square Footage: 5,500; 6,000
Preferred Location Types: Freestanding; Hotel/Motel
Alcohol Served: Beer, Wine, Liquor
Primary Menu: American (6); Coffee (1); Snacks (1); Southern (4)
Areas of Operation: NC
Type of Foodservice: Casual Dining (11); Fine Dining (1)
Catering Services: Yes
Primary Distributors: (Full Line) US Foods, FORT MILL, SC
Notes: Restaurants located in, but not owned by hotels.

Key Personnel
BILL CECIL - CEO; President
STEPHEN WATSON - CFO; Senior VP
CHUCK PICKERING - Exec VP; Director Development, Design
MARK PICKEL - Senior VP Finance
PAULA WILBER - VP Sales; Manager Marketing
THERESA PIWOWAR - VP Accounting, Tax
TIM ROSEBROCK - VP; Director Business Development
MARK HEMPHILL - VP Marketing
GEOFF GARDNER - VP Menu Development, Food and Beverage
LEE SCOTT - Treasurer; Director Finance
KATHLEEN MOSHER - Senior Director Communications
HEATHER NORTON - Senior Director Accounting
MELODY RIGDON - Senior Director Marketing
CHRIS MASLIN - Senior Director Development, Talent
KATHY MINTER - Director Benefits, Compensation
HEATHER JORDAN - Director Marketing
PAUL KRUEGER - Director Sustainability, Technology, Infrastructure
TIM HILL - Director Sales
CHRISTY HODGINS - Director Marketing
BARBARA CLARIZIO - Director Marketing
KEITH CAMPBELL - Director Marketing
LAURA CARIDEO - Director Purchasing, Supply Chain
ANNA SULLINS - Director Development
TRAVIS TATHAM - Director Promotion, Event Planning, Strategic Planning
JILL WHITFIELD - Senior Manager Marketing

ELIZABETH FORD - Senior Manager Marketing
MARTHA HOWARD - Manager Sales
LINDSEY LUPFER - Manager Email Marketing
CHRIS CONLEY - Manager Information Technology
BETH POSLUSNY - Manager Catering
JEAN SEXTON - Manager Communications
SCOTT HOLBROOK - Supervisor Facility/Maintenance
ABIGAIL ODETTE - Corporate Manager Accounting
ROBERT GRACE - Corporate Director Technology
ELIZABETH STAHL - Coordinator E-Commerce

Travinia Italian Kitchen
264 Thetford St
Asheville, NC 28803

Telephone: (828) 684-8060
Internet Homepage: traviniaitaliankitchen.com
Company Email: travinia1@yahoo.com
Type of Business: Chain Restaurant Operator
Year Founded: 2002
Total Sales: $8,693,000 (e)
Number of Employees: 200
Total Units: 6
Trade Names: Travinia Italian Kitchen (6)
Company-Owned Units: 6
Primary Menu: Italian (6)
Areas of Operation: NC, SC, VA
Type of Foodservice: Casual Dining (6)

Key Personnel
MARK CRAIG - Founder; CEO
DAVE HERRINGTON - General Manager
BRANDY SKINNER - Director Marketing

Tupelo Honey Cafe
1200 Ridgefield Blvd Ste 290
Asheville, NC 28806-2280

Telephone: (828) 255-4404
Internet Homepage: tupelohoneycafe.com
Type of Business: Chain Restaurant Operator
Total Sales: $43,030,000 (e)
Total Units: 15
Trade Names: Tupelo Honey Cafe (15)
Company-Owned Units: 15
Preferred Location Types: Freestanding
Primary Menu: Southern (15)
Areas of Operation: CO, GA, NC, SC, TN, TX, VA
Type of Foodservice: Casual Dining (15)

Key Personnel
STEPHEN FRABITORE - Founder; CEO
NICK SCHULZ - CFO
CAROLINE SKINNER - Senior VP Human Resources
CAITLIN MCMAHON - VP Purchasing

MICHAEL VESS - General Manager
STEPHANIE PARSONS - General Manager
DANIEL SERAFINI - Senior Director Operations
KARA VERINGA - Director Branding
ROBYN KESLER - Director Information Technology
ELENA CAPOBIANCO - Manager Operations
JOHN WILSON - Manager Beverages
AMANDA STEVENS - Manager Digital Marketing
CODY REID - Manager Network, Network-Hardware
ANNIE ELAM - Analyst Finance

Twin Subs, Inc.
1341 Parkwood Ave Ste 103
Asheville, NC 28806-8703

Telephone: (828) 271-4612
Type of Business: Chain Restaurant Operator
Total Sales: $6,795,000 (e)
Total Units: 5
Trade Names: Jersey Mike's Subs (5)
Units Franchised From: 5
Primary Menu: Sandwiches/Deli (5)
Areas of Operation: NC
Type of Foodservice: Quick Serve (5)
Franchise Affiliation: Jersey Mike's Franchise Systems, MANASQUAN, NJ

Key Personnel
PATRICK DILLINGHAM - Partner
PHIL DILLINGHAM - Partner

Tar Heel Capital Corp.
166 Southgate Dr Ste 10
Boone, NC 28607-2905

Telephone: (828) 262-1811
Fax Number: (828) 262-0015
Internet Homepage: tarheelcapital.com
Company Email: comments@tarheelcapital.com
Type of Business: Chain Restaurant Operator
Year Founded: 1977
Total Sales: $188,700,000 (e)
Number of Employees: 2,310
Average Check: Lunch(8); Dinner(8)
Total Units: 70
Trade Names: Wendy's Old Fashioned Hamburgers (70)
Units Franchised From: 70
Preferred Square Footage: 2,200
Preferred Location Types: Freestanding
Primary Menu: Hamburger (70)
Projected Remodelings: 6
Areas of Operation: NC, SC
Type of Foodservice: Quick Serve (70)
Franchise Affiliation: The Wendy's Company, DUBLIN, OH
Primary Distributors: (Full Line) The SYGMA Network Inc. - Carolina, CHARLOTTE, NC

Key Personnel
TAD DOLBIER - President; VP Purchasing
BOB GASBARRO - VP Operations
MICHAEL BUTTON - Director Human Resources
JAMES WOMACK - Director Information Technology
HEATH BETCHLEY - Regional Director Operations
TODD OWENS - Regional Director

The Hastings Company
805 State Farm Rd Ste 201
Boone, NC 28607-4914

Mailing Address: PO Box 2327, BOONE, NC, 28607-2327
Telephone: (828) 262-5335
Fax Number: (828) 264-9535
Type of Business: Chain Restaurant Operator
Total Sales: $7,852,000 (e)
Number of Employees: 140
Average Check: Breakfast(8); Lunch(8); Dinner(8)
Total Units: 4
Trade Names: Hardee's (4)
Units Franchised From: 4
Preferred Square Footage: 3,000; 3,500
Preferred Location Types: Freestanding
Primary Menu: Hamburger (4)
Areas of Operation: NC
Type of Foodservice: Quick Serve (4)
Franchise Affiliation: Hardee's Food Systems Inc., FRANKLIN, TN
Primary Distributors: (Food) McLane/Rocky Mount, ROCKY MOUNT, NC

Key Personnel
BRYAN HAAS - President; General Manager; General Buyer
JIM HASTINGS - Owner

JOR Foods Inc.
205 Asheville Hwy
Brevard, NC 28712-3490

Telephone: (828) 884-7071
Type of Business: Chain Restaurant Operator
Total Sales: $14,719,000 (e)
Total Units: 4
Trade Names: Zaxby's (4)
Units Franchised From: 4
Primary Menu: Chicken (4)
Areas of Operation: NC
Type of Foodservice: Fast Casual (4)
Franchise Affiliation: Zaxby's Franchising Inc., ATHENS, GA

Key Personnel
JAMES O. RODGERS - President

Blue Ribbon Diner
2465 S Church St
Burlington, NC 27215-5201

Telephone: (336) 570-1120
Internet Homepage: bestfoodintown.com
Company Email: brdburlington@bestfoodintown.com
Type of Business: Chain Restaurant Operator
Year Founded: 1989
Total Sales: $7,785,000 (e)
Alcohol Sales: 5%
Number of Employees: 150
Average Check: Lunch(18); Dinner(34)
Total Units: 3
Trade Names: Blue Ribbon Diner (2); The Village Grill (1)
Company-Owned Units: 3
Preferred Location Types: Freestanding; Regional Mall
Alcohol Served: Beer, Wine, Liquor
Primary Menu: American (2); Steak/Seafood (1)
Areas of Operation: NC
Type of Foodservice: Casual Dining (3)
Primary Distributors: (Full Line) US Foods, CHARLOTTE, NC

Key Personnel
RANDY COX - Partner; General Buyer
PAM HESTER - General Manager
RODNEY MATTHEWS - General Manager
MITCH BARKER - General Manager

Creamery at the Crossing, LLC
3160 Walden Ln
Burlington, NC 27215-8236

Telephone: (336) 538-1338
Type of Business: Chain Restaurant Operator
Total Sales: $1,183,000 (e)
Total Units: 2
Trade Names: Cold Stone Creamery (2)
Units Franchised From: 2
Primary Menu: Snacks (2)
Areas of Operation: NC
Type of Foodservice: Quick Serve (2)
Franchise Affiliation: Kahala Brands, SCOTTSDALE, AZ

Key Personnel
TRENT REISBERGER - Partner
ERICA REISBERGER - Partner

Dejas Enterprises
2966 S Church St
Burlington, NC 27215-5108

Mailing Address: PO Box 27404, BURLINGTON, NC, 27404
Telephone: (336) 584-1382
Fax Number: (336) 389-0039
Type of Business: Chain Restaurant Operator
Total Sales: $15,284,000 (e)
Total Units: 3
Trade Names: McDonald's (3)
Units Franchised From: 3
Primary Menu: Hamburger (3)
Areas of Operation: NC
Type of Foodservice: Quick Serve (3)
Franchise Affiliation: McDonald's Corporation, CHICAGO, IL

Key Personnel
JAMES N. SMITH - President; General Buyer

Domino's Franchisee
2447 N Church St
Burlington, NC 27217-3242

Telephone: (336) 229-1199
Type of Business: Chain Restaurant Operator
Total Sales: $12,191,000 (e)
Total Units: 6
Trade Names: Domino's (6)
Units Franchised From: 6
Primary Menu: Pizza (6)
Areas of Operation: NC
Type of Foodservice: Quick Serve (6)
Franchise Affiliation: Domino's Pizza Inc, ANN ARBOR, MI

Key Personnel
CLYDE P. STOKES - Owner; General Buyer

Shuckin' Shack Franchising, LLC
6A Lake Park Blvd N
Carolina Beach, NC 28428-4925

Telephone: (910) 228-8103
Internet Homepage: shuckinshackfranchise.com; theshuckinshack.com
Company Email: marketing@theshuckinshack.com
Type of Business: Chain Restaurant Operator
Year Founded: 2007
Systemwide Sales: $17,680,000 (e)
Total Sales: $14,600,000 (e)
Total Units: 17
Trade Names: Shuckin' Shack (17)
Company-Owned Units: 2
Units Franchised To: 15
Preferred Square Footage: 1,800; 2,800
Preferred Location Types: Freestanding; Strip Mall
Primary Menu: Seafood (17)
Projected Openings: 8
Areas of Operation: GA, MD, NC, SC
Type of Foodservice: Casual Dining (17)

Key Personnel
MATT PICCININ - Co-Founder; COO
SEAN COOK - Co-Founder
JONATHAN WEATHINGTON - CEO
BILL BARTLETT - VP Operations
WENDY KOONCE - Director Marketing

Amante Pizza Corp.
300 E Main St Ste F
Carrboro, NC 27510-2359

Telephone: (919) 929-3330
Fax Number: (919) 969-6645
Internet Homepage: amantefranchise.com; amantepizza.com
Company Email: amante@amantepizza.com
Type of Business: Chain Restaurant Operator
Year Founded: 1991
Systemwide Sales: $3,792,000 (e)
Total Sales: $1,990,000 (e)
Alcohol Sales: 3%
Number of Employees: 40
Average Check: Lunch(10); Dinner(12)
Total Units: 4
Trade Names: Amante Gourmet Pizza (4)
Company-Owned Units: 2
Units Franchised To: 2
Preferred Location Types: Strip Mall
Alcohol Served: Beer, Wine
Primary Menu: Pizza (4)
Areas of Operation: NC
Type of Foodservice: Casual Dining (4)

Key Personnel
C. MICHAEL VILOPOTO - President; Manager Menu Development; General Buyer
DAVE PARKER - General Manager

Smithfield's Chicken 'N Bar-B-Q
431 Keisler Dr Ste 201
Cary, NC 27518-7064

Mailing Address: PO Box 979, CARY, NC, 27512
Telephone: (919) 852-1722
Fax Number: (919) 852-5268
Internet Homepage: scnbnc.com
Company Email: feedback@scnbnc.com
Type of Business: Chain Restaurant Operator
Systemwide Sales: $39,498,000 (e)

Total Sales: $32,380,000 (e)
Number of Employees: 358
Average Check: Lunch(10); Dinner(14)
Internet Order Processing: Yes
Internet Sales: 1.00%
Total Units: 39
Trade Names: Smithfield's Chicken 'N Bar-B-Q (39)
Company-Owned Units: 14
Units Franchised To: 25
Preferred Square Footage: 4,900; 5,500; 6,000
Preferred Location Types: Freestanding
Primary Menu: Bar-B-Q (39)
Areas of Operation: NC
Type of Foodservice: Casual Dining (39)
Catering Services: Yes
Primary Distributors: (Food) US Foods, CHARLOTTE, NC

Key Personnel
GREGORY MOORE - President; CFO; Executive Chef
CHRISTOPHER DRUM - General Manager

The Richards Advantage
100 Cascade Pointe Ln Ste 102
Cary, NC 27513-5761

Telephone: (919) 677-2700
Fax Number: (919) 677-3007
Internet Homepage: mcdonaldsadvantage.com
Company Email: info@mcdonaldsadvantage.com
Type of Business: Chain Restaurant Operator
Year Founded: 1999
Total Sales: $37,350,000 (e)
Number of Employees: 370
Average Check: Breakfast(8); Lunch(10); Dinner(10)
Total Units: 8
Trade Names: McDonald's (8)
Units Franchised From: 8
Preferred Square Footage: 3,000
Preferred Location Types: Freestanding
Primary Menu: Hamburger (8)
Areas of Operation: NC
Type of Foodservice: Quick Serve (8)
Foodservice Management Venues: College & University
Franchise Affiliation: McDonald's Corporation, CHICAGO, IL
Primary Distributors: (Food) The Martin-Brower Co., LEXINGTON, SC

Key Personnel
RIC RICHARDS - President; Director Finance; Manager Purchasing, Information Systems, Real Estate

Tobacco Road Restaurant Group Inc
3490 Kildaire Farm Rd Ste 172
Cary, NC 27518-2287

Telephone: (919) 363-7827
Type of Business: Chain Restaurant Operator
Total Sales: $4,502,000 (e)
Total Units: 3
Trade Names: Jersey Mike's Subs (3)
Units Franchised From: 3
Primary Menu: Sandwiches/Deli (3)
Areas of Operation: NC
Type of Foodservice: Quick Serve (3)
Franchise Affiliation: Jersey Mike's Franchise Systems, MANASQUAN, NJ

Key Personnel
AL HARDIE - Owner

Chapel Hill Restaurant Group
1201 Fordham Blvd
Chapel Hill, NC 27514-7094

Mailing Address: PO Box 7, CHAPEL HILL, NC, 27514-0007
Telephone: (919) 929-1262
Fax Number: (919) 929-0780
Internet Homepage: chapelhillrestaurantgroup.com; 518w.com
Company Email: office@chapelhillrestaurantgroup.com
Type of Business: Chain Restaurant Operator
Year Founded: 1978
Total Sales: $12,790,000 (e)
Alcohol Sales: 18%
Number of Employees: 350
Average Check: Lunch(12); Dinner(18)
Internet Order Processing: Yes
Total Units: 5
Trade Names: Four Eleven West (1); Mez (1); Page Road Grill (1); Spanky's (1); Squid's (1)
Company-Owned Units: 5
Preferred Location Types: Freestanding
Alcohol Served: Beer, Wine, Liquor
Primary Menu: American (2); Italian (1); Seafood (1); Southwest/Tex-Mex (1)
Projected Openings: 1
Areas of Operation: NC
Type of Foodservice: Casual Dining (5)
Catering Services: Yes
Primary Distributors: (Equipment) United Restaurant Equipment Co., RALEIGH, NC; (Food) US Foods, CHARLOTTE, NC; (Supplies) US Foods, CHARLOTTE, NC

Key Personnel
JENNIFER ANDERSON - Partner; General Manager
KEN CARLSON - Partner; Manager Operations, Real Estate
PETE DORRANCE - Partner; Director Menu Development; Manager Operations, Purchasing
TOM HERZOG - Partner
JAMIE LAFORCE - Partner; General Manager
THOMAS O'CONNELL - Partner; General Manager
GREG OVERBECK - Partner; Director Marketing
MARK TACHMAN - Corporate Chef
ALEX STEWART - Executive Chef
JON DOWSE - Executive Chef
JOEY GUENETTE - Executive Chef
JOSEPH GUENETTE - Executive Chef

AMC Ventures, Inc.
2700 W Mallard Creek Church Rd
Charlotte, NC 28262-2304

Telephone: (704) 548-9650
Type of Business: Chain Restaurant Operator
Total Sales: $1,813,000 (e)
Total Units: 3
Trade Names: Cold Stone Creamery (3)
Units Franchised From: 3
Primary Menu: Snacks (3)
Areas of Operation: NC
Type of Foodservice: Quick Serve (3)
Franchise Affiliation: Kahala Brands, SCOTTSDALE, AZ

Key Personnel
ANDREW MARTINEZ - Owner; General Buyer

Amergent Hospitality Group, Inc.
7529 Red Oak Ln Ste 414
Charlotte, NC 28226

Telephone: (704) 366-5122
Internet Homepage: americanburgerco.com; bgrtheburgerjoint.com; chanticleerholdings.com; justfresh.com; littlebigburger.com
Company Email: IR@chanticleerholdings.com
Type of Business: Chain Restaurant Operator
Publicly Held: Yes
Total Sales: $30,700,000 (e)
Total Units: 35
Trade Names: American Burger Co. (3); BGR Burgers Grilled Right (16); Hooters (1); Little Big Burger (15)
Company-Owned Units: 26
Units Franchised To: 9
Primary Menu: American (1); Hamburger (34)
Areas of Operation: DC, GA, MD, NJ, NY, SC, TN, UT, VA
Type of Foodservice: Casual Dining (1); Fast

Casual (34)

Key Personnel
MICHAEL D. PRUITT - Chairman; CEO
MICHELLE ARCIDIACONO - Manager Accounting

Big Bran Corporation
1111 Central Ave Ste 300
Charlotte, NC 28204-2257

Telephone: (704) 376-0975
Fax Number: (704) 376-7393
Type of Business: Chain Restaurant Operator
Year Founded: 1979
Total Sales: $41,170,000 (e)
Number of Employees: 770
Average Check: Breakfast(8); Lunch(8); Dinner(8)
Total Units: 18
Trade Names: Burger King (18)
Units Franchised From: 18
Preferred Square Footage: 3,000
Preferred Location Types: Convenience Store/Gas Station; Freestanding
Primary Menu: Hamburger (18)
Areas of Operation: NC, SC
Type of Foodservice: Quick Serve (18)
Franchise Affiliation: Burger King Worldwide Inc., MIAMI, FL
Primary Distributors: (Equipment) QualServ Corporation, FORT SMITH, AR; (Food) McLane/Rocky Mount, ROCKY MOUNT, NC

Key Personnel
HUGH E. BIGHAM - President; Director Facility/Maintenance, Real Estate, Franchising, Store Fixtures
LINDA LAROCQUE - CFO; Director Finance
WILLIAM J. BRANSTROM - VP

BlackFinn Ameripub
210 E Trade St Ste B120
Charlotte, NC 28202-2413

Telephone: (704) 971-4440
Internet Homepage: blackfinncharlotte.com
Company Email: Community@BlackfinnAmeripub.com
Type of Business: Chain Restaurant Operator
Year Founded: 2008
Total Units: 6
Trade Names: Blackfinn Ameripub (6)
Company-Owned Units: 6
Alcohol Served: Beer, Wine, Liquor
Primary Menu: American (6)
Areas of Operation: AL, DC, NC, VA
Type of Foodservice: Casual Dining (6)
Catering Services: Yes

Key Personnel
GREGG MCCONNELL - Partner Region
CHAD SMITH - Executive Chef
SARAH SPITLER-MITCHELL - Manager Marketing, Sales
THERESE SLIWINSKI - Manager Marketing, Sales

Bojangles Restaurants Inc.
9432 Southern Pine Blvd
Charlotte, NC 28273-5553

Mailing Address: PO Box 240239, CHARLOTTE, NC, 28224-0239
Telephone: (704) 527-2675
Fax Number: (704) 523-6803
Internet Homepage: bojangles-franchise.com; bojangles.com
Company Email: bojadmin@bojangles.com
Type of Business: Chain Restaurant Operator
Year Founded: 1977
Systemwide Sales: $1,963,400,000 (e)
Total Sales: $888,720,000 (e)
Number of Employees: 7,162
Average Check: Breakfast(6); Lunch(8); Dinner(10)
Internet Order Processing: Yes
Internet Sales: 1.00%
Total Units: 759
Trade Names: Bojangles' Famous Chicken 'n Biscuits (759)
Company-Owned Units: 319
Units Franchised To: 440
Preferred Square Footage: 2,750; 3,550; 3,654; 3,800; 4,075
Preferred Location Types: Airports; Community Mall; Convenience Store/Gas Station; Downtown; Freestanding; Grocery Stores; Institution (college/hospital); Mobile Unit; Office Complex; Stadiums; Strip Mall; Travel Plazas
Primary Menu: Chicken (759)
Projected Openings: 20
Areas of Operation: AL, DC, FL, GA, KY, MD, NC, PA, SC, TN, VA, WV
Foreign Countries: HONDURAS
Type of Foodservice: Quick Serve (759)
Catering Services: Yes
Primary Distributors: (Full Line) Cheney Bros., GOLDSBORO, NC

Key Personnel
KENNETH KOZIOL - Chief Restaurant Operations Officer
JOSE ARMARIO - CEO
RANDY ICARD - President Region
REESE STEWART - CFO
MARK KISKUNAS - CFO
DAVID WHITAKER - COO
LAURA ROBERTS - Chief Compliance Officer; VP; Corporate Secretary; General Counsel
JAYSON ROMEO - Chief of Staff; VP Training
MELISSA NAYSMITH - Area Director
MARIO DRUMMOND - Area Director
KEITH VIGNESS - VP Finance
ROBERT GARCIA - VP Franchise Operations, Development, Training
PATRICIA HALPIN - VP
CATHY CHASE - VP People
STACEY MCCRAY - VP Communications
GRANT WILLIAMS - VP Omnichannel, Digital Marketing
KRISTAL BEAVER - Executive Director
KELLY VU - Senior Director
SERGIO PEREZ - Senior Director
DARREN WEBB - Director Real Estate
SUZANNE YOUNG - Director Human Resources, Recruitment
JERRY BROWDER - Director Facility/Maintenance
KEN REYNOLDS - Director Corporate Affairs, Community Relations
ROBERT PURSER - Director Information Technology
KEVIN MORRIS - Director POS/Scanning
ALLYSON CAMPBELL - Director Marketing, Social Media
LELA DINAKARAN - Director Marketing
ALLISON ATKINSON - Senior Manager
DORRANCE DAVIS - Manager Marketing, Franchise Development
TONI TOLBERT - Manager Marketing, Merchandising
APRIL ANDERSON - Manager Training
ANITA ISENHOUR - Assistant Training

Burke Hospitality Group
1111 Metropolitan Ave Ste 725
Charlotte, NC 28204-3425

Telephone: (704) 375-9715
Fax Number: (704) 358-0702
Internet Homepage: harpersgroup.com; harpersrestaurants.com
Company Email: contactus@harpersgroup.com
Type of Business: Chain Restaurant Operator
Year Founded: 1987
Total Sales: $20,510,000 (e)
Alcohol Sales: 10%
Number of Employees: 340
Average Check: Lunch(22); Dinner(42)
Total Units: 6
Trade Names: 1801 Grille (1); Harper's Restaurants (3); Mimosa Grill (1); Upstream (1)
Company-Owned Units: 6
Preferred Square Footage: 5,000
Preferred Location Types: Downtown; Freestanding; Strip Mall
Alcohol Served: Beer, Wine, Liquor
Primary Menu: American (5); Steak/Seafood (1)
Areas of Operation: NC, SC
Type of Foodservice: Casual Dining (6)
Catering Services: Yes

Primary Distributors: (Full Line) US Foods, FORT MILL, SC

Key Personnel
BILL BRANSTROM - Partner
APRYL HEIL - Controller; Manager Administration
SCOTT WALLEN - Executive Chef; Director Menu Development
SARAH WRENN - Manager Catering

Canteen Vending Services
2400 Yorkmont Rd
Charlotte, NC 28217-4511

Telephone: (704) 328-4000
Fax Number: (704) 328-4010
Internet Homepage: canteen.com
Type of Business: Foodservice Management Operator
Year Founded: 1929
Total Sales: $1,869,807,000 (e)
Number of Employees: 42,000
Number of Locations Served: 19,000
Total Foodservice Mgmt Accounts: 19,000
Areas of Operation: NC
Type of Foodservice: Vending machines (19,000)
Foodservice Management Venues: Business & Industry; College & University; Schools
Primary Distributors: (Full Line) SYSCO Food Services of Charlotte LLC, CONCORD, NC
Parent Company: Compass Group PLC, LONDON, ENG
Headquarters: Compass Group The Americas, CHARLOTTE, NC
Divisional Offices: Canteen Vending Services, DALLAS, TX
Regional Offices: Canteen Vending Services, GREENVILLE, SC

Key Personnel
PETER FETHERSTON - CEO
KARL BEHRENS - COO
SAM THAYER - Senior Director
BETSY O'BRIEN - Director Communications

Carolina Restaurant Group Inc.
8040 Arrowridge Blvd Ste 100
Charlotte, NC 28273-5604

Telephone: (704) 525-3434
Fax Number: (800) 780-5208
Internet Homepage: classicburgers.com
Type of Business: Chain Restaurant Operator
Year Founded: 1975
Total Sales: $342,920,000 (e)
Number of Employees: 2,808
Average Check: Lunch(8); Dinner(10)
Total Units: 122
Trade Names: Wendy's Old Fashioned Hamburgers (122)
Units Franchised From: 122
Preferred Square Footage: 3,000
Preferred Location Types: Convenience Store/Gas Station; Freestanding
Primary Menu: Hamburger (122)
Areas of Operation: NC, SC
Type of Foodservice: Quick Serve (122)
Franchise Affiliation: The Wendy's Company, DUBLIN, OH
Primary Distributors: (Equipment) Aydelott Equipment Inc., CENTERVILLE, OH; (Food) The SYGMA Network, Inc., DUBLIN, OH; (Supplies) The SYGMA Network, Inc., DUBLIN, OH
Notes: Carolina Restaurant Group Inc. operates as Palmetto Restaurant Group LLC & Florida Restaurant Group LLC.

Key Personnel
ERIC DORNHEIM - VP Operations
MIKE PANNILL - General Manager
HOPE MCGARRIGLE - Director Risk Management
JOHN SMILEY - Manager District

Chick-fil-A Franchisee
9801 South Blvd
Charlotte, NC 28273-6904

Telephone: (704) 552-7997
Internet Homepage: chick-fil-a.com/Locations/NC/Carolina-Pavilion
Type of Business: Chain Restaurant Operator
Total Sales: $18,532,000 (e)
Average Check: Dinner(14)
Total Units: 2
Trade Names: Chick-fil-A (2)
Units Franchised From: 2
Primary Menu: Chicken (2)
Areas of Operation: NC
Type of Foodservice: Quick Serve (2)
Franchise Affiliation: Chick-fil-A Inc., ATLANTA, GA

Key Personnel
TERRY SHELTON - President; General Buyer

Clean Juice
10000 Twin Lakes Pkwy Ste B
Charlotte, NC 28269

Telephone: (704) 918-1217
Fax Number: (704) 918-4451
Internet Homepage: cleanjuice.com
Company Email: franchise@cleanjuice.com
Type of Business: Chain Restaurant Operator
Year Founded: 2015
Total Sales: $113,010,000 (e)
Total Units: 114
Trade Names: Clean Juice (114)
Company-Owned Units: 6
Units Franchised To: 108
Primary Menu: Health Foods (114)
Projected Openings: 25
Areas of Operation: AL, CA, CO, FL, GA, IL, IN, LA, MI, NC, OH, PA, SC, TN, TX
Type of Foodservice: Quick Serve (114)

Key Personnel
KAT ECKLES - Co-Founder; VP
CHARLIE WIGGINS - Partner
ASHLEY LOVE - CFO
TRIPP SETLIFF - COO
SCOTT BRAINARD - VP Supply Chain
BRENNAN KERR - Director Operations
MACKENZIE KRUISE - Director Training
KEREN FREDERICK - Director Human Resources
AARON BONDS - Director Training
VINCENT GRAZIDEI - Manager Franchise Operations

Compass Group The Americas
2400 Yorkmont Rd
Charlotte, NC 28217-4511

Telephone: (704) 328-4000
Fax Number: (704) 328-6058
Internet Homepage: cgnad.com
Listing Type: Corporate Office
Type of Business: Foodservice Management Operator
Year Founded: 1987
Publicly Held: Yes
Total Sales: $29,689,823,000 (e)
Number of Employees: 220,000
Number of Locations Served: 34,000
Total Foodservice Mgmt Accounts: 34,000
Trade Names: Burger King (2); Denny's (2); IHOP Restaurant (1); Moe's Southwest Grill (6); Quiznos (3); Subway (14); Wendy's Old Fashioned Hamburgers(4)
Areas of Operation: NC
Type of Foodservice: Cafeteria; Full-service sit-down dining; Mobile units/kiosks; Quick Serve; Vending machines
Foodservice Management Venues: Business & Industry; College & University; Health Care; Military Feeding; Other; Prison Feeding; Schools; Sports Venues; Transportation
Subsidiaries: Compass Group Canada Ltd., MISSISSAUGA, ON CANADA
Parent Company: Compass Group PLC, LONDON, ENG
Headquarter Offices: Bon Appetit Management Co., PALO ALTO, CA; Canteen Vending Services, CHARLOTTE, NC; Chartwells Educational Dining Services, RYE BROOK, NY; Eurest Dining Services, CHESTERBROOK, PA; Levy Restaurants,

CHICAGO, IL; Morrison Healthcare, SANDY SPRINGS, GA; Restaurant Associates Managed Services, NEW YORK, NY
Divisional Offices: Canteen Vending Services, BLOOMINGDALE, IL; Canteen Vending Services, DALLAS, TX; Eurest Dining Services, FORT WASHINGTON, PA
Regional Offices: Canteen Vending Services, GREENVILLE, SC; Eurest Dining Services, NORMAL, IL; Groupe Compass (Quebec) Ltee, LASALLE, QC CANADA

Key Personnel
WARREN THOMPSON - Chairman Group; President Group
RICK POSTIGLIONE - CEO Group
ANDY LANSING - CEO Group; President Group
FEDELE BAUCCIO - CEO Division
BOBBY KUTTEH - CEO Group
SAAJID KHAN - CEO International Division
TIM PIERCE - CEO Group
ADRIAN MEREDITH - CFO
PALMER BROWN - Chief Strategy Officer
AMY KNEPP - Exec VP Strategic Services, Group
CHRIS KOWALEWSKI - Exec VP Business Development
JENNIFER MCCONNELL - Exec VP; General Counsel
SAM THAYER - Director Human Resources
GREG MAURO - Manager Internal Audit
BROOKE LEHMANN - Manager Strategic Planning
JOSEPH CANADAY - Project Manager Information Technology

Erwen Management Corp
8552 University City Blvd
Charlotte, NC 28213-3579

Telephone: (704) 549-8519
Fax Number: (980) 833-1539
Type of Business: Chain Restaurant Operator
Total Sales: $3,467,000 (e)
Total Units: 6
Trade Names: Subway (6)
Units Franchised From: 6
Primary Menu: American (6)
Areas of Operation: NC
Type of Foodservice: Quick Serve (6)
Franchise Affiliation: Doctor's Associates Inc., MILFORD, CT

Key Personnel
WENDELL ROWELL - President; General Buyer
MARTHA ASHLEY - District Manager

Ewing-Dunn, Inc
5501 Josh Birmingham Pkwy
Charlotte, NC 28208

Telephone: (704) 359-4610
Type of Business: Chain Restaurant Operator
Total Sales: $1,567,000 (e)
Total Units: 2
Trade Names: Auntie Anne's Hand Rolled Soft Pretzels (1); Brioche Doree (1)
Units Franchised From: 2
Areas of Operation: NC
Franchise Affiliation: Auntie Anne's Inc., LANCASTER, PA; Cinnabon Inc., ATLANTA, GA

Key Personnel
SANDY DUNN - President

Firebirds International
13850 Ballantyne Corporate Pl Ste 450
Charlotte, NC 28277-4200

Telephone: (704) 944-5180
Fax Number: (704) 944-5181
Internet Homepage: firebirdsrestaurants.com
Type of Business: Chain Restaurant Operator
Year Founded: 2000
Total Sales: $274,280,000 (e)
Alcohol Sales: 20%
Number of Employees: 1,555
Average Check: Lunch(32); Dinner(32)
Internet Order Processing: Yes
Total Units: 64
Trade Names: Firebirds Wood Fired Grill (64)
Company-Owned Units: 64
Preferred Square Footage: 6,000; 7,500
Preferred Location Types: Freestanding; Regional Mall
Alcohol Served: Beer, Wine, Liquor
Primary Menu: American (64)
Areas of Operation: AL, AZ, DE, FL, GA, IA, IN, KS, MD, MO, MS, NC, NE, NJ, OH, OK, PA, SC, TN, TX, VA
Type of Foodservice: Casual Dining (64)
Primary Distributors: (Equipment) Edward Don & Co., WOODRIDGE, IL; (Food) US Foods, FAIRBURN, GA; (Supplies) Edward Don & Co., WOODRIDGE, IL
Parent Company: J.H. Whitney & Co., NEW CANAAN, CT

Key Personnel
STEPHEN KISLOW - CEO
STEVE STRUM - COO
CHARLES BLANKENSHIP - Senior VP
STEVE CROUCH - VP Purchasing
STEPHEN LOFTIS - VP Marketing
ANDY SEIPLE - Executive Chef
CHRISTINE LORUSSO - Director Digital Marketing

Graham Foods
4324 Revolution Park Dr Ste 101
Charlotte, NC 28217-1500

Mailing Address: PO Box 19928, CHARLOTTE, NC, 28219
Telephone: (704) 527-7996
Fax Number: (704) 529-7496
Company Email: grahamfoods@carolina.rr.com
Type of Business: Chain Restaurant Operator
Year Founded: 1980
Total Sales: $27,630,000 (e)
Number of Employees: 560
Average Check: Breakfast(10); Lunch(10); Dinner(12)
Total Units: 13
Trade Names: Captain D's Seafood (9); Shoney's (4)
Units Franchised From: 13
Preferred Square Footage: 10,000
Preferred Location Types: Freestanding
Primary Menu: American (4); Seafood (9)
Areas of Operation: NC, SC
Type of Foodservice: Family Restaurant (4); Fast Casual (9)
Franchise Affiliation: Captain D's LLC, NASHVILLE, TN; Shoney's North America Corp., NASHVILLE, TN
Primary Distributors: (Full Line) McLane/Rocky Mount, ROCKY MOUNT, NC

Key Personnel
CHARLES GRAHAM - President; Controller; General Manager; Director Information Systems, Supply Chain, Real Estate; General Buyer
CONNIE JOHNS - Director Human Resources

Great Food Services LLC
6634 Old Statesville Rd
Charlotte, NC 28269-6768

Telephone: (704) 599-9890
Fax Number: (704) 599-9945
Internet Homepage: greatfoodserv.com
Company Email: gfs@greatfoodserv.com
Type of Business: Chain Restaurant Operator
Year Founded: 1999
Total Sales: $13,560,000 (e)
Number of Employees: 150
Average Check: Breakfast(8); Lunch(10); Dinner(12)
Total Units: 6
Trade Names: Burger King (6)
Units Franchised From: 6
Preferred Square Footage: 1,500
Preferred Location Types: Freestanding
Primary Menu: Hamburger (6)

Areas of Operation: NC, SC
Type of Foodservice: Quick Serve (6)
Franchise Affiliation: Burger King Worldwide Inc., MIAMI, FL

Key Personnel
JACQUELINE G. FORD - President; Director Finance; General Buyer
KELVIN D. FORD - President
THELMA ALLEN - Director Operations, Facility/Maintenance
CAMERON WELLS - Director Information Technology
VALERIE JONES - Manager Accounting, Branch

Johnson & Wales University Charlotte Campus
801 W Trade St
Charlotte, NC 28202-1122

Telephone: (866) 598-2427
Fax Number: (980) 598-1111
Internet Homepage: jwu.edu/charlotte
Type of Business: Culinary Schools
Areas of Operation: NC

Key Personnel
TODD SLAHERTY - President Interim

Krispy Kreme Doughnut Corporation
2116 Hawkins Street
Charlotte, NC 28203

Mailing Address: PO Box 83, WINSTON SALEM, NC, 27102-0083
Telephone: (800) 457-4779
Fax Number: (336) 733-3791
Internet Homepage: krispykreme.com
Company Email: customer@krispykreme.com
Type of Business: Chain Restaurant Operator
Year Founded: 1937
Systemwide Sales: $5,460,714,000 (e)
Publicly Held: Yes
Total Sales: $1,947,982,000 (e)
Number of Employees: 4,500
Average Check: Breakfast(8); Lunch(8); Dinner(10)
Internet Order Processing: Yes
Internet Sales: 1.00%
Total Units: 2,177
Trade Names: Insomnia Cookies (267); Krispy Kreme Doughnuts (1,910)
Company-Owned Units: 1,012
Units Franchised To: 1,165
Preferred Square Footage: 688; 1,500; 2,000; 2,400; 4,000
Preferred Location Types: Airports; Convenience Store/Gas Station; Discount Dept. Stores; Freestanding; Hotel/Motel; Institution (college/hospital); Regional Mall; Stadiums; Strip Mall
Primary Menu: Snacks (2,177)
Projected Openings: 20
Areas of Operation: AL, AR, AZ, CA, CO, CT, DC, FL, GA, HI, IA, ID, IL, IN, KS, KY, LA, MD, MI, MO, MS, MT, NC, NE, NJ, NM, NV, NY, OH, OK, OR, PA, PR, SC, TN, TX, UT, VA, WA, WI, WV, FC, BC, ON, QC
Foreign Countries: AUSTRALIA; BAHRAIN; BOLIVIA; CANADA; CHINA; COLOMBIA; DOMINICAN REPUBLIC; ENGLAND; INDIA; INDONESIA; JAPAN; KUWAIT; LEBANON; MALAYSIA; MEXICO; PERU; QATAR; RUSSIA; SAUDI ARABIA; SINGAPORE; SOUTH KOREA; TAIWAN; THAILAND; THE PHILIPPINES; TURKEY; UNITED ARAB EMIRATES
Type of Foodservice: Quick Serve (2,177)
Foodservice Management Venues: College & University
Distribution Centers: WINSTON-SALEM, NC
On-site Distribution Center: Yes
Primary Distributors: (Food) S&D Coffee & Tea Inc., CONCORD, NC
Parent Company: JAB Holding Company, LUDWIGSHAFEN, GER
Headquarter Offices: Insomnia Cookies, NEWTOWN SQUARE, PA
Notes: The company derives approximately 25% of its revenue from its KK Supply Chain segment, supplying food & equipment to Krispy Kreme units.

Key Personnel
JOSH CHARLESWORTH - CEO; President Global
MATTHEW SPANJERS - President International; Chief Growth Officer International
RAPHAEL DUVIVIER - President International
JEREMIAH ASHUKIAN - CFO; Exec VP
JOEY PRUITT - Chief Accounting Officer
NICOLA STEELE - COO
TERRI ZANDHUIS - Chief People Officer
BEN HALL - CIO
IRINY ATALLA - Chief Procurement Officer
DAVID SKENA - Chief Growth Officer
BILL LORD - Chief Information Security Officer
ALISON HOLDER - Chief Product Officer
ERIC HARTMAN - VP Supply Chain, Logistics
KAREN CHILCOTT - Controller
KITTIE PEARSON - Senior Director Information/Data Security, Compliance
RICHARD BELL - Senior Director Information Technology, Applications, Infrastructure
LUKE RUPERT - Director E-Commerce
CAROLYN LANGHANS - Director Consumer Insights
HOLLY SHANKLE - Director
LAURIE MARAVICH - Director Procurement, Global
HUGO RODRIGUEZ-MEDINA - Manager Quality Assurance
BETSY CLARKE - Manager Information Systems
MANUEL DE LA ROSA - Manager Sales
OLIVIA LIU - Associate Manager Loyalty Program
ALLISON PENNINGTON - Brand Manager
JEFF BAKER - Systems Analyst

Matt's Chicago Dog
435 S Tryon St Ste 140
Charlotte, NC 28202-1933

Telephone: (704) 333-3650
Fax Number: (704) 333-3748
Internet Homepage: eatatmatts.com
Company Email: Info@mattschicagodog.com
Type of Business: Chain Restaurant Operator
Year Founded: 2002
Total Sales: $1,844,000 (e)
Number of Employees: 18
Average Check: Lunch(8); Dinner(12)
Internet Sales: 4.00%
Total Units: 2
Trade Names: Matt's Chicago Deep Dish and Chicago Dog (1); Matt's Chicago Dog (1)
Company-Owned Units: 2
Preferred Location Types: Freestanding
Primary Menu: Hot Dogs (1); Pizza (1)
Areas of Operation: NC
Type of Foodservice: Quick Serve (2)
Catering Services: Yes

Key Personnel
MARLYS SIELSKY - President; Partner; Director Menu Development; General Buyer
JILL SAUER - Partner
EDWARD SIELSKY - Partner
STEVIE WOLFE - General Manager

New South Pizza Inc.
1817 E Center St
Charlotte, NC 28202

Telephone: (704) 247-9736
Internet Homepage: brixxpizza.com
Company Email: info@brixxpizza.com
Type of Business: Chain Restaurant Operator
Year Founded: 1998
Systemwide Sales: $67,767,000 (e)
Total Sales: $37,150,000 (e)
Alcohol Sales: 20%
Average Check: Dinner(14)
Total Units: 26
Trade Names: Brixx Wood-Fired Pizza (29)
Company-Owned Units: 15
Units Franchised To: 14
Preferred Location Types: Freestanding; Lifestyle Center; Strip Mall
Alcohol Served: Beer, Wine, Liquor
Primary Menu: Pizza (29)
Areas of Operation: AL, IN, NC, SC, TN, VA
Type of Foodservice: Casual Dining (29)

Catering Services: Yes

Key Personnel
JEFF VAN DYKE - President; Partner
BARBARA BODFORD-MORGAN - Partner; COO
ERIC HORSLEY - Partner; COO
CODY INNES - General Manager
TIM MINOR - Director Marketing
ROB RICHWALSKI - Director Training

Noble's Restaurants
6601 Carnegie Blvd
Charlotte, NC 28211-3538

Telephone: (704) 366-8688
Fax Number: (704) 366-0788
Internet Homepage: noblesgrille.com; roosterskitchen.com; kingskitchen.org; noblesrestaurant.com
Type of Business: Chain Restaurant Operator
Year Founded: 1983
Total Sales: $9,011,000 (e)
Alcohol Sales: 30%
Number of Employees: 200
Average Check: Lunch(12); Dinner(36)
Total Units: 4
Trade Names: Noble's Grille (1); Rooster @ Southpark (1); Rooster Uptown (1); The King's Kitchen (1)
Company-Owned Units: 4
Preferred Location Types: Freestanding; Regional Mall
Alcohol Served: Beer, Wine, Liquor
Primary Menu: American (4)
Areas of Operation: NC
Type of Foodservice: Casual Dining (1); Fine Dining (3)
Catering Services: Yes
Primary Distributors: (Food) US Foods, FORT MILL, SC; (Supplies) US Foods, FORT MILL, SC

Key Personnel
JIM NOBLE - Partner; General Manager; General Buyer

OSAAT Enterprises LLC
4118 Waterford Dr
Charlotte, NC 28226-7826

Telephone: (704) 341-3054
Type of Business: Chain Restaurant Operator
Total Sales: $20,413,000 (e)
Number of Employees: 200
Total Units: 4
Trade Names: McDonald's (4)
Units Franchised From: 4
Preferred Square Footage: 2,500
Primary Menu: Hamburger (4)
Areas of Operation: NC, SC
Type of Foodservice: Quick Serve (4)
Franchise Affiliation: McDonald's Corporation, CHICAGO, IL

Key Personnel
ANN FOX BAUM - President; General Buyer

Phoenix Taco, LLC
8702 Red Oak Blvd Ste A
Charlotte, NC 28217-5913

Telephone: (704) 523-0216
Fax Number: (704) 523-0682
Type of Business: Chain Restaurant Operator
Total Sales: $102,080,000 (e)
Number of Employees: 547
Total Units: 37
Trade Names: Taco Bell (25); Taco Bell/KFC (12)
Units Franchised From: 37
Primary Menu: Chicken (12); Taco (25)
Areas of Operation: NC, SC
Type of Foodservice: Quick Serve (37)
Franchise Affiliation: Taco Bell Corp., IRVINE, CA

Key Personnel
CHARLES FULENWIDER - Owner; General Buyer
J. W. WEST - VP Operations

Prairie Pizza
9107 S Tryon St Ste F
Charlotte, NC 28273-3125

Telephone: (704) 588-2611
Fax Number: (704) 588-2613
Internet Homepage: dominos.com
Company Email: comments@prairiepizza.com
Type of Business: Chain Restaurant Operator
Year Founded: 1981
Total Sales: $117,532,000 (e)
Number of Employees: 700
Average Check: Lunch(14); Dinner(24)
Internet Order Processing: Yes
Total Units: 59
Trade Names: Domino's (59)
Units Franchised From: 59
Preferred Square Footage: 1,200
Preferred Location Types: Convenience Store/Gas Station; Strip Mall
Primary Menu: Pizza (59)
Areas of Operation: NC, SC
Type of Foodservice: Quick Serve (59)
Foodservice Management Venues: Schools
Franchise Affiliation: Domino's Pizza Inc, ANN ARBOR, MI
Primary Distributors: (Full Line) Domino's Distribution Center, GARNER, NC

Key Personnel
MACK PATTERSON - President; Controller; Manager Facility/Maintenance, Information Systems, Risk Management, Marketing, Real Estate, Human Resources, Business Development, Store Planning, Food Safety
JODIE TAYLOR - Controller
J. T. ANDERSON - Director Operations, Purchasing, Loss Prevention
KYLE BROWN - Director Area

Salsarita's Holdings LLC
4601 Charlotte Park Dr Ste 250
Charlotte, NC 28217-1593

Telephone: (704) 540-9447
Fax Number: (704) 329-1718
Internet Homepage: salsaritas.com
Company Email: info@salsaritas.com
Type of Business: Chain Restaurant Operator
Year Founded: 1999
Systemwide Sales: $80,055,000 (e)
Total Sales: $3,571,000 (e)
Alcohol Sales: 5%
Number of Employees: 12
Average Check: Lunch(8); Dinner(10)
Total Units: 76
Trade Names: Salsarita's Fresh Cantina (79)
Company-Owned Units: 11
Units Franchised To: 68
Preferred Square Footage: 2,000
Preferred Location Types: Freestanding; Institution (college/hospital); Office Complex; Strip Mall
Alcohol Served: Beer, Wine, Liquor
Primary Menu: Mexican (79)
Areas of Operation: AL, FL, GA, KS, KY, LA, MD, MI, MN, MS, NC, NJ, NY, OH, PA, PR, SC, TN, TX, VA
Type of Foodservice: Fast Casual (79)
Catering Services: Yes
Primary Distributors: (Full Line) Reinhart FoodService, LOUISVILLE, TN
Parent Company: Mississippi Restaurant Group LLC, RIDGELAND, MS

Key Personnel
PHIL FRIEDMAN - Chairman; CEO
TIM CARTER - Chief Administrative Officer
SHANNON GLASER - VP Franchise Development
KELLY O'DELL - Director Marketing

Showmars of America Inc.
2127 S Tryon St
Charlotte, NC 28203-4957

Telephone: (704) 376-7469
Fax Number: (704) 335-0093
Internet Homepage: showmars.com
Type of Business: Chain Restaurant Operator

Year Founded: 1963
Total Sales: $33,340,000 (e)
Alcohol Sales: 20%
Number of Employees: 120
Average Check: Breakfast(6); Lunch(8); Dinner(8)
Total Units: 31
Trade Names: Showmars Restaurant (31)
Company-Owned Units: 31
Preferred Square Footage: 900
Preferred Location Types: Community Mall; Downtown; Freestanding; Strip Mall
Alcohol Served: Beer, Wine
Primary Menu: Greek/Mediterranean (31)
Areas of Operation: NC, SC
Type of Foodservice: Quick Serve (31)
On-site Distribution Center: Yes
Primary Distributors: (Full Line) US Foods, FORT MILL, SC

Key Personnel
GEORGE J. COUCHELL - Chairman; President; Manager Finance, Operations, Purchasing, Facility/Maintenance, Information Systems, Supply Chain, Ethnic Marketing, Real Estate, Design, Menu Development

Sonoma Restaurant Group
100 N Tryon St Ste 200
Charlotte, NC 28202-4028

Telephone: (704) 376-8880
Fax Number: (704) 376-8737
Internet Homepage: ariacharlotte.com; cicchetticlt.com
Type of Business: Chain Restaurant Operator
Year Founded: 1995
Total Sales: $9,477,000 (e)
Alcohol Sales: 20%
Number of Employees: 25
Average Check: Lunch(24); Dinner(60)
Internet Order Processing: Yes
Total Units: 1
Trade Names: Aria Tuscan Grill (1)
Company-Owned Units: 1
Preferred Location Types: Downtown
Alcohol Served: Beer, Wine, Liquor
Primary Menu: Italian (1)
Areas of Operation: NC
Type of Foodservice: Fine Dining (1)
Catering Services: Yes
Primary Distributors: (Full Line) US Foods, CHARLOTTE, NC

Key Personnel
PIERRE BADER - Owner; General Manager; General Buyer
FRANK ALTOMARE - Executive Chef; Director Catering
BRIANA COHEN - Director Operations
DEAN JORDAN - Coordinator Sales

T & B Concepts LLC
13900 Conlan Cir Ste 240
Charlotte, NC 28277-0675

Telephone: (704) 752-9600
Fax Number: (704) 405-4185
Internet Homepage: thehickorytavern.com
Type of Business: Chain Restaurant Operator
Year Founded: 1997
Total Sales: $96,040,000 (e)
Alcohol Sales: 20%
Total Units: 28
Trade Names: Hickory Tavern (28)
Company-Owned Units: 28
Preferred Location Types: Freestanding
Alcohol Served: Beer, Wine, Liquor
Primary Menu: American (28)
Areas of Operation: AL, NC, SC, TN
Type of Foodservice: Casual Dining (28)

Key Personnel
PAUL BALDASARO - CEO
MONTE OLSON - VP Purchasing; Director Operations
TIM FOUGNIE - VP Operations
KATHIE RAY - Director Human Resources
TAMMY LUCICH - Director Marketing
JOHN MESSINA - Manager Operations, Region
JOE SKOCZYLAS - Manager Operations

Tricor Inc.
7422 Carmel Executive Park Dr Ste 201
Charlotte, NC 28226-0425

Telephone: (704) 541-9316
Fax Number: (704) 542-7066
Type of Business: Chain Restaurant Operator
Year Founded: 1978
Total Sales: $14,170,000 (e)
Alcohol Sales: 10%
Number of Employees: 250
Average Check: Breakfast(10); Lunch(10); Dinner(14)
Total Units: 5
Trade Names: Sonny's Real Pit Bar-B-Q (5)
Units Franchised From: 5
Preferred Square Footage: 5,400
Preferred Location Types: Freestanding; Strip Mall
Alcohol Served: Beer
Primary Menu: Bar-B-Q (5)
Areas of Operation: NC, SC
Type of Foodservice: Casual Dining (5)
Catering Services: Yes
Franchise Affiliation: Sonny's Franchise Company, MAITLAND, FL
Primary Distributors: (Full Line) SYSCO Corporation, HOUSTON, TX

Key Personnel
ED TUBEL - CEO; Director Finance, Operations, Purchasing, Quality Assurance, Real Estate, Franchising
THERESA RANDALL - President; General Buyer
DERICK BYRUM - Director Training
STEVE TUBEL - Supervisor Area

Ava's Cupcakes, LLC
1483 River Ridge Dr
Clemmons, NC 27012

Telephone: (336) 283-9021
Internet Homepage: avascupcakes.com
Company Email: info@avascupcakes.com
Type of Business: Chain Restaurant Operator
Year Founded: 2011
Total Units: 3
Trade Names: Ava's Cupcakes (3)
Company-Owned Units: 3
Primary Menu: Snacks (3)
Areas of Operation: NC, NJ
Type of Foodservice: Quick Serve (3)

Key Personnel
MICHELLE SPELL - Founder; Owner

Auntie Anne's Franchise
8111 Concord Mills Blvd Ste 745
Concord, NC 28027-4407

Telephone: (704) 979-7912
Type of Business: Chain Restaurant Operator
Total Sales: $20,450,000 (e)
Total Units: 28
Trade Names: Auntie Anne's Hand-Rolled Soft Pretzels (28)
Units Franchised From: 28
Primary Menu: Snacks (28)
Areas of Operation: NC
Type of Foodservice: Quick Serve (28)
Franchise Affiliation: Auntie Anne's Inc., LANCASTER, PA

Key Personnel
ANTHONY KING - Owner; General Buyer

Carolina Pizza Huts, Inc.
2331 Concord Lake Rd
Concord, NC 28025-2813

Telephone: (704) 786-7627
Fax Number: (704) 786-8519
Internet Homepage: carolinapizzahuts.com
Type of Business: Chain Restaurant Operator
Year Founded: 1980
Total Sales: $18,600,000 (e)
Alcohol Sales: 1%
Number of Employees: 377
Average Check: Lunch(12); Dinner(16)

2025 Chain Restaurant Operators 659

Internet Order Processing: Yes
Total Units: 15
Trade Names: Pizza Hut (15)
Units Franchised From: 15
Preferred Square Footage: 4,200
Preferred Location Types: Freestanding; Regional Mall
Alcohol Served: Beer
Primary Menu: Pizza (15)
Areas of Operation: NC, SC
Type of Foodservice: Quick Serve (15)
Franchise Affiliation: Pizza Hut Inc., PLANO, TX
Primary Distributors: (Full Line) McLane/Concord, CONCORD, NC

Key Personnel
ROGER SINK - President; Treasurer; Manager Franchising
DOUG CLEVELAND - VP Operations; Manager Supply Chain, Marketing
BUDDY POLLOCK - VP Operations; Manager Supply Chain

What-A-Burger Drive-Ins Inc.
2036 Wilshire Ct SW
Concord, NC 28025-6403

Mailing Address: PO Box 566, CONCORD, NC, 28026-0566
Telephone: (704) 786-4101
Fax Number: (704) 723-9402
Company Email: wabinc@windstream.net
Type of Business: Chain Restaurant Operator
Year Founded: 1956
Total Sales: $6,151,000 (e)
Number of Employees: 100
Average Check: Breakfast(8); Lunch(10); Dinner(12)
Total Units: 4
Trade Names: What-A-Burger Drive-In (4)
Units Franchised From: 4
Preferred Location Types: Freestanding
Primary Menu: Hamburger (4)
Areas of Operation: NC
Type of Foodservice: Quick Serve (4)
On-site Distribution Center: Yes
Primary Distributors: (Food) US Foods, CHARLOTTE, NC

Key Personnel
MICHAEL L. BOST - President; Director Operations, Real Estate, Menu Development; General Buyer
DON HURRELL - Regional Director

Waters of Hickory, Inc
318 2nd St SW
Conover, NC 28613-2136

Mailing Address: PO Box 1029, CONOVER, NC, 28613-1029
Telephone: (828) 464-2812
Fax Number: (828) 464-8673
Type of Business: Chain Restaurant Operator
Total Sales: $6,113,000 (e)
Total Units: 3
Trade Names: Arby's (3)
Units Franchised From: 3
Primary Menu: Sandwiches/Deli (3)
Areas of Operation: NC
Type of Foodservice: Quick Serve (3)
Franchise Affiliation: Arby's Restaurant Group, ATLANTA, GA

Key Personnel
STEVE MAST - President; General Buyer

Famous Toastery
445 S Main St
Davidson, NC 28036

Telephone: (704) 997-5471
Internet Homepage: famoustoastery.com
Company Email: catering@famoustoastery.com
Type of Business: Chain Restaurant Operator
Year Founded: 2005
Total Sales: $35,350,000 (e)
Internet Order Processing: Yes
Total Units: 28
Trade Names: Famous Toastery (28)
Units Franchised To: 28
Primary Menu: American (28)
Areas of Operation: CO, GA, NC, NY, PA, SC, VA
Type of Foodservice: Family Restaurant (28)

Key Personnel
ROBERT MAYNARD - CEO; Partner
BRIAN BURCHILL - Partner; COO

Canteen Vending Services
1716 Camden Ave
Durham, NC 27704-4614

Telephone: (919) 771-1671
Fax Number: (919) 771-1691
Listing Type: Branch Office
Type of Business: Foodservice Management Operator
Year Founded: 1929
Number of Employees: 35
Number of Locations Served: 200
Total Foodservice Mgmt Accounts: 200
Areas of Operation: NC
Type of Foodservice: Vending machines (200)
Foodservice Management Venues: Business & Industry; College & University; Health Care; Schools
Parent Company: Compass Group The Americas, CHARLOTTE, NC
Headquarters: Canteen Vending Services, CHARLOTTE, NC

Key Personnel
CHRIS TAYLOR - District Manager

Domino's Franchisee
1201 Cole Mill Rd
Durham, NC 27705-2901

Telephone: (919) 383-8399
Type of Business: Chain Restaurant Operator
Total Sales: $4,087,000 (e)
Total Units: 2
Trade Names: Domino's (2)
Units Franchised From: 2
Primary Menu: Pizza (2)
Areas of Operation: NC
Type of Foodservice: Quick Serve (2)
Franchise Affiliation: Domino's Pizza Inc, ANN ARBOR, MI

Key Personnel
AUSTIN MITCHELL - Owner; General Buyer

Domino's Franchisee
3205 University Dr
Durham, NC 27707-3770

Telephone: (919) 493-8484
Company Email: dominos5508@outlook.com
Type of Business: Chain Restaurant Operator
Total Sales: $4,084,000 (e)
Total Units: 2
Trade Names: Domino's (2)
Units Franchised From: 2
Primary Menu: Pizza (2)
Areas of Operation: NC
Type of Foodservice: Quick Serve (2)
Franchise Affiliation: Domino's Pizza Inc, ANN ARBOR, MI

Key Personnel
TAMIR STUCHINER - Owner; General Buyer

Domino's Franchisee
4502 N Roxboro St
Durham, NC 27704-1832

Telephone: (919) 477-1966
Internet Homepage: dominosdfa.com
Type of Business: Chain Restaurant Operator
Total Sales: $8,020,000 (e)
Total Units: 4
Trade Names: Domino's (4)
Units Franchised From: 4
Primary Menu: Pizza (4)
Areas of Operation: NC
Type of Foodservice: Quick Serve (4)

Franchise Affiliation: Domino's Pizza Inc, ANN ARBOR, MI

Key Personnel
RANDALL L. EASTER - Owner; General Buyer

MSWG Chapel Hill, LLC
5332 McFarland Rd
Durham, NC 27707-6866

Telephone: (919) 493-6637
Type of Business: Chain Restaurant Operator
Total Sales: $5,250,000 (e)
Total Units: 3
Trade Names: Moe's Southwest Grill (3)
Units Franchised From: 3
Primary Menu: Southwest/Tex-Mex (3)
Areas of Operation: NC
Type of Foodservice: Fast Casual (3)
Franchise Affiliation: Moe's Southwest Grill LLC, ATLANTA, GA

Key Personnel
DAVID WILSON - Owner; General Buyer

Oxford Common's Submarines Inc
3500 N Roxboro St Ste 40
Durham, NC 27704-2765

Telephone: (919) 220-1474
Fax Number: (919) 220-1492
Type of Business: Chain Restaurant Operator
Total Sales: $5,755,000 (e)
Total Units: 10
Trade Names: Subway (10)
Units Franchised From: 10
Primary Menu: Sandwiches/Deli (10)
Areas of Operation: NC
Type of Foodservice: Quick Serve (10)
Franchise Affiliation: Doctor's Associates Inc., MILFORD, CT

Key Personnel
SHAKEEL ANSARI - President; General Buyer

RBS Subs, Inc.
3600 N Duke St Ste 37
Durham, NC 27704-1788

Telephone: (919) 620-7808
Type of Business: Chain Restaurant Operator
Total Sales: $5,977,000 (e)
Total Units: 4
Trade Names: Jersey Mike's Subs (4)
Units Franchised From: 4
Primary Menu: Sandwiches/Deli (4)
Areas of Operation: NC

Type of Foodservice: Quick Serve (4)
Franchise Affiliation: Jersey Mike's Franchise Systems, MANASQUAN, NJ

Key Personnel
BRENDA SMITH - Owner

Rise Southern Biscuits & Righteous Chicken
8200 Renaissance Pkwy
Durham, NC 27713-7747

Telephone: (919) 248-2992
Internet Homepage: risebiscuitsdonuts.com
Company Email: durham@risebiscuitsdonuts.com
Type of Business: Chain Restaurant Operator
Year Founded: 2012
Total Sales: $15,040,000 (e)
Total Units: 16
Trade Names: Rise Biscuits and Donuts (16)
Company-Owned Units: 4
Units Franchised To: 12
Primary Menu: Snacks (16)
Areas of Operation: FL, GA, MD, NC, SC, TN, TX, VA
Type of Foodservice: Fast Casual (16)

Key Personnel
TOM FERGUSON - Founder; CEO; Partner; General Buyer
BRIAN WILES - Founder; COO

Walker Holding LLC
3211 Shannon Rd Ste 225
Durham, NC 27707-6324

Telephone: (888) 961-3332
Type of Business: Chain Restaurant Operator
Year Founded: 1994
Total Sales: $36,040,000 (e)
Number of Employees: 455
Average Check: Breakfast(8); Lunch(8); Dinner(10)
Total Units: 13
Trade Names: Wendy's Old Fashioned Hamburgers (13)
Units Franchised From: 13
Preferred Square Footage: 3,000
Preferred Location Types: Freestanding
Primary Menu: Hamburger (13)
Areas of Operation: NC, VA
Type of Foodservice: Quick Serve (13)
Franchise Affiliation: The Wendy's Company, DUBLIN, OH
Primary Distributors: (Full Line) The SYGMA Network, Inc., DUBLIN, OH

Key Personnel
BURT WALKER - President; Director Finance,

Purchasing, Real Estate; General Buyer
PHIL MANTZ - Director Operations, Facility/Maintenance, Human Resources
LINDA RILEY - Manager Administration
JAIMIE RUTH - Supervisor District
RICH MILNER - Supervisor District

Tandem Inc.
202 W Main St
Elizabeth City, NC 27909-4327

Mailing Address: PO Box 709, ELIZABETH CITY, NC, 27907-0709
Telephone: (252) 338-1793
Fax Number: (252) 331-7713
Type of Business: Chain Restaurant Operator
Year Founded: 1976
Total Sales: $71,930,000 (e)
Number of Employees: 600
Average Check: Breakfast(8); Lunch(8); Dinner(10)
Total Units: 15
Trade Names: McDonald's (15)
Units Franchised From: 15
Preferred Square Footage: 2,000
Preferred Location Types: Convenience Store/Gas Station; Freestanding
Primary Menu: Hamburger (15)
Areas of Operation: NC, VA
Type of Foodservice: Quick Serve (15)
Franchise Affiliation: McDonald's Corporation, CHICAGO, IL
Primary Distributors: (Food) Golden State Foods (QCDS), SUFFOLK, VA

Key Personnel
BILL TAYLOR - President; General Buyer
JEANETTE DOUGLAS - Director Operations
RON MOSLEY - Manager Facility/Maintenance

3M & N, Inc.
501 E Jackson Blvd
Erwin, NC 28339-9630

Telephone: (910) 892-3964
Type of Business: Chain Restaurant Operator
Total Sales: $11,226,000 (e)
Total Units: 3
Trade Names: Zaxby's (3)
Units Franchised From: 3
Primary Menu: Chicken (3)
Areas of Operation: NC
Type of Foodservice: Fast Casual (3)
Franchise Affiliation: Zaxby's Franchising Inc., ATHENS, GA

Key Personnel
NANCY JACKSON - President
BRIAN RICE - Senior VP Design, Global

Auntie Anne's Franchise
1550 Skibo Rd
Fayetteville, NC 28303-3478

Telephone: (910) 867-4261
Type of Business: Chain Restaurant Operator
Total Sales: $1,568,000 (e)
Total Units: 2
Trade Names: Auntie Anne's Hand-Rolled Soft Pretzels (2)
Units Franchised From: 2
Primary Menu: Snacks (2)
Areas of Operation: NC
Type of Foodservice: Quick Serve (2)
Franchise Affiliation: Auntie Anne's Inc., LANCASTER, PA

Key Personnel
MARIA GUEDES - Owner; General Buyer

Baldinos Giant Jersey Subs & Salads
304 Owen Dr
Fayetteville, NC 28304-3415

Telephone: (910) 483-1053
Fax Number: (910) 484-6505
Internet Homepage: baldinosnc.com
Type of Business: Chain Restaurant Operator
Year Founded: 1973
Total Sales: $8,459,000 (e)
Number of Employees: 45
Average Check: Dinner(8)
Internet Order Processing: Yes
Total Units: 6
Trade Names: Baldino's Giant Jersey Subs (6)
Units Franchised From: 6
Preferred Square Footage: 3,000
Preferred Location Types: Freestanding
Primary Menu: Sandwiches/Deli (6)
Areas of Operation: NC
Type of Foodservice: Quick Serve (6)
Franchise Affiliation: Baldino's Inc., GLENNVILLE, GA

Key Personnel
MARIA PAPPAS - VP; Director Information Systems, Marketing, Real Estate, Human Resources

Canteen Vending Services
3524 Claude Lee Rd
Fayetteville, NC 28306-7100

Telephone: (910) 484-8157
Fax Number: (910) 484-8157
Listing Type: Branch Office
Type of Business: Foodservice Management Operator
Year Founded: 1929
Number of Employees: 20
Number of Locations Served: 100
Total Foodservice Mgmt Accounts: 100
Areas of Operation: NC
Type of Foodservice: Vending machines (100)
Foodservice Management Venues: Business & Industry; College & University; Health Care; Schools; Travel Plazas
Parent Company: Compass Group The Americas, CHARLOTTE, NC
Headquarters: Canteen Vending Services, CHARLOTTE, NC

Key Personnel
CHRIS BRUCE - General Manager
TAMMY FOX - Manager Accounting, District

Dino's Pizza USA Inc.
150 Andrews Rd Ste 9A
Fayetteville, NC 28311-1129

Telephone: (910) 488-6100
Fax Number: (919) 676-1080
Internet Homepage: dinospizza-nc.com
Company Email: dinospizza@aol.com
Type of Business: Chain Restaurant Operator
Year Founded: 1992
Systemwide Sales: $20,292,000 (e)
Total Sales: $2,029,000 (e)
Number of Employees: 300
Average Check: Lunch(14); Dinner(28)
Total Units: 2
Trade Names: Dino's Pizza & Subs (2)
Units Franchised To: 2
Preferred Location Types: Freestanding; Strip Mall
Primary Menu: Pizza (2)
Areas of Operation: NC
Type of Foodservice: Quick Serve (2)
Catering Services: Yes
Primary Distributors: (Full Line) Performance Foodservice, ORLANDO, FL

Key Personnel
JOHN E. RAY - President; CFO; Director Operations, Purchasing, Information Systems, Marketing, Real Estate, Menu Development
AARON RAY - Manager Operations

James Mack
201 N McPherson Church Rd
Fayetteville, NC 28303-4403

Telephone: (910) 826-6637
Type of Business: Chain Restaurant Operator
Total Sales: $8,254,000 (e)
Total Units: 5
Trade Names: Moe's Southwest Grill (5)
Units Franchised From: 5
Primary Menu: Southwest/Tex-Mex (5)
Areas of Operation: NC
Type of Foodservice: Fast Casual (5)
Franchise Affiliation: Moe's Southwest Grill LLC, ATLANTA, GA

Key Personnel
JAMES MACK - Owner

K-1 Enterprises, Inc.
2043 Skibo Rd Ste 204
Fayetteville, NC 28314-0254

Telephone: (910) 860-9494
Type of Business: Chain Restaurant Operator
Total Sales: $5,779,000 (e)
Total Units: 4
Trade Names: Jersey Mike's Subs (4)
Units Franchised From: 4
Primary Menu: Sandwiches/Deli (4)
Areas of Operation: NC
Type of Foodservice: Quick Serve (4)
Franchise Affiliation: Jersey Mike's Franchise Systems, MANASQUAN, NJ

Key Personnel
ARASH AINOLHAYAT - Owner; General Buyer

Paris and Potter Management Corporation
430 Ramsey St Ste 106
Fayetteville, NC 28301-4910

Telephone: (910) 323-2211
Fax Number: (910) 323-0038
Company Email: pnpkfc@aol.com
Type of Business: Chain Restaurant Operator
Year Founded: 1969
Total Sales: $50,240,000 (e)
Number of Employees: 440
Average Check: Lunch(10); Dinner(12)
Total Units: 27
Trade Names: KFC (27)
Units Franchised From: 27
Preferred Square Footage: 4,200
Preferred Location Types: Freestanding; Strip Mall
Primary Menu: Chicken (27)
Projected Openings: 10
Areas of Operation: NC, SC
Type of Foodservice: Quick Serve (27)
Franchise Affiliation: CiCi Enterprises L.P., COPPELL, TX; KFC Corporation, LOUISVILLE, KY
Primary Distributors: (Food) US Foods, CHARLOTTE, NC; (Food) JMC Restaurant Distribution LP, COPPELL, TX

Key Personnel
STEVE WEST - CEO
STEVE PARIS - Partner; Director Finance, Real

Estate
NICK POTTER - Partner; Director Purchasing, Supply Chain, Design, Store Fixtures
KATHY LOCKLEAR - CFO
RAY WOOD - Manager Loss Prevention
SHANEATHA COUSAR - Administrator Payroll, Human Resources

SGS Creamery, Inc.
5075 Morganton Rd
Fayetteville, NC 28314-1587

Telephone: (910) 868-4323
Type of Business: Chain Restaurant Operator
Total Sales: $1,217,000 (e)
Total Units: 2
Trade Names: Cold Stone Creamery (2)
Units Franchised From: 2
Primary Menu: Snacks (2)
Areas of Operation: NC
Type of Foodservice: Quick Serve (2)
Franchise Affiliation: Kahala Brands, SCOTTSDALE, AZ

Key Personnel
KENT HARMON - Partner
MICHAEL QUEEN - Partner
BARBARA QUEEN - Partner

In the Ballpark Inc.
30 McMurray Rd
Flat Rock, NC 28731-5810

Telephone: (828) 697-7277
Fax Number: (828) 697-7277
Type of Business: Chain Restaurant Operator
Total Sales: $11,477,000 (e)
Number of Employees: 12
Average Check: Lunch(8); Dinner(14)
Total Units: 3
Trade Names: Zaxby's (3)
Units Franchised From: 3
Preferred Location Types: Freestanding
Primary Menu: Chicken (3)
Areas of Operation: NC
Type of Foodservice: Fast Casual (3)
Franchise Affiliation: Zaxby's Franchising Inc., ATHENS, GA

Key Personnel
BARRY TAYLOR - Owner; General Buyer

David A & Kathryn Hunt Inc
599 S Broadway St
Forest City, NC 28043

Telephone: (828) 245-9915
Type of Business: Chain Restaurant Operator
Total Sales: $62,450,000 (e)
Total Units: 13
Trade Names: McDonald's (13)
Units Franchised From: 13
Primary Menu: Hamburger (13)
Areas of Operation: NC
Type of Foodservice: Quick Serve (13)
Franchise Affiliation: McDonald's Corporation, CHICAGO, IL

Key Personnel
DAVID A. HUNT - President; General Buyer

Domino's Distribution Center
3100 Waterfield Dr
Garner, NC 27529-8575

Telephone: (919) 779-5252
Fax Number: (919) 779-7473
Internet Homepage: dominos.com
Listing Type: Distribution Center
Type of Business: Chain Restaurant Operator
Year Founded: 1960
Number of Employees: 145
Internet Order Processing: Yes
Areas of Operation: NC, SC, VA, WV
Parent Company: Domino's Pizza Inc, ANN ARBOR, MI

Key Personnel
ULLIC YOUNG - General Manager

F & D Huebner LLC
52 Glen Rd Ste 101
Garner, NC 27529-7972

Telephone: (919) 772-1677
Fax Number: (919) 772-6944
Type of Business: Chain Restaurant Operator
Year Founded: 1986
Total Sales: $48,650,000 (e)
Number of Employees: 600
Average Check: Breakfast(8); Lunch(10); Dinner(10)
Total Units: 10
Trade Names: McDonald's (10)
Units Franchised From: 10
Preferred Square Footage: 3,000
Preferred Location Types: Freestanding
Primary Menu: Hamburger (10)
Areas of Operation: NC
Type of Foodservice: Quick Serve (10)
Franchise Affiliation: McDonald's Corporation, CHICAGO, IL

Key Personnel
FREDERICK HUEBNER III - President; Partner; Director Finance, Supply Chain; General Buyer
DORIS HUEBNER - Partner; VP; Director Information Systems, Real Estate, Human Resources
BRAD JENKINS - Controller
GARY COOK - General Manager; Director Operations, Facility/Maintenance, Store Fixtures
MIKE SKOG - Manager Information Technology

Papa John's Distribution Center
5301 Waterfield Dr
Garner, NC 27529-6988

Telephone: (919) 772-5116
Fax Number: (919) 772-8402
Listing Type: Distribution Center
Type of Business: Chain Restaurant Operator
Number of Employees: 150
Areas of Operation: GA, NC, SC, VA, WV
Parent Company: Papa Johns International Inc., LOUISVILLE, KY

Key Personnel
CARLOS CUSTODIO - President International
BRIAN MAGUIRE - Representative Customer Service

Domino's Franchisee
530 Dudley Shoals Rd
Granite Falls, NC 28630-8443

Telephone: (828) 313-0555
Type of Business: Chain Restaurant Operator
Total Sales: $8,124,000 (e)
Total Units: 4
Trade Names: Domino's (4)
Units Franchised From: 4
Primary Menu: Pizza (4)
Areas of Operation: NC
Type of Foodservice: Quick Serve (4)
Franchise Affiliation: Domino's Pizza Inc, ANN ARBOR, MI

Key Personnel
MITCHELL L. YOUNG - Owner; General Buyer

Battleground Restaurants Inc.
1337 Winstead Pl
Greensboro, NC 27408-8024

Mailing Address: PO Box 10398, GREENSBORO, NC, 27404-0398
Telephone: (336) 272-9355
Fax Number: (336) 272-5568
Internet Homepage: brginc.com; kbjacks.com; trippsrestaurants.com
Type of Business: Chain Restaurant Operator
Year Founded: 1981

Total Sales: $89,030,000 (e)
Alcohol Sales: 25%
Number of Employees: 2,023
Average Check: Lunch(10); Dinner(14)
Internet Order Processing: Yes
Total Units: 19
Trade Names: Kickback Jack's (18); Tripps Restaurant (1)
Company-Owned Units: 19
Preferred Square Footage: 5,000
Preferred Location Types: Freestanding
Alcohol Served: Beer, Wine, Liquor
Primary Menu: American (19)
Areas of Operation: NC, VA
Type of Foodservice: Casual Dining (19); Fast Casual (18)
Primary Distributors: (Food) Cheney Bros., GOLDSBORO, NC

Key Personnel
THOMAS D. MINCHER - President; Manager Franchise Development
MATT STALL - VP Finance
TOM MINCHER JR - Director Real Estate, Design
ASHBY GRAY - Director Personnel, Training

Biscuitville Inc.
1414 Yanceyville St Ste 300
Greensboro, NC 27405-6963

Telephone: (336) 553-3717
Fax Number: (336) 553-3701
Internet Homepage: biscuitville.com
Company Email: info@biscuitville.com
Type of Business: Chain Restaurant Operator
Year Founded: 1975
Total Sales: $45,620,000 (e)
Number of Employees: 950
Average Check: Breakfast(6); Lunch(6);
Internet Order Processing: Yes
Internet Sales: 0.50%
Total Units: 62
Trade Names: Biscuitville (62)
Company-Owned Units: 62
Preferred Square Footage: 2,200
Preferred Location Types: Freestanding
Primary Menu: Southern (62)
Areas of Operation: NC, VA
Type of Foodservice: Fast Casual (62)
On-site Distribution Center: Yes
Primary Distributors: (Food) US Foods, FORT MILL, SC

Key Personnel
BURNEY JENNINGS JR - Executive Chairman
KATHIE NIVEN - CEO; President
JEFF ARCHER - CIO
KRISTIE MITCHELL - VP Marketing, Branding
JESS WILLIAMS - VP Human Resources
JAMES MCCURLEY - VP Culinary Operations
LARRY WILLIAMS - Director Supply Chain, Product Development

RYAN HILTON - Director Finance
LEE EASLEY - Manager Real Estate
CHARLES ALSTON - Manager Operations
JASON MALONE - Manager Culinary Operations, Quality Assurance
CORLINDIUS MANLEY - Manager Restaurant Operations

Deep River Partners
804 Green Valley Rd Ste 204
Greensboro, NC 27408-7044

Telephone: (336) 617-2000
Fax Number: (336) 617-2001
Internet Homepage: deepriver.com
Company Email: info@deepriver.com
Type of Business: Chain Restaurant Operator
Total Units: 5
Trade Names: IHOP (5)
Units Franchised From: 5
Primary Menu: American (5)
Areas of Operation: IA, ND, SD
Type of Foodservice: Family Restaurant (5)
Notes: Steen Spove is the Partner in charge of and primary contact for IHOP of Krispy Kreme development.
IHOP units are held under GPRG, LLC.
Deep River Partners is a diverse development and property management organzation with eight partners on the development side of the business.

Key Personnel
BILL HANSEN - Co-Founder; CEO; Partner
STEEN SPOVE - Partner
SUSAN OAKLEY - Senior Manager Real Estate
DOUG BARKER - Senior Manager Real Estate
TERRY CASH - Administrator Accounting

Elizabeth's Pizza
2116 Lawndale Dr
Greensboro, NC 27408-7102

Telephone: (336) 370-0800
Internet Homepage: elizabethpizza.com
Company Email: comments@elizabethpizza.com
Type of Business: Chain Restaurant Operator
Year Founded: 1978
Total Sales: $10,050,000 (e)
Alcohol Sales: 15%
Number of Employees: 100
Average Check: Dinner(18)
Total Units: 7
Trade Names: Elizabeth's Pizza (7)
Company-Owned Units: 7
Preferred Location Types: Downtown; Freestanding
Alcohol Served: Beer, Wine, Liquor
Primary Menu: Italian (7)
Areas of Operation: NC

Type of Foodservice: Family Restaurant (7)

Key Personnel
FRANK ERRICHIELLO - CEO; President
MIKE MATARESE - General Manager
MARIO PUGLESI - Director Menu Development; General Buyer

Food Express Inc.
7901 Thorndike Rd
Greensboro, NC 27409-9425

Telephone: (336) 393-0031
Fax Number: (336) 393-0190
Internet Homepage: foodexpress.com
Type of Business: Foodservice Management Operator
Year Founded: 1985
Total Sales: $28,693,000 (e)
Number of Employees: 220
Number of Locations Served: 125
Total Foodservice Mgmt Accounts: 100
Areas of Operation: NC
Type of Foodservice: Cafeteria (50); Vending machines (50)
Foodservice Management Venues: Business & Industry
Primary Distributors: (Full Line) US Foods, FORT MILL, SC

Key Personnel
WILLIAM J. WHITACRE - Chairman
BILL SEAWELL - COO; Director Foodservice, Menu Development
WILLIAM J. WHITACRE III - CTO; General Buyer
DAVID ROBINSON - Senior VP Operations
BARBARA FITZPATRICK - Director Information Systems; Manager Finance, Risk Management, Human Resources
CHRISTIE STRUPE - Director; Customer Care

Franchise Finders Inc
2609 Battleground Ave
Greensboro, NC 27408-4005

Telephone: (336) 282-3828
Company Email: subway1413@bellsouth.com
Type of Business: Chain Restaurant Operator
Total Sales: $4,275,000 (e)
Total Units: 7
Trade Names: Subway (7)
Units Franchised From: 7
Primary Menu: Sandwiches/Deli (7)
Areas of Operation: NC
Type of Foodservice: Quick Serve (7)
Franchise Affiliation: Doctor's Associates Inc., MILFORD, CT

Key Personnel
THOMAS L. KIRKMAN II - President; General Buyer
JOEL NEUMANN - Owner

Ghassan's Inc.
1605 Battleground Ave
Greensboro, NC 27408-8005

Telephone: (336) 272-8400
Fax Number: (336) 273-2266
Internet Homepage: ghassans.com
Company Email: info@ghassans.com
Type of Business: Chain Restaurant Operator
Year Founded: 1975
Total Sales: $4,413,000 (e)
Alcohol Sales: 3%
Number of Employees: 50
Average Check: Dinner(14)
Internet Order Processing: Yes
Total Units: 4
Trade Names: Ghassan's (4)
Company-Owned Units: 4
Preferred Location Types: Freestanding
Alcohol Served: Beer, Wine
Primary Menu: Sandwiches/Deli (4)
Areas of Operation: NC
Type of Foodservice: Casual Dining (4)
Catering Services: Yes
Primary Distributors: (Full Line) US Foods, FORT MILL, SC

Key Personnel
KHALED FLEIHAN - President; General Manager; Executive Chef; General Buyer
MAY FLEIHAN - VP
ZIAD FLEIHAN - VP; General Manager

Libby Hill Seafood Restaurant Inc.
4517 W Market St Ste B
Greensboro, NC 27407-1541

Telephone: (336) 294-0505
Fax Number: (336) 292-6005
Internet Homepage: libbyhill.com
Type of Business: Chain Restaurant Operator
Year Founded: 1953
Systemwide Sales: $20,844,000 (e)
Total Sales: $9,046,000 (e)
Number of Employees: 20
Average Check: Lunch(8); Dinner(10)
Total Units: 6
Trade Names: Libby Hill Seafood Restaurant (6)
Company-Owned Units: 3
Units Franchised To: 3
Preferred Square Footage: 6,000
Preferred Location Types: Freestanding
Primary Menu: Seafood (6)
Areas of Operation: NC
Type of Foodservice: Family Restaurant (4)
On-site Distribution Center: Yes

Key Personnel
JUSTIN CONRAD - President; General Buyer

Quaintance-Weaver
324 W Wendover Ave Ste 300
Greensboro, NC 27408-8440

Telephone: (336) 370-0966
Fax Number: (336) 370-0965
Internet Homepage: qwrh.com
Company Email: qwrhinfo@qwrh.com
Type of Business: Chain Restaurant Operator
Year Founded: 1989
Total Sales: $24,288,000 (e)
Alcohol Sales: 20%
Number of Employees: 600
Average Check: Lunch(14); Dinner(20)
Total Units: 4
Trade Names: Green Valley Grill (1); Lucky 32 (2); Print Works Bistro (1)
Company-Owned Units: 4
Preferred Square Footage: 5,500; 6,000
Preferred Location Types: Freestanding
Alcohol Served: Beer, Wine, Liquor
Primary Menu: American (2); Eastern European (1); French/Continental (1)
Areas of Operation: NC
Type of Foodservice: Casual Dining (2); Fine Dining (2)
Primary Distributors: (Food) SYSCO Food Services of Virginia LLC, HARRISONBURG, VA
Notes: The company derives approximately 40% of its revenue from hotel operations.

Key Personnel
DENNIS QUAINTANCE - CEO; President; Director Finance, Real Estate; General Buyer
TONY VILLIER - Director Sales
THERESA MARTIN - Project Manager Design

Sebis Inc
2910 W Gate City Blvd
Greensboro, NC 27403-3159

Telephone: (336) 294-7766
Type of Business: Chain Restaurant Operator
Total Sales: $1,863,000 (e)
Total Units: 3
Trade Names: Subway (3)
Units Franchised From: 3
Primary Menu: Sandwiches/Deli (3)
Areas of Operation: NC
Type of Foodservice: Quick Serve (3)
Franchise Affiliation: Doctor's Associates Inc., MILFORD, CT

Key Personnel
RAKEN SHAH - President; General Buyer

TBL Investments
1 Centerview Dr Ste 215
Greensboro, NC 27407-3712

Mailing Address: PO Box 10361, GREENSBORO, NC, 27404-0361
Telephone: (336) 292-5151
Fax Number: (336) 292-5510
Internet Homepage: chophousesofnc.com
Company Email: info@tblinvestments.net
Type of Business: Chain Restaurant Operator
Year Founded: 1992
Total Sales: $16,157,000 (e)
Alcohol Sales: 25%
Number of Employees: 400
Average Check: Lunch(18); Dinner(34)
Total Units: 3
Trade Names: Capital City Chop House (1); Chop House at Mendenhall (1); Port City Chop House (1)
Company-Owned Units: 3
Preferred Square Footage: 5,500; 6,000
Preferred Location Types: Freestanding
Alcohol Served: Beer, Wine, Liquor
Primary Menu: Steak/Seafood (3)
Areas of Operation: NC
Type of Foodservice: Casual Dining (3)
Primary Distributors: (Food) US Foods, CHARLOTTE, NC

Key Personnel
D. KEITH HALL - President; Corporate Chef; Director Finance, Facility/Maintenance, Information Systems, Real Estate, Design; General Buyer
ROBYN WAYMAN - Director Administration

TRACK Investments, LLC
3105 Northline Ave
Greensboro, NC 27408-7817

Telephone: (336) 294-6100
Type of Business: Chain Restaurant Operator
Total Sales: $1,184,000 (e)
Total Units: 2
Trade Names: Cold Stone Creamery (2)
Units Franchised From: 2
Primary Menu: Snacks (2)
Areas of Operation: NC
Type of Foodservice: Quick Serve (2)
Franchise Affiliation: Kahala Brands, SCOTTSDALE, AZ

Key Personnel
RODNEY SHOAF - Partner
SHERRYL SHOAF - Partner

Coastal Plains Restaurants LLC
3204 Bismarck St
Greenville, NC 27834-6862

Telephone: (252) 355-5315
Fax Number: (252) 355-0387
Internet Homepage: nri-restaurants.com
Type of Business: Chain Restaurant Operator
Year Founded: 1998
Total Sales: $192,720,000 (e)
Number of Employees: 800
Average Check: Lunch(10); Dinner(10)
Total Units: 75
Trade Names: KFC (15); Taco Bell (60)
Units Franchised From: 75
Preferred Square Footage: 3,500
Preferred Location Types: Freestanding
Primary Menu: Chicken (15); Taco (60)
Projected Openings: 1
Areas of Operation: NC, SC, WA
Type of Foodservice: Quick Serve (75)
Franchise Affiliation: KFC Corporation, LOUISVILLE, KY; Taco Bell Corp., IRVINE, CA
Primary Distributors: (Food) US Foods, CHARLOTTE, NC

Key Personnel
SAM SIBERT - CEO; President; Owner
KELLY SMITH - Controller
ERIC COATES - General Manager; Director Operations, Facility/Maintenance, Human Resources; General Buyer
DAVID DEAN - Director Training
GINGER FOSTER - Director Development, People
GAYLE JOHNSON - Director Training
DREW PAGE - Director Training
CHIP JONES - Manager Facility/Maintenance

Domino's Franchisee
2305 Dickinson Ave
Greenville, NC 27834-5005

Telephone: (252) 756-9998
Type of Business: Chain Restaurant Operator
Total Sales: $6,065,000 (e)
Total Units: 3
Trade Names: Domino's (3)
Units Franchised From: 3
Primary Menu: Pizza (3)
Areas of Operation: NC
Type of Foodservice: Quick Serve (3)
Franchise Affiliation: Domino's Pizza Inc, ANN ARBOR, MI

Key Personnel
KERMIT A. LYLE - Owner; General Buyer

Parker's Barbeque
3109 S Memorial Dr
Greenville, NC 27834-6716

Telephone: (252) 756-2388
Fax Number: (252) 756-6950
Internet Homepage: parkersbbq.com
Type of Business: Chain Restaurant Operator
Year Founded: 1971
Total Sales: $5,137,000 (e)
Number of Employees: 130
Average Check: Lunch(8); Dinner(10)
Internet Order Processing: Yes
Total Units: 3
Trade Names: Parker's Barbeque (3)
Company-Owned Units: 3
Preferred Location Types: Freestanding
Primary Menu: Bar-B-Q (3)
Areas of Operation: NC
Type of Foodservice: Family Restaurant (3)
Catering Services: Yes
Primary Distributors: (Full Line) Cheney Bros., GOLDSBORO, NC

Key Personnel
ROBERT BULLOCK - Partner; General Buyer
BARBARA PARKER - Partner; General Manager
WILLIAM PARKER - Partner; Executive Chef; Director Catering; General Buyer

SDS Restaurant Group, LLC
3280 Charles Blvd
Greenville, NC 27858-8875

Telephone: (252) 301-2391
Type of Business: Chain Restaurant Operator
Total Sales: $62,430,000 (e)
Total Units: 51
Trade Names: Pizza Hut (51)
Units Franchised From: 51
Primary Menu: Pizza (51)
Areas of Operation: NC
Type of Foodservice: Quick Serve (51)
Franchise Affiliation: Pizza Hut Inc., PLANO, TX

Key Personnel
RYAN O'CONNELL - Director Operations
MELANIE G. MILLER - Manager Human Resources
GRAHAM WILLIAMS - Manager Marketing

Subway Franchisee
566 US Highway 70 W
Havelock, NC 28532-9569

Telephone: (252) 444-4408
Type of Business: Chain Restaurant Operator
Total Sales: $725,000 (e)
Total Units: 2
Trade Names: Subway (2)
Units Franchised From: 2
Areas of Operation: NC
Franchise Affiliation: Doctor's Associates Inc., MILFORD, CT

Key Personnel
GURINDER DHILLON - Owner; General Buyer

PPV Inc.
1333 2nd St NE Ste 300
Hickory, NC 28601-2594

Telephone: (828) 322-2505
Fax Number: (828) 322-4408
Type of Business: Chain Restaurant Operator
Year Founded: 1983
Total Sales: $42,330,000 (e)
Number of Employees: 343
Average Check: Breakfast(8); Lunch(8); Dinner(8)
Total Units: 9
Trade Names: McDonald's (9)
Units Franchised From: 9
Preferred Square Footage: 2,500
Preferred Location Types: Freestanding
Primary Menu: Hamburger (9)
Areas of Operation: NC
Type of Foodservice: Quick Serve (9)
Franchise Affiliation: McDonald's Corporation, CHICAGO, IL

Key Personnel
JOHN LINK - President; Director Finance; General Buyer
JOE THUNEY - President
KATHY BUCHANAN - Manager Marketing

J & S Cafeterias
110 Westover Dr
High Point, NC 27265-2869

Telephone: (336) 884-0404
Fax Number: (336) 884-0815
Internet Homepage: jscafeteria.com
Type of Business: Chain Restaurant Operator
Year Founded: 1984
Total Sales: $7,888,000 (e)
Number of Employees: 375
Average Check: Breakfast(8); Lunch(10); Dinner(14)
Total Units: 3
Trade Names: J & S Cafeteria (3)
Company-Owned Units: 3
Preferred Square Footage: 5,500; 6,000
Preferred Location Types: Freestanding
Primary Menu: American (3)
Projected Openings: 1
Areas of Operation: NC
Type of Foodservice: Cafeteria (3)

Primary Distributors: (Full Line) SYSCO Food Services of Charlotte LLC, CONCORD, NC

Key Personnel
F. B. NOWLAN - President; Director Finance, Purchasing, Supply Chain, Menu Development; General Buyer

Scott Hiatt Sport, Inc.
2200 N Main St Ste 103
High Point, NC 27262-7744

Telephone: (336) 885-3970
Type of Business: Chain Restaurant Operator
Total Sales: $2,880,000 (e)
Total Units: 2
Trade Names: Jersey Mike's Subs (2)
Units Franchised From: 2
Primary Menu: Sandwiches/Deli (2)
Areas of Operation: NC
Type of Foodservice: Quick Serve (2)
Franchise Affiliation: Jersey Mike's Franchise Systems, MANASQUAN, NJ

Key Personnel
SCOTT HIATT - Owner; General Buyer

Subway Sandwiches & Salads
3792 Samet Dr
High Point, NC 27265-3504

Telephone: (336) 885-4444
Fax Number: (336) 885-4466
Internet Homepage: subway.com
Type of Business: Chain Restaurant Operator
Total Sales: $4,589,000 (e)
Total Units: 8
Trade Names: Subway (8)
Units Franchised From: 8
Primary Menu: Sandwiches/Deli (8)
Areas of Operation: NC
Type of Foodservice: Quick Serve (8)
Franchise Affiliation: Doctor's Associates Inc., MILFORD, CT

Key Personnel
SAL JUDEH - President; Owner

Wake Pizza LLC
112 John Earl St
Hillsborough, NC 27278-2672

Telephone: (919) 732-3001
Type of Business: Chain Restaurant Operator
Total Sales: $26,803,000 (e)
Total Units: 13
Trade Names: Domino's (13)
Units Franchised From: 13
Primary Menu: Pizza (13)
Areas of Operation: NC
Type of Foodservice: Quick Serve (13)
Franchise Affiliation: Domino's Pizza Inc, ANN ARBOR, MI

Key Personnel
GALE W. EBERT - Owner; General Buyer

Bad Daddy's International
8625 Lindholm Dr Ste A
Huntersville, NC 28078-1892

Telephone: (704) 237-4055
Internet Homepage: baddaddysburgerbar.com
Listing Type: Subsidiary
Type of Business: Chain Restaurant Operator
Year Founded: 2007
Total Sales: $152,310,000 (e)
Average Check: Lunch(14); Dinner(16)
Total Units: 39
Trade Names: Bad Daddy's Burger Bar (39)
Company-Owned Units: 39
Preferred Square Footage: 3,300; 3,600
Preferred Location Types: Airports; Downtown; Lifestyle Center; Regional Mall
Alcohol Served: Beer, Wine, Liquor
Primary Menu: Hamburger (39)
Areas of Operation: AL, CO, GA, NC, OK, SC, TN
Type of Foodservice: Casual Dining (39)
Franchise Affiliation: Good Times Restaurants Inc., LAKEWOOD, CO
Parent Company: Good Times Restaurants Inc., LAKEWOOD, CO

Key Personnel
BRUCE FISHER - General Manager
AMANDA SEVIN - General Manager
JULIAN DOUGLAS - General Manager
TRISTA SCHAMBOW - General Manager
JON ASKIN - General Manager
DEAN KEITH - General Manager
HAAKON CURRIE - General Manager
MICHAEL MAGUIRE - General Manager
JASON GAGNON - General Manager
JAMES BAIRD - Manager
MCKENNA SNYDER - Manager Restaurant Operations

Boykin Lodging Company
8015 W Kenton Cir Ste 220
Huntersville, NC 28078-4848

Telephone: (704) 896-2880
Fax Number: (704) 896-8887
Internet Homepage: boykin.com
Company Email: info@boykin.com
Listing Type: Subsidiary
Type of Business: Foodservice Operations - Hotel/Motels
Year Founded: 1996
Total Sales: $337,610,000 (e)
Alcohol Sales: 23%
Number of Employees: 1,450
Total Units: 22
Restaurants in Hotels: 22
Trade Names: Best Western (2); Courtyard by Marriott (1); DoubleTree by Hilton (7); Embassy Suites (1); Hilton (2); Holiday Inn (1); Marriott (3); Pink Shell Beach Resort (2); Radisson (3)
Company-Owned Units: 22
Alcohol Served: Beer, Wine, Liquor
Projected Remodelings: 6
Areas of Operation: FL, GA, NC, OH, PA, TX
Type of Foodservice: Casual Dining (22)
Primary Distributors: (Food) SYSCO Food Services of Cincinnati, CINCINNATI, OH
Parent Company: Westmont Hospitality Group, HOUSTON, TX
Notes: The company derives approximately 71% of its revenue from hotel operations and other activities.

Key Personnel
ROBERT W. BOYKIN - Chairman; CEO
RICHARD LONGO - President; CFO; Chief Administrative Officer
JOHN "JACK" BOYKIN - Exec VP; Senior VP Operations, Marketing, Food and Beverage
BILL WAICHULIS - Senior VP Operations

Platinum Corral LLC
521 New Bridge St
Jacksonville, NC 28540-5430

Telephone: (910) 347-3971
Fax Number: (910) 347-4616
Internet Homepage: platinumcorral.com
Company Email: customerservice@platinumcorral.com
Type of Business: Chain Restaurant Operator
Year Founded: 1996
Total Sales: $63,590,000 (e)
Number of Employees: 1,400
Average Check: Breakfast(10); Lunch(12); Dinner(16)
Total Units: 12
Trade Names: Golden Corral Buffet & Grill (12)
Units Franchised From: 12
Preferred Square Footage: 7,800; 10,300; 11,500
Preferred Location Types: Freestanding
Primary Menu: American (12)
Areas of Operation: NC, VA
Type of Foodservice: Family Restaurant (12)
Franchise Affiliation: Golden Corral Corp., RALEIGH, NC
Primary Distributors: (Food) McLane/Rocky Mount, ROCKY MOUNT, NC

Anjusam, LLC
4835 W Wendover Ave Ste 144
Jamestown, NC 27282-8599

Telephone: (336) 856-0010
Type of Business: Chain Restaurant Operator
Total Sales: $3,012,000 (e)
Total Units: 2
Trade Names: Jersey Mike's Subs (2)
Units Franchised From: 2
Primary Menu: Sandwiches/Deli (2)
Areas of Operation: NC
Type of Foodservice: Quick Serve (2)
Franchise Affiliation: Jersey Mike's Franchise Systems, MANASQUAN, NJ

Key Personnel
BILLY SEWELL - CEO; President; Director Information Systems, Real Estate, Design
MATT SHARKEY - General Manager
KIM ALLGEIER - General Manager
MICHAEL BURTON - General Manager
JEFF LEPPER - Director Human Resources
RICK TRANT - Director Operations, Facility/Maintenance, Store Fixtures; General Buyer
DEBRA SMITH - Specialist Payroll
DEBI BOETTNER - Coordinator Accounting

Key Personnel
JEREMY JHINGREE - Owner; General Buyer

Be Rich Buns, Inc.
1413 Trail Ln
Kernersville, NC 27284

Telephone: (336) 996-7006
Type of Business: Chain Restaurant Operator
Total Sales: $735,000 (e)
Total Units: 2
Trade Names: Cinnabon (2)
Units Franchised From: 2
Primary Menu: Snacks (2)
Areas of Operation: NC
Type of Foodservice: Quick Serve (2)
Franchise Affiliation: Cinnabon Inc., ATLANTA, GA

Key Personnel
RICHARD MUNSON - Owner; General Buyer

JS2 Services LLC
960 S Main St Ste E
Kernersville, NC 27284-7095

Telephone: (336) 992-2524
Type of Business: Chain Restaurant Operator
Total Sales: $1,311,000 (e)
Total Units: 2
Trade Names: Cold Stone Creamery (2)
Units Franchised From: 2
Primary Menu: Snacks (2)
Areas of Operation: NC
Type of Foodservice: Quick Serve (2)
Franchise Affiliation: Kahala Brands, SCOTTSDALE, AZ

Key Personnel
HARRY KIM - Owner; General Buyer

Kelly's Hospitality Group
1004 9th Ave
Kill Devil Hills, NC 27948

Mailing Address: PO Box 1089, NAGS HEAD, NC, 27959-1089
Telephone: (252) 441-4116
Fax Number: (252) 480-2665
Internet Homepage: makomikes.com; pamlicojacks.com
Company Email: kellysrestaurant@earthlink.net
Type of Business: Chain Restaurant Operator
Year Founded: 1985
Total Sales: $7,146,000 (e)
Alcohol Sales: 20%
Number of Employees: 125
Average Check: Dinner(30)
Total Units: 2
Trade Names: Mako Mike's (1); Pamlico Jack's (1)
Company-Owned Units: 2
Preferred Location Types: Freestanding
Alcohol Served: Beer, Wine, Liquor
Primary Menu: American (1); Seafood (1)
Areas of Operation: NC
Type of Foodservice: Casual Dining (2)
Catering Services: Yes
Primary Distributors: (Full Line) Sysco Eastern Maryland Inc., POCOMOKE CITY, MD

Key Personnel
MIKE KELLY - President; General Manager
MARYANN NEWMAN - Manager Catering

King's Restaurants Inc.
405 E New Bern Rd
Kinston, NC 28504-6737

Telephone: (800) 332-6465
Fax Number: (252) 522-4373
Internet Homepage: kingsbbq.com
Type of Business: Chain Restaurant Operator
Year Founded: 1946
Total Sales: $5,824,000 (e)
Alcohol Sales: 1%
Number of Employees: 200
Average Check: Lunch(18); Dinner(18)
Internet Order Processing: Yes
Internet Sales: 0.50%
Total Units: 4
Trade Names: King's Barbecue & Chicken (4)
Company-Owned Units: 4
Preferred Square Footage: 3,500
Preferred Location Types: Freestanding
Alcohol Served: Beer, Wine, Liquor
Primary Menu: Bar-B-Q (4)
Areas of Operation: NC
Type of Foodservice: Casual Dining (4)
Catering Services: Yes
On-site Distribution Center: Yes
Primary Distributors: (Equipment) Jacobi-Lewis Co., WILMINGTON, NC; (Food) Sysco Eastern Maryland Inc., POCOMOKE CITY, MD

Key Personnel
JOE HARGITT - Owner; Executive Chef; Director Catering; General Buyer
BARBARA GOODING - Manager Operations
WILBUR KING JR - Consultant

Tands Inc.
335 N Queen St
Kinston, NC 28501-4931

Mailing Address: PO Box 277, KINSTON, NC, 28502-0277
Telephone: (252) 522-0191
Fax Number: (252) 522-3602
Internet Homepage: becajun.com; bojangles.com
Company Email: aniro@becajun.com
Type of Business: Chain Restaurant Operator
Year Founded: 1979
Total Sales: $188,580,000 (e)
Number of Employees: 1,985
Average Check: Breakfast(8); Lunch(8); Dinner(10)
Total Units: 69
Trade Names: Bojangles' Famous Chicken 'n Biscuits (69)
Units Franchised From: 69
Preferred Square Footage: 3,000
Preferred Location Types: Freestanding
Primary Menu: Chicken (60)
Areas of Operation: NC
Type of Foodservice: Quick Serve (69)
Franchise Affiliation: Bojangles Restaurants Inc., CHARLOTTE, NC

Key Personnel
CAMERON MCRAE - CEO; President; Manager Real Estate
REESE STEWART - CFO
JACKIE WOODWARD - Chief Marketing Officer
JOSE COSTA - Chief Growth Officer; VP
SCOTT MCRAE - VP
ADAM PADGETT - VP Information Technology
JEFF MCKIMMIE - VP Operations
NICK SWANSON - Senior Director Consumer Insights
DONNA RODWELL - Director Marketing
GERALD FORREST - Director Business

Development
JOHN LEQUIRE - Regional Director Operations
LISA DUER - Senior Manager Quality Assurance
ALLISON ANSELMO - Manager Finance
TALIA CRACKEL - Manager Digital Media
JONI MCRAE - Manager Research & Development
NATHAN PARIS - Manager Marketing

R.M. Gibson, Inc.
12280 McColl Rd
Laurinburg, NC 28352-7921

Telephone: (910) 266-0013
Type of Business: Chain Restaurant Operator
Total Sales: $2,992,000 (e)
Total Units: 2
Trade Names: Jersey Mike's Subs (2)
Units Franchised From: 2
Primary Menu: Sandwiches/Deli (2)
Areas of Operation: NC
Type of Foodservice: Quick Serve (2)
Franchise Affiliation: Jersey Mike's Franchise Systems, MANASQUAN, NJ

Key Personnel
RONALD GIBSON - Owner; General Buyer

Scottish Food Systems Inc.
452 Atkinson St
Laurinburg, NC 28352-3714

Mailing Address: PO Box 1469, LAURINBURG, NC, 28353-1469
Telephone: (910) 276-6740
Fax Number: (910) 276-7588
Internet Homepage: scottishfoodsystemsinc.com
Type of Business: Chain Restaurant Operator
Year Founded: 1964
Total Sales: $56,930,000 (e)
Alcohol Sales: 1%
Number of Employees: 2,020
Average Check: Lunch(6); Dinner(10)
Total Units: 31
Trade Names: KFC (27); Pizza Inn (4)
Units Franchised From: 31
Preferred Square Footage: 2,700; 3,200; 4,000
Preferred Location Types: Freestanding; Strip Mall
Primary Menu: Chicken (27); Pizza (4)
Areas of Operation: NC, SC
Type of Foodservice: Family Restaurant (4); Quick Serve (27)
Franchise Affiliation: KFC Corporation, LOUISVILLE, KY; RAVE Restaurant Group Inc., THE COLONY, TX
Parent Company: Z.V. Pate Inc., LAUREL HILL, NC

Key Personnel
HEW FULTON - President; VP Division
BRUCE T. GOODWIN - VP Administration; Controller

Domino's Franchisee
114 E Center St
Lexington, NC 27292-3312

Telephone: (336) 238-7272
Type of Business: Chain Restaurant Operator
Total Sales: $20,353,000 (e)
Total Units: 10
Trade Names: Domino's (10)
Units Franchised From: 10
Primary Menu: Pizza (10)
Areas of Operation: NC
Type of Foodservice: Quick Serve (10)
Franchise Affiliation: Domino's Pizza Inc, ANN ARBOR, MI

Key Personnel
SHANE GRAHAM - Partner; General Buyer
KORI GRAHAM - Partner

KTL McDonald's LLC
1208 S Main St
Lillington, NC 27546-7924

Telephone: (910) 814-3636
Fax Number: (910) 814-0381
Company Email: ktlmcdonalds@embarqmail.com
Type of Business: Chain Restaurant Operator
Total Sales: $23,270,000 (e)
Number of Employees: 250
Total Units: 5
Trade Names: McDonald's (5)
Units Franchised From: 5
Preferred Square Footage: 2,500
Primary Menu: Hamburger (5)
Areas of Operation: NC
Type of Foodservice: Quick Serve (5)
Franchise Affiliation: McDonald's Corporation, CHICAGO, IL

Key Personnel
THOMAS HAYNIE - President; Partner; General Buyer
ARLENE HAYNIE - Partner

Domino's Franchisee
8551 NC 56 Hwy
Louisburg, NC 27549-8636

Telephone: (919) 497-0400
Type of Business: Chain Restaurant Operator
Total Sales: $12,466,000 (e)
Total Units: 6
Trade Names: Domino's (6)
Units Franchised From: 6
Primary Menu: Pizza (6)
Areas of Operation: NC
Type of Foodservice: Quick Serve (6)
Franchise Affiliation: Domino's Pizza Inc, ANN ARBOR, MI

Key Personnel
BART H. CRUM - Owner; General Buyer

Bullard Restaurant Group
1901 N Pine St
Lumberton, NC 28358-3969

Mailing Address: PO Box 1886, LUMBERTON, NC, 28359-1886
Telephone: (910) 738-7183
Fax Number: (910) 738-1821
Internet Homepage: bullardrestaurants.com
Type of Business: Chain Restaurant Operator
Year Founded: 1980
Total Sales: $51,420,000 (e)
Number of Employees: 2,325
Average Check: Breakfast(8); Lunch(8); Dinner(8)
Total Units: 57
Trade Names: Burger King (19); BurgerFI (2); CoreLife Eatery (2); Moe's Southwest Grill (26); Smithfield's Chicken 'N Bar-B-Q (8)
Units Franchised From: 57
Preferred Square Footage: 2,600
Preferred Location Types: Freestanding; Regional Mall
Primary Menu: Chicken (8); Hamburger (21); Health Foods (2); Southwest/Tex-Mex (26)
Projected Openings: 2
Areas of Operation: NC, SC
Type of Foodservice: Quick Serve (57)
Franchise Affiliation: Burger King Worldwide Inc., MIAMI, FL; CoreLife Eatery, LLC, VESTAL, NY; FIC Restaurants, WILBRAHAM, MA; Moe's Southwest Grill LLC, ATLANTA, GA; Smithfield's Chicken 'N Bar-B-Q, CARY, NC
Primary Distributors: (Food) McLane/Rocky Mount, ROCKY MOUNT, NC

Key Personnel
DEBBIE ARMSTEAD - CFO
HELEN PODRUCHNY - Senior VP Operations
CLIFF JONES - Senior VP Operations
RACHELLE BULLARD - Director Marketing
JOSEPH RICHARDSON - Director Information Technology
JASON PUHLMAN - Area Manager
MICHAEL MERRY - Area Manager
CHRIS FRAZIER - Specialist POS/Scanning

Rust Enterprise
4260 Fayetteville Rd Ste A
Lumberton, NC 28358-2726

Telephone: (910) 738-1428
Fax Number: (910) 738-5183
Company Email: mcddata@aol.com
Type of Business: Chain Restaurant Operator
Total Sales: $37,540,000 (e)
Total Units: 8
Trade Names: McDonald's (8)
Units Franchised From: 8
Preferred Square Footage: 2,500
Primary Menu: Hamburger (8)
Areas of Operation: NC
Type of Foodservice: Quick Serve (8)
Franchise Affiliation: McDonald's Corporation, CHICAGO, IL

Key Personnel
KENNETH RUST - President; General Buyer

Delights of Carolina Inc.
640 Matthews Mint Hill Rd Ste A
Matthews, NC 28105-1759

Mailing Address: PO Box 2349, MATTHEWS, NC, 28106-2349
Telephone: (704) 845-8215
Company Email: delights@windstream.net
Type of Business: Chain Restaurant Operator
Total Sales: $6,439,000 (e)
Total Units: 11
Trade Names: Subway (11)
Units Franchised From: 11
Primary Menu: Sandwiches/Deli (11)
Areas of Operation: NC
Type of Foodservice: Quick Serve (11)
Franchise Affiliation: Doctor's Associates Inc., MILFORD, CT

Key Personnel
PHYLLIS M. CURTIS - President

Jenick Professional Services, LLC
102 Millstead Dr
Mebane, NC 27302-7165

Telephone: (919) 563-8800
Type of Business: Chain Restaurant Operator
Total Sales: $6,006,000 (e)
Total Units: 4
Trade Names: Jersey Mike's Subs (4)
Units Franchised From: 4
Primary Menu: Sandwiches/Deli (4)
Areas of Operation: NC
Type of Foodservice: Quick Serve (4)
Franchise Affiliation: Jersey Mike's Franchise Systems, MANASQUAN, NJ

Key Personnel
JEFFREY JOHNSON - Owner; General Buyer

CharBar7
Town View Dr
Mint Hill, NC 28227

Telephone: (704) 573-4336
Internet Homepage: charbar7.com
Type of Business: Chain Restaurant Operator
Year Founded: 2011
Total Units: 6
Trade Names: CharBar 7 (6)
Company-Owned Units: 6
Primary Menu: American (6)
Areas of Operation: NC
Type of Foodservice: Casual Dining (6)

Key Personnel
TYLER HAGER - Owner
GREGG BIBIK - Manager Region
KARA HAGER - Manager Design
JEROME CLYBURN - Manager Culinary Development

Slip Management
PO Box 2026
Monroe, NC 28111-2016

Telephone: (336) 681-8713
Type of Business: Chain Restaurant Operator
Total Sales: $15,096,000 (e)
Total Units: 3
Trade Names: McDonald's (3)
Units Franchised From: 3
Preferred Square Footage: 2,500
Primary Menu: Hamburger (3)
Areas of Operation: NC
Type of Foodservice: Quick Serve (3)
Franchise Affiliation: McDonald's Corporation, CHICAGO, IL

Key Personnel
JEROME DAVIS - President; General Buyer

Clutch Coffee Bar
154 W Plaza Dr
Mooresville, NC 28117

Telephone: (669) 800-9172
Internet Homepage: clutchcoffeebar.com
Type of Business: Chain Restaurant Operator
Year Founded: 2018
Total Sales: $13,700,000 (e)
Total Units: 9
Trade Names: Clutch Coffee Bar (9)
Company-Owned Units: 9
Primary Menu: American (9); Coffee (9)
Type of Foodservice: Casual Dining (9); Quick Serve (9)

Key Personnel
DARREN SPICER - Co-Founder; CEO
ANDERSON JOHN - Owner

JP Steakhouse LLC
129 Fast Ln
Mooresville, NC 28117-6421

Telephone: (704) 660-5939
Fax Number: (704) 799-6199
Internet Homepage: sagebrushsteakhouse.com
Type of Business: Chain Restaurant Operator
Year Founded: 1970
Systemwide Sales: $89,428,000 (e)
Total Sales: $53,427,000 (e)
Alcohol Sales: 15%
Number of Employees: 720
Average Check: Lunch(14); Dinner(14)
Internet Order Processing: Yes
Total Units: 20
Trade Names: Sagebrush Steakhouse & Saloon (19); Western Steer (1)
Company-Owned Units: 19
Units Franchised To: 1
Preferred Square Footage: 7,500
Preferred Location Types: Freestanding; Strip Mall
Alcohol Served: Beer, Wine, Liquor
Primary Menu: Steak (20)
Areas of Operation: KY, NC, TN, VA
Type of Foodservice: Casual Dining (20)
Catering Services: Yes
Notes: Formerly known as Claremont Restaurant Group LLC.

Key Personnel
JIM L. PETERSON - CEO; President; CFO; Director Real Estate, Menu Development
CANDICE B - Manager

Fulenwider Enterprises
104 Mull St
Morganton, NC 28655-3315

Telephone: (828) 437-8000
Fax Number: (828) 430-8463
Internet Homepage: fulenwider.net
Type of Business: Chain Restaurant Operator
Year Founded: 1965
Total Sales: $242,490,000 (e)
Number of Employees: 4,634
Average Check: Breakfast(12); Lunch(8); Dinner(10)
Total Units: 152
Trade Names: Butch's BBQ (1); KCF/ Taco Bell (21); KFC (81); Taco Bell (49)

Company-Owned Units: 1
Units Franchised From: 152
Preferred Square Footage: 3,500
Preferred Location Types: Freestanding
Primary Menu: Bar-B-Q (1); Chicken (102); Sandwiches/Deli (0); Taco (49)
Areas of Operation: GA, NC, SC, TN, WV
Type of Foodservice: Casual Dining (0); Fast Casual (1); Quick Serve (151)
Franchise Affiliation: KFC Corporation, LOUISVILLE, KY; Taco Bell Corp., IRVINE, CA

Key Personnel
MICHAEL FULENWIDER - CEO; Partner
BRIAN GOLDSTEIN - President; Partner; COO
VIRGINIA FULENWIDER - Partner; Manager Marketing
KELLY BUNYEA - CFO
MARY CAMPBELL - Chief People Officer
MARY ANN CAMPBELL - Chief People Officer
ARIC WHISNANT - CIO
GARY MINGO - VP Division
MICHAEL AUDETTE - VP Division
ANDRES CHAVEZ - General Manager
KEVIN COFFEY - Director Development
MICHAEL COOK - Director Operations
PAMELA BRABB - Director Training
LUIS SANDOVAL - Director Operations
TIJWANNA KETTER - Director Human Resources
TERESA EDWARDS - Director Marketing
ADAM MCCURRY - Director Development
IA VUE - Manager Payroll
ERSKINE WHITE - Manager Human Resources
STEVEN YANG - Manager Information Technology
LUIS CORONA - Manager
TOMRA MARTIN - Administrative Assistant; Office Manager

Luihn Four Inc.
2950 Gateway Centre Blvd
Morrisville, NC 27560-9615

Telephone: (919) 850-0558
Fax Number: (919) 850-0727
Internet Homepage: hurricanewings.com; luihnfood.com
Company Email: luihn@luihnfood.com
Type of Business: Chain Restaurant Operator
Year Founded: 1966
Total Sales: $268,030,000 (e)
Number of Employees: 3,000
Total Units: 132
Trade Names: KFC (32); Long John Silver's (2); Taco Bell (98)
Units Franchised From: 132
Preferred Square Footage: 2,500; 3,000
Preferred Location Types: Freestanding
Primary Menu: Chicken (32); Seafood (2); Taco (98)
Areas of Operation: FL, NC, SC, VA
Type of Foodservice: Quick Serve (132)

Franchise Affiliation: KFC Corporation, LOUISVILLE, KY; Long John Silver's Inc., LOUISVILLE, KY; Pizza Hut Inc., PLANO, TX; Taco Bell Corp., IRVINE, CA

Key Personnel
CRAIG BARTLES - CEO
JODY J. LUIHN - President; Director Finance, Franchising; Manager Operations; General Buyer
S. ALLAN LUIHN - Owner
MICHELLE FUNK - CFO
JAMEY LUIHN - VP Operations, Real Estate, Construction, Store Fixtures
SANDRA LUIHN ARGAY - Treasurer
ANDREA ROBERSON - Controller; Manager Risk Management
KAITLIN LEWIS - General Manager
BRET HOOPPAW - Director Operations
TAYLOR BOYETTE - Director Human Resources
CHIP DAVIS - Director Operations
MARIO FLORES - Senior Manager

The Little Mint Inc.
102 Commercial Ave
Mount Olive, NC 28365-8695

Telephone: (919) 635-0902
Fax Number: (919) 635-3660
Internet Homepage: hwy55burgers.com
Type of Business: Chain Restaurant Operator
Year Founded: 1991
Systemwide Sales: $73,694,000 (e)
Total Sales: $49,750,000 (e)
Number of Employees: 1,155
Average Check: Lunch(10); Dinner(10)
Total Units: 138
Trade Names: Hwy 55 Burgers Shakes & Fries (138)
Company-Owned Units: 48
Units Franchised To: 90
Preferred Square Footage: 2,500
Preferred Location Types: Freestanding; Strip Mall
Primary Menu: Hamburger (138)
Projected Openings: 3
Areas of Operation: AL, AR, FL, GA, NC, OH, SC, TX, VA, WV
Foreign Countries: DENMARK; UNITED ARAB EMIRATES
Type of Foodservice: Quick Serve (138)
On-site Distribution Center: Yes

Key Personnel
KENNY MOORE - CEO; President; General Buyer
DAVE THOMPSON - Senior VP Business Development

Wild Wing Cafe
205 Regncy Ex Pk Dr
Mount Pleasant, NC 28217

Telephone: (843) 216-7601
Fax Number: (843) 216-7602
Internet Homepage: wildwingcafe.com
Company Email: contactus@wildwingcafe.com
Type of Business: Chain Restaurant Operator
Year Founded: 1990
Systemwide Sales: $172,578,000 (e)
Total Sales: $77,190,000 (e)
Alcohol Sales: 40%
Number of Employees: 88
Average Check: Lunch(12); Dinner(20)
Internet Order Processing: Yes
Total Units: 44
Trade Names: Wild Wing Cafe (44)
Company-Owned Units: 11
Units Franchised To: 33
Preferred Square Footage: 6,500; 7,500; 8,000
Preferred Location Types: Freestanding
Alcohol Served: Beer, Wine, Liquor
Primary Menu: American (44)
Projected Openings: 10
Areas of Operation: FL, GA, NC, SC, TN, TX, VA
Type of Foodservice: Casual Dining (44)
Catering Services: Yes
Primary Distributors: (Full Line) US Foods, MANASSAS, VA
Parent Company: Axum Capital Partners, CHARLOTTE, NC

Key Personnel
TOM LEWISON - CEO; President; General Buyer
JEFFREY WAKEM - Senior Director Operations
KEITH HUME - Director Operations
JAMES REEVES - Director Operations

Hagan & Hagan Inc.
3968 M L King Jr Blvd
New Bern, NC 28562-2297

Telephone: (252) 634-9760
Fax Number: (252) 634-9759
Type of Business: Chain Restaurant Operator
Year Founded: 1982
Total Sales: $13,740,000 (e)
Number of Employees: 150
Average Check: Lunch(8); Dinner(8)
Total Units: 5
Trade Names: Taco Bell (5)
Units Franchised From: 5
Preferred Square Footage: 2,500; 3,200
Preferred Location Types: Freestanding
Primary Menu: Taco (5)
Areas of Operation: NC
Type of Foodservice: Quick Serve (5)

Franchise Affiliation: Taco Bell Corp., IRVINE, CA

Key Personnel
SANDRA HAGAN - President; Partner; General Buyer
ANTHONY WOOD - Partner; VP; Manager Human Resources, Food Safety
JAMES HAGAN IV - Partner; Treasurer; Director Real Estate
KELLY WOOD - Partner; Corporate Secretary

Purcell Foods Inc
1002 US Highway 70 E
New Bern, NC 28560

Telephone: (252) 637-8061
Internet Homepage: purcellfoods.com
Company Email: jean.pmc5370@gmail.com
Type of Business: Chain Restaurant Operator
Total Sales: $64,900,000 (e)
Total Units: 14
Trade Names: McDonald's (14)
Units Franchised From: 14
Primary Menu: Hamburger (14)
Areas of Operation: NC
Type of Foodservice: Quick Serve (14)
Franchise Affiliation: McDonald's Corporation, CHICAGO, IL

Key Personnel
DULCY PURCELL - Partner
WILLIAM PURCELL - Partner; General Buyer
MIKE HALDER - COO
BERNIE JONES - Coordinator Marketing

Pretzel Twister Inc.
3705 Mason Rd
New Hill, NC 27562-9171

Telephone: (919) 387-8929
Fax Number: (919) 363-6945
Internet Homepage: pretzeltwister.com
Type of Business: Chain Restaurant Operator
Year Founded: 1992
Systemwide Sales: $4,110,000 (e)
Total Sales: $6,208,000 (e)
Number of Employees: 8
Average Check: Lunch(8); Dinner(8)
Total Units: 37
Trade Names: Pretzel Twister (37)
Units Franchised To: 37
Preferred Square Footage: 200; 900
Preferred Location Types: Airports; Community Mall; Downtown; Kiosk; Outlet Mall; Regional Mall; Strip Mall
Primary Menu: Snacks (37)
Areas of Operation: AL, FL, GA, IN, KY, LA, MA, MD, MS, NC, NY, OH, SC, VA, WA, WV
Type of Foodservice: Quick Serve (37)
Primary Distributors: (Food) Ferraro Foods, PISCATAWAY, NJ

Key Personnel
CATHERINE HUNG - Coordinator Accounting

Lamar, Inc.
PO Box 1323
Newton, NC 28658-8710

Mailing Address: P.O. Box 1323, Newton, NC, 28658
Telephone: (828) 465-6366
Type of Business: Chain Restaurant Operator
Total Sales: $3,170,000 (e)
Number of Employees: 90
Total Units: 5
Trade Names: Little Caesars Pizza (5)
Units Franchised From: 5
Preferred Location Types: Strip Mall
Primary Menu: Pizza (5)
Areas of Operation: NC
Type of Foodservice: Quick Serve (5)
Franchise Affiliation: Little Caesar Enterprises Inc., DETROIT, MI

Key Personnel
DAVE KASTELIC - President; General Buyer
JEREMY KADOICH - Account Executive
STEVE GILLIGAN - Account Executive

Pinehurst Resort LLC
80 Carolina Vis
Pinehurst, NC 28374

Mailing Address: PO Box 4000, PINEHURST, NC, 28374-4000
Telephone: (910) 295-6811
Fax Number: (910) 235-8402
Internet Homepage: pinehurst.com
Company Email: info@pinehurst.com
Type of Business: Foodservice Operations - Hotel/Motels
Year Founded: 1895
Total Sales: $90,260,000 (e)
Alcohol Sales: 28%
Number of Employees: 1,000
Total Units: 10
Restaurants in Hotels: 10
Trade Names: 1895 Grille (1); 91st Hole (1); Centennail Number 8 (1); Fairwoods on Seven Dining Room (1); The Carolina Coffee Shop (1); The Carolina Dining Room (1); The Centennial Dining Room (1); The Donald Ross Grill (1); The Ryder Cup Lounge (1); The Tavern at The Holly (1)
Company-Owned Units: 10
Alcohol Served: Beer, Wine, Liquor
Areas of Operation: NC
Type of Foodservice: Casual Dining (6); Fine Dining (4)
Parent Company: KSL Capital Partners, DENVER, CO
Headquarters: ClubCorp Inc., DALLAS, TX
Notes: The company derives approximately 72% of its revenue from hotel operations.

Key Personnel
TOM PASHLLEY - President
DICK HIGGINBOTHAM - Exec VP Finance
ERICK KUESTER - VP Marketing
THIERRY DEBAILLEUL - Executive Chef
RAY CASTILLO - Director Purchasing
ED NICKELSON - Director Information Systems
EDWARD PECKELS - Director Foodservice, Menu Development, Food Safety, Food and Beverage

Viva Chicken
10915 Southern Loop Blvd
Pineville, NC 28134

Internet Homepage: vivachicken.com
Type of Business: Chain Restaurant Operator
Total Sales: $16,940,000 (e)
Total Units: 14
Trade Names: Viva Chicken (14)
Company-Owned Units: 14
Primary Menu: Chicken (14)
Areas of Operation: DE, NC, SC, UT
Type of Foodservice: Fast Casual (14)

Key Personnel
RANDY GARCIA - Founder; President
GERALD PULSINELLI - CEO
TREVOR SCOTT - VP Operations

Fearrington House
240 Market St
Pittsboro, NC 27312

Telephone: (919) 542-2121
Fax Number: (919) 542-4202
Internet Homepage: fearrington.com
Company Email: fhouse@fearrington.com
Type of Business: Chain Restaurant Operator
Year Founded: 1980
Total Sales: $10,055,000 (e)
Alcohol Sales: 20%
Number of Employees: 50
Average Check: Breakfast(8); Lunch(24); Dinner(120)
Internet Order Processing: Yes
Internet Sales: 1.00%
Total Units: 3
Trade Names: Fearrington House Restaurant (1); Roost Beer Garden (1); The Belted Goat (1)
Company-Owned Units: 3
Preferred Location Types: Hotel/Motel
Alcohol Served: Beer, Wine, Liquor
Primary Menu: American (1); Pizza (1); Sandwiches/Deli (1)

Areas of Operation: NC
Type of Foodservice: Casual Dining (2); Fine Dining (1)
Primary Distributors: (Food) Southern Foods LLC, GREENSBORO, NC; (Supplies) US Foods, FORT MILL, SC

Key Personnel
R. B. FITCH - President
THERESA CHIETTINI - General Manager
COLIN BEDFORD - Executive Chef; General Buyer
LAURA MORGAN - Director Real Estate, Construction
DANEEN GRIFFIN - Manager Merchandising
GILDA MCDANIEL - Manager Promotion

321 Coffee
1202 Agriculture St Slot 48
Raleigh, NC 27603

Internet Homepage: 321coffee.com
Company Email: info@321coffee.com
Type of Business: Chain Restaurant Operator
Year Founded: 2017
Total Sales: $3,887,000 (e)
Total Units: 3
Trade Names: 321 Coffee (3)
Company-Owned Units: 3
Primary Menu: Coffee (3)
Areas of Operation: NC
Type of Foodservice: Quick Serve (3)

Key Personnel
LINDSAY WREGE - Founder; CEO
MALLORY BRYAN - Director Marketing
TAYLOR MCGOVERN - Director People

Ag of Raleigh, Inc.
601 W Peace St
Raleigh, NC 27605-1519

Telephone: (919) 832-3499
Company Email: raleigh@mellowmushroominfo.com
Type of Business: Chain Restaurant Operator
Total Units: 4
Trade Names: Mellow Mushroom Pizza Bakers (4)
Units Franchised From: 4
Primary Menu: Pizza (4)
Areas of Operation: NC
Type of Foodservice: Casual Dining (4)
Franchise Affiliation: Home-Grown Industries Of Georgia, ATLANTA, GA

Key Personnel
CASEY FOX - President; General Buyer

Ashley Christensen Restaurants
426 S McDowell St
Raleigh, NC 27601-1727

Telephone: (919) 832-4477
Internet Homepage: ac-restaurants.com
Company Email: info@ac-restaurants.com
Type of Business: Chain Restaurant Operator
Year Founded: 2007
Total Units: 5
Trade Names: Beasley's Chicken & Honey (1); Chuck's (1); Death & Taxes (1); Fox Liquor Bar (1); Poole's (1)
Company-Owned Units: 5
Primary Menu: American (2); Hamburger (1); Snacks (1); Southern (1)
Areas of Operation: NC
Type of Foodservice: Casual Dining (5)

Key Personnel
ASHLEY CHRISTENSEN - Owner; Executive Chef

Bryant Restaurants Inc.
3105 Glenwood Ave Ste 103
Raleigh, NC 27612-5059

Telephone: (919) 787-0036
Fax Number: (919) 787-7769
Type of Business: Chain Restaurant Operator
Year Founded: 1960
Total Sales: $55,270,000 (e)
Number of Employees: 650
Average Check: Lunch(8); Dinner(10)
Total Units: 20
Trade Names: Wendy's Old Fashioned Hamburgers (20)
Units Franchised From: 20
Preferred Square Footage: 3,000
Preferred Location Types: Freestanding
Primary Menu: Hamburger (20)
Areas of Operation: NC, SC
Type of Foodservice: Quick Serve (20)
Franchise Affiliation: The Wendy's Company, DUBLIN, OH
Primary Distributors: (Food) The SYGMA Network, Inc., DUBLIN, OH; (Supplies) The SYGMA Network, Inc., DUBLIN, OH

Key Personnel
DOUGLAS BRYANT - CEO; General Manager; Director Finance, Facility/Maintenance, Risk Management, Real Estate, Store Fixtures
RICHARD BRYANT - President; Director Information Systems, Marketing; General Buyer
SHANNON SAMUEL - General Manager
KAREN ALLEN - Manager Operations, Design
LINDA HAITH - Manager Human Resources
CHERYL KLACK - Manager

Cardinal Management Co Inc
3424 Poole Rd
Raleigh, NC 27610-2902

Telephone: (919) 250-0072
Fax Number: (919) 250-9025
Type of Business: Chain Restaurant Operator
Total Sales: $20,169,000 (e)
Total Units: 4
Trade Names: McDonald's (4)
Company-Owned Units: 4
Primary Menu: Hamburger (4)
Areas of Operation: NC
Type of Foodservice: Quick Serve (4)
Franchise Affiliation: McDonald's Corporation, CHICAGO, IL

Key Personnel
WILLIM HOLDER - President; General Buyer
DON MAZZEI - Owner; COO
VICTORIA GARNER - VP

Concord Hospitality Enterprises Co.
11410 Common Oaks Dr
Raleigh, NC 27614-7002

Telephone: (919) 455-2900
Fax Number: (919) 455-2909
Internet Homepage: concordhotels.com
Company Email: information@concordhotels.com
Type of Business: Foodservice Operations - Hotel/Motels
Year Founded: 1985
Total Sales: $337,550,000 (e)
Alcohol Sales: 8%
Number of Employees: 5,600
Total Units: 120
Trade Names: 41Hundred (1); AC Hotels (5); Beaufort Hotel an Ascend Collection (1); Cambria Suites (10); Canopy by Hilton Atlanta Midtown (1); Canopy Washington DC | The Wharf (1); Clinton Inn (1); Courtyard (24); Dewberry 1850 (1); DoubleTree (2); Embassy Suites Uptown Charlotte (1); Fairfield Inn &Suites (4); Four Points (1); Hampton Inn (5); Hilton Garden Inn (8); Holiday Inn (1); Holiday Inn Express (2); Homewood Suites (8); Hyatt (11); Marriott (3);Renaissance (3); Residence Inn (13); SpringHill Suites (8); The Ben, Autograph Collection (1); The Oaklander Hotel an Autograph Collection (1); TownePlace Suites (3)
Company-Owned Units: 120
Alcohol Served: Beer, Wine, Liquor
Areas of Operation: CT, GA, IA, NC, NJ, OH
Primary Distributors: (Food) SYSCO Food Services of Cincinnati, CINCINNATI, OH

Notes: The company derives approximately 80% of its revenue from hotel operations.

Key Personnel
MARK G. LAPORT - CEO; President
JULIE RICHTER - CFO
NICK KELLOCK - COO
BRIAN CORNELL - CIO
JARED GARNER - Chief Compliance Officer; General Counsel
CARL HREN - Senior VP Development
DEBRA PUNKE - Senior VP Communications, Human Resources
KEVIN MCATEER - Senior VP Marketing, Sales
SCOTT NESS - Senior VP Accounting; Controller
GRANT SABROFF - Senior VP Business Development
DEAN WENDEL - VP Food and Beverage
LYLA HEDLUND - VP Human Resources
ANDY BURCH - Regional VP
DAN FREELAND - Regional VP
BILL GANT - Regional VP
KENNETH POLO - Regional VP
MICHAEL ROBERTS - Regional VP
WILL FLEMING - Director Information Technology, Human Resources

Crab Du Jour
6320 Plantation Center Dr
Raleigh, NC 27616

Telephone: (347) 654-9410
Internet Homepage: crabdujour.com
Company Email: info@crabdujour.com
Type of Business: Chain Restaurant Operator
Year Founded: 2019
Number of Employees: 800
Total Units: 41
Trade Names: Crab Du Jour (41)
Company-Owned Units: 41
Primary Menu: Seafood (41)
Areas of Operation: AL, CT, DE, FL, GA, IL, NC, NJ, NY, PA, SC, VA
Type of Foodservice: Casual Dining (41)

Key Personnel
BEAU STICKLEY - VP Business Development

CRC Brier Creek, LLC
10251 Little Brier Creek Ln
Raleigh, NC 27617-4268

Telephone: (919) 806-3900
Type of Business: Chain Restaurant Operator
Total Sales: $4,984,000 (e)
Total Units: 4
Trade Names: Firehouse Subs (4)
Units Franchised From: 4
Preferred Location Types: Strip Mall
Primary Menu: Sandwiches/Deli (4)
Areas of Operation: NC
Type of Foodservice: Fast Casual (4)
Franchise Affiliation: Firehouse Restaurant Group Inc., JACKSONVILLE, FL

Key Personnel
AMISH DESAI - President; General Buyer

Domino's Franchisee
2881 Jones Franklin Rd
Raleigh, NC 27606-4007

Telephone: (919) 235-0808
Type of Business: Chain Restaurant Operator
Total Sales: $9,901,000 (e)
Total Units: 5
Trade Names: Domino's (5)
Units Franchised From: 5
Primary Menu: Pizza (5)
Areas of Operation: NC
Type of Foodservice: Quick Serve (5)
Franchise Affiliation: Domino's Pizza Inc, ANN ARBOR, MI

Key Personnel
MARK S. FARRIOR - Owner; General Buyer

Food Masters, Inc.
10224 Durant Rd
Raleigh, NC 27614

Mailing Address: PO Box 58399, RALEIGH, NC, 27658-8399
Telephone: (919) 876-0957
Fax Number: (919) 876-0958
Internet Homepage: foodmastersinc.com
Type of Business: Chain Restaurant Operator
Total Sales: $14,180,000 (e)
Total Units: 10
Trade Names: Dairy Queen (4); DQ Grill & Chill (1); Huddle House (1); Milestone Diner (1); Orange Julius (1); Quiznos Sub (1); Roadhouse Restaurant (1)
Company-Owned Units: 4
Units Franchised From: 6
Primary Menu: American (8); Sandwiches/Deli (1); Snacks (1)
Areas of Operation: NC, PA, SC, VA
Type of Foodservice: Family Restaurant (4); Quick Serve (6)
Franchise Affiliation: International Dairy Queen Inc., BLOOMINGTON, MN; The Quiznos Master LLC, DENVER, CO
Notes: The company also operates several convenience stores in NC.

Key Personnel
WAYNE RICE - President
MATT MOORE - VP; Director Purchasing
BILL CASTEEN - Treasurer; Corporate Secretary
CHARLES CASTEEN - Controller

Golden Corral Corp.
5151 Glenwood Ave
Raleigh, NC 27612-3240

Mailing Address: PO Box 29502, RALEIGH, NC, 27626-0502
Telephone: (919) 781-9310
Fax Number: (919) 881-5252
Internet Homepage: goldencorral.com; goldencorralfranchise.com
Company Email: support@goldencorral.net
Type of Business: Chain Restaurant Operator
Year Founded: 1972
Systemwide Sales: $2,458,687,000 (e)
Total Sales: $802,800,000 (e)
Number of Employees: 9,759
Average Check: Breakfast(8); Lunch(8); Dinner(12)
Total Units: 452
Trade Names: Golden Corral Buffet & Grill (452)
Company-Owned Units: 100
Units Franchised To: 352
Preferred Square Footage: 7,800; 11,100; 11,600; 14,000
Preferred Location Types: Freestanding; Strip Mall
Primary Menu: American (452)
Projected Openings: 10
Areas of Operation: AK, AL, AR, AZ, CA, CO, CT, FL, GA, IA, ID, IL, IN, KS, KY, LA, MA, MD, MI, MO, MS, MT, NC, ND, NE, NJ, NM, NV, NY, OH, OK, PA, SC, SD, TN, TX, UT, VA, WA, WI, WV, WY
Type of Foodservice: Family Restaurant (452)
Subsidiaries: Coastal Equipment, JACKSONVILLE, NC
Primary Distributors: (Full Line) McLane/Rocky Mount, ROCKY MOUNT, NC
Parent Company: Investors Management Corp., RALEIGH, NC
Regional Offices: Golden Corral East Region, RALEIGH, NC

Key Personnel
JAMES H. MAYNARD - Chairman
ROY HINOJOSA - President West Division
KIM DAVIS - President Division
DAWN GILLIS - CIO
SKIP HANKE - Chief Marketing Officer
JAMES D. LAVERTY - Senior VP Finance, Administration
DAVID CONKLIN - Senior VP Development
SHELLEY WOLFORD - Senior VP Strategy, Communications
CHAPPELL PHILLIPS - Senior VP; Corporate Secretary; General Counsel
DARRYL MICKLER - Senior VP Food
GORDON POULSON - VP Real Estate
MIKE LARSEN - Senior Director Information

Technology
TERRY MCDONALD - Director Operations
JEFFREY SCHAUFEL - Director Operations
TODD KAUFMAN - Director Operations
NICKI MILES - Director Legal
DEBRA OLSON - Senior Manager Menu Development
DENISE HIGGS - Manager Tax

Golden Corral East Region
5151 Glenwood Ave
Raleigh, NC 27612-3240

Mailing Address: PO Box 29502, RALEIGH, NC, 27626-0502
Telephone: (919) 781-9310
Fax Number: (919) 881-4485
Listing Type: Regional Office
Type of Business: Chain Restaurant Operator
Total Units: 500
Company-Owned Units: 500
Areas of Operation: AL, DE, FL, GA, IL, IN, KY, LA, MD, MI, MS, NC, NJ, NY, OH, SC, TN, VA, WV
Parent Company: Golden Corral Corp., RALEIGH, NC

Key Personnel
LANCE TRENARY - CEO; President

Gunter Enterprises, Inc.
PO Box 61398
Raleigh, NC 27661-1398

Telephone: (919) 850-0011
Fax Number: (919) 850-0017
Internet Homepage: raleighmcd.com
Company Email: rakiaadmin@raleighmcd.com
Type of Business: Chain Restaurant Operator
Total Sales: $56,930,000 (e)
Number of Employees: 400
Total Units: 12
Trade Names: McDonald's (12)
Units Franchised From: 12
Preferred Square Footage: 2,500
Preferred Location Types: Freestanding; Regional Mall
Primary Menu: Hamburger (12)
Areas of Operation: NC
Type of Foodservice: Quick Serve (12)
Franchise Affiliation: McDonald's Corporation, CHICAGO, IL

Key Personnel
SHEILA GUNTER - CEO
GAFFNEY GUNTER SR - Partner; General Buyer
GAFFNEY GUNTER JR - Partner; General Buyer
GAFFNEY GUNTER II - Partner

ANA DEDHO - Administrator

Happy + Hale
200 Park at North Hills St
Raleigh, NC 27609

Telephone: (984) 200-3802
Internet Homepage: happyandhale.com
Type of Business: Chain Restaurant Operator
Total Sales: $4,728,000 (e)
Total Units: 4
Trade Names: Happy + Hale (4)
Company-Owned Units: 4
Primary Menu: Health Foods (4)
Areas of Operation: NC
Type of Foodservice: Fast Casual (4)

Key Personnel
MATT WHITLEY - Co-Founder
TYLER HELIKSON - Co-Founder; CEO
ELENA CARON - Creative Director
JORDAN PERILI - Director Operations

La Car Of N C, Inc
10532 Byrum Woods Dr
Raleigh, NC 27613-6596

Telephone: (919) 841-0347
Type of Business: Chain Restaurant Operator
Total Sales: $38,670,000 (e)
Total Units: 8
Trade Names: McDonald's (8)
Units Franchised From: 8
Primary Menu: Hamburger (8)
Areas of Operation: NC
Type of Foodservice: Quick Serve (8)
Franchise Affiliation: McDonald's Corporation, CHICAGO, IL

Key Personnel
CHARLES REID - President; General Buyer
LINDA F. REID - VP

LM Restaurants Inc.
6510 Chapel Hill Rd Ste 200
Raleigh, NC 27607-5010

Telephone: (919) 851-0858
Fax Number: (919) 851-0857
Internet Homepage: bluewaterdining.com; carolinaalehouse.com; henrysrestaurant.com; hopssupplyco.com; lmrest.com; oceanicrestaurant.com; romanellisrestaurant.com; tavernaagora.com
Company Email: lmrest@lmrest.com
Type of Business: Chain Restaurant Operator
Year Founded: 1992
Total Sales: $67,110,000 (e)
Alcohol Sales: 20%
Number of Employees: 1,473
Average Check: Lunch(18); Dinner(36)
Internet Order Processing: Yes
Total Units: 34
Trade Names: Bluewater (1); Carolina Ale House (27); Henry's (1); Hops Supply Co. (1); Oceanic (2); Tavern Agora (1); Vidrio (1)
Company-Owned Units: 35
Preferred Square Footage: 3,000
Preferred Location Types: Freestanding
Alcohol Served: Beer, Wine, Liquor
Primary Menu: American (32); Greek/Mediterranean (2); Seafood (1)
Areas of Operation: FL, GA, NC, SC
Type of Foodservice: Casual Dining (35)
Primary Distributors: (Full Line) SYSCO Food Services of Columbia, COLUMBIA, SC

Key Personnel
DYLAN B. CHASE - VP Operations
AMBER MOSHAKOS - VP Corporate Affairs
TONYA TOLLER - Controller
KATHERINE GOLDFADEN - Director Marketing
BOB SAVAGE - Manager Purchasing

Milton's Pizza & Pasta
14520 Falls of Neuse Rd
Raleigh, NC 27614-8232

Telephone: (919) 570-9099
Fax Number: (919) 570-3309
Internet Homepage: miltonspizza.com
Type of Business: Chain Restaurant Operator
Year Founded: 1983
Total Sales: $6,300,000 (e)
Alcohol Sales: 10%
Number of Employees: 35
Average Check: Lunch(12); Dinner(14)
Internet Order Processing: Yes
Internet Sales: 5.00%
Total Units: 2
Trade Names: Milton's Pizza & Pasta (2)
Company-Owned Units: 2
Preferred Location Types: Freestanding; Strip Mall
Alcohol Served: Beer, Wine, Liquor
Primary Menu: Italian (2)
Areas of Operation: NC
Type of Foodservice: Casual Dining (2)
Catering Services: Yes

Key Personnel
JEFF JANIK - President; Director Menu Development
PATTY IMPERIAL - General Manager; Manager Operations, Purchasing, Human Resources

Pinecrest Subway Inc
4112 Pleasant Valley Rd Ste 116
Raleigh, NC 27612-2634

Telephone: (919) 787-7981
Fax Number: (919) 787-9663
Type of Business: Chain Restaurant Operator
Total Sales: $5,642,000 (e)
Total Units: 9
Trade Names: Subway (9)
Units Franchised From: 9
Primary Menu: Sandwiches/Deli (10)
Areas of Operation: NC
Type of Foodservice: Quick Serve (9)
Franchise Affiliation: Doctor's Associates Inc., MILFORD, CT

Key Personnel
EMAD KHAMIL - President

R&L Subs, Inc.
200 W Peace St
Raleigh, NC 27603-1184

Telephone: (919) 832-7972
Type of Business: Chain Restaurant Operator
Total Sales: $2,862,000 (e)
Total Units: 2
Trade Names: Jersey Mike's Subs (2)
Units Franchised From: 2
Primary Menu: Sandwiches/Deli (2)
Areas of Operation: NC
Type of Foodservice: Quick Serve (2)
Franchise Affiliation: Jersey Mike's Franchise Systems, MANASQUAN, NJ

Key Personnel
RICHARD J. DOMANSKI - Owner; General Buyer

Rudino's Pizza & Grinders
8800 Harvest Oaks Dr Ste 102
Raleigh, NC 27615-2075

Telephone: (919) 848-8899
Internet Homepage: rudinos.com
Type of Business: Chain Restaurant Operator
Year Founded: 1996
Total Sales: $12,700,000 (e)
Alcohol Sales: 10%
Number of Employees: 50
Average Check: Lunch(10); Dinner(14)
Total Units: 11
Trade Names: Rudino's Pizza & Grinders (11)
Company-Owned Units: 5
Units Franchised To: 6
Preferred Square Footage: 3,000
Preferred Location Types: Freestanding
Alcohol Served: Beer, Wine, Liquor

Primary Menu: Italian (11)
Areas of Operation: NC, OH, TX, VA
Type of Foodservice: Fast Casual (11)
Primary Distributors: (Full Line) US Foods, CHARLOTTE, NC

Key Personnel
DANIEL JEEVES - President
LUISA BALDERRAMA - Owner; Manager
TOM RUDD - Partner

Tri-Arc Food Systems Inc.
4905 Waters Edge Dr
Raleigh, NC 27606-2405

Telephone: (919) 859-1131
Fax Number: (919) 859-9361
Internet Homepage: bojanglesrdu.com
Type of Business: Chain Restaurant Operator
Year Founded: 1980
Total Sales: $146,260,000 (e)
Number of Employees: 3,000
Average Check: Lunch(8); Dinner(12)
Total Units: 51
Trade Names: Bojangles' Famous Chicken 'n Biscuits (51)
Units Franchised From: 51
Preferred Square Footage: 4,000
Preferred Location Types: Freestanding
Primary Menu: Chicken (51)
Areas of Operation: NC, VA
Type of Foodservice: Quick Serve (51)
Catering Services: Yes
Franchise Affiliation: Bojangles Restaurants Inc., CHARLOTTE, NC
Primary Distributors: (Food) Cheney Bros., GOLDSBORO, NC

Key Personnel
TOMMY HADDOCK - President; Director Finance, Information Systems, Real Estate
JIM DEVIVO - CFO
KENNETH AVERY - COO
GARNELL VALENTINE - VP Information Technology
DONNA HADDOCK - Treasurer
LYNN BRITT - Director Operations; General Buyer
AMANDA ARNOLD - Director Human Resources

Domino's Franchisee
1570 Freeway Dr
Reidsville, NC 27320-7149

Telephone: (336) 342-3555
Type of Business: Chain Restaurant Operator
Total Sales: $13,924,000 (e)
Total Units: 7
Trade Names: Domino's (7)
Units Franchised From: 7
Primary Menu: Pizza (7)

Areas of Operation: NC
Type of Foodservice: Quick Serve (7)
Franchise Affiliation: Domino's Pizza Inc, ANN ARBOR, MI

Key Personnel
MICHAEL L. TINGEN - Owner; General Buyer

BHT Inc.
3054 Zebulon Rd
Rocky Mount, NC 27804-2421

Mailing Address: P. O. Box 7908, ROCKY MOUNT, NC, 27804
Telephone: (252) 443-0001
Fax Number: (252) 443-2910
Type of Business: Chain Restaurant Operator
Year Founded: 1983
Total Sales: $38,390,000 (e)
Number of Employees: 454
Average Check: Breakfast(8); Lunch(8); Dinner(8)
Total Units: 8
Trade Names: McDonald's (8)
Units Franchised From: 8
Preferred Square Footage: 2,500
Preferred Location Types: Convenience Store/Gas Station; Discount Dept. Stores; Freestanding
Primary Menu: Hamburger (8)
Areas of Operation: NC
Type of Foodservice: Quick Serve (8)
Franchise Affiliation: McDonald's Corporation, CHICAGO, IL
Primary Distributors: (Food) Golden State Foods (QCDS), SUFFOLK, VA

Key Personnel
BARRY TRAUB - Owner; Director Real Estate; General Buyer
LARRY WINBOURNE - Director Operations, Purchasing, Information Systems, Supply Chain
NITA SWAMINATHAN - Manager Accounting, Human Resources

Boddie-Noell Enterprises Inc.
1021 Noell Ln
Rocky Mount, NC 27804-1761

Mailing Address: PO Box 1908, ROCKY MOUNT, NC, 27802-1908
Telephone: (252) 937-2000
Fax Number: (252) 937-2978
Internet Homepage: bneinc.com
Company Email: generalmail@bneinc.com
Type of Business: Chain Restaurant Operator
Year Founded: 1962
Total Sales: $629,500,000 (e)

Number of Employees: 9,106
Average Check: Lunch(8); Dinner(10)
Total Units: 342
Trade Names: Hardee's (341); The Highway Diner (1)
Company-Owned Units: 1
Units Franchised From: 341
Preferred Square Footage: 3,000; 3,600
Preferred Location Types: Community Mall; Downtown; Freestanding; Hotel/Motel; Office Complex; Strip Mall
Primary Menu: American (1); Hamburger (341)
Areas of Operation: KY, NC, SC, VA
Type of Foodservice: Family Restaurant (1); Quick Serve (341)
Catering Services: Yes
Franchise Affiliation: Hardee's Food Systems Inc., FRANKLIN, TN
Primary Distributors: (Equipment) HED Foodservice Equipment, ROCKY MOUNT, NC; (Food) McLane/Rocky Mount, ROCKY MOUNT, NC; (Supplies) McLane/Rocky Mount, ROCKY MOUNT, NC

Key Personnel
BILL BODDIE - CEO; President
MIKE BODDIE - President Division
TERRY LEWIS - President Restaurant Operations
W. CRAIG WORTHY - CFO
JERRY ALLSBROOK - Chief Marketing Officer
MICHAEL HANCOCK - Exec VP
DOUGLAS E. ANDERSON - Exec VP
BOB CRUMLEY - Senior VP Human Resources
DAVID SCHMITT - VP Finance, Accounting
KATHLEEN TRUSCH - VP Human Resources
TIM LANE - VP Supply Chain, Product Development
KEVIN BOUDREAU - VP
BOB LARIMER - VP Information Systems
NANETTE HERBERT - VP Benefits, Compensation
MIKE HANCOCK - VP
JON GRANT - VP Finance
REGGIE BARNACASCEL - VP Development
JUSTIN REYNOLDS - General Manager
ADAM IPOCK - Senior Director Information Systems
GEORGE CRANE - Senior Director Operations
JACKIE WILLIAMS - Senior Director Training
LAURA JOYNER - Director Product Development, Quality Control
JIM REID - Director Financial Planning
GLORIA DUNN - Director Supply Chain
PHYLLIS HARDEE - Director Software Development
JODY SMITH - Director Restaurant Operations
WAYNE CLARK - Director Human Resources
PAT CYRUS-KARR - Director Tax
GIL STEPHENS - Director Facility/Maintenance
SCOTT KEENE - Director Real Estate
MITZI ALDRIDGE - Director Human Resources
ANN LUPTON - Director Loss Prevention
DON MACK - Director Operations
RYAN CARTER - Director Restaurant Operations
BUNN BODDIE - Director Operations
BECKY OWENS - Director Employee Benefits
JAIME BOSTIC - Regional Director Operations
STEWART SCHUYLER - Regional Director Operations
TONY FISHER - Senior Manager Facility/Maintenance, Region
PAM SPIVEY - Senior Manager Branding
BRIAN MILBURN - Senior Manager Network, Security
STAN HARWOOD - Senior Manager Human Resources
JOHNNY THOMPSON - Manager Store Fixtures, Kitchen Equipment, Refrigeration Equipment, Restaurant Operations-Refrigeration Equipment; Buyer Foodservice Equip/Supplies, Kitchen Equipment
SUSAN MIZELLE - Manager Accounting
KEVIN BENSON - Manager Facility/Maintenance
LEO PITTMAN - Manager Technology
JUNE GARDNER - Manager Information Technology, Information/Data Security
JENNA GREEN - Manager Marketing
BARBARA HENDRICKS - Manager Human Resources
ANGELA LANGLEY-DAVIS - Manager Marketing; Analyst
TIM KILLEBREW - Manager
KALEIGH YENNEY - Manager Fleet
MONICA PATSEL - Manager Human Resources

Cliett Inc.
143 May Dr
Rocky Mount, NC 27804-2507

Telephone: (252) 977-1735
Fax Number: (252) 977-9737
Internet Homepage: cliettinc.com
Company Email: office@cliettinc.com
Type of Business: Chain Restaurant Operator
Year Founded: 1973
Total Sales: $5,276,000 (e)
Number of Employees: 250
Average Check: Lunch(10); Dinner(10)
Total Units: 1
Trade Names: WesterN SizzliN Steak & More (1)
Units Franchised From: 1
Preferred Location Types: Freestanding
Primary Menu: Steak (1)
Areas of Operation: NC
Type of Foodservice: Family Restaurant (1)
Franchise Affiliation: The Western Sizzlin Corp., ROANOKE, VA
Primary Distributors: (Full Line) US Foods, CHARLOTTE, NC

Key Personnel
CINDY WILDER - President; General Manager; General Buyer
TOMMY CLIETT - Owner
DAN HOWELL - Controller; Manager Loss Prevention
RON WILDER - Director Operations, Purchasing; Manager Marketing, Human Resources

Wade Cary Enterprise Inc.
1029 Hammond St
Rocky Mount, NC 27803

Mailing Address: PO Box 4305, ROCKY MOUNT, NC, 27803-0305
Telephone: (252) 977-3221
Fax Number: (252) 972-3556
Type of Business: Chain Restaurant Operator
Year Founded: 1970
Total Sales: $21,630,000 (e)
Number of Employees: 450
Average Check: Breakfast(8); Lunch(8); Dinner(8)
Total Units: 12
Trade Names: Hardee's (12)
Units Franchised From: 12
Preferred Square Footage: 3,000
Preferred Location Types: Freestanding
Primary Menu: Hamburger (12)
Areas of Operation: NC
Type of Foodservice: Quick Serve (12)
Franchise Affiliation: Hardee's Food Systems Inc., FRANKLIN, TN
Primary Distributors: (Equipment) HED Foodservice Equipment, ROCKY MOUNT, NC; (Food) McLane/Rocky Mount, ROCKY MOUNT, NC; (Supplies) HED Foodservice Equipment, ROCKY MOUNT, NC

Key Personnel
JOHN G. GARDNER JR - CEO; President
JAMES B. GARDNER - VP; Director Finance, Facility/Maintenance, Design, Store Fixtures
KELLY BATTS - Representative

Domino's Franchisee
6110 Rogers Rd
Rolesville, NC 27571-9369

Telephone: (919) 453-2324
Type of Business: Chain Restaurant Operator
Total Sales: $3,992,000 (e)
Total Units: 2
Trade Names: Domino's (2)
Units Franchised From: 2
Primary Menu: Pizza (2)
Areas of Operation: NC
Type of Foodservice: Quick Serve (2)
Franchise Affiliation: Domino's Pizza Inc, ANN ARBOR, MI

Key Personnel
STEVEN FERONE - Owner; General Buyer

GBR Pizza Inc
1600 S Horner Blvd
Sanford, NC 27331

Telephone: (919) 774-4881
Fax Number: (919) 775-4304
Type of Business: Chain Restaurant Operator
Total Sales: $27,912,000 (e)
Total Units: 14
Trade Names: Domino's (14)
Units Franchised From: 14
Primary Menu: Pizza (14)
Areas of Operation: NC
Type of Foodservice: Quick Serve (14)
Franchise Affiliation: Domino's Pizza Inc, ANN ARBOR, MI

Key Personnel
GERALD B. RHODES - Owner; General Buyer

Durhan Sub Shop
4600 Main St Ste 150-4
Shallotte, NC 28470-1902

Telephone: (910) 754-7760
Type of Business: Chain Restaurant Operator
Total Sales: $2,455,000 (e)
Total Units: 4
Trade Names: Subway (4)
Units Franchised From: 4
Primary Menu: American (4)
Areas of Operation: NC
Type of Foodservice: Quick Serve (4)
Franchise Affiliation: Doctor's Associates Inc., MILFORD, CT

Key Personnel
CHARLES DURHAN - President; General Buyer

Ray Lackey Enterprises
1523 E Broad St
Statesville, NC 28625-4301

Telephone: (828) 838-1497
Fax Number: (828) 838-1499
Internet Homepage: villageinnpizza.com
Company Email: office@villageinnpizza.com
Type of Business: Chain Restaurant Operator
Year Founded: 1967
Total Sales: $9,211,000 (e)
Alcohol Sales: 15%
Number of Employees: 300
Average Check: Lunch(8); Dinner(10)
Internet Order Processing: Yes
Total Units: 12
Trade Names: Village Inn Pizza Parlor (12)
Company-Owned Units: 12
Preferred Square Footage: 2,500
Preferred Location Types: Freestanding; Strip Mall
Alcohol Served: Beer
Primary Menu: Pizza (12)
Areas of Operation: NC
Type of Foodservice: Fast Casual (10); Quick Serve (2)
Franchise Affiliation: Village Inn, MINNETONKA, MN

Key Personnel
JIM MARTIN - President
WILL LACKEY - Manager Operations; General Buyer

Domino's Franchisee
204 N New River Dr Ste B
Surf City, NC 28445-7034

Telephone: (910) 328-8888
Type of Business: Chain Restaurant Operator
Total Sales: $4,071,000 (e)
Total Units: 2
Trade Names: Domino's (2)
Units Franchised From: 2
Primary Menu: Pizza (2)
Areas of Operation: NC
Type of Foodservice: Quick Serve (2)
Franchise Affiliation: Domino's Pizza Inc, ANN ARBOR, MI

Key Personnel
CRAIG W. BRANNAN - Owner; General Buyer

Abrams Family Restaurants
609 W Wilson St
Tarboro, NC 27886-4240

Telephone: (252) 823-4522
Fax Number: (252) 641-0261
Internet Homepage: abramsweb.com
Company Email: abrams@abramsweb.com
Type of Business: Chain Restaurant Operator
Year Founded: 1973
Total Sales: $9,873,000 (e)
Number of Employees: 140
Average Check: Breakfast(6); Lunch(8); Dinner(8)
Total Units: 7
Trade Names: Abrams Family Restaurant (7)
Company-Owned Units: 7
Preferred Location Types: Downtown; Freestanding
Primary Menu: American (7)
Areas of Operation: NC
Type of Foodservice: Family Restaurant (7)
Catering Services: Yes
Primary Distributors: (Equipment) United Restaurant Equipment Co., RALEIGH, NC; (Food) SYSCO Food Services of Charlotte LLC, CONCORD, NC

Key Personnel
GERALD ABRAMS - President; Controller; Executive Chef; General Buyer
JERRY ABRAMS - VP Operations; General Manager; Manager Catering
BETH ABRAMS - Treasurer; Manager Accounting
WENDY BRADY - General Manager

Cook Out Restaurant
2 Regency Industrial Blvd
Thomasville, NC 27360-4929

Telephone: (336) 431-1094
Fax Number: (336) 431-3053
Internet Homepage: cookout.com
Company Email: comments@cookout.com
Type of Business: Chain Restaurant Operator
Year Founded: 1989
Total Sales: $331,000,000 (e)
Total Units: 359
Trade Names: Cook Out Restaurant (359)
Company-Owned Units: 359
Preferred Location Types: Downtown; Freestanding; Strip Mall
Primary Menu: American (359)
Projected Openings: 5
Areas of Operation: AL, GA, KY, MD, MS, NC, SC, TN, VA, WV
Type of Foodservice: Quick Serve (359)

Key Personnel
JEREMY REAVES - CEO
MORRIS REAVES - Owner; General Buyer
ROB BOLD - VP Finance
JARED RAVELING - Director Operations
CLAUDIA FARR - Regional Manager
CRYSTAL CAUSEY - Manager Payroll
BRIAN SEGERS - Project Manager
TROY MCCRARY - Administrator Human Resources
SARAHI RUIZ - Administrator Accounting
RENEE MAY - Administrator Payroll

Caison Enterprises
205 E Main St
Wallace, NC 28466-2721

Telephone: (910) 285-2848
Fax Number: (910) 285-2852
Type of Business: Chain Restaurant Operator
Total Sales: $28,500,000 (e)
Total Units: 6
Trade Names: McDonald's (6)
Units Franchised From: 6
Preferred Location Types: Freestanding
Primary Menu: Hamburger (6)
Areas of Operation: NC
Type of Foodservice: Quick Serve (6)
Franchise Affiliation: McDonald's Corporation,

CHICAGO, IL

Key Personnel
HUGH CAISON - CEO; President; General Buyer

Auntie Anne's Franchise
5226 Sigmon Rd
Wilmington, NC 28403-1666

Telephone: (910) 392-8299
Type of Business: Chain Restaurant Operator
Total Sales: $1,581,000 (e)
Total Units: 2
Trade Names: Auntie Anne's Hand-Rolled Soft Pretzels (2)
Units Franchised From: 2
Primary Menu: Snacks (2)
Areas of Operation: NC
Type of Foodservice: Quick Serve (2)
Franchise Affiliation: Auntie Anne's Inc., LANCASTER, PA

Key Personnel
GEORGE LEVITON - Owner; General Buyer

Bradford & Lee Inc.
1707 Dawson St
Wilmington, NC 28403-2326

Telephone: (910) 763-5313
Fax Number: (910) 251-9642
Type of Business: Chain Restaurant Operator
Year Founded: 1982
Total Sales: $6,561,000 (e)
Number of Employees: 80
Average Check: Breakfast(8); Lunch(8); Dinner(10)
Total Units: 8
Trade Names: Subway (8)
Units Franchised From: 8
Preferred Square Footage: 1,200
Preferred Location Types: Downtown; Strip Mall
Primary Menu: Sandwiches/Deli (8)
Areas of Operation: NC
Type of Foodservice: Quick Serve (8)
Catering Services: Yes
Franchise Affiliation: Doctor's Associates Inc., MILFORD, CT
Primary Distributors: (Full Line) US Foods, CHARLOTTE, NC

Key Personnel
TAMMY YARBOROUGH - President; Partner; Controller; Director Finance, Facility/Maintenance, Information Systems, Real Estate, Store Fixtures; General Buyer
DALE YARBOROUGH - Partner; Manager Operations, Human Resources; General Buyer

Canteen Vending Services
3008 Orville Wright Way
Wilmington, NC 28405-8761

Telephone: (910) 763-3487
Fax Number: (910) 343-2965
Listing Type: Branch Office
Type of Business: Foodservice Management Operator
Year Founded: 1929
Number of Employees: 7
Number of Locations Served: 40
Total Foodservice Mgmt Accounts: 40
Areas of Operation: NC
Type of Foodservice: Vending machines (40)
Foodservice Management Venues: Business & Industry; College & University; Health Care; Schools
Parent Company: Compass Group The Americas, CHARLOTTE, NC
Headquarters: Canteen Vending Services, CHARLOTTE, NC

Key Personnel
TONY SPENCER - General Manager; Director Operations
MARCUS SPENCER - Manager District

Charlie Graingers Franchising LLC
702 S 17th St
Wilmington, NC 28401

Telephone: (910) 769-3720
Internet Homepage: charliegraingers.com
Type of Business: Chain Restaurant Operator
Year Founded: 2016
Total Sales: $1,059,000 (e)
Total Units: 8
Trade Names: Charlie Graingers (8)
Company-Owned Units: 2
Units Franchised To: 14
Primary Menu: American (8)
Projected Openings: 41
Areas of Operation: FL, GA, LA, NC, SC, WV
Type of Foodservice: Fast Casual (8)

Key Personnel
LOUIS NORTH - Founder; President; Executive Chef
MORGAN COOK - General Manager
GREG GEORGE - Director Franchise Development
SCOTT STUCK - Representative Southeast Region

Clean Eatz
203 Racine Dr
Wilmington, NC 28403

Telephone: (910) 452-3733
Internet Homepage: cleaneatz.net
Company Email: opportunity@Cleaneatz.net
Type of Business: Chain Restaurant Operator
Year Founded: 2013
Total Sales: $55,100,000 (e)
Number of Employees: 230
Total Units: 46
Trade Names: Clean Eatz (46)
Units Franchised To: 46
Primary Menu: Health Foods (46)
Projected Openings: 3
Areas of Operation: AL, FL, GA, IL, IN, NC, OH, PA, SC, TN, VA
Type of Foodservice: Quick Serve (46)

Key Personnel
DON VARADY - Co-Founder; Partner; General Manager
EVONNE VARADY - Co-Founder; Partner; General Manager
ERIC WYATT - CEO
JOSH SHANAHAN - Owner
GARY SACHS - CFO
SARAH CHIRCO - Controller
WALTER VOIGHT - Director Operations
KARLEY GREER - Director Catering

Crave Hot Dogs & Barbecue
1407 Barclay Pointe Blvd Building 4
Unit 401
Wilmington, NC 28412

Telephone: (910) 399-5550
Internet Homepage: iwantcrave.com
Type of Business: Chain Restaurant Operator
Year Founded: 2018
Total Sales: $12,720,000 (e)
Total Units: 18
Trade Names: Crave Hot Dogs & BBQ (18)
Company-Owned Units: 7
Units Franchised To: 11
Preferred Location Types: Strip Mall
Primary Menu: Bar-B-Q (18)
Projected Openings: 8
Areas of Operation: GA, NC, OK, TX
Type of Foodservice: Fast Casual (18)

Key Personnel
SALVATORE RINCIONE - Co-Founder; President; Chief Development Officer
SAMANTHA RINCIONE - Co-Founder; CEO; COO
JAKE MORAN - Director Operations, Training

Peno Mediterranean Grill
351 S College Rd Ste 29
Wilmington, NC 28403-1626

Telephone: (910) 769-1056
Internet Homepage: penogrill.com
Type of Business: Chain Restaurant Operator
Year Founded: 2001
Total Units: 8
Trade Names: Peno Mediterranean Grill (8)
Company-Owned Units: 2
Units Franchised To: 6
Primary Menu: Greek/Mediterranean (8)
Projected Openings: 1
Areas of Operation: NC, SC
Type of Foodservice: Fast Casual (8)

Key Personnel
JAMAL HADDAD - Founder; Partner

Port City Java Inc.
101 Portwatch Way
Wilmington, NC 28412-7010

Telephone: (910) 796-6646
Fax Number: (910) 796-6611
Internet Homepage: portcityjava.com
Type of Business: Chain Restaurant Operator
Year Founded: 1995
Systemwide Sales: $9,673,000 (e)
Total Sales: $11,830,000 (e)
Number of Employees: 189
Average Check: Breakfast(10); Lunch(10); Dinner(10)
Internet Order Processing: Yes
Internet Sales: 1.00%
Total Units: 26
Trade Names: Port City Java (26)
Company-Owned Units: 10
Units Franchised To: 16
Preferred Square Footage: 4,500
Preferred Location Types: Airports; Community Mall; Convenience Store/Gas Station; Downtown; Freestanding; Grocery Stores; Institution (college/hospital); Kiosk; Office Complex; Regional Mall; Strip Mall
Primary Menu: Coffee (26)
Areas of Operation: DC, NC, SC, FC
Foreign Countries: COSTA RICA; INDONESIA; SAUDI ARABIA
Type of Foodservice: Quick Serve (26)
Distribution Centers: WILMINGTON, NC
On-site Distribution Center: Yes
Primary Distributors: (Full Line) US Foods, BOCA RATON, FL

Key Personnel
STEVE SCHNITZLER - CEO; President; COO; Executive Chef; Director Finance, Real Estate, Design; General Buyer
ROSEANN HELMS - CFO
KIM CRUSE - Director
NEAL ENGLAND - Manager
KEVIN WELCH - Manager District

Dixon Foods Group
2500 Wooten Blvd SW
Wilson, NC 27893-4427

Mailing Address: P.O. Box 3976, WILSON, NC, 27895
Telephone: (252) 291-0886
Fax Number: (252) 243-4277
Internet Homepage: dixonfoods.com
Type of Business: Chain Restaurant Operator
Year Founded: 1970
Total Sales: $135,110,000 (e)
Total Units: 29
Trade Names: McDonald's (29)
Units Franchised From: 29
Preferred Square Footage: 2,500
Primary Menu: Hamburger (29)
Areas of Operation: NC
Type of Foodservice: Quick Serve (29)
Franchise Affiliation: McDonald's Corporation, CHICAGO, IL

Key Personnel
WADE DIXON - Owner; General Buyer
TIM SOLLARS - Director Operations; General Buyer

SanLar Enterprises
2520 Ward Blvd
Wilson, NC 27893-1600

Telephone: (252) 291-5335
Fax Number: (252) 237-7194
Type of Business: Chain Restaurant Operator
Year Founded: 1980
Total Sales: $20,540,000 (e)
Number of Employees: 315
Average Check: Breakfast(10); Lunch(10); Dinner(10)
Total Units: 9
Trade Names: Burger King (9)
Units Franchised From: 9
Preferred Square Footage: 4,000
Preferred Location Types: Freestanding
Primary Menu: Hamburger (9)
Areas of Operation: NC
Type of Foodservice: Quick Serve (9)
Franchise Affiliation: Burger King Worldwide Inc., MIAMI, FL
Primary Distributors: (Full Line) McLane/Rocky Mount, ROCKY MOUNT, NC

Key Personnel
ROBERT REARDON - President; Manager Purchasing, Marketing
STEVE CLAYTON - Controller; Director Information Systems, Risk Management, Human Resources
CRAIG HANSEN - Manager Operations, Facility/Maintenance, Supply Chain, Real Estate, Food Safety

D E B Foods Inc
1332 Westgate Center Dr
Winston Salem, NC 27103-2933

Mailing Address: PO Box 2444, KERNERSVILLE, NC, 27285
Telephone: (336) 765-8960
Internet Homepage: yourmcd.com
Company Email: Support@yourmcd.com
Type of Business: Chain Restaurant Operator
Total Sales: $32,090,000 (e)
Total Units: 7
Trade Names: McDonald's (7)
Units Franchised From: 7
Primary Menu: Hamburger (7)
Areas of Operation: NC
Type of Foodservice: Quick Serve (7)
Franchise Affiliation: McDonald's Corporation, CHICAGO, IL

Key Personnel
DICKIE J. BRITT - President; General Buyer

Domino's Franchisee
450 Knollwood St
Winston Salem, NC 27103-3426

Telephone: (336) 659-0065
Type of Business: Chain Restaurant Operator
Total Sales: $11,979,000 (e)
Total Units: 6
Trade Names: Domino's (6)
Units Franchised From: 6
Primary Menu: Pizza (6)
Areas of Operation: NC
Type of Foodservice: Quick Serve (6)
Franchise Affiliation: Domino's Pizza Inc, ANN ARBOR, MI

Key Personnel
SEAN T. HEANEY - Owner; General Buyer

East Coast Wings Corp.
100 Cambridge Plaza Dr
Winston Salem, NC 27104-3556

Telephone: (336) 760-4985
Fax Number: (336) 760-4516
Internet Homepage: eastcoastwings.com
Type of Business: Chain Restaurant Operator
Year Founded: 1995
Systemwide Sales: $53,961,000 (e)
Total Sales: $20,090,000 (e)
Alcohol Sales: 10%

Number of Employees: 1,900
Average Check: Lunch(10); Dinner(22)
Total Units: 38
Trade Names: East Coast Wings & Grill (38)
Company-Owned Units: 2
Units Franchised To: 36
Preferred Square Footage: 1,400; 1,700; 1,800; 2,500; 4,000
Preferred Location Types: Freestanding; Strip Mall
Alcohol Served: Beer, Wine, Liquor
Primary Menu: Chicken (38)
Areas of Operation: FL, NC, SC, TX, VA
Type of Foodservice: Casual Dining (38)
Primary Distributors: (Full Line) US Foods, CHARLOTTE, NC
Parent Company: ZorAbility, Inc., WINSTON SALEM, NC

Key Personnel
SAM BALLAS - CEO; President; Owner
TOM SCALESE - COO
MARK LYSO - Exec VP Operations
FREDDY DUPUY - VP
JIM OVERBECK - Director Operations; Manager Supply Chain

GC Partners Inc.
3816 Forrestgate Dr
Winston Salem, NC 27103-2929

Telephone: (336) 767-1600
Fax Number: (336) 744-2610
Internet Homepage: gcpartners.com
Company Email: tammyt@gcpartners.com
Type of Business: Chain Restaurant Operator
Total Sales: $38,330,000 (e)
Number of Employees: 665
Average Check: Lunch(8); Dinner(10)
Total Units: 8
Trade Names: Golden Corral Buffet & Grill (8)
Units Franchised From: 8
Preferred Square Footage: 7,800; 10,300; 13,000
Preferred Location Types: Freestanding
Primary Menu: American (8)
Areas of Operation: FL, NC, SC
Type of Foodservice: Family Restaurant (8)
Catering Services: Yes
Franchise Affiliation: Golden Corral Corp., RALEIGH, NC
Primary Distributors: (Full Line) McLane/Rocky Mount, ROCKY MOUNT, NC

Key Personnel
DAVE GRONEWOLLER - CEO; President; General Manager; General Buyer
TIM WEAVIL - CFO

GetFried Franchise USA LLC
100 Cambridge Plaza Dr
Winston Salem, NC 27104-3556

Telephone: (336) 760-4985
Internet Homepage: getfried.com
Type of Business: Chain Restaurant Operator
Year Founded: 2015
Total Units: 12
Trade Names: #getfried fry Cafe (12)
Units Franchised From: 12
Preferred Square Footage: 900; 1,400
Preferred Location Types: Community Mall; Mobile Unit
Primary Menu: Snacks (12)
Projected Openings: 200
Areas of Operation: CA, FL, NY, PA, TX
Type of Foodservice: Quick Serve (12)
Parent Company: ZorAbility, Inc., WINSTON SALEM, NC

Key Personnel
CHRIS COVELLI - Co-Founder
GARRETT GREEN - Co-Founder
MARK LYSO - President

K&W Cafeterias Inc.
1391 Plaza West Rd
Winston Salem, NC 27103-1419

Mailing Address: PO Box 25048, WINSTON SALEM, NC, 27114-5048
Telephone: (336) 760-0526
Fax Number: (336) 659-0032
Internet Homepage: kwcafeterias.com
Type of Business: Chain Restaurant Operator
Year Founded: 1937
Total Sales: $46,590,000 (e)
Number of Employees: 3,000
Average Check: Lunch(8); Dinner(8)
Total Units: 11
Trade Names: K & W Cafeteria (11)
Company-Owned Units: 11
Preferred Square Footage: 10,000
Preferred Location Types: Freestanding; Strip Mall
Primary Menu: American (11)
Areas of Operation: NC, SC, VA, WV
Type of Foodservice: Cafeteria (11)
Primary Distributors: (Full Line) E.G. Forrest Co. Inc., WINSTON SALEM, NC

Key Personnel
DAX ALLRED - President; Partner
TODD SMITH - Exec VP
ROBERT D. COX - VP Region
R LEO SASAKI - VP Finance, Administration
BILL ALLRED - Assistant Director Purchasing

Krispy Kreme Distribution Center
1814 Ivy Ave
Winston Salem, NC 27105-5216

Telephone: (336) 725-2981
Listing Type: Distribution Center
Type of Business: Chain Restaurant Operator
Areas of Operation: AL, AZ, CA, DC, HI, IL, KY, LA, MI, MO, NC, NV, OH, OR, UT, WA, AB, BC
Foreign Countries: CANADA
Parent Company: Krispy Kreme Doughnut Corporation, CHARLOTTE, NC

Key Personnel
MIKE JENNINGS - General Manager
WILL CASH - Senior Director Sourcing

RJD Management
154 Charlois Blvd
Winston Salem, NC 27103-1567

Telephone: (336) 714-1510
Fax Number: (336) 714-1520
Internet Homepage: redhotandblue.com; stickyfingers.com
Company Email: info@redhotandblue.com
Type of Business: Chain Restaurant Operator
Year Founded: 1988
Systemwide Sales: $50,917,000 (e)
Total Sales: $11,790,000 (e)
Alcohol Sales: 10%
Number of Employees: 300
Average Check: Lunch(8); Dinner(12)
Internet Order Processing: Yes
Internet Sales: 2.00%
Total Units: 25
Trade Names: Red Hot & Blue (14); Sticky Fingers (11)
Company-Owned Units: 17
Units Franchised To: 8
Preferred Square Footage: 7,800
Preferred Location Types: Community Mall; Downtown; Freestanding
Alcohol Served: Beer, Wine, Liquor
Primary Menu: Bar-B-Q (25)
Areas of Operation: FL, GA, MD, MI, MO, NC, NJ, SC, TN, TX, VA
Type of Foodservice: Casual Dining (25)
Catering Services: Yes
Primary Distributors: (Food) US Foods, MANASSAS, VA
Headquarter Offices: Sticky Fingers, MT PLEASANT, SC

Key Personnel
RANDY MCCANN - Chairman; President; Partner
JOHN WALKER - Partner
SONNY MCKNIGHT - Executive Chef; Director

Operations, Product Development, Franchise Development

Triad Hotspots, Inc.
205 S Stratford Rd Ste F
Winston Salem, NC 27103-1858

Telephone: (336) 972-2051
Type of Business: Chain Restaurant Operator
Total Sales: $2,534,000 (e)
Total Units: 2
Trade Names: Firehouse Subs (2)
Units Franchised From: 2
Primary Menu: Sandwiches/Deli (2)
Areas of Operation: NC
Type of Foodservice: Fast Casual (2)
Catering Services: Yes
Franchise Affiliation: Firehouse Restaurant Group Inc., JACKSONVILLE, FL

Key Personnel
MARK WHITLEY - CEO

Village Tavern Inc.
102 Reynolda Vlg
Winston Salem, NC 27106-5123

Telephone: (336) 724-0102
Fax Number: (336) 714-4004
Internet Homepage: villagetavern.com
Type of Business: Chain Restaurant Operator
Year Founded: 1984
Total Sales: $41,630,000 (e)
Alcohol Sales: 15%
Number of Employees: 605
Average Check: Lunch(14); Dinner(24)
Total Units: 8
Trade Names: Village Tavern (8)
Company-Owned Units: 7
Units Franchised To: 1
Preferred Square Footage: 3,500
Preferred Location Types: Freestanding; Office Complex
Alcohol Served: Beer, Wine, Liquor
Primary Menu: American (8)
Areas of Operation: AL, AZ, CO, FL, GA, NC
Foreign Countries: THE PHILIPPINES
Type of Foodservice: Casual Dining (8)
Primary Distributors: (Full Line) US Foods, CHARLOTTE, NC

Key Personnel
SCOTT RICHARDSON - Chairman; Founder; CEO; Director Purchasing, Facility/Maintenance, Information Systems, Real Estate, Human Resources, Menu Development; General Buyer
ANTHONY SANTARELLI - President; COO; Director Supply Chain, Design, Store Fixtures
BILL BUITENDORP - Controller

MARY GRACE VIADO - Corporate Chef

NORTH DAKOTA

A & B Pizza Inc.
311 S 7th St
Bismarck, ND 58504-5682

Telephone: (701) 222-3108
Fax Number: (701) 222-8945
Internet Homepage: a-bpizza.com
Type of Business: Chain Restaurant Operator
Year Founded: 1969
Total Sales: $4,956,000 (e)
Alcohol Sales: 5%
Average Check: Lunch(14); Dinner(16)
Total Units: 4
Trade Names: A & B Pizza (4)
Company-Owned Units: 4
Preferred Location Types: Strip Mall
Alcohol Served: Beer
Primary Menu: Pizza (4)
Areas of Operation: ND
Type of Foodservice: Fast Casual (4)
Primary Distributors: (Equipment) Capital City Restaurant Supply Inc., BISMARCK, ND; (Food) Performance Foodservice, RICE, MN; (Supplies) Capital City Restaurant Supply Inc., BISMARCK, ND

Key Personnel
CLINT BARTH - President; Partner; General Manager; Executive Chef; General Buyer
DAVE BARTH - Partner; Manager Operations; General Buyer

Dacla Foods Inc
1911 N 13th St
Bismarck, ND 58501-1973

Telephone: (701) 223-7547
Fax Number: (701) 223-8832
Type of Business: Chain Restaurant Operator
Total Sales: $5,381,000 (e)
Average Check: Dinner(8)
Total Units: 5
Trade Names: Taco John's (5)
Units Franchised From: 5
Primary Menu: Taco (5)
Areas of Operation: ND
Type of Foodservice: Quick Serve (5)
Franchise Affiliation: Taco John's International Inc., CHEYENNE, WY

Key Personnel
CATHY GOSSETT - President; General Buyer

DDS Partnership
1401 E Calgary Ave
Bismarck, ND 58503-0938

Telephone: (701) 224-0350
Fax Number: (701) 224-9451
Type of Business: Chain Restaurant Operator
Year Founded: 1970
Total Sales: $29,170,000 (e)
Number of Employees: 300
Average Check: Breakfast(5); Lunch(8); Dinner(8)
Total Units: 6
Trade Names: McDonald's (6)
Units Franchised From: 6
Preferred Square Footage: 3,000
Preferred Location Types: Freestanding
Primary Menu: Hamburger (6)
Areas of Operation: ND
Type of Foodservice: Quick Serve (6)
Franchise Affiliation: McDonald's Corporation, CHICAGO, IL
Primary Distributors: (Food) The Martin-Brower Co., FRIDLEY, MN

Key Personnel
DENNIS SOTEBEER - President; Director Finance, Operations, Facility/Maintenance, Information Systems, Real Estate, Design, Human Resources; General Buyer
JOSH WIENS - CFO

Dome Pizza Inc
1031 S Washington St
Bismarck, ND 58504-6262

Telephone: (701) 222-3100
Fax Number: (701) 258-1480
Type of Business: Chain Restaurant Operator
Total Sales: $6,041,000 (e)
Total Units: 3
Trade Names: Domino's (3)
Units Franchised From: 3
Primary Menu: Pizza (3)
Areas of Operation: ND
Type of Foodservice: Quick Serve (3)
Franchise Affiliation: Domino's Pizza Inc, ANN ARBOR, MI

Key Personnel
MIKE SCOTT - President; General Buyer

Grand Junction Subs
4303 Ottawa St
Bismarck, ND 58503

Telephone: (701) 751-0375
Internet Homepage: grandjunctionsubs.com
Type of Business: Chain Restaurant Operator

Total Sales: $4,451,000 (e)
Total Units: 7
Trade Names: Grand Junction Subs (7)
Company-Owned Units: 1
Units Franchised To: 6
Primary Menu: Sandwiches/Deli (7)
Areas of Operation: MN, ND
Type of Foodservice: Fast Casual (7)

Key Personnel
VU TRUONG - Founder; Partner
COLTON SHOULTS - Partner

Roughrider Pizza Hut Inc
513 Elks Dr
Dickinson, ND 58601-2947

Telephone: (701) 264-7052
Fax Number: (701) 483-7051
Company Email: pizzahut@ndsupernet.com
Type of Business: Chain Restaurant Operator
Total Sales: $3,904,000 (e)
Total Units: 3
Trade Names: Pizza Hut (3)
Units Franchised From: 3
Primary Menu: Pizza (3)
Areas of Operation: ND
Type of Foodservice: Quick Serve (3)
Franchise Affiliation: Pizza Hut Inc., PLANO, TX

Key Personnel
ROBERT HEIN - President; General Buyer

Atlas Foods Inc.
3330 Fiechtner Dr S Ste 204
Fargo, ND 58103-2321

Mailing Address: PO Box 9013, FARGO, ND, 58106-9013
Telephone: (701) 280-0809
Fax Number: (701) 280-0842
Internet Homepage: paradiso.com
Company Email: corporate@paradiso.com
Type of Business: Chain Restaurant Operator
Year Founded: 1979
Total Sales: $19,250,000 (e)
Alcohol Sales: 10%
Number of Employees: 375
Average Check: Breakfast(16); Lunch(20); Dinner(22)
Internet Order Processing: Yes
Total Units: 5
Trade Names: Paradiso Cantina (5)
Company-Owned Units: 5
Preferred Square Footage: 5,000; 7,000; 10,000
Preferred Location Types: Freestanding
Alcohol Served: Beer, Wine, Liquor
Primary Menu: Mexican (5)
Areas of Operation: ND

Type of Foodservice: Casual Dining (5)
Catering Services: Yes
Franchise Affiliation: Fat Brands, Inc., BEVERLY HILLS, CA
Primary Distributors: (Full Line) SYSCO Food Services of North Dakota, FARGO, ND

Key Personnel
GREG PUNG - CFO; Controller; Manager Operations, Purchasing, Facility/Maintenance, Supply Chain, Design, Human Resources

Deep Roots FGO, Inc.
4501 15th Ave S Ste 109
Fargo, ND 58103-8956

Telephone: (701) 365-8515
Type of Business: Chain Restaurant Operator
Total Sales: $1,186,000 (e)
Total Units: 3
Trade Names: Cold Stone Creamery (3)
Units Franchised From: 3
Primary Menu: Snacks (3)
Areas of Operation: ND
Type of Foodservice: Quick Serve (3)
Franchise Affiliation: Kahala Brands, SCOTTSDALE, AZ

Key Personnel
JUSTIN TURNQUIST - Owner

FAF Incorporated
3008 26th Ave S
Fargo, ND 58103-5072

Telephone: (701) 234-9040
Fax Number: (701) 234-9860
Type of Business: Chain Restaurant Operator
Year Founded: 1996
Total Sales: $15,354,000 (e)
Number of Employees: 135
Average Check: Breakfast(8); Lunch(10); Dinner(12)
Total Units: 3
Trade Names: McDonald's (3)
Units Franchised From: 3
Preferred Square Footage: 2,500; 3,000
Preferred Location Types: Freestanding
Primary Menu: Hamburger (3)
Areas of Operation: MN, ND
Type of Foodservice: Quick Serve (3)
Franchise Affiliation: McDonald's Corporation, CHICAGO, IL
Primary Distributors: (Food) The Martin-Brower Co., FRIDLEY, MN

Key Personnel
TODD AXTMAN - VP; Director Human Resources
DEBBIE KNIGHT - Manager Administration, Branch

Global Development LLC
16 Broadway N Ste 208
Fargo, ND 58102-5238

Mailing Address: PO Box 2043, FARGO, ND, 58107-2043
Telephone: (701) 237-5151
Fax Number: (701) 237-3189
Internet Homepage: borrowedbucks.com; jlbeers.com; theoldbroadway.com; vinyltaco.com
Company Email: info@jlbeers.com
Type of Business: Chain Restaurant Operator
Year Founded: 1981
Total Sales: $55,430,000 (e)
Alcohol Sales: 20%
Number of Employees: 1,062
Average Check: Lunch(12); Dinner(12)
Total Units: 18
Trade Names: Borrowed Bucks Roadhouse (2); J L Beers (12); Old Broadway (1); Vinyl Taco (3)
Company-Owned Units: 17
Units Franchised From: 1
Preferred Square Footage: 2,500; 3,200
Preferred Location Types: Freestanding; Regional Mall
Alcohol Served: Beer, Wine, Liquor
Primary Menu: American (3); Hamburger (12); Taco (3)
Areas of Operation: MN, ND, SD
Type of Foodservice: Casual Dining (18)
Primary Distributors: (Full Line) Food Services of America, FARGO, ND

Key Personnel
RANDY THORSON - CEO; President; Director Facility/Maintenance, Real Estate, Design, Human Resources, Store Fixtures
WARREN ACKLEY - VP Operations, Marketing, Menu Development; Treasurer; General Buyer
PAT KNOLL - Controller; Director Purchasing, Information Systems, Supply Chain
KAREN KAHLER - Director Finance; Manager Accounting

Izumi Sushi & Hibachi
5675 26th Ave S #108
Fargo, ND 58104

Telephone: (701) 356-8556
Internet Homepage: izumirestaurant.com
Type of Business: Chain Restaurant Operator
Total Sales: $8,079,000 (e)
Total Units: 4
Trade Names: Izumi Sushi & Hibachi (4)
Company-Owned Units: 4
Primary Menu: Asian (4)
Areas of Operation: IA, ND

Type of Foodservice: Casual Dining (4)

Key Personnel
JOHN WENG - Manager

JL Beers
16 Broadway N Ste 208
Fargo, ND 58102-5238

Telephone: (701) 237-5151
Internet Homepage: jlbeers.com
Type of Business: Chain Restaurant Operator
Year Founded: 2009
Total Sales: $10,000,000 (e)
Total Units: 11
Trade Names: JL Beers (11)
Company-Owned Units: 11
Units Franchised To: 2
Primary Menu: Hamburger (11)
Areas of Operation: MN, ND, SD
Type of Foodservice: Casual Dining (11)

Key Personnel
LANCE THORSON - Co-Founder; Director Franchise Development
WARREN ACKLEY - Co-Founder; VP
RANDY THORSON - Co-Founder; CEO; President
BONNIE BIRMINGHAM - Director Franchising, Licensing

K F C of St Peter, Inc
115 Broadway N
Fargo, ND 58102-4925

Telephone: (701) 237-6470
Type of Business: Chain Restaurant Operator
Total Sales: $2,785,000 (e)
Total Units: 5
Trade Names: Subway (5)
Units Franchised From: 5
Primary Menu: Sandwiches/Deli (5)
Areas of Operation: ND
Type of Foodservice: Quick Serve (5)
Franchise Affiliation: Doctor's Associates Inc., MILFORD, CT

Key Personnel
LEE FOWLER - Owner; General Buyer

Kroll's Diner
1033 45th St S
Fargo, ND 58103

Telephone: (701) 492-2319
Type of Business: Chain Restaurant Operator
Year Founded: 1969
Total Sales: $8,334,000 (e)
Total Units: 4
Trade Names: Kroll's Diner (4)
Company-Owned Units: 4
Primary Menu: American (4)
Areas of Operation: ND
Type of Foodservice: Casual Dining (4)

Key Personnel
EDWARD WETSCH - Partner

March Investment Inc
3201 13th Ave S
Fargo, ND 58103-3402

Telephone: (701) 293-5918
Type of Business: Chain Restaurant Operator
Total Sales: $5,960,000 (e)
Average Check: Dinner(12)
Total Units: 4
Trade Names: Dairy Queen (4)
Units Franchised From: 4
Primary Menu: American (4)
Areas of Operation: ND
Type of Foodservice: Quick Serve (4)
Franchise Affiliation: International Dairy Queen Inc., BLOOMINGTON, MN

Key Personnel
GAYLON ANDERSON - Owner; General Buyer

Paradiso Mexican Restaurant
801 38th St S
Fargo, ND 58103

Telephone: (701) 282-5747
Internet Homepage: paradiso.com
Company Email: corporate@paradiso.com
Type of Business: Chain Restaurant Operator
Year Founded: 1979
Total Sales: $8,673,000 (e)
Total Units: 5
Trade Names: Paradiso Mexican Restaurant (5)
Company-Owned Units: 5
Primary Menu: Mexican (5)
Type of Foodservice: Casual Dining (5)

Key Personnel
JAKE WOINAROWICZ - General Manager

Rhombus Guys
606 Main Ave
Fargo, ND 58103

Telephone: (701) 540-4534
Internet Homepage: rhombusguyspizza.com
Type of Business: Chain Restaurant Operator
Year Founded: 2002
Total Sales: $3,766,000 (e)
Total Units: 2
Trade Names: Rhombus Guys (2)
Company-Owned Units: 2
Primary Menu: Pizza (2)
Areas of Operation: ND
Type of Foodservice: Fast Casual (2)

Key Personnel
MATT WINJUM - Partner
ARRON HENDRICKS - Partner

Sickies Garage
3431 Fiechtner Dr S
Fargo, ND 58103

Telephone: (701) 478-7425
Internet Homepage: sickiesburgers.com
Type of Business: Chain Restaurant Operator
Year Founded: 2012
Total Sales: $13,080,000 (e)
Total Units: 8
Trade Names: Sickies Garage (8)
Company-Owned Units: 8
Primary Menu: American (8)
Areas of Operation: FL, MA, ND, NV, SD
Type of Foodservice: Casual Dining (8)

Key Personnel
KENNETH HARRIS - CEO; Owner

Spicy Pie
322 Broadway N
Fargo, ND 58102

Telephone: (701) 356-7437
Internet Homepage: pizzagrindersbeer.com
Type of Business: Chain Restaurant Operator
Year Founded: 2010
Total Sales: $7,779,000 (e)
Trade Names: Spicy Pie (4)
Company-Owned Units: 4
Primary Menu: Pizza (4)
Areas of Operation: ND
Type of Foodservice: Fast Casual (4)

Key Personnel
LEXI ROESNTHAL - Director Marketing

Taco Shop
420 University Dr N
Fargo, ND 58102

Telephone: (701) 232-7734
Internet Homepage: tacoshopsfargo.com
Type of Business: Chain Restaurant Operator
Total Sales: $5,474,000 (e)
Total Units: 3
Trade Names: Taco Shop (3)

Company-Owned Units: 3
Primary Menu: Taco (3)
Areas of Operation: ND
Type of Foodservice: Fast Casual (3)

Key Personnel
TROY THOMSON - Owner

Deek's Pizza
512 N Washington St
Grand Forks, ND 58203

Internet Homepage: deekspizza.com
Type of Business: Chain Restaurant Operator
Total Sales: $6,365,000 (e)
Total Units: 3
Trade Names: Deek's Pizza (3)
Company-Owned Units: 3
Primary Menu: Pizza (3)
Areas of Operation: ND
Type of Foodservice: Fast Casual (3)

Key Personnel
TYLER KUENZEL - Owner

O K Enterprises, Inc.
5550 1st Ave N
Grand Forks, ND 58203-2502

Telephone: (701) 746-5493
Fax Number: (701) 746-1324
Type of Business: Chain Restaurant Operator
Total Sales: $23,690,000 (e)
Total Units: 5
Trade Names: McDonald's (5)
Units Franchised From: 5
Preferred Square Footage: 2,500
Primary Menu: Hamburger (5)
Areas of Operation: MN, ND
Type of Foodservice: Quick Serve (5)
Franchise Affiliation: McDonald's Corporation, CHICAGO, IL

Key Personnel
BILL O'KEEFE - Partner; General Buyer
MICHAEL O'KEEFE - Partner; General Buyer

Red Pepper
1011 University Ave
Grand Forks, ND 58203

Telephone: (701) 775-9671
Internet Homepage: redpepper.com
Type of Business: Chain Restaurant Operator
Year Founded: 1961
Total Sales: $8,655,000 (e)
Total Units: 4
Trade Names: Red Pepper (4)
Company-Owned Units: 4

Primary Menu: Mexican (4)
Type of Foodservice: Casual Dining (4)

Key Personnel
JEFF TELLMANN - Partner
NICKI TELLMANN - Partner

The Toasted Frog
124 N 3rd St
Grand Forks, ND 58203

Telephone: (701) 772-3764
Internet Homepage: toastedfrog.com
Type of Business: Chain Restaurant Operator
Total Sales: $7,237,000 (e)
Total Units: 3
Trade Names: The Toasted Frog (3)
Company-Owned Units: 3
Primary Menu: American (3)
Areas of Operation: ND
Type of Foodservice: Casual Dining (3)

Key Personnel
SHAWN CLAPP - Partner
JONATHAN HOLTH - Partner

Dakota Pizza, LLC
PO Box 113
Mandan, ND 58554-0113

Telephone: (701) 471-9451
Type of Business: Chain Restaurant Operator
Total Sales: $5,939,000 (e)
Total Units: 5
Trade Names: Dickey's Barbecue Pit (5); Little Caesars Pizza (5)
Units Franchised From: 5
Primary Menu: Bar-B-Q (5); Pizza (5)
Areas of Operation: ND
Type of Foodservice: Fast Casual (5); Quick Serve (5)
Franchise Affiliation: Little Caesar Enterprises Inc., DETROIT, MI

Key Personnel
RANDY RHONE - President; General Buyer

Apple Core Enterprises, Inc
509 30th Ave NW
Minot, ND 58703-0607

Mailing Address: PO Box 969, MINOT, ND, 58702-0969
Telephone: (701) 838-2822
Type of Business: Chain Restaurant Operator
Year Founded: 1989
Total Sales: $89,690,000 (e)
Alcohol Sales: 18%
Number of Employees: 1,875

Average Check: Breakfast(14); Lunch(16); Dinner(22)
Total Units: 23
Trade Names: Applebee's Neighborhood Grill & Bar (23)
Units Franchised From: 23
Preferred Square Footage: 3,600; 5,000
Preferred Location Types: Freestanding
Alcohol Served: Beer, Wine, Liquor
Primary Menu: American (23)
Areas of Operation: AZ, CA, MN, MT, ND
Type of Foodservice: Casual Dining (23)
Catering Services: Yes
Franchise Affiliation: Applebee's Services Inc., KANSAS CITY, MO

Key Personnel
MYRON THOMPSON - President; General Buyer
BOB LAMONT - CFO
CHAD THOMPSON - Chief Brand Officer
MARK GIROUX - Area Director
DUSTIN JENSEN - VP Operations
MISTY MAHANY - Director Human Resources
TOM WEAVER - Director Human Resources-Training
GIL SKARPHOL - Manager Branch
BRUCE BERG - Manager Purchasing
JASON ADKINS - Supervisor Information Technology

Herslip Management
2000 Burdick Expy E Ste A
Minot, ND 58701-5028

Telephone: (701) 852-6303
Fax Number: (701) 838-6323
Company Email: receptionist@srt.com
Type of Business: Chain Restaurant Operator
Total Sales: $15,686,000 (e)
Average Check: Dinner(6)
Total Units: 3
Trade Names: Buffalo Wild Wings (3)
Units Franchised From: 3
Alcohol Served: Beer, Wine
Primary Menu: Chicken (3)
Areas of Operation: ND
Type of Foodservice: Casual Dining (3)
Franchise Affiliation: Buffalo Wild Wings Inc., ATLANTA, GA

Key Personnel
JANELLE HERSLIP - President; General Buyer

Minking Inc.
1509 S Broadway
Minot, ND 58701-5934

Telephone: (701) 838-2022
Type of Business: Chain Restaurant Operator
Total Sales: $4,919,000 (e)

Number of Employees: 25
Average Check: Breakfast(8); Lunch(8); Dinner(8)
Total Units: 2
Trade Names: Burger King (2)
Units Franchised From: 2
Preferred Square Footage: 2,500; 4,000
Preferred Location Types: Freestanding; Regional Mall
Primary Menu: Hamburger (2)
Areas of Operation: ND
Type of Foodservice: Quick Serve (2)
Franchise Affiliation: Burger King Worldwide Inc., MIAMI, FL
Primary Distributors: (Full Line) Reinhart FoodService, AUSTELL, GA

Key Personnel
DON HUMMEL - President; General Manager; General Buyer
JOSH HUMMEL - Manager Finance, Operations, Purchasing, Information Systems

Outlaws' Bar & Grill
120 North Main Street
Watford City, ND 58854

Telephone: (701) 842-6859
Internet Homepage: outlawsbarngrill.com/owc
Type of Business: Chain Restaurant Operator
Year Founded: 2006
Total Sales: $15,390,000 (e)
Total Units: 8
Trade Names: JL Beers (1); Meadowlark Public House (1); Outlaws' Bar & Grill (2); Six Shooters (1); Stonehome Brew Pub (2); Wildcow Coffee & Cream (1)
Company-Owned Units: 7
Units Franchised From: 1
Primary Menu: American (7); Coffee (1)
Areas of Operation: ND
Type of Foodservice: Casual Dining (6); Quick Serve (2)

Key Personnel
ANGIE PELTON - Partner
AARON PELTON - Partner

B T N D, LLC
405 Main Ave W Unit 2D
West Fargo, ND 58078-1663

Telephone: (701) 277-0080
Fax Number: (701) 282-2663
Internet Homepage: itsburgertime.com
Company Email: sharlene.krogh@itsburgertime.com
Type of Business: Chain Restaurant Operator
Year Founded: 1987
Total Sales: $14,550,000 (e)
Number of Employees: 169

Average Check: Lunch(8); Dinner(10)
Total Units: 9
Trade Names: Burger Time (9)
Company-Owned Units: 9
Preferred Square Footage: 2,500
Preferred Location Types: Freestanding
Primary Menu: Hamburger (9)
Areas of Operation: MN, ND, SD
Type of Foodservice: Quick Serve (9)

Key Personnel
GARY COPPERUD - Owner; General Buyer
MARK PETRI - Manager Region

Dakota Farms Family Restaurant
1906 2nd Ave W
Williston, ND 58801

Telephone: (701) 572-4480
Internet Homepage: dakotafarmsrestaurants.com
Type of Business: Chain Restaurant Operator
Total Sales: $9,155,000 (e)
Total Units: 4
Trade Names: Dakota Farms Family Restaurant (4)
Company-Owned Units: 4
Primary Menu: American (4)
Areas of Operation: ND
Type of Foodservice: Family Restaurant (4)

Key Personnel
SHIL PATEL - Owner

NEBRASKA

D & D Berg, LLC
824 E 3rd St
Alliance, NE 69301-3946

Telephone: (308) 762-6590
Fax Number: (308) 762-3714
Company Email: tj2001@tacojohns.net
Type of Business: Chain Restaurant Operator
Total Sales: $2,312,000 (e)
Total Units: 2
Trade Names: Taco John's (2)
Units Franchised From: 2
Primary Menu: Taco (2)
Areas of Operation: NE
Type of Foodservice: Quick Serve (2)
Franchise Affiliation: Taco John's International Inc., CHEYENNE, WY

Key Personnel
DANIELLE PIRELLE - General Manager; General Buyer

MCD Management
1449 W 3rd St
Alliance, NE 69301-3127

Telephone: (308) 762-8762
Company Email: mcdofficene@gmail.com
Type of Business: Chain Restaurant Operator
Total Sales: $28,700,000 (e)
Total Units: 6
Trade Names: McDonald's (6)
Units Franchised From: 6
Preferred Location Types: Freestanding
Primary Menu: Hamburger (6)
Areas of Operation: NE
Type of Foodservice: Quick Serve (6)
Franchise Affiliation: McDonald's Corporation, CHICAGO, IL

Key Personnel
CHRISTIAN MILLER - Owner; General Buyer

S-N-C, Inc.
652 Lakeside Cir
Ashland, NE 68003-7405

Telephone: (402) 944-6090
Company Email: pattyjofish@windstream.net
Type of Business: Chain Restaurant Operator
Total Sales: $732,000 (e)
Total Units: 2
Trade Names: Cinnabon (2)
Units Franchised From: 2
Primary Menu: Snacks (2)
Areas of Operation: NE
Type of Foodservice: Quick Serve (2)
Franchise Affiliation: Cinnabon Inc., ATLANTA, GA

Key Personnel
STEVE FISHER - Owner; General Buyer

1502 J F K Inc
1502 Galvin Rd S Ste 1B
Bellevue, NE 68005-3048

Telephone: (402) 291-8818
Fax Number: (402) 291-1933
Type of Business: Chain Restaurant Operator
Total Sales: $2,962,000 (e)
Total Units: 4
Trade Names: Subway (4)
Units Franchised From: 4
Primary Menu: Sandwiches/Deli (4)
Areas of Operation: NE
Type of Foodservice: Quick Serve (4)
Franchise Affiliation: Doctor's Associates Inc., MILFORD, CT

Key Personnel
ROB KIRK - Owner; General Buyer

Hart Management Inc.
940 N 28th Ave
Blair, NE 68008-1021

Telephone: (402) 426-5015
Company Email: chartvigsen@huntel.net
Type of Business: Chain Restaurant Operator
Year Founded: 1975
Total Sales: $6,098,000 (e)
Alcohol Sales: 1%
Number of Employees: 200
Average Check: Lunch(16); Dinner(22)
Total Units: 5
Trade Names: Pizza Hut (5)
Units Franchised From: 5
Preferred Square Footage: 4,200
Preferred Location Types: Freestanding
Alcohol Served: Beer
Primary Menu: Pizza (5)
Areas of Operation: IA, KS, MO, ND, NE
Type of Foodservice: Quick Serve (5)
Franchise Affiliation: Pizza Hut Inc., PLANO, TX
Primary Distributors: (Full Line) McLane/Shawnee, SHAWNEE, KS

Key Personnel
CAROL HARTVIGSEN - Partner; Manager Finance, Information Systems, Real Estate, Design; General Buyer
KEITH HARTVIGSEN - Partner; General Buyer
TROY HARTVIGSEN - Manager Operations, Supply Chain, Human Resources

H H Hall Management Corp
3210 23rd St
Columbus, NE 68601-3126

Telephone: (402) 564-6600
Company Email: mcdonalds@neb.rr.com
Type of Business: Chain Restaurant Operator
Total Sales: $46,760,000 (e)
Total Units: 10
Trade Names: McDonald's (10)
Units Franchised From: 10
Preferred Location Types: Freestanding
Primary Menu: Hamburger (10)
Areas of Operation: NE
Type of Foodservice: Quick Serve (10)
Franchise Affiliation: McDonald's Corporation, CHICAGO, IL

Key Personnel
GREG HALL - President; General Buyer

Dough Pac, Inc.
20507 Nicholas Cir Ste 106
Elkhorn, NE 68022-4686

Telephone: (402) 614-4405
Fax Number: (402) 496-0338
Internet Homepage: samandlouiesnyp.com
Company Email: info@samandlouiesnyp.com
Type of Business: Chain Restaurant Operator
Year Founded: 1994
Systemwide Sales: $3,316,000 (e)
Total Sales: $3,587,000 (e)
Alcohol Sales: 5%
Number of Employees: 108
Average Check: Dinner(14)
Internet Order Processing: Yes
Total Units: 9
Trade Names: Sam & Louie's NY Pizza (9)
Company-Owned Units: 4
Units Franchised To: 5
Preferred Location Types: Freestanding; Strip Mall
Alcohol Served: Beer, Wine
Primary Menu: Italian (9)
Areas of Operation: IA, MT, NE, SD, WI
Type of Foodservice: Casual Dining (9)
Catering Services: Yes

Key Personnel
MICHAEL NOLAN - Director Franchising

Leonard Management
1408 Veterans Dr Ste 202
Elkhorn, NE 68022-6912

Telephone: (402) 932-6550
Fax Number: (402) 932-6680
Internet Homepage: leonardmcd.com
Type of Business: Chain Restaurant Operator
Year Founded: 1993
Total Sales: $124,070,000 (e)
Number of Employees: 930
Average Check: Breakfast(8); Lunch(8); Dinner(8)
Total Units: 32
Trade Names: McDonald's (32)
Units Franchised From: 32
Preferred Square Footage: 2,500; 3,000
Preferred Location Types: Discount Dept. Stores; Freestanding
Primary Menu: Hamburger (32)
Areas of Operation: IA, NE
Type of Foodservice: Quick Serve (32)
Franchise Affiliation: McDonald's Corporation, CHICAGO, IL
Primary Distributors: (Food) Earp Distribution, EDWARDSVILLE, KS

Key Personnel
STEVEN LEONARD - President; General Manager; Director Facility/Maintenance, Supply Chain, Real Estate, Design; General Buyer
DANIEL WOJTALEWICZ - Executive Director Human Resources
TOBY REES - Director Human Resources
DENISE TROUT - Director Human Resources
ERIC LEONARD - Manager Human Resources

Degen Properties
1320 W 2nd St
Grand Island, NE 68801-5712

Telephone: (308) 382-6780
Fax Number: (308) 381-6445
Type of Business: Chain Restaurant Operator
Total Sales: $7,314,000 (e)
Number of Employees: 100
Average Check: Breakfast(5); Lunch(8); Dinner(8)
Total Units: 3
Trade Names: Burger King (3)
Units Franchised From: 3
Preferred Square Footage: 2,500; 4,000
Preferred Location Types: Freestanding; Strip Mall
Primary Menu: Hamburger (3)
Areas of Operation: NE
Type of Foodservice: Quick Serve (3)
Franchise Affiliation: Burger King Worldwide Inc., MIAMI, FL
Primary Distributors: (Full Line) Reinhart FoodService LLC, CHICAGO, IL

Key Personnel
BILL DEGEN - President; Director Operations; General Buyer

Jomida Inc.
1804 N Webb Rd
Grand Island, NE 68803-2323

Telephone: (308) 381-1415
Type of Business: Chain Restaurant Operator
Year Founded: 1982
Total Sales: $7,833,000 (e)
Number of Employees: 40
Average Check: Lunch(10); Dinner(10)
Total Units: 4
Trade Names: KFC (4)
Units Franchised From: 4
Preferred Square Footage: 3,000
Preferred Location Types: Freestanding
Primary Menu: Chicken (4)
Areas of Operation: NE
Type of Foodservice: Quick Serve (4)
Catering Services: Yes
Franchise Affiliation: KFC Corporation, LOUISVILLE, KY

Key Personnel
DALE BLACK - President; General Manager;

Director Finance, Operations, Purchasing, Facility/Maintenance, Information Systems, Supply Chain, Real Estate, Design; General Buyer
CINDY HAWTHORNE - Manager Human Resources

Otte Restaurants Inc
2341 N Webb Rd
Grand Island, NE 68803-1743

Telephone: (308) 384-7300
Fax Number: (308) 384-7370
Company Email: otterestaurants@gmail.com
Type of Business: Chain Restaurant Operator
Total Sales: $15,331,000 (e)
Total Units: 3
Trade Names: McDonald's (3)
Units Franchised From: 3
Preferred Square Footage: 2,500
Primary Menu: Hamburger (3)
Areas of Operation: NE
Type of Foodservice: Quick Serve (3)
Franchise Affiliation: McDonald's Corporation, CHICAGO, IL

Key Personnel
DOUG OTTE - President; General Buyer
ADAM OTTE - Director Operations

Staab Management Co. Inc.
3048 W Stolley Park Rd
Grand Island, NE 68801-7227

Telephone: (308) 382-1053
Fax Number: (308) 382-7315
Internet Homepage: staabmgt.com
Type of Business: Chain Restaurant Operator
Year Founded: 1966
Total Sales: $105,790,000 (e)
Alcohol Sales: 2%
Number of Employees: 1,632
Average Check: Lunch(16); Dinner(16)
Total Units: 89
Trade Names: Pizza Hut (89)
Units Franchised From: 89
Preferred Square Footage: 2,500
Preferred Location Types: Freestanding
Alcohol Served: Beer
Primary Menu: Pizza (89)
Areas of Operation: IA, MN, MO, NE, SD
Type of Foodservice: Quick Serve (89)
Franchise Affiliation: Pizza Hut Inc., PLANO, TX

Key Personnel
DAVE STAAB - President
KIRK SHUCK - CFO
MARC JULIAN - Controller
JIM MOLACEK - Director Operations
KRISSA ABRAHAM - Manager Marketing

LOIS SMIDT - Coordinator Human Resources

Subway Development
3221 Ramada Rd Ste 10
Grand Island, NE 68801-8800

Telephone: (308) 389-3243
Fax Number: (308) 381-0893
Type of Business: Chain Restaurant Operator
Year Founded: 1989
Total Sales: $22,500,000 (e)
Number of Employees: 208
Average Check: Breakfast(6); Lunch(8); Dinner(12)
Total Units: 17
Trade Names: Subway (17)
Units Franchised From: 17
Preferred Square Footage: 300; 1,200; 2,000
Preferred Location Types: Freestanding
Primary Menu: Sandwiches/Deli (17)
Projected Openings: 20
Areas of Operation: NE, SD
Type of Foodservice: Quick Serve (17)
Catering Services: Yes
Franchise Affiliation: Doctor's Associates Inc., MILFORD, CT
Primary Distributors: (Food) US Foods, OMAHA, NE

Key Personnel
DEBORA CARPENTER - Partner; Director Operations
TODD CARPENTER - Partner; Director Store Development; General Buyer

Restaurant Concepts Inc.
1312 2nd Ave
Kearney, NE 68847-6734

Telephone: (308) 234-2757
Fax Number: (308) 237-9539
Internet Homepage: whiskeycreek.com
Company Email: info@whiskeycreek.com
Type of Business: Chain Restaurant Operator
Year Founded: 1991
Total Sales: $20,580,000 (e)
Alcohol Sales: 13%
Number of Employees: 462
Average Check: Breakfast(5); Lunch(10); Dinner(24)
Internet Order Processing: Yes
Total Units: 5
Trade Names: Whiskey Creek (5)
Company-Owned Units: 5
Preferred Square Footage: 5,000
Preferred Location Types: Freestanding; Hotel/Motel
Alcohol Served: Beer, Wine, Liquor
Primary Menu: Steak (5)
Areas of Operation: KS, NE, SD
Type of Foodservice: Casual Dining (5)

Catering Services: Yes
Primary Distributors: (Food) Cash-Wa Distributing Co. Inc., KEARNEY, NE

Key Personnel
JIM GARDNER - President; Director Information Systems, Real Estate, Design
ROBBY YENDRA - Director Operations; General Buyer

Concord Hospitality Inc.
1701 Windhoek Dr
Lincoln, NE 68512-1204

Mailing Address: PO Box 22579, LINCOLN, NE, 68542-2579
Telephone: (402) 421-2551
Fax Number: (402) 421-7563
Internet Homepage: concordei.com
Company Email: internal@concordei.com
Type of Business: Chain Restaurant Operator
Year Founded: 1987
Total Sales: $15,640,000 (e)
Alcohol Sales: 25%
Number of Employees: 325
Average Check: Breakfast(8); Lunch(10); Dinner(14)
Total Units: 6
Trade Names: Famous Dave's (4); Slim Chickens (2)
Units Franchised From: 6
Preferred Square Footage: 3,600; 5,000
Preferred Location Types: Downtown; Freestanding; Hotel/Motel; Regional Mall
Alcohol Served: Beer, Wine
Primary Menu: Bar-B-Q (4); Chicken (2)
Projected Openings: 1
Areas of Operation: KS, MO, NE
Type of Foodservice: Casual Dining (4); Fast Casual (2)
Franchise Affiliation: BBQ Holdings, Inc., MINNETONKA, MN
Primary Distributors: (Food) The SYGMA Network Inc.- San Antonio, SAN ANTONIO, TX

Key Personnel
IMELDA KUCHLE - CEO
LARRY BIRD - President
NANCY BIRD - VP
STACIE HOOKS - VP Operations
JOHN HANUS - Director Facility/Maintenance
DAWN RUDD - Director Operations

Cornhusker Pj LLC
621 N 48th St
Lincoln, NE 68504-3442

Telephone: (402) 465-4800
Type of Business: Chain Restaurant Operator
Total Sales: $15,350,000 (e)

Total Units: 11
Trade Names: Papa John's Pizza (11)
Units Franchised From: 11
Primary Menu: Pizza (11)
Areas of Operation: NE
Type of Foodservice: Quick Serve (11)
Franchise Affiliation: Papa Johns International Inc., LOUISVILLE, KY

Key Personnel
TROY POST - President

Growth Management Corporation
4200 S 14th St
Lincoln, NE 68502-5321

Telephone: (402) 488-8500
Fax Number: (402) 488-0926
Internet Homepage: amigoskings.com
Company Email: info@amigoskings.com
Type of Business: Chain Restaurant Operator
Year Founded: 1980
Total Sales: $36,280,000 (e)
Number of Employees: 951
Average Check: Breakfast(8); Lunch(10); Dinner(14)
Total Units: 31
Trade Names: Amigos (31)
Company-Owned Units: 21
Units Franchised To: 10
Preferred Square Footage: 3,800
Preferred Location Types: Community Mall; Freestanding; Regional Mall; Strip Mall
Primary Menu: Mexican (31)
Areas of Operation: NE
Type of Foodservice: Family Restaurant (31)
Catering Services: Yes

Key Personnel
ROGER MOORE - President; Controller; Director Finance, Risk Management
STEVE TALBOT - CIO; Director Information Systems
JANICE MOORE - VP Marketing; Director Food Safety

Kedds Inc.
1431 S 33rd St
Lincoln, NE 68506-1002

Telephone: (402) 434-3300
Fax Number: (402) 434-3303
Internet Homepage: davincis.com
Company Email: comments@davincis.com
Type of Business: Chain Restaurant Operator
Year Founded: 1978
Total Sales: $7,016,000 (e)
Number of Employees: 165
Average Check: Lunch(10); Dinner(14)
Internet Order Processing: Yes
Internet Sales: 1.00%
Total Units: 5
Trade Names: DaVinci's (5)
Company-Owned Units: 5
Preferred Square Footage: 5,500; 6,000
Preferred Location Types: Freestanding; Strip Mall
Primary Menu: Italian (5)
Areas of Operation: NE
Type of Foodservice: Family Restaurant (5)
Catering Services: Yes

Key Personnel
KENT KNUDSON - President; VP Catering; Executive Chef
KELLY KNUDSON - VP Operations, Food Safety; Manager Finance, Purchasing, Loss Prevention, Supply Chain, Human Resources, Product Development; General Buyer

Lazlo Inc.
729 Q St
Lincoln, NE 68508-1536

Telephone: (402) 434-5960
Fax Number: (402) 434-3291
Internet Homepage: fireworksrestaurant.com; lazlosbreweryandgrill.com; telesis-inc.com
Type of Business: Chain Restaurant Operator
Year Founded: 1994
Total Sales: $18,804,000 (e)
Alcohol Sales: 25%
Number of Employees: 200
Average Check: Lunch(18); Dinner(32)
Internet Order Processing: Yes
Total Units: 4
Trade Names: Fireworks Restaurant (1); Lazlo's Brewery & Grill (3)
Company-Owned Units: 4
Preferred Square Footage: 2,200
Preferred Location Types: Downtown; Freestanding
Alcohol Served: Beer, Wine, Liquor
Primary Menu: American (4)
Areas of Operation: NE
Type of Foodservice: Casual Dining (4)

Key Personnel
JAY JARVIS - Owner; COO; General Manager; Executive Chef; General Buyer
LOWELL LAZARUS - Director

Runza Restaurants Inc.
8800 Firethorn Ln Ste 300
Lincoln, NE 68520

Telephone: (180) 092-92394
Internet Homepage: runza.com
Type of Business: Chain Restaurant Operator
Year Founded: 1949
Systemwide Sales: $70,075,000 (e)
Total Sales: $49,190,000 (e)
Number of Employees: 1,062
Average Check: Breakfast(8); Lunch(8); Dinner(8)
Internet Order Processing: Yes
Internet Sales: 1.00%
Total Units: 85
Trade Names: Runza Restaurant (85)
Company-Owned Units: 40
Units Franchised To: 45
Preferred Square Footage: 2,500; 3,000; 3,600
Preferred Location Types: Community Mall; Downtown; Freestanding; Regional Mall; Strip Mall
Primary Menu: American (80)
Areas of Operation: CO, IA, KS, NE
Type of Foodservice: Quick Serve (85)
Catering Services: Yes
Primary Distributors: (Full Line) Cash-Wa Lincoln, LINCOLN, NE

Key Personnel
DONALD EVERETT JR - President
RENEE SJULIN - VP
NOLAN NAFFZIGER - General Manager
CHRIS ZEEB - Executive Chef
DAWN AMEND - Director Product Development; General Buyer
LINDA DENNIS - Director Operations
DAN RUDOLPH - Director Facility/Maintenance, Real Estate, Construction, Site Selection
BECKY PERRETT - Director Marketing
JON WURST - Director Business Development, Franchising
SARAH ZACH - Director Human Resources
TRENTON T. VARGASON - Director Information Technology
KERRY AMEND - Manager Accounting, Information Systems

Taco Inn
245 S 70th St
Lincoln, NE 68510

Telephone: (402) 488-6114
Internet Homepage: tacoinnlincoln.com
Type of Business: Chain Restaurant Operator
Total Units: 4
Trade Names: Taco Inn (4)
Company-Owned Units: 4
Primary Menu: Taco (4)
Areas of Operation: NE
Type of Foodservice: Fast Casual (4)

Key Personnel
ROGER LEISING - Founder
BJ KREIFELS - Owner

Valentino's of America Inc.
2601 S 70th St
Lincoln, NE 68506-2960

Telephone: (402) 434-9350
Fax Number: (402) 434-9325
Internet Homepage: valentinos.com
Company Email: sbowen@valscorp.com
Type of Business: Chain Restaurant Operator
Year Founded: 1957
Systemwide Sales: $65,982,000 (e)
Total Sales: $43,000,000 (e)
Alcohol Sales: 1%
Number of Employees: 565
Average Check: Lunch(6); Dinner(6)
Internet Order Processing: Yes
Total Units: 36
Trade Names: Valentino's (36)
Company-Owned Units: 22
Units Franchised To: 14
Preferred Square Footage: 1,500; 6,500
Preferred Location Types: Freestanding; Strip Mall
Alcohol Served: Beer, Wine
Primary Menu: Italian (36)
Areas of Operation: IA, KS, MN, NE, SD
Type of Foodservice: Casual Dining (2); Family Restaurant (12); Quick Serve (22)
Foodservice Management Venues: College & University
Catering Services: Yes

Key Personnel
MICHAEL A. ALESIO - Exec VP
MICHAEL MESSINEO - Director Operations, Purchasing, Human Resources

Rosberg Management
206 W Madison Ave
Norfolk, NE 68701-5338

Telephone: (402) 379-9867
Fax Number: (402) 379-4243
Type of Business: Chain Restaurant Operator
Total Sales: $8,984,000 (e)
Number of Employees: 70
Average Check: Dinner(12)
Total Units: 16
Trade Names: Subway (16)
Units Franchised From: 16
Preferred Square Footage: 300; 2,000
Preferred Location Types: Downtown; Freestanding; Strip Mall
Primary Menu: Sandwiches/Deli (16)
Areas of Operation: NE
Type of Foodservice: Quick Serve (16)
Franchise Affiliation: Doctor's Associates Inc., MILFORD, CT

Key Personnel
JOHN ROSBERG - President; General Buyer
CARL ROSBERG - CFO
ROB POTTER - Director Operations

Blackshirt Investments, Inc.
17304 Davenport St
Omaha, NE 68118-2906

Telephone: (402) 505-4192
Type of Business: Chain Restaurant Operator
Total Sales: $2,454,000 (e)
Total Units: 4
Trade Names: Cold Stone Creamery (4)
Units Franchised From: 4
Primary Menu: Snacks (4)
Areas of Operation: NE
Type of Foodservice: Quick Serve (4)
Franchise Affiliation: Kahala Brands, SCOTTSDALE, AZ

Key Personnel
SHAWN WILLIAMS - Owner

Bronco's Holding Company
1123 S 120th St
Omaha, NE 68144

Telephone: (402) 551-7477
Fax Number: (402) 391-0122
Internet Homepage: broncoburgers.com
Company Email: info@broncoburgers.com
Type of Business: Chain Restaurant Operator
Year Founded: 1959
Total Sales: $3,332,000 (e)
Number of Employees: 100
Average Check: Breakfast(8); Lunch(8); Dinner(10)
Total Units: 2
Trade Names: Bronco's (2)
Company-Owned Units: 2
Preferred Location Types: Freestanding
Primary Menu: Hamburger (2)
Areas of Operation: NE
Type of Foodservice: Quick Serve (2)

Key Personnel
STEVE BARNES - President; General Manager; Executive Chef; General Buyer

Canteen Vending Services
2631 S 156th Cir
Omaha, NE 68130

Telephone: (402) 592-3150
Fax Number: (402) 592-2076
Listing Type: Branch Office
Type of Business: Foodservice Management Operator
Year Founded: 1929
Number of Employees: 40
Number of Locations Served: 120
Total Foodservice Mgmt Accounts: 120
Areas of Operation: NE
Type of Foodservice: Vending machines (120)
Foodservice Management Venues: Business & Industry; College & University; Health Care; Travel Plazas
Primary Distributors: (Food) Vistar Kansas City, RIVERSIDE, MO
Parent Company: Compass Group The Americas, CHARLOTTE, NC
Headquarters: Canteen Vending Services, CHARLOTTE, NC

Key Personnel
DOUG ROOT - General Manager

CCW LLC
752 N 129th St
Omaha, NE 68154

Telephone: (402) 697-0057
Fax Number: (402) 697-1125
Internet Homepage: frcgroup.net
Type of Business: Chain Restaurant Operator
Year Founded: 1985
Total Sales: $20,570,000 (e)
Alcohol Sales: 5%
Number of Employees: 70
Average Check: Breakfast(8); Lunch(14); Dinner(18)
Internet Order Processing: Yes
Total Units: 26
Trade Names: Cowboy Chicken (3); HuHot Mongolian Grill (23)
Units Franchised From: 26
Preferred Location Types: Downtown; Freestanding; Strip Mall
Alcohol Served: Beer, Wine, Liquor
Primary Menu: Asian (23); Chicken (3)
Areas of Operation: IA, KS, NE, SD
Type of Foodservice: Casual Dining (26)
Franchise Affiliation: HuHot Mongolian Grills LLC, MISSOULA, MT
Parent Company: Sun Capital Partners Inc., BOCA RATON, FL

Key Personnel
WILL GROSZ - President
BRENDAN CROWLEY - Partner; General Buyer
TRENT SMITH - VP Operations

Cutchall Management Co.
13305 Birch Dr Ste 201
Omaha, NE 68164-5451

Telephone: (402) 558-3333
Fax Number: (402) 558-1512
Internet Homepage: cutchallmanagement.com; paradisebakery.com; tinstartacobar.com
Company Email:

inquiry@cutchallmanagement.com
Type of Business: Chain Restaurant Operator
Year Founded: 1986
Total Sales: $72,350,000 (e)
Alcohol Sales: 2%
Number of Employees: 200
Average Check: Breakfast(8); Lunch(20); Dinner(26)
Total Units: 49
Trade Names: Dominos (14); First Watch (5); Jams (3); Kasai Asian Grill (1); Kith & Kin Southern Kitchen (1); Lo-lo's (1); Oklahoma Joe's Bar-B-Cue (1); Paradise Bakery & Cafe (8); Salty Senorita (1); Sonic America's Drive-In (13); Tin Star (1)
Company-Owned Units: 9
Units Franchised From: 40
Preferred Square Footage: 1,000; 2,000; 3,000
Preferred Location Types: Freestanding; Parks; Regional Mall
Alcohol Served: Beer, Wine, Liquor
Primary Menu: American (8); Asian (1); Bar-B-Q (1); Chicken (2); Hamburger (13); Mexican (1); Pizza (14); Snacks (8); Southern (1); Southwest/Tex-Mex (1)
Areas of Operation: IA, KS, NE, TX
Type of Foodservice: Casual Dining (13); Quick Serve (32)
Catering Services: Yes
Franchise Affiliation: BBQ Holdings, Inc., MINNETONKA, MN; Domino's Pizza Inc, ANN ARBOR, MI; Sonic Corp., OKLAHOMA CITY, OK
Primary Distributors: (Equipment) TriMark Hockenbergs, OMAHA, NE; (Food) SYSCO Food Services of Idaho Inc., BOISE, ID; (Supplies) TriMark Hockenbergs, OMAHA, NE

Key Personnel
GREG CUTCHALL - Founder; CEO; Executive Chef; Manager Real Estate, Design; General Buyer
TIM GRIGGS - COO; VP
CHRISTINE CHARLESTON - Controller
JULIE HANSEN - Director Marketing, Sales
BRIAN LARSON - Director Operations
ABBY BINDERUP - Manager Human Resources

D.R.M. Inc.
5324 N 134th Ave
Omaha, NE 68164-6326

Telephone: (402) 573-1216
Fax Number: (402) 573-0171
Internet Homepage: drmarbys.com
Company Email: customer-service@drmarbys.com
Type of Business: Chain Restaurant Operator
Year Founded: 1968
Total Sales: $187,550,000 (e)
Number of Employees: 2,760
Average Check: Lunch(8); Dinner(8)
Total Units: 99
Trade Names: Arby's (99)
Units Franchised From: 99
Preferred Square Footage: 2,000
Preferred Location Types: Convenience Store/Gas Station; Freestanding
Primary Menu: Sandwiches/Deli (99)
Projected Openings: 1
Areas of Operation: IA, IL, NE, WI
Type of Foodservice: Quick Serve (99)
Franchise Affiliation: Arby's Restaurant Group, ATLANTA, GA
Primary Distributors: (Food) McLane/Elkhorn, ELKHORN, WI

Key Personnel
MATT JOHNSON - CEO; President; Partner
MARC JOHNSON - Partner; COO
MICHAEL SWOPE - CFO
ABBEY RAMSEY - Director Marketing, Design
MITCHELL JOHNSON - Director Operations
MICHELE HARVIEUX - Director Training
JULIE SHOWERS - Manager District
PATRICK MORGAN - Manager District
HANNAH WHALEY - Coordinator Marketing, Communications

Darmco Corp.
10235 Wiesman Dr Ste 1
Omaha, NE 68134-1520

Telephone: (402) 431-1558
Fax Number: (402) 431-1879
Type of Business: Chain Restaurant Operator
Total Sales: $66,820,000 (e)
Number of Employees: 660
Total Units: 14
Trade Names: McDonald's (14)
Units Franchised From: 14
Preferred Square Footage: 2,500
Primary Menu: Hamburger (14)
Areas of Operation: NE
Type of Foodservice: Quick Serve (14)
Franchise Affiliation: McDonald's Corporation, CHICAGO, IL

Key Personnel
JAMES DARMODY - President; General Buyer

Davden, Inc.
2410 Cuming St
Omaha, NE 68131-1630

Telephone: (402) 342-1226
Type of Business: Chain Restaurant Operator
Total Sales: $15,511,000 (e)
Total Units: 3
Trade Names: McDonald's (3)
Units Franchised From: 3
Preferred Location Types: Freestanding
Primary Menu: Hamburger (3)
Areas of Operation: NE
Type of Foodservice: Quick Serve (3)
Franchise Affiliation: McDonald's Corporation, CHICAGO, IL

Key Personnel
STEVE LENORD - Owner; General Buyer

Flagship Restaurant Group
14450 Eagle Run Dr Ste 100
Omaha, NE 68116-1464

Telephone: (402) 498-9660
Internet Homepage: flagshiprestaurantgroup.com; blattbeer.com; bluesushisakegrill.com; plankseafood.com
Type of Business: Chain Restaurant Operator
Year Founded: 2002
Total Sales: $95,040,000 (e)
Total Units: 24
Trade Names: Blatt Beer & Table (3); Blue Sushi Sake Grill (17); Flagship Commons Foodhall (1); Plank Seafood Provisions (1); Roja Mexican Grill (2)
Company-Owned Units: 24
Primary Menu: American (3); Japanese (17); Mexican (2); Miscellaneous (1); Seafood (1)
Projected Openings: 3
Areas of Operation: CO, KS, NE, TX
Type of Foodservice: Casual Dining (23); Fast Casual (1)

Key Personnel
NICK HOGAN - CEO; Partner
ANTHONY HITCHCOCK - Partner; COO
TONY GENTILE - Partner; Corporate Chef; Executive Chef
TOM ALLISMA - Partner; Director Design
MICHAEL BOLER - CFO
NESTOR REBOLLEDO - Corporate Chef
PERRY PARRIGIN - Director Training
DEVIN JACOBSON - Director
KELLI PILKINGTON - Director Marketing
MICHELE OTERO - Director Sales
JAKE MASON - Regional Manager Operations
MARK KANTARAS - Manager Operations
JAY GOULD - Manager Real Estate
AMY HALE - Manager
MEGAN SIMPSON - Manager Human Resources
TRACY AKERS - Manager Benefits, Human Resources
RYA MITCHELL - Assistant

Godfather's Pizza, Inc.
2808 N 108th St
Omaha, NE 68164-3702

Telephone: (402) 391-1452
Fax Number: (402) 255-2687
Internet Homepage: godfathers.com

Type of Business: Chain Restaurant Operator
Year Founded: 1973
Systemwide Sales: $335,960,000 (e)
Total Sales: $23,740,000 (e)
Alcohol Sales: 1%
Number of Employees: 3,900
Average Check: Lunch(8); Dinner(10)
Total Units: 409
Trade Names: Godfather's Pizza (465)
Company-Owned Units: 15
Units Franchised To: 450
Preferred Square Footage: 4,000
Preferred Location Types: Freestanding; Strip Mall
Alcohol Served: Beer, Wine
Primary Menu: Pizza (465)
Projected Openings: 10
Areas of Operation: AK, AL, AR, AZ, CA, CO, FL, GA, IA, ID, IL, IN, KS, KY, MA, MI, MN, MO, MT, NC, ND, NE, NH, NJ, NM, NV, NY, OH, OK, OR, PA, SC, SD, TN, TX, UT, VA, WA, WI, WV, WY
Type of Foodservice: Casual Dining (465)
Catering Services: Yes
Primary Distributors: (Full Line) Food Services of America, KENT, WA
Notes: Systemwide sales reflect results from traditional stores only & exclude results from nontraditional locations such as convenience stores.

Key Personnel
RONALD B. GARTLAN - CEO; President; COO; Director Real Estate, Design, Franchising
LINDA MEYER - CFO; VP
KATHLEEN M. JOHNSON - Senior VP
DAVID GARTLAN - VP Development
DAVE GARTLAN - VP Development
BRUCE JUST - Director Franchise Operations
MATTHEW COMBS - Director Safety, Human Resources-Training
NADINE HOFFMAN - Senior Manager Training
TOM PERINA - Manager Loss Prevention, Risk Management
PAM FOX - Manager Procurement
ASHLEY SMITH - Manager Marketing, Sales
DALE O'BRIEN - Assistant Marketing, Public Relations

Little King Inc.
14005 Q St
Omaha, NE 68137

Telephone: (402) 330-8019
Fax Number: (402) 330-3221
Internet Homepage: littlekingsubs.com
Company Email: info@littlekingsubs.com
Type of Business: Chain Restaurant Operator
Year Founded: 1968
Systemwide Sales: $41,782,000 (e)
Total Sales: $441,000 (e)
Alcohol Sales: 1%
Number of Employees: 3
Average Check: Lunch(10); Dinner(10)
Total Units: 7
Trade Names: Little King Restaurant (7)
Units Franchised To: 7
Preferred Square Footage: 1,500
Preferred Location Types: Community Mall; Downtown; Freestanding; Grocery Stores; Office Complex; Regional Mall; Strip Mall
Alcohol Served: Beer
Primary Menu: Sandwiches/Deli (7)
Areas of Operation: NE
Type of Foodservice: Quick Serve (7)
Foodservice Management Venues: Business & Industry
Catering Services: Yes
Primary Distributors: (Food) Cash-Wa Lincoln, LINCOLN, NE

Key Personnel
SID WERTHEIM - CEO; Director Franchising; General Buyer
VIJAY MALLIK - VP Operations

Panda Inc.
13911 Gold Cir Ste 130
Omaha, NE 68144-2376

Telephone: (402) 333-0203
Fax Number: (402) 333-3260
Internet Homepage: arbysomaha.com
Type of Business: Chain Restaurant Operator
Year Founded: 1981
Total Sales: $37,190,000 (e)
Number of Employees: 541
Average Check: Lunch(8); Dinner(8)
Total Units: 20
Trade Names: Arby's (20)
Units Franchised From: 20
Preferred Square Footage: 2,600
Preferred Location Types: Community Mall; Freestanding
Primary Menu: Sandwiches/Deli (20)
Areas of Operation: IA, NE
Type of Foodservice: Quick Serve (20)
Foodservice Management Venues: Schools
Catering Services: Yes
Franchise Affiliation: Arby's Restaurant Group, ATLANTA, GA
Primary Distributors: (Food) McLane/Lagrange, LAGRANGE, GA

Key Personnel
ALAN D'AGOSTO - President; Manager Purchasing, Facility/Maintenance, Real Estate, Design
GREG SHERLOCK - Controller; Director Finance, Information Systems, Human Resources
ANDREW D'AGOSTO - Director Operations

Peak Interest LLC
4938 S 114th St
Omaha, NE 68137-2324

Telephone: (402) 592-5591
Fax Number: (402) 592-5899
Company Email: peak@peakinterests.com
Type of Business: Chain Restaurant Operator
Year Founded: 1995
Total Sales: $49,830,000 (e)
Alcohol Sales: 1%
Number of Employees: 1,200
Average Check: Lunch(14); Dinner(16)
Total Units: 41
Trade Names: Pizza Hut (41)
Units Franchised From: 41
Preferred Square Footage: 2,500
Preferred Location Types: Downtown; Freestanding; Strip Mall
Alcohol Served: Beer
Primary Menu: Pizza (41)
Areas of Operation: IA, NE
Type of Foodservice: Quick Serve (41)
Foodservice Management Venues: Schools
Catering Services: Yes
Franchise Affiliation: Pizza Hut Inc., PLANO, TX
Primary Distributors: (Full Line) McLane/Shawnee, SHAWNEE, KS

Key Personnel
JOE ARAGON - President; Director Finance, Operations, Information Systems; General Buyer
RICH JASPER - Manager Store Fixtures

Romeo's Inc.
2731 S 87th Ave
Omaha, NE 68124-3044

Telephone: (402) 390-0561
Fax Number: (402) 390-6222
Internet Homepage: romeosomaha.com
Type of Business: Chain Restaurant Operator
Year Founded: 1975
Total Sales: $9,128,000 (e)
Alcohol Sales: 15%
Number of Employees: 300
Average Check: Lunch(8); Dinner(14)
Total Units: 5
Trade Names: Romeo's Mexican Food & Pizza (5)
Company-Owned Units: 5
Preferred Square Footage: 5,000
Preferred Location Types: Freestanding; Strip Mall
Alcohol Served: Beer, Wine, Liquor
Primary Menu: Mexican (5)
Areas of Operation: NE
Type of Foodservice: Casual Dining (5)
Primary Distributors: (Food) Cash-Wa Lincoln,

LINCOLN, NE

Key Personnel
SAM AMENTA - CEO; President; Executive Chef; Director Finance, Purchasing, Facility/Maintenance, Supply Chain, Real Estate, Design, Menu Development; General Buyer
DENISE ROBINSON - Manager Human Resources

Scooter's Coffee LLC
10500 Sapp Brothers Dr
Omaha, NE 68138

Telephone: (402) 614-1723
Fax Number: (402) 614-3702
Internet Homepage: scooterscoffee.com
Type of Business: Chain Restaurant Operator
Year Founded: 1998
Total Sales: $10,510,000 (e)
Number of Employees: 360
Average Check: Breakfast(8); Lunch(8); Dinner(8)
Internet Order Processing: Yes
Internet Sales: 3.00%
Total Units: 486
Trade Names: Scooter's Coffee (486)
Company-Owned Units: 5
Units Franchised To: 481
Preferred Square Footage: 500; 1,600; 1,800
Preferred Location Types: Downtown; Freestanding; Strip Mall
Primary Menu: Coffee (486)
Projected Openings: 80
Areas of Operation: CA, CO, FL, IA, KS, MO, NE, SD, TX, UT
Type of Foodservice: Quick Serve (486)
Foodservice Management Venues: College & University; Lodging
Catering Services: Yes

Key Personnel
JOE THORNTON - CEO; President
BILL BLACK - Chief Marketing Officer
DAVE ANDERSON - Chief Legal Officer
RICHARD HEYMAN - Chief Strategy Officer
MITCH WALDEN - Senior Director Digital Marketing, Loyalty Program
AARON KECK - Director Facility/Maintenance
SARA QUAM - Director Procurement
JENNA EAGLETON - Director Brand Marketing

Welsh Family Holdings, LLC
2221 N 90th St
Omaha, NE 68134-6005

Telephone: (586) 899-9787
Type of Business: Chain Restaurant Operator
Total Sales: $1,595,000 (e)
Total Units: 2

Trade Names: Little Caesars Pizza (2)
Units Franchised From: 2
Primary Menu: Pizza (2)
Areas of Operation: NE
Type of Foodservice: Quick Serve (2)
Franchise Affiliation: Little Caesar Enterprises Inc., DETROIT, MI

Key Personnel
CHUCK WELSH - President; General Buyer

Bentley-Miller Inc
801 Ferdinand Plz
Scottsbluff, NE 69361-4401

Telephone: (308) 632-5559
Fax Number: (308) 632-5589
Company Email: owners@bentley-miller.com
Type of Business: Chain Restaurant Operator
Year Founded: 1988
Total Sales: $45,450,000 (e)
Number of Employees: 472
Average Check: Lunch(10); Dinner(12)
Total Units: 24
Trade Names: Arby's (24)
Units Franchised From: 24
Preferred Square Footage: 1,400; 3,200
Preferred Location Types: Freestanding; Regional Mall
Primary Menu: Sandwiches/Deli (24)
Areas of Operation: NE
Type of Foodservice: Quick Serve (24)
Franchise Affiliation: Arby's Restaurant Group, ATLANTA, GA

Key Personnel
CHRISTY HENRY - President
CARTER MILLER - President; Partner
AL JOHNSON - VP Operations
STEVEN SMITH - Director Information Technology

Svoboda and Henk Inc.
122 N 5th St
Seward, NE 68434-2147

Telephone: (402) 643-4524
Type of Business: Chain Restaurant Operator
Total Sales: $1,903,000 (e)
Total Units: 3
Trade Names: Godfather's Pizza (3)
Units Franchised From: 3
Primary Menu: Pizza (3)
Areas of Operation: NE
Type of Foodservice: Casual Dining (3)
Franchise Affiliation: Godfather's Pizza, Inc., OMAHA, NE

Key Personnel
MARK HENK - Partner; General Buyer

TIM SVOBODA - Partner; General Buyer

NEW HAMPSHIRE

The Napoli Group
5 Overlook Dr Unit 2
Amherst, NH 03031-2831

Mailing Address: PO Box 6300, AMHERST, NH, 03031-6300
Telephone: (603) 732-0864
Fax Number: (603) 732-0877
Type of Business: Chain Restaurant Operator
Year Founded: 1978
Total Sales: $264,940,000 (e)
Number of Employees: 3,304
Average Check: Breakfast(8); Lunch(10); Dinner(12)
Total Units: 56
Trade Names: McDonald's (56)
Units Franchised From: 56
Preferred Square Footage: 2,500; 3,000
Preferred Location Types: Discount Dept. Stores; Freestanding; Regional Mall
Primary Menu: Hamburger (56)
Areas of Operation: ME, NH, NY, VT
Type of Foodservice: Quick Serve (56)
Franchise Affiliation: McDonald's Corporation, CHICAGO, IL
Primary Distributors: (Food) The Martin-Brower Co., ENFIELD, CT
Notes: Formerly known as Colley/McCoy Management Group Inc.

Key Personnel
FRANK NAPOLI - CEO; President
PETER NAPOLI - President; Director Real Estate, Design, Store Fixtures
JACK LOFTUS - CFO
LYNN SHIELDS - VP; Director Purchasing, Information Systems
RICK OSNER - Controller
SAL NAPOLI - Director Operations, Facility/Maintenance, Supply Chain
STEPHANIE NAPOLI - Director Operations
LINDA WRIGHT - Director Human Resources
TOM WIRT - Manager Sales

The Common Man Family of Restaurants
59 Main St
Ashland, NH 03217

Mailing Address: PO Box 581, ASHLAND, NH, 03217-0581
Telephone: (603) 968-9330
Fax Number: (603) 968-2123
Internet Homepage: thecman.com
Company Email: info@thecman.com
Type of Business: Chain Restaurant Operator

Year Founded: 1971
Total Sales: $37,440,000 (e)
Alcohol Sales: 1%
Number of Employees: 1,049
Average Check: Breakfast(10); Lunch(14); Dinner(42)
Internet Order Processing: Yes
Internet Sales: 1.00%
Total Units: 17
Trade Names: 104 Diner (1); Airport Diner (1); Camp (1); Common Man Ashland (1); Common Man at Hooksertt Welcome Center (1); Common Man Clairmont (1); Common Man Concord (1); Common Man Lincoln (1); Common Man Merrimack (1); Common Man Windham (1); Foster's Boiler Room (1); ItalianFarmhouse (1); Lago (1); Lakehouse (1); Rise and Shine Cafe (1); Tilt'n Diner (1); Town Docks (1)
Company-Owned Units: 17
Preferred Square Footage: 3,000; 5,000; 7,000
Preferred Location Types: Freestanding
Alcohol Served: Beer, Wine, Liquor
Primary Menu: American (12); French/Continental (1); Italian (2); Seafood (1); Steak/Seafood (1)
Areas of Operation: NH
Type of Foodservice: Casual Dining (11); Family Restaurant (5); Fine Dining (1)
Catering Services: Yes
Primary Distributors: (Equipment) Kittredge Equipment, BOW, NH; (Supplies) Kittredge Equipment, BOW, NH

Key Personnel
ALEX RAY - Founder; President; Director Real Estate
VINCENT VELLA - CEO
SEAN BROWN - COO
DIANE DOWNING - VP
SALVATORE DELORENZO - Director Operations
CINDY BATES - Director Training
JENNIFER TOWER WHITFIELD - Director Sales
SALLY MOLTON - Manager Risk Management, Human Resources

Crescent Group
2 Cote Ln Unit 5
Bedford, NH 03110-5842

Mailing Address: P O Box 10117, BEDFORD , NH, 03110
Telephone: (603) 625-1517
Fax Number: (603) 625-1022
Type of Business: Chain Restaurant Operator
Year Founded: 1983
Total Sales: $42,610,000 (e)
Number of Employees: 405
Average Check: Breakfast(8); Lunch(10); Dinner(12)
Total Units: 9
Trade Names: McDonald's (9)
Units Franchised From: 9
Preferred Square Footage: 1,600
Preferred Location Types: Freestanding
Primary Menu: Hamburger (9)
Areas of Operation: NH
Type of Foodservice: Quick Serve (9)
Franchise Affiliation: McDonald's Corporation, CHICAGO, IL
Primary Distributors: (Food) The Martin-Brower Co. LLC, ROSEMONT, IL

Key Personnel
MICHAEL GAMBINO - President; General Buyer

T Bones Great American Eatery
124 Bedford Center Rd Ste B
Bedford, NH 03110-5448

Telephone: (603) 488-2820
Fax Number: (603) 676-1984
Internet Homepage: copperdoorrestaurant.com; go2cjs.com; t-bones.com
Company Email: info@GreatNHRestaurants.com
Type of Business: Chain Restaurant Operator
Year Founded: 1984
Total Sales: $35,530,000 (e)
Alcohol Sales: 18%
Number of Employees: 608
Average Check: Lunch(28); Dinner(28)
Internet Order Processing: Yes
Internet Sales: 1.00%
Total Units: 9
Trade Names: Cactus Jack's (1); CJ's Great West Grill (1); Copper Door (2); T. Bone's Great American Eatery (5)
Company-Owned Units: 9
Preferred Square Footage: 5,500; 6,000
Preferred Location Types: Freestanding
Alcohol Served: Beer, Wine, Liquor
Primary Menu: American (7); Steak/Seafood (2)
Areas of Operation: NH
Type of Foodservice: Casual Dining (7); Fine Dining (2)
Primary Distributors: (Full Line) Performance Foodservice - Springfield, SPRINGFIELD, MA

Key Personnel
TOM BOUCHER - President; Partner; CFO; Director Operations, Real Estate, Store Planning
MARK FENSKE - Partner; Director Store Operations, Facility/Maintenance; General Buyer
DAN FRASER - Partner
BOB SULLIVAN - Manager Purchasing, Supply Chain
ZACHARY GALVIN - Manager

Homestead Restaurant & Lounge
1567 Summer St
Bristol, NH 03222-3238

Telephone: (603) 744-2022
Fax Number: (603) 744-3603
Internet Homepage: fratellos.com; homesteadnh.com
Company Email: mark@fratellos.com
Type of Business: Chain Restaurant Operator
Year Founded: 1978
Total Sales: $8,005,000 (e)
Alcohol Sales: 20%
Number of Employees: 170
Average Check: Lunch(22); Dinner(42)
Internet Order Processing: Yes
Internet Sales: 1.00%
Total Units: 5
Trade Names: Fratellos (3); Homestead Restaurant of Bristol (1); Homestead Restaurant of Merrimack (1)
Company-Owned Units: 5
Preferred Square Footage: 5,500; 6,000
Preferred Location Types: Freestanding
Alcohol Served: Beer, Wine, Liquor
Primary Menu: American (2); Italian (3)
Areas of Operation: NH
Type of Foodservice: Fine Dining (5)
Catering Services: Yes

Key Personnel
MARK MCDONOUGH - President; Director Real Estate, Catering; General Buyer

Jamar Donuts Inc.
5 Crystal Ave
Derry, NH 03038-2415

Telephone: (603) 432-9797
Type of Business: Chain Restaurant Operator
Total Sales: $7,848,000 (e)
Number of Employees: 100
Average Check: Dinner(8)
Total Units: 5
Trade Names: Dunkin' Donuts (5)
Units Franchised From: 5
Preferred Square Footage: 1,500; 2,200
Preferred Location Types: Freestanding; Strip Mall
Primary Menu: Snacks (5)
Areas of Operation: NH
Type of Foodservice: Quick Serve (5)
Franchise Affiliation: DD IP Holder, CANTON, MA

Key Personnel
ANTONIO TRAVASSOS - President; General

Buyer
JASON TRAVASSOS - General Manager

Great American Hotel Group, Inc
180 Locust St Ste 2
Dover, NH 03820-4033

Telephone: (603) 373-1510
Fax Number: (603) 559-2195
Internet Homepage: greatamericanhg.com
Company Email: info@greatamericanhg.com
Type of Business: Foodservice Operations - Hotel/Motels
Year Founded: 1979
Total Sales: $72,110,000 (e)
Alcohol Sales: 10%
Number of Employees: 3,904
Total Units: 16
Restaurants in Hotels: 16
Trade Names: Marriott (3); Other Concepts (13)
Company-Owned Units: 16
Alcohol Served: Beer, Wine, Liquor
Projected Openings: 2
Projected Remodelings: 3
Areas of Operation: AK, CO, CT, FL, KY, MA, NC, NH, NJ, NY, OH, TN, VA, VT, WI, BC, NS, ON, QC
Foreign Countries: CANADA
Type of Foodservice: Casual Dining (49)
Primary Distributors: (Food) Cheney Bros. Inc., RIVIERA BEACH, FL
Notes: The company derives approximately 85% of its revenue from hotel operations. Included in the company-owned count are units managed by Ocean Hospitalities.

Key Personnel
WILLIAM D. AKRIDGE - President
GABRIELLE SMITH - Controller; Director Finance
SUZANNE BAELE - Director Human Resources
LINDA KOMORNIK - Director Marketing, Sales

Ashworth By The Sea Hotel & Restaurant
295 Ocean Blvd
Hampton, NH 03842-3629

Telephone: (603) 926-6762
Fax Number: (603) 926-2002
Internet Homepage: ashworthhotel.com
Company Email: ashworthinfo@ashworthhotel.com
Type of Business: Chain Restaurant Operator
Year Founded: 1953
Total Sales: $3,901,000 (e)
Alcohol Sales: 10%
Number of Employees: 55
Average Check: Breakfast(14); Lunch(30); Dinner(42)
Total Units: 3
Trade Names: Breakers Restaurant and Bar (1); Sandbar (1); Wharfside Cafe (1)
Company-Owned Units: 3
Preferred Location Types: Hotel/Motel
Alcohol Served: Beer, Wine, Liquor
Primary Menu: American (2); Snacks (1)
Areas of Operation: NH
Type of Foodservice: Casual Dining (3)
Primary Distributors: (Full Line) SYSCO of Boston, PLYMPTON, MA

Key Personnel
JOE PRIMAVERA - Executive Chef; General Buyer

Flatbread, Inc.
4 High St Ste 5
Hampton, NH 03842-2220

Telephone: (603) 926-9401
Internet Homepage: flatbreadcompany.com
Type of Business: Chain Restaurant Operator
Year Founded: 1998
Total Sales: $7,214,000 (e)
Total Units: 8
Trade Names: Flatbread Company (8)
Company-Owned Units: 8
Primary Menu: Pizza (8)
Areas of Operation: CT, HI, MA, ME, NH, RI, BC
Foreign Countries: CANADA
Type of Foodservice: Fast Casual (8)

Key Personnel
JAY GOULD - Co-Founder; Partner
MEREDITH MORRISSETTE - Account Executive

Blue Sky Restaurant Group
224 Lebanon St
Hanover, NH 03755-3225

Mailing Address: PO Box 665, HANOVER, NH, 03755-0665
Telephone: (603) 643-4111
Fax Number: (603) 643-3340
Internet Homepage: blueskyrestaurants.com
Company Email: jennifer@blueskyrestaurants.com
Type of Business: Chain Restaurant Operator
Year Founded: 1978
Total Sales: $11,388,000 (e)
Alcohol Sales: 20%
Number of Employees: 325
Average Check: Lunch(22); Dinner(34)
Internet Order Processing: Yes
Internet Sales: 0.50%
Total Units: 2
Trade Names: Jesse's Restaurant (1); Molly's Restaurant (1)
Company-Owned Units: 2
Preferred Location Types: Freestanding
Alcohol Served: Beer, Wine, Liquor
Primary Menu: American (2)
Areas of Operation: NH
Type of Foodservice: Casual Dining (2)
Primary Distributors: (Equipment) Kittredge Equipment, BOW, NH; (Food) US Foods, CLIFTON PARK, NY; (Supplies) Kittredge Equipment, BOW, NH

Key Personnel
ANTHONY BARNETT - Owner; General Buyer
JENNIFER PACKARD - Director Human Resources

Andrade Management Group
146 Eddy Rd
Manchester, NH 03102-3231

Telephone: (603) 647-4488
Fax Number: (603) 647-2757
Internet Homepage: andradenh.com
Company Email: hroffice@andradesnh.com
Type of Business: Chain Restaurant Operator
Year Founded: 1990
Total Sales: $200,620,000 (e)
Number of Employees: 680
Average Check: Breakfast(5); Lunch(5); Dinner(5)
Total Units: 129
Trade Names: Dunkin' Donuts (129)
Units Franchised From: 129
Preferred Location Types: Convenience Store/Gas Station; Freestanding; Other
Primary Menu: Snacks (129)
Areas of Operation: NH
Type of Foodservice: Quick Serve (129)
Franchise Affiliation: DD IP Holder, CANTON, MA
Primary Distributors: (Full Line) SYSCO Food Services of Northern New England Inc., WESTBROOK, ME

Key Personnel
CARL ANDRADE - President; Partner; General Buyer
LORI ANDRADE-HILLIARD - Partner
VERONICA NIXON - General Manager
JEANNETTE PLUMPTON - General Manager

Cidas, LLC
581 2nd St
Manchester, NH 03102-5237

Telephone: (603) 641-4040
Fax Number: (603) 626-1476
Type of Business: Chain Restaurant Operator
Total Sales: $3,916,000 (e)
Total Units: 3

Trade Names: Little Caesars Pizza (3)
Units Franchised From: 3
Primary Menu: Pizza (3)
Areas of Operation: NH
Type of Foodservice: Quick Serve (3)
Franchise Affiliation: Little Caesar Enterprises Inc., DETROIT, MI

Key Personnel
JOSEPH STANLEY - President; General Buyer

Fantabulous Cakes and Cones
2 Cellu Dr Ste 111
Nashua, NH 03063-1000

Telephone: (603) 882-0550
Type of Business: Chain Restaurant Operator
Total Sales: $1,832,000 (e)
Total Units: 3
Trade Names: Cold Stone Creamery (3)
Units Franchised From: 3
Primary Menu: Snacks (3)
Areas of Operation: NH
Type of Foodservice: Quick Serve (3)
Franchise Affiliation: Kahala Brands, SCOTTSDALE, AZ

Key Personnel
CHRISTOPHER PERRY - Owner

Lilac Blossom
650 Amherst St Unit 22
Nashua, NH 03063-4017

Mailing Address: 385 East Dunstable, NASHUA, NH, 03062-2258
Telephone: (603) 886-8420
Fax Number: (603) 888-9588
Internet Homepage: lilacblossom-nh.com
Company Email: customerservice@lilacblossom.us
Type of Business: Chain Restaurant Operator
Year Founded: 1980
Total Sales: $3,116,000 (e)
Alcohol Sales: 8%
Number of Employees: 15
Average Check: Lunch(12); Dinner(30)
Total Units: 2
Trade Names: Lilac Blossom (2)
Company-Owned Units: 2
Preferred Location Types: Downtown
Alcohol Served: Beer, Wine, Liquor
Primary Menu: Chinese (2)
Areas of Operation: NH
Type of Foodservice: Casual Dining (2)
Primary Distributors: (Food) SYSCO of Boston, PLYMPTON, MA

Key Personnel
SOPHIA CHU - Partner; General Manager; General Buyer
HARRY KU - Partner

Sepco Inc
29 Lafayette Rd Ste A3
North Hampton, NH 03862-2437

Mailing Address: PO Box 986, NORTH HAMPTON, NH, 03862-0986
Telephone: (603) 964-7275
Fax Number: (603) 964-6514
Type of Business: Chain Restaurant Operator
Total Sales: $6,117,000 (e)
Average Check: Dinner(16)
Total Units: 3
Trade Names: Domino's (3)
Units Franchised From: 3
Primary Menu: Pizza (3)
Areas of Operation: NH
Type of Foodservice: Quick Serve (3)
Franchise Affiliation: Domino's Pizza Inc, ANN ARBOR, MI

Key Personnel
STEPHEN GALLUP - President; General Buyer

Margaritas Management Group
200 Griffin Rd Ste 1
Portsmouth, NH 03801-7145

Telephone: (603) 430-8905
Fax Number: (603) 430-8927
Internet Homepage: margs.com; margs.com
Type of Business: Chain Restaurant Operator
Year Founded: 1984
Total Sales: $50,710,000 (e)
Alcohol Sales: 45%
Number of Employees: 1,478
Average Check: Lunch(12); Dinner(24)
Total Units: 25
Trade Names: Tio Juan's Margaritas Restaurant & Watering Hole (25)
Company-Owned Units: 25
Preferred Square Footage: 3,800
Preferred Location Types: Downtown; Freestanding
Alcohol Served: Beer, Wine, Liquor
Primary Menu: Mexican (25)
Projected Openings: 10
Areas of Operation: CT, MA, ME, NH, NJ, PA
Type of Foodservice: Casual Dining (25)
Primary Distributors: (Equipment) TriMark USA Inc., MANSFIELD, MA; (Supplies) TriMark USA Inc., MANSFIELD, MA

Key Personnel
JOHN PELLETIER - Chairman; Partner; Director Design
DAVID PELLETIER - Partner
TOM RADOMSKI - VP Real Estate Development, Franchise Development
KELLY TOBEY - Director Payroll

Twin Coast Enterprises, Inc.
23 Stiles Rd Ste 219
Salem, NH 03079

Telephone: (603) 296-4930
Fax Number: (603) 296-4932
Internet Homepage: twincoastenterprises.com
Company Email: lapierce@tcewendys.com
Type of Business: Chain Restaurant Operator
Total Sales: $21,290,000 (e)
Total Units: 8
Trade Names: Wendy's Old Fashioned Hamburgers (8)
Units Franchised From: 8
Primary Menu: Hamburger (8)
Areas of Operation: MA, NH
Type of Foodservice: Quick Serve (8)
Franchise Affiliation: The Wendy's Company, DUBLIN, OH

Key Personnel
CHRISTOPHER BAKER - President; Director Operations; General Buyer
DENNIS BLANCO - Director Operations

NEW JERSEY

Doherty Enterprises Inc.
7 Pearl Ct Ste F
Allendale, NJ 07401-1654

Telephone: (201) 818-4669
Fax Number: (201) 818-0807
Internet Homepage: spuntinowinebar.com; DohertyInc.com; theshannonrose.com
Type of Business: Chain Restaurant Operator
Year Founded: 1985
Total Sales: $741,800,000 (e)
Alcohol Sales: 15%
Number of Employees: 7,652
Average Check: Breakfast(6); Lunch(12); Dinner(18)
Total Units: 150
Trade Names: Applebee's Neighborhood Grill & Bar (100); Chevys Fresh Mex (2); Panera Bread (41); Quaker Steak (3); Spuntino (2); The Shannon Rose Irish Pub (2)
Company-Owned Units: 4
Units Franchised From: 146
Preferred Square Footage: 5,500
Preferred Location Types: Community Mall; Freestanding; Strip Mall
Alcohol Served: Beer, Wine, Liquor
Primary Menu: American (103); Italian (2);

Mexican (2); Miscellaneous (2); Sandwiches/Deli (41)
Areas of Operation: FL, GA, NJ, NY
Type of Foodservice: Casual Dining (109); Fast Casual (41)
Franchise Affiliation: Applebee's Services Inc., KANSAS CITY, MO; Fired Up Inc., AUSTIN, TX; Noodles & Company, BROOMFIELD, CO; Panera Bread Company, SAINT LOUIS, MO; Xperience Restaurant Group, CYPRESS, CA
Primary Distributors: (Food) Maines Paper & Food Service Inc., CONKLIN, NY

Key Personnel
EDWARD DOHERTY - Chairman; CEO
TIMOTHY DOHERTY - President; COO; Manager Information Technology
JERRY MARCOPOULOS - CFO; Exec VP
KATHY COUGHLIN - Chief People Officer; VP Human Resources, Training
JASON SICIGNANO - Area Director
TIFFANY HUFF - Area Director
DAVID DIBARTOLO - VP Operations, Group
MICHAEL VENEZIANO - VP Finance
GREGORY K. GEORGE - VP Restaurant Operations, Group
KURT PAHLITZSCH - VP Franchise Operations
SHANNON PORTELL - VP Marketing, Branding, Business Development
BOB GAUTHIER - VP; Manager
TOM MACDONNELL - General Manager
CESAR RAMOS - General Manager
JAMES BURGSTAHLER - General Manager
DANIELLE QUIGLEY - General Manager Training
REGAN DEBENEDETTO - Director Operations, Group
GORDON A. GROSS - Director Construction
JAMES F. REILLY - Director Training
RANDY DEVELVIS - Director Group
ADAM EURY - Director Group
SAM HALIM - Director Group
WAYNE KAISER - Director Group
BRIAN MCDONNELL - Director Operations
MICHAEL MCKEE - Director Group
MICHELLE DIAMOND - Director Marketing
MELISSA MACDONNELL - Director Training
JOANNE SHANNON - Director Talent Acquisitions
RONALD BLAIS - Director Purchasing
LEIGH SALZBERG - Director Marketing
PATRICIO AROSTEGUI - Senior Manager Information Technology
CAILEY DIMITROPOULOS - Manager Marketing
MELISSA MCCORMICK - Manager Human Resources
BRYAN YOUNGHANS - Manager Marketing
LISA DANILOW - Manager Payroll
TRACY PRYDE - Executive Assistant
CHRISTIE PATTMAN - Executive Assistant; Office Manager

Shore Thing Restaurants, LLC
PO Box 357
Allenhurst, NJ 07711-0357

Telephone: (703) 405-8512
Type of Business: Chain Restaurant Operator
Total Sales: $9,693,000 (e)
Number of Employees: 90
Total Units: 5
Trade Names: Five Guys Burgers and Fries (5)
Units Franchised From: 5
Preferred Square Footage: 3,000
Primary Menu: Hamburger (5)
Areas of Operation: NJ
Type of Foodservice: Fast Casual (5)
Franchise Affiliation: Five Guys Holdings Inc., LORTON, VA

Key Personnel
JOHN GILMARTIN - Partner
JAMES RODIO - Partner
BRETT ROSELY - Partner
ROBERT WOLF - Partner
CHRISTOPHER DRUMMOND - Partner

Borgata Hotel, Casino & Spa
1 Borgata Way
Atlantic City, NJ 08401-1946

Telephone: (609) 317-1000
Fax Number: (609) 317-1100
Internet Homepage: theborgata.com
Company Email: info@theborgata.com
Type of Business: Foodservice Operations - Casinos
Total Sales: $1,122,441,000 (e)
Alcohol Sales: 14%
Number of Employees: 7,000
Total Units: 1
Restaurants in Hotels: 15
Trade Names: Borgata Hotel Casino & Spa (1)
Company-Owned Units: 15
Alcohol Served: Beer, Wine, Liquor
Areas of Operation: NJ
Type of Foodservice: Casual Dining (7); Family Restaurant (2); Fine Dining (5); Quick Serve (1)

Key Personnel
MARCUS GLOVER - President; COO
BECKY SCHULTZ - VP Food and Beverage
THOMAS BIGLAN - Executive Chef
CHRIS RYNKIEWICZ - Director Finance
PRESTON PATTERSON - Director Food and Beverage
CHELSEA REYES - Manager Marketing
LAURA TURENNE - Manager Alcoholic Beverages
CARIE WOJDYLA - Manager Social Media

Growth Restaurants Inc.
55 S Finley Ave
Basking Ridge, NJ 07920

Telephone: (908) 766-0166
Fax Number: (908) 766-0942
Internet Homepage: growthrestaurants.com
Company Email: info@growthrestaurants.com
Type of Business: Chain Restaurant Operator
Year Founded: 1971
Total Sales: $15,364,000 (e)
Alcohol Sales: 30%
Number of Employees: 320
Average Check: Lunch(24); Dinner(24)
Total Units: 3
Trade Names: The Famished Frog (1); Thirsty Turtle (2)
Company-Owned Units: 3
Preferred Square Footage: 5,500; 6,000
Preferred Location Types: Freestanding
Alcohol Served: Beer, Wine, Liquor
Primary Menu: American (3)
Areas of Operation: NJ
Type of Foodservice: Fine Dining (3)
Catering Services: Yes
Primary Distributors: (Equipment) SYSCO Food Services of Metro New York, JERSEY CITY, NJ; (Food) SYSCO Food Services of Metro New York, JERSEY CITY, NJ; (Supplies) M. Tucker, a divison of Singer NY LLC, PATERSON, NJ

Key Personnel
JACK WELCH - President; Partner
JEFFREY BEERS - Partner; Treasurer; Director Finance
JIM FINNEGAN - Partner; General Manager
KEN RAYMOND - Executive Chef; General Buyer

Domino's Franchisee
1051 Broadway
Bayonne, NJ 07002-4157

Telephone: (201) 339-3030
Type of Business: Chain Restaurant Operator
Total Sales: $14,603,000 (e)
Total Units: 7
Trade Names: Domino's (7)
Units Franchised From: 7
Primary Menu: Pizza (7)
Areas of Operation: NJ
Type of Foodservice: Quick Serve (7)
Franchise Affiliation: Domino's Pizza Inc, ANN ARBOR, MI

Key Personnel
FRANK J. LAZAUSKAS - Owner; General Buyer

Playa Bowls
803 Ocean Ave
Belmar, NJ 07719

Telephone: (732) 556-6897
Internet Homepage: playabowls.com
Company Email: info@playabowls.com
Type of Business: Chain Restaurant Operator
Total Sales: $160,910,000 (e)
Total Units: 123
Trade Names: Playa Bowls (123)
Company-Owned Units: 123
Primary Menu: Health Foods (123)
Areas of Operation: CT, DE, FL, GA, MD, NJ, NY, PA, PR, SC
Type of Foodservice: Fast Casual (123)

Key Personnel
ROBERT GIULIANI - Co-Founder
ABBY TAYLOR - Co-Founder
DAN HARMON - CEO
GARY MOSS - VP Operations, Business Development
DARLENE SCHOENEBERG - VP Operations
DANIELLE DEANGELO - General Manager Operations
DANIELLE PANIKIEWSKY - Director Finance
MARISA AUSTIN - Director Sourcing, Supply Chain
RACHEL VOGEL - Director Marketing
BRENNA TRUMPER - Director Marketing, Communications
MIKE SNYDER - Regional Manager Operations
MELISSA MCCORMACK - Manager Human Resources
DANIELLE GRIECO - Manager Business Development
DAISY WILEY - Manager Operations

Domino's Franchisee
5051 Route 42
Blackwood, NJ 08012-1703

Telephone: (856) 232-3333
Type of Business: Chain Restaurant Operator
Total Sales: $5,985,000 (e)
Total Units: 3
Trade Names: Domino's (3)
Units Franchised From: 3
Primary Menu: Pizza (3)
Areas of Operation: NJ
Type of Foodservice: Quick Serve (3)
Franchise Affiliation: Domino's Pizza Inc, ANN ARBOR, MI

Key Personnel
THOMAS J. WHITMAN - Owner; General Buyer

Macalibur Limited
901 Route 168 Ste 401
Blackwood, NJ 08012-3237

Telephone: (856) 228-5511
Fax Number: (856) 228-0061
Type of Business: Chain Restaurant Operator
Total Sales: $10,186,000 (e)
Average Check: Breakfast(8); Lunch(8); Dinner(8)
Total Units: 2
Trade Names: McDonald's (2)
Units Franchised From: 2
Preferred Square Footage: 2,500; 3,000
Preferred Location Types: Freestanding
Primary Menu: Hamburger (2)
Areas of Operation: NJ
Type of Foodservice: Quick Serve (2)
Franchise Affiliation: McDonald's Corporation, CHICAGO, IL

Key Personnel
SAM RABINOWITZ - President; General Manager; General Buyer

CRI Longhill
800 Thompson Ave
Bound Brook, NJ 08805-1124

Mailing Address: PO Box 638, MARTINSVILLE, NJ, 08836
Telephone: (732) 469-4600
Fax Number: (732) 271-8187
Internet Homepage: chimneyrockinn.com
Company Email: info@chimneyrockinn.com
Type of Business: Chain Restaurant Operator
Year Founded: 1995
Total Sales: $4,825,000 (e)
Alcohol Sales: 15%
Number of Employees: 150
Average Check: Lunch(14); Dinner(18)
Internet Order Processing: Yes
Total Units: 3
Trade Names: Chimmney Rock Inn (3)
Company-Owned Units: 3
Preferred Square Footage: 1,200; 1,500
Preferred Location Types: Freestanding
Alcohol Served: Beer, Wine, Liquor
Primary Menu: Italian (3)
Areas of Operation: NJ
Type of Foodservice: Casual Dining (3)
Primary Distributors: (Food) US Foods, NORWICH, CT

Key Personnel
ALAN FRANK - President; General Manager; Executive Chef; General Buyer
WINFIELD CHASMAR - General Manager

Fins Tropicali Cuisine
120 Main St
Bradley Beach, NJ 07720-1030

Telephone: (732) 897-8600
Fax Number: (732) 897-1926
Internet Homepage: finsusa.com
Company Email: finsusa@gmail.com
Type of Business: Chain Restaurant Operator
Total Units: 3
Trade Names: Fins Tropcali Cuisine (3)
Company-Owned Units: 3
Primary Menu: Mexican (3)
Areas of Operation: NJ
Type of Foodservice: Fast Casual (3)

Key Personnel
SHAWN RYAN - Partner; General Buyer
PATRICK CUOZZO - Partner; General Buyer

B & J Food Enterprises, Inc.
56 Chambers Bridge Rd Ste 101
Brick, NJ 08723

Telephone: (732) 477-5700
Type of Business: Chain Restaurant Operator
Total Sales: $28,170,000 (e)
Total Units: 20
Trade Names: Jersey Mike's Subs (20)
Units Franchised From: 20
Primary Menu: Sandwiches/Deli (20)
Areas of Operation: NJ
Type of Foodservice: Quick Serve (20)
Franchise Affiliation: Jersey Mike's Franchise Systems, MANASQUAN, NJ

Key Personnel
JOHN HELM - Partner; General Buyer
JOHN CATANIA - Partner

Dunkin' Donuts Franchise
1960 Route 88
Brick, NJ 08724

Telephone: (732) 245-1454
Internet Homepage: dunkindonuts.com
Type of Business: Chain Restaurant Operator
Total Sales: $10,720,000 (e)
Number of Employees: 50
Average Check: Lunch(6); Dinner(8)
Total Units: 7
Trade Names: Dunkin' Donuts (7)
Units Franchised From: 7
Preferred Square Footage: 1,500; 2,200
Preferred Location Types: Freestanding; Strip Mall
Primary Menu: Snacks (7)
Areas of Operation: NJ
Type of Foodservice: Quick Serve (7)

Franchise Affiliation: DD IP Holder, CANTON, MA

Key Personnel
RAHUL SHAH - President; General Buyer

410 Bank Street Restaurant
410 Bank St
Cape May, NJ 08204-1404

Mailing Address: PO Box 518, CAPE MAY, NJ, 08204-0518
Telephone: (609) 884-2127
Fax Number: (609) 846-7647
Internet Homepage: frescoscapemay.com; 410bankstreet.com; bankstreetrestaurants.com
Company Email: 410bankstreetcm@gmail.com
Type of Business: Chain Restaurant Operator
Year Founded: 1984
Total Sales: $3,131,000 (e)
Alcohol Sales: 2%
Number of Employees: 75
Average Check: Dinner(38)
Internet Order Processing: Yes
Total Units: 2
Trade Names: 410 Bank Street Restaurant (1); Fresco's Ristorante (1)
Company-Owned Units: 2
Preferred Location Types: Freestanding
Alcohol Served: Wine
Primary Menu: French/Continental (1); Italian (1)
Areas of Operation: NJ
Type of Foodservice: Fine Dining (2)
Primary Distributors: (Full Line) US Foods, ALLENTOWN, PA

Key Personnel
JANET MILLER - Partner; VP
STEVE MILLER - Partner; General Manager; General Buyer
CHET SAIGN - Executive Chef; General Buyer
IDA SHAPIRA - Executive Chef; General Buyer

Baim Enterprises
57 Haddonfield Rd Ste 100
Cherry Hill, NJ 08002-4807

Telephone: (856) 667-6656
Fax Number: (856) 667-9723
Type of Business: Chain Restaurant Operator
Year Founded: 1975
Total Sales: $28,810,000 (e)
Number of Employees: 280
Average Check: Breakfast(6); Lunch(8); Dinner(8)
Total Units: 6
Trade Names: McDonald's (6)
Units Franchised From: 6
Preferred Square Footage: 3,300
Preferred Location Types: Freestanding; Regional Mall
Primary Menu: Hamburger (6)
Areas of Operation: NJ, PA
Type of Foodservice: Quick Serve (6)
Franchise Affiliation: McDonald's Corporation, CHICAGO, IL

Key Personnel
ED BAIM - President; Manager Finance, Real Estate, Franchising
GARY BEERS - Controller
KATHY CLEMENTS - Manager Human Resources

Cozco Management
1873 Marlton Pike E Ste 2-D
Cherry Hill, NJ 08003-2012

Telephone: (856) 722-0111
Fax Number: (856) 722-7066
Type of Business: Chain Restaurant Operator
Year Founded: 1983
Systemwide Sales: $3,874,000 (e)
Total Sales: $3,874,000 (e)
Number of Employees: 25
Average Check: Breakfast(8); Lunch(10); Dinner(16)
Total Units: 2
Trade Names: Philly Steak & Gyro (2)
Company-Owned Units: 2
Preferred Square Footage: 500; 2,500; 4,000
Preferred Location Types: Airports; Community Mall; Office Complex; Strip Mall
Primary Menu: Sandwiches/Deli (2)
Areas of Operation: NJ, PA
Type of Foodservice: Quick Serve (2)
Catering Services: Yes
Primary Distributors: (Food) US Foods, PITTSTON, PA

Key Personnel
ANDREW COSENZA JR - CEO; President; Partner; CFO; Director Operations, Facility/Maintenance, Information Systems, Loss Prevention, Real Estate, Design, Menu Development, Catering; General Buyer

Lamberti Restaurant Consulting
6 Grove St Rear
Cherry Hill, NJ 08002-2788

Telephone: (856) 663-7887
Fax Number: (856) 663-1312
Internet Homepage: lambertis.com
Company Email: lambertimarketing@comcast.net
Type of Business: Chain Restaurant Operator
Year Founded: 1994
Total Sales: $17,470,000 (e)
Alcohol Sales: 15%
Number of Employees: 290
Average Check: Lunch(20); Dinner(36)
Total Units: 8
Trade Names: Aldo Lamberti Trattoria (1); Caffe Aldo Lamberti (1); Lamberti's Cucina (1); Lamberti's Tutti Toscani (1); Luna Rossa Biagio Lamberti (1); Palat Miami (1); Pizza Fresca (1); Postiano Coast by Aldo Lamberti (1)
Company-Owned Units: 8
Preferred Square Footage: 3,000
Preferred Location Types: Freestanding; Strip Mall
Alcohol Served: Beer, Wine, Liquor
Primary Menu: Italian (8)
Areas of Operation: FL, NJ, PA
Type of Foodservice: Casual Dining (5); Fine Dining (2); Quick Serve (1)
Catering Services: Yes
Primary Distributors: (Food) SYSCO Food Services of Metro New York, JERSEY CITY, NJ

Key Personnel
ALDO LAMBERTI - Owner; CFO; Director Facility/Maintenance, Real Estate, Design
ANNA MARIA FERRARO - Director Operations, Supply Chain, Menu Development, Catering; General Buyer
REBECCA GURZO - Manager Marketing
CARLA BEDFORD - Manager Human Resources

Micale Management
11 Sayer Ave Ste 202
Cherry Hill, NJ 08002-2739

Telephone: (856) 665-8622
Fax Number: (856) 665-8904
Company Email: micalemcdonalds@comcast.net
Type of Business: Chain Restaurant Operator
Year Founded: 1974
Total Sales: $23,050,000 (e)
Number of Employees: 280
Average Check: Breakfast(8); Lunch(8); Dinner(8)
Total Units: 5
Trade Names: McDonald's (5)
Units Franchised From: 5
Preferred Square Footage: 2,500; 3,000
Preferred Location Types: Freestanding
Primary Menu: Hamburger (5)
Areas of Operation: PA
Type of Foodservice: Quick Serve (5)
Franchise Affiliation: McDonald's Corporation, CHICAGO, IL

Key Personnel
ANTHONY MICALE - Owner; Director Finance, Operations, Facility/Maintenance, Information

Systems, Real Estate, Design, Human Resources; General Buyer
ANTHONY MICALE III - Controller

Tarantini Panzarotti Inc.
2060 Springdale Rd Ste 300
Cherry Hill, NJ 08003-4028

Telephone: (856) 489-0026
Fax Number: (856) 489-0027
Internet Homepage: francosplace.com
Company Email: leo@panzarotti.net
Type of Business: Chain Restaurant Operator
Year Founded: 1963
Total Sales: $3,610,000 (e)
Number of Employees: 40
Average Check: Lunch(14); Dinner(16)
Total Units: 2
Trade Names: Franco's Place (1); Panzarotti's (1)
Company-Owned Units: 2
Preferred Location Types: Freestanding; Strip Mall
Primary Menu: Italian (1); Pizza (1)
Areas of Operation: NJ
Type of Foodservice: Family Restaurant (1); Quick Serve (1)
Foodservice Management Venues: College & University; Schools
Distribution Centers: CAMDEN, NJ

Key Personnel
PAUL TARANTINI - VP

Domino's Franchisee
1821 Cinnaminson Ave
Cinnaminson, NJ 08077-2856

Telephone: (856) 786-0100
Type of Business: Chain Restaurant Operator
Total Sales: $4,103,000 (e)
Total Units: 2
Trade Names: Domino's (2)
Units Franchised From: 2
Primary Menu: Pizza (2)
Areas of Operation: NJ
Type of Foodservice: Quick Serve (2)
Franchise Affiliation: Domino's Pizza Inc, ANN ARBOR, MI

Key Personnel
CHRISTOPHER W. WITTING - Owner; General Buyer

P & D Hamburgers
185 Center St
Clinton, NJ 08809-1364

Mailing Address: PO Box 5276, Clinton, NJ, 08809
Telephone: (908) 735-4499
Fax Number: (908) 735-0377
Type of Business: Chain Restaurant Operator
Total Sales: $9,948,000 (e)
Total Units: 2
Trade Names: McDonald's (2)
Units Franchised From: 2
Preferred Location Types: Freestanding
Primary Menu: Hamburger (2)
Areas of Operation: NJ
Type of Foodservice: Quick Serve (2)
Franchise Affiliation: McDonald's Corporation, CHICAGO, IL

Key Personnel
PHILIP KOURY - President; General Buyer

Domino's Franchisee
28 W Blackwell St
Dover, NJ 07801-3837

Telephone: (973) 328-3233
Type of Business: Chain Restaurant Operator
Total Sales: $6,192,000 (e)
Total Units: 3
Trade Names: Domino's (3)
Units Franchised From: 3
Primary Menu: Pizza (3)
Areas of Operation: NJ
Type of Foodservice: Quick Serve (3)
Franchise Affiliation: Domino's Pizza Inc, ANN ARBOR, MI

Key Personnel
VINCENT M. CASTELLANO - Owner; General Buyer

MSK Management
441 Main St Ste 200
East Orange, NJ 07018-3211

Telephone: (973) 672-9900
Fax Number: (973) 672-9960
Company Email: office@mskmgt.com
Type of Business: Chain Restaurant Operator
Total Sales: $90,123,000 (e)
Average Check: Dinner(28)
Total Units: 45
Trade Names: Domino's (45)
Units Franchised From: 45
Preferred Location Types: Strip Mall
Primary Menu: Pizza (45)
Projected Openings: 2
Areas of Operation: NJ, NY, PA
Type of Foodservice: Quick Serve (45)
Franchise Affiliation: Domino's Pizza Inc, ANN ARBOR, MI

Key Personnel
MOHAMMAD KHAN - President; General Manager; General Buyer
MIKE KHAN - President

Sidmar Management Corp.
685 Avon Dr State Hwy 33
East Windsor, NJ 08520

Telephone: (609) 443-8210
Fax Number: (609) 443-8535
Type of Business: Chain Restaurant Operator
Total Sales: $7,267,000 (e)
Total Units: 3
Trade Names: Burger King (3)
Units Franchised From: 3
Primary Menu: Hamburger (3)
Areas of Operation: NJ
Type of Foodservice: Quick Serve (3)
Franchise Affiliation: Burger King Worldwide Inc., MIAMI, FL

Key Personnel
SIDNEY KESSOUS - President; General Buyer

The River Palm Terrace
1416 River Rd
Edgewater, NJ 07020-1537

Telephone: (201) 224-2013
Fax Number: (201) 224-7625
Internet Homepage: riverpalm.com
Company Email: riverpalmterrace@aol.com
Type of Business: Chain Restaurant Operator
Year Founded: 1983
Total Sales: $12,581,000 (e)
Alcohol Sales: 25%
Number of Employees: 58
Average Check: Lunch(36); Dinner(78)
Internet Order Processing: Yes
Total Units: 3
Trade Names: The River Palm Terrace (3)
Company-Owned Units: 3
Preferred Location Types: Freestanding
Alcohol Served: Beer, Wine, Liquor
Primary Menu: Steak/Seafood (3)
Areas of Operation: NJ
Type of Foodservice: Fine Dining (3)
Primary Distributors: (Full Line) US Foods, SWEDESBORO, NJ

Key Personnel
JOHN CAMPBELL - President; General Manager; General Buyer
STEPHEN RUSS - General Manager
LUIS "WIIIE" MONTESINOS - Executive Chef; General Buyer

QSC Enterprises
2 Ethel Rd Ste 206A
Edison, NJ 08817-2839

Telephone: (732) 819-9777
Fax Number: (732) 819-3553
Type of Business: Chain Restaurant Operator
Year Founded: 1980
Total Sales: $28,310,000 (e)
Number of Employees: 255
Average Check: Breakfast(8); Lunch(10); Dinner(10)
Total Units: 6
Trade Names: McDonald's (6)
Units Franchised From: 6
Preferred Square Footage: 2,500
Preferred Location Types: Freestanding
Primary Menu: Hamburger (6)
Areas of Operation: NJ
Type of Foodservice: Quick Serve (6)
Franchise Affiliation: McDonald's Corporation, CHICAGO, IL

Key Personnel
SEBASTIAN LENTINI - President; General Buyer
MARY MELANDO - Assistant Administration

QSR Management Inc
1714 Woodbridge Ave
Edison, NJ 08817-4901

Mailing Address: PO Box 560, EDISON, 08818-0560
Telephone: (732) 572-5000
Fax Number: (732) 572-5003
Type of Business: Chain Restaurant Operator
Total Sales: $61,660,000 (e)
Average Check: Dinner(8)
Total Units: 39
Trade Names: Dunkin' Donuts (39)
Units Franchised From: 39
Preferred Square Footage: 1,500; 2,200
Primary Menu: Snacks (39)
Areas of Operation: NJ, NY
Type of Foodservice: Quick Serve (39)
Franchise Affiliation: DD IP Holder, CANTON, MA

Key Personnel
ANTON NADER - President; General Buyer
JAY DREICER - COO
JASON JARRAR - COO

Quick Quality Restaurants
2 Ethel Rd Ste 205A
Edison, NJ 08817-2839

Mailing Address: PO Box 3145, EDISON, NJ, 08818-3145
Telephone: (732) 248-8200
Fax Number: (732) 248-9115
Type of Business: Chain Restaurant Operator
Year Founded: 1968
Total Sales: $42,580,000 (e)
Number of Employees: 600
Average Check: Breakfast(8); Lunch(14); Dinner(22)
Total Units: 19
Trade Names: Burger King (18); Popeyes Louisiana Kitchen (1)
Units Franchised From: 19
Preferred Square Footage: 3,200
Preferred Location Types: Freestanding
Primary Menu: Chicken (1); Hamburger (18)
Areas of Operation: NJ, NY
Type of Foodservice: Quick Serve (19)
Franchise Affiliation: Burger King Worldwide Inc., MIAMI, FL; Popeyes Louisiana Kitchen Inc., ATLANTA, GA
Primary Distributors: (Full Line) Maines Paper & Food Service Inc., CONKLIN, NY

Key Personnel
ALBERT BIJOU - VP Finance, Operations, Facility/Maintenance, Construction
DENNIS BANDOLA - Manager Accounting, Marketing

Food Service Property Corporation
29 Main Ave
Elmwood Park, NJ 07407-2727

Telephone: (201) 797-4100
Fax Number: (201) 797-7512
Type of Business: Chain Restaurant Operator
Year Founded: 1969
Total Sales: $11,400,000 (e)
Number of Employees: 265
Average Check: Breakfast(12); Lunch(10); Dinner(10)
Total Units: 5
Trade Names: Burger King (5)
Units Franchised From: 5
Preferred Square Footage: 3,500
Preferred Location Types: Freestanding; Strip Mall
Primary Menu: Hamburger (5)
Areas of Operation: NJ
Type of Foodservice: Quick Serve (5)
Franchise Affiliation: Burger King Worldwide Inc., MIAMI, FL
Primary Distributors: (Full Line) Maines Paper & Food Service Inc., CONKLIN, NY

Key Personnel
JIM HUFNAGEL - President; Director Purchasing, Real Estate
PAUL KUHN - CFO; Controller
ROBERT LAURIE - Director Operations, Advertising; General Buyer
TIM BRIGHT - Manager Information Systems

Wenesco Restaurants Inc.
910 Sylvan Ave
Englewood Cliffs, NJ 07632-3306

Telephone: (201) 567-4900
Fax Number: (201) 567-5949
Type of Business: Chain Restaurant Operator
Year Founded: 1986
Total Sales: $33,130,000 (e)
Number of Employees: 222
Average Check: Lunch(8); Dinner(10)
Total Units: 12
Trade Names: Wendy's Old Fashioned Hamburgers (12)
Units Franchised From: 12
Preferred Square Footage: 2,100; 2,900
Preferred Location Types: Downtown; Freestanding; Regional Mall
Primary Menu: Hamburger (12)
Areas of Operation: NJ, NY
Type of Foodservice: Quick Serve (12)
Franchise Affiliation: The Wendy's Company, DUBLIN, OH
Primary Distributors: (Full Line) The SYGMA Network Inc. - Pennsylvania, HARRISBURG, PA

Key Personnel
KEVIN WOODSIDE - President; COO; VP; Director Real Estate; Manager Information Technology; General Buyer
NANCY DI GIACOMO - Manager Human Resources

Raven and the Peach
740 River Rd Ste 100
Fair Haven, NJ 07704-3357

Telephone: (732) 747-4666
Fax Number: (732) 747-3633
Internet Homepage: nauvoogrillclub.com; ravenandthepeach.net
Type of Business: Chain Restaurant Operator
Year Founded: 1982
Total Sales: $7,715,000 (e)
Alcohol Sales: 20%
Number of Employees: 50
Average Check: Breakfast(10); Lunch(22); Dinner(54)
Total Units: 3
Trade Names: Blue Peach (1); Nauvoo Grill (1); Raven and the Peach (1)
Company-Owned Units: 3
Preferred Location Types: Freestanding
Alcohol Served: Beer, Wine, Liquor
Primary Menu: American (3)
Areas of Operation: NJ
Type of Foodservice: Casual Dining (2); Fine

Dining (1)
Catering Services: Yes
Primary Distributors: (Full Line) Dairyland, The Chefs' Warehouse, BRONX, NY

Key Personnel
RICHARD BAHADURIAN - President; General Manager; Director Menu Development, Catering; General Buyer

ADF Companies
350 Passaic Ave Fl 2
Fairfield, NJ 07004-2025

Telephone: (973) 808-9525
Fax Number: (973) 808-9526
Internet Homepage: adfcompanies.com
Company Email: info@adfmgt.com
Type of Business: Chain Restaurant Operator
Year Founded: 1998
Total Sales: $271,520,000 (e)
Alcohol Sales: 3%
Number of Employees: 8,500
Average Check: Lunch(14); Dinner(22)
Total Units: 337
Trade Names: KFC (45); Pizza Hut (83); Pizza Hut/WingStreet (209)
Units Franchised From: 337
Preferred Square Footage: 2,500; 3,200; 5,000; 7,000
Preferred Location Types: Freestanding; Strip Mall
Alcohol Served: Beer
Primary Menu: Chicken (45); Pizza (292)
Areas of Operation: AL, CT, DC, FL, GA, MD, NJ, NY, PA, TN, VA, WV
Type of Foodservice: Quick Serve (337)
Franchise Affiliation: KFC Corporation, LOUISVILLE, KY; Pizza Hut Inc., PLANO, TX
Primary Distributors: (Food) McLane/Burlington, BURLINGTON, NJ
Notes: ADF Companies is the second largest Pizza Hut franchisee in the United States and the eighth in the world.

Key Personnel
DONALD K. HARTY - Owner
SPENCER MANKE - CFO
GURVINDER SETHI - General Manager
JOHN ALTON - General Manager
JAN LITZBURG - Senior Director Human Resources
KEVIN DUNLAP - Director Loss Prevention
KRISTIN HAIRABEDIAN - Director Marketing
JOHN SHEPPARD - Regional Manager
DON BLUE - Manager District
DOROTHY DUNLAP - Manager Benefits
KEVIN LUCKMAN - Manager District
TAE KIM - Manager District

bb.q Chicken
2134 North Central Rd
Fort Lee, NJ 07024

Telephone: (201) 921-0473
Internet Homepage: bbqchicken.com
Type of Business: Chain Restaurant Operator
Year Founded: 1995
Total Sales: $11,964,000 (e)
Trade Names: bb.q Chicken
Areas of Operation: AL, AZ, CA, DE, FL, GA, IL, KS, MA, MD, MI, MN, NC, NJ, NV, NY, OH, OK, PA, RI, TN, TX, VA, WA
Type of Foodservice: Casual Dining

Key Personnel
YOON HONG-GUEN - Founder
JOSEPH KIM - CEO

Domino's Franchisee
540 Park Ave
Freehold, NJ 07728-2377

Telephone: (732) 577-9400
Type of Business: Chain Restaurant Operator
Total Sales: $10,107,000 (e)
Total Units: 5
Trade Names: Domino's (5)
Units Franchised From: 5
Primary Menu: Pizza (5)
Areas of Operation: NJ
Type of Foodservice: Quick Serve (5)
Franchise Affiliation: Domino's Pizza Inc, ANN ARBOR, MI

Key Personnel
SUBHASH C. TALWAR - Owner; General Buyer

Frutta Bowls Franchising LLC
51 Hudson St
Freehold, NJ 07728

Telephone: (732) 740-1960
Company Email: franchise@fruttabowls.com
Type of Business: Chain Restaurant Operator
Total Units: 38
Trade Names: Frutta Bowls (38)
Company-Owned Units: 37
Units Franchised To: 1
Primary Menu: Health Foods (38)
Areas of Operation: AL, FL, GA, KY, LA, MD, MS, NC, NJ, OH, PA, SC, TN, VA, WI
Type of Foodservice: Quick Serve (38)
Parent Company: WOWorks, CONSHOHOCKEN, PA

Key Personnel
BROOKE GAGLIANO - Founder; CEO
JOHN O'NEILL - Chief Strategy Officer

Harvey Management Corporation
55 Harristown Rd Ste 304
Glen Rock, NJ 07452-3303

Telephone: (201) 445-0055
Fax Number: (201) 445-4692
Type of Business: Chain Restaurant Operator
Year Founded: 1969
Total Sales: $13,690,000 (e)
Number of Employees: 225
Average Check: Breakfast(10); Lunch(12); Dinner(12)
Total Units: 6
Trade Names: Burger King (6)
Units Franchised From: 6
Preferred Square Footage: 2,500
Preferred Location Types: Freestanding; Regional Mall
Primary Menu: Hamburger (6)
Areas of Operation: NJ, NY, PA
Type of Foodservice: Quick Serve (6)
Franchise Affiliation: Burger King Worldwide Inc., MIAMI, FL
Primary Distributors: (Full Line) Maines Paper & Food Service Inc., CONKLIN, NY

Key Personnel
MICHAEL WALLSTEIN - CEO
DREW PATERNO - President; CIO; Director Operations, Information Systems, Real Estate, Design, Store Fixtures, E-Commerce, Internet Development

Dunkin' Donuts Franchise
455 S Broadway
Gloucester City, NJ 08030-2319

Telephone: (856) 456-5007
Internet Homepage: dunkindonuts.com
Type of Business: Chain Restaurant Operator
Total Sales: $6,740,000 (e)
Average Check: Dinner(8)
Total Units: 4
Trade Names: Dunkin' Donuts (4)
Units Franchised From: 4
Preferred Square Footage: 1,500; 2,200
Preferred Location Types: Freestanding
Primary Menu: Snacks (4)
Areas of Operation: NJ
Type of Foodservice: Quick Serve (4)
Franchise Affiliation: DD IP Holder, CANTON, MA

Key Personnel
KALPESH SHAH - President; General Buyer

5877 Corporation
314 W Pleasantview Ave
Hackensack, NJ 07601-1003

Telephone: (201) 342-5877
Fax Number: (201) 342-4282
Internet Homepage: bkpf.com
Company Email: bkpf@bkpf.com
Type of Business: Chain Restaurant Operator
Year Founded: 1988
Total Sales: $12,600,000 (e)
Alcohol Sales: 8%
Number of Employees: 70
Average Check: Breakfast(8); Lunch(12); Dinner(14)
Total Units: 5
Trade Names: Burger King (1); Popeyes Louisiana Kitchen (4)
Units Franchised From: 5
Preferred Square Footage: 2,000; 4,300; 9,000
Preferred Location Types: Community Mall; Freestanding; Regional Mall
Alcohol Served: Wine
Primary Menu: Chicken (4); Hamburger (1)
Areas of Operation: NJ
Type of Foodservice: Quick Serve (5)
Franchise Affiliation: Burger King Worldwide Inc., MIAMI, FL; Popeyes Louisiana Kitchen Inc., ATLANTA, GA

Key Personnel
STEVE COX - President; General Buyer
LARRY FOSTER - Director Operations

NYC Bagel & Sandwich Shop
2 University Plz
Hackensack, NJ 07601

Telephone: (844) 348-6098
Internet Homepage: nycbagelsandwichshop.com
Type of Business: Chain Restaurant Operator
Year Founded: 2004
Total Sales: $10,380,000 (e)
Total Units: 9
Trade Names: NYC Bagel & Sandwich Shop (9)
Units Franchised To: 9
Projected Openings: 10
Areas of Operation: AL, CO, FL, LA, NC, OH, PA, TX

Key Personnel
JOSEPH SMITH - CEO
TRISTAN HARMON - Owner

Harvey Cedars Shellfish Co.
7904 Long Beach Blvd
Harvey Cedars, NJ 08008-5952

Telephone: (609) 494-7112
Fax Number: (609) 494-7108
Internet Homepage: harveycedarsshellfish.com
Company Email: shellfishco@harveycedarsshellfishco.com
Type of Business: Chain Restaurant Operator
Year Founded: 1976
Total Sales: $1,736,000 (e)
Number of Employees: 50
Average Check: Lunch(14); Dinner(24)
Total Units: 2
Trade Names: Harvey Cedars Shellfish Co. (1); The Clam Bar (1)
Company-Owned Units: 2
Preferred Location Types: Freestanding
Primary Menu: Seafood (2)
Areas of Operation: NJ
Type of Foodservice: Family Restaurant (2)
Primary Distributors: (Equipment) Johnson's Restaurant Equipment & Supply, NEPTUNE, NJ; (Food) US Foods, ALLENTOWN, PA; (Supplies) SYSCO Food Services of Metro New York, JERSEY CITY, NJ
Notes: The company derives approximately 20% of its total sales from retail operations.

Key Personnel
JOHN GAROFALO - Partner; Manager Finance; General Buyer

Hillsborough Donuts Inc.
315 US Highway 206
Hillsborough, NJ 08844-4627

Telephone: (732) 926-9100
Fax Number: (732) 926-9115
Internet Homepage: hillsborough.cit-e.net
Company Email: ddqueenmary@aol.com
Type of Business: Chain Restaurant Operator
Total Sales: $38,920,000 (e)
Average Check: Dinner(8)
Total Units: 25
Trade Names: Dunkin' Donuts (25)
Units Franchised From: 25
Preferred Square Footage: 1,500; 2,200
Primary Menu: Snacks (25)
Areas of Operation: NJ
Type of Foodservice: Quick Serve (25)
Franchise Affiliation: DD IP Holder, CANTON, MA

Key Personnel
THOMAS MASCIA - President; General Buyer

Sweetberry Bowls
649 US Highway 206 Unit 1B
Hillsborough, NJ 08844

Telephone: (908) 829-5964
Internet Homepage: sweetberrybowls.com
Company Email: info@sweetberrybowls.com
Type of Business: Chain Restaurant Operator
Year Founded: 2017
Total Units: 15
Trade Names: Sweetberry Bowls (15)
Company-Owned Units: 15
Primary Menu: Health Foods (15)
Areas of Operation: FL, IL, NC, NJ
Type of Foodservice: Quick Serve (15)

Key Personnel
DESI SARAN - Founder; CEO
KYLE KISSANE - Partner
KEVIN O'TOOLE - Partner

Ascott
620 Ramsey Ave
Hillside, NJ 07205-1010

Telephone: (908) 436-1800
Type of Business: Chain Restaurant Operator
Total Sales: $752,000 (e)
Total Units: 2
Trade Names: Cinnabon (2)
Units Franchised From: 2
Primary Menu: Snacks (2)
Areas of Operation: NJ
Type of Foodservice: Quick Serve (2)
Franchise Affiliation: Cinnabon Inc., ATLANTA, GA

Key Personnel
SCOTT GILLMAN - Owner; General Buyer

Mascott Corporation
620 Ramsey Ave
Hillside, NJ 07205-1010

Telephone: (908) 436-1800
Fax Number: (908) 436-1700
Internet Homepage: mascott.com
Company Email: adriana@mascott.com
Type of Business: Chain Restaurant Operator
Year Founded: 1989
Total Sales: $21,748,000 (e)
Alcohol Sales: 5%
Number of Employees: 65
Average Check: Breakfast(6); Lunch(12); Dinner(14)
Total Units: 10
Trade Names: Carvel Ice Cream (1); Cinnabon (3); Markers (1); Markers Express (1); Noodles & Co. (2); Seattle's Best Coffee (1);

Smashburger (1)
Company-Owned Units: 2
Units Franchised To: 8
Preferred Square Footage: 850; 7,000
Preferred Location Types: Community Mall; Downtown; Freestanding; Strip Mall
Alcohol Served: Beer, Wine, Liquor
Primary Menu: American (2); Coffee (1); Hamburger (1); Miscellaneous (2); Snacks (4)
Areas of Operation: NJ
Type of Foodservice: Casual Dining (1); Quick Serve (9)
Foodservice Management Venues: Business & Industry
Catering Services: Yes
Primary Distributors: (Equipment) M. Tucker, a divison of Singer NY LLC, PATERSON, NJ; (Food) Performance Foodservice - AFI, ELIZABETH, NJ;(Supplies) M. Tucker, a divison of Singer NY LLC, PATERSON, NJ

Key Personnel
SCOTT GILLMAN - Chairman; CEO
GUY STANTON - Controller
JOHN WHITE - Director Human Resources
MARYBETH DE LA CRUZ - Manager Administration, Marketing

Greek From Greece - GFG Bakery
221 River St
Hoboken, NJ 07030

Telephone: (201) 533-1040
Internet Homepage: gfg-bakery.com
Company Email: info@gfg-bakery.com
Type of Business: Chain Restaurant Operator
Year Founded: 2017
Systemwide Sales: $25,955,000 (e)
Total Sales: $21,140,000 (e)
Total Units: 28
Trade Names: Greek From Greece - GFG Bakery (28)
Company-Owned Units: 1
Units Franchised To: 27
Primary Menu: Greek/Mediterranean (28)
Areas of Operation: NY
Type of Foodservice: Fast Casual (28)

Key Personnel
GEORGIOS DROSOS - Founder; Owner

Onieal's Restaurant & Bar
343 Park Ave
Hoboken, NJ 07030-3805

Telephone: (201) 653-1492
Fax Number: (201) 653-9264
Internet Homepage: onieals.com
Company Email: iloveonieals@gmail.com
Type of Business: Chain Restaurant Operator
Year Founded: 1983
Total Sales: $3,149,000 (e)
Alcohol Sales: 10%
Number of Employees: 50
Average Check: Lunch(18); Dinner(30)
Total Units: 2
Trade Names: Onieal's on Grand Restaurant (1); Onieal's Restaurant & Bar (1)
Company-Owned Units: 2
Preferred Location Types: Freestanding
Alcohol Served: Beer, Wine, Liquor
Primary Menu: American (2)
Areas of Operation: NJ, NY
Type of Foodservice: Casual Dining (2)
Primary Distributors: (Food) SYSCO Food Services of Metro New York, JERSEY CITY, NJ; (Supplies) SYSCO Food Services of Metro New York, JERSEY CITY, NJ

Key Personnel
CHRIS ONIEAL - President; General Manager; Executive Chef; General Buyer
BRIAN SCHORGL - Owner

Alliance Management Dunkin' Donuts
838 Green St Ste 101
Iselin, NJ 08830

Telephone: (732) 882-1890
Fax Number: (732) 882-1890
Internet Homepage: alliancemanagementqsr.com
Type of Business: Chain Restaurant Operator
Total Sales: $48,490,000 (e)
Number of Employees: 510
Average Check: Breakfast(8); Lunch(8); Dinner(8)
Total Units: 31
Trade Names: Dunkin' Donuts (31)
Units Franchised From: 31
Preferred Square Footage: 1,500; 2,200
Primary Menu: Snacks (31)
Projected Openings: 10
Areas of Operation: NJ
Type of Foodservice: Fast Casual (31)
Franchise Affiliation: DD IP Holder, CANTON, MA

Key Personnel
KAUSHIK PATEL - President; General Buyer
AHMED RASSWAN - Director Operations

Inn America Hospitality Inc.
517 US Highway 1 S Ste 2100
Iselin, NJ 08830-3023

Telephone: (732) 283-9700
Fax Number: (732) 283-1009
Internet Homepage: americanproperties.net
Company Email: md@americanproperties.net
Type of Business: Foodservice Operations - Hotel/Motels
Year Founded: 1987
Total Sales: $26,341,000 (e)
Alcohol Sales: 20%
Number of Employees: 300
Total Units: 3
Restaurants in Hotels: 2
Trade Names: Courtyard Marriott (1); Element By Westin (1); Renaissance (1)
Company-Owned Units: 2
Alcohol Served: Beer, Wine, Liquor
Areas of Operation: NJ
Type of Foodservice: Casual Dining (2)
Primary Distributors: (Food) SYSCO Food Services of Metro New York, JERSEY CITY, NJ
Parent Company: Weingarten Group, EDISON, NJ
Notes: The company derives approximately 65% of its revenue from hotel operations.

Key Personnel
PAUL T. CSIK - Senior VP Marketing, Sales

Domino's Franchisee
55 E Railroad Ave
Jamesburg, NJ 08831-1462

Telephone: (732) 521-4800
Type of Business: Chain Restaurant Operator
Total Sales: $8,021,000 (e)
Total Units: 4
Trade Names: Domino's (4)
Units Franchised From: 4
Primary Menu: Pizza (4)
Areas of Operation: NJ
Type of Foodservice: Quick Serve (4)
Franchise Affiliation: Domino's Pizza Inc, ANN ARBOR, MI

Key Personnel
HADI VAHIDI - Owner; General Buyer

Restaurant Development Group Ltd
212 Washington St
Jersey City, NJ 07302-4567

Telephone: (201) 435-5151
Internet Homepage: restaurantdevelopmentgroupltd.com
Company Email: info@RestaurantDevelopmentGroupLTD.com
Type of Business: Chain Restaurant Operator
Year Founded: 2010
Total Units: 3
Trade Names: Lucky 7 Tavern (1); Satis Bistro

(2)
Company-Owned Units: 3
Primary Menu: American (3)
Projected Openings: 1
Areas of Operation: NJ
Type of Foodservice: Casual Dining (3)

Key Personnel
GEZA GULAS - President; General Buyer

NATC Donuts Inc.
740 Jefferson Ave
Kenilworth, NJ 07033-1762

Telephone: (908) 241-7585
Fax Number: (908) 241-8514
Internet Homepage: trymydunkindonuts.com; natcdonuts.com
Company Email: info@natcdonuts.com
Type of Business: Chain Restaurant Operator
Total Sales: $29,710,000 (e)
Average Check: Lunch(6); Dinner(8)
Total Units: 19
Trade Names: Dunkin' Donuts (19)
Units Franchised From: 19
Preferred Square Footage: 1,500; 2,200
Preferred Location Types: Freestanding; Strip Mall
Primary Menu: Snacks (19)
Areas of Operation: NJ
Type of Foodservice: Quick Serve (19)
Franchise Affiliation: DD IP Holder, CANTON, MA

Key Personnel
ANTHONY D'AMORE - CEO; President; General Buyer
CHRIS FOX - Director Operations
RICK FRANKS - Director Human Resources

Terra Momo Restaurant Group
4478 Route 27
Kingston, NJ 08528-9613

Mailing Address: PO Box 446, PRINCETON, NJ, 08542-0446
Telephone: (609) 924-4009
Fax Number: (609) 924-4074
Internet Homepage: terramomo.com
Company Email: info@terramomo.com
Type of Business: Chain Restaurant Operator
Year Founded: 1982
Total Sales: $13,720,000 (e)
Alcohol Sales: 20%
Number of Employees: 150
Average Check: Lunch(14); Dinner(32)
Internet Order Processing: Yes
Internet Sales: 1.00%
Total Units: 5
Trade Names: Eno Terra (1); Mediterra (1); Tapas (1); Teresa Caffe (1); Terra MoMo (1)
Company-Owned Units: 5
Preferred Location Types: Freestanding
Alcohol Served: Beer, Wine, Liquor
Primary Menu: Greek/Mediterranean (1); Italian (2); Snacks (1); Spanish (1)
Areas of Operation: NJ
Type of Foodservice: Casual Dining (3); Fine Dining (2)
Primary Distributors: (Full Line) SYSCO Food Services of Metro New York, JERSEY CITY, NJ

Key Personnel
CARLO MOMO - Partner
RAOUL MOMO - Partner
JOHN PERKOWSKI - CFO; Controller; General Buyer
JOHN SHAW - CFO
CARMINE DEPASUALE - General Manager

Nuop Corp
924 New Hampshire Ave
Lakewood, NJ 08701-5958

Telephone: (732) 370-2700
Fax Number: (732) 370-2811
Type of Business: Chain Restaurant Operator
Year Founded: 1983
Total Sales: $113,460,000 (e)
Number of Employees: 1,000
Average Check: Breakfast(8); Lunch(10); Dinner(12)
Total Units: 24
Trade Names: McDonald's (24)
Units Franchised From: 24
Preferred Square Footage: 2,500
Preferred Location Types: Freestanding
Primary Menu: Hamburger (24)
Areas of Operation: NJ
Type of Foodservice: Quick Serve (24)
Franchise Affiliation: McDonald's Corporation, CHICAGO, IL

Key Personnel
HARRY CHAPMAN - President; General Manager; Director Operations, Real Estate; General Buyer
GIOVANNI LASALANDRA - Director Business Development

Triumph Brewing Company
287 S Main St Ste 16
Lambertville, NJ 08530-1869

Telephone: (609) 773-0111
Fax Number: (888) 740-5829
Internet Homepage: triumphbrewing.com
Company Email: info@triumphbrew.com
Type of Business: Chain Restaurant Operator
Year Founded: 1995
Total Sales: $7,635,000 (e)
Alcohol Sales: 30%
Number of Employees: 95
Average Check: Lunch(12); Dinner(24)
Total Units: 3
Trade Names: Triumph Brewing Company (3)
Company-Owned Units: 3
Alcohol Served: Beer, Wine, Liquor
Primary Menu: American (3)
Areas of Operation: NJ, PA
Type of Foodservice: Casual Dining (3)
Primary Distributors: (Food) Novick Brothers Corp., PHILADELPHIA, PA

Key Personnel
ADAM RECHNITZ - Owner; Executive Chef; General Buyer
ERIC NUTT - Manager Sales

Auntie Anne's Franchise
112 Eisenhower Pkwy
Livingston, NJ 07039-4995

Telephone: (973) 992-9122
Type of Business: Chain Restaurant Operator
Total Sales: $1,597,000 (e)
Total Units: 2
Trade Names: Auntie Anne's Hand-Rolled Soft Pretzels (2)
Units Franchised From: 2
Primary Menu: Snacks (2)
Areas of Operation: NJ
Type of Foodservice: Quick Serve (2)
Franchise Affiliation: Auntie Anne's Inc., LANCASTER, PA

Key Personnel
KEVIN ROSENBLATT - Owner; General Buyer

The Briad Group
78 Okner Pkwy
Livingston, NJ 07039-1604

Telephone: (973) 597-6433
Fax Number: (973) 597-6422
Internet Homepage: briad.com
Company Email: guestcomments@briad.com
Type of Business: Chain Restaurant Operator
Year Founded: 1988
Total Sales: $487,480,000 (e)
Alcohol Sales: 20%
Number of Employees: 10,624
Average Check: Lunch(12); Dinner(14)
Total Units: 116
Trade Names: Wendy's Old Fashioned Hamburgers (114); Zinburger (2)
Company-Owned Units: 2
Units Franchised From: 114
Preferred Square Footage: 3,300; 4,000; 6,000; 7,200

Preferred Location Types: Community Mall; Downtown; Freestanding; Hotel/Motel; Lifestyle Center; Office Complex; Regional Mall; Strip Mall
Alcohol Served: Beer, Wine, Liquor
Primary Menu: Hamburger (116)
Areas of Operation: AZ, CA, CT, FL, NC, NJ, NM, NV, NY, PA, VA
Type of Foodservice: Fast Casual (2); Quick Serve (114)
Franchise Affiliation: Fox Restaurant Concepts, PHOENIX, AZ; T.G.I. Friday's Inc., DALLAS, TX; The Wendy's Company, DUBLIN, OH
Primary Distributors: (Full Line) US Foods- San Francisco, LIVERMORE, CA; (Full Line) Performance Foodservice - AFI, ELIZABETH, NJ; (Full Line) The SYGMA Network Inc. - Pennsylvania, HARRISBURG, PA
Notes: In addition to its restaurants, the company also operates several hotels & derives approximately 5% of its revenue from these operations.

Key Personnel
BRAD HONIGFELD - Chairman; Founder; Co-CEO
RICK BARBRICK - Co-CEO; President; COO
DAVE CAHILL - CFO; Senior VP
STEVE SCHARF - Senior VP Development
DAN SHEA - VP Finance
MICHAEL SPELMAN - Controller
CHARLA KIMBRELL - Controller
JAMES TALERICO - Senior Director Development
HIMANSHU TRIPATHI - Director Development
BOB LAYMAN - Director Operations
JORDYN HONIGFELD SUCHOFF - Director Human Resources
JOHN BOGLE - Director Operations
COLIN KELLY - Director Operations
TINA CLEMENTS - Director Talent Acquisitions
THOMAS CORNELL - Director Information Systems, Information Technology
TOM CORNELL - Director Information Systems
ALEXANDRA SEWARD - Senior Manager Marketing
SANDRA KANTOR - Manager
JORDYN HONIGFELD Manager Human Resources
ALICIA CHERNIAK - Manager Risk Management
MICHAEL BASICH - Manager Information Systems
OLISA SMALL - Manager Human Resources

McLoone's Restaurants
1 Ocean Ave
Long Branch, NJ 07740

Telephone: (732) 923-1006
Internet Homepage: mcloones.com
Company Email: corporate@mcloones.com
Type of Business: Chain Restaurant Operator
Total Sales: $13,410,000 (e)
Total Units: 11
Trade Names: CJ McLoone's (1); McLoone's Bayonne Grille (1); McLoone's Boathouse (1); McLoone's Clubhouse Pub (1); McLoone's Pier House (2); McLoone's Woodbridge Grille (1); Rum Runner (1); The Robinson Ale House (2); Tim McLoone's Supper Club (1)
Company-Owned Units: 11
Primary Menu: American (11)
Areas of Operation: MD, NJ
Type of Foodservice: Casual Dining (11)

Key Personnel
TIM MCLOONE - Founder; CEO; General Buyer
LAUREN COUTU - Senior VP Operations
RACHEL GANLEY - Director Marketing

Ruoff Management Group
92 Ocean Ave
Long Branch, NJ 07740-6728

Telephone: (732) 923-1104
Fax Number: (732) 923-1106
Internet Homepage: theturningpoint.biz
Type of Business: Chain Restaurant Operator
Year Founded: 1998
Total Sales: $18,530,000 (e)
Internet Order Processing: Yes
Total Units: 21
Trade Names: Turning Point (21)
Company-Owned Units: 21
Preferred Square Footage: 3,000; 4,000
Primary Menu: American (21)
Areas of Operation: NJ, PA
Type of Foodservice: Family Restaurant (21)

Key Personnel
KIRK RUOFF - CEO; Partner
BONNIE IAVARONI - CEO
MATTHEW ALKON - Partner; Regional Manager
CHARLES RUOFF - VP Finance
JOANN SALAYI - Controller

Windmill Franchise Corp.
200 Ocean Ave N
Long Branch, NJ 07740-7461

Telephone: (732) 870-8282
Fax Number: (732) 870-9613
Internet Homepage: windmillhotdogs.com
Company Email: rdlevy@windmillhotdogs.com
Type of Business: Chain Restaurant Operator
Year Founded: 1964
Systemwide Sales: $8,551,000 (e)
Total Sales: $4,822,000 (e)
Alcohol Sales: 5%
Number of Employees: 60
Average Check: Lunch(14); Dinner(26)
Total Units: 6
Trade Names: Windmill Gourmet Fast Foods (6)
Company-Owned Units: 4
Units Franchised To: 2
Preferred Square Footage: 800; 3,000
Preferred Location Types: Freestanding; Strip Mall
Alcohol Served: Beer
Primary Menu: American (6)
Projected Openings: 1
Areas of Operation: NJ
Type of Foodservice: Quick Serve (6)
Catering Services: Yes
Distribution Centers: NEPTUNE, NJ
Primary Distributors: (Supplies) Edward Don & Co., WESTAMPTON, NJ

Key Personnel
JOE PRECOPIO - CFO; General Manager
SANDY LEVINE - Director Customer Service, Human Resources

La Rosa Chicken & Grill
300 Craig Rd
Manalapan, NJ 07726

Telephone: (732) 972-0019
Internet Homepage: larosagrill.com
Type of Business: Chain Restaurant Operator
Year Founded: 1994
Systemwide Sales: $2,380,000 (e)
Total Sales: $1,055,000 (e)
Total Units: 14
Trade Names: La Rosa Chicken & Grill (14)
Units Franchised To: 14
Primary Menu: Chicken (14)
Areas of Operation: NJ, NY
Type of Foodservice: Fast Casual (14)

Key Personnel
VINCENZO PUGLIESE - Founder; CEO

Jersey Mike's Franchise Systems
2251 Landmark Pl
Manasquan, NJ 08736-1026

Telephone: (732) 223-4044
Fax Number: (732) 223-0777
Internet Homepage: jerseymikes.com
Company Email: info@jerseymikes.com
Type of Business: Chain Restaurant Operator
Year Founded: 1986
Systemwide Sales: $2,241,736,000 (e)
Total Sales: $447,110,000 (e)
Number of Employees: 456
Average Check: Lunch(16); Dinner(16)
Internet Order Processing: Yes
Total Units: 1,978
Trade Names: Jersey Mike's Subs (1,978)

Company-Owned Units: 87
Units Franchised To: 1,891
Preferred Square Footage: 1,200; 1,500; 1,600
Preferred Location Types: Airports; Freestanding; Strip Mall
Primary Menu: Sandwiches/Deli (1,978)
Projected Openings: 155
Areas of Operation: AL, AZ, CA, CO, CT, DC, DE, FL, GA, IA, IL, IN, KS, KY, MA, MD, MI, MN, MO, MT, NC, NE, NH, NJ, NV, NY, OH, OK, OR, PA, RI, SC, TN, TX, UT, VA, WA, WI, WV, WY
Type of Foodservice: Quick Serve (1,978)
Catering Services: Yes
Primary Distributors: (Full Line) SYSCO Food Services of Columbia, COLUMBIA, SC

Key Personnel
PETER CANCRO - CEO
MICHAEL J. MANZO - COO
SCOTT SCHERER - CIO
RICHARD HOPE - Chief Marketing Officer
DANIEL KAPELLA - Chief Supply Chain Officer
CODY WALDRON - Area Director
JOHN E. HUGHES - Senior VP
KEITH HERTLING - VP Franchise Operations
JOSEPHINE CAPOZZI - VP Communications
JEFF BERNS - VP Franchise Development
BRIAN SOMMERS - VP Franchise Development
JOHN FUNDERBURK - VP; Director Training
JOHN GELSON - VP; General Counsel
JEFF HEMSCHOOT - VP Marketing
ROBERT STAWIARSKI - VP Operations
LANDON CORKREN - VP Operations
PAT GILLMANN - Controller
JAMIE KAPALKA - General Counsel
RICK BUCKLEY - Director Construction
RODNEY TAYLOR - Director Construction
BRIAN LOUGHRAN - Director Training
CHRIS CZASZYNSKI - Director Development
CORBY CRONIN - Director Franchise Sales
EDWARD BASCH - Director
CHRISTINE CRANE - Director Development
LAUREN BELLINGHAM - Director Development
KELLY MCGEE - Director Digital Marketing
BILL NEWELL - Director Operations
CAROL RORKE - Director Media
ELIZABETH HUTCHISON - Director Real Estate
BROOKE CABRERA - Director Real Estate
HEATHER BOGDEN - Director Real Estate
JAMIE NICHOLSON - Director Real Estate
NATALIE PEBBLES - Director Real Estate
BILL URADNIK - Director Real Estate
BILL MAPES - Manager Real Estate
CATHY BROWN - Manager Real Estate
BRIAN KENNEY - Manager Real Estate
JOE RYBOWICZ - Manager Real Estate
GREG MCMENAMAN - Manager Real Estate
DAVE BOCKSTAHLER - Manager Real Estate
DAN SHANAHAN - Manager Real Estate
CHRIS DANIELS - Manager Real Estate
HENRY GALLO - Manager Real Estate
JOHN GRIPARIS - Manager Real Estate
CHARLIE BROWN - Manager Real Estate
JAY YATES - Manager Real Estate
DALTON STEWART - Manager Real Estate
ALYSSA GILLMANN LAW - Manager Marketing
JESSE GIOULIS - Senior Designer

Lufrankton LLC
2517 Highway 35 Ste H101
Manasquan, NJ 08736-1987

Telephone: (732) 528-1852
Fax Number: (732) 298-8599
Internet Homepage: lufrankton.com
Company Email: lufrankton@lufrankton.com
Type of Business: Chain Restaurant Operator
Year Founded: 1998
Total Sales: $32,990,000 (e)
Number of Employees: 699
Average Check: Breakfast(8); Lunch(8); Dinner(8)
Total Units: 21
Trade Names: Dunkin' Donuts (21)
Units Franchised From: 21
Preferred Square Footage: 1,800
Preferred Location Types: Freestanding; Grocery Stores; Strip Mall
Primary Menu: Snacks (21)
Areas of Operation: NJ
Type of Foodservice: Quick Serve (21)
Franchise Affiliation: DD IP Holder, CANTON, MA

Key Personnel
JIM CRISMALE - CFO
DAWN PAGANO - VP Operations
BARBARA CANNAMELA - VP Human Resources
JAY SIMAS - Manager Area

SUDH Management
2891 Route 73 S Ste 7
Maple Shade, NJ 08052-1881

Telephone: (856) 667-7341
Fax Number: (856) 667-7340
Company Email: info@smqs.com
Type of Business: Chain Restaurant Operator
Total Sales: $23,690,000 (e)
Number of Employees: 265
Average Check: Dinner(8)
Total Units: 15
Trade Names: Dunkin' Donuts (15)
Units Franchised From: 15
Preferred Square Footage: 1,500; 2,200
Preferred Location Types: Community Mall; Freestanding
Primary Menu: Snacks (15)
Areas of Operation: PA
Type of Foodservice: Quick Serve (15)
Franchise Affiliation: DD IP Holder, CANTON, MA

Key Personnel
VIPUL PATEL - President; General Manager; General Buyer

Earle Enterprises LP
60 E Main St Ste A
Marlton, NJ 08053-2176

Telephone: (856) 797-9870
Fax Number: (856) 797-8005
Type of Business: Chain Restaurant Operator
Year Founded: 2007
Total Sales: $28,210,000 (e)
Number of Employees: 340
Average Check: Breakfast(8); Lunch(10); Dinner(12)
Total Units: 6
Trade Names: McDonald's (6)
Units Franchised From: 6
Preferred Square Footage: 2,400; 3,000
Preferred Location Types: Freestanding
Primary Menu: Hamburger (6)
Areas of Operation: NJ, PA
Type of Foodservice: Quick Serve (6)
Franchise Affiliation: McDonald's Corporation, CHICAGO, IL

Key Personnel
JOHN EARLE - President; Partner; Director Finance, Information Systems, Real Estate; General Buyer
JACK EARLE - Partner
STEPHANIE SCHWARZ - Director Operations, Facility/Maintenance

Auntie Anne's Franchise
4403 Black Horse Pike Ste 1126
Mays Landing, NJ 08330-3144

Telephone: (609) 383-1200
Type of Business: Chain Restaurant Operator
Total Sales: $1,524,000 (e)
Total Units: 2
Trade Names: Auntie Anne's Hand-Rolled Soft Pretzels (2)
Units Franchised From: 2
Primary Menu: Snacks (2)
Areas of Operation: NJ
Type of Foodservice: Quick Serve (2)
Franchise Affiliation: Auntie Anne's Inc., LANCASTER, PA

Key Personnel
DANIEL BROWN - Owner; General Buyer

CS CHUNG, INC
1650 Nixon Dr
Moorestown, NJ 08057-2675

Telephone: (856) 866-0200
Type of Business: Chain Restaurant Operator
Total Sales: $6,214,000 (e)
Total Units: 3
Trade Names: Five Guys Burgers and Fries (3)
Units Franchised From: 3
Primary Menu: Hamburger (3)
Areas of Operation: NJ
Type of Foodservice: Fast Casual (3)
Franchise Affiliation: Five Guys Holdings Inc., LORTON, VA

Key Personnel
CHA CHUNG - President; General Buyer

Harvest Restaurants
2230 State Route 10 Ste 2
Morris Plains, NJ 07950

Telephone: (973) 656-1881
Fax Number: (973) 656-1828
Internet Homepage: harvestrestaurants.com
Company Email: events@harvestrestaurants.com
Type of Business: Chain Restaurant Operator
Year Founded: 1996
Total Sales: $19,520,000 (e)
Total Units: 14
Trade Names: 3 West (1); Addams Tavern (1); Agricola Eatery (1); Agricola Morristown (1); Grato (1); Grato Ristorante (1); Huntley Taverne (1); Roots Ocean Prime (1); Roots Steakhouse (3); Tabor Road Tavern (1); The Dinky Bar (1); Trap Rock Restaurant & Brewery (1)
Company-Owned Units: 14
Primary Menu: American (9); Italian (1); Seafood (1); Steak (3)
Areas of Operation: NJ
Type of Foodservice: Casual Dining (11); Fine Dining (3)

Key Personnel
CHIP GRABOWSKI - Owner
CALLIE GRABOWSKI - Director Human Resources

Tiffany's Restaurant Inc.
231 Speedwell Ave
Morris Plains, NJ 07950-2308

Telephone: (973) 290-9777
Fax Number: (973) 290-9778
Internet Homepage: tiffsmorrisplains.com
Type of Business: Chain Restaurant Operator
Year Founded: 1982
Total Sales: $13,750,000 (e)
Alcohol Sales: 1.50%
Number of Employees: 80
Total Units: 4
Trade Names: Tiffany's Casual Grill & Bar (4)
Company-Owned Units: 4
Preferred Location Types: Freestanding
Alcohol Served: Beer, Wine, Liquor
Primary Menu: American (4)
Areas of Operation: NJ
Type of Foodservice: Casual Dining (4)

Key Personnel
MICHAEL ROMANELLI SR - CEO; Owner
MICHAEL ROMANELLI JR - Executive Chef

Villa Restaurant Group
25 Washington St
Morristown, NJ 07960-3995

Telephone: (973) 285-4800
Fax Number: (973) 285-5252
Internet Homepage: villarestaurantgroup.com
Type of Business: Chain Restaurant Operator
Year Founded: 1964
Total Sales: $63,330,000 (e)
Alcohol Sales: 1%
Number of Employees: 740
Average Check: Breakfast(6); Lunch(8); Dinner(10)
Total Units: 220
Trade Names: Bananas Ultimate Juice Bar; Cozzoli's Pizzeria; George & Martha's American Grille; Green Leaf's Grill; Piattino; South Philly Steaks & Fries; Steelworks Buffet & Grill; The Black Horse Pub; The Black Horse Tavern; The Office Beer Bar & Grill; Tony + Benny's Authentic Brooklyn Pizzeria; Treat Street; Villa Fresh Italian Kitchen; Villa Pizza; Villa Pronto
Company-Owned Units: 135
Units Franchised To: 85
Preferred Square Footage: 550; 700; 1,500; 3,000
Preferred Location Types: Airports; Community Mall; Institution (college/hospital); Kiosk; Outlet Mall; Regional Mall; Strip Mall
Alcohol Served: Beer, Wine, Liquor
Projected Openings: 10
Areas of Operation: AK, AL, AR, AZ, CA, CO, CT, DC, DE, FL, GA, IA, ID, IL, IN, KS, KY, LA, MA, MD, ME, MI, MO, MS, NC, NH, NJ, NM, NV, NY, OK, OR, PA, RI, SC, TN, TX, UT, VA, VT, WA
Foreign Countries: AZERBAIJAN; COLOMBIA; EGYPT; ITALY; KUWAIT; LIBYA; MEXICO; SAINT MAARTEN; TURKEY; UNITED ARAB EMIRATES
Type of Foodservice: Casual Dining; Quick Serve
Foodservice Management Venues: College & University
Primary Distributors: (Food) Ferraro Foods, PISCATAWAY, NJ

Key Personnel
MICHELE SCOTTO - Founder
ANTHONY SCOTTO - CEO
BIAGIO SCOTTO - President
FRANK CLARK - CFO
ANDREW STEINBERG - COO
KELLY HERNANDEZ - VP Operations
STEVEN BALIVA - VP
BIAGIO PUGLIESE - Corporate Secretary; Director Security, Risk Management
BEN SCOTTO - Director Facility/Maintenance, Design
KIM PERROTTA - Director Franchise Development
MIKE SERCHIA - Director Human Resources
MEKKI LAHOUARI - Director Information Technology
STANLEY LICAIRAC - Director Operations
KEVIN FELICE - Director Operations-Food
CHERYL KEMPF - Senior Manager Sales, Leasing
MERRILL LAMB - Consultant Real Estate

A & J Produce
506 Atkins Ave
Neptune, NJ 07753-5156

Telephone: (732) 774-7755
Listing Type: Distribution Center
Type of Business: Chain Restaurant Operator
Number of Employees: 2
Areas of Operation: NJ, NY
Parent Company: Windmill Franchise Corp., LONG BRANCH, NJ

Key Personnel
BILLY MANA - General Manager; Manager Distribution; General Buyer

Destination Dogs
101 Paterson St
New Brunswick, NJ 08901-1912

Telephone: (732) 993-1016
Internet Homepage: destinationdogs.com
Company Email: contact@destinationdogs.com
Type of Business: Chain Restaurant Operator
Total Units: 2
Trade Names: Destination Dogs (2)
Company-Owned Units: 2
Primary Menu: American (2)
Areas of Operation: NJ, PA
Type of Foodservice: Casual Dining (2)

Key Personnel
JIMMY CRONK - Partner; Executive Chef;

General Buyer
SEAN HOSTY - Partner; Executive Chef; General Buyer
MICHAEL PARKER - Partner

Newmad Corporation
360 Mulberry St
Newark, NJ 07102-3415

Telephone: (973) 642-7577
Fax Number: (973) 642-1730
Type of Business: Chain Restaurant Operator
Year Founded: 1990
Total Sales: $23,350,000 (e)
Number of Employees: 235
Average Check: Breakfast(8); Lunch(8); Dinner(10)
Total Units: 5
Trade Names: McDonald's (5)
Units Franchised From: 5
Preferred Square Footage: 3,000
Preferred Location Types: Freestanding
Primary Menu: Hamburger (5)
Areas of Operation: NJ
Type of Foodservice: Quick Serve (5)
Franchise Affiliation: McDonald's Corporation, CHICAGO, IL

Key Personnel
ROBERTO MADAN - President; Director Finance, Information Systems, Real Estate, Human Resources; General Buyer
STEVE SAMUEL - Director Operations, Facility/Maintenance
CATHY POLANCO - Manager Accounting, Branch

Seabra Group
574 Ferry St
Newark, NJ 07105-4402

Telephone: (973) 491-0399
Fax Number: (973) 491-5296
Internet Homepage: casaseabra.com; seabragroup.com
Type of Business: Chain Restaurant Operator
Year Founded: 1994
Total Sales: $6,743,000 (e)
Alcohol Sales: 25%
Number of Employees: 120
Average Check: Lunch(18); Dinner(26)
Total Units: 2
Trade Names: Casa Seabra (1); Mediterranean Manor (1)
Company-Owned Units: 2
Preferred Location Types: Freestanding
Alcohol Served: Beer, Wine, Liquor
Primary Menu: Greek/Mediterranean (2)
Areas of Operation: NJ
Type of Foodservice: Casual Dining (2)
Catering Services: Yes
On-site Distribution Center: Yes
Primary Distributors: (Full Line) SYSCO Food Services of Metro New York, JERSEY CITY, NJ

Key Personnel
ALBANO SEABRA - Partner; Director Real Estate; General Buyer
ALBERTO B - Director Information Technology
BRUNO NOGUEIRA - Art Director

Auntie Anne's Franchise
10 Upper Brook Dr
North Brunswick, NJ 08902-1211

Telephone: (732) 780-9024
Type of Business: Chain Restaurant Operator
Total Sales: $2,307,000 (e)
Total Units: 3
Trade Names: Auntie Anne's Hand-Rolled Soft Pretzels (3)
Units Franchised From: 3
Primary Menu: Snacks (3)
Areas of Operation: NJ
Type of Foodservice: Quick Serve (3)
Franchise Affiliation: Auntie Anne's Inc., LANCASTER, PA

Key Personnel
MANISH KHANNA - Owner; General Buyer

JMC Holdings Inc
527 High Mountain Rd
North Haledon, NJ 07508-2603

Telephone: (914) 337-3370
Internet Homepage: jmcholdingsllc.com
Company Email: info@jmcholdingsllc.com
Type of Business: Chain Restaurant Operator
Total Sales: $36,152,000 (e)
Total Units: 18
Trade Names: Domino's (18)
Units Franchised From: 18
Primary Menu: Pizza (18)
Areas of Operation: NJ
Type of Foodservice: Quick Serve (18)
Franchise Affiliation: Domino's Pizza Inc, ANN ARBOR, MI

Key Personnel
JOHN M. CILMI - Owner; General Buyer

Classic Restaurant Group
247 Livingston St
Northvale, NJ 07647-1901

Telephone: (201) 767-6267
Fax Number: (201) 784-7427
Internet Homepage: northvaleclassicdiner.com; spartaclassicdiner.com; tenaflyclassicdiner.com; classicrestaurantgroup.com; orangetownclassicdiner.com
Company Email: info@classicrestaurantgroup.com
Type of Business: Chain Restaurant Operator
Year Founded: 1980
Total Sales: $41,126,000 (e)
Alcohol Sales: 2%
Average Check: Dinner(16)
Internet Order Processing: Yes
Total Units: 4
Trade Names: Northvale Classic Diner (1); Orangetown Classic Diner (1); Sparta Classic Diner (1); Tenafly Classic Diner (1)
Company-Owned Units: 3
Preferred Location Types: Freestanding
Alcohol Served: Beer, Wine, Liquor
Primary Menu: American (4)
Areas of Operation: NJ
Type of Foodservice: Casual Dining (4)
Catering Services: Yes
Primary Distributors: (Full Line) SYSCO Food Services of Metro New York, JERSEY CITY, NJ

Key Personnel
DIMITRI KONTOLIOS - President; Partner; General Manager; Executive Chef; General Buyer
MICHAEL KONTOLIOS - Partner
JACOB PERRY - General Manager

Domino's Franchisee
10 Franklin Ave
Nutley, NJ 07110-3223

Telephone: (973) 667-2222
Type of Business: Chain Restaurant Operator
Total Sales: $6,247,000 (e)
Total Units: 3
Trade Names: Domino's (3)
Units Franchised From: 3
Primary Menu: Pizza (3)
Areas of Operation: NJ
Type of Foodservice: Quick Serve (3)
Franchise Affiliation: Domino's Pizza Inc, ANN ARBOR, MI

Key Personnel
MOHAMMAD I. KHOKHAR - Owner; General Buyer

Parade Enterprises
105 White Oak Ln Ste 201B
Old Bridge, NJ 08857-1975

Telephone: (732) 698-7725
Fax Number: (732) 698-7726
Internet Homepage: bkparade.com

Type of Business: Chain Restaurant Operator
Total Sales: $139,200,000 (e)
Total Units: 63
Trade Names: Burger King (63)
Units Franchised From: 63
Preferred Square Footage: 2,500
Primary Menu: Hamburger (63)
Projected Remodelings: 10
Areas of Operation: NJ, NY, PA
Type of Foodservice: Quick Serve (63)
Franchise Affiliation: Burger King Worldwide Inc., MIAMI, FL

Key Personnel
BHAVESH PATEL - CEO; CFO; General Buyer
MAHESH PATEL - Owner

Albert DiPrizito, Jr
175 N State Rt 17
Paramus, NJ 07652-2903

Telephone: (201) 262-0591
Type of Business: Chain Restaurant Operator
Total Sales: $9,659,000 (e)
Total Units: 6
Trade Names: Moe's Southwest Grill (6)
Units Franchised From: 6
Primary Menu: Southwest/Tex-Mex (6)
Areas of Operation: NJ
Type of Foodservice: Fast Casual (6)
Franchise Affiliation: Moe's Southwest Grill LLC, ATLANTA, GA

Key Personnel
ALBERT L. DIPRIZITO - Owner; General Buyer

Dunkin' Donuts Franchise
147 US Highway 46
Parsippany, NJ 07054-2300

Telephone: (732) 986-2369
Internet Homepage: dunkindonuts.com
Type of Business: Chain Restaurant Operator
Total Sales: $8,001,000 (e)
Number of Employees: 35
Average Check: Dinner(8)
Total Units: 5
Trade Names: Dunkin' Donuts (5)
Units Franchised From: 5
Preferred Square Footage: 1,500; 2,200
Preferred Location Types: Freestanding; Strip Mall
Primary Menu: Snacks (5)
Areas of Operation: NJ
Type of Foodservice: Quick Serve (5)
Franchise Affiliation: DD IP Holder, CANTON, MA

Key Personnel
HARENDRA TOLIA - President; General Buyer

Wyndham Hotel Group
22 Sylvan Way Ste 1
Parsippany, NJ 07054-3801

Telephone: (973) 753-6000
Fax Number: (973) 446-2408
Internet Homepage: wyndham.com
Type of Business: Foodservice Operations - Hotel/Motels
Year Founded: 1981
Publicly Held: Yes
Total Sales: $2,122,800,000 (e)
Alcohol Sales: 25%
Number of Employees: 16,200
Total Units: 8,941
Trade Names: Baymont Inn & Suites; Days Inn; Dream; Hawthorn Suites; Howard Johnson; Knights Inn; Microtel Inns & Suites; Night; Ramada Inn; Super 8; Travelodge; TRYP by Wyndham; Wingate by Wyndham; Wyndham Hotel; Wyndham Resort
Company-Owned Units: 9,157
Alcohol Served: Beer, Wine, Liquor
Projected Openings: 7
Areas of Operation: AR, CA, CO, DC, FL, GA, IA, IL, IN, KS, KY, LA, MA, MD, ME, MI, MN, MO, MS, MT, NC, ND, NE, NJ, NM, NV, NY, OH, OK, PA, PR, RI, SD, TN, TX, VA, VI, WA, WI, WV, WY, AB, ON, QC, SK
Foreign Countries: ARGENTINA; AUSTRALIA; AUSTRIA; BAHAMAS; BAHRAIN; BELGIUM; BRAZIL; CANADA; CAYMAN ISLANDS; CHINA; COLOMBIA; COSTA RICA; CURACAO; CZECH REPUBLIC; DOMINICAN REPUBLIC; ECUADOR; EGYPT; ENGLAND; ETHIOPIA; FRANCE; GERMANY; GHANA; GUATEMALA; HONG KONG; HUNGARY; INDIA; INDONESIA; IRAQ; IRELAND; ISRAEL; ITALY; JAMAICA; JAPAN; JORDAN; KUWAIT; LATVIA; LEBANON; LIBYA; LITHUANIA; MACEDONIA; MALTA; MEXICO; MOROCCO; NIGERIA; NORTHERN IRELAND; OMAN; PAKISTAN; PANAMA; PARAGUAY; PERU; PORTUGAL; QATAR; ROMANIA; RUSSIA; SAUDI ARABIA; SCOTLAND; SOUTH KOREA; SRI LANKA; SWITZERLAND; THAILAND; THE NETHERLANDS; THE PHILIPPINES; TUNISIA; TURKEY; UNITED ARAB EMIRATES; URUGUAY; VENEZUELA; WALES
Type of Foodservice: Casual Dining; Fine Dining
Primary Distributors: (Food) SYSCO Food Services of North Texas, LEWISVILLE, TX
Parent Company: Wyndham Worldwide Corporation, PARSIPPANY, NJ
Headquarters: Wyndham Hotels and Resorts LLC, PARSIPPANY, NJ
Notes: The company derives approximately 75% of its revenue from hotel operations and management/service fees. Not all of the hotels listed in "Trade Names" operate on-site foodservice.

Key Personnel
STEPHEN P. HOLMES - Chairman; CEO
GEOFF A. BALLOTTI - CEO Group; President Group
NICOLA ROSSI - Chief Accounting Officer; Senior VP Accounting
BOB LOEWEN - COO; Exec VP
SCOTT STRICKLAND - CIO
CHIP OHLSSON - Chief Development Officer; Exec VP
KERI PUTERA - VP Marketing, Division
BARRY ROBINSON - VP Operations, Sales
SUZANNE GREGORY - VP Human Resources
EDUARDO CRUZ DEL RIO - VP Operations, International Division
ALYSSA BARNES - VP Legal
MATT CAPUZZI - VP Investor Relations
PAUL CASH - General Counsel
AMRITA MUKUNDAN - Senior Director
EDWARD BURGOS - Director Operations
DORAL WHISMAN SHRM-SCP - Director Employee Benefits
MICHELE FERNANDEZ - Manager Administration
SCOTT GIFFIN - Manager Business Development

Rackson Corporation
780 Main Ave
Passaic, NJ 07055-8430

Telephone: (973) 890-1245
Company Email: info@racksoncorp.com
Type of Business: Chain Restaurant Operator
Total Sales: $98,400,000 (e)
Total Units: 43
Trade Names: Burger King (43)
Units Franchised From: 43
Primary Menu: Hamburger (43)
Areas of Operation: CT, DE, MD, NJ, NY, PA
Type of Foodservice: Quick Serve (43)
Franchise Affiliation: Burger King Worldwide Inc., MIAMI, FL

Key Personnel
CHRIS JOHNSON - President; Owner; General Buyer

Cook's Restaurant Group
60 Main St
Pennsville, NJ 08070-2039

Telephone: (856) 678-3700
Fax Number: (856) 678-1299
Internet Homepage: riverviewinn.net/cooks-restaurant-group; carolinabluerestaurant.com;

telfordinn.com/cooks-restaurant-group
Type of Business: Chain Restaurant Operator
Total Sales: $6,050,000 (e)
Alcohol Sales: 25%
Average Check: Lunch(22); Dinner(36)
Total Units: 3
Trade Names: Carolina Blue (1); J.G. Cook's Riverview Inn (1); Telford Inn (1)
Company-Owned Units: 3
Preferred Location Types: Downtown; Freestanding
Alcohol Served: Beer, Wine, Liquor
Primary Menu: American (2); Steak/Seafood (1)
Areas of Operation: NJ
Type of Foodservice: Casual Dining (2); Fine Dining (1)

Key Personnel
JEFF COOK - Partner; General Manager
JIM COOK - Partner; General Manager
LINDA COOK - Partner; General Manager; General Buyer
ROBERT THREN - Executive Chef; General Buyer

Pat's Management LLC
102 S Broadway
Pennsville, NJ 08070-2069

Telephone: (856) 678-5888
Fax Number: (856) 678-4436
Internet Homepage: patsfamilyrestaurant.com
Type of Business: Chain Restaurant Operator
Year Founded: 1974
Total Sales: $32,560,000 (e)
Alcohol Sales: 1%
Number of Employees: 605
Average Check: Lunch(22); Dinner(22)
Internet Order Processing: Yes
Total Units: 51
Trade Names: Pat's Pizzeria (51)
Company-Owned Units: 51
Preferred Square Footage: 2,200; 5,000
Preferred Location Types: Freestanding
Alcohol Served: Beer, Wine
Primary Menu: Pizza (51)
Areas of Operation: DE, MD, NJ, PA
Type of Foodservice: Quick Serve (51)
Foodservice Management Venues: College & University; Schools
Catering Services: Yes
Primary Distributors: (Food) P.K.'s Wholesale Grocer Inc., WILMINGTON, DE

Key Personnel
JOHN KARAKASIDIS - President; CFO; General Manager; Director Facility/Maintenance, Information Systems, Marketing, Real Estate, Human Resources, Menu Development; General Buyer

Gencarelli's
1 Hook Mountain Rd
Pine Brook, NJ 07058-9727

Mailing Address: PO Box 164, Pinebrook, NJ, 07058
Telephone: (973) 575-6745
Internet Homepage: gencarellis.com
Type of Business: Chain Restaurant Operator
Year Founded: 1982
Total Sales: $1,563,000 (e)
Internet Order Processing: Yes
Total Units: 2
Trade Names: Gencarelli's (2)
Company-Owned Units: 2
Primary Menu: Italian (2)
Areas of Operation: NJ
Type of Foodservice: Family Restaurant (2)
Catering Services: Yes

Key Personnel
GUY GENCARELLI - Partner; General Buyer
JULIANNA COPPOLA - Partner; General Buyer
MICHAEL COPPOLA - Partner; General Buyer

NorJam, LLC
604 Bartholomew Rd
Piscataway, NJ 08854-8074

Telephone: (732) 297-6637
Type of Business: Chain Restaurant Operator
Total Sales: $11,350,000 (e)
Total Units: 7
Trade Names: Moe's Southwest Grill (7)
Units Franchised From: 7
Primary Menu: Southwest/Tex-Mex (7)
Areas of Operation: NJ
Type of Foodservice: Fast Casual (7)
Franchise Affiliation: Moe's Southwest Grill LLC, ATLANTA, GA

Key Personnel
NORAIZ KAHN - Partner; General Buyer
KASHIF KAHN - Partner

TRAA Corporation
776 Black Horse Pike
Pleasantville, NJ 08232-2340

Telephone: (609) 645-1840
Type of Business: Chain Restaurant Operator
Total Sales: $23,760,000 (e)
Total Units: 5
Trade Names: McDonald's (5)
Units Franchised From: 5
Preferred Square Footage: 2,500
Preferred Location Types: Freestanding; Strip Mall
Primary Menu: Hamburger (5)
Areas of Operation: NJ
Type of Foodservice: Quick Serve (5)
Franchise Affiliation: McDonald's Corporation, CHICAGO, IL

Key Personnel
ROBERT TRAA - President; General Buyer

Chefs International Inc
62 Broadway
Point Pleasant Beach, NJ 08742-2606

Mailing Address: PO Box 1332, POINT PLEASANT BEACH, NJ, 08742-1332
Telephone: (732) 295-0350
Fax Number: (732) 295-4514
Internet Homepage: 9thavepier.com; anchortavernnj.com; bakersamerican.com; bakerswaterstreet.com; escondidos.com; jackbakerslobstershanty.com; moorestavern.com; patiobarnj.com; wharfsidenj.com; chefsinternationalnj.com
Type of Business: Chain Restaurant Operator
Year Founded: 1975
Total Sales: $39,314,000 (e)
Alcohol Sales: 25%
Number of Employees: 490
Average Check: Lunch(72); Dinner(120)
Total Units: 11
Trade Names: 9th Avenue Pier (1); Anchor Tavern (1); Baker's American Bar & Grille (1); Baker's Water Street Bar & Grille (1); Escondido's Mexican Restaurant (1); Jack Baker's Lobster Shanty (1); Jack Baker's Wharfside Restaurant (1); Marina Grille (1); Moore's Tavern and Restaurant (1); The Sunset Ballroom (1); Wharfside Patio Bar (1)
Company-Owned Units: 11
Preferred Square Footage: 5,000; 6,000; 17,000
Preferred Location Types: Freestanding
Alcohol Served: Beer, Wine, Liquor
Primary Menu: American (7); Mexican (1); Seafood (3)
Areas of Operation: NJ, PA
Type of Foodservice: Casual Dining (9); Fine Dining (2)
Catering Services: Yes
Primary Distributors: (Full Line) SYSCO Food Services of Metro New York, JERSEY CITY, NJ
Notes: Chefs International also operates The Sunset Ballroom special occasion venue.

Key Personnel
ROBERT M. LOMBARDI - Chairman; Executive Chef
BOB COOPER - CEO; President
MARTIN W. FLETCHER - CFO; VP Real Estate; Treasurer; Corporate Secretary; Manager Facility/Maintenance, Information Systems, Human Resources
JEFF HAVENS - Manager Purchasing, Supply

Chain

Surf Taco
1300 Richmond Ave
Point Pleasant Beach, NJ 08742-3053

Telephone: (732) 701-9000
Internet Homepage: surftaco.com
Type of Business: Chain Restaurant Operator
Total Sales: $12,130,000 (e)
Total Units: 13
Trade Names: Surf Taco (13)
Company-Owned Units: 13
Primary Menu: Taco (13)
Areas of Operation: FL, NJ
Type of Foodservice: Fast Casual (13)

Key Personnel
ROBERT NAGEL - Founder; President; Partner
MICHAEL COURTNEY - Partner; Director Operations
GREGORY CARTNICK - Partner
SHAWN GRAUL - General Manager
VERONICA SANCHEZ - Manager Administration

Plaza 23 Diner
411 State Rt 23
Pompton Plains, NJ 07444-1812

Telephone: (973) 835-1952
Fax Number: (973) 835-7848
Type of Business: Chain Restaurant Operator
Year Founded: 1981
Total Sales: $4,730,000 (e)
Alcohol Sales: 20%
Number of Employees: 40
Average Check: Breakfast(8); Lunch(10); Dinner(14)
Total Units: 3
Trade Names: Heritage Restaurant (1); Plaza 23 Diner (1); Suburban (1)
Company-Owned Units: 3
Preferred Location Types: Freestanding
Alcohol Served: Beer, Wine, Liquor
Primary Menu: American (3)
Areas of Operation: NJ
Type of Foodservice: Casual Dining (3)
Primary Distributors: (Food) Performance Foodservice - AFI, ELIZABETH, NJ

Key Personnel
NICK KOUTSOURIS - Owner; General Manager; Executive Chef; General Buyer

JM Group
256 Nassau St
Princeton, NJ 08542-4623

Telephone: (609) 924-8431
Fax Number: (609) 924-5336
Internet Homepage: jmgroupprinceton.com
Company Email: info@jmgroupprinceton.com
Type of Business: Chain Restaurant Operator
Year Founded: 1982
Number of Employees: 100
Average Check: Dinner(24)
Internet Order Processing: Yes
Total Units: 3
Trade Names: Blue Point Grill (1); Nassau Street Seafood (1); Witherspoon Grill (1)
Company-Owned Units: 3
Preferred Location Types: Downtown; Freestanding
Alcohol Served: Beer, Wine, Liquor
Primary Menu: Seafood (3)
Areas of Operation: NJ
Type of Foodservice: Casual Dining (3)
Catering Services: Yes

Key Personnel
JACK MORRISON - President; General Buyer
DIMITRI ANDREADIS - Controller
STEVE MURRAY - General Manager
COLIN ROONEY - General Manager
EDGAR URIAS - Executive Chef

Princeton Food Services Inc.
444 Wall St
Princeton, NJ 08540-1504

Mailing Address: PO Box 670, ROCKY HILL, NJ, 08553-0670
Telephone: (609) 924-2262
Fax Number: (609) 924-0184
Type of Business: Chain Restaurant Operator
Year Founded: 1977
Total Sales: $44,100,000 (o)
Number of Employees: 735
Average Check: Lunch(5); Dinner(5)
Total Units: 16
Trade Names: Wendy's Old Fashioned Hamburgers (16)
Units Franchised From: 16
Preferred Square Footage: 3,300
Preferred Location Types: Freestanding; Strip Mall
Primary Menu: Hamburger (16)
Areas of Operation: NJ, NY
Type of Foodservice: Quick Serve (16)
Franchise Affiliation: The Wendy's Company, DUBLIN, OH
Primary Distributors: (Full Line) The SYGMA Network Inc. - Pennsylvania, HARRISBURG, PA

Key Personnel
JOHN V. RAWSON - Chairman; Owner; Director Finance, Real Estate
LAURA BUTRICO - President; Director Operations; General Buyer
SCOTT CHRISTINE - Controller
ALEIDA MARANGELLA - Director Marketing
LYNN MORAN - Manager Risk Management, Human Resources

Molly Pitcher Inn
88 Riverside Ave
Red Bank, NJ 07701-1005

Telephone: (732) 747-2500
Fax Number: (732) 747-2713
Internet Homepage: mollypitcher-oysterpoint.com
Company Email: info@mollypitcher-oysterpoint.com
Type of Business: Chain Restaurant Operator
Year Founded: 1928
Total Sales: $4,636,000 (e)
Alcohol Sales: 33%
Number of Employees: 150
Average Check: Breakfast(8); Lunch(14); Dinner(36)
Total Units: 2
Trade Names: International Bar (1); Molly Pitcher Inn (1)
Company-Owned Units: 2
Preferred Location Types: Freestanding
Alcohol Served: Beer, Wine, Liquor
Primary Menu: American (2)
Areas of Operation: NJ
Type of Foodservice: Casual Dining (1); Fine Dining (1)
Primary Distributors: (Food) Performance Foodservice - AFI, ELIZABETH, NJ

Key Personnel
KEVIN BARRY - VP; Manager Operations
WILLIAM ROLL - Executive Chef; General Buyer

Auntie Anne's Franchise
301 Mount Hope Ave Ste 1048
Rockaway, NJ 07866-2156

Telephone: (973) 442-1898
Type of Business: Chain Restaurant Operator
Total Sales: $1,526,000 (e)
Total Units: 2
Trade Names: Auntie Anne's Hand-Rolled Soft Pretzels (2)
Units Franchised From: 2
Primary Menu: Snacks (2)
Areas of Operation: NJ
Type of Foodservice: Quick Serve (2)
Franchise Affiliation: Auntie Anne's Inc.,

LANCASTER, PA

Key Personnel
STEPHEN CHAN - Owner; General Buyer

Domino's Franchisee
102 Main St
Sayreville, NJ 08872-1565

Telephone: (732) 613-4200
Type of Business: Chain Restaurant Operator
Total Sales: $9,974,000 (e)
Total Units: 5
Trade Names: Domino's (5)
Units Franchised From: 5
Primary Menu: Pizza (5)
Areas of Operation: NJ
Type of Foodservice: Quick Serve (5)
Franchise Affiliation: Domino's Pizza Inc, ANN ARBOR, MI

Key Personnel
SYED S. ZAIDI - Owner; General Buyer

JDKD Enterprises
9 Doe Ct
Sewell, NJ 08080-3339

Telephone: (856) 582-6843
Fax Number: (856) 256-9236
Type of Business: Chain Restaurant Operator
Total Sales: $61,780,000 (e)
Total Units: 13
Trade Names: McDonald's (13)
Units Franchised From: 13
Preferred Square Footage: 2,500
Primary Menu: Hamburger (13)
Areas of Operation: NJ
Type of Foodservice: Quick Serve (13)
Franchise Affiliation: McDonald's Corporation, CHICAGO, IL

Key Personnel
JOHN DURANTE - President; General Buyer

Cape Atlantic Food Service, LLC
91 Mays Landing Rd
Somers Point, NJ 08244-1111

Telephone: (609) 927-9622
Fax Number: (609) 927-9635
Company Email: cafs_bk@yahoo.com
Type of Business: Chain Restaurant Operator
Year Founded: 2010
Total Sales: $15,830,000 (e)
Number of Employees: 300
Average Check: Breakfast(8); Lunch(10); Dinner(12)
Total Units: 7
Trade Names: Burger King (7)
Units Franchised From: 7
Preferred Square Footage: 3,000
Preferred Location Types: Freestanding
Primary Menu: Hamburger (7)
Areas of Operation: NJ
Type of Foodservice: Quick Serve (7)
Franchise Affiliation: Burger King Worldwide Inc., MIAMI, FL
Primary Distributors: (Full Line) Maines Paper & Food Service Inc., CONKLIN, NY

Key Personnel
JERRY KLAUS - Partner; Controller; Manager Real Estate; General Buyer
FRANK LAMB - Partner; Director Finance, Operations, Facility/Maintenance

Domino's Franchisee
60 Main St Ste C
South Bound Brook, NJ 08880-1476

Telephone: (732) 563-0330
Type of Business: Chain Restaurant Operator
Total Sales: $33,888,000 (e)
Total Units: 17
Trade Names: Domino's (17)
Units Franchised From: 17
Primary Menu: Pizza (17)
Areas of Operation: NJ
Type of Foodservice: Quick Serve (17)
Franchise Affiliation: Domino's Pizza Inc, ANN ARBOR, MI

Key Personnel
MASOOB ANSARI - Owner; General Buyer

Domino's Franchisee
41 Park Ave
Summit, NJ 07901-5928

Telephone: (908) 273-9550
Type of Business: Chain Restaurant Operator
Total Sales: $10,189,000 (e)
Total Units: 5
Trade Names: Domino's (5)
Units Franchised From: 5
Primary Menu: Pizza (5)
Areas of Operation: NJ
Type of Foodservice: Quick Serve (5)
Franchise Affiliation: Domino's Pizza Inc, ANN ARBOR, MI

Key Personnel
WAHEED JAHANGIR - Owner; General Buyer

TR Worldwide Phillyfood LLC
300 Heron Dr
Swedesboro, NJ 08085-1707

Telephone: (215) 892-1010
Internet Homepage: tonylukes.com
Company Email: info@tonylukes.com
Type of Business: Chain Restaurant Operator
Year Founded: 1992
Total Units: 15
Trade Names: Tony Luke's (15)
Units Franchised To: 15
Preferred Square Footage: 1,100
Preferred Location Types: Airports; Community Mall; Freestanding; Stadiums; Strip Mall
Primary Menu: Sandwiches/Deli (15)
Areas of Operation: DE, MD, NJ, PA, FC
Foreign Countries: BAHRAIN
Type of Foodservice: Quick Serve (15)
Notes: Partner/President Ray Rastelli is co-owner of Rastelli Foods Group, Inc. dba Rastelli Market Fresh.
COO John Moser is also CEO of MBB Management (http://www.mbbmanagement.com/).
Franchise/expansion plans focus on the East Coat I-95 corridor south of New Jersey.

Key Personnel
TONY LUKE (LUCIDONIO) JR - Founder; CEO; Partner
RAY RASTELLI JR - President; Partner
JOHN MOSER - COO
ALBERT MISCI - Director Marketing, Sales

Mangia Brick Oven Pizza
1 Route 37 W
Toms River, NJ 08753-6500

Telephone: (732) 557-5000
Internet Homepage: joeydsbrickovenpizza.com; mangiabrickovenpizza.com
Type of Business: Chain Restaurant Operator
Total Units: 5
Trade Names: Joey D's Brick Oven Pizzeria & Restaurant (2); Mangia Brick Oven Pizza (3)
Company-Owned Units: 5
Primary Menu: Pizza (5)
Areas of Operation: NJ
Type of Foodservice: Fast Casual (5)
Notes: Family-owned business. First franchisees of Bubbakoo's Burritos (Toms River, NJ)
Address and phone are Toms River Mangia Location.

Key Personnel
ANTHONY DI PIERRO - Partner; General Buyer

GREGG DI PIERRO - Partner
DANIEL DI PIERRO - Partner
JOSEPH DI PIERRO - Partner

Anthony Palagano Enterprises, Inc.
1540 Kuser Rd Ste A6
Trenton, NJ 08619-3828

Telephone: (609) 581-0606
Fax Number: (609) 581-8805
Type of Business: Chain Restaurant Operator
Total Sales: $4,975,000 (e)
Total Units: 2
Trade Names: Burger King (1); Cosi (1)
Units Franchised From: 2
Preferred Location Types: Freestanding; Strip Mall
Primary Menu: American (1); Hamburger (1)
Areas of Operation: NJ, PA
Type of Foodservice: Casual Dining (1); Quick Serve (1)
Franchise Affiliation: Burger King Worldwide Inc., MIAMI, FL; Cosi Inc., BOSTON, MA

Key Personnel
TONY PALAGANO - President; General Buyer

Delectabell Management Inc.
3200 S Broad St
Trenton, NJ 08610-2602

Mailing Address: PO Box 8635, Hamilton, NJ, 08650-0635
Telephone: (609) 298-1008
Fax Number: (609) 298-1239
Type of Business: Chain Restaurant Operator
Total Sales: $13,640,000 (e)
Average Check: Lunch(10); Dinner(10)
Total Units: 5
Trade Names: Taco Bell (5)
Units Franchised From: 5
Primary Menu: Taco (5)
Areas of Operation: NJ
Type of Foodservice: Quick Serve (5)
Franchise Affiliation: Taco Bell Corp., IRVINE, CA
Primary Distributors: (Food) McLane/Burlington, BURLINGTON, NJ

Key Personnel
JOHN TOMASULO - President; General Manager; General Buyer

Smolar Management Company
2556 S Broad St
Trenton, NJ 08610-4010

Telephone: (609) 888-3532
Fax Number: (609) 888-3847
Type of Business: Chain Restaurant Operator
Total Sales: $46,920,000 (e)
Number of Employees: 690
Total Units: 10
Trade Names: McDonald's (10)
Units Franchised From: 10
Preferred Square Footage: 2,500
Primary Menu: Hamburger (10)
Areas of Operation: NJ
Type of Foodservice: Quick Serve (10)
Franchise Affiliation: McDonald's Corporation, CHICAGO, IL

Key Personnel
THOMAS SMOLAR - President; General Buyer
NICKI THOMAS - General Manager
JAMIE SMOLAR - Manager Accounting

Dominate Food Services L.P
1600 US Highway 22 E Ste 100
Union, NJ 07083-3410

Telephone: (908) 686-2223
Fax Number: (908) 686-2503
Type of Business: Chain Restaurant Operator
Total Sales: $25,500,000 (e)
Number of Employees: 214
Total Units: 11
Trade Names: Burger King (11)
Units Franchised From: 11
Preferred Square Footage: 2,500
Preferred Location Types: Freestanding
Primary Menu: Hamburger (11)
Areas of Operation: NJ
Type of Foodservice: Quick Serve (11)
Franchise Affiliation: Burger King Worldwide Inc., MIAMI, FL

Key Personnel
NATHAN BLAU - President
DOMINICK VESPOLI - Owner; General Buyer

Domino's Franchisee
524 31st St
Union City, NJ 07087-3907

Telephone: (201) 319-9000
Type of Business: Chain Restaurant Operator
Total Sales: $5,965,000 (e)
Total Units: 3
Trade Names: Domino's (3)
Units Franchised From: 3
Primary Menu: Pizza (3)
Areas of Operation: NJ
Type of Foodservice: Quick Serve (3)
Franchise Affiliation: Domino's Pizza Inc, ANN ARBOR, MI

Key Personnel
SHAFIQ A. KHAN - Owner; General Buyer

SMS Enterprises Inc
395 S Main Rd
Vineland, NJ 08360-7895

Telephone: (856) 794-2530
Type of Business: Chain Restaurant Operator
Total Sales: $9,759,000 (e)
Total Units: 4
Trade Names: Burger King (4)
Units Franchised From: 4
Primary Menu: Hamburger (4)
Areas of Operation: NJ
Type of Foodservice: Quick Serve (4)
Franchise Affiliation: Burger King Worldwide Inc., MIAMI, FL

Key Personnel
ERIC SALISBURY - President; General Buyer

Bubbakoo's Burritos
1670 State Route 34 Ste 1C
Wall, NJ 07727-3988

Telephone: (732) 974-8444
Internet Homepage: bubbakoos.com
Type of Business: Chain Restaurant Operator
Year Founded: 2008
Systemwide Sales: $11,389,000 (e)
Total Sales: $31,120,000 (e)
Total Units: 25
Trade Names: Bubbakoo's Burritos (25)
Company-Owned Units: 11
Units Franchised To: 14
Primary Menu: Mexican (25)
Projected Openings: 3
Areas of Operation: NJ
Type of Foodservice: Fast Casual (25)
Notes: Founders are Johnny Rockets veterans.

Key Personnel
PAUL ALTERO - Co-Founder; Partner
BILL HART - Co-Founder; Partner
TOM MIRABELLA - Partner
CHRISTOPHER IVES - CFO
CHRIS IVES - CFO
GUS DIGIOVANNI - VP Operations, Development
RON BIDINOST - VP Construction
SALLY FINEGAN - Director Foodservice
BENJAMIN GRANNICK - Director Marketing
STEPHEN FINEGAN - Director Operations

KEVIN LAWLOR - Director Purchasing
KEVIN OLIVO - Director Training
GERRY MIGUEL - District Manager
KYLE ANDERSON - Supervisor

Charlie Brown's Corporation
95 Linwood Ave
Washington Township, NJ 07676

Telephone: (888) 616-4664
Fax Number: (973) 232-6564
Internet Homepage: charliebrowns.com; texassteakhouse.com
Type of Business: Chain Restaurant Operator
Year Founded: 1966
Total Sales: $24,520,000 (e)
Alcohol Sales: 2%
Number of Employees: 1,896
Average Check: Lunch(14); Dinner(24)
Internet Order Processing: Yes
Internet Sales: 2.00%
Total Units: 6
Trade Names: Charlie Brown's Steakhouse (1); Texas Steakhouse & Saloon (5)
Company-Owned Units: 6
Preferred Square Footage: 3,000; 7,300; 9,000
Preferred Location Types: Downtown; Freestanding; Strip Mall
Alcohol Served: Beer, Wine, Liquor
Primary Menu: Steak (6)
Areas of Operation: NC, NJ, NY, PA, VA, WV
Type of Foodservice: Casual Dining (6)
Catering Services: Yes
Parent Company: Praesidian Capital, NEW YORK, NY

Key Personnel
ROB MARQUARDT - CEO; Executive Chef; General Buyer

Lenfam Management Co.
1534 State Route 23
Wayne, NJ 07470-7516

Telephone: (973) 785-1424
Fax Number: (973) 785-3024
Type of Business: Chain Restaurant Operator
Year Founded: 1969
Total Sales: $35,550,000 (e)
Alcohol Sales: 7%
Number of Employees: 407
Average Check: Lunch(8); Dinner(8)
Total Units: 13
Trade Names: Wendy's Old Fashioned Hamburgers (13)
Units Franchised From: 13
Preferred Square Footage: 3,300
Preferred Location Types: Freestanding
Primary Menu: Hamburger (13)
Areas of Operation: NJ
Type of Foodservice: Quick Serve (13)
Franchise Affiliation: The Wendy's Company, DUBLIN, OH
Primary Distributors: (Food) Willow Run Foods Inc., KIRKWOOD, NY; (Supplies) Willow Run Foods Inc., KIRKWOOD, NY

Key Personnel
CONSTANTINE LENAS - President; Director Finance, Real Estate
ANTHONY CHRISTIANO - CFO
ARISTOTLE SCLAVOUNOS - COO
SANDA LUPULESCU - Coordinator Human Resources

Lenfam Management Co.
1534 State Route 23
Wayne, NJ 07470-7516

Telephone: (973) 785-1424
Fax Number: (973) 785-3024
Type of Business: Chain Restaurant Operator
Total Sales: $40,800,000 (e)
Total Units: 15
Trade Names: Wendy's Old Fashioned Hamburgers (15)
Units Franchised From: 15
Primary Menu: Hamburger (15)
Areas of Operation: NJ
Type of Foodservice: Quick Serve (15)
Franchise Affiliation: The Wendy's Company, DUBLIN, OH

Key Personnel
CONSTANTINE LENAS - President
ANTHONY CHRISTIANO - CFO; Controller
SANDA LUPULESCU - Manager Risk Management, Human Resources
RICH GRECCO - Manager Payroll

F.J.D. Fast Food Corp.
6201 Bergenline Ave
West New York, NJ 07093-1605

Telephone: (201) 854-3921
Fax Number: (201) 854-0075
Type of Business: Chain Restaurant Operator
Total Sales: $4,895,000 (e)
Total Units: 2
Trade Names: Burger King (2)
Units Franchised From: 2
Preferred Location Types: Freestanding
Primary Menu: Hamburger (2)
Areas of Operation: NJ
Type of Foodservice: Quick Serve (2)
Franchise Affiliation: Burger King Worldwide Inc., MIAMI, FL

Key Personnel
CHARLES VARESANO - President; General Buyer

The Knowles Restaurants
111 Prospect Ave
West Orange, NJ 07052-4202

Telephone: (973) 731-2360
Fax Number: (973) 731-5168
Internet Homepage: highlawn.com; knowleshospitality.com; ramsheadinn.com; themanorrestaurant.com
Company Email: info@themanorrestaurant.com
Type of Business: Chain Restaurant Operator
Year Founded: 1956
Total Sales: $27,600,000 (e)
Alcohol Sales: 40%
Number of Employees: 450
Average Check: Lunch(30); Dinner(62)
Internet Order Processing: Yes
Total Units: 2
Trade Names: Highlawn Pavillion (1); The Manor (1)
Company-Owned Units: 2
Preferred Location Types: Freestanding
Alcohol Served: Beer, Wine, Liquor
Primary Menu: American (2)
Projected Remodelings: 1
Areas of Operation: NJ
Type of Foodservice: Fine Dining (2)
Primary Distributors: (Full Line) SYSCO Food Services of Metro New York, JERSEY CITY, NJ

Key Personnel
HARRY KNOWLES - President
WADE KNOWLES - VP
KURT KNOWLES - VP Purchasing; Director Corporate Affairs
CATHY VASTOLA - Controller
MICHAEL CAMMARANO - General Manager
ELIO GRACIA - Executive Chef
ROBERT ALBERS - Executive Chef
TRISTAN TEVROW - Executive Chef
MAURICE ALAMEDA - Director Operations, Purchasing
KURT KNOWLES JR - Director Operations
KEITH SLY - Director Communications
JENNIFER COOPER - Director Sales

P.J.W. Restaurant Group
222 Haddon Ave Ste 200
Westmont, NJ 08108

Telephone: (856) 216-0656
Fax Number: (856) 216-8447
Internet Homepage: pjwrestaurantgroup.com
Type of Business: Chain Restaurant Operator
Year Founded: 1983
Total Sales: $71,190,000 (e)
Alcohol Sales: 15%

Number of Employees: 2,240
Internet Order Processing: Yes
Total Units: 26
Trade Names: Central Taco and Tequila (1); Chophouse Grille (1); P.J. Whelihan's Pub and Restaurant (19); The Chophouse (1); The Pour House (3); Treno Pizza Bar (1)
Company-Owned Units: 26
Alcohol Served: Beer, Wine, Liquor
Primary Menu: American (23); Pizza (1); Steak/Seafood (2)
Projected Openings: 2
Areas of Operation: NJ, PA
Type of Foodservice: Casual Dining (25); Fine Dining (1)

Key Personnel
BOB PLATZER - Chairman
JIM FRIS - CEO
WILLIAM LOVE - CFO
JESSICA BRESLOW - COO
MICHAEL PERRO - Director Operations
CHRISTOPHER WEBB - Director Operations
JIM AMATO - Director Operations
THOMAS GARRO - Director Information Technology
MICHAEL RUDDY - Director Operations
CARLA ADAMS - Director Operations-Training
JACQUELINE PLATZER - Assistant Director Culinary Operations

PrimoHoagies Franchising, Inc.
610 Ryan Ave Ste 4
Westville, NJ 08093-1588

Telephone: (856) 742-1999
Fax Number: (856) 742-5000
Internet Homepage: primohoagies.com
Company Email: info@primohoagies.com
Type of Business: Chain Restaurant Operator
Year Founded: 1992
Total Sales: $44,450,000 (e)
Total Units: 80
Trade Names: PrimoHoagies (80)
Company-Owned Units: 80
Primary Menu: Sandwiches/Deli (80)
Areas of Operation: DE, FL, MD, NJ, PA, SC, VA
Type of Foodservice: Fast Casual (80)

Key Personnel
NICK PAPANIER - Owner; COO; General Buyer
ERIC BONNER - COO
KARLIE DIPIETRO - Director Marketing

Dartcor Enterprises Inc.
40 S Jefferson Rd Ste 1
Whippany, NJ 07981-1011

Telephone: (973) 739-9060
Fax Number: (973) 739-9361
Internet Homepage: dartcor.com
Company Email: info@dartcor.com
Type of Business: Foodservice Management Operator
Year Founded: 1985
Total Sales: $36,016,000 (e)
Number of Employees: 150
Number of Locations Served: 45
Total Foodservice Mgmt Accounts: 45
Total Units: 30
Company-Owned Units: 30
Projected Remodelings: 2
Areas of Operation: NJ
Type of Foodservice: Cafeteria (45)
Foodservice Management Venues: Business & Industry
Primary Distributors: (Full Line) Performance Foodservice - AFI, ELIZABETH, NJ; (Full Line) US Foods, ALLENTOWN, PA

Key Personnel
WARREN LEEDS - President

Big Fish Restaurant Group
588 W Rio Grande Ave
Wildwood, NJ 08260-1526

Telephone: (609) 522-7761
Fax Number: (609) 522-0938
Internet Homepage: beachcreek.net; bigfish6.net; boathouseonline.net; uries.net
Company Email: bigfishgroup@comcast.net
Type of Business: Chain Restaurant Operator
Year Founded: 1997
Total Sales: $11,649,000 (e)
Alcohol Sales: 30%
Number of Employees: 300
Average Check: Lunch(24); Dinner(44)
Total Units: 3
Trade Names: Beachcreek Oyster Bar & Grill (1); Boathouse Restaurant (1); Urie's Waterfront (1)
Company-Owned Units: 3
Preferred Square Footage: 5,500; 6,000
Preferred Location Types: Freestanding
Alcohol Served: Beer, Wine, Liquor
Primary Menu: Seafood (3)
Areas of Operation: NJ
Type of Foodservice: Casual Dining (3)

Key Personnel
MICHAEL DIANTONIO - Partner; Director Real Estate; General Buyer
PAT DIANTONIO - Partner; Manager Information Systems; General Buyer
JOE RYMER - Partner; General Buyer
DAN POWELL - Executive Director Operations
BROOKE BENNETT - General Manager
ANDREW MALLON - Executive Chef; Manager Menu Development, Food Safety, Catering
RORY NEWCOMB - Director Human Resources

Two Mile Landing Restaurant & Marina
1 Fish Dock Rd
Wildwood Crest, NJ 08260

Mailing Address: PO Box 1528, WILDWOOD, NJ, 08260-8098
Telephone: (609) 522-1341
Internet Homepage: twomilelanding.com
Company Email: twomile@eclipse.com
Type of Business: Chain Restaurant Operator
Year Founded: 1983
Total Sales: $8,130,000 (e)
Alcohol Sales: 5%
Number of Employees: 240
Average Check: Lunch(12); Dinner(24)
Total Units: 2
Trade Names: 2 Mile Landing (1); Crab House (1)
Company-Owned Units: 2
Preferred Square Footage: 3,000
Preferred Location Types: Freestanding
Alcohol Served: Beer, Wine, Liquor
Primary Menu: Seafood (2)
Projected Remodelings: 1
Areas of Operation: NJ
Type of Foodservice: Casual Dining (2)
Catering Services: Yes
Primary Distributors: (Food) W.E. Ryan Co. Inc., PHILADELPHIA, PA

Key Personnel
RACHEL HANSEN - Owner
LORI LANE - General Manager; Executive Chef; Director Operations; General Buyer

Blue Moon Mexican Cafe
291 Wiley Pl Ste B
Wyckoff, NJ 07481-2833

Mailing Address: PO Box 92, WYCKOFF, NJ, 07481
Telephone: (201) 848-4088
Fax Number: (201) 891-8484
Internet Homepage: bluemoonmexicancafe.com
Company Email: contact@bluemoonmexicancafe.com
Type of Business: Chain Restaurant Operator
Total Sales: $3,083,000 (e)
Total Units: 4
Trade Names: Blue Moon Mexican Cafe (4)
Company-Owned Units: 4
Alcohol Served: Beer, Wine, Liquor

Primary Menu: Mexican (4)
Areas of Operation: FL, NJ, NY
Type of Foodservice: Casual Dining (4)

Key Personnel
HOWIE FELIXBROD - CEO; Partner; Executive Chef; General Buyer
COLLEEN GRENNAN - VP Operations

NEW MEXICO

IGT Enterprises
PO Box 968
Alamogordo, NM 88311-0968

Telephone: (575) 443-1277
Internet Homepage: alamomcds.com
Type of Business: Chain Restaurant Operator
Total Sales: $10,207,000 (e)
Total Units: 2
Trade Names: McDonald's (2)
Units Franchised From: 2
Preferred Location Types: Discount Dept. Stores; Freestanding
Primary Menu: Hamburger (2)
Areas of Operation: NM
Type of Foodservice: Quick Serve (2)
Franchise Affiliation: McDonald's Corporation, CHICAGO, IL

Key Personnel
MALCOLMN RAMSEY - President; Partner; General Buyer
KATHY RAMSEY - Partner

Alamos LS LLC
6100 Seagull St NE
Albuquerque, NM 87109

Telephone: (505) 346-5468
Internet Homepage: texaslandandcattle.com; yourlonestar.com
Type of Business: Chain Restaurant Operator
Year Founded: 1989
Total Sales: $21,450,000 (e)
Alcohol Sales: 10%
Number of Employees: 10,710
Average Check: Lunch(14); Dinner(22)
Internet Order Processing: Yes
Internet Sales: 1.00%
Total Units: 5
Trade Names: Lone Star Steakhouse & Saloon (3); Texas Land & Cattle Steak House (3)
Company-Owned Units: 6
Preferred Square Footage: 5,800; 6,800; 7,300; 9,000; 11,000; 12,000; 16,500
Preferred Location Types: Community Mall; Downtown; Freestanding; Regional Mall; Strip Mall
Alcohol Served: Beer, Wine, Liquor

Primary Menu: Steak (6)
Areas of Operation: IL, MO, OK, TX
Type of Foodservice: Casual Dining (6)
Primary Distributors: (Full Line) McLane/Fort Worth, FORT WORTH, TX

Key Personnel
ART CARRASCO - CEO

Annapurna's World Vegetarian Cafe
2201 Silver Ave SE
Albuquerque, NM 87106-3532

Mailing Address: PO Box 40317, Albuquerque, NM, 87196
Telephone: (505) 262-2424
Internet Homepage: chaishoppe.com
Company Email: info@chaishoppe.com
Type of Business: Chain Restaurant Operator
Year Founded: 2002
Total Units: 4
Trade Names: Annapurna's World Vegetarian Cafe (4)
Company-Owned Units: 4
Primary Menu: Vegetarian (4)
Areas of Operation: NM
Type of Foodservice: Casual Dining (4)

Key Personnel
YASHODA NAIDOO - Owner; Executive Chef; General Buyer

Auntie Anne's Franchise
6600 Menaul Blvd NE Ste E1
Albuquerque, NM 87110-3448

Telephone: (505) 888-1915
Type of Business: Chain Restaurant Operator
Total Sales: $1,591,000 (e)
Total Units: 2
Trade Names: Auntie Anne's Hand-Rolled Soft Pretzels (2)
Units Franchised From: 2
Primary Menu: Snacks (2)
Areas of Operation: NM
Type of Foodservice: Quick Serve (2)
Franchise Affiliation: Auntie Anne's Inc., LANCASTER, PA

Key Personnel
LUCY LARRANAGA - Owner; General Buyer

Blake's Lotaburger LLC
3205 Richmond Dr NE
Albuquerque, NM 87107-1922

Telephone: (505) 884-2160

Fax Number: (505) 884-0343
Internet Homepage: lotaburger.com
Type of Business: Chain Restaurant Operator
Year Founded: 1952
Total Sales: $44,990,000 (e)
Number of Employees: 1,021
Average Check: Breakfast(6); Lunch(8); Dinner(8)
Internet Order Processing: Yes
Total Units: 72
Trade Names: Blake's Lotaburger (72)
Company-Owned Units: 72
Preferred Square Footage: 2,300
Preferred Location Types: Freestanding
Primary Menu: Hamburger (72)
Projected Openings: 1
Areas of Operation: AZ, NM, TX
Type of Foodservice: Quick Serve (72)
On-site Distribution Center: Yes

Key Personnel
RON RULE - CEO
BRIAN RULE - President
DAVID WILTON - VP Operations
PAULA HAYDEN - Director Development, Construction
ROSS BROWN - Manager Facility/Maintenance, Development
KEN REEVES - Supervisor Warehouse

Cooperage
7220 Lomas Blvd NE
Albuquerque, NM 87110-7146

Telephone: (505) 255-1657
Internet Homepage: cooperageabq.com; scarpaspizza.com
Company Email: info@cooperageabq.com
Type of Business: Chain Restaurant Operator
Year Founded: 1976
Total Sales: $9,057,000 (e)
Alcohol Sales: 20%
Number of Employees: 90
Average Check: Lunch(20); Dinner(30)
Internet Order Processing: Yes
Total Units: 3
Trade Names: Cooperage (1); Scarpas (2)
Company-Owned Units: 3
Preferred Location Types: Freestanding
Alcohol Served: Beer, Wine, Liquor
Primary Menu: Italian (2); Steak/Seafood (1)
Areas of Operation: NM
Type of Foodservice: Casual Dining (3)
Catering Services: Yes

Key Personnel
JIM SHUMACHER - CEO; President
C.C. MARTINEZ - General Manager; Director Menu Development, Catering
ANTONIO EBELL - Executive Chef; Manager Menu Development, Catering; General Buyer

D & D Enterprises
9680 Eagle Ranch Rd NW Ste E
Albuquerque, NM 87114-1581

Telephone: (505) 896-1040
Fax Number: (505) 896-2171
Type of Business: Chain Restaurant Operator
Total Sales: $16,530,000 (e)
Total Units: 6
Trade Names: Taco Bell (6)
Units Franchised From: 6
Primary Menu: Taco (6)
Areas of Operation: NM
Type of Foodservice: Quick Serve (6)
Franchise Affiliation: Taco Bell Corp., IRVINE, CA

Key Personnel
DAVID SPARKS - President; General Buyer
ROGER SPARKS - Director Operations
LISA BROOKS - Coordinator Accounting

Dancel, L.L.C.
3501 State Highway 528 NW
Albuquerque, NM 87114

Telephone: (505) 898-5205
Type of Business: Chain Restaurant Operator
Total Sales: $14,950,000 (e)
Total Units: 6
Trade Names: Jack in the Box (6)
Units Franchised From: 6
Primary Menu: Hamburger (6)
Areas of Operation: AZ
Type of Foodservice: Quick Serve (6)
Franchise Affiliation: Jack in the Box Restaurants, SAN DIEGO, CA

Key Personnel
LAURA OLGUIN - CEO; Owner; General Buyer

Domino's Franchisee
1209 Menaul Blvd NW
Albuquerque, NM 87107-1022

Telephone: (505) 345-9936
Type of Business: Chain Restaurant Operator
Total Sales: $14,577,000 (e)
Total Units: 7
Trade Names: Domino's (7)
Units Franchised From: 7
Primary Menu: Pizza (7)
Areas of Operation: NM
Type of Foodservice: Quick Serve (7)
Franchise Affiliation: Domino's Pizza Inc, ANN ARBOR, MI

Key Personnel
GORDON E. NELSON - Owner; General Buyer

Flying Star Cafe
2701 Broadway Blvd NE Ste A
Albuquerque, NM 87107-1530

Telephone: (505) 255-1128
Fax Number: (505) 254-7655
Internet Homepage: flyingstarcafe.com; satellitecoffee.com
Company Email: info@flyingstarcafe.com
Type of Business: Chain Restaurant Operator
Year Founded: 1987
Total Sales: $25,320,000 (e)
Alcohol Sales: 1%
Number of Employees: 480
Average Check: Breakfast(5); Lunch(12); Dinner(14)
Internet Order Processing: Yes
Total Units: 12
Trade Names: Flying Star Cafe (6); Satellite Coffee (6)
Company-Owned Units: 12
Preferred Square Footage: 2,000; 2,700
Preferred Location Types: Freestanding
Alcohol Served: Beer, Wine
Primary Menu: American (6); Coffee (6)
Areas of Operation: NM
Type of Foodservice: Fast Casual (12)
Catering Services: Yes
On-site Distribution Center: Yes
Primary Distributors: (Full Line) SYSCO New Mexico, ALBUQUERQUE, NM

Key Personnel
JEAN BERNSTEIN - CEO; President; General Buyer
JOHN JONES - CFO; VP
ALICE GARCIA - Chief People Officer
JESSICA VARGAS - Controller
MARK LOVATO - General Manager
WILLEM BLOM - Executive Chef
JARED TRUJILLO - Director Operations
CARISSA RIVERA - Manager Human Resources
RODNEY BURR - Manager Purchasing
JAMES KALIVODA - Manager Culinary Development

Fresquez Inc.
8218 Louisiana Blvd NE Ste B
Albuquerque, NM 87113-2382

Telephone: (505) 884-7484
Fax Number: (505) 880-1015
Internet Homepage: fresquezcompanies.com
Company Email: info@fresquezcompanies.com
Type of Business: Chain Restaurant Operator
Year Founded: 1984
Total Sales: $12,100,000 (e)
Alcohol Sales: 10%
Number of Employees: 800
Average Check: Breakfast(6); Lunch(10); Dinner(16)
Total Units: 20
Trade Names: Comida Buena (1); Dunkin Donuts (1); Freckles Frozen Custard (1); La Trattoria (1); Mac's Steak in the Rough (2); Panda Express (1); Quiznos (3); Rio Grande Brew Pub And Grill (1); Route 66 Lounge (1); Slice (1); Subway (1); Tia Juanita's Full Service (1); Tia Juanita's Pronto (1); Tia's (1); Village Inn(1); Watch! Sports Bar (1); Wendy's (1)
Company-Owned Units: 12
Units Franchised From: 8
Preferred Square Footage: 5,400
Preferred Location Types: Airports; Community Mall; Freestanding
Alcohol Served: Beer, Wine, Liquor
Primary Menu: American (5); Asian (1); Hamburger (1); Italian (1); Mexican (5); Sandwiches/Deli (5); Snacks (2)
Areas of Operation: CO, NM, TX
Type of Foodservice: Casual Dining (6); Family Restaurant (3); Quick Serve (11)
Catering Services: Yes
Franchise Affiliation: The Quiznos Master LLC, DENVER, CO; Village Inn, MINNETONKA, MN
Primary Distributors: (Full Line) SYSCO New Mexico, ALBUQUERQUE, NM

Key Personnel
LENNY FRESQUEZ - CEO; Controller; Executive Chef; Director Operations, Purchasing, Loss Prevention, Marketing, Real Estate, Design, Menu Development
LINDA FRESQUEZ - President; VP Operations, Purchasing, Supply Chain, Marketing; Controller; General Manager
MARY MONTANO - VP Human Resources

Gardunos
201 3rd St NW Ste 1310
Albuquerque, NM 87102-3373

Telephone: (505) 298-5514
Fax Number: (505) 298-5549
Internet Homepage: gardunosrestaurants.com
Type of Business: Chain Restaurant Operator
Year Founded: 1969
Systemwide Sales: $69,733,000 (e)
Total Sales: $55,786,000 (e)
Alcohol Sales: 20%
Number of Employees: 332
Average Check: Lunch(14); Dinner(18)
Internet Order Processing: Yes
Internet Sales: 2.00%
Total Units: 4
Trade Names: Garduno's of Mexico (4)
Company-Owned Units: 4

Preferred Square Footage: 5,000; 15,000
Preferred Location Types: Freestanding; Strip Mall
Alcohol Served: Beer, Wine, Liquor
Primary Menu: Mexican (4)
Areas of Operation: NM, NV
Type of Foodservice: Casual Dining (4)
Catering Services: Yes
Primary Distributors: (Full Line) SYSCO New Mexico, ALBUQUERQUE, NM

Key Personnel
TUG HERIG - Owner; Executive Chef; General Buyer

GLS Foods LLC
4240 San Mateo Blvd NE
Albuquerque, NM 87110-1236

Mailing Address: PO Box 66408, ALBUQUERQUE, NM, 87193-6408
Telephone: (505) 730-5900
Fax Number: (505) 830-1302
Company Email: glsfoods@comcast.net
Type of Business: Chain Restaurant Operator
Year Founded: 2004
Total Sales: $5,336,000 (e)
Number of Employees: 90
Average Check: Lunch(12); Dinner(12)
Total Units: 2
Trade Names: Popeyes Louisiana Kitchen (2)
Units Franchised From: 2
Preferred Location Types: Freestanding
Primary Menu: Chicken (2)
Areas of Operation: NM
Type of Foodservice: Quick Serve (2)
Franchise Affiliation: Popeyes Louisiana Kitchen Inc., ATLANTA, GA

Key Personnel
GREG TAYLOR - President; Director Real Estate
BEN MILLER - VP Operations, Purchasing; General Buyer
NIKKI MILLER - VP Finance, Human Resources

Il Vicino Holding Company
2201 San Pedro Dr NE Bldg 2-107
Albuquerque, NM 87110-5942

Telephone: (505) 262-4717
Internet Homepage: canteenbrewhouse.com; ilvicino.com
Company Email: IVinfo@ilvicino.com
Type of Business: Chain Restaurant Operator
Year Founded: 1986
Total Sales: $24,050,000 (e)
Alcohol Sales: 25%
Number of Employees: 270
Average Check: Lunch(18); Dinner(24)
Total Units: 10
Trade Names: Canteen Brewhouse (1); Canteen Taproom (1); Il Vicino Wood Oven Pizza (8)
Company-Owned Units: 10
Preferred Square Footage: 5,500; 6,000
Preferred Location Types: Freestanding; Strip Mall
Alcohol Served: Beer, Wine
Primary Menu: Pizza (10)
Areas of Operation: CO, KS, NM
Type of Foodservice: Casual Dining (10)
Primary Distributors: (Food) Shamrock Foods Colorado Division, COMMERCE CITY, CO

Key Personnel
GREG ATKIN - Partner; Manager Facility/Maintenance, District
TOM WHITE - Partner; VP Operations; Executive Chef; General Buyer
RICK POST - Manager Information Systems

Kenric Management, Inc.
210 Montano Rd NW
Albuquerque, NM 87107-5220

Telephone: (505) 343-0066
Fax Number: (505) 343-0073
Type of Business: Chain Restaurant Operator
Total Sales: $41,930,000 (e)
Total Units: 9
Trade Names: McDonald's (9)
Company-Owned Units: 9
Primary Menu: Hamburger (9)
Areas of Operation: NM
Type of Foodservice: Quick Serve (9)
Franchise Affiliation: McDonald's Corporation, CHICAGO, IL

Key Personnel
KENRIC GARCIA - Owner; General Buyer
CHERYL HERBERT - Director Operations

Keva Juice Southwest
201 3rd St NW Ste D
Albuquerque, NM 87102

Telephone: (505) 242-5382
Fax Number: (505) 298-5549
Internet Homepage: kevajuicesw.com
Company Email: comments@kevajuice.com
Type of Business: Chain Restaurant Operator
Year Founded: 1996
Total Sales: $4,465,000 (e)
Average Check: Dinner(12)
Total Units: 13
Trade Names: Keva Juice (13)
Company-Owned Units: 13
Preferred Location Types: Downtown; Strip Mall
Primary Menu: Snacks (13)
Areas of Operation: NM
Type of Foodservice: Quick Serve (13)

Key Personnel
RICHARD HERIG - President; General Buyer

L.P.G. Enterprises
12854 Eastridge Dr NE
Albuquerque, NM 87112-4715

Telephone: (505) 299-4155
Fax Number: (505) 299-4158
Company Email: ana.ibarra@comcast.net
Type of Business: Chain Restaurant Operator
Year Founded: 1984
Total Sales: $33,700,000 (e)
Number of Employees: 350
Average Check: Breakfast(8); Lunch(10); Dinner(12)
Total Units: 7
Trade Names: McDonald's (7)
Units Franchised From: 7
Preferred Square Footage: 2,500; 3,000
Preferred Location Types: Discount Dept. Stores; Freestanding
Primary Menu: Hamburger (7)
Areas of Operation: NM
Type of Foodservice: Quick Serve (7)
Franchise Affiliation: McDonald's Corporation, CHICAGO, IL
Primary Distributors: (Food) Mile Hi Foods, DENVER, CO

Key Personnel
LARRY GARCIA - President; Partner; Director Purchasing, Facility/Maintenance, Real Estate, Design; General Buyer
MIKE GARCIA - Partner; Director Operations, Information Systems
ROBERT BUONO - Manager Accounting

Little Anita's Mexican Food
2105 Mountain Rd NW
Albuquerque, NM 87104

Telephone: (505) 242-3102
Internet Homepage: foodsofnewmexico.com; loscuatesrestaurants.com; littleanitas.com
Company Email: littleanitas02@gmail.com
Type of Business: Chain Restaurant Operator
Year Founded: 1974
Systemwide Sales: $20,017,000 (e)
Total Sales: $11,209,000 (e)
Alcohol Sales: 15%
Number of Employees: 435
Average Check: Lunch(8); Dinner(12)
Total Units: 12
Trade Names: Little Anita's Mexican Foods (9); Los Cuates (3)
Company-Owned Units: 9
Units Franchised To: 3
Preferred Square Footage: 2,000

Preferred Location Types: Downtown; Strip Mall
Alcohol Served: Beer, Wine, Liquor
Primary Menu: Mexican (12)
Areas of Operation: CO, NM
Type of Foodservice: Casual Dining (12)
Catering Services: Yes
Primary Distributors: (Full Line) SYSCO Food Services of Denver, DENVER, CO

Key Personnel
CAROL SEDILLO - Director Human Resources

Peter DeFries Corporation
8525 Jefferson St NE
Albuquerque, NM 87113-1603

Telephone: (505) 858-1010
Fax Number: (505) 858-2421
Internet Homepage: dions.com
Type of Business: Chain Restaurant Operator
Year Founded: 1978
Total Sales: $42,540,000 (e)
Number of Employees: 891
Average Check: Lunch(6); Dinner(6)
Internet Order Processing: Yes
Total Units: 25
Trade Names: Dion's Pizza (25)
Company-Owned Units: 25
Preferred Square Footage: 3,500; 4,000
Preferred Location Types: Freestanding
Primary Menu: Pizza (25)
Projected Openings: 1
Areas of Operation: CO, NM, TX
Type of Foodservice: Family Restaurant (25)
Foodservice Management Venues: Schools
Distribution Centers: ALBUQUERQUE, NM
Primary Distributors: (Equipment) McComas Sales Company Inc., ALBUQUERQUE, NM; (Supplies) McComas Sales Company Inc., ALBUQUERQUE, NM

Key Personnel
JON PATTEN - Co-Founder
MARK HERMAN - CEO
BLAIR BOYER - Senior Director Human Resources
DEENA CRAWLEY - Director Supply Chain, Marketing, Research & Development, Menu Development
JASON SAVAGE - Director Store Operations
DAVID GALBRAITH - Director Training
BRIAN MAGEE - Director Supply Chain

Peter DeFries Distribution Center
5388 Pan American East Fwy NE
Albuquerque, NM 87109-2306

Telephone: (505) 889-3503

Fax Number: (505) 872-8313
Listing Type: Distribution Center
Type of Business: Foodservice Operations - Bowling Alley
Number of Employees: 60
Areas of Operation: CO, NM, TX
Parent Company: Peter DeFries Corporation, ALBUQUERQUE, NM

Key Personnel
BRIAN MAGEE - Manager Distribution, Warehouse, Transportation

Pizza 9 Franchise Corporation
5643 Jefferson St NE Ste A
Albuquerque, NM 87109-3405

Mailing Address: PO Box 21614, ALBUQUERQUE, NM, 87154
Telephone: (505) 764-3780
Fax Number: (505) 715-5962
Internet Homepage: pizzanine.com
Company Email: wedeliver@pizzanine.com
Type of Business: Chain Restaurant Operator
Year Founded: 2008
Systemwide Sales: $11,199,000 (e)
Total Sales: $1,901,000 (e)
Number of Employees: 765
Total Units: 17
Trade Names: Pizza 9 (17)
Units Franchised To: 17
Preferred Location Types: Strip Mall
Primary Menu: Pizza (17)
Areas of Operation: NM, NV, OK, TX
Type of Foodservice: Quick Serve (17)
Primary Distributors: (Food) Performance Foodservice, PHOENIX, AZ

Key Personnel
HASS ASLAMI - CEO; Partner
BEHRAD ETEMADI - President; Partner; Director Real Estate, Construction

Weck's Inc.
3921 Louisiana Blvd NE
Albuquerque, NM 87110-1444

Telephone: (505) 881-0152
Fax Number: (505) 881-0183
Internet Homepage: lepeepabq.com; wecksinc.com
Company Email: info@lepeepabq.com
Type of Business: Chain Restaurant Operator
Year Founded: 1991
Total Sales: $14,540,000 (e)
Number of Employees: 410
Average Check: Dinner(12)
Total Units: 16
Trade Names: Le Peep (1); Weck's (14); Wecks

Select (1)
Company-Owned Units: 16
Preferred Location Types: Freestanding
Primary Menu: American (16)
Areas of Operation: NM
Type of Foodservice: Family Restaurant (16)

Key Personnel
ART KAPLAN - Owner; General Buyer
DANIELLE MONTOYA - Director Human Resources
JOE GARCIA - Director Operations

Willis Investments Corporation
3222 Central Ave SE Ste B
Albuquerque, NM 87106-1458

Telephone: (505) 265-3150
Internet Homepage: wicinvest.com
Type of Business: Chain Restaurant Operator
Total Sales: $2,841,000 (e)
Total Units: 5
Trade Names: Cold Stone Creamery (5)
Units Franchised From: 5
Primary Menu: Snacks (5)
Areas of Operation: NM
Type of Foodservice: Quick Serve (5)
Franchise Affiliation: Kahala Brands, SCOTTSDALE, AZ

Key Personnel
TOM WILLIS - Partner
CHRISTINE WILLIS - Partner

The Range Cafe
925 S Camino Del Pueblo
Bernalillo, NM 87004

Mailing Address: PO Box 1780, BERNALILLO, NM, 87004
Telephone: (505) 867-1700
Fax Number: (505) 867-7256
Internet Homepage: fr8house.com; rangecafe.com; standarddiner.com
Company Email: contact@rangecafe.com
Type of Business: Chain Restaurant Operator
Year Founded: 1992
Total Sales: $8,193,000 (e)
Alcohol Sales: 10%
Total Units: 9
Trade Names: The Freight House (1); The Range (7); The Standard Diner (1)
Company-Owned Units: 9
Alcohol Served: Beer, Wine, Liquor
Primary Menu: American (9)
Areas of Operation: NM
Type of Foodservice: Casual Dining (8); Family Restaurant (1)

Key Personnel
MATT DIGREGORY - Owner; VP
ANN FISHER-IVES - General Manager
JEFF BARNES - Manager Operations; General Buyer

Macatak Inc
2600 E 21st St
Clovis, NM 88101-8618

Mailing Address: PO Box 250, CLOVIS, NM, 88102-2268
Telephone: (575) 762-6010
Type of Business: Chain Restaurant Operator
Total Sales: $27,510,000 (e)
Total Units: 6
Trade Names: McDonald's (6)
Units Franchised From: 6
Primary Menu: Hamburger (6)
Areas of Operation: NM
Type of Foodservice: Quick Serve (6)
Franchise Affiliation: McDonald's Corporation, CHICAGO, IL

Key Personnel
JOHN SNOWBERGER - President; General Buyer

Four Corners Taco Inc.
2216 E Main St
Farmington, NM 87401-7718

Telephone: (505) 327-0745
Fax Number: (505) 327-5734
Type of Business: Chain Restaurant Operator
Total Sales: $8,554,000 (e)
Number of Employees: 70
Average Check: Lunch(8); Dinner(8)
Total Units: 3
Trade Names: Taco Bell (3)
Units Franchised From: 3
Preferred Location Types: Freestanding
Primary Menu: Taco (3)
Areas of Operation: NM
Type of Foodservice: Quick Serve (3)
Franchise Affiliation: Taco Bell Corp., IRVINE, CA
Primary Distributors: (Food) McLane /Aurora, COMMERCE CITY, CO

Key Personnel
MARILYN ANDERSON - President; General Buyer
SHEILA WICKEN - General Manager

De La Riva Enterprises
2300 E Historic Highway 66
Gallup, NM 87301-4769

Telephone: (505) 722-4055
Fax Number: (505) 722-4833
Company Email: mayradelariva@msn.com
Type of Business: Chain Restaurant Operator
Total Sales: $47,760,000 (e)
Number of Employees: 622
Average Check: Breakfast(8); Lunch(8); Dinner(8)
Total Units: 10
Trade Names: McDonald's (10)
Units Franchised From: 10
Preferred Square Footage: 2,500; 3,000
Preferred Location Types: Discount Dept. Stores; Freestanding
Primary Menu: Hamburger (10)
Areas of Operation: NM
Type of Foodservice: Quick Serve (10)
Franchise Affiliation: McDonald's Corporation, CHICAGO, IL
Primary Distributors: (Full Line) Mile Hi Foods, DENVER, CO

Key Personnel
J. MARTIN DE LA RIVA - President; General Buyer
CATHY DURAN - Department Manager

Taira's Inc.
911 W Coal Ave
Gallup, NM 87301-6643

Mailing Address: PO Box 3069, GALLUP, NM, 87305-3069
Telephone: (505) 722-3849
Fax Number: (505) 722-7274
Internet Homepage: tairasinc.com
Type of Business: Chain Restaurant Operator
Year Founded: 1956
Total Sales: $24,370,000 (e)
Number of Employees: 270
Average Check: Lunch(10); Dinner(10)
Total Units: 9
Trade Names: Taco Bell (8); Taco Bell/Pizza Hut (1)
Units Franchised From: 9
Preferred Square Footage: 1,600
Preferred Location Types: Freestanding
Primary Menu: Pizza (1); Taco (8)
Areas of Operation: AZ, CO, NM
Type of Foodservice: Quick Serve (9)
Franchise Affiliation: Pizza Hut Inc., PLANO, TX; Taco Bell Corp., IRVINE, CA
Primary Distributors: (Full Line) McLane /Aurora, COMMERCE CITY, CO

Key Personnel
GEORGE TAIRA - President; Partner; CFO; Director Loss Prevention, Real Estate
JAMES RICH - Partner; General Manager; Director Operations, Facility/Maintenance; General Buyer
WILMA TAIRA - Partner; Manager Finance, Purchasing, Information Systems; General Buyer
KIM RICH - Partner; Director Human Resources

McFadke Inc.
1515 W Calle Sur St
Hobbs, NM 88240-0998

Mailing Address: PO Box 5528, HOBBS, NM, 88241-5909
Telephone: (575) 393-0331
Type of Business: Chain Restaurant Operator
Total Sales: $19,842,000 (e)
Number of Employees: 210
Average Check: Breakfast(8); Lunch(12); Dinner(12)
Total Units: 4
Trade Names: McDonald's (4)
Units Franchised From: 4
Preferred Square Footage: 2,500; 3,000
Preferred Location Types: Freestanding
Primary Menu: Hamburger (4)
Areas of Operation: NM
Type of Foodservice: Quick Serve (4)
Franchise Affiliation: McDonald's Corporation, CHICAGO, IL
Primary Distributors: (Food) The Martin-Brower Co., CONROE, TX

Key Personnel
KENNETH FADKE - President; General Buyer

Allen Theatres Inc.
1401 S Don Roser Dr Ste C
Las Cruces, NM 88011-4577

Telephone: (575) 524-7933
Fax Number: (575) 527-0068
Internet Homepage: allentheatresinc.com
Company Email: lcoffice@allentheatersinc.com
Type of Business: Foodservice Operations - Movie Theatre
Year Founded: 1912
Total Sales: $40,130,000 (e)
Number of Employees: 391
Average Check: Lunch(8); Dinner(8)
Total Units: 17
Trade Names: Allen Theatres (17)
Company-Owned Units: 17
Preferred Location Types: Other
Primary Menu: Snacks (17)
Areas of Operation: CO, NM
Type of Foodservice: In-Store Feeder (17)
Notes: The company derives approximately 72% of its revenue from theatre ticket sales,

on-screen advertising and other operations.

Key Personnel
LARRY ALLEN - President
NATHAN ALLEN - VP Finance
RUSSELL ALLEN - VP Operations
MICHELLE GOODWIN - General Manager
CHARLES GREEN - General Manager
AMANDA SHARP - Director Marketing
IRMA HOLGUIN - Manager Social Media

●▲
Auntie Anne's Franchise
700 S Telshor Blvd
Las Cruces, NM 88011-4669

Telephone: (575) 532-1378
Type of Business: Chain Restaurant Operator
Total Sales: $4,479,000 (e)
Total Units: 6
Trade Names: Auntie Anne's Hand-Rolled Soft Pretzels (6)
Units Franchised From: 6
Primary Menu: Snacks (6)
Areas of Operation: NM
Type of Foodservice: Quick Serve (6)
Franchise Affiliation: Auntie Anne's Inc., LANCASTER, PA

Key Personnel
MILAP MANIAR - Owner; General Buyer

●▲
Lavin Enterprises
151 S Walnut St Ste C3
Las Cruces, NM 88001-2617

Telephone: (575) 524-2912
Fax Number: (575) 524-8375
Type of Business: Chain Restaurant Operator
Year Founded: 1985
Total Sales: $37,680,000 (e)
Number of Employees: 300
Average Check: Breakfast(10); Lunch(10); Dinner(10)
Total Units: 8
Trade Names: McDonald's (8)
Units Franchised From: 8
Preferred Square Footage: 2,500; 3,000
Preferred Location Types: Discount Dept. Stores; Freestanding
Primary Menu: Hamburger (8)
Areas of Operation: NM
Type of Foodservice: Quick Serve (8)
Franchise Affiliation: McDonald's Corporation, CHICAGO, IL
Primary Distributors: (Full Line) The Martin-Brower Co., CONROE, TX

Key Personnel
MICHAEL LAVIN - President; General Manager; Director Operations, Facility/Maintenance, Real Estate; General Buyer

●▲
The Merritt Group
750 N 17th St
Las Cruces, NM 88005-4153

Telephone: (575) 524-8998
Fax Number: (575) 525-9232
Type of Business: Chain Restaurant Operator
Year Founded: 1972
Total Sales: $244,850,000 (e)
Number of Employees: 5,000
Average Check: Breakfast(6); Lunch(8); Dinner(8)
Total Units: 147
Trade Names: Sonic America's Drive-In (147)
Units Franchised From: 147
Preferred Square Footage: 1,200; 1,400
Preferred Location Types: Freestanding
Primary Menu: Hamburger (142)
Areas of Operation: AZ, CO, FL, GA, NM, NV, TX
Type of Foodservice: Quick Serve (142)
Franchise Affiliation: Sonic Corp., OKLAHOMA CITY, OK
Primary Distributors: (Full Line) US Foods, ALBUQUERQUE, NM

Key Personnel
BOB MERRITT - Chairman
BARBARA STAMNER - President; General Buyer
AHMAD MERRITT - Partner
TOM RICE - Partner; VP
JAYSON SCHKLOVEN - Partner; Senior VP
HAMILTON MERRITT - Partner
SHAHED AHMED - Partner; Senior VP
LESLIE BERRYMAN - CFO
MELISSA CHADWICK - Senior VP
COLLEEN HILL - VP Human Resources
MIKE PAULOWSKY - VP Loss Prevention, Real Estate, Human Resources
DONNA VOLZ - Senior Director Marketing
KATIE PESEK - Director
JULIA MCGAVRAN - Director Security
J. D. MERRITT - Director Facility/Maintenance, Information Systems, Construction, Design, Store Fixtures
KATHERINE NANNEY - Director Government Affairs

Inn of the Mountain Gods Resort and Casino
287 Carrizo Canyon Rd
Mescalero, NM 88340-9641

Mailing Address: PO Box 269, MESCALERO, NM, 88340-0269
Telephone: (575) 464-7777
Fax Number: (575) 464-7005
Internet Homepage: innofthemountaingods.com
Type of Business: Foodservice Operations - Casinos
Total Sales: $190,212,000 (e)
Alcohol Sales: 10%
Number of Employees: 1,515
Average Check: Breakfast(10); Lunch(16); Dinner(30)
Total Units: 7
Trade Names: Apache Tee (1); Big Game Sports Bar (1); Broken Arrow Tap House (1); Gathering of Nations Buffet (1); Ski Apache (1); Smokey B (1); Wendell's Steak & Seafood (1)
Company-Owned Units: 7
Preferred Square Footage: 5,500; 6,000
Preferred Location Types: Freestanding; Hotel/Motel; Travel Plazas
Alcohol Served: Beer, Wine, Liquor
Primary Menu: American (3); Bar-B-Q (1); Miscellaneous (1); Steak/Seafood (2)
Areas of Operation: NM
Type of Foodservice: Casual Dining (7)
Primary Distributors: (Food) US Foods, ALBUQUERQUE, NM
Notes: The company derives approximately 89% of its revenue from gaming, recreation, retail, hotel and other operations.

Key Personnel
JAMES MULDOWNEY - Executive Chef; General Buyer
MICHELLE PAPE - Director Information Technology
MONICA PINO - Director Operations
ELGIN TOCLANNY - Director Operations
BERNALYN VIA - Manager Operations
DENNY WARD - Manager Event Planning
SHAWN YOUNGMAN - Manager Food and Beverage
DENISE MATCHER - Supervisor Gaming/Entertainment
STEVEN PAWLYSHYN - Corporate Director Human Resources
KARIN STEWART - Analyst Marketing

●▲
Phelan Management Services, Inc
542 Clayton Rd
Raton, NM 87740-2368

Mailing Address: P O Box 2, TRINIDAD, CO, 81082
Telephone: (575) 445-4018
Fax Number: (575) 445-4018
Internet Homepage: phelaninc.us/home.html
Company Email: comments@phelaninc.us
Type of Business: Chain Restaurant Operator
Year Founded: 2001
Total Sales: $20,607,000 (e)
Number of Employees: 90
Average Check: Breakfast(8); Lunch(8); Dinner(8)

Total Units: 4
Trade Names: McDonald's (4)
Units Franchised From: 4
Preferred Square Footage: 2,500; 3,000
Preferred Location Types: Freestanding
Primary Menu: Hamburger (4)
Areas of Operation: CO, NM
Type of Foodservice: Quick Serve (4)
Franchise Affiliation: McDonald's Corporation, CHICAGO, IL
Primary Distributors: (Food) Mile Hi Foods, DENVER, CO

Key Personnel
GISELA PHELAN - CEO; General Manager; General Buyer
LEE PHELAN SR - Owner; COO; General Buyer
NANCY DROSTE - Controller

McDonald's of Corrales
PO Box 45688
Rio Rancho, NM 87174-5688

Telephone: (505) 892-4748
Fax Number: (505) 891-1044
Type of Business: Chain Restaurant Operator
Total Sales: $55,170,000 (e)
Number of Employees: 600
Average Check: Breakfast(8); Lunch(8); Dinner(8)
Total Units: 12
Trade Names: McDonald's (12)
Units Franchised From: 12
Preferred Square Footage: 2,500; 3,000
Preferred Location Types: Convenience Store/Gas Station; Discount Dept. Stores; Freestanding
Primary Menu: Hamburger (12)
Areas of Operation: NM
Type of Foodservice: Quick Serve (12)
Franchise Affiliation: McDonald's Corporation, CHICAGO, IL

Key Personnel
JULIAN GARZA - President; General Buyer

Cattle Baron Restaurants Inc.
901 S Main St Ste A
Roswell, NM 88203-5700

Mailing Address: PO Box 1654, Roswell, NM, 88202-1654
Telephone: (575) 622-3311
Fax Number: (575) 623-8801
Internet Homepage: cattlebaron.com
Company Email: marketing@cattlebaron.com
Type of Business: Chain Restaurant Operator
Year Founded: 1976
Total Sales: $42,250,000 (e)
Alcohol Sales: 2%
Number of Employees: 1,080
Average Check: Lunch(8); Dinner(20)
Total Units: 13
Trade Names: Cattle Baron Steak and Seafood (9); Farley's Food, Fun & Pub (3); Pasta Cafe (1)
Company-Owned Units: 13
Preferred Square Footage: 5,500; 6,000
Preferred Location Types: Freestanding
Alcohol Served: Beer, Wine, Liquor
Primary Menu: American (3); Italian (1); Steak/Seafood (9)
Areas of Operation: NM, TX
Type of Foodservice: Casual Dining (13)
Primary Distributors: (Full Line) SYSCO New Mexico, ALBUQUERQUE, NM

Key Personnel
TIM DOLAN - President
DENISE TODD - CFO
DOUGLAS WIESER - Senior VP
AMBER LUNDQUIST - General Manager

MJG Corporation
204 W 4th St
Roswell, NM 88201-4629

Telephone: (575) 622-8711
Fax Number: (575) 623-3075
Internet Homepage: mjgcorparbys.com
Company Email: nm_arbys_feedback@qwestoffice.net
Type of Business: Chain Restaurant Operator
Year Founded: 1979
Total Sales: $42,010,000 (e)
Number of Employees: 713
Average Check: Breakfast(5); Lunch(8); Dinner(12)
Total Units: 22
Trade Names: Arby's (22)
Units Franchised From: 22
Preferred Square Footage: 2,000; 2,300; 3,000
Preferred Location Types: Convenience Store/Gas Station; Downtown; Freestanding; Regional Mall
Primary Menu: Sandwiches/Deli (22)
Projected Remodelings: 4
Areas of Operation: CO, NM, TX
Type of Foodservice: Quick Serve (22)
Catering Services: Yes
Franchise Affiliation: Arby's Restaurant Group, ATLANTA, GA; International Dairy Queen Inc., BLOOMINGTON, MN
Primary Distributors: (Full Line) McLane/Rocky Mount, ROCKY MOUNT, NC

Key Personnel
JAY GLUCK - President; Director Purchasing, Facility/Maintenance, Real Estate, Design, Store Fixtures
GARY CHAVES - VP Operations, Human Resources, Training, Food Safety; Director Risk Management
PHIL CARBAJAL - VP Finance

Pecos Valley Pizza Incorporated dba Dominos Pizza
1114 S Union Ave
Roswell, NM 88203-2732

Mailing Address: PO Box 6030, ROSWELL, NM, 88202-6030
Telephone: (575) 637-3030
Fax Number: (575) 627-1330
Internet Homepage: dominosnm.com
Type of Business: Chain Restaurant Operator
Total Sales: $144,347,000 (e)
Total Units: 72
Trade Names: Domino's (72)
Units Franchised From: 72
Primary Menu: Pizza (72)
Areas of Operation: CO, NM, TX
Type of Foodservice: Quick Serve (72)
Franchise Affiliation: Domino's Pizza Inc, ANN ARBOR, MI

Key Personnel
BRIAN BAILEY - President
PAT CHANDLER - VP Administration
ANTHONY FISH - VP Operations; General Buyer
DIEDRA DUVALL - Director Marketing
VINCENT ALTON - Regional Director Operations

City Different Enterprises Inc.
1508 S Saint Francis Dr
Santa Fe, NM 87505-4040

Telephone: (505) 982-1831
Type of Business: Chain Restaurant Operator
Year Founded: 1973
Total Sales: $11,877,000 (e)
Number of Employees: 200
Average Check: Lunch(8); Dinner(8)
Total Units: 4
Trade Names: Taco Bell (4)
Units Franchised From: 4
Preferred Location Types: Freestanding
Primary Menu: Taco (4)
Areas of Operation: NM
Type of Foodservice: Quick Serve (4)
Franchise Affiliation: Taco Bell Corp., IRVINE, CA
Primary Distributors: (Full Line) McLane/Aurora, COMMERCE CITY, CO

Key Personnel
PAM LENHARD - President; Director

Advertising, Store Planning
JACK PELL - VP Marketing, Real Estate; General Buyer
ROBERT GRIEGO - Treasurer; Director Accounting
JORGE COBLENTZ - Director Operations, Purchasing, Food Safety
MICHELLE EVANS - Manager Administration

Santa Fe Dining
4056 Cerrillos Rd Ste F-6
Santa Fe, NM 87507-2605

Telephone: (505) 424-0303
Fax Number: (505) 424-1206
Internet Homepage: kellysbrewpub.com; santafedining.com
Type of Business: Chain Restaurant Operator
Year Founded: 1989
Total Sales: $20,130,000 (e)
Alcohol Sales: 20%
Number of Employees: 500
Average Check: Breakfast(10); Lunch(16); Dinner(28)
Total Units: 10
Trade Names: 35 North Coffee (1); Blue Corn Brewery (1); Blue Corn Cafe (1); Chama River Brewing Company (1); Draft Station (1); Kellys Brew Pub (1); La Casa Sena (1); Maria's New Mexican Kitchen (1); Rio Chama Steakhouse (1); Roof Top Pizzeria (1)
Company-Owned Units: 10
Preferred Square Footage: 10,000
Preferred Location Types: Freestanding; Outlet Mall
Alcohol Served: Beer, Wine, Liquor
Primary Menu: American (2); Coffee (2); Miscellaneous (1); Pizza (1); Southwest/Tex-Mex (2); Steak (1); Steak/Seafood (1)
Areas of Operation: NM
Type of Foodservice: Casual Dining (7); Fine Dining (2); Quick Serve (2)
Catering Services: Yes
Primary Distributors: (Food) SYSCO New Mexico, ALBUQUERQUE, NM

Key Personnel
ROBERT GRIEGO - VP Operations; General Manager Operations; Manager Operations
RENICK SARO - Controller
JON PAUL LEOS - General Manager
DAN LISS - General Manager
YMANDA CHAVEZ - General Manager
YOLANDA CATANACH - Director Payroll, Risk Management
NICOLE KULLER - Director Marketing
BLAINE MARTINEZ - Manager Restaurant Operations

The Coyote Cafe
132 W Water St
Santa Fe, NM 87501-2137

Telephone: (505) 983-1615
Fax Number: (505) 983-1615
Internet Homepage: coyotecafe.com
Company Email: coyotecafeoffice@gmail.com
Type of Business: Chain Restaurant Operator
Year Founded: 1987
Total Sales: $7,642,000 (e)
Alcohol Sales: 40%
Number of Employees: 60
Average Check: Lunch(36); Dinner(60)
Total Units: 2
Trade Names: Coyote Cafe (1); La Rooftop Cantina (1)
Company-Owned Units: 2
Preferred Location Types: Freestanding
Alcohol Served: Beer, Wine, Liquor
Primary Menu: Mexican (1); Southwest/Tex-Mex (1)
Areas of Operation: NM
Type of Foodservice: Casual Dining (1); Fine Dining (1)
Primary Distributors: (Full Line) SYSCO New Mexico, ALBUQUERQUE, NM

Key Personnel
QUINN STEPHENSON - Owner
EDUARDO RODRIGUEZ - Executive Chef

NEVADA

Carson Nugget Inc.
507 N Carson St
Carson City, NV 89701-4222

Telephone: (775) 882-1626
Fax Number: (775) 883-1106
Internet Homepage: ccnugget.com
Company Email: ccnugget@ccnugget.com
Type of Business: Foodservice Operations - Casinos
Year Founded: 1950
Total Sales: $20,408,000 (e)
Alcohol Sales: 25%
Number of Employees: 550
Total Units: 3
Trade Names: Alatte Coffee, Wine & Deli (1); Angelina's Italian Bistro (1); Eatery (1)
Company-Owned Units: 3
Preferred Square Footage: 10,000; 15,000
Preferred Location Types: Freestanding
Alcohol Served: Beer, Wine, Liquor
Primary Menu: American (2); Italian (1)
Areas of Operation: NV
Type of Foodservice: Casual Dining (3)
Primary Distributors: (Full Line) US Foods, RENO, NV

Key Personnel
DENISE DARLING - Controller; Manager Finance
DAVID SELLERS - Executive Chef
BILL ELDRED - Director Facility/Maintenance

Mi Casa Too
3809 N Carson St
Carson City, NV 89706-1935

Telephone: (775) 882-4080
Internet Homepage: mi-casa-too-carsoncity.com; mi-casa-too-reno.com
Company Email: info@mi-casa-too-carsoncity.com
Type of Business: Chain Restaurant Operator
Year Founded: 1975
Total Sales: $6,117,000 (e)
Alcohol Sales: 33%
Number of Employees: 110
Average Check: Lunch(14); Dinner(20)
Total Units: 2
Trade Names: Mi Casa Too (2)
Company-Owned Units: 2
Preferred Location Types: Freestanding
Alcohol Served: Beer, Wine, Liquor
Primary Menu: Mexican (2)
Areas of Operation: CA, NV
Type of Foodservice: Casual Dining (2)
On-site Distribution Center: Yes

Key Personnel
CINDY GOWER - Manager

Feel Good Brands, LLC
2230 Corporate Cir Ste 200
Henderson, NV 89074

Telephone: (702) 795-4100
Fax Number: (702) 795-4149
Internet Homepage: feelgoodbrandscorp.com
Company Email: hello@feelgoodbrands.com
Type of Business: Chain Restaurant Operator
Year Founded: 1999
Total Sales: $31,880,000 (e)
Number of Employees: 350
Average Check: Breakfast(8); Lunch(8); Dinner(8)
Total Units: 18
Trade Names: Auntie Anne's Hand-Rolled Soft Pretzels (2); Cinnabon (1); Einstein Bros Bagels (1); Frites (1); Hot Dog On A Stick (1); Krispy Kreme Doughnuts (8); Pick Up Stix Fresh Asian Kitchen (1); Popcornopolis (1); Popeyes Louisiana Kitchen (1); Schlotzsky's (1)
Units Franchised From: 18
Preferred Square Footage: 2,000; 4,000
Preferred Location Types: Other

Primary Menu: American (1); Asian (1); Bagels (1); Chicken (1); Hot Dogs (1); Sandwiches/Deli (1); Snacks (12)
Areas of Operation: CO, NV
Type of Foodservice: Fast Casual (3); In-Store Feeder (8); Quick Serve (7)
Franchise Affiliation: Auntie Anne's Inc., LANCASTER, PA; Cinnabon Inc., ATLANTA, GA; HDOS Enterprises, BEVERLY HILLS, CA; Krispy Kreme Doughnut Corporation, CHARLOTTE, NC; Pick Up Stix Inc., LAGUNA HILLS, CA; Popeyes Louisiana Kitchen Inc., ATLANTA, GA; Schlotzsky's Ltd., ATLANTA,GA; Tropical Smoothie Franchise Development Corp., ATLANTA, GA
Primary Distributors: (Full Line) SYSCO Food Services of Las Vegas, LAS VEGAS, NV

Key Personnel
LINCOLN SPOOR - CEO; Director Purchasing, Facility/Maintenance, Supply Chain, Real Estate, Design; General Buyer
MICHAEL GONZALEZ - VP Operations
JASON PEREIRA - General Manager
JULIE JEWELS BERRIER - Director Operations

Snowed Inn LLC.
2217 N Green Valley Pkwy
Henderson, NV 89014-5024

Telephone: (702) 454-1956
Fax Number: (702) 454-4332
Type of Business: Chain Restaurant Operator
Total Sales: $43,310,000 (e)
Total Units: 9
Trade Names: McDonald's (9)
Units Franchised From: 9
Preferred Square Footage: 2,500
Primary Menu: Hamburger (9)
Areas of Operation: NV
Type of Foodservice: Quick Serve (9)
Franchise Affiliation: McDonald's Corporation, CHICAGO, IL

Key Personnel
JAMES VANCE - President; General Buyer

The Dapper Doughnut
1000 N Green Valley Pkwy
Henderson, NV 89074

Telephone: (702) 546-9230
Internet Homepage: thedapperdoughnut.com
Type of Business: Chain Restaurant Operator
Total Sales: $10,950,000 (e)
Total Units: 11
Trade Names: The Dapper Doughnut (11)
Company-Owned Units: 1
Units Franchised To: 10
Primary Menu: Snacks (11)

Type of Foodservice: Quick Serve (11)

Key Personnel
MARK PUBLICOVER - Founder; CEO

American Casino & Entertainment Properties LLC
2000 Las Vegas Blvd S
Las Vegas, NV 89104-2507

Telephone: (702) 380-7777
Fax Number: (702) 383-4734
Internet Homepage: acepllc.com; arizonacharlies.com; stratospherehotel.com; theaquarius.com
Company Email: info@stratospherehotel.com
Type of Business: Foodservice Operations - Casinos
Year Founded: 1996
Total Sales: $675,490,000 (e)
Alcohol Sales: 10%
Number of Employees: 6,400
Total Units: 27
Restaurants in Hotels: 27
Trade Names: Buffet (1); Cafe Aquarius (1); Charlie's Cheesesteak Deli (1); Dreyers Ice Cream (1); Fellini's Ristorante (1); Frisco Market Buffet (1); Level 107 Lounge (1); Level 8 Pool Cafe (1); McCall's Heartland Grill (1); McDonald's (1); Noble Roman's Pizza (1); Outback Steakhouse (1); Panda Express (1); Ron's Steakhouse (1); Roxy's Diner (1); Sandwich Carvery 108 (1); Sourdough Cafe (2); Starbucks Coffee (1); Subway (2); The Vineyard Ristorante (1); Top of the World (1); Tower Pizzeria (1); Wild West Buffet (1); Windows on the River Buffet (1); Yukon Grille (1)
Company-Owned Units: 20
Units Franchised From: 7
Alcohol Served: Beer, Wine, Liquor
Areas of Operation: NV
Type of Foodservice: Casual Dining; Family Restaurant; Fast Casual; Fine Dining; Quick Serve
Franchise Affiliation: Burger King Worldwide Inc., MIAMI, FL; Doctor's Associates Inc., MILFORD, CT; Noble Roman's Inc., INDIANAPOLIS, IN; Outback Steakhouse Restaurants, TAMPA, FL; Panda Restaurant Group Inc., ROSEMEAD, CA; Sbarro Holdings LLC, COLUMBUS, OH; Starbucks Corporation, SEATTLE, WA
Primary Distributors: (Food) US Foods, NORTH LAS VEGAS, NV; (Specialty Foods) BakeMark - Las Vegas, NORTH LAS VEGAS, NV
Parent Company: Goldman, Sachs & Co. (GS Capital Partners), NEW YORK, NY
Notes: The company derives approximately 78% of its revenue from hotel/casino operations.

Key Personnel
MARK MAJETICH - Senior VP; General Manager Division

Auntie Anne's Franchise
5757 Wayne Newton Blvd
Las Vegas, NV 89111-8037

Telephone: (702) 261-7052
Internet Homepage: auntieannes.com
Type of Business: Chain Restaurant Operator
Total Sales: $2,325,000 (e)
Total Units: 3
Trade Names: Auntie Anne's Hand-Rolled Soft Pretzels (3)
Units Franchised From: 3
Primary Menu: Snacks (3)
Areas of Operation: NV
Type of Foodservice: Quick Serve (3)
Franchise Affiliation: Auntie Anne's Inc., LANCASTER, PA

Key Personnel
VICKI RICHARDSON - Owner; General Buyer

Big Chicken
10845 Griffith Peak Dr Ste 520
Las Vegas, NV 89135

Internet Homepage: bigchicken.com
Type of Business: Chain Restaurant Operator
Year Founded: 2018
Total Units: 14
Trade Names: Big Chicken (14)
Company-Owned Units: 14
Primary Menu: Chicken (14)
Projected Openings: 5
Areas of Operation: AZ, CA, FL, IL, LA, MD, MO, NV, NY, OH, TN, TX, WA
Type of Foodservice: Fast Casual (14)

Key Personnel
SHAQUILLE O'NEAL - Founder; Owner
JOSH HALPERN - CEO
MICHAEL FONTES - VP Construction
STEPHANIE BITTERS - Controller
BRIAN COCHRAN - Director Operations
JOSHUA SIMS SR - Director Marketing

Bok Bok Chicken
2900 E Patrick Ln Suite 3
Las Vegas, NV 89120

Telephone: (702) 761-9207
Internet Homepage: bokbokchicken.com
Company Email: info@bokbokchicken.com
Type of Business: Chain Restaurant Operator

Year Founded: 2018
Total Units: 7
Trade Names: Bok Bok Chicken (7)
Company-Owned Units: 5
Units Franchised To: 2
Preferred Location Types: Community Mall; Freestanding; Hotel/Motel; Strip Mall
Primary Menu: Greek/Mediterranean (7)
Projected Openings: 3
Areas of Operation: CA, NV
Type of Foodservice: Fast Casual (7)

Key Personnel
SILVA CHAMANIAN - Owner
JEONGHOON KANG - Manager

Boyd Gaming Corporation
6465 S Rainbow Blvd
Las Vegas, NV 89118-3215

Telephone: (702) 792-7200
Fax Number: (702) 696-1194
Internet Homepage: boydgaming.com
Type of Business: Foodservice Operations - Casinos
Year Founded: 1974
Publicly Held: Yes
Total Sales: $3,470,000,000 (e)
Alcohol Sales: 10%
Number of Employees: 23,477
Total Units: 29
Restaurants in Hotels: 100
Trade Names: Aliante Casino (1); Amelia Belle Casino (1); Ameristar Casino Hotel (1); Ameristar Casino Resort Spa (1); Belterra Casino Resort (1); Blue Chip Casino Hotel Spa (1); Borgata Hotel, Casino & Spa (1); California Hotel & Casino (1); Cannery Casino Hotel (1); Delta Downs Racetrack Casino Hotel (1);Diamond Jo Dubuque (1); Diamond Jo Worth (1); Eastside Cannery Casino (1); Eldorado (1); Evangeline Downs Racetrack, Casino, Hotel (1); Fremont Hotel & Casino (1); Gold Coast Hotel & Casino (1); IP Casino Resort Spa (1); Jokers Wild (1); Kansas Star (1); Main Street Station Casino, Brewery & Hotel (1); Par-A-Dice Hotel & Casino (1); Sam's Town Hotel & Casino Shreveport (1); Sam's Town Hotel & Gambling Hall Las Vegas (1); Sam's Town Hotel & Gambling HallTunica (1); Suncoast Hotel & Casino (1); The Orleans Hotel & Casino (1); Treasure Chest Casino (1); Valley Forge Casino Resort (1)
Company-Owned Units: 24
Alcohol Served: Beer, Wine, Liquor
Areas of Operation: IA, IL, IN, LA, MS, NJ, NV
Type of Foodservice: Casual Dining; Fast Casual; Fine Dining; Quick Serve
Notes: The company derives approximately 91% of its revenue from casino/hotel operations & other business ventures.

Key Personnel
WILLIAM S. BOYD - Executive Chairman
MARIANNE JOHNSON - Vice Chairman; Chief Diversity Officer; Exec VP
KEITH E. SMITH - CEO; President
JOSH HIRSBERG - CFO; Exec VP; Treasurer
TED BOGICH - Exec VP Operations, Midwest Region
STEPHEN S. THOMPSON - Exec VP Operations
TONY TAEUBEL - Senior VP Operations; General Manager
STEVE SCHUTTE - Senior VP Operations
VINCE SCHWARTZ - Senior VP Operations
BILL NOONAN - Senior VP Government Affairs
STAN SMITH - VP
THOMAS F. TWESME - VP; General Counsel
RON FRYE - VP Construction, Design
DAVID KRASN - VP Tax
WILLIAM R. BOYD - VP
JAMES W. CARTER - VP Strategic Planning
RICH ARON - VP Legal; General Counsel
DAVID DALEY - VP
KIM ETLAND - General Manager Division
BILLY MCCOY - Director
CARLOS CASTANO - Director Compliance
MS KATHY VOGEL - Director Operations
JEFF RAMSEY - Director Finance
KAREN STEPHENS - Senior Manager Risk Management
PATRICK QUINN - Manager Engineering
MIKE WISEMAN - Manager Data Quality
SYLVIA BAUER - Manager Benefits
OTIS EDWARDS - Supervisor Security
ARLENE CECKA - Specialist Human Resources
JENNIFER JUDKINS - Coordinator Marketing
DEBI KLOEK - Analyst Operations
LISA WAMSLEY - Analyst Finance
CARMEN RESTIVO - Senior Engineer Security

Caesars Entertainment Corporation
1 Caesars Palace Dr
Las Vegas, NV 89109-8969

Telephone: (702) 407-6000
Fax Number: (702) 407-6037
Internet Homepage: caesars.com
Type of Business: Foodservice Operations - Casinos
Year Founded: 1937
Publicly Held: Yes
Total Sales: $12,530,700,000 (e)
Alcohol Sales: 15%
Number of Employees: 66,000
Foodservice Sales: $2,255,526,000 (e)
Total Units: 55
Restaurants in Hotels: 53
Trade Names: Alea Glasgow (1); Alea Nottingham (1); Bally's Atlantic City (1); Bally's Las Vegas (1); Bluegrass Downs (1); Caesars Atlantic City (1); Caesars Cairo (1); Caesars Dubai (1); Caesars Palace Las Vegas (1); Caesars Southern Indiana (1); Caesars Windsor (1); Emerald Casino Resort (1); Flamingo LasVegas (1); Harrah's Atlantic City (1); Harrah's Cherokee (1); Harrah's Chrokee Valley River (1); Harrah's Council Bluffs (1); Harrah's Gulf Coast (1); Harrah's Joliet (1); Harrah's Lake Tahoe (1); Harrah's Las Vegas (1); Harrah's Laughlin (1); Harrah's Louisiana Downs (1); Harrah's Metropolis (1); Harrah's New Orleans (1); Harrah's North Kansas City (1); Harrah's Northern California (1); Harrah's Philadelphia (1); Harrah's Phoenix Ak-Chin (1); Harrah's Reno (1); Harrah's Resort Southern California (1); Harvey's Lake Tahoe (1); Hoosier Park (1); Horseshoe Casino Bossier City (1); Horseshoe Casino Council Bluffs (1); HorseshoeCasino Hammond (1); Horseshoe Casino Southern Indiana (1); Horseshoe Casino Tunica (1); Indiana Grand (1); Kings & Queens Casino (1); Manchester235 (1); Nobu Hotel at Caesars Palace (1); Paris Las Vegas (1); Planet Hollywood (1); Playboy Club London (1); Ramses Casino (1); Rendezvous Brighton (1);Rendezvous Southend-on-Sea (1); Rio All-Suite Hotel & Casino (1); The Cromwell (1); The Empire Casino (1); The LINQ Hotel & Casino (2); The Sportsman (1); Tunica Roadhouse (1)
Company-Owned Units: 55
Alcohol Served: Beer, Wine, Liquor
Areas of Operation: AZ, CA, IA, IL, IN, LA, MD, MO, MS, NC, NJ, NV, OH, PA, ON
Foreign Countries: CANADA; EGYPT; ENGLAND; SCOTLAND; SOUTH AFRICA; URUGUAY
Type of Foodservice: Cafeteria; Casual Dining; Family Restaurant; Fast Casual; Fine Dining; Quick Serve
Primary Distributors: (Food) SYSCO Food Services of Las Vegas, LAS VEGAS, NV
Notes: The company derives approximately 82% of its revenue from hotel/casino operations.

Key Personnel
GARY W. LOVEMAN - Chairman
TONY RODIO - CEO
GARY SELESNER - President Division
DAN NITA - President Division
THOMAS M. JENKIN - President Group
JOHN KOSTER - President Region
ERIC HESSION - CFO; Exec VP
MARCO CECCARELLI - CIO Division; Senior VP
TIMOTHY DONOVAN - Chief Compliance Officer; Exec VP; General Counsel
GEOFF BREACH - Chief Engineering Officer
FERNANDO ROSETE - Chief Engineering Officer
KEITH K. ALEXANDER - Chief Security Officer
JAN JONES BLACKHURST - Exec VP Communications
CHRISTIAN STUART - Exec VP Gaming/Entertainment
TY STEWART - Senior VP Digital Media;

Executive Director Operations
NINA BARIAS - Senior VP Gaming/Entertainment
BRANDI ELLIS - Senior VP Marketing
TOM COOK - Senior VP; General Manager Division
NAPOLEON CHIO - VP Marketing
MARILYN ELLIS-VISSER - VP Information Technology, Security
TIM BOWEN - VP Culinary Operations
PAUL BRECI - VP Operations
DIANA CABALLERO - VP Strategic Sourcing
AMBER HERRINGTON - VP Sales
CARA HUEY - VP Finance
NADEEN HUGHES - VP
DHIVY JAYASEELAN - VP Labor Relations
KARIE HALL - VP; General Manager
MIKE HARTY - VP Information Technology
CRAIG FJELSTED - VP Tax
BILL GORMLEY - VP Credit
MARK KELLY - VP Operations
LYNN JUAN - VP
KARYN STEENKAMP - VP Construction, Design
JOHN VISCOSI - VP Gaming/Entertainment
LORI WARE - VP Finance
NORA WEST - VP Marketing
DAVID WOLKOFF - VP Information Systems
DONALD ROSS - VP Catering
JANA RYGIEL - VP Marketing
SUSAN MOORE - VP Sales
DEBBIE MUNCH - VP Public Relations
AMBER NADEAU - VP
CHRIS NEMENZO - Executive Director Gaming/Entertainment
DAN NEWTON - Executive Director Gaming/Entertainment
BEVERLY SHAHAN - Executive Director Gaming/Entertainment
CINDY SAXON - Executive Director Gaming/Entertainment
HEIDE SMITH - Executive Director Sales
JENNIFER READ - Executive Director Sales
SCOTT REATH - Executive Director Sales
BRITTANY WOLFORD - Executive Director Sales
PAUL STEWART - Executive Director Marketing
CAROL THOMPSON - Executive Director Gaming/Entertainment
CAROL TOWNS - Executive Director Gaming/Entertainment
LARRY GLANTZ - Executive Director Sales
CELIA GERONIMO - Executive Director Gaming/Entertainment
CINDY HINKLEY - Executive Director Gaming/Entertainment
MICHAEL BURNAM - Executive Director Sales
GRETCHEN BROUGHER - Executive Director Gaming/Entertainment
SANDRA ARAGON - Executive Director Sales
MICHAEL DORSZ - Executive Director Sales
TAMMY LEE - Controller
C. GEORGE WOO - Controller
ASHLEY SANDERSON - Controller Accounting
THOMAS LYNN - General Counsel

GOMEZ MARISELA - General Manager
MICHELLE LLEWELLYN - General Manager
CRISTOBAL JINGER - General Manager
JOSEPH JARMUZ - General Manager Food and Beverage
KRYSTAL GRIER - General Manager
NIESHA FORTSON - General Manager
COLLEEN DEC - General Manager
RAY ANGELES - General Manager
SANDRA AYALA - General Manager
DONALD BISHOP - General Manager
ELOISE SCAVELLA - General Manager
JASON RABON - General Manager
SEAN MCBURNEY - General Manager
MICHAEL NOONE - General Manager
JACKIE PETERSON - General Manager
LIANETTY PINTO - General Manager
STEPHANIE WHATLEY-HEINLE - General Manager
KAREN TACCONA - General Manager
MARLENE STICKNEY - Director Information Technology
PAT TAYLOR - Director Logistics
FRANKIE WILLETT - Director Marketing
BARRY WITT - Director Operations
CHERECE VINA - Director Human Resources, Region
MICHELE POLCI CPCE - Director Catering
MATT NITSCHE - Director Event Planning
DAVID O'HARRA - Director Operations, Logistics
SANDRA MORRIS - Director Infrastructure
LORENA MOTA - Director Marketing
ADRIENNE PRATHER-MARCOS - Director Communications
STEPHANIE RICHTER - Director Operations
MORGAN RICK - Director Human Resources
DAVID SCHERER - Director Operations
LINDA SCHMITZ - Director Finance
WILLIAM SATTLER - Director Gaming/Entertainment
CHAD SIMMONS - Director Marketing
PETER SCHUCH - Director Finance
ROGER BISSELL - Director
GARY BOGAN - Director Construction
MOSTAFA BOUTAJRIT - Director Customer Service
KARLA CALMELAT - Director Marketing
GARY AUSTIN - Director Operations
JOHN AVEIRO - Director Operations
WENDY BENNECKE - Director Sales
DAVID BERONI - Director Marketing
SETA ARTINIAN - Director Gaming/Entertainment
EDWARD DAVIS - Director Finance
KEVIN DOUGLAS - Director Security
VICTOR ECHENIQUE - Director Internal Audit
SABRA ELGES - Director Event Planning, Region
EDMOND ELIAS - Director Development
JESSICA CHOY - Director Real Estate
DARRELL CLULOW - Director Technology
OLGA CHAPLYGINA - Director Marketing
MICHAEL CAPPARELLI - Director Operations
TONYA CARPENTER - Director Marketing

RICARDO CORNEJO - Director Real Estate
BRENT COX - Director Marketing
ERIK CHAVEZ - Director Finance
LINDA FOLLOSCO - Director Administration
DEREK FOPPES - Director Marketing
FRANK FRANCOIS - Director Marketing, Region
MELISSA FIELDING - Director Operations
GABRIEL GARCIA - Director Design
KENT HOUSTON - Director Customer Analytics
ANDY HERROLD - Director Marketing
LUTHER GUELKER - Director Accounting
MARC HADDAD - Director Marketing
MICHALA JOELS - Director Information Technology
TONY KORKOW - Director Strategic Sourcing
KAREN LO - Director Design
GINA LUCARELLA - Director Marketing
MAJA LUKIC - Director Business Development
MARTIN TURNER - Regional Director Procurement
DENNIS EASTERDAY - Assistant Director Security
ELOISE DE LA TORRE - Assistant Director Retail Operations
STEPHEN LUEBBERT - Senior Manager Information Technology, Risk Management, Compliance
SONJA KNEISSL-PARK - Senior Manager Finance
ROBIN HUDGENS - Senior Manager Sales
THOMAS GOLANICS - Senior Manager Tax
CINDY GOLDBERG - Senior Manager Sales
MARK FLETCHER - Senior Manager
JOAN TAYLOR - Senior Manager Sales
PANKAJ PATEL - Senior Manager Database
STEPHANIE NICHOLS - Business Manager Accounting
JASON PARKER - Business Manager Accounting
RYAN NEPOMUCENO - Business Manager Accounting
DIANE MYERS - Business Manager Accounting
MIROSLAVA SAPUNDZHIEVA - Business Manager Accounting
TINA WHEELER - Business Manager Accounting
TRAVIS WHITAKER - Business Manager Accounting
MUI HUNG-STEELE - Business Manager Accounting
LAURA GUTIERREZ - Business Manager Accounting
RITA LIMEHOUSE - Business Manager Accounting
STEPHANIE LIANG - Business Manager Accounting
MARICEL DONNELLY - Business Manager Accounting
APRIL CVETNICH - Business Manager Accounting
JONATHAN ALVAREZ - Business Manager Accounting
AMY BAZE - Business Manager Accounting
JOHN BLANCHARD - Regional Manager

Wholesale
FAVIAN CONTRERAS - Regional Manager Information Systems
ROSIE PARRA - Regional Manager Talent
MARTIN PERTEET II - Manager Gaming/Entertainment
DARLENE PHILLIPS - Manager Sales
ROBIN PHILLIPS - Manager Media
KEVIN POND - Manager Internal Audit
QIAN (Q) QIAN - Manager Operations
KEVIN QUAGLIO - Manager Security
SUE QUINLAN - Manager Security
JOSEPH NOEL - Manager Gaming/Entertainment
DEAN NOTLEY - Manager Gaming/Entertainment
KIMBERLY PATTERSON - Manager Sales
MATT PATULSKI - Manager Gaming/Entertainment
J.C. PENNY - Manager Security
JOSE OSORIO - Manager Customer Service
JUDITH PALMA - Manager Sales
ANNE NASH - Manager Database
PAULINE NGUYEN - Manager Marketing
JESUS MORENO - Manager Accounting
DION MORIC - Manager
HEATHER MURRAY - Manager Restaurant Operations
KATHLEEN MCCUE - Manager Marketing
JAMES MCDERMOTT - Manager Security
SUSAN MCNAMARA - Manager Information Technology
DAVID B. MELTON - Manager Retail Operations
MICHAEL MENDOZA - Manager Restaurant Operations
JANICE MILLER - Manager Security
LAILA MITRI - Manager Accounting
TRACEY MONROE - Manager Sales
GRACE MARTIN-NOEL - Manager Sales
ELISABETH MARTINEZ - Manager Marketing
THOMAS SAWYER - Manager Information Technology
MAYRA SANDOVAL - Manager Gaming/Entertainment
VERONICA SALAS - Manager Human Resources
ANDREW SCLATER-BOOTH - Manager Gaming/Entertainment
KAREN SCOFIELD - Manager Compliance
MATT SINIBALDI - Manager Sales
DENNIS SIXBERY - Manager Alcoholic Beverages
NANCY SMALSKAS - Manager Sales
JEFFREY SMITH - Manager Restaurant Operations
JASON RINTA - Manager Human Resources
LINDSAY RADIC - Manager Event Planning
NICHOLE RADCLIFF - Manager Human Resources
JEANNE ROY - Manager Sales
LISA RUBIN - Manager Credit
KURT RUCHABER - Manager Retail Operations
JUDY RUFFINI - Manager Sales
JEFFREY RUSKOWITZ - Manager Engineering
DANA ROGERS - Manager

ANGIE ROMIN - Manager Sales
MARYDALIA ROSAS - Manager Gaming/Entertainment
AVA WIDEEN - Manager Marketing
SHAUN WAYNE - Manager Design
PHILLIP WILSON - Manager General Merchandise
STEWART WITHEY - Manager Security
WARREN WOODARD - Manager Security
ALISON WOODWARD - Manager Event Planning
VALERIE TURNER - Manager Gaming/Entertainment
STEPHANIE VAN ORSOW - Manager Marketing
JAZMIN VARGAS-CAMACHO - Manager Customer Service
EDEN VIRAY - Manager Customer Service
RICK VONFELDT - Manager Legal
MORGAN TAYLOR - Manager Security
HENRY THAI - Manager Accounting
KELLY STONE - Manager Sales
KRISHANA THOMAS - Manager Catering
BARBARA TURNER - Manager Sales
DANIEL TICKNER - Manager Gaming/Entertainment
TIMOTHIE TINSLEY - Manager Information Systems, Sales
LISA STEWART - Manager Gaming/Entertainment
LIZ SOTOMAYOR - Manager Facility/Maintenance
OPHELIA WONG - Manager Tax
SHANNON COLDON - Manager Sales
ANGELA COLEMAN - Manager Human Resources
JENNIFER COGNITORE - Manager Internal Audit
JANA DANIELS - Manager Compliance
JANA DANIELS CICA - Manager Internal Audit
CHRISTOPHER CARRAHER - Manager Operations
GEORGE CARTER - Manager Operations
GEORGE CATACALOS - Manager Restaurant Operations
CHRIS COXSEY - Manager Gaming/Entertainment
JAKE EATON - Manager Restaurant Operations
LISA EBELTOFT - Manager Digital Marketing
JUDY DUPREY - Manager Food and Beverage
KEVIN ELLER - Manager Customer Service
GEORGE FARRELL - Manager POS/Scanning
JESSICA FERNANDEZ - Manager Marketing
SKIP BLANCHARD - Manager Wholesale
JOEL BLAKEMORE - Manager Marketing
HAZEL BRANCH - Manager Human Resources
JAMES BROWN - Manager Tax
SHAUN BURNETT - Manager Information Technology
SEAN BURNEY - Manager Operations
DUSTIN BROWN - Manager Gaming/Entertainment
HOPE BUCHANAN - Manager Catering
PAMELA BUCKLEY - Manager Sales
MICHAEL BECERRA-GUTIERREZ - Manager

Payroll
ZACHARY BARRUS - Manager Finance
CHRISTINE BERRY - Manager Catering
YALDA AYOUB - Manager Real Estate
CONNIE ANDERSEN - Manager Gaming/Entertainment
PHIL ANDERSEN - Manager Infrastructure
TINA ANDERSON - Manager Database
TYLER ADAMS - Manager POS/Scanning
PARRILLO LISA - Manager Media Relations
RAQUEL LUCERO - Manager Database
LU LU - Manager Digital Marketing
FAVIOLA LOPEZ - Manager Accounting
KELLEY MAGDALUYO - Manager Government Affairs, Compliance
POOJA MAHESHWARI - Manager Accounting
CHRISTINE MAHONEY - Manager Customer Service
JOHN M. MARTIN - Manager Gaming/Entertainment
CYNTHIA MARCUS - Manager Group
JOSEPH MAIDMAN - Manager Gaming/Entertainment
DAWN MALONE - Manager Information Systems
MASSIMO MANIERI - Manager Food and Beverage
VINCE KONG - Manager Catering
KATHY KELLEY - Manager Accounting
BARBARA KILLEN - Manager Operations
SCOTT KINGHAM - Manager Tax
JONETTE KITCH - Manager Operations
SCOTT KRAMER - Manager Restaurant Operations
SALINA KRAVETZ - Manager Sales
MARY LABARRE - Manager Payroll
ASHLEY LAWSON - Manager Marketing
AMBER JOHNSON - Manager Restaurant Operations
DAWN JENNINGS - Manager Sales
AL JIANNOTTI - Manager Gaming/Entertainment
ALBERT JIANNOTTI - Manager Gaming/Entertainment
MICKI JORDAN - Manager Risk Management
MARY GRIEGO - Manager Human Resources
DUANE HASHIRO - Manager Information Technology
MARK GUTHRIE - Manager Beverages, Food
MARLIES HARDY - Manager Restaurant Operations
REGINA IBARRA - Manager Catering
OZZY ISLAS - Manager Alcoholic Beverages
AMBER JACKSON - Manager Marketing
JEFF JARBOE - Manager Gaming/Entertainment
KIM HUCKABAY - Manager Gaming/Entertainment
KIERRA HOSANNAH - Manager Digital
MARY FERRIS - Manager Catering
RACHAEL GABEL - Manager Catering
ADRIAN GAINES - Manager Information Technology
THOMAS GAMBLE - Manager Gaming/Entertainment

DAVID FOSTER - Manager Marketing
JAMIE FOX - Manager Catering
TIM GRIFFIN - Manager Gaming/Entertainment
BECKY GARRISON SPENIA - Manager Credit
DANA GEORGE - Manager
ALEX GILMOUR - Manager HRIS
GRETCHEN GERSKI - Manager Sales
STACY GERSTEIN - Manager Catering
JULIA GRAHAM - Supervisor
CATHY GRAY - Supervisor
DERICK GOOD - Supervisor Gaming/Entertainment
BRENDA GARCIA - Supervisor Gaming/Entertainment
JEFFREY FITI - Supervisor Security
HUGO FLORES - Supervisor Marketing
SHERRY HANKINS - Supervisor Training
THOMAS HEATH - Supervisor Security
ANGELA GUADAGNO - Supervisor
TAYLOR KURTIK - Supervisor Security
KIMO MAIWELA - Supervisor Security
MICHELLE MARE-OBERLAY - Supervisor Gaming/Entertainment
BRIAN LOUVIERE - Supervisor Gaming/Entertainment
ANTHONY ARCHULETA - Supervisor Training
NELLY AZUCAR AZUCAR - Supervisor Production
CHUCK BABBISH - Supervisor Training
MICHAEL BAILEY - Supervisor Retail Operations
ERIK BALBUENA - Supervisor Information Technology
JOLETTA BIBBS - Supervisor Security
CHARMAINE BIRD - Supervisor
GERALD BEER - Supervisor
GARY BROWN - Supervisor Gaming/Entertainment
ADAM BYCINA - Supervisor Gaming/Entertainment
MICHAEL BROWN - Supervisor Security
STEPHIE BROWN - Supervisor
RON BOYLAND - Supervisor Gaming/Entertainment
CHRISTINE BLUNK - Supervisor
DAVID FANTAUZZO - Supervisor Gaming/Entertainment
RYAN DOUGHERTY - Supervisor Security
JARROD CHAPMAN - Supervisor Security
JUAN CARLOS CARRERA PENA - Supervisor Gaming/Entertainment
RONALD CAMPOS - Supervisor Retail Operations
HECTOR CARIAS - Supervisor Gaming/Entertainment
ANDRE DAVID - Supervisor Gaming/Entertainment
SCOTT COX - Supervisor Gaming/Entertainment
MARIE COHEN - Supervisor Accounting
RON YEE - Supervisor
DEBORAH YOUNG'S-GRAVES - Supervisor Customer Service
DAN SPENCE - Supervisor Gaming/Entertainment

JOHN STALLINGS - Supervisor
MAGGI STARKWEATHER - Supervisor Retail Operations
CHRIS SOENARIE - Supervisor Gaming/Entertainment
JEREMY STONE - Supervisor Production
DAVID TILLEMANS - Supervisor
BOB WEISMAN - Supervisor Gaming/Entertainment
RENATA RODRIGUEZ - Supervisor Development
JOSHUA SOBOTTA - Supervisor Security
TERRI SCAROLA - Supervisor
GINGER SHEA - Supervisor
RALPH SANTIAGO - Supervisor Security
ALLEN H. MALLAD JR - Supervisor Security
JOSH MOORE - Supervisor Security
NATE MONDELL - Supervisor Production
MICHAEL MURRAY - Supervisor Recruitment
WILLIAM MUNSON - Supervisor Security
MATTHEW QUINTERO - Supervisor Retail Operations
JESSICA RABINO - Supervisor
CINDY PONTECORVO - Supervisor
BARBARA ROSE CAMS - Project Manager
MICHAEL WALKER - Project Manager Information Technology
LISA COBB - Project Manager
TAMMY FERRENBURG - Project Manager
KATHY ELDER - Project Manager Information Technology
AL JIMENEZ - Project Manager Information Technology
RAMONA MAHUNA - Administrator Human Resources
VICTORIA BUNTING - Administrator Benefits
JASON ALLEN - Administrator Security
ANIA PINO O'REILLY - Administrator Human Resources
TERRI WAUGH - General Buyer
DELIA SAMSON - Senior Buyer Region
SLOBODANKA CAVIC - Senior Buyer Sourcing
VICTOR CHAVEZ - Specialist Marketing
KATHLEEN DUNBAR - Specialist Event Planning
DENNIS DOMPKE - Specialist
CAROLINE APP - Specialist Training
GWENDOLYN ARTIS - Specialist Customer Service
MEAGAN ALBAN - Specialist Event Planning
LESA CAMPBELL - Specialist Marketing
MATTHEW BLUNK - Specialist Digital
SUSAN BOZELL - Specialist Credit
CHRISTOPHER BOWERS - Specialist Communications
DEBBIE MALDONADO - Specialist Benefits
MARJET LUCKING - Specialist Event Planning
AMY JO JOHNSON - Specialist Payroll
JAMIE KELLETT - Specialist Event Planning
JOHNNY LEAL - Specialist Information Technology
CHRISTIAN GUNGON - Specialist Operations
DEANNA HUDSON - Specialist Payroll
DEANNA SANTARELLI - Specialist Marketing
KRISTEN SANTERO - Specialist Marketing

JUSTIN SCHOLZ - Specialist Distribution
TONY SODA - Specialist Inventory
ANTHONY RATTANA - Specialist Information Technology
ERISA PRIFTI - Specialist Operations
JULIE PRUSSACK - Specialist Talent
CRAIG RICHARDS - Specialist Marketing
DAVID RYAN - Specialist Marketing
GLEN PETERS - Specialist Information Systems
SUNITA VILLADROIN - Specialist Marketing
ERICA TURNER-MARTIN - Specialist Training
TASHA TORGENSEN - Specialist Payroll
D'ANDRE THOMPSON - Specialist Marketing
SHERRY THORNLEY - Specialist Information Systems
JOHN STUART - Specialist Marketing
KRISTIN SOO HOO - Specialist Public Relations
GREG THEVENIN - Buyer General Merchandise
NANCY NOBLE-BASCH - Buyer Accessories - Fine Jewelry
DEBBI LONGCHAMPS - Buyer
CYNTHIA BONILLA - Buyer
RHONDA BURKE - Coordinator Event Planning
ELLEN BANAG - Coordinator Event Planning
MARCIE ALLEN - Coordinator Database
ANDREA CRUMMEY - Coordinator Sales
FATIMA EHLERS - Coordinator Sales
ROMAN DAVID - Coordinator Marketing
JANET LUIB - Coordinator Database
SHEILA MANTES-CHAVEZ - Coordinator Media
MICHELLE MARTIN - Coordinator Sales
CHRISTOPHER LAPENA - Coordinator Marketing
EDLYN KAANOI - Coordinator
NATALIE KANIAN - Coordinator Product Development
GARY JIORAS - Coordinator Operations
JUSTINE HEW - Coordinator Marketing
ANDREA HACK - Coordinator Event Planning
MARGARITA HERRERA MAGGIE - Coordinator Marketing
REBECCA FLEMING - Coordinator
JANET GAGNE - Coordinator Group
BELINDA GAUTHIER - Coordinator Operations
TERRI NORTH - Coordinator Group
JACLYN OCONNOR - Coordinator Human Resources
BRITTANY MILES - Coordinator Event Planning
BRANDY MASTERSON - Coordinator
GABRIEL J. MARTINEZ - Coordinator Gaming/Entertainment
RICARDO REGINO - Coordinator Administration
DANIELLE RIOLO - Coordinator Event Planning
KAMEELAH SHAREEF-SIMS - Coordinator Branding
MICHELLE SABORIDO - Coordinator Branch
LAJUANA TRAYLOR - Coordinator Compliance
MIKE TODD - Coordinator Marketing
YADIRA VALENCIA - Coordinator Human Resources
JANICE WRIGHT - Coordinator Marketing
CORINNE WITTIG - Coordinator Marketing
SERENA WETCHER - Agent Sales

MARILYN SAENZ - Agent Customer Service
KACHINA JOHNSTON - Agent Gaming/Entertainment
MICHAEL LUKSAVAGE - Agent Security
CHARLES LEWIS - Agent Sales
ARACELI CASTRILLO - Agent Customer Service
CARLOS CASTRO - Agent Security
PATRICIA (PATTI) DILLON - Agent Customer Service
GLEN ALIRE - Agent Security
CHRIS DIX - Representative Customer Service
VICKY LICOMITROS - Representative Sales
PATSY GOODMAN - Representative Accounting
NATALIE HALEY - Representative Gaming/Entertainment
GINGER RILEY - Representative Marketing
DESYRAE REED - Representative Sales
CESAR MARTINEZ - Representative Customer Analytics
KEVIN METCALF - Representative Customer Service
ROSE NEWMAN - Representative
SCOTT GIBSON - Consultant
RYAN HAY - Designer Graphic Design
MARIA DJALOVA - Designer Production
JESSICA DRUMMOND - Designer Graphic Design
ANTHONY CARDUCCI - Systems Analyst
MICHAEL CONTRERAS - Systems Analyst
BOB BATES - Systems Analyst
MARLENE GRUBICH - Systems Analyst
FELIX RODRIGUEZ - Systems Analyst
HOWARD VAIL - Systems Analyst
SARAH TARANTO - Senior Analyst Purchasing
NANCY RIVAS - Senior Analyst
MIKE GURLIDES - Senior Analyst
LILLIAN BLASCO - Senior Analyst
JENNIFER DELUCA - Senior Analyst
PAUL CRIPE - Senior Analyst Marketing
STEPHANIE DAVIS - Analyst Information Systems
KELLY EASON - Analyst Payroll
DANIELLE COLL - Analyst Accounting
STACEY AWLS-IGELEKE - Analyst Credit
CHRIS JONES - Analyst Information Technology
TAYLOR RADFORD - Analyst Marketing
ERIC SIMON - Analyst Information Systems
AVETIS MAZMANYAN - Analyst Marketing
RICH PORTNOY - Analyst; Senior Programmer
SVETLANA VAYSMAN - Analyst Gaming/Entertainment
CATHY YEE - Analyst Compliance
JOHN VALLE - Architect
ADNAN KHAWAJA - Architect Information Systems
REY E. MADRID - Developer
TRAVIS PIERCE - Senior Engineer Security
TIM MAXSON - Senior Engineer Communications
HECTOR MARTINEZ - Engineer Network
JIM PERRY - Engineer
RICHARD O'BRIEN - Engineer
TOM SHELLABARGER - Engineer Operations
AREND SCHOUTEN - Engineer
JESSE RODRIGUEZ - Engineer
JASON VAN DER ELST - Engineer Operations
ERNESTO VILLAGRANA - Engineer Information Technology
MICHAEL STEPZINSKI - Engineer Information Technology
JAMES JOHNSON - Engineer
JIMMY JIMENEZ - Engineer
CHASE HILL - Engineer
ANTHONY BALISACAN - Engineer
GARY DESJARLAIS - Engineer
DAVID DRYE - Engineer
DAVID TROMBLEE - Assistant Engineering
TIGIST SHIFERAW - Administrative Assistant
KATE LAW - Administrative Assistant
CATALINA DUBBS - Generalist Human Resources
GERMANN BRIZUELA - Advisor Human Resources
NICOLE HALIBURTON - Advisor Human Resources
STEPHANIE REEDER - Advisor Human Resources
LINDA FIATO - Senior Programmer
SIAVASH AKRAMI - Programmer
EDMUND SULLIVAN - Programmer

Capriotti's Sandwich Shop Inc.
6056 S Durango Dr Ste 100
Las Vegas, NV 89113-1782

Telephone: (866) 959-3737
Fax Number: (702) 736-9878
Internet Homepage: capriottis.com
Company Email: info@capriottis.com
Type of Business: Chain Restaurant Operator
Year Founded: 1976
Systemwide Sales: $134,098,000 (e)
Total Sales: $15,900,000 (e)
Number of Employees: 1,188
Average Check: Lunch(8); Dinner(8)
Total Units: 176
Trade Names: Capriotti's Sandwich Shop (115); Wing Zone (61)
Company-Owned Units: 7
Units Franchised To: 169
Preferred Square Footage: 650; 1,200; 1,500; 1,700
Preferred Location Types: Airports; Freestanding; Regional Mall; Strip Mall
Primary Menu: Chicken (61); Sandwiches/Deli (115)
Areas of Operation: AZ, CA, DC, DE, FL, GA, IA, IN, MA, MD, NC, NE, NV, PA, TX, UT, VA, WA, WI
Type of Foodservice: Quick Serve (176)
Catering Services: Yes
Subsidiaries: Wing Zone Franchise Corp., ATLANTA, GA

Key Personnel
GEORGE J. CHANOS - Chairman
ASHLEY I. MORRIS - CEO
JASON M. SMYLIE - President
DAVID BLOOM - Chief Development Officer
BRENT ERWIN - Senior VP Finance
AMI LINDSAY - Senior VP Supply Chain
JANE MCPHERSON - Senior VP Marketing
BRUCE EVANS - VP Franchise Sales
MYLES GIFT - VP Operations
VINNIE CALCAGNIE - VP Operations
JAKE HUBER - General Manager
JOHN LEHNER - Director Operations
SHAWNA DECKER - Director Transportation
FREDDIE BACCARI - Director Operations
JA HADDAD - Director Construction, Design
HUONG NGUYEN - Director Catering
ELENA VANDOVER - Director Finance
BENNY J. WILLEFORD JR, MBA - Director Information Technology
BRANDI COCHRAN - Senior Manager Marketing
GRACANN HOPPE - Manager Purchasing
GLYNN CHAMBERS - Manager Training
SARA TAYLOR - Manager Real Estate
JIM LOLLEY - Project Manager Construction
BRENDA ANDERSON - Assistant

Desert Venture LLC
6400 W Charleston Blvd
Las Vegas, NV 89146

Telephone: (702) 870-1550
Type of Business: Chain Restaurant Operator
Total Sales: $35,930,000 (e)
Total Units: 14
Trade Names: Jack in the Box (14)
Units Franchised From: 14
Primary Menu: Hamburger (14)
Areas of Operation: NV
Type of Foodservice: Quick Serve (14)
Franchise Affiliation: Jack in the Box Restaurants, SAN DIEGO, CA

Key Personnel
SHEHZAD GILL - Owner; General Buyer

Don Tortaco
6628 Chardonay Way
Las Vegas, NV 89108

Internet Homepage: dontortaco.com
Type of Business: Chain Restaurant Operator
Total Sales: $26,720,000 (e)
Total Units: 23
Trade Names: Don Tortaco (23)
Company-Owned Units: 23
Primary Menu: Mexican (23)
Type of Foodservice: Quick Serve (23)

Key Personnel
APOLINAR IBARRA - Founder; Owner

Dona Maria Tamales
3250 N Tenaya Way
Las Vegas, NV 89129-7430

Telephone: (702) 656-1600
Fax Number: (702) 656-1500
Internet Homepage: donamariatamales.com
Company Email: customerservice@donamariatamales.com
Type of Business: Chain Restaurant Operator
Total Sales: $3,052,000 (e)
Alcohol Sales: 10%
Number of Employees: 32
Average Check: Breakfast(6); Lunch(6); Dinner(10)
Total Units: 2
Trade Names: Dona Maria (2)
Company-Owned Units: 2
Preferred Location Types: Freestanding
Alcohol Served: Beer, Wine, Liquor
Primary Menu: Mexican (2)
Areas of Operation: NV
Type of Foodservice: Casual Dining (2)
Catering Services: Yes
Primary Distributors: (Food) SYSCO Food Services of Arizona Inc., TOLLESON, AZ

Key Personnel
NERIZA MARTINEZ-JOHNSON - Owner
RAFAEL RUIZ - General Manager; Executive Chef; General Buyer

Egg Works
4533 W Sahara Ave
Las Vegas, NV 89102-3675

Telephone: (702) 364-9686
Fax Number: (702) 364-9008
Internet Homepage: theeggworks.com
Company Email: eggworks@theeggworks.com
Type of Business: Chain Restaurant Operator
Year Founded: 1988
Total Sales: $6,405,000 (e)
Number of Employees: 23
Average Check: Breakfast(10); Lunch(10);
Internet Order Processing: Yes
Total Units: 7
Trade Names: The Egg & I (1); The Egg Works (6)
Company-Owned Units: 7
Preferred Location Types: Strip Mall
Primary Menu: American (7)
Projected Openings: 1
Areas of Operation: NV
Type of Foodservice: Family Restaurant (7)
Catering Services: Yes
Primary Distributors: (Food) US Foods, NORTH LAS VEGAS, NV

Key Personnel
BRAD BURDSALL - Owner; Executive Chef; Director Catering; General Buyer
GIA KATZ - General Manager

Four Queens Inc.
202 Fremont St
Las Vegas, NV 89101-5606

Telephone: (702) 385-4011
Fax Number: (702) 387-5120
Internet Homepage: fourqueens.com
Company Email: fnb@fourqueens.com
Type of Business: Foodservice Operations - Casinos
Year Founded: 1966
Total Sales: $69,407,000 (e)
Alcohol Sales: 3%
Number of Employees: 1,200
Total Units: 1
Restaurants in Hotels: 4
Trade Names: 4 Queens Hotel & Casino (1)
Company-Owned Units: 4
Alcohol Served: Beer, Wine, Liquor
Areas of Operation: NV
Type of Foodservice: Casual Dining (3); Quick Serve (1)
Primary Distributors: (Specialty Foods) Pacific Seafood of Las Vegas, LAS VEGAS, NV
Notes: The company derives approximately 80% of its revenue from casino/hotel operations.
Restaurants within the hotel include: Hugo's Cellar, Magnolia's Veranda, Chicago Brewing Co. and Patio Bar.

Key Personnel
TERRY CAUDILL - Chairman; CEO; President; General Manager
TINA M. KOTULA - Executive Director Marketing
BUTCH LIDGETT - Executive Chef; General Buyer
KEN JOHNSON - Director Purchasing, Quality Assurance, Menu Development, Food Safety, Food and Beverage

Full House Resorts Inc.
1980 Festival Plaza Dr Ste 680
Las Vegas, NV 89135

Telephone: (702) 221-7800
Fax Number: (702) 221-8101
Internet Homepage: fullhouseresorts.com
Company Email: fhri@fullhouseresorts.com
Type of Business: Foodservice Operations - Casinos
Publicly Held: Yes
Total Sales: $215,531,000 (e)
Alcohol Sales: 10%
Number of Employees: 942
Total Units: 6
Trade Names: American Place (1); Bronco Billy's Casino (1); Grand Lodge Casino (1); Rising Star Casino Resort (1); Silver Slipper Casino (1); Stockman's Casino (1)
Company-Owned Units: 6
Alcohol Served: Beer, Wine, Liquor
Areas of Operation: CO, IN, MS, NV
Type of Foodservice: Casual Dining; Family Restaurant; Fine Dining
Notes: Full House Resorts derives approximately 80% of its total revenue from casino and management operations. The company manages gaming operations at several full-service resorts in addition to operating its own casinos.

Key Personnel
CARL G. BRAUNLICH - Vice Chairman
DANIEL R. LEE - CEO; President
LEWIS FANGER - CFO; Senior VP; Treasurer
ALEX J. STOLYAR - Chief Development Officer; Senior VP
JIM DACEY - VP Development
ELAINE L. GUIDROZ - Corporate Secretary; General Counsel
JOHN N. FERRUCCI - General Manager Division
DANE HANSEN - General Manager; Assistant
DANIELLE STRONG - Director Human Resources
JACKIE SUNSHINE - Director Human Resources
JILL STEWART - Director Marketing
GREG TUFTS - Director Operations
CHRISTIAN PEEK - Director Information Technology
JOHN JOHNSON - Director Food
BRETT MODEL - Director Operations
NATHAN KIRBY - Director Information Technology
ERIC MCDONALD - Director Operations
BILLY MOHR - Director Operations
KATHLEEN MARSHALL - Director Internal Audit

Gen3 Hospitality
395 E Sunset Rd
Las Vegas, NV 89119

Telephone: (702) 866-2159
Internet Homepage: elephantbar.com
Type of Business: Chain Restaurant Operator
Year Founded: 1993
Total Sales: $24,550,000 (e)
Alcohol Sales: 24%
Number of Employees: 1,441
Average Check: Lunch(14); Dinner(18)
Total Units: 11
Trade Names: Elephant Bar (6); Flour & Barley - Brick Oven Pizza's (2); Haute Doggery (1); Holsteins Shakes and Buns (1); The Barrymore (1)
Company-Owned Units: 11
Preferred Square Footage: 8,000
Preferred Location Types: Freestanding
Alcohol Served: Beer, Wine, Liquor

Primary Menu: American (8); Hot Dogs (1); Pizza (2)
Areas of Operation: CA, NM, NV
Type of Foodservice: Casual Dining (11)
Primary Distributors: (Full Line) Goldberg & Solovy Foods Inc., VERNON, CA

Key Personnel
BILLY RICHARDSON - President
REINHARD DORFHUBER - Senior VP Culinary Development
JEFF MARSHALL - VP Operations, Training
TRAVIS ANDERSON - Director Finance

Glencoe Management, Inc.
7548 W Sahara Ave Ste 102
Las Vegas, NV 89117-2779

Telephone: (702) 254-7400
Fax Number: (702) 254-7494
Internet Homepage: glencoemanagement.com
Type of Business: Chain Restaurant Operator
Total Sales: $98,300,000 (e)
Number of Employees: 2,702
Average Check: Breakfast(8); Lunch(12); Dinner(16)
Total Units: 44
Trade Names: Burger King (44)
Units Franchised From: 44
Preferred Square Footage: 2,500; 2,900; 4,000
Preferred Location Types: Freestanding
Primary Menu: Hamburger (44)
Areas of Operation: NV
Type of Foodservice: Quick Serve (44)
Foodservice Management Venues: Schools
Franchise Affiliation: Burger King Worldwide Inc., MIAMI, FL
Primary Distributors: (Full Line) Nicholas & Co. Inc., SALT LAKE CITY, UT

Key Personnel
TOM MCDONALD - President; Director Real Estate; General Buyer
STEVE KEITH - Owner
LLINDA MERZ - Controller
TOM PIKE - Director Operations
BETHANY STERNBERG - District Manager

Golden Entertainment
6595 S Jones Blvd
Las Vegas, NV 89118-3337

Telephone: (702) 893-7777
Internet Homepage: ggilv.com; goldenent.com; ptstaverns.com
Type of Business: Foodservice Operations - Casinos
Year Founded: 2001
Publicly Held: Yes
Total Sales: $1,211,534,000 (e)
Alcohol Sales: 5%
Number of Employees: 5,584
Average Check: Dinner(12)
Foodservice Sales: $121,153,000 (e)
Internet Order Processing: Yes
Total Units: 104
Trade Names: Aquarius (8); Arizona Charlie's Casino Restaurants (5); Edgewater (5); Gold Town (1); Lakeside Casino (1); Lucky's Lounge & Restaurant (4); Pahrump Nugget (3); PT's Taverns (65); Rocky Gap Casino Resort Restaurants (3); The Strat Restaurants (9)
Company-Owned Units: 104
Alcohol Served: Beer, Wine, Liquor
Primary Menu: American (104)
Areas of Operation: MD, NV
Type of Foodservice: Casual Dining (69); Fine Dining (35)
Primary Distributors: (Full Line) US Foods, NORTH LAS VEGAS, NV

Key Personnel
BLAKE SARTINI - Chairman; CEO
CHARLES PROTELL - President; CFO
STEVE ARCANA - COO; Exec VP
BRAD GOLDBERG - Chief Marketing Officer
SEAN T. HIGGINS - Exec VP Government Affairs
KATHERINE RODEN - Senior VP Human Resources
JOE ROMANO - VP Food and Beverage
AL SALINAS - VP Security
ELIOT RIPOLL - VP; General Manager
TRAVIS J WOLTERMANN - VP Operations
BRIAN LAMBERT - VP Purchasing
KIM AST - VP Strategy, Digital
JAY FENNEL - VP Gaming/Entertainment
RICARDO FIGUEROA - VP Facility/Maintenance
ROSS GDOVIN - VP Marketing
RAY GENTRY - VP Security
SKYLAR DICE - General Manager; Assistant
JEFFREY COFFMAN - Senior Director Information Technology, Security
JUAN ALVAREZ - Director
BENITO BIANCANIELLO - Director Operations
BRENT EDLAND - Director Operations
LAURA PAMPLONA - Director Operations
ROBERT KLAUS - Director Security, Safety
TYZA GURLEY - Director Information Technology
DARIN YUNEK - Regional Manager Operations
GIAN SAPIENZA - Regional Manager
ANNE LALAMA - Manager Human Resources
RAYMOND GRAHAM - Manager Security
MORGAN EVANS-HAMMOND - Project Manager
JOE PHOMNINH - Project Manager

Golden Nugget Inc.
129 Fremont St
Las Vegas, NV 89101-5603

Telephone: (702) 385-7111
Fax Number: (702) 382-9092
Internet Homepage: goldennugget.com
Type of Business: Foodservice Operations - Casinos
Year Founded: 2003
Total Sales: $353,260,000 (e)
Alcohol Sales: 25%
Number of Employees: 2,000
Total Units: 5
Trade Names: Golden Nugget Atlantic City (1); Golden Nugget Biloxi (1); Golden Nugget Lake Charles (1); Golden Nugget Las Vegas (1); Golden Nugget Laughlin (1)
Company-Owned Units: 5
Alcohol Served: Beer, Wine, Liquor
Areas of Operation: MS, NJ, NV, TX
Type of Foodservice: Casual Dining; Fine Dining
Parent Company: Landry's Restaurants Inc., HOUSTON, TX
Notes: The company derives approximately 78% of its revenue from casino and hotel operations.

Key Personnel
TILMAN J. FERTITTA - Chairman; CEO; President
CHRIS LATIL - CFO; Senior VP
ANDREW GAUL - Director Food and Beverage

Hakkasan Group
6385 S Rainbow Blvd Ste 800
Las Vegas, NV 89118-3201

Telephone: (702) 212-8804
Fax Number: (702) 964-1424
Internet Homepage: angelmg.com/venues/social-house; hakkasan.com; hakkasangroup.com; hkklondon.com; sakenohana.com; herringboneeats.com; searsucker.com; yauatcha.com
Company Email: info@hakkasangroup.com
Type of Business: Chain Restaurant Operator
Year Founded: 2001
Total Units: 37
Trade Names: Casa Calavera (1); Fix (1); Hakkasan (12); Herringbone (4); Ling Ling (3); Sake no Hana (3); Searsucker (3); Shorebar (1); Stack Steakhouse(1); Yauatcha (7); Yellow Tail (1)
Company-Owned Units: 37
Alcohol Served: Beer, Wine, Liquor
Primary Menu: American (4); Chinese (22); Japanese (4); Mexican (2); Seafood (4); Steak (1)

Areas of Operation: CA, FL, NV, NY, TX, FC
Foreign Countries: CHINA; ENGLAND; INDIA; QATAR; UNITED ARAB EMIRATES
Type of Foodservice: Casual Dining (18); Fast Casual (1); Fine Dining (18)

Key Personnel
KHALIFA BIN BUTTI - Chairman
MARK WERLINGER - Executive Director Finance
JON AMORIN - Executive Chef Group
MIGUEL ROMAN - Executive Chef
IRENE PHAM - Director Customer Service
DAN REID - Director Sales
GERARDO GONZALEZ - Director
MIGUEL DROZ - Manager Production
GLADDYS GARCIA-TUNGPALAN - Manager Human Resources
JOHNNY MARTINO - Manager Promotion
VERONICA STILES - Manager Risk Management
SAEED A. MALIK - Manager Security
ERICK HONG - Manager Information Technology
TAMMI M. WILLIAMS - Manager Safety
JARED KELLER - Manager Technology
DOMENIC TORRES - Specialist Security
MICHELLE SCARONE - Specialist Accounting
ANN HIRD - Agent Purchasing
CYNTHIA ADAMS CEBS, SPHR - Consultant Employee Benefits
MARIO GARCIA - Developer Database

Indo Cal Foods, Inc.
4866 S Maryland Pkwy
Las Vegas, NV 89119-6314

Telephone: (702) 736-2812
Type of Business: Chain Restaurant Operator
Total Sales: $57,190,000 (e)
Number of Employees: 410
Total Units: 22
Trade Names: Jack in the Box (22)
Units Franchised From: 22
Primary Menu: Hamburger (22)
Areas of Operation: NV
Type of Foodservice: Quick Serve (22)
Franchise Affiliation: Jack in the Box Restaurants, SAN DIEGO, CA

Key Personnel
JYOTI MADHURA - Owner; General Buyer
MARLENE PADILLA - Manager
JENNIE BEERS - Manager

Las Vegas Sands Corp.
3355 Las Vegas Blvd S
Las Vegas, NV 89109-8941

Telephone: (702) 414-1000
Fax Number: (702) 783-5499
Internet Homepage: palazzo.com; lasvegassands.com; pasands.com; venetian.com
Company Email: reservations@sands.com
Type of Business: Foodservice Operations - Casinos
Publicly Held: Yes
Total Sales: $6,162,350,000 (e)
Alcohol Sales: 20%
Number of Employees: 50,000
Total Units: 3
Restaurants in Hotels: 49
Trade Names: Sands Bethlehem (1); The Palazzo (1); The Venetian Resort-Hotel-Casino (1)
Company-Owned Units: 49
Alcohol Served: Beer, Wine, Liquor
Areas of Operation: NV, PA
Foreign Countries: MACAO
Type of Foodservice: Casual Dining; Fast Casual; Fine Dining; Quick Serve
Subsidiaries: The Venetian Resort-Hotel-Casino, LAS VEGAS, NV; Wind Creek Bethlehem, BETHLEHEM, PA
Notes: Las Vegas Sands operates The Venetian Resort Hotel Casino, The Palazzo, and Sands Casino Resort Bethlehem in the U.S. and The Venetian Macao, Sands Macao, Four Seasons Hotel Macao, Plaza Casino, and Sands Macao in China and Marina Bay Sands in Singapore. Trade names include only those found in NV and PA locations. The company derives approximately 93% of its revenue from hotel/casino/retail operations.

Key Personnel
ROBERT G. GOLDSTEIN - President; COO
PATRICK DUMONT - CFO; Exec VP
KATARINA TESAROVA - Chief Sustainability Officer; Senior VP
CALVIN SIEMER - Senior VP
GIDEON BERKOWITZ - Senior VP Information Technology
DANIEL BRIGGS - Senior VP Investor Relations
AMY LEE CCP, GRP - Senior VP Human Resources
RON REESE - Senior VP Public Relations
ALISTAIR SCOBIE - VP Investor Relations
MIKE MERLIN - VP Procurement
PETE BOYD - VP Operations
CHRISTINE SOMMELLA - VP Real Estate Development; General Counsel
RYAN YEE - Executive Director
PHILIPP BATALLIA - Executive Director
GAYLE GOSSELIN - Executive Director Information Technology
JOHN EDWARDS - Executive Director Design
KRISTIN KOCA MCLARTY - Executive Director Communications
D. ZACHARY HUDSON - General Counsel Global
DAVID NASSER - Director Procurement
JONATHAN KELLY - Director Security
CULLEN PARKER - Director Accounting
KATHLEEN POTTER - Director Internal Audit
RICHARD SEDLACEK - Director Information Technology
LEESANNE GUTHRIE - Director Information Technology, Quality Assurance
SELENA DURBIN - Director Design
MICHAEL ECHOLS - Director Information/Data Security
ALI TORAL - Director Information Technology
REGINA CONCEPCION CISA - Senior Manager Information Technology
JESSIE GAO - Manager Finance
ANDREA TORRES - Manager Compliance
RYAN WAAS - Manager Gaming/Entertainment
JON SOBB - Manager Supply Chain
SOC TIENG - Manager Security
DAVE WOOD - Supervisor
ELAINE I. IWASE - Project Manager Procurement
TIARA BINGHAM - Specialist Accounting
CINDY BAKER - Specialist Human Resources
VIVIAN NEUBAUER - Coordinator Development
NATHAN NITZEL - Systems Engineer
MICHAEL ROA - Senior Analyst Security
ALEX COLOM - Analyst Quality Assurance
JOSH HUDDLESTON - Analyst Security
JOE SABELKO - Analyst Finance
JERRY BRACAMONTE - Engineer
DAVID ADAMS - Engineer
MIKE S. - Engineer
LORENZO PALUZZI - Engineer Operations
BETTY AN YURCICH - Executive Assistant

Lipscomb-Smith Enterprises, Inc.
6840 S Durango Dr
Las Vegas, NV 89113

Telephone: (702) 263-3569
Type of Business: Chain Restaurant Operator
Total Sales: $62,480,000 (e)
Total Units: 13
Trade Names: McDonald's (13)
Units Franchised From: 13
Primary Menu: Hamburger (13)
Areas of Operation: NV
Type of Foodservice: Quick Serve (13)
Franchise Affiliation: McDonald's Corporation, CHICAGO, IL

Key Personnel
JIM LIPSCOMB - President

Magic Wok Management
10175 W Twain Ave
Las Vegas, NV 89147

Telephone: (702) 463-8000
Fax Number: (702) 427-4879
Internet Homepage: higmgt.com
Type of Business: Chain Restaurant Operator
Year Founded: 1984

Systemwide Sales: $100,490,000 (e)
Total Sales: $36,680,000 (e)
Number of Employees: 35
Average Check: Lunch(8); Dinner(8)
Total Units: 183
Trade Names: Cajun Cafe (50); China Max (91); Little Tokyo (38); Thai Max (4)
Company-Owned Units: 1
Units Franchised To: 183
Preferred Square Footage: 600; 800
Preferred Location Types: Freestanding; Regional Mall
Primary Menu: Asian (4); Cajun/Creole (50); Chinese (91); Japanese (38)
Areas of Operation: AL, CA, CT, DC, FL, GA, IL, IN, KS, KY, LA, MA, MI, MN, MO, MS, NC, NE, NH, NJ, NM, NV, NY, OH, OR, PA, PR, SC, SD, TN, TX, VA, WA, WI, WV
Foreign Countries: CANADA
Type of Foodservice: Quick Serve (219)
Primary Distributors: (Full Line) SYSCO Food Services of South Florida Inc., MEDLEY, FL

Key Personnel
DAVID WU - Co-Founder; CEO; Director Facility/Maintenance, Real Estate; General Buyer
BOBBY SABAS - Director Operations
MASUMI SCOTT - Manager Marketing, Promotion
LEON WU - Manager Real Estate

Martin Enterprises
PO Box 370035
Las Vegas, NV 89137-0035

Telephone: (702) 242-8865
Type of Business: Chain Restaurant Operator
Total Sales: $15,199,000 (e)
Total Units: 3
Trade Names: McDonald's (3)
Units Franchised From: 3
Preferred Location Types: Freestanding
Primary Menu: Hamburger (3)
Areas of Operation: NV
Type of Foodservice: Quick Serve (3)
Franchise Affiliation: McDonald's Corporation, CHICAGO, IL

Key Personnel
EVA MARTIN - President; General Buyer
ERIC MANNING - Manager Production

MEGHA INVESTMENTS, LLC
7435 S Durango Dr Ste 103
Las Vegas, NV 89113-3610

Telephone: (702) 228-2300
Type of Business: Chain Restaurant Operator
Total Sales: $2,598,000 (e)
Total Units: 4
Trade Names: Cold Stone Creamery (4)
Units Franchised From: 4
Primary Menu: Snacks (4)
Areas of Operation: NV
Type of Foodservice: Quick Serve (4)
Franchise Affiliation: Kahala Brands, SCOTTSDALE, AZ

Key Personnel
JAY MEGHA - Owner; General Buyer

Memphis Championship Barbecue
2250 Warm Springs Rd
Las Vegas, NV 89119

Telephone: (702) 260-6909
Internet Homepage: 17bbq.com; memphis-bbq.com
Company Email: talk2us@memphis-bbq.com
Type of Business: Chain Restaurant Operator
Total Sales: $10,604,000 (e)
Alcohol Sales: 7%
Number of Employees: 180
Average Check: Lunch(18); Dinner(24)
Internet Order Processing: Yes
Internet Sales: 2.00%
Total Units: 3
Trade Names: 17th Street Barbeque (2); Memphis Championship Barbecue (1)
Company-Owned Units: 3
Preferred Location Types: Freestanding
Alcohol Served: Beer, Wine, Liquor
Primary Menu: Bar-B-Q (3)
Areas of Operation: IL, NV
Type of Foodservice: Casual Dining (3)
Catering Services: Yes

Key Personnel
MIKE MILLS - President; Partner; Executive Chef
CARLOS SILVA - Partner
JUDY HERKERT - Controller
CINDY LORENZ - Director Catering
CHRISTINE PACIOLLA - Director Catering

MGM Resorts International
3600 Las Vegas Blvd S
Las Vegas, NV 89109-4303

Telephone: (702) 693-7120
Internet Homepage: mgmresorts.com
Type of Business: Foodservice Operations - Casinos
Year Founded: 2000
Publicly Held: Yes
Total Sales: $8,427,600,000 (e)
Alcohol Sales: 10%
Number of Employees: 72,000
Total Units: 19
Restaurants in Hotels: 145
Trade Names: Beau Rivage (1); Bellagio (1); Borgata (1); Circus Circus Las Vegas (1); Delano Las Vegas (1); Excalibur (1); Four Seasons (1); Gold Strike Tunica (1); Luxor (1); Mandalay Bay Resort and Casino (1); MGM Grand Detroit (2); MGM Grand Las Vegas (1); MGM Grand Signature (1); MGM National Harbor (1); New York-New York Hotel & Casino (1); NoMad Las Vegas (1); The Mirage (1); The Park (1)
Company-Owned Units: 28
Alcohol Served: Beer, Wine, Liquor
Areas of Operation: IL, MI, MS, NV
Foreign Countries: MACAO
Type of Foodservice: Casual Dining; Family Restaurant; Fast Casual; Fine Dining; Quick Serve
Franchise Affiliation: Ben & Jerry's Franchising Inc., SOUTH BURLINGTON, VT; Burger King Worldwide Inc., MIAMI, FL; Doctor's Associates Inc., MILFORD, CT; International Dairy Queen Inc., BLOOMINGTON, MN; Krispy Kreme Doughnut Corporation, CHARLOTTE, NC; La Salsa Fresh Mexican Grill,THOUSAND OAKS, CA; Little Caesar Enterprises Inc., DETROIT, MI; McDonald's Corporation, CHICAGO, IL; Nathan's Famous Inc., JERICHO, NY; Noble Roman's Inc., INDIANAPOLIS, IN; Panda Restaurant Group Inc., ROSEMEAD, CA; Pizza Hut Inc., PLANO, TX; Sbarro Holdings LLC, COLUMBUS, OH; Starbucks Corporation, SEATTLE, WA; The Haagen-Dazs Shoppe Company Inc., MINNEAPOLIS, MN; The Quiznos Master LLC, DENVER, CO
Notes: The company derives approximately 84% of its revenue from hotel/casino operations.

Key Personnel
CHUCK BOWLING - President Division
PAULA GENTILE - President; Senior VP Risk Management
WILLIAM J. HORNBUCKLE - President
JENNIFER LANCER - President Logistics
RANDY MORTON - President Group; COO
KENNETH ROSEVEAR - President Business Development
SCOTT SIBELLA - President Division; COO Division
RICHARD STURM - President; COO
LISA VALENTINE - Partner Communications; General Manager
JOSHUA WHITE - Partner
SONDRA MOWER - Partner
KEITH MICHAELS - Partner
MICHAEL NAVARRETE - Partner
JACQUELINE LOMANTO - Partner
CATALINA LOPEZ VELAZQUEZ - Partner
EMILY IVIE - Partner
DARREL JORDAN - Partner
LORENA GIL - Partner
JESSICA HARBAUGH - Partner
CALLIE DRIEHORST - Partner

Communications; General Manager
JESSE ANTONIO - Partner Communications
JACKI BURKE - Partner
JEFF ELLIS - CFO; VP
DANIEL J. D'ARRIGO - CFO; Exec VP; Treasurer
JONATHAN HALKYARD - CFO
ROB FITZPATRICK - CFO
ROBERT C. SELWOOD - Chief Accounting Officer; Exec VP
COREY I. SANDERS - COO
MICHAEL EVANS - COO
ANTON NIKODEMUS - COO Region
LILIAN TOMOVICH - Chief People Officer
STACEY TAYLOR - Chief Procurement Officer
BENJAMIN LACORTE - Chief Security Officer
DAVE COX - Senior Exec VP
ALAN FELDMAN - Exec VP Communications
EMILY LEW - Exec VP
JOHN M. MCMANUS - Exec VP; Corporate Secretary; General Counsel
LI CHUN RADIUM - Exec VP Marketing
NICK RAIN - Senior VP
THOMAS REICH - Senior VP Legal
SHAWN SANI - Senior VP Tax
BILL SOU - Senior VP
HEIDI SEALY - Senior VP
KRISTEN E. SCHOONMAKER - Senior VP Gaming/Entertainment
KATE VUTURO-WIK - Senior VP Marketing
JUNE YI - Senior VP Marketing
JUSTIN MANACHER - Senior VP
JENN MICHAELS - Senior VP Public Relations
PAUL MURRAY - Senior VP Finance
WENDY NUTT - Senior VP Human Resources
CINDY ORTEGA - Senior VP Facility/Maintenance
KELLY LITSTER - Senior VP
LAURA LEE - Senior VP Human Resources; VP Human Resources
ARI KASTRATI - Senior VP Strategic Sourcing
ARCHITECTS JOYEN - Senior VP Design; VP Development
DIMA HOWARD - Senior VP Marketing
JAMES A. FREEMAN - Senior VP Strategic Planning
JIM FREEMAN - Senior VP
MAGDY GAYED - Senior VP Marketing
JEFF GEBBEN - Senior VP Strategic Planning
CLARK DUMONT - Senior VP Communications
H. FLETCH BRUNELLE - Senior VP Marketing
KIM CIMINI - Senior VP Operations
JESSICA CIPOLLA-TARIO - Senior VP Advertising
URI CLINTON - Senior VP; General Counsel
CHRIS BALDIZAN - Senior VP Development
ED BOWERS - Senior VP Gaming/Entertainment
RICK BERNINGER - VP Human Resources
MELODY BITTINGER - VP Finance
BRUCE BARCLAY CAPP - VP
BRUCE BELCHER MBA - VP Human Resources
GORDON ABSHER - VP Public Relations
ANGELA CHAN - VP
CHAD BROWN - VP Marketing
BRENDA BRADBURY - VP
ADAM BRAVO - VP Marketing
VANESA BUI - VP
ANTHONY CARATOZZOLO - VP Food and Beverage
ASHLEY EDDY - VP Legal
TERESA COOKSON - VP Marketing
ARNIE COPE - VP Marketing
JESSICA CUNNINGHAM - VP; General Counsel
RANDY DEARBORN - VP Technology
DON GILLETTE - VP Human Resources
SARAH FULTS - VP Distribution
MIKE GATTEN - VP Marketing
THOMAS FANGER - VP Media
MISSY HALLEAD - VP Human Resources
TONY GLADNEY - VP Diversity
DIANE GONZALES - VP Finance
CHRISTOPHER HUME - VP
KEVIN HOLYFIELD - VP Strategic Planning
PEGGY JACOBS - VP Compliance
JOHN LAI - VP
EDWARD LEE - VP; General Counsel
ALAN PALARDY - VP Construction
JODI MYERS - VP Development
DENISE NEGREL - VP
NICK NAGGAR - VP Finance
MIKE PISTANA - VP Sales
GLENN POLLACK - VP Development
ED MULHOLLAND - VP; General Counsel
CECILE MAINO - VP Human Resources
RICHARD MCMILLON - VP Facility/Maintenance
STEFAN WISTORF - VP Finance
TED WHITING - VP Security
THERESA THOMPSON - VP
MEGAN TOBIN-ESTRADA - VP Media
CHRIS SHERLOCK - VP Strategic Planning
YALMAZ SIDDIQUI - VP Sustainability
JAY SIMPSON - VP Sales
JOSHUA SMITH - VP
LILY SU - VP Marketing
MARK STONER - VP Food and Beverage
DANIEL RUSH - VP Sales
TIMOTHY RYAN - VP Food and Beverage
BRIAN ROBISON CSM - VP; General Manager
PAUL ROERSMA - VP Operations
TOM REICH - VP; General Counsel
CHRISTY REYNOLDS - VP Development
GREG RICHES - VP Legal
JOE SAUCEDO - Assistant VP
JORGE MELATTI - Assistant VP Marketing
RICKY ARORA - Assistant VP
VICTOR AZEVEDO - Executive Director Sales
MATT BALL - Executive Director Architecture
BELINDA BRISSETTE-MATHIAS - Executive Director Risk Management
LOURDES CHAVEZ POGOLOWITZ - Executive Director Marketing
BRIAN CHILTON - Executive Director
ROBERTO GONZALEZ - Executive Director Sales
TAYLOR GWIAZDON - Executive Director Marketing
ANNE HANSON - Executive Director Strategy
ASHLEY FARKAS - Executive Director Public Relations
SCOTT FITZGERALD - Executive Director Strategy
DERYCK FULLER - Executive Director Internal Audit
DARYL DANIELS - Executive Director Accounting
MICHAEL DAMATO - Executive Director Business Development
JAY CLINE - Executive Director Production
DEREK EBLING - Executive Director Accounting
TODD MEGRATH - Executive Director Development
JOHN MEISNER - Executive Director Procurement
MATT MORRISON - Executive Director Operations
KEVIN MOCHRIE - Executive Director Technology
KATHARINE MECZKA - Executive Director Strategy
STEPHANIE MAES - Executive Director Sales
CHRIS MAGEE - Executive Director Facility/Maintenance
NANETTE PIETREWICZ - Executive Director Accounting
TASSOS PANAGAKOS - Executive Director Distribution
CATHERINE PARK - Executive Director
PAUL PACE - Executive Director Food and Beverage
ANTHONY OLHEISER - Executive Director Branding
KENYATTA LEWIS - Executive Director Diversity
NATALIYA LOYER - Executive Director Sales
MICHAEL KLEIN - Executive Director Finance
CRAIG JACOBS - Executive Director Information Technology
LORI JOHNSON LABARBERA - Executive Director Finance
KATHY SPRINGSTEAD - Executive Director Operations
MAHMOUD SLEIMAN - Executive Director Quality Assurance
STACY SOLOVEY - Executive Director Public Relations
RICHARD SHIELDS - Executive Director Security
KARLA TUCKER - Executive Director Strategic Sourcing
ANN WILLIAMS - Executive Director Compliance
GREG WILLIAMS - Executive Director Marketing
LOVELL WALKER - Executive Director Development
ELLEN VILLARS - Executive Director Strategic Sourcing
JOHN WINDON - Executive Director Finance
PAULA ZAPPIA - Executive Director Branding
DUANE ZOOK - Controller
GARY BRUNER - Controller Risk Management
ANDREW HAGOPIAN III - General Counsel
RALPH GOOD - General Manager

JASON GORDON - General Manager Restaurant Operations
MARY GIULIANO - General Manager
PASCAL DESVAUX - General Manager
PAMELA DE BLANC - General Manager; Merchandise Manager Visual Merchandising
MARCOS CABRERA - General Manager
BERNARD CLAEYS - General Manager
JELENA BAHR - General Manager
ANTHONY BAILEY - General Manager
ANTHONY JEMISON - General Manager
VESTA LAMMERDING - General Manager
TAMMI NAKAGAWARA - General Manager
AMI ZIPP - General Manager
NIK RYTTERSTROM - General Manager
PATRICIA ROGERS - General Manager
EDMUND WONG - Executive Chef Group
DANIEL MCGOWEN - Executive Chef
PATRICK HOEFLER - Executive Chef
ANTHONY AMOROSO - Executive Chef
DIANA CASTRILLON - Senior Director Labor Relations
CARMEN KINSMAN-PYPER - Senior Director
MILLET PEZZI - Senior Director Media
MELISSA PAULSON CPA - Director Accounting
SID PIKE - Director Operations
JEFFREY PARK - Director Marketing
NATALIE PEDRAZA - Director Accounting
STEVEN PELLETIER - Director Production
SHERI NIKISHIN - Director Technology
MARGO O'NEILL - Director Product Development
BRIAN PACKER - Director Construction
MICHELE OWENS - Director Human Resources
RANDY MCFADDEN - Director Infrastructure
RYAN MCGAHAN - Director Strategy
TIMOTHY MARTIN - Director Digital
MICHELLE MARTINEZ - Director Operations
JOLEEN MORROW - Director Finance
ZACHARY LEVINE - Director Games
ROSE MCKINNEY-JAMES - Director
CASEY MERSCH - Director Human Resources
CHRISTA MEYRICK - Director Production
JIM KIMBALL - Director Communications
DEBBIE KLEIN - Director Payroll
GARY LARSON - Director Accounting
KURT ZEPPENFELD KURT ZEPPENFELD - Director Operations
ELLEN MA - Director Finance
ANGELA MAC CFE - Director Finance
AMY LI - Director Marketing
JEREMY LIMUN - Director Government Affairs
VANESSA LEE - Director Tax
DEAN HUEBNER - Director Purchasing, Food and Beverage
FREDERICA HARVEY - Director Employee Compensation
MICHAEL HARRIS - Director Food and Beverage
PAUL HER-STURM - Director Content Marketing
G.E. JINGJING - Director
ALFRED JANG - Director Accounting
NEIL JOHNSON - Director Global sales
JOHNNIE JOHNSON - Director Compliance

EDWARD KANG - Director
LINDA CASSONE - Director Operations
ERICKA CARR - Director Media
SCOTTIE CHANCE - Director Strategic Sourcing
MUDIT CHANDRA - Director Finance
STEPHANIE CLOUD - Director Marketing, Sales
APRIL CHAPARIAN - Director Real Estate
LAUREN BURNETT - Director Brand Marketing
JEFF BUEME - Director Finance, Administration
AMY BREWSTER - Director Accounting
AMY BRILLANTES - Director
FE ALLEN - Director Talent
ENYEW ALEMAYEHU - Director Accounting
MICHAEL ABURAS - Director Media
BRYAN ANDERSON - Director Operations
JOSH APANA - Director Finance
DOLLY BALI - Director Risk Management
VIKRANT BODALIA - Director Information Technology
PAVAN BHARGAVA - Director Finance
ADAM BOURCIER - Director Brand Marketing, Food and Beverage
MIKE COOK - Director Network
JAMES CZARNECKI - Director Procurement
TOM CUDDY - Director Marketing
PAUL CULLEY - Director Strategy
EDDY COLLIER - Director Technology
DON DRISCOLL - Director Operations
JULIE DONOHUE - Director Benefits
TERRY DRACHLER - Director Strategic Sourcing
LESLIE ESPY - Director Development
NATHAN DUNN - Director Finance
ROSEMARY GWIZDALOSKI - Director Compliance
DIANE GUBERTI - Director Branding
LINDA FOLLOSCO - Director Procurement
KRISTIAN FORTUNE - Director Retail Operations
ED FIEGER - Director Special Projects
BOBBY WINGO - Director Marketing
SUSAN YATES - Director Finance
ORCUN YESILCIMEN - Director Marketing
JONNECE WRIGHT - Director Accounting
ERNESTO ZITA - Director Operations
WATSON YUEN - Director Marketing
CHRIS ZACHRITZ - Director Operations
SAM ZANINI - Director Strategy
MATTHEW VASQUEZ - Director Finance
JASON B. WILK - Director Food and Beverage
ALISA WILLIAMSON - Director
ANGELA WINCHESTER - Director Compliance
JILLIAN WINDER - Director Finance
COURTNEY TODD - Director Product Development
JASON ROSEWELL - Director Construction
CARLY ROSICH - Director Marketing
ROBYN RUSSO - Director Operations
GRANT RILEY - Director Sales
BRENDA REICHERT - Director Event Planning
WENDY PRICE - Director Safety
RUDY PULIDO - Director Labor Relations
BRITTANY PRICE - Director Operations
JANE SIERRAS - Director Purchasing

MELISSA SMITH - Director Design, Visual Merchandising
REVA SHAW - Director Marketing
AMBER SCHMAELING - Director Marketing
BERNADETTE SCHMITZ - Director Internal Audit
DEREK SCHOEN - Director Media
NADIA STRATILA - Director Marketing
SAM STEWART - Director Procurement
JACK STONE - Director Strategic Sourcing
JANON BOURGEOIS - Assistant Director Marketing
GINA HERNANDEZ - Assistant Director Human Resources
PATTI HEISER - Senior Manager Procurement
NICHOLAS DODSON - Senior Manager Procurement
CHRIS SZYMANSKI - Senior Manager Applications
HEATHER STEPHENS PMP - Senior Manager Information Technology
DAVE PETROSKI - Senior Manager Network
GREGORY VALDOV - Senior Manager Quality Assurance
ANGELA TURNER - Manager Business Development
SUSAN VALLONE - Manager Finance
THOMAS VAN BREDA - Manager Development
JACQUELYN TRUJILLO - Manager Operations
NICHOLAS TSO - Manager Strategic Services
BRIAN TRUAX - Manager Risk Management
EVANS TINA - Manager Payroll
FLOYD TIFFANI - Manager Accounting
THERESA TILLMAN - Manager Facility/Maintenance
MAUREEN TOPSCHER - Manager Accounting
CAROLINA TORRES - Manager Accounting
SCOTT TOWNSEND - Manager Sales
FERNANDEZ TRACY - Manager Compliance
HA TRAN - Manager Finance
LINH TRAN - Manager Internal Audit
KRIS WILKE - Manager Digital
NATASHA WILLIAMS - Manager Accounting
TRACY WILLIAMS PMP - Manager Information Technology
MARISOL WENK - Manager Sales
AIMEE WENSKE - Manager Branding
MARCUS VILLEGOS - Manager Marketing
JOSE VILLAR - Manager Visual Merchandising
ROBIN WALKER - Manager Sales
LINDSEY WALTER - Manager Accounting
ROBERT CONNOR WARK - Manager Accounting
MICHAEL WAVERLY - Manager Security
HENRY YUAN - Manager Marketing
ROXANNE WRIGHT - Manager Marketing
SUSAN WU - Manager Marketing
DANIELLE YANKOWSKY - Manager Finance
COLLIN WISEMAN - Manager Strategy
LAUREN WOJTASZEK - Manager Marketing
JOEL WOLF - Manager Sales
STEPHEN PRICE - Manager Security
TARIK PORTER - Manager Security
SIN RADIC - Manager Security
GINA RICHARDS - Manager Design

JAE YOON RIM - Manager Compliance
MARTHA RIVERA - Manager Sales
DOUGLAS ROBERTS - Manager Inventory
LYNN ROBINSON - Manager Administration
GINA RIDDLE - Manager Operations
DAVE RUTTENBERG - Manager Facility/Maintenance
PATRICIA RULLO - Manager Operations
CAMERON SCHARCHBURG BEYER - Manager Sales
STEVE SCHEPPMANN - Manager Internal Audit
CARISSA SANDOVAL - Manager Security
LAURINDA ROSE - Manager Marketing
UNCLE ROGER - Manager Engineering
DAVID D. REED - Manager Marketing
CHRISTYNE RIGGS - Manager Employee Benefits
ARGUELLO SUSAN - Manager
LISA SUSANY PURSEL - Manager Accounting
ROCKWELL SUTTON - Manager Strategy
ERIC SWANSON - Manager Technology
COURTNEY THERIAULT - Manager Training
JOHN THOMPSON - Manager Engineering
GARY SCOTT - Manager Operations
KATHARINE SHERRER - Manager Public Relations
MARTINA SMITH - Manager Accounting
NICOLE DONES - Manager Sales
ROSA DELGADO - Manager Sales
JAMES DERELLA - Manager Marketing
YULIYA DIDIN - Manager Operations
ALFRED DORAN - Manager Security
KEITH DOTSON - Manager Branding
CURTIS DUBOIS - Manager Safety
CHELSEA DUENO - Manager Food and Beverage
GENIA DUFFELL BASILE - Manager Production
HAROLD EDWARDS - Manager Security
WILLIE EDWARDS - Manager Development
ISELA ESCOBEDO - Manager Operations
MAZONE CONSTANCE - Manager Training
WILLIAM CORONEL - Manager Information Technology
PRINCE COSIO - Manager Food and Beverage
VICTORIA COX - Manager Finance
LAURA DAMORE - Manager Sourcing
RUIZ DANNY - Manager Human Resources
LOLA FAKOYA - Manager Accounting
GARY FARMER - Manager Security
NICOLE FOURNIER - Manager Design
KARLA GILLETT - Manager Accounting
RON GETZ - Manager Human Resources
LAUREN GIGLIOLI - Manager Sales
AARON HAID - Manager Finance
BRITTANY HAID - Manager Marketing
BEINI HAO - Manager Business Development
MARY HANDWERKER - Manager Marketing
KATY HANKINS - Manager Accounting
BREE GOLDMAN - Manager Customer Service
CESAR GONZALES - Manager Customer Service
WALTER BEHRE - Manager Sales
RANDALL BALTIMORE - Manager Security
EMILY BARAN - Manager Recruitment
ALLISON BARANICK-STEVENSON CPA - Manager Finance
ANNA BARANTEZ MBA, PMP - Manager Information Technology
DAVE BELMONTE - Manager Warehouse
MARIA BEMENT - Manager Production
MARK BASHAM - Manager Accounting
SANDRA APFEL - Manager Procurement
CHRISTOPHER APGAR - Manager Distribution
MARK ANTUNES - Manager Security, Safety
ROBERT A'HEARN - Manager Operations
JANICE ABAD - Manager Marketing
JAIME AKERS - Manager Human Resources
ARLENE ALANO-RAMISCAL - Manager Integration
DENISE ALLEN - Manager Retail Information Systems
NELI ALVAREZ - Manager Sales
DON ALVES - Manager Production
NELLY ANAYA - Manager Internal Audit
JANELLE BRADY - Manager Marketing
JENNA BRONZ - Manager Operations
NASHAE BROWN - Manager Accounting
OFELIA (FELY) BROWN - Manager Real Estate
PETE BUSH - Manager Security
SHALITA BUTLER - Manager Strategic Sourcing
BRITTANY BUYHER - Manager Sales
FAITH CABILLO - Manager Marketing
ANGELIQUE CABRERA - Manager Sales
JONATHAN CHUNG - Manager Food and Beverage
RYAN COCHRAN - Manager Operations
SESE CLARENCE SESEPASARA - Manager Group
MONICA CIRILLO - Manager Advertising
JASON CASARREAL - Manager Food and Beverage
SCOTT CELESTINO - Manager Marketing
JOSHUA CAREY - Manager Operations
BRENDA HEALEA - Manager Marketing
AL HECK - Manager Production
ELAINE HEDLUND - Manager Human Resources
VERONICA HAYES - Manager Global sales
TROY HATCH - Manager Security
BENTON HUI - Manager Distribution
JOLENA HUANG - Manager Accounting
JUN HUNG - Manager Marketing
SCOTT HOOKER - Manager Facility/Maintenance
NICOLE HEROD - Manager Sourcing
GEORGE KASTNER - Manager Sales
MAI L. JOHNSON CGMP - Manager Sales
JOE HYNES - Manager Labor Relations
JEREMY JERRY-REFFNER - Manager Facility/Maintenance
YEN LE - Manager Accounting
FELISSA LINDSEY - Manager Compliance
AMY LINK - Manager Marketing
ANGIE LIBA - Manager Warehouse
RACHEL LEWIS - Manager Procurement
KRIS LUMAGUE - Manager Social Media
DEANNA LORUSSO - Manager Training
KATIE LOPER - Manager Investor Relations
ADOLFO LOPEZ - Manager Sales
JOSEPH LOPEZ - Manager Visual Merchandising
ANDREW LANZINO III - Manager Strategic Services
MARTIN LAPISKA - Manager Operations
KRISTYN LAPORTE - Manager Operations
COLEEN KRAMER - Manager Inventory
AMY KIWANUKA - Manager Strategy
SHANNON KEENE CPA - Manager Finance
NICHOLAS MENCARELLI - Manager Warehouse
SEAN MULLANEY - Manager Gaming/Entertainment
CHARLOTTE MOLENDA - Manager Strategy
YVETTE MONET - Manager Public Relations
BEALS MARLON - Manager Security
DONTA LYNCH - Manager Food and Beverage
SHAUNA LYNN - Manager Marketing
QUINN LYTTLE - Manager Design
JOHN PAUL MALIMBAN - Manager Internal Audit
KRISTI MCKEE - Manager Sourcing
MITZEL MEDICA LANDERO MBA - Manager Internal Audit
MITZEL MEDICA LANDERO - Manager Internal Audit
MATTHEW MAYNARD - Manager Media
DARYL MCALLISTER - Manager Security
JENNIFER MCBEATH-STRICKLAND - Manager Gaming/Entertainment
MAGHAN MCCLUNG - Manager Operations
RICHARD MCCLUNG - Manager Security
BILL OTT - Manager Security
NYI NYI - Manager
MARISSA NORTON - Manager Human Resources
COLE NIKODEMUS - Manager Advertising
ANGELA PALOMBARO - Manager Operations
LORI PASTOR - Manager Customer Service
CAMILLE PARADISE - Manager Accounting
ADRIANA PILON - Manager Marketing, Sales
JESSICA PERKINS - Manager Sales
LIZA CEJA - Brand Manager
MONIQUE GATEL - Brand Manager Marketing
DENIS DARVEAU - Senior Program Manager Information/Data Security
VICTORIA TAMAYO - Senior Program Manager Information Technology
ELEANOR STEVENS - Supervisor Gaming/Entertainment
JENNIFER STEVENS - Supervisor Gaming/Entertainment
DEE SMITH - Supervisor Food and Beverage
RONALD SMITH - Supervisor
JILL SILVERMAN - Supervisor Gaming/Entertainment
TINA SHELTON - Supervisor Event Planning
VICTORIA ROSE - Supervisor Gaming/Entertainment
ROBERT RUSSELL - Supervisor Security
MARTHA SALSMAN - Supervisor Internal Audit
GREGORY VUKASOVIC - Supervisor
KELLY WATTERS - Supervisor Operations
CAROL WASSON - Supervisor Gaming/Entertainment
PATY VERDUZCO - Supervisor

YAZMIN WHITEHEAD - Supervisor
NICOLE WHITLEY - Supervisor Communications
ANDREA TIMBOL - Supervisor Operations
MEGAN THORNTON - Supervisor Accounting
TY TONEY - Supervisor Accounting
JOHN TUPPER - Supervisor Gaming/Entertainment
HAE MEE CREEDON - Supervisor Branding
CASEY COWDEN - Supervisor Special Projects
ASHLEY E. EDGEWORTH - Supervisor Special Projects
FRANK DIMARTINO - Supervisor Gaming/Entertainment
SOPHIA GATCHALIAN - Supervisor Special Projects
JOHN PAUL FRANCO - Supervisor Facility/Maintenance
KELLY FINK - Supervisor Benefits
MEGAN HANLEY - Supervisor Marketing
TIMOTHY HARD - Supervisor Production
WESLEY BURTS - Supervisor Security
GRETA BRENNA - Supervisor Gaming/Entertainment
ANGELA BOZA - Supervisor
DANIELLE BATES - Supervisor Accounting
DEYANIRA BELL - Supervisor Accounting
ERNESTO PERDOMO - Supervisor Gaming/Entertainment
JOSEPH PORRELLO - Supervisor Event Planning
ABIGAIL PANCOAST - Supervisor Marketing
NATALYA PARMELEY - Supervisor Procurement
JONG NOH - Supervisor Security
MAXINE NICOL - Supervisor Accounting
CRISTINA MUNGARAY - Supervisor Internal Audit
JULIO PADILLA - Supervisor Gaming/Entertainment
KRISTINE KELEHER - Supervisor Accounting
KAYLA KIMDY - Supervisor Gaming/Entertainment
MARKO KUSTURA - Supervisor
ALEXA KOHOUTEK - Supervisor Event Planning
HECTOR LOZANO - Supervisor Gaming/Entertainment
EDWIN LUXOR - Supervisor
JOHNNY LEE - Supervisor Accounting
JOHN LEJK - Supervisor
TOM JATCZAK - Supervisor Gaming/Entertainment
WIL JONES - Supervisor Information Technology
SHARON JONES-CISA - Supervisor Internal Audit
ALAN HESTER ARM - Supervisor Accounting
ANGELA GUTIERREZ - Supervisor Payroll
JAMIE HATHAWAY - Supervisor Purchasing
BARRIS KAISER - Senior Project Manager
SUANN LESTER PMP, CSM - Senior Project Manager
VANYA M. LAMBERT - Senior Project Manager Construction
TAMARA BEARD - Senior Project Manager E-Commerce
LORI DAHL - Senior Project Manager
RAYMOND DEFILIPPIS - Project Manager Design
CLAUDIA ESCOBEDO - Project Manager
CRAIG HARADA - Project Manager
MOHAMED R. BAHAJ - Project Manager Procurement
STEVE KNISLEY - Project Manager Network
R JOHNSON - Project Manager Information Technology
TRAVIS OCONNOR - Project Manager
GUSTAVO MARTINES - Project Manager
JOHN J. WOO - Project Manager
RITA YOUNG - Project Manager Design
JACOB ZEPEDA - Project Manager
ROB RAYMOND - Project Manager Design
DREW POULSON - Project Manager Information Technology
JOANNE SHAY - Project Manager
SUSAN RYAN - Project Manager Information Technology
DONNA TACHERA - Project Manager
GEOFF RENNE - Administrator Risk Management
JOE PASCOE - Administrator Marketing
SELINA LUPISAN - Administrator Benefits
JOHN CONNER - Administrator Accounting
MITCHELL BIGDA - Senior Buyer Procurement
MARIA BLACKWELL - Senior Buyer Purchasing
ALI AL MAHASNEH - Senior Buyer
CHARLES MOCHRIE - Senior Buyer Food and Beverage
BELINDA MILLER - Senior Buyer Food and Beverage
KELLY SOUTHARD - Senior Buyer
PAMELA TRUAX - Senior Buyer
CHRISTOPHER WIECZORKOWSKI - Senior Buyer
TERESA VERADEJ - Specialist Distribution
DENA WEBBER - Specialist Safety
ERIC TREJO - Specialist Branding
CRYSTAL TRICOLO - Specialist Distribution
MICHELLE ZENAROSA - Specialist Recruitment
DIANE WOHLMAN - Specialist Event Planning
JOHNATHAN TATUM - Specialist Accounting
AMELIA TAYLOR - Specialist Finance
TIM SHALHOOB - Specialist Security
MICHAEL SOLAS - Specialist Payroll
GEORGE PREDESCU - Specialist Group
ALARICE RAINEY - Specialist Finance
MELISSA RAMIREZ-VALDEZ - Specialist Human Resources
JORG RADTKE - Specialist Security
NAOMI RUCKER - Specialist Marketing
NATALIE ROSENBERG - Specialist Distribution
SUSAN ROJAS - Specialist
POOLE MISSY - Specialist Human Resources
ANN MILLER - Specialist Payroll
JOANNA M. MENDOZA - Specialist
COLEMAN MERCEDES - Specialist Payroll
ALEJANDRA MORALES - Specialist Payroll
WENDY MORAN - Specialist Wholesale
BEVERLY MARTINEZ - Specialist Employee Compensation
JUSTIN MATHER - Specialist Finance
JACQUELINE MANGINI - Specialist Accounting
MAUREEN MCCONNELL - Specialist Business Development
LUCIO PAROLISI - Specialist Recruitment
CINDY PARULSKI - Specialist Benefits
CHRIS PAONE - Specialist Finance
LESTER PARILLON - Specialist Data Quality
LEIGHANN OSGOOD - Specialist Accounting
MATTHEW LEBARON - Specialist Distribution
ROLAND LLAPITAN - Specialist Communications
BRIANA KNOWLTON - Specialist Communications
JENNIFER JOHNSON - Specialist Distribution
DEBBIE KASPRZYK - Specialist Accounting
KIWA JEFFERSON - Specialist Information Systems
TAYLOR JANISON - Specialist Marketing
LETICIA HERNANDEZ MELCHOR - Specialist Payroll
JOHN HILLENBRAND - Specialist Security
ROSALIE HITECHEW - Specialist Human Resources
CHRISTINE HOLLOWAY - Specialist Payroll
JESSICA BAAL - Specialist Distribution
ASHLEY BURLEY - Specialist Internal Audit
JOSE CAMACHO - Specialist Media
FILOMENA CASTELO - Specialist Payroll
MERCEDES COLEMAN - Specialist Payroll
RANDALL CHERYL - Specialist Talent
BRET COX - Specialist Talent
JESS DAVIS - Specialist Talent
RUIZ DANY - Specialist Human Resources
DARLA ENGLAND - Specialist Human Resources
RANDALL GOINS - Specialist Finance
SARAH FELKER - Specialist Human Resources
ASHLEY L. FORD-FERGUSON - Specialist Event Planning
JASMINE FURLOW - Specialist Compliance
ANNAMARIE GALINDO - Specialist
CHELSEY GAMBINO - Specialist Accounting
ERICK GONZALEZ - Buyer
MIRIAM HABER - Buyer
CHRIS CONEDY - Buyer
CHRISTOPHER CONEDY - Buyer Procurement
NANCY HOLMAN - Buyer
RAY JESKA - Buyer
KWAN KIM - Buyer Jewelry, Watches
JUDITH LAINEZ - Buyer
BILLIE NAKAGAWA - Buyer Purchasing
KERI NUNEZ - Buyer
VALDEZ PAULA - Buyer Purchasing
AMANDA QUINTANILLA - Buyer
NOLAN VIOLA - Buyer Food and Beverage
CATHY TEIXEIRA - Associate Buyer
ALEXA PAGLIA - Associate Buyer
TAMARA NORMAN - Coordinator Brand Marketing
JOANNA PETROFF - Coordinator Human Resources
STEFANIE MCCUE - Coordinator Sales
JULIANA MCBRIDE - Coordinator Sales
RIANNE MARR - Coordinator Sales

VASANTI KUMAR - Coordinator Diversity
AZIZAH KEO-ZEISS - Coordinator Talent
EVETTE MADERE - Coordinator Purchasing
KATHERINE HEFFERNAN-SNIFFEN - Coordinator Purchasing
PATRICIA CONLEY - Coordinator Development
BRADLEY ELLINGTON - Coordinator Sales
JO EMON - Coordinator Design
RENAE HALBAKKEN-SCHULZ - Coordinator Human Resources
JOSLYN GARCIA - Coordinator Public Relations
KAYLA FIORE - Coordinator Marketing
MIKE BRIDGES - Coordinator Sales
NATALIE BORGES - Coordinator Sales
JESSICA BERCAW - Coordinator Sales
CAITLIN TATE - Coordinator Training
JANICE SWENSON - Coordinator Benefits
NOLA SHEPARD - Coordinator Accounting
PETER RAYNOLDS - Coordinator Marketing
NICHOLAS ZOZAYA - Coordinator Marketing
ANDREA WILLIAMS - Agent Sales
BOB RICHMOND - Agent Sales
PAULINE GALERA - Agent Sales
LISA LITTLE LVNE - Agent Sales
MARIE MORALES - Agent Sales
MARSHA MULLERA - Representative Accounting
STEVEN PEDERSON - Representative Risk Management
JAMES MORGAN - Representative Sales
CRYSTAL HAYDEN - Representative Sales
CAROLINA JENNINGS - Representative Sales
SUSIE JEON - Representative Sales
CHARLES IRION - Representative Sales
MISTY ESCALERA - Representative Customer Service
FERNANDA AGUILAR - Representative Marketing
NICOLE BROWN - Representative Customer Service
TREASURE ROYAL - Representative Sales
BRIAN RODRIGUEZ - Representative Talent
LAURIE WEISER - Representative Sales
JACQUELINE YU - Representative Marketing
SHULMAN SANDRA - Consultant Development
NINA QUEEN - Consultant Training
LORENA CABRERA - Consultant Talent
JONATHAN BAILEY - Consultant Development
ARUN KUMAR - Consultant
ANTONIO MONTANO - Consultant Design
WILLIAM MITCHEM - Consultant Security
BELLA MATI - Consultant
CHAN RYAN - Senior Designer
RICH SCALLAN - Designer
GARY SHARPLES - Designer
VISA SENAMONTRI - Designer
EMILY WATSON - Designer
CAMIE MUMPOWER - Designer
OSCAR MORENO - Designer
OLIVIER S. NOLOS - Designer
KRIS PLOWDEN - Designer
JACK PENAFIEL - Designer Floral
JANNA HVEEM - Designer
KERON ARTHUR - Designer
JESSICA DRUMMOND - Designer

JOHN CONDEMI - Designer
ABEBE AZENE - Senior Analyst Marketing
TYLER CLARK - Senior Analyst Finance
BARNEY CARVILLE - Senior Analyst Finance
JUN HE - Senior Analyst Business Development
TAMARA JOHNSON - Senior Analyst Employee Compensation
CHRISTOPHER LAM - Senior Analyst Finance
ROBERT MADRID - Senior Analyst Technology
BRIAN PATJE - Senior Analyst Operations
CHRIS STARESINIC - Senior Analyst Business Development
CHARLES STEVE MCPARTLAND - Analyst Information/Data Security
WARREN STENDER - Analyst Finance
ERIK SARVELA - Analyst Information Technology
DAVID WEST - Analyst Enterprise Solutions
KEVIN ZADNIK - Analyst Finance
TERRY PHILLIPS - Analyst Technology
ENRIQUE MENDEZ - Analyst Finance
JAN MITCHELL-VILLAVICENCIO - Analyst Information/Data Security
AKRAM MAHESH - Analyst Digital
ISAIAS LOZANO - Analyst Information/Data Security
JODIE LAU - Analyst Finance
JUDY LAURVICK - Analyst Security
DONALD JOHNSON - Analyst Applications
CHRISTOPHER HODGES - Analyst Infrastructure
TIFFANY CARDOSO - Analyst HRIS
TINA BUENO - Analyst Finance
MICHAEL ALEMAYEHU - Analyst Accounting
JEFF BEEDHAM - Analyst Operations
LIZA BEZORE - Analyst Information Systems, Database
THOMAS CONTRERAS - Analyst Finance
CARLO DAMOT - Analyst Information/Data Security
MARY DIDONNA - Analyst Compliance
CINDY GARCIA - Analyst Finance
MELISSA GINSBURG - Analyst Finance
MARY GUERRA-SAENZ - Analyst Finance
SHIRLEY GLENN - Analyst Benefits
JASON HAGEMAN CISA - Architect Information/Data Security, Risk Management
MARC HALL - Architect Design
LUIS FRANCO - Architect Information Technology
DAVID DIETZ - Architect Information Systems
MARK CRONIN - Architect Network
RICK BOYD - Architect
JOSEPH BALZER - Architect Infrastructure
EDISON BARRETO - Architect Enterprise Solutions
JOSE ACEBAL - Architect Network
KEVIN BROWNING - Architect Infrastructure
TIFFANY CARIASO - Architect Information Technology
CORKY CHANDLER - Architect Applications
NITEEN CHAUDHARI - Architect Web Design
VIJAYA BHASKARAREDDY CHEJERLA - Architect Applications
KEITH MASSNER - Architect Database

MATTHEW PARKER - Architect
PRASAD NAGENDRA - Architect Enterprise Solutions
T. RICHARD VAN BREDA - Architect Database
JOSEPH POWERS - Architect Enterprise Solutions
RAJEEV PRATHI - Architect Applications
JASON RIDDLE - Architect Design
JOSE ROSARIO-LOPEZ - Developer Media
VANITHA VENKATANARAYANAN - Developer
NIMA MOHSENI - Developer Software
JEFF PINEDA - Senior Engineer Information Systems
EVA HIBNER - Senior Engineer Information Systems
CLIFF HARRISON III - Senior Engineer Digital
MATTHEW ILER - Senior Engineer Applications
REBECCA JOHNSON LUXOR - Senior Engineer
AMIT KAPOOR - Senior Engineer
JAMES KOENIG - Senior Engineer Hardware
CRAIG KERSEY - Senior Engineer
CESAR ABREGO - Senior Engineer Information Systems
ROBERT ALBANEZ - Senior Engineer Information Systems
CORY ARENA - Senior Engineer Hardware
ROBERT BOLLINGER - Senior Engineer Security
JOANNE CRISTINE BONITA - Senior Engineer Applications
JEFFREY VANCOBB - Senior Engineer Network
SCOTT VALLINE - Senior Engineer Information Systems
MATTHEW ROJAS - Senior Engineer Information Systems
PAUL STEFFENER - Senior Engineer Hardware
RANDY SWENSON - Senior Engineer
KALMAN SHOR - Senior Engineer Software
ROSALIA SKLARIS - Engineer
ROBERT SHENO - Engineer Operations
STEPHEN THOMAS - Engineer
GRANT VAN OSTROM - Engineer Applications
REGINALD VANCE - Engineer
BRANDON TRIPLETT - Engineer Applications
JESSE THORNTON - Engineer
GREG WILHELMS - Engineer
TONY BLOCK - Engineer
DOUG BOSZE - Engineer
MARK ARMSTRONG - Engineer Hardware
JAMES ARNETT - Engineer Store Systems
ETHAN ANDREWS - Engineer
BRADLEY BAGASANI - Engineer Network
JAMES BALDWIN - Engineer Information Systems
SEAN CHILIPKA - Engineer Applications
PAM CHANIN - Engineer
GIL CHAIDEZ - Engineer
AARON CAVANAUGH-WEBB - Engineer
H BURRIS - Engineer Technology
CHRIS FAGNANT - Engineer Network
ROBERT FERGUSON - Engineer
SALOMON GIRON - Engineer Applications
KEVIN HARE - Engineer
WILLIAM HAMPTON - Engineer Hardware

DOUGLAS GRANGAARD - Engineer
LISA GRAY - Engineer
MICHAEL GREENE - Engineer
ERIC LOWE - Engineer Applications
MARK JONES - Engineer Facility/Maintenance
JIM JACOBSON - Engineer
MARK HENNINGS - Engineer Network
MARK HURST - Engineer Information Systems
MICHAEL PENNETT - Engineer
FRANK PALOMARES - Engineer Facility/Maintenance
JEFF MILES - Engineer
SHELLEY MCGINN - Executive Assistant Labor Relations

Omelet House
2160 W Charleston Blvd Ste A
Las Vegas, NV 89102-2243

Telephone: (702) 384-6868
Fax Number: (702) 212-9496
Internet Homepage: omelethouse.net
Company Email: Comments@omelethouse.net
Type of Business: Chain Restaurant Operator
Year Founded: 1979
Total Sales: $3,895,000 (e)
Number of Employees: 60
Average Check: Breakfast(10); Lunch(14); Dinner(18)
Total Units: 3
Trade Names: Omelet House (3)
Company-Owned Units: 3
Preferred Location Types: Freestanding; Office Complex; Strip Mall
Primary Menu: American (3)
Areas of Operation: NV
Type of Foodservice: Family Restaurant (3)
Primary Distributors: (Food) US Foods, NORTH LAS VEGAS, NV

Key Personnel
MIKE MCGOWAN - Partner; General Manager; Executive Chef; General Buyer
KEVIN MILLS - Partner; General Manager; General Buyer
FRED OSTERTAG - Partner; General Manager; General Buyer

Paymon's Mediterranean Cafe and Hookah Lounge
8380 W Sahara Ave
Las Vegas, NV 89117

Telephone: (702) 804-0293
Internet Homepage: hookahlounge.com; paymons.com
Type of Business: Chain Restaurant Operator
Total Sales: $5,867,000 (e)
Alcohol Sales: 10%
Number of Employees: 50
Average Check: Lunch(10); Dinner(20)
Internet Order Processing: Yes
Total Units: 2
Trade Names: Paymon's Mediterranean Cafe (2)
Company-Owned Units: 2
Preferred Location Types: Strip Mall
Alcohol Served: Beer, Wine, Liquor
Primary Menu: Greek/Mediterranean (2)
Areas of Operation: NV
Type of Foodservice: Casual Dining (2)

Key Personnel
JEFF ECKER - President; General Manager; Director Human Resources
PAYMON RAOUF - Owner; Director Menu Development

Pinkbox Doughnuts
7531 W Lake Mead Blvd
Las Vegas, NV 89128

Telephone: (702) 478-7465
Internet Homepage: pinkboxdoughnuts.com
Company Email: contact@pinkboxdoughnuts.com
Type of Business: Chain Restaurant Operator
Year Founded: 2012
Total Units: 3
Trade Names: Pinkbox Doughnuts (3)
Company-Owned Units: 3
Preferred Location Types: Strip Mall
Primary Menu: Snacks (3)
Projected Openings: 13
Areas of Operation: NV
Type of Foodservice: Quick Serve (3)

Key Personnel
STEPHEN SIEGEL - Partner
JUDI SIEGEL - Partner
ANTHONY RAMIREZ - General Manager

Rachel's Kitchen
9640 W Tropicana Ave Ste 117
Las Vegas, NV 89147

Telephone: (702) 629-6100
Internet Homepage: rachelskitchen.com
Company Email: preferredguest@rachelskitchen.com
Type of Business: Chain Restaurant Operator
Year Founded: 2006
Total Units: 8
Trade Names: Rachel's Kitchen (8)
Company-Owned Units: 5
Units Franchised To: 3
Preferred Location Types: Airports; Freestanding; Institution (college/hospital); Strip Mall
Primary Menu: American (8)
Projected Openings: 2
Areas of Operation: NV
Type of Foodservice: Fast Casual (8)

Key Personnel
DEBBIE ROXARZADE - Founder; CEO; General Buyer

Silver State Restaurants Inc
1591 S Main St
Las Vegas, NV 89104

Telephone: (702) 383-6908
Type of Business: Chain Restaurant Operator
Total Sales: $78,470,000 (e)
Total Units: 31
Trade Names: Jack in the Box (31)
Units Franchised From: 31
Primary Menu: Hamburger (31)
Areas of Operation: NV
Type of Foodservice: Quick Serve (31)
Franchise Affiliation: Jack in the Box Restaurants, SAN DIEGO, CA

Key Personnel
ALI NAVAIE - Owner; General Buyer

Station Casinos Inc.
1505 S Pavilion Center Dr
Las Vegas, NV 89135-1403

Telephone: (702) 495-3000
Fax Number: (702) 367-2426
Internet Homepage: sclv.com
Company Email: info@stationcasinos.com
Type of Business: Foodservice Operations - Casinos
Year Founded: 1976
Total Sales: $2,379,100,000 (e)
Alcohol Sales: 30%
Number of Employees: 9,163
Total Units: 18
Restaurants in Hotels: 49
Trade Names: Barley's Casino & Brewing Company (1); Boulder Station Hotel & Casino (1); Fiesta Henderson Casino Hotel (1); Fiesta Rancho Casino Hotel(1); Graton Resort & Casino (1); Green Valley Ranch Resort, Spa & Casino (1); Lake Mead Casino (1); Palace Station Hotel & Casino (1); Palms Casino Resort(1); Red Rock Casino (1); Santa Fe Station Hotel & Casino (1); Sunset Station Hotel & Casino (1); Texas Station Gambling Hall & Hotel (1); The Greens (1); Wild Wild West Gambling Hall & Hotel (1); Wildfire Anthem (1); Wildfire Boulder (1); Wildfire Lanes (1); Wildfire Rancho (1); Wildfire Sunset (1); Wildfire ValleyView (1)
Company-Owned Units: 49
Alcohol Served: Beer, Wine, Liquor
Areas of Operation: CA, NV
Type of Foodservice: Casual Dining (26); Family Restaurant (13); Fine Dining (10)

Primary Distributors: (Food) US Foods, NORTH LAS VEGAS, NV
Parent Company: Fertitta Colony Partners LLC, LAS VEGAS, NV
Notes: The company derives approximately 81% of its revenue from casino/hotel operations.

Key Personnel
FRANK J. FERTITTA III - Chairman; CEO
RICHARD J. HASKINS - President; Corporate Secretary; General Counsel
THOMAS M. FRIEL - CFO Division; Exec VP Division
STEPHEN L. COOTEY - CFO; Chief Administrative Officer; Exec VP
WES D. ALLISON - Chief Accounting Officer; Senior VP
JEFFREY T. WALSH - Chief Legal Officer; Exec VP

Tacotarian
1130 S. Casino Center Blvd. #170
Las Vegas, NV 89104

Telephone: (725) 251-3853
Internet Homepage: eattacotarian.com
Type of Business: Chain Restaurant Operator
Year Founded: 2018
Total Sales: $4,625,000 (e)
Total Units: 5
Trade Names: Tacotarian (5)
Company-Owned Units: 5
Primary Menu: Taco (5)
Areas of Operation: CA, NV
Type of Foodservice: Fast Casual (5)

Key Personnel
REGINA SIMMONS - Co-Founder; Director Culinary Operations, Food Safety
DAN SIMMONS - Co-Founder; CFO
CARLOS CORRAL - Co-Founder; Director Operations
KRISTEN CORRAL - Co-Founder; Director Public Relations

The Grove, Inc.
5757 Wayne Newton Blvd
Las Vegas, NV 89111-8037

Telephone: (702) 468-1433
Internet Homepage: tgiconcessions.com
Type of Business: Chain Restaurant Operator
Total Sales: $84,630,000 (e)
Total Units: 50
Trade Names: Auntie Anne's Hand-Rolled Soft Pretzels (2); Dunkin' Donuts (8); Famous Famiglia (1); Great Wraps Grill (1); Grove Snacks (10); Jamba Juice(3); Jersey Mike's Subs (3); Krispy Kreme Doughnuts (1); Manchu Wok (2); Moe's Southwest Grill (1); Nathan's Famous Hot Dogs (1); Red Mango (6); Smoothie King (7); Villa Fresh Italian Kitchen (1); Wendy's Old Fashioned Hamburgers (3)
Units Franchised From: 50
Areas of Operation: DC, DE, GA, IL, NV, NY, PA, TX, UT
Franchise Affiliation: Auntie Anne's Inc., LANCASTER, PA; DD IP Holder, CANTON, MA; Famiglia - DeBartolo, LLC, WHITE PLAINS, NY; GoTo Foods, ATLANTA, GA; Great Wraps Inc., ATLANTA, GA; Jamba Inc., FRISCO, TX; Jersey Mike's Franchise Systems, MANASQUAN, NJ; Krispy Kreme Doughnut Corporation, CHARLOTTE, NC; Moe's Southwest Grill LLC, ATLANTA, GA; MTY Food Group Inc., SAINT-LAURENT, QC; Nathan's Famous Inc., JERICHO, NY; Red Mango FC LLC, DALLAS, TX; Smoothie King Franchises Inc., DALLAS, TX; The Wendy's Company, DUBLIN, OH; Villa Restaurant Group, MORRISTOWN, NJ

Key Personnel
MICHELLE DUKLER - CEO; President; General Buyer
NINA MADONIA - CEO
BRIAN ANDERSON - CFO
TOM WARDELL - CFO
ANGELA ALESKY - Director Human Resources
TIFFANY HOVEN - Director Operations
JIM PEDZIWATER - Corporate Director Technology

The Palms Casino Resort
4321 W Flamingo Rd
Las Vegas, NV 89103-3903

Telephone: (702) 942-7777
Internet Homepage: palms.com
Company Email: info@palms.com
Type of Business: Chain Restaurant Operator
Year Founded: 1999
Total Sales: $43,640,000 (e)
Alcohol Sales: 10%
Number of Employees: 266
Average Check: Dinner(98)
Internet Order Processing: Yes
Internet Sales: 1.00%
Total Units: 12
Trade Names: A.Y.C.E Buffett (1); Greene St. Kitchen (1); Laguna Pool House (1); Lucky Penny (1); Mabel's BBQ (1); Sara's (1); Scotch 80 Prime (1); Send Noodles (1); Shark (1); The Eatery (1); Tim Ho Wan (1); Vetri Cucina (1)
Company-Owned Units: 12
Preferred Square Footage: 5,500; 6,000
Preferred Location Types: Hotel/Motel; Other
Alcohol Served: Beer, Wine, Liquor
Primary Menu: American (6); Asian (2); Bar-B-Q (1); Italian (1); Seafood (1); Steak (1)
Projected Remodelings: 2
Areas of Operation: NV
Type of Foodservice: Casual Dining (10); Family Restaurant (1); Quick Serve (1)
Primary Distributors: (Full Line) SYSCO Detroit LLC, CANTON, MI

Key Personnel
JAKE JOYCE - VP Marketing
ALEX SCHNOELLER - VP Food and Beverage
SCOTT SMITH - Director Food and Beverage

WBF Management Inc.
1775 N Martin L King Blvd Ste 200
Las Vegas, NV 89106-2101

Telephone: (702) 384-3950
Fax Number: (702) 384-2410
Type of Business: Chain Restaurant Operator
Year Founded: 1972
Total Sales: $176,310,000 (e)
Number of Employees: 2,075
Average Check: Breakfast(8); Lunch(8); Dinner(10)
Total Units: 37
Trade Names: McDonald's (37)
Units Franchised From: 37
Preferred Square Footage: 2,500
Preferred Location Types: Discount Dept. Stores; Freestanding
Primary Menu: Hamburger (37)
Areas of Operation: FL, NV
Type of Foodservice: Quick Serve (37)
Franchise Affiliation: McDonald's Corporation, CHICAGO, IL
Primary Distributors: (Full Line) The Martin-Brower Co., POMPANO BEACH, FL

Key Personnel
MARK WATSON - President; Partner; Director Finance, Operations, Purchasing, Facility/Maintenance, Loss Prevention, Supply Chain, Real Estate, Design, Store Fixtures, Food Safety

Wolfgang Puck Inc.
955 Kelly Johnson Dr Ste A
Las Vegas, NV 89119

Telephone: (702) 737-9600
Fax Number: (310) 432-1640
Internet Homepage: wolfgangpuck.com
Company Email: contactus@wolfgangpuck.com
Type of Business: Chain Restaurant Operator
Year Founded: 1982
Total Sales: $220,580,000 (e)
Alcohol Sales: 20%
Number of Employees: 5,400
Average Check: Dinner(24)
Internet Order Processing: Yes
Internet Sales: 1.00%

Total Units: 60
Trade Names: Cafe At The End Of The Universe (1); Chinois (1); Culture Kitchen (1); CUT (6); re Asian Cuisine (1); Spago (6); The Kitchen (1); Wolfgang Puck American Grille (1); Wolfgang Puck at Hotel Bel-Air (1); Wolfgang Puck Bar & Grill (3); Wolfgang Puck Bistro (2); Wolfgang Puck Express (28); WolfgangPuck Grand Cafe (1); Wolfgang Puck Pizza | Bar (2); Wolfgang Puck Pizzeria & Cucina (2); Wolfgang Puck Steak (1); WP Kitchen + Bar (1); WP24 by Wolfgang Puck (1)
Company-Owned Units: 39
Units Franchised To: 21
Preferred Square Footage: 4,000
Preferred Location Types: Airports; Community Mall; Downtown; Freestanding; Grocery Stores; Institution (college/hospital); Kiosk; Outlet Mall; Strip Mall
Alcohol Served: Beer, Wine, Liquor
Primary Menu: American (39); Asian (3); Californian (7); Italian (2); Pizza (2); Steak (7)
Projected Openings: 1
Areas of Operation: CA, CO, DC, FL, GA, HI, IL, IN, MA, MI, NC, NJ, NV, NY, OH, PA, RI, TX, ON
Foreign Countries: CANADA; FRANCE; SINGAPORE; UNITED ARAB EMIRATES
Type of Foodservice: Casual Dining (9); Fast Casual (28); Fine Dining (23)
Catering Services: Yes
Primary Distributors: (Full Line) US Foods-Los Angeles, LA MIRADA, CA

Key Personnel
BARBARA LAZAROFF - Co-Founder; Partner
TOM KAPLAN - President Division; Partner
VINCE MODICA - President Licensing
LEE HEFTER - Partner; Corporate Chef
DAVID ROBINS - Partner; Corporate Chef; Director Operations
ARI ROSENSON - VP
DAVID MORRIS - Director
SCOTT IRESTONE - Director Culinary Operations
GINA BOROWITZ - Director Human Resources
DOUG CHIPPEWA - Director Food
GENNARO SBARRO - Director Operations, Development
EDGAR SUGAY - Manager Accounting
JAKE HALL - Manager Operations

Yogurtland Franchisee
9516 W Flamingo Rd Ste 105
Las Vegas, NV 89147-5756

Telephone: (702) 243-1774
Type of Business: Chain Restaurant Operator
Total Sales: $4,270,000 (e)
Total Units: 4
Trade Names: Yogurtland (4)
Units Franchised From: 4
Primary Menu: Snacks (4)
Areas of Operation: NV
Type of Foodservice: Quick Serve (4)
Franchise Affiliation: Yogurtland Franchising Inc., FARMERS BRANCH, TX

Key Personnel
CHAD SMITH - Owner; General Buyer

The Carson Valley Inn and Casino
1627 US Highway 395 N
Minden, NV 89423-4301

Telephone: (775) 782-9711
Fax Number: (775) 782-7479
Internet Homepage: carsonvalleyinn.com
Company Email: info@http://www.carsonvalleyinn.com/
Type of Business: Foodservice Operations - Casinos
Year Founded: 1985
Total Sales: $8,267,000 (e)
Alcohol Sales: 20%
Number of Employees: 60
Average Check: Breakfast(12); Lunch(24); Dinner(42)
Total Units: 3
Trade Names: C V's Steak (1); Job's Perk (1); Katie's Country Kitchen (1)
Company-Owned Units: 3
Preferred Location Types: Other
Alcohol Served: Beer, Wine, Liquor
Primary Menu: American (1); Snacks (1); Steak/Seafood (1)
Areas of Operation: NV
Type of Foodservice: Casual Dining (2); Fine Dining (1)
Primary Distributors: (Full Line) US Foods, RENO, NV

Key Personnel
RICK MURDOCK - Partner

Bully's Sports Bar & Grill Inc.
3724 Lakeside Dr Ste 200
Reno, NV 89509-5293

Telephone: (775) 825-4333
Fax Number: (775) 825-4454
Internet Homepage: bullyssportsbar.com
Type of Business: Chain Restaurant Operator
Year Founded: 1994
Systemwide Sales: $27,602,000 (e)
Total Sales: $21,250,000 (e)
Alcohol Sales: 40%
Number of Employees: 375
Average Check: Breakfast(24); Lunch(24); Dinner(24)
Total Units: 11
Trade Names: Bully's Sports Bar & Grill (7); Smokin Bullys (4)
Company-Owned Units: 11
Preferred Square Footage: 5,500; 6,000
Preferred Location Types: Freestanding; Strip Mall
Alcohol Served: Beer, Wine, Liquor
Primary Menu: American (11)
Areas of Operation: NV
Type of Foodservice: Casual Dining (11)
Primary Distributors: (Food) BakeMark - Reno, RENO, NV

Key Personnel
JO SONNER - President; General Manager Finance, Supply Chain, Real Estate, Design, Store Fixtures; Executive Chef; General Buyer
MARLENE SCHWARTZ - Director Finance

Caesars Entertainment Corporation
100 W Liberty St Ste 1150
Reno, NV 89501-1960

Telephone: (775) 328-0100
Internet Homepage: eldoradoresorts.com
Company Email: investorrelations@eldoradoresorts.com
Type of Business: Foodservice Operations - Casinos
Year Founded: 2014
Publicly Held: Yes
Total Sales: $5,760,700,000 (e)
Alcohol Sales: 15%
Foodservice Sales: $921,712,000 (e)
Total Units: 23
Trade Names: Belle of Baton Rouge Casino & Hotel; Circus Circus Reno; Eldorado Gaming Scioto Downs; Eldorado Resort Casino Reno; Eldorado Resort Casino Shreveport; Isle Casino Bettendorf; Isle Casino Hotel-Black Hawk; Isle Casino Racing Pompano Park; Isle Casino Waterloo; Isle of Capri CasinoBoonville; Isle of Capri Casino Hotel Lake Charles; Isle of Capri Casino Kansas City; Isle of Capri Casino Lula; Lady Luck Casino Black Hawk; Lady LuckCasino Vicksburg; Lumière Place Casino; MontBleu Casino Resort & Spa; Mountaineer Casino Racetrack & Resort; Silver Legacy Resort Casino; Trop Casino Greenville; Tropicana Casino and Resort, Atlantic City; Tropicana Evansville; Tropicana Laughlin Hotel and Casino
Company-Owned Units: 23
Areas of Operation: CO, FL, IA, IL, IN, LA, MO, MS, NJ, NV, OH, WV
Type of Foodservice: Casual Dining; Fast Casual; Fine Dining; Quick Serve

Key Personnel
GARY CARANO - Chairman
THOMAS R. REEG - CEO

ANTHONY CARANO - President; COO
THOMAS ROBERT REEG - President
BRET YUNKER - CFO
STEPHANIE D. LEPORI - Chief Administrative Officer
EDMUND QUATMANN JR - Chief Legal Officer; Exec VP
ROBERT B. MOUCHOU - Senior VP Operations
GLENN CARANO - Senior VP Operations, Central Region
GREGG CARANO - Senior VP Food and Beverage
MATT MIELE - Senior VP Procurement, Quality Assurance
JOSH JONES - Senior VP Operations
STEWART MASSIE - Senior VP Operations, West Region
BARRON FULLER - Senior VP Operations, South Region
STEVE CALLENDER - Senior VP Operations, East Region
TODD CONNELLY - Senior VP Operations, Midwest Region
BESSIE SACCO - VP Legal
BILL REEG - VP Operations
TONY PHELPS - VP Information Technology
MIKE LAPOINTE - VP Information Technology, Infrastructure
PETER LARRAGUETA - Director Finance
NINA CARANO - Director Advertising
BRIAN SMITH - Director Information Technology
JOSH SCHWARZ - Director
JENNIFER FITZPATRICK - Director Catering
TRACI ADAMSON - Director Development
MICHAEL NIX - Director Information Technology
BRAD STEGMAN - Director Operations
JOHN BIRCHFIELD - Regional Director Information Technology
RALONDA GREEN - Regional Manager Talent
JOE ALVAREZ - Manager Marketing

Club Cal-Neva Hotel Casino
38 E 2nd St
Reno, NV 89501-1410

Mailing Address: PO Box 2071, Reno, NV, 89505
Telephone: (775) 323-1046
Fax Number: (775) 785-3246
Internet Homepage: clubcalneva.com
Company Email: customerservice@calneva.net
Type of Business: Foodservice Operations - Casinos
Year Founded: 1962
Total Sales: $131,785,000 (e)
Alcohol Sales: 8%
Number of Employees: 1,000
Average Check: Dinner(6)
Total Units: 1
Restaurants in Hotels: 4
Trade Names: Club Cal Neva Hotel Casino (1)
Company-Owned Units: 4
Alcohol Served: Beer, Wine, Liquor
Areas of Operation: NV
Type of Foodservice: Casual Dining (4)
Notes: The company derives approximately 78% of its revenue from hotel/casino operations.

Key Personnel
JEFF SIRI - CEO; President; General Manager
RON SWIFT - Executive Chef
JOHN MACARTHUR - Manager Purchasing

Emerald Cascade Restaurant Systems, Inc.
4655 Longley Ln Ste 105
Reno, NV 89502-7904

Telephone: (775) 322-7799
Type of Business: Chain Restaurant Operator
Total Sales: $50,250,000 (e)
Total Units: 20
Trade Names: Jack in the Box (20)
Units Franchised From: 20
Primary Menu: Hamburger (20)
Areas of Operation: NV
Type of Foodservice: Quick Serve (20)
Franchise Affiliation: Jack in the Box Restaurants, SAN DIEGO, CA

Key Personnel
ADAM GONZALES - Owner; General Buyer

Little Bonanza Casino
4720 N Virginia St
Reno, NV 89506-9031

Telephone: (775) 323-2724
Fax Number: (775) 323-5788
Internet Homepage: bonanzacasino.com
Company Email: contact@bonanzacasino.com
Type of Business: Foodservice Operations - Casinos
Year Founded: 1945
Total Sales: $3,794,000 (e)
Alcohol Sales: 20%
Number of Employees: 85
Average Check: Breakfast(8); Lunch(8); Dinner(10)
Total Units: 2
Trade Names: Branding Iron Cafe (1); Cactus Creek Prime Steakhouse (1)
Company-Owned Units: 2
Preferred Location Types: Hotel/Motel
Alcohol Served: Beer, Wine, Liquor
Primary Menu: Southwest/Tex-Mex (1); Steak (1)
Areas of Operation: NV
Type of Foodservice: Casual Dining (1); Fine Dining (1)
Primary Distributors: (Food) US Foods, NORTH LAS VEGAS, NV

Key Personnel
RYAN SHELTRA - President; General Manager; General Buyer

Monarch Casino & Resort Inc.
3800 S Virginia St
Reno, NV 89502-6005

Telephone: (775) 335-4600
Fax Number: (775) 332-9171
Internet Homepage: atlantiscasino.com; monarchblackhawk.com; monarchcasino.com
Company Email: info@monarchcasino.com
Type of Business: Foodservice Operations - Casinos
Year Founded: 1993
Publicly Held: Yes
Total Sales: $310,760,000 (e)
Alcohol Sales: 25%
Number of Employees: 1,900
Total Units: 2
Restaurants in Hotels: 12
Trade Names: Atlantis Casino Resort (1); Monarch Casino (1)
Company-Owned Units: 2
Alcohol Served: Beer, Wine, Liquor
Areas of Operation: CO, NV
Primary Distributors: (Food) US Foods, NORTH LAS VEGAS, NV; (Specialty Foods) US Foods, NORTH LAS VEGAS, NV
Notes: The company derives approximately 76% of its revenue from casino/hotel operations.

Key Personnel
JOHN FARAHI - CEO
ED KOENIG - Chief Accounting Officer
DAVID FARAHI - COO

MRB Holdings
3983 S McCarran Blvd
Reno, NV 89502-7510

Telephone: (775) 996-1162
Type of Business: Chain Restaurant Operator
Total Sales: $50,610,000 (e)
Total Units: 23
Trade Names: Burger King (23)
Units Franchised From: 23
Preferred Square Footage: 2,500
Primary Menu: Hamburger (23)
Areas of Operation: CA, NV
Type of Foodservice: Quick Serve (23)
Franchise Affiliation: Burger King Worldwide Inc., MIAMI, FL

Key Personnel
SANJAY LILLANEY - CEO; General Buyer
SAMANTHA C - VP Operations

Peg's Glorified Ham n Eggs
420 S Sierra St
Reno, NV 89501

Telephone: (775) 329-2600
Internet Homepage: eatatpegs.com
Type of Business: Chain Restaurant Operator
Year Founded: 1999
Total Units: 9
Trade Names: Peg's Glorified Ham n Eggs (9)
Company-Owned Units: 9
Preferred Location Types: Downtown; Strip Mall
Primary Menu: American (9)
Areas of Operation: CA, NV
Type of Foodservice: Family Restaurant (9)
Notes: This chain is run by the children of founders Fred and JoAnna Lee.

Key Personnel
DAVID FARRELL - Partner
JEWEL FARRELL - Partner
FRED LEE JR - Partner

▲
Port of Subs Inc.
5365 Mae Anne Ave Ste A29
Reno, NV 89523-1841

Telephone: (775) 747-0555
Fax Number: (775) 747-1510
Internet Homepage: portofsubs.com
Company Email: info@portofsubs.com
Type of Business: Chain Restaurant Operator
Year Founded: 1972
Systemwide Sales: $91,894,000 (e)
Total Sales: $17,770,000 (e)
Number of Employees: 381
Average Check: Breakfast(8); Lunch(10); Dinner(10)
Internet Order Processing: Yes
Total Units: 126
Trade Names: Port of Subs (127)
Company-Owned Units: 21
Units Franchised To: 94
Preferred Square Footage: 1,500; 1,600
Preferred Location Types: Community Mall; Convenience Store/Gas Station; Freestanding; Lifestyle Center; Other; Strip Mall
Primary Menu: Sandwiches/Deli (127)
Areas of Operation: AZ, CA, ID, NV, OR, UT, WA
Type of Foodservice: Quick Serve (127)
Primary Distributors: (Full Line) US Foods, RENO, NV

Key Personnel
MIKE POWELL - President

LISA MOORE - CFO
THERESA AULD - VP Human Resources
MICHELLE SCHROEDER - Director Human Resources

● ▲
Tom McKennie Group
1547 S Virginia St Ste 1
Reno, NV 89502-2818

Telephone: (775) 322-0414
Fax Number: (775) 322-2517
Type of Business: Chain Restaurant Operator
Total Sales: $62,280,000 (e)
Number of Employees: 470
Average Check: Breakfast(8); Lunch(8); Dinner(10)
Total Units: 13
Trade Names: McDonald's (13)
Units Franchised From: 13
Preferred Square Footage: 2,500; 3,000
Preferred Location Types: Discount Dept. Stores; Freestanding; Regional Mall
Primary Menu: Hamburger (13)
Areas of Operation: NV
Type of Foodservice: Quick Serve (13)
Franchise Affiliation: McDonald's Corporation, CHICAGO, IL
Primary Distributors: (Food) The Martin-Brower Co., STOCKTON, CA

Key Personnel
THOMAS MCKENNIE - President; General Buyer
ROBERT SIDORSKI - Director Operations, Purchasing, Real Estate, Design

---

NEW YORK

● ▲
Domino's Franchisee
263 New Scotland Ave
Albany, NY 12208-3123

Telephone: (518) 438-3030
Type of Business: Chain Restaurant Operator
Total Sales: $8,124,000 (e)
Total Units: 4
Trade Names: Domino's (4)
Units Franchised From: 4
Primary Menu: Pizza (4)
Areas of Operation: NY
Type of Foodservice: Quick Serve (4)
Franchise Affiliation: Domino's Pizza Inc, ANN ARBOR, MI

Key Personnel
SHAHID MAHMOOD - Owner; General Buyer

● ▲
Draper Development LLC
4 Fritz Blvd Ste 2
Albany, NY 12205-4966

Telephone: (518) 869-3986
Fax Number: (518) 869-3989
Internet Homepage: draperdevllc.com
Type of Business: Chain Restaurant Operator
Total Sales: $6,450,000 (e)
Number of Employees: 230
Average Check: Dinner(12)
Total Units: 3
Trade Names: Subway (3)
Units Franchised From: 3
Preferred Square Footage: 300; 2,000
Primary Menu: Sandwiches/Deli (3)
Areas of Operation: NY
Type of Foodservice: Quick Serve (3)
Franchise Affiliation: Doctor's Associates Inc., MILFORD, CT

Key Personnel
LAWRENCE JASENSKI JR - CEO
ROB JASENSKI - Director Facility/Maintenance, Construction
BRITTANY LANNING - Director Marketing

Paesan's Pizza & Restaurant
1785 Western Ave
Albany, NY 12203-4601

Telephone: (518) 464-0725
Fax Number: (518) 464-0722
Internet Homepage: paesanspizza.com
Type of Business: Chain Restaurant Operator
Year Founded: 1994
Total Sales: $4,762,000 (e)
Number of Employees: 20
Average Check: Lunch(10); Dinner(14)
Internet Order Processing: Yes
Total Units: 5
Trade Names: Paesan's Pizza & Restaurant (5)
Company-Owned Units: 5
Preferred Location Types: Freestanding; Strip Mall
Primary Menu: Pizza (5)
Areas of Operation: NY
Type of Foodservice: Family Restaurant (5)
Catering Services: Yes
Primary Distributors: (Full Line) SYSCO Food Services of Albany, HALFMOON, NY

Key Personnel
FRANK SCAVIO - Partner; Director Human Resources
VINNIE SCAVIO - Partner; Director Construction

The Desmond Hotel
660 Albany Shaker Rd
Albany, NY 12211-1056

Telephone: (518) 869-8100
Fax Number: (518) 869-7659
Internet Homepage: desmondhotels.com
Type of Business: Foodservice Operations - Hotel/Motels
Year Founded: 1974
Total Sales: $23,068,000 (e)
Alcohol Sales: 20%
Number of Employees: 100
Average Check: Lunch(14); Dinner(34)
Total Units: 2
Restaurants in Hotels: 6
Trade Names: The Desmond Hotel (2)
Company-Owned Units: 2
Units Franchised From: 4
Alcohol Served: Beer, Wine, Liquor
Areas of Operation: NY, PA
Type of Foodservice: Casual Dining (6)
Primary Distributors: (Food) SYSCO Food Services of Albany, HALFMOON, NY
Notes: The company derives approximately 70% of its revenue from hotel operations. Restaurants within the hotel include: The Tavern, Scrimshaw, Simpson's, Hunt Room, Fox and Hounds Pub and Sunset Grille.

Key Personnel
JOSHUA K. DESMOND - VP Operations
CHERYL BOYKO - Controller
MICHAEL CHAIN - General Manager
TYLER DESMOND - General Manager
MICHAEL ST. JOHN - Executive Chef; General Buyer
JACK RODDY - Director Sales
SHARI EDWARDS - Director Finance
ANGELA KELLY - Manager Sales

The Halal Shack
1400 Washington Ave
Albany, NY 12206

Internet Homepage: thehalalshack.com
Type of Business: Chain Restaurant Operator
Total Sales: $2,325,000 (e)
Total Units: 2
Trade Names: The Halal Shack (2)
Company-Owned Units: 2
Primary Menu: Greek/Mediterranean (2)
Areas of Operation: CA, NY
Type of Foodservice: Fast Casual (2)

Key Personnel
JAMAL RASOULLY - CEO

Edgewood Resort & Conference Center
22467 Edgewood Rd
Alexandria Bay, NY 13607-2415

Mailing Address: PO Box 600, ALEXANDRIA BAY, NY, 13607-0600
Telephone: (315) 482-9923
Fax Number: (315) 482-5210
Internet Homepage: theedgewoodresort.com
Company Email: info@theedgewoodresort.com
Type of Business: Chain Restaurant Operator
Year Founded: 1997
Total Sales: $6,241,000 (e)
Alcohol Sales: 10%
Number of Employees: 50
Average Check: Breakfast(8); Lunch(10); Dinner(22)
Total Units: 2
Trade Names: CB Bakers At Riverfront Cafe (1); Oscar's Harborside (1)
Company-Owned Units: 2
Preferred Location Types: Hotel/Motel
Alcohol Served: Beer, Wine, Liquor
Primary Menu: American (1); Italian (1)
Areas of Operation: NY
Type of Foodservice: Casual Dining (1); Fine Dining (1)
Primary Distributors: (Food) US Foods, BUFFALO, NY

Key Personnel
BENJAMIN RIDLEY - Partner; General Manager; General Buyer
JANINE RIDLEY - Partner; Executive Chef; Buyer Beverages, Food
CHRISTIAN IVES - Executive Chef

Bareburger Group LLC
3101 Vernon Blvd
Astoria, NY 11106-4870

Telephone: (718) 777-2273
Internet Homepage: bareburger.com
Company Email: franchise@bareburger.com
Type of Business: Chain Restaurant Operator
Year Founded: 2009
Systemwide Sales: $152,621,000 (e)
Total Sales: $4,409,000 (e)
Alcohol Sales: 10%
Average Check: Lunch(34); Dinner(54)
Total Units: 37
Trade Names: Bareburger (37)
Units Franchised To: 347
Preferred Square Footage: 2,500; 5,000
Preferred Location Types: Downtown
Alcohol Served: Beer, Wine
Primary Menu: Hamburger (37)
Projected Openings: 15
Areas of Operation: CA, CT, DC, IL, NJ, NY, OH, PA, FC, ON
Foreign Countries: CANADA; GERMANY; JAPAN; UNITED ARAB EMIRATES
Type of Foodservice: Fast Casual (37)

Key Personnel
EURIPIDES PELEKANOS - CEO
JIMMY PELEKANOS - President
GEORGIOS RODAS - COO
SAVVAS XANTHOS - CIO
GEORGE DELLIS - Chief Compliance Officer; Director Construction
JOHN SIMEONIDIS JR - Chief Design Officer
MISHA LEVIN - Director Culinary Operations
ASHLEY OTT - Director Training

The Halal Guys Inc.
1002 34th Ave
Astoria, NY 11106

Telephone: (347) 527-1505
Fax Number: (347) 763-8619
Internet Homepage: thehalalguysny.com; thehalalguysfranchise.com
Company Email: Info@thehalalguysny.com
Type of Business: Chain Restaurant Operator
Year Founded: 1990
Systemwide Sales: $89,258,000 (e)
Total Sales: $8,496,000 (e)
Total Units: 100
Trade Names: The Halal Guys (100)
Company-Owned Units: 2
Units Franchised To: 98
Preferred Location Types: Freestanding
Primary Menu: Middle Eastern (100)
Projected Openings: 13
Areas of Operation: AZ, CA, CT, DC, FL, GA, IL, LA, MA, NJ, NV, NY, PA, TX, VA, WA, WI, ON, QC
Foreign Countries: CANADA; THE PHILIPPINES
Type of Foodservice: Quick Serve (100)
Catering Services: Yes

Key Personnel
MUHAMMED ABOUELENEIN - Co-Founder; President
AHMED ELSAKA - Co-Founder; VP; Treasurer
ABDELBASET ELSAYED - Co-Founder; VP
AHMED ABOUELENEIN - CEO
TERRY WILSON - COO
HESHAM HEGAZY - General Manager
MELISSA CURTIN - Director Operations, Franchising
JOSEPH HAFEZ - Director Operations
MATT BORGEN - Director Operations

Domino's Franchisee
19 Dill St
Auburn, NY 13021-3605

Telephone: (315) 252-4440
Type of Business: Chain Restaurant Operator
Total Sales: $6,142,000 (e)
Total Units: 3
Trade Names: Domino's (3)
Units Franchised From: 3
Primary Menu: Pizza (3)
Areas of Operation: NY
Type of Foodservice: Quick Serve (3)
Franchise Affiliation: Domino's Pizza Inc, ANN ARBOR, MI

Key Personnel
GREGORY E. GRAY - Owner; General Buyer

Del Fuego
117 Deer Park Ave
Babylon, NY 11702-2830

Telephone: (631) 620-3700
Internet Homepage: latavolasayville.com; ruvorestaurant.com; delfuegorestaurant.com
Company Email: info@DeNicolaBrothersConcepts.com
Type of Business: Chain Restaurant Operator
Year Founded: 2011
Internet Order Processing: Yes
Total Units: 8
Trade Names: Del Fuego (4); La Tavola (1); NOCO (1); Ruvo (2)
Company-Owned Units: 8
Preferred Location Types: Freestanding; Strip Mall
Alcohol Served: Beer, Wine, Liquor
Primary Menu: American (1); Italian (3); Mexican (4)
Areas of Operation: NY
Type of Foodservice: Casual Dining (7); Fine Dining (1)
Catering Services: Yes
Notes: The DeNicola family owns and operates the following restaurants: (2) Del Fuego, (2) Ruvo, and (1) La Travola.

Key Personnel
JOSEPH DENICOLA - Partner; Executive Chef; General Buyer
LEO DENICOLA - General Manager
ANTHONY D'AMICO - Executive Chef

Tully's
522 E Main St
Batavia, NY 14020

Telephone: (585) 343-9030
Internet Homepage: tullysgoodtimes.com
Type of Business: Chain Restaurant Operator
Year Founded: 1991
Total Sales: $16,820,000 (e)
Total Units: 14
Trade Names: Tully's (14)
Company-Owned Units: 14
Primary Menu: American (14)
Areas of Operation: NY, PA
Type of Foodservice: Casual Dining (14)

Key Personnel
JOHN PAUL GIAMARTINO - Owner

Constant Rock
355 W Morris St Ste 101
Bath, NY 14810-1059

Mailing Address: PO Box 400, CORNING, NY, 14830-0400
Telephone: (607) 776-3457
Fax Number: (607) 776-5080
Type of Business: Chain Restaurant Operator
Total Sales: $15,374,000 (e)
Total Units: 3
Trade Names: McDonald's (3)
Units Franchised From: 3
Preferred Location Types: Freestanding
Primary Menu: Hamburger (3)
Areas of Operation: NY
Type of Foodservice: Quick Serve (3)
Franchise Affiliation: McDonald's Corporation, CHICAGO, IL

Key Personnel
W. DAVID FOSTER II - President; General Buyer

Auntie Anne's Franchise
1701 Sunrise Hwy
Bay Shore, NY 11706-6091

Telephone: (631) 665-6175
Type of Business: Chain Restaurant Operator
Total Sales: $2,320,000 (e)
Total Units: 3
Trade Names: Auntie Anne's Hand-Rolled Soft Pretzels (3)
Units Franchised From: 3
Primary Menu: Snacks (3)
Areas of Operation: NY
Type of Foodservice: Quick Serve (3)
Franchise Affiliation: Auntie Anne's Inc., LANCASTER, PA

Key Personnel
KEN KUGLER - Owner; General Buyer

Uncle Jack's Steakhouse
3940 Bell Blvd
Bayside, NY 11361-2061

Telephone: (718) 229-1100
Fax Number: (718) 229-1119
Internet Homepage: jacksshack.com; unclejacks.com; unclejacksmeathouse.com
Company Email: uncle@unclejacks.com
Type of Business: Chain Restaurant Operator
Year Founded: 1996
Total Sales: $11,945,000 (e)
Alcohol Sales: 12%
Number of Employees: 100
Average Check: Lunch(60); Dinner(120)
Internet Order Processing: Yes
Internet Sales: 5.00%
Total Units: 4
Trade Names: Uncle Jack's Meat House (2); Uncle Jack's Steakhouse (2)
Company-Owned Units: 4
Preferred Square Footage: 5,000; 7,000
Preferred Location Types: Freestanding
Alcohol Served: Beer, Wine, Liquor
Primary Menu: Steak (2); Steak/Seafood (2)
Projected Openings: 1
Areas of Operation: GA, NY
Type of Foodservice: Casual Dining (2); Fine Dining (2)
Primary Distributors: (Food) Dairyland, The Chefs' Warehouse, BRONX, NY

Key Personnel
WILLIAM DEGEL - President; Executive Chef
TOM CARPENTER - Director Operations

Chick-N-Bap
4400 Vestal Pkwy E
Binghampton, NY 13902

Telephone: (347) 414-3258
Internet Homepage: chicknbap.com; linkedin.com/company/chick-n-bap/about
Company Email: contact@chicknbap.com
Type of Business: Chain Restaurant Operator
Year Founded: 2013
Total Units: 2
Trade Names: Chick-N-Bap (2)
Company-Owned Units: 2
Primary Menu: Korean (2)
Projected Openings: 1
Areas of Operation: NY
Type of Foodservice: Fast Casual (2)

Key Personnel
SUNG KIM - Co-Founder; CEO
CHRISTIAN KO - Co-Founder; COO

99 Subway Inc
33 Court St
Binghamton, NY 13901-3104

Mailing Address: PO Box 103, BINGHAMTON, NY, 13903-0103
Telephone: (607) 723-3434
Internet Homepage: 99subwayeatfresh.com
Type of Business: Chain Restaurant Operator
Total Sales: $2,692,000 (e)
Total Units: 4
Trade Names: Subway (4)
Units Franchised From: 4
Primary Menu: Sandwiches/Deli (4)
Areas of Operation: NY
Type of Foodservice: Quick Serve (4)
Franchise Affiliation: Doctor's Associates Inc., MILFORD, CT

Key Personnel
FRANK STENTO - Owner

Larry Wilson, LLC
1257 Upper Front St
Binghamton, NY 13905

Telephone: (607) 217-4608
Type of Business: Chain Restaurant Operator
Total Sales: $36,460,000 (e)
Total Units: 22
Trade Names: Moe's Southwest Grill (22)
Units Franchised From: 22
Primary Menu: Southwest/Tex-Mex (22)
Areas of Operation: NY
Type of Foodservice: Fast Casual (22)
Franchise Affiliation: Moe's Southwest Grill LLC, ATLANTA, GA

Key Personnel
LARRY WILSON - Owner; General Buyer

Number 5
28 Mary St
Binghamton, NY 13903-1706

Mailing Address: PO Box 118, BINGHAMTON, NY, 13903-0118
Telephone: (607) 723-1600
Fax Number: (607) 723-3030
Internet Homepage: lampysrestaurant.com; number5restaurant.com
Company Email: info@number5restaurant.com
Type of Business: Chain Restaurant Operator
Year Founded: 1978
Total Sales: $5,434,000 (e)
Alcohol Sales: 15%
Number of Employees: 60
Average Check: Lunch(20); Dinner(54)
Total Units: 2
Trade Names: Lampy's Mediterranean Grill (1); Number 5 (1)
Company-Owned Units: 2
Preferred Location Types: Freestanding
Alcohol Served: Beer, Wine, Liquor
Primary Menu: Greek/Mediterranean (1); Steak/Seafood (1)
Areas of Operation: NY
Type of Foodservice: Fine Dining (2)
Catering Services: Yes
Primary Distributors: (Full Line) Maines Paper & Food Service New York Metro, FARMINGDALE, NY

Key Personnel
JIM MCCOY - President; General Manager; Executive Chef; General Buyer
AMBER AYERS - Manager Digital Marketing

The Sagamore
110 Sagamore Rd
Bolton Landing, NY 12814-7735

Mailing Address: PO Box 450, BOLTON LANDING, NY, 12814-0450
Telephone: (518) 644-9400
Fax Number: (518) 743-6211
Internet Homepage: thesagamore.com
Type of Business: Foodservice Operations - Hotel/Motels
Year Founded: 1985
Total Sales: $46,592,000 (e)
Alcohol Sales: 25%
Number of Employees: 850
Total Units: 1
Restaurants in Hotels: 8
Trade Names: The Sagamore Resort (1)
Company-Owned Units: 8
Alcohol Served: Beer, Wine, Liquor
Areas of Operation: NY
Type of Foodservice: Casual Dining (8)
Primary Distributors: (Food) SYSCO Food Services of Albany, HALFMOON, NY; (Specialty Foods) Dairyland, The Chefs' Warehouse, BRONX, NY
Notes: The company derives approximately 70% of its revenue from hotel operations.

Key Personnel
TOM GUAY - General Manager; Director Operations
DARCY MCINNIS - Director Purchasing
LORI REHM - Director Sales

Domino's Franchisee
167 Clarke St
Brentwood, NY 11717-2043

Telephone: (631) 747-4517
Type of Business: Chain Restaurant Operator
Total Sales: $8,103,000 (e)
Total Units: 4
Trade Names: Domino's (4)
Units Franchised From: 4
Primary Menu: Pizza (4)
Areas of Operation: NY
Type of Foodservice: Quick Serve (4)
Franchise Affiliation: Domino's Pizza Inc, ANN ARBOR, MI

Key Personnel
RAJA S. ALI - Owner; General Buyer

Bobby Van's
2393 Montauk Hwy
Bridgehampton, NY 11932

Mailing Address: PO Box 3055, BRIDGEHAMPTON, NY, 11932-3055
Telephone: (631) 537-0590
Fax Number: (631) 537-1983
Internet Homepage: bobbyvans.com
Company Email: bobbyvans@aol.com
Type of Business: Chain Restaurant Operator
Year Founded: 1969
Total Sales: $4,855,000 (e)
Alcohol Sales: 10%
Number of Employees: 25
Average Check: Lunch(24); Dinner(60)
Internet Order Processing: Yes
Total Units: 9
Trade Names: Bobby Van's (9)
Company-Owned Units: 9
Preferred Square Footage: 5,500; 6,000
Preferred Location Types: Freestanding
Alcohol Served: Beer, Wine, Liquor
Primary Menu: Steak (9)
Areas of Operation: DC, NY
Type of Foodservice: Casual Dining (9)
Primary Distributors: (Food) Dairyland, The Chefs' Warehouse, BRONX, NY

Key Personnel
JOSEPH PHAIR - President; General Manager
JAMES PHAIR - General Manager; Buyer Beverages
JOHN STELLA - Executive Chef; Manager Purchasing, Risk Management, Food Safety; Buyer Food

3C Blessing, Inc.
623 E Tremont Ave
Bronx, NY 10457-4801

Telephone: (347) 271-5300
Type of Business: Chain Restaurant Operator
Total Sales: $5,128,000 (e)
Total Units: 4
Trade Names: Little Caesars Pizza (4)
Units Franchised From: 4
Primary Menu: Pizza (4)
Areas of Operation: NJ, NY

Type of Foodservice: Quick Serve (4)
Franchise Affiliation: Little Caesar Enterprises Inc., DETROIT, MI

Key Personnel
ADE OTUFALE - Owner; General Buyer

Detail Systems Inc.
2065 Jerome Ave
Bronx, NY 10453

Telephone: (718) 733-2819
Fax Number: (718) 733-2647
Type of Business: Chain Restaurant Operator
Total Sales: $14,740,000 (e)
Total Units: 3
Trade Names: McDonald's (3)
Units Franchised From: 3
Preferred Location Types: Freestanding
Primary Menu: Hamburger (3)
Areas of Operation: NY
Type of Foodservice: Quick Serve (3)
Franchise Affiliation: McDonald's Corporation, CHICAGO, IL

Key Personnel
DAVID MOYETT - President; General Buyer

Golden Krust Caribbean Bakery Inc.
3958 Park Ave
Bronx, NY 10457-8014

Telephone: (718) 655-7878
Fax Number: (718) 583-1883
Internet Homepage: goldenkrustbakery.com
Type of Business: Chain Restaurant Operator
Year Founded: 1989
Systemwide Sales: $143,098,000 (e)
Total Sales: $41,740,000 (e)
Alcohol Sales: 2%
Number of Employees: 1,800
Average Check: Breakfast(12); Lunch(16); Dinner(20)
Internet Order Processing: Yes
Internet Sales: 1.00%
Total Units: 93
Trade Names: Golden Krust Caribbean Bakery & Grill (127)
Company-Owned Units: 3
Units Franchised To: 124
Preferred Square Footage: 250; 500; 3,500
Preferred Location Types: Downtown; Strip Mall
Primary Menu: Caribbean (127)
Areas of Operation: FL, GA, MA, MD, NC, NJ, NY
Type of Foodservice: Quick Serve (127)
Distribution Centers: BRONX, NY
On-site Distribution Center: Yes

Primary Distributors: (Food) US Foods, BUFFALO, NY

Key Personnel
JACQUELINE HAWTHORNE-ROBINSON - Chairman; CEO
DAREN HAWTHORNE ESQ - President Restaurant Operations; Exec VP Franchising
GLENN FANCIE - CFO
LORRAINE HAWTHORNE-MORRISON - Chief Administrative Officer
HAYWOOD HAWTHORNE - CIO; VP Information Technology, Manufacturing
STEVEN AMENT - VP Operations, Franchising
STEVEN CLARKE - Director Marketing, Public Relations
OMAR HAWTHORNE - Director Franchise Development
CHRISTOPHER HYLTON - Director Quality Assurance, Research & Development
ORLEAN LUNAN - Director Training
GARNETT MORRISON - Director Operations
ZAIDA DE LA ROSA - Manager Quality Assurance

Great Bons, Inc.
290 Baychester Ave
Bronx, NY 10475-4575

Telephone: (518) 325-9717
Type of Business: Chain Restaurant Operator
Total Sales: $1,528,000 (e)
Total Units: 4
Trade Names: Cinnabon (4)
Units Franchised From: 4
Primary Menu: Snacks (4)
Areas of Operation: NY
Type of Foodservice: Quick Serve (4)
Franchise Affiliation: Cinnabon Inc., ATLANTA, GA

Key Personnel
BILL GELLERT - Owner; General Buyer

Perna Group
300 E 204th St
Bronx, NY 10467-4602

Telephone: (718) 405-6510
Fax Number: (718) 882-0887
Type of Business: Chain Restaurant Operator
Year Founded: 1994
Total Sales: $33,200,000 (e)
Number of Employees: 200
Average Check: Breakfast(8); Lunch(12); Dinner(12)
Total Units: 7
Trade Names: McDonald's (7)
Units Franchised From: 7
Preferred Square Footage: 3,000
Preferred Location Types: Freestanding

Primary Menu: Hamburger (7)
Areas of Operation: NY
Type of Foodservice: Quick Serve (7)
Franchise Affiliation: McDonald's Corporation, CHICAGO, IL

Key Personnel
CATHERINE PERNA - President; Partner; Director Finance, Information Systems, Supply Chain, Real Estate, Design; General Buyer
RICHARD PERNA - Partner; Director Operations, Facility/Maintenance
SALAM ABDUL - General Manager; Manager Operations, Facility/Maintenance, Human Resources
MICHELLE PERNA - Manager Accounting

Sam's Restaurant Systems
41 City Island Ave
Bronx, NY 10464-1612

Telephone: (718) 885-0949
Fax Number: (718) 885-0187
Internet Homepage: shrimpboxrestaurant.com; pierrestaurantandtikibar.com; seashorerestaurant.com; seasidejohnnies.net; sammysfishbox.com
Type of Business: Chain Restaurant Operator
Year Founded: 1967
Total Sales: $22,684,000 (e)
Alcohol Sales: 25%
Number of Employees: 500
Average Check: Lunch(30); Dinner(42)
Total Units: 4
Trade Names: Pier Restaruant & Tiki Bar (1); Sammy's Fish Box (1); Sammy's Shrimp Box (1); Sea Shore Restaurant (1)
Company-Owned Units: 4
Preferred Location Types: Freestanding
Alcohol Served: Beer, Wine, Liquor
Primary Menu: American (1); Seafood (3)
Areas of Operation: NY
Type of Foodservice: Casual Dining (1); Fine Dining (3)
Primary Distributors: (Food) SYSCO Food Services of Syracuse, WARNERS, NY

Key Personnel
SAM CHERNIN - President; General Manager; Executive Chef; Director Real Estate; General Buyer
JOHN CARFAGNO - Controller
STEVE GILMORE - General Manager; Manager Risk Management, Human Resources

Zaro's Bake Shop Inc.
138 Bruckner Blvd
Bronx, NY 10454-4620

Telephone: (718) 993-5600

Fax Number: (718) 292-9353
Internet Homepage: zaro.com
Type of Business: Chain Restaurant Operator
Year Founded: 1935
Total Sales: $14,080,000 (e)
Number of Employees: 550
Average Check: Lunch(10); Dinner(16)
Total Units: 9
Trade Names: Zaro's Bread Basket (9)
Company-Owned Units: 9
Preferred Square Footage: 4,000
Preferred Location Types: Freestanding
Primary Menu: American (9)
Areas of Operation: NY
Type of Foodservice: Quick Serve (9)
Catering Services: Yes
On-site Distribution Center: Yes

Key Personnel
LARRY MARCO - Controller
RALPH BEN-SHALOM - Manager Facility/Maintenance, Store Fixtures

Auntie Anne's Franchise
5100 Kings Plz
Brooklyn, NY 11234-5208

Telephone: (718) 692-2200
Type of Business: Chain Restaurant Operator
Total Sales: $1,595,000 (e)
Total Units: 2
Trade Names: Auntie Anne's Hand-Rolled Soft Pretzels (2)
Units Franchised From: 2
Primary Menu: Snacks (2)
Areas of Operation: NY
Type of Foodservice: Quick Serve (2)
Franchise Affiliation: Auntie Anne's Inc., LANCASTER, PA

Key Personnel
SHARON DYM - Owner; General Buyer

Auntie Anne's Franchise
625 Atlantic Ave
Brooklyn, NY 11217-2169

Telephone: (718) 398-4390
Type of Business: Chain Restaurant Operator
Total Sales: $1,535,000 (e)
Total Units: 2
Trade Names: Auntie Anne's Hand-Rolled Soft Pretzels (2)
Units Franchised From: 2
Primary Menu: Snacks (2)
Areas of Operation: NY
Type of Foodservice: Quick Serve (2)
Franchise Affiliation: Auntie Anne's Inc., LANCASTER, PA

Key Personnel
CHERYL WITTE - Owner; General Buyer

Cafe Grumpy
199 Diamond St
Brooklyn, NY 11222-2406

Telephone: (718) 383-0748
Internet Homepage: cafegrumpy.com
Company Email: info@cafegrumpy.com
Type of Business: Chain Restaurant Operator
Year Founded: 2005
Total Units: 11
Trade Names: Cafe Grumpy (11)
Company-Owned Units: 11
Primary Menu: Coffee (11)
Projected Openings: 1
Areas of Operation: NY
Type of Foodservice: Quick Serve (11)

Key Personnel
CAROLINE BELL - Co-Founder; CEO; Partner; General Buyer
CHRIS TIMBRELL - Co-Founder; Partner

Junior's Restaurants
386 Flatbush Avenue Ext
Brooklyn, NY 11201-5331

Telephone: (718) 852-5257
Fax Number: (718) 260-9849
Internet Homepage: juniorscheesecake.com
Company Email: info@juniorscheesecake.com
Type of Business: Chain Restaurant Operator
Year Founded: 1950
Total Sales: $9,828,000 (e)
Alcohol Sales: 15%
Number of Employees: 125
Average Check: Breakfast(10); Lunch(16); Dinner(24)
Internet Order Processing: Yes
Internet Sales: 1.00%
Total Units: 4
Trade Names: Junior's Most Fabulous Cheesecake (4)
Company-Owned Units: 4
Preferred Location Types: Downtown; Freestanding; Strip Mall
Alcohol Served: Beer, Wine, Liquor
Primary Menu: American (4)
Areas of Operation: FL, NY
Type of Foodservice: Casual Dining (4)
Catering Services: Yes
Primary Distributors: (Full Line) SYSCO Food Services of Syracuse, WARNERS, NY

Key Personnel
KEVIN ROSEN - President; Partner; Director Operations; General Buyer
ALAN ROSEN - Partner; Director Finance
LOU INCHEASCIAGO - Manager Accounting

Mimi's Hummus
1209 Cortelyou Rd
Brooklyn, NY 11218-5403

Telephone: (718) 284-4444
Internet Homepage: mimishummus.com
Company Email: info@mimishummus.com
Type of Business: Chain Restaurant Operator
Year Founded: 2009
Total Units: 2
Trade Names: Mimi's Hummus (2)
Company-Owned Units: 2
Primary Menu: Middle Eastern (2)
Areas of Operation: NY
Type of Foodservice: Casual Dining (2)

Key Personnel
MIMI KITAN - President; Executive Chef; General Buyer

Peter Luger Inc.
178 Broadway
Brooklyn, NY 11211-6131

Telephone: (718) 387-7400
Fax Number: (718) 387-3523
Internet Homepage: peterluger.com
Company Email: info@peterluger.com
Type of Business: Chain Restaurant Operator
Year Founded: 1887
Total Sales: $10,784,000 (e)
Alcohol Sales: 25%
Number of Employees: 160
Average Check: Lunch(66); Dinner(90)
Internet Order Processing: Yes
Total Units: 2
Trade Names: Peter Luger Steak House (2)
Company-Owned Units: 2
Preferred Location Types: Freestanding
Alcohol Served: Beer, Wine, Liquor
Primary Menu: Steak (2)
Areas of Operation: NY
Type of Foodservice: Fine Dining (2)
Primary Distributors: (Food) US Foods New York Metro, PERTH AMBOY, NJ

Key Personnel
MARILYN SPIERA - President
JODY STORCH - VP Operations, Purchasing; General Buyer
AMY RUBINSTEIN - Treasurer
MIRTHA HERNANDEZ - General Buyer

Pizza Loves Emily Group
919 Fulton St
Brooklyn, NY 11238

Telephone: (347) 844-9588
Internet Homepage: emmysquaredpizza.com; pizzalovesemily.com; violeteastvillage.com
Company Email: info@pizzalovesemily.com
Type of Business: Chain Restaurant Operator
Year Founded: 2016
Total Units: 8
Trade Names: Emmy Squared (5); Pizza Loves Emily (2); Violet (1)
Company-Owned Units: 8
Preferred Location Types: Downtown; Strip Mall
Primary Menu: Pizza (8)
Projected Openings: 1
Areas of Operation: NY, PA, TN
Type of Foodservice: Casual Dining (8)

Key Personnel
EMILY HYLAND - Co-Founder; Partner
MATT HYLAND - Co-Founder; Partner
KEN LEVITAN - Partner
MELISSA RIORDAN - General Manager

Posh Tomato
252 Conover St
Brooklyn, NY 11231-1020

Telephone: (347) 227-0172
Internet Homepage: poshtomato.com
Company Email: cs@poshtomato.com
Type of Business: Chain Restaurant Operator
Total Units: 3
Trade Names: Posh Tomato (3)
Units Franchised To: 3
Primary Menu: Pizza (3)
Areas of Operation: NJ, NY
Type of Foodservice: Fast Casual (3)

Key Personnel
SOLOMON SARWAY - Partner; Executive Chef
MORRIS SARWAY - Partner; General Buyer
IKE SARWAY - Partner

Sweet Chick
164 Bedford Ave
Brooklyn, NY 11211

Telephone: (347) 725-4793
Internet Homepage: sweetchick.com
Type of Business: Chain Restaurant Operator
Total Sales: $6,083,000 (e)
Total Units: 5
Trade Names: Sweet Chick (5)
Company-Owned Units: 5
Primary Menu: Chicken (5)

Type of Foodservice: Fast Casual (5)

Key Personnel
JOHN SEYMOUR - Founder; Owner

Sweetleaf Coffee Roasters
159 Freeman St
Brooklyn, NY 11222

Internet Homepage: sweetleafcoffee.com
Company Email: shop@sweetleafcoffee.com
Type of Business: Chain Restaurant Operator
Year Founded: 2008
Number of Employees: 25
Total Units: 4
Trade Names: Sweetleaf Coffee Roasters (4)
Company-Owned Units: 4
Primary Menu: Coffee (4)
Areas of Operation: NY
Type of Foodservice: Quick Serve (4)

Key Personnel
RICH NIETO - Founder

The Butcher's Daughter
271 Metropolitan Ave
Brooklyn, NY 11211

Telephone: (347) 763-1421
Internet Homepage: thebutchersdaughter.com
Company Email: brooklyn@thebutchersdaughter.com
Type of Business: Chain Restaurant Operator
Total Units: 5
Trade Names: The Butcher's Daughter (5)
Company-Owned Units: 5
Primary Menu: Health Foods (5)
Areas of Operation: CA, NY
Type of Foodservice: Casual Dining (5)

Key Personnel
HEATHER TIERNEY - Founder; Creative Director
RICHARD REA - Executive Chef
MIKA CALI - Creative Director
KARI HENDRICK - Director Operations

†▲ Delaware North
250 Delaware Ave
Buffalo, NY 14202-2200

Telephone: (716) 858-5000
Fax Number: (716) 858-5187
Internet Homepage: delawarenorth.com
Company Email: info@delawarenorth.com
Type of Business: Foodservice Management Operator
Year Founded: 1915
Total Sales: $17,798,000 (e)
Number of Employees: 100
Number of Locations Served: 14
Total Foodservice Mgmt Accounts: 14
Trade Names: Delaware North Companies Parks and Resorts
Areas of Operation: AR, AZ, CA, CO, FL, GA, IA, ID, IL, LA, MA, MD, MI, MN, MO, MT, NJ, NY, OH, OK, PA, RI, SC, TN, TX, VA, WA, WI, WV, AB, ON
Foreign Countries: AUSTRALIA; CANADA; NEW ZEALAND
Type of Foodservice: Full-service sit-down dining (14); Quick Serve (14)
Foodservice Management Venues: Parks & Recreation
Primary Distributors: (Full Line) SYSCO Food Services of Albany, HALFMOON, NY
Parent Company: Delaware North Companies Inc., BUFFALO, NY
Headquarter Offices: Delaware North Parks & Resorts At Yosemite, YOSEMITE NATIONAL PARK, CA

Key Personnel
JEREMY M. JACOBS - Chairman
CHARLIE JACOBS - CEO Division
JERRY JACOBS JR - Co-CEO
LOUIS JACOBS - Co-CEO
E. BRIAN HANSBERRY - President Division
JIM HOUSER - President
SCOTT SOCHA - President; VP; Treasurer
CHRISTOPHER J. FEENEY - CFO; Exec VP
DAVID FRANKHOUSER - COO
JEFF WILKINSON - CIO
TODD MERRY - Chief Marketing Officer
KALA IYENGAR - Chief Data Officer
BARRY FREILICHER - Senior VP Business Development
JAMES OBLETZ - Senior VP Corporate Development
LUISA WOODS - VP Marketing
JEFF TAIPS - VP Finance, Gaming/Entertainment
DANIEL ZIMMER - VP Finance, Development
MICHAEL CARRUTHERS - VP Gaming/Entertainment
JAMES CLARKE - VP Human Resources
LYNN CONSTABLE - VP Finance
LATEYFA ALI - VP Employee Development
ALLISON APPOLONEY - VP Operations
DONNA GENESKY - VP
KATHY GILL - VP Marketing, Communications
SEAN GAVIGAN - General Manager Operations-Food
MICHAEL ZIELINSKI - General Manager
ROB PUHALSKI - General Manager
MARK SZUBECZAK - Executive Chef
STEVE MARTIN - Senior Director Marketing
TIM BARTHOLD - Senior Director Risk Management, Compliance; Director Risk Management
ANDREW ANDORF - Director
DAISY HALL - Director Marketing, Sales
PAULA HALLIGAN - Director Retail Operations
KELLY MILBRANDT - Director Information

Technology
JIM ZILLIOX - Director Information Technology
WES TRUMP - Director Visual Merchandising
BRIAN ESCOBAR - Regional Director Information Technology
SAMANTHA EYGENDAAL - Regional Director Technology
JANA JARED - Regional Director Information Technology
LIZ COLOSIMO - Manager Marketing
DAVID BOLZ - Manager Human Resources
LEANNE PAWLAK - Manager Human Resources
BRIAN MERCER - Manager Information Technology
KATARINA STIGLICH - Manager Talent, Talent Acquisitions
GABE GIGLIOTTI - Supervisor Security
JEREMIAH COLLINS - Project Manager Construction
DIANE CZORA - Administrator Payroll
KAREN JORDAN - Administrator Security
MICHAEL LAJEWSKI - Administrator Retail Information Systems
DARRYLL POPIELARSKI - Senior Buyer
MEGAN SUDORE - Specialist Digital Marketing
CHARLES ROBERTS - Specialist Communications
JOHNATHAN WORDEN - Specialist Training, Talent
LINDSAY TRUESDELL - Specialist Communications
AMANDA BOCKRATH - Specialist Human Resources
BETH MURPHY - Buyer; Analyst
SHARMIN SULTANA - Representative Customer Service
DEBRA GRADZEWICZ - Representative Customer Service
CARLA KLINE - Senior Analyst Business Development
TRACI ARCHER - Senior Analyst Employee Compensation
ABBIGAIL BINGA - Analyst Finance
AMBER KURAS - Analyst HRIS
ANTHONY LYNCH - Analyst Information/Data Security
COLLIN MCARDLE - Analyst Information/Data Security
CHRISTOPHER TURNER - Analyst Security
BRIAN TECHMAN - Analyst Help Desk
AARON DEROOY - Engineer Network

‡

Hart Hotels Inc.
617 Dingens St
Buffalo, NY 14206-2400

Telephone: (716) 893-6551
Fax Number: (716) 893-6517
Internet Homepage: harthotels.com
Company Email: hart@harthotels.com
Type of Business: Foodservice Operations - Hotel/Motels
Year Founded: 1985
Total Sales: $42,680,000 (e)
Alcohol Sales: 20%
Number of Employees: 384
Total Units: 6
Restaurants in Hotels: 6
Trade Names: Candlewood Suites (1); Doubletree by Hilton (1); Green Mountain Suites (1); Holiday Inn (1); Hotel at Batavia Downs (1); Hotel Ithaca (1)
Company-Owned Units: 6
Alcohol Served: Beer, Wine, Liquor
Areas of Operation: ME, NY, VT
Type of Foodservice: Casual Dining (6)
Primary Distributors: (Food) SYSCO Food Services of Albany, HALFMOON, NY
Notes: The company derives approximately 80% of its revenue from hotel operations.

Key Personnel
DAVID HART - CEO; President
ALAN INCORVAIA - VP Operations
LINDA COSTELLO - VP Human Resources
AARON SYPNIEWSKI - Controller

†

Personal Touch Food Service Inc.
120 W Tupper St Ste 101
Buffalo, NY 14201-2170

Telephone: (716) 883-1998
Fax Number: (716) 883-0672
Internet Homepage: ptfswny.com
Type of Business: Foodservice Management Operator
Year Founded: 1985
Total Sales: $21,488,000 (e)
Number of Employees: 400
Number of Locations Served: 85
Total Foodservice Mgmt Accounts: 43
Areas of Operation: NY
Type of Foodservice: Cafeteria (43)
Foodservice Management Venues: Business & Industry; College & University; Schools
Primary Distributors: (Full Line) Maple Leaf Foods, CHEEKTOWAGA, NY

Key Personnel
DAVE CERVI - President; Manager Operations, Purchasing, Information Systems, Foodservice, Food Safety, Food and Beverage
PAUL TYRPAK - CFO; Controller; Director Risk Management, Human Resources

Rich Products Corp.
1 Robert Rich Way
Buffalo, NY 14213-1701

Telephone: (716) 878-8000
Fax Number: (716) 878-8130
Internet Homepage: richs.com/about/subsidiary-businesses
Type of Business: Chain Restaurant Operator
Year Founded: 1986
Total Sales: $27,150,000 (e)
Alcohol Sales: 25%
Number of Employees: 400
Average Check: Breakfast(16); Lunch(20); Dinner(32)
Total Units: 5
Trade Names: Glen Iris Inn (1); Green Turtle Inn Restaurant (1); Kaiyo Grill (1); Palm Beach CC Grill (1); Pettibones Grill (1)
Company-Owned Units: 5
Preferred Location Types: Freestanding; Hotel/Motel; Mixed-use Center
Alcohol Served: Beer, Wine, Liquor
Primary Menu: American (4); Asian (1)
Areas of Operation: FL, NY
Type of Foodservice: Casual Dining (4); Quick Serve (1)
Catering Services: Yes
Primary Distributors: (Full Line) US Foods, BUFFALO, NY

Key Personnel
ROBERT RICH JR - Chairman; Partner
MINDY RICH - Vice Chairman; Partner; Exec VP; General Buyer
RICHARD FERRANTI - CEO
BILL GISEL - CEO
JIM KIM - President Global Marketing
STEVE KING - President Business Development
MIHIR RAJOPADHYE - President
MIKE SIMS - President Information Systems
KEN LOCKWOOD - President Information Systems
BETTY ZAWADA - President Finance
ED MOORE - Chief Human Resources Officer; Exec VP
MONICA NOVOMISLE - Chief Product Officer; Exec VP
TED RICH - Exec VP
GEORGIA DACHILLE - Exec VP Information Technology, Supply Chain
JILL DAVISON - VP Strategic Planning
KARA BURKE - VP Innovation
MOODIE CORETTI - VP E-Commerce
MARIE-CLAUDE LAPRADE - VP Strategy, Marketing
MIKE RUDNEY - VP Procurement
JACK SCHUYLER - VP Procurement
MAUREEN LYNCH - VP Supply Chain
WILLIAM KREINER - General Manager; Executive Chef; Manager Menu Development
PREETIKA GHAI - Senior Director Manufacturing
VIC GILMORE - Director Information Technology
NICK CORCORAN - Director Applications, Infrastructure, Global
JASON DELAPLANE - Director Sales
KEN KWASNIEWSKI - Director Supply Chain; Transformation

JACK JOSEPH - Director Research & Development
KEVIN MALCHOFF - Director
ROB MCCOY - Director Sales
MITCH MIRSKY - Director Digital Marketing, Global
SCOTT OLSON - Director Distribution, Sales
DON SMYCZYNSKI - Director Security, Global
JON ZIRNHELD - Director Information Systems
JAMES TOOMEY - Director Technology, Digital, Innovation
CIERA WOMACK - Director Marketing
KERRY SWARTZ - Senior Manager Supply Chain
NICOLE OWCZARCZAK - Senior Manager Marketing
JESSICA ENGLISH - Manager Innovation

Ted's Jumbo Red Hots Inc.
301 Ohio St Ste 200
Buffalo, NY 14204

Telephone: (716) 691-3731
Fax Number: (716) 691-3776
Internet Homepage: tedshotdogs.com
Company Email: info@tedshotdogs.com
Type of Business: Chain Restaurant Operator
Year Founded: 1927
Total Sales: $14,560,000 (e)
Number of Employees: 310
Average Check: Lunch(8); Dinner(8)
Internet Order Processing: Yes
Total Units: 10
Trade Names: Ted's Jumbo Red Hots (10)
Company-Owned Units: 10
Preferred Square Footage: 1,800
Preferred Location Types: Freestanding; Regional Mall
Primary Menu: Hot Dogs (10)
Projected Openings: 1
Areas of Operation: AZ, NY
Type of Foodservice: Quick Serve (10)
Catering Services: Yes
Primary Distributors: (Equipment) BHS Foodservice Solutions, AMHERST, NY; (Food) Tarantino Foods LLC, BUFFALO, NY; (Supplies) BHS Foodservice Solutions, AMHERST, NY

Key Personnel
PETER LIAROS - Owner; Treasurer

Villa Roma Resort Hotel Inc.
356 Villa Roma Rd
Callicoon, NY 12723-6816

Telephone: (845) 887-4880
Fax Number: (845) 887-4824
Internet Homepage: villaroma.com
Type of Business: Chain Restaurant Operator
Year Founded: 1980
Total Sales: $20,440,000 (e)
Alcohol Sales: 30%
Number of Employees: 400
Average Check: Breakfast(18); Lunch(24); Dinner(36)
Total Units: 8
Trade Names: Dolce's Ice Cream Parlor (1); Eleanor's (1); Pool Grill (1); The Clubhouse Dining Room (1); The Grille Room (1); The Main Dining Room (1); The Roman Garden Cafe (1); The Ski Chalet Snack Bar (1)
Company-Owned Units: 8
Preferred Location Types: Hotel/Motel
Alcohol Served: Beer, Wine, Liquor
Primary Menu: American (5); Sandwiches/Deli (2); Snacks (1)
Areas of Operation: NY
Type of Foodservice: Casual Dining (5); Fast Casual (1); Fine Dining (1); Quick Serve (1)
Primary Distributors: (Full Line) Maines Paper & Food Service Inc., CONKLIN, NY

Key Personnel
MARTIN PASSANTE - President
PAUL CARLUCCI - VP; General Manager
DORIS MOYER - Director Human Resources
ADAM JACOBSON - Director Marketing, Sales
JOAN STODDARD - Manager Accounting
LINDA POLTERSDORF - Manager Information Systems

Southwest Grill of New York, LLC
5256 W Genesee St
Camillus, NY 13031-2254

Telephone: (315) 468-6637
Type of Business: Chain Restaurant Operator
Total Sales: $23,330,000 (e)
Total Units: 14
Trade Names: Moe's Southwest Grill (14)
Units Franchised From: 14
Primary Menu: Southwest/Tex-Mex (14)
Areas of Operation: NY, PA
Type of Foodservice: Fast Casual (14)
Franchise Affiliation: Moe's Southwest Grill LLC, ATLANTA, GA

Key Personnel
SCOTT SEARLES - Owner; General Buyer

Frant Corporation Inc.
3892 Rileys Run
Canandaigua, NY 14424-9038

Telephone: (585) 396-9483
Type of Business: Chain Restaurant Operator
Year Founded: 1989
Total Sales: $11,420,000 (e)
Number of Employees: 20
Average Check: Dinner(10)
Total Units: 6
Trade Names: Arby's (6)
Units Franchised From: 6
Preferred Square Footage: 1,400; 3,200
Primary Menu: Sandwiches/Deli (6)
Areas of Operation: NY
Type of Foodservice: Quick Serve (6)
Franchise Affiliation: Arby's Restaurant Group, ATLANTA, GA

Key Personnel
FRANK MUGNOLA - President; General Buyer
JERRY GREGORY - District Manager

Shiro of Japan
401 Old Country Rd
Carle Place, NY 11514-2122

Telephone: (516) 997-4770
Fax Number: (516) 997-4772
Internet Homepage: shiroofjapan.com
Company Email: david@shiroofjapan.com/
Type of Business: Chain Restaurant Operator
Year Founded: 1973
Total Sales: $5,842,000 (e)
Number of Employees: 35
Average Check: Lunch(14); Dinner(24)
Total Units: 1
Trade Names: Shiro of Japan (1)
Company-Owned Units: 1
Alcohol Served: Beer, Wine, Liquor
Primary Menu: Japanese (1)
Areas of Operation: NY
Type of Foodservice: Casual Dining (1); Quick Serve (0)
Primary Distributors: (Food) Landmark Food Corp., HOLTSVILLE, NY

Key Personnel
PETER FACCIBENE - CEO
Y. UCHIDA - Executive Chef; General Buyer
T. MEGURO - General Buyer

Windram Enterprises, Inc.
1891 Route 6
Carmel, NY 10512

Telephone: (845) 228-4898
Fax Number: (845) 855-0794
Type of Business: Chain Restaurant Operator
Total Sales: $9,076,000 (e)
Number of Employees: 500
Average Check: Lunch(8); Dinner(10)
Internet Order Processing: Yes
Total Units: 5
Trade Names: KFC (5)
Units Franchised From: 5
Preferred Square Footage: 2,500; 3,200
Preferred Location Types: Freestanding
Primary Menu: Chicken (5)

Areas of Operation: NY
Type of Foodservice: Quick Serve (5)
Franchise Affiliation: KFC Corporation, LOUISVILLE, KY

Key Personnel
ARTHUR WINDRAM - President; Owner; General Buyer
DAVID ROSE - Director Operations; Manager Information Systems
DEBBIE TAFFE - Manager Accounting

Charlie's Food Co. Inc.
618 Saratoga St
Cohoes, NY 12047-4609

Telephone: (518) 462-3505
Internet Homepage: hotdogcharlies.com
Company Email: custservice@hotdogcharlies.com
Type of Business: Chain Restaurant Operator
Year Founded: 1922
Total Sales: $1,893,000 (e)
Number of Employees: 25
Average Check: Lunch(6); Dinner(6)
Internet Order Processing: Yes
Total Units: 4
Trade Names: Hot Dog Charlie's (4)
Company-Owned Units: 4
Preferred Square Footage: 2,000
Preferred Location Types: Community Mall; Downtown; Strip Mall
Primary Menu: Hot Dogs (4)
Areas of Operation: NY
Type of Foodservice: Quick Serve (4)

Key Personnel
CHARLES FENTEKES - President; Treasurer; General Manager
FLORENCE DIMITRIADIS - VP Distribution; General Manager; General Buyer

Mr. Subb Inc.
601 Columbia St
Cohoes, NY 12047-3802

Telephone: (518) 783-0276
Fax Number: (518) 783-0294
Internet Homepage: mrsubb.com
Type of Business: Chain Restaurant Operator
Year Founded: 1976
Systemwide Sales: $40,534,000 (e)
Total Sales: $32,630,000 (e)
Number of Employees: 256
Average Check: Lunch(10); Dinner(10)
Internet Order Processing: Yes
Total Units: 16
Trade Names: Mr. Subb (16)
Company-Owned Units: 16
Preferred Square Footage: 1,000; 1,600
Preferred Location Types: Freestanding; Regional Mall; Strip Mall; Travel Plazas
Primary Menu: Sandwiches/Deli (16)
Areas of Operation: NY
Type of Foodservice: Quick Serve (16)
Primary Distributors: (Food) Ginsberg's Foods, HUDSON, NY

Key Personnel
WILLIAM F. POMPA - President; Manager Purchasing, Menu Development
MICHAEL MALIN - Director Information Systems, Marketing
HAROLD E. WOOD - Director Operations; Manager Sales
CARMELLA POMPA - Manager Human Resources

The Xaviars Restaurant Group
117 N Route 303
Congers, NY 10920-1734

Telephone: (845) 268-6555
Internet Homepage: xaviars.com
Company Email: info@xaviars.com
Type of Business: Chain Restaurant Operator
Total Sales: $2,321,000 (e)
Alcohol Sales: 35%
Number of Employees: 95
Average Check: Lunch(30); Dinner(60)
Total Units: 2
Trade Names: Restaurant X and Bully Boy Bar (1); X2O (1)
Company-Owned Units: 2
Preferred Location Types: Freestanding
Alcohol Served: Beer, Wine, Liquor
Primary Menu: American (2)
Areas of Operation: NY
Type of Foodservice: Fine Dining (2)
Catering Services: Yes
Primary Distributors: (Specialty Foods) D'Artagnan Inc., UNION, NJ

Key Personnel
PETER X. KELLY - President; Executive Chef; General Buyer

J.C. Wong Management
3001 E Main St
Cortlandt Manor, NY 10567-2689

Telephone: (914) 739-6605
Fax Number: (914) 739-6628
Company Email: mcdbibiampinc@gmail.com
Type of Business: Chain Restaurant Operator
Total Sales: $23,940,000 (e)
Total Units: 5
Trade Names: McDonald's (5)
Units Franchised From: 5
Preferred Square Footage: 2,500
Primary Menu: Hamburger (5)
Areas of Operation: NY
Type of Foodservice: Quick Serve (5)
Franchise Affiliation: McDonald's Corporation, CHICAGO, IL

Key Personnel
JOY CARLOS WONG - President; General Buyer

Dean W. Colley Organization
4 Front St
Croton Falls, NY 10519

Mailing Address: PO Box 779, CROTON FALLS, NY, 10519-0779
Telephone: (914) 277-4800
Fax Number: (914) 277-8096
Internet Homepage: dwco.org
Company Email: dcolley@dwco.org
Type of Business: Chain Restaurant Operator
Year Founded: 1991
Total Sales: $233,010,000 (e)
Number of Employees: 4,700
Average Check: Breakfast(8); Lunch(10); Dinner(10)
Total Units: 60
Trade Names: McDonald's (60)
Units Franchised From: 60
Preferred Square Footage: 2,500; 3,000
Preferred Location Types: Freestanding; Regional Mall
Primary Menu: Hamburger (60)
Areas of Operation: NJ, NY, PA
Type of Foodservice: Quick Serve (60)
Franchise Affiliation: McDonald's Corporation, CHICAGO, IL

Key Personnel
BRUCE COLLEY - Partner; Director Information Systems, Real Estate
DEAN W. COLLEY - Partner
JIM DORSEY - Partner; Director Operations, Purchasing, Facility/Maintenance, Supply Chain, Design, Store Fixtures; Manager Finance
JOANN SEYMOUR - COO
BARBARA QUINN - Director Operations

Domino's Franchisee
853 Long Island Ave
Deer Park, NY 11729-3449

Telephone: (631) 242-6771
Type of Business: Chain Restaurant Operator
Total Sales: $9,928,000 (e)
Total Units: 5
Trade Names: Domino's (5)
Units Franchised From: 5
Primary Menu: Pizza (5)
Areas of Operation: NY

Type of Foodservice: Quick Serve (5)
Franchise Affiliation: Domino's Pizza Inc, ANN ARBOR, MI

Key Personnel
JOHN R. HALL - Owner; General Buyer

Domino's Franchisee
10506 Bennett Rd
Dunkirk, NY 14048-3511

Telephone: (716) 363-2227
Type of Business: Chain Restaurant Operator
Total Sales: $6,255,000 (e)
Total Units: 3
Trade Names: Domino's (3)
Units Franchised From: 3
Primary Menu: Pizza (3)
Areas of Operation: NY
Type of Foodservice: Quick Serve (3)
Franchise Affiliation: Domino's Pizza Inc, ANN ARBOR, MI

Key Personnel
ADAM P. BALDWIN - Owner; General Buyer

Mighty Taco Inc.
9362 Transit Rd
East Amherst, NY 14051-1495

Telephone: (716) 636-1097
Fax Number: (716) 636-4520
Internet Homepage: mightytaco.com
Type of Business: Chain Restaurant Operator
Year Founded: 1973
Total Sales: $21,030,000 (e)
Number of Employees: 378
Average Check: Lunch(8); Dinner(10)
Internet Order Processing: Yes
Total Units: 21
Trade Names: Mighty Taco (21)
Company-Owned Units: 21
Preferred Square Footage: 1,300
Preferred Location Types: Freestanding
Primary Menu: Taco (21)
Areas of Operation: NY
Type of Foodservice: Fast Casual (21)
Primary Distributors: (Full Line) US Foods, BUFFALO, NY

Key Personnel
DANIEL SCEPKOWSKI - CEO; President; Director Facility/Maintenance, Real Estate, Design, Store Fixtures, Menu Development
RUSSELL JASULEVICH - COO

Pio Pio
3268 85th St
East Elmhurst, NY 11370-2012

Telephone: (718) 803-8242
Fax Number: (718) 803-3993
Internet Homepage: piopio.com
Company Email: contact@piopio.com
Type of Business: Chain Restaurant Operator
Year Founded: 1994
Total Units: 8
Trade Names: Pio Pio (8)
Company-Owned Units: 8
Alcohol Served: Beer, Wine, Liquor
Primary Menu: Miscellaneous (8)
Areas of Operation: NY
Type of Foodservice: Fine Dining (8)

Key Personnel
AUGUSTO YALLICO - President; General Manager; Executive Chef; General Buyer
EDDIE B - General Manager

Nick & Toni's Cafe
136 N Main St
East Hampton, NY 11937-2619

Telephone: (631) 324-3550
Internet Homepage: nickandtonis.com
Company Email: info@nickandtonis.com
Type of Business: Chain Restaurant Operator
Year Founded: 1990
Total Sales: $10,691,000 (e)
Alcohol Sales: 30%
Number of Employees: 55
Average Check: Lunch(30); Dinner(60)
Total Units: 4
Trade Names: La Fondita Mexican (1); Nick & Toni's Cafe (1); Rowdy Hall (1); Townline BBQ (1)
Company-Owned Units: 1
Preferred Location Types: Downtown; Freestanding
Alcohol Served: Beer, Wine, Liquor
Primary Menu: American (1); Bar-B-Q (1); Italian (1); Mexican (1)
Areas of Operation: NY
Type of Foodservice: Casual Dining (4)
Primary Distributors: (Food) Dairyland, The Chefs' Warehouse, BRONX, NY

Key Personnel
MARK SMITH - Owner; Buyer Beverages
LAURIE TOMASINO - General Manager
JOE REALMUTO - Executive Chef; Manager Menu Development; General Buyer

Domino's Franchisee
517 Larkfield Rd Ste C
East Northport, NY 11731-4208

Telephone: (631) 269-2690
Type of Business: Chain Restaurant Operator
Total Sales: $6,133,000 (e)
Total Units: 3
Trade Names: Domino's (3)
Units Franchised From: 3
Primary Menu: Pizza (3)
Areas of Operation: NY
Type of Foodservice: Quick Serve (3)
Franchise Affiliation: Domino's Pizza Inc, ANN ARBOR, MI

Key Personnel
NUR MOHAMMED - Owner; General Buyer

Mario's Restaurant & Bar
212 Main St
East Setauket, NY 11733-2851

Telephone: (631) 751-8840
Internet Homepage: colosseorestaurant.net; mariositalianrestaurantny.com
Company Email: info@mariositalianrestaurantny.com
Type of Business: Chain Restaurant Operator
Year Founded: 1965
Total Sales: $5,277,000 (e)
Alcohol Sales: 15%
Number of Employees: 45
Average Check: Breakfast(10); Lunch(14); Dinner(30)
Total Units: 4
Trade Names: Brancinelli's Italian Restaurant (2); Colosseo Pizza (1); Mario's Bar & Restaurant (1)
Company-Owned Units: 4
Preferred Location Types: Freestanding; Strip Mall
Alcohol Served: Beer, Wine, Liquor
Primary Menu: Italian (4)
Areas of Operation: CT, NY
Type of Foodservice: Casual Dining (4)

Key Personnel
MARIO BRANCINELLI - Owner; General Manager; Executive Chef; General Buyer
MARCO BRANCINELLI - General Manager

Frederick & Palmer, Inc
5781 Bridge St
East Syracuse, NY 13057-2964

Telephone: (315) 251-2500
Fax Number: (315) 251-1080
Internet Homepage: pavonespizza.com

Type of Business: Chain Restaurant Operator
Year Founded: 1971
Total Sales: $6,900,000 (e)
Number of Employees: 40
Average Check: Lunch(8); Dinner(10)
Total Units: 4
Trade Names: Pavone's Pizza & Eatery (4)
Company-Owned Units: 4
Preferred Square Footage: 2,500
Preferred Location Types: Freestanding; Strip Mall
Primary Menu: Pizza (4)
Areas of Operation: NY
Type of Foodservice: Family Restaurant (4)
Primary Distributors: (Full Line) Gerharz Equipment Inc., EAST SYRACUSE, NY

Key Personnel
AVERY BURKE - President; General Buyer
FRANK PAVONE - Partner
ANGELA PAVONE - Partner

M.P. Cleary Inc.
350 S Main St
Elmira, NY 14904-1342

Telephone: (607) 734-4869
Fax Number: (607) 734-4983
Internet Homepage: pudgiespizza.com
Company Email: dsharp@pudgiespizza.com
Type of Business: Chain Restaurant Operator
Year Founded: 1963
Total Sales: $9,159,000 (e)
Number of Employees: 228
Internet Order Processing: Yes
Total Units: 8
Trade Names: Pudgie's Pizza, Pasta & Subs (8)
Company-Owned Units: 8
Primary Menu: Pizza (8)
Areas of Operation: NY, PA
Type of Foodservice: Quick Serve (8)

Key Personnel
DAVID CLEARY - Partner
ROBERT CLEARY - Partner; General Buyer

Eldorado Diner Corp.
55 W Main St
Elmsford, NY 10523-2404

Telephone: (914) 592-6197
Fax Number: (914) 592-6885
Internet Homepage: eldoradodiners.com
Company Email: elmsford@EldoradoDiners.com
Type of Business: Chain Restaurant Operator
Year Founded: 1983
Total Sales: $4,649,000 (e)
Alcohol Sales: 30%
Number of Employees: 50

Average Check: Breakfast(8); Lunch(10); Dinner(12)
Total Units: 3
Trade Names: Bull's Head Diner (1); Eldorado Diner (1); Eldorado Three (1)
Company-Owned Units: 3
Preferred Location Types: Freestanding
Alcohol Served: Beer, Wine, Liquor
Primary Menu: American (3)
Areas of Operation: NY
Type of Foodservice: Casual Dining (3)
Catering Services: Yes
Primary Distributors: (Full Line) SYSCO Food Services of Albany, HALFMOON, NY

Key Personnel
JIMMY KITSIOS - Owner; General Manager; Executive Chef; Director Real Estate, Design; General Buyer

Sto-Mac
205 Harrison Ave
Endicott, NY 13760-5119

Telephone: (607) 785-1999
Fax Number: (607) 785-2085
Type of Business: Chain Restaurant Operator
Total Sales: $23,870,000 (e)
Number of Employees: 285
Total Units: 5
Trade Names: McDonald's (5)
Units Franchised From: 5
Preferred Square Footage: 2,500
Preferred Location Types: Freestanding
Primary Menu: Hamburger (5)
Areas of Operation: NY
Type of Foodservice: Quick Serve (5)
Franchise Affiliation: McDonald's Corporation, CHICAGO, IL

Key Personnel
BETH DIBBLE - President; General Buyer
KATHY NICHOLS - Manager Marketing, Customer Service

LC of Watertown, LLC
26461 Johnson Rd
Evans Mills, NY 13637-3271

Telephone: (315) 317-0487
Company Email: mantova13041@yahoo.com
Type of Business: Chain Restaurant Operator
Total Sales: $2,623,000 (e)
Total Units: 2
Trade Names: Little Caesars Pizza (2)
Units Franchised From: 2
Primary Menu: Pizza (2)
Areas of Operation: NY
Type of Foodservice: Quick Serve (2)
Catering Services: Yes
Franchise Affiliation: Little Caesar Enterprises Inc., DETROIT, MI

Key Personnel
RICHARD JACOBSEN - President; General Buyer

Mark's Pizzeria
7450 Pittsford Palmyra Rd
Fairport, NY 14450-9516

Mailing Address: PO Box 1367, Fairport, NY, 14450
Telephone: (585) 223-3120
Internet Homepage: markspizzeria.com
Company Email: info@markspizzeria.com
Type of Business: Chain Restaurant Operator
Year Founded: 1982
Systemwide Sales: $45,697,000 (e)
Total Sales: $40,508,000 (e)
Number of Employees: 295
Average Check: Dinner(22)
Internet Order Processing: Yes
Total Units: 29
Trade Names: Mark's Pizzeria (29)
Company-Owned Units: 29
Preferred Location Types: Downtown; Freestanding; Strip Mall
Primary Menu: Pizza (29)
Areas of Operation: NY
Type of Foodservice: Quick Serve (29)

Key Personnel
CONNOR SULLIVAN - Director Information Technology

Bouley International
31 W 21st St
Flatiron, NY 10010

Telephone: (212) 964-2525
Fax Number: (212) 349-8626
Internet Homepage: davidbouley.com
Company Email: connect@bouleyathome.com
Type of Business: Chain Restaurant Operator
Year Founded: 1987
Total Sales: $6,529,000 (e)
Alcohol Sales: 20%
Number of Employees: 100
Average Check: Breakfast(12); Lunch(72); Dinner(126)
Internet Order Processing: Yes
Total Units: 1
Trade Names: Bouley (1)
Company-Owned Units: 1
Preferred Location Types: Freestanding
Alcohol Served: Beer, Wine, Liquor
Primary Menu: French/Continental (1)
Areas of Operation: NY
Type of Foodservice: Fine Dining (1)
Catering Services: Yes
Primary Distributors: (Full Line) SYSCO Food

Services of Albany, HALFMOON, NY

Key Personnel
DAVID BOULEY - President; General Manager; Executive Chef; General Buyer
BILJANA BOSANAC - Executive Chef
OLIVIA WHEAT - Director Marketing

Yellow Cab Holdings Pennsylvania LLC
1 Commercial Dr
Florida, NY 10921-1055

Type of Business: Chain Restaurant Operator
Year Founded: 2019
Total Sales: $21,789,000 (e)
Trade Names: Wendy's Old Fashioned Hamburgers (81)
Units Franchised From: 81
Primary Menu: Hamburger (81)
Areas of Operation: NJ, PA
Type of Foodservice: Quick Serve (81)
Franchise Affiliation: The Wendy's Company, DUBLIN, OH
Notes: Acquired 54 Wendy's locations from NPC International.

Key Personnel
ZACHARY CALINOFF - President; Partner
JARED YAVERS - Partner
CATHY TOBOZ - Director Marketing

Hook & Reel Cajun Seafood & Bar
3808 Union St #11d
Flushing, NY 11354

Telephone: (929) 380-7536
Company Email: info@hookreel.com
Type of Business: Chain Restaurant Operator
Year Founded: 2013
Total Sales: $67,270,000 (e)
Total Units: 71
Trade Names: Hook & Reel Cajun Seafood & Bar (71)
Company-Owned Units: 71
Preferred Square Footage: 6,500
Primary Menu: Seafood (71)
Projected Openings: 21
Areas of Operation: FL, MA, MD, NC, NJ, NY, SC, UT
Type of Foodservice: Casual Dining (71)

Key Personnel
CHRISTOPHER MERIDETH - VP Operations
EASON LI - Director Operations

McDonald's Franchise
4018 Main St
Flushing, NY 11354-5519

Telephone: (718) 939-1881
Company Email: dedbreed@aol.com
Type of Business: Chain Restaurant Operator
Total Sales: $10,038,000 (e)
Total Units: 2
Trade Names: McDonald's (2)
Units Franchised From: 2
Primary Menu: Hamburger (2)
Areas of Operation: NY
Type of Foodservice: Quick Serve (2)
Franchise Affiliation: McDonald's Corporation, CHICAGO, IL

Key Personnel
LUIGI SOLIMEO - Owner; General Buyer

Creative Foods Corporation
200 Garden City Plz Ste 105
Garden City, NY 11530-3338

Telephone: (516) 746-6800
Fax Number: (516) 746-3464
Internet Homepage: creativefoodscorp.com
Type of Business: Chain Restaurant Operator
Year Founded: 1968
Total Sales: $68,687,000 (e)
Number of Employees: 1,232
Average Check: Lunch(5); Dinner(5)
Total Units: 28
Trade Names: Burger King (28)
Units Franchised From: 28
Preferred Square Footage: 2,000; 3,000
Preferred Location Types: Freestanding
Primary Menu: Hamburger (28)
Projected Openings: 1
Areas of Operation: NY
Type of Foodservice: Quick Serve (28)
Franchise Affiliation: Burger King Worldwide Inc., MIAMI, FL
Primary Distributors: (Full Line) Maines Paper & Food Service Inc., CONKLIN, NY

Key Personnel
JAY DELLA MONICA - President; Director Operations; General Buyer
DONALD LANCIOTTI - VP Finance

Domino's Franchisee
481 Hamilton St
Geneva, NY 14456-3058

Telephone: (315) 789-3090
Type of Business: Chain Restaurant Operator
Total Sales: $12,482,000 (e)
Total Units: 6
Trade Names: Domino's (6)
Units Franchised From: 6
Primary Menu: Pizza (6)
Areas of Operation: NY
Type of Foodservice: Quick Serve (6)
Franchise Affiliation: Domino's Pizza Inc, ANN ARBOR, MI

Key Personnel
CHRISTOPHER J. MACPHERSON - Owner; General Buyer

Flynn/Meyer Co.
7511 Myrtle Ave
Glendale, NY 11385-7434

Telephone: (718) 386-5800
Fax Number: (718) 628-7397
Type of Business: Chain Restaurant Operator
Total Sales: $28,920,000 (e)
Number of Employees: 290
Total Units: 6
Trade Names: McDonald's (6)
Units Franchised From: 6
Preferred Square Footage: 2,500
Primary Menu: Hamburger (6)
Areas of Operation: NY
Type of Foodservice: Quick Serve (6)
Franchise Affiliation: McDonald's Corporation, CHICAGO, IL

Key Personnel
EDWARD FLYNN - President; General Buyer

Domino's Franchisee
132 W Fulton St
Gloversville, NY 12078-2800

Telephone: (518) 725-1100
Type of Business: Chain Restaurant Operator
Total Sales: $4,141,000 (e)
Total Units: 2
Trade Names: Domino's (2)
Units Franchised From: 2
Primary Menu: Pizza (2)
Areas of Operation: NY
Type of Foodservice: Quick Serve (2)
Franchise Affiliation: Domino's Pizza Inc, ANN ARBOR, MI

Key Personnel
MATTHEW J. DENMAN - Owner; General Buyer

Metro Franchising
98 Cuttermill Rd Ste 364
Great Neck, NY 11021-3036

Telephone: (516) 472-7100
Type of Business: Chain Restaurant Operator

Total Sales: $75,730,000 (e)
Average Check: Dinner(8)
Total Units: 49
Trade Names: Dunkin' Donuts (49)
Units Franchised From: 49
Preferred Square Footage: 1,500; 2,200
Preferred Location Types: Freestanding
Primary Menu: Snacks (49)
Areas of Operation: NY
Type of Foodservice: Quick Serve (49)
Franchise Affiliation: DD IP Holder, CANTON, MA

Key Personnel
STUART COHEN - President; General Buyer
JOSEPH GIACALONE - CFO
SCOTT CAMPBELL - COO
CHRIS LIDES - VP Operations
CHRIS HASSAN - Director Operations

Lessing's Inc.
3500 Sunrise Hwy Ste 100
Great River, NY 11739-1001

Telephone: (631) 567-8200
Fax Number: (631) 567-8746
Internet Homepage: lessings.com
Type of Business: Foodservice Management Operator
Year Founded: 1890
Total Sales: $21,597,000 (e)
Number of Employees: 370
Number of Locations Served: 120
Total Foodservice Mgmt Accounts: 120
Total Units: 9
Trade Names: Finnegan's (1); Maxwell's (1); Mirabelle Tavern (1); Post Office Cafe (1); Restaurant Mirabelle (1); Sandbar (1); The Library Cafe (1); The Southside Hotel (1); View (1)
Company-Owned Units: 9
Areas of Operation: NY
Type of Foodservice: Cafeteria (20); Full-service sit-down dining (100)
Foodservice Management Venues: Business & Industry; Other; Parks & Recreation; Schools
Primary Distributors: (Full Line) J. Kings Food Services Professionals Inc., HOLTSVILLE, NY

Key Personnel
JOHN LESSING SR - CEO; Director Operations
LAWRENCE LESSING III - President
MICHAEL LESSING - President; COO
SCOTT MCKELVEY - CFO
JOHN LESSING JR - Exec VP Business Development
MARK LESSING - Exec VP Marketing
KEVIN LESSING - Exec VP; Director Business Development
PETER LESSING - Director

ELLEN BARRETT - Director Human Resources

Reaal Inc.
13 Morris Ln
Halfmoon, NY 12065

Mailing Address: PO Box 441, CLIFTON PARK, NY, 12065-0441
Telephone: (518) 348-1840
Type of Business: Chain Restaurant Operator
Year Founded: 1976
Total Sales: $23,540,000 (e)
Number of Employees: 225
Average Check: Breakfast(8); Lunch(10); Dinner(12)
Total Units: 5
Trade Names: McDonald's (5)
Units Franchised From: 5
Preferred Square Footage: 2,500; 3,000
Preferred Location Types: Community Mall; Freestanding
Primary Menu: Hamburger (5)
Areas of Operation: NY
Type of Foodservice: Quick Serve (5)
Franchise Affiliation: McDonald's Corporation, CHICAGO, IL
Primary Distributors: (Food) The Martin-Brower Co., ENFIELD, CT

Key Personnel
ROGER GROUT - President; Director Finance, Operations, Purchasing, Real Estate; General Buyer
KIM JURCSAK - Manager Facility/Maintenance, Information Systems, Human Resources

Apple-Metro Inc.
550 Mamaroneck Ave Ste 204
Harrison, NY 10528-1617

Telephone: (914) 777-2331
Fax Number: (914) 777-2615
Internet Homepage: applebeesny.com; applemetrorestaurants.com; pizzastudio.com
Company Email: comments@applemetro.com
Type of Business: Chain Restaurant Operator
Year Founded: 1994
Total Sales: $145,200,000 (e)
Alcohol Sales: 20%
Number of Employees: 1,905
Average Check: Lunch(12); Dinner(20)
Total Units: 36
Trade Names: Applebee's Neighborhood Grill & Bar (34); Pizza Studio (2)
Units Franchised From: 36
Preferred Square Footage: 3,600; 5,000
Preferred Location Types: Community Mall; Freestanding
Alcohol Served: Beer, Wine, Liquor
Primary Menu: American (34); Pizza (2)
Areas of Operation: NY

Type of Foodservice: Casual Dining (36)
Franchise Affiliation: Applebee's Services Inc., KANSAS CITY, MO
Primary Distributors: (Food) Maines Paper & Food Service Inc., CONKLIN, NY; (Supplies) Maines Paper & Food Service Inc., CONKLIN, NY

Key Personnel
ZANE TANKEL - Chairman; CEO
ROY RAEBURN - President; Director Information Systems, Design
FRANK VENICE - Exec VP; Director Purchasing
KEN FELDMAN - VP Marketing
NEESHA SEERVAI - Executive Director Operations
TRINI SANTOS - Controller
DARREN EPPERSON - Director Consumer Insights
SHANNON LONG - Director Human Resources-Training
MICHAEL BERRY - Director Construction
KELLY CASTRO - Manager Human Resources

Hunt Enterprises
10 Rabro Dr
Hauppauge, NY 11788-4211

Telephone: (631) 582-6665
Fax Number: (631) 582-6707
Internet Homepage: huntent.com
Company Email: acooper@huntent.com
Type of Business: Chain Restaurant Operator
Year Founded: 1971
Total Sales: $129,170,000 (e)
Number of Employees: 1,049
Average Check: Breakfast(8); Lunch(10); Dinner(12)
Total Units: 27
Trade Names: McDonald's (27)
Units Franchised From: 27
Preferred Square Footage: 2,500; 3,000
Preferred Location Types: Freestanding
Primary Menu: Hamburger (27)
Areas of Operation: NY
Type of Foodservice: Quick Serve (27)
Franchise Affiliation: McDonald's Corporation, CHICAGO, IL
Primary Distributors: (Food) The Martin-Brower Co., ENFIELD, CT

Key Personnel
PETER HUNT - President; Director Finance, Real Estate; General Buyer
RALPH MOORE - COO; VP
MICHAEL PRESTRIDGE - Director Special Projects
JOE TALENTO - Director Operations
ROBERT JOHNSON - Director Operations
CHRISTOPHER WATSON - Manager Operations

MIKE YOVINO - Manager Information Systems

Mount Fuji Japanese Steak House
296 Route 17
Hillburn, NY 10931-9003

Mailing Address: PO Box 1218, HILLBURN, NY, 10931-1218
Telephone: (845) 357-4167
Fax Number: (845) 357-8631
Internet Homepage: mtfujirestaurants.com
Company Email: info@mtfujirestaurants.com
Type of Business: Chain Restaurant Operator
Year Founded: 1969
Total Sales: $8,492,000 (e)
Alcohol Sales: 20%
Number of Employees: 150
Average Check: Lunch(36); Dinner(38)
Total Units: 2
Trade Names: Mount Fuji Japanese Steak House (2)
Company-Owned Units: 2
Preferred Location Types: Freestanding
Alcohol Served: Beer, Wine, Liquor
Primary Menu: Japanese (2)
Areas of Operation: NJ, NY
Type of Foodservice: Fine Dining (2)
Catering Services: Yes

Key Personnel
NANCY FUJITA - President; General Buyer
ANDREA SMITH - Manager Operations

Four Cousins Burgers & Fries of NH. LLC
173 Whippoorwill Rd
Hillsdale, NY 12529-6015

Telephone: (914) 643-2180
Type of Business: Chain Restaurant Operator
Total Sales: $47,500,000 (e)
Number of Employees: 845
Total Units: 24
Trade Names: Five Guys Burgers and Fries (24)
Units Franchised From: 24
Preferred Location Types: Freestanding; Strip Mall
Primary Menu: Hamburger (24)
Areas of Operation: NH
Type of Foodservice: Fast Casual (24)
Franchise Affiliation: Five Guys Holdings Inc., LORTON, VA

Key Personnel
BILL GELLERT - Owner

Alfalfa
1110 Washington St.
Hoboken, NY 07030

Telephone: (201) 790-0491
Internet Homepage: eatalfalfa.com
Type of Business: Chain Restaurant Operator
Year Founded: 2019
Total Sales: $3,958,000 (e)
Total Units: 4
Trade Names: Alfalfa (4)
Company-Owned Units: 4
Primary Menu: Health Foods (4)
Areas of Operation: CA, NJ
Type of Foodservice: Fast Casual (4)

Key Personnel
ANDREW ARROSPIDE - Co-Founder; Partner
DANIEL LONDONO - Co-Founder; Partner
BEN SOBSEY - Co-Founder; Partner
DAN SOBSEY - Co-Founder; Partner

J&B Restaurant Partners
4250 Veterans Memorial Hwy Ste 1070
Holbrook, NY 11741-4032

Telephone: (631) 218-9067
Fax Number: (631) 218-8019
Internet Homepage: jbrestaurants.net
Type of Business: Chain Restaurant Operator
Year Founded: 1998
Total Sales: $52,930,000 (e)
Number of Employees: 1,013
Average Check: Breakfast(8); Lunch(10); Dinner(10)
Total Units: 25
Trade Names: Friendly's (25)
Units Franchised From: 25
Preferred Square Footage: 2,500; 3,200
Preferred Location Types: Freestanding; Regional Mall; Strip Mall
Primary Menu: American (25)
Areas of Operation: NY
Type of Foodservice: Family Restaurant (25)
Foodservice Management Venues: College & University; Recreational
Franchise Affiliation: FIC Restaurants, WILBRAHAM, MA
Primary Distributors: (Full Line) SYSCO Food Services of Syracuse, WARNERS, NY

Key Personnel
JOSEPH VITRANO - CEO; President; Partner; Director Operations; General Buyer
WILLIAM MURPHY - Partner; Director Supply Chain; General Buyer
ELYSE REMIGIO - Director Sales
CONLAN SHEA - Manager Operations

Oak Hotels Inc
2424 Route 52
Hopewell Junction, NY 12533-3221

Telephone: (845) 223-3603
Fax Number: (845) 223-7340
Internet Homepage: oakhotels.com
Company Email: rrickards@oakhotels.com
Type of Business: Foodservice Operations - Hotel/Motels
Year Founded: 1978
Total Sales: $162,470,000 (e)
Alcohol Sales: 25%
Number of Employees: 2,688
Total Units: 14
Trade Names: Days Inn (7); Holiday Inn (1); Independent (5); Motel 6 (1)
Company-Owned Units: 14
Alcohol Served: Beer, Wine, Liquor
Areas of Operation: AZ, CT, FL, GA, MN, NC, NY, PA
Primary Distributors: (Food) SYSCO Food Services of Albany, HALFMOON, NY
Notes: The company derives approximately 80% of its revenue from hotel operations.

Key Personnel
CRAIG KENDZIERA - Chairman; Exec VP
JAN BATEMAN - VP Marketing, Sales
BETTY FOUNTAIN - Director Information Systems

La Villa Pizzeria
8207 153rd Ave
Howard Beach, NY 11414-1751

Telephone: (718) 641-8259
Fax Number: (718) 641-8505
Internet Homepage: lavillaparkslope.com
Type of Business: Chain Restaurant Operator
Total Sales: $5,660,000 (e)
Alcohol Sales: 10%
Number of Employees: 50
Average Check: Lunch(14); Dinner(14)
Total Units: 4
Trade Names: La Villa Pizzeria (4)
Company-Owned Units: 4
Preferred Location Types: Freestanding; Strip Mall
Alcohol Served: Beer, Wine
Primary Menu: Pizza (4)
Areas of Operation: NY
Type of Foodservice: Casual Dining (4)

Key Personnel
ALFRED DISIPIO - Owner; Executive Chef; General Buyer
TONY MANZA - General Manager

Domino's Franchisee
209 Main St
Hudson Falls, NY 12839-1841

Telephone: (518) 747-7700
Type of Business: Chain Restaurant Operator
Total Sales: $4,051,000 (e)
Total Units: 2
Trade Names: Domino's (2)
Units Franchised From: 2
Primary Menu: Pizza (2)
Areas of Operation: NY
Type of Foodservice: Quick Serve (2)
Franchise Affiliation: Domino's Pizza Inc, ANN ARBOR, MI

Key Personnel
BYRON O'HARA - Owner; General Buyer

Liedtke Enterprises
344 W Jericho Tpke
Huntington, NY 11743-6361

Telephone: (631) 321-0243
Fax Number: (631) 421-1337
Type of Business: Chain Restaurant Operator
Year Founded: 1980
Total Sales: $28,230,000 (e)
Number of Employees: 215
Average Check: Breakfast(8); Lunch(8); Dinner(8)
Total Units: 6
Trade Names: McDonald's (6)
Units Franchised From: 6
Preferred Square Footage: 2,500; 3,000
Preferred Location Types: Freestanding
Primary Menu: Hamburger (6)
Areas of Operation: NY
Type of Foodservice: Quick Serve (6)
Franchise Affiliation: McDonald's Corporation, CHICAGO, IL

Key Personnel
ANTHONY LIEDTKE - President; General Buyer

Piccolo Restaurant
215 Wall St
Huntington, NY 11743-2060

Telephone: (631) 424-5592
Fax Number: (631) 421-5555
Internet Homepage: millpondrestaurant.com; piccolorestaurant.net
Company Email: piccolohuntington@gmail.com
Type of Business: Chain Restaurant Operator
Year Founded: 1988
Total Sales: $9,180,000 (e)
Alcohol Sales: 10%
Number of Employees: 30
Average Check: Lunch(34); Dinner(48)
Total Units: 3
Trade Names: Crabtrees (1); Mill Pond House (1); Piccolo Restaurant (1)
Company-Owned Units: 3
Preferred Location Types: Freestanding
Alcohol Served: Beer, Wine, Liquor
Primary Menu: American (1); Italian (1); Spanish (1)
Areas of Operation: NY
Type of Foodservice: Casual Dining (1); Fine Dining (2)
Catering Services: Yes
Primary Distributors: (Food) Dairyland, The Chefs' Warehouse, BRONX, NY

Key Personnel
DEAN PHILIPPIS - Partner; General Manager; Executive Chef; General Buyer
DINO PHILIPPIS - Partner; General Manager; Director Catering
ANDREW CRABTREE - Executive Chef

Red Bar & Restaurant
417 New York Ave
Huntington, NY 11743-3435

Telephone: (631) 673-0304
Internet Homepage: redrestaurant.com
Company Email: comments@redrestaurantli.com
Type of Business: Chain Restaurant Operator
Total Sales: $9,011,000 (e)
Alcohol Sales: 20%
Number of Employees: 45
Average Check: Lunch(22); Dinner(34)
Total Units: 4
Trade Names: Cafe Red (1); Ostria Da Nino (1); Red Bar & Restaurant (1); Sapsuckers (1)
Company-Owned Units: 4
Preferred Location Types: Downtown; Freestanding
Alcohol Served: Beer, Wine, Liquor
Primary Menu: American (3); Italian (1)
Areas of Operation: NY
Type of Foodservice: Casual Dining (2); Fine Dining (2)
Catering Services: Yes

Key Personnel
NINO ANTUZZI - Owner; Executive Chef; General Buyer
KELLEY DANEK - General Manager; Director Purchasing-Beverages; General Buyer

Kaufman Enterprises
134 W Hills Rd
Huntington Station, NY 11746-3140

Telephone: (631) 271-8055
Fax Number: (631) 271-8066
Internet Homepage: macpride.net
Type of Business: Chain Restaurant Operator
Year Founded: 1989
Total Sales: $75,620,000 (e)
Number of Employees: 515
Average Check: Breakfast(8); Lunch(10); Dinner(12)
Total Units: 16
Trade Names: McDonald's (16)
Units Franchised From: 16
Preferred Square Footage: 3,000
Preferred Location Types: Freestanding
Primary Menu: Hamburger (16)
Areas of Operation: NY
Type of Foodservice: Quick Serve (16)
Franchise Affiliation: McDonald's Corporation, CHICAGO, IL

Key Personnel
JONAH KAUFMAN - Co-President; Director Information Systems, Real Estate, Human Resources; General Buyer
JOSH KAUFMAN - Co-President
LONNY WEINER - Chief Marketing Officer; VP Finance
JOHN RAMPOLLO - VP; Director Operations
RICK DISNEY - VP Facility/Maintenance
STEPHANIE BELLEW - Director Operations

Culinary Institute of America
1946 Campus Dr
Hyde Park, NY 12538-1430

Telephone: (845) 452-9600
Internet Homepage: ciachef.edu
Type of Business: Culinary Schools
Areas of Operation: NY

Key Personnel
TIMOTHY L. RYAN - President
RHETT REIDY - Chief Engineering Officer
ELANCE DONNADAVIES - Director Web Design
PETER GRIMM - Assistant Director Communications
LISA PAQUIN - Assistant Director Menu Development
NICOLE GIUSTI - Manager Operations
BRIDGET RUGGIERO - Manager Media
EDWARD BAKTER - Manager Purchasing
ALLISON BUSH - Manager Training

Whitsons Culinary Group
1800 Motor Pkwy
Islandia, NY 11749-5216

Telephone: (631) 424-2700
Fax Number: (631) 424-2745
Internet Homepage: whitsons.com
Company Email: information@whitsons.com

Type of Business: Foodservice Management Operator
Year Founded: 1979
Total Sales: $141,052,000 (e)
Number of Employees: 1,900
Number of Locations Served: 250
Total Foodservice Mgmt Accounts: 150
Areas of Operation: NY
Type of Foodservice: Cafeteria (150)
Foodservice Management Venues: Business & Industry; College & University; Health Care; Other; Prison Feeding; Schools
Primary Distributors: (Full Line) DiCarlo Distributors Inc., HOLTSVILLE, NY; (Full Line) J. Kings Food Services Professionals Inc., HOLTSVILLE, NY

Key Personnel
PAUL WHITCOMB - CEO; President
DOUGLAS WHITCOMB - President
BETH BUNSTER - CFO
KELLYANN FRIEND - COO
ROBERT E. WHITCOMB - Chief Innovation Officer
JOHN WHITCOMB - Chief Innovation Officer
JOHN GERSBECK - Senior VP
OZZIE ORSILLO - Senior VP Business Development
S. CHRIS FAUTAS - Senior VP Operations
MICHAEL WHITCOMB - VP Customer Service
MICHAEL MARINARO - VP Supply Chain; Director Purchasing
KAREN SCOTT - VP Finance
CRAIG WHITCOMB - Regional VP
MARK SIMKISS - Regional VP Business Development
BILL WHITCOMB JR - Corporate Secretary
JOHN KOUTRAS - Corporate Chef; District Manager
RICHARD SANDMANN - Corporate Chef
PETER JOHNSON - Corporate Chef
ANDREW WHITCOMB - Executive Chef; Manager Foodservice, Food Safety, Food and Beverage
WILLIAM WHITCOMB - Director Compliance
BRENNA SCHETTINO - Director Human Resources
JEANINE WALSHON - Director Business Development
ERIN NORTON - Director Recruitment
GUS TRAVASSOS - Director
MARY DISTEFANO - Director Marketing
TONY DISTEFANO - Director Strategy
KIM PARKER - Regional Director; Customer Care
CHRISTINE KUNNMANN - District Manager
JOHN PRUNIER - District Manager
RICK EMERY - District Manager
JOSEPH ARMENTI - District Manager
MARK KIRN - District Manager
SCOTT BERRY - District Manager
JOHNNY TEAGUE - Manager Foodservice
KATHERINE BARFUSS - Agent

Bohlsen Restaurant Group
577 Main St
Islip, NY 11751-3528

Telephone: (631) 277-4831
Fax Number: (631) 857-7913
Internet Homepage: brgroup.biz; h2oseafoodgrill.com; pizzaparmislip.com; tellersrestaurant.com
Company Email: info@brgroup.biz
Type of Business: Chain Restaurant Operator
Total Sales: $26,400,000 (e)
Alcohol Sales: 30%
Number of Employees: 135
Average Check: Lunch(36); Dinner(72)
Internet Order Processing: Yes
Internet Sales: 1.00%
Total Units: 9
Trade Names: H2O (2); Harbor Club (1); Monsoon (1); Pizza Parm (1); Prime (2); Tellers (1); Verace (1)
Company-Owned Units: 9
Preferred Square Footage: 5,500; 6,000
Preferred Location Types: Freestanding
Alcohol Served: Beer, Wine, Liquor
Primary Menu: American (4); Asian (1); Italian (2); Steak/Seafood (2)
Areas of Operation: NY
Type of Foodservice: Casual Dining (3); Fine Dining (6)
Primary Distributors: (Food) DiCarlo Distributors Inc., HOLTSVILLE, NY

Key Personnel
KURT BOHLSEN - Partner; Manager Facility/Maintenance, Supply Chain; General Buyer
MICHAEL BOHLSEN - Partner; Manager Information Systems, Real Estate, Design; General Buyer
ROBERT DIPIERRO - General Manager; Director Operations
JAMES MCDEVITT - Corporate Chef; Executive Chef
PAULO VILLELA - Director Beverages
KATIE CANELLA - Director Customer Service, Training

Delectable Capital
121 Dryden Rd
Ithaca, NY 14850

Telephone: (607) 319-4664
Internet Homepage: wingsover.com
Type of Business: Chain Restaurant Operator
Total Units: 40
Trade Names: Wings Over . . . (40)
Company-Owned Units: 2
Units Franchised To: 38
Primary Menu: Chicken (40)
Areas of Operation: CT, MA, MI, NC, NJ, NY, OH, PA, RI, TN, VA, WI
Type of Foodservice: Fast Casual (40)

Key Personnel
KEVIN MOK - Partner
RAUNAK NIRMAL - Partner

Gimme! Coffee
3201 Krums Corners Rd
Ithaca, NY 14850

Telephone: (877) 446-6325
Internet Homepage: gimmecoffee.com
Type of Business: Chain Restaurant Operator
Year Founded: 2000
Total Sales: $10,119,000 (e)
Total Units: 5
Trade Names: Gimme! Coffee (5)
Company-Owned Units: 5
Primary Menu: American (5); Coffee (5)
Type of Foodservice: Casual Dining (5); Quick Serve (5)

Key Personnel
KEVIN CUDDEBACK - Founder

Lawrence Enterprises
Jfk International Airport Bldg 151 Fl 2 Rm 319
Jamaica, NY 11430

Telephone: (718) 656-4890
Type of Business: Chain Restaurant Operator
Total Sales: $23,720,000 (e)
Total Units: 5
Trade Names: McDonald's (5)
Units Franchised From: 5
Preferred Square Footage: 2,500
Primary Menu: Hamburger (5)
Areas of Operation: NY
Type of Foodservice: Quick Serve (5)
Franchise Affiliation: McDonald's Corporation, CHICAGO, IL

Key Personnel
JACQUES LAWRENCE - President; General Buyer

Parsons QSR, LLC
14712 105th Ave
Jamaica, NY 11435-4918

Telephone: (718) 846-2371
Fax Number: (718) 846-2374
Type of Business: Chain Restaurant Operator
Total Sales: $13,590,000 (e)
Total Units: 9
Trade Names: Checkers (9)
Units Franchised From: 9

Primary Menu: Hamburger (9)
Areas of Operation: FL, NY
Type of Foodservice: Quick Serve (9)
Franchise Affiliation: Checkers Drive-In Restaurants Inc., TAMPA, FL

Key Personnel
ROD VALENCIA - President; General Buyer
REX VALENCIA - VP

A&T Food Development, Llc
804 Fairmount Ave
Jamestown, NY 14701-2517

Telephone: (716) 664-0519
Internet Homepage: bemuspointcasino.com; wingcitygrille.com
Company Email: comments@bemuspointcasino.com
Type of Business: Chain Restaurant Operator
Year Founded: 1993
Total Sales: $8,880,000 (e)
Alcohol Sales: 25%
Number of Employees: 100
Average Check: Breakfast(6); Lunch(14); Dinner(24)
Total Units: 4
Trade Names: Arby's (1); Village Casino (1); Wing City Grille (2)
Company-Owned Units: 3
Units Franchised From: 1
Preferred Square Footage: 5,500; 6,000
Preferred Location Types: Freestanding; Strip Mall
Alcohol Served: Beer, Wine, Liquor
Primary Menu: American (3); Sandwiches/Deli (1)
Areas of Operation: NY, PA
Type of Foodservice: Casual Dining (3); Quick Serve (1)
Catering Services: Yes
Franchise Affiliation: Arby's Restaurant Group, ATLANTA, GA
Primary Distributors: (Equipment) Bezac Equipment, YOUNGSTOWN, OH; (Food) Willow Run Foods Inc., KIRKWOOD, NY

Key Personnel
ANDREW CARLSON - President; Controller; Manager Finance, Operations, Loss Prevention, Marketing, Product Development, Food Safety; General Buyer

Canyon Properties Inc
575 Jericho Tpke Ste 102
Jericho, NY 11753-1847

Telephone: (516) 433-4870
Fax Number: (516) 433-4191
Type of Business: Chain Restaurant Operator
Total Sales: $12,370,000 (e)

Number of Employees: 96
Average Check: Breakfast(14); Lunch(10); Dinner(10)
Total Units: 8
Trade Names: Dunkin' Donuts (6); Dunkin' Donuts/Baskin-Robbins (2)
Units Franchised From: 8
Preferred Square Footage: 1,500; 2,200
Preferred Location Types: Downtown; Freestanding; Strip Mall
Primary Menu: Snacks (8)
Areas of Operation: NY
Type of Foodservice: Quick Serve (8)
Franchise Affiliation: DD IP Holder, CANTON, MA

Key Personnel
CHERYL PORTNOY - CFO
BRET NADLER - VP; General Buyer

Gong Cha Tea, LLC
425 N. Broadway STE #287
Jericho, NY 11753

Telephone: (516) 813-5642
Internet Homepage: gongchausa.com
Company Email: inquiries@gongchausa.com
Type of Business: Chain Restaurant Operator
Year Founded: 2006
Systemwide Sales: $63,000,000 (e)
Total Sales: $53,760,000 (e)
Total Units: 140
Trade Names: Gong Cha (140)
Company-Owned Units: 1
Units Franchised To: 139
Primary Menu: Asian (140)
Areas of Operation: CT, FL, GA, MA, NC, NH, NJ, NY, OK, PA, RI, SC, TX
Type of Foodservice: Quick Serve (140)

Key Personnel
MARTIN BERRY - Founder
PAUL REYNISH - CEO
GEOFF HENRY - President United States
KIKI JIN - Chief Marketing Officer Global
PIP MCKENZIE - General Counsel
MISSY MAIO - Director Brand Marketing
REBECCA KAHN - Director Franchising

Nathan's Famous Inc.
1 Jericho Plz Fl 2
Jericho, NY 11753-1680

Telephone: (516) 338-8500
Fax Number: (516) 338-7220
Internet Homepage: nathansfamous.com
Company Email: info@nathansfamous.com
Type of Business: Chain Restaurant Operator
Year Founded: 1916
Systemwide Sales: $149,956,000 (e)
Publicly Held: Yes

Total Sales: $129,676,000 (e)
Alcohol Sales: 2%
Number of Employees: 228
Average Check: Breakfast(5); Lunch(12); Dinner(16)
Foodservice Sales: $64,838,000 (e)
Internet Order Processing: Yes
Internet Sales: 1.00%
Total Units: 224
Trade Names: Nathan's Famous Hot Dogs (224)
Company-Owned Units: 5
Units Franchised To: 219
Preferred Square Footage: 300; 4,000
Preferred Location Types: Airports; Community Mall; Convenience Store/Gas Station; Discount Dept. Stores; Downtown; Freestanding; Grocery Stores; Hotel/Motel; Institution (college/hospital); Kiosk; Mobile Unit; Office Complex; Other; Outlet Mall; Parks; Regional Mall; Stadiums; Strip Mall; Travel Plazas
Alcohol Served: Beer
Primary Menu: Hot Dogs (224)
Projected Openings: 3
Areas of Operation: AL, AZ, CA, CT, FL, GA, IL, KY, MA, MD, MI, MO, MS, NC, NH, NJ, NM, NV, NY, OH, PA, RI, SC, TN, TX, VA, VT
Foreign Countries: CANADA; CAYMAN ISLANDS; COSTA RICA; DOMINICAN REPUBLIC; EGYPT; JAMAICA; KUWAIT; MALAYSIA; MEXICO; RUSSIA; SAUDI ARABIA; TURKEY
Type of Foodservice: Quick Serve (224)
Foodservice Management Venues: Business & Industry; College & University; Health Care; Lodging; Military Feeding; Parks & Recreation; Schools; Transportation
Primary Distributors: (Food) SYSCO Food Services of Syracuse, WARNERS, NY; (Full Line) US Foods Holding Corp., ROSEMONT, IL
Notes: In addition to its Nathan's Famous concept restaurants, the company can be found in all 50 states through its Branded Products Program. The number of franchised units includes locations such as Kmart and Bruster's which sell Nathan's products through its Branded Menu Program. Nathan's derives approximately 67% of its revenue from sales of the company's products through its Branded Product Program and other investment activities.

Key Personnel
HOWARD M. LORBER - Chairman
ROBERT STEINBERG - CFO
LEIGH PLATTE - VP Foodservice
PHIL MCCANN - Senior Director Marketing
SHARON WERNIKOWSKI - Director Accounting
BRUCE J. MILLER - Director Company Operations
RICH LINDWALL - Director Construction, Design

JIM HICKS - Director Operations-Training

Auntie Anne's Franchise
601-635 Harry L Dr
Johnson City, NY 13790

Telephone: (607) 770-1228
Internet Homepage: auntieannes.com
Type of Business: Chain Restaurant Operator
Total Sales: $2,357,000 (e)
Total Units: 3
Trade Names: Auntie Anne's Hand-Rolled Soft Pretzels (3)
Units Franchised From: 3
Primary Menu: Snacks (3)
Areas of Operation: NY
Type of Foodservice: Quick Serve (3)
Franchise Affiliation: Auntie Anne's Inc., LANCASTER, PA

Key Personnel
DAPHNE DOW - Owner; General Buyer

Domino's Franchisee
122 Baldwin St
Johnson City, NY 13790-2148

Telephone: (607) 798-7177
Type of Business: Chain Restaurant Operator
Total Sales: $5,990,000 (e)
Total Units: 3
Trade Names: Domino's (3)
Units Franchised From: 3
Primary Menu: Pizza (3)
Areas of Operation: NY
Type of Foodservice: Quick Serve (3)
Franchise Affiliation: Domino's Pizza Inc, ANN ARBOR, MI

Key Personnel
LARRY DE BUSK - Owner; General Buyer

Gialil Food Services
4 Wells St
Johnstown, NY 12095-2005

Telephone: (518) 762-2445
Fax Number: (518) 762-2822
Type of Business: Chain Restaurant Operator
Total Sales: $57,250,000 (e)
Number of Employees: 600
Total Units: 12
Trade Names: McDonald's (12)
Units Franchised From: 12
Preferred Square Footage: 2,500
Primary Menu: Hamburger (12)
Areas of Operation: NY
Type of Foodservice: Quick Serve (12)
Franchise Affiliation: McDonald's Corporation, CHICAGO, IL

Key Personnel
JOE GIALIL - Owner; General Buyer

Dunkin' Donuts Franchise
1285 Ulster Ave
Kingston, NY 12401-1527

Telephone: (845) 336-5241
Type of Business: Chain Restaurant Operator
Total Sales: $6,814,000 (e)
Total Units: 4
Trade Names: Dunkin' Donuts (4)
Company-Owned Units: 4
Primary Menu: Snacks (4)
Areas of Operation: NY
Type of Foodservice: Quick Serve (4)
Franchise Affiliation: DD IP Holder, CANTON, MA

Key Personnel
MARIO SARDINHA - President

Bread Alone Bakery and Cafe
2121 Ulster Ave
Lake Katrine, NY 12449-5446

Telephone: (845) 657-3328
Fax Number: (845) 657-6228
Internet Homepage: breadalone.com
Company Email: info@breadalone.com
Type of Business: Chain Restaurant Operator
Year Founded: 1983
Systemwide Sales: $8,178,000 (e)
Total Sales: $9,404,000 (e)
Number of Employees: 60
Average Check: Breakfast(10); Lunch(10); Dinner(10)
Internet Order Processing: Yes
Internet Sales: 2.00%
Total Units: 4
Trade Names: Boiceville Cafe (1); Bread Alone Bakery and Cafe (1); Rhinebeck Cafe (1); Woodstock Cafe (1)
Company-Owned Units: 4
Preferred Square Footage: 1,400
Preferred Location Types: Freestanding; Mixed-use Center
Alcohol Served: Beer, Wine
Primary Menu: Sandwiches/Deli (4)
Areas of Operation: NY
Type of Foodservice: Quick Serve (4)
Catering Services: Yes
Primary Distributors: (Food) SYSCO Food Services of Albany, HALFMOON, NY
Notes: The company derives approximately 50% of its revenue from wholesale operations.

Key Personnel
DANIEL M. LEADER - CEO; Partner; Director Finance, Facility/Maintenance, Information Systems, Real Estate, Design, Research & Development, Menu Development; General Buyer
SHARON BURNS-LEADER - President; Partner; Director Finance, Operations, Purchasing, Facility/Maintenance, Information Systems, Real Estate, Design
NELS LEADER - VP
IAN MARTIN - VP Finance

American Food & Vending
124 Metropolitan Park Dr
Liverpool, NY 13088-5342

Telephone: (315) 457-9950
Internet Homepage: afvusa.com
Type of Business: Foodservice Management Operator
Year Founded: 1970
Total Sales: $21,731,000 (e)
Number of Employees: 150
Number of Locations Served: 2,000
Total Foodservice Mgmt Accounts: 250
Areas of Operation: NY
Type of Foodservice: Cafeteria (250)
Foodservice Management Venues: Business & Industry
Primary Distributors: (Full Line) US Foods, CLIFTON PARK, NY

Key Personnel
J. MICHAEL HADLEY - CFO
JOSHUA WELLS - COO
PAT SHERIDAN - Exec VP
CHARLES HAVEN - Exec VP Human Resources
CARRIE ROBERSON - Senior Director Business Development
OSCAR M. PEREZ - Director Operations
AMANDA SPRINGSTEAD - Director Catering
SAMUEL MELAMEDAS - Director Purchasing
KRISTEN PESSIRILO - Director Retail Operations

Hospitality Restaurant Group Inc.
290 Elwood Davis Rd Ste 320
Liverpool, NY 13088

Mailing Address: PO Box 1269, TRAVERSE CITY, MI, 49685-1269
Telephone: (315) 451-1957
Fax Number: (315) 451-9603
Internet Homepage: hrgweb.com
Company Email: info@hrgonline.net
Type of Business: Chain Restaurant Operator
Year Founded: 1985
Total Sales: $147,080,000 (e)

Number of Employees: 2,635
Average Check: Lunch(8); Dinner(10)
Total Units: 89
Trade Names: Pizza Hut (21); Taco Bell (52); Taco Bell / Long John Silver (4); Taco Bell/KFC (4)
Units Franchised From: 89
Preferred Square Footage: 2,500
Preferred Location Types: Community Mall; Freestanding
Primary Menu: Chicken (4); Pizza (21); Seafood (4); Taco (59)
Areas of Operation: MA, MI, NY, TN
Type of Foodservice: Quick Serve (81)
Catering Services: Yes
Franchise Affiliation: KFC Corporation, LOUISVILLE, KY; Long John Silver's Inc., LOUISVILLE, KY; Pizza Hut Inc., PLANO, TX; Taco Bell Corp., IRVINE, CA
Primary Distributors: (Food) McLane/Guilderland Center, GUILDERLAND CENTER, NY
Divisional Offices: Hospitality Syracuse, LIVERPOOL, NY
Notes: The company also does business as Hospitality Syracuse Inc., Hospitality West LLC, WKSC LLC, & Lobdell Management.

Key Personnel
MARTY LOBDELL - CEO; Partner; VP Operations, Purchasing, Marketing, Sales, Store Fixtures; Director Finance, Facility/Maintenance, Information Systems, Real Estate, Design
STEVE PINKERTON - President; Partner; Manager Operations, Supply Chain
DIANE BURNS - Controller; Manager Risk Management, Human Resources
WALTER RUTA - Director Operations
WAHID AKL - Director Operations
JESSICA WOODBURN - Director Marketing
MARK FORAKER - Manager Recruitment
BRANDY CARR - Product Manager

Hospitality Syracuse
290 Elwood Davis Rd Ste 320
Liverpool, NY 13088-2105

Telephone: (315) 451-1957
Fax Number: (315) 451-9603
Listing Type: Divisional Office
Type of Business: Chain Restaurant Operator
Year Founded: 1988
Number of Employees: 20
Average Check: Dinner(8)
Total Units: 52
Projected Openings: 3
Projected Remodelings: 6
Areas of Operation: MA, NY, VT
Parent Company: Hospitality Restaurant Group Inc., LIVERPOOL, NY

Key Personnel
MARTY LOBDELL - CEO; Partner; VP Operations, Purchasing, Marketing, Sales
STEVE PINKERTON - Partner; Director Facility/Maintenance, Information Systems, Real Estate, Human Resources; General Buyer
WALTER RUTA - Director Operations

Domino's Franchisee
269 W Park Ave
Long Beach, NY 11561-3222

Telephone: (516) 432-1234
Type of Business: Chain Restaurant Operator
Total Sales: $8,003,000 (e)
Total Units: 4
Trade Names: Domino's (4)
Units Franchised From: 4
Primary Menu: Pizza (4)
Areas of Operation: NY
Type of Foodservice: Quick Serve (4)
Franchise Affiliation: Domino's Pizza Inc, ANN ARBOR, MI

Key Personnel
MILI A. BHUYAN - Owner; General Buyer

Ambassador Food Services Corporation
4012 28th St
Long Island City, NY 11101-3308

Telephone: (718) 361-2512
Fax Number: (718) 786-4572
Internet Homepage: ambassadorfoodservice.com
Company Email: ambassadorsquire@aol.com
Type of Business: Foodservice Management Operator
Year Founded: 1961
Total Sales: $11,929,000 (e)
Number of Employees: 85
Number of Locations Served: 30
Total Foodservice Mgmt Accounts: 30
Areas of Operation: NY
Type of Foodservice: Quick Serve (30)
Foodservice Management Venues: Health Care
Notes: The company derives approximately 9% of its revenue from janitorial services.

Key Personnel
ARTHUR D. STEVENS - Chairman
ROBERT A. LAUDICINA PH.D. - CEO; President; Treasurer
JOHN A. MAKULA - COO; VP Finance, Operations, Marketing, Human Resources; Corporate Secretary
ANTHONY R. ZACCARIO - Senior VP

P. Hendel Products Partnership
146 Horton Ave
Lynbrook, NY 11563-2331

Telephone: (516) 256-0200
Fax Number: (516) 256-0285
Type of Business: Chain Restaurant Operator
Year Founded: 1992
Total Sales: $111,850,000 (e)
Number of Employees: 1,073
Average Check: Breakfast(8); Lunch(10); Dinner(12)
Total Units: 24
Trade Names: McDonald's (24)
Units Franchised From: 24
Preferred Square Footage: 1,500; 3,000
Preferred Location Types: Freestanding
Primary Menu: Hamburger (24)
Areas of Operation: NY
Type of Foodservice: Quick Serve (24)
Franchise Affiliation: McDonald's Corporation, CHICAGO, IL

Key Personnel
PAUL HENDEL - President; General Manager; Director Finance, Real Estate; General Buyer
KATHY SALERNO - Manager Human Resources

Toli Management
510 Broadhollow Rd Ste 304
Melville, NY 11747-3606

Telephone: (631) 427-0178
Fax Number: (631) 427-0179
Company Email: mcsmile@toli-mgmt.com
Type of Business: Chain Restaurant Operator
Total Sales: $71,230,000 (e)
Number of Employees: 350
Average Check: Breakfast(8); Lunch(8); Dinner(8)
Total Units: 15
Trade Names: McDonald's (15)
Units Franchised From: 15
Preferred Square Footage: 2,500; 3,000
Preferred Location Types: Freestanding
Primary Menu: Hamburger (15)
Areas of Operation: NY
Type of Foodservice: Quick Serve (15)
Franchise Affiliation: McDonald's Corporation, CHICAGO, IL

Key Personnel
JUAN RODRIGUEZ - President; General Buyer
LUIS NINA - Controller
PATTI ORSO BUTLER - Manager Accounting

Domino's Franchisee
50 Carpenter Ave Ste 1
Middletown, NY 10940-2418

Telephone: (845) 342-4200
Type of Business: Chain Restaurant Operator
Total Sales: $10,024,000 (e)
Total Units: 5
Trade Names: Domino's (5)
Units Franchised From: 5
Primary Menu: Pizza (5)
Areas of Operation: NY
Type of Foodservice: Quick Serve (5)
Franchise Affiliation: Domino's Pizza Inc, ANN ARBOR, MI

Key Personnel
MUHAMMAD R. KHAN - Owner; General Buyer

Planet Wings Enterprises
253 Route 211 E Fl 2
Middletown, NY 10940-3107

Telephone: (845) 344-8000
Fax Number: (845) 344-9435
Internet Homepage: planetwings.com
Company Email: contact@planetwings.com
Type of Business: Chain Restaurant Operator
Year Founded: 1995
Systemwide Sales: $29,688,000 (e)
Total Sales: $8,998,000 (e)
Average Check: Dinner(10)
Total Units: 15
Trade Names: Planet Wings (20)
Units Franchised To: 20
Preferred Location Types: Freestanding; Regional Mall; Strip Mall
Primary Menu: Chicken (20)
Areas of Operation: NJ, NY
Type of Foodservice: Quick Serve (20)

Key Personnel
FRANCO FIDANZA - CEO; Partner; General Buyer
PAULA FIDANZA - Partner; CFO

Kings Point Ventures, LLC
555 S Columbus Ave Ste 203
Mount Vernon, NY 10550-4742

Telephone: (914) 664-4255
Fax Number: (914) 664-4266
Internet Homepage: kpvllc.com; kpvllc.com
Company Email: info@kpvllc.com
Type of Business: Chain Restaurant Operator
Year Founded: 2007
Total Sales: $104,000,000 (e)
Average Check: Lunch(5); Dinner(5)
Total Units: 67
Trade Names: Dunkin' Donuts (67)
Units Franchised From: 67
Preferred Square Footage: 1,500; 2,200
Preferred Location Types: Freestanding; Strip Mall
Primary Menu: Snacks (67)
Areas of Operation: CT, IN, NC, NJ, NY, PA
Type of Foodservice: Quick Serve (67)
Franchise Affiliation: DD IP Holder, CANTON, MA

Key Personnel
ALEX SMIGELSKI - CEO; Partner
THOMAS P. CARPENTER - Partner; COO
BOB CARPENTER - Director Development, Construction
ROBERT RUFO - Area Manager District

Auntie Anne's Franchise
Route 5 and 5A
New Hartford, NY 13413

Telephone: (315) 733-8470
Type of Business: Chain Restaurant Operator
Total Sales: $1,561,000 (e)
Total Units: 2
Trade Names: Auntie Anne's Hand-Rolled Soft Pretzels (2)
Units Franchised From: 2
Primary Menu: Snacks (2)
Areas of Operation: NY
Type of Foodservice: Quick Serve (2)
Franchise Affiliation: Auntie Anne's Inc., LANCASTER, PA

Key Personnel
STUART DIAMOND - Owner; General Buyer

Subway 21139, Inc
234 Main St Ste 4
New Paltz, NY 12561-1352

Telephone: (845) 256-6425
Type of Business: Chain Restaurant Operator
Total Sales: $2,510,000 (e)
Total Units: 4
Trade Names: Subway (4)
Units Franchised From: 4
Primary Menu: Sandwiches/Deli (4)
Areas of Operation: NY
Type of Foodservice: Quick Serve (4)
Franchise Affiliation: Doctor's Associates Inc., MILFORD, CT

Key Personnel
PATRICK RYDER - President; General Buyer
KEVIN RYDER - Director Operations, Sales

Cafe Spice
677 Little Britain Rd
New Windsor, NY 12553-6152

Telephone: (845) 863-0910
Fax Number: (845) 863-0918
Internet Homepage: cafespice.com
Company Email: info@cafespice.com
Type of Business: Chain Restaurant Operator
Total Sales: $3,564,000 (e)
Number of Employees: 12
Total Units: 2
Trade Names: Cafe Spice (2)
Company-Owned Units: 2
Preferred Location Types: Institution (college/hospital); Kiosk; Other
Primary Menu: Indian (2)
Areas of Operation: CT, MA, MI, NY
Type of Foodservice: Quick Serve (2)

Key Personnel
SUSHIL MALHOTRA - CEO; Partner; General Buyer
SAMEER MALHOTRA - President; Partner
RYAN BAKST - Manager Research & Development

Cosimo's Restaurant Group
1089 Little Britain Rd
New Windsor, NY 12553-7215

Telephone: (845) 564-5571
Fax Number: (845) 564-5577
Internet Homepage: cosimospizzacafe.com; cosimosrestaurantgroup.com; cosimosunion.com; pizza-shop.com
Company Email: info@http://cosimospizzacafe.com/
Type of Business: Chain Restaurant Operator
Year Founded: 1980
Total Sales: $5,790,000 (e)
Alcohol Sales: 3%
Number of Employees: 65
Average Check: Dinner(34)
Total Units: 6
Trade Names: Cosimo's Brick Oven (4); Cosimo's Pizza Cafe (1); Pizza Shop (1)
Company-Owned Units: 6
Preferred Square Footage: 4,000
Preferred Location Types: Freestanding; Strip Mall
Alcohol Served: Beer, Wine, Liquor
Primary Menu: Pizza (6)
Areas of Operation: NY
Type of Foodservice: Casual Dining (6)
Primary Distributors: (Food) Lisanti Foodservice of Texas, FLOWER MOUND, TX

Key Personnel
CARLO CITERA - Partner; CIO; VP Operations, Information Systems; Director Finance,

Human Resources
NICK CITERA - Partner; General Buyer
ELISA DIBRIZZI - Partner
JASON COOPERMAN - General Manager; Executive Chef
DAMIEN BRADY - Director Operations
KAITLYN FESTA - Manager

5 Napkin Burger
630 9th Ave Ste 311
New York, NY 10036-4751

Telephone: (212) 757-2277
Internet Homepage: 5napkinburger.com
Company Email: info@5napkinburger.com
Type of Business: Chain Restaurant Operator
Year Founded: 2003
Total Sales: $40,150,000 (e)
Alcohol Sales: 15%
Average Check: Lunch(26); Dinner(26)
Internet Order Processing: Yes
Total Units: 4
Trade Names: 5 Napkin Burger (4)
Company-Owned Units: 4
Alcohol Served: Beer, Wine, Liquor
Primary Menu: Hamburger (4)
Areas of Operation: MA, NY
Type of Foodservice: Fast Casual (4)

Key Personnel
ROBERT GUARINO - CEO
ANDY D'AMICO - Partner
SIMON OREN - Partner
MARIA ROSSI - General Manager
PEDRO I. LOPEZ - General Manager
ROMAN CHURSIN - General Manager
VIJAY RAGHAVAN - Executive Chef
VANESSA FANNING - Director Operations
SHELLY ATKIN - Manager Accounting
KYLE PRUITT - Manager

Alicart Restaurant Group
1501 Broadway Ste 515
New York, NY 10036-5505

Telephone: (212) 675-9790
Fax Number: (212) 675-9756
Internet Homepage: alicart.com; carminesnyc.com; virgilsbbq.com
Company Email: info@carminesnyc.com
Type of Business: Chain Restaurant Operator
Year Founded: 1990
Total Sales: $33,140,000 (e)
Alcohol Sales: 20%
Number of Employees: 1,800
Average Check: Lunch(14); Dinner(24)
Internet Order Processing: Yes
Total Units: 9
Trade Names: Carmine's Restaurant (6); Virgil's Real BBQ (3)
Company-Owned Units: 9
Preferred Square Footage: 5,500; 6,000
Preferred Location Types: Downtown; Hotel/Motel; Office Complex
Alcohol Served: Beer, Wine, Liquor
Primary Menu: Bar-B-Q (3); Italian (6)
Areas of Operation: DC, NV, NY, FC
Foreign Countries: BAHAMAS
Type of Foodservice: Casual Dining (9)
Catering Services: Yes
Primary Distributors: (Food) SYSCO Food Services of Albany, HALFMOON, NY

Key Personnel
JEFFREY BANK - CEO; General Manager
DREW KURUC - CFO
RANDY TALBOT - COO
JAMES YACYSHYN - General Manager
GLENN ROLNICK - Corporate Chef; Director Culinary Development
PHILIP DIXON - Director Information Technology
KAY KOLBO - Director Event Planning
LAURA O'NEILL - Director Human Resources
ERIKA RODRIGUEZ - Director Training
GIANNA LEFLAR - Director Digital Marketing
JULY MARTINEZ - Director Operations, Event Planning, Catering
CAROLYN MORRISON - Director Operations
KAREN BANK - Manager Recruitment
KONRAD BOLKUN - Manager Operations, Facility/Maintenance
KATHY CICHA - Manager Human Resources
ANDREW KURUC - Manager Information Technology
LYNNE WILKINSON - Manager Sales
PAULA MUNIZ - Specialist Information Technology

Altamarea Group
611 Broadway Rm 415
New York, NY 10012-2653

Telephone: (347) 854-0150
Fax Number: (212) 219-8509
Internet Homepage: altamareagroup.com
Company Email: info@altamareagroup.com
Type of Business: Chain Restaurant Operator
Total Sales: $7,732,000 (e)
Total Units: 12
Trade Names: Ai Fiori (1); Al Molo (1); Costata (1); Due Mari (1); Marea (1); Nicoletta Restaruant (2); Osteria Morini (3); Ristorante Morini (1); Vaucluse (1)
Company-Owned Units: 12
Alcohol Served: Beer, Wine, Liquor
Primary Menu: French/Continental (1); Italian (2); Pizza (2); Steak/Seafood (7)
Areas of Operation: DC, NJ, NY
Foreign Countries: ENGLAND; HONG KONG; TURKEY
Type of Foodservice: Casual Dining (3); Fine Dining (9)

Key Personnel
AHMASS FAKAHANY - CEO; Partner; General Buyer
MICHAEL WHITE - Partner; Executive Chef
ARTHUR LI - CFO; Chief Administrative Officer
BRIAN LAUCK - General Counsel
ALEXANDRIA KENNEDY - General Manager
DOLLY NACARIO - Director Human Resources
UZMA AMANAT - Director Finance
ROBERTO RECCHIONE - Director Alcoholic Beverages
JENNIFER MURRI - Director Compliance
ELIZA POEHLMAN - Director Talent
REBECCA LEVINE - Director
LIS SILVEIRA - Manager Finance
FABIAN ROMERO - Manager Facility/Maintenance

Ark Restaurants Corp.
85 5th Ave Fl 14
New York, NY 10003-3019

Telephone: (212) 206-8800
Fax Number: (212) 206-8845
Internet Homepage: arkrestaurants.com; arkvegas.com
Company Email: info@arkrestaurants.com
Type of Business: Chain Restaurant Operator
Year Founded: 1983
Publicly Held: Yes
Total Sales: $192,757,000 (e)
Alcohol Sales: 30%
Number of Employees: 2,000
Average Check: Breakfast(10); Lunch(20); Dinner(26)
Total Units: 19
Trade Names: America (1); Blue Moon Fish Comapny (1); Broadway Burger Bar & Grill (1); Bryant Park Grill (1); Fever-Tree Porch (1); Gallagher's Steakhouse (2); Gonzalez y Gonzalez (1); Hard Rock Hotel & Casino Hollywood Food Court (1); Hard Rock Hotel & Casino Tampa Food Court (1); JB's On the Beach (1); Oyster House (2); Robert (1); Rustic Inn (1); Sequoia (1); Shuckers (1); Village Eateries (1); Yolos Mexican Grill (1)
Company-Owned Units: 19
Preferred Square Footage: 800; 1,000
Preferred Location Types: Downtown; Freestanding; Hotel/Motel; Other
Alcohol Served: Beer, Wine, Liquor
Primary Menu: American (8); Hamburger (1); Mexican (2); Seafood (6); Steak (2)
Areas of Operation: CT, DC, FL, MA, NJ, NV, NY
Type of Foodservice: Casual Dining (8); Fast Casual (1); Fine Dining (7); Quick Serve (3)
Catering Services: Yes
On-site Distribution Center: Yes
Primary Distributors: (Food) Cheney Bros. Inc., RIVIERA BEACH, FL

Key Personnel
ANTHONY J. SIRCIA - CFO
VINCENT PASCAL - COO; Senior VP
SERGIO SOTO - Executive Chef
JOHN OLDWEILER - Director Purchasing
LINDA CLOUS - Director Facility/Maintenance
RUBEN REY CASAS - Director Event Planning
KRISTI OHLIN - Manager Catering
EMMA WEINSTEIN - Manager Catering
ANDREA O'BRIEN - Manager Event Planning

Artichoke Basille's Pizza
321 E 14th St
New York, NY 10003

Telephone: (212) 228-2004
Internet Homepage: artichokepizza.com
Type of Business: Chain Restaurant Operator
Year Founded: 2008
Total Sales: $43,350,000 (e)
Average Check: Lunch(18); Dinner(20)
Total Units: 17
Trade Names: Artichoke Basilles's Pizza (17)
Company-Owned Units: 13
Units Franchised To: 4
Preferred Square Footage: 1,400
Primary Menu: Pizza (17)
Projected Openings: 15
Areas of Operation: CT, NY
Type of Foodservice: Casual Dining (17)
Catering Services: Yes

Key Personnel
SAL BASILLE - Partner
FRANCIS GARCIA - Partner
BRANDON R. LINKER - Senior VP Operations

Aurify Brands LLC
56 W 22nd St Rm 200
New York, NY 10010-7296

Telephone: (212) 505-5861
Fax Number: (646) 687-7752
Internet Homepage: aurifybrands.com; fieldsgoodchicken.com; meltshop.com; thelittlebeet.com
Company Email: info@aurifybrands.com
Type of Business: Chain Restaurant Operator
Total Sales: $40,230,000 (e)
Total Units: 94
Trade Names: Fields Good Chicken (4); Five Guys Burgers and Fries (13); Le Pain Quotidien (50); Little Beet Table (2); The Little Beet (10); The Melt Shop (15)
Company-Owned Units: 81
Units Franchised From: 13
Preferred Location Types: Downtown
Primary Menu: American (16); Hamburger (13); Sandwiches/Deli (15); Sandwiches/Deli (50)
Projected Openings: 5
Areas of Operation: DC, IL, NY, PA
Type of Foodservice: Casual Dining (2); Fast Casual (92)
Catering Services: Yes
Subsidiaries: Le Pain Quotidien, NEW YORK, NY
Franchise Affiliation: Five Guys Holdings Inc., LORTON, VA
Notes: The Little Beet Table has an average per-person check of $54 at dinner and $30 at lunch.

Key Personnel
BECKY MULLIGAN - CEO
ANDREW L. STERN - Co-CEO; General Buyer
JOHN RIGGOS - Co-CEO
SPENCER RUBIN - Partner
FIELD FAILING - Partner
ROB GARRETT - CFO
MARINA ROULIS - Chief Human Resources Officer; Chief of Staff
JASON ANELLO - Chief Marketing Officer
TONY MINELLA - Chief Investment Officer
LOUIS RIGOS - Director Operations
JUANINA KOCHER - Director Event Planning, Catering
DOMINIC VALERIO - Director Operations
JENNIFER MELECK - Director Operations, Event Planning, Catering
LUIS NICOLAS - Manager District
JOHN Z. RIGOS - General Buyer

B & B Hospitality Group
45 E 20th St
New York, NY 10003-1308

Telephone: (212) 397-2471
Fax Number: (212) 677-2917
Internet Homepage: babbonyc.com; bandbhg.com; carnevino.com; casamononyc.com; delposto.com; esca-nyc.com; luparestaurant.com; mariobatali.com; mozza-la.com; ottopizzeria.com
Type of Business: Chain Restaurant Operator
Year Founded: 1998
Total Sales: $40,900,000 (e)
Alcohol Sales: 10%
Number of Employees: 354
Average Check: Lunch(30); Dinner(42)
Total Units: 12
Trade Names: Babbo (1); Bar Jamon (1); Becco (1); Casa Mono (1); Chi Spacca (1); Eataly (2); Lidia's (1); Lupa (1); Osteria Mozza (1); Pizzeria Mozza (1); Tarry Lodge (1)
Company-Owned Units: 12
Preferred Square Footage: 5,500; 6,000
Preferred Location Types: Freestanding
Alcohol Served: Beer, Wine, Liquor
Primary Menu: Italian (9); Pizza (1); Spanish (2)
Areas of Operation: CA, CT, MO, NJ, NV, NY, PA, FC
Type of Foodservice: Casual Dining (12)
Primary Distributors: (Food) Dairyland, The Chefs' Warehouse, BRONX, NY

Key Personnel
JOE BASTIANICH - Partner; General Buyer
LIDIA BASTIANICH - Partner
NANCY SILVERTON - Partner
KASIA MANCHISI - CFO
MARIE O'BRIEN - General Manager
DAVID PASTERNACK - Executive Chef
CHEF NUSSER - Executive Chef
FRANK LANGELLO - Executive Chef Division

Balthazar
80 Spring St
New York, NY 10012-3907

Mailing Address: 568 Broadway, NEW YORK, NY, 10012-3235
Telephone: (212) 925-5340
Fax Number: (212) 925-6299
Internet Homepage: luckystrikeny.com; balthazarny.com; minettatavernny.com; morandiny.com; pastisny.com
Type of Business: Chain Restaurant Operator
Year Founded: 1997
Total Sales: $14,510,000 (e)
Alcohol Sales: 20%
Number of Employees: 779
Average Check: Breakfast(5); Lunch(20); Dinner(32)
Total Units: 7
Trade Names: Augustine (1); Balthazar (1); Balthazar Bakery (1); Lucky Strike (1); Minetta (1); Morandi (1); Patis (1)
Company-Owned Units: 7
Preferred Square Footage: 5,500; 6,000
Preferred Location Types: Freestanding
Alcohol Served: Beer, Wine, Liquor
Primary Menu: American (2); French/Continental (4); Italian (1)
Areas of Operation: NY
Type of Foodservice: Casual Dining (7)
Primary Distributors: (Food) Balter Sales Co Inc., NEW YORK, NY

Key Personnel
ROBERTA DELICE - CFO
KEITH MCNALLY - President; Owner; General Manager; Director Real Estate, Design; General Buyer
ANNELENE RAMOS - CFO
ERIN WENDT - Director Operations
DIANNE AGUAS - Manager
NICHOLAS G. RIDLEY - Manager Training

Barnes & Noble Inc.
122 5th Ave Fl 2
New York, NY 10011-5634

Telephone: (212) 633-3300
Fax Number: (212) 633-3578

Internet Homepage: barnesandnoble.com; bncollege.com
Company Email: customerservice@bn.com
Type of Business: Nontraditional Foodservice Operator
Year Founded: 1990
Total Sales: $3,239,459,000 (e)
Number of Employees: 33,000
Average Check: Breakfast(8); Lunch(10); Dinner(10)
Foodservice Sales: $226,762,000 (e)
Internet Order Processing: Yes
Total Units: 769
Trade Names: Barnes & Noble Cafe (769)
Company-Owned Units: 769
Preferred Square Footage: 10,000; 60,000
Preferred Location Types: Downtown; Freestanding; Lifestyle Center; Regional Mall; Strip Mall
Primary Menu: American (769)
Areas of Operation: AK, AL, AR, AZ, CA, CO, CT, DC, DE, FL, GA, HI, IA, ID, IL, IN, KS, KY, LA, MA, MD, ME, MI, MN, MO, MS, MT, NC, ND, NE, NH, NJ, NM, NV, NY, OH, OK, OR, PA, RI, SC, SD, TN, TX, UT, VA, VT, WA, WI, WV, WY
Type of Foodservice: In-Store Feeder (769)
Primary Distributors: (Food) US Foods Holding Corp., ROSEMONT, IL
Parent Company: Elliott Advisors, NEW YORK, NY
Notes: Total store count includes some locations without in-store cafes. Total sales reflect results from Barnes & Noble retail stores only & exclude results from B&N College stores, NOOK, and BN.com. The company derives approximately 93% of its revenue from retail operations.

Key Personnel
JAMES DAUNT - CEO
CARLO POCHINTESTA - CIO
JOE GORMAN - Exec VP Operations
BRAD FEUER - VP; Corporate Secretary; General Counsel
MICHELLE SMITH - VP Human Resources
SARA ROSOFF - Senior Director Digital Experience
CHRISTIAN RODRIGUEZ - Director Technology, Information Technology, E-Commerce
CHRISTIAN KIM - Director Security
RITA BERTONE - Manager Procurement

Barnes & Noble The Kitchen
122 5th Ave
New York, NY 10011-5634

Telephone: (212) 633-3300
Internet Homepage: barnesandnoblekitchen.com
Company Email: kitchen@bn.com
Type of Business: Chain Restaurant Operator
Total Units: 5
Trade Names: Barnes & Noble Kitchen (5)
Company-Owned Units: 5
Primary Menu: American (5)
Areas of Operation: CA, MN, NY, TX
Type of Foodservice: Casual Dining (5)

Key Personnel
ALLEN LINDSTROM - CFO
CARLO POCHINTESTA - CIO
NURI ONGAN - Director Logistics

Benares
45 Murray St
New York, NY 10007

Telephone: (212) 766-4900
Internet Homepage: benaresnyc.com
Company Email: info@benaresnyc.com
Type of Business: Chain Restaurant Operator
Year Founded: 1993
Total Sales: $984,000 (e)
Alcohol Sales: 30%
Number of Employees: 30
Average Check: Lunch(36); Dinner(36)
Total Units: 1
Trade Names: Bennares (1)
Company-Owned Units: 1
Preferred Square Footage: 1,000; 1,400
Preferred Location Types: Freestanding
Alcohol Served: Beer, Wine, Liquor
Primary Menu: Indian (1)
Areas of Operation: NY
Type of Foodservice: Casual Dining (1)
Catering Services: Yes
Primary Distributors: (Full Line) Maya Overseas Foods Inc., GARDEN CITY PARK, NY

Key Personnel
INDER KUMAR - Owner; General Buyer
DHANDU RAM - Executive Chef

Benchmarc Restaurants
13 Laight St Ste 17
New York, NY 10013-2119

Telephone: (212) 625-8265
Internet Homepage: marc-murphy.com
Company Email: info@benchmarc-restaurants.com
Type of Business: Chain Restaurant Operator
Total Units: 3
Trade Names: Ditch Plains (1); Landmarc (2)
Company-Owned Units: 3
Preferred Location Types: Downtown
Alcohol Served: Beer, Wine, Liquor
Primary Menu: French/Continental (2); Seafood (1)
Areas of Operation: NY
Type of Foodservice: Casual Dining (3)
Catering Services: Yes
Notes: In addition to restaurants, the company also operates Benchmarc Events.

Key Personnel
MARC MURPHY - Partner; Executive Chef
YVETTE FEINBERG - Director Human Resources
STEVE MARTIN - Manager Inventory
NIGEL LAFORCE - Manager Transportation
GIANNY ABEL DES SOURCES - Manager
LEROY LA FORCE - Manager

Black Tap Craft Burgers & Beer
529 Broome St
New York, NY 10013

Telephone: (917) 639-3089
Internet Homepage: blacktap.com
Company Email: press@blacktapnyc.com
Type of Business: Chain Restaurant Operator
Year Founded: 2015
Total Units: 14
Trade Names: Black Tap Craft Burgers & Beer (14)
Company-Owned Units: 5
Units Franchised To: 9
Primary Menu: Hamburger (14)
Projected Openings: 2
Areas of Operation: CA, NV, NY
Foreign Countries: BAHRAIN; KUWAIT; SINGAPORE; SWITZERLAND; UNITED ARAB EMIRATES
Type of Foodservice: Casual Dining (14)

Key Personnel
CHRIS BARISH - Co-Founder; Partner
JOE ISIDORI - Co-Founder; Executive Chef
JULIE MULLIGAN - Partner; Director Development, Design
JULIE MULLIGAN BARISH - Partner Design; Director Development
STEVE PARKER - Corporate Chef
COURTNEY WRIGHT - Creative Director

Blockheads Burritos
104 E 121st St
New York, NY 10035-2812

Telephone: (212) 860-4737
Fax Number: (212) 725-6884
Internet Homepage: blockheads.com
Company Email: blockheads@blockheads.com
Type of Business: Chain Restaurant Operator
Total Sales: $8,346,000 (e)
Alcohol Sales: 15%
Number of Employees: 40
Average Check: Lunch(8); Dinner(18)
Total Units: 7

Trade Names: Benny's Burritos (1); Blockheads Burritos (5); MTHR Vegan (1)
Company-Owned Units: 7
Preferred Square Footage: 5,500; 6,000
Preferred Location Types: Freestanding
Alcohol Served: Beer, Wine, Liquor
Primary Menu: Hamburger (1); Mexican (6)
Areas of Operation: NY
Type of Foodservice: Casual Dining (7)
Catering Services: Yes
Primary Distributors: (Full Line) US Foods, BUFFALO, NY

Key Personnel
DON SOFER - Partner; VP; Executive Chef; Director Information Systems, Real Estate, Design; General Buyer
KEN SOFER - Partner; Director Operations, Facility/Maintenance, Supply Chain; General Buyer
JOEL ANDUJAR - General Manager

BLT Restaurant Group
145 E 57th St Fl 11
New York, NY 10022-2889

Telephone: (212) 688-2700
Fax Number: (212) 688-7908
Internet Homepage: bltsteak.com; bltrestaurantgroup.com
Company Email: info@bltrestaurantgroup.com
Type of Business: Chain Restaurant Operator
Year Founded: 2004
Total Sales: $58,150,000 (e)
Alcohol Sales: 12%
Number of Employees: 110
Average Check: Lunch(36); Dinner(78)
Total Units: 18
Trade Names: BLT Burger (1); BLT Prime (3); BLT Steak (11); Casa Nonna (2); The Florentine (1)
Company-Owned Units: 18
Alcohol Served: Beer, Wine, Liquor
Primary Menu: Hamburger (1); Italian (3); Steak (14)
Areas of Operation: AZ, CA, DC, FL, GA, HI, IL, MO, NC, NV, NY, PR, FC
Foreign Countries: JAPAN
Type of Foodservice: Casual Dining (17); Fine Dining (1)
Notes: Formerly known as BLT Restaurant Group.

Key Personnel
JIMMY HARBER - CEO
DAVID BURKE - Partner
SCOTT CRONIN - Exec VP Operations
RICK WELLS - Director; Manager
MATTHEW ACKLAND - Director
CAMILLE GONZALEZ - Manager Event Planning

Blue Ribbon Restaurants
97 Sullivan St Frnt A
New York, NY 10012-3663

Telephone: (212) 229-0404
Fax Number: (212) 219-2049
Internet Homepage: blueribbonrestaurants.com
Company Email: email@blueribbonrestaurants.com
Type of Business: Chain Restaurant Operator
Year Founded: 1992
Total Sales: $18,850,000 (e)
Total Units: 19
Trade Names: Blue Ribbon Bar (4); Blue Ribbon Brasserie (2); Blue Ribbon Fried Chicken (1); Blue Ribbon Sushi (6); Brooklyn Bowl (4); The Fountain (1); Weki Sushi (1)
Company-Owned Units: 19
Primary Menu: American (10); Asian (8); Chicken (1); Sandwiches/Deli (0)
Projected Openings: 3
Areas of Operation: NV, NY
Foreign Countries: ENGLAND
Type of Foodservice: Casual Dining (19)

Key Personnel
ERIC BROMBERG - CEO; Partner
BRUCE BROMBERG - Partner
AARON L. BAUM - Partner
DONNA LACHMAN - CFO
RICHARD HO - General Manager
DAISY GOGEL - General Manager

Bluestone Lane Coffee
51 Astor Pl
New York, NY 10003-7139

Telephone: (646) 863-3197
Internet Homepage: bluestonelaneny.com
Company Email: info@BluestoneLaneNY.com
Type of Business: Chain Restaurant Operator
Year Founded: 2013
Total Sales: $67,890,000 (e)
Internet Order Processing: Yes
Total Units: 51
Trade Names: Bluestone Lane Cafe (18); Bluestone Lane Coffee Shop (33)
Company-Owned Units: 51
Primary Menu: American (18); Snacks (33)
Areas of Operation: CA, DC, NJ, NY, PA
Type of Foodservice: Fast Casual (18); Quick Serve (33)

Key Personnel
NICK STONE - Executive Chairman; Co-Founder
EDIE AMES - CEO
ANDREW STONE - VP Marketing
LIAM FARROW - VP Digital
ARIANA SOTO - General Manager
SHUHANA ISLAM - General Manager
MELISSA HOWIE - Manager Operations

Bold Food
152 W 52nd St
New York, NY 10019-6004

Mailing Address: PO Box 1102, NEW YORK, NY, 10159-1102
Telephone: (212) 460-0928
Fax Number: (212) 265-9025
Internet Homepage: gatonyc.com; baramericain.com; bobbysburgerpalace.com; boldfood.net; mesagrill.com
Company Email: info@gatonyc.com
Type of Business: Chain Restaurant Operator
Year Founded: 1991
Total Sales: $50,580,000 (e)
Alcohol Sales: 30%
Number of Employees: 580
Average Check: Lunch(46); Dinner(78)
Internet Order Processing: Yes
Internet Sales: 2.00%
Total Units: 18
Trade Names: Bar Americain (1); Bobby Flay Steak (1); Bobby's Burger Palace (13); Gato (1); Mesa Grill Las Vegas (1); Shark (1)
Company-Owned Units: 17
Units Franchised To: 1
Preferred Location Types: Freestanding; Hotel/Motel
Alcohol Served: Beer, Wine, Liquor
Primary Menu: American (10); Greek/Mediterranean (1); Seafood (1); Southwest/Tex-Mex (1); Steak (1)
Projected Openings: 2
Areas of Operation: CT, DC, FL, MA, MD, NJ, NV, NY, OH, PA, VA
Type of Foodservice: Casual Dining (14); Fine Dining (1)
Primary Distributors: (Food) SYSCO Food Services of Syracuse, WARNERS, NY

Key Personnel
BOBBY FLAY - Partner; Executive Chef
MANNY GATDULA - Controller
SHARON COOPER - Director Marketing
SHAFEEZA DAIKALO - Coordinator Accounting

Branded Restaurants
235 Park Ave S Fl 8
New York, NY 10003-1405

Telephone: (212) 388-0688
Fax Number: (212) 473-8030
Internet Homepage: brandedrestaurants.com
Company Email: info@brandedrestaurants.com
Type of Business: Chain Restaurant Operator
Year Founded: 1992
Total Sales: $19,970,000 (e)

Alcohol Sales: 15%
Number of Employees: 70
Average Check: Lunch(18); Dinner(24)
Total Units: 4
Trade Names: Big Daddie's (2); Duke's (2)
Company-Owned Units: 4
Preferred Square Footage: 5,500; 6,000
Preferred Location Types: Freestanding
Alcohol Served: Beer, Wine, Liquor
Primary Menu: American (4)
Areas of Operation: NY, FC
Type of Foodservice: Casual Dining (4)
Primary Distributors: (Food) US Foods, BUFFALO, NY

Key Personnel
JAMES FRISCHLING - Partner; Director Finance
MICHAEL SCHATZBERG - Partner; General Buyer
MICHAEL SIRY - Corporate Chef
JULIE ZUCKER - Director Marketing
MIRA SHIMUNOVA - Specialist Accounting

Bubby's Pie Co.
120 Hudson St
New York, NY 10013-2317

Telephone: (212) 219-0666
Internet Homepage: bubbys.com
Company Email: adriana@bubbys.com
Type of Business: Chain Restaurant Operator
Year Founded: 1990
Total Sales: $6,165,000 (e)
Alcohol Sales: 10%
Number of Employees: 14
Average Check: Breakfast(20); Lunch(20); Dinner(28)
Total Units: 2
Trade Names: Bubby's Pie Co. (2)
Company-Owned Units: 2
Preferred Location Types: Freestanding; Other
Alcohol Served: Beer, Wine, Liquor
Primary Menu: American (2)
Areas of Operation: NY
Type of Foodservice: Casual Dining (2)
Catering Services: Yes
Primary Distributors: (Full Line) SYSCO Food Services of Albany, HALFMOON, NY

Key Personnel
RON SILVER - Owner; Executive Chef; General Buyer
ADRIANA DIAZ ALVAREZ - General Manager; Manager Catering
ANTONELA PINA - Manager Catering

By Chloe
60 W 22nd St
New York, NY 10010

Telephone: (347) 620-9662
Internet Homepage: eatbychloe.com; linkedin.com/company/by-chloe
Company Email: hello@eatbychloe.com
Type of Business: Chain Restaurant Operator
Year Founded: 2015
Total Sales: $54,896,000 (e)
Total Units: 14
Trade Names: By Chloe (14)
Company-Owned Units: 14
Primary Menu: Health Foods (14)
Areas of Operation: CA, MA, NY, RI
Foreign Countries: ENGLAND
Type of Foodservice: Fast Casual (14)

Key Personnel
CHLOE COSCARELLI - Co-Founder
SAMANTHA WASSER - Co-Founder

Carlyle
35 E 76th St
New York, NY 10021-1827

Telephone: (212) 744-1600
Fax Number: (212) 439-5810
Internet Homepage: rosewoodhotels.com/en/the-carlyle-new-york
Company Email: thecarlyle@rosewoodhotels.com
Type of Business: Chain Restaurant Operator
Year Founded: 1926
Total Sales: $12,512,000 (e)
Alcohol Sales: 30%
Number of Employees: 100
Average Check: Lunch(54); Dinner(78)
Total Units: 3
Trade Names: Cafe Carlyle (1); Carlyle Restaurant (1); The Gallery (1)
Company-Owned Units: 3
Preferred Location Types: Hotel/Motel
Alcohol Served: Beer, Wine, Liquor
Primary Menu: French/Continental (3)
Areas of Operation: NY
Type of Foodservice: Fine Dining (3)
Primary Distributors: (Food) Performance Foodservice - AFI, ELIZABETH, NJ

Key Personnel
TERRY TOLAN - Director Purchasing; General Buyer

Catch Hospitality Group
426 W 14th St 6th Floor
New York, NY 10014

Telephone: (212) 627-1235
Internet Homepage: catchrestaurants.com
Company Email: info@catchhg.com
Type of Business: Chain Restaurant Operator
Year Founded: 2006
Average Check: Breakfast(18); Lunch(30); Dinner(60)
Total Units: 6
Trade Names: Catch (4); Catch Roof (1); Lexington Brass Bar & Grill (1)
Company-Owned Units: 6
Primary Menu: American (1); Seafood (5)
Projected Openings: 1
Areas of Operation: CA, NV, NY
Foreign Countries: MEXICO
Type of Foodservice: Fine Dining (6)
Catering Services: Yes

Key Personnel
EUGENE REMM - Partner
MARK BIRNBAUM - Partner
TILMAN J. FERTITTA - Partner
GREGORY GILDEA - General Manager
MICHAEL VIGNOLA - Executive Chef
LUCAS ROBINSON - Director Division
MICHAEL ILIC - Director Operations
SOY CHIEVER - Director Operations
ALEC SIKAR - Manager Event Planning
MELYSSA GRANAT - Manager Event Planning

Charlie Palmer Group
1460 Broadway Ste 9028
New York, NY 10036-7306

Telephone: (212) 755-7050
Fax Number: (646) 755-6143
Internet Homepage: charliepalmer.com
Company Email: info@charliepalmer.com
Type of Business: Chain Restaurant Operator
Year Founded: 1988
Total Sales: $106,670,000 (e)
Alcohol Sales: 40%
Number of Employees: 1,453
Average Check: Lunch(66); Dinner(130)
Internet Order Processing: Yes
Internet Sales: 2.00%
Total Units: 17
Trade Names: Aureole (3); Charlie Palmer at The Knick (1); Charlie Palmer Steak (5); Crimson & Rye (1); Dry Ceek Kitchen (1); Dry Creek Kitchen (1); Jake's @ The Knick (1); Sky & Vine (1); Spirit Bar (1); St. Cloud (1); Upper Story By Charlie Palmer (1)
Company-Owned Units: 17
Preferred Square Footage: 3,000; 7,000
Preferred Location Types: Downtown; Freestanding; Hotel/Motel; Lifestyle Center;

Regional Mall
Alcohol Served: Beer, Wine, Liquor
Primary Menu: American (8); Californian (1); Steak (5); Steak/Seafood (3)
Areas of Operation: CA, DC, NV, NY
Type of Foodservice: Casual Dining (7); Fine Dining (9); Quick Serve (1)
Catering Services: Yes
Primary Distributors: (Food) Dairyland, The Chefs' Warehouse, BRONX, NY

Key Personnel
CHARLIE PALMER - President; General Manager; Executive Chef
PAVLA KOVAROVA - General Manager
THADEE ZACHARIASEN - General Manager
DAVE HOLMAN - Executive Chef
CHARLES POUCHOT - Director Operations

China Grill Management Inc.
60 W 53rd St
New York, NY 10019-6106

Telephone: (212) 262-0028
Fax Number: (212) 956-7062
Internet Homepage: asiadecuba.com; chinagrillrestaurant.com
Type of Business: Chain Restaurant Operator
Year Founded: 1995
Total Sales: $13,230,000 (e)
Alcohol Sales: 10%
Number of Employees: 617
Average Check: Breakfast(12); Lunch(24); Dinner(60)
Internet Order Processing: Yes
Total Units: 8
Trade Names: Asia de Cuba (3); China Grill (3); Chowder House Raw Bar (1); Plunge (1)
Company-Owned Units: 8
Preferred Square Footage: 1,500; 30,000
Preferred Location Types: Freestanding; Hotel/Motel
Alcohol Served: Beer, Wine, Liquor
Primary Menu: Asian (4); Chinese (3); Seafood (1)
Areas of Operation: FL, NY, FC
Foreign Countries: ENGLAND; MEXICO
Type of Foodservice: Casual Dining (6); Fine Dining (3)
Primary Distributors: (Food) SYSCO Food Services of Syracuse, WARNERS, NY

Key Personnel
JEFFREY CHODOROW - CEO; Manager Human Resources
LINDA CHODOROW - President; Partner; Director Finance, Real Estate, Design; General Buyer
JOHN POLSENBERG - CFO
JT MCKAY - Creative Director; Director Marketing
NICK DIXIT - Assistant Director Development

Chopt Creative Salad Company
850 Broadway Ste 606
New York, NY 10003

Telephone: (646) 233-2923
Internet Homepage: choptsalad.com
Type of Business: Chain Restaurant Operator
Year Founded: 2001

Key Personnel
COLIN MCCABE - Co-Founder
TOM KELLEHER - COO
CATHERINE LEDERER - Senior VP Beverages, Food
ALI BANKS - Director Culinary Operations

Cipriani International
110 E 42nd St
New York, NY 10017-5611

Telephone: (212) 499-0599
Fax Number: (212) 499-0776
Internet Homepage: cipriani.com
Company Email: sgirobelli@cipriani.com
Type of Business: Chain Restaurant Operator
Year Founded: 1962
Total Sales: $44,010,000 (e)
Alcohol Sales: 30%
Number of Employees: 825
Average Check: Lunch(32); Dinner(54)
Internet Order Processing: Yes
Internet Sales: 2.00%
Total Units: 15
Trade Names: Cipriani Riyadh (1); Cipriani Downtown (1); Cipriani Mexico City (1); Cipriani 55 Wall Street (1); Cipriani Abu Dhabi (1); Cipriani Dubai (1); Cipriani Las Vegas (1); Cipriani Le Specialita (1); Cipriani Monte Carlo (1); Cirpriani Dolci (1); Downtown Ibiza (1); Downtown Miami (1); Harry Cipriani (1); Harry's Bar -Venice (1); Harry's Dolci Venice (1)
Company-Owned Units: 15
Preferred Square Footage: 5,500; 6,000
Preferred Location Types: Downtown; Freestanding; Lifestyle Center; Office Complex
Alcohol Served: Beer, Wine, Liquor
Primary Menu: American (1); Indian (1); Italian (13)
Areas of Operation: FL, NV, NY, FC
Foreign Countries: HONG KONG; ITALY; MONACO; SPAIN; UNITED ARAB EMIRATES; UNITED STATES OF AMERICA
Type of Foodservice: Casual Dining (5); Fine Dining (10)
Catering Services: Yes
Primary Distributors: (Full Line) SYSCO Food Services of Albany, HALFMOON, NY

Key Personnel
GIUSSEPPE CIPRIANI - CEO; CFO; Director Purchasing, Supply Chain, Real Estate, Design
MAX BURGIO - Owner
ARRIGO CIPRIANI - Owner
LUIS GALAN - Manager Information Technology

City Winery
233 West St
New York, NY 10013

Telephone: (212) 608-0555
Internet Homepage: citywinery.com
Company Email: info@citywinery.com
Type of Business: Chain Restaurant Operator
Year Founded: 2008
Total Units: 8
Trade Names: City Vineyard at Pier 26 (1); City Winery (7)
Company-Owned Units: 8
Preferred Location Types: Downtown
Primary Menu: American (8)
Areas of Operation: DC, GA, IL, MA, NY, PA, TN
Type of Foodservice: Casual Dining (8)

Key Personnel
DAVID LECOMTE - Chief Culinary Officer
MICHAEL DORF - Founder; CEO
JACK LASCHEVER - Chief Growth Officer
SHLOMO LIPETZ - VP
LAURA ALBERS - VP Marketing
SARAH WEISS - Director Marketing
MIA MARCHESE - Director Customer Service
THOMAS FALLON - Director Customer Service
KAROLINA BARTNIK-BARROS - Director Payroll; Manager Payroll
GRACE BLAKE - Director
MEGAN MOORE - Manager Operations
SCOTT FELDMAN - Manager Marketing
CHRISTIAN COPELAND - Manager Operations

Connollys Pub & Restaurant
121 W 45th St
New York, NY 10036-4004

Telephone: (212) 597-5126
Fax Number: (212) 852-9065
Internet Homepage: connollyspubandrestaurant.com
Company Email: connollys47st@nyct.net
Type of Business: Chain Restaurant Operator
Year Founded: 1992
Total Sales: $9,059,000 (e)
Alcohol Sales: 40%
Number of Employees: 80
Average Check: Lunch(22); Dinner(34)
Internet Order Processing: Yes

Total Units: 3
Trade Names: Connolly Pub & Restaurant (3)
Company-Owned Units: 3
Preferred Location Types: Freestanding
Alcohol Served: Beer, Wine, Liquor
Primary Menu: American (3)
Areas of Operation: NY
Type of Foodservice: Casual Dining (3)
Primary Distributors: (Food) Woolco Foods Inc., JERSEY CITY, NJ

Key Personnel
DANIEL O'CONNOR - General Manager
WINSTON HERNANDEZ - Executive Chef; General Buyer

Coppola's Italian Restaurant
206 W 79th St
New York, NY 10024-6235

Telephone: (212) 877-3840
Fax Number: (212) 874-2583
Internet Homepage: coppolas-nyc.com
Company Email: events@coppolas-nyc.com
Type of Business: Chain Restaurant Operator
Year Founded: 1986
Total Sales: $4,088,000 (e)
Alcohol Sales: 18%
Number of Employees: 35
Average Check: Lunch(18); Dinner(36)
Internet Order Processing: Yes
Total Units: 2
Trade Names: Coppola's Italian Restaurant (2)
Company-Owned Units: 2
Preferred Location Types: Freestanding
Alcohol Served: Beer, Wine, Liquor
Primary Menu: Italian (2)
Areas of Operation: NY
Type of Foodservice: Casual Dining (2)
Catering Services: Yes
Primary Distributors: (Full Line) SYSCO Food Services of Albany, HALFMOON, NY

Key Personnel
SALVATORE COPPOLA - President; General Manager; Executive Chef; General Buyer

Corner Table Restaurants, LLC
270 Lafayette St Suite 1500
New York, NY 10012

Telephone: (212) 966-3250
Internet Homepage: ctrnyc.com
Company Email: info@ctrnyc.com
Type of Business: Chain Restaurant Operator
Year Founded: 2001
Total Units: 7
Trade Names: The Smith Restaurant & Bar (7)
Company-Owned Units: 7
Preferred Location Types: Downtown
Primary Menu: American (7)
Projected Openings: 1
Areas of Operation: DC, IL, NY
Type of Foodservice: Casual Dining (7)

Key Personnel
JEFFREY LEFCOURT - Founder; CEO; Partner
MICHAEL JACOBS - Partner
ADAM BURKE - VP Operations
BRIAN ELLIS - VP Culinary Development; Executive Chef
ERIC SIMKIN - Controller
AMANDO AULELEY - Corporate Chef
LUIS NIETO - Corporate Chef
KEN LARSEN - Corporate Chef
JUAN C. LUCERO - Executive Chef
VINCENT MARTINEZ - Executive Chef
JENNIFER WOODHULL - Director Operations
JOSH BIDWELL - Director Operations
MAY COHEN - Director Event Planning, Catering
DANA BALDING - Manager Design; Brand Manager
JARED BAILEY - Manager Information Technology
KEVIN MURRAY - Manager Payroll
THAISIS CONYERS - Manager Human Resources
KIMARA MCGEE - Manager
JAWAINN BOND - Manager Restaurant Operations
WEIHONG LU - Assistant Manager Construction
CANDICE WEIHONG LU - Assistant Manager Construction
SHENA VAGLIANO - Coordinator Marketing
ANDREA ORAN - Analyst Finance

Cowgirl Inc.
519 Hudson St
New York, NY 10014-2601

Telephone: (212) 633-1133
Internet Homepage: cowgirlseahorse.com; cowgirlnyc.com
Company Email: info@cowgirlnyc.com
Type of Business: Chain Restaurant Operator
Year Founded: 1989
Total Sales: $10,514,000 (e)
Alcohol Sales: 40%
Number of Employees: 130
Average Check: Breakfast(14); Lunch(20); Dinner(26)
Total Units: 2
Trade Names: Cowgirl (1); Seahorse (1)
Company-Owned Units: 2
Preferred Square Footage: 3,000; 5,000
Preferred Location Types: Freestanding
Alcohol Served: Beer, Wine, Liquor
Primary Menu: American (2)
Areas of Operation: NY
Type of Foodservice: Casual Dining (2)
Catering Services: Yes
Primary Distributors: (Equipment) US Foods New York Metro, PERTH AMBOY, NJ; (Supplies) US Foods New York Metro, PERTH AMBOY, NJ

Key Personnel
SHERRY DELAMARTER - President; Controller; Executive Chef; Director Finance, Information Systems, Marketing, Advertising, Real Estate, Design, Research & Development
JOEL GORDIN - Exec VP; General Manager; Director Operations, Purchasing, Risk Management, Quality Assurance, Store Fixtures, Food Safety, Facility/Maintenance-Beverages; General Buyer
MICHELLE WAKEFIELD - Manager Human Resources

Craft Hospitality
43 E 19th St
New York, NY 10003-1304

Telephone: (212) 780-0880
Internet Homepage: craftedhospitality.com; craftrestaurant.com
Company Email: info@craftedhospitality.com
Type of Business: Chain Restaurant Operator
Total Units: 7
Trade Names: Craft (2); Craft Steak (1); Heritage (1); Riverpark (1); Small Batch (1); Temple Court (1)
Company-Owned Units: 7
Primary Menu: American (4); Miscellaneous (1); Steak (2)
Areas of Operation: CA, FL, NV, NY
Type of Foodservice: Fine Dining (7)

Key Personnel
TOM COLICCHIO - Owner; Executive Chef
GREGORY TOMICICH - Director Restaurant Operations
BRYAN HUNT - Director Culinary Operations

Craveable Hospitality Group
170 E 61st St Fl 4
New York, NY 10065-8551

Telephone: (917) 521-5277
Internet Homepage: craveablehospitalitygroup.com
Company Email: info@craveablehg.com
Type of Business: Chain Restaurant Operator
Year Founded: 2003
Total Sales: $20,010,000 (e)
Alcohol Sales: 20%
Internet Order Processing: Yes
Total Units: 9
Trade Names: Angry Taco (1); Babe's Bacon Bar (1); Bacon Bar (1); Canal Street Noodle (1); Caputo Trattoria (1); Clam Shack (1); Jimmy (1); Prime Steakhouse (1); Saltbrick

Burger (1)
Company-Owned Units: 9
Preferred Location Types: Downtown; Fashion/Specialty Center; Hotel/Motel
Alcohol Served: Beer, Wine, Liquor
Primary Menu: American (1); Asian (1); Hamburger (1); Italian (1); Miscellaneous (1); Sandwiches/Deli (1); Snacks (1); Steak (1); Taco (1)
Areas of Operation: CT, IL, NJ, NY
Type of Foodservice: Casual Dining (7); Quick Serve (2)
Catering Services: Yes

Key Personnel
DAVID BURKE - Founder
STEPHEN GOGLIA - CEO; President; General Buyer
PEDRO AVILA - Executive Chef Division
CHRIS SHEA - Executive Chef Division
CHRIS CUBBERLEY - Executive Chef Division
ANGELO SCHIFILLITI - Executive Chef

Denihan Hospitality Group LLC
551 5th Ave Fl 10
New York, NY 10176-0901

Telephone: (212) 465-3700
Fax Number: (212) 465-3511
Internet Homepage: affinia.com; denihan.com; jameshotels.com
Company Email: information@affinia.com
Type of Business: Foodservice Operations - Hotel/Motels
Year Founded: 1963
Total Sales: $86,220,000 (e)
Alcohol Sales: 30%
Number of Employees: 1,000
Total Units: 10
Restaurants in Hotels: 5
Trade Names: Carlton (1); Dumont NYC (1); Fifty NYC (1); Gardens NYC (1); Manhattan NYC (1); Shelburne NYC (1); The Benjamin (1); The James Chicago - Magnificent Mile (1); The James New York - Soho (1); The Surrey (1)
Company-Owned Units: 5
Alcohol Served: Beer, Wine, Liquor
Areas of Operation: NY
Type of Foodservice: Casual Dining (5)
Primary Distributors: (Food) SYSCO Food Services of Albany, HALFMOON, NY
Notes: The company derives approximately 75% of its revenue from hotel operations.

Key Personnel
PATRICK DENIHAN - CEO; Executive Director Food and Beverage
TOM FELDERMAN - CFO
BROOKE D. BARRETT - Exec VP Food and Beverage
ELLEN BROWN - Exec VP Business Development
JOHN CHAN - Senior VP Development
DAVID SANDLER - General Manager
CHRISSY DENIHAN - Director
CASSANDRA SALDUTTI - Manager Brand Marketing

Dig Inn
1235 Broadway
New York, NY 10001

Internet Homepage: diginn.com
Type of Business: Chain Restaurant Operator
Year Founded: 2011
Total Sales: $28,140,000 (e)
Number of Employees: 360
Total Units: 12
Trade Names: Dig Inn Seasonal Market (12)
Company-Owned Units: 12
Primary Menu: American (12)
Areas of Operation: MA, NY, PA
Type of Foodservice: Fast Casual (12)

Key Personnel
MATT WEINGARTEN - Chief Culinary Officer
ADAM ESKIN - Co-Founder; CEO
CHRISTIAN TROESCH - CFO
ALYSON BASSO - Director Talent
MIKE MERLESENA - Manager Commercial Sales, National
CINDY LIN - Manager Operations
MELINA HSIAO - Manager Operations
DANIEL DRENNEN - Principal
MAKINA CELESTINE - Administrator Information Technology, Systems
KRISTEN WILSON - Coordinator Talent

Dig Seasonal Market
1235 Broadway Fl 2
New York, NY 10001-4393

Telephone: (212) 545-7867
Fax Number: (212) 545-7866
Internet Homepage: diginn.com
Company Email: contact@diginn.com
Type of Business: Chain Restaurant Operator
Year Founded: 1997
Total Sales: $6,418,000 (e)
Average Check: Dinner(10)
Total Units: 28
Trade Names: Dig Seasonal Market (28)
Company-Owned Units: 28
Preferred Location Types: Downtown
Primary Menu: Health Foods (28)
Projected Openings: 7
Areas of Operation: MA, NY
Type of Foodservice: Fast Casual (28)
Catering Services: Yes

Key Personnel
ADAM ESKIN - Co-Founder; CEO
TRISTAN SILVERIO - General Manager
MATT WEINGARTEN - Director Culinary Development
SOMIRAN GUPTA - Director Strategy
BRENNA MILLER - Director Marketing, Communications
DUKE PILGREM - Director Operations
XAVIER DONNELLY - Designer

Dill & Parsley Natural Mediterranean
1155 Avenue of the Americas
New York, NY 10036

Telephone: (646) 362-9920
Internet Homepage: dillandparsley.com
Type of Business: Chain Restaurant Operator
Year Founded: 2015
Total Sales: $9,978,000 (e)
Total Units: 5
Trade Names: Dill & Parsley (5)
Company-Owned Units: 5
Primary Menu: Greek/Mediterranean (5)
Type of Foodservice: Fast Casual (5)

Key Personnel
BALAHAN BOBUS - Founder; CEO

Dining Entertainment Group
350 7th Ave Rm 301
New York, NY 10001-1957

Telephone: (212) 244-3503
Fax Number: (212) 629-3617
Internet Homepage: brotherjimmys.com
Company Email: info@diningentertainmentgroup.com
Type of Business: Chain Restaurant Operator
Year Founded: 2000
Total Sales: $11,101,000 (e)
Alcohol Sales: 20%
Number of Employees: 280
Average Check: Lunch(18); Dinner(26)
Internet Order Processing: Yes
Internet Sales: 1.00%
Total Units: 5
Trade Names: Brother Jimmy's Bar-B-Que (5)
Company-Owned Units: 5
Preferred Location Types: Downtown; Freestanding; Office Complex; Other; Stadiums
Alcohol Served: Beer, Wine, Liquor
Primary Menu: Bar-B-Q (5)
Areas of Operation: CT, FL, MD, NJ, NY
Type of Foodservice: Casual Dining (5)
Primary Distributors: (Full Line) SYSCO Food Services of Albany, HALFMOON, NY

Key Personnel
JENNA FRITSCHE - Director Catering

Domino's Franchisee
181 Church St
New York, NY 10007-1829

Telephone: (212) 566-8888
Type of Business: Chain Restaurant Operator
Total Sales: $8,298,000 (e)
Total Units: 4
Trade Names: Domino's (4)
Units Franchised From: 4
Primary Menu: Pizza (4)
Areas of Operation: NY
Type of Foodservice: Quick Serve (4)
Franchise Affiliation: Domino's Pizza Inc, ANN ARBOR, MI

Key Personnel
SHUEB AHMED - Owner; General Buyer

Domino's Franchisee
2554 Adam Clayton Powell Jr Blvd
New York, NY 10039-3536

Telephone: (212) 283-1100
Type of Business: Chain Restaurant Operator
Total Sales: $3,982,000 (e)
Total Units: 2
Trade Names: Domino's (2)
Units Franchised From: 2
Primary Menu: Pizza (2)
Areas of Operation: NY
Type of Foodservice: Quick Serve (2)
Franchise Affiliation: Domino's Pizza Inc, ANN ARBOR, MI

Key Personnel
ANTHONY MAESTRI - Owner; General Buyer

Dos Toros
41 Union Sq W Ste 820
New York, NY 10003-3229

Telephone: (510) 290-5207
Internet Homepage: dostoros.com
Company Email: info@dostoros.com
Type of Business: Chain Restaurant Operator
Year Founded: 2009
Total Sales: $59,940,000 (e)
Total Units: 20
Trade Names: Dos Toros (20)
Company-Owned Units: 20
Primary Menu: Mexican (20)
Projected Openings: 3
Areas of Operation: IL, NY
Type of Foodservice: Fast Casual (20)

Catering Services: Yes

Key Personnel
LEO KREMER - Partner; General Buyer
OLIVER KREMER - Partner
ERICA RETBLATT - VP Human Resources
PATRICK FITZGERALD - VP Area
WES MAPLES - General Manager
GUSTAVO ENRIQUE ARELLANES BRACHO - General Manager
ROSIE MOLINA - General Manager
DAWN MAUBERRET - Director Catering
DWAYNE HOWELL - Area Manager
INOCENTE RAMIREZ - Manager Restaurant Operations
GABRIEL GONZALEZ - Manager

Doughnuttery
425 W 15th St
New York, NY 10011

Telephone: (212) 633-4359
Internet Homepage: doughnuttery.com
Company Email: info@doughnuttery.com
Type of Business: Chain Restaurant Operator
Year Founded: 2012
Total Units: 4
Trade Names: Doughnuttery (4)
Company-Owned Units: 4
Preferred Location Types: Community Mall; Downtown; Hotel/Motel
Primary Menu: Snacks (4)
Areas of Operation: NY, SC
Type of Foodservice: Quick Serve (4)

Key Personnel
EVAN FELDMAN - Founder; CEO
BRIAN BURWELL - Owner

Elephant & Castle Inc.
68 Greenwich Ave
New York, NY 10011-8307

Telephone: (212) 243-1400
Internet Homepage: elephantandcastle.com; keens.com
Type of Business: Chain Restaurant Operator
Year Founded: 1977
Total Sales: $12,985,000 (e)
Alcohol Sales: 25%
Number of Employees: 160
Average Check: Breakfast(14); Lunch(18); Dinner(24)
Total Units: 2
Trade Names: Elephant & Castle Restaurant (1); Keens Steak House (1)
Company-Owned Units: 2
Preferred Square Footage: 5,500; 6,000
Preferred Location Types: Freestanding
Alcohol Served: Beer, Wine, Liquor
Primary Menu: American (1); Steak (1)
Areas of Operation: NY
Foreign Countries: IRELAND
Type of Foodservice: Casual Dining (1); Fine Dining (1)
Primary Distributors: (Food) Dairyland, The Chefs' Warehouse, BRONX, NY
Notes: This company is not affiliated with the Elephant & Castle chain of Boston, MA, and has the rights to the name in NY and CA.

Key Personnel
RICK SALAS - General Manager Information Systems, Human Resources, Store Fixtures

Eli Zabar Inc.
1064 Madison Ave
New York, NY 10028-0242

Telephone: (212) 772-0022
Fax Number: (212) 628-1625
Internet Homepage: elizabar.com
Company Email: info@elizabar.com
Type of Business: Chain Restaurant Operator
Year Founded: 2000
Total Sales: $8,016,000 (e)
Alcohol Sales: 15%
Number of Employees: 50
Average Check: Lunch(14); Dinner(48)
Total Units: 5
Trade Names: E.A.T. (1); Eli's Bread (1); Eli's Manhattan (1); Eli's Table (1); Eli's Vinegar Factory (1)
Company-Owned Units: 5
Preferred Square Footage: 2,500; 5,500; 6,000
Preferred Location Types: Freestanding
Alcohol Served: Beer, Wine
Primary Menu: American (4); Asian (1)
Areas of Operation: NY
Type of Foodservice: Casual Dining (5)
Primary Distributors: (Food) SYSCO Food Services of Albany, HALFMOON, NY

Key Personnel
ELI ZABAR - Owner; Director Finance, Supply Chain, Real Estate, Design; General Buyer
RUBEN FLORES - Manager Operations, Facility/Maintenance
NATALIE STETTNER - Manager Information Systems, Human Resources

Estiatorio Milos
125 W 55th St
New York, NY 10019-5369

Telephone: (212) 245-7400
Fax Number: (212) 245-4828
Internet Homepage: miloscafe.nyc; estiatoriomilos.com
Company Email: newyork@estiatoriomilos.com
Type of Business: Chain Restaurant Operator

Year Founded: 1996
Total Sales: $57,470,000 (e)
Alcohol Sales: 10%
Number of Employees: 135
Total Units: 9
Trade Names: Estiatorio Milos (7); Milos Cafe (1); Milos Motor Yacht (1)
Company-Owned Units: 9
Alcohol Served: Beer, Wine, Liquor
Primary Menu: Greek/Mediterranean (9)
Areas of Operation: FL, NV, NY, FC, QC
Foreign Countries: CANADA; GREECE
Type of Foodservice: Fast Casual (1); Fine Dining (8)

Key Personnel
COSTAS SPILIADIS - President; General Buyer
MARIA ARHONTOULIS - Director Marketing
GIULIA NICOLOTTI - Director Event Planning
DIMITRIS ZAFEIROPOULOS - Director Global
VICKY HOLDMAN - Manager Event Planning
MERCEDES LORA - Manager Logistics

F&J Ventures
320 W 46th St
New York, NY 10036-3845

Telephone: (212) 997-9494
Fax Number: (212) 997-6851
Internet Homepage: frankieandjohnnies.com
Company Email: fj46steaks@gmail.com
Type of Business: Chain Restaurant Operator
Total Sales: $6,122,000 (e)
Alcohol Sales: 5%
Average Check: Dinner(60)
Internet Order Processing: Yes
Total Units: 3
Trade Names: Frankie and Johnnie's Steakhouse (3)
Company-Owned Units: 3
Preferred Location Types: Freestanding
Alcohol Served: Beer, Wine, Liquor
Primary Menu: Steak (3)
Areas of Operation: NY
Type of Foodservice: Casual Dining (3)
Catering Services: Yes

Key Personnel
GUS CHIMOS - Partner; COO; General Manager; General Buyer

Fig & Olive Holding LLC
254 W 31st St 7th Floor
New York, NY 10011

Telephone: (855) 344-6548
Internet Homepage: figandolive.com
Company Email: info@figandolive.com
Type of Business: Chain Restaurant Operator
Year Founded: 2006
Internet Order Processing: Yes
Total Units: 9
Trade Names: FIG & OLIVE (9)
Company-Owned Units: 9
Preferred Location Types: Downtown
Alcohol Served: Wine, Liquor
Primary Menu: Greek/Mediterranean (9)
Areas of Operation: CA, DC, IL, NY
Type of Foodservice: Fine Dining (9)
Catering Services: Yes

Key Personnel
PHILIP J. MARANO - Director Information Technology
JULIEN MALAGUARNERA NOLAN - Director; Client Services
KEN SISTRUNK - Director Beverages

Fireman Hospitality Group
888 7th Ave Ste 203
New York, NY 10106-0298

Telephone: (212) 399-1325
Fax Number: (212) 977-3044
Internet Homepage: thefiremangroup.com
Company Email: info@thefiremangroup.com
Type of Business: Chain Restaurant Operator
Year Founded: 1972
Total Sales: $87,260,000 (e)
Alcohol Sales: 35%
Number of Employees: 1,000
Average Check: Breakfast(10); Lunch(26); Dinner(40)
Total Units: 9
Trade Names: Bond 45 (2); BROOKLYN DELICATESSEN (1); Brooklyn Diner (2); Cafe Fiorello (1); Fiorella Italian Kitchen (1); Redeye Grill (1); Trattoria dell'Arte (1)
Company-Owned Units: 9
Preferred Square Footage: 6,000
Preferred Location Types: Downtown; Freestanding; Office Complex
Alcohol Served: Beer, Wine, Liquor
Primary Menu: American (3); Italian (5); Seafood (1)
Areas of Operation: MD, NY
Type of Foodservice: Casual Dining (8); Fine Dining (2)
Primary Distributors: (Food) Dairyland, The Chefs' Warehouse, BRONX, NY

Key Personnel
SHELDON FIREMAN - President; Partner; Executive Chef; Director Purchasing, Research & Development, Menu Development
JERRY DISTEFANO - Partner; COO
ROCKY LUCIA - Director Information Technology
ANDREA ROMAN - Director Sales
ERIKA FARBER - Manager Sales
KIRA ARCIAGA - Manager Restaurant Operations

Founders Table Restaurant Group
853 Broadway Ste 606
New York, NY 10003-4723

Telephone: (212) 524-4619
Fax Number: (646) 695-0563
Internet Homepage: choptsalad.com
Company Email: cassie@choptsalad.com
Type of Business: Chain Restaurant Operator
Year Founded: 2001
Total Sales: $75,390,000 (e)
Total Units: 80
Trade Names: Chopt Creative Salad Company (59); Dos Toros Taqueria (21)
Company-Owned Units: 80
Primary Menu: Sandwiches/Deli (59); Southwest/Tex-Mex (21)
Projected Openings: 1
Areas of Operation: CT, DC, GA, MD, NC, NJ, NY, TN, VA
Type of Foodservice: Fast Casual (80)

Key Personnel
TONY SHURE - Co-Founder
NICHOLAS MARSH - CEO; General Buyer
CATHERINE LEDERER - VP Food and Beverage
MICHAEL LAPLACA - VP Operations
DENNIS LEE - VP Development
ALI BANKS - VP Culinary Operations
JENNIFER ALBERTS - Senior Director Digital Marketing
AMANDA-LOUISE EHRLICH - Director Design
MEGAN RUSTUM - Director Digital
BRANDI M. FANNELL - Director People
KAWSU SILLAH - Manager Information Technology

Fresco by Scotto
34 E 52nd St
New York, NY 10022-5914

Telephone: (212) 935-3434
Fax Number: (212) 935-3436
Internet Homepage: frescobyscotto.com
Type of Business: Chain Restaurant Operator
Year Founded: 1993
Total Sales: $15,004,000 (e)
Alcohol Sales: 25%
Number of Employees: 85
Average Check: Lunch(42); Dinner(54)
Total Units: 2
Trade Names: Fresco by Scotto (1); Fresco by Scotto on the go (1)
Company-Owned Units: 2
Preferred Location Types: Freestanding
Alcohol Served: Beer, Wine, Liquor
Primary Menu: Italian (2)

Areas of Operation: NY
Type of Foodservice: Casual Dining (1); Fine Dining (1)
Catering Services: Yes
Primary Distributors: (Food) M. Tucker, a divison of Singer NY LLC, PATERSON, NJ

Key Personnel
MARION SCOTTO - President; Partner; General Buyer
ROSANNA SCOTTO - Partner
ANTHONY SCOTTO JR - Partner; General Manager; General Buyer
ELAINA SCOTTO - Partner
JOHN SCOTTO - Partner

Gallagher's Steak House
228 W 52nd St
New York, NY 10019-5802

Telephone: (212) 245-5336
Fax Number: (212) 245-5426
Internet Homepage:
  gallaghersfranchising.com;
  gallaghersnysteakhouse.com;
  thecentralparkboathouse.com
Company Email: info@gallagherssteak.com
Type of Business: Chain Restaurant Operator
Year Founded: 1927
Total Sales: $21,781,000 (e)
Alcohol Sales: 20%
Number of Employees: 100
Average Check: Lunch(36); Dinner(58)
Internet Order Processing: Yes
Internet Sales: 5.00%
Total Units: 4
Trade Names: Gallagher's Steakhouse (3); The Loeb Boathouse Central Park (1)
Company-Owned Units: 3
Units Franchised To: 1
Preferred Square Footage: 5,500; 6,000
Preferred Location Types: Freestanding
Alcohol Served: Beer, Wine, Liquor
Primary Menu: American (1); Steak (3)
Areas of Operation: NJ, NV, NY
Type of Foodservice: Fine Dining (4)
Primary Distributors: (Food) SYSCO Food Services of Albany, HALFMOON, NY

Key Personnel
DEAN POLL - Owner
MICHAEL AMORE - General Manager
BRIAN JONTOW - General Manager; General Buyer

Glazier Works
535 5th Ave Fl 16
New York, NY 10017-3689

Telephone: (212) 406-7900
Fax Number: (212) 406-7890
Internet Homepage: michaeljordansnyc.com; striphouse.com
Type of Business: Chain Restaurant Operator
Year Founded: 1985
Total Sales: $265,680,000 (e)
Alcohol Sales: 30%
Number of Employees: 500
Average Check: Lunch(22); Dinner(44)
Total Units: 12
Trade Names: BRIDGEWATERS (1); GIANNI'S (1); Michael Jordan's The Steak House (1); MONKEY BAR (1); MORGANS BROOKLYN BARBEQUE (1); STICKY FINGERS (1); Strip House (4); TAPIKA (1); TWENTY FOUR FIFTH (1)
Company-Owned Units: 12
Preferred Square Footage: 5,500; 6,000
Preferred Location Types: Freestanding; Hotel/Motel; Other; Strip Mall
Alcohol Served: Beer, Wine, Liquor
Primary Menu: American (11); Steak (1)
Areas of Operation: NV, NY
Type of Foodservice: Fine Dining (12)
Catering Services: Yes
Primary Distributors: (Food) Dairyland, The Chefs' Warehouse, BRONX, NY
Notes: Bridgewaters operates as a private event/catering facility

Key Personnel
PETER H. GLAZIER - CEO; Partner
MATTHEW P. GLAZIER - President; General Counsel; Director Operations
PENNY GLAZIER - Partner; Director Communications
CHRISTY PHILLIPS - CFO
JUAN DELEON - Controller
JONO MORATIS - Director Operations, Purchasing, Information Systems, E-Commerce, Internet Development

Goa Taco
79 Delancey St
New York, NY 10002

Telephone: (347) 276-5103
Internet Homepage: goataco.com
Company Email: les@goataco.com
Type of Business: Chain Restaurant Operator
Year Founded: 2014
Total Units: 4
Trade Names: Goa Taco (4)
Company-Owned Units: 4
Preferred Square Footage: 300
Primary Menu: Taco (4)
Areas of Operation: CA, NY
Type of Foodservice: Fast Casual (4)

Key Personnel
RYAN CHADWICK - Partner; General Buyer

Gotham City Restaurant Group
29 Union Sq W Ste 500
New York, NY 10003-3305

Telephone: (212) 243-7969
Fax Number: (212) 243-4187
Internet Homepage: livebaitnyc.com; thecoffeeshopnyc.com; unionsquareballroom.com
Company Email: info@unionsquareballroom.com
Type of Business: Chain Restaurant Operator
Year Founded: 1987
Total Sales: $15,587,000 (e)
Alcohol Sales: 25%
Number of Employees: 300
Average Check: Breakfast(10); Lunch(14); Dinner(22)
Total Units: 2
Trade Names: The Coffee Shop (1); Union Square (1)
Company-Owned Units: 2
Preferred Square Footage: 2,500; 5,000
Preferred Location Types: Downtown; Mixed-use Center
Alcohol Served: Beer, Wine, Liquor
Primary Menu: American (2)
Areas of Operation: NY
Type of Foodservice: Casual Dining (2)
Catering Services: Yes
Primary Distributors: (Full Line) Dairyland, The Chefs' Warehouse, BRONX, NY

Key Personnel
CAROLYN BENITEZ - Partner
ERIC PETTERSON - Partner; Director Catering
SERENA JONES - General Manager
RAYMOND MOHAN - Executive Chef
JOEL OBERLANDER - Executive Chef
RAMON GOMEZ - Manager Purchasing

Grand Central Restaurant Group
3 E 40th St
New York, NY 10016-0101

Telephone: (212) 481-7887
Fax Number: (212) 481-4510
Internet Homepage:
  grandcentralrestaurantgroup.com;
  houseoflasagnanyc.com; lastanzanyc.com
Company Email:
  jack@grandcentralrestaurantgroup.com
Type of Business: Chain Restaurant Operator
Year Founded: 1980
Total Sales: $5,760,000 (e)
Alcohol Sales: 25%
Number of Employees: 65
Average Check: Breakfast(22); Lunch(42); Dinner(54)

Internet Order Processing: Yes
Total Units: 2
Trade Names: House of Lasagna (1); La Stanza (1)
Company-Owned Units: 2
Preferred Location Types: Freestanding
Alcohol Served: Beer, Wine, Liquor
Primary Menu: Italian (2)
Areas of Operation: NY
Type of Foodservice: Casual Dining (2)
Catering Services: Yes
Primary Distributors: (Food) US Foods, BUFFALO, NY

Key Personnel
JACK O'BRIEN - President; Partner; General Manager; Executive Chef; General Buyer

Hale and Hearty Soups Inc.
75 9th Ave Frnt 9
New York, NY 10011

Telephone: (212) 255-2400
Fax Number: (212) 929-9588
Internet Homepage: haleandhearty.com
Type of Business: Chain Restaurant Operator
Year Founded: 1995
Total Sales: $13,090,000 (e)
Number of Employees: 931
Internet Order Processing: Yes
Total Units: 22
Trade Names: Hale and Hearty Soups (22)
Company-Owned Units: 22
Preferred Location Types: Downtown
Primary Menu: American (22)
Projected Openings: 3
Areas of Operation: MA, NY
Type of Foodservice: Fast Casual (22)
Catering Services: Yes

Key Personnel
MARIAMA MASSALY - District Manager
ALBERT J. CALCATERRA - Manager Purchasing

Heartland Brewery Inc.
1430 Broadway Rm 1513
New York, NY 10018-3367

Telephone: (212) 400-2300
Internet Homepage: heartlandbrewery.com
Company Email: info@heartlandbrewery.com
Type of Business: Chain Restaurant Operator
Year Founded: 1995
Total Sales: $7,694,000 (e)
Alcohol Sales: 10%
Number of Employees: 43
Average Check: Dinner(24)
Total Units: 3
Trade Names: HB Burger (1); Heartland Brewery (1); Heartland Brewery Chophouse (1)
Company-Owned Units: 3
Preferred Location Types: Downtown; Freestanding; Strip Mall
Alcohol Served: Beer, Wine, Liquor
Primary Menu: American (2); Hamburger (1)
Areas of Operation: NY
Type of Foodservice: Casual Dining (3)
Catering Services: Yes

Key Personnel
JON BLOOSTEIN - President; Executive Chef; General Buyer
IVAN CORDERO - Senior Manager Operations

HPH
93 Pearl St
New York, NY 10004-2713

Telephone: (212) 344-0500
Internet Homepage: hphnyc.com
Company Email: info@hphnyc.com
Type of Business: Chain Restaurant Operator
Total Sales: $18,110,000 (e)
Total Units: 19
Trade Names: Adrienne's (1); Bathtub Gin (1); Beaubourg (1); Financier (1); Harry's (1); Harry's Italian (2); L'Appart (1); Le District (1); Pennsy (1); Pier A (1); Stone Street Coffee Company (1); The 18th Room (1); The Dead Rabbit (1); Two Forks (1); Ulysses' Folk House (1); Underdog (1); Vintry Wine & Whiskey (1);Wintry Fine Wines (1)
Company-Owned Units: 21
Primary Menu: American (5); French/Continental (3); Italian (3); Pizza (2); Steak (1)
Projected Openings: 1
Areas of Operation: NY
Type of Foodservice: Casual Dining (11); Fine Dining (1)

Key Personnel
PETER POULAKAKOS - Partner; General Buyer
PAUL LAMAS - Partner
DORIS JIMENEZ - Manager Public Relations

Il Postino
337 E 49th St Frnt A
New York, NY 10017-7326

Telephone: (212) 688-0033
Fax Number: (212) 644-8937
Internet Homepage: ilpostinony.com
Company Email: info@ilpostinony.com
Type of Business: Chain Restaurant Operator
Year Founded: 1996
Total Sales: $6,209,000 (e)
Alcohol Sales: 20%
Number of Employees: 70
Average Check: Lunch(36); Dinner(78)
Total Units: 2
Trade Names: Il Postino (1); Scalinatella (1)
Company-Owned Units: 2
Preferred Location Types: Downtown; Mixed-use Center; Office Complex
Alcohol Served: Beer, Wine, Liquor
Primary Menu: Italian (2)
Areas of Operation: NY
Type of Foodservice: Fine Dining (2)

Key Personnel
ALFIO RUOCCO - Partner
LUIGI RUSSO - Partner; Executive Chef; General Buyer

Jean-Georges Enterprises LLC
111 Prince St Fl 2
New York, NY 10012-3102

Telephone: (212) 358-0688
Fax Number: (212) 358-0685
Internet Homepage: jean-georges.com
Company Email: comments@jean-georges.com
Type of Business: Chain Restaurant Operator
Year Founded: 1991
Total Sales: $66,950,000 (e)
Alcohol Sales: 25%
Number of Employees: 1,466
Average Check: Breakfast(24); Lunch(24); Dinner(24)
Total Units: 25
Trade Names: ABC Cocina (1); ABC Kitchen (1); ABCV (1); Jean - George at Topping Rose House (1); Jean - George Beverly Hills (1); Jean George Steak House (1); Jean-Georges (1); JoJo (1); Le Dock (1); Louis (1); Market at Edition (1); Matador Room (1); Nougatine (1); On the Rocks (1); Perry Street (1); PrimeSteakhouse (1); Public Litchen (1); Seared (1); Simply Chicken (1); Terrace at Jean George (1); The Inn at Pound Ridge (1); The Mark (1); The Mercer Kitchen(1); The Rooftop by JG (1); Tropicale (1)
Company-Owned Units: 25
Preferred Square Footage: 5,500; 6,000
Preferred Location Types: Freestanding; Office Complex
Alcohol Served: Beer, Wine, Liquor
Primary Menu: American (8); Asian (1); Caribbean (1); Chicken (1); Chinese (1); French/Continental (5); Italian (1); Japanese (1); Miscellaneous (3); Steak (3); Thai (1)
Areas of Operation: FL, NV, NY, FC
Foreign Countries: BAHAMAS; CHINA; FRANCE; HONG KONG; JAPAN; MEXICO; UNITED ARAB EMIRATES
Type of Foodservice: Casual Dining (14); Family Restaurant (1); Fine Dining (11)
Primary Distributors: (Food) Riviera Produce

Inc., ENGLEWOOD, NJ

Key Personnel
LOIS FREEDMAN - President; Partner; Director Operations
PHIL SUAREZ - Partner; Manager Finance, Menu Development
JEAN-GEORGES VONGERICHTEN - Partner; General Buyer
DOMINIC PASCARELLA - Controller
GREGORY BRAININ - Director Culinary Development
OZGE GUVEN - Director Restaurant Operations

Joe & The Juice
1350 Avenue of the Americas
New York, NY 10019

Telephone: (718) 427-6608
Internet Homepage: joejuice.com
Company Email: info@joejuice.com
Type of Business: Chain Restaurant Operator
Year Founded: 2002
Total Sales: $88,420,000 (e)
Number of Employees: 800
Total Units: 60
Trade Names: Joe & The Juice (60)
Company-Owned Units: 60
Primary Menu: Snacks (60)
Projected Openings: 3
Areas of Operation: CA, DC, FL, IL, MD, MN, NY, WA
Type of Foodservice: Quick Serve (60)
Notes: Profile is for US locations only.

Key Personnel
KASPAR BASSE - Founder
VALDEMAR HALBYE - Director Retail Operations
VAINIUS JASEVICIUS - Director Supply Chain
SAMMY EINSTEIN - Director Human Resources
ANDREAS PETER DIPO-ZIMMERMANN - Regional Director
ALAN GURUNG - Regional Manager
ANDREAS S. KNUDSEN - Regional Manager
VALERIE SIMMONDS - Regional Manager
CRISTI COSMA - Regional Manager
FRANK LINDGREN - Area Manager
CHRISTIAN BJORN - Manager Purchasing
GEORGIOS MOYZAKIS - Manager Employee Development-Training
BRENT GOMISH - Manager Supply Chain
MUHAMMAD HAQ - Product Manager
CESAR VELASQUEZ - Project Manager Construction

Juice Press
1 W 22nd St
New York, NY 10010

Telephone: (212) 777-0034
Internet Homepage: juicepress.com
Company Email: customerservice@juicepress.com
Type of Business: Chain Restaurant Operator
Year Founded: 2010
Internet Order Processing: Yes
Total Units: 85
Trade Names: Juice Press (85)
Company-Owned Units: 85
Primary Menu: Health Foods (85)
Areas of Operation: CT, DC, MA, NJ, NV, NY, WA
Type of Foodservice: Quick Serve (85)

Key Personnel
MICHAEL KARSCH - Chairman; Co-Founder
PETER KAY - COO
DANIEL CEBALLOS - Chief Innovation Officer
SOPHIE BIKOFSKY - Director Business Development
SARAH BIKOFSKY - Senior Manager Marketing

Just Salad LLC
663 Lexington Ave Frnt 1
New York, NY 10022-3636

Telephone: (212) 244-1111
Internet Homepage: justsalad.com
Company Email: comments@justsalad.com
Type of Business: Chain Restaurant Operator
Year Founded: 2006
Total Sales: $49,280,000 (e)
Average Check: Breakfast(14); Lunch(14);
Total Units: 34
Trade Names: Just Salad (34)
Company-Owned Units: 34
Preferred Square Footage: 1,600
Preferred Location Types: Community Mall; Fashion/Specialty Center
Primary Menu: Health Foods (34)
Areas of Operation: IL, NY, PA, FC
Foreign Countries: HONG KONG; UNITED ARAB EMIRATES
Type of Foodservice: Quick Serve (34)

Key Personnel
NICK KENNER - Founder; CEO; Partner
ROB CRESPI - Partner
JARED GARBER - CFO
APOLINAR CHAVEZ - COO
MADELINE PENA - General Manager
BOBBIE PALCHEVA - Area Manager
KELVIND PEREZ - Manager Catering
JULIA JENKINS - Brand Manager
MELISSA BURGOS - Senior Designer

Kung Fu Tea Franchising LLC
589 8th Ave
New York, NY 10018

Telephone: (855) 538-9888
Fax Number: (718) 728-8866
Internet Homepage: kfteausa.com
Company Email: info@kfteausa.com
Type of Business: Chain Restaurant Operator
Total Sales: $4,886,000 (e)
Total Units: 184
Trade Names: Kung Fu Tea (184)
Company-Owned Units: 15
Units Franchised To: 169
Primary Menu: Coffee (184)
Areas of Operation: CA, FL, GA, IL, IN, MA, MD, MN, NJ, NV, NY, OH, OK, PA, RI, TX, VA, WA, WI
Foreign Countries: AUSTRALIA
Type of Foodservice: Quick Serve (184)

Key Personnel
HUNG-JEN WANG - CFO
JUI CHIU - Chief Marketing Officer
DAVID CHIANG - Director Operations
WEN-CHI LEE - Manager Quality Assurance, Research & Development, Product Development
MICHAEL PAN - Manager Sales

Le Pain Quotidien
50 Broad St Fl 12
New York, NY 10004-2790

Telephone: (212) 359-9000
Fax Number: (212) 359-9029
Internet Homepage: lepainquotidien.com
Company Email: questions@lepainquotidien.com
Listing Type: Subsidiary
Type of Business: Chain Restaurant Operator
Year Founded: 1990
Total Sales: $246,700,000 (e)
Alcohol Sales: 2%
Number of Employees: 1,500
Average Check: Breakfast(10); Lunch(12); Dinner(18)
Total Units: 44
Trade Names: Le Pain Quotidien (44)
Company-Owned Units: 44
Preferred Square Footage: 5,500; 6,000
Preferred Location Types: Freestanding
Alcohol Served: Beer, Wine
Primary Menu: Sandwiches/Deli (44)
Areas of Operation: CA, CT, DC, IL, MD, NY, PA, VA
Type of Foodservice: Fast Casual (44)
Catering Services: Yes
Primary Distributors: (Food) Baldor Specialty Foods Inc., BRONX, NY

Parent Company: Aurify Brands LLC, NEW YORK, NY
Notes: Store count represents US locations only.

Key Personnel
ALAIN COUMONT - Founder; Chief Creative Officer
STEPHEN SMITTLE - Senior VP Operations
PHILIPPE GATTO - Executive Director Production
OUMOU K. DIAGNE - General Manager
ANDREW ALI - General Manager Training
RAUL MIRA - General Manager
KAELYN TOMASZEWSKI - Director Procurement, Supply Chain
CRUICKSHANK TYRELL - Manager District
OLIVER OLIVER - Manager Restaurant Operations
RACHID AZALA - Manager Distribution
TINA B - Manager District
NASSER JABER - Manager Business Development
RANICH MAHAMUD - Manager Customer Service
CHRIS MARS - Manager Loss Prevention

Livanos Restaurant Group
120 W 49th St
New York, NY 10020

Telephone: (212) 759-5941
Fax Number: (212) 688-7494
Internet Homepage: citylimitsdiner.com; livanosrestaurantgroup.com; modernebarn.com; molyvos.com; oceanarestaurant.com
Company Email: eat@oceanarestaurant.com
Type of Business: Chain Restaurant Operator
Year Founded: 1992
Total Sales: $19,130,000 (e)
Alcohol Sales: 2%
Number of Employees: 360
Average Check: Lunch(36); Dinner(78)
Internet Order Processing: Yes
Internet Sales: 1.00%
Total Units: 6
Trade Names: City Limits Diner (1); Moderne Barn (1); Molyvos (1); Oceana Poke (1); Oceana Restaurant (1); Ousia (1)
Company-Owned Units: 6
Preferred Square Footage: 5,500; 6,000
Preferred Location Types: Downtown; Freestanding; Lifestyle Center; Office Complex
Alcohol Served: Beer, Wine, Liquor
Primary Menu: American (2); Greek/Mediterranean (3); Seafood (1)
Areas of Operation: NY
Type of Foodservice: Casual Dining (4); Fine Dining (2)
Primary Distributors: (Full Line) Dairyland, The Chefs' Warehouse, BRONX, NY

Key Personnel
NICK LIVANOS - President; Partner; Director Finance, Facility/Maintenance, Real Estate, Design, Store Fixtures; General Buyer
PAUL MCLAUGHLIN - Partner; General Manager; Director Menu Development
BILL LIVANOS - Partner
JOHN LIVANOS - Partner
LORENA LIVANOS - Partner
PAVLA KOVAROVA - General Manager
DARLENE GUAJARDO - General Manager
PETER ASSUE - Corporate Chef
BILL TELEPAN - Executive Chef; General Buyer
SENTA CONNELLY - Manager Catering
GEORGE KAVALIS - Manager Restaurant Operations
MARGARET MOSCATO - Manager Central Division
MARY PAULA - Manager Human Resources

Loews Hotel Holding Corporation
667 Madison Ave
New York, NY 10065-8029

Telephone: (212) 521-2000
Fax Number: (212) 521-2379
Internet Homepage: loewshotels.com
Type of Business: Foodservice Operations - Hotel/Motels
Year Founded: 1960
Publicly Held: Yes
Total Sales: $450,900,000 (e)
Alcohol Sales: 30%
Number of Employees: 9,947
Total Units: 27
Restaurants in Hotels: 49
Trade Names: Bisha Hotel Toronto (1); Hard Rock Hotel (1); Live! (2); Loews Hotel (19); Universal (4)
Company-Owned Units: 29
Alcohol Served: Beer, Wine, Liquor
Areas of Operation: AZ, CA, CO, DC, FL, GA, LA, MD, NV, NY, PA, TN, QC
Foreign Countries: CANADA
Type of Foodservice: Casual Dining (44); Fine Dining (1); Quick Serve (4)
Franchise Affiliation: Ruth's Hospitality Group Inc., WINTER PARK, FL; Starbucks Corporation, SEATTLE, WA
Primary Distributors: (Food) SYSCO Food Services of Syracuse, WARNERS, NY
Parent Company: Loews Corporation, NEW YORK, NY
Notes: The company derives approximately 80% of its revenue from hotel operations.

Key Personnel
JONATHAN M. TISCH - Chairman; President
ANDREW H. TISCH - Chairman; President
PAUL WHETSELL - Vice Chairman
JAMES S. TISCH - CEO; President
VINCE DUNLEAVY - CFO
DAVID B. EDELSON - CFO; Senior VP
MARK S. SCHWARTZ - Chief Accounting Officer; VP
JOHN COTTRILL - COO
RICHARD W. SCOTT - CIO Canada; Senior VP Canada
RICHARD SENECHAL - Exec VP Facility/Maintenance
MONICA XUEREB - Exec VP Finance
ANTHONY DEL GAUDIO - Senior VP Sales
DAVID WIENER - Senior VP Sales
MICHAEL PALMERI - Senior VP Real Estate
HERBERT E. HOFMANN - Senior VP Information Technology
MARC A. ALPERT - Senior VP; General Counsel
MARY SKAFIDAS - VP Public Relations, Investor Relations
SARAH MUROV - VP Public Relations
DAVID WEIDLICH - VP Operations, East Region
SUSAN BECKER - VP Tax
JOHNATHAN KOPLOVITZ - VP Corporate Development
AUDREY A. RAMPINELLI - VP Risk Management
LAURA K. CUSHING - VP Human Resources
ALISHA WAID - Executive Director Sales, East Region
PATTY METCALF-SOBCZAK - Executive Director Sales, Southeast Region
MARY REID - Executive Director Sales, Midwest Region
JIM CAUL - Director Marketing, Sales
DAVE MERKLINGER - Director
HALEY INGRAHAM - Director Gaming/Entertainment
ANTONELLA MIGLIONICO - Manager Finance

Luke's Lobster
93 E 7th St Frnt A
New York, NY 10009-5730

Telephone: (860) 391-4123
Internet Homepage: lukeslobster.com
Company Email: lukeslobster@gmail.com
Type of Business: Chain Restaurant Operator
Year Founded: 2009
Total Sales: $47,440,000 (c)
Total Units: 40
Trade Names: Luke's Lobster (40)
Company-Owned Units: 40
Preferred Location Types: Freestanding
Alcohol Served: Beer
Primary Menu: Seafood (40)
Projected Openings: 10
Areas of Operation: DC, IL, MA, ME, NJ, NV, NY, PA
Foreign Countries: JAPAN; TAIWAN
Type of Foodservice: Fast Casual (40)
Catering Services: Yes
Primary Distributors: (Food) Cape Seafood LLC, SACO, ME

Notes: Company operates its own processing plant, Cape Seafood in Saco, Me.

Key Personnel
LUKE HOLDEN - Founder; CEO; Partner
BEN CONNIFF - Co-Founder; Chief Marketing Officer
JEFF HOLDEN - Partner
STEVEN SONG - CFO
VIRGINIA RECTOR - COO
BRYAN HOLDEN - Chief Development Officer
HALEIGH PETROE - VP; Director Human Resources
EMILY FELDMAN - VP Operations
MEAGHAN DILLON - VP Marketing
SKYLER SKYLER - General Manager
JODIE ZHAO - General Manager
KEVIN MICHAEL CASEY - General Manager
LAUREN GIBSON - Director Culinary Development
GARRET CURRIER - Director Development
MICHAEL HOLDEN - Director Store Planning
MICHAEL RATULOWSKI - Coordinator Catering

Lusardi's
1494 2nd Ave Apt 3B
New York, NY 10075-1308

Telephone: (212) 249-2020
Fax Number: (212) 585-2941
Internet Homepage: uvanyc.com; duenyc.com; lukesbarandgrill.com; lusardis.com
Type of Business: Chain Restaurant Operator
Year Founded: 1982
Total Sales: $6,211,000 (e)
Alcohol Sales: 40%
Number of Employees: 75
Average Check: Lunch(36); Dinner(42)
Total Units: 4
Trade Names: Due (1); Lukes Bar & Grill (1); Lusardi's (1); Uva (1)
Company-Owned Units: 4
Preferred Location Types: Office Complex
Alcohol Served: Beer, Wine, Liquor
Primary Menu: American (1); Italian (3)
Areas of Operation: NY
Type of Foodservice: Casual Dining (4)
Primary Distributors: (Food) SYSCO Food Services of Albany, HALFMOON, NY

Key Personnel
MAURO LUSARDI - President; Partner
LUIGI LUSARDI - Partner; General Manager; Executive Chef; General Buyer
IMER DJAKAJ - Partner
CLAUDO MENEGHINI - Executive Chef; General Buyer

Maison Kayser
1535 3rd Ave
New York, NY 10028-2111

Telephone: (212) 348-8400
Internet Homepage: maison-kayser-usa.com
Company Email: info@maisonkayserusa.com
Type of Business: Chain Restaurant Operator
Year Founded: 1996
Total Sales: $18,420,000 (e)
Total Units: 20
Trade Names: Maison Kayser (20)
Company-Owned Units: 20
Primary Menu: American (20)
Areas of Operation: NY
Type of Foodservice: Family Restaurant (20)

Key Personnel
ERIC KAYSER - President; Executive Chef
CARL LUKACH - CFO
HUGO MESSERSCHMITT - General Manager
MANUEL PENA - General Manager
EVAN JAY - General Manager
YANN LEDOUX - Executive Chef
ALEXIS JEBEJIAN - Director Catering
RON NG - Manager Accounting
CHEIKH DIOUM - Manager Facility/Maintenance
LETICIA BAEZ - Manager Talent Acquisitions
STEEVE KNOLL - Manager Bakery
TIM PINKOWSKI - Manager Bakery
JOHAN DURAN - Manager Operations

Major Food Group
248 Mulberry St
New York, NY 10012-4164

Telephone: (212) 993-7189
Internet Homepage: majorfood.com
Company Email: events@majorfood.com
Type of Business: Chain Restaurant Operator
Year Founded: 2010
Total Sales: $13,400,000 (e)
Total Units: 15
Trade Names: Carbone (1); Dirty French (1); Don Camillo (1); Golda's (1); Parm (4); Sadelle's (1); Santina (1); The Grill (1); The Lobster Club (1); The Polynesian (1); The Pool (1); ZZ's Clam Bar (1)
Company-Owned Units: 15
Preferred Location Types: Downtown; Stadiums
Primary Menu: American (2); French/Continental (1); Italian (7); Japanese (1); Sandwiches/Deli (1); Seafood (2); Snacks (1)
Areas of Operation: NY
Type of Foodservice: Casual Dining (9); Fast Casual (1); Fine Dining (5)

Key Personnel
JULIA PEI - President Business Development
JEFF ZALAZNICK - Partner
RICH TORRISI - Partner
MARIO CARBONE - Partner; Executive Chef
CLIFF FEIBUS - CFO
LONN COWARD - General Manager
KYRA SUKI BURNER - Director Customer Service
CASEY WOLEN - Director Operations, Marketing
CARLEEN KRIEB - Senior Manager Event Planning
JENNIFER AKIYOSHI - Manager Operations
WILLIAM TISCH - Manager Special Projects
CARLI ABRAHAM - Manager Event Planning
JESSICA WALTON - Manager Event Planning, Sales

Mamoun's Falafel
119 MacDougal St
New York, NY 10012-1202

Telephone: (646) 870-5785
Internet Homepage: mamouns.com; mamounsfranchise.com
Company Email: info@mamouns.com
Type of Business: Chain Restaurant Operator
Year Founded: 1971
Total Sales: $8,174,000 (e)
Average Check: Lunch(14); Dinner(14)
Total Units: 9
Trade Names: Mamoun's Falafel (9)
Company-Owned Units: 9
Primary Menu: Middle Eastern (9)
Projected Openings: 19
Areas of Operation: CT, NJ, NY, TX
Type of Foodservice: Fast Casual (9)
Catering Services: Yes

Key Personnel
HUSSAM CHATER - CEO; Partner; General Buyer
MAMOUN CHATER JR - Partner
HEATHER KOLESER - Director Franchise Operations

Maoz Vegetarian U.S.A. Inc.
213 W 40th St Fl 3
New York, NY 10018-1627

Telephone: (646) 722-8191
Fax Number: (646) 722-8192
Internet Homepage: maozusa.com
Company Email: info@maozusa.com
Type of Business: Chain Restaurant Operator
Year Founded: 2002
Systemwide Sales: $14,860,000 (e)
Total Sales: $748,000 (e)
Average Check: Breakfast(12); Lunch(12); Dinner(12)

Total Units: 12
Trade Names: maoz vegetarian (12)
Company-Owned Units: 4
Units Franchised To: 8
Preferred Square Footage: 600; 1,500
Primary Menu: Miscellaneous (12)
Areas of Operation: FL, NY, PA
Foreign Countries: BRAZIL; FRANCE; SPAIN; THE NETHERLANDS
Type of Foodservice: Quick Serve (12)
Parent Company: Maoz Franchise B.V., AMSTERDAM, NLD
Notes: The company also operates in The Netherlands, Spain, France, and England; these locations are not included in total store count or total sales.

Key Personnel
BOAZ SCHWEITZER - Chairman; CEO; President; General Buyer
AVIV SCHWEITZER - General Manager

McDonalds Franchise
208 Dyckman St
New York, NY 10040-1004

Telephone: (212) 569-2909
Fax Number: (212) 942-2932
Type of Business: Chain Restaurant Operator
Total Sales: $19,961,000 (e)
Total Units: 4
Trade Names: McDonald's (4)
Units Franchised From: 4
Preferred Location Types: Freestanding
Primary Menu: Hamburger (4)
Areas of Operation: NY
Type of Foodservice: Quick Serve (4)
Franchise Affiliation: McDonald's Corporation, CHICAGO, IL

Key Personnel
SAM DELUCA - Owner; General Buyer

Meatball Management LLC
108 E 16th St Ste 6B
New York, NY 10003-2111

Telephone: (718) 551-0525
Internet Homepage: themeatballshop.com
Company Email: info@themeatballshop.com
Type of Business: Chain Restaurant Operator
Year Founded: 2010
Total Sales: $10,270,000 (e)
Alcohol Sales: 25%
Average Check: Lunch(22); Dinner(26)
Internet Order Processing: Yes
Total Units: 6
Trade Names: The Meatball Shop (6)
Company-Owned Units: 6
Alcohol Served: Beer, Wine, Liquor
Primary Menu: American (6)
Projected Openings: 2
Areas of Operation: NY
Type of Foodservice: Casual Dining (6)

Key Personnel
DANIEL HOLZMAN - Partner; General Manager
MICHAEL CHERNOW - Partner
DANIEL SHARP - Corporate Chef

Merchants Hospitality
111 Broadway Rm 1202
New York, NY 10006-1916

Telephone: (212) 871-4000
Fax Number: (212) 716-1143
Internet Homepage: merchantshospitality.com; merchantsny.com; nyccigarbar.com; poundandpence.com; southwestny.com
Company Email: info@merchantshospitality.com
Type of Business: Chain Restaurant Operator
Year Founded: 1989
Total Sales: $38,750,000 (e)
Alcohol Sales: 35%
Number of Employees: 487
Average Check: Lunch(24); Dinner(42)
Total Units: 13
Trade Names: Art Bar (1); Industry Kitchen (1); Merchants NY (1); Merchants Riverhouse (1); Ophelia Lounge NYC (1); Philippe Chow (1); Pound & Pence (1); SouthWest NY (1); Sugar East (1); The Black Hound (1); Treadwell Park (2); WaterMark Bar (1)
Company-Owned Units: 13
Preferred Square Footage: 5,500; 6,000
Preferred Location Types: Downtown; Freestanding; Office Complex
Alcohol Served: Beer, Wine, Liquor
Primary Menu: American (6); Asian (1); Miscellaneous (4); Pizza (1); Southern (1)
Areas of Operation: NY
Type of Foodservice: Casual Dining (10); Fine Dining (3)
Primary Distributors: (Food) SYSCO Food Services of Metro New York, JERSEY CITY, NJ

Key Personnel
ABRAHAM MERCHANT - CEO; President; COO; Director Facility/Maintenance, Real Estate, Menu Development
RICHARD COHN - Chief Administrative Officer; Exec VP Purchasing; Director Finance, Operations, Information Systems, Supply Chain
DANIEL HANNAGAN - VP Operations
KEN ANDREWS - VP Human Resources
BRAULIO BUNAY - Executive Chef
PHILLIPPE CHOW - Executive Chef
ANTELMO AMBROSIO - Executive Chef
GREG CLICK - Director Information Technology
FERNANDO RODRIGUEZ - Director Operations
JEREMY STRAWN - Director

Mexicue
225 5th Ave
New York, NY 10010-1102

Telephone: (646) 922-7289
Internet Homepage: mexicue.com
Company Email: info@mexicueny.com
Type of Business: Chain Restaurant Operator
Total Sales: $20,450,000 (e)
Internet Order Processing: Yes
Total Units: 5
Trade Names: Mexicue (5)
Company-Owned Units: 5
Primary Menu: Mexican (5)
Areas of Operation: NY
Type of Foodservice: Casual Dining (5)

Key Personnel
DAVE SCHILLACE - Co-Founder
DAVID SCHILLACE - CEO; Partner
THOMAS KELLY - Partner; Executive Chef Culinary Development; Director Culinary Development
EMILY BAUMANN - General Manager

Mighty Quinn's Barbecue
103 E 6th St
New York, NY 10003-8336

Telephone: (212) 677-3733
Internet Homepage: mightyquinnsbbq.com
Company Email: info@mightyquinnsbbq.com
Type of Business: Chain Restaurant Operator
Total Units: 15
Trade Names: Mighty Quinn's Barbeque (15)
Company-Owned Units: 8
Units Franchised To: 4
Areas of Operation: NJ, NY
Foreign Countries: TAIWAN; THE PHILIPPINES; UNITED ARAB EMIRATES

Key Personnel
MICHA MAGID - Co-Founder; Partner
CHRISTOS GOURMOS - Co-Founder; Partner
HUGH MANGUM - Co-Founder; Partner; Executive Chef

Mimi Cheng's
179 2nd Ave
New York, NY 10003-5752

Telephone: (212) 533-2007
Internet Homepage: mimichengs.com
Company Email: info@mimichengs.com
Type of Business: Chain Restaurant Operator
Internet Order Processing: Yes
Total Units: 2

Trade Names: Mimi Cheng's (2)
Company-Owned Units: 2
Areas of Operation: NY

Key Personnel
HANNAH CHENG - Partner; Executive Chef; General Buyer

Momofuku Restaurants
171 1st Ave
New York, NY 10003-2949

Telephone: (212) 777-7773
Fax Number: (212) 228-7493
Internet Homepage: momofuku.com
Type of Business: Chain Restaurant Operator
Total Sales: $10,960,000 (e)
Alcohol Sales: 30%
Number of Employees: 75
Average Check: Lunch(32); Dinner(32)
Internet Order Processing: Yes
Total Units: 11
Trade Names: Bang Bar (1); Fuku (1); Kawi (1); Kojin (1); Majordomo (1); Momofuku Ko (1); Momofuku Noodle Bar (2); Momofuku Ssam Bar (1); Peach Mart(1); Seiobo (1)
Company-Owned Units: 11
Alcohol Served: Beer, Wine, Liquor
Primary Menu: Japanese (11)
Areas of Operation: DC, NY, FC, ON
Foreign Countries: AUSTRALIA; CANADA
Type of Foodservice: Casual Dining (10); Quick Serve (1)
Primary Distributors: (Full Line) SYSCO Food Services of Albany, HALFMOON, NY

Key Personnel
MARGUERITE ZABAR MARISCAL - CEO
DAVID CHANG - Owner; Executive Chef; General Buyer
RYAN HEALEY - VP Marketing

Muginoho USA Inc.
2167 Broadway
New York, NY 10024-6603

Internet Homepage: beardpapas.com
Company Email: info@muginohointl.com
Type of Business: Chain Restaurant Operator
Systemwide Sales: $7,512,000 (e)
Total Sales: $4,787,000 (e)
Average Check: Dinner(12)
Total Units: 32
Trade Names: Beard Papa's Sweets Cafe (32)
Company-Owned Units: 5
Units Franchised To: 27
Preferred Location Types: Freestanding; Kiosk; Outlet Mall
Primary Menu: Snacks (32)
Areas of Operation: CA, DC, GU, HI, KS, MA, NY, OR, VA, WA, FC, BC, ON
Foreign Countries: CANADA
Type of Foodservice: Quick Serve (32)
Parent Company: Muginoho Co. Ltd., OSAKA-SHI, JAPAN
Notes: There are more than 300 Beard Papa's Sweets Cafes outside the U.S.

Key Personnel
AKIRA OKURA - Senior Manager Training, West Region
MASASHI WADA - Manager Operations, Marketing

Myriad Restaurant Group
249 W Broadway Ste 2E
New York, NY 10013-2463

Telephone: (212) 219-9500
Fax Number: (212) 219-2380
Internet Homepage: myriadrestaurantgroup.com
Company Email: info@myriadrestaurantgroup.com
Type of Business: Chain Restaurant Operator
Year Founded: 1993
Total Sales: $44,320,000 (e)
Alcohol Sales: 30%
Number of Employees: 550
Average Check: Breakfast(38); Lunch(46); Dinner(64)
Internet Order Processing: Yes
Internet Sales: 3.00%
Total Units: 8
Trade Names: Batard (1); Crush Wine Co. (1); Daily Burger (1); Nobu (1); Nobu 57 (1); Nobu London (1); Porsche Grille (1); Tribeca Grill (1)
Company-Owned Units: 8
Preferred Square Footage: 2,500; 4,000
Preferred Location Types: Downtown; Hotel/Motel; Office Complex; Stadiums
Alcohol Served: Beer, Wine, Liquor
Primary Menu: American (2); French/Continental (1); Greek/Mediterranean (1); Hamburger (1); Japanese (1); Middle Eastern (1); Miscellaneous (1)
Areas of Operation: CA, NY, FC
Foreign Countries: GREAT BRITAIN
Type of Foodservice: Casual Dining (1); Fine Dining (6); Quick Serve (1)
Catering Services: Yes
Primary Distributors: (Food) Baldor Specialty Foods Inc., BRONX, NY
Notes: Daily Burger is a foodservice stand located at Madison Square Garden. Acela Club is a four-floor casual restaurant located at Citi Field.

Key Personnel
DREW NIEPORENT - Partner
TRACY NIEPORENT - Partner; Director Information Systems, Marketing
MARTIN SHAPIRO - Partner; Manager Risk Management, Human Resources
AGNES CHIAO - Partner; CFO; Controller; Director Finance, Operations, Purchasing, Facility/Maintenance, Real Estate, Design, Business Development
OSCAR HERNANDEZ - General Manager
COURTNEY WIELAND - General Manager
AMANDA IGER - Manager Special Projects

Nobu Restaurants
40 W 57th St Suite 320
New York, NY 10019

Telephone: (121) 275-73374
Internet Homepage: noburestaurants.com
Type of Business: Chain Restaurant Operator
Total Sales: $113,450,000 (e)
Total Units: 23
Trade Names: Nobu Restaurants (23)
Company-Owned Units: 23
Primary Menu: Seafood (23)
Type of Foodservice: Fine Dining (23)

Key Personnel
MEIR TEPER - Partner
NOBU MATSUHISA - Partner
ROBERT DE NIRO - Partner
CHRISTINE PRESTAGE LONGFIELD - CFO
LUKE BJOIN - Director Food
YVONNE LOPEZ - Director Human Resources, Region
JAD MAROUCHE - Regional Director

Num Pang
1129 Broadway
New York, NY 10010-2006

Telephone: (212) 647-8889
Internet Homepage: numpangnyc.com
Company Email: info@numpankitchenc.com
Type of Business: Chain Restaurant Operator
Year Founded: 2009
Total Units: 7
Trade Names: Num Pang (7)
Company-Owned Units: 7
Primary Menu: Sandwiches/Deli (7)
Areas of Operation: MA, NY
Type of Foodservice: Fast Casual (7)

Key Personnel
BEN DAITZ - Co-Founder; Owner
PETER LAGADAS - Director Operations

Osteria al Doge
142 W 44th St
New York, NY 10036-4013

Telephone: (212) 944-3643
Fax Number: (212) 944-5754
Internet Homepage: osteriaaldogenyc.com;

osterialagunanyc.com
Type of Business: Chain Restaurant Operator
Year Founded: 1993
Total Sales: $7,593,000 (e)
Alcohol Sales: 30%
Number of Employees: 55
Average Check: Lunch(36); Dinner(66)
Total Units: 2
Trade Names: Osteria Al Doge (1); Osteria Laguna (1)
Company-Owned Units: 2
Preferred Location Types: Downtown; Mixed-use Center
Alcohol Served: Beer, Wine, Liquor
Primary Menu: Italian (2)
Areas of Operation: NY
Type of Foodservice: Fine Dining (2)
Catering Services: Yes

Key Personnel
PHILIPPE BERNARD - President; Executive Chef; General Buyer
MADDALENA CINQUE - General Manager
MARC JACKSON - Manager Accounting

Papaya King Operations Inc.
179 E 86th St
New York, NY 10028-2106

Telephone: (212) 369-0648
Internet Homepage: papayaking.com
Company Email: franchise@papayaking.com
Type of Business: Chain Restaurant Operator
Year Founded: 1932
Systemwide Sales: $3,821,000 (e)
Total Sales: $1,910,000 (e)
Number of Employees: 25
Average Check: Lunch(8); Dinner(8)
Internet Order Processing: Yes
Internet Sales: 5.00%
Total Units: 3
Trade Names: Papaya King (3)
Company-Owned Units: 3
Primary Menu: Hot Dogs (3)
Areas of Operation: NV, NY
Type of Foodservice: Quick Serve (3)
Catering Services: Yes
Primary Distributors: (Supplies) Imperial Bag & Paper LLC, JERSEY CITY, NJ

Key Personnel
AMZAD HOSSAIN - Director Operations; General Buyer

Patina Restaurant Group LLC
60 E 42nd St Ste 1730
New York, NY 10165-6223

Telephone: (212) 789-8100
Fax Number: (212) 302-8032
Internet Homepage: patinagroup.com
Company Email: ContactUs@patinagroup.com
Type of Business: Chain Restaurant Operator
Year Founded: 1989
Total Sales: $220,030,000 (e)
Alcohol Sales: 35%
Number of Employees: 3,305
Average Check: Breakfast(14); Lunch(20); Dinner(34)
Internet Order Processing: Yes
Internet Sales: 5.00%
Total Units: 41
Trade Names: Banners (1); Brooklyn Botanic (1); C+M (2); Catal Restaurant & UVA Bar (1); Chef Street (1); Enzo's Hideaway (1); George's Cafe (1); Hub Hall(1); Jake's Cafe (1); LACMA Cafe (1); Leatherby's Cafe Rouge (1); Lincoln Ristorante (1); Maple Descanso Gardens (1); Maria & Enzo's Ristorante (1); Market Cafe (1); Market Cafe at 550 St (1); Market Cafe at Westwood (1); Morimoto Asia (1); Naples Ristorante & Pizzeria (1); Napolini Pizzeria (1); New England Aquarium (1); Nick & Stef's Steakhouse (2); Norton Simon Cafe at Norton Simon Museum (1); Panevino Ristorante (1); Patina (2); Pizza Ponte (1); Ray's and Stark Bar at LACMA (1); Rowlands Bar & Grill (1); State Grill & Bar (1); Stella 34 Trattoria (1); Tangata (1); Taqueria (1); The Edison (1); The Grand Tier Restaurant (1); Tortilla Jo's (1); Tutto Italia (1); Via Napoli (1); Yellow Magnolia Cafe (1)
Company-Owned Units: 41
Preferred Square Footage: 5,000; 6,000
Preferred Location Types: Downtown; Freestanding; Hotel/Motel; Institution (college/hospital); Office Complex; Other
Alcohol Served: Beer, Wine, Liquor
Primary Menu: American (13); Bar-B-Q (0); Californian (0); Coffee (1); French/Continental (5); Greek/Mediterranean (5); Hamburger (0); Italian (8); Mexican(1); Pizza (1); Sandwiches/Deli (5); Seafood (0); Southwest/Tex-Mex (1); Spanish (0); Steak (3)
Areas of Operation: CA, FL, NJ, NV, NY
Type of Foodservice: Casual Dining (28); Fast Casual (1); Fine Dining (12)
Foodservice Management Venues: Parks & Recreation
Catering Services: Yes
Primary Distributors: (Full Line) SYSCO Food Services of Central California Inc., MODESTO, CA
Parent Company: Delaware North Companies Inc., BUFFALO, NY

Key Personnel
JOACHIM SPLICHAL - Founder; Executive Chef
JOE POLIDORA - Exec VP Operations
PETER WYSS - Senior VP Operations
OLIVIER RASSINOUX - VP Operations
SETH ROSE - VP Operations
DAVID RUEDE - VP Construction, Design
LEWIS SCHWARTZ - VP Operations
MARC SMITH - VP Information Technology
STEPHANIE EDENS - VP Event Planning, Catering
AFRANNA YAMEEN - Senior Director Sales
GABRIELE UBERTI - Director Operations
YUHI FUJINAGA - Director Culinary Operations
PHILIP POTTHOFF - Director Operations
ANTONIO PRONTELLI - Director Culinary Operations
ANDRAS HAMZA - Director Food and Beverage
DWIGHT HOOVER - Director Operations
JACQUELINE KELLY - Director Culinary Operations
ANGIE LONG - Director Purchasing
ADAM OLLAND - Director Business Development
KYLE BEAUREGARD - Director Operations
MATTHEW CARRALEJO - Director Operations
LAURA CHRISTOPHER - Director Event Planning
SHARON COLABELLO - Director Catering
KYLE COLLINS - Director Marketing
ERIC CUSTIS - Director Operations, West Region
CEASAR DE LA CRUZ - Director Human Resources
FRANCK DELETRAIN - Director Food
ALISON GARTNER GIUNTA - Senior Designer

Peking Duck House
236 E 53rd St
New York, NY 10022-5201

Telephone: (212) 759-8260
Fax Number: (212) 753-0236
Internet Homepage: pekingduckhousenyc.com
Type of Business: Chain Restaurant Operator
Year Founded: 1980
Total Sales: $3,399,000 (e)
Alcohol Sales: 20%
Number of Employees: 25
Average Check: Lunch(30); Dinner(42)
Total Units: 2
Trade Names: Peking Duck House (2)
Company-Owned Units: 2
Preferred Location Types: Downtown; Mixed-use Center
Alcohol Served: Beer, Wine, Liquor
Primary Menu: Asian (2)
Areas of Operation: NY
Type of Foodservice: Fine Dining (2)

Key Personnel
WNYIN WU - President
ALEX LOW - VP
TOM TSE - Executive Chef; General Buyer

Pret A Manger (USA) Ltd
30 Irving Pl Fl 2
New York, NY 10003

Telephone: (646) 728-0505
Fax Number: (646) 728-0858
Internet Homepage: pret.com
Company Email: customerservice@pret.com
Type of Business: Chain Restaurant Operator
Year Founded: 1999
Total Sales: $404,045,000 (e)
Number of Employees: 915
Average Check: Breakfast(10); Lunch(14); Dinner(16)
Internet Order Processing: Yes
Internet Sales: 15.00%
Total Units: 65
Trade Names: Pret A Manger (65)
Company-Owned Units: 65
Preferred Square Footage: 1,500; 3,000
Preferred Location Types: Airports; Downtown; Office Complex; Strip Mall
Primary Menu: Sandwiches/Deli (65)
Projected Openings: 10
Areas of Operation: CA, DC, DE, IL, MA, NC, NJ, NV, NY, PA
Foreign Countries: ENGLAND; HONG KONG; JAPAN; SCOTLAND
Type of Foodservice: Fast Casual (65)
Catering Services: Yes
Parent Company: Pret A Manger (Europe) Ltd, LONDON, ENG
Notes: Store count and sales reflect only US operations.

Key Personnel
SINCLAIR BEECHAM - Co-Founder
JULIAN METCALFE - Co-Founder
PANO CHRISTOU - CEO
THOMAS TRAUTMANN - Senior VP Finance
MARK THOMAS - VP Food; Director Quality Assurance
PIERCE HORAN - VP Operations, Store Development
HEIDI LANG - Director Retail Information Systems
MADELINE MELLY - Director; Transformation
PATRICK HOKE - Director Purchasing-Food
MEL DE FARIA - Director Systems, Compliance
MOLLY GATELY - Director Finance
CHRISTIAN ACHENBACH - Director Real Estate
JEAN-BAPTISTE THOUVENIN - Director Finance
FREIDA HIRSCH - Senior Manager Innovation
JESSICA P. MITIC - Senior Manager Development, Training
STEPHANIE PEREZ - Senior Manager Marketing, Social Media, Digital Marketing
ERIC SILVA - Senior Manager Training
FRANCISCO TAVAREZ - Senior Manager Operations
NICOLLE MONROY - Manager Catering
KARINES AYALA - Manager Operations
JAMES BUSSANDRI - Manager Internal Audit
TARA GREEN - Manager Training
JOSHUA DIJKSTRA - Manager Logistics
ZACHARY THOMAS - Manager Product Development

Quality Branded
880 3rd Ave Ste 400
New York, NY 10022-4760

Telephone: (212) 838-2061
Fax Number: (212) 308-3521
Internet Homepage: qualitybranded.com
Type of Business: Chain Restaurant Operator
Year Founded: 2007
Total Sales: $73,993,000 (e)
Alcohol Sales: 5%
Number of Employees: 160
Average Check: Lunch(30); Dinner(48)
Total Units: 8
Trade Names: Don Angie (1); Park Avenue (1); Quality Eats (2); Quality Italian Steakhouse (2); Quality Meats NYC (1); Smith & Wollensky (1)
Company-Owned Units: 11
Preferred Square Footage: 7,000; 9,000; 19,000
Preferred Location Types: Freestanding; Hotel/Motel
Alcohol Served: Beer, Wine, Liquor
Primary Menu: American (8); Steak (3)
Areas of Operation: CO, FL, NY
Type of Foodservice: Casual Dining (3); Fine Dining (8)
Catering Services: Yes
Primary Distributors: (Full Line) SYSCO Food Services of West Coast Florida Inc., PALMETTO, FL
Notes: The company derives approximately 1% of its revenue from management fees of The Post House.

Key Personnel
ALAN STILLMAN - Co-Founder
MICHAEL STILLMAN - Co-Founder; CEO
CRAIG KOKETSU - Partner; Executive Chef
STEVEN JOLTON - CFO
KEVIN DILLON - COO
JENNIFER RACKOFF - VP; General Counsel
SUSAN SPIKES - VP Human Resources
ROGER MORLOCK - General Manager
CORY COLTON - Executive Chef
RODRIGO RODRIGUEZ - Senior Director Operations
DENISE BRYANT - Director Event Planning
DAVID COHEN - Director Information Technology
BRIAN SCHNEIDER - Director
JOEY SMITH - Director Alcoholic Beverages
BILLY BARLOW - Director Operations
ALEXANDER PFAFFENBACH - Director Operations

Reading International Inc.
189 Second Avenue Suite 2S
New York, NY 10003

Telephone: (213) 235-2240
Fax Number: (213) 235-2229
Internet Homepage: angelicafilmcenter.com; consolidatedtheatres.com; readingcinemasus.com; readingrdi.com
Company Email: citycinema@aol.com
Type of Business: Foodservice Operations - Movie Theatre
Year Founded: 1994
Publicly Held: Yes
Total Sales: $115,154,000 (e)
Number of Employees: 60
Average Check: Lunch(10); Dinner(10)
Foodservice Sales: $28,788,000 (e)
Total Units: 61
Trade Names: Angelika Film Center & Cafe (7); Consolidated Theatre (9); Reading (45)
Company-Owned Units: 61
Preferred Square Footage: 5,000; 20,000
Preferred Location Types: Freestanding
Alcohol Served: Beer, Wine, Liquor
Primary Menu: Snacks (61); Steak (1)
Projected Openings: 1
Areas of Operation: CA, HI, NY, TX
Foreign Countries: AUSTRALIA; NEW ZEALAND
Type of Foodservice: In-Store Feeder (61)
Primary Distributors: (Full Line) Continental Restaurant & Bar Supply, HEMPSTEAD, NY
Notes: The company derives approximately 75% of its revenue from theater admissions, on-screen advertising, & other sales. Total units include two locations managed by Reading International; total sales excludes revenues from real estate activities.

Key Personnel
ELLEN M. COTTER - Chairman; CEO; President; COO
MARGARET COTTER - Vice Chairman; Exec VP Real Estate
ROBERT F. SMERLING - President; Director Real Estate, Construction, Site Selection, Business Development; General Buyer
GILBERT AVANES - CFO Interim; Treasurer
ANDRZEJ MATYCZYNSKI - Exec VP Operations, Global
MARCELO AXARLIAN - Director National
KEN GILLICH - Director Food and Beverage
JOHN GOEDDEL - Director Information Technology
ARTURO JIMENEZ - Manager Information Technology
DANIEL KOEHLER - Manager
XIAORU LAZARUS CPA - Manager Finance
LAUREN MARTZ - Manager Financial Planning

Restaurant Associates Managed Services
132 W 31st St Rm 601
New York, NY 10001-3470

Telephone: (212) 613-5500
Fax Number: (212) 613-4697
Internet Homepage: restaurantassociates.com
Company Email:
   info@restaurantassociates.com
Type of Business: Foodservice Management Operator
Year Founded: 1930
Total Sales: $625,126,000 (e)
Number of Employees: 8,500
Number of Locations Served: 200
Total Foodservice Mgmt Accounts: 100
Trade Names: American Museum of Natural History; Boston Children's Museum; Brooklyn Museum; Carnegie Hall; Carnival Center for the Performing Arts; Central Park Zoo; City Center; Cooper Hewitt, National Design Museum; Georgia Aquarium; High Museum of Art; Intrepid Sea, Air & Space Museum; John F. Kennedy Center for the Performing Arts; Liberty Science Center; Lincoln Center, Alice Tully Hall; Lincoln Center, Avery Fisher Hall; Lincoln Center, KaplanPenthouse; Lincoln Center, New York State Theater; Lincoln Center, The Tent; Museum of Fine Arts, Boston; Museum of Science; National Gallery of Art;National Museum of American History; National Museum of Natural History; National Museum of the American Indian; National Portrait Gallery; Newseum; Philadelphia Museum of Art; Royal Ontario Museum; Smithsonian Institution, The Castle; Solomon R. Guggenheim Museum; Sports Museum of America; Strathmore; The Kimmel Center; The Metropolitan Museum of Art; The Morgan Library & Museum; Winterthur Museum; Woodruff Arts Center
Areas of Operation: NY
Type of Foodservice: Cafeteria; Full-service sit-down dining; Mobile units/kiosks; Quick Serve
Foodservice Management Venues: Business & Industry; College & University; Other; Sports Venues
Primary Distributors: (Food) Performance Food Group, RICHMOND, VA
Parent Company: Compass Group PLC, LONDON, ENG
Headquarters: Compass Group The Americas, CHARLOTTE, NC
Notes: Trade names represents the venues at which the company operates foodservice facilities.

Key Personnel
RICHARD CATTANI - CEO
ED BROWN - President Restaurant Operations
MICHAEL GALLAGHER - Exec VP Operations
TIMOTHY MCLAUGHLIN - Senior VP Catering; Executive Chef Division

Riese Restaurants
560 5th Ave
New York, NY 10036-5005

Telephone: (212) 563-7440
Fax Number: (212) 613-1904
Type of Business: Chain Restaurant Operator
Year Founded: 1943
Total Sales: $84,250,000 (e)
Alcohol Sales: 33%
Number of Employees: 1,200
Total Units: 20
Trade Names: Haagen-Dazs (1); KFC (2); Lindy's (1); Nathan's Famous Hot Dogs (2); Pizza Hut (2); T.G.I. Friday's (8); Taco Bell (1); Tad's Broiled Steaks (1); Tim Hortons (2)
Units Franchised From: 20
Preferred Square Footage: 2,500; 3,000; 12,000; 18,000
Preferred Location Types: Downtown; Freestanding; Hotel/Motel; Kiosk; Mobile Unit
Alcohol Served: Beer, Wine, Liquor
Primary Menu: American (8); Chicken (2); Hot Dogs (2); Pizza (2); Sandwiches/Deli (1); Snacks (3); Steak (1); Taco (1)
Areas of Operation: NY
Type of Foodservice: Casual Dining (9); Fast Casual (1); Quick Serve (10)
Catering Services: Yes
On-site Distribution Center: Yes
Franchise Affiliation: KFC Corporation, LOUISVILLE, KY; Nathan's Famous Inc., JERICHO, NY; Pizza Hut Inc., PLANO, TX; Plamondon Companies Inc., FREDERICK, MD; T.G.I. Friday's Inc., DALLAS, TX; Taco Bell Corp., IRVINE, CA; The Haagen-Dazs Shoppe Company Inc., MINNEAPOLIS, MN; Tim Hortons Inc., OAKVILLE, ON
Primary Distributors: (Full Line) US Foods New York Metro, PERTH AMBOY, NJ
Parent Company: The Riese Organization, NEW YORK, NY

Key Personnel
DENNIS RIESE - Chairman; CEO
ANN MARTINEZ - CFO; VP Finance; Controller; Director Information Systems

Ristorante II Cantinori
32 E 10th St Frnt 1
New York, NY 10003-6238

Telephone: (212) 673-6044
Fax Number: (212) 353-0534
Internet Homepage: amalinyc.com; barsixny.com; ilcantinori.com; periyali.com; thebarroomnyc.com
Company Email: ilcantinori@gmail.com
Type of Business: Chain Restaurant Operator
Year Founded: 1983
Total Sales: $5,141,000 (e)
Alcohol Sales: 22%
Number of Employees: 160
Average Check: Lunch(60); Dinner(96)
Total Units: 5
Trade Names: Amali (1); Bar Six Restaurant (1); Periyali (1); Ristorante II Cantinori (1); The Bar Room (1)
Company-Owned Units: 5
Preferred Square Footage: 5,500; 6,000
Preferred Location Types: Freestanding
Alcohol Served: Beer, Wine, Liquor
Primary Menu: American (1); Greek/Mediterranean (3); Italian (1)
Areas of Operation: NY
Type of Foodservice: Casual Dining (1); Fine Dining (4)
Primary Distributors: (Food) SYSCO Food Services of Albany, HALFMOON, NY

Key Personnel
STEVE TZOLIS - President; Partner; Director Finance, Operations, Facility/Maintenance, Real Estate, Design
NICOLA KOTSONI - Partner; Controller; Director Supply Chain; Buyer Food
FRANK MINIERI - Partner; General Manager; Director Information Systems; Buyer Beverages, Food
ANTONIO CINARDI - Executive Chef
MASSIMILANO VELFIORE - Director Human Resources

RM Hospitality Group
264 W 40th St Fl 18
New York, NY 10018

Telephone: (212) 397-0666
Fax Number: (212) 397-0999
Internet Homepage: rosamexicano.com
Company Email: comments@rosamexicano.com
Type of Business: Chain Restaurant Operator
Year Founded: 1984
Total Sales: $31,540,000 (e)
Alcohol Sales: 22%
Number of Employees: 360
Average Check: Lunch(24); Dinner(50)
Internet Order Processing: Yes
Internet Sales: 1.00%
Total Units: 10
Trade Names: Rosa Mexicano (10)
Company-Owned Units: 10
Preferred Square Footage: 5,500; 6,000
Preferred Location Types: Freestanding; Other
Alcohol Served: Beer, Wine, Liquor
Primary Menu: Mexican (10)
Areas of Operation: CA, DC, FL, GA, MA, MD, MN, NJ, NY, PR
Foreign Countries: UNITED ARAB EMIRATES

Type of Foodservice: Fine Dining (10)
Catering Services: Yes
Primary Distributors: (Full Line) Performance Foodservice - AFI, ELIZABETH, NJ

Key Personnel
STEVEN WEISSMAN - CFO
AMIRA GERTZ - Director Event Planning, Catering

Roast Kitchen
740 7th Ave
New York, NY 10019

Telephone: (212) 399-9100
Internet Homepage: roast-kitchen.com
Type of Business: Chain Restaurant Operator
Year Founded: 2012
Total Sales: $28,400,000 (e)
Number of Employees: 200
Internet Order Processing: Yes
Total Units: 8
Trade Names: Roast Kitchen (8)
Company-Owned Units: 8
Primary Menu: Greek/Mediterranean (8)
Areas of Operation: NY
Type of Foodservice: Fast Casual (8)

Key Personnel
ALEXANDER XENOPOULOS - CEO
GISELLE TSIKARIDIS - General Manager; Manager Human Resources

Samba Brands Management
17 E 16th St Fl 2
New York, NY 10003-3146

Telephone: (212) 604-0600
Fax Number: (212) 366-1606
Internet Homepage: sugarcanerawbargrill.com; sushisamba.com
Type of Business: Chain Restaurant Operator
Year Founded: 1999
Total Sales: $23,280,000 (e)
Alcohol Sales: 10%
Number of Employees: 800
Average Check: Lunch(18); Dinner(54)
Internet Order Processing: Yes
Internet Sales: 0.50%
Total Units: 8
Trade Names: SUGARCANE Raw Bar Grill (3); SUSHISAMBA (5)
Company-Owned Units: 8
Preferred Square Footage: 5,500; 6,000
Preferred Location Types: Freestanding; Hotel/Motel
Alcohol Served: Beer, Wine, Liquor
Primary Menu: Miscellaneous (8)
Areas of Operation: FL, NV, NY, FC
Foreign Countries: ENGLAND; THE NETHERLANDS; UNITED ARAB EMIRATES

Type of Foodservice: Fine Dining (8)
Primary Distributors: (Full Line) SYSCO Food Services of Metro New York, JERSEY CITY, NJ

Key Personnel
DANIELLE BILLERA - Partner
SHIMON BOKOVZA - Partner; CFO; General Buyer
MATTHEW JOHNSON - Partner
PATRICIA GONZALES - COO
DANA RICCOBONO - COO
KOJI KAGAWA - Corporate Chef

Scalini Fedeli
165 Duane St Frnt 2
New York, NY 10013-3332

Telephone: (212) 528-0400
Fax Number: (212) 587-8773
Internet Homepage: ilmondovecchio.com; scalinifedeli.com
Type of Business: Chain Restaurant Operator
Total Sales: $7,507,000 (e)
Alcohol Sales: 10%
Number of Employees: 100
Average Check: Lunch(50); Dinner(72)
Total Units: 3
Trade Names: Il Mondo Vecchio (1); Scalini Fedeli (2)
Company-Owned Units: 3
Preferred Location Types: Downtown
Alcohol Served: Beer, Wine, Liquor
Primary Menu: Italian (3)
Areas of Operation: NJ, NY
Type of Foodservice: Fine Dining (3)

Key Personnel
MICHAEL CETRULO - President; Executive Chef; General Buyer
SHUHANA KHAN - Administrative Assistant

Schnippers
620 8th Ave
New York, NY 10018-1618

Telephone: (212) 921-2400
Internet Homepage: schnippers.com
Company Email: info@schnippers.com
Type of Business: Chain Restaurant Operator
Total Units: 5
Trade Names: Schnippers (4); Thunder Bun (1)
Company-Owned Units: 5
Primary Menu: Hamburger (5)
Areas of Operation: NY
Type of Foodservice: Fast Casual (5)

Key Personnel
JONATHAN SCHNIPPER - Partner

ANDREW SCHNIPPER - Partner

Serafina Restaurant Group
1740 Broadway
New York, NY 10019-4315

Telephone: (646) 368-1110
Internet Homepage: cognacrestaurant.com; serafinarestaurant.com; serafinarestaurant.com
Company Email: info@serafinarestaurant.com
Type of Business: Chain Restaurant Operator
Year Founded: 1995
Total Sales: $28,330,000 (e)
Total Units: 34
Trade Names: Cognac (1); Serafina (33)
Company-Owned Units: 34
Preferred Location Types: Downtown; Hotel/Motel; Strip Mall
Alcohol Served: Beer, Wine, Liquor
Primary Menu: French/Continental (1); Italian (33)
Projected Openings: 2
Areas of Operation: MA, NY, PA
Foreign Countries: BRAZIL; JAPAN; SOUTH KOREA; UNITED ARAB EMIRATES
Type of Foodservice: Casual Dining (33); Fine Dining (1)
Catering Services: Yes
Notes: Serafina Restaurant Group will be reopening its Japanese restaurant, Geisha, at its new location: 27 East 61st Street New York, NY 10065.

Key Personnel
VITTORIO ASSAF - Partner
FABIO GRANATO - Partner
KEITH SANTANGELO - CFO
MICHELLE SARRIA - Director Human Resources
KEVIN DEL CASALE - Director Purchasing, Development, Compliance

Shake Shack Inc.
225 Varick St Ste 301
New York, NY 10014

Telephone: (646) 747-7200
Internet Homepage: shakeshack.com
Type of Business: Chain Restaurant Operator
Year Founded: 2004
Systemwide Sales: $1,663,348,000 (e)
Publicly Held: Yes
Total Sales: $1,062,773,000 (e)
Number of Employees: 6,100
Total Units: 334
Trade Names: Shake Shack (334)
Company-Owned Units: 295
Units Franchised To: 39
Preferred Location Types: Airports; Downtown; Lifestyle Center; Regional Mall;

Stadiums
Alcohol Served: Beer, Wine
Primary Menu: Hamburger (334)
Projected Openings: 65
Areas of Operation: AL, AZ, CA, CO, CT, DC, DE, FL, GA, IL, KY, LA, MA, MD, MI, MN, MO, NC, NJ, NV, NY, OH, PA, RI, TN, TX, UT, VA, WA, WI, FC
Foreign Countries: BAHRAIN; CHINA; ENGLAND; JAPAN; KUWAIT; MEXICO; OMAN; QATAR; RUSSIA; SAUDI ARABIA; SINGAPORE; SOUTH KOREA; THE PHILIPPINES; TURKEY; UNITED ARAB EMIRATES
Type of Foodservice: Casual Dining (334)

Key Personnel
ROB LYNCH - CEO
KATHERINE FOGERTEY - CFO
STEPHANIE SENTELL - COO
DIANE NEVILLE - Chief People Officer
DAVE HARRIS - CIO
JAY LIVINGSTON - Chief Marketing Officer
ANDREW MCCAUGHAN - Chief Development Officer
CARLOS VISCARRA - Area Director
WADE HOUSKEN - Area Director
MARCELO SOSA - Area Director
DANNY SZYMANSKI - Area Director
MIKE KARK - Exec VP Licensing
RON PALMESE - Senior VP; General Counsel
CHRISTINA VAUGHAN - Senior VP Operations
CINDY BIRNBAUM RONSON - Senior VP Real Estate
JEFFREY AMOSCATO - VP Supply Chain, Innovation, Menu Development
JOHN KARANGIS - VP Culinary Development; Executive Chef
JEFFREY RAUSCH - VP Digital
BRIAN SEELY - VP
KELLY VONDRAK - VP Training
LORIN CIPOLLA DUNPHY - VP People
LOU DEANGELIS - Senior Director Facility/Maintenance, Construction
LISA KARTZMAN - Senior Director Supply Chain; Director Purchasing
ALLISON OESTERLE - Senior Director Quality Assurance, Product Development
CHARLIE FRANKIEVICH - Senior Director Consumer Insights
JONATHAN VANDEGRIFT - Director Operations
JOHN BERBERICH - Director Business Development
EDDIE LAU - Director Accounting
DANNY VASQUEZ - Director Information Technology, Security
GREGORY KOIZIM - Director Technology, Marketing
BEN SCHEIN - Director Product Development
MICHAEL BOYAN - Director Digital
ADAM CLATTERBUCK - Director Technology, Digital
MATT ANDERSON - Director Foodservice
KEVIN HWANG - Director Information Technology
LARAMIE ARONSON - Director Operations
ANASTASIA KOUIMELIS - Director Real Estate
STEPH SO - Director Digital
MIKE IAIA - Regional Director Operations
CATHIE URUSHIBATA - Art Director
JULIE ZISFEIN - Senior Manager Marketing, Business Development, Licensing
JOANNA SIEGEL - Senior Manager Training
MATTHEW MATHIS - Manager Licensing
ERNIE ROGERS - Manager Accounting
ANDREW TRINCHITELLA - Manager Operations
ALAN ELLIFF - Manager Quality Assurance
KARVEN BOWENS - Manager Facility/Maintenance, Region
IDRIS HUTHMAN - Manager Tax
CHELSEA DEKIS - Project Manager Construction
JEANNETTE CASTRO - Administrator Systems
KEARNEY SNEATH - Designer

Shun Lee Palace
155 E 55th St Frnt 2
New York, NY 10022-4038

Telephone: (212) 371-8844
Fax Number: (212) 752-1936
Internet Homepage: shunleepalace.net
Type of Business: Chain Restaurant Operator
Year Founded: 1971
Total Sales: $13,999,000 (e)
Alcohol Sales: 20%
Number of Employees: 55
Average Check: Lunch(36); Dinner(60)
Internet Order Processing: Yes
Total Units: 3
Trade Names: Shun Lee Cafe (1); Shun Lee Palace (1); Shun Lee West Restaurant (1)
Company-Owned Units: 3
Preferred Location Types: Mixed-use Center
Alcohol Served: Beer, Wine, Liquor
Primary Menu: Chinese (3)
Areas of Operation: NY
Type of Foodservice: Fine Dining (3)
Catering Services: Yes
Primary Distributors: (Full Line) SYSCO Food Services of Syracuse, WARNERS, NY

Key Personnel
MICHAEL TONG - President; Director Food and Beverage
SIMON TAM - General Manager; Executive Chef; General Buyer

Snowdays
241 E 10th St
New York, NY 10003

Telephone: (212) 982-8881
Internet Homepage: snowdaysnyc.com
Type of Business: Chain Restaurant Operator
Total Units: 2
Trade Names: Snowdays (2)
Company-Owned Units: 2
Primary Menu: Snacks (2)
Type of Foodservice: Quick Serve (2)

Key Personnel
TONY QUACH - Founder; Owner

Sophie's Cuban Cuisine Franchising Inc.
262 W 38th St Rm 1604
New York, NY 10018-1134

Telephone: (212) 382-2226
Fax Number: (212) 382-2227
Internet Homepage: sophiescuban.com
Company Email: vsantacruz@sophiescuban.com
Type of Business: Chain Restaurant Operator
Year Founded: 1998
Total Sales: $4,427,000 (e)
Average Check: Lunch(12); Dinner(14)
Internet Order Processing: Yes
Total Units: 10
Trade Names: Sophie's Cuban Cuisine (10)
Company-Owned Units: 10
Preferred Location Types: Freestanding; Office Complex
Primary Menu: Latin American/Cuban (10)
Areas of Operation: NY
Type of Foodservice: Family Restaurant (10)
Catering Services: Yes
Primary Distributors: (Full Line) SYSCO Food Services of Metro New York, JERSEY CITY, NJ

Key Personnel
SOFIA LUNA - Co-Founder; President
MANUELA MATOS - Co-Founder; Corporate Secretary
INES LUNA - VP Operations
EDUARDO MORGADO - Director Product Development

Southern Hospitality Restaurant & Bar
645 9th Ave Frnt 1
New York, NY 10036-3606

Telephone: (212) 249-1001
Fax Number: (646) 915-1572
Internet Homepage: southernhospitalitybbq.com
Company Email: info@southernhospitalitybbq.com
Type of Business: Chain Restaurant Operator
Year Founded: 2007
Average Check: Lunch(42); Dinner(48)
Total Units: 1

Trade Names: Southern Hospitality BBQ & Bar (1)
Company-Owned Units: 1
Alcohol Served: Beer, Wine, Liquor
Primary Menu: Bar-B-Q (1)
Projected Openings: 3
Areas of Operation: NY
Type of Foodservice: Casual Dining (1)

Key Personnel
RYAN TEDDER - Partner
EYTAN SUGARMAN - Partner
NELSON BRAFF - Partner; General Buyer
JUSTIN TIMBERLAKE - Partner

ST Management Group
130 W 37th St 2nd Floor
New York, NY 10018

Telephone: (212) 983-7474
Fax Number: (212) 983-7444
Internet Homepage: cafemetrony.com; freshandco.com
Company Email: info@freshandcofranchise.com
Type of Business: Chain Restaurant Operator
Year Founded: 1982
Total Sales: $69,330,000 (e)
Number of Employees: 529
Average Check: Breakfast(10); Lunch(10); Dinner(12)
Total Units: 22
Trade Names: Cafe Metro (4); Fresh & Co (18)
Company-Owned Units: 23
Preferred Square Footage: 3,000
Preferred Location Types: Downtown; Office Complex; Other
Primary Menu: American (4); Health Foods (18)
Areas of Operation: NY
Type of Foodservice: Fast Casual (23)
Catering Services: Yes
Primary Distributors: (Full Line) SYSCO Food Services of Albany, HALFMOON, NY

Key Personnel
STEVE TENEDIOS - President
KONSTANTINOS ZAMFOTIS - CFO
ALEX PEREZ - COO
SANDRA POPE - Director Marketing
HANS ROMAIN - Director Information Technology
TY SULLIVAN - Director Development, Training
LUIS ARIAS - Director Security

Tacombi
262 Bowery
New York, NY 10012

Telephone: (212) 967-5555
Internet Homepage: tacombi.com
Company Email: info@tacombi.com
Type of Business: Chain Restaurant Operator
Year Founded: 2006
Total Sales: $29,927,000 (e)
Total Units: 20
Trade Names: Tacombi (20)
Company-Owned Units: 20
Primary Menu: Mexican (20)
Areas of Operation: CT, FL, IL, MD, NY, VA
Type of Foodservice: Casual Dining (20)

Key Personnel
DARIO WOLOS - Founder; CEO; Owner
CARLOS DE COSÍO - Chief Supply Chain Officer
JESSICA DAY - VP People
RORY MULCAHY - Senior Director Sales
CESAR CASTRO - Director Manufacturing
JAZMIN GAC - Director Business Development
SHANNON RYOO - Director Accounting

Taim Holdings LLC
45 Spring St
New York, NY 10012

Telephone: (212) 219-0600
Internet Homepage: taimfalafel.com
Company Email: info@taimfalafel.com
Type of Business: Chain Restaurant Operator
Year Founded: 2005
Total Units: 8
Trade Names: Balaboosta (1); Kish-Kash (1); Taim Falafel (6)
Company-Owned Units: 8
Preferred Location Types: Downtown
Primary Menu: Middle Eastern (8)
Areas of Operation: DC, NY
Type of Foodservice: Casual Dining (2); Fast Casual (6)

Key Personnel
EINAT ADMONY - Co-Founder; Partner; Corporate Chef
STEFAN NAFZIGER - Co-Founder; Partner
JERRY SHEETS - General Manager
CINDY GUEVARA - General Manager

Tao Group
42 E 58th St
New York, NY 10022-1910

Telephone: (212) 888-2288
Fax Number: (212) 888-4148
Internet Homepage: taogroup.com; taorestaurant.com
Company Email: info@taogroup.com
Type of Business: Chain Restaurant Operator
Year Founded: 2001
Total Sales: $24,930,000 (e)
Number of Employees: 39
Average Check: Lunch(24); Dinner(72)
Total Units: 7
Trade Names: LAVO Italian Restaurant and Lounge (2); Tao Asian Bistro (5)
Company-Owned Units: 7
Preferred Location Types: Freestanding
Alcohol Served: Beer, Wine, Liquor
Primary Menu: Asian (5); Italian (2)
Areas of Operation: CA, IL, NV, NY
Type of Foodservice: Casual Dining (7)

Key Personnel
LOUIS ABIN - President; General Buyer
RICHARD WOLFE - President; General Buyer
MARK PACKER - Partner
PAUL GOLDSTEIN - Partner; COO
KIM KURLANCHIK RUSSEN - Partner
SUSAN NUGRAHA - VP Development, Design
BRANDON WERGELES - General Manager
TINA JONICA - General Manager
MICHELLE ALDEN - General Manager
CESAR ANTIPAS - General Manager
JASON CORREA - General Manager
CHARLIE OU - Executive Chef; Manager Operations
RALPH SCAMARDILLA - Executive Chef; General Buyer
DREW SWEENEY - Director Food and Beverage
KEVIN SWEENEY - Director Operations
BRITTANY WEINGART - Director Event Planning
YVONNE NAJOR - Director Marketing
ALVIN CHEUNG - Director Accounting
ADAM GEWANTER - Director Store Operations
TOM GILLESPIE - Director Purchasing
MORGAN MANN - Director Human Resources
NIKKI MCCUTCHEON - Manager Food and Beverage
JUSTIN LEVY - Manager Digital Marketing
KRYSTIAN EKLUND - Manager Event Planning
LAUREN FOLEY - Manager Restaurant Operations
JOE FRIEDMAN - Manager Marketing
BILL NICHOLAS - Manager Food and Beverage
CORY WILSON - Manager Marketing

The Dinex Group LLC
16 E 40th St Fl 5
New York, NY 10016-0113

Telephone: (212) 794-2329
Fax Number: (212) 794-2600
Internet Homepage: danielboulud.com; danielnyc.com
Company Email: info@danielnyc.com
Type of Business: Chain Restaurant Operator
Year Founded: 1992
Total Sales: $80,660,000 (e)
Alcohol Sales: 35%
Number of Employees: 1,463
Average Check: Lunch(66); Dinner(144)
Internet Order Processing: Yes
Internet Sales: 1.00%

Total Units: 19
Trade Names: Bar at Danie (1); Bar Boulud (3); Bar Pleiades (1); Boulud Sud (1); Cafe Boulud (3); Daniel (1); DB Bistro Moderne (3); DBGB Kitchen & Bar (1); DiBar (1); Epicerie Boulud (3); Maison Boulud (1)
Company-Owned Units: 19
Preferred Square Footage: 5,500; 6,000
Preferred Location Types: Freestanding; Hotel/Motel
Alcohol Served: Beer, Wine, Liquor
Primary Menu: French/Continental (19)
Projected Openings: 2
Areas of Operation: DC, FL, MA, NV, NY, FC, ON, QC
Foreign Countries: CANADA; ENGLAND; SINGAPORE
Type of Foodservice: Casual Dining (10); Fine Dining (9)
Catering Services: Yes
Primary Distributors: (Food) SYSCO Food Services of Albany, HALFMOON, NY

Key Personnel
DANIEL BOULUD - CEO; President; Director Real Estate
SEBASTIEN SILVESTRI - CEO
BRIAN DIAMOND - CFO
JEAN FRANCOIS BRUEL - Executive Chef Division
DANIEL BOYCE - Director Operations

The Hummus & Pita Co.
585 Avenue of the Americas
New York, NY 10011-2004

Telephone: (212) 510-7405
Fax Number: (212) 510-7409
Internet Homepage: hummusandpitas.com
Company Email: contact@HummusAndPitas.com
Type of Business: Chain Restaurant Operator
Year Founded: 2012
Internet Order Processing: Yes
Total Units: 8
Trade Names: The Hummus & Pita Co. (8)
Company-Owned Units: 3
Primary Menu: Sandwiches/Deli (8)
Projected Openings: 7
Areas of Operation: NY
Type of Foodservice: Quick Serve (8)
Notes: Partnering with Fransmart in franchising efforts.

Key Personnel
DAVID PESSO - Co-Founder; Director Operations, Business Development
JANICE AXELROD - Co-Founder; CEO; Partner
STEVE PESSO - Partner

The International Culinary Center New York
462 Broadway
New York, NY 10013-2618

Telephone: (888) 324-2433
Fax Number: (212) 431-3065
Internet Homepage: internationalculinarycenter.com
Company Email: info@culinarycenter.com
Type of Business: Culinary Schools
Areas of Operation: NY

Key Personnel
MARC BAUER - Senior Director Culinary Operations

The Kati Roll Company Franchising Corporation
222 W 37th St Fl 14
New York, NY 10018-9027

Telephone: (212) 730-6740
Internet Homepage: thekatirollcompany.com
Company Email: tkrc@thekatirollcompany.com
Type of Business: Chain Restaurant Operator
Year Founded: 2002
Total Units: 8
Trade Names: The Kati Roll Company (8)
Company-Owned Units: 8
Primary Menu: Indian (8)
Projected Openings: 2
Areas of Operation: NY
Foreign Countries: ENGLAND
Type of Foodservice: Quick Serve (8)
Notes: Personnel note: Anil Bathwal is founder Payal Saha's husband.
Locations note: The chain operates a commissary in the Bronx.

Key Personnel
PAYAL SAHA - Founder; General Buyer
ANIL BATHWAL - Executive Chef; Director
SCOTT WEISSMAN - Manager Catering

The ONE Group LLC
411 W 14th St Fl 3
New York, NY 10014-1082

Telephone: (646) 624-2400
Internet Homepage: togrp.com
Company Email: info@togrp.com
Type of Business: Chain Restaurant Operator
Year Founded: 2004
Publicly Held: Yes
Total Sales: $394,357,000 (e)
Alcohol Sales: 41%
Number of Employees: 3,364
Average Check: Dinner(152)
Total Units: 63
Trade Names: Angel (1); Bao Yum (1); Heliot (1); Heliot Steak House (1); Hideout (1); Kona Grill (27); Radio Rooftop (8); Rivershore Bar & Grill (1); STK (28); The Marconi Lounge (1)
Company-Owned Units: 63
Preferred Square Footage: 8,000; 10,000
Alcohol Served: Beer, Wine, Liquor
Primary Menu: American (28); Asian (1); German (0); Greek/Mediterranean (1); Italian (1); Steak (39)
Projected Openings: 3
Areas of Operation: CA, DC, FL, GA, IL, NV, NY, FC, ON
Foreign Countries: CANADA; ENGLAND; ITALY
Type of Foodservice: Casual Dining (56); Fast Casual (1); Fine Dining (13)
Parent Company: The ONE Group Hospitality Inc., NEW YORK, NY
Headquarter Offices: Kona Grill Inc., SCOTTSDALE, AZ

Key Personnel
JONATHAN SEGAL - Executive Chairman
EMANUEL HILARIO - CEO; President
TYLER LOY - CFO
CAROLINE O'MAHONY-BAKER - Senior VP Operations
KEITHA FRANCIS - VP Human Resources
STACEY PERRONE - VP Restaurant Operations
MICHAEL TORRES - Assistant VP Training
QUINCY FITZWATER - Senior Director Operations, International Division
KATIE CHAPMAN - Senior Director Marketing
ERIC MARQUARDT - Senior Director Operations
SARA MALONEY TRUITT - Director Human Resources
DOUG VAN NORT - Director Purchasing
BAILEY KEEFE - Director
SARA BECK - Director Human Resources
JASON BANNERMAN - Director Operations
DAVID-ALEX STEELE - Director Operations
STEVE CHANG - Director Purchasing
HEATH HIUDT - Director Beverages
AMBER THOMPSON - Director Event Planning
KEITH ROCHE - Regional Director Operations
EMILY MARTESE - Manager Operations

The Restaurant Group
522 Columbus Ave
New York, NY 10024-3404

Telephone: (212) 579-3195
Fax Number: (212) 362-3004
Internet Homepage: therestaurantgroup.com
Type of Business: Chain Restaurant Operator
Year Founded: 1998
Total Sales: $66,740,000 (e)
Alcohol Sales: 10%

Number of Employees: 130
Average Check: Lunch(8); Dinner(12)
Total Units: 12
Trade Names: A.G. Kitchen (1); Brad's Burgers (1); Fuel Pizza (7); Good Enough To Eat (1); Harlem Taco (1); Zen Taco (1)
Company-Owned Units: 12
Preferred Location Types: Freestanding; Strip Mall
Alcohol Served: Beer, Wine, Liquor
Primary Menu: American (1); Asian (1); Hamburger (1); Latin American/Cuban (1); Pizza (7); Taco (1)
Areas of Operation: DC, NC, NY
Type of Foodservice: Casual Dining (11); Fast Casual (1)
Primary Distributors: (Full Line) US Foods, CLIFTON PARK, NY

Key Personnel
JEREMY WLADIS - President
EDDIE SCHWARTZ - CFO
PATRICK FAUP - COO
WILLIAM LEHMAN - Executive Chef
LINCOLN CLARK - Executive Chef; Director Operations; General Buyer

Three Guys Restaurant
960 Madison Ave Frnt 1
New York, NY 10021-2637

Telephone: (212) 628-8108
Type of Business: Chain Restaurant Operator
Year Founded: 1978
Total Sales: $1,666,000 (e)
Alcohol Sales: 10%
Number of Employees: 45
Average Check: Breakfast(12); Lunch(18); Dinner(30)
Total Units: 1
Trade Names: Three Guys Restaurant (1)
Company-Owned Units: 1
Preferred Location Types: Freestanding
Alcohol Served: Beer, Wine, Liquor
Primary Menu: American (1)
Areas of Operation: NY
Type of Foodservice: Casual Dining (1)
Parent Company: Zanimed Foods, NEW YORK, NY

Key Personnel
HERCULES KATAIN - Partner; General Manager; General Buyer
ARGIROS SPIRO - Partner; General Manager; General Buyer

Tour de France
630 9th Ave
New York, NY 10036-3708

Telephone: (212) 333-2323
Fax Number: (212) 799-4041
Internet Homepage: tourdefrancenyc.com; cafedalsace.com; lemondenyc.com; lexpressnyc.com; marseillenyc.com; nicematinnyc.com
Company Email: d.meyers@chefdriven.com,b.perez@chefdriven.com
Type of Business: Chain Restaurant Operator
Total Sales: $43,280,000 (e)
Number of Employees: 177
Average Check: Dinner(90)
Internet Order Processing: Yes
Internet Sales: 1.00%
Total Units: 6
Trade Names: Cafe D'Alsace (1); French Roast (1); L'Express (1); Le Monde (1); Marseille (1); Nice Matin (1)
Company-Owned Units: 6
Preferred Location Types: Downtown
Alcohol Served: Beer, Wine, Liquor
Primary Menu: French/Continental (6)
Areas of Operation: NY
Type of Foodservice: Casual Dining (6)
Primary Distributors: (Full Line) US Foods, BUFFALO, NY

Key Personnel
ANDY D'AMICO - Partner; Executive Chef; General Buyer
SIMON OREN - Partner; CFO; COO
BLANCA PEREZ - Corporate Secretary Human Resources
JHONY ALAM - General Manager

TRUFOODS, LLC
666 5th Ave Fl 27
New York, NY 10103-0001

Telephone: (212) 359-3600
Fax Number: (212) 359-3601
Internet Homepage: arthurtreachersfranchising.com/index.php; pudgies.com; ritters.com; trufoods.com; wallstreetdeli.com
Company Email: info@trufoods.com
Type of Business: Chain Restaurant Operator
Year Founded: 1969
Systemwide Sales: $2,501,000 (e)
Total Sales: $6,887,000 (e)
Number of Employees: 186
Total Units: 39
Trade Names: Arthur Treacher's Fish & Chips (7); Pudgie's Famous Chicken (3); Ritter's Frozen Custard (21); Wall Street Deli (8)
Units Franchised To: 39
Preferred Square Footage: 1,200
Preferred Location Types: Airports; Community Mall; Convenience Store/Gas Station; Freestanding; Institution (college/hospital); Office Complex; Parks; Regional Mall; Strip Mall; Travel Plazas
Primary Menu: Chicken (3); Sandwiches/Deli (8); Seafood (7); Snacks (21)
Areas of Operation: AL, DC, FL, IN, KY, MD, MI, NY, OH, PA, SC, TX, VA
Foreign Countries: CAYMAN ISLANDS
Type of Foodservice: Quick Serve (39)
Catering Services: Yes
Primary Distributors: (Food) US Foods, BUFFALO, NY; (Supplies) US Foods, CLIFTON PARK, NY

Key Personnel
ANDY UNANUE - CEO
STEW STOLZ - Executive Director Operations

Tutti A Tavola LLC
243 E 58th St
New York, NY 10022-1201

Telephone: (212) 758-1479
Internet Homepage: felidia-nyc.com
Company Email: info@felidia-nyc.com
Type of Business: Chain Restaurant Operator
Year Founded: 1981
Total Sales: $30,000,000 (e)
Alcohol Sales: 10%
Number of Employees: 140
Average Check: Lunch(60); Dinner(90)
Total Units: 13
Trade Names: Becco (1); Del Posto (1); Eataly (7); Esca (1); Felidia (1); Lidia's (2)
Company-Owned Units: 13
Preferred Location Types: Freestanding
Alcohol Served: Beer, Wine, Liquor
Primary Menu: Italian (7)
Areas of Operation: MO, NY, PA
Type of Foodservice: Fine Dining (13)
Primary Distributors: (Food) SYSCO Food Services of Albany, HALFMOON, NY

Key Personnel
OLIVER CROM - Vice Chairman
MIKE D. - CEO
ELENA FOGG - CEO
VALENCIA VALCIN - CEO
DORIS PEARSON - President
BRIAN SCHMIDT - President
ARNOLD SCHNEIDER - President
MORRY KUBASHKY - President
JIM DUGANDZIC - President
KURT ABISCH - President
TOM ALLEN - Owner
LIDIA BASTIANICH - Owner; Director Finance
RICHARD FAIRCHILD - Owner
RALPH DIBIASI - Owner
LINDA LANDA-STOLER - Owner
DEANA LARKIN - Owner
DOUGLAS LAVIANO - Owner
THOMAS KENNEDY - Owner
BRIAN GAUCI - Owner
RENEE GILDERSLEEVE - Owner
PARKER HOUGH - Owner
BILL SCULLY - Owner
GEOFF PORTEUS - Owner

AMIR YUZARY - Owner
ANTHONY NOZZOLILLO - CFO
DAVID DUFFY - CFO
TOM DONALDSON - VP
DAN ONEILL - VP
NORMAN LEAKE - VP Marketing
BRUCE BAXTER - General Manager
MIKE BESTWINA - General Manager
FORTUNATO NICOTRA - Executive Chef; General Buyer
DAVID MAXEY - Director
BARBARA NEVES - Manager Customer Service
ANDREA IPPOLITO - Manager Administration
STEVEN GUSMEROTTI - Manager Warehouse
STACY FREMGEN - Manager
MARLENE FRIEDLANDER - Manager
LARRY BLAIR - Manager POS/Scanning
DANNY CINTRON - Manager
SANDY CORTESE - Manager Sales
ROY BERNSTEN - Manager Warehouse
MATUZAK DAN - Manager Sales
HOLIDAY ROSE - Manager Administration
QUINCY WIELINGEN - Manager
JOSEPH TERICO - Manager
RICHARD PRUNESTI - Project Manager
BILLY GEE - Project Manager
ROSA ESCOTO - Principal

Two Boots
176 E 3rd St Apt B1
New York, NY 10009-7745

Telephone: (212) 777-2668
Fax Number: (212) 777-2631
Internet Homepage: twoboots.com
Company Email: info@twoboots.com
Type of Business: Chain Restaurant Operator
Year Founded: 1987
Total Sales: $15,770,000 (e)
Alcohol Sales: 1%
Number of Employees: 185
Average Check: Lunch(10); Dinner(14)
Internet Order Processing: Yes
Total Units: 16
Trade Names: Two Boots (16)
Company-Owned Units: 16
Preferred Location Types: Freestanding; Strip Mall
Alcohol Served: Beer
Primary Menu: Pizza (16)
Projected Openings: 1
Areas of Operation: CA, CT, MD, NJ, NY, TN
Type of Foodservice: Fast Casual (16)
Primary Distributors: (Full Line) US Foods, BUFFALO, NY

Key Personnel
PHIL HARTMAN - President; Manager Real Estate
DENNIS ESCHENBERG - VP Operations; General Buyer
ANTHONY JORDAN - General Manager
EDGAR LOPEZ - General Manager
SAMI AKLEH - General Manager
EDWARD ALVAREZ - General Manager

Union Square Hospitality Group
853 Broadway Fl 17
New York, NY 10003

Telephone: (212) 228-3585
Fax Number: (212) 228-3622
Internet Homepage: ushgnyc.com
Company Email: info@ushgnyc.com
Listing Type: Corporate Office
Type of Business: Chain Restaurant Operator
Year Founded: 1985
Total Sales: $72,220,000 (e)
Alcohol Sales: 20%
Number of Employees: 484
Average Check: Lunch(26); Dinner(52)
Internet Order Processing: Yes
Internet Sales: 2.00%
Total Units: 23
Trade Names: Bay Room (1); Blue Smoke (2); Cafe 2 (1); Cafe Marchio (1); Daily Provisions (1); Gramercy Tavern (1); Gramercy Terrace (1); Intersect By Lexus-NYC (1); Maialino (1); Manhatta (1); Marta (1); Martina (1); North End Grill (1); Porchlight (1); Studio Cafe (1); Taco Cina (1); Terrace Cafe (1); The Modern (1); The Redbury New York Hotel (1); Union Square Cafe (1); Untitled at the Whitney (1); Vini e Fritti (1)
Company-Owned Units: 23
Preferred Square Footage: 5,500; 6,000
Preferred Location Types: Downtown; Freestanding; Lifestyle Center; Office Complex; Other
Alcohol Served: Beer, Wine, Liquor
Primary Menu: American (13); Bar-B-Q (2); French/Continental (1); Italian (1); Mexican (1); Miscellaneous (1); Pizza (2); Snacks (1)
Projected Openings: 2
Areas of Operation: IL, NY
Foreign Countries: ENGLAND; JAPAN; LEBANON; QATAR; RUSSIA; SOUTH KOREA; TURKEY; UNITED ARAB EMIRATES
Type of Foodservice: Casual Dining (15); Fast Casual (1); Fine Dining (5); Quick Serve (2)
Catering Services: Yes
Primary Distributors: (Food) D'Artagnan Inc., UNION, NJ
Notes: Union Square Hospitality also provides food at various venues throughout New York City through its Hudson Yards Catering operation.

Key Personnel
CHIP WADE - CEO; President
MICHAEL ANTHONY - Partner; Executive Chef
MICHAEL ROMANO - Partner; Executive Chef; Director Operations, Information Systems
TIFFANY DANIELE - CFO
PATTI H. SIMPSON - Chief Administrative Officer
RICHARD CORAINE - Chief Investment Officer
DOROTHY VIRAY - Controller; Director Accounting
JOSEPH TARASCO - Director Operations
JOHN RAGAN - Director Operations
JENNI GUIZIO - Director
GRETCHEN GARRY - Assistant Director Development
AMY GOLDBERG - Manager Sales
AMANDA LIPP - Manager Operations
RIZZO DEVIN - Manager Operations
LUCIANO CASTANEDA - Manager Restaurant Operations
BRETT ROMBERG - Manager Culinary Development
ASHLEY ROACHE - Supervisor
RUBEN LORA - Specialist Transportation

Van Leeuwen Ice Cream
61 W Houston St
New York, NY 10012

Telephone: (917) 639-3691
Internet Homepage: vanleeuwenicecream.com
Type of Business: Chain Restaurant Operator
Year Founded: 2008
Total Sales: $3,262,000 (e)
Total Units: 24
Trade Names: Van Leeuwen Ice Cream (24)
Company-Owned Units: 24
Primary Menu: Ice Cream (24)
Type of Foodservice: Fast Casual (24)

Key Personnel
BEN VAN LEEUWEN - Founder; CEO
COREY SEGAL - COO
ALEXANDRA WRIGHT - VP Sales
JENNA PEZZOLO - VP Retail Operations
CADY ROBERTS - Director Marketing

Water Club Restaurants
500 E 30th St
New York, NY 10016-8382

Telephone: (212) 683-3333
Fax Number: (212) 696-4099
Internet Homepage: brooklynicecreamfactory.com; pershingsquare.com; rivercafe.com; thewaterclub.com
Type of Business: Chain Restaurant Operator
Year Founded: 1982
Total Sales: $44,310,000 (e)
Alcohol Sales: 35%
Number of Employees: 250
Average Check: Breakfast(20); Lunch(32); Dinner(46)
Internet Sales: 1.00%
Total Units: 5
Trade Names: Pershing Square (1); River Cafe

(1); The Brooklyn Ice Cream Factory (2); Water Club (1)
Company-Owned Units: 5
Preferred Location Types: Freestanding
Alcohol Served: Beer, Wine, Liquor
Primary Menu: American (3); Snacks (2)
Areas of Operation: NY
Type of Foodservice: Fine Dining (3); Quick Serve (2)
Catering Services: Yes
Primary Distributors: (Food) Dairyland, The Chefs' Warehouse, BRONX, NY

Key Personnel
MICHAEL O'KEEFFE - President; CFO; Director Advertising; General Buyer
RICHARD DEAN - Controller
SCOTT STAMFORD - General Manager
BRAD STEELMAN - Executive Chef

Wolfnights
99 Riv-Ing-Ton Street
New York, NY 10002

Telephone: (646) 669-8070
Internet Homepage: wolfnightsusa.com
Type of Business: Chain Restaurant Operator
Year Founded: 2011
Total Sales: $7,895,000 (e)
Total Units: 2
Trade Names: Wolfnights (2)
Company-Owned Units: 2
Primary Menu: American (2)
Type of Foodservice: Fast Casual (2)

Key Personnel
ITAI AFEK - Founder; CEO
LOLA TOTS - Manager

Xi'an Famous Foods
38 E 23rd St
New York, NY 10010

Telephone: (212) 786-2068
Internet Homepage: xianfoods.com
Type of Business: Chain Restaurant Operator
Year Founded: 2005
Total Sales: $25,370,000 (e)
Number of Employees: 150
Total Units: 15
Trade Names: Xi'an Famous Foods (15)
Company-Owned Units: 15
Primary Menu: Chinese (15)
Areas of Operation: NY
Type of Foodservice: Fast Casual (15)
Notes: Total locations includes a tentatively open location in Woodside, Queens.

Key Personnel
JASON WANG - CEO; President; General Buyer

CHRISTINA BRONNE - Manager Operations

Yo Fresh Inc. LLC
362 5th Ave Suite 804
New York, NY 10001

Telephone: (212) 260-4416
Fax Number: (646) 626-6450
Internet Homepage: 16handles.com
Company Email: info@16handles.com
Type of Business: Chain Restaurant Operator
Year Founded: 2008
Systemwide Sales: $36,712,000 (e)
Total Sales: $26,620,000 (e)
Total Units: 33
Trade Names: 16 Handles (33)
Company-Owned Units: 12
Units Franchised To: 21
Preferred Square Footage: 1,200; 1,500
Preferred Location Types: Downtown; Regional Mall
Primary Menu: Health Foods (33)
Projected Openings: 23
Areas of Operation: CT, FL, MA, MD, NJ, NY
Type of Foodservice: Quick Serve (33)

Key Personnel
SOLOMON CHOI - CEO
ALEX CHOI - CFO; VP Operations; Controller
ROBYNNE MA'I'I - Corporate Chef

Zuma
261 Madison Ave
New York, NY 10016

Telephone: (212) 544-9862
Internet Homepage: zumarestaurant.com
Type of Business: Chain Restaurant Operator
Year Founded: 2002
Total Sales: $12,660,000 (e)
Number of Employees: 150
Total Units: 3
Trade Names: Zuma (3)
Company-Owned Units: 3
Primary Menu: Japanese (3)
Projected Openings: 1
Areas of Operation: FL, NV, NY
Type of Foodservice: Fine Dining (3)

Key Personnel
RAINER BECKER - Co-Founder
ARJUN WANEY - Co-Founder
IRFANKHAN PATHAN - Director Finance

Boqueria Restaurants
53 W 19th St
New York City, NY 10011

Telephone: (212) 255-4160

Internet Homepage: boqueriarestaurant.com
Company Email: Flatiron@BoqueriaNYC.com
Type of Business: Chain Restaurant Operator
Year Founded: 2006
Total Units: 6
Trade Names: Boqueria Tapas Bar & Spanish Restaurant (6)
Company-Owned Units: 6
Primary Menu: Spanish (6)
Projected Openings: 1
Areas of Operation: DC, NY
Type of Foodservice: Casual Dining (6)

Key Personnel
YANN DE ROCHEFORT - Founder
EMMA BLECKER - Chief of Staff
RACHEL KORNAFEL - VP Marketing
FRANSHELLY M - General Manager
OMAR G - General Manager
MEG GRACE LARCOM - Corporate Chef
PAUL FLEMING - Director
RICK FREDERICO - Director
SIMONE CAREAGA - Director Marketing
MATTHEW TANNENBAUM - Director Design
RUBEN RAMIREZ - Manager

R.E. Weichbrodt Inc.
218 Ford St
Newark, NY 14513-1104

Telephone: (315) 946-0027
Fax Number: (315) 946-3374
Type of Business: Chain Restaurant Operator
Year Founded: 1986
Total Sales: $23,700,000 (e)
Number of Employees: 250
Average Check: Breakfast(8); Lunch(8); Dinner(8)
Total Units: 5
Trade Names: McDonald's (5)
Units Franchised From: 5
Preferred Square Footage: 2,500; 3,000
Preferred Location Types: Freestanding
Primary Menu: Hamburger (5)
Areas of Operation: NY
Type of Foodservice: Quick Serve (5)
Franchise Affiliation: McDonald's Corporation, CHICAGO, IL
Primary Distributors: (Food) The Anderson-DuBose, ROCHESTER, NY

Key Personnel
WARREN WEICHBRODT - Partner; Director Facility/Maintenance, Information Systems, Human Resources, Store Fixtures; General Buyer
NANCY WILKES - Partner; General Buyer

Seneca Gaming Corporation
310 4th St
Niagara Falls, NY 14303-1242

Telephone: (716) 299-1100
Fax Number: (716) 299-1200
Internet Homepage: senecacasinos.com
Company Email:
info@SenecaGamingCorporation.com
Type of Business: Foodservice Operations - Casinos
Year Founded: 2002
Total Sales: $1,118,100,000 (e)
Alcohol Sales: 15%
Number of Employees: 4,800
Average Check: Breakfast(14); Lunch(18); Dinner(40)
Foodservice Sales: $111,810,000 (e)
Total Units: 13
Trade Names: Blues Burger Bar (1); Koi (1); Lounge 101 (1); Morrie's Express (1); Seneca Cafe (1); Seneca Cafe Express (1); The Creek (1); The Creek Stop (1); The Western Door: A Seneca Steakhouse (2); Three Sisters Cafe (1); Thunder Mountain Buffet (1); Tim Hortons Cafe (1)
Company-Owned Units: 10
Units Franchised From: 3
Preferred Square Footage: 2,500; 5,500; 6,000
Preferred Location Types: Other
Alcohol Served: Beer, Wine, Liquor
Primary Menu: American (6); Snacks (1)
Areas of Operation: NY
Type of Foodservice: Casual Dining (4); Family Restaurant (2); Fast Casual (3)
Franchise Affiliation: Kahala Brands, SCOTTSDALE, AZ
Primary Distributors: (Full Line) US Foods, BUFFALO, NY
Notes: Seneca Gaming does business as Seneca Niagara Casino and Hotel, Seneca Allegany Casino and Hotel, and Seneca Buffalo Creek Casino. The company derives approximately 90% of its revenue from casino, hotel, and retail operations.

Key Personnel
DAVID SHERIDAN - CFO; Senior VP Finance
ROBERT CHAMBERLAIN - Senior VP Construction, Design
MELISSA FREE - Senior VP Marketing
MICHAEL R. KIMELBERG - Senior VP Strategy, Corporate Development
LES LEONARD - VP
LISA CHAN - VP Marketing
DAVID FOX - VP Development
VINCE NARDANGELI - Executive Director Strategy
BETH NEPHEW - Executive Director Operations, Marketing
LINDA HITCHCOCK - General Manager
CHAMA DARCY - Director Operations
JILL CHRISTENSEN - Manager Sales
ANTHONY BENNETT - Manager Operations, Security
DAVID HOLLAND - Manager Production
MIKE GREEN - Manager Warehouse
LORETTA LIGAMMARI - Manager Marketing
KIM SUMBLER - Manager Safety
RHONDA ZORNICK - Manager Talent
MICHAEL RIVERA - Manager Customer Service
CARMEN GENOVESE - Administrator Inventory
LISA FITTANTE - General Buyer
CHRISTOPHER DUFFIN - Specialist Recruitment
JENNIFER HILL SKYE - Specialist Gaming/Entertainment
JOHN POSCH - Specialist Applications
JENNIFER PEREZ - Representative Marketing

The Como Restaurant
2220 Pine Ave
Niagara Falls, NY 14301-2330

Telephone: (716) 285-9341
Fax Number: (716) 282-5195
Internet Homepage: comorestaurant.com
Company Email:
comorestaurant@hotmail.com
Type of Business: Chain Restaurant Operator
Year Founded: 1927
Total Sales: $14,232,000 (e)
Alcohol Sales: 25%
Number of Employees: 150
Average Check: Lunch(8); Dinner(22)
Total Units: 3
Trade Names: The Como Restaurant (1); The Como Restaurant at the Airport (1); The Como Restaurant Deli (1)
Company-Owned Units: 3
Preferred Location Types: Freestanding; Strip Mall
Alcohol Served: Beer, Wine, Liquor
Primary Menu: Italian (3)
Areas of Operation: NY
Type of Foodservice: Casual Dining (3)
Catering Services: Yes

Key Personnel
DOMINIC COLUCCI - President; General Manager; General Buyer
STEVE HALL - Executive Chef
FRANK ANTONACCI - Buyer Beverages

Consumer Food Services, L.L.C.
60 Wheatley Rd
Old Westbury, NY 11568-1212

Mailing Address: PO Box 775, OAKHURST, NJ, 07755-0775
Telephone: (516) 626-0157
Type of Business: Chain Restaurant Operator
Total Sales: $20,370,000 (e)
Total Units: 9
Trade Names: Burger King (9)
Units Franchised From: 9
Primary Menu: Hamburger (9)
Areas of Operation: NY
Type of Foodservice: Quick Serve (9)
Franchise Affiliation: Burger King Worldwide Inc., MIAMI, FL

Key Personnel
CHARLES MAZZOCCHI - President; General Buyer

Domino's Franchisee
2626 W State St Unit 1
Olean, NY 14760-1858

Telephone: (716) 373-4210
Type of Business: Chain Restaurant Operator
Total Sales: $4,139,000 (e)
Total Units: 2
Trade Names: Domino's (2)
Units Franchised From: 2
Primary Menu: Pizza (2)
Areas of Operation: NY
Type of Foodservice: Quick Serve (2)
Franchise Affiliation: Domino's Pizza Inc, ANN ARBOR, MI

Key Personnel
WILLIAM H. PARRIS - Owner; General Buyer

Danny's
4300 Abbott Rd
Orchard Park, NY 14127-4219

Telephone: (716) 649-1194
Fax Number: (716) 649-4969
Internet Homepage: dannysrestaurant.com
Type of Business: Chain Restaurant Operator
Year Founded: 1958
Total Sales: $7,277,000 (e)
Alcohol Sales: 20%
Number of Employees: 70
Average Check: Lunch(10); Dinner(16)
Total Units: 2
Trade Names: Danny's (2)
Company-Owned Units: 2
Preferred Location Types: Freestanding
Alcohol Served: Beer, Wine, Liquor
Primary Menu: American (2)
Areas of Operation: NY
Type of Foodservice: Casual Dining (2)
Catering Services: Yes
Primary Distributors: (Food) Curtze Food Service, ERIE, PA

Key Personnel
MARK EBLING - Partner; General Manager;

Executive Chef; Director Catering

Domino's Franchisee
60 SW 9th St
Oswego, NY 13126-2402

Telephone: (315) 343-7250
Type of Business: Chain Restaurant Operator
Total Sales: $4,135,000 (e)
Total Units: 2
Trade Names: Domino's (2)
Units Franchised From: 2
Primary Menu: Pizza (2)
Areas of Operation: NY
Type of Foodservice: Quick Serve (2)
Franchise Affiliation: Domino's Pizza Inc, ANN ARBOR, MI

Key Personnel
TOM MATWEECHA - Owner; General Buyer

SoBol Inc.
185 Waverly Ave
Patchogue, NY 11772

Telephone: (631) 419-3470
Internet Homepage: mysobol.com; linkedin.com/company/sobol-inc
Type of Business: Chain Restaurant Operator
Year Founded: 2014
Total Sales: $25,350,000 (e)
Total Units: 36
Trade Names: Sobol Acai Bowls & Beyond (36)
Company-Owned Units: 1
Units Franchised To: 35
Preferred Square Footage: 1,800
Primary Menu: Health Foods (36)
Areas of Operation: CT, NY, PA
Type of Foodservice: Fast Casual (36)

Key Personnel
JASON MAZZARONE - Founder; CEO; President
PAUL GUCCIARDO - President Branding; Director Operations
NICK PESKO - Director Marketing
RICKEY STUEBER - Coordinator Development, Training

Coriale Enterprises
298 Lake St Ste 1
Penn Yan, NY 14527-1834

Telephone: (315) 536-3290
Fax Number: (315) 536-1113
Type of Business: Chain Restaurant Operator
Total Sales: $14,961,000 (e)
Total Units: 3
Trade Names: McDonald's (3)
Units Franchised From: 3
Primary Menu: Hamburger (3)
Areas of Operation: NY
Type of Foodservice: Quick Serve (3)
Franchise Affiliation: McDonald's Corporation, CHICAGO, IL

Key Personnel
JAMES CORIALE - President; General Buyer

CulinArt Inc.
175 Sunnyside Blvd Ste 200
Plainview, NY 11803-1521

Telephone: (516) 437-2700
Fax Number: (516) 437-6680
Internet Homepage: culinartinc.com
Company Email: info@culinartinc.com
Type of Business: Foodservice Management Operator
Year Founded: 1969
Total Sales: $146,899,000 (e)
Number of Employees: 2,000
Number of Locations Served: 160
Total Foodservice Mgmt Accounts: 160
Trade Names: Burger King (23); Carvel Ice Cream (5); Nathan's Famous Hot Dogs (12); Starbucks Coffee (21)
Units Franchised From: 61
Areas of Operation: NY
Type of Foodservice: Cafeteria (160)
Foodservice Management Venues: Business & Industry; College & University; Parks & Recreation
Franchise Affiliation: Burger King Worldwide Inc., MIAMI, FL; Carvel Corporation, ATLANTA, GA; Nathan's Famous Inc., JERICHO, NY; Starbucks Corporation, SEATTLE, WA
Primary Distributors: (Full Line) US Foods, BUFFALO, NY

Key Personnel
THOMAS EICH - CEO
MIKE PURCELL - President
TOM WIGGINTON - VP Corporate Development
MIKE PITKEWICZ - VP Risk Management, Human Resources
ALI BERNARDI - VP Marketing, Branding
JOSEPH SARGIS - VP Finance
LOU VOGT - VP Logistics
BOB KELLY - VP Business Development
PETER KLEIN - Director Culinary Development
ERIK BUCKHOLTZ - Director Human Resources
JOHN DREXEL - District Manager

Dame Bros Corporation
35 McKinley Ave
Plattsburgh, NY 12901-3815

Telephone: (518) 563-7786
Type of Business: Chain Restaurant Operator
Total Sales: $3,129,000 (e)
Total Units: 5
Trade Names: Subway (5)
Units Franchised From: 5
Primary Menu: Sandwiches/Deli (5)
Areas of Operation: NY
Type of Foodservice: Quick Serve (5)
Franchise Affiliation: Doctor's Associates Inc., MILFORD, CT

Key Personnel
RANDY DAME - Owner; General Buyer

Domino's Franchisee
331 Cornelia St
Plattsburgh, NY 12901-2316

Telephone: (518) 563-0600
Type of Business: Chain Restaurant Operator
Total Sales: $10,232,000 (e)
Total Units: 5
Trade Names: Domino's (5)
Units Franchised From: 5
Primary Menu: Pizza (5)
Areas of Operation: NY
Type of Foodservice: Quick Serve (5)
Franchise Affiliation: Domino's Pizza Inc, ANN ARBOR, MI

Key Personnel
TIMOTHY R. JARVIS - Owner; General Buyer

Burger Brothers Restaurant Group, Inc
20 Soundview Market Pl Ste 22
Port Washington, NY 11050-2221

Telephone: (516) 767-1472
Fax Number: (516) 767-3594
Type of Business: Chain Restaurant Operator
Total Sales: $71,690,000 (e)
Total Units: 32
Trade Names: Burger King (32)
Units Franchised From: 32
Primary Menu: Hamburger (32)
Areas of Operation: NY
Type of Foodservice: Quick Serve (32)
Franchise Affiliation: Burger King Worldwide Inc., MIAMI, FL

Key Personnel
JOHN FROCCARO - Partner; General Buyer
JEFF FROCCARO - Partner; General Buyer
JACQUELINE F - Assistant Controller
KEVIN PATERA - District Manager
JAMES R. FROCCARO III - Manager Operations

Lal Restaurant Group
21814 Jamaica Ave Ste 2
Queens Village, NY 11428-2153

Telephone: (718) 736-0999
Fax Number: (718) 736-0995
Company Email: sharmi.lalgroup@gmail.com
Type of Business: Chain Restaurant Operator
Year Founded: 2008
Total Sales: $206,970,000 (e)
Total Units: 89
Trade Names: Burger King (8); Dunkin' Donuts (6); Popeyes Louisiana Kitchen (75)
Units Franchised From: 89
Primary Menu: Chicken (75); Hamburger (8); Snacks (6)
Areas of Operation: NJ, NY, PA
Type of Foodservice: Quick Serve (89)
Franchise Affiliation: DD IP Holder, CANTON, MA; Popeyes Louisiana Kitchen Inc., ATLANTA, GA

Key Personnel
LALMIR SULTANZADA - President; General Buyer
SHARMILA ABRAHAM - Manager Real Estate
DAVID DRAKE - Designer

Abbott's Frozen Custard Inc.
4791 Lake Ave
Rochester, NY 14612-2154

Telephone: (585) 865-7400
Fax Number: (585) 865-6034
Internet Homepage: abbottscustard.com
Company Email: contactus@abbottscustard.com
Type of Business: Chain Restaurant Operator
Year Founded: 1902
Systemwide Sales: $37,332,000 (e)
Total Sales: $4,424,000 (e)
Number of Employees: 137
Average Check: Lunch(8); Dinner(12)
Internet Order Processing: Yes
Internet Sales: 1.00%
Total Units: 45
Trade Names: Abbott's Frozen Custard (35)
Company-Owned Units: 6
Units Franchised To: 29
Preferred Square Footage: 700; 1,000; 1,500
Preferred Location Types: Community Mall; Freestanding; Strip Mall
Primary Menu: Snacks (35)
Areas of Operation: FL, MA, NY, SC
Foreign Countries: CANADA; JAPAN
Type of Foodservice: Quick Serve (35)
Primary Distributors: (Food) Concord Foods Inc., ONTARIO, CA

Key Personnel
GAIL DREW - President; Director Operations, Purchasing, Facility/Maintenance, Real Estate, Design
ROBERT AMICO - VP; Director Finance, Information Systems, Human Resources, Menu Development
JOE ORDEN - Director Franchising

DiBella's Old Fashioned Submarines Inc.
180 Canal View Blvd Ste 600
Rochester, NY 14623-2849

Telephone: (585) 641-2210
Fax Number: (585) 641-2212
Internet Homepage: dibellas.com
Company Email: feedback@dibellas.com
Type of Business: Chain Restaurant Operator
Year Founded: 1918
Total Sales: $31,400,000 (e)
Number of Employees: 470
Total Units: 47
Trade Names: DiBella's Old Fashioned Submarines (47)
Company-Owned Units: 47
Preferred Square Footage: 3,300; 3,500; 3,900
Preferred Location Types: Community Mall; Strip Mall
Primary Menu: Sandwiches/Deli (47)
Areas of Operation: CT, IN, MI, NY, OH, PA
Type of Foodservice: Quick Serve (47)
Catering Services: Yes

Key Personnel
PETER FOX - VP Operations

India House
998 Clinton Ave S
Rochester, NY 14620-2025

Telephone: (585) 461-0880
Fax Number: (585) 461-5818
Internet Homepage: Indiahouse.com
Company Email: support@indiahouse.com
Type of Business: Chain Restaurant Operator
Total Sales: $6,529,000 (e)
Alcohol Sales: 5%
Average Check: Dinner(18)
Total Units: 4
Trade Names: India House Express (1); India House Restaurant (3)
Company-Owned Units: 4
Alcohol Served: Beer, Wine, Liquor
Primary Menu: Indian (4)
Areas of Operation: NY
Type of Foodservice: Fast Casual (1); Fine Dining (3)
Catering Services: Yes

Key Personnel
OM SUD - Owner; Executive Chef; General Buyer
AMIT SUD - General Manager; General Buyer

MSWG of Rochester, Inc.
186 Sylvania Rd
Rochester, NY 14618-3706

Telephone: (585) 424-6637
Type of Business: Chain Restaurant Operator
Total Sales: $8,189,000 (e)
Total Units: 5
Trade Names: Moe's Southwest Grill (5)
Units Franchised From: 5
Primary Menu: Southwest/Tex-Mex (5)
Areas of Operation: NY
Type of Foodservice: Fast Casual (5)
Franchise Affiliation: Moe's Southwest Grill LLC, ATLANTA, GA

Key Personnel
BRADLEY DEGRAZIA - Partner; General Buyer
DREW DEGRAZIA - Partner

Rayner Enterprises
3280 Monroe Ave
Rochester, NY 14618-4608

Telephone: (585) 586-1867
Type of Business: Chain Restaurant Operator
Total Sales: $10,033,000 (e)
Total Units: 2
Trade Names: McDonald's (2)
Units Franchised From: 2
Primary Menu: Hamburger (2)
Areas of Operation: NY
Type of Foodservice: Quick Serve (2)
Franchise Affiliation: McDonald's Corporation, CHICAGO, IL

Key Personnel
RON FITHEN - Owner; General Buyer

Dodici
12 N Park Ave
Rockville Centre, NY 11570-5223

Telephone: (516) 764-3000
Fax Number: (516) 678-4813
Internet Homepage: bluemoonpizzeria.com; dodicirestaurant.com
Company Email: dodicirestaurant@yahoo.com
Type of Business: Chain Restaurant Operator
Total Sales: $4,553,000 (e)
Alcohol Sales: 15%
Number of Employees: 20
Average Check: Dinner(36)
Total Units: 2

Trade Names: Blue Moon (1); Dodici (1)
Company-Owned Units: 2
Preferred Location Types: Freestanding
Alcohol Served: Beer, Wine, Liquor
Primary Menu: Italian (2)
Areas of Operation: NY
Type of Foodservice: Casual Dining (2)
Primary Distributors: (Food) US Foods, BUFFALO, NY

Key Personnel
ROBERTO NALDINI - Manager

George Martin Restaurant Group
65 N Park Ave
Rockville Centre, NY 11570-4105

Telephone: (516) 678-7225
Fax Number: (516) 594-9356
Internet Homepage:
 georgemartinsstripsteak.com;
 georgemartintheoriginal.com;
 georgemartingroup.com;
 georgemartinsgrillfire.com; gmburgerbar.com;
 vivotrattoria.com
Company Email: info@georgemartingroup.com
Type of Business: Chain Restaurant Operator
Year Founded: 1989
Total Sales: $11,040,000 (e)
Alcohol Sales: 30%
Number of Employees: 108
Average Check: Lunch(22); Dinner(42)
Total Units: 6
Trade Names: George Martin Grill Fire (2); George Martin Original (1); George Martin Strip Steak (1); GM Burger Bar (1); Vivo Trattoria (1)
Company-Owned Units: 6
Preferred Location Types: Freestanding
Alcohol Served: Beer, Wine, Liquor
Primary Menu: Hamburger (1); Italian (1); Steak (4)
Areas of Operation: MD, NY
Type of Foodservice: Casual Dining (6)
Catering Services: Yes
Primary Distributors: (Full Line) US Foods, BUFFALO, NY; (Full Line) Landmark Food Corp., HOLTSVILLE, NY

Key Personnel
GEORGE KORTEN - President; Owner; General Buyer
SUZANNE RASPANTI - General Manager; General Buyer
FRANK GRECO - Executive Chef; General Buyer

Kotobuki
1530 Old Northern Blvd
Roslyn, NY 11576-1126

Telephone: (516) 621-5312
Fax Number: (516) 621-5313
Internet Homepage: kotobukinewyork.com
Type of Business: Chain Restaurant Operator
Total Sales: $6,006,000 (e)
Alcohol Sales: 15%
Average Check: Lunch(30); Dinner(42)
Internet Order Processing: Yes
Total Units: 4
Trade Names: Kotobuki (4)
Company-Owned Units: 4
Preferred Location Types: Downtown; Freestanding
Alcohol Served: Beer, Wine
Primary Menu: Japanese (4)
Areas of Operation: NY
Type of Foodservice: Family Restaurant (4)

Key Personnel
YOSHI NARITA - Owner; General Manager; Executive Chef; General Buyer
ERIC KIM - Director Operations

Poll Restaurants
2 Middleneck Rd
Roslyn, NY 11576-1348

Telephone: (516) 627-0021
Internet Homepage: pollrestaurants.com
Type of Business: Chain Restaurant Operator
Year Founded: 1986
Total Sales: $25,090,000 (e)
Alcohol Sales: 18%
Total Units: 7
Trade Names: Bar Frites (1); Bryant & Cooper (1); Cipollini Trattoria & Bar (1); Hendrick's Tavern (1); Majors Steakhouse (1); The Bryant (1); TOKU (1)
Company-Owned Units: 7
Preferred Location Types: Community Mall; Regional Mall
Alcohol Served: Beer, Wine, Liquor
Primary Menu: American (1); Asian (1); French/Continental (1); Italian (1); Steak (3)
Projected Openings: 1
Areas of Operation: NY
Type of Foodservice: Casual Dining (4); Fine Dining (3)

Key Personnel
GEORGE POLL - Partner; General Buyer
GILLIS POLL - Partner; General Buyer

Pearl Restaurant Group
PO Box 1027
Rye, NY 10580-0827

Telephone: (914) 921-8132
Internet Homepage: pearlrestaurantgroup.com
Company Email: hello@pearlrestaurantgroup.com
Type of Business: Chain Restaurant Operator
Year Founded: 1992
Total Sales: $18,470,000 (e)
Alcohol Sales: 18%
Number of Employees: 200
Average Check: Lunch(30); Dinner(46)
Total Units: 7
Trade Names: Elm Street Oyster House (1); Lexington Square Cafe (1); Morgan's Fish House (1); Ruby's Oyster Bar & Bistro (1); Rye Grill & Bar (1); Ten Twenty Post (1); The Tap House (1)
Company-Owned Units: 7
Preferred Square Footage: 5,500; 6,000
Preferred Location Types: Freestanding
Alcohol Served: Beer, Wine
Primary Menu: American (4); Seafood (3)
Areas of Operation: CT, NY
Type of Foodservice: Casual Dining (7)
Primary Distributors: (Food) Ace Endico Corporation, BREWSTER, NY; (Supplies) Ace Endico Corporation, BREWSTER, NY

Key Personnel
JAMES SULLIVAN - President; Partner; Director Operations, Real Estate, Design, Store Fixtures
WILLIAM KULHANEK - Partner; General Manager; Executive Chef; General Buyer
JAN FABRY - COO
NANCY DILEO - Controller

Z Hospitality Group
60 Purchase St
Rye, NY 10580-3009

Telephone: (914) 921-2333
Internet Homepage: auroraofrye.com; mediterraneoofgreenwich.com; soleofnewcanaan.com; terraofgreenwich.com; zhospitalitygroup.com
Type of Business: Chain Restaurant Operator
Year Founded: 1997
Total Sales: $24,250,000 (e)
Alcohol Sales: 15%
Number of Employees: 210
Average Check: Lunch(24); Dinner(54)
Total Units: 8
Trade Names: Aurora (1); Eastend (1); Mediterraneo (3); Sole (1); Terra Ristorante Italiano (2)
Company-Owned Units: 8
Preferred Square Footage: 5,500; 6,000

Preferred Location Types: Freestanding
Alcohol Served: Beer, Wine, Liquor
Primary Menu: Italian (8)
Areas of Operation: CT, NY
Type of Foodservice: Fine Dining (8)
Primary Distributors: (Full Line) Dairyland, The Chefs' Warehouse, BRONX, NY

Key Personnel
RAMZE ZAKKA - President; Partner; Director Finance, Information Systems, Real Estate
ADAM ZAKKA - Partner; COO
ALBERT DEANGELIS - Executive Chef; Director Menu Development
JOSEPH G. HAMBOUSSI - Director Operations

Chartwells Educational Dining Services
2 International Dr
Rye Brook, NY 10573-1094

Telephone: (914) 935-5300
Fax Number: (914) 935-5550
Internet Homepage: eatlearnlive.com
Type of Business: Foodservice Management Operator
Year Founded: 1965
Total Sales: $3,564,664,000 (e)
Number of Employees: 30,000
Number of Locations Served: 975
Total Foodservice Mgmt Accounts: 975
Total Units: 880
Company-Owned Units: 880
Areas of Operation: NY
Type of Foodservice: Cafeteria (975)
Foodservice Management Venues: College & University; Schools
Primary Distributors: (Full Line) Performance Food Group, RICHMOND, VA
Parent Company: Compass Group PLC, LONDON, ENG
Headquarters: Compass Group The Americas, CHARLOTTE, NC

Key Personnel
RAY MULLIGAN - President
PHIL DELGIUDICE - VP Business Development

Rye Ridge Deli & Restaurant
126 S Ridge St
Rye Brook, NY 10573-2813

Telephone: (914) 937-2131
Fax Number: (914) 937-4289
Internet Homepage: ryeridgedeli.com
Company Email: ryeridgedelinyct@gmail.com
Type of Business: Chain Restaurant Operator
Year Founded: 1983
Total Sales: $18,241,000 (e)
Alcohol Sales: 20%
Number of Employees: 40
Average Check: Breakfast(8); Lunch(10); Dinner(20)
Total Units: 3
Trade Names: Rye Ridge Deli & Restaurant (3)
Company-Owned Units: 3
Preferred Location Types: Strip Mall
Alcohol Served: Beer, Wine
Primary Menu: American (3)
Areas of Operation: CT, NY
Type of Foodservice: Casual Dining (3)
Catering Services: Yes
Primary Distributors: (Food) Tufo's Food's, BRONX, NY

Key Personnel
HARRY MARTIN - President; Partner; General Buyer
SCOTT MARTIN - Partner
LEVID AGUIRE - Executive Chef; Director Menu Development, Catering
JAVIER SOSA - Assistant Manager

Domino's Franchisee
5640 Sunrise Hwy Ste 300
Sayville, NY 11782-1016

Telephone: (631) 567-0600
Type of Business: Chain Restaurant Operator
Total Sales: $20,514,000 (e)
Total Units: 10
Trade Names: Domino's (10)
Units Franchised From: 10
Primary Menu: Pizza (10)
Areas of Operation: NY
Type of Foodservice: Quick Serve (10)
Franchise Affiliation: Domino's Pizza Inc, ANN ARBOR, MI

Key Personnel
CHRISTOPHER M. HANLEY - Owner; General Buyer

Pasta Pasta/Cafe Joelle
25 Main St
Sayville, NY 11782-2501

Telephone: (631) 589-4600
Fax Number: (631) 589-4632
Internet Homepage: pastapasta.net; cafejoelle.com
Company Email: cafejoelle@yahoo.com
Type of Business: Chain Restaurant Operator
Year Founded: 1995
Total Sales: $3,755,000 (e)
Alcohol Sales: 15%
Number of Employees: 50
Average Check: Lunch(18); Dinner(38)
Total Units: 2
Trade Names: Cafe Joelle (1); Pasta Pasta (1)
Company-Owned Units: 2
Preferred Location Types: Downtown
Alcohol Served: Beer, Wine, Liquor
Primary Menu: Italian (2)
Areas of Operation: NY
Type of Foodservice: Casual Dining (2)
Catering Services: Yes
Primary Distributors: (Food) SYSCO Food Services of Syracuse, WARNERS, NY

Key Personnel
JULES BUITRON - Partner; Executive Chef; General Buyer
STEVE SANDS - Partner; General Buyer

Dining Associates
26 W Genesee St
Skaneateles, NY 13152-1020

Mailing Address: PO Box 529, SKANEATELES, NY, 13152-0529
Telephone: (315) 685-3405
Fax Number: (315) 685-8983
Internet Homepage: gildasskaneateles.com; phoebessyracuse.com; sherwoodinnproperties.com; thesherwoodinn.com; thesherwoodinn.com/patisserie
Company Email: info@thesherwoodinn.com
Type of Business: Chain Restaurant Operator
Year Founded: 1971
Total Sales: $8,112,000 (e)
Alcohol Sales: 30%
Number of Employees: 300
Average Check: Breakfast(14); Lunch(20); Dinner(28)
Total Units: 6
Trade Names: Bluewater Grill (1); Gilda's (1); Patisserie (1); Phoebe's Garden Cafe (1); Sherwood Inn (1); The Tavern (1)
Company-Owned Units: 6
Preferred Square Footage: 5,500; 6,000
Preferred Location Types: Downtown; Freestanding; Hotel/Motel
Alcohol Served: Beer, Wine, Liquor
Primary Menu: American (5); Sandwiches/Deli (1)
Areas of Operation: NY
Type of Foodservice: Casual Dining (6); Quick Serve (1)
Catering Services: Yes
Primary Distributors: (Full Line) US Foods, PITTSTON, PA

Key Personnel
BILL EBERHARDT - CEO; President; Manager Operations, Purchasing, Real Estate, Design, Human Resources, Menu Development
SAM MASON - General Manager
NANCY RANIERI - Director Sales, Catering

RSVT Holding, LLC
29 Windsor Ct
Slingerlands, NY 12159-3713

Telephone: (518) 488-4060
Type of Business: Chain Restaurant Operator
Total Sales: $35,610,000 (e)
Total Units: 18
Trade Names: Five Guys Burgers and Fries (18)
Units Franchised From: 18
Preferred Square Footage: 3,000
Primary Menu: Hamburger (18)
Areas of Operation: NY
Type of Foodservice: Fast Casual (18)
Franchise Affiliation: Five Guys Holdings Inc., LORTON, VA

Key Personnel
TEJRAJ HADA - Partner; General Buyer
SAVITA HADA - Partner

Golden Pear Corp.
99 Main St
Southampton, NY 11968-4808

Mailing Address: PO Box 5080, SOUTHAMPTON, NY, 11969-5080
Telephone: (631) 287-4242
Fax Number: (631) 283-7799
Internet Homepage: goldenpear.com; goldenpearcafe.com
Company Email: info@goldenpearcafe.com
Type of Business: Chain Restaurant Operator
Year Founded: 1987
Total Sales: $4,079,000 (e)
Number of Employees: 60
Average Check: Breakfast(10); Lunch(10);
Internet Order Processing: Yes
Total Units: 4
Trade Names: The Golden Pear Cafe (4)
Company-Owned Units: 4
Preferred Square Footage: 3,600
Preferred Location Types: Freestanding; Strip Mall
Areas of Operation: NY
Type of Foodservice: Family Restaurant (4)
Catering Services: Yes
Primary Distributors: (Equipment) Imperial Bag & Paper Co LLC Center Moriches Paper, JERSEY CITY, NJ; (Food) J. Kings Food Services Professionals Inc., HOLTSVILLE, NY

Key Personnel
KEITH E. DAVIS - President; General Manager; Executive Chef; Director Facility/Maintenance, Real Estate, Design, Catering; General Buyer
KATIE BRANDT - VP Risk Management
GINA BIAMONTE - Controller; Director Catering

Arlekan, Inc.
135 Kelvin Ave
Staten Island, NY 10306-3743

Telephone: (646) 379-6955
Company Email: reskander@email.com
Type of Business: Chain Restaurant Operator
Total Sales: $2,648,000 (e)
Total Units: 2
Trade Names: Little Caesars Pizza (2)
Units Franchised From: 2
Primary Menu: Pizza (2)
Areas of Operation: NY
Type of Foodservice: Quick Serve (2)
Franchise Affiliation: Little Caesar Enterprises Inc., DETROIT, MI

Key Personnel
RAMY IBRAHIM - President; General Buyer

Golden Ice Cream LLC
2341 Richmond Ave
Staten Island, NY 10314-3918

Telephone: (718) 983-5700
Type of Business: Chain Restaurant Operator
Total Sales: $1,200,000 (e)
Total Units: 1
Trade Names: Cold Stone Creamery (1)
Units Franchised From: 1
Primary Menu: Snacks (1)
Areas of Operation: NY
Type of Foodservice: Quick Serve (2)
Franchise Affiliation: Kahala Brands, SCOTTSDALE, AZ

Key Personnel
YAN SHI CREGAN - Owner

Parikh Network
15 Nicolosi Dr
Staten Island, NY 10312

Telephone: (732) 318-6269
Type of Business: Chain Restaurant Operator
Total Sales: $218,580,000 (e)
Total Units: 94
Trade Names: Arby's (12); Popeyes Louisiana Kitchen (82)
Units Franchised From: 94
Areas of Operation: CT, DE, IL, MA, MD, NJ, NY, PA
Franchise Affiliation: Popeyes Louisiana Kitchen Inc., ATLANTA, GA

Key Personnel
AMISH PARIKH - Co-Founder; President
ASHISH PARIKH - CEO

KINJAL SHAH - CFO; Controller

Patrick Marianne Corp
653 Edgegrove Ave
Staten Island, NY 10312-2762

Telephone: (718) 967-8713
Fax Number: (718) 967-5135
Type of Business: Chain Restaurant Operator
Total Sales: $28,230,000 (e)
Number of Employees: 100
Total Units: 6
Trade Names: McDonald's (6)
Units Franchised From: 6
Preferred Square Footage: 2,500
Primary Menu: Hamburger (6)
Areas of Operation: NY
Type of Foodservice: Quick Serve (6)
Franchise Affiliation: McDonald's Corporation, CHICAGO, IL

Key Personnel
MARIANNE SPILLANE - Partner; General Buyer
PATRICK SPILLANE - Partner; General Buyer

Sweeney Enterprises
3267 Richmond Ave
Staten Island, NY 10312-2123

Telephone: (718) 948-3800
Type of Business: Chain Restaurant Operator
Total Sales: $9,995,000 (e)
Total Units: 2
Trade Names: McDonald's (2)
Units Franchised From: 2
Primary Menu: Hamburger (2)
Areas of Operation: NY
Type of Foodservice: Quick Serve (2)
Franchise Affiliation: McDonald's Corporation, CHICAGO, IL

Key Personnel
MICHAEL SWEENEY - President; General Buyer

Uncle Louie G
115 Johnson St
Staten Island, NY 10309-1114

Telephone: (718) 966-3763
Fax Number: (718) 966-3764
Internet Homepage: unclelouiegee.com
Company Email: dinoices@aol.com
Type of Business: Chain Restaurant Operator
Year Founded: 1999
Total Sales: $2,167,000 (e)
Average Check: Dinner(8)
Total Units: 50
Trade Names: Uncle Louie G (50)

Units Franchised To: 50
Primary Menu: Snacks (50)
Areas of Operation: CT, FL, GA, MD, NC, NJ, NY, PA
Type of Foodservice: Quick Serve (50)
Catering Services: Yes
Distribution Centers: STATEN ISLAND, NY
On-site Distribution Center: Yes

Key Personnel
DINO RUSSO - Owner; General Buyer

C & B Restaurant Corporation
14 John St
Stony Point, NY 10980-1917

Telephone: (845) 429-7504
Fax Number: (845) 429-7564
Type of Business: Chain Restaurant Operator
Year Founded: 1977
Total Sales: $19,490,000 (e)
Number of Employees: 260
Average Check: Lunch(10); Dinner(10)
Total Units: 10
Trade Names: KFC (7); KFC/Taco Bell (3)
Units Franchised From: 10
Preferred Square Footage: 2,200
Preferred Location Types: Freestanding; Strip Mall
Primary Menu: Chicken (7); Taco (3)
Areas of Operation: NJ, NY
Type of Foodservice: Quick Serve (10)
Franchise Affiliation: KFC Corporation, LOUISVILLE, KY
Primary Distributors: (Full Line) McLane/Guilderland Center, GUILDERLAND CENTER, NY

Key Personnel
JOSEPH CAVEGN - President; Director Finance, Supply Chain, Real Estate, Design

Auntie Anne's Franchise
9677 Destiny Usa Dr
Syracuse, NY 13204-9621

Telephone: (315) 466-4012
Type of Business: Chain Restaurant Operator
Total Sales: $1,596,000 (e)
Total Units: 2
Trade Names: Auntie Anne's Hand-Rolled Soft Pretzels (2)
Units Franchised From: 2
Primary Menu: Snacks (2)
Areas of Operation: NY
Type of Foodservice: Quick Serve (2)
Franchise Affiliation: Auntie Anne's Inc., LANCASTER, PA

Key Personnel
DAVID MARGOLIS - Owner; General Buyer

Bart-Rich Enterprises
6060 Court Street Rd Ste 2
Syracuse, NY 13206-1746

Telephone: (315) 463-7181
Fax Number: (315) 463-4627
Internet Homepage: bartrich.com
Company Email: info@bartrich.com
Type of Business: Chain Restaurant Operator
Year Founded: 1975
Total Sales: $46,620,000 (e)
Number of Employees: 450
Average Check: Breakfast(8); Lunch(8); Dinner(8)
Total Units: 21
Trade Names: Burger King (21)
Units Franchised From: 21
Preferred Square Footage: 3,000
Preferred Location Types: Freestanding; Strip Mall
Primary Menu: Hamburger (21)
Areas of Operation: NY, PA
Type of Foodservice: Quick Serve (21)
Franchise Affiliation: Burger King Worldwide Inc., MIAMI, FL
Primary Distributors: (Full Line) Maines Paper & Food Service Inc., CONKLIN, NY

Key Personnel
RICK BARTLETT - Director Supply Chain, Marketing, Real Estate; General Buyer

Dinosaur Bar-B-Que
234 W Genesee St
Syracuse, NY 13202-1020

Telephone: (315) 476-1662
Fax Number: (315) 476-1663
Internet Homepage: dinosaurbarbque.com
Type of Business: Chain Restaurant Operator
Year Founded: 1983
Total Sales: $10,790,000 (e)
Alcohol Sales: 25%
Number of Employees: 270
Average Check: Lunch(12); Dinner(16)
Internet Order Processing: Yes
Internet Sales: 5.00%
Total Units: 8
Trade Names: Dinosaur Bar-B-Que (8)
Company-Owned Units: 8
Preferred Location Types: Freestanding
Alcohol Served: Beer, Wine, Liquor
Primary Menu: Bar-B-Q (8)
Areas of Operation: CT, NJ, NY
Type of Foodservice: Casual Dining (8)
Catering Services: Yes
Primary Distributors: (Full Line) SYSCO Food Services of Albany, HALFMOON, NY

Key Personnel
JOHN STAGE - Chairman; Founder; CFO; Executive Chef
MIKE NUGENT - COO
LINDSAY AMORESE - VP Operations
LELAND AVELLINO - Executive Chef
JIM CLANCY - Director Operations

Paul Ross
117 N Townsend St
Syracuse, NY 13203-2336

Telephone: (315) 472-5556
Fax Number: (315) 478-1209
Company Email: cindy.tyrrell@cnymcd1.com
Type of Business: Chain Restaurant Operator
Year Founded: 1970
Total Sales: $61,550,000 (e)
Number of Employees: 500
Average Check: Breakfast(8); Lunch(8); Dinner(10)
Total Units: 13
Trade Names: McDonald's (13)
Units Franchised From: 13
Preferred Square Footage: 3,000
Preferred Location Types: Freestanding
Primary Menu: Hamburger (13)
Areas of Operation: NY
Type of Foodservice: Quick Serve (13)
Franchise Affiliation: McDonald's Corporation, CHICAGO, IL
Primary Distributors: (Full Line) The Anderson-DuBose, ROCHESTER, NY

Key Personnel
PAUL ROSS - President; Director Finance, Operations, Facility/Maintenance, Information Systems, Supply Chain, Real Estate, Design, Store Fixtures; General Buyer
CINDY TYRRELL - Manager Accounting, Branch

Franco's Pizza
2714 Sheridan Dr Ste 1
Tonawanda, NY 14150-9458

Telephone: (716) 833-5633
Fax Number: (716) 833-6426
Internet Homepage: francospizza.com
Company Email: franco@francospizza.com
Type of Business: Chain Restaurant Operator
Year Founded: 1979
Total Sales: $5,446,000 (e)
Number of Employees: 75
Average Check: Lunch(8); Dinner(8)
Internet Order Processing: Yes
Total Units: 5
Trade Names: Franco's Pizza (5)
Company-Owned Units: 5
Preferred Square Footage: 1,500

Preferred Location Types: Freestanding
Primary Menu: Pizza (5)
Areas of Operation: NY
Type of Foodservice: Quick Serve (5)
Primary Distributors: (Full Line) US Foods, BUFFALO, NY

Key Personnel
MARIO KROESE - VP

Domino's Franchisee
198 Hoosick St
Troy, NY 12180-2326

Telephone: (518) 273-3030
Type of Business: Chain Restaurant Operator
Total Sales: $16,473,000 (e)
Total Units: 8
Trade Names: Domino's (8)
Units Franchised From: 8
Primary Menu: Pizza (8)
Areas of Operation: NY
Type of Foodservice: Quick Serve (8)
Franchise Affiliation: Domino's Pizza Inc, ANN ARBOR, MI

Key Personnel
ALAN ERWIN - Owner; General Buyer

TBG Food Acquisition Corp.
68 Main St
Tuckahoe, NY 10707

Telephone: (914) 779-7878
Type of Business: Chain Restaurant Operator
Total Sales: $55,900,000 (e)
Total Units: 36
Trade Names: Dunkin' Donuts (36)
Units Franchised From: 36
Primary Menu: Snacks (36)
Projected Openings: 3
Areas of Operation: NY, SC, VA
Type of Foodservice: Quick Serve (36)
Franchise Affiliation: DD IP Holder, CANTON, MA
Parent Company: The Beekman Group, NEW YORK, NY

Key Personnel
PETER MARRINAN - President
LENA VLADSKY - Director Human Resources

Mac-Clark Restaurants Inc.
185 Genesee St Ste 1505
Utica, NY 13501-2109

Telephone: (315) 735-1240
Fax Number: (315) 732-0857
Type of Business: Chain Restaurant Operator
Year Founded: 1989
Total Sales: $93,930,000 (e)
Number of Employees: 600
Average Check: Breakfast(8); Lunch(10); Dinner(12)
Total Units: 20
Trade Names: McDonald's (20)
Units Franchised From: 20
Preferred Square Footage: 2,500; 3,000
Preferred Location Types: Freestanding
Primary Menu: Hamburger (20)
Areas of Operation: NY
Type of Foodservice: Quick Serve (20)
Franchise Affiliation: McDonald's Corporation, CHICAGO, IL
Primary Distributors: (Food) The Anderson-DuBose, ROCHESTER, NY

Key Personnel
HAROLD CLARK JR - President; Partner; Director Information Systems, Real Estate; General Buyer
TOM CLARK III - Partner; Director Finance
DONNA ARMSTRONG - Director Human Resources
JOAN GRANDY - Director Customer Service
DEBRA SALTIS - Manager Business Development
JOSEPH ADAMCZYK - Manager Human Resources
ALBERT DOHN - Manager Operations, Facility/Maintenance

ROBWAT Management Inc.
41 Notre Dame Ln Ste 1
Utica, NY 13502-4800

Telephone: (315) 735-9918
Fax Number: (315) 797-0482
Type of Business: Chain Restaurant Operator
Year Founded: 1966
Total Sales: $5,698,000 (e)
Number of Employees: 70
Average Check: Lunch(8); Dinner(8)
Total Units: 3
Trade Names: KFC (3)
Units Franchised From: 3
Preferred Square Footage: 3,000
Preferred Location Types: Freestanding
Primary Menu: American (3); Chicken (3)
Areas of Operation: NY
Type of Foodservice: Quick Serve (3)
Franchise Affiliation: KFC Corporation, LOUISVILLE, KY
Primary Distributors: (Full Line) McLane/Guilderland Center, GUILDERLAND CENTER, NY

Key Personnel
JOSEPHINE KRAUSE - General Manager; Director Operations, Information Systems, Food Safety; General Buyer

Laurino Enterprises
806 W Merrick Rd
Valley Stream, NY 11580-4829

Telephone: (516) 872-3700
Fax Number: (516) 872-4742
Type of Business: Chain Restaurant Operator
Total Sales: $68,040,000 (e)
Total Units: 14
Trade Names: McDonald's (14)
Units Franchised From: 14
Preferred Square Footage: 2,500
Primary Menu: Hamburger (14)
Areas of Operation: NY
Type of Foodservice: Quick Serve (14)
Franchise Affiliation: McDonald's Corporation, CHICAGO, IL

Key Personnel
GERALD LAURINO - President; General Buyer

CoreLife Eatery, LLC
4700 Vestal Pkwy E
Vestal, NY 13850-3770

Telephone: (607) 203-2977
Internet Homepage: corelifeeatery.com
Company Email: info@eatatcore.com
Type of Business: Chain Restaurant Operator
Year Founded: 2015
Total Sales: $37,930,000 (e)
Total Units: 52
Trade Names: CoreLife Eatery (52)
Company-Owned Units: 52
Primary Menu: Health Foods (52)
Projected Openings: 20
Areas of Operation: IL, IN, KY, MI, NY, OH, PA, TN, UT
Type of Foodservice: Fast Casual (52)
Notes: CEO and Chairman Larry Wilson is also a Moe's Southwest Grill franchisee (Larry Wilson, LLC).

Key Personnel
LARRY WILSON - Chairman; Co-Founder; CEO; Partner
TODD MANSFIELD - Co-Founder; Chief Culture Officer; Exec VP
SCOTT DAVIS - President; Partner
JEFFREY COGHLAN - Chief Administrative Officer
JULIA SIMON - VP Marketing
RYAN TIMMONS - Director Operations

Metro Bd LLC
160 Vestal Pkwy E
Vestal, NY 13850-1618

Telephone: (607) 748-8299
Company Email: subway11076@yahoo.com
Type of Business: Chain Restaurant Operator
Total Sales: $1,516,000 (e)
Total Units: 2
Trade Names: Subway (2)
Units Franchised From: 2
Primary Menu: Sandwiches/Deli (2)
Areas of Operation: NY
Type of Foodservice: Quick Serve (2)
Franchise Affiliation: Doctor's Associates Inc., MILFORD, CT

Key Personnel
THADDEUS SISSON - President; General Buyer

Sboro's Family Restaurants
820 Huntington St
Watertown, NY 13601-2822

Telephone: (315) 782-9764
Fax Number: (315) 788-8077
Internet Homepage: artsjug.com; sborosrestaurant.com
Type of Business: Chain Restaurant Operator
Total Sales: $3,640,000 (e)
Total Units: 2
Trade Names: Art's Jug (1); Sboro's Restaurant (1)
Company-Owned Units: 2
Primary Menu: Italian (2)
Areas of Operation: NY
Type of Foodservice: Casual Dining (2)

Key Personnel
STEVEN SBORO - Owner; General Manager; General Buyer

Ted's Fish Fry Inc.
447 3rd Ave
Watervliet, NY 12189-3808

Telephone: (518) 273-0232
Fax Number: (518) 273-1418
Internet Homepage: tedsfishfry.net
Company Email: tedsfishfry@nycap.rr.com
Type of Business: Chain Restaurant Operator
Year Founded: 1950
Total Sales: $3,823,000 (e)
Number of Employees: 90
Average Check: Lunch(12); Dinner(14)
Total Units: 6
Trade Names: Ted's Fish Fry (6)
Company-Owned Units: 6
Preferred Location Types: Freestanding
Primary Menu: Seafood (6)
Areas of Operation: NY
Type of Foodservice: Quick Serve (6)

Key Personnel
S.K. DEEB - President; General Manager; Executive Chef; General Buyer

Bill Gray's Inc.
964 Ridge Rd
Webster, NY 14580-2555

Telephone: (585) 787-0150
Fax Number: (585) 787-0816
Internet Homepage: billgrays.com
Company Email: feedback@BillGrays.com
Type of Business: Chain Restaurant Operator
Year Founded: 1938
Total Sales: $23,930,000 (e)
Number of Employees: 586
Average Check: Breakfast(8); Lunch(18); Dinner(24)
Internet Order Processing: Yes
Total Units: 22
Trade Names: Bill Gray's (15); Bill Gray's Tap Room (6); Flaherty's (1)
Company-Owned Units: 20
Preferred Square Footage: 10,000
Preferred Location Types: Freestanding; Regional Mall
Alcohol Served: Beer, Wine, Liquor
Areas of Operation: NY
Type of Foodservice: Casual Dining (7); Family Restaurant (15)
Primary Distributors: (Full Line) Maines Paper & Food Service New York Metro, FARMINGDALE, NY

Key Personnel
JOHN GONZALEZ - CEO; CFO
RICHARD MASTIN - VP Operations; Manager Operations, Purchasing, Supply Chain, Real Estate, Business Development

Sagebrook Restaurant Management
1177 Corporate Dr
Westbury, NY 11590

Telephone: (516) 222-7010
Fax Number: (516) 222-7014
Internet Homepage: cozymels.com/store_longisland.htm
Type of Business: Chain Restaurant Operator
Year Founded: 1995
Total Sales: $4,709,000 (e)
Alcohol Sales: 25%
Number of Employees: 240
Average Check: Lunch(8); Dinner(18)
Internet Order Processing: Yes
Internet Sales: 1.00%
Total Units: 1
Trade Names: Cozymel's Mexican Grill (1)
Company-Owned Units: 1
Preferred Square Footage: 7,500
Preferred Location Types: Downtown; Freestanding; Regional Mall
Alcohol Served: Beer, Wine, Liquor
Primary Menu: Mexican (1)
Areas of Operation: NY
Type of Foodservice: Casual Dining (1)
Catering Services: Yes
Primary Distributors: (Full Line) SYSCO Corporation, HOUSTON, TX

Key Personnel
JACK BAUM - Chairman; CEO
RUSSELL BIRK - Founder

Famiglia - DeBartolo, LLC
245 Main St Ste 410
White Plains, NY 10601-2406

Telephone: (914) 328-4444
Fax Number: (914) 328-4479
Internet Homepage: famousfamiglia.com
Company Email: info@famousfamiglia.com
Type of Business: Chain Restaurant Operator
Year Founded: 1986
Systemwide Sales: $87,094,000 (e)
Total Sales: $43,130,000 (e)
Number of Employees: 189
Average Check: Lunch(16); Dinner(26)
Total Units: 50
Trade Names: Famous Famiglia (50)
Company-Owned Units: 43
Units Franchised To: 7
Preferred Square Footage: 750; 1,000; 2,500
Preferred Location Types: Airports; Institution (college/hospital); Other; Parks; Regional Mall; Stadiums; Strip Mall
Primary Menu: Pizza (50)
Areas of Operation: AZ, CA, CT, DC, DE, FL, GA, IA, KY, MA, MN, NJ, NV, NY, OH, PA, RI, TN, TX, VA, WI, BC
Foreign Countries: CANADA; CHINA; ECUADOR; MEXICO; UNITED ARAB EMIRATES
Type of Foodservice: Quick Serve (50)
Primary Distributors: (Full Line) Ferraro Foods, PISCATAWAY, NJ

Key Personnel
JOHN KOLAJ - Co-Founder; COO
PAUL KOLAJ - Co-Founder; CEO; Director Finance, Real Estate, Design

Four M Capital LLC
7 Renaissance Sq Fl 5
White Plains, NY 10601-3056

Telephone: (914) 747-2552
Fax Number: (914) 769-1851
Type of Business: Chain Restaurant Operator
Total Sales: $74,520,000 (e)
Alcohol Sales: 24%
Number of Employees: 610
Total Units: 15
Trade Names: Buffalo Wild Wings (15)
Units Franchised From: 15
Preferred Square Footage: 4,500; 9,800
Preferred Location Types: Freestanding; Strip Mall
Alcohol Served: Beer, Wine, Liquor
Primary Menu: Chicken (15)
Areas of Operation: CT, NY
Type of Foodservice: Casual Dining (15)
Franchise Affiliation: Buffalo Wild Wings Inc., ATLANTA, GA

Key Personnel
JAMES BITZONIS - President; General Buyer
MICHAEL MEHIEL - Partner; CFO; COO
OSCAR TORRES - Manager

Anderson's Management Associates Inc.
6075 Main St
Williamsville, NY 14221-6836

Telephone: (716) 633-2302
Fax Number: (716) 633-2671
Internet Homepage: andersonscustard.com
Company Email: corp@andersonscustard.com
Type of Business: Chain Restaurant Operator
Year Founded: 1946
Systemwide Sales: $10,911,000 (e)
Total Sales: $10,560,000 (e)
Number of Employees: 170
Average Check: Lunch(12); Dinner(12)
Internet Order Processing: Yes
Internet Sales: 3.00%
Total Units: 6
Trade Names: Anderson's Frozen Custard and Roast Beef (6)
Company-Owned Units: 6
Preferred Square Footage: 2,500
Preferred Location Types: Freestanding; Strip Mall
Primary Menu: Sandwiches/Deli (6)
Areas of Operation: NY
Type of Foodservice: Quick Serve (6)
Catering Services: Yes
Distribution Centers: WILLIAMSVILLE, NY
On-site Distribution Center: Yes

Key Personnel
KEITH F. ANDERSON - President; Partner;
Executive Chef; Director Operations, Facility/Maintenance, Information Systems, Real Estate, Food Safety
HOLLY ANDERSON - Partner; Director Finance, Design, Human Resources, Franchising
LISA SORRENTINO - Director Marketing, Training

Dipson Theatres Inc.
388 Evans St Ste 3A
Williamsville, NY 14221-5626

Telephone: (716) 626-9613
Fax Number: (716) 626-9614
Internet Homepage: dipsontheatres.com
Company Email: info@dipsontheatres.com
Type of Business: Foodservice Operations - Movie Theatre
Year Founded: 1939
Total Sales: $15,160,000 (e)
Number of Employees: 70
Average Check: Lunch(6); Dinner(6)
Total Units: 7
Trade Names: Dipson Theatre (7)
Company-Owned Units: 7
Preferred Location Types: Community Mall; Freestanding; Regional Mall
Primary Menu: Snacks (7)
Areas of Operation: NY
Type of Foodservice: In-Store Feeder (7)
Primary Distributors: (Food) Sanarak Products Inc., BUFFALO, NY
Notes: The company derives approximately 72% of its revenue from theater admissions, on-screen advertising, and other sales.

Key Personnel
MICHAEL CLEMENT - President; Partner; CFO; Director Information Systems, Risk Management, Supply Chain, Real Estate, Design, Menu Development; General Buyer
BRYAN SPOKANE - Partner; VP; Director Foodservice
CONNIE TARTICK - Controller
JEREMY MILLS - General Manager Marketing; Coordinator

ROC N Burgers, LLC
5330 Main St
Williamsville, NY 14221-5360

Telephone: (716) 633-2529
Company Email: ap@fiveguysbuffalo.com
Type of Business: Chain Restaurant Operator
Total Sales: $25,710,000 (e)
Number of Employees: 350
Total Units: 13
Trade Names: Five Guys Burgers and Fries (13)
Units Franchised From: 13
Preferred Square Footage: 3,000
Preferred Location Types: Strip Mall
Primary Menu: Hamburger (13)
Projected Openings: 2
Areas of Operation: NY
Type of Foodservice: Fast Casual (13)
Franchise Affiliation: Five Guys Holdings Inc., LORTON, VA

Key Personnel
REID RICHARDS - Partner; General Buyer
STEVEN CHRISTENSEN - Partner

La Parma
707 Willis Ave Unit A
Williston Park, NY 11596-1177

Telephone: (516) 294-6610
Fax Number: (516) 294-4825
Internet Homepage: laparma.com
Type of Business: Chain Restaurant Operator
Year Founded: 1984
Total Sales: $7,914,000 (e)
Alcohol Sales: 20%
Number of Employees: 100
Average Check: Lunch(24); Dinner(48)
Total Units: 4
Trade Names: La Parma (1); La Parma II (1); La Parma III (1); La Parma IV (1)
Company-Owned Units: 4
Preferred Square Footage: 4,000
Preferred Location Types: Freestanding
Alcohol Served: Beer, Wine, Liquor
Primary Menu: Italian (4)
Areas of Operation: NY
Type of Foodservice: Casual Dining (4)
Catering Services: Yes
Primary Distributors: (Food) C & S Wholesale Grocers, NEWBURGH, NY

Key Personnel
ANTHONY CASTELLI - Partner; Executive Chef; Director Menu Development, Catering
RICHARD FAILA - Partner; General Manager
ANTHONY GRALTO - Partner; Executive Chef; General Buyer
DOMINICK GREGORIO - Partner; Executive Chef
GUIDO IENPPOLI - Partner; Executive Chef

Scotto Bros. LLC
40 Crossways Park Dr Ste 100
Woodbury, NY 11797-2039

Telephone: (516) 333-8777
Fax Number: (516) 997-8554
Internet Homepage:
  blackstonesteakhouse.com;
  insigniasteakhouse.com;
  onenorthrestaurant.com; rare650.com;
  scottobrothers.com
Company Email: vickic@scottobrothers.com

Type of Business: Chain Restaurant Operator
Total Sales: $12,436,000 (e)
Alcohol Sales: 5%
Internet Order Processing: Yes
Total Units: 4
Trade Names: Blackstone Steakhouse (1); Insignia Prime Steak & Sushi (1); One North (1); Rare 650 Steakhouse (1)
Company-Owned Units: 4
Preferred Location Types: Freestanding
Alcohol Served: Beer, Wine, Liquor
Primary Menu: Greek/Mediterranean (1); Steak/Seafood (3)
Areas of Operation: NY
Type of Foodservice: Fine Dining (4)

Key Personnel
ANTHONY SCOTTO - CEO; President; Partner
ARTHUR VIANA - Partner; Controller
VICKI COLACICCO - Manager Marketing, Business Development

Auntie Anne's Franchise
6 Mall Walk
Yonkers, NY 10704

Telephone: (914) 423-6300
Type of Business: Chain Restaurant Operator
Total Sales: $5,711,000 (e)
Total Units: 8
Trade Names: Auntie Anne's Hand-Rolled Soft Pretzels (8)
Units Franchised From: 8
Primary Menu: Snacks (8)
Areas of Operation: CT
Type of Foodservice: Quick Serve (8)
Franchise Affiliation: Auntie Anne's Inc., LANCASTER, PA

Key Personnel
RANJAN WHADWA - Owner; General Buyer
KATHLEEN DERUSHA - Director Operations

Fordham Foods (USA), Inc.
135 Timberlane Ct
Yorktown Heights, NY 10598-1820

Telephone: (914) 424-7000
Fax Number: (914) 233-5677
Type of Business: Chain Restaurant Operator
Total Sales: $7,409,000 (e)
Total Units: 5
Trade Names: Checkers (5)
Units Franchised From: 5
Primary Menu: Hamburger (5)
Areas of Operation: NY
Type of Foodservice: Quick Serve (5)
Franchise Affiliation: Checkers Drive-In Restaurants Inc., TAMPA, FL

Key Personnel
VIJAY GHEI - President; General Buyer

OHIO

M.E. Theatres Inc.
215 S Main St
Ada, OH 45810-1413

Telephone: (419) 634-9127
Internet Homepage: adatheatre.com; metheatres.com
Type of Business: Foodservice Operations - Movie Theatre
Total Sales: $3,419,000 (e)
Average Check: Dinner(8)
Total Units: 3
Trade Names: Ada Theatre (1); M.E. Theatres Inc. (2)
Company-Owned Units: 3
Preferred Location Types: Freestanding
Primary Menu: Snacks (3)
Areas of Operation: OH
Type of Foodservice: In-Store Feeder (3)

Key Personnel
BECKY MILLER - Partner; Director Operations, Marketing
RODNEY MILLER - Partner; CFO; Director Operations

Domino's Franchisee
4037 S Main St
Akron, OH 44319-3668

Telephone: (330) 245-1444
Type of Business: Chain Restaurant Operator
Total Sales: $10,254,000 (e)
Total Units: 5
Trade Names: Domino's (5)
Units Franchised From: 5
Primary Menu: Pizza (5)
Areas of Operation: OH
Type of Foodservice: Quick Serve (5)
Franchise Affiliation: Domino's Pizza Inc, ANN ARBOR, MI

Key Personnel
KARL J. WALLER - Owner; General Buyer

Rubber City LLC
500 Grant St
Akron, OH 44311-1121

Telephone: (330) 535-8400
Fax Number: (330) 535-1441
Type of Business: Chain Restaurant Operator
Year Founded: 1959
Total Sales: $89,010,000 (e)
Number of Employees: 1,090
Average Check: Breakfast(8); Lunch(8); Dinner(8)
Total Units: 19
Trade Names: McDonald's (19)
Units Franchised From: 19
Preferred Square Footage: 2,500
Preferred Location Types: Freestanding
Primary Menu: Hamburger (19)
Areas of Operation: OH
Type of Foodservice: Quick Serve (19)
Franchise Affiliation: McDonald's Corporation, CHICAGO, IL
Primary Distributors: (Full Line) The Anderson-DuBose Co., WARREN, OH

Key Personnel
JOHN BLICKLE - Chairman; President; Director Facility/Maintenance, Real Estate
CHARLES BOOTH - Treasurer; Director Finance, Purchasing, Loss Prevention
CHRIS PRESTON - Director Operations, Information Systems, Human Resources; General Buyer

Swensons Drive In
680 E Cuyahoga Falls Ave
Akron, OH 44310-1553

Telephone: (330) 928-3797
Internet Homepage: swensonsdriveins.com
Company Email: info@swensonsdriveins.com
Type of Business: Chain Restaurant Operator
Total Units: 12
Trade Names: Swensons Drive In (12)
Company-Owned Units: 12
Primary Menu: Hamburger (12)
Areas of Operation: OH
Type of Foodservice: Quick Serve (12)

Key Personnel
JEFF FLOWERS - CEO; President

We're Rolling Pretzel Company
2700 W State St
Alliance, OH 44601

Telephone: (330) 821-5937
Internet Homepage: wererolling.com
Type of Business: Chain Restaurant Operator
Year Founded: 1996
Systemwide Sales: $4,334,000 (e)
Total Sales: $1,927,000 (e)
Number of Employees: 59
Average Check: Breakfast(8); Lunch(8); Dinner(8)
Total Units: 13
Trade Names: We're Rolling (13)

Company-Owned Units: 10
Units Franchised To: 3
Preferred Square Footage: 350; 1,000
Preferred Location Types: Discount Dept. Stores; Regional Mall
Primary Menu: Snacks (13)
Areas of Operation: IN, KY, MI, OH, PA, WV
Type of Foodservice: In-Store Feeder (13)
Primary Distributors: (Full Line) Avalon Foodservice Inc., CANAL FULTON, OH

Key Personnel
KEVIN KRABILL - President; Director Real Estate; Manager Menu Development; General Buyer

J J M Associates Inc
1200 S Defiance St
Archbold, OH 43502-1620

Telephone: (419) 445-7827
Fax Number: (419) 445-8646
Type of Business: Chain Restaurant Operator
Total Sales: $3,160,000 (e)
Total Units: 5
Trade Names: Subway (5)
Units Franchised From: 5
Primary Menu: Sandwiches/Deli (5)
Areas of Operation: OH
Type of Foodservice: Quick Serve (5)
Franchise Affiliation: Doctor's Associates Inc., MILFORD, CT

Key Personnel
MELODIE RUPP - President; Partner; General Buyer
KYI FOSTER - President
JEFF RUPP - Partner
BROOKE MCKINNEY-FOSTER - CFO

Wenco Wooster Inc.
400 Claremont Ave
Ashland, OH 44805-3008

Telephone: (419) 289-3628
Fax Number: (419) 281-0256
Internet Homepage: wencowendys.com
Type of Business: Chain Restaurant Operator
Year Founded: 1976
Total Sales: $71,350,000 (e)
Number of Employees: 1,511
Average Check: Lunch(6); Dinner(6)
Total Units: 63
Trade Names: Wendy's Old Fashioned Hamburgers (63)
Units Franchised From: 63
Preferred Square Footage: 2,500; 2,800
Preferred Location Types: Freestanding
Primary Menu: Hamburger (63)
Areas of Operation: IN, MI, OH
Type of Foodservice: Quick Serve (63)

Franchise Affiliation: The Wendy's Company, DUBLIN, OH
Primary Distributors: (Equipment) The Wasserstrom Co., COLUMBUS, OH; (Food) The SYGMA Network, Inc., DUBLIN, OH; (Supplies) The Wasserstrom Co., COLUMBUS, OH

Key Personnel
ZANE GROSS JR - President; Director Operations, Purchasing, Food and Beverage
RACHEL WEBER - Director Finance
JAMIE JACKSON - Director Operations
ROGER ROMAN - Director Information Technology

Domino's Franchisee
5817 Main Ave
Ashtabula, OH 44004-7563

Telephone: (440) 992-6060
Type of Business: Chain Restaurant Operator
Total Sales: $8,095,000 (e)
Total Units: 4
Trade Names: Domino's (4)
Units Franchised From: 4
Primary Menu: Pizza (4)
Areas of Operation: OH
Type of Foodservice: Quick Serve (4)
Franchise Affiliation: Domino's Pizza Inc, ANN ARBOR, MI

Key Personnel
ROBERT MCNICHOLAS - Owner; General Buyer

Burrito Partners, LLC
10 S Court St
Athens, OH 45701

Telephone: (740) 566-4100
Internet Homepage: bigmammasonline.com
Company Email: mammasbbb@gmail.com
Type of Business: Chain Restaurant Operator
Year Founded: 2005
Total Units: 2
Trade Names: Big Mamma's Burritos (2)
Company-Owned Units: 2
Preferred Location Types: Downtown; Strip Mall
Primary Menu: Mexican (2)
Projected Openings: 2
Areas of Operation: OH
Type of Foodservice: Fast Casual (2)

Key Personnel
JERRY DEPIZZO - Partner
MATT CRUMPTON - Partner
GEORGEINA ORNELAS - Creative Director

White House Chicken Systems Inc.
180 Wooster Rd N
Barberton, OH 44203-2561

Telephone: (330) 745-0449
Fax Number: (330) 745-0009
Internet Homepage: whitehousechicken.com
Type of Business: Chain Restaurant Operator
Year Founded: 1942
Total Sales: $4,736,000 (e)
Number of Employees: 125
Average Check: Lunch(12); Dinner(12)
Total Units: 3
Trade Names: White House Chicken (3)
Company-Owned Units: 3
Preferred Square Footage: 1,200; 1,500
Preferred Location Types: Freestanding
Primary Menu: Chicken (3)
Areas of Operation: OH
Type of Foodservice: Quick Serve (3)
Primary Distributors: (Food) The Tasty Pure Food Co., AKRON, OH

Key Personnel
BRIAN CANALE - President; Director Finance, Operations, Purchasing, Information Systems, Supply Chain, Real Estate, Design, Human Resources, Menu Development

Psl Enterprises Ltd
146 W Main St
Barnesville, OH 43713-1066

Telephone: (740) 425-9999
Type of Business: Chain Restaurant Operator
Total Sales: $26,972,000 (e)
Total Units: 13
Trade Names: Domino's (13)
Units Franchised From: 13
Primary Menu: Pizza (13)
Areas of Operation: OH
Type of Foodservice: Quick Serve (13)
Franchise Affiliation: Domino's Pizza Inc, ANN ARBOR, MI

Key Personnel
MORGAN T. LACEFIELD - Owner; General Buyer

Ho Wah
2101 Richmond Rd Ste G3
Beachwood, OH 44122-1390

Telephone: (216) 831-2327
Fax Number: (216) 364-0380
Internet Homepage: howahrestaurant.com; kingwahrestaurant.biz; liwahrestaurant.com
Type of Business: Chain Restaurant Operator

Year Founded: 1980
Total Sales: $6,878,000 (e)
Alcohol Sales: 10%
Number of Employees: 70
Average Check: Lunch(14); Dinner(22)
Total Units: 3
Trade Names: Ho Wah (1); King Wah (1); Li Wah (1)
Company-Owned Units: 3
Preferred Location Types: Strip Mall
Alcohol Served: Beer, Wine, Liquor
Primary Menu: Chinese (3)
Areas of Operation: OH
Type of Foodservice: Casual Dining (3)
Catering Services: Yes
Primary Distributors: (Food) Gordon Food Service, SPRINGFIELD, OH

Key Personnel
MICHAEL SETO - President; Executive Chef; Director Catering; General Buyer

Hyde Park Restaurant Systems Inc.
21945 Chagrin Blvd
Beachwood, OH 44122-5309

Telephone: (216) 514-1777
Fax Number: (216) 514-1995
Internet Homepage: blackpointrestaurant.com; elevenatthecap.com; hydeparkrestaurants.com; jekyllskitchen.com
Type of Business: Chain Restaurant Operator
Year Founded: 1988
Total Sales: $20,510,000 (e)
Alcohol Sales: 30%
Number of Employees: 767
Average Check: Lunch(26); Dinner(38)
Internet Order Processing: Yes
Total Units: 18
Trade Names: Black Point (1); Bull & Bird Steakhouse (1); Eleven (1); Hyde Park Steakhouse (13); Jekyll's Kitchen (1); ML Tavern (1)
Company-Owned Units: 18
Preferred Square Footage: 5,500; 7,400
Preferred Location Types: Downtown; Freestanding
Alcohol Served: Beer, Wine, Liquor
Primary Menu: American (3); Steak (14); Steak/Seafood (1)
Projected Openings: 1
Areas of Operation: OH
Type of Foodservice: Casual Dining (1); Fine Dining (17)
Primary Distributors: (Food) SYSCO Food Services of Cincinnati, CINCINNATI, OH; (Supplies) SYSCO Food Services of Cleveland Inc., CLEVELAND, OH

Key Personnel
RICK HAUCK - Chairman; Partner; Director Operations, Risk Management, Human Resources, Food Safety
JOE SACCONE - President; Partner; CFO; Director Real Estate; General Buyer
KELLY FENSKE - VP Operations
ROB KIHLSTROM - Director Internet Development
LISA MATTHEWS - Manager Sales
RON WALKER - Manager Human Resources

Red Restaurant Group
3355 Richmond Rd
Beachwood, OH 44122-4100

Telephone: (216) 831-2252
Internet Homepage: redthesteakhouse.com
Type of Business: Chain Restaurant Operator
Total Units: 4
Trade Names: Moxie, The Restaurant (1); RED (3)
Company-Owned Units: 4
Primary Menu: Steak (4)
Areas of Operation: OH
Type of Foodservice: Fine Dining (4)

Key Personnel
PETER VAUTHY - Partner; VP; Executive Chef
JONATHAN BENNETT - VP
MARY ANNE HEINTZELMAN - Controller
SHAWN CLINE - Executive Chef
DAVID SCHNEIDER - Director Operations
MELISSA WRIGHT - Director Sales, Catering

Winking Lizard Inc.
25380 Miles Rd
Bedford Heights, OH 44146-1322

Telephone: (216) 831-0022
Fax Number: (216) 831-7999
Internet Homepage: lizardville.net; winkinglizard.com
Company Email: info@winkinglizard.com
Type of Business: Chain Restaurant Operator
Year Founded: 1981
Total Sales: $23,630,000 (e)
Alcohol Sales: 35%
Number of Employees: 1,076
Average Check: Lunch(14); Dinner(18)
Total Units: 22
Trade Names: Lizardville (4); Winking Lizard Tavern (18)
Company-Owned Units: 22
Preferred Square Footage: 3,500
Preferred Location Types: Freestanding; Strip Mall
Alcohol Served: Beer, Wine, Liquor
Primary Menu: American (22)
Areas of Operation: OH
Type of Foodservice: Casual Dining (23)
Catering Services: Yes
On-site Distribution Center: Yes
Primary Distributors: (Full Line) US Foods, CINCINNATI, OH

Key Personnel
JIM CALLAM - President; Partner; Director Design
FRED KOBZOWICZ - Partner; Director Finance, Real Estate
JOHN LANE - Partner; Director Operations; Manager Information Systems

Zeppes Franchise Co.
25780 Miles Rd Ste A
Bedford Heights, OH 44146-1418

Telephone: (216) 360-9100
Fax Number: (216) 360-9888
Internet Homepage: zeppes.com
Type of Business: Chain Restaurant Operator
Year Founded: 1990
Total Sales: $18,620,000 (e)
Alcohol Sales: 5%
Number of Employees: 297
Average Check: Dinner(16)
Internet Order Processing: Yes
Total Units: 35
Trade Names: Zeppe's Pizzeria (32); Zeppes Tavern (2); Zeppes's Bistro (1)
Company-Owned Units: 5
Units Franchised To: 30
Preferred Square Footage: 2,500; 5,500; 6,000
Preferred Location Types: Freestanding; Strip Mall
Alcohol Served: Beer, Wine, Liquor
Primary Menu: American (3); Pizza (32)
Areas of Operation: OH
Type of Foodservice: Quick Serve (35)
Catering Services: Yes
Primary Distributors: (Food) Hillcrest FoodService Co., CLEVELAND, OH

Key Personnel
JOSEPH T. CIRESI - President; Director Operations, Information Systems, Menu Development
CASSIE CIRESI - Director Marketing

Dunn-Bowling LLC
1109 Mead Rd
Bellbrook, OH 45305-8747

Telephone: (937) 372-5223
Fax Number: (937) 372-5233
Type of Business: Chain Restaurant Operator
Year Founded: 2001
Total Sales: $3,856,000 (e)
Number of Employees: 90
Average Check: Lunch(12); Dinner(12)
Total Units: 2
Trade Names: KFC (2)

Units Franchised From: 2
Preferred Square Footage: 2,500; 3,200
Preferred Location Types: Freestanding
Primary Menu: Chicken (2)
Areas of Operation: OH
Type of Foodservice: Quick Serve (2)
Franchise Affiliation: KFC Corporation, LOUISVILLE, KY
Primary Distributors: (Full Line) SYSCO Food Services of Cleveland Inc., CLEVELAND, OH

Key Personnel
JOAN BOWLING - President; Owner; General Manager; General Buyer

Best Quality Pizza Group Inc
815 S Main St
Bellefontaine, OH 43311-1612

Telephone: (937) 592-1100
Fax Number: (937) 592-9249
Type of Business: Chain Restaurant Operator
Total Sales: $2,986,000 (e)
Total Units: 2
Trade Names: Donatos Pizza (2)
Units Franchised From: 2
Primary Menu: Pizza (2)
Areas of Operation: OH
Type of Foodservice: Family Restaurant (2)
Franchise Affiliation: Donatos Pizzeria LLC, COLUMBUS, OH

Key Personnel
BILL YORK - President; General Buyer

COBCO Enterprises
10250 Alliance Rd Ste 223
Blue Ash, OH 45242-4737

Telephone: (513) 841-2444
Fax Number: (513) 841-2555
Internet Homepage: cobco-ent.com
Type of Business: Chain Restaurant Operator
Total Sales: $36,089,000 (e)
Total Units: 7
Trade Names: McDonald's (7)
Units Franchised From: 7
Primary Menu: Hamburger (7)
Areas of Operation: OH
Type of Foodservice: Quick Serve (7)
Franchise Affiliation: McDonald's Corporation, CHICAGO, IL

Key Personnel
DAVE IMES - Director Technology
COURTNEY SNOW - Director Human Resources

Eurest Dining Services
4545 Creek Rd
Blue Ash, OH 45242-2803

Telephone: (513) 337-8336
Fax Number: (513) 337-8459
Listing Type: Branch Office
Type of Business: Foodservice Management Operator
Year Founded: 1929
Number of Employees: 25
Number of Locations Served: 80
Total Foodservice Mgmt Accounts: 80
Areas of Operation: OH
Type of Foodservice: Full-service sit-down dining (80)
Foodservice Management Venues: Business & Industry
Primary Distributors: (Food) Performance Food Group, RICHMOND, VA
Parent Company: Compass Group The Americas, CHARLOTTE, NC
Headquarters: Eurest Dining Services, CHESTERBROOK, PA

Key Personnel
JULIE AKERS - Director Foodservice

Ison Management
11333 Deerfield Rd
Blue Ash, OH 45242-2104

Telephone: (513) 672-3500
Fax Number: (513) 672-3504
Internet Homepage: isonfamilymcd.com
Type of Business: Chain Restaurant Operator
Year Founded: 1994
Total Sales: $84,930,000 (e)
Number of Employees: 150
Average Check: Breakfast(8); Lunch(10); Dinner(12)
Total Units: 18
Trade Names: McDonald's (18)
Units Franchised From: 18
Preferred Square Footage: 2,500
Preferred Location Types: Freestanding
Primary Menu: Hamburger (18)
Areas of Operation: OH
Type of Foodservice: Quick Serve (18)
Franchise Affiliation: McDonald's Corporation, CHICAGO, IL
Primary Distributors: (Full Line) The Martin-Brower Co. LLC, ROSEMONT, IL

Key Personnel
LEIGH CHAMNESS - CEO
JEFF HINE - Director Operations
LISA WISE - Manager Customer Service
LOGAN BROWN - Manager Human Resources

Winegardner & Hammons Inc.
4243 Hunt Rd
Blue Ash, OH 45242-6645

Telephone: (513) 891-1066
Fax Number: (513) 794-2590
Internet Homepage: whihotels.com
Company Email: ops@whihotels.com
Type of Business: Foodservice Operations - Hotel/Motels
Year Founded: 1965
Total Sales: $183,860,000 (e)
Alcohol Sales: 20%
Number of Employees: 2,100
Total Units: 26
Restaurants in Hotels: 26
Trade Names: Alexander's (2); Baxter's (1); Capitol City Grille (2); Cutler's (1); Jersey's Sports Pub (1); Kokomo's Cafe (1); McKenna's (3); River City Grille(12); The Atrium Cafe (1); The Greenery (1); Water Colour (1)
Company-Owned Units: 26
Alcohol Served: Beer, Wine, Liquor
Areas of Operation: AL, CA, CT, FL, IL, KY, MI, OH, PA, TX, VA
Type of Foodservice: Casual Dining
Primary Distributors: (Food) SYSCO Food Services of Cincinnati, CINCINNATI, OH; (Specialty Foods) US Foods, GRAND FORKS, ND
Notes: The company derives approximately 78% of its revenue from hotel operations.

Key Personnel
KENT BRUGGEMAN - CFO
TERRY DAMMEYER - Chief Development Officer; Senior VP Construction, Business Development
BILL BOGGESS - VP; Controller
GARY BRITTON - Executive Chef

Lewis Family McDonald's
7 Airport Dr
Bluffton, OH 45817

Mailing Address: P O Box 29, BLUFFTON, OH, 45817
Telephone: (419) 225-5916
Fax Number: (888) 481-1792
Internet Homepage: lewisfamilymcdonalds.com; mcohio.com
Type of Business: Chain Restaurant Operator
Year Founded: 2000
Total Sales: $80,880,000 (e)
Number of Employees: 686
Average Check: Breakfast(8); Lunch(10); Dinner(12)
Total Units: 17
Trade Names: McDonald's (17)
Units Franchised From: 17

Preferred Square Footage: 2,500; 3,000
Preferred Location Types: Discount Dept. Stores; Freestanding
Primary Menu: Hamburger (17)
Areas of Operation: OH
Type of Foodservice: Quick Serve (8)
Franchise Affiliation: McDonald's Corporation, CHICAGO, IL

Key Personnel
JERRY A. LEWIS - President; Partner; Director Purchasing, Facility/Maintenance, Real Estate
JESSICA HALL - Owner
JONATHAN LEWIS - Partner
SARA POWERS - CFO
SCOTT SHAW - Director Operations
BOB LEWIS - Director Finance, Supply Chain
SHERRI MATTER - Director Human Resources
MIKE MAURER - Manager Information Technology

●▲
Ed Reese
7322 Market St
Boardman, OH 44512-5610

Telephone: (330) 629-8038
Type of Business: Chain Restaurant Operator
Total Sales: $6,226,000 (e)
Total Units: 3
Trade Names: Five Guys Burgers and Fries (3)
Units Franchised From: 3
Primary Menu: Hamburger (3)
Areas of Operation: OH
Type of Foodservice: Fast Casual (3)
Franchise Affiliation: Five Guys Holdings Inc., LORTON, VA

Key Personnel
ED REESE - President; General Buyer

●▲
Hlw Fasttrack Inc.
4900 Market St
Boardman, OH 44512-2130

Telephone: (330) 783-5659
Fax Number: (330) 783-5610
Internet Homepage: hlwfasttrack.com
Company Email: tkeel@hlwfasttrack.com
Type of Business: Chain Restaurant Operator
Total Sales: $87,890,000 (e)
Total Units: 23
Trade Names: McDonald's (23)
Units Franchised From: 23
Primary Menu: Hamburger (23)
Projected Openings: 3
Areas of Operation: OH, PA
Type of Foodservice: Quick Serve (23)
Franchise Affiliation: McDonald's Corporation, CHICAGO, IL

Key Personnel
HERB WASHINGTON - President
RICHARD PRICE - VP; Director Operations
GISELE WASHINGTON - VP
BECKY CARTAGENA - General Manager
JOE PRATT - Director

Rise Pies Handcrafted Pizza
7629 Market St Ste 200
Boardman, OH 44512-6082

Telephone: (330) 729-7400
Internet Homepage: risepies.com
Company Email: information@risepies.com
Type of Business: Chain Restaurant Operator
Year Founded: 2013
Internet Order Processing: Yes
Total Units: 17
Trade Names: Rise Pies Handcrafted Pizza (17)
Company-Owned Units: 17
Primary Menu: Pizza (17)
Projected Openings: 3
Areas of Operation: CO, FL, GA, IL, MI, MS, OH

Key Personnel
ED MURANSKY - Chairman
EDDIE MURANSKY - President
GARY LOCKHART - CFO
VERNON CESTA - Executive Chef
BEKAH MARSTELLAR - Director Human Resources
EDDIE MOSES - Manager Operations

●▲
The Chestnut Land Co
7629 Market St
Boardman, OH 44512-6075

Telephone: (330) 729-7430
Internet Homepage: chestnutland.com
Type of Business: Chain Restaurant Operator
Total Sales: $65,880,000 (e)
Total Units: 92
Trade Names: Auntie Anne's Hand-Rolled Soft Pretzels (92)
Units Franchised From: 92
Primary Menu: Snacks (92)
Areas of Operation: AL, FL, GA, MI, NC, OH, SC, TN, VA, WV
Type of Foodservice: Quick Serve (92)
Franchise Affiliation: Auntie Anne's Inc., LANCASTER, PA

Key Personnel
GARY LOCKHART - CFO
CHRIS SAMMARTINO - COO
BRYAN O'SHAUGHNESSY - CIO
BEKAH MARSTELLAR - Director Human Resources

MELISSA BOHR - Manager Operations

Gerald M. Liss Co. Inc.
203 N Main St
Bowling Green, OH 43402-2421

Telephone: (419) 352-5166
Fax Number: (419) 352-5160
Internet Homepage: pisanellos.com
Type of Business: Chain Restaurant Operator
Year Founded: 1955
Systemwide Sales: $9,513,000 (e)
Total Sales: $719,000 (e)
Number of Employees: 19
Average Check: Lunch(8); Dinner(12)
Total Units: 19
Trade Names: Pisanello's (19)
Company-Owned Units: 1
Units Franchised To: 18
Preferred Square Footage: 1,800; 3,000
Preferred Location Types: Downtown; Freestanding; Strip Mall
Primary Menu: Pizza (19)
Areas of Operation: OH
Type of Foodservice: Fast Casual (19)
Catering Services: Yes
Primary Distributors: (Food) Sofo Foods, TOLEDO, OH

Key Personnel
MIRANDA LISS - Owner; Director Human Resources; Manager Information Systems, POS/Scanning

Antonio's Inc.
2906 Center Rd
Brunswick, OH 44212

Telephone: (440) 345-5138
Internet Homepage: antoniospizza.net
Type of Business: Chain Restaurant Operator
Year Founded: 1969
Total Sales: $21,590,000 (e)
Alcohol Sales: 20%
Number of Employees: 495
Average Check: Lunch(10); Dinner(12)
Internet Order Processing: Yes
Total Units: 15
Trade Names: Antonio's Pizza (15)
Company-Owned Units: 15
Preferred Square Footage: 2,000; 6,000
Preferred Location Types: Freestanding; Strip Mall
Alcohol Served: Beer, Wine, Liquor
Primary Menu: Pizza (15)
Areas of Operation: OH
Type of Foodservice: Casual Dining (15)
Catering Services: Yes
Primary Distributors: (Full Line) SYSCO Food Services of Cleveland Inc., CLEVELAND, OH

Key Personnel
FRED LOSCHIAVO - CEO; Partner; General Manager; Director Operations, Facility/Maintenance, Catering; General Buyer
JASON COOPER - Manager District
GEORGE FOYTIK - Manager District

Theo's Restaurant
632 Wheeling Ave
Cambridge, OH 43725-2252

Telephone: (740) 432-3878
Internet Homepage: theforumrestaurant.com; theosrestaurant.us
Company Email: info@theosrestaurant.us
Type of Business: Chain Restaurant Operator
Year Founded: 1931
Total Sales: $4,528,000 (e)
Alcohol Sales: 15%
Number of Employees: 50
Average Check: Lunch(14); Dinner(26)
Total Units: 2
Trade Names: The Forum (1); Theo's Restaurant (1)
Company-Owned Units: 2
Preferred Location Types: Freestanding
Alcohol Served: Beer, Wine, Liquor
Primary Menu: American (2)
Areas of Operation: OH
Type of Foodservice: Casual Dining (2)
Catering Services: Yes
Primary Distributors: (Equipment) The Wasserstrom Co., COLUMBUS, OH; (Food) Gordon Food Service Inc., WYOMING, MI; (Supplies) The Wasserstrom Co., COLUMBUS, OH

Key Personnel
ALEX THEODOSOTOULOS - Partner; Executive Chef; General Buyer
STEVE THEODOSOTOULOS - Partner; General Manager; General Buyer

Bajco Group
3695 Boardman Canfield Rd Ste 200
Canfield, OH 44406-9009

Telephone: (330) 533-0900
Fax Number: (330) 533-6993
Internet Homepage: bajco.net
Company Email: info@bajco.net
Type of Business: Chain Restaurant Operator
Total Sales: $173,290,000 (e)
Total Units: 129
Trade Names: Papa John's Pizza (129)
Units Franchised From: 129
Primary Menu: Pizza (129)
Areas of Operation: FL, IL, IN, MI, NY, OH, PA, ON
Foreign Countries: CANADA
Type of Foodservice: Quick Serve (129)
Franchise Affiliation: Papa Johns International Inc., LOUISVILLE, KY

Key Personnel
NADEEM BAJWA - CEO; Partner
MALIK BAJWA - President; Partner
JEROME BETTIS - Partner
RAZI BILAL KHAN - Senior VP Finance, Accounting
SUJIT PAL - VP Administration
EUSHA BAJWA - VP Technology
RAZI KHAN - Controller
NICHOLAS ARTURO - Director Operations
SAEED RAZI - Director Operations
GARY LUTTON - Manager Purchasing, Systems

Handel's Homemade Ice Cream & Yogurt
3830 Starrs Centre Dr
Canfield, OH 44406-7037

Telephone: (330) 702-8270
Fax Number: (330) 702-8290
Internet Homepage: handelsicecream.com
Company Email: info@handelsicecream.com
Type of Business: Chain Restaurant Operator
Year Founded: 1945
Systemwide Sales: $35,849,000 (e)
Total Sales: $16,850,000 (e)
Number of Employees: 198
Average Check: Lunch(8); Dinner(8)
Internet Order Processing: Yes
Internet Sales: 1.00%
Total Units: 46
Trade Names: Handel's Homemade Ice Cream & Yogurt (46)
Company-Owned Units: 13
Units Franchised To: 33
Preferred Square Footage: 2,500
Preferred Location Types: Freestanding; Strip Mall
Primary Menu: Snacks (46)
Projected Openings: 2
Areas of Operation: AL, CA, FL, IN, NV, OH, PA, VA
Type of Foodservice: Quick Serve (46)
Primary Distributors: (Full Line) SYSCO Food Services of Cleveland Inc., CLEVELAND, OH

Key Personnel
JENNIFER SCHULER - CEO
LEONARD FISHER - President; General Buyer
JAMES BROWN - COO; Director Franchising
JODY NERONE - Director Marketing

Bear Management Company
4084 Holiday St NW
Canton, OH 44718-2513

Telephone: (330) 493-3377
Fax Number: (330) 493-3443
Internet Homepage: pizzaovenpapabears.com
Type of Business: Chain Restaurant Operator
Year Founded: 1956
Total Sales: $12,430,000 (e)
Alcohol Sales: 3%
Number of Employees: 400
Average Check: Lunch(14); Dinner(16)
Total Units: 8
Trade Names: Papa Bear's Italian Restaurant/Pizza Oven (1); Pizza Oven (7)
Company-Owned Units: 8
Preferred Square Footage: 3,000; 7,500
Preferred Location Types: Freestanding
Alcohol Served: Beer, Wine, Liquor
Primary Menu: Italian (1); Pizza (7)
Areas of Operation: OH
Type of Foodservice: Casual Dining (1); Quick Serve (7)
Foodservice Management Venues: Schools
Catering Services: Yes
On-site Distribution Center: Yes

Key Personnel
DAVID M. DIPIETRO - Partner; VP Purchasing, Human Resources; Controller; Executive Chef; Director Finance, Facility/Maintenance, Real Estate, Design, Catering
STEVE DIPIETRO - Partner; VP Operations, Information Systems, Supply Chain

Italo's Pizza Shop Inc.
3560 Middlebranch Ave NE
Canton, OH 44705-5012

Telephone: (330) 455-6428
Fax Number: (330) 455-7443
Internet Homepage: italospizza.com
Type of Business: Chain Restaurant Operator
Year Founded: 1966
Systemwide Sales: $10,753,000 (e)
Total Sales: $2,521,000 (e)
Number of Employees: 60
Average Check: Lunch(8); Dinner(14)
Total Units: 7
Trade Names: Italo's Pizza Shop (7)
Company-Owned Units: 2
Units Franchised To: 5
Preferred Square Footage: 1,000; 1,500
Preferred Location Types: Freestanding; Strip Mall
Primary Menu: Pizza (7)
Areas of Operation: OH
Type of Foodservice: Family Restaurant (7)
Primary Distributors: (Equipment) Rizzi Distributors Inc., AKRON, OH

Key Personnel
JAMES P. VENTURA - President; VP Operations, Information Systems, Marketing; Controller; General Manager

Holland Subs, Inc.
6002 Far Hills Ave
Centerville, OH 45459-1924

Telephone: (937) 439-3840
Type of Business: Chain Restaurant Operator
Total Sales: $6,803,000 (e)
Total Units: 5
Trade Names: Jersey Mike's Subs (5)
Units Franchised From: 5
Primary Menu: Sandwiches/Deli (5)
Areas of Operation: OH
Type of Foodservice: Quick Serve (5)
Franchise Affiliation: Jersey Mike's Franchise Systems, MANASQUAN, NJ

Key Personnel
TEDDY L. TOLLIVER - Owner; General Buyer

MAK Management
7227 Chagrin Rd Ste B
Chagrin Falls, OH 44023-1131

Telephone: (440) 247-9180
Fax Number: (440) 247-9197
Type of Business: Chain Restaurant Operator
Total Sales: $33,130,000 (e)
Total Units: 7
Trade Names: McDonald's (7)
Units Franchised From: 7
Preferred Square Footage: 2,500
Primary Menu: Hamburger (7)
Areas of Operation: OH
Type of Foodservice: Quick Serve (7)
Franchise Affiliation: McDonald's Corporation, CHICAGO, IL

Key Personnel
MARGO KAROS - Owner; General Buyer
JOHN VERES - Controller
PAUL CZERNICKI - Director Operations; Supervisor

Mel K Management
10160 Queens Way Unit 6
Chagrin Falls, OH 44023-5434

Telephone: (440) 543-1011
Fax Number: (440) 543-1013
Company Email: office@mel-k.com
Type of Business: Chain Restaurant Operator
Total Sales: $28,440,000 (e)
Number of Employees: 200
Total Units: 6
Trade Names: McDonald's (6)
Units Franchised From: 6
Preferred Square Footage: 2,500
Primary Menu: Hamburger (6)
Areas of Operation: OH

Type of Foodservice: Quick Serve (6)
Franchise Affiliation: McDonald's Corporation, CHICAGO, IL

Key Personnel
MELONEY KAROS HERRICK - President; General Buyer

Shibley Management Inc.
30 N Main St
Chagrin Falls, OH 44022-3006

Telephone: (440) 247-8338
Internet Homepage: shibleyproperties.com; ytr.com
Company Email: info@ytr.com
Type of Business: Chain Restaurant Operator
Year Founded: 1981
Total Sales: $20,850,000 (e)
Alcohol Sales: 10%
Number of Employees: 510
Average Check: Breakfast(10); Lunch(12); Dinner(18)
Internet Order Processing: Yes
Internet Sales: 2.00%
Total Units: 9
Trade Names: Yours Truly (9)
Company-Owned Units: 9
Preferred Square Footage: 4,000
Preferred Location Types: Freestanding; Strip Mall
Alcohol Served: Beer, Wine, Liquor
Primary Menu: American (9)
Areas of Operation: OH
Type of Foodservice: Casual Dining (9)
Catering Services: Yes
Primary Distributors: (Full Line) Gordon Food Service Inc., WYOMING, MI

Key Personnel
DIXIE SINGER - President; Partner; General Buyer
LINDSAY ROYER - Partner; Director
KRISTEN PHELPS - Chief Accounting Officer
DICK HUMPHREY - COO; VP; Manager Facility/Maintenance, Region; General Buyer
DAMON SUNDMAN - Regional Manager
SARAH HOOVER - Coordinator Development

Salem Management Company, Inc
209 Center St Unit F
Chardon, OH 44024-1189

Telephone: (440) 286-2030
Type of Business: Chain Restaurant Operator
Total Sales: $4,503,000 (e)
Total Units: 3
Trade Names: Jersey Mike's Subs (3)
Units Franchised From: 3

Primary Menu: Sandwiches/Deli (3)
Areas of Operation: OH
Type of Foodservice: Quick Serve (3)
Franchise Affiliation: Jersey Mike's Franchise Systems, MANASQUAN, NJ

Key Personnel
MICHAEL SALEM - Owner; General Buyer

Goodwin Family Foods, LLC
184 Township Road Ste 1290
Chesapeake, OH 45619

Telephone: (740) 886-0951
Fax Number: (740) 886-7425
Type of Business: Chain Restaurant Operator
Total Sales: $5,315,000 (e)
Total Units: 9
Trade Names: Little Caesars Pizza (9)
Units Franchised From: 9
Primary Menu: Pizza (9)
Areas of Operation: KY, OH, WV
Type of Foodservice: Quick Serve (9)
Franchise Affiliation: Little Caesar Enterprises Inc., DETROIT, MI

Key Personnel
WILLIAM GOODWIN - President; Partner; General Buyer
SCOTT GOODWIN - Partner
CASSIE GOODWIN - Manager Marketing

RHF Enterprises
1256 Western Ave
Chillicothe, OH 45601-1105

Telephone: (740) 773-4177
Fax Number: (740) 775-1039
Company Email: rhfent@yahoo.com
Type of Business: Chain Restaurant Operator
Total Sales: $20,307,000 (e)
Number of Employees: 100
Total Units: 4
Trade Names: McDonald's (4)
Units Franchised From: 4
Preferred Square Footage: 2,500
Primary Menu: Hamburger (4)
Areas of Operation: OH
Type of Foodservice: Quick Serve (4)
Franchise Affiliation: McDonald's Corporation, CHICAGO, IL

Key Personnel
RONALD FEWSTER - President; General Buyer
JAN DETTY - Manager Human Resources

AED Enterprises LLC
300 Main St Ste 1
Cincinnati, OH 45202-4123

Telephone: (513) 362-1265
Fax Number: (513) 362-1333
Internet Homepage: deweyspizza.com
Company Email: deweysmail@deweyspizza.com
Type of Business: Chain Restaurant Operator
Year Founded: 1998
Total Sales: $65,970,000 (e)
Alcohol Sales: 12%
Number of Employees: 760
Average Check: Lunch(16); Dinner(32)
Total Units: 24
Trade Names: Dewey's Pizza (25)
Company-Owned Units: 25
Preferred Square Footage: 5,500; 6,000
Preferred Location Types: Community Mall; Freestanding
Alcohol Served: Beer, Wine
Primary Menu: Pizza (25)
Projected Openings: 2
Areas of Operation: IL, KS, KY, MO, OH
Type of Foodservice: Casual Dining (25)

Key Personnel
ANDREW DEWITT - President; Owner; Director Real Estate, Menu Development; General Buyer
CHUCK LIPP - Director Operations, Facility/Maintenance
STEPHANIE MCCALL - Director Marketing
JOE SCHLOTMAN - Director Information Systems

Anderson Larosa's
7756 Beechmont Ave
Cincinnati, OH 45255-4214

Telephone: (513) 347-1111
Fax Number: (513) 232-5491
Internet Homepage: larosas.com
Type of Business: Chain Restaurant Operator
Year Founded: 1973
Total Sales: $6,053,000 (e)
Alcohol Sales: 3%
Number of Employees: 90
Average Check: Lunch(6); Dinner(10)
Internet Order Processing: Yes
Internet Sales: 1.00%
Total Units: 3
Trade Names: LaRosa's Pizzeria (3)
Units Franchised From: 3
Preferred Square Footage: 4,000
Preferred Location Types: Freestanding
Alcohol Served: Beer, Wine, Liquor
Primary Menu: Italian (3)
Areas of Operation: OH
Type of Foodservice: Casual Dining (3)
Franchise Affiliation: LaRosa's Inc., CINCINNATI, OH

Key Personnel
NICK FUCITO - President; General Buyer
PHIL MOHAT - General Manager
KEN ANNIS - Area Manager Operations

Angilo's Pizza
607 Shepherd Dr
Cincinnati, OH 45215-2152

Telephone: (513) 821-6292
Fax Number: (513) 821-4491
Internet Homepage: angilospizza.com
Company Email: info@angilospizza.com
Type of Business: Chain Restaurant Operator
Year Founded: 1958
Systemwide Sales: $12,918,000 (e)
Total Sales: $328,000 (e)
Number of Employees: 11
Average Check: Lunch(12); Dinner(14)
Total Units: 18
Trade Names: Angilo's Pizza (18)
Company-Owned Units: 1
Units Franchised To: 17
Preferred Square Footage: 4,000
Preferred Location Types: Community Mall; Freestanding; Strip Mall
Primary Menu: Pizza (18)
Areas of Operation: KY, OH
Type of Foodservice: Quick Serve (18)
Primary Distributors: (Food) The Chefs' Warehouse, CINCINNATI, OH

Key Personnel
GREG BERTRAM - CEO; Partner
TERESA BERTRAM - Partner

Auntie Anne's Franchise
7875 Montgomery Rd Spc L121
Cincinnati, OH 45236-4344

Telephone: (513) 791-8804
Internet Homepage: auntieannesfranchising.com
Type of Business: Chain Restaurant Operator
Total Sales: $3,575,000 (e)
Total Units: 5
Trade Names: Auntie Anne's Hand-Rolled Soft Pretzels (5)
Units Franchised From: 5
Primary Menu: Snacks (5)
Areas of Operation: OH
Type of Foodservice: Quick Serve (5)
Franchise Affiliation: Auntie Anne's Inc., LANCASTER, PA

Key Personnel
KENNETH DIXON - Owner; General Buyer

Boca Restaurant Group
114 E 6th St
Cincinnati, OH 45202-3202

Telephone: (513) 542-2022
Internet Homepage: bocacincinnati.com; eatdrinknada.com; sottocincinnati.com
Company Email: info@bocacincinnati.com
Type of Business: Chain Restaurant Operator
Year Founded: 2001
Total Units: 7
Trade Names: Boca (1); Nada (5); Sotto (1)
Company-Owned Units: 7
Primary Menu: American (1); Italian (1); Mexican (5)
Areas of Operation: IN, OH, TN
Type of Foodservice: Casual Dining (6); Fine Dining (1)

Key Personnel
DAVID FALK - Owner
KELLY HICKEY - Director Operations
KENZIE GOODWIN - Director Event Planning
BRENDAN MARTIN - Assistant Director Operations
TAYLER RITCHER - Manager Event Planning

Domino's Franchisee
3250 Brotherton Rd
Cincinnati, OH 45209-1314

Telephone: (513) 321-7770
Type of Business: Chain Restaurant Operator
Total Sales: $4,048,000 (e)
Total Units: 2
Trade Names: Domino's (2)
Units Franchised From: 2
Primary Menu: Pizza (2)
Areas of Operation: OH
Type of Foodservice: Quick Serve (2)
Franchise Affiliation: Domino's Pizza Inc, ANN ARBOR, MI

Key Personnel
JEFFERY S. DUVALL - Owner; General Buyer

E.L.F. Development
1143 Saint Gregory St
Cincinnati, OH 45202-1734

Telephone: (513) 421-2660
Fax Number: (513) 421-2662
Type of Business: Chain Restaurant Operator
Year Founded: 1982
Total Sales: $11,810,000 (e)
Number of Employees: 1,500

Average Check: Breakfast(8); Lunch(10); Dinner(12)
Total Units: 20
Trade Names: Subway (20)
Units Franchised From: 20
Preferred Square Footage: 900
Preferred Location Types: Convenience Store/Gas Station; Freestanding; Strip Mall; Travel Plazas
Primary Menu: Sandwiches/Deli (20)
Areas of Operation: KY, OH
Type of Foodservice: Quick Serve (20)
Catering Services: Yes
Franchise Affiliation: Doctor's Associates Inc., MILFORD, CT

Key Personnel
ERIC FRANKE - President; Partner; CFO; Director Finance, Real Estate; General Buyer
KAREN FRANKE - Partner; Director Accounting
BEVERLY CENTERS - General Manager
DAVE NEIDER - Director Facility/Maintenance

Frisch's Restaurants Inc.
2800 Gilbert Ave
Cincinnati, OH 45206-1206

Telephone: (513) 961-2660
Fax Number: (513) 559-5160
Internet Homepage: frischs.com
Company Email: bigboy@frischs.com
Type of Business: Chain Restaurant Operator
Year Founded: 1947
Systemwide Sales: $261,672,000 (e)
Total Sales: $283,880,000 (e)
Number of Employees: 6,100
Average Check: Breakfast(8); Lunch(10); Dinner(10)
Total Units: 119
Trade Names: Frisch's Big Boy (119)
Company-Owned Units: 94
Units Franchised To: 25
Preferred Square Footage: 5,000; 5,600; 10,300
Preferred Location Types: Freestanding
Primary Menu: American (119)
Projected Remodelings: 10
Areas of Operation: IN, KY, OH
Type of Foodservice: Family Restaurant (119)
On-site Distribution Center: Yes
Primary Distributors: (Food) McLane/Columbus, COLUMBUS, OH
Parent Company: NRD Capital Management II LLC, BROOKHAVEN, GA
Notes: The company derives approximately 3% of its revenue from wholesale operations.

Key Personnel
DON SHORT - Owner
CHERYL WHITE - Owner
MATT STELLETELL - Area Director
EDWARD CHIARELLI - General Manager
JOE ROMAN - Director Information Technology
TIM REILLEY - Director Facility/Maintenance, Construction
TERRY MCQUERY - Director Employee Compensation, Employee Benefits
JEFFREY KITCHEN - Director Safety, Quality Assurance
WILLIAM PHIPPS - Regional Director
ED GIBSON - Manager Information Technology
RICHARD CONRAD - Manager Marketing
TONY STEELE - Manager Restaurant Operations
KELLY MASSEY - Manager Restaurant Operations
SUSAN GARVEY - Manager Restaurant Operations
SIERRA COMBS - Manager Restaurant Operations
DEL FUGATE - Supervisor Facility/Maintenance

Gold Star Chili Inc.
650 Lunken Park Dr
Cincinnati, OH 45226-1800

Telephone: (513) 231-4541
Fax Number: (513) 624-4415
Internet Homepage: goldstarchili.com
Company Email: contact@goldstarchili.com
Type of Business: Chain Restaurant Operator
Year Founded: 1965
Systemwide Sales: $117,472,000 (e)
Total Sales: $13,670,000 (e)
Number of Employees: 2,577
Average Check: Lunch(10); Dinner(10)
Internet Order Processing: Yes
Internet Sales: 2.00%
Total Units: 116
Trade Names: Gold Star Chili (90); Tom+Chee (26)
Company-Owned Units: 7
Units Franchised To: 109
Preferred Square Footage: 650; 2,000
Preferred Location Types: Airports; Freestanding; Regional Mall; Stadiums; Strip Mall
Primary Menu: Hot Dogs (90); Sandwiches/Deli (26)
Projected Remodelings: 22
Areas of Operation: IN, KY, OH
Type of Foodservice: Fast Casual (26); Quick Serve (90)
Foodservice Management Venues: Health Care; Parks & Recreation
Catering Services: Yes
On-site Distribution Center: Yes
Primary Distributors: (Full Line) The Wasserstrom Co., CINCINNATI, OH
Headquarter Offices: Tom and Chee Worldwide LLC, CINCINNATI, OH

Key Personnel
LYNN S. JOHNSON - Partner; Director Human Resources
JAMES CONOVER - CFO
JESSICA ALLCOCK - VP Marketing
BRIAN HARPER - Director Store Operations
HAROLD FINK - Director Purchasing
JOE CLARK - Director Franchise Sales
JAMIE POLLARD - Manager Field Marketing
JEREMY HILDEBRAND - Project Manager
STEPHEN R. SCHLAGBAUM - Project Manager Facility/Maintenance

Graeter's Inc.
1175 Regina Graeter Way
Cincinnati, OH 45216

Telephone: (513) 721-3323
Fax Number: (513) 721-3385
Internet Homepage: graeters.com
Company Email: cincinnati@graeters.com
Type of Business: Chain Restaurant Operator
Year Founded: 1870
Systemwide Sales: $20,098,000 (e)
Total Sales: $7,508,000 (e)
Number of Employees: 728
Average Check: Lunch(6); Dinner(6)
Internet Order Processing: Yes
Internet Sales: 1.00%
Total Units: 57
Trade Names: Graeter's Ice Cream (57)
Company-Owned Units: 35
Units Franchised To: 22
Preferred Square Footage: 2,500
Preferred Location Types: Freestanding
Primary Menu: Snacks (57)
Areas of Operation: IL, IN, KY, OH, PA
Type of Foodservice: Quick Serve (57)
Primary Distributors: (Full Line) US Foods, CINCINNATI, OH

Key Personnel
RICHARD A. GRAETER II - CEO; President; Exec VP; Director Loss Prevention, Risk Management, Real Estate, Construction
ROBERT GRAETER - Chief Compliance Officer
CHIP GRAETER - Chief Retail Officer; VP Retail Operations
GEORGE DENMAN - VP Sales
TOM KUNZELMAN - VP Manufacturing
TIM PHILPOTT - VP Marketing

Izzy's
602 Main St Ste 601
Cincinnati, OH 45202-2521

Telephone: (513) 369-0245
Fax Number: (513) 369-0247
Internet Homepage: izzys.com
Company Email: customerservice@izzys.com
Type of Business: Chain Restaurant Operator
Year Founded: 1901
Total Sales: $12,130,000 (e)
Alcohol Sales: 5%
Number of Employees: 212

Average Check: Breakfast(8); Lunch(10); Dinner(10)
Internet Order Processing: Yes
Internet Sales: 2.00%
Total Units: 7
Trade Names: Izzy's (7)
Company-Owned Units: 7
Preferred Square Footage: 2,600
Preferred Location Types: Downtown; Strip Mall
Alcohol Served: Beer
Primary Menu: American (7)
Areas of Operation: KY, OH
Type of Foodservice: Casual Dining (7)
Catering Services: Yes
On-site Distribution Center: Yes
Primary Distributors: (Full Line) The Chefs' Warehouse, CINCINNATI, OH
Notes: The company derives approximately 7% of its revenue from wholesale operations.

Key Personnel
JOHN GEISEN - President; Owner; Director Information Systems, Ethnic Marketing, Real Estate, Design; General Buyer
AMY GEISEN - Controller; Director Finance, Supply Chain, Human Resources, Catering

Jeff Ruby Culinary Entertainment
700 Walnut St Ste 200
Cincinnati, OH 45202-2015

Telephone: (513) 321-8080
Fax Number: (513) 533-6161
Internet Homepage: jeffruby.com
Company Email: comments@jeffruby.com
Type of Business: Chain Restaurant Operator
Year Founded: 1981
Total Sales: $14,700,000 (e)
Alcohol Sales: 30%
Number of Employees: 325
Average Check: Lunch(36); Dinner(90)
Internet Order Processing: Yes
Internet Sales: 2.00%
Total Units: 7
Trade Names: Carlo & Johnny (1); Jeff Ruby's Steakhouse (5); The Precinct (1)
Company-Owned Units: 7
Preferred Square Footage: 5,500; 6,000
Preferred Location Types: Downtown; Freestanding; Office Complex
Alcohol Served: Beer, Wine, Liquor
Primary Menu: Steak (7)
Projected Openings: 1
Areas of Operation: KY, OH
Type of Foodservice: Fine Dining (7)
Primary Distributors: (Equipment) The Wasserstrom Co., CINCINNATI, OH; (Food) SYSCO Food Services of Cincinnati, CINCINNATI, OH; (Supplies) The Wasserstrom Co., CINCINNATI, OH

Key Personnel
BRITNEY RUBY MILLER - President; General Buyer
JEFF RUBY - Owner; Executive Chef; Director Facility/Maintenance, Advertising, Real Estate, Design, Store Fixtures, Menu Development; General Buyer
NANCY WEBER - Controller
MICHAEL MORGAN - General Manager
JUSTIN LEIDENHEIMER - Executive Chef
ANDI SEMPIER - Director Sales
BAWE C. SHINHOLSTER - Director Quality Assurance, Training
PEGGY SULLIVAN - Director Inventory
VICTORIA YERDEN - Manager Accounting
TODD SHREVE - Manager Beverages
CHIP MULLEN - Manager Sales

L & P Company
7707 Montgomery Rd
Cincinnati, OH 45236-4243

Telephone: (513) 791-7902
Type of Business: Chain Restaurant Operator
Total Units: 5
Trade Names: Skyline Chili (4); The Root Cellar (1)
Units Franchised From: 5
Alcohol Served: Beer
Primary Menu: American (5)
Areas of Operation: OH
Type of Foodservice: Casual Dining (1); Family Restaurant (4)
Franchise Affiliation: Skyline Chili Inc., FAIRFIELD, OH

Key Personnel
JAMES CHANTILAS - President; General Buyer

LaRosa's Inc.
2334 Boudinot Ave
Cincinnati, OH 45238-3417

Telephone: (513) 347-5660
Fax Number: (513) 922-2710
Internet Homepage: larosas.com
Company Email: contactus@larosas.com
Type of Business: Chain Restaurant Operator
Year Founded: 1954
Systemwide Sales: $167,487,000 (e)
Total Sales: $43,990,000 (e)
Alcohol Sales: 10%
Number of Employees: 2,990
Average Check: Lunch(10); Dinner(14)
Internet Order Processing: Yes
Internet Sales: 5.00%
Total Units: 61
Trade Names: LaRosa's Pizzeria (65)
Company-Owned Units: 20
Units Franchised To: 45
Preferred Square Footage: 1,200; 4,000
Preferred Location Types: Freestanding; Strip Mall
Alcohol Served: Beer, Wine, Liquor
Primary Menu: Pizza (65)
Projected Openings: 2
Areas of Operation: IN, KY, OH
Type of Foodservice: Casual Dining (65)
Foodservice Management Venues: Health Care
Catering Services: Yes
Primary Distributors: (Food) Presto Foods, MONROE, OH

Key Personnel
DONALD S. LAROSA - Chairman
MICHAEL T. LAROSA - Chairman; CEO
PETE BUSCANI - Exec VP Marketing
MICHELLE MCMAHON - VP Franchise Development
SUZIE PFEIFFER - VP Finance
STEVEN BROWNE - VP Human Resources
KYLE WELCH - Director Information Systems, Information Technology
MEGAN TORBECK - Director Marketing
SHAUNA DUVALL - Manager Human Resources
K. JAKE WARREN - Designer

Lee's Famous Recipe of Cincinnati Inc.
3638 Round Bottom Rd
Cincinnati, OH 45244-2431

Telephone: (513) 272-4100
Fax Number: (513) 272-4108
Type of Business: Chain Restaurant Operator
Year Founded: 1967
Total Sales: $2,891,000 (e)
Number of Employees: 140
Average Check: Lunch(12); Dinner(12)
Total Units: 9
Trade Names: Lee's Famous Recipe Chicken (9)
Units Franchised From: 9
Preferred Square Footage: 2,500
Preferred Location Types: Freestanding
Primary Menu: Chicken (9)
Areas of Operation: KY, OH
Type of Foodservice: Quick Serve (9)
Franchise Affiliation: Lee's Famous Recipes Inc., FORT WALTON BEACH, FL

Key Personnel
TOM CUMMINS - President; General Manager; Director Finance, Operations, Purchasing, Facility/Maintenance, Information Systems, Real Estate; General Buyer
CHRIS CALLAHAN - Controller; Manager Supply Chain, Human Resources

Montgomery Inn Inc.
925 Riverside Dr
Cincinnati, OH 45202

Telephone: (513) 791-3482
Internet Homepage: montgomeryinn.com
Type of Business: Chain Restaurant Operator
Year Founded: 1951
Total Sales: $30,601,000 (e)
Alcohol Sales: 20%
Number of Employees: 500
Average Check: Lunch(26); Dinner(38)
Internet Order Processing: Yes
Internet Sales: 15.00%
Total Units: 2
Trade Names: Montgomery Inn (1); Montgomery Inn Boat House (1)
Company-Owned Units: 2
Preferred Location Types: Freestanding
Alcohol Served: Beer, Wine, Liquor
Primary Menu: Bar-B-Q (3)
Areas of Operation: OH
Type of Foodservice: Casual Dining (2)
Foodservice Management Venues: Parks & Recreation
Catering Services: Yes
On-site Distribution Center: Yes

Key Personnel
C. DEAN GREGORY - Exec VP
EVAN ANDREWS - Exec VP Operations, Marketing
RICK KNAPP - General Manager
ANDY HICKS - Executive Chef; Manager Menu Development; General Buyer
JIM BOMKAMP - Manager

Pickard Enterprises
3870 Virginia Ave Ste 210
Cincinnati, OH 45227-3431

Telephone: (513) 527-5900
Fax Number: (513) 527-5906
Type of Business: Chain Restaurant Operator
Year Founded: 1999
Total Sales: $37,580,000 (e)
Number of Employees: 400
Average Check: Breakfast(8); Lunch(10); Dinner(10)
Total Units: 8
Trade Names: McDonald's (8)
Units Franchised From: 8
Preferred Square Footage: 2,500
Preferred Location Types: Freestanding
Primary Menu: Hamburger (8)
Areas of Operation: KY, OH
Type of Foodservice: Quick Serve (8)
Franchise Affiliation: McDonald's Corporation, CHICAGO, IL

Key Personnel
JUDSON PICKARD JR - President; Director Information Systems, Real Estate; General Buyer
MELVIN PICKARD - Owner
CLARENCE ANDERSON - Director Operations
TIM MASSEY - Director Operations, Purchasing, Facility/Maintenance, Supply Chain
TIFFANY BOLES - Manager Human Resources

PS Management Inc
1225 Birney Ln
Cincinnati, OH 45230-2926

Telephone: (513) 231-8539
Type of Business: Chain Restaurant Operator
Total Units: 17
Trade Names: Penn Station Steak & Sub (17)
Units Franchised From: 17
Primary Menu: Sandwiches/Deli (17)
Areas of Operation: OH
Type of Foodservice: Quick Serve (17)

Key Personnel
KEVIN OSTERFELD - President; General Buyer

Restaurant Management Inc.
300 Main St Fl 2
Cincinnati, OH 45202-4123

Telephone: (513) 362-8900
Fax Number: (513) 362-1328
Internet Homepage: arbys-rmi.com
Company Email: info@arbys-rmi.com
Type of Business: Chain Restaurant Operator
Year Founded: 1965
Total Sales: $120,070,000 (e)
Number of Employees: 1,720
Average Check: Lunch(8); Dinner(8)
Total Units: 65
Trade Names: Arby's (65)
Units Franchised From: 65
Preferred Square Footage: 3,000
Preferred Location Types: Freestanding; Regional Mall
Primary Menu: Sandwiches/Deli (65)
Areas of Operation: AL, GA, IN, KY, NC, OH, TN
Type of Foodservice: Quick Serve (65)
Franchise Affiliation: Arby's Restaurant Group, ATLANTA, GA
Primary Distributors: (Food) I Supply Co., FAIRBORN, OH

Key Personnel
DAVE RAAB - Senior VP Operations; General Manager; Director Facility/Maintenance, Information Systems, Real Estate, Design, Human Resources; General Buyer
DAVID KONERMAN - Director Purchasing
PATTY ORSE - District Manager
MICHELLE CORNELISSEN - Manager Restaurant Operations
KAREN DUMFORD - Specialist Accounting

Skyline Chili of Oakley
2951 Madison Rd
Cincinnati, OH 45209-2027

Telephone: (513) 841-9285
Fax Number: (513) 841-9287
Internet Homepage: skylinechili.com
Type of Business: Chain Restaurant Operator
Total Sales: $4,998,000 (e)
Number of Employees: 85
Average Check: Dinner(10)
Total Units: 6
Trade Names: Skyline Chili (6)
Units Franchised From: 6
Preferred Square Footage: 2,800
Primary Menu: American (6)
Areas of Operation: OH
Type of Foodservice: Family Restaurant (6)
Catering Services: Yes
Franchise Affiliation: Skyline Chili Inc., FAIRFIELD, OH
Primary Distributors: (Full Line) US Foods, CINCINNATI, OH

Key Personnel
MIKE MISLEH - President; General Buyer

Tavern Restaurant Group Inc.
11340 Montgomery Rd Ste 214
Cincinnati, OH 45249-2377

Telephone: (513) 605-4700
Fax Number: (513) 605-4706
Internet Homepage: tavernrestaurantgroup.com
Company Email: info@tavernrestaurantgroup.com
Type of Business: Chain Restaurant Operator
Year Founded: 1973
Total Sales: $32,850,000 (e)
Alcohol Sales: 23%
Number of Employees: 650
Average Check: Lunch(10); Dinner(16)
Internet Order Processing: Yes
Total Units: 12
Trade Names: DeSha's American Tavern (2); Horse & Barrel (1); Nicholson's Tavern & Pub (1); Pub Cincinnati (1); Pub Nashville (1); Pub Orlando (1); Pub Tampa (1); The Pub Beavercreek (1); The Pub Crestview Hills (1); The Pub Naples (1); The Pub Pembroke Pines (1)
Company-Owned Units: 12
Preferred Square Footage: 8,000
Preferred Location Types: Downtown; Freestanding; Other; Regional Mall

Alcohol Served: Beer, Wine, Liquor
Primary Menu: American (12)
Projected Openings: 2
Areas of Operation: FL, GA, KY, OH, TN
Type of Foodservice: Casual Dining (12)
Primary Distributors: (Equipment) SYSCO Food Services of Louisville, LOUISVILLE, KY; (Food) US Foods, CINCINNATI, OH; (Supplies) SYSCO Food Services of Louisville, LOUISVILLE, KY

Key Personnel
W. NICK SANDERS - Founder; CEO
TOM HENSLEY - CFO
DAVID BELL - VP
PAUL DAGENBACH - Corporate Chef
KATHY FRENCH - Director Human Resources; Manager Payroll
DANIELLE CARLISLE - Director Operations, Facility/Maintenance, Information Systems, Risk Management, Real Estate; Manager Administration

Tom and Chee Worldwide LLC
125 E Court St
Cincinnati, OH 45202-1212

Telephone: (513) 381-8500
Internet Homepage: tomandchee.com
Type of Business: Chain Restaurant Operator
Year Founded: 2009
Systemwide Sales: $6,030,000 (e)
Total Sales: $16,890,000 (e)
Average Check: Lunch(10); Dinner(10)
Internet Order Processing: Yes
Internet Sales: 1.00%
Total Units: 26
Trade Names: Tom+Chee (26)
Company-Owned Units: 3
Units Franchised To: 23
Primary Menu: Sandwiches/Deli (26)
Areas of Operation: CO, FL, GA, IN, KY, LA, MI, MO, NE, NJ, OH, PA, TN, TX, WI
Type of Foodservice: Fast Casual (26)
Catering Services: Yes
Parent Company: Gold Star Chili Inc., CINCINNATI, OH

Key Personnel
COREY WARD - Partner; Chief Marketing Officer; Director Franchise Development
JENNIFER QUACKENBUSH - Director Franchise Operations
JENNIFER RACHFORD - Manager Human Resources

Virginia Wings of Norfolk Lc
3825 Edwards Rd Ste 200
Cincinnati, OH 45209-1288

Telephone: (513) 241-5800
Type of Business: Chain Restaurant Operator
Total Sales: $18,000,000 (e)
Total Units: 6
Trade Names: Hooters (6)
Units Franchised From: 6
Alcohol Served: Beer, Wine, Liquor
Primary Menu: American (6)
Areas of Operation: OH
Type of Foodservice: Casual Dining (6)
Franchise Affiliation: HOA Restaurant Group LLC, ATLANTA, GA

Key Personnel
JEFFREY R. ANDERSON - President; General Buyer

White Castle System Inc.
3400 Central Pkwy
Cincinnati, OH 45223-2611

Telephone: (513) 559-0575
Fax Number: (513) 559-1101
Listing Type: Regional Office
Type of Business: Chain Restaurant Operator
Total Units: 39
Areas of Operation: IN, KY, OH
On-site Distribution Center: Yes
Parent Company: White Castle Management Co., COLUMBUS, OH

Key Personnel
TOMMY LOVEBERRY - Regional Director

A.E.S. Management Corp.
11811 Shaker Blvd Ste 206
Cleveland, OH 44120-1933

Telephone: (216) 721-4765
Fax Number: (216) 721-4769
Type of Business: Chain Restaurant Operator
Total Sales: $39,210,000 (e)
Number of Employees: 386
Average Check: Lunch(8); Dinner(12)
Total Units: 15
Trade Names: Popeyes Louisiana Kitchen (15)
Units Franchised From: 15
Preferred Square Footage: 2,000
Preferred Location Types: Freestanding
Primary Menu: Chicken (15)
Areas of Operation: OH
Type of Foodservice: Quick Serve (15)
Franchise Affiliation: Popeyes Louisiana Kitchen Inc., ATLANTA, GA
Primary Distributors: (Food) I Supply Co.,
FAIRBORN, OH

Key Personnel
VANESSA WHITING - President; General Buyer
ANTHONY SMITH - Director Operations
TAYLOR SMITH - Director Marketing

Auntie Anne's Franchise
3400 Steelyard Dr
Cleveland, OH 44109-2386

Telephone: (216) 398-9750
Internet Homepage: auntieannesfranchising.com
Type of Business: Chain Restaurant Operator
Total Sales: $1,568,000 (e)
Total Units: 2
Trade Names: Auntie Anne's Hand-Rolled Soft Pretzels (1); Subway (1)
Units Franchised From: 2
Primary Menu: Sandwiches/Deli (1); Snacks (1)
Areas of Operation: OH
Type of Foodservice: Quick Serve (2)
Franchise Affiliation: Auntie Anne's Inc., LANCASTER, PA

Key Personnel
IMAD NADER - Owner; General Buyer

Auntie Anne's Franchise
5300 Riverside Dr
Cleveland, OH 44135-3130

Telephone: (216) 265-8468
Internet Homepage: auntieannesfranchising.com
Type of Business: Chain Restaurant Operator
Total Sales: $4,970,000 (e)
Total Units: 7
Trade Names: Auntie Anne's Hand-Rolled Soft Pretzels (7)
Units Franchised From: 7
Primary Menu: Snacks (7)
Areas of Operation: OH
Type of Foodservice: Quick Serve (7)
Franchise Affiliation: Auntie Anne's Inc., LANCASTER, PA

Key Personnel
GENE WEISS - Owner; General Buyer

Epoch Five Enterprises LLC
24050 Commerce Park
Cleveland, OH 44122-5833

Telephone: (216) 514-9798
Type of Business: Chain Restaurant Operator
Total Sales: $1,535,000 (e)

Total Units: 2
Trade Names: Auntie Anne's (1); Cinnabon (1)
Units Franchised From: 2
Primary Menu: Snacks (2)
Areas of Operation: OH
Type of Foodservice: Quick Serve (2)
Franchise Affiliation: Auntie Anne's Inc., LANCASTER, PA; Cinnabon Inc., ATLANTA, GA

Key Personnel
GEAN WEISS - Owner; General Buyer

Hot Sauce Williams Barbeque
3770 Lee Rd
Cleveland, OH 44128-1410

Telephone: (216) 921-4704
Type of Business: Chain Restaurant Operator
Year Founded: 1963
Total Sales: $2,290,000 (e)
Number of Employees: 100
Average Check: Lunch(12); Dinner(14)
Total Units: 2
Trade Names: Hot Sauce Williams Barbeque (2)
Company-Owned Units: 2
Preferred Square Footage: 1,500
Preferred Location Types: Freestanding
Primary Menu: Bar-B-Q (2)
Areas of Operation: OH
Type of Foodservice: Quick Serve (2)
Catering Services: Yes
On-site Distribution Center: Yes

Key Personnel
ELVIN WILLIAMS - General Manager

Johnny's Downtown
1406 W 6th St
Cleveland, OH 44113-1300

Telephone: (216) 623-0055
Fax Number: (216) 623-1248
Internet Homepage: johnnyscleveland.com; johnnysonfulton.com
Type of Business: Chain Restaurant Operator
Total Sales: $6,919,000 (e)
Alcohol Sales: 25%
Number of Employees: 100
Average Check: Lunch(28); Dinner(60)
Total Units: 3
Trade Names: Johnny's Bar (1); Johnny's Downtown (1); Johnny's Little Bar (1)
Company-Owned Units: 3
Preferred Location Types: Downtown
Alcohol Served: Beer, Wine, Liquor
Primary Menu: American (1); Italian (2)
Areas of Operation: OH
Type of Foodservice: Casual Dining (1); Fine Dining (2)
Primary Distributors: (Full Line) SYSCO Food Services of Cincinnati, CINCINNATI, OH

Key Personnel
JOSEPH SANTOSUOSSO - President; General Manager
DAVE FLOWERS - Controller; General Manager; General Buyer

McNulty's Bier Markt/Bar Cento
1948 W 25th St
Cleveland, OH 44113-3438

Telephone: (216) 274-1010
Internet Homepage: bier-markt.com; marketgardenbrewery.com; nanobrewcleveland.com; barcento.com
Type of Business: Chain Restaurant Operator
Year Founded: 2004
Total Units: 5
Trade Names: Barcento (1); Market Garden Brewery (1); McNulty's Bier Markt (1); Nanobrew (1); Speakesy (1)
Company-Owned Units: 5
Preferred Location Types: Downtown; Freestanding
Alcohol Served: Beer, Wine, Liquor
Primary Menu: American (5)
Areas of Operation: OH
Type of Foodservice: Casual Dining (5)

Key Personnel
SAM MCNULTY - Partner; General Buyer
MARK PRIEMER - Partner
LOU LANG - Partner
MICHAEL FORAN - COO; General Manager

Michael Symon Restaurants
2058 E 4th St
Cleveland, OH 44115-1024

Telephone: (216) 621-6662
Internet Homepage: bspotburgers.com; lolabistro.com; michaelsymon.com; roastdetroit.com; unitedconcessionsgroup.com
Company Email: michael@lolabistro.com
Type of Business: Chain Restaurant Operator
Total Sales: $9,532,000 (e)
Total Units: 11
Trade Names: Angeline (1); B Spot Burgers (3); Bar Symon (2); Lola (1); Mabel's BBQ (2); Roast (1); Sara's (1)
Company-Owned Units: 9
Units Franchised To: 2
Primary Menu: American (3); Bar-B-Q (2); French/Continental (1); Hamburger (3); Italian (1); Steak (1)
Projected Openings: 1
Areas of Operation: DC, IN, MI, OH, PA
Type of Foodservice: Casual Dining (8); Fine Dining (3)

Key Personnel
DOUG PETKOVIC - Partner
CARRIE SILLIA - CFO
AMANDA SMITH - COO
KELLY CREER - Controller
SAM LINDSLEY - Director Operations
KEVIN FLANNERY - Manager Warehouse

Morgan's Foods Inc
4829 Galaxy Pkwy Ste S
Cleveland, OH 44128

Telephone: (800) 869-8692
Internet Homepage: morgansfoods.com
Type of Business: Chain Restaurant Operator
Total Sales: $125,558,000 (e)
Average Check: Dinner(12)
Total Units: 70
Trade Names: KFC (55); KFC/Taco Bell (8); Taco Bell (3); Taco Bell/Pizza Hut Express (4)
Units Franchised To: 70
Primary Menu: Chicken (66); Pizza (3); Taco (4)
Areas of Operation: NY
Type of Foodservice: Quick Serve (73)
Franchise Affiliation: Taco Bell Corp., IRVINE, CA

Key Personnel
LEONARD R. STEIN-SAPIR - Chairman
KENNETH L. HIGNETT - CFO; Exec VP
VINCENT J. ODDI - VP Development

Paladar Restaurant Group
3615 Superior Ave E Ste 4403C
Cleveland, OH 44114

Telephone: (216) 591-1625
Fax Number: (216) 591-1628
Internet Homepage: bombatacos.com; paladarlatinkitchen.com
Type of Business: Chain Restaurant Operator
Year Founded: 2007
Total Units: 7
Trade Names: Bomba Tacos & Rum (3); Paladar Latin Kitchen & Rum Bar (4)
Company-Owned Units: 7
Primary Menu: Latin American/Cuban (7)
Areas of Operation: FL, MD, OH, VA
Type of Foodservice: Casual Dining (4); Fast Casual (3)

Key Personnel
ANDY HIMMEL - Founder; CEO

JOHN PETRUC - CFO; Controller

Restaurant Developers Corporation
7002 Engle Rd Ste 100
Cleveland, OH 44130-3474

Telephone: (440) 625-3080
Fax Number: (440) 625-3081
Internet Homepage: mrhero.com
Type of Business: Chain Restaurant Operator
Year Founded: 1965
Total Sales: $9,768,000 (e)
Number of Employees: 325
Average Check: Breakfast(5); Lunch(8); Dinner(16)
Total Units: 115
Trade Names: Mr. Hero (115)
Units Franchised To: 115
Preferred Square Footage: 1,800
Preferred Location Types: Convenience Store/Gas Station; Freestanding; Regional Mall; Stadiums; Travel Plazas
Primary Menu: Sandwiches/Deli (115)
Areas of Operation: OH
Type of Foodservice: Quick Serve (115)
Foodservice Management Venues: Schools
Catering Services: Yes
Primary Distributors: (Full Line) SYSCO Food Services of Cleveland Inc., CLEVELAND, OH
Notes: Systemwide sales reflect Mr. Hero operations only.

Key Personnel
TIMOTHY FREEMAN - Director Franchise Sales
KATHLEEN A. MOORMAN - Director Accounting, Human Resources
SHARON MERICO - Director Operations
BILL MAXFIELD - Supervisor Area

Select Restaurants Inc.
2000 Auburn Dr Ste 410
Cleveland, OH 44122-4327

Telephone: (216) 464-6606
Fax Number: (216) 464-8565
Internet Homepage: selectrestaurants.com
Company Email: info@selectrestaurants.com
Type of Business: Chain Restaurant Operator
Year Founded: 1992
Total Sales: $55,130,000 (e)
Alcohol Sales: 26%
Number of Employees: 1,090
Average Check: Lunch(22); Dinner(48)
Internet Order Processing: Yes
Internet Sales: 1.00%
Total Units: 9
Trade Names: Black Powder Tavern (1); County Line Tavern (1); Parker Restaurant & Bar (1); Parker's Lighthouse (1); Pier W (1); Queensview Steakhouse(1); Rusty Scupper (1); Winberie Restaurant & Bar (2)
Company-Owned Units: 9
Preferred Square Footage: 6,000; 15,000
Preferred Location Types: Downtown; Freestanding; Strip Mall
Alcohol Served: Beer, Wine, Liquor
Primary Menu: American (10); Seafood (3)
Projected Remodelings: 4
Areas of Operation: CA, IL, MA, MD, NJ, OH, PA
Type of Foodservice: Casual Dining (8); Fine Dining (5)
Primary Distributors: (Full Line) SYSCO Food Services of Cleveland Inc., CLEVELAND, OH

Key Personnel
WILL GREEN - VP Operations, Information Systems
JULIAN DEMIRI - General Manager

Strang Corporation
8905 Lake Ave Fl 2
Cleveland, OH 44102-6316

Telephone: (216) 961-6767
Fax Number: (216) 961-1966
Internet Homepage: americanbreadcompany.net; donslighthouse.com; donspomeroy.com; strangcorp.com
Company Email: feedback@strangcorp.com
Type of Business: Chain Restaurant Operator
Year Founded: 1941
Total Sales: $184,840,000 (e)
Alcohol Sales: 17%
Number of Employees: 1,791
Average Check: Lunch(8); Dinner(20)
Internet Order Processing: Yes
Total Units: 43
Trade Names: Don's Lighthouse (1); Don's Pomeroy (1); Panera Bread (41)
Company-Owned Units: 2
Units Franchised From: 41
Preferred Square Footage: 5,000
Preferred Location Types: Freestanding; Strip Mall
Alcohol Served: Beer, Wine, Liquor
Primary Menu: Sandwiches/Deli (41); Seafood (2)
Areas of Operation: DE, NJ, OH, PA
Type of Foodservice: Fast Casual (41); Fine Dining (2)
Franchise Affiliation: Fired Up Inc., AUSTIN, TX; Panera Bread Company, SAINT LOUIS, MO
Primary Distributors: (Food) SYSCO Food Services of Cincinnati, CINCINNATI, OH
Notes: The Panera Bread restaurants operate as American Bread Company.

Key Personnel
DONALD STRANG III - Chairman; CEO
PETER STRANG - President
IULIAN BULUCEA - VP Information Technology
JOHN CHAMP - Controller
DAVID BURDETTE - Manager Information Technology
MICHELE LEARY-POELKING - Supervisor Accounting
JONATHAN BARKER - Senior Analyst Accounting

Tri-Arch
22535 Lorain Rd
Cleveland, OH 44126-2211

Telephone: (440) 734-9504
Fax Number: (440) 734-7504
Company Email: mcdtri@fbcglobal.net
Type of Business: Chain Restaurant Operator
Year Founded: 1989
Total Sales: $94,770,000 (e)
Number of Employees: 1,185
Average Check: Breakfast(8); Lunch(8); Dinner(10)
Total Units: 20
Trade Names: McDonald's (20)
Units Franchised From: 20
Preferred Square Footage: 2,500
Preferred Location Types: Freestanding; Regional Mall
Primary Menu: Hamburger (20)
Projected Openings: 1
Areas of Operation: OH
Type of Foodservice: Quick Serve (20)
Franchise Affiliation: McDonald's Corporation, CHICAGO, IL
Primary Distributors: (Full Line) The Anderson-DuBose Co., WARREN, OH

Key Personnel
STEVE PAYNE - President; Director Finance, Facility/Maintenance, Information Systems, Real Estate; General Buyer

Asian Concepts Inc.
3120 Valleyview Dr
Columbus, OH 43204-2023

Telephone: (614) 737-2550
Fax Number: (614) 737-2547
Internet Homepage: markpi.com
Type of Business: Chain Restaurant Operator
Year Founded: 1978
Systemwide Sales: $16,078,000 (e)
Total Sales: $1,584,000 (e)
Alcohol Sales: 20%
Number of Employees: 5
Average Check: Lunch(10); Dinner(16)
Total Units: 13
Trade Names: Mark Pi's China Gate (3); Mark Pi's Express (9); Mark Pis Asian Diner (1)
Units Franchised To: 13
Preferred Square Footage: 1,500; 4,500;

5,000
Preferred Location Types: Community Mall; Downtown; Freestanding; Regional Mall; Strip Mall
Alcohol Served: Beer, Wine, Liquor
Primary Menu: Chinese (13)
Areas of Operation: CA, IN, OH
Foreign Countries: INDIA
Type of Foodservice: Casual Dining (4); Quick Serve (9)
Catering Services: Yes
Distribution Centers: COLUMBUS, OH

Key Personnel
LILIAN CHEN - Manager Accounting

Calimira LLC
390 W Nationwide Blvd
Columbus, OH 43215-2392

Telephone: (614) 621-1105
Fax Number: (614) 280-8026
Internet Homepage: myrustybucket.com; rustybuckettavern.com
Type of Business: Chain Restaurant Operator
Year Founded: 2002
Total Sales: $61,970,000 (e)
Alcohol Sales: 24%
Number of Employees: 166
Average Check: Dinner(12)
Total Units: 23
Trade Names: Rusty Bucket Restaurant and Tavern (23)
Company-Owned Units: 23
Preferred Location Types: Freestanding; Strip Mall
Alcohol Served: Beer, Wine, Liquor
Primary Menu: American (23)
Areas of Operation: CO, FL, IN, MI, NC, OH
Type of Foodservice: Casual Dining (23)
Catering Services: Yes
Notes: Rusty Bucket Corner Tavern operations are co-located with Cameron Mitchell Restaurants which handles back-office functions for both groups.

Key Personnel
GARY CALLICOAT - Founder; President; Partner; General Buyer
KATE SUMPTION - Partner; Director Marketing
RICK LINDEBOOM - Manager Region

Cameron Mitchell Restaurants LLC
390 W Nationwide Blvd
Columbus, OH 43215-2392

Telephone: (877) 491-1267
Fax Number: (614) 621-1020
Internet Homepage: cameronmitchell.com
Company Email: media@cameronmitchell.com
Type of Business: Chain Restaurant Operator
Year Founded: 1993
Total Sales: $194,400,000 (e)
Alcohol Sales: 25%
Number of Employees: 2,635
Average Check: Lunch(30); Dinner(42)
Internet Order Processing: Yes
Internet Sales: 1.00%
Total Units: 35
Trade Names: Barn at Rocky Fork Creek (1); Cameron's American Bistro (1); Cap City Fine Diner (3); Del Mar Kitchen (1); Guild House (1); Hudson 29 (2); Lincoln Social (1); M (1); Marcella's Ristorante, Pizzeria and Wine Bar (2); Martini Modern Italian (1); Mitchell's Ocean Club (16); Molly Woo's (1); The Avenue (2); The Guild House (1); The Pearl (1)
Company-Owned Units: 35
Preferred Square Footage: 7,500
Preferred Location Types: Downtown; Freestanding; Office Complex; Regional Mall; Strip Mall
Alcohol Served: Beer, Wine, Liquor
Primary Menu: American (9); Asian (1); Italian (4); Miscellaneous (2); Steak (3); Steak/Seafood (16)
Projected Openings: 2
Areas of Operation: AZ, CA, CO, FL, GA, IN, MI, OH, PA, TX
Type of Foodservice: Casual Dining (16); Fine Dining (19)
Catering Services: Yes
Primary Distributors: (Equipment) The Wasserstrom Co., COLUMBUS, OH; (Food) Michael's Finer Meats and Seafoods, COLUMBUS, OH; (Supplies) The Wasserstrom Co., COLUMBUS, OH

Key Personnel
CAMERON MITCHELL - Founder; CEO
DAVID MILLER - President; COO
GARY CALLICOAT - President
JR DEHRING - CFO
DIANE SMULLEN - CFO; VP
WAYNE A. SCHICK - Senior VP Procurement, Store Planning; VP Store Planning
CHARLES KLINE - Senior VP Operations
BRIAN HINSHAW - Senior VP Food and Beverage; Executive Chef
KATIE LAUDICK - VP Human Resources
HEATHER LEONARD - VP Marketing
STACEY L. CONNAUGHTON - VP Corporate Affairs
STEVE WEIS - VP Business Development
MITCH MILLER - VP
DONALD PIETRZYK - Director
MICHAEL REDCAY - Director Event Planning
RANDY ROBERTY AIA - Director Architecture, Design
MARK WEISS - Director Operations
ORLANDO SPROCKEL - Director Information Technology
DON WALLER - Director Construction
VERONICA MATHENY - Director E-Commerce
MAUREEN DELUCA - Director Training
KIMBERLY HO - Director Accounting
MELISSA JOHNSON - Director Catering
ADAM JUSTI - Director Facility/Maintenance
AARON WESLEY - Regional Director Operations
BRIAN SCHEREN - Regional Director Operations
GRETCHEN MOORE - Senior Manager Marketing
DANI LINDEBOOM - Senior Manager Accounting
HOLLY HARRAH - Manager Finance
CAITLIN CEPLUCH - Manager Human Resources
NICK ANSARA - Manager Operations
RUSSELL BLANKS - Manager Information Systems
ERIN SCHROCK - Manager Human Resources

Capitol Foods Inc
947 E Johnstown Rd Ste 273
Columbus, OH 43230-1851

Telephone: (614) 855-4763
Type of Business: Chain Restaurant Operator
Total Sales: $13,290,000 (e)
Number of Employees: 200
Average Check: Lunch(10); Dinner(10)
Total Units: 7
Trade Names: Arby's (7)
Units Franchised From: 7
Preferred Square Footage: 1,400; 3,200
Preferred Location Types: Freestanding
Primary Menu: Sandwiches/Deli (7)
Areas of Operation: OH
Type of Foodservice: Quick Serve (7)
Franchise Affiliation: Arby's Restaurant Group, ATLANTA, GA

Key Personnel
BOB MCDONALD - President; Director Operations; Manager Information Systems, Real Estate; General Buyer

Donatos Pizzeria LLC
935 Taylor Station Rd
Columbus, OH 43230-6657

Telephone: (614) 416-7700
Fax Number: (614) 416-7702
Internet Homepage: donatos.com
Type of Business: Chain Restaurant Operator
Year Founded: 1963
Systemwide Sales: $470,916,000 (e)
Total Sales: $130,110,000 (e)
Alcohol Sales: 1%
Number of Employees: 6,039
Average Check: Lunch(16); Dinner(16)
Internet Order Processing: Yes
Total Units: 240

Trade Names: Donatos Pizza (240)
Company-Owned Units: 55
Units Franchised To: 185
Preferred Square Footage: 2,000; 2,100; 2,400
Preferred Location Types: Freestanding; Stadiums; Strip Mall
Alcohol Served: Beer
Primary Menu: Pizza (240)
Projected Openings: 1
Areas of Operation: AL, IN, KY, NC, OH, SC, VA
Type of Foodservice: Casual Dining (240)
Catering Services: Yes
Primary Distributors: (Equipment) The Wasserstrom Co., COLUMBUS, OH; (Food) The SYGMA Network, Inc., DUBLIN, OH; (Supplies) The Wasserstrom Co., COLUMBUS, OH

Key Personnel
KEVIN KING - CEO; President
DOUG KOURIE - CFO
AMOS DURBIN - COO
CHRISTINA JACKSON - Chief People Officer
STEVEN GRAVES - CIO
JODIE CONRAD - Chief Marketing Officer
JEFF BALDWIN - VP Franchise Development, Franchising
CHERYL BERGSMAN - VP Operations
MARK REED - Executive Director Purchasing
CAROLYN DELP - Executive Director Marketing
CAROLYN C. BUTLER - Executive Director Branding
LAURA FORDING - Controller
CYNTHIA OTTAVIO - Director Menu Development
SCOTT STONAKER - Director Information Systems
KAREN KUNTZ - Director Business Development

El Vaquero
2195 Riverside Dr
Columbus, OH 43221-4020

Telephone: (614) 486-4547
Fax Number: (614) 486-4050
Internet Homepage: elvaquerorestaurants.com
Type of Business: Chain Restaurant Operator
Year Founded: 1993
Total Sales: $12,160,000 (e)
Alcohol Sales: 40%
Number of Employees: 308
Average Check: Lunch(8); Dinner(18)
Internet Order Processing: Yes
Total Units: 18
Trade Names: El Vaquero (18)
Company-Owned Units: 18
Preferred Square Footage: 6,000
Preferred Location Types: Freestanding
Alcohol Served: Beer, Wine, Liquor
Primary Menu: Mexican (18)
Areas of Operation: MI, OH
Type of Foodservice: Casual Dining (18)
Primary Distributors: (Full Line) US Foods, CINCINNATI, OH

Key Personnel
FERNANDO MORALES - President; Partner; General Manager; Director Finance, Operations, Purchasing, Facility/Maintenance, Information Systems, Supply Chain, Real Estate, Design, Human Resources; General Buyer
SERGIO MORALES - Partner
JORGE ORNELAS - Executive Chef; General Buyer

Escape Enterprises Ltd.
1099 Sullivant Ave
Columbus, OH 43223

Telephone: (614) 224-0300
Fax Number: (614) 224-6460
Internet Homepage: steakescape.com
Type of Business: Chain Restaurant Operator
Year Founded: 1982
Systemwide Sales: $59,262,000 (e)
Total Sales: $2,135,000 (e)
Number of Employees: 36
Average Check: Breakfast(8); Lunch(14); Dinner(16)
Total Units: 36
Trade Names: Steak Escape (34); Steak Escape Express (1); Steak Escape Sandwich Grill (1)
Company-Owned Units: 4
Units Franchised To: 32
Preferred Square Footage: 500; 3,000
Preferred Location Types: Airports; Community Mall; Convenience Store/Gas Station; Downtown; Regional Mall; Strip Mall
Primary Menu: Sandwiches/Deli (36)
Projected Openings: 1
Areas of Operation: AR, AZ, CA, CO, DE, IN, LA, MD, MN, MS, NC, OH, SD, TN, WI, WV
Foreign Countries: MEXICO; SAUDI ARABIA
Type of Foodservice: Fast Casual (1); Quick Serve (35)

Key Personnel
ANTHONY TICCONI - VP Franchise Development
DIRK AHLGRIM - Director Purchasing, Loss Prevention, Quality Assurance, Training, Menu Development, Food Safety

Figlio Wood-Fired Pizza
1369 Grandview Ave
Columbus, OH 43212-2802

Telephone: (614) 481-8850
Fax Number: (614) 481-8810
Internet Homepage: figliopizza.com
Company Email: peterandlaurie@figliopizza.com
Type of Business: Chain Restaurant Operator
Year Founded: 1991
Total Sales: $4,507,000 (e)
Alcohol Sales: 20%
Number of Employees: 60
Average Check: Lunch(12); Dinner(18)
Total Units: 4
Trade Names: Figlio Wood-Fired Pizza (3); Vino Vino Wine Bar & Restaurant (1)
Company-Owned Units: 4
Preferred Location Types: Freestanding; Strip Mall
Alcohol Served: Beer, Wine, Liquor
Primary Menu: Italian (4)
Areas of Operation: OH
Type of Foodservice: Casual Dining (4)

Key Personnel
LAURIE DANIS - Partner
PETER DANIS - Partner; General Manager; General Buyer
JEN ARDEN - Buyer Beverages

FUSIAN
855 W 5th Ave
Columbus, OH 43212

Telephone: (614) 670-4323
Internet Homepage: fusian.com
Company Email: info@fusian.com
Type of Business: Chain Restaurant Operator
Year Founded: 2010
Total Sales: $8,514,000 (e)
Total Units: 12
Trade Names: FUSIAN (12)
Company-Owned Units: 12
Primary Menu: Japanese (12)
Projected Openings: 1
Areas of Operation: OH
Type of Foodservice: Fast Casual (12)

Key Personnel
STEPHAN HARMAN - Co-Founder
ERIC ROSENBERG - Controller
STEVEN PAVELKA - Specialist Digital

Gosh Enterprises Inc.
2500 Farmers Dr Ste 140
Columbus, OH 43235-5706

Telephone: (614) 923-4700
Fax Number: (614) 923-4701
Internet Homepage: bibibop.com/contact; charleys.com
Type of Business: Chain Restaurant Operator
Year Founded: 1986
Systemwide Sales: $315,406,000 (e)
Total Sales: $42,000,000 (e)

Number of Employees: 750
Average Check: Breakfast(8); Lunch(10); Dinner(16)
Total Units: 638
Trade Names: Bibibop Asian Grill (38); Charley's Philly Steaks (600)
Company-Owned Units: 65
Units Franchised To: 573
Preferred Square Footage: 700; 1,800; 2,200
Preferred Location Types: Airports; Community Mall; Convenience Store/Gas Station; Downtown; Freestanding; Institution (college/hospital); Office Complex; Regional Mall; Stadiums; Strip Mall
Primary Menu: Asian (38); Sandwiches/Deli (600)
Areas of Operation: AK, AL, AZ, CA, CO, CT, DC, FL, GA, GU, HI, IL, IN, KS, KY, MA, MD, MI, MO, NC, NJ, NM, NY, OH, OK, OR, PA, SC, TN, TX, UT, VA, WI, ON
Foreign Countries: BAHAMAS; BAHRAIN; BRAZIL; CANADA; EGYPT; ENGLAND; GERMANY; GUATEMALA; HONDURAS; ITALY; JAPAN; KUWAIT; MAURITIUS; OMAN; PANAMA; POLAND; RUSSIA; SAUDI ARABIA; SOUTH KOREA; UNITED ARAB EMIRATES; VENEZUELA
Type of Foodservice: Fast Casual (38); Quick Serve (600)
Primary Distributors: (Equipment) Best Restaurant Equipment & Design Inc., COLUMBUS, OH

Key Personnel
CHARLEY M. SHIN - Chairman; CEO
CANDRA ALISISWANTO - CFO
JOHN WOO - VP Real Estate, Business Development
SEOK SOONG KIM - Director Business Development
DORI NORTH - Director Business Development
RICHARD PAGE - Director Franchise Sales
KEN KANZAKI - Senior Manager Franchise Development
AMY HAYES - Senior Manager Employee Compensation, Employee Benefits
SARAH WINTERS - Specialist Information Technology

Hunan Lion
2038 Crown Plaza Dr
Columbus, OH 43235

Telephone: (614) 459-3933
Fax Number: (614) 459-9675
Internet Homepage: hunancolumbus.com
Type of Business: Chain Restaurant Operator
Year Founded: 1986
Total Sales: $5,055,000 (e)
Alcohol Sales: 12%
Number of Employees: 25
Average Check: Lunch(18); Dinner(28)
Total Units: 2
Trade Names: Hunan House (1); Hunan Lion (1)
Company-Owned Units: 2
Preferred Location Types: Strip Mall
Alcohol Served: Beer, Wine, Liquor
Primary Menu: Chinese (2)
Areas of Operation: OH
Type of Foodservice: Casual Dining (2)
Catering Services: Yes

Key Personnel
JASON CHANG - President; Partner; General Manager; General Buyer
ALLISON CHANG - Partner; General Manager; General Buyer

Jeni's Splendid Ice Cream
401 N Front St
Columbus, OH 43215-2254

Telephone: (614) 488-3224
Fax Number: (614) 488-3236
Internet Homepage: jenis.com
Company Email: contact@jenis.com
Type of Business: Chain Restaurant Operator
Total Sales: $11,760,000 (e)
Number of Employees: 995
Total Units: 71
Trade Names: Jeni's Splendid Ice Creams (71)
Company-Owned Units: 71
Preferred Location Types: Freestanding; Strip Mall
Primary Menu: Snacks (71)
Areas of Operation: CA, FL, GA, IL, MO, OH, SC, TN
Type of Foodservice: Quick Serve (71)

Key Personnel
STACY PETERSON - CEO
JENI BRITTON BAUER - President; General Buyer
CHARLY BAUER - Director Finance
RYAN MORGAN - Director Customer Service

JTN Commercial Investments
1899 Lockbourne Rd
Columbus, OH 43207-1421

Telephone: (614) 444-6868
Fax Number: (614) 443-5003
Type of Business: Chain Restaurant Operator
Systemwide Sales: $2,505,000 (e)
Total Sales: $1,085,000 (e)
Alcohol Sales: 1%
Number of Employees: 20
Average Check: Lunch(14); Dinner(24)
Total Units: 2
Trade Names: Pa-Pa Joe's Pizza (2)
Units Franchised To: 2
Preferred Location Types: Freestanding
Alcohol Served: Beer, Wine
Primary Menu: Pizza (2)
Areas of Operation: OH
Type of Foodservice: Casual Dining (2)
Primary Distributors: (Full Line) RDP Foodservice, LLC, HILLIARD, OH

Key Personnel
SAM SABIR - Owner; General Buyer

Massey's Pizza Inc.
5310 E Main St Ste 101
Columbus, OH 43213-2598

Telephone: (614) 866-0700
Fax Number: (614) 866-8126
Internet Homepage: masseyspizza.com
Company Email: info@masseyspizza.com
Type of Business: Chain Restaurant Operator
Year Founded: 1949
Systemwide Sales: $10,904,000 (e)
Total Sales: $8,447,000 (e)
Alcohol Sales: 1%
Number of Employees: 102
Average Check: Lunch(8); Dinner(18)
Internet Order Processing: Yes
Total Units: 14
Trade Names: Massey's Pizza (14)
Company-Owned Units: 3
Units Franchised To: 11
Preferred Square Footage: 2,000; 4,000
Preferred Location Types: Freestanding; Strip Mall
Alcohol Served: Beer
Primary Menu: Pizza (14)
Areas of Operation: OH
Type of Foodservice: Casual Dining (14)
Catering Services: Yes
Primary Distributors: (Food) Presto Foods, MONROE, OH

Key Personnel
DAVE PALLONE - President; Partner
RICHARD FOLK - Manager Operations
KRISTEN CARTER - Manager Human Resources

Miller Managment LLC
4683 Winterset Dr
Columbus, OH 43220-8113

Telephone: (614) 451-6363
Fax Number: (614) 451-9724
Internet Homepage: millerbkcareers.com
Type of Business: Chain Restaurant Operator
Year Founded: 1981
Total Sales: $40,720,000 (e)
Number of Employees: 900
Average Check: Breakfast(8); Lunch(10); Dinner(10)

Total Units: 18
Trade Names: Burger King (18)
Units Franchised From: 18
Preferred Square Footage: 3,000
Preferred Location Types: Freestanding
Primary Menu: Hamburger (18)
Areas of Operation: OH
Type of Foodservice: Quick Serve (18)
Franchise Affiliation: Burger King Worldwide Inc., MIAMI, FL
Primary Distributors: (Full Line) McLane/Frankfort, FRANKFORT, KY

Key Personnel
STEPHEN MILLER - President; Partner; Controller; General Manager; Director Risk Management, Real Estate, Franchising
NANCY MILLER - Partner; Director Promotion, Customer Service
TIMOTHY NEFF - Controller; Manager Finance
JOHN STAHL - Director Information Technology
SHAWN MILLER - Director Operations, Purchasing

MJPT II & Associates, LTD
1333 Oakview Dr
Columbus, OH 43235-1134

Telephone: (614) 431-5774
Fax Number: (614) 431-5738
Company Email: mcdonalds@columbus.rr.com
Type of Business: Chain Restaurant Operator
Total Sales: $47,660,000 (e)
Number of Employees: 380
Total Units: 10
Trade Names: McDonald's (10)
Units Franchised From: 10
Preferred Square Footage: 2,500
Primary Menu: Hamburger (10)
Areas of Operation: OH
Type of Foodservice: Quick Serve (10)
Franchise Affiliation: McDonald's Corporation, CHICAGO, IL

Key Personnel
MICHAEL J.P. TELICH - President; General Buyer

Northstar Cafe
4241 N High St
Columbus, OH 43214-3049

Telephone: (614) 784-2233
Internet Homepage: bassicas.com; thenorthstarcafe.com
Company Email: info@brassicas.com
Type of Business: Chain Restaurant Operator
Year Founded: 2004
Total Units: 9
Trade Names: Brassica (4); Northstar Cafe (5)
Company-Owned Units: 9
Primary Menu: American (5); Greek/Mediterranean (4)
Areas of Operation: OH
Type of Foodservice: Casual Dining (9)

Key Personnel
KEVIN MALHAME - Partner; Executive Chef; General Buyer
KATY MALHAME - Partner; Executive Chef; General Buyer
DARREN MALHAME - Partner
GREG HEINE - Partner
LEIGH ALLARDYCE NORDIN - Partner Recruitment
LISA NAVOJOSKY - Partner
DAMON BURNEY - Director Operations
JEN O'LEARY - Director Food
LEIGH NORDIN - Director Talent

Olde Towne Partners LLC
889 Oak St
Columbus, OH 43205

Telephone: (614) 252-2955
Internet Homepage: cornerstonecolumbus.com; pecanpennys.com; theoldetownetavern.com; thewalruscolumbus.com
Type of Business: Chain Restaurant Operator
Total Units: 4
Trade Names: Corner Stone Craft Beer & Wine (1); Olde Towne Tavern (1); Pecan Penny's (1); The Walrus (1)
Company-Owned Units: 4
Areas of Operation: OH
Franchise Affiliation: Duck Donuts Franchising Company, MECHANICSBURG, PA

Key Personnel
KEVIN BURNS - Partner
BRAD HOBBS - Partner
KRISTA HOBBS - Partner
PHIL RICHARDSON - General Manager

Plank's Bier Garden
888 S High St
Columbus, OH 43206-1929

Telephone: (614) 443-4570
Internet Homepage: planksbeergarden.com
Type of Business: Chain Restaurant Operator
Year Founded: 1960
Total Sales: $1,569,000 (e)
Alcohol Sales: 40%
Number of Employees: 40
Average Check: Lunch(6); Dinner(12)
Total Units: 2
Trade Names: Plank's Beer Garden (1); Planks on Broadway (1)
Company-Owned Units: 2
Preferred Location Types: Freestanding
Alcohol Served: Beer, Wine, Liquor
Primary Menu: American (2)
Areas of Operation: OH
Type of Foodservice: Casual Dining (2)
Primary Distributors: (Full Line) Louis R. Polster Co., COLUMBUS, OH; (Full Line) The Wasserstrom Co., CINCINNATI, OH

Key Personnel
CHRIS PLANK - President; General Buyer
BILL PLANK - General Manager

Purdum Restaurants
1331 Walcutt Rd
Columbus, OH 43228-9348

Telephone: (614) 870-3273
Fax Number: (614) 870-3274
Internet Homepage: oldbagofnails.com
Type of Business: Chain Restaurant Operator
Year Founded: 1985
Total Sales: $25,730,000 (e)
Alcohol Sales: 25%
Number of Employees: 570
Average Check: Lunch(8); Dinner(14)
Total Units: 14
Trade Names: The Old Bag of Nails Pub (14)
Company-Owned Units: 14
Preferred Square Footage: 5,500; 6,000
Preferred Location Types: Downtown; Freestanding
Alcohol Served: Beer, Wine, Liquor
Primary Menu: American (14)
Areas of Operation: OH
Type of Foodservice: Casual Dining (14)
Catering Services: Yes
Primary Distributors: (Food) Globe Food Service Equipment, WALTHAM, MA

Key Personnel
GAYLORD WIRRICK - Founder
MIKE PURDUM - Owner; Executive Chef; Manager Real Estate, Menu Development, Catering; General Buyer
MIKE ALLEN - Controller; Manager Finance

Rise & Dine Restaurants, Inc.
274 Marconi Blvd Ste 260
Columbus, OH 43215-2399

Telephone: (614) 396-5030
Fax Number: (614) 396-5035
Internet Homepage: sunnystreetcafe.com
Company Email: info@sunnystreetcafe.com
Type of Business: Chain Restaurant Operator
Systemwide Sales: $35,784,000 (e)
Total Sales: $23,380,000 (e)
Number of Employees: 145
Average Check: Breakfast(8); Lunch(14);
Total Units: 25
Trade Names: Sunny Street Cafe (25)

Units Franchised To: 25
Preferred Square Footage: 2,400; 2,800; 3,200
Preferred Location Types: Freestanding; Strip Mall
Primary Menu: American (25)
Areas of Operation: AL, IL, MO, OH, TX
Foreign Countries: CANADA
Type of Foodservice: Family Restaurant (25)
Primary Distributors: (Full Line) SYSCO Food Services of Jacksonville Inc., JACKSONVILLE, FL
Notes: The company has a development agreement for 50 units in OH. The "company-owned" locations are owned and operated by Peach's Restaurants, a separate corporation but operating out of the same location.

Key Personnel

MICHAEL STASKO SR - Chairman; Partner; Director Operations, Design
SCOTT MOFFITT - President
MICHAEL LUCIANO - Partner; Director Franchising, Menu Development; General Buyer
GARWIN P. VELIE - Partner; Exec VP; General Counsel; Director Franchise Development; General Buyer
SHAWN BELL - VP Operations
MIKE STASKO JR - Director Business Development
MIKE MINNIEAR - Director Operations
HEIDI SMITH - Director Marketing, Communications

Sbarro Holdings LLC

1328 Dublin Rd Ste 300
Columbus, OH 43215-1054

Telephone: (614) 769-9911
Fax Number: (614) 294-1648
Internet Homepage: sbarro.com
Company Email: generalcomments@sbarro.com
Type of Business: Chain Restaurant Operator
Year Founded: 1959
Systemwide Sales: $854,807,000 (e)
Total Sales: $267,697,000 (e)
Alcohol Sales: 0.50%
Number of Employees: 5,300
Average Check: Lunch(10); Dinner(10)
Total Units: 641
Trade Names: Pizza Cucinova (3); Sbarro (638)
Company-Owned Units: 180
Units Franchised To: 461
Preferred Square Footage: 500; 750; 1,000; 1,500; 2,500; 3,000
Preferred Location Types: Airports; Community Mall; Downtown; Freestanding; Hotel/Motel; Institution (college/hospital); Lifestyle Center; Office Complex; Other; Outlet Mall; Regional Mall; Stadiums; Strip Mall; Travel Plazas
Alcohol Served: Beer, Wine
Primary Menu: Italian (0); Pizza (641)
Areas of Operation: AL, AR, AZ, CA, CO, CT, DC, DE, FL, GA, GU, HI, IA, ID, IL, IN, KS, KY, LA, MA, MD, ME, MI, MN, MO, MS, NC, ND, NE, NH, NJ, NM, NV, NY, OH, OK, OR, PA, PR, RI, SC, SD, TN, TX, UT, VA, VT, WA, WI, WV, WY, AB, ON
Foreign Countries: ARUBA; AZERBAIJAN; BAHAMAS; BELGIUM; BOLIVIA; CANADA; CHILE; CYPRUS; CZECH REPUBLIC; DOMINICAN REPUBLIC; ECUADOR; EGYPT; GREECE; GUATEMALA; ICELAND; INDIA; IRELAND; ISRAEL; JAPAN; JORDAN; KUWAIT; MEXICO; NICARAGUA; PANAMA; QATAR; RUSSIA; SAUDI ARABIA; SLOVAKIA; SWEDEN; THE NETHERLANDS; THE PHILIPPINES; TURKEY; UNITED ARAB EMIRATES
Type of Foodservice: Fast Casual (3); Quick Serve (638)
Primary Distributors: (Food) VISTAR Specialty, ENGLEWOOD, CO
Parent Company: MidOcean Partners, NEW YORK, NY

Key Personnel

J. DAVID KARAM - Chairman; CEO
BRIAN DANIELS - CFO
ROHAN SHEARER - Chief People Officer
MARK INZETTA - Chief Legal Officer; Corporate Secretary
HARRY ERARDI - VP Training
AURELIEN ORPHANIDES - VP Operations, International Division
ROBERT GERLACH - VP Supply Chain
DWAYNE ADAMS - VP Culinary Development
VICKI BESWICK - VP Marketing
MICHAEL SCHADE - VP Operations
IVANA HESLOP - VP Design
PHILIPPE JORE - VP International
JOSE RODRIGUEZ - VP Operations, Central Region
MICHAEL KARAM - General Counsel
LAURIE CHRISTENSEN - Senior Director Development, Real Estate
SHONTYL SHUPPS - Senior Director
HOWARD ISRAEL - Director Operations, Southeast Region
CARLO ACOSTINELLI - Director Real Estate
MIKE ALBERT - Director Facility/Maintenance
MIKE ABUSWAY - Director Operations
JAMIE WARDEN - Director Operations
EVER RODAS - Director Operations
JAY VANDERKOOI - Director New Store Development
DIANE NORRIS - Manager Payroll
MARLEE SHELDON - Manager Payroll

Stauf's Coffee

705 Hadley Dr
Columbus, OH 43228-1029

Telephone: (614) 487-6050
Fax Number: (614) 358-8986
Internet Homepage: staufs.com
Company Email: info@cupojoe.com
Type of Business: Chain Restaurant Operator
Year Founded: 1988
Total Sales: $6,544,000 (e)
Number of Employees: 171
Average Check: Lunch(10); Dinner(12)
Internet Order Processing: Yes
Total Units: 8
Trade Names: Cup o' Joe (2); Stauf's Coffee Roasters (6)
Company-Owned Units: 8
Preferred Square Footage: 2,500
Preferred Location Types: Freestanding
Primary Menu: Coffee (8)
Areas of Operation: OH
Type of Foodservice: Quick Serve (7)
Primary Distributors: (Food) Gordon Food Service Inc., WYOMING, MI

Key Personnel

MARK SWANSON - President; Director Operations, Facility/Maintenance, Information Systems, Real Estate, Design, Human Resources
ANDY TANG - Owner; Manager Menu Development; General Buyer
WILLIAM STURGES - CFO; VP; Director Finance, Supply Chain
BOYD JARVIS - Area Manager

Tee Jaye's Country Place Inc.

1363 Parsons Ave
Columbus, OH 43206-3644

Mailing Address: PO Box 6646, COLUMBUS, OH, 43206
Telephone: (614) 443-1938
Fax Number: (614) 443-0613
Internet Homepage: teejayes.com
Company Email: teejayes@barnyardbuster.com
Type of Business: Chain Restaurant Operator
Year Founded: 1970
Total Sales: $13,460,000 (e)
Number of Employees: 575
Average Check: Breakfast(12); Lunch(14); Dinner(18)
Internet Order Processing: Yes
Total Units: 8
Trade Names: Tee Jaye's Country Place (8)
Company-Owned Units: 8
Preferred Square Footage: 5,000
Preferred Location Types: Freestanding

Primary Menu: American (8)
Areas of Operation: OH
Type of Foodservice: Family Restaurant (8)

Key Personnel
JULES SOKOL - Co-Founder
DAYNA SOKOL - President; General Manager; Executive Chef; General Buyer

The Piada Group, LLC
1440 King Ave
Columbus, OH 43212-2107

Telephone: (614) 487-9140
Internet Homepage: mypiada.com
Type of Business: Chain Restaurant Operator
Year Founded: 2011
Total Sales: $34,367,000 (e)
Average Check: Lunch(12); Dinner(12)
Internet Order Processing: Yes
Total Units: 42
Trade Names: Piada Italian Street Food (42)
Company-Owned Units: 42
Alcohol Served: Beer, Wine
Primary Menu: Italian (42)
Projected Openings: 3
Areas of Operation: IN, KY, MI, MN, OH, PA, TX
Type of Foodservice: Fast Casual (42)

Key Personnel
MATT HARDING - Director Culinary Operations

Tommy's Pizza Inc.
1350 W Lane Ave
Columbus, OH 43221-3530

Telephone: (614) 486-2969
Internet Homepage: tommyspizza.com
Type of Business: Chain Restaurant Operator
Year Founded: 1952
Total Sales: $5,879,000 (e)
Alcohol Sales: 10%
Number of Employees: 100
Average Check: Lunch(10); Dinner(14)
Total Units: 3
Trade Names: Tommy's Pizza (3)
Company-Owned Units: 3
Preferred Square Footage: 6,000
Preferred Location Types: Freestanding; Strip Mall
Alcohol Served: Beer, Wine
Primary Menu: Pizza (3)
Areas of Operation: OH
Type of Foodservice: Casual Dining (3)
Primary Distributors: (Equipment) The Wasserstrom Co., COLUMBUS, OH; (Food) Gordon Food Service Inc., WYOMING, MI; (Supplies) Gordon Food Service Inc., WYOMING, MI

Key Personnel
RICK IACONO - President; Controller; Executive Chef; Manager Operations, Facility/Maintenance, Information Systems, Risk Management, Real Estate, Design, Human Resources, Menu Development; General Buyer

White Castle Management Co.
555 Edgar Waldo Way
Columbus, OH 43215-1104

Mailing Address: PO Box 1498, COLUMBUS, OH, 43216-1498
Telephone: (614) 228-5781
Fax Number: (614) 464-0596
Internet Homepage: whatyoucrave.com; whitecastle.com
Type of Business: Chain Restaurant Operator
Year Founded: 1921
Systemwide Sales: $816,353,000 (e)
Total Sales: $887,290,000 (e)
Number of Employees: 8,360
Average Check: Breakfast(8); Lunch(8); Dinner(8)
Internet Order Processing: Yes
Internet Sales: 0.50%
Total Units: 377
Trade Names: White Castle (377)
Company-Owned Units: 377
Preferred Square Footage: 2,000
Preferred Location Types: Convenience Store/Gas Station; Freestanding; Mobile Unit
Primary Menu: Hamburger (377)
Projected Openings: 10
Areas of Operation: IL, IN, KY, MI, MN, MO, NJ, NY, OH, PA, TN, WI
Type of Foodservice: Quick Serve (377)
Distribution Centers: CHICAGO, IL; INDIANAPOLIS, IN; LOUISVILLE, KY; FARMINGTON HILLS, MI; ST PAUL, MN; ST LOUIS, MO; WOODSIDE, NY; CINCINNATI, OH; COLUMBUS, OH
On-site Distribution Center: Yes
Regional Offices: White Castle System Inc., CHICAGO, IL; White Castle System Inc., CINCINNATI, OH; White Castle System Inc., COLUMBUS, OH; White Castle System Inc., FARMINGTON HILLS, MI; White Castle System Inc., LOUISVILLE, KY; White Castle System Inc., SAINT LOUIS, MO
Notes: The company also operates a number of manufacturing facilities (bakeries, meat processing plants) that provide products to its stores; sales from these operations are not included in total sales. Also excluded from total sales are revenues derived from retail sale of White Castle branded products in grocery stores.

Key Personnel
LISA INGRAM - CEO; President
JEFFREY D. CARPER - COO
ANTHONY JOSEPH - Chief Administrative Officer; General Counsel
KIM KELLEY-BARTLEY - Chief Marketing Officer
SUSAN CARROLL-BOSER - VP Technology
JOHN KELLEY - VP Human Resources, Training
JAMIE RICHARDSON - VP Marketing, Communications
ANDREW F. PRAKEL - VP; Controller
MICHAEL GUINAN - VP Operations
DAVID RIFE - VP Manufacturing
RIFE DAVID - VP Manufacturing
CHRIS SHAFFERY - Regional VP
PHILLIP BACH - Corporate Chef; Director Product Development
HEATHER WARD - Senior Director Benefits
TIM MURRIN - Director Purchasing, Supply Chain, Distribution
MICHAEL TOLLE - Director Accounting
DON DESENDER - Director Risk Management
RANDY EMBREE - Director Information Technology
MASON WOLF - Director Operations, Midwest Region
SHAWNA JONES - Director Operations, Southeast Region
NINA MARATTO - Director Benefits
BARBARA WILSON - Director Tax
CHIP STALTER - Director Compensation
STEVE FOREMAN - Director Operations
BOZANA BYERS - Director Member Services
TOBY REEL - Director Accounting
THERESA KASZUBSKI - Regional Director
DARRIN COTTON - Regional Director Restaurant Operations
BRIAN WALKERLY - Senior Manager Real Estate
SHANNON TOLLIVER - Manager Sustainability
MISSY HARRISON - Manager Risk Management
SARAH PAULSON - Manager Branding
STEVE ZVONEK - Manager
MARIE COTTRELL - Manager
AARON LAHMAN - Manager Digital Marketing
VANESSA HAYSLIP - Manager Purchasing
MISHALEE BALLARD - Manager Human Resources
CIERRA FRASER - Manager Plant
BRIAN INGRAM - Supervisor Technology
CRAIG EILERS - Project Manager Engineering
MERI OLDHAM - Category Manager
COLLEEN KELLEY - General Buyer

White Castle System Inc.
915 W 5th Ave
Columbus, OH 43212-2635

Telephone: (614) 294-3753
Fax Number: (614) 294-8516

Listing Type: Regional Office
Type of Business: Chain Restaurant Operator
Number of Employees: 1,000
Total Units: 27
Areas of Operation: OH
Parent Company: White Castle Management Co., COLUMBUS, OH

Key Personnel
THERESA KASZUBSKI - Director Operations, Region

Domino's Franchisee
1450 Kuntz Rd
Dayton, OH 45404-1231

Telephone: (937) 228-3030
Type of Business: Chain Restaurant Operator
Total Sales: $42,411,000 (e)
Total Units: 21
Trade Names: Domino's (21)
Units Franchised From: 21
Primary Menu: Pizza (21)
Areas of Operation: OH
Type of Foodservice: Quick Serve (21)
Franchise Affiliation: Domino's Pizza Inc, ANN ARBOR, MI

Key Personnel
CHRISTOPHER T. KOEHLER - Owner; General Buyer

J. Thomas & Co. Inc.
7231 Taylorsville Rd Ste 110
Dayton, OH 45424-2380

Telephone: (937) 235-0021
Fax Number: (937) 235-2721
Type of Business: Chain Restaurant Operator
Year Founded: 1983
Total Sales: $38,290,000 (e)
Number of Employees: 685
Average Check: Breakfast(8), Lunch(8), Dinner(10)
Total Units: 29
Trade Names: Waffle House (29)
Units Franchised From: 29
Preferred Square Footage: 500
Preferred Location Types: Freestanding
Primary Menu: American (29)
Projected Openings: 1
Projected Remodelings: 2
Areas of Operation: OH
Type of Foodservice: Family Restaurant (29)
Franchise Affiliation: Waffle House Inc., NORCROSS, GA
Primary Distributors: (Full Line) US Foods, MANASSAS, VA

Key Personnel
JOHN BLANTON - Partner
TOM BLANTON - Partner
TOM KEARNEY - Controller
RUTH GRUBB - Manager Human Resources

Marene Inc.
711 Shroyer Rd
Dayton, OH 45419-3611

Telephone: (937) 293-6993
Fax Number: (937) 293-2725
Internet Homepage: marionspiazza.com
Type of Business: Chain Restaurant Operator
Year Founded: 1965
Total Sales: $25,250,000 (e)
Alcohol Sales: 10%
Number of Employees: 250
Average Check: Lunch(8); Dinner(12)
Total Units: 9
Trade Names: Marion's Piazza (9)
Company-Owned Units: 9
Preferred Square Footage: 5,500; 6,000
Preferred Location Types: Freestanding
Alcohol Served: Beer, Wine
Primary Menu: Pizza (9)
Areas of Operation: OH
Type of Foodservice: Casual Dining (9)
Catering Services: Yes
On-site Distribution Center: Yes
Primary Distributors: (Full Line) SYSCO Food Services of Cincinnati, CINCINNATI, OH

Key Personnel
ROGER GLASS - President; Executive Chef; Director Operations, Supply Chain, Real Estate, Design, Product Development, Store Fixtures, Food Safety, Catering; General Buyer
DAN FEUCHT - Manager Human Resources

Mosher Management
1219 N Gettysburg Ave
Dayton, OH 45417

Telephone: (937) 687-3334
Fax Number: (937) 687-8303
Type of Business: Chain Restaurant Operator
Total Sales: $10,119,000 (e)
Number of Employees: 250
Average Check: Breakfast(8); Lunch(8); Dinner(8)
Total Units: 2
Trade Names: McDonald's (2)
Units Franchised From: 2
Preferred Square Footage: 2,400; 3,000
Preferred Location Types: Freestanding
Primary Menu: Hamburger (2)
Areas of Operation: OH
Type of Foodservice: Quick Serve (2)
Franchise Affiliation: McDonald's Corporation, CHICAGO, IL

Key Personnel
TIMOTHY MOSHER - Owner; Director Operations, Purchasing, Real Estate, Design

Submarine House
1137 Brown St
Dayton, OH 45409-2603

Telephone: (937) 222-7939
Fax Number: (937) 222-8440
Internet Homepage: submarinehouse.com
Type of Business: Chain Restaurant Operator
Year Founded: 1973
Total Sales: $2,010,000 (e)
Total Units: 9
Trade Names: Submarine House (3); Submarine House Bar & Grill (6)
Units Franchised To: 9
Primary Menu: Sandwiches/Deli (9)
Areas of Operation: OH
Type of Foodservice: Casual Dining (9)

Key Personnel
GARY DANNER - Partner; General Buyer
BRODY DANNER - Partner; Exec VP Franchise Development
JASON DANNER - Partner
NATE EARLY - General Manager
CRAIG CYPHERS - General Manager

Super Subby's Inc.
8924 N Dixie Dr
Dayton, OH 45414-1806

Telephone: (937) 898-0996
Fax Number: (937) 898-2367
Internet Homepage: subbys.com
Company Email: subs@subbys.com
Type of Business: Chain Restaurant Operator
Year Founded: 1978
Systemwide Sales: $16,070,000 (o)
Total Sales: $9,938,000 (e)
Alcohol Sales: 5%
Number of Employees: 114
Average Check: Breakfast(8); Lunch(12); Dinner(12)
Total Units: 8
Trade Names: Super Subby's (8)
Company-Owned Units: 8
Preferred Square Footage: 2,500
Preferred Location Types: Downtown; Strip Mall
Alcohol Served: Beer
Primary Menu: Sandwiches/Deli (8)
Areas of Operation: OH
Type of Foodservice: Quick Serve (8)

Key Personnel
JODY NEAL - Manager Accounting, Operations

Data Group/Boes Management
20269 County Road 424
Defiance, OH 43512

Telephone: (419) 399-4062
Type of Business: Chain Restaurant Operator
Total Sales: $6,717,000 (e)
Total Units: 12
Trade Names: Subway (12)
Units Franchised From: 12
Primary Menu: Sandwiches/Deli (12)
Areas of Operation: OH
Type of Foodservice: Quick Serve (12)
Franchise Affiliation: Doctor's Associates Inc., MILFORD, CT

Key Personnel
JIM BOES - Partner
DAN BOES - Partner; General Buyer

City Barbeque Inc.
6175 Emerald Pkwy Ste M
Dublin, OH 43016-3248

Telephone: (614) 583-0999
Fax Number: (614) 583-0998
Internet Homepage: citybbq.com
Company Email: info@citybbq.com
Type of Business: Chain Restaurant Operator
Year Founded: 1999
Total Sales: $48,780,000 (e)
Alcohol Sales: 3%
Number of Employees: 1,465
Average Check: Lunch(10); Dinner(14)
Internet Order Processing: Yes
Internet Sales: 3.00%
Total Units: 47
Trade Names: City Barbeque (43)
Company-Owned Units: 43
Preferred Square Footage: 3,000; 5,400
Preferred Location Types: Freestanding; Strip Mall
Alcohol Served: Beer
Primary Menu: Bar-B-Q (43)
Areas of Operation: GA, IL, IN, KY, MI, NC, OH
Type of Foodservice: Casual Dining (43)
Catering Services: Yes

Key Personnel
RICK MALIR - Chairman
MIKE MULDOON - CEO; President
DIANE REED - CFO
RONNIE BERRY - Chief People Officer
BRYAN MYERS - CIO
MONTI TARMEY - Exec VP Operations

KEITH WILLIS - Director Facility/Maintenance, Construction, Design
JENNIFER HAMILTON - Director Human Resources
MIKE CONDON - Director Information Technology
RACHEL DEMERS - Director Supply Chain
SCOTT ERWIN - Regional Director Catering
STEVE LILLY - Manager Human Resources

CLB Restaurants
4330 Tuller Rd
Dublin, OH 43017-5008

Telephone: (614) 760-0432
Internet Homepage: clbrestaurants.com
Type of Business: Chain Restaurant Operator
Year Founded: 2010
Total Units: 7
Trade Names: Matt the Miller's Tavern (6); Tucci's (1)
Company-Owned Units: 7
Primary Menu: American (7)
Areas of Operation: IN, OH
Type of Foodservice: Casual Dining (6); Fine Dining (1)

Key Personnel
CRAIG BARNUM - President; Owner
ROB HOERSDIG - VP; Director Operations; General Buyer
BRYAN HOPPING - Executive Chef
PATTY QUARANTO - Manager Human Resources

J, T and T Irrevocable Trust
7038 Hospital Dr
Dublin, OH 43016-8462

Telephone: (614) 718-0333
Type of Business: Chain Restaurant Operator
Total Sales: $4,672,000 (e)
Total Units: 2
Trade Names: Cold Stone Creamery (2)
Units Franchised From: 2
Primary Menu: Snacks (2)
Areas of Operation: OH
Type of Foodservice: Quick Serve (2)
Franchise Affiliation: Kahala Brands, SCOTTSDALE, AZ

Key Personnel
JAMES GRUBE - Partner
ADAM COLLIER - Partner

Rooster's Inc.
6140 Dublin Rd
Dublin, OH 43017-1406

Telephone: (614) 774-9573
Fax Number: (614) 761-1956
Internet Homepage: roosterswings.com
Type of Business: Chain Restaurant Operator
Year Founded: 1985
Total Sales: $30,350,000 (e)
Alcohol Sales: 15%
Number of Employees: 682
Average Check: Lunch(8); Dinner(10)
Internet Order Processing: Yes
Total Units: 42
Trade Names: Rooster's (42)
Company-Owned Units: 17
Units Franchised To: 27
Preferred Square Footage: 2,500
Preferred Location Types: Freestanding; Strip Mall
Alcohol Served: Beer, Wine, Liquor
Primary Menu: American (42)
Projected Openings: 1
Areas of Operation: IN, KY, OH, WV
Type of Foodservice: Casual Dining (42)
Primary Distributors: (Food) US Foods, CINCINNATI, OH

Key Personnel
DAN PONTON - CEO; President; Director Finance; General Buyer
TANNY FEERER - VP Purchasing
STEVE FERGUSON - VP Franchising
NICOLE COX - Director Marketing

The Wendy's Company
1 Dave Thomas Blvd
Dublin, OH 43017-5452

Mailing Address: 4288 W Dublin Granville Rd, DUBLIN, OH, 43017-1442
Telephone: (614) 764-3100
Fax Number: (614) 766-3979
Internet Homepage: wendys.com; wendysenespanol.com
Type of Business: Chain Restaurant Operator
Year Founded: 1969
Systemwide Sales: $17,677,622,000 (e)
Publicly Held: Yes
Total Sales: $2,737,530,000 (e)
Number of Employees: 13,300
Average Check: Lunch(8); Dinner(8)
Total Units: 7,240
Trade Names: Wendy's Old Fashioned Hamburgers (7,240)
Company-Owned Units: 403
Units Franchised To: 6,837
Preferred Square Footage: 2,100; 2,900
Preferred Location Types: Airports; Community Mall; Convenience Store/Gas

Station; Downtown; Freestanding; Institution (college/hospital); Outlet Mall; Regional Mall; Strip Mall; Travel Plazas
Primary Menu: Hamburger (7,240)
Areas of Operation: AK, AL, AR, AZ, CA, CO, CT, DC, DE, FL, GA, GU, HI, IA, ID, IL, IN, KS, KY, LA, MA, MD, ME, MI, MN, MO, MS, MT, NC, ND, NE, NH, NJ, NM, NV, NY, OH, OK, OR, PA, PR, RI, SC, SD, TN, TX, UT, VA, VI, VT, WA, WI, WV, WY, FC, AB, BC, MB, NB, NL, NS, ON, PE, QC, SK
Foreign Countries: ARGENTINA; ARUBA; BAHAMAS; BRAZIL; CANADA; CAYMAN ISLANDS; CHILE; CURACAO; DOMINICAN REPUBLIC; ECUADOR; EL SALVADOR; GEORGIA; GUATEMALA; HONDURAS; INDIA; INDONESIA; JAMAICA; JAPAN; KUWAIT; MALAYSIA; MEXICO; NEW ZEALAND; PANAMA; QATAR; THE PHILIPPINES; TRINIDAD & TOBAGO; UNITED ARAB EMIRATES; VENEZUELA
Type of Foodservice: Quick Serve (7,240)
Distribution Centers: ZANESVILLE, OH
Primary Distributors: (Full Line) The SYGMA Network, Inc., DUBLIN, OH
Divisional Offices: The Wendy's Company, AURORA, CO; The Wendy's Company, TAMPA, FL; The Wendy's Company-Atlanta Division, ALPHARETTA, GA
Notes: Wendy's derives approximately 1% of its total revenue from the sale of bakery items and kids' meal promotional items to its franchisees.

Key Personnel
ARTHUR WINKLEBLACK - Chairman
KIRK TANNER - CEO; President
ABIGAIL PRINGLE - President United States
E.J. WUNSCH - President International
DEEPAK AJMANI - President Company Operations
MARK EGANHOUSE - President Supply Chain
LAURA FREEMAN - President Development
BEVERLY STALLINGS-JOHNSON - President Diversity
GUNTHER PLOSCH - CFO
COLEY O'BRIEN - Chief People Officer
KEVIN VASCONI - CIO
LIZ GERAGHTY - Chief Marketing Officer
IAN ROWDEN - Chief Marketing Officer
TATIANA LAMBERT - Chief Development Officer United States
LILIANA ESPOSITO - Chief Communications Officer; Senior VP
JOHN MIN - Chief Legal Officer
STEVEN DERWOED - Global VP Design
TOM RICHERT - Area Director Franchising
MARY GREENLEE - Senior VP United States
KRIS KAFFENBARGER - VP Franchise Development
LINDSAY RADKOSKI - VP Brand Marketing
JORGE HERNANDEZ - VP Quality Assurance
JIM BENDER - VP Branding
JAIME WEEKS - VP Training
MICHAEL GIST - VP Division
AARON KALE - VP Tax
JEFF ROBERTS - VP Division
WHITNEY GRETZ - VP Digital Marketing
HEIDI SCHAUER - Senior Director Communications
LISA SMITH - Senior Director Communications
KRIS MIOTKE - Senior Director Marketing, International
AMY WOODS - Senior Director
MELTEM EDIN - Senior Director Advertising, Brand Marketing, International
JEFF SCHILT - Director Quality Assurance, Customer Service
STEVE TROTH - Director Accounting, Payroll
MICHELLE RYMAN - Director Development
TARA FITZPATRICK - Director Operations, Training
BOB BOWMAN - Director Risk Management
TODD CHRISTENSEN - Director Training
LYNN BAUMAN - Director Employee Benefits
WAYNE BUCK - Director Strategic Planning
CYNTHIA HOFFMAN - Director Tax, International
GARY KEITH - Director Operations
JIM KLEVA - Director Engineering
KATHY MCDERMOTT - Director Technology
DENNIS OSBORNE - Director Engineering
CHERI ROELL - Director Engineering, North America
ANDREW SCHNEIDER - Director Advertising, Production
JULIE SCOTT - Director Talent
BOB STOWE - Director Marketing
MELISSA C - Director
MELANIE TRUDELL - Director Technology
SCOTT WENSYEL - Director Operations
ELIZABETH WINICK - Director Digital Marketing
RAYMOND ARRUDA - Director Field Marketing
ANDREW VICKS - Director Operations
CLARK ELMS - Director Real Estate
ASHLEY SPERLING - Director Real Estate
SHELLY THOBE - Senior Manager
GREG CORNISH - Senior Manager Marketing
RAY ARRUDA - Manager Field Marketing
JANE DANN - Manager Franchising, Strategic Planning
DONALD BARKER - Manager Security
KATE BENTLEY - Manager Operations; Customer Care Digital Media
LARRY G BURKE - Manager Quality Assurance-Dairy
ALISSA CALDWELL - Manager Communications
ROBIN CAMPBELL - Manager Marketing, Communications
BRYAN CLABAUGH - Manager Information Technology, Development
KELLY COLE - Manager Accounting
JIM GATTO - Manager Store Systems
CHERYL GERSTENBERGER - Manager Accounting
LUIS GONZALEZ - Manager Infrastructure
KAREN HAMILTON - Manager Administration, Benefits
NEIL HERTENSTEIN - Manager Financial Planning
KEITH KUHN - Manager Administration, Database
VICKI LAPKA BESWICK - Manager Strategy, Digital, Innovation
SARAH MORAN - Manager Finance, Marketing, Innovation
ERIC NAYLOR - Manager
LARRY NOBLE - Manager Product Development
BRYANN ROTH - Manager Communications
MIKE SPIVEY - Manager Engineering
ALEXANDER STOUT - Manager
LAKSHMI SURAPANENI - Manager Architecture
THADDEUS WOODS - Manager Internal Audit
AMANDA ZAZA - Manager Development, Global
MAT KNUPP - Manager Construction
TOMMY MORGAN - Manager Construction
LINDA CORBET - Manager Technology
SOPHIE CHOGOVADZE - Manager Marketing, International
TRAVIS MARTIN - Brand Manager Innovation
TIM LENTZ - Project Manager; Engineer
KEITH PUSATERI - Project Manager Integration
EVAN HORTON - Senior Analyst

Thomas 5 Ltd.
5131 Post Rd Ste 203
Dublin, OH 43017-1197

Telephone: (614) 764-9495
Type of Business: Chain Restaurant Operator
Total Sales: $141,790,000 (e)
Number of Employees: 675
Total Units: 52
Trade Names: Wendy's Old Fashioned Hamburgers (52)
Units Franchised From: 52
Primary Menu: Hamburger (52)
Areas of Operation: OH
Type of Foodservice: Quick Serve (52)
Franchise Affiliation: The Wendy's Company, DUBLIN, OH

Key Personnel
WENDY MORSE - President; Partner; General Buyer
PAM THOMAS - President; Partner
RICK RIEBOLD - COO

Midwest R Corporation
356 2nd St
Elyria, OH 44035-5527

Telephone: (440) 322-6060
Fax Number: (440) 322-6070
Type of Business: Chain Restaurant Operator
Year Founded: 1968
Total Sales: $49,700,000 (e)
Number of Employees: 800
Average Check: Breakfast(10); Lunch(10);

Dinner(10)
Total Units: 22
Trade Names: Burger King (22)
Units Franchised From: 22
Preferred Square Footage: 2,500
Preferred Location Types: Freestanding
Primary Menu: Hamburger (22)
Areas of Operation: OH
Type of Foodservice: Quick Serve (22)
Franchise Affiliation: Burger King Worldwide Inc., MIAMI, FL
Primary Distributors: (Full Line) Maines Paper & Food Services Ohio, OAKWOOD VILLAGE, OH

Key Personnel
SULLIVAN RENUART - President; Director Finance, Operations, Facility/Maintenance, Supply Chain, Real Estate; General Buyer
HEATHER COSTELLO - Manager Information Systems, Human Resources

Mahendra Patel
4820 Dixie Hwy
Fairfield, OH 45014-1911

Mailing Address: PO Box 18036, FAIRFIELD, OH, 45018-0036
Telephone: (513) 829-1986
Type of Business: Chain Restaurant Operator
Total Sales: $2,694,000 (e)
Total Units: 4
Trade Names: Subway (4)
Units Franchised From: 4
Primary Menu: Sandwiches/Deli (4)
Areas of Operation: OH
Type of Foodservice: Quick Serve (4)
Franchise Affiliation: Doctor's Associates Inc., MILFORD, CT

Key Personnel
MAHENDRA PATEL - President; General Buyer

Skyline Chili Inc.
4180 Thunderbird Ln
Fairfield, OH 45014-2235

Telephone: (513) 874-1188
Fax Number: (513) 874-3591
Internet Homepage: skylinechili.com
Company Email: restaurant_team@skylinechili.com
Type of Business: Chain Restaurant Operator
Year Founded: 1949
Systemwide Sales: $137,703,000 (e)
Total Sales: $65,960,000 (e)
Number of Employees: 952
Average Check: Lunch(10); Dinner(10)
Internet Order Processing: Yes
Internet Sales: 1.00%
Total Units: 136
Trade Names: Skyline Chili (136)
Company-Owned Units: 36
Units Franchised To: 100
Preferred Square Footage: 2,800
Preferred Location Types: Downtown; Freestanding; Institution (college/hospital); Office Complex; Stadiums; Strip Mall
Primary Menu: Greek/Mediterranean (136)
Projected Openings: 2
Areas of Operation: FL, IN, KY, OH
Type of Foodservice: Fast Casual (136)
Foodservice Management Venues: College & University
Catering Services: Yes
On-site Distribution Center: Yes
Notes: The company derives approximately 40% of its revenue from retail operations.

Key Personnel
KEVIN MCDONNELL - CEO; President
MIKE LYNCH - VP Business Development
SHARON SCOTT - Director Supply Chain, Store Fixtures
JODI PRICE - Manager Payroll

Cow Licks, Inc.
3900 Medina Rd STE G
Fairlawn, OH 44333

Telephone: (330) 665-4466
Type of Business: Chain Restaurant Operator
Total Sales: $1,789,000 (e)
Total Units: 3
Trade Names: Cold Stone Creamery (3)
Units Franchised From: 3
Primary Menu: Snacks (3)
Areas of Operation: OH
Type of Foodservice: Quick Serve (3)
Franchise Affiliation: Kahala Brands, SCOTTSDALE, AZ

Key Personnel
SHELDON MCDOUGAL - Partner
MARJORIE MCDOUGAL - Partner

Sugar Creek Pizza, LLC
3610 W Market St Ste 102
Fairlawn, OH 44333

Mailing Address: PO Box 4279, COPLEY, OH, 44321-0279
Telephone: (216) 642-3750
Internet Homepage: pizzahut.com
Company Email: cflocken@sugarcreekpizza.com
Type of Business: Chain Restaurant Operator
Year Founded: 2010
Total Sales: $38,100,000 (e)
Alcohol Sales: 11%
Number of Employees: 700
Average Check: Dinner(16)
Total Units: 31
Trade Names: Pizza Hut (31)
Units Franchised From: 31
Preferred Square Footage: 4,000; 4,500
Preferred Location Types: Downtown; Freestanding
Alcohol Served: Beer, Wine
Primary Menu: Pizza (31)
Areas of Operation: MD, OH, WV
Type of Foodservice: Quick Serve (31)
Franchise Affiliation: Pizza Hut Inc., PLANO, TX

Key Personnel
CHARLES D. HUDSON - CEO; President; Partner; General Buyer
CHRISTOPHER M. FLOCKEN - Partner; CFO
PEGGY ANDRYSZAK - Manager Accounting

Domino's Franchisee
21154 Lorain Rd
Fairview Park, OH 44126-2129

Telephone: (440) 333-5544
Type of Business: Chain Restaurant Operator
Total Sales: $4,078,000 (e)
Total Units: 2
Trade Names: Domino's (2)
Units Franchised From: 2
Primary Menu: Pizza (2)
Areas of Operation: OH
Type of Foodservice: Quick Serve (2)
Franchise Affiliation: Domino's Pizza Inc, ANN ARBOR, MI

Key Personnel
SAIDE S. FRANCIS - Owner; General Buyer

Hospitality Restaurants Inc.
22005 Mastick Rd
Fairview Park, OH 44126-3157

Telephone: (440) 356-7202
Fax Number: (440) 356-7206
Internet Homepage: hrcleveland.com
Company Email: information@hrcleveland.com
Type of Business: Chain Restaurant Operator
Year Founded: 1983
Total Sales: $31,670,000 (e)
Alcohol Sales: 25%
Number of Employees: 580
Average Check: Lunch(22); Dinner(46)
Internet Order Processing: Yes
Internet Sales: 2.00%
Total Units: 9
Trade Names: Blue Point Grille (1); Delmonico's Steakhouse (1); Kingfish (1); Rosewood Grill (3); Salmon Dave's (1); The Cabin Club (1); Thirsty Parrot (1)
Company-Owned Units: 9
Preferred Square Footage: 5,500; 6,000

Preferred Location Types: Downtown; Freestanding
Alcohol Served: Beer, Wine, Liquor
Primary Menu: American (2); Seafood (2); Steak/Seafood (5)
Areas of Operation: OH
Type of Foodservice: Casual Dining (4); Fine Dining (5)

Key Personnel
DAVID R. HALE - Partner; Executive Chef; Director Operations, Real Estate; General Buyer
GEORGE SCHINDLER - Partner
CHRIS KNEELAND - General Manager
CHRISTOPHER MALOY - General Manager
LINDA EKEY - Director Human Resources

Bellevue Restaurants Inc.
2738 N Main St Ste A
Findlay, OH 45840-4035

Telephone: (419) 422-3437
Fax Number: (419) 422-3535
Type of Business: Chain Restaurant Operator
Year Founded: 1984
Total Sales: $75,490,000 (e)
Number of Employees: 65
Average Check: Lunch(8); Dinner(8)
Total Units: 27
Trade Names: Taco Bell (27)
Units Franchised From: 27
Preferred Square Footage: 2,500; 3,200
Preferred Location Types: Freestanding
Primary Menu: Taco (27)
Areas of Operation: OH
Type of Foodservice: Quick Serve (27)
Franchise Affiliation: Taco Bell Corp., IRVINE, CA
Primary Distributors: (Full Line) McLane/Hebron, HEBRON, KY

Key Personnel
GEORGE KENTRIS - President; CFO; Treasurer; General Buyer
MATT ARTHUR - VP

Humbard Enterprises
833 Barker Rd
Fremont, OH 43420-3104

Telephone: (419) 332-0398
Fax Number: (419) 332-8687
Type of Business: Chain Restaurant Operator
Total Sales: $67,130,000 (e)
Number of Employees: 570
Total Units: 14
Trade Names: McDonald's (14)
Units Franchised From: 14
Preferred Square Footage: 2,500
Primary Menu: Hamburger (14)
Areas of Operation: OH
Type of Foodservice: Quick Serve (14)
Franchise Affiliation: McDonald's Corporation, CHICAGO, IL

Key Personnel
THOMAS HUMBARD - President; General Buyer
DORITA STEINLE SNYDER - CFO

The Hickory House
550 Officenter Pl
Gahanna, OH 43230-5314

Telephone: (614) 428-7427
Fax Number: (614) 428-7514
Internet Homepage: thehickoryhouse.com
Type of Business: Chain Restaurant Operator
Year Founded: 1985
Total Sales: $3,564,000 (e)
Alcohol Sales: 30%
Number of Employees: 55
Average Check: Lunch(14); Dinner(26)
Total Units: 2
Trade Names: Hickory House (2)
Company-Owned Units: 2
Preferred Location Types: Freestanding
Alcohol Served: Beer, Wine, Liquor
Primary Menu: American (2)
Areas of Operation: OH
Type of Foodservice: Casual Dining (2)
Primary Distributors: (Food) Gordon Food Service Inc., WYOMING, MI

Key Personnel
CHAD HUNTER - Partner; General Buyer
JIMMY TORCHIA - Partner; General Manager

Westaar V, Inc.
332 S Hamilton Rd
Gahanna, OH 43230-3350

Telephone: (614) 337-1884
Type of Business: Chain Restaurant Operator
Total Sales: $6,811,000 (e)
Total Units: 5
Trade Names: Jersey Mike's Subs (5)
Units Franchised From: 5
Primary Menu: Sandwiches/Deli (5)
Areas of Operation: OH
Type of Foodservice: Quick Serve (5)
Franchise Affiliation: Jersey Mike's Franchise Systems, MANASQUAN, NJ

Key Personnel
PAM WESTERLUND - Partner; General Buyer
TOM WESTERLUND - Partner

Domino's Franchisee
1200 Jackson Pike
Gallipolis, OH 45631-1384

Telephone: (740) 446-4040
Type of Business: Chain Restaurant Operator
Total Sales: $8,106,000 (e)
Total Units: 4
Trade Names: Domino's (4)
Units Franchised From: 4
Primary Menu: Pizza (4)
Areas of Operation: OH
Type of Foodservice: Quick Serve (4)
Franchise Affiliation: Domino's Pizza Inc, ANN ARBOR, MI

Key Personnel
DONALD L. SMITH - Owner; General Buyer

R. J. Management
5252 Turney Rd
Garfield Heights, OH 44125-2642

Telephone: (216) 581-6464
Fax Number: (216) 581-6259
Type of Business: Chain Restaurant Operator
Total Sales: $14,849,000 (e)
Number of Employees: 55
Total Units: 3
Trade Names: McDonald's (3)
Units Franchised From: 3
Preferred Square Footage: 2,500
Primary Menu: Hamburger (3)
Areas of Operation: OH
Type of Foodservice: Quick Serve (3)
Franchise Affiliation: McDonald's Corporation, CHICAGO, IL

Key Personnel
ROBERT JURSICH JR - President; General Buyer

Pro Mac Inc
8027 State St
Garrettsville, OH 44231-1022

Telephone: (330) 527-4876
Type of Business: Chain Restaurant Operator
Total Sales: $28,830,000 (e)
Total Units: 6
Trade Names: McDonald's (6)
Units Franchised From: 6
Primary Menu: Hamburger (6)
Areas of Operation: OH
Type of Foodservice: Quick Serve (6)
Franchise Affiliation: McDonald's Corporation, CHICAGO, IL

Key Personnel
WILL GALLOWAY - President; General Buyer

Jib Jab Inc.
313 S State St
Girard, OH 44420-2952

Telephone: (330) 545-1129
Type of Business: Chain Restaurant Operator
Year Founded: 1946
Total Sales: $4,511,000 (e)
Number of Employees: 70
Average Check: Breakfast(10); Lunch(10); Dinner(14)
Total Units: 3
Trade Names: The Hot Dog Shoppe (3)
Company-Owned Units: 3
Preferred Location Types: Freestanding
Primary Menu: American (3)
Areas of Operation: OH
Type of Foodservice: Family Restaurant (3)
On-site Distribution Center: Yes
Primary Distributors: (Full Line) SYSCO Food Services of Cleveland Inc., CLEVELAND, OH

Key Personnel
DIRK DOVERSPIKE - Owner; General Manager; Executive Chef; General Buyer
CHRIS CONWAY - General Manager; General Buyer

●▲
Queen Enterprises Inc
92 Wexford Dr
Granville, OH 43023-9275

Telephone: (740) 587-3933
Type of Business: Chain Restaurant Operator
Total Sales: $6,821,000 (e)
Total Units: 12
Trade Names: Subway (12)
Units Franchised From: 12
Primary Menu: Sandwiches/Deli (12)
Areas of Operation: OH
Type of Foodservice: Quick Serve (12)
Franchise Affiliation: Doctor's Associates Inc., MILFORD, CT

Key Personnel
DARLENE QUEEN - President; General Buyer
PAUL QUEEN JR - VP

●▲
Marich Inc.
4213 Hoover Rd
Grove City, OH 43123-3617

Telephone: (614) 277-1398
Fax Number: (614) 277-9740
Type of Business: Chain Restaurant Operator
Year Founded: 1988

Total Sales: $24,100,000 (e)
Number of Employees: 250
Average Check: Breakfast(8); Lunch(10); Dinner(12)
Total Units: 5
Trade Names: McDonald's (5)
Units Franchised From: 5
Preferred Square Footage: 2,500
Preferred Location Types: Freestanding
Primary Menu: Hamburger (5)
Areas of Operation: OH
Type of Foodservice: Quick Serve (5)
Franchise Affiliation: McDonald's Corporation, CHICAGO, IL

Key Personnel
JOLENE MIERZEJEWSKI - President; Director Finance, Real Estate, Human Resources
MARK CASSELL - General Manager; Director Operations, Purchasing, Facility/Maintenance, Supply Chain, Store Fixtures
RACHEL BISHOP - Manager Branch

●▲
Total Quality Inc.
6077 Landings Pond Pl
Grove City, OH 43123-9444

Telephone: (614) 277-9100
Fax Number: (614) 277-9555
Type of Business: Chain Restaurant Operator
Year Founded: 1994
Total Sales: $27,620,000 (e)
Number of Employees: 350
Average Check: Lunch(8); Dinner(8)
Total Units: 10
Trade Names: Wendy's Old Fashioned Hamburgers (10)
Units Franchised From: 10
Preferred Square Footage: 2,100; 2,900
Preferred Location Types: Freestanding
Primary Menu: Hamburger (10)
Areas of Operation: OH
Type of Foodservice: Quick Serve (10)
Franchise Affiliation: The Wendy's Company, DUBLIN, OH
Primary Distributors: (Full Line) The SYGMA Network, Inc., DUBLIN, OH

Key Personnel
JOHN ROME - President; Manager Real Estate; General Buyer
KIM ROBERTS - VP Operations
DONNA CAWOOD - Manager Accounting, Information Systems, Human Resources

†
Franklin Services
4600 Homer Ohio Ln
Groveport, OH 43125-9288

Telephone: (614) 863-8700
Fax Number: (614) 482-8100

Internet Homepage: cuyahogagroup.com
Company Email: franklin@cuygroup.com
Listing Type: Subsidiary
Type of Business: Foodservice Management Operator
Year Founded: 1988
Total Sales: $5,890,000 (e)
Number of Employees: 25
Number of Locations Served: 250
Total Foodservice Mgmt Accounts: 250
Areas of Operation: OH
Type of Foodservice: Vending machines (250)
Foodservice Management Venues: Business & Industry; College & University; Health Care; Lodging; Military Feeding; Parks & Recreation; Prison Feeding; Schools
Primary Distributors: (Food) Vistar of Ohio, TWINSBURG, OH

Key Personnel
VINCE VARIGLOTTI - President; General Manager; General Buyer
KIM MATTINGLY - Manager Branch

●▲
Paws Inc.
1230 Eaton Ave
Hamilton, OH 45013-1405

Telephone: (513) 894-0800
Fax Number: (513) 894-0208
Type of Business: Chain Restaurant Operator
Year Founded: 1994
Total Sales: $27,750,000 (e)
Number of Employees: 300
Average Check: Breakfast(8); Lunch(8); Dinner(10)
Total Units: 6
Trade Names: McDonald's (6)
Units Franchised From: 6
Preferred Square Footage: 1,600
Preferred Location Types: Freestanding
Primary Menu: Hamburger (6)
Areas of Operation: IN, OH
Type of Foodservice: Quick Serve (6)
Franchise Affiliation: McDonald's Corporation, CHICAGO, IL

Key Personnel
PATRICK J. PAWLING - President; General Manager; Director Finance, Purchasing, Facility/Maintenance, Information Systems, Real Estate, Human Resources; General Buyer
MARK ACEY - Director
CURT HOWARD - Manager

Thunderdome Restaurant Group
188 N Brookwood Ave Ste 100
Hamilton, OH 45013-1304

Telephone: (513) 896-9695
Fax Number: (513) 896-3750
Internet Homepage: currito.com;
 bakersfieldtacos.com; eaglerestaurant.com;
 sohisandwich.com;
 thunderdomerestaurants.com
Type of Business: Chain Restaurant Operator
Year Founded: 2004
Total Sales: $16,500,000 (e)
Total Units: 42
Trade Names: Bakersfield Tacos (8); CityBird (2); Currito Burritos Without Borders (21); Kaze (2); Krueger's Tavern (2); Maplewood (2); SoHi Grilled Sandwiches (1); The Eagle (4)
Company-Owned Units: 15
Units Franchised To: 27
Preferred Square Footage: 1,800; 2,500
Preferred Location Types: Airports; Institution (college/hospital); Regional Mall; Strip Mall
Alcohol Served: Beer
Primary Menu: American (8); Chicken (2); Japanese (2); Mexican (29); Sandwiches/Deli (1)
Projected Openings: 1
Areas of Operation: IN, KY, MA, MD, NJ, OH, PA
Type of Foodservice: Casual Dining (20); Fast Casual (22)

Key Personnel
JOE LANNI - President; Partner
JOHN LANNI - Partner; COO
CHAS BARACATO - Executive Chef
ROBERT CREAGER - Director Purchasing

McDonald's of Harrison
375 Industrial Dr
Harrison, OH 45030-1483

Mailing Address: PO Box 218, HARRISON, OH, 45030-0218
Telephone: (513) 367-2649
Fax Number: (513) 367-4107
Company Email: archways.sei@gmail.com
Type of Business: Chain Restaurant Operator
Year Founded: 1986
Total Sales: $20,214,000 (e)
Number of Employees: 295
Average Check: Breakfast(8); Lunch(8); Dinner(8)
Total Units: 4
Trade Names: McDonald's (4)
Units Franchised From: 4
Preferred Square Footage: 2,500
Preferred Location Types: Discount Dept. Stores; Freestanding
Primary Menu: Hamburger (4)
Areas of Operation: IN, OH
Type of Foodservice: Quick Serve (4)
Franchise Affiliation: McDonald's Corporation, CHICAGO, IL

Key Personnel
ROBERT CUMMINGS - Partner; Manager Purchasing, Risk Management
ED CUMMINGS - Partner; Manager Operations, Purchasing, Risk Management, Real Estate
CRAIG PETERS - Partner; Manager Information Systems
PATRICIA PETERS - Partner; General Buyer
LYNNE KORTE - Director Human Resources
LISA CREECH - Manager Finance, Accounting

GT Pizza Inc.
3730 Main St
Hilliard, OH 43026-1321

Telephone: (614) 771-1181
Type of Business: Chain Restaurant Operator
Total Sales: $30,133,000 (e)
Total Units: 15
Trade Names: Domino's (15)
Units Franchised From: 15
Primary Menu: Pizza (15)
Areas of Operation: OH
Type of Foodservice: Quick Serve (15)
Franchise Affiliation: Domino's Pizza Inc, ANN ARBOR, MI

Key Personnel
ERIC POTTERTON - Director Operations

Holowicki Enterprises Inc.
5049 Cemetery Rd
Hilliard, OH 43026-1642

Telephone: (614) 876-3509
Fax Number: (614) 876-9729
Type of Business: Chain Restaurant Operator
Total Sales: $126,580,000 (e)
Number of Employees: 1,589
Total Units: 27
Trade Names: McDonald's (27)
Units Franchised From: 27
Preferred Square Footage: 2,500
Preferred Location Types: Discount Dept. Stores; Freestanding
Primary Menu: Hamburger (27)
Areas of Operation: OH
Type of Foodservice: Quick Serve (27)
Franchise Affiliation: McDonald's Corporation, CHICAGO, IL

Key Personnel
JAMES HOLOWICKI - Partner; General Buyer
SCOTT HOLOWICKI - Partner
COURTNEY PAUL - Director Accounting, Human Resources
RICHARD ZITZKE - Director Business Development
SANDY ZITZKE - Director Operations

JUMP Asian Express
3395 Eastwoodlands Trl
Hilliard, OH 43026-9346

Telephone: (614) 529-7110
Fax Number: (614) 529-7112
Internet Homepage: jumpasian.com
Company Email: info@jumpasian.com
Type of Business: Chain Restaurant Operator
Year Founded: 1996
Systemwide Sales: $124,144,000 (e)
Total Sales: $9,866,000 (e)
Alcohol Sales: 1%
Number of Employees: 9
Average Check: Lunch(10); Dinner(10)
Total Units: 127
Trade Names: Jump Asian Express (127)
Units Franchised To: 127
Preferred Square Footage: 2,500
Preferred Location Types: Institution (college/hospital); Kiosk; Office Complex; Outlet Mall; Stadiums; Strip Mall
Primary Menu: Asian (127)
Projected Openings: 20
Areas of Operation: CA, CT, GA, IA, IL, IN, KS, MA, MI, MO, NC, NJ, NY, OH, PA, RI, SC, TX, VA, VT
Foreign Countries: QATAR
Type of Foodservice: Quick Serve (127)
Foodservice Management Venues: Business & Industry; College & University; Health Care; Lodging; Military Feeding; Prison Feeding; Recreational; Schools; Transportation
Primary Distributors: (Full Line) Ferraro Foods, PISCATAWAY, NJ

Key Personnel
DAISY CORRIGAN - CEO
MARC BUTTS - COO

Goldwing Ventures Inc
7015 Spring Meadows Dr W Ste 103
Holland, OH 43528-9299

Telephone: (419) 861-2600
Fax Number: (419) 861-2603
Internet Homepage: imasubwayfan.com
Company Email: customerservice@imasubwayfan.com.
Type of Business: Chain Restaurant Operator
Total Sales: $6,164,000 (e)
Internet Order Processing: Yes
Total Units: 11
Trade Names: Subway (11)

Units Franchised From: 11
Primary Menu: Sandwiches/Deli (11)
Areas of Operation: OH
Type of Foodservice: Quick Serve (11)
Franchise Affiliation: Doctor's Associates Inc., MILFORD, CT

Key Personnel
PAULA J. BERRY - Partner; General Buyer
KIMBERLY SWAN - Manager Human Resources

Brown Derby Roadhouse Inc.
72 N Main St Ste 208
Hudson, OH 44236-2883

Telephone: (330) 528-3227
Fax Number: (888) 239-9108
Internet Homepage: brownderbyusa.com
Company Email: info@brownderbyusa.com
Type of Business: Chain Restaurant Operator
Year Founded: 1941
Systemwide Sales: $11,524,000 (e)
Total Sales: $10,100,000 (e)
Alcohol Sales: 10%
Number of Employees: 1,430
Average Check: Lunch(14); Dinner(28)
Internet Order Processing: Yes
Total Units: 5
Trade Names: Brown Derby Roadhouse (5)
Company-Owned Units: 5
Units Franchised To: 1
Preferred Square Footage: 5,500; 6,000
Preferred Location Types: Freestanding; Strip Mall
Alcohol Served: Beer, Wine, Liquor
Primary Menu: Steak (5)
Areas of Operation: OH
Type of Foodservice: Casual Dining (5)
Primary Distributors: (Food) US Foods, HURRICANE, WV

Key Personnel
PARIS GIRVES - President; Executive Chef; Director Finance, Operations, Purchasing, Information Systems, Human Resources, Menu Development
MICHAEL HADZIGEORGE - General Manager

CIELEC-IRONTON, INC.
1001 E Ring Rd
Ironton, OH 45638-9610

Telephone: (614) 886-8700
Type of Business: Chain Restaurant Operator
Total Sales: $33,930,000 (e)
Total Units: 7
Trade Names: McDonald's (7)
Units Franchised From: 7
Primary Menu: Hamburger (7)
Areas of Operation: OH
Type of Foodservice: Quick Serve (7)
Franchise Affiliation: McDonald's Corporation, CHICAGO, IL

Key Personnel
STEPHEN CIELEC - President; General Buyer

Pulp Franchising Inc.
1708 E Main St
Kent, OH 44240

Telephone: (330) 256-2950
Internet Homepage: pulpjuiceandsmoothie.com
Type of Business: Chain Restaurant Operator
Year Founded: 2005
Systemwide Sales: $31,500,000 (e)
Total Sales: $15,560,000 (e)
Total Units: 45
Trade Names: Pulp Juice and Smoothie Bar (45)
Company-Owned Units: 1
Units Franchised To: 44
Primary Menu: Snacks (45)
Type of Foodservice: Quick Serve (45)

Key Personnel
CHRIS IGHNAT - President
ANTHONY ROBINSON JR - VP Operations, Employee Development

Cassano's Inc.
1700 E Stroop Rd
Kettering, OH 45429-5040

Telephone: (937) 294-8400
Fax Number: (937) 294-8107
Internet Homepage: cassanos.com
Type of Business: Chain Restaurant Operator
Year Founded: 1953
Total Sales: $37,226,000 (e)
Alcohol Sales: 2%
Number of Employees: 390
Average Check: Lunch(8); Dinner(12)
Internet Order Processing: Yes
Total Units: 33
Trade Names: Cassano's Pizza King (33)
Company-Owned Units: 33
Preferred Square Footage: 1,800
Preferred Location Types: Community Mall; Freestanding; Strip Mall
Alcohol Served: Beer, Wine
Primary Menu: Pizza (33)
Projected Openings: 2
Areas of Operation: OH
Type of Foodservice: Casual Dining (33)
Catering Services: Yes
Primary Distributors: (Food) Presto Foods, MONROE, OH

Key Personnel
TIM SAYER - VP; Treasurer; Controller; Manager Finance, Purchasing, Risk Management, Human Resources
JANET HURLEY - VP; Director Operations

Hot Head Burritos
2795 Culver Ave
Kettering, OH 45429

Telephone: (937) 723-8556
Fax Number: (937) 410-3050
Internet Homepage: hotheadburritos.com
Company Email: office@hotheadburritos.com
Type of Business: Chain Restaurant Operator
Year Founded: 2007
Systemwide Sales: $66,996,000 (e)
Total Sales: $12,580,000 (e)
Number of Employees: 330
Average Check: Dinner(10)
Total Units: 75
Trade Names: Hot Head Burritos (78); Hot Head Burritos Cantina (4)
Company-Owned Units: 13
Units Franchised To: 69
Preferred Location Types: Freestanding; Strip Mall
Primary Menu: Mexican (82)
Projected Openings: 2
Areas of Operation: FL, IN, KY, MI, OH, PA
Type of Foodservice: Casual Dining (4); Quick Serve (78)
Notes: Founder Ray Wiley is also co-founder of the Rapid Fired Pizza chain.

Key Personnel
CYNTHIA WILEY - Co-Founder; Partner; Executive Chef
RAY WILEY - Co-Founder; CEO; President; Partner; General Buyer
ZACHARY HUGHES - Owner Operations; Director
RYAN CANCINO - Director Operations
MATTHEW CURTIS - Developer Area

Rapid Fired Pizza LLC
2795 Culver Ave
Kettering, OH 45429-3723

Telephone: (800) 465-9910
Internet Homepage: rapidfiredpizza.com
Company Email: contact@rapidfiredpizza.com
Type of Business: Chain Restaurant Operator
Year Founded: 2015
Systemwide Sales: $31,668,000 (e)
Total Sales: $18,160,000 (e)
Total Units: 35
Trade Names: Rapid Fired Pizza (35)
Company-Owned Units: 19

Units Franchised To: 16
Primary Menu: Pizza (35)
Projected Openings: 3
Areas of Operation: CA, IN, KY, OH, SC, TX
Type of Foodservice: Fast Casual (35)
Notes: Co-founder Ray Wiley is also founder of the Hot Head Burritos chain.

Key Personnel
RAY WILEY - Co-Founder; Director Franchise Development
MATT CURTIS - Co-Founder; VP Development
TIM TEFS - Co-Founder
PETER WILEY - Director Marketing, Branding
MATTHEW HORTON - Director Operations

Aladdin's Eatery Systems Inc
14518 Detroit Ave
Lakewood, OH 44107-4367

Telephone: (216) 226-2020
Fax Number: (216) 226-2083
Internet Homepage: aladdinseatery.com
Type of Business: Chain Restaurant Operator
Year Founded: 1994
Total Sales: $39,770,000 (e)
Alcohol Sales: 1%
Number of Employees: 290
Average Check: Breakfast(8); Lunch(10); Dinner(14)
Total Units: 31
Trade Names: Aladdin's Eatery (31)
Company-Owned Units: 31
Preferred Square Footage: 4,000
Preferred Location Types: Freestanding; Regional Mall
Alcohol Served: Beer
Primary Menu: Miscellaneous (31)
Areas of Operation: IN, NC, OH, PA, VA
Type of Foodservice: Casual Dining (31)
Distribution Centers: CLEVELAND, OH
Primary Distributors: (Full Line) US Foods, CINCINNATI, OH

Key Personnel
FADY CHAMOUN - President; General Manager Operations, Supply Chain, Real Estate; Manager Menu Development; General Buyer
FARES CHAMOUN - CFO
BRITTANY CALVIN - Area Director
GEORGE ISKANDAR - Area Director
PAUL CHAMOUN - Director Operations, Development
RUTH GOLOMB - Director Training

Melt Bar & Grilled
14718 Detroit Ave
Lakewood, OH 44107-4102

Mailing Address: PO Box 771150, LAKEWOOD, OH, 44107
Telephone: (216) 431-7760
Internet Homepage: meltbarandgrilled.com
Company Email: info@meltbarandgrilled.com
Type of Business: Chain Restaurant Operator
Year Founded: 2006
Total Sales: $57,160,000 (e)
Alcohol Sales: 20%
Average Check: Lunch(14); Dinner(24)
Internet Order Processing: Yes
Total Units: 13
Trade Names: Melt Bar & Grilled (13)
Company-Owned Units: 13
Alcohol Served: Beer, Wine, Liquor
Primary Menu: Sandwiches/Deli (13)
Areas of Operation: OH
Type of Foodservice: Casual Dining (13)

Key Personnel
MATT FISH - President; General Buyer
RICHARD LEDBETTER - Controller
ANDREA PRICE - General Manager
BOB GOULD - Director Operations

Cristy's Pizza
1424 Tiki Ln
Lancaster, OH 43130

Telephone: (740) 681-4691
Internet Homepage: cristyspizza.com; papaboos.com
Type of Business: Chain Restaurant Operator
Total Units: 8
Trade Names: Cristy's Pizza (7); Papa Boo's (1)
Company-Owned Units: 8
Primary Menu: American (1); Pizza (7)
Areas of Operation: OH
Type of Foodservice: Casual Dining (1); Fast Casual (7)

Key Personnel
JASON BIGGS - President
CHRIS HAMMACK - VP
JENNA MALCOLM - Manager Marketing

Dairy Queen of Lancaster Inc
1150 E Main St
Lancaster, OH 43130-4055

Telephone: (740) 653-7257
Fax Number: (740) 653-5772
Type of Business: Chain Restaurant Operator
Total Sales: $6,032,000 (e)
Total Units: 4
Trade Names: Dairy Queen Store (4)
Units Franchised From: 4
Primary Menu: Snacks (4)
Areas of Operation: OH
Type of Foodservice: Quick Serve (4)
Franchise Affiliation: International Dairy Queen Inc., BLOOMINGTON, MN

Key Personnel
BOYD WARNER - President; General Buyer

W.G. Grinders Inc.
9002 Cotter St Ste M
Lewis Center, OH 43035-7101

Telephone: (614) 766-2313
Fax Number: (614) 766-4030
Internet Homepage: wggrinders.com
Type of Business: Chain Restaurant Operator
Year Founded: 1989
Systemwide Sales: $13,304,000 (e)
Total Sales: $2,465,000 (e)
Alcohol Sales: 0.50%
Number of Employees: 39
Average Check: Lunch(12); Dinner(12)
Internet Order Processing: Yes
Total Units: 5
Trade Names: W.G. Grinders (5)
Company-Owned Units: 5
Units Franchised To: 4
Preferred Square Footage: 2,400
Preferred Location Types: Downtown; Strip Mall
Primary Menu: Sandwiches/Deli (5)
Projected Openings: 3
Areas of Operation: MI, OH
Type of Foodservice: Quick Serve (5)
Catering Services: Yes

Key Personnel
CONSTANCE BELLISARI - CEO; Partner
MIKE BELLISARI - President; Partner; Executive Chef; Director Purchasing, Risk Management, Research & Development, Product Development, Menu Development
DEE WEST - CFO
LARRY ROBBINS - Director Operations

D's of Kentucky, Inc.
2530 Balyeat Dr
Lima, OH 45805-4019

Telephone: (419) 999-3333
Fax Number: (419) 999-1994
Type of Business: Chain Restaurant Operator
Total Sales: $7,896,000 (e)
Total Units: 7
Trade Names: Captain D's Seafood Kitchen (7)
Units Franchised From: 7
Primary Menu: Seafood (7)
Areas of Operation: OH
Type of Foodservice: Quick Serve (7)
Franchise Affiliation: Captain D's LLC, NASHVILLE, TN

Key Personnel
LOWELL HUGHES - President; General Buyer

D's of Ohio
2020 Harding Hwy
Lima, OH 45804-3420

Telephone: (419) 223-8899
Type of Business: Chain Restaurant Operator
Year Founded: 1969
Total Sales: $20,580,000 (e)
Number of Employees: 400
Average Check: Lunch(8); Dinner(10)
Total Units: 14
Trade Names: Captain D's Seafood (14)
Units Franchised From: 14
Preferred Square Footage: 2,500
Preferred Location Types: Freestanding
Primary Menu: Seafood (14)
Areas of Operation: KY, LA, OH
Type of Foodservice: Quick Serve (14)
Franchise Affiliation: Captain D's LLC, NASHVILLE, TN

Key Personnel
TOM SIMS - President; Partner; Manager Information Systems, Real Estate
LOWELL HUGHES - Partner; VP Operations, Purchasing, Supply Chain
CARL SCHIMMOELLER - General Manager

Domino's Franchisee
2400 Cable Ct
Lima, OH 45805-3406

Telephone: (419) 222-3030
Type of Business: Chain Restaurant Operator
Total Sales: $24,580,000 (e)
Total Units: 12
Trade Names: Domino's (12)
Units Franchised From: 12
Primary Menu: Pizza (12)
Areas of Operation: OH
Type of Foodservice: Quick Serve (12)
Franchise Affiliation: Domino's Pizza Inc, ANN ARBOR, MI

Key Personnel
STEPHAN DEPUGH - Owner; General Buyer

East of Chicago Pizza Company
121 W High St Fl 12
Lima, OH 45801-4349

Telephone: (419) 225-7116
Fax Number: (419) 225-7138
Internet Homepage: eastofchicago.com
Type of Business: Chain Restaurant Operator
Year Founded: 1990
Systemwide Sales: $50,114,000 (e)
Total Sales: $1,635,000 (e)
Alcohol Sales: 1%
Number of Employees: 53
Average Check: Lunch(12); Dinner(16)
Internet Order Processing: Yes
Total Units: 80
Trade Names: East of Chicago Pizza (80)
Company-Owned Units: 5
Units Franchised To: 75
Preferred Square Footage: 1,200; 2,400
Preferred Location Types: Freestanding; Regional Mall; Strip Mall
Alcohol Served: Beer, Wine, Liquor
Primary Menu: Pizza (80)
Projected Openings: 10
Projected Remodelings: 10
Areas of Operation: GA, IN, NY, OH, SC, TN, WV
Type of Foodservice: Quick Serve (80)
Foodservice Management Venues: College & University; Schools
Catering Services: Yes
Primary Distributors: (Food) Sofo Foods, TOLEDO, OH

Key Personnel
ANTHONY COLLINS - President
ANGIE FINNERTY - Senior VP Accounting
MICHAEL WILLIAMS - VP Purchasing, Quality Assurance, Real Estate, Design, Training, Store Fixtures
ALLIE BETTAC - Manager Marketing
CONNIE SMITH - Manager Operations, Research & Development

Famous Recipe Fried Chicken of Lima Inc
959 Bellefontaine Ave
Lima, OH 45804-2875

Telephone: (419) 227-4877
Fax Number: (419) 227-1153
Internet Homepage: leeschickenoflima.com
Type of Business: Chain Restaurant Operator
Total Units: 2
Trade Names: Lee's Famous Recipe Chicken (2)
Units Franchised From: 2
Primary Menu: Chicken (2)
Areas of Operation: OH
Type of Foodservice: Quick Serve (2)
Franchise Affiliation: Lee's Famous Recipes Inc., FORT WALTON BEACH, FL

Key Personnel
SUSAN YOHE - VP

The Kewpee Inc.
111 N Elizabeth St
Lima, OH 45801-4334

Telephone: (419) 228-1778
Internet Homepage: kewpeehamburgers.com
Type of Business: Chain Restaurant Operator
Year Founded: 1928
Total Sales: $4,157,000 (e)
Number of Employees: 110
Average Check: Breakfast(8); Lunch(10); Dinner(12)
Total Units: 3
Trade Names: Kewpee's Hamburgers (3)
Company-Owned Units: 3
Preferred Location Types: Freestanding
Primary Menu: Hamburger (3)
Areas of Operation: OH
Type of Foodservice: Quick Serve (3)
Primary Distributors: (Equipment) The Wasserstrom Co., COLUMBUS, OH; (Supplies) The Wasserstrom Co., COLUMBUS, OH

Key Personnel
HARRY SHUTT - VP; General Manager; Executive Chef; General Buyer
SCOTT SHUTT - VP; General Manager; General Buyer
EMILY SHUTT - Manager Accounting

Logan Enterprises
12904 State Route 664 S
Logan, OH 43138-8564

Telephone: (740) 385-7860
Fax Number: (740) 385-7860
Type of Business: Chain Restaurant Operator
Total Sales: $37,640,000 (e)
Total Units: 8
Trade Names: McDonald's (8)
Units Franchised From: 8
Primary Menu: Hamburger (8)
Areas of Operation: OH
Type of Foodservice: Quick Serve (8)
Franchise Affiliation: McDonald's Corporation, CHICAGO, IL

Key Personnel
ESAU LOGAN - CEO; President
MATTHEW HARPER - Owner; General Manager; General Buyer

Mio's Development LLC
732 Middleton Way
Loveland, OH 45140-6989

Telephone: (513) 697-6467
Internet Homepage: miospizza.com

Type of Business: Chain Restaurant Operator
Year Founded: 1975
Systemwide Sales: $29,600,000 (e)
Total Sales: $3,364,000 (e)
Alcohol Sales: 15%
Number of Employees: 162
Average Check: Lunch(16); Dinner(24)
Internet Order Processing: Yes
Total Units: 6
Trade Names: Mio's Pizzeria (6)
Units Franchised To: 6
Preferred Square Footage: 5,500; 6,000
Preferred Location Types: Community Mall; Freestanding
Alcohol Served: Beer, Wine, Liquor
Primary Menu: Italian (6)
Projected Openings: 1
Areas of Operation: OH
Type of Foodservice: Casual Dining (6)
Catering Services: Yes

Key Personnel
JENNIFER HARLESS - VP
AMY HARLESS - VP

Wings and Rings
396 Wards Corner Rd
Loveland, OH 45140

Telephone: (513) 831-9464
Fax Number: (513) 831-9463
Internet Homepage: buffalowingsandrings.com
Type of Business: Chain Restaurant Operator
Year Founded: 1984
Systemwide Sales: $104,827,000 (e)
Total Sales: $18,870,000 (e)
Alcohol Sales: 28%
Number of Employees: 85
Average Check: Lunch(12); Dinner(20)
Total Units: 56
Trade Names: Wings and Rings (56)
Company-Owned Units: 2
Units Franchised To: 54
Preferred Square Footage: 4,500; 5,500
Preferred Location Types: Freestanding; Strip Mall
Alcohol Served: Beer, Wine, Liquor
Primary Menu: American (56)
Areas of Operation: CA, FL, IL, IN, KS, KY, ND, NE, OH, SD, TX
Foreign Countries: JORDAN; SAUDI ARABIA
Type of Foodservice: Casual Dining (56)
Primary Distributors: (Food) SYSCO Food Services of Cleveland Inc., CLEVELAND, OH

Key Personnel
NADER MASADEH - CEO; President; CFO; Exec VP Finance, Human Resources
MICHAEL DAVID - President Operations
BOB BAFUNDO - COO
THOMAS FLAHERTY - Chief Development Officer
PHILIP SCHRAM - Chief Development Officer
NANCY FRIEND-SCHNURPEL - VP People
GIORGOS HOFMANN - Director International
TRAVIS JOHNSON - Director Construction
LINSEY CASE - Director Marketing
DAN DOULEN - Director Real Estate, Franchise Development
TERRA KELLER-GARMON - Manager Purchasing

Pertoria, Inc.
236 Main St
Luckey, OH 43443

Telephone: (419) 833-3534
Fax Number: (419) 833-3535
Internet Homepage: pertoria.com
Type of Business: Chain Restaurant Operator
Total Sales: $5,796,000 (e)
Total Units: 2
Trade Names: Wendy's Old Fashioned Hamburgers (2)
Units Franchised From: 2
Primary Menu: Hamburger (2)
Areas of Operation: OH
Type of Foodservice: Quick Serve (2)
Franchise Affiliation: The Wendy's Company, DUBLIN, OH

Key Personnel
REBECCA WILLIAMS - CEO; President; General Buyer
EMILY DAY - Manager HRIS

Finally Fondue
24741 Cedar Rd
Lyndhurst, OH 44124-3786

Telephone: (216) 381-2700
Fax Number: (216) 381-5042
Type of Business: Chain Restaurant Operator
Year Founded: 1974
Total Sales: $19,542,000 (e)
Average Check: Dinner(44)
Total Units: 3
Trade Names: District (1); The Melting Pot (2)
Company-Owned Units: 1
Units Franchised From: 2
Preferred Location Types: Strip Mall
Alcohol Served: Beer, Wine, Liquor
Primary Menu: American (3)
Areas of Operation: OH
Type of Foodservice: Casual Dining (3)
Franchise Affiliation: The Melting Pot Restaurants Inc., TAMPA, FL

Key Personnel
SETH BROMBERG - Partner
ERIC MCINTYRE - Partner; General Buyer

Damon Morgan Corp.
PO Box 280
Madison, OH 44057-0280

Telephone: (440) 350-0080
Fax Number: (440) 350-9909
Type of Business: Chain Restaurant Operator
Year Founded: 1970
Total Sales: $42,950,000 (e)
Number of Employees: 400
Average Check: Breakfast(8); Lunch(8); Dinner(8)
Total Units: 9
Trade Names: McDonald's (9)
Units Franchised From: 9
Preferred Square Footage: 1,600
Preferred Location Types: Freestanding
Primary Menu: Hamburger (9)
Areas of Operation: OH
Type of Foodservice: Quick Serve (9)
Franchise Affiliation: McDonald's Corporation, CHICAGO, IL
Primary Distributors: (Full Line) The Anderson-DuBose Co., WARREN, OH

Key Personnel
ALLEN D. SMITH - President; Controller; Manager Operations, Purchasing, Information Systems, Supply Chain, Sales, Real Estate, Store Planning; General Buyer
LINDA MCCREADY - Manager Human Resources

Bellville Arch, Inc.
58 W 3rd St Ste C
Mansfield, OH 44902-1251

Telephone: (419) 522-0707
Fax Number: (419) 526-1831
Company Email: ssm@mcmonica.com
Type of Business: Chain Restaurant Operator
Total Sales: $37,690,000 (e)
Number of Employees: 405
Total Units: 8
Trade Names: McDonald's (8)
Units Franchised From: 8
Preferred Square Footage: 2,500
Primary Menu: Hamburger (8)
Areas of Operation: OH
Type of Foodservice: Quick Serve (8)
Franchise Affiliation: McDonald's Corporation, CHICAGO, IL

Key Personnel
JEFFREY MONICA - President; Owner; General Buyer

Domino's Franchisee
625 Lexington Ave Ste 1
Mansfield, OH 44907-1579

Telephone: (419) 756-3030
Type of Business: Chain Restaurant Operator
Total Sales: $8,011,000 (e)
Total Units: 4
Trade Names: Domino's (4)
Units Franchised From: 4
Primary Menu: Pizza (4)
Areas of Operation: OH
Type of Foodservice: Quick Serve (4)
Franchise Affiliation: Domino's Pizza Inc, ANN ARBOR, MI

Key Personnel
ANTHONY SATTERWHITE - Owner; General Buyer

Performance Foods Corporation
441 Lexington Ave
Mansfield, OH 44907-1501

Mailing Address: PO Box 3643, MANSFIELD, OH, 44907-0643
Telephone: (419) 756-4233
Fax Number: (419) 756-7437
Internet Homepage: oldcarolina.com
Type of Business: Chain Restaurant Operator
Year Founded: 1983
Total Sales: $39,129,000 (e)
Number of Employees: 540
Average Check: Lunch(8); Dinner(12)
Total Units: 35
Trade Names: Long John Silver's (34); Old Carolina Barbecue Co (1)
Units Franchised From: 35
Preferred Square Footage: 2,400
Preferred Location Types: Freestanding
Primary Menu: Bar-B-Q (1); Seafood (34)
Areas of Operation: KY, OH, PA, WV
Type of Foodservice: Family Restaurant (1); Quick Serve (34)
Franchise Affiliation: Long John Silver's Inc., LOUISVILLE, KY

Key Personnel
JOSEPH FEENEY - CEO; President; General Buyer
MARK FEENEY - General Manager Restaurant Operations

Worthington Enterprises
282 Lexington Ave
Mansfield, OH 44907-1239

Telephone: (419) 756-2333
Type of Business: Chain Restaurant Operator
Total Sales: $2,135,000 (e)
Total Units: 3
Trade Names: Subway (3)
Units Franchised From: 3
Primary Menu: Sandwiches/Deli (3)
Areas of Operation: OH
Type of Foodservice: Quick Serve (3)
Franchise Affiliation: Doctor's Associates Inc., MILFORD, CT

Key Personnel
ASHLEY SOSNER - CEO; President
CHARLES WORTHINGTON - President; General Buyer
DONNY WORTHINGTON - Manager Business Development

McDonald's of Marietta
215 Ohio St
Marietta, OH 45750-3137

Telephone: (740) 374-6004
Fax Number: (740) 374-6906
Type of Business: Chain Restaurant Operator
Total Sales: $15,389,000 (e)
Number of Employees: 220
Total Units: 3
Trade Names: McDonald's (3)
Units Franchised From: 3
Preferred Square Footage: 2,500
Preferred Location Types: Convenience Store/Gas Station; Discount Dept. Stores; Freestanding
Primary Menu: Hamburger (3)
Areas of Operation: OH
Type of Foodservice: Quick Serve (3)
Franchise Affiliation: McDonald's Corporation, CHICAGO, IL

Key Personnel
LAURIE STRAHLER - President; General Buyer

Focused Management Experts Inc.
PO Box 305
Marysville, OH 43040-0305

Telephone: (937) 642-7847
Fax Number: (937) 642-0600
Type of Business: Chain Restaurant Operator
Total Sales: $9,609,000 (e)
Total Units: 4
Trade Names: Burger King (4)
Units Franchised From: 4
Primary Menu: Hamburger (4)
Areas of Operation: OH
Type of Foodservice: Quick Serve (4)
Franchise Affiliation: Burger King Worldwide Inc., MIAMI, FL

Key Personnel
DAVID LASLOW - President; Partner; General Buyer
LAURA LASLOW - Partner

Kendall House Inc.
1207 Lincoln Way E
Massillon, OH 44646-6952

Telephone: (330) 837-5041
Fax Number: (330) 837-1207
Type of Business: Chain Restaurant Operator
Year Founded: 1961
Total Sales: $36,530,000 (e)
Number of Employees: 320
Average Check: Lunch(12); Dinner(12)
Total Units: 19
Trade Names: KFC (18); Taco Bell (1)
Units Franchised From: 19
Preferred Square Footage: 3,000
Preferred Location Types: Freestanding
Primary Menu: Chicken (18); Taco (1)
Areas of Operation: OH
Type of Foodservice: Quick Serve (19)
Franchise Affiliation: KFC Corporation, LOUISVILLE, KY; Taco Bell Corp., IRVINE, CA
Primary Distributors: (Supplies) McLane/Columbus, COLUMBUS, OH

Key Personnel
GEORGE LAMBOS - President; Director Purchasing, Information Systems; General Buyer
NICK LAMBOS - Treasurer
MARK LAMBOS - Controller
PAULA STANLEY - Manager Human Resources

Your Pizza Shop Corp.
3161 Lincoln Way NW
Massillon, OH 44647

Telephone: (330) 837-5700
Internet Homepage: yourpizzashop.com
Company Email: yps@sssnet.com
Type of Business: Chain Restaurant Operator
Year Founded: 1950
Total Sales: $1,416,000 (e)
Average Check: Dinner(12)
Internet Order Processing: Yes
Total Units: 11
Trade Names: Your Pizza Shop (11)
Company-Owned Units: 11
Preferred Location Types: Freestanding; Strip Mall
Alcohol Served: Beer, Wine, Liquor
Primary Menu: Pizza (11)
Areas of Operation: FL, OH
Type of Foodservice: Fast Casual (11)

Key Personnel
DAVE NEWSTETTER - Owner; General Manager; General Buyer

Bennett Management Corp
1412 Arrowhead Dr
Maumee, OH 43537-4016

Telephone: (419) 865-0232
Fax Number: (419) 865-0912
Internet Homepage: bennettmanagement.com
Company Email: bennett@bennettmanagement.com
Type of Business: Chain Restaurant Operator
Year Founded: 1967
Total Sales: $55,350,000 (e)
Number of Employees: 770
Average Check: Breakfast(8); Lunch(8); Dinner(8)
Total Units: 25
Trade Names: Burger King (25)
Units Franchised From: 25
Preferred Square Footage: 3,800
Preferred Location Types: Freestanding
Primary Menu: Hamburger (25)
Projected Remodelings: 3
Areas of Operation: IN, MI, OH
Type of Foodservice: Quick Serve (25)
Franchise Affiliation: Burger King Worldwide Inc., MIAMI, FL
Primary Distributors: (Full Line) Maines Paper & Food Services Ohio, OAKWOOD VILLAGE, OH

Key Personnel
EMILY E. BENNETT - Chairman; President
JIMMY HARMON - CEO; Director Operations
ROBERT BENNETT - Owner
DAVE PRUSS - CFO
LINDSEY BOND - Director Training, Recruitment
JOHN SHORTRIDGE - Director Information Systems
JIM RUBLE - Director Information Technology
JULIE BAIR - Manager Purchasing, Supply Chain
TODI HUNTER - Specialist Human Resources

Golden Alliance, Inc.
5681 River Styx Rd
Medina, OH 44256-6869

Telephone: (330) 723-3197
Company Email: goldenallianceinc@zoominternet.net
Type of Business: Chain Restaurant Operator
Total Sales: $20,399,000 (e)
Total Units: 4
Trade Names: McDonald's (4)
Units Franchised From: 4
Primary Menu: Hamburger (4)

Areas of Operation: OH
Type of Foodservice: Quick Serve (4)
Franchise Affiliation: McDonald's Corporation, CHICAGO, IL

Key Personnel
LEA ANNE HEIDMAN - President; General Buyer

Romeo's Pizza Inc
1113 Medina Rd Ste 200
Medina, OH 44256-5913

Telephone: (234) 248-4549
Internet Homepage: romeospizza.com
Type of Business: Chain Restaurant Operator
Year Founded: 2001
Total Sales: $32,510,000 (e)
Average Check: Lunch(8); Dinner(16)
Internet Order Processing: Yes
Internet Sales: 1.00%
Total Units: 35
Trade Names: Romeo's Pizza (35)
Company-Owned Units: 2
Units Franchised To: 33
Primary Menu: Pizza (35)
Areas of Operation: OH
Type of Foodservice: Fast Casual (35)
Catering Services: Yes

Key Personnel
TOM FIALA - Director Operations
THOMAS FIALA - Director Operations

Primo Inc.
7314 Lake Shore Blvd
Mentor, OH 44060-3030

Mailing Address: PO Box 270, MENTOR, OH, 44061-0270
Telephone: (440) 946-8222
Internet Homepage: pastinarusticitalian.com; joeysitaliangrille.com; longospizza.com
Company Email: info@longospizza.com
Type of Business: Chain Restaurant Operator
Year Founded: 1969
Total Sales: $7,796,000 (e)
Alcohol Sales: 8%
Number of Employees: 300
Average Check: Lunch(14); Dinner(14)
Total Units: 5
Trade Names: Joey's Italian Grille (2); Longo's Pizzeria (2); Pastina Rustic Italian Kitchen (1)
Company-Owned Units: 5
Preferred Location Types: Strip Mall
Alcohol Served: Beer, Wine
Primary Menu: Italian (3); Pizza (2)
Areas of Operation: OH
Type of Foodservice: Casual Dining (5)
Primary Distributors: (Equipment) TriMark SS Kemp, CLEVELAND, OH; (Food) SYSCO Food Services of Cleveland Inc., CLEVELAND, OH; (Supplies) TriMark SS Kemp, CLEVELAND, OH

Key Personnel
JOSEPH LONGO SR - President; Controller; Executive Chef; General Buyer
JOSEPH LONGO JR - VP Operations, Purchasing, Marketing; Director Quality Assurance, Food Safety
ADAM ABRAHAM - VP Sales
JOSEPHINE TODD - Executive Chef

Fricker's USA
228 Byers Rd Ste 100
Miamisburg, OH 45342-3675

Telephone: (937) 865-9242
Fax Number: (937) 865-9579
Internet Homepage: frickers.com
Company Email: mail@frickers.com
Type of Business: Chain Restaurant Operator
Year Founded: 1985
Systemwide Sales: $22,510,000 (e)
Total Sales: $21,780,000 (e)
Alcohol Sales: 10%
Number of Employees: 1,275
Average Check: Lunch(12); Dinner(14)
Internet Order Processing: Yes
Internet Sales: 1.00%
Total Units: 24
Trade Names: Fricker's (24)
Company-Owned Units: 16
Units Franchised To: 8
Preferred Square Footage: 5,500; 6,000
Preferred Location Types: Freestanding
Alcohol Served: Beer, Wine, Liquor
Primary Menu: Chicken (24)
Areas of Operation: IN, MI, OH
Type of Foodservice: Casual Dining (24)
Primary Distributors: (Full Line) SYSCO Food Services of Cleveland Inc., CLEVELAND, OH

Key Personnel
CRIS D'ANDREA - COO
CAMILLE NUCKOLS - Director Talent
MATT THATCHER - Director Human Resources; Manager Training
JIM MANLEY - Manager Marketing

Dutchman Hospitality
4985 State Route 515
Middlesburg, OH 44654

Mailing Address: PO Box 158, WALNUT CREEK, OH, 44687-0158
Telephone: (330) 893-2926
Fax Number: (330) 893-2637
Internet Homepage: dhgroup.com; dutchmanhospitality.com
Company Email: custservice@dhgroup.com

Type of Business: Chain Restaurant Operator
Year Founded: 1969
Total Sales: $51,062,000 (e)
Number of Employees: 1,020
Average Check: Breakfast(10); Lunch(14); Dinner(14)
Internet Order Processing: Yes
Internet Sales: 2.00%
Total Units: 6
Trade Names: Berlin Farmstead (1); Der Dutchman (4); Dutch Valley (1)
Company-Owned Units: 6
Preferred Square Footage: 20,000
Preferred Location Types: Freestanding
Primary Menu: Miscellaneous (6)
Areas of Operation: FL, OH
Type of Foodservice: Family Restaurant (6)
Catering Services: Yes
Distribution Centers: SUGARCREEK, OH
Primary Distributors: (Food) Dutch Creek Foods, SUGARCREEK, OH
Headquarter Offices: Dutch Creek Foods, SUGARCREEK, OH
Notes: The company derives approximately 25% of its revenue from retail operations.

Key Personnel
MIKE PALMER - President; Executive Chef; Director Real Estate, Menu Development
TOM TROYER - Controller
MIKE MILLER - Director Operations
VICKI VANNATTA - Manager Public Relations
KAREN MILLER - Administrator Payroll

BCC Direct LLC
5991 Meijer Dr Ste 24
Milford, OH 45150-1531

Telephone: (513) 697-6610
Internet Homepage: bluechipcookiesdirect.com
Company Email: info@bluechipcookies.com
Type of Business: Chain Restaurant Operator
Systemwide Sales: $4,116,000 (e)
Total Sales: $1,930,000 (e)
Number of Employees: 35
Average Check: Breakfast(8); Lunch(10); Dinner(14)
Internet Order Processing: Yes
Internet Sales: 15.00%
Total Units: 4
Trade Names: Blue Chip Cookies (4)
Units Franchised To: 4
Preferred Square Footage: 600
Preferred Location Types: Freestanding; Regional Mall; Strip Mall
Primary Menu: Snacks (4)
Areas of Operation: KS, OH, FC
Type of Foodservice: Quick Serve (4)
Catering Services: Yes
Primary Distributors: (Food) The Chefs' Warehouse, CINCINNATI, OH

Key Personnel
DONNA DRURY-HEINE - President; COO; General Buyer

Carpe Diems Inc.
5989 Meijer Dr Ste 6
Milford, OH 45150-1544

Telephone: (513) 576-6160
Fax Number: (513) 576-6260
Type of Business: Chain Restaurant Operator
Total Sales: $4,480,000 (e)
Number of Employees: 25
Average Check: Dinner(14)
Total Units: 4
Trade Names: Donatos Pizza (4)
Units Franchised From: 4
Preferred Square Footage: 2,200
Preferred Location Types: Freestanding; Strip Mall
Primary Menu: Pizza (4)
Areas of Operation: OH
Type of Foodservice: Family Restaurant (4)
Catering Services: Yes
Franchise Affiliation: Donatos Pizzeria LLC, COLUMBUS, OH
Primary Distributors: (Food) The SYGMA Network Inc. - Columbus, COLUMBUS, OH

Key Personnel
DON JOHNSON - President; General Manager; General Buyer

Penn Station Inc.
1226 US Route 50
Milford, OH 45150-9518

Telephone: (513) 474-5957
Fax Number: (513) 474-7116
Internet Homepage: penn-station.com
Type of Business: Chain Restaurant Operator
Year Founded: 1985
Systemwide Sales: $270,510,000 (e)
Total Sales: $20,800,000 (e)
Number of Employees: 2,261
Average Check: Lunch(8); Dinner(8)
Total Units: 306
Trade Names: Penn Station East Coast Subs (306)
Company-Owned Units: 1
Units Franchised To: 306
Preferred Square Footage: 1,500; 1,800
Preferred Location Types: Community Mall; Downtown; Freestanding; Regional Mall; Strip Mall
Primary Menu: Sandwiches/Deli (313)
Areas of Operation: GA, IL, IN, KS, KY, MI, MO, NC, OH, PA, SC, TN, TX, VA, WV
Type of Foodservice: Fast Casual (313)
Catering Services: Yes
Primary Distributors: (Full Line) US Foods, CINCINNATI, OH

Key Personnel
JEFFREY J. OSTERFELD - CEO
CRAIG N. DUNAWAY - President; General Buyer
KIRK W. DURCHHOLZ - VP Construction
SHERI S. OSTERFELD - Treasurer
CYNTHIA D. STENGER - Corporate Secretary; Director Administration
LARRY HAUG - Director Information Technology
R. LANCE VAUGHT - Director Operations

Q S C Inc
882 Business 28
Milford, OH 45150-1952

Telephone: (513) 831-3392
Fax Number: (513) 831-1475
Type of Business: Chain Restaurant Operator
Total Sales: $4,921,000 (e)
Average Check: Dinner(12)
Total Units: 2
Trade Names: Burger King (2)
Units Franchised From: 2
Primary Menu: Hamburger (2)
Areas of Operation: OH
Type of Foodservice: Quick Serve (2)
Franchise Affiliation: Burger King Worldwide Inc., MIAMI, FL

Key Personnel
DON ROOKS - President; General Buyer
JAKE CORLETT - Manager Sales, Canada

The Twins Group Inc.
3019 Kettering Blvd
Moraine, OH 45439-1921

Telephone: (937) 262-7536
Fax Number: (937) 262-7905
Internet Homepage: thetwinsgroup.com
Type of Business: Chain Restaurant Operator
Year Founded: 1998
Total Sales: $105,790,000 (e)
Alcohol Sales: 5%
Number of Employees: 1,365
Average Check: Lunch(10); Dinner(14)
Total Units: 41
Trade Names: Taco Bell (38); Taco Bell/Pizza Hut Express (3)
Units Franchised From: 41
Preferred Square Footage: 2,500; 3,500
Preferred Location Types: Freestanding; Strip Mall
Alcohol Served: Beer
Primary Menu: Pizza (3); Taco (38)
Areas of Operation: IL, OH
Type of Foodservice: Quick Serve (41)
Franchise Affiliation: Pizza Hut Inc., PLANO, TX; Taco Bell Corp., IRVINE, CA

Primary Distributors: (Food) McLane/Midwest, DANVILLE, IL

Key Personnel
GILBERT HUNT - Director Operations
JEAN LESLIE - Director Human Resources

Domino's Franchisee
321 S Main St
Mount Vernon, OH 43050-3305

Telephone: (740) 397-3151
Type of Business: Chain Restaurant Operator
Total Sales: $6,200,000 (e)
Total Units: 3
Trade Names: Domino's (3)
Units Franchised From: 3
Primary Menu: Pizza (3)
Areas of Operation: OH
Type of Foodservice: Quick Serve (3)
Franchise Affiliation: Domino's Pizza Inc, ANN ARBOR, MI

Key Personnel
RUSSELL D. MENTZER - Owner; General Buyer

Bob Evans Farms Inc.
8200 Walton Pkwy
New Albany, OH 43054

Mailing Address: PO Box 07863, COLUMBUS, OH, 43207
Telephone: (614) 491-2225
Fax Number: (614) 492-4949
Internet Homepage: bobevans.com
Company Email: customer_support@bobevans.com
Type of Business: Chain Restaurant Operator
Year Founded: 1953
Systemwide Sales: $2,034,933,000 (e)
Total Sales: $2,180,285,000 (e)
Number of Employees: 32,350
Average Check: Breakfast(10); Lunch(10); Dinner(12)
Foodservice Sales: $1,548,001,000 (e)
Internet Order Processing: Yes
Internet Sales: 0.50%
Total Units: 439
Trade Names: Bob Evans Restaurant (439)
Company-Owned Units: 439
Preferred Square Footage: 3,600; 5,400; 6,600; 9,800
Preferred Location Types: Airports; Freestanding
Primary Menu: American (439)
Areas of Operation: DE, FL, IL, IN, KS, KY, MD, MI, MO, NC, NJ, NY, OH, PA, SC, TN, VA, WV
Type of Foodservice: Family Restaurant (439)
Distribution Centers: SPRINGFIELD, OH

Primary Distributors: (Equipment) The Wasserstrom Co., COLUMBUS, OH; (Food) Mattingly Foods Inc., ZANESVILLE, OH; (Supplies) Acorn Distributors, COLUMBUS, OH
Parent Company: Golden Gate Capital, SAN FRANCISCO, CA
Notes: The company derives approximately 28% of its revenue from retail food products.

Key Personnel
MICHAEL TOWNSLEY - Chairman
MIKE MCCOY - CFO; VP
MICKEY MILLS - COO; Senior VP Restaurant Operations
JOHN CAROTHERS - Chief People Officer; Senior VP Human Resources
JIM ROBERTS - Senior VP
ROBERT D. SPEIRS - VP Operations
DEVRA CORNELL - VP Human Resources
THYME H. - VP Marketing
ROBERT FRADETTE - VP Marketing
ADAM GONSIOROWSKI - VP Finance
JESSE DAVIS - VP Region
COLIN M. DALY - Corporate Secretary; General Counsel
MEL VALIQUETT - Senior Director Real Estate
DEAN BOEGEMAN - Senior Director Marketing, Customer Service
MARIA GARDINA - Director Purchasing
IMAD MUSTAFA - Director Operations
JAY EXTINE - Director Operations
DAVID RAVELLETTE - Director Operations
GLENDA CAMPBELL - Director Operations
MELISSA GILBERT - Director Operations
STEPHEN WILKES - Director Operations
CYNTHIA DAVIS - Director Operations
TONY FUNG - Director Marketing, E-Commerce
JONATHAN THRASHER - Director Marketing
JASON WALTERS - Director Branding
LOGAN KAHLE - Senior Manager Marketing
VICTOR LAYNE - Manager Real Estate
ALI VAN LOON - Manager Branding

Subway Operation of Ohio
494 S Washington St
New Bremen, OH 45869

Telephone: (419) 629-3770
Fax Number: (419) 629-2439
Type of Business: Chain Restaurant Operator
Total Sales: $2,809,000 (e)
Total Units: 5
Trade Names: Subway (5)
Units Franchised From: 5
Primary Menu: Sandwiches/Deli (5)
Areas of Operation: OH
Type of Foodservice: Quick Serve (5)
Franchise Affiliation: Doctor's Associates Inc., MILFORD, CT

Key Personnel
TY MINNICK - Owner; General Buyer

Frfc Springfield, Inc
301 N Main St
New Carlisle, OH 45344-1840

Mailing Address: PO Box 383, NEW CARLISLE, OH, 45344-0383
Telephone: (937) 845-2142
Fax Number: (937) 845-1705
Internet Homepage: leeschicken.net
Type of Business: Chain Restaurant Operator
Total Sales: $7,194,000 (e)
Total Units: 7
Trade Names: Lee's Famous Recipe Chicken (7)
Units Franchised From: 7
Primary Menu: Chicken (7)
Areas of Operation: OH
Type of Foodservice: Quick Serve (7)
Franchise Affiliation: Lee's Famous Recipes Inc., FORT WALTON BEACH, FL

Key Personnel
SCOTT GRIFFITH - President; General Buyer

DJB Bott LLC
590 Carroll St
New Lexington, OH 43764-1050

Telephone: (740) 342-1147
Type of Business: Chain Restaurant Operator
Total Sales: $20,443,000 (e)
Total Units: 4
Trade Names: McDonald's (4)
Units Franchised From: 4
Preferred Location Types: Freestanding
Primary Menu: Hamburger (4)
Areas of Operation: OH
Type of Foodservice: Quick Serve (4)
Franchise Affiliation: McDonald's Corporation, CHICAGO, IL

Key Personnel
RECINA BOTT - President; General Buyer
LIBBIE WYER - Director Operations; General Buyer

Domino's Franchisee
122 N Main St
New Lexington, OH 43764-1261

Telephone: (740) 342-5141
Type of Business: Chain Restaurant Operator
Total Sales: $26,715,000 (e)
Total Units: 13
Trade Names: Domino's (13)
Units Franchised From: 13

Primary Menu: Pizza (13)
Areas of Operation: OH
Type of Foodservice: Quick Serve (13)
Franchise Affiliation: Domino's Pizza Inc, ANN ARBOR, MI

Key Personnel
CHRISTOPHER J. BAKER - Owner; General Buyer

Auntie Anne's Franchise
400 Mill Ave SE Ste 433
New Philadelphia, OH 44663-3877

Telephone: (330) 339-3278
Type of Business: Chain Restaurant Operator
Total Sales: $3,114,000 (e)
Total Units: 4
Trade Names: Auntie Anne's Hand-Rolled Soft Pretzels (4)
Units Franchised From: 4
Primary Menu: Snacks (4)
Areas of Operation: OH
Type of Foodservice: Quick Serve (4)
Franchise Affiliation: Auntie Anne's Inc., LANCASTER, PA

Key Personnel
CHARLES BAUER - Owner; General Buyer

Golden Spirit, LTD
139 Beech Ln NE
New Philadelphia, OH 44663

Mailing Address: PO Box 604, NEW PHILADELPHIA, OH, 44663
Telephone: (330) 308-5018
Fax Number: (330) 308-5019
Type of Business: Chain Restaurant Operator
Total Sales: $14,740,000 (e)
Total Units: 3
Trade Names: McDonald's (3)
Units Franchised From: 3
Preferred Square Footage: 2,500
Primary Menu: Hamburger (3)
Areas of Operation: OH
Type of Foodservice: Quick Serve (3)
Franchise Affiliation: McDonald's Corporation, CHICAGO, IL

Key Personnel
VIRGINIA LEWIS - Owner; General Buyer

Mortellaro's Mcdonalds
15 Sandalwood Dr
Newark, OH 43055-9232

Telephone: (740) 522-2054
Fax Number: (740) 522-2059

Type of Business: Chain Restaurant Operator
Total Sales: $73,480,000 (e)
Number of Employees: 1,000
Average Check: Breakfast(8); Lunch(12); Dinner(12)
Total Units: 16
Trade Names: McDonald's (16)
Units Franchised From: 16
Preferred Square Footage: 2,500
Primary Menu: Hamburger (16)
Areas of Operation: OH
Type of Foodservice: Quick Serve (16)
Franchise Affiliation: McDonald's Corporation, CHICAGO, IL

Key Personnel
BRIAN MORTELLARO - Co-President; Partner; General Buyer
JOSEPH MORTELLARO - Co-President; Partner; General Buyer

Skip Salome Enterprises Inc
1005 W Main St
Newark, OH 43055-2554

Telephone: (740) 344-4178
Internet Homepage: leesfamousrecipe.com/locations/ohio/newark-main
Type of Business: Chain Restaurant Operator
Total Sales: $2,931,000 (e)
Total Units: 2
Trade Names: Lee's Famous Recipe Chicken (2)
Units Franchised From: 2
Primary Menu: Chicken (2)
Areas of Operation: OH
Type of Foodservice: Quick Serve (2)
Franchise Affiliation: Lee's Famous Recipes Inc., FORT WALTON BEACH, FL

Key Personnel
TODD SALOME - President; Owner; General Buyer

Patrick Anderson
224 E Canal St
Newcomerstown, OH 43832-1201

Telephone: (740) 498-4131
Type of Business: Chain Restaurant Operator
Total Sales: $4,148,000 (e)
Average Check: Dinner(16)
Total Units: 2
Trade Names: Domino's (2)
Units Franchised From: 2
Primary Menu: Pizza (2)
Areas of Operation: OH
Type of Foodservice: Quick Serve (2)
Franchise Affiliation: Domino's Pizza Inc, ANN ARBOR, MI

Key Personnel
PATRICK ANDERSON - President; General Buyer

Ichor Restaurant Group LLC
5757 Mayfair Rd
North Canton, OH 44720-1546

Mailing Address: PO Box 2850, North Canton, OH,
Telephone: (330) 433-2197
Internet Homepage: ichorgroup.com; oldcarolina.com
Company Email: info@oldcarolina.com
Type of Business: Chain Restaurant Operator
Year Founded: 2002
Total Sales: $23,830,000 (e)
Total Units: 17
Trade Names: Old Carolina Barbecue Company (4); Smoke The Burger Joint (13)
Company-Owned Units: 9
Units Franchised To: 5
Primary Menu: American (13); Bar-B-Q (4)
Areas of Operation: MI, OH, PA
Type of Foodservice: Fast Casual (17)
Catering Services: Yes

Key Personnel
BRIAN BAILEY - Partner; Executive Chef
TIM HUG - Partner; Executive Chef

J & K Subway Inc
5441 Global Gtwy
North Canton, OH 44720-1376

Telephone: (330) 497-4484
Fax Number: (330) 497-8102
Internet Homepage: jandkrestaurants.com
Company Email: info@jandkrestarants.com
Type of Business: Chain Restaurant Operator
Total Sales: $28,000,000 (e)
Total Units: 49
Trade Names: Subway (49)
Units Franchised From: 49
Primary Menu: Sandwiches/Deli (49)
Areas of Operation: OH
Type of Foodservice: Quick Serve (49)
Franchise Affiliation: Doctor's Associates Inc., MILFORD, CT

Key Personnel
KRIS NONNAMAKER - President; Partner; General Buyer
JOE NONNAMAKER - Partner

Franchise Operations Inc.
24950 Country Club Blvd Ste 104
North Olmsted, OH 44070-5334

Telephone: (440) 801-1620
Fax Number: (440) 801-1621
Type of Business: Chain Restaurant Operator
Year Founded: 1969
Total Sales: $44,760,000 (e)
Number of Employees: 785
Average Check: Breakfast(8); Lunch(10); Dinner(10)
Total Units: 20
Trade Names: Burger King (20)
Units Franchised From: 20
Preferred Square Footage: 1,500
Preferred Location Types: Freestanding
Primary Menu: Hamburger (20)
Projected Remodelings: 3
Areas of Operation: OH
Type of Foodservice: Quick Serve (20)
Franchise Affiliation: Burger King Worldwide Inc., MIAMI, FL
Primary Distributors: (Full Line) Maines Paper & Food Services Ohio, OAKWOOD VILLAGE, OH

Key Personnel
MICHAEL SHOWALTER - President
RANDALL SHOWALTER - VP Purchasing, Real Estate, Design
JAN LAWLOR - Controller; Director Supply Chain
JEANNE MARTIN - General Manager

Domino's Franchisee
25 E Main St
Orwell, OH 44076

Telephone: (440) 437-3030
Type of Business: Chain Restaurant Operator
Total Sales: $5,955,000 (e)
Total Units: 3
Trade Names: Domino's (3)
Units Franchised From: 3
Primary Menu: Pizza (3)
Areas of Operation: OH
Type of Foodservice: Quick Serve (3)
Franchise Affiliation: Domino's Pizza Inc, ANN ARBOR, MI

Key Personnel
MUHAMMAD B. QURESHI - Owner; General Buyer

Grinders Above & Beyond
1216 Fox Ave SE
Paris, OH 44669-9794

Telephone: (330) 862-9001
Internet Homepage: grinders.net
Type of Business: Chain Restaurant Operator
Year Founded: 1976
Systemwide Sales: $18,241,000 (e)
Total Sales: $14,740,000 (e)
Alcohol Sales: 1%
Number of Employees: 210
Average Check: Lunch(16); Dinner(24)
Internet Order Processing: Yes
Internet Sales: 1.00%
Total Units: 7
Trade Names: Grinders Above & Beyond (7)
Company-Owned Units: 4
Units Franchised To: 3
Preferred Square Footage: 4,200
Preferred Location Types: Downtown; Strip Mall
Primary Menu: American (7)
Areas of Operation: OH
Type of Foodservice: Casual Dining (7)
Catering Services: Yes
Primary Distributors: (Food) US Foods, TWINSBURG, OH; (Supplies) US Foods, TWINSBURG, OH

Key Personnel
DEBRA HOSTERMAN - CEO; President; Partner; CFO; Executive Chef; Director Real Estate, Design, Catering
DOUG HOSTERMAN - Partner; VP Facility/Maintenance; Buyer Foodservice Equip/Supplies
CASEY LOGSDON - VP Information Systems, Marketing
BRADLEY MORGAN - VP Operations, Purchasing, Supply Chain, Business Development, Food Safety

Domino's Franchisee
7406 Broadview Rd
Parma, OH 44134-5718

Telephone: (216) 236-6933
Type of Business: Chain Restaurant Operator
Total Sales: $36,035,000 (e)
Total Units: 18
Trade Names: Domino's (18)
Units Franchised From: 18
Primary Menu: Pizza (18)
Areas of Operation: OH
Type of Foodservice: Quick Serve (18)
Franchise Affiliation: Domino's Pizza Inc, ANN ARBOR, MI

Key Personnel
STEPHEN L. GFELL - Owner; General Buyer

Navco Corp.
7505 Day Dr
Parma, OH 44129-5602

Telephone: (440) 888-4652
Type of Business: Chain Restaurant Operator
Total Sales: $23,640,000 (e)
Number of Employees: 300
Total Units: 5
Trade Names: McDonald's (5)
Units Franchised From: 5
Preferred Square Footage: 2,500
Primary Menu: Hamburger (5)
Areas of Operation: OH
Type of Foodservice: Quick Serve (5)
Franchise Affiliation: McDonald's Corporation, CHICAGO, IL

Key Personnel
CRAIG NAVRATIL - President; Owner
PAIGE NAVRATIL - VP; General Buyer

Bennett Enterprises Inc.
27476 Holiday Ln
Perrysburg, OH 43551-3345

Mailing Address: PO Box 670, PERRYSBURG, OH, 43552-0670
Telephone: (419) 874-1933
Fax Number: (419) 874-2615
Internet Homepage: bennett-enterprises.com
Type of Business: Chain Restaurant Operator
Year Founded: 1955
Total Sales: $70,710,000 (e)
Alcohol Sales: 5%
Number of Employees: 1,083
Average Check: Breakfast(6); Lunch(8); Dinner(12)
Total Units: 19
Trade Names: Big Boy (11); J. Patrick's (1); Ralphie's (7)
Company-Owned Units: 8
Units Franchised From: 11
Preferred Square Footage: 4,000; 6,000
Preferred Location Types: Freestanding; Hotel/Motel
Alcohol Served: Beer, Wine, Liquor
Primary Menu: American (19)
Areas of Operation: OH
Type of Foodservice: Casual Dining (19)
Primary Distributors: (Full Line) Gordon Food Service Inc., WYOMING, MI
Notes: The company derives approximately 35% of its revenue from hotel operations.

Key Personnel
ROB ARMSTRONG - CEO
DAVID P. BENNETT - President; VP Operations;

Director Menu Development; General Buyer
GARY SADDLER - Director Information Systems, E-Commerce, Internet Development
TONYA PICCIUTO - Director Personnel
PAULA DURAN - Supervisor Area

Scott M & A Corporation
218 W Ash St
Piqua, OH 45356-2202

Telephone: (937) 773-7200
Fax Number: (937) 773-1195
Internet Homepage: scottmcdonalds.com
Type of Business: Chain Restaurant Operator
Year Founded: 1974
Total Sales: $56,730,000 (e)
Alcohol Sales: 3%
Number of Employees: 400
Average Check: Breakfast(8); Lunch(8); Dinner(10)
Total Units: 12
Trade Names: McDonald's (12)
Units Franchised From: 12
Preferred Square Footage: 1,600
Preferred Location Types: Discount Dept. Stores; Freestanding
Primary Menu: Hamburger (12)
Areas of Operation: OH
Type of Foodservice: Quick Serve (12)
Franchise Affiliation: McDonald's Corporation, CHICAGO, IL

Key Personnel
BEN SCOTT JR - President Finance, Real Estate; General Buyer
KEN ROOSA - Director Operations
CLEDITH ROOSA - Manager Human Resources
DAVE MIZEK - Supervisor Region

SCHMIDT FAMILY RESTAURANT GROUP
1735 Waller St
Portsmouth, OH 45662-3540

Telephone: (740) 353-0990
Fax Number: (740) 353-1576
Internet Homepage: schmidtgroup.us
Type of Business: Chain Restaurant Operator
Total Sales: $157,430,000 (e)
Total Units: 55
Trade Names: Buffalo Wild Wings (5); Wendy's Old Fashioned Hamburgers (50)
Units Franchised From: 55
Alcohol Served: Beer
Primary Menu: Chicken (5); Hamburger (40)
Areas of Operation: OH
Type of Foodservice: Casual Dining (5); Quick Serve (40)
Franchise Affiliation: The Wendy's Company, DUBLIN, OH

Key Personnel
JUSTIN SCHMIDT - President; Partner
STACEY HUMPHREYS - CFO
JUD WHITE - Controller
SUARRA SPARKS - Director Human Resources
PATRICK BURNETT - Director Facility/Maintenance
KATIE VETTER - Director Marketing
SHAWN BROWN - Regional Director
JEANNIE MURPHY - Regional Director Operations
DEEDEE ROBERTS - District Manager

Iacono's
9303 Dublin Rd
Powell, OH 43065-9656

Telephone: (614) 766-0444
Internet Homepage: iaconos.com
Type of Business: Chain Restaurant Operator
Year Founded: 1977
Total Sales: $6,873,000 (e)
Alcohol Sales: 15%
Number of Employees: 95
Average Check: Lunch(14); Dinner(22)
Total Units: 3
Trade Names: Iacono's (3)
Company-Owned Units: 3
Preferred Location Types: Freestanding; Strip Mall
Alcohol Served: Beer, Wine, Liquor
Primary Menu: Italian (3)
Areas of Operation: OH
Type of Foodservice: Casual Dining (3)
Foodservice Management Venues: Health Care
Primary Distributors: (Full Line) RDP Foodservice, LLC, HILLIARD, OH

Key Personnel
STEPHEN IACONO SR - President; Executive Chef; General Buyer
STEPHEN TRENT IACONO JR - VP Operations; General Manager

T & C Foods Inc
10691 Scarborough Way
Powell, OH 43065-8769

Telephone: (614) 889-4739
Type of Business: Chain Restaurant Operator
Total Sales: $19,060,000 (e)
Total Units: 7
Trade Names: Wendy's Old Fashioned Hamburgers (7)
Units Franchised From: 7
Primary Menu: Hamburger (7)
Areas of Operation: OH
Type of Foodservice: Quick Serve (7)
Franchise Affiliation: The Wendy's Company, DUBLIN, OH

Key Personnel
JEROME L. TRUBY - President; General Buyer

Minuteman Pizza
2723 Independence Village Ctr
Reynoldsburg, OH 43068-3989

Telephone: (614) 575-0033
Fax Number: (614) 864-6190
Internet Homepage: minutemanpizza.com
Type of Business: Chain Restaurant Operator
Total Sales: $2,360,000 (e)
Total Units: 2
Trade Names: Minuteman Pizza (2)
Company-Owned Units: 2
Primary Menu: Pizza (2)
Areas of Operation: OH
Type of Foodservice: Quick Serve (2)

Key Personnel
RICK JACKSON - President; General Buyer

Medina County Foods Inc
19071 Old Detroit Rd Ste 301
Rocky River, OH 44116-1767

Telephone: (440) 331-3555
Fax Number: (440) 331-3492
Type of Business: Chain Restaurant Operator
Total Sales: $24,170,000 (e)
Total Units: 9
Trade Names: Wendy's Old Fashioned Hamburgers (9)
Units Franchised From: 9
Primary Menu: Hamburger (9)
Areas of Operation: OH
Type of Foodservice: Quick Serve (9)
Franchise Affiliation: The Wendy's Company, DUBLIN, OH

Key Personnel
WILLIAM M. HENNINGS - President; General Buyer
MARI ENGELHART - Director Technology

Cedar Fair LLP
1 Cedar Point Dr
Sandusky, OH 44870-5259

Telephone: (419) 626-0830
Internet Homepage: cedarfair.com; cedarpoint.com
Company Email: info@cedarfair.com
Type of Business: Foodservice Operations - Theme Parks
Year Founded: 1870
Publicly Held: Yes

Total Sales: $292,860,000 (e)
Alcohol Sales: 5%
Number of Employees: 2,000
Average Check: Breakfast(8); Lunch(10); Dinner(10)
Foodservice Sales: $58,572,000 (e)
Total Units: 13
Trade Names: California's Great America (1); Canada's Wonderland (1); Carowinds (1); Cedar Point (1); Dorney Park (1); Kings Dominion (1); Kings Island (1); Knott's Berry Farm (1); Michigan's Adventure (1); Schlitterbahn Waterpark and Resort New Braunfels (1); Schlitterbahn Waterpark Galveston (1); Valleyfair (1); Worlds of Fun (1)
Company-Owned Units: 13
Preferred Square Footage: 2,500; 6,000
Preferred Location Types: Parks
Alcohol Served: Beer, Wine, Liquor
Primary Menu: Miscellaneous (13)
Areas of Operation: CA, MI, MN, MO, NC, OH, PA, SC, TX, VA, ON
Foreign Countries: CANADA
Type of Foodservice: Cafeteria; Casual Dining; Family Restaurant; Fine Dining; In-Store Feeder
Franchise Affiliation: Quaker Steak & Lube, WESTLAKE, OH
Primary Distributors: (Food) Gordon Food Service Inc., WYOMING, MI
Headquarter Offices: Virginia's Gift Shop, BUENA PARK, CA
Divisional Offices: Cedar Point, SANDUSKY, OH; Dorney Park & Wildwater Kingdom, ALLENTOWN, PA; Valleyfair, SHAKOPEE, MN; Worlds of Fun & Oceans of Fun, KANSAS CITY, MO
Notes: The company derives approximately 80% of its revenue from amusement park operations. Total employees represents full-time employees; during operating seasons, the parks employ 42,000 seasonal and part-time workers.

Key Personnel
MATTHEW A. OUIMET - Executive Chairman
RICHARD A. ZIMMERMAN - CEO; President
BETH PAINTER - President
DICK KINZEL - President
JASON MCCLURE - President; VP Operations; General Manager
BRIAN C. WITHEROW - CFO; Exec VP
DAVID R. HOFFMAN - Chief Accounting Officer; Senior VP
TIM FISHER - COO
KELLEY SEMMELROTH - Chief Marketing Officer; Exec VP
H. PHILIP BENDER - Exec VP Operations
DUFFIELD E. MILKIE - Exec VP; Corporate Secretary; General Counsel
CRAIG HECKMAN - Senior VP Human Resources
ROBERT DECKER - Senior VP Design, Store Planning
SCOTT TANNER - Senior VP Sales
MATT SHAFER - VP Business Development
TODD SASALA - VP Information Technology
KEN PARKS - VP
STEVEN TOMASULA - VP; Controller
JIM DENNY - VP E-Commerce
TONY CAROVILLANO - VP; General Manager
MIKE HASMAN - VP Compliance
ROGER ALLEN - VP; Treasurer
CARRIE BOLDMAN - VP Merchandising
JACK HIGHSMITH - VP Operations
MONTY JASPER - VP Engineering, Safety
BOB WHITE - Regional VP
DUFF MILKIE - General Counsel
JAMES D. - Executive Chef
TONY CLARK - Director Communications
SCOTT CLEMONS - Director Marketing
DWIGHT DRISKILL - Director Sales
JUSTIN BRADY - Director Operations
LISA BRADY - Director Business Development
KATHLEEN BODDIE - Director Finance
AUGUST LOCOCO - Director Development
MELISSA LUTZ - Director Human Resources
SISSY MACKORELL - Director Applications
LYNN WEBB - Director Sales
CARSON WEINGART - Director Operations
CAMERON TYER - Director Sales
JOE VIVIANO - Director Procurement
CHAD SHOWALTER - Director Communications
HARRY SMITH - Director Food
KASIE SPENCE - Director
HEIDI PECK - Director Human Resources
BRIAN RATH - Director Operations
PETE SCARPERO - Director Sales
SHAUNA B. WISE - Senior Manager Finance
AUSTIN THIMLAR-COFFMAN - Area Manager
STEPHANIE SIMONELLI - Area Manager Food
STEPHANIE CALDWELL - Area Manager
ANDREW GREEN - Area Manager Technology
SARA MAINE - Manager Information Technology
DUBELL JENNIFER - Manager HRIS
JENNIFER HOFFMAN - Manager E-Commerce
ADAM WATTRICK - Manager
DANIEL ROBINSON - Manager Operations
DAVE O'HARE - Manager Internal Audit
AMY WIKE - Manager Administration
MICHAEL RUSSELL - Corporate Director Investor Relations
JEFF SHEPARD - Corporate Director Purchasing-Food
CRAIG KSENICH - Corporate Director Tax
JERRY NIEDERHELMAN - Corporate Director Security
BRIDGETTE BYWATER - Corporate Director Operations

Cedar Point
1 Cedar Point Dr
Sandusky, OH 44870-5259

Telephone: (419) 626-0830
Fax Number: (419) 627-2200
Company Email: info@cedarpoint.com
Listing Type: Divisional Office
Type of Business: Foodservice Operations - Theme Parks
Number of Employees: 3,500
Total Units: 70
Areas of Operation: OH
Parent Company: Cedar Fair LLP, SANDUSKY, OH

Key Personnel
MISSY SMITH - VP Finance
JOSEPH VIVIANO - Director Purchasing
LYNN WEBB - Director Group
KEN BERRYHILL - Director Safety
TONY CLARK - Director Communications
LISA SMITH - Area Manager
DAN MCMANUS - Manager Internal Audit
JOHN TAYLOR - Manager Restaurant Operations
PATRICK CHAMBERS - Coordinator Training

S Group
4000 Columbus Ave
Sandusky, OH 44870-7325

Telephone: (419) 625-7003
Fax Number: (419) 625-7219
Type of Business: Chain Restaurant Operator
Year Founded: 1985
Total Sales: $65,730,000 (e)
Number of Employees: 1,200
Average Check: Breakfast(8); Lunch(8); Dinner(8)
Total Units: 24
Trade Names: Wendy's Old Fashioned Hamburgers (24)
Units Franchised From: 24
Preferred Square Footage: 3,300
Preferred Location Types: Freestanding; Regional Mall
Primary Menu: Hamburger (24)
Areas of Operation: OH, PA
Type of Foodservice: Quick Serve (24)
Franchise Affiliation: The Wendy's Company, DUBLIN, OH
Primary Distributors: (Full Line) The Wasserstrom Co., COLUMBUS, OH

Key Personnel
JOHN STOCK - President; Manager Purchasing, Real Estate

The Barn Restaurant
877 W Main St
Smithville, OH 44677-9401

Mailing Address: PO Box 125, SMITHVILLE, OH, 44677-0125
Telephone: (330) 669-2555
Internet Homepage: dravenstotts.com; thebarnrest.com
Type of Business: Chain Restaurant Operator

Year Founded: 1983
Total Sales: $6,912,000 (e)
Number of Employees: 130
Average Check: Breakfast(8); Lunch(10); Dinner(14)
Total Units: 2
Trade Names: Dravenstott's Restaurant (1); The Barn Restaurant (1)
Company-Owned Units: 2
Preferred Location Types: Freestanding
Primary Menu: American (2)
Areas of Operation: OH
Type of Foodservice: Family Restaurant (2)
Primary Distributors: (Full Line) Gordon Food Service Inc., WYOMING, MI

Key Personnel
MARK DRAVENSTOTT - President
KELLY MYERS - General Manager; General Buyer

Buckeye Valley/White River Valley Pizza Hut
65 S Main St
Springboro, OH 45066-1321

Telephone: (937) 748-3338
Fax Number: (937) 748-3339
Type of Business: Chain Restaurant Operator
Year Founded: 1998
Total Sales: $20,810,000 (e)
Total Units: 17
Trade Names: Pizza Hut (17)
Units Franchised From: 17
Primary Menu: Pizza (17)
Areas of Operation: IN, OH
Type of Foodservice: Quick Serve (17)
Franchise Affiliation: Pizza Hut Inc., PLANO, TX

Key Personnel
GARY COOMER - President; General Buyer

Southern Ohio Pizza Inc
64 W Eleanor Dr
Springboro, OH 45066-1616

Telephone: (937) 746-1005
Fax Number: (937) 746-8678
Type of Business: Chain Restaurant Operator
Total Sales: $39,598,000 (e)
Average Check: Dinner(16)
Total Units: 20
Trade Names: Domino's (20)
Units Franchised From: 20
Primary Menu: Pizza (20)
Areas of Operation: OH
Type of Foodservice: Quick Serve (20)
Franchise Affiliation: Domino's Pizza Inc, ANN ARBOR, MI

Key Personnel
LOU METRO - President; General Buyer
KAREN METRO - VP; General Buyer

Chakeres Theatres Inc.
222 N Murray St
Springfield, OH 45503

Mailing Address: PO Box 1200, SPRINGFIELD, OH, 45501-1200
Telephone: (937) 323-6447
Fax Number: (937) 325-1100
Internet Homepage: chakerestheatres.com
Company Email: info@chakerestheatres.com
Type of Business: Foodservice Operations - Movie Theatre
Year Founded: 1908
Total Sales: $3,235,000 (e)
Number of Employees: 75
Average Check: Lunch(6); Dinner(6)
Total Units: 3
Trade Names: Chakeres Cinema (3)
Company-Owned Units: 3
Preferred Square Footage: 20,000
Preferred Location Types: Community Mall; Freestanding; Other; Regional Mall
Primary Menu: Snacks (3)
Areas of Operation: KY, OH
Type of Foodservice: In-Store Feeder (3)
Primary Distributors: (Food) Gordon Food Service Inc., WYOMING, MI
Notes: The company derives approximately 72% of its revenue from theater admissions, on-screen advertising, and other sales.

Key Personnel
MARK BOOTH - General Manager; General Buyer
CHRIS STEVENS - General Manager
PAUL DOUGLAS - Manager Purchasing, Supply Chain, Warehouse
DEBI HOLLIS - Manager Accounting

Sheehan Brothers
1740 Commerce Rd
Springfield, OH 45504-2018

Telephone: (937) 325-2357
Fax Number: (937) 325-7004
Internet Homepage: sheehanvending.com
Type of Business: Foodservice Management Operator
Year Founded: 1956
Total Sales: $14,459,000 (e)
Number of Employees: 60
Number of Locations Served: 300
Total Foodservice Mgmt Accounts: 300
Total Units: 300
Trade Names: Sheehan Brothers (300)
Company-Owned Units: 300
Projected Openings: 20
Areas of Operation: OH
Type of Foodservice: Vending machines (300)
Foodservice Management Venues: Business & Industry; College & University
Primary Distributors: (Food) Vistar Michigan, BELLEVILLE, MI

Key Personnel
PATRICK SHEEHAN - President
PAUL SHEEHAN - VP Marketing, Sales
DAN SHEEHAN - VP Operations, Risk Management; General Buyer
MICHAEL SHEEHAN - VP
KAITLIN DOBSON - Director Operations
MICHAEL ORF - Manager Food
JOHN SHAW - Manager Fleet
KEN COLEMAN - Manager Division

Hallrich Incorporated
3747 Fishcreek Rd
Stow, OH 44224-5404

Mailing Address: PO Box 370, KENT, OH, 44240-0007
Telephone: (330) 678-0684
Fax Number: (330) 673-5291
Internet Homepage: innercrust.com
Type of Business: Chain Restaurant Operator
Year Founded: 1968
Total Sales: $156,720,000 (e)
Alcohol Sales: 5%
Number of Employees: 3,510
Average Check: Lunch(10); Dinner(22)
Internet Order Processing: Yes
Total Units: 128
Trade Names: Pizza Hut (128)
Units Franchised From: 128
Preferred Square Footage: 5,000
Preferred Location Types: Freestanding; Strip Mall
Alcohol Served: Beer, Wine
Primary Menu: Pizza (128)
Areas of Operation: OH, WV
Type of Foodservice: Quick Serve (128)
Foodservice Management Venues: Schools
Franchise Affiliation: Pizza Hut Inc., PLANO, TX
Primary Distributors: (Full Line) McLane Foodservice, CARROLLTON, TX

Key Personnel
ANTHONY SZAMBECKI - CEO; Director Operations, Purchasing, Facility/Maintenance, Food Safety
SCOTT ARBUTHNOT - President; CFO
DAN WRIGHT - VP Real Estate
HEATHER WIETHOLTER MEADOWS - VP Operations
CAROL KLINGER - VP Real Estate

Auntie Anne's Franchise
9115 Southpark Center
Strongsville, OH 44136

Telephone: (440) 238-9722
Type of Business: Chain Restaurant Operator
Total Sales: $3,648,000 (e)
Total Units: 5
Trade Names: Auntie Anne's Hand-Rolled Soft Pretzels (5)
Units Franchised From: 5
Primary Menu: Snacks (5)
Areas of Operation: OH
Type of Foodservice: Quick Serve (5)
Franchise Affiliation: Auntie Anne's Inc., LANCASTER, PA

Key Personnel
RAYMOND MCCONNELL - Owner; General Buyer

PS Cleveland
1958 E Kerry Pl
Strongsville, OH 44136

Telephone: (440) 572-0880
Internet Homepage: pscleveland.com
Type of Business: Chain Restaurant Operator
Total Units: 10
Trade Names: Penn Station East Coast Subs (10)
Units Franchised From: 10
Primary Menu: Sandwiches/Deli (10)
Areas of Operation: OH
Type of Foodservice: Quick Serve (10)

Key Personnel
MIKE OSTERFELD - Owner

Gionino's Pizzeria Inc.
676 Eastwood Ave
Tallmadge, OH 44278-3139

Telephone: (330) 630-2010
Internet Homepage: gioninos.com
Type of Business: Chain Restaurant Operator
Year Founded: 1988
Total Sales: $21,600,000 (e)
Number of Employees: 12
Average Check: Lunch(8); Dinner(12)
Internet Order Processing: Yes
Total Units: 49
Trade Names: Gionino's Pizzeria (49)
Units Franchised To: 49
Preferred Square Footage: 2,500
Preferred Location Types: Freestanding; Strip Mall
Primary Menu: Pizza (49)
Projected Openings: 2
Projected Remodelings: 2
Areas of Operation: OH, SC
Type of Foodservice: Quick Serve (49)
Primary Distributors: (Food) Hillcrest FoodService Co., CLEVELAND, OH

Key Personnel
SAM OWEN - President; Partner; VP Marketing; Executive Chef; General Buyer
CHUCK OWEN - Partner; General Buyer

Barry Bagels
3715 King Rd
Toledo, OH 43617-1417

Telephone: (419) 885-1000
Fax Number: (419) 885-5400
Internet Homepage: barrybagels.com
Company Email: feedback@barrybagels.com
Type of Business: Chain Restaurant Operator
Year Founded: 1972
Total Sales: $18,590,000 (e)
Number of Employees: 233
Average Check: Breakfast(10); Lunch(12); Dinner(12)
Internet Order Processing: Yes
Total Units: 14
Trade Names: Barry Bagels (14)
Company-Owned Units: 14
Preferred Square Footage: 2,500
Preferred Location Types: Outlet Mall; Strip Mall
Primary Menu: Bagels (14)
Areas of Operation: MI, OH
Type of Foodservice: Quick Serve (14)
Catering Services: Yes
On-site Distribution Center: Yes
Franchise Affiliation: Global Orange Development, EAST LANSING, MI
Primary Distributors: (Full Line) US Foods, WIXOM, MI

Key Personnel
MARK GREENBLATT - President; Director Facility/Maintenance, Real Estate, Design, Menu Development, Catering; General Buyer
ANGIE BUGERT - Chief Marketing Officer
LES GREENBLATT - Director Promotion, Customer Service
MARILYN SHARP - Director Purchasing
ROSE ANN KENNY - Manager Accounting

Mancy's Family
953 Phillips Ave
Toledo, OH 43612-1336

Telephone: (419) 476-4154
Internet Homepage: mancys.com
Type of Business: Chain Restaurant Operator
Year Founded: 1997
Total Sales: $10,300,000 (e)
Alcohol Sales: 10%
Number of Employees: 75
Average Check: Lunch(18); Dinner(26)
Internet Order Processing: Yes
Total Units: 6
Trade Names: Mancy's Bluewater Grille (1); Mancy's Ideal (1); Mancy's Italian (1); Mancy's Steak (1); Mancy's Steakhose at the Hancock Hotel (1); Shorty's True American Roadhouse (1)
Company-Owned Units: 6
Preferred Location Types: Freestanding
Alcohol Served: Beer, Wine, Liquor
Primary Menu: Bar-B-Q (1); Italian (1); Steak (3); Steak/Seafood (1)
Areas of Operation: OH
Type of Foodservice: Casual Dining (6)
Catering Services: Yes
Primary Distributors: (Food) US Foods, WIXOM, MI

Key Personnel
GEORGE MANCY - Partner; Executive Chef; Director Catering; General Buyer
GUS MANCY - Partner
JOHN MANCY - Partner; General Manager
MIKE MANCY - Partner
NICK MANCY - Partner

Marco's Franchising LLC
5252 Monroe St
Toledo, OH 43623-3140

Telephone: (419) 885-7000
Fax Number: (419) 885-5215
Internet Homepage: marcos.com
Type of Business: Chain Restaurant Operator
Year Founded: 1978
Systemwide Sales: $806,737,000 (e)
Total Sales: $50,320,000 (e)
Alcohol Sales: 1%
Number of Employees: 11,450
Average Check: Lunch(16); Dinner(20)
Internet Order Processing: Yes
Total Units: 1,101
Trade Names: Marco's Pizza (1,101)
Company-Owned Units: 51
Units Franchised To: 1,050
Preferred Square Footage: 1,200; 1,400; 1,600
Preferred Location Types: Airports; Community Mall; Freestanding; Mobile Unit; Stadiums; Strip Mall
Primary Menu: Pizza (1,101)
Projected Openings: 91
Areas of Operation: AL, AR, AZ, CA, CO, FL, GA, IA, IL, IN, KS, KY, LA, MI, MN, MO, MS, NC, ND, NE, NJ, NV, NY, OH, OK, PA, PR, SC, SD, TN, TX, VA, WI, WV
Foreign Countries: BAHAMAS; INDIA
Type of Foodservice: Quick Serve (1,101)
Foodservice Management Venues: College & University; Schools

Catering Services: Yes
Primary Distributors: (Full Line) Sofo Foods, TOLEDO, OH

Key Personnel
PASQUALE GIAMMARCO - Founder
TONY LIBARDI - Co-CEO; President
JEFFREY RAGER - CFO
JOHN MEYERS - COO
RICHARD STANBRIDGE - CIO; VP
STEVE SEYFERTH - Chief Marketing Officer; Chief Experience Officer; Senior VP
GERARDO FLORES - Chief Development Officer
TODD WATSON - Chief Legal Officer; VP; General Counsel
RODERICK SANDERS - VP Talent
SHAWN CHOWDHARY - VP Administration
APRIL MILLER - VP Operations
RYAN JUSTUS - VP Operations
KRISTIN CORCORAN - VP; General Counsel
ANGELICA LARA - Senior Director Operations
JESSICA EMERY - Senior Director Consumer Insights
EMILY ALT - Director Talent
CATHY KINZER - Director Purchasing
ALEX TOKATLIAN - Director Brand Marketing
JEFF TISDEL - Director Development
ELLEN SMITH - Assistant Director Logistics
BECKY BOYLE - Manager Supply Chain
EMILY CROLL - Manager Brand Marketing
NICOLE JAMES - Specialist Communications
WHITNEY KEELER - Senior Analyst Finance

N S & T Inc.
3352 W Laskey Rd
Toledo, OH 43623-4030

Telephone: (419) 531-1818
Fax Number: (419) 531-1819
Internet Homepage: magicwok.com
Company Email: themagic@magicwok.com
Type of Business: Chain Restaurant Operator
Year Founded: 1983
Systemwide Sales: $12,265,000 (e)
Total Sales: $7,109,000 (e)
Number of Employees: 333
Average Check: Lunch(10); Dinner(16)
Total Units: 15
Trade Names: Magic Wok (13); Tropical Grill & Juices (2)
Company-Owned Units: 15
Preferred Square Footage: 1,200
Preferred Location Types: Freestanding; Office Complex; Regional Mall; Strip Mall
Primary Menu: Chinese (13)
Projected Openings: 1
Areas of Operation: MI, OH, FC
Foreign Countries: BAHRAIN
Type of Foodservice: Quick Serve (15)
Catering Services: Yes
Primary Distributors: (Full Line) Gordon Food Service Inc., WYOMING, MI

Key Personnel
TOMMY PIPATJARASGIT - President; CFO; VP; General Manager; Executive Chef; Director Finance, Ethnic Marketing, Store Fixtures; General Buyer
DEBBIE MAHLMAN - Controller; Director Information Technology, Human Resources
ANNIE PIPATJARASGIT - Director Risk Management, Marketing, Food Safety

Rudy's Hot Dog Inc.
946 W Sylvania Ave
Toledo, OH 43612-1317

Telephone: (419) 478-7095
Internet Homepage: rudyshotdog.com
Company Email: info@rudyshotdog.com
Type of Business: Chain Restaurant Operator
Year Founded: 1922
Total Sales: $8,058,000 (e)
Alcohol Sales: 10%
Number of Employees: 84
Average Check: Breakfast(6); Lunch(8); Dinner(8)
Internet Order Processing: Yes
Total Units: 6
Trade Names: Rudy's Hot Dogs (6)
Company-Owned Units: 6
Preferred Square Footage: 2,000
Preferred Location Types: Freestanding
Alcohol Served: Beer
Primary Menu: Hot Dogs (6)
Areas of Operation: OH
Type of Foodservice: Quick Serve (6)
Primary Distributors: (Food) Gordon Food Service Inc., WYOMING, MI

Key Personnel
HARRY DIONYSSIOU - VP Food Safety
ROBIN WHITE - General Manager; Director Information Systems, Human Resources

Ten Star Enterprises Inc.
2778 Centennial Rd
Toledo, OH 43617-3117

Telephone: (419) 868-9858
Internet Homepage: scramblermaries.com
Company Email: corporate@scramblermaries.com
Type of Business: Chain Restaurant Operator
Year Founded: 1991
Systemwide Sales: $14,190,000 (e)
Total Sales: $3,873,000 (e)
Number of Employees: 414
Average Check: Dinner(24)
Total Units: 28
Trade Names: Scrambler Marie's Breakfast Bistro (28)
Company-Owned Units: 10
Units Franchised To: 18
Primary Menu: American (28)
Areas of Operation: MI, OH
Type of Foodservice: Family Restaurant (28)

Key Personnel
SHAIN BUERK - President; General Buyer

Tony Packo's Inc.
1902 Front St
Toledo, OH 43605-1226

Telephone: (419) 691-1953
Fax Number: (419) 691-8358
Internet Homepage: tonypackos.com
Company Email: eat@tonypackos.com
Type of Business: Chain Restaurant Operator
Year Founded: 1932
Total Sales: $5,929,000 (e)
Alcohol Sales: 20%
Number of Employees: 150
Average Check: Lunch(18); Dinner(22)
Total Units: 5
Trade Names: Packo's (4); Tony Packo's Cafe (1)
Company-Owned Units: 5
Preferred Location Types: Freestanding
Alcohol Served: Beer, Wine, Liquor
Primary Menu: Eastern European (5)
Areas of Operation: OH
Type of Foodservice: Fast Casual (5)
Primary Distributors: (Food) SYSCO Food Services of Cleveland Inc., CLEVELAND, OH

Key Personnel
JIMMY HARMON - CEO
EMILY BENNETT - President; Director Operations
JASON MANDEL - General Manager; Director Operations, Menu Development; General Buyer
SCOTT MCDOLE - Manager Operations

Dominos Franchisee
1377 Franklin St
Tornonto, OH 43964

Telephone: (740) 537-3537
Internet Homepage: dominos.com
Type of Business: Chain Restaurant Operator
Total Sales: $62,954,000 (e)
Total Units: 31
Trade Names: Domino's (31)
Units Franchised From: 31
Primary Menu: Pizza (31)
Areas of Operation: MI
Type of Foodservice: Quick Serve (31)
Franchise Affiliation: Domino's Pizza Inc, ANN ARBOR, MI

Key Personnel
AMMAR JALI - Owner; General Buyer

Doane Family Enterprises
1408 Franklin St
Toronto, OH 43964-1028

Telephone: (610) 356-8775
Fax Number: (740) 537-2199
Type of Business: Chain Restaurant Operator
Total Sales: $56,190,000 (e)
Total Units: 12
Trade Names: McDonald's (12)
Units Franchised From: 12
Primary Menu: Hamburger (12)
Areas of Operation: OH
Type of Foodservice: Quick Serve (12)
Franchise Affiliation: McDonald's Corporation, CHICAGO, IL

Key Personnel
RICH DOANE - Owner; General Buyer

Lepsco Inc.
1829 W Main St
Troy, OH 45373-2303

Telephone: (937) 339-6263
Fax Number: (937) 335-5748
Type of Business: Chain Restaurant Operator
Total Sales: $4,775,000 (e)
Number of Employees: 198
Total Units: 2
Trade Names: Burger King (2)
Units Franchised From: 2
Preferred Square Footage: 2,500
Preferred Location Types: Freestanding
Primary Menu: Hamburger (2)
Areas of Operation: OH
Type of Foodservice: Quick Serve (2)
Franchise Affiliation: Burger King Worldwide Inc., MIAMI, FL

Key Personnel
JOSH LEPHARDT - Partner; General Buyer
PAUL SCORDIA - Partner
JENNIFER CASSIDY - General Manager; General Buyer

Liquid Living
9453 Ravenna Rd
Twinsburg, OH 44087

Telephone: (440) 919-0425
Internet Homepage: flipsideburger.com; liquidliving.com
Company Email: info@flipsideburger.com
Type of Business: Chain Restaurant Operator
Total Units: 11
Trade Names: 3 Palms Pizzeria (3); Flip Side (6); One Red Door (1); The Bone Yard (1)
Company-Owned Units: 11
Primary Menu: American (2); Hamburger (6); Pizza (3)
Areas of Operation: CO, OH
Type of Foodservice: Casual Dining (11)

Key Personnel
SHAWN MONDAY - Partner; Executive Chef; General Buyer
TIFFANY MONDAY - Partner
MICHAEL SCHWARTZ - Partner

CAM/RB, Inc
1525 Corporate Woods Pkwy Ste 100
Uniontown, OH 44685-7883

Mailing Address: PO Box 3515, AKRON, OH, 44309-3515
Telephone: (330) 896-3253
Fax Number: (330) 896-3304
Internet Homepage: camincorp.com
Type of Business: Chain Restaurant Operator
Total Sales: $5,882,000 (e)
Average Check: Dinner(12)
Total Units: 3
Trade Names: Arby's (3)
Units Franchised From: 3
Primary Menu: Sandwiches/Deli (3)
Areas of Operation: OH
Type of Foodservice: Quick Serve (3)
Franchise Affiliation: Arby's Restaurant Group, ATLANTA, GA

Key Personnel
JEFF MOCKBEE - CEO; General Buyer
VICTOR MAINI - President
JOHN KAUFFMAN - Manager Facility/Maintenance

Tomtreyco, Inc.
11350 Cleveland Ave NW
Uniontown, OH 44685-8078

Telephone: (330) 966-4976
Fax Number: (330) 966-6776
Company Email: tomtreyco@gmail.com
Type of Business: Chain Restaurant Operator
Total Sales: $143,400,000 (e)
Number of Employees: 2,000
Total Units: 45
Trade Names: McDonald's (45)
Units Franchised From: 45
Preferred Square Footage: 2,500
Primary Menu: Hamburger (45)
Areas of Operation: OH, PA, WV
Type of Foodservice: Quick Serve (45)
Franchise Affiliation: McDonald's Corporation, CHICAGO, IL

Key Personnel
THOMAS LOCKE - President; General Buyer
JOSH BARNETT - Chief Strategy Officer
KYLE CANO - Director Operations
JENNIFER SHORT - Director Operations
SPRING ASHMORE - Manager Information Technology

Domino's Franchisee
128 E Wyandot Ave
Upper Sandusky, OH 43351-1430

Telephone: (419) 294-5741
Type of Business: Chain Restaurant Operator
Total Sales: $16,220,000 (e)
Total Units: 12
Trade Names: Domino's (12)
Units Franchised From: 12
Primary Menu: Pizza (12)
Areas of Operation: OH
Type of Foodservice: Quick Serve (12)
Franchise Affiliation: Domino's Pizza Inc, ANN ARBOR, MI

Key Personnel
BRIAN L. EDLER - Owner; General Buyer

Covelli Enterprises
3900 E Market St
Warren, OH 44484-4708

Telephone: (330) 856-3176
Fax Number: (330) 856-6752
Internet Homepage: covelli.com
Company Email: info@paneracovelli.com
Type of Business: Chain Restaurant Operator
Year Founded: 1968
Total Sales: $1,090,900,000 (e)
Alcohol Sales: 1%
Number of Employees: 2,797
Average Check: Breakfast(8); Lunch(10); Dinner(10)
Total Units: 294
Trade Names: Dairy Queen (7); O'Charley's (5); Panera Bread (282)
Units Franchised From: 294
Preferred Square Footage: 3,200; 4,800
Preferred Location Types: Freestanding; Regional Mall; Strip Mall
Alcohol Served: Beer, Wine, Liquor
Primary Menu: American (14); Sandwiches/Deli (280)
Projected Openings: 10
Areas of Operation: FL, GA, KY, NC, OH, PA, SC, TN
Foreign Countries: CANADA
Type of Foodservice: Casual Dining (5); Fast Casual (280); Quick Serve (9)
Distribution Centers: ORLANDO, FL; WARREN, OH
Franchise Affiliation: A&W Restaurants Inc.,

LEXINGTON, KY; International Dairy Queen Inc., BLOOMINGTON, MN; O'Charley's Restaurants, NASHVILLE, TN; Panera Bread Company, SAINT LOUIS, MO
Primary Distributors: (Food) The SYGMA Network Inc. - Columbus, COLUMBUS, OH
Notes: The Panera Bread restaurants operate as Candall Group Inc. The O'Charley's restaurants operate as O'Candall Group Inc.

Key Personnel
SAM COVELLI - CEO; President
DOUG SMITH - Area Director Operations
VALARIE CAMPBELL - VP Finance
KATEY CHILDERS - Director Marketing
ANTHONY ARDIZZONE - Director Accounting
DAN BROWN - Director Operations, Region
DANIELLE COVELLI - Director Marketing
DAVE SUTPHIN - Director Information Technology
JEFFREY VICKERS - Director
KELLIE GUTIERREZ - Director Leasing
KRISTINA HERMANN - Director Human Resources
AARON HINTON - Director Operations
RYAN PESCE - Director Operations
AMY DUCAT - Regional Director Operations
MARISSA CLEVER - Regional Director Operations
LUANNE WEISMILLER - Manager Sales, Catering
ANTHONY BIEGACKI - Engineer Network, Security
JENNIFER HUFFMAN - Office Manager

Commac Foods
120 E Mulberry St
West Union, OH 45693-1344

Telephone: (937) 544-5529
Fax Number: (937) 544-2395
Type of Business: Chain Restaurant Operator
Year Founded: 1991
Total Sales: $3,546,000 (e)
Number of Employees: 225
Average Check: Breakfast(12); Lunch(16); Dinner(28)
Total Units: 4
Trade Names: Big Boy Restaurant (1); Little Ceasars (2); Ponderosa Steakhouse (1)
Units Franchised From: 4
Preferred Square Footage: 5,000
Preferred Location Types: Freestanding
Primary Menu: Hamburger (1); Pizza (2); Steak (1)
Areas of Operation: KY, OH
Type of Foodservice: Casual Dining (1); Quick Serve (3)
Franchise Affiliation: Fat Brands, Inc., BEVERLY HILLS, CA; Long John Silver's Inc., LOUISVILLE, KY
Primary Distributors: (Food) McLane/Midwest, DANVILLE, IL

Key Personnel
STEVE CACARO - President; Partner; Director Finance, Purchasing, Supply Chain, Real Estate, Design
TINA CACARO - Partner; General Manager; Director Menu Development; General Buyer
MARLA MAY - Manager Operations, Information Systems

Variety Management
314 E Main St
West Union, OH 45693-1449

Telephone: (937) 544-5709
Type of Business: Chain Restaurant Operator
Total Sales: $19,669,000 (e)
Total Units: 4
Trade Names: McDonald's (4)
Units Franchised From: 4
Preferred Location Types: Freestanding
Primary Menu: Hamburger (4)
Areas of Operation: OH
Type of Foodservice: Quick Serve (4)
Franchise Affiliation: McDonald's Corporation, CHICAGO, IL

Key Personnel
SUZANNE HEAD - General Manager; General Buyer
CONNIE SCHMACHER - General Manager; General Buyer

C L Inc.
114 Dorchester Sq N
Westerville, OH 43081-7300

Telephone: (614) 898-5482
Fax Number: (614) 898-9615
Type of Business: Chain Restaurant Operator
Year Founded: 1977
Total Sales: $92,510,000 (e)
Number of Employees: 633
Average Check: Lunch(8); Dinner(12)
Total Units: 37
Trade Names: KFC/Taco Bell (1); Taco Bell (35); Taco Bell/Long John Silvers (1)
Units Franchised From: 37
Preferred Square Footage: 2,500; 3,200
Preferred Location Types: Community Mall; Freestanding
Primary Menu: Chicken (1); Seafood (1); Taco (35)
Areas of Operation: OH
Type of Foodservice: Quick Serve (37)
Franchise Affiliation: Taco Bell Corp., IRVINE, CA

Key Personnel
CARL CRISTMAN - CEO; Director Facility/Maintenance, Real Estate
ERIC LAEUFER - President; General Buyer
BILL WOOD - VP Operations
PAM CONNELLY - Controller; Manager Finance, Accounting
JASON WAKEFIELD - Director Information Technology

Domino's Franchisee
26063 Detroit Rd
Westlake, OH 44145-2428

Telephone: (440) 892-0030
Type of Business: Chain Restaurant Operator
Total Sales: $6,052,000 (e)
Total Units: 3
Trade Names: Domino's (3)
Units Franchised From: 3
Primary Menu: Pizza (3)
Areas of Operation: OH
Type of Foodservice: Quick Serve (3)
Franchise Affiliation: Domino's Pizza Inc, ANN ARBOR, MI

Key Personnel
BRIAN T. DISTIN - Owner; General Buyer

Quaker Steak & Lube
24601 Center Ridge Rd
Westlake, OH 44145-5634

Telephone: (440) 808-9100
Fax Number: (724) 981-5946
Internet Homepage: quakersteakandlube.com
Type of Business: Chain Restaurant Operator
Year Founded: 1974
Systemwide Sales: $62,138,000 (e)
Total Sales: $51,420,000 (e)
Alcohol Sales: 25%
Number of Employees: 420
Average Check: Lunch(12); Dinner(14)
Internet Order Processing: Yes
Internet Sales: 2.00%
Total Units: 42
Trade Names: Quaker Steak & Lube (42)
Company-Owned Units: 11
Units Franchised To: 31
Preferred Square Footage: 4,000; 5,500; 7,400; 8,700
Preferred Location Types: Freestanding; Stadiums
Alcohol Served: Beer, Wine, Liquor
Primary Menu: American (42)
Projected Openings: 2
Areas of Operation: CO, FL, IA, IN, KY, LA, MI, NC, NJ, NY, OH, PA, SC, TN, VA, WI, WV, ON
Foreign Countries: CANADA
Type of Foodservice: Casual Dining (42)
Catering Services: Yes

Primary Distributors: (Full Line) Reinhart FoodService, MOUNT PLEASANT, PA
Parent Company: TravelCenters of America Inc., WESTLAKE, OH

Key Personnel
BOB DEBOIS - VP Operations
RACHEL MESZAROS - Director Franchise Operations
CONNIE SCHENKER - Director Human Resources
JUDY RADKOWSKI - Director Franchise Operations
AMBER DAVIS - Director Marketing
JOHN NORTON - Director Operations
JEFFREY MUIRHEAD - Regional Director Operations

● ▲
TravelCenters of America Inc.
24601 Center Ridge Rd Ste 200
Westlake, OH 44145-5677

Telephone: (440) 808-9100
Fax Number: (440) 808-3303
Internet Homepage: petrotruckstops.com; tatravelcenters.com; thelube.com
Company Email: info@tatravelcenters.com
Type of Business: Nontraditional Foodservice Operator
Year Founded: 1970
Publicly Held: Yes
Total Sales: $8,206,996,000 (e)
Number of Employees: 14,250
Average Check: Breakfast(10); Lunch(10); Dinner(12)
Foodservice Sales: $984,839,000 (e)
Total Units: 314
Trade Names: Atlanta South Family Restaurant; Berky's; Black Bear Diner; Bonnie's Kitchen; Buckhorn Family Restaurant; Coburg Crossing Cafe; Country Fare; Country Pride; Davy Crockett; Fork in the Road; Fuddruckers; Full Service Restaurant; Iowa 80 Kitchen; Iron Skillet; Johnson's Corner; Nelson Brothers; Petro Diner; Popeyes Louisiana Kitchen; Quaker Steak & Lube; Quick Skillet; R Place; The Hub Room
Company-Owned Units: 297
Units Franchised To: 17
Preferred Square Footage: 3,000
Preferred Location Types: Freestanding; Travel Plazas
Projected Openings: 20
Areas of Operation: AL, AR, AZ, CA, CO, CT, FL, GA, IA, ID, IL, IN, KS, KY, LA, MD, MI, MN, MO, MS, NC, NE, NH, NJ, NM, NV, NY, OH, OK, OR, PA, RI, SC, TN, TX, UT, VA, WA, WI, WV, WY, ON
Foreign Countries: CANADA
Type of Foodservice: Casual Dining; Family Restaurant; Quick Serve

Distribution Centers: NASHVILLE, TN
Franchise Affiliation: Kahala Brands, SCOTTSDALE, AZ
Primary Distributors: (Equipment) Edward Don & Co., WOODRIDGE, IL; (Food) US Foods, CINCINNATI, OH; (Supplies) US Foods, TWINSBURG, OH
Parent Company: Hospitality Properties Trust, NEWTON, MA
Headquarter Offices: Quaker Steak & Lube, WESTLAKE, OH
Notes: Total units represents the number of travel plazas in the TravelCenters' system and freestanding Quaker Steak & Lube restaurants; most centers have multiple food venues. The company derives approximately 86% of its revenue from fueling & truck stop operations.

Key Personnel
DEBI BOFFA - CEO
LLOYD SANFORD - Exec VP Sales
MARK R. YOUNG - Exec VP; General Counsel
RODNEY BRESNAHAN - Exec VP Retail Operations
MIKE POLACHEK - Senior VP East Region
DAVID THORNTON - Director Asset Management
JOCELYN ALBRECHT - Director Marketing, Loyalty Program
RICK HOLLEY - Manager Store Systems

Freeway Lanes Bowling Group
28801 Euclid Ave
Wickliffe, OH 44092-2528

Telephone: (440) 585-5800
Fax Number: (440) 585-1297
Internet Homepage: bowlthegame.com; therollhouse.com/wickliffe
Type of Business: Foodservice Operations - Bowling Alley
Total Sales: $2,733,000 (e)
Alcohol Sales: 5%
Number of Employees: 320
Average Check: Dinner(6)
Total Units: 7
Trade Names: Capri Lanes (1); Freeway Lanes Of Solon (2); Game of Fairfield (1); Game of Mentor (1); Game of Western Columbus (1); Game of Wickliffe (1)
Company-Owned Units: 7
Alcohol Served: Beer, Wine, Liquor
Primary Menu: American (7)
Areas of Operation: OH
Type of Foodservice: In-Store Feeder (7)

Key Personnel
MICHAEL J. IRWIN - Partner
MARY KRAHE - COO; General Buyer

Panini's Franchise Group
37333 Euclid Ave Fl 2
Willoughby, OH 44094-5617

Telephone: (440) 942-7140
Fax Number: (440) 951-8827
Internet Homepage: paninisgrill.com
Company Email: paninis@paninisgrill.com
Type of Business: Chain Restaurant Operator
Total Sales: $18,030,000 (e)
Alcohol Sales: 5%
Number of Employees: 295
Average Check: Dinner(8)
Internet Order Processing: Yes
Total Units: 16
Trade Names: Panini's Bar & Grill (16)
Company-Owned Units: 16
Alcohol Served: Beer
Primary Menu: Sandwiches/Deli (16)
Areas of Operation: FL, OH
Type of Foodservice: Casual Dining (16)

Key Personnel
JOHN FRECH - Partner
ROBERT ROBERTS - Partner; Executive Chef; General Buyer

FRC Enterprises
29025 Lake Shore Blvd
Willowick, OH 44095-4658

Telephone: (440) 585-4800
Fax Number: (440) 585-4815
Internet Homepage: mrchickencater.com
Type of Business: Chain Restaurant Operator
Year Founded: 1958
Total Sales: $13,100,000 (e)
Number of Employees: 200
Average Check: Lunch(10); Dinner(10)
Total Units: 8
Trade Names: Mr. Chicken (8)
Company-Owned Units: 8
Preferred Square Footage: 2,000
Preferred Location Types: Freestanding
Primary Menu: Chicken (8)
Areas of Operation: OH
Type of Foodservice: Quick Serve (8)

Key Personnel
MICHAEL SIMENS - President; Partner; General Buyer
GLORIA SIMENS - Partner; Manager Finance
VICKIE DEBICK - Director Human Resources

● ▲
Subway Franchisee
18862 State Route 136
Winchester, OH 45697-9793

Telephone: (937) 695-0405

Type of Business: Chain Restaurant Operator
Total Sales: $1,431,000 (e)
Total Units: 2
Trade Names: Subway (2)
Units Franchised From: 2
Areas of Operation: OH
Franchise Affiliation: Doctor's Associates Inc., MILFORD, CT

Key Personnel
LARRY SINGER - Owner; General Buyer

Abalar Fast Foods, INC.
815 Middlebury Dr
Worthington, OH 43085-3463

Telephone: (419) 668-4121
Type of Business: Chain Restaurant Operator
Total Sales: $3,867,000 (e)
Average Check: Dinner(12)
Total Units: 2
Trade Names: KFC (2)
Units Franchised From: 2
Preferred Location Types: Freestanding
Primary Menu: Chicken (2)
Areas of Operation: OH
Type of Foodservice: Quick Serve (2)
Franchise Affiliation: KFC Corporation, LOUISVILLE, KY; Long John Silver's Inc., LOUISVILLE, KY

Key Personnel
DON ROBINSON - Partner; General Buyer

Young's Jersey Dairy
6880 Springfield Xenia Rd
Yellow Springs, OH 45387-9610

Telephone: (937) 325-0629
Fax Number: (937) 325-3226
Internet Homepage: youngsdairy.com
Type of Business: Chain Restaurant Operator
Year Founded: 1960
Total Sales: $7,538,000 (e)
Number of Employees: 210
Average Check: Breakfast(5); Lunch(6); Dinner(8)
Internet Order Processing: Yes
Total Units: 2
Trade Names: The Golden Jersey Inn (1); Young's Jersey Dairy (1)
Company-Owned Units: 2
Preferred Location Types: Other
Primary Menu: American (2)
Areas of Operation: OH
Type of Foodservice: Family Restaurant (2)
Catering Services: Yes
Primary Distributors: (Full Line) Gordon Food Service Inc., WYOMING, MI
Notes: The company derives approximately 45% of its revenue from miniature golf course operations.

Key Personnel
DAN YOUNG - CEO; General Manager; Executive Chef; General Buyer
DEB WHITKER - CFO
BRIAN PATTERSON - General Manager; General Buyer

Belleria Franchise Corporation
3460 S Meridian Rd
Youngstown, OH 44511-2619

Telephone: (330) 792-0338
Fax Number: (330) 965-9013
Internet Homepage: belleriaitalianrestaurant.com
Type of Business: Chain Restaurant Operator
Year Founded: 1957
Systemwide Sales: $33,683,000 (e)
Total Sales: $4,063,000 (e)
Alcohol Sales: 9%
Number of Employees: 13
Average Check: Lunch(12); Dinner(16)
Total Units: 13
Trade Names: Belleria Pizzeria (13)
Company-Owned Units: 1
Units Franchised To: 12
Preferred Square Footage: 3,000
Preferred Location Types: Freestanding; Strip Mall
Alcohol Served: Beer, Wine
Primary Menu: Pizza (13)
Areas of Operation: OH
Type of Foodservice: Casual Dining (6); Quick Serve (7)
Primary Distributors: (Food) Youngstown Wholesale Grocery Inc., YOUNGSTOWN, OH

Key Personnel
WILLIAM LIBERATO - President; Partner; Manager Operations, Human Resources, Franchise Development, Menu Development; General Buyer
MARY JANE LIBERATO - Partner; Manager Accounting, Information Systems, Real Estate, Franchising

The Sandwich Factory
15 N Canfield Niles Rd
Youngstown, OH 44515-2303

Telephone: (330) 793-4084
Internet Homepage: austintownsandwichfactory.net
Type of Business: Chain Restaurant Operator
Year Founded: 1973
Systemwide Sales: $7,044,000 (e)
Total Sales: $5,666,000 (e)
Number of Employees: 30
Average Check: Lunch(10); Dinner(10)
Total Units: 4
Trade Names: Sandwich Factory (4)
Company-Owned Units: 3
Units Franchised To: 1
Preferred Location Types: Office Complex; Strip Mall
Primary Menu: Sandwiches/Deli (4)
Areas of Operation: OH
Type of Foodservice: Quick Serve (4)
Primary Distributors: (Supplies) The Hearn Paper Co., YOUNGSTOWN, OH

Key Personnel
JOSEPH LOREE JR - President; Treasurer; Manager Franchising
KAREN GARCIA - General Manager

Adornetto's Selected Italian Foods
2224 Maple Ave
Zanesville, OH 43701-2027

Telephone: (740) 453-0780
Fax Number: (740) 450-7492
Internet Homepage: adornettos.com
Company Email: corporate@adornettos.com
Type of Business: Chain Restaurant Operator
Year Founded: 1974
Total Sales: $8,270,000 (e)
Alcohol Sales: 5%
Number of Employees: 105
Average Check: Breakfast(6); Lunch(12); Dinner(24)
Internet Order Processing: Yes
Internet Sales: 0.50%
Total Units: 3
Trade Names: Adornetto's Pizzeria (1); Giacomo's Bread & More (1); Old Market House Inn (1)
Company-Owned Units: 3
Preferred Location Types: Freestanding
Alcohol Served: Beer, Wine
Primary Menu: Italian (1); Sandwiches/Deli (1); Steak/Seafood (1)
Areas of Operation: OH
Type of Foodservice: Casual Dining (2); Fine Dining (1)
Catering Services: Yes
Primary Distributors: (Full Line) RDP Foodservice, LLC, HILLIARD, OH

Key Personnel
ADRIAN ADORNETTO - President; General Manager; Executive Chef; General Buyer
JODIE SPENCER - General Manager

Domino's Franchisee
1645 Maysville Ave
Zanesville, OH 43701-5866

Telephone: (740) 455-3161
Type of Business: Chain Restaurant Operator
Total Sales: $8,073,000 (e)
Total Units: 4
Trade Names: Domino's (4)
Units Franchised From: 4
Primary Menu: Pizza (4)
Areas of Operation: OH
Type of Foodservice: Quick Serve (4)
Franchise Affiliation: Domino's Pizza Inc, ANN ARBOR, MI

Key Personnel
LISA M. BURKETT - Owner; General Buyer

Primary Aim LLC
947 Adair Ave
Zanesville, OH 43701-2841

Telephone: (740) 454-2568
Fax Number: (740) 454-6056
Internet Homepage: primaryaimllc.com
Type of Business: Chain Restaurant Operator
Year Founded: 1999
Total Sales: $166,470,000 (e)
Number of Employees: 2,736
Average Check: Breakfast(5); Lunch(8); Dinner(8)
Total Units: 73
Trade Names: Wendy's Old Fashioned Hamburgers (73)
Units Franchised From: 73
Preferred Square Footage: 3,000
Preferred Location Types: Downtown; Freestanding; Regional Mall
Primary Menu: Hamburger (73)
Areas of Operation: OH, PA, WV
Type of Foodservice: Quick Serve (73)
Franchise Affiliation: The Wendy's Company, DUBLIN, OH
Primary Distributors: (Full Line) The SYGMA Network, Inc., DUBLIN, OH

Key Personnel
STEPHEN THOMPSON - CFO
CAROL FRIEL - Director Accounting; Manager Finance, Information Systems
ROBIN DENMAN - Director Payroll
JASNA KELLER - Director Human Resources
JEREMY NORWOOD - District Manager
WENDY WARD - Administrator Payroll

OKLAHOMA

RtK, Inc.
901 N Monte Vista St
Ada, OK 74820-7728

Telephone: (580) 436-1724
Fax Number: (580) 436-1237
Type of Business: Chain Restaurant Operator
Total Sales: $28,130,000 (e)
Number of Employees: 119
Total Units: 6
Trade Names: McDonald's (6)
Units Franchised From: 6
Preferred Square Footage: 2,500
Preferred Location Types: Freestanding
Primary Menu: Hamburger (6)
Areas of Operation: OK
Type of Foodservice: Quick Serve (6)
Franchise Affiliation: McDonald's Corporation, CHICAGO, IL

Key Personnel
RICK THORLEY - President; General Buyer

Burger Baron Inc.
401 S Dewey Ave Ste 214
Bartlesville, OK 74003-3537

Telephone: (918) 336-1818
Fax Number: (918) 338-0888
Type of Business: Chain Restaurant Operator
Year Founded: 1951
Total Sales: $6,244,000 (e)
Number of Employees: 66
Average Check: Lunch(8); Dinner(12)
Total Units: 7
Trade Names: Lot-A-Burgers (7)
Company-Owned Units: 7
Preferred Square Footage: 2,000
Preferred Location Types: Freestanding
Primary Menu: Hamburger (7)
Areas of Operation: OK
Type of Foodservice: Quick Serve (7)

Key Personnel
JOHN P. AKERS - President; Director Site Selection, Design; General Buyer
JOHNNY D. AKERS - CFO; Treasurer; Director Supply Chain, Real Estate, Store Fixtures; Manager Information Systems, Advertising
JUDY GRAY - Director Operations, Facility/Maintenance, Advertising, Sales, Human Resources
STAN BRANSON - Director Finance, Accounting, Purchasing, Supply Chain, Menu Development
GINA OWENS - Director Food Safety; Supervisor Risk Management
HABIBUR RAHMAN - Manager Operations, Risk Management, Food Safety

M.E.K. Corp.
901 N 9th St
Broken Arrow, OK 74012-2805

Telephone: (918) 251-1242
Internet Homepage: coneyi-lander.com
Type of Business: Chain Restaurant Operator
Year Founded: 1926
Total Sales: $6,811,000 (e)
Number of Employees: 65
Average Check: Lunch(6); Dinner(6)
Total Units: 7
Trade Names: Coney I-Lander (7)
Company-Owned Units: 7
Preferred Square Footage: 2,000
Preferred Location Types: Freestanding; Strip Mall
Primary Menu: Hot Dogs (7)
Areas of Operation: OK
Type of Foodservice: Quick Serve (7)
Catering Services: Yes
Primary Distributors: (Food) Ben E. Keith Foods, EDMOND, OK

Key Personnel
KAREN LITCHFIELD - VP; Director Risk Management, Design, Human Resources, Food Safety
MICHAEL KINGSLEY - General Buyer

City Bites Inc.
2608 E Memorial Rd
Edmond, OK 73013-5522

Telephone: (405) 607-8100
Fax Number: (405) 607-8200
Internet Homepage: citybites.net
Company Email: CustomerService@citybites.net
Type of Business: Chain Restaurant Operator
Year Founded: 1986
Total Sales: $18,120,000 (e)
Alcohol Sales: 1%
Number of Employees: 220
Average Check: Lunch(12); Dinner(16)
Total Units: 18
Trade Names: City Bites (18)
Company-Owned Units: 18
Preferred Square Footage: 2,000; 3,500
Preferred Location Types: Downtown; Freestanding; Strip Mall
Primary Menu: Sandwiches/Deli (18)
Areas of Operation: KS, OK
Type of Foodservice: Quick Serve (18)
Catering Services: Yes
Primary Distributors: (Full Line) Ben E. Keith Foods, EDMOND, OK

Key Personnel
MARK BLEVINS - President; Partner; CFO; Controller; General Manager; Director

Finance, Operations, Risk Management, Real Estate, Human Resources
MIKE WOLF - Controller; Director Real Estate

Domino's Franchisee
740 W Danforth Rd
Edmond, OK 73003-5004

Telephone: (405) 340-0300
Type of Business: Chain Restaurant Operator
Total Sales: $30,338,000 (e)
Total Units: 15
Trade Names: Domino's (15)
Units Franchised From: 15
Primary Menu: Pizza (15)
Areas of Operation: OK
Type of Foodservice: Quick Serve (15)
Franchise Affiliation: Domino's Pizza Inc, ANN ARBOR, MI

Key Personnel
JOHN E. HALL - Owner; General Buyer

Restaurant Concepts Inc.
1100 E 2nd St
Edmond, OK 73034-5315

Telephone: (405) 705-5800
Fax Number: (405) 775-9494
Type of Business: Chain Restaurant Operator
Year Founded: 1993
Total Sales: $14,780,000 (e)
Alcohol Sales: 15%
Number of Employees: 2,500
Total Units: 5
Trade Names: Denny's (5)
Units Franchised From: 5
Preferred Square Footage: 3,000; 5,000
Preferred Location Types: Freestanding; Strip Mall
Alcohol Served: Beer, Wine, Liquor
Primary Menu: American (5)
Areas of Operation: OK
Type of Foodservice: Family Restaurant (5)
Franchise Affiliation: Denny's Corporation, SPARTANBURG, SC

Key Personnel
ALI H. ANVAR - Partner; General Buyer
ARDESHIR BOOZARY - Partner; Manager Purchasing, Supply Chain; General Buyer
SUDIE ANVAR - Director Human Resources

Wagner & Son LLC
1400 S Fretz Ave Ste 110
Edmond, OK 73003-5845

Telephone: (405) 359-7928
Fax Number: (405) 359-7565

Type of Business: Chain Restaurant Operator
Total Sales: $93,460,000 (e)
Total Units: 20
Trade Names: McDonald's (20)
Units Franchised From: 20
Preferred Square Footage: 2,500
Preferred Location Types: Freestanding
Primary Menu: Hamburger (20)
Areas of Operation: OK
Type of Foodservice: Quick Serve (20)
Franchise Affiliation: McDonald's Corporation, CHICAGO, IL

Key Personnel
ROBERT WAGNER - Owner; General Buyer

Castleberry Investments Inc.
1920 W 20th St
Elk City, OK 73644-9252

Mailing Address: PO Box 2009, ELK CITY, OK, 73648-2009
Telephone: (580) 225-6041
Fax Number: (580) 225-6056
Internet Homepage: cisonic.com
Company Email: jamieb@cisonic.com
Type of Business: Chain Restaurant Operator
Year Founded: 1986
Total Sales: $71,200,000 (e)
Number of Employees: 900
Average Check: Breakfast(6); Lunch(10); Dinner(16)
Total Units: 33
Trade Names: Sonic America's Drive-In (33)
Units Franchised From: 33
Preferred Square Footage: 1,200
Preferred Location Types: Freestanding
Primary Menu: Hamburger (33)
Areas of Operation: OK, TX
Type of Foodservice: Quick Serve (33)
Franchise Affiliation: Sonic Corp., OKLAHOMA CITY, OK
Primary Distributors: (Full Line) Ben E. Keith Foods, AMARILLO, TX
Divisional Offices: R-C Investments, AMARILLO, TX

Key Personnel
THOMAS D. CASTLEBERRY - President; CFO; General Manager; Director Facility/Maintenance, Supply Chain, Real Estate, Design; General Buyer
ROGER CASTLEBERRY - VP Operations; Director Finance, Purchasing, Information Systems, Human Resources

Domino's Franchisee
1119 S Van Buren St
Enid, OK 73703-7133

Telephone: (580) 242-2004

Type of Business: Chain Restaurant Operator
Total Sales: $9,997,000 (e)
Total Units: 5
Trade Names: Domino's (5)
Units Franchised From: 5
Primary Menu: Pizza (5)
Areas of Operation: OK
Type of Foodservice: Quick Serve (5)
Franchise Affiliation: Domino's Pizza Inc, ANN ARBOR, MI

Key Personnel
KELLY W. LESSERT - Owner; General Buyer

McDonald's of Enid
853 Commercial Cir
Enid, OK 73703-4318

Telephone: (580) 242-5704
Fax Number: (580) 242-0612
Internet Homepage: mcdonalds.com
Type of Business: Chain Restaurant Operator
Total Sales: $19,843,000 (e)
Number of Employees: 200
Average Check: Breakfast(8); Lunch(8); Dinner(8)
Total Units: 4
Trade Names: McDonald's (4)
Units Franchised From: 4
Preferred Square Footage: 2,500; 3,000
Preferred Location Types: Freestanding
Primary Menu: Hamburger (4)
Areas of Operation: OK
Type of Foodservice: Quick Serve (4)
Franchise Affiliation: McDonald's Corporation, CHICAGO, IL
Primary Distributors: (Full Line) The Martin-Brower Co., NORTH LITTLE ROCK, AR

Key Personnel
LYNETTE BIDDLE - Partner; General Buyer
STEVE BIDDLE - Partner; General Buyer
BECKY WILSON - Director Operations
SARA WALLACE - Manager Human Resources

J&H Foods Inc.
12175 S Yukon Ave
Glenpool, OK 74033-6621

Telephone: (918) 496-1272
Fax Number: (918) 493-6516
Internet Homepage: cheeziespizza.com; simplesimonspizza.com
Type of Business: Chain Restaurant Operator
Year Founded: 1982
Systemwide Sales: $67,884,000 (e)
Total Sales: $5,252,000 (e)
Number of Employees: 75
Average Check: Lunch(10); Dinner(28)
Internet Order Processing: Yes
Total Units: 179

Trade Names: CheeZies Pizza (9); Simple Simon's Pizza (170)
Company-Owned Units: 4
Units Franchised To: 175
Preferred Square Footage: 2,000
Preferred Location Types: Community Mall; Convenience Store/Gas Station; Downtown; Freestanding; Strip Mall; Travel Plazas
Primary Menu: Pizza (179)
Projected Openings: 3
Areas of Operation: AL, AR, GA, KS, LA, MO, OK, TX
Type of Foodservice: Quick Serve (179)
Foodservice Management Venues: Schools
Primary Distributors: (Full Line) Performance Foodservice, SPRINGFIELD, MO
Notes: J & H Foods has developed a second concept called CheeZies Pizza which it is beginning to franchise.

Key Personnel
B. J. DUMOND - CEO; President; Owner; Director Real Estate
BECKY DUMOND - CFO
JOE LITTLE - Exec VP Purchasing, Franchising; Director Design

Morris Food Service
Hwy 51
Mannford, OK 74044

Telephone: (918) 865-3346
Type of Business: Chain Restaurant Operator
Total Sales: $2,576,000 (e)
Total Units: 2
Trade Names: Pizza Hut (2)
Units Franchised From: 2
Primary Menu: Pizza (2)
Areas of Operation: OK
Type of Foodservice: Quick Serve (2)
Franchise Affiliation: Pizza Hut Inc., PLANO, TX
Notes: Address and Phone are for PH location.

Key Personnel
PAUL MORRIS - Partner; General Buyer
TIMOTHY JOHNSON - Partner

Kentucky Fried Chicken of McAlester
1808 S Peaceable Rd
Mcalester, OK 74501-7242

Mailing Address: PO Box 608, MCALESTER, OK, 74502-0608
Telephone: (918) 426-0790
Fax Number: (918) 426-3063
Type of Business: Chain Restaurant Operator
Year Founded: 1968
Total Sales: $7,846,000 (e)
Number of Employees: 195
Average Check: Lunch(6); Dinner(8)
Total Units: 4
Trade Names: KFC (4)
Units Franchised From: 4
Preferred Square Footage: 2,500
Preferred Location Types: Freestanding
Primary Menu: Chicken (4)
Areas of Operation: OK
Type of Foodservice: Quick Serve (4)
Franchise Affiliation: KFC Corporation, LOUISVILLE, KY
Primary Distributors: (Food) Quality Foods Inc., MCALESTER, OK

Key Personnel
DEBBIE ASHMORE - President; Director Marketing, Real Estate, Store Fixtures; Buyer Beverages
GEORGE NEWSOM - Controller; Manager Operations

McDonald's Franchise
1758 E Carl Albert Pkwy
Mcalester, OK 74501-5138

Telephone: (918) 423-8050
Type of Business: Chain Restaurant Operator
Total Sales: $20,234,000 (e)
Number of Employees: 115
Total Units: 4
Trade Names: McDonald's (4)
Units Franchised From: 4
Preferred Square Footage: 2,500
Primary Menu: Hamburger (4)
Areas of Operation: OK
Type of Foodservice: Quick Serve (4)
Franchise Affiliation: McDonald's Corporation, CHICAGO, IL

Key Personnel
BILLY SAMPSON - President; General Buyer

Kreeger Enterprises
314 N Main St
Miami, OK 74354-5920

Telephone: (918) 542-6642
Fax Number: (918) 542-6643
Type of Business: Chain Restaurant Operator
Total Sales: $7,283,000 (e)
Number of Employees: 163
Total Units: 6
Trade Names: Pizza Hut (6)
Units Franchised From: 6
Preferred Square Footage: 2,500
Preferred Location Types: Freestanding
Primary Menu: Pizza (6)
Areas of Operation: OK
Type of Foodservice: Family Restaurant (6)
Foodservice Management Venues: Business & Industry; Schools
Catering Services: Yes
Franchise Affiliation: Pizza Hut Inc., PLANO, TX

Key Personnel
RENICK KREEGER - Owner; General Manager; General Buyer
SCOTT KREEGER - Director Operations

Larco Enterprises Inc.
29 S Main St Ste 200
Miami, OK 74354-7022

Telephone: (918) 542-1679
Fax Number: (918) 542-7611
Type of Business: Chain Restaurant Operator
Year Founded: 1980
Total Sales: $19,120,000 (e)
Number of Employees: 295
Average Check: Breakfast(8); Lunch(8); Dinner(8)
Total Units: 9
Trade Names: Sonic America's Drive-In (8); Stonehill Grill (1)
Units Franchised From: 9
Preferred Square Footage: 2,500
Preferred Location Types: Freestanding
Primary Menu: Hamburger (8); Steak (1)
Areas of Operation: GA, KS, OK
Type of Foodservice: Family Restaurant (1); Quick Serve (8)
Franchise Affiliation: Sonic Corp., OKLAHOMA CITY, OK

Key Personnel
LARRY SMITH - CEO; General Buyer
KRISTI BASHORE - VP; Controller
STUART MCMILLAN - Manager Operations, Purchasing, Supply Chain

Culinary Institute of Platt College - Moore
201 N Eastern Ave
Moore, OK 73160-6917

Telephone: (405) 912-3260
Fax Number: (405) 912-4360
Internet Homepage: plattcolleges.edu/campuses/moore-ok
Type of Business: Culinary Schools
Areas of Operation: OK

Key Personnel
JAMES COOPER - Executive Director

Charlie's Chicken Franchise Systems
3325 W Okmulgee St
Muskogee, OK 74401-5070

Telephone: (918) 687-8741
Internet Homepage: charlieschicken.com
Company Email:
  questions@charlieschicken.com
Type of Business: Chain Restaurant Operator
Year Founded: 1955
Systemwide Sales: $32,158,000 (e)
Total Sales: $3,403,000 (e)
Number of Employees: 30
Average Check: Lunch(10); Dinner(12)
Total Units: 24
Trade Names: Charlie's Chicken (24)
Company-Owned Units: 1
Units Franchised To: 23
Preferred Square Footage: 2,500
Preferred Location Types: Freestanding
Primary Menu: Chicken (24)
Areas of Operation: MO, OK
Type of Foodservice: Quick Serve (24)
Catering Services: Yes
Primary Distributors: (Full Line) US Foods, OKLAHOMA CITY, OK

Key Personnel
CHARLES C. RANDOLPH - President; Director Finance, Real Estate, Design; General Buyer
SUSANA STEPHENS - General Manager
DARREN KILPATRICK - General Manager; Director Facility/Maintenance

Great White Bites, LLC
1204 N Interstate Dr Ste 150
Norman, OK 73072-3355

Telephone: (405) 321-5100
Type of Business: Chain Restaurant Operator
Total Sales: $6,931,000 (e)
Total Units: 5
Trade Names: Jersey Mike's Subs (5)
Units Franchised From: 5
Primary Menu: Sandwiches/Deli (5)
Areas of Operation: OK
Type of Foodservice: Quick Serve (5)
Franchise Affiliation: Jersey Mike's Franchise Systems, MANASQUAN, NJ

Key Personnel
CHARLIE BROWN - Owner; General Buyer

Hal Smith Restaurant Group
3101 W Tecumseh Rd Ste 200
Norman, OK 73072-1817

Telephone: (405) 321-2600
Fax Number: (405) 321-2992
Internet Homepage: charlestons.com; ehsrg.com; louiesgrillandbar.com; mahoganyprime.com; redrockcanyongrill.com
Company Email: charlestons@nsis.net
Type of Business: Chain Restaurant Operator
Year Founded: 1987
Total Sales: $196,570,000 (e)
Alcohol Sales: 10%
Number of Employees: 4,110
Average Check: Lunch(16); Dinner(32)
Total Units: 83
Trade Names: Charleston's Restaurant (17); El Huevo (1); Hefner Grill (1); Hollies Flatiron Steakhouse (1); Louie's Grill and Bar (15); Mahogany Prime Steak House (4); Mama Roja (1); Neighborhood JA.M. (5); Notorious Pie (1); Pub W (5); Red Rock Canyon Grille (6); Smitty's Garage (20); The Winston (1); Toby Keith's I Love This Bar & Grill (2); Upper Crust Wood Fired Pizza (3)
Company-Owned Units: 78
Units Franchised From: 5
Preferred Square Footage: 7,500
Preferred Location Types: Freestanding; Strip Mall
Alcohol Served: Beer, Wine, Liquor
Primary Menu: American (45); Hamburger (11); Italian (1); Mexican (2); Pizza (3); Seafood (1); Snacks (2); Steak (11)
Projected Openings: 1
Areas of Operation: AR, AZ, FL, IN, KS, MD, MO, NE, OK, TX, VA
Type of Foodservice: Casual Dining (78); Fast Casual (11); Fine Dining (4); Quick Serve (2)
Primary Distributors: (Full Line) SYSCO Food Services of Oklahoma Inc., NORMAN, OK

Key Personnel
HAL W. SMITH - President
DAVID BRAUCKMANN - CFO; VP Finance, Loss Prevention, Risk Management, Quality Assurance, Real Estate, Human Resources, Business Development, Food Safety; Controller; Director Purchasing, Supply Chain
DIANE FAIR - Director Accounting
SARA MCDANEL - Director Development-Training
EMILY MILLER - Director Marketing
KATELYN SCHMIDT - Assistant Director Training
MIKE TURMAN - Manager Restaurant Operations
DAVE ZIMMER - Manager Facility/Maintenance, Construction, Design, Store Fixtures
DINA FORD - Manager Operations
JEREMY GILBERT - Manager Restaurant Operations

Interurban Management Inc.
1150 Ed Noble Pkwy
Norman, OK 73072

Telephone: (405) 307-9200
Fax Number: (405) 307-8556
Internet Homepage: baxtersgrill.com; interurban.us
Type of Business: Chain Restaurant Operator
Year Founded: 1976
Systemwide Sales: $29,247,000 (e)
Total Sales: $28,570,000 (e)
Alcohol Sales: 20%
Number of Employees: 1,400
Average Check: Breakfast(8); Lunch(8); Dinner(12)
Total Units: 8
Trade Names: Baxters Interurban Grill (1); Interurban Restaurant (7)
Company-Owned Units: 2
Units Franchised To: 6
Preferred Square Footage: 8,000
Preferred Location Types: Freestanding; Office Complex; Strip Mall
Alcohol Served: Beer, Wine, Liquor
Primary Menu: American (8)
Areas of Operation: OK
Type of Foodservice: Casual Dining (8)
Catering Services: Yes
Primary Distributors: (Full Line) SYSCO Food Services of Oklahoma Inc., NORMAN, OK

Key Personnel
RUSTY LEOFFLER - Partner; Director Finance, Real Estate; Manager Menu Development; General Buyer
ROBERT ROSS - Partner; Director Finance, Operations, Purchasing, Catering
ABBY BILLINGSLY - Manager Human Resources, Recruitment

La Baguette
620 N Berry Rd
Norman, OK 73069-7542

Telephone: (405) 329-4910
Fax Number: (405) 329-0093
Internet Homepage: labaguette.com
Type of Business: Chain Restaurant Operator
Year Founded: 1984
Systemwide Sales: $4,113,000 (e)
Total Sales: $4,318,000 (e)
Alcohol Sales: 9%
Number of Employees: 155
Average Check: Breakfast(8); Lunch(14); Dinner(30)
Total Units: 2
Trade Names: La Baguette (2)
Company-Owned Units: 2
Preferred Location Types: Mixed-use Center
Alcohol Served: Beer, Wine, Liquor

Primary Menu: French/Continental (2)
Areas of Operation: OK
Type of Foodservice: Casual Dining (2)
Catering Services: Yes
Primary Distributors: (Full Line) SYSCO Food Services of Oklahoma Inc., NORMAN, OK

Key Personnel
JOHNNY JAZZAR - Partner; Manager Operations, Purchasing, Advertising; General Buyer
RUDY KHOURI - Partner; Executive Chef; General Buyer

Pizza Shuttle
1506 W Lindsey St
Norman, OK 73069-4302

Telephone: (405) 364-4440
Internet Homepage: pizzashuttlenorman.com
Company Email: mikey@pizzashuttle.biz
Type of Business: Chain Restaurant Operator
Year Founded: 1982
Total Sales: $4,082,000 (e)
Number of Employees: 110
Average Check: Lunch(12); Dinner(14)
Internet Order Processing: Yes
Total Units: 3
Trade Names: Pizza Shuttle (3)
Company-Owned Units: 3
Preferred Location Types: Strip Mall
Primary Menu: Pizza (3)
Areas of Operation: OK
Type of Foodservice: Quick Serve (3)

Key Personnel
FRANK SCARBOROUGH - President; Partner; Executive Chef; Director Information Systems, Loss Prevention, Risk Management, Marketing, Advertising, Real Estate, Human Resources, Menu Development
CINDA NABINGER - Treasurer

Sonic of Nowata
327 S Ash St
Nowata, OK 74040-4020

Telephone: (918) 273-3400
Fax Number: (918) 273-3616
Type of Business: Chain Restaurant Operator
Year Founded: 1979
Total Sales: $34,410,000 (e)
Number of Employees: 75
Average Check: Breakfast(8); Lunch(12); Dinner(12)
Total Units: 16
Trade Names: Sonic America's Drive-In (16)
Units Franchised From: 16
Preferred Square Footage: 5,000
Preferred Location Types: Freestanding
Primary Menu: Hamburger (16)
Areas of Operation: OK
Type of Foodservice: Quick Serve (16)
Franchise Affiliation: Sonic Corp., OKLAHOMA CITY, OK
Primary Distributors: (Full Line) US Foods, OKLAHOMA CITY, OK

Key Personnel
MARION BARNES - President; CFO; Manager Operations, Facility/Maintenance, Information Systems, Loss Prevention, Risk Management, Marketing, Real Estate, Design, Human Resources; General Buyer

Jimmy's Egg Franchise Systems
14504 Hertz Quail Springs Pkwy
Okalahoma City, OK 73134

Telephone: (720) 556-3877
Internet Homepage: jimmysegg.com
Company Email: comments@jimmysegg.com
Type of Business: Chain Restaurant Operator
Year Founded: 1980
Total Sales: $24,480,000 (e)
Total Units: 64
Trade Names: Jimmy's Egg (64)
Company-Owned Units: 64
Preferred Square Footage: 3,200; 3,600
Primary Menu: American (64)
Areas of Operation: KS, MO, NE, OK, TX
Type of Foodservice: Casual Dining (64)

Key Personnel
KEVIN BURKE - President
JIM BURKE - Owner; Director Purchasing, Menu Development
JAMES NGUYEN - Controller
ALEX BERTHOLDI - Director Real Estate
MENDI LANDGRAF - Manager Marketing

Bricktown Brewery
1 N Oklahoma Ave
Oklahoma City, OK 73104

Internet Homepage: bricktownbrewery.com
Type of Business: Chain Restaurant Operator
Year Founded: 1992
Number of Employees: 250
Total Units: 22
Trade Names: Bricktown Brewery (22)
Company-Owned Units: 22
Primary Menu: American (22)
Areas of Operation: AR, KS, MO, OK, TX, VA
Type of Foodservice: Casual Dining (22)

Key Personnel
MATT THOMAS - President
JOHN M. WATSON - Regional Director Operations

DCW Investments
2701 W I 44 Service Rd
Oklahoma City, OK 73112-3775

Telephone: (405) 942-2936
Fax Number: (405) 942-7242
Type of Business: Chain Restaurant Operator
Year Founded: 1960
Total Sales: $104,720,000 (e)
Number of Employees: 800
Average Check: Breakfast(6); Lunch(8); Dinner(8)
Total Units: 48
Trade Names: Sonic America's Drive-In (48)
Units Franchised From: 48
Preferred Square Footage: 1,320
Preferred Location Types: Freestanding
Primary Menu: Hamburger (48)
Areas of Operation: NM, OK, TX
Type of Foodservice: Quick Serve (48)
Franchise Affiliation: Sonic Corp., OKLAHOMA CITY, OK

Key Personnel
DAN WINTERS - President; Partner; Director Operations, Purchasing, Facility/Maintenance, Supply Chain, Real Estate, Design, Store Fixtures
CHRIS WINTERS - Partner
MARVIN JIROUS - Partner; Treasurer; Director Finance
KATHY MOTE - Director Information Systems, Risk Management, Human Resources; General Buyer

Domino's Franchisee
2724 N Pennsylvania Ave
Oklahoma City, OK 73107-2547

Telephone: (405) 525-8300
Type of Business: Chain Restaurant Operator
Total Sales: $3,968,000 (e)
Total Units: 2
Trade Names: Domino's (2)
Units Franchised From: 2
Primary Menu: Pizza (2)
Areas of Operation: OK
Type of Foodservice: Quick Serve (2)
Franchise Affiliation: Domino's Pizza Inc, ANN ARBOR, MI

Key Personnel
LINDA J. BURGAT - Owner; General Buyer

Domino's Franchisee
3445 W Memorial Rd
Oklahoma City, OK 73134-7001

Telephone: (405) 755-3030
Type of Business: Chain Restaurant Operator
Total Sales: $8,120,000 (e)
Total Units: 4
Trade Names: Domino's (4)
Units Franchised From: 4
Primary Menu: Pizza (4)
Areas of Operation: OK
Type of Foodservice: Quick Serve (4)
Franchise Affiliation: Domino's Pizza Inc, ANN ARBOR, MI

Key Personnel
ALLEN J. OPIE - Owner; General Buyer

Emerging Brands Inc
6205 N Bryant Ave
Oklahoma City, OK 73121-1405

Telephone: (405) 478-2515
Fax Number: (405) 478-2517
Internet Homepage: henryhudsonspub.com; poblanogrill.net; sandbburgers.com
Type of Business: Chain Restaurant Operator
Year Founded: 1968
Total Sales: $38,660,000 (e)
Alcohol Sales: 30%
Number of Employees: 424
Average Check: Lunch(18); Dinner(30)
Total Units: 31
Trade Names: Henry Hudson's Pub (10); Jimmy's Egg (10); Poblano Grill (1); S&B Burgers (10)
Company-Owned Units: 31
Preferred Square Footage: 2,700; 4,000
Preferred Location Types: Freestanding; Strip Mall
Alcohol Served: Beer, Wine, Liquor
Primary Menu: American (30); Mexican (1)
Areas of Operation: OK
Type of Foodservice: Casual Dining (24); Family Restaurant (5)
On-site Distribution Center: Yes
Primary Distributors: (Food) Ben E. Keith Foods, EDMOND, OK

Key Personnel
KIM MCLENDON - CEO; President; Executive Chef; Manager Menu Development
MIKE BEIGHEY - VP Operations
JB EDWARDS - VP
BILL LIEDTKE - VP Administration, Legal

FTM Enterprises, LLC
1630 NW 23rd St Ste D
Oklahoma City, OK 73106-3625

Telephone: (405) 524-1200
Type of Business: Chain Restaurant Operator
Total Sales: $4,402,000 (e)
Total Units: 3
Trade Names: Jersey Mike's Subs (3)
Units Franchised From: 3
Primary Menu: Sandwiches/Deli (3)
Areas of Operation: OK
Type of Foodservice: Quick Serve (3)
Franchise Affiliation: Jersey Mike's Franchise Systems, MANASQUAN, NJ

Key Personnel
MICHAEL ZIMMER - President
KEVIN BROWN - Owner; General Buyer

Johnnie's Charcoal Broiler
6641 NW Expressway
Oklahoma City, OK 73132-4404

Telephone: (405) 721-7974
Fax Number: (405) 722-1146
Internet Homepage: johnniesburgers.com
Type of Business: Chain Restaurant Operator
Year Founded: 1971
Systemwide Sales: $10,134,000 (e)
Total Sales: $10,880,000 (e)
Number of Employees: 430
Average Check: Lunch(10); Dinner(14)
Total Units: 8
Trade Names: Johnnie's Charcoal Broiler (6); Johnnie's Charcoal Broiler Express (2)
Company-Owned Units: 5
Units Franchised To: 3
Preferred Location Types: Freestanding
Primary Menu: Hamburger (8)
Areas of Operation: OK
Type of Foodservice: Family Restaurant (6); Quick Serve (2)
Primary Distributors: (Food) US Foods, OKLAHOMA CITY, OK

Key Personnel
RICK HAYNES - CEO; General Buyer
DAVID R. HAYNES - CFO; Executive Chef; Director Real Estate, Design
VICKIE ALLEN - Chief Accounting Officer
JACK BOBRITT - District Manager

Kinslow and Kinslow
9050 NE 23rd St
Oklahoma City, OK 73141-3010

Telephone: (405) 769-7956
Type of Business: Chain Restaurant Operator
Total Sales: $84,590,000 (e)
Total Units: 40
Trade Names: Sonic America's Drive-In (40)
Units Franchised From: 40
Primary Menu: Hamburger (40)
Areas of Operation: OK
Type of Foodservice: Quick Serve (40)
Franchise Affiliation: Sonic Corp., OKLAHOMA CITY, OK

Key Personnel
GARY KINSLOW - President

Magnum Foods Inc.
7205 N Robinson Ave
Oklahoma City, OK 73116-7710

Telephone: (405) 767-3313
Fax Number: (405) 767-9963
Type of Business: Chain Restaurant Operator
Year Founded: 1983
Total Sales: $42,920,000 (e)
Number of Employees: 750
Average Check: Lunch(8); Dinner(8)
Total Units: 36
Trade Names: Little Caesars Pizza (36)
Units Franchised From: 36
Preferred Square Footage: 3,000
Preferred Location Types: Freestanding
Primary Menu: Pizza (36)
Areas of Operation: OK, TX
Type of Foodservice: Quick Serve (36)
Foodservice Management Venues: Schools
Franchise Affiliation: Little Caesar Enterprises Inc., DETROIT, MI
Primary Distributors: (Food) Performance Foodservice, DALLAS, TX; (Full Line) Blue Line, GRAND PRAIRIE, TX

Key Personnel
STEVE PRICE - President; Partner; Manager Supply Chain; General Buyer
CARL MESSER - Partner
TERESA COFFMAN - Controller; Manager Finance, Security, Inventory, Loss Prevention, Risk Management, Quality Assurance, Real Estate, Human Resources, Food Safety
LUKE MCFADDEN - Controller
COLIN GILMARTIN - Director Operations
RUSTY ALLEN - Manager Facility/Maintenance

Mason Harrison Ratliff Enterprises
5725 NW 132nd St
Oklahoma City, OK 73142-4437

Mailing Address: PO Box 22775, OKLAHOMA CITY, OK, 73123-1775
Telephone: (405) 722-9390
Fax Number: (405) 720-9113

Type of Business: Chain Restaurant Operator
Year Founded: 1973
Total Sales: $442,920,000 (e)
Number of Employees: 8,320
Average Check: Breakfast(6); Lunch(8); Dinner(8)
Total Units: 209
Trade Names: Sonic America's Drive-In (209)
Units Franchised From: 209
Preferred Square Footage: 1,200
Preferred Location Types: Freestanding
Primary Menu: Hamburger (209)
Areas of Operation: AR, AZ, GA, KS, LA, MS, OK, SC, TN, TX
Type of Foodservice: Quick Serve (209)
Franchise Affiliation: Sonic Corp., OKLAHOMA CITY, OK
Primary Distributors: (Food) US Foods, OKLAHOMA CITY, OK

Key Personnel
RALPH L. MASON - CEO; Partner
REEDER RATLIFF - President; Partner
CHUCK HARRISON - Partner; CFO; Manager Operations, Purchasing, Supply Chain
LORETTA LACY - Controller
PAM WHINERY - Director Finance
NICOLE HERBERT - Regional Director Finance
CHERYL CHARTNEY - Project Manager
PAUL RATLIFF - Project Manager Operations
CHRIS STARR - Analyst

O&M Restaurant Group
6533 N Classen Blvd
Oklahoma City, OK 73116-7309

Telephone: (405) 840-4180
Fax Number: (405) 260-9721
Internet Homepage: 180business.com
Company Email: david@180business.com
Type of Business: Chain Restaurant Operator
Year Founded: 2002
Total Sales: $64,490,000 (e)
Number of Employees: 150
Average Check: Breakfast(8); Lunch(8); Dinner(8)
Total Units: 28
Trade Names: Burger King (13); Taco Bell (15)
Units Franchised From: 28
Preferred Square Footage: 2,500
Preferred Location Types: Freestanding
Primary Menu: Hamburger (13); Taco (15)
Areas of Operation: LA, OK
Type of Foodservice: Casual Dining (4); Quick Serve (14)
Franchise Affiliation: Burger King Worldwide Inc., MIAMI, FL

Key Personnel
DAVID OSTROWE - President; Partner
TIM MORGAN - Partner; VP Operations; General Buyer
BOBBY PATEL - Regional Director Operations
SARAH BAGGETT - Manager Accounting, Human Resources

OK Sub of OKC Inc
11647 S Western Ave
Oklahoma City, OK 73170-5801

Telephone: (405) 692-0773
Type of Business: Chain Restaurant Operator
Total Sales: $3,396,000 (e)
Total Units: 6
Trade Names: Subway (6)
Units Franchised From: 6
Primary Menu: Sandwiches/Deli (6)
Areas of Operation: OK
Type of Foodservice: Quick Serve (6)
Franchise Affiliation: Doctor's Associates Inc., MILFORD, CT

Key Personnel
TIM OGG - President
MISTY OGG - VP
DIANE SMITH - General Manager

Pearl's Restaurant Group
5641 N Classen Blvd
Oklahoma City, OK 73118-4015

Telephone: (405) 842-2174
Fax Number: (405) 840-0382
Internet Homepage: funfresh.com; pearlsokc.com
Company Email: comments@pearlsokc.com
Type of Business: Chain Restaurant Operator
Year Founded: 1984
Systemwide Sales: $17,212,000 (e)
Total Sales: $12,239,000 (e)
Alcohol Sales: 25%
Number of Employees: 300
Average Check: Lunch(16); Dinner(38)
Total Units: 3
Trade Names: Pearl's Crabtown (1); Pearl's Oyster Bar (1); Trapper's Fishcamp & Grill (1)
Company-Owned Units: 3
Preferred Square Footage: 5,000; 22,000
Preferred Location Types: Freestanding
Alcohol Served: Beer, Wine, Liquor
Primary Menu: Seafood (3)
Areas of Operation: OK
Type of Foodservice: Casual Dining (3)
Primary Distributors: (Food) SYSCO Food Services of Oklahoma Inc., NORMAN, OK
Notes: Formerly known as Mid-South Restaurant Management Co.

Key Personnel
STEVE GRIFFIN - President; COO; Director Operations, Information Systems, Human Resources
PAUL SEIKEL - Owner; Executive Chef; Director Menu Development; General Buyer
SHAVONDA PICKETT - CFO; VP

Shorty Smalls Restaurant Group Inc.
5030 N May Ave Ste 334
Oklahoma City, OK 73112-6010

Telephone: (888) 419-6754
Fax Number: (405) 946-6632
Internet Homepage: shortysmalls.com
Type of Business: Chain Restaurant Operator
Year Founded: 1954
Total Sales: $10,091,000 (e)
Alcohol Sales: 12%
Number of Employees: 170
Average Check: Lunch(14); Dinner(20)
Internet Order Processing: Yes
Total Units: 3
Trade Names: Shorty Small's (3)
Company-Owned Units: 3
Preferred Square Footage: 6,500
Preferred Location Types: Freestanding
Alcohol Served: Beer, Wine, Liquor
Primary Menu: American (3)
Areas of Operation: AR, MO, OK
Type of Foodservice: Casual Dining (3)
Catering Services: Yes

Key Personnel
CINDY HARSHA - COO; VP; Director Information Systems, Advertising, Human Resources

Sonic Corp.
300 Johnny Bench Dr Ste 300
Oklahoma City, OK 73104-2469

Telephone: (405) 225-5000
Fax Number: (405) 225-4003
Internet Homepage: sonicdrivein.com
Company Email: marketinginquiries@sonicdrivein.com
Type of Business: Chain Restaurant Operator
Year Founded: 1953
Systemwide Sales: $6,469,439,000 (e)
Total Sales: $667,080,000 (e)
Number of Employees: 11,200
Average Check: Breakfast(6); Lunch(8); Dinner(8)
Total Units: 3,548
Trade Names: Sonic America's Drive-In (3,548)
Company-Owned Units: 230
Units Franchised To: 3,318
Preferred Square Footage: 1,100; 1,200; 1,350
Preferred Location Types: Community Mall; Downtown; Freestanding
Primary Menu: Hamburger (3,548)
Projected Openings: 50
Areas of Operation: AL, AR, AZ, CA, CO, CT, DE, FL, GA, IA, ID, IL, IN, KS, KY, LA, MA,

MD, MI, MN, MO, MS, MT, NC, ND, NE, NJ, NM, NV, NY, OH, OK, OR, PA, RI, SC, SD, TN, TX, UT, VA, WA, WI, WV, WY
Type of Foodservice: Quick Serve (3,548)
Primary Distributors: (Food) Willow Run Foods Inc., KIRKWOOD, NY; (Food) McLane Foodservice, CARROLLTON, TX; (Full Line) Ben E. Keith Foods, NORTH LITTLE ROCK, AR; (Full Line) US Foods, OKLAHOMA CITY, OK; (Full Line) Ben E. Keith Foods, AMARILLO, TX; (Supplies) Willow Run Foods Inc., KIRKWOOD, NY
Parent Company: Inspire Brands, ATLANTA, GA
Notes: Systemwide sales for Sonic are presented on a fiscal year basis.

Key Personnel
ANDY ALSOBROOK - Partner; COO
VICKI JOYNER - Partner
HEATH R BYRD - CFO
E. EDWARD SAROCH - Senior VP Operations, Training, Franchise Development
DIANE L. PREM - VP Operations
BARBARA WILLIAMS - VP Branding, Customer Care
TANISHIA M. BEACHAM - VP Franchise Operations
SCOT TREADWELL - VP Construction, Design
RAY HASSELL - VP International
SCOTT MARKET - VP Operations
ANDREW PIEC - VP Operations, Sales
NANCY ROBERTSON - VP Communications
TODD WEKENBORG - Regional VP Operations
TAMARA STANLEY - Senior Director Integration, Marketing
MACKENZIE GIBSON - Senior Director Marketing, Culinary Development
JOHN ROBINSON - Director Information Technology, POS/Scanning, Retail Information Systems
WADE HARDEN - Director Architecture, Engineering
MICHAEL KISNER - Director Operations, Technology
BYRON BUTLER - Director Operations
MICHELLE LEBLANC - Regional Director Marketing
BETH MEIER - Senior Manager Brand Marketing
TINA FANCHER - Senior Manager Safety-Food
CINDY BURT - Project Manager Information Technology
MARSHA ORR - Administrator Franchising

Swadley's Barbeque Restaurants & Catering Co.
7156 NW 80th St
Oklahoma City, OK 73132-4149

Telephone: (405) 413-7333
Fax Number: (405) 603-6918
Internet Homepage: swadleys.com
Company Email: info@swadleys.com
Type of Business: Chain Restaurant Operator
Total Sales: $7,203,000 (e)
Average Check: Lunch(12); Dinner(12)
Total Units: 8
Trade Names: Jim's Chicken (1); Swadley's Bar-B-Q (7)
Company-Owned Units: 8
Preferred Location Types: Freestanding
Primary Menu: Bar-B-Q (7); Chicken (1)
Areas of Operation: OK
Type of Foodservice: Family Restaurant (8)
Catering Services: Yes

Key Personnel
BRENT SWADLEY - President; Partner; Executive Chef; General Buyer

Taco Mayo Franchise Systems Inc.
10405 Greenbriar Pl
Oklahoma City, OK 73159-7636

Telephone: (405) 691-8226
Fax Number: (405) 691-2572
Internet Homepage: tacomayo.com
Company Email: customerservices@tacomayo.com
Type of Business: Chain Restaurant Operator
Year Founded: 1978
Systemwide Sales: $45,206,000 (e)
Total Sales: $9,236,000 (e)
Number of Employees: 115
Average Check: Lunch(8); Dinner(8)
Total Units: 53
Trade Names: Taco Mayo (53)
Company-Owned Units: 25
Units Franchised To: 28
Preferred Square Footage: 2,200
Preferred Location Types: Freestanding
Primary Menu: Taco (53)
Projected Openings: 3
Areas of Operation: AR, KS, OK, TX
Type of Foodservice: Quick Serve (53)
Foodservice Management Venues: College & University
Catering Services: Yes
Primary Distributors: (Full Line) US Foods, OKLAHOMA CITY, OK

Key Personnel
KEITH HOCKER - CEO; General Counsel
BRYAN GWINN - President; Director Purchasing, Quality Assurance, Product Development; General Buyer
RUSS MCREYNOLDS - CFO
JIM FAREWELL - Director Operations
ELIZABETH SPEAKS - Director Operations
J'LAYNE COSBY - Manager Supply Chain, Marketing, Franchise Development, Franchising
RUTH ANN RICKEY - Manager Payroll, Human Resources

Ted's Cafe Escondido
8500 S Western Ave
Oklahoma City, OK 73139-9243

Mailing Address: PO Box 890240, OKLAHOMA CITY, OK, 73189
Telephone: (405) 632-3325
Fax Number: (405) 632-7907
Internet Homepage: tedscafe.com
Type of Business: Chain Restaurant Operator
Year Founded: 1991
Total Sales: $12,860,000 (e)
Alcohol Sales: 5%
Number of Employees: 872
Average Check: Lunch(14); Dinner(18)
Total Units: 10
Trade Names: Ted's Cafe Escondido (10)
Company-Owned Units: 10
Preferred Location Types: Freestanding
Alcohol Served: Beer, Liquor
Primary Menu: Mexican (11)
Areas of Operation: KS, MO, OK
Type of Foodservice: Casual Dining (10)
Catering Services: Yes
Primary Distributors: (Food) Ben E. Keith Foods, EDMOND, OK

Key Personnel
KEITH MILLER - CFO
DAVID FOXX - VP Operations
BRYAN WELCH - General Manager
ANDY GUERRERO - Director Development-Training
KRISTEN HALLCROFT - Director Catering
ERIN BARRESI - Manager Human Resources

The Metro Wine Bar & Bistro
6418 N Western Ave
Oklahoma City, OK 73116-7322

Telephone: (405) 840-9463
Internet Homepage: metrowinebar.com
Company Email: metrowinebar@coxinet.net
Type of Business: Chain Restaurant Operator
Year Founded: 1985
Total Sales: $1,668,000 (e)
Alcohol Sales: 30%
Number of Employees: 150
Average Check: Lunch(18); Dinner(48)
Total Units: 1
Trade Names: Metro Wine Bar & Bistro (1)
Company-Owned Units: 1
Preferred Location Types: Freestanding
Alcohol Served: Beer, Wine, Liquor
Primary Menu: French/Continental (1)
Areas of Operation: OK
Type of Foodservice: Fine Dining (1)
Catering Services: Yes
Primary Distributors: (Full Line) Ben E. Keith

Foods, EDMOND, OK

Key Personnel
CHRIS LOWER - Partner
LAVERYL LOWER - Partner; General Manager; General Buyer
LEANN MARSHALL - General Manager; General Buyer
DAVE LIEBLED - General Buyer

The Petroleum Club
100 N Broadway Ave Ste 3400
Oklahoma City, OK 73102-8824

Telephone: (405) 232-1184
Fax Number: (405) 232-1187
Internet Homepage: petroleumclubokc.com
Company Email: verej@petroleumclubokc.com
Type of Business: Chain Restaurant Operator
Year Founded: 1957
Total Sales: $6,175,000 (e)
Alcohol Sales: 25%
Number of Employees: 75
Average Check: Lunch(20); Dinner(48)
Total Units: 2
Trade Names: The Petroleum Club (1); The Petroleum Club North (1)
Company-Owned Units: 2
Preferred Location Types: Downtown; Freestanding
Alcohol Served: Beer, Wine, Liquor
Primary Menu: American (2)
Areas of Operation: OK
Type of Foodservice: Fine Dining (2)
Catering Services: Yes
Primary Distributors: (Food) Ben E. Keith Foods, EDMOND, OK

Key Personnel
VEREJ JAZZIRVAR - President; General Manager; General Buyer

W.H. Braum Inc.
3000 NE 63rd St
Oklahoma City, OK 73121-1202

Mailing Address: PO Box 25429, OKLAHOMA CITY, OK, 73125-0429
Telephone: (405) 478-1656
Fax Number: (405) 475-2460
Internet Homepage: braums.com
Type of Business: Chain Restaurant Operator
Year Founded: 1968
Total Sales: $385,380,000 (e)
Number of Employees: 7,580
Average Check: Lunch(8); Dinner(8)
Total Units: 285
Trade Names: Braum's Ice Cream & Dairy Store (285)
Company-Owned Units: 285
Preferred Square Footage: 5,800
Preferred Location Types: Freestanding
Primary Menu: American (285)
Areas of Operation: AR, KS, MO, OK, TX
Type of Foodservice: Quick Serve (285)
Distribution Centers: TUTTLE, OK

Key Personnel
DREW BRAUM - CEO; President
MARK GODWIN - CFO
PAUL CLARK - CIO
JIM DEATON - Controller
JIM CARWILE - Director Construction
ROBERT BAYLESS - Director Operations
AMANDA BEUCHAW - Director Public Relations
MANDY MERRIFIELD - Director Marketing, Advertising
BOBBY SANDERS - Director Manufacturing
CHRIS MOUTTET - Director Operations
PAUL ENRIGHT - Manager POS/Scanning
SCOTT BEARPAW-BUTLER - Manager Transportation

Walker Subway Development Corp
9107 SE 29th St Ste C
Oklahoma City, OK 73130-7163

Telephone: (405) 741-2214
Fax Number: (474) 122-1305
Type of Business: Chain Restaurant Operator
Total Sales: $11,240,000 (e)
Total Units: 18
Trade Names: Subway (18)
Units Franchised From: 18
Primary Menu: Sandwiches/Deli (18)
Areas of Operation: OK
Type of Foodservice: Quick Serve (18)
Franchise Affiliation: Doctor's Associates Inc., MILFORD, CT

Key Personnel
SHANNON SMITH - CEO; Director Operations
RAYMOND P. WALKER - President; Partner
MERI WALKER - Partner; VP

Western Management
2113 1/2 W Britton Rd
Oklahoma City, OK 73120-1505

Telephone: (405) 755-8761
Fax Number: (405) 755-8764
Internet Homepage: mackiessteakhouse.com
Type of Business: Chain Restaurant Operator
Year Founded: 1975
Total Sales: $20,733,000 (e)
Alcohol Sales: 0.50%
Number of Employees: 170
Total Units: 4
Trade Names: Mackie McNear's Steakhouse (1); WesterN SizzliN Steak & More (3)
Company-Owned Units: 1
Units Franchised From: 3
Preferred Square Footage: 7,500
Preferred Location Types: Freestanding
Alcohol Served: Beer
Primary Menu: Steak (4)
Areas of Operation: OK
Type of Foodservice: Casual Dining (1); Family Restaurant (3)
Franchise Affiliation: The Western Sizzlin Corp., ROANOKE, VA
Primary Distributors: (Full Line) US Foods, OKLAHOMA CITY, OK

Key Personnel
MACKIE MCNEAR - President; Director Supply Chain, Real Estate, Design
KELLY PINDEL - Controller; Manager Human Resources
GREG WRIGHT - General Manager; Executive Chef; Director Finance, Operations, Information Systems, Menu Development; General Buyer
CHARLES BROOKS - Manager Facility/Maintenance, Risk Management

Coolgreens
914 NW 73rd St
Oklanhoma City, OK 73116

Telephone: (850) 333-8260
Internet Homepage: coolgreens.com
Company Email: info@coolgreens.com
Type of Business: Chain Restaurant Operator
Year Founded: 2009
Total Sales: $8,134,000 (e)
Total Units: 9
Trade Names: Coolgreens (9)
Company-Owned Units: 7
Units Franchised To: 2
Primary Menu: Health Foods (9)
Projected Openings: 24
Areas of Operation: OK, TX
Type of Foodservice: Fast Casual (9)

Key Personnel
TOM WOLFE - Founder
ROBERT LEE - CEO
MARK RAMAGE - VP Franchise Development

The Moore Sonic Group
517 S Willow St
Pauls Valley, OK 73075

Mailing Address: PO Box 1069, PAULS VALLEY, OK, 73075-1069
Telephone: (405) 238-7594
Type of Business: Chain Restaurant Operator
Year Founded: 1977
Total Sales: $68,210,000 (e)
Number of Employees: 1,530

Average Check: Breakfast(8); Lunch(12); Dinner(12)
Total Units: 32
Trade Names: Sonic America's Drive-In (32)
Units Franchised From: 32
Preferred Square Footage: 1,200
Preferred Location Types: Freestanding
Primary Menu: Hamburger (32)
Projected Openings: 20
Areas of Operation: AR, OK
Type of Foodservice: Quick Serve (32)
Franchise Affiliation: Sonic Corp., OKLAHOMA CITY, OK
Primary Distributors: (Full Line) US Foods, LUBBOCK, TX

Key Personnel
JOE MOORE - President; CFO; Director Purchasing, Facility/Maintenance, Loss Prevention, Real Estate
JANET MOORE - VP
ALLEN RUDE - Director Operations, Information Systems, Supply Chain; General Buyer
KRISTI BOURNE - Manager Human Resources

Kinslow Sonic Group
507 N Jim Thorpe Blvd
Prague, OK 74864-4565

Telephone: (405) 567-4901
Fax Number: (405) 567-4903
Internet Homepage: kinslowsonicgroup.com
Company Email: info@kinslowsonicgroup.com
Type of Business: Chain Restaurant Operator
Year Founded: 1985
Total Sales: $126,130,000 (e)
Number of Employees: 900
Average Check: Breakfast(8); Lunch(8); Dinner(8)
Total Units: 59
Trade Names: Sonic America's Drive-In (59)
Units Franchised From: 59
Preferred Square Footage: 1,200
Preferred Location Types: Freestanding
Primary Menu: Hamburger (59)
Areas of Operation: MS, OK, TX
Type of Foodservice: Quick Serve (59)
Franchise Affiliation: Sonic Corp., OKLAHOMA CITY, OK
Primary Distributors: (Full Line) US Foods, OKLAHOMA CITY, OK

Key Personnel
GARY KINSLOW - President; General Manager; Director Finance, Operations, Facility/Maintenance, Store Fixtures
LARRY KINSLOW - Owner
KAREN LADD - Manager Information Systems, Human Resources

Newton Investments Inc
PO Box 3909
Shawnee, OK 74802-3909

Telephone: (405) 275-5910
Type of Business: Chain Restaurant Operator
Total Sales: $9,139,000 (e)
Total Units: 4
Trade Names: Sonic America's Drive-In (4)
Units Franchised From: 4
Primary Menu: Hamburger (4)
Areas of Operation: OK
Type of Foodservice: Quick Serve (4)
Franchise Affiliation: Sonic Corp., OKLAHOMA CITY, OK

Key Personnel
ROBERT NEWTON - President; Partner; General Buyer
MYRA NEWTON - Partner; Treasurer; Corporate Secretary

Van's Pig Stand
717 E Highland St
Shawnee, OK 74801-7159

Telephone: (405) 273-8704
Internet Homepage: pigstands.com
Company Email: info@pigstands.com
Type of Business: Chain Restaurant Operator
Year Founded: 1930
Total Sales: $7,510,000 (e)
Alcohol Sales: 5%
Number of Employees: 50
Average Check: Lunch(10); Dinner(10)
Internet Order Processing: Yes
Internet Sales: 0.50%
Total Units: 5
Trade Names: Van's Pig Stand (5)
Company-Owned Units: 5
Preferred Location Types: Freestanding
Alcohol Served: Beer
Primary Menu: Bar-B-Q (5)
Areas of Operation: OK
Type of Foodservice: Casual Dining (5)
Catering Services: Yes
Primary Distributors: (Food) US Foods, OKLAHOMA CITY, OK

Key Personnel
JERRY VANDEGRIFT - Owner
JEV VANDEGRIFT - General Manager; Executive Chef; General Buyer
HARVEY VALENTINE - Manager; Supervisor

Wintco Inc.
22 W Main St Ste A
Shawnee, OK 74801-6854

Mailing Address: PO Box 1809, SHAWNEE, OK, 74802-1809
Telephone: (405) 275-0881
Fax Number: (405) 275-0107
Internet Homepage: wintco.com
Company Email: wintco@sonicpartnernet.com
Type of Business: Chain Restaurant Operator
Year Founded: 1983
Total Sales: $52,740,000 (e)
Number of Employees: 1,257
Average Check: Breakfast(6); Lunch(6); Dinner(6)
Total Units: 20
Trade Names: Sonic America's Drive-In (20)
Units Franchised From: 20
Preferred Square Footage: 1,600
Preferred Location Types: Freestanding
Primary Menu: American (20)
Areas of Operation: ID, OK, TX
Type of Foodservice: Quick Serve (20)
Franchise Affiliation: Sonic Corp., OKLAHOMA CITY, OK

Key Personnel
BRIAN J. WINTERRINGER - President; Director Operations; General Buyer
JOHN WINTERRINGER - VP; Director Information Systems, Real Estate

Stan Clark Companies
501 W Elm Ave
Stillwater, OK 74074-3014

Mailing Address: PO Box 729, STILLWATER, OK, 74076-0729
Telephone: (405) 377-4232
Fax Number: (405) 377-0825
Internet Homepage: stanclarkcompanies.com; eskimojoes.com; mexicojoes.com
Company Email: caseyb@scc.eskimojoes.com
Type of Business: Chain Restaurant Operator
Year Founded: 1975
Total Sales: $6,310,000 (e)
Alcohol Sales: 25%
Number of Employees: 850
Average Check: Lunch(14); Dinner(22)
Internet Order Processing: Yes
Internet Sales: 0.50%
Total Units: 2
Trade Names: Eskimo Joe's (1); Mexico Joe's (1)
Company-Owned Units: 2
Preferred Location Types: Freestanding
Alcohol Served: Beer, Wine, Liquor
Primary Menu: American (1); Mexican (1)
Areas of Operation: OK
Type of Foodservice: Casual Dining (2)

Catering Services: Yes
Primary Distributors: (Full Line) Ben E. Keith Foods, EDMOND, OK

Key Personnel
STAN CLARK - CEO
SHEILA PARSON - CFO
ROBERT WILLIAMS - Director Operations, Purchasing, Store Planning, Catering
JASON RAYMON - Coordinator Digital

●▲
Atherton Restaurant Systems
1924 S Utica Ave Ste 1018
Tulsa, OK 74104-6522

Telephone: (918) 749-4423
Fax Number: (918) 749-6159
Type of Business: Chain Restaurant Operator
Year Founded: 1989
Total Sales: $12,030,000 (e)
Number of Employees: 230
Average Check: Lunch(18); Dinner(26)
Total Units: 10
Trade Names: Pizza Hut (10)
Units Franchised From: 10
Preferred Square Footage: 2,500
Preferred Location Types: Freestanding
Primary Menu: Pizza (10)
Areas of Operation: AR, MO
Type of Foodservice: Fast Casual (10)
Franchise Affiliation: Pizza Hut Inc., PLANO, TX
Primary Distributors: (Full Line) McLane Foodservice, CARROLLTON, TX

Key Personnel
JAMES T. ATHERTON - President; Director Real Estate, Design, Franchising
TOM ATHERTON - President
SHARON HUGHES - Controller; Director Finance, Information Systems, Human Resources
LESTER SMITH Manager Operations, Purchasing, Supply Chain; General Buyer

Billy Sims BBQ Restaurants
6570B E 51st St
Tulsa, OK 74145-7603

Telephone: (855) 266-6371
Fax Number: (918) 828-9692
Internet Homepage: billysimsbbq.com
Company Email: info@billysimsbbq.com
Type of Business: Chain Restaurant Operator
Total Sales: $22,740,000 (e)
Average Check: Lunch(8); Dinner(14)
Total Units: 42
Trade Names: Billy Sims Barbeque (54)
Units Franchised To: 54
Alcohol Served: Beer
Primary Menu: Bar-B-Q (53)
Projected Openings: 15
Areas of Operation: AR, CA, CO, IA, KS, MI, MO, OK, TX
Type of Foodservice: Fast Casual (53)
Catering Services: Yes

Key Personnel
JEFF JACKSON - Partner; General Buyer
BILLY SIMS - Partner
STEVEN DEGEORGE - Director Franchise Development
TENA WOOLDRIDGE - Manager Marketing, Compliance

●
Costley Enterprises, Inc.
8955 S Memorial Dr
Tulsa, OK 74133-4306

Telephone: (918) 254-4775
Fax Number: (918) 254-4657
Company Email: store90@cicispizza.com
Type of Business: Chain Restaurant Operator
Total Sales: $13,500,000 (e)
Total Units: 18
Trade Names: Cici's Pizza (18)
Units Franchised From: 18
Primary Menu: Pizza (18)
Areas of Operation: OK
Type of Foodservice: Family Restaurant (18)
Franchise Affiliation: CiCi Enterprises L.P., COPPELL, TX

Key Personnel
GREG COSTLEY - President; General Buyer
FRED RUSH - VP
TAYLOR CARTER - General Manager
ANDY DELOSSANTOS - Manager Marketing, District

Culinary Institute of Platt College - Tulsa
3801 S Sheridan Rd
Tulsa, OK 74145-1111

Telephone: (918) 663-9000
Fax Number: (918) 622-1240
Internet Homepage: plattcolleges.edu/campuses/tulsa-ok
Type of Business: Culinary Schools
Areas of Operation: OK

Key Personnel
CHERYL BEESE - Executive Director
SPENCER MILLS - Executive Chef; Director Culinary Operations

Daylight Donut Flour Company LLC
11707 E 11th St
Tulsa, OK 74128-4401

Mailing Address: PO Box 691150, TULSA, OK, 74169-1150
Telephone: (918) 438-0800
Fax Number: (918) 438-0804
Internet Homepage: daylightdonuts.com
Company Email: info@daylightdonuts.com
Type of Business: Chain Restaurant Operator
Year Founded: 1954
Systemwide Sales: $451,536,000 (e)
Total Sales: $257,850,000 (e)
Number of Employees: 60
Average Check: Breakfast(8); Lunch(8);
Internet Order Processing: Yes
Total Units: 915
Trade Names: Daylight Donuts (915)
Units Franchised To: 915
Preferred Square Footage: 1,200
Preferred Location Types: Community Mall; Downtown; Freestanding; Regional Mall; Strip Mall
Primary Menu: Snacks (915)
Projected Openings: 25
Areas of Operation: AK, AL, AR, AZ, CO, CT, DC, DE, FL, GA, HI, IA, ID, IL, IN, KS, KY, LA, ME, MI, MN, MO, MS, MT, NC, ND, NE, NH, NJ, NM, NY, OH, OK, OR, PA, SC, SD, TN, TX, UT, VA, WA, WV, WY
Foreign Countries: AUSTRALIA; CHINA; MEXICO; ROMANIA
Type of Foodservice: Quick Serve (915)
On-site Distribution Center: Yes
Primary Distributors: (Full Line) SYSCO Food Services of Oklahoma Inc., NORMAN, OK
Notes: This company does not collect franchise fees or license fees. Daylight Donut licensees, however, agree to purchase food & equipment from Daylight Corporation. The company derives approximately 95% of its revenue from wholesale food & equipment. The systemwide sales figure reflects estimated sales of the 600 current Daylight units.

Key Personnel
JOHN BOND - CEO; President; Partner
SARETH CHEA - Owner
BRIAN VAN NORMAN - Owner
SHEILA BOND - Partner
JIMMY KEETER - CFO; Director Human Resources
MIKE CARPENTER - VP Sales, Real Estate, Design
DALTON ORBAND - Director Transportation
DUSTEN HOBSON - Manager Accounting
JASON BOND - Manager Information Technology
JON DAVIS - Manager Operations, Facility/Maintenance, Risk Management, Quality Assurance, Marketing, Research &

Development, Product Development, Menu Development, Food Safety
DUSTIN CARPENTER - General Buyer

Domino's Franchisee
5108 S 33rd Ave W
Tulsa, OK 74107

Telephone: (918) 446-4444
Type of Business: Chain Restaurant Operator
Total Sales: $27,937,000 (e)
Total Units: 14
Trade Names: Domino's (14)
Units Franchised From: 14
Primary Menu: Pizza (14)
Areas of Operation: OK
Type of Foodservice: Quick Serve (14)
Franchise Affiliation: Domino's Pizza Inc, ANN ARBOR, MI

Key Personnel
MARIA D. WILLS - Owner; General Buyer

Java Dave's Executive Coffee Service
6239 E 15th St
Tulsa, OK 74112-6407

Mailing Address: P. O. Box 58123, TULSA, OK, 74158
Telephone: (918) 836-5570
Fax Number: (918) 835-4348
Internet Homepage: javadavescoffee.com
Company Email: online@javadavescoffee.com
Type of Business: Chain Restaurant Operator
Year Founded: 1988
Systemwide Sales: $20,107,000 (e)
Total Sales: $2,178,000 (e)
Number of Employees: 39
Average Check: Breakfast(8); Lunch(10); Dinner(10)
Internet Order Processing: Yes
Internet Sales: 1.00%
Total Units: 21
Trade Names: Java Dave's Coffee (21)
Company-Owned Units: 1
Units Franchised To: 20
Preferred Square Footage: 1,500
Preferred Location Types: Community Mall; Freestanding; Strip Mall
Primary Menu: Coffee (21)
Areas of Operation: AR, MO, OK
Foreign Countries: OMAN
Type of Foodservice: Quick Serve (21)
On-site Distribution Center: Yes
Primary Distributors: (Supplies) Vistar Kansas City, RIVERSIDE, MO

Key Personnel
MARK CONE - VP; General Manager

MIKE TIERNAN - Manager Wholesale

Mazzio's Corporation
4441 S 72nd East Ave
Tulsa, OK 74145-4610

Telephone: (918) 663-8880
Fax Number: (918) 641-1236
Internet Homepage: mazzios.com; olivetobistro.com
Type of Business: Chain Restaurant Operator
Year Founded: 1961
Systemwide Sales: $151,657,000 (e)
Total Sales: $89,380,000 (e)
Alcohol Sales: 3%
Number of Employees: 2,686
Average Check: Lunch(8); Dinner(14)
Internet Order Processing: Yes
Internet Sales: 1.00%
Total Units: 143
Trade Names: Mazzio's Italian Eatery (140); Oliveto Italian Bistro (3)
Company-Owned Units: 95
Units Franchised To: 48
Preferred Square Footage: 2,100; 2,500; 3,000; 4,000
Preferred Location Types: Convenience Store/Gas Station; Freestanding; Regional Mall; Strip Mall
Alcohol Served: Beer, Wine, Liquor
Primary Menu: Italian (143)
Projected Openings: 3
Areas of Operation: AR, GA, IA, IL, KS, MO, MS, OK, TX, VA
Type of Foodservice: Casual Dining (3); Quick Serve (140)
Catering Services: Yes
Primary Distributors: (Equipment) Joe Harding Inc., JOPLIN, MO; (Supplies) Joe Harding Inc., JOPLIN, MO

Key Personnel
LORI CARVER - CEO; President
BRADFORD J. WILLIAMS JR - Senior VP
DAVE POTH - VP Marketing
PAT PATTERSON - VP Information Systems
STUART MYERS - VP Marketing, Sales
NICOLE MOORE - Director Operations
JONNA WILKINSON - Director Human Resources
NAHLA LEEPER - Manager Marketing

RibCrib Corporation
4535 S Harvard Ave
Tulsa, OK 74135-2905

Telephone: (918) 712-7427
Fax Number: (918) 728-6945
Internet Homepage: ribcrib.com
Company Email: ribcrib@ribcrib.com
Type of Business: Chain Restaurant Operator
Year Founded: 1992
Systemwide Sales: $110,583,000 (e)
Total Sales: $81,810,000 (e)
Alcohol Sales: 10%
Number of Employees: 1,640
Average Check: Lunch(12); Dinner(16)
Internet Order Processing: Yes
Total Units: 54
Trade Names: RibCrib BBQ & Grill (54)
Company-Owned Units: 54
Preferred Square Footage: 2,600; 4,000; 6,000
Preferred Location Types: Downtown; Freestanding; Lifestyle Center; Power Center
Alcohol Served: Beer, Wine, Liquor
Primary Menu: Bar-B-Q (60)
Projected Openings: 3
Areas of Operation: AR, FL, IA, KS, MO, NM, OK, TX
Type of Foodservice: Casual Dining (60)
Catering Services: Yes
Primary Distributors: (Food) Ben E. Keith Foods, EDMOND, OK

Key Personnel
BRET CHANDLER - Owner
BRAD DENTIS - VP Operations
BOB LUKE - Director Facility/Maintenance
VANESSA ZELLNER - Manager Restaurant Operations

Southwest KFC
7707 E 111th St Ste 104
Tulsa, OK 74133-2555

Telephone: (918) 970-4296
Company Email: sdecou@swkfc.com
Type of Business: Chain Restaurant Operator
Year Founded: 1952
Total Sales: $58,390,000 (e)
Number of Employees: 750
Average Check: Lunch(8); Dinner(8)
Total Units: 32
Trade Names: KFC (29); KFC/Taco Bell (2); Taco Bell (1)
Units Franchised From: 32
Preferred Square Footage: 1,500
Preferred Location Types: Freestanding
Primary Menu: Chicken (31); Taco (3)
Areas of Operation: NM, TX
Type of Foodservice: Quick Serve (32)
Franchise Affiliation: KFC Corporation, LOUISVILLE, KY; Taco Bell Corp., IRVINE, CA
Primary Distributors: (Full Line) McLane/Shawnee, SHAWNEE, KS

Key Personnel
RANDY BURNETT - Supervisor Risk Management, Food Safety

Braum Distribution Center
491 County Street 2880
Tuttle, OK 73089

Mailing Address: PO Box 725, TUTTLE, OK, 73089-0725
Telephone: (405) 381-4427
Fax Number: (405) 381-2137
Internet Homepage: braums.com
Listing Type: Distribution Center
Type of Business: Chain Restaurant Operator
Year Founded: 1968
Number of Employees: 100
Trade Names: Braums Ice Cream & Dairy Store (277)
Company-Owned Units: 277
Areas of Operation: AR, KS, MO, OK, TX
Distribution Centers: TUTTLE, OK
Parent Company: W.H. Braum Inc., OKLAHOMA CITY, OK

Key Personnel
DAVID JOHNSON - Regional Director Operations
MATTHEW WILLIAMS - Manager Operations, Area

OREGON

Allan's Coffee & Tea
1852 Fescue St SE
Albany, OR 97322-7075

Telephone: (541) 812-8000
Fax Number: (541) 812-8010
Internet Homepage: allanscoffee.com
Company Email: Feedback@AllanBrosCoffee.com
Type of Business: Chain Restaurant Operator
Year Founded: 1972
Total Sales: $3,085,000 (e)
Alcohol Sales: 2%
Number of Employees: 1,153
Average Check: Breakfast(6); Lunch(8); Dinner(8)
Internet Order Processing: Yes
Internet Sales: 4.00%
Total Units: 4
Trade Names: The Beanery (4)
Company-Owned Units: 4
Preferred Square Footage: 800
Preferred Location Types: Freestanding; Strip Mall
Alcohol Served: Beer, Wine
Primary Menu: Coffee (4)
Areas of Operation: OR
Type of Foodservice: Quick Serve (4)
Catering Services: Yes
On-site Distribution Center: Yes
Primary Distributors: (Food) SYSCO Food Services of Portland Inc., WILSONVILLE, OR

Key Personnel
ROBERT MORGAN - CEO; Manager Finance
ALLAN STUART - President; Owner; Director Real Estate, Design
KATRINA LARSEN - Director Human Resources
TIM WIDMER - Manager Sales

Izzy's Franchise Systems, LLC
128 3rd Ave SW
Albany, OR 97321-2241

Mailing Address: PO Box 1689, ALBANY, OR, 97321-0422
Telephone: (541) 926-8693
Fax Number: (541) 928-8127
Internet Homepage: izzysonline.com; izzysonline.com
Company Email: info@izzyspizza.com
Type of Business: Chain Restaurant Operator
Year Founded: 1979
Systemwide Sales: $33,421,000 (e)
Total Sales: $16,360,000 (e)
Alcohol Sales: 1%
Number of Employees: 100
Average Check: Lunch(10); Dinner(14)
Internet Order Processing: Yes
Total Units: 11
Trade Names: Izzy's Pizza Restaurant (11)
Units Franchised To: 11
Preferred Square Footage: 5,000
Preferred Location Types: Freestanding; Strip Mall
Alcohol Served: Beer, Wine, Liquor
Primary Menu: Pizza (11)
Areas of Operation: OR, WA
Type of Foodservice: Casual Dining (11)
Catering Services: Yes
Primary Distributors: (Full Line) SYSCO Food Services of Portland Inc., WILSONVILLE, OR

Key Personnel
DEAN JANSEN - Chairman; Co-Founder
DAVE FREEMAN - CEO; President; Director Finance, Purchasing, Marketing, Real Estate, Menu Development
HEATHER LONG - VP Marketing
TONY DAVID - General Buyer

Coming Attractions Theatres
2200 Ashland St
Ashland, OR 97520-1406

Telephone: (541) 488-1021
Fax Number: (541) 482-9290
Internet Homepage: catheatres.com
Company Email: cati@catheatres.com
Type of Business: Foodservice Operations - Movie Theatre
Year Founded: 1986
Total Sales: $37,470,000 (e)
Number of Employees: 275
Average Check: Lunch(12); Dinner(12)
Total Units: 18
Trade Names: Coming Attractions Theatres (18)
Company-Owned Units: 18
Preferred Location Types: Downtown; Freestanding
Alcohol Served: Beer, Wine
Primary Menu: Snacks (18)
Areas of Operation: AK, CA, OR, WA
Type of Foodservice: In-Store Feeder (18)

Key Personnel
JOHN SCHWEIGER - Executive Chairman; CEO
MICHAEL GUYTON - CEO
DESAREE HALL - VP; Controller
SARAH HEIKEN - Director Human Resources
KIM NEUFELD - Director Administration, Marketing, Promotion, Sales

Chang's Mongolian Grill
1935 NW 167th Pl
Beaverton, OR 97006-4829

Telephone: (503) 645-7718
Fax Number: (503) 655-2323
Internet Homepage: changsmongoliangrill.com
Type of Business: Chain Restaurant Operator
Year Founded: 1985
Total Sales: $5,836,000 (e)
Alcohol Sales: 2%
Number of Employees: 145
Average Check: Lunch(10); Dinner(14)
Total Units: 7
Trade Names: Chang's Mongolian Grill (7)
Company-Owned Units: 7
Preferred Square Footage: 4,000
Preferred Location Types: Freestanding
Alcohol Served: Beer, Wine
Primary Menu: Asian (7)
Projected Openings: 1
Areas of Operation: OR, WA
Type of Foodservice: Casual Dining (7)

Key Personnel
TABON CHANG - Owner; Executive Chef; Director Finance, Operations, Facility/Maintenance, Supply Chain, Real Estate, Design, Human Resources, Menu Development; General Buyer
TANA TROST - General Manager; Director Information Systems

Domino's Franchisee
10081 SW Nimbus Ave
Beaverton, OR 97008-7122

Telephone: (503) 626-3030
Type of Business: Chain Restaurant Operator
Total Sales: $8,152,000 (e)
Total Units: 4
Trade Names: Domino's (4)
Units Franchised From: 4
Primary Menu: Pizza (4)
Areas of Operation: OR
Type of Foodservice: Quick Serve (4)
Franchise Affiliation: Domino's Pizza Inc, ANN ARBOR, MI

Key Personnel
TROY HAMILTON - Owner

JTS BBQ, Inc.
14700 SW Murray Scholls Dr
Beaverton, OR 97007-9278

Telephone: (503) 746-5299
Type of Business: Chain Restaurant Operator
Total Sales: $3,731,000 (e)
Total Units: 3
Trade Names: Dickey's Barbecue Pit (3)
Units Franchised From: 3
Areas of Operation: OR
Franchise Affiliation: Dickey's Barbecue Restaurants Inc., DALLAS, TX

Key Personnel
TODD SAPERSTEIN - Owner; General Buyer

Cascade Culinary Institute
2555 NW Campus Village Way
Bend, OR 97703-7366

Telephone: (541) 383-7700
Fax Number: (541) 383-7508
Internet Homepage: cascadeculinary.com
Company Email: info@cascadeculinary.com/
Type of Business: Culinary Schools
Areas of Operation: OR

Key Personnel
THOR ERIKSON - Chairman

McDonald's of Bend OR
390 NE Emerson Ave Ste 101
Bend, OR 97701-4900

Telephone: (541) 389-6479
Fax Number: (541) 389-5174
Internet Homepage: mcoregon.com
Type of Business: Chain Restaurant Operator
Total Sales: $27,870,000 (e)
Number of Employees: 210
Average Check: Breakfast(8); Lunch(8); Dinner(8)
Total Units: 6
Trade Names: McDonald's (6)
Units Franchised From: 6
Preferred Square Footage: 2,500; 3,000
Preferred Location Types: Discount Dept. Stores; Freestanding
Primary Menu: Hamburger (6)
Areas of Operation: OR
Type of Foodservice: Quick Serve (6)
Franchise Affiliation: McDonald's Corporation, CHICAGO, IL
Primary Distributors: (Full Line) The Martin-Brower Co., PORTLAND, OR

Key Personnel
NANETTE BITTLER - President; Partner; General Buyer
MICK BITTLER - Partner; General Manager Operations, Human Resources
LYNNDEE HARGOUS - Director Operations
MIKE HARGOUS - Manager Marketing

Next Level Burger Company, Inc.
70 SW Century Dr Ste 120
Bend, OR 97702-3562

Telephone: (541) 306-6778
Internet Homepage: nextlevelburger.com
Company Email: chitchat@nextlevelburger.com
Type of Business: Chain Restaurant Operator
Total Units: 8
Trade Names: Next Level Burger (8)
Company-Owned Units: 8
Preferred Location Types: Downtown; Freestanding; Grocery Stores
Primary Menu: Hamburger (8)
Areas of Operation: OR
Type of Foodservice: Fast Casual (8)

Key Personnel
MATT DE GRUYTER - Co-Founder; General Buyer
CIERRA DE GRUYTER - Co-Founder
PATRICK BUCHANAN - CFO

McDonald's Franchise
772 S Broadway
Coos Bay, OR 97420-1542

Telephone: (541) 267-2688
Fax Number: (541) 267-2688
Type of Business: Chain Restaurant Operator
Total Sales: $14,952,000 (e)
Total Units: 3
Trade Names: McDonald's (3)
Units Franchised From: 3
Primary Menu: Hamburger (3)
Areas of Operation: OR
Type of Foodservice: Quick Serve (3)
Franchise Affiliation: McDonald's Corporation, CHICAGO, IL

Key Personnel
CARL ARMSTRONG - President; General Buyer

VPS Inc.
1525 Gateway Blvd
Cottage Grove, OR 97424-1225

Telephone: (541) 942-7010
Type of Business: Chain Restaurant Operator
Total Sales: $42,800,000 (e)
Total Units: 17
Trade Names: Jack in the Box (17)
Units Franchised From: 17
Primary Menu: Hamburger (17)
Areas of Operation: OR
Type of Foodservice: Quick Serve (17)
Franchise Affiliation: Jack in the Box Restaurants, SAN DIEGO, CA

Key Personnel
MIGUEL PALOS - Owner; General Buyer

Wack Company Restaurant
14539 SE Berry Cane Ln
Damascus, OR 97089-7261

Telephone: (503) 314-8019
Fax Number: (503) 698-6370
Company Email: jlwack@comcast.net
Type of Business: Chain Restaurant Operator
Total Sales: $10,052,000 (e)
Total Units: 2
Trade Names: McDonald's (2)
Units Franchised From: 2
Preferred Location Types: Freestanding; Regional Mall
Primary Menu: Hamburger (2)
Areas of Operation: OR
Type of Foodservice: Quick Serve (2)
Franchise Affiliation: McDonald's Corporation, CHICAGO, IL

Key Personnel
DOUG WACKER - President; General Buyer
JOAN WACKER - VP

Abby's Inc.
1960 River Rd
Eugene, OR 97404-2502

Telephone: (541) 689-0019
Fax Number: (541) 689-2588
Internet Homepage: abbys.com
Company Email: info@abbys.com
Type of Business: Chain Restaurant Operator
Year Founded: 1964
Systemwide Sales: $104,284,000 (e)
Total Sales: $42,340,000 (e)
Alcohol Sales: 10%
Number of Employees: 805
Average Check: Breakfast(8); Lunch(8); Dinner(10)
Total Units: 36
Trade Names: Abby's Legendary Pizza (36)
Company-Owned Units: 34
Units Franchised To: 2
Preferred Square Footage: 4,000
Preferred Location Types: Community Mall; Freestanding
Alcohol Served: Beer, Wine
Primary Menu: Pizza (36)
Areas of Operation: OR, WA
Type of Foodservice: Casual Dining (36)
Primary Distributors: (Full Line) Vistar Rocky Mountain, DENVER, CO

Key Personnel
B. MILLS SINCLAIR - CEO; President
DOUG PHILLIPS - VP Marketing; Director Menu Development
DEBI HORN - Controller
GORDON TOLMAN - Director Operations; Manager Facility/Maintenance, Design
NESOL TURNER - Director Information Technology, POS/Scanning
BETH KAILIULI - Manager Human Resources

Cafe Yumm
456 Charnelton St
Eugene, OR 97401-2626

Telephone: (541) 683-9866
Fax Number: (541) 685-9137
Internet Homepage: cafeyumm.com
Company Email: Info@cafeyumm.com
Type of Business: Chain Restaurant Operator
Year Founded: 1997
Systemwide Sales: $35,009,000 (e)
Total Sales: $13,230,000 (e)
Alcohol Sales: 3%
Average Check: Dinner(10)
Total Units: 23
Trade Names: Cafe Yumm! (23)
Company-Owned Units: 7
Units Franchised To: 16
Alcohol Served: Beer, Wine
Primary Menu: Health Foods (23)
Areas of Operation: OR, WA
Type of Foodservice: Casual Dining (23)

Key Personnel
HOLLY OWENS - Director Finance
MARCELLA EASTON - Associate Director Administration
MARNE DUNDER - Manager Marketing

Domino's Franchisee
1690 Coburg Rd
Eugene, OR 97401-4848

Telephone: (541) 255-2284
Type of Business: Chain Restaurant Operator
Total Sales: $12,490,000 (e)
Total Units: 6
Trade Names: Domino's (6)
Units Franchised From: 6
Primary Menu: Pizza (6)
Areas of Operation: OR
Type of Foodservice: Quick Serve (6)
Franchise Affiliation: Domino's Pizza Inc, ANN ARBOR, MI

Key Personnel
DANIEL P. CATES - Owner; General Buyer

Eagle Eye Pizza
54 Division Ave Ste B
Eugene, OR 97404-5420

Telephone: (541) 461-7272
Fax Number: (541) 484-1872
Type of Business: Chain Restaurant Operator
Total Sales: $2,918,000 (e)
Total Units: 2
Trade Names: Papa John's Pizza (2)
Units Franchised From: 2
Primary Menu: Pizza (2)
Areas of Operation: OR
Type of Foodservice: Quick Serve (2)
Franchise Affiliation: Papa Johns International Inc., LOUISVILLE, KY

Key Personnel
TIM MITCHELL - President; General Buyer

KB Restaurants Inc.
875 Country Club Rd
Eugene, OR 97401-6009

Telephone: (541) 342-6557
Fax Number: (541) 743-0202
Internet Homepage: jckstar.com
Company Email: admin@jckstar.com
Type of Business: Chain Restaurant Operator
Total Sales: $124,630,000 (e)
Total Units: 57
Trade Names: Carl's Jr. (57)
Units Franchised From: 57
Primary Menu: Hamburger (57)
Areas of Operation: OR
Type of Foodservice: Quick Serve (57)
Franchise Affiliation: Carl's Jr., FRANKLIN, TN

Key Personnel
JOSEPH C. KARCHER - President
CORINNA J. MEARS - Director Human Resources

M-D Sanders Restaurants Inc.
2896 Crescent Ave Ste 105
Eugene, OR 97408-7422

Telephone: (541) 431-0885
Fax Number: (541) 431-0906
Type of Business: Chain Restaurant Operator
Year Founded: 1997
Total Sales: $52,430,000 (e)
Number of Employees: 700
Average Check: Breakfast(8); Lunch(10); Dinner(12)
Total Units: 11
Trade Names: McDonald's (11)
Units Franchised From: 11
Preferred Square Footage: 3,000
Preferred Location Types: Discount Dept. Stores; Freestanding
Primary Menu: Hamburger (11)
Areas of Operation: OR
Type of Foodservice: Quick Serve (11)
Franchise Affiliation: McDonald's Corporation, CHICAGO, IL
Primary Distributors: (Full Line) The Martin-Brower Co., SUMNER, WA

Key Personnel
PATRICE SANDERS - President; Director Finance, Operations, Facility/Maintenance, Information Systems, Real Estate; General Buyer
DEBI BODINE - Manager Human Resources

Papa's Pizza Inc.
2706 Willakenzie Rd
Eugene, OR 97401-5229

Telephone: (541) 686-2237
Fax Number: (541) 683-0915
Internet Homepage: papaspizza.net
Company Email: dori@papaspizza.net
Type of Business: Chain Restaurant Operator
Year Founded: 1971
Total Sales: $7,932,000 (e)
Alcohol Sales: 4%
Number of Employees: 225
Average Check: Lunch(8); Dinner(14)

Internet Order Processing: Yes
Internet Sales: 1.00%
Total Units: 5
Trade Names: Papa's Pizza (5)
Company-Owned Units: 5
Preferred Square Footage: 5,000; 12,000
Preferred Location Types: Freestanding; Strip Mall
Alcohol Served: Beer, Wine
Primary Menu: Pizza (5)
Areas of Operation: OR
Type of Foodservice: Casual Dining (5)
Catering Services: Yes
Primary Distributors: (Full Line) McDonald Wholesale Co., EUGENE, OR

Key Personnel
SUSAN MOORE - President; General Buyer
DORI KELTY - Manager Human Resources

Steelhead Brewing Co.
199 E 5th Ave
Eugene, OR 97401-8715

Telephone: (541) 686-2739
Fax Number: (541) 342-5338
Internet Homepage: steelheadbrewery.com
Company Email: Eugene@steelheadbrewery.com
Type of Business: Chain Restaurant Operator
Year Founded: 1990
Total Sales: $3,148,000 (e)
Alcohol Sales: 25%
Number of Employees: 90
Average Check: Lunch(18); Dinner(24)
Total Units: 2
Trade Names: Steelhead Brewing Co. (2)
Company-Owned Units: 2
Preferred Square Footage: 5,500; 6,000
Preferred Location Types: Freestanding
Alcohol Served: Beer, Wine, Liquor
Primary Menu: American (2)
Areas of Operation: CA, OR
Type of Foodservice: Casual Dining (2)
Primary Distributors: (Full Line) SYSCO Food Services of Portland Inc., WILSONVILLE, OR
Notes: The company derives approximately 30% of its revenue from brewing operations.

Key Personnel
CORDY JENSEN - Owner; Executive Chef; General Buyer
DOMINGO GARCIA - Manager Facility/Maintenance
REBECKA MATHIAS - Office Manager

Weber Enterprises
840 Conger St
Eugene, OR 97402-2721

Mailing Address: PO Box 23408, EUGENE, OR, 97402-0428
Telephone: (541) 687-8445
Fax Number: (541) 344-3742
Internet Homepage: webertacobells.com
Type of Business: Chain Restaurant Operator
Year Founded: 1969
Total Sales: $118,100,000 (e)
Number of Employees: 700
Average Check: Lunch(8); Dinner(8)
Total Units: 43
Trade Names: Taco Bell (43)
Units Franchised From: 43
Preferred Square Footage: 3,000
Preferred Location Types: Freestanding
Primary Menu: Seafood (43); Taco (43)
Areas of Operation: OR, WA
Type of Foodservice: Quick Serve (43)
Franchise Affiliation: Long John Silver's Inc., LOUISVILLE, KY; Taco Bell Corp., IRVINE, CA
Primary Distributors: (Full Line) McLane/Tualatin, TUALATIN, OR

Key Personnel
MICHELE WEBER - General Counsel
DAN WEBER - Director Real Estate
NICOLE MCCREARY WEBER - Director
ALISHA CANTWELL - Director Human Resources
JOE JOHNSTON - Manager Facility/Maintenance
JULIANN JOHNSTON - Manager Human Resources

Domino's Franchisee
2835 19th Ave Ste 200
Forest Grove, OR 97116-0016

Telephone: (503) 992-7722
Type of Business: Chain Restaurant Operator
Total Sales: $4,082,000 (e)
Total Units: 2
Trade Names: Domino's (2)
Units Franchised From: 2
Primary Menu: Pizza (2)
Areas of Operation: OR
Type of Foodservice: Quick Serve (2)
Franchise Affiliation: Domino's Pizza Inc, ANN ARBOR, MI

Key Personnel
TINA K. KASUBA - Owner; General Buyer

Dutch Bros. Coffee
110 SW 4th St
Grants Pass, OR 97526

Mailing Address: PO Box 1929, GRANTS PASS, OR, 97526
Telephone: (541) 955-4700
Fax Number: (541) 471-0330
Internet Homepage: dutchbros.com
Company Email: customerexperience@dutchbros.com
Type of Business: Chain Restaurant Operator
Year Founded: 1992
Systemwide Sales: $835,919,000 (e)
Total Sales: $53,840,000 (e)
Number of Employees: 11,400
Average Check: Breakfast(8); Lunch(8); Dinner(8)
Total Units: 471
Trade Names: Dutch Bros. Coffee (471)
Company-Owned Units: 207
Units Franchised To: 264
Preferred Square Footage: 375; 400
Preferred Location Types: Freestanding
Primary Menu: Coffee (471)
Projected Openings: 80
Areas of Operation: AZ, CA, CO, ID, NV, OR, WA
Type of Foodservice: Quick Serve (471)
Distribution Centers: GRANTS PASS, OR

Key Personnel
CHRISTINE BARONE - CEO; President
BRENT WILSON - CEO; President
CHARLES SWINDLER - VP Field Marketing
KRISTIN ROHLFING - VP Finance
BRIAN MAXWELL - VP
ALEX OLIVA - VP Information Technology
JOSHUA LUTE - General Counsel
MIKAELA COX - Senior Director
BRENDON GILBERT - Director Operations
SARAH HANSEN - Director Human Resources
JOSH KIMZEY - Director Special Projects
JENNIFER LEWIS - Director Compliance, Compensation
LANCE RISSER - Director Operations
TINA TODD - Director Database, Human Resources
SARAH WILLIAMS - Director Marketing, Social Media
RACHEL LAHORGUE - Regional Manager
AUSTIN SANDERS - Manager Retail Information Systems
CHRISTINE SCHMIDT - Manager Finance
BRANDON STELTER - Manager Help Desk
JEFF WEST - Broker Real Estate

Southern Oregon Elmer's, L.L.C.
206 NE 7th St
Grants Pass, OR 97526-2126

Telephone: (541) 955-9506
Fax Number: (541) 474-4560
Internet Homepage: elmersrestaurants.com
Type of Business: Chain Restaurant Operator
Total Units: 29
Trade Names: Egg N Joe (3); Elmer's Pancake & Steak House (26)
Company-Owned Units: 29
Alcohol Served: Beer, Wine
Primary Menu: American (29)

Areas of Operation: AZ, CA, ID, OR, WA
Type of Foodservice: Casual Dining (29)

Key Personnel
DAVID THOMASON - President; General Buyer
TERRY HOPKINS - VP
TRACY BRINK - Controller

Northwest Burgers and Fries Inc.
8305 SE Monterey Ave
Happy Valley, OR 97086-7725

Telephone: (818) 399-3544
Type of Business: Chain Restaurant Operator
Total Sales: $23,200,000 (e)
Total Units: 12
Trade Names: Five Guys Burgers and Fries (12)
Units Franchised From: 12
Preferred Square Footage: 3,000
Preferred Location Types: Community Mall; Regional Mall; Strip Mall
Primary Menu: Hamburger (12)
Projected Openings: 1
Areas of Operation: OR, WA
Type of Foodservice: Fast Casual (12)
Franchise Affiliation: Five Guys Holdings Inc., LORTON, VA

Key Personnel
WILLIAM MARBLE - President; General Buyer

Twin Scoop, L.L.C.
2355 SE Tualatin Valley Hwy
Hillsboro, OR 97123-7976

Telephone: (503) 597-6038
Type of Business: Chain Restaurant Operator
Total Sales: $1,846,000 (e)
Total Units: 4
Trade Names: Cold Stone Creamery (4)
Units Franchised From: 4
Primary Menu: Snacks (4)
Areas of Operation: OR
Type of Foodservice: Quick Serve (4)
Franchise Affiliation: Kahala Brands, SCOTTSDALE, AZ

Key Personnel
ROB CRUZ - Partner

Domino's Franchisee
2025 Cascade Ave Ste 102
Hood River, OR 97031-1272

Telephone: (541) 386-7600
Type of Business: Chain Restaurant Operator
Total Sales: $5,965,000 (e)
Total Units: 3
Trade Names: Domino's (3)
Units Franchised From: 3
Primary Menu: Pizza (3)
Areas of Operation: OR
Type of Foodservice: Quick Serve (3)
Franchise Affiliation: Domino's Pizza Inc, ANN ARBOR, MI

Key Personnel
DENNIS POE - Owner; General Buyer

325 Roseway
5462 River Rd N
Keizer, OR 97303-4483

Telephone: (503) 390-6273
Type of Business: Chain Restaurant Operator
Total Sales: $2,561,000 (e)
Total Units: 4
Trade Names: Subway (4)
Units Franchised From: 4
Primary Menu: Sandwiches/Deli (4)
Areas of Operation: OR
Type of Foodservice: Quick Serve (4)
Franchise Affiliation: Doctor's Associates Inc., MILFORD, CT

Key Personnel
KYLE MESSMER - Owner; General Buyer

Willadsen Enterprises
2308 Island Ave
La Grande, OR 97850-3938

Telephone: (541) 963-9015
Fax Number: (541) 963-6719
Type of Business: Chain Restaurant Operator
Year Founded: 1987
Total Sales: $20,533,000 (e)
Number of Employees: 200
Average Check: Breakfast(6); Lunch(8); Dinner(12)
Total Units: 4
Trade Names: McDonald's (4)
Units Franchised From: 4
Preferred Square Footage: 2,500; 3,000
Preferred Location Types: Freestanding
Primary Menu: Hamburger (4)
Projected Remodelings: 1
Areas of Operation: OR
Type of Foodservice: Quick Serve (4)
Franchise Affiliation: McDonald's Corporation, CHICAGO, IL
Primary Distributors: (Food) The Martin-Brower Co., PORTLAND, OR

Key Personnel
BEAU WILLADSEN - President; General Manager; General Buyer
ROBBIE WINDE - Store Manager

BAM Enterprises, Inc.
1265 SW Booth Bend Rd
Mcminnville, OR 97128-9730

Telephone: (503) 472-0200
Type of Business: Chain Restaurant Operator
Total Sales: $4,392,000 (e)
Total Units: 7
Trade Names: Subway (7)
Units Franchised From: 7
Primary Menu: Sandwiches/Deli (7)
Areas of Operation: OR
Type of Foodservice: Quick Serve (7)
Franchise Affiliation: Doctor's Associates Inc., MILFORD, CT

Key Personnel
KYLE MESSMER - Owner; General Buyer
KEVIN HEFFLER - COO

Domino's Franchisee
51 E Stewart Ave Ste 103
Medford, OR 97501-7924

Telephone: (541) 245-2682
Type of Business: Chain Restaurant Operator
Total Sales: $6,203,000 (e)
Total Units: 3
Trade Names: Domino's (3)
Units Franchised From: 3
Primary Menu: Pizza (3)
Areas of Operation: OR
Type of Foodservice: Quick Serve (3)
Franchise Affiliation: Domino's Pizza Inc, ANN ARBOR, MI

Key Personnel
TIMMY L. REVARD - Owner; General Buyer

Hill Management LLC
724 S Central Ave Ste 104
Medford, OR 97501-7808

Telephone: (541) 858-9541
Fax Number: (541) 858-9507
Type of Business: Chain Restaurant Operator
Year Founded: 1993
Total Sales: $33,160,000 (e)
Number of Employees: 230
Average Check: Breakfast(8); Lunch(8); Dinner(10)
Total Units: 7
Trade Names: McDonald's (7)
Units Franchised From: 7
Preferred Square Footage: 2,500; 3,000
Preferred Location Types: Discount Dept.

Stores; Freestanding
Primary Menu: Hamburger (7)
Areas of Operation: OR
Type of Foodservice: Quick Serve (7)
Franchise Affiliation: McDonald's Corporation, CHICAGO, IL
Primary Distributors: (Full Line) The Martin-Brower Co., PORTLAND, OR

Key Personnel
LYLE EUGENE HILL III - President; Partner; Director Operations, Facility/Maintenance; General Buyer
GENE HILL - Partner
JILL HILL - Partner; Director Supply Chain, Real Estate, Design; General Buyer
MELISSA MCCARTHY - General Manager
SUZANNE ALGER - Director Accounting, Information Systems, Human Resources

The Human Bean
623 Rossanley Drive
Medford, OR 97501

Telephone: (541) 608-0564
Fax Number: (541) 608-3757
Internet Homepage: thehumanbean.com
Type of Business: Chain Restaurant Operator
Year Founded: 1998
Systemwide Sales: $170,640,000 (e)
Total Sales: $75,840,000 (e)
Number of Employees: 155
Average Check: Breakfast(6); Lunch(6); Dinner(6)
Total Units: 185
Trade Names: The Human Bean (185)
Company-Owned Units: 13
Units Franchised To: 172
Preferred Location Types: Freestanding
Primary Menu: Coffee (185)
Projected Openings: 50
Areas of Operation: AZ, CA, CO, DC, FL, GA, ID, IL, IN, KY, MO, NC, NJ, NM, NV, OH, OR, UT, VA, WA, WV, WY
Type of Foodservice: Quick Serve (185)

Key Personnel
TOM CASEY - Co-Founder; Partner; VP; General Buyer
DAN HAWKINS - Co-Founder; CEO; President; Director Operations; General Buyer
SCOTT ANDERSON - COO
JANIE PAGE - Chief Marketing Officer
JEAN SCHNEIDER - Director Franchise Development
KIM STEENSLID - Director Operations
LESLEE SWANSON - Director Franchise Operations
ANGELA BEEKS - Director Franchise Sales
JUSTIN HAWKINS - Director Franchise Development
LILY HAWKINS - Director Training

ALEXA CORDING - Specialist Real Estate

Domino's Franchisee
10586 SE 32nd Ave
Milwaukie, OR 97222-6522

Telephone: (503) 659-5585
Type of Business: Chain Restaurant Operator
Total Sales: $6,081,000 (e)
Total Units: 3
Trade Names: Domino's (3)
Units Franchised From: 3
Primary Menu: Pizza (3)
Areas of Operation: OR
Type of Foodservice: Quick Serve (3)
Franchise Affiliation: Domino's Pizza Inc, ANN ARBOR, MI

Key Personnel
CLINT R. SCHAFFER - Owner; General Buyer

Rogue Ales Brewery
2320 SE Osu Dr
Newport, OR 97365-5261

Telephone: (541) 867-3660
Fax Number: (503) 423-8148
Internet Homepage: rogue.com
Company Email: brewdawg@rogue.com
Type of Business: Chain Restaurant Operator
Total Sales: $8,116,000 (e)
Number of Employees: 200
Average Check: Dinner(26)
Internet Order Processing: Yes
Total Units: 8
Trade Names: Brewer's On The Bay (8)
Company-Owned Units: 8
Preferred Square Footage: 5,500; 6,000
Preferred Location Types: Freestanding
Alcohol Served: Beer, Wine, Liquor
Primary Menu: American (8)
Areas of Operation: CA, OR, WA
Type of Foodservice: Casual Dining (8)
On-site Distribution Center: Yes
Primary Distributors: (Food) SYSCO Food Services of Portland Inc., WILSONVILLE, OR

Key Personnel
RUSS MENEGAT - General Manager

Biscuits Cafe, Inc.
19273 Molalla Ave Suite H
Oregon City, OR 97045

Mailing Address: 19273 Molalla Ave, Suite H, OREGON CITY, OR, 97045
Telephone: (503) 655-3612
Internet Homepage: biscuitscafe.com
Type of Business: Chain Restaurant Operator
Year Founded: 1998
Total Units: 22
Trade Names: Biscuits Cafe (22)
Company-Owned Units: 22
Primary Menu: American (22)
Areas of Operation: AZ, NV, OR, WA
Type of Foodservice: Family Restaurant (22)
Notes: Address is owner's home. Phone is Oregon City location.

Key Personnel
SHANNON PRESTON - Owner; General Buyer

All American Specialty Restaurants Inc.
1201 SW 12th Ave Ste 415
Portland, OR 97205-2031

Telephone: (503) 224-6199
Fax Number: (503) 224-5042
Internet Homepage: allamericanrestaurants.com; sertinoscafe.com; sertinoscoffee.com
Type of Business: Chain Restaurant Operator
Year Founded: 1986
Systemwide Sales: $11,333,000 (e)
Total Sales: $2,765,000 (e)
Number of Employees: 415
Average Check: Breakfast(5); Lunch(10); Dinner(10)
Total Units: 33
Trade Names: All American Ice Cream & Frozen Yogurt Shops (16); Sertino's Cafe (9); Sertino's Coffee (8)
Company-Owned Units: 5
Units Franchised To: 28
Preferred Square Footage: 1,000; 2,600
Preferred Location Types: Freestanding; Regional Mall
Primary Menu: Coffee (8); Sandwiches/Deli (9); Snacks (16)
Areas of Operation: FL, NJ, NY, OR, TX, WA
Type of Foodservice: Casual Dining (9); Quick Serve (24)
Primary Distributors: (Full Line) US Foods, FIFE, WA

Key Personnel
C. R. DUFFIE - President; Controller; Manager Real Estate; General Buyer

Bruce Carey Restaurants
250 NW 13th Ave
Portland, OR 97209-2953

Telephone: (503) 226-3394
Fax Number: (503) 221-3005
Internet Homepage: bluehouronline.com; brucecareyrestaurants.com; saucebox.com
Company Email: info@bluehouronline.com

Type of Business: Chain Restaurant Operator
Year Founded: 1990
Total Sales: $5,835,000 (e)
Alcohol Sales: 35%
Number of Employees: 75
Average Check: Lunch(16); Dinner(36)
Total Units: 4
Trade Names: 23 Hoyt (1); Bluehour (1); Clark Lewis (1); Sauce Box Cafe Bar (1)
Company-Owned Units: 4
Preferred Location Types: Freestanding
Alcohol Served: Beer, Wine, Liquor
Primary Menu: American (2); Asian (1); Californian (1)
Areas of Operation: OR
Type of Foodservice: Casual Dining (3); Fine Dining (1)

Key Personnel
JOE ROGERS - Partner; Executive Chef
MINOO OMNIVAR - Controller

Bunk Sandwiches Ltd
1028 SE Water Ave Ste 130
Portland, OR 97214-2186

Telephone: (503) 328-2865
Internet Homepage: bunksandwiches.com
Company Email: bunk@bunksandwiches.com
Type of Business: Chain Restaurant Operator
Year Founded: 2008
Total Units: 4
Trade Names: Bunk Sandwiches (4)
Company-Owned Units: 4
Primary Menu: Sandwiches/Deli (4)
Projected Openings: 1
Areas of Operation: OR
Type of Foodservice: Fast Casual (4)

Key Personnel
MATT BROWN - Partner
NICK WOOD - Partner; General Buyer
TOMMY HABETZ - Partner; Executive Chef
ALEXANDER PEKAR - Manager
VICTORIA OLSON - Manager Social Media

Concept Entertainment Group
829 SE 9th Ave Ste 202
Portland, OR 97214-2260

Telephone: (503) 222-4174
Fax Number: (503) 221-2152
Internet Homepage: ceghospitality.com
Type of Business: Chain Restaurant Operator
Year Founded: 1990
Total Sales: $34,580,000 (e)
Alcohol Sales: 10%
Number of Employees: 570
Total Units: 11
Trade Names: Grand Central Restaurant and Bowling Lounge (1); Thirsty Lion Pub and Grill (10)
Company-Owned Units: 11
Preferred Square Footage: 7,000
Preferred Location Types: Freestanding
Alcohol Served: Beer, Wine, Liquor
Primary Menu: American (11)
Projected Openings: 5
Areas of Operation: AZ, CO, OR
Type of Foodservice: Casual Dining (11)

Key Personnel
JOHN PLEW - CEO; President; Partner; General Buyer
RUSS TEISING - Partner
WES CURL - COO; VP Restaurant Operations
KEITH CASTRO - VP Food and Beverage; Executive Chef

Elephants Delicatessen
700 SE Clay St
Portland, OR 97214-3511

Telephone: (503) 224-3955
Fax Number: (503) 224-4097
Internet Homepage: elephantsdeli.com
Type of Business: Chain Restaurant Operator
Total Units: 7
Trade Names: Elephants Delicatessen (7)
Company-Owned Units: 7
Primary Menu: Sandwiches/Deli (7)
Areas of Operation: OR
Type of Foodservice: Fast Casual (7)

Key Personnel
ANNE WEAVER - CEO
NICK DOUGHTY - General Manager
SCOTT WEAVER - Executive Chef
RUSSELL SPEES - Director Operations
KATIE ARNOLD - Director Sales
CHRIS MATHIEU - Director Wholesale; Manager Operations
LOUISE LOUD - Manager Operations
SARAH WOELFLE - Manager Event Planning
DILLON RUSSELL - Manager; Buyer
MARCETT BANKS - Manager Human Resources
RICHARD MCKENZIE - Supervisor Catering
NICHOLAS DOUGHTY - Store Director
JUSTIN HOWARD - Assistant Marketing

Elmer's Restaurants Inc.
8338 NE Alderwood Rd Ste 175
Portland, OR 97220-6800

Telephone: (503) 252-1485
Fax Number: (503) 257-7448
Internet Homepage: eatatelmers.com
Company Email: jessica@eatatelmers.com
Type of Business: Chain Restaurant Operator
Year Founded: 1960
Total Sales: $40,659,000 (e)
Alcohol Sales: 5%
Number of Employees: 1,955
Average Check: Breakfast(12); Lunch(14); Dinner(16)
Total Units: 29
Trade Names: Egg N' Joe (1); Elmer's (28)
Units Franchised To: 29
Preferred Square Footage: 5,500
Preferred Location Types: Community Mall; Freestanding; Strip Mall
Alcohol Served: Beer, Wine, Liquor
Primary Menu: American (29)
Areas of Operation: CA, ID, OR, WA
Type of Foodservice: Casual Dining (29)
Catering Services: Yes
Notes: The company derives approximately 13% of its revenue from video lottery terminals in some of its restaurants.

Key Personnel
GERALD SCOTT - Chairman; CEO; President; Exec VP Menu Development
JILL RAMOS - VP Restaurant Operations
TRAVIS CALDWELL - Director Purchasing

Flying Pie
7804 SE Stark St
Portland, OR 97215-2340

Telephone: (503) 254-2016
Fax Number: (503) 254-1687
Internet Homepage: flying-pie.com
Company Email: fpstark@comcast.net
Type of Business: Chain Restaurant Operator
Year Founded: 2003
Total Sales: $8,089,000 (e)
Alcohol Sales: 4.75%
Number of Employees: 80
Average Check: Lunch(8); Dinner(18)
Total Units: 5
Trade Names: Flying Pie Pizzeria (5)
Company-Owned Units: 5
Alcohol Served: Beer, Wine
Primary Menu: Pizza (5)
Areas of Operation: OR
Type of Foodservice: Casual Dining (5)
Catering Services: Yes
Primary Distributors: (Full Line) SYSCO Food Services of Portland Inc., WILSONVILLE, OR

Key Personnel
TY DUPUIS - President; Executive Chef; General Buyer

GBMO LLC
522 SW 5th Ave Ste 925
Portland, OR 97204-2126

Telephone: (503) 906-1290

Internet Homepage: bkgbmo.com
Company Email: lgalanto@bkgbmo.com
Type of Business: Chain Restaurant Operator
Year Founded: 1992
Total Sales: $151,280,000 (e)
Number of Employees: 4,000
Average Check: Breakfast(8); Lunch(10); Dinner(10)
Total Units: 66
Trade Names: Burger King (66)
Units Franchised From: 66
Preferred Square Footage: 2,500; 3,000; 4,000; 5,000
Preferred Location Types: Freestanding; Regional Mall
Primary Menu: Hamburger (66)
Areas of Operation: OR, WA
Type of Foodservice: Quick Serve (66)
Franchise Affiliation: Burger King Worldwide Inc., MIAMI, FL

Key Personnel
SYED AHMAD - President; General Manager Real Estate
MOHAMMED KAHN - Corporate Secretary

Grand Central Baking Comany
2249 NW York St
Portland, OR 97210-2110

Telephone: (503) 232-0575
Internet Homepage: grandcentralbakery.com
Company Email: gcb.info@grandcentralbaking.com
Type of Business: Chain Restaurant Operator
Year Founded: 1993
Total Units: 11
Trade Names: Grand Central Bakery (11)
Company-Owned Units: 11
Primary Menu: Snacks (10)
Areas of Operation: OR, WA
Type of Foodservice: Fast Casual (11)

Key Personnel
BEN DAVIS - Partner
BOB KERR - Partner; CFO
SAMANTHA KENNEN - Director Human Resources

Guten Foods, Inc.
5035 NE Sandy Blvd
Portland, OR 97213-1941

Telephone: (503) 249-0507
Internet Homepage: gutenfoods.com
Type of Business: Chain Restaurant Operator
Year Founded: 1963
Total Units: 6
Trade Names: Gustav's (3); Gustav's Bargarten (2); Hatch + Hooves (1)
Company-Owned Units: 6
Primary Menu: German (6)
Projected Openings: 1
Areas of Operation: OR, WA
Type of Foodservice: Casual Dining (5); Fast Casual (1)

Key Personnel
SUZEANNE MAGER - CEO; General Buyer
JUERGEN DAVIS - CFO

Heart Coffee Roasters
923 SE Hawthorne
Portland, OR 97214

Telephone: (503) 235-8276
Internet Homepage: heartroasters.com
Company Email: coffee@heartroasters.com
Type of Business: Chain Restaurant Operator
Year Founded: 2009
Total Sales: $3,539,000 (e)
Total Units: 2
Trade Names: Heart Coffee Roasters (2)
Company-Owned Units: 2
Primary Menu: Coffee (2)
Type of Foodservice: Quick Serve (2)

Key Personnel
WILLE YLI-LUOMA - Owner
REBEKAH YLI-LUOMA - Owner

Hero Systems Inc.
333 SW Taylor St
Portland, OR 97204

Telephone: (503) 228-4376
Fax Number: (503) 228-8778
Internet Homepage: bigtownhero.com; bth.com
Company Email: mail@bth.com
Type of Business: Chain Restaurant Operator
Year Founded: 1982
Systemwide Sales: $12,719,000 (e)
Total Sales: $683,000 (e)
Number of Employees: 6
Average Check: Breakfast(5); Lunch(8); Dinner(14)
Total Units: 14
Trade Names: Big Town Hero Submarine Sandwiches (14)
Units Franchised To: 14
Preferred Square Footage: 1,500
Preferred Location Types: Community Mall; Freestanding
Primary Menu: Sandwiches/Deli (14)
Areas of Operation: AZ, OR
Type of Foodservice: Family Restaurant (14)
Catering Services: Yes
Primary Distributors: (Full Line) SYSCO Food Services of Portland Inc., WILSONVILLE, OR

Key Personnel
KELLEN EGGERT - VP Operations

Hot Lips Pizza
1432 SE 22nd Ave
Portland, OR 97214-3901

Telephone: (503) 224-2069
Fax Number: (503) 224-4814
Internet Homepage: hotlipspizza.com
Company Email: comments@hotlipspizza.com
Type of Business: Chain Restaurant Operator
Year Founded: 1985
Total Sales: $5,305,000 (e)
Alcohol Sales: 3%
Number of Employees: 80
Average Check: Lunch(10); Dinner(10)
Internet Order Processing: Yes
Total Units: 6
Trade Names: Hot Lips Pizza (6)
Company-Owned Units: 6
Preferred Square Footage: 2,000
Preferred Location Types: Freestanding
Alcohol Served: Beer, Wine
Primary Menu: Pizza (6)
Areas of Operation: OR
Type of Foodservice: Casual Dining (6)
Catering Services: Yes

Key Personnel
DAVID YUDKIN - President; General Manager; General Buyer

Killer Burger, Inc.
4644 NE Sandy Blvd
Portland, OR 97213-2074

Mailing Address: PO BOX 301037, Portland, OR, 97294
Telephone: (971) 544-7521
Internet Homepage: killerburger.com
Type of Business: Chain Restaurant Operator
Year Founded: 2010
Total Sales: $16,360,000 (e)
Total Units: 14
Trade Names: Killer Burger (14)
Company-Owned Units: 14
Preferred Location Types: Downtown; Freestanding; Stadiums
Primary Menu: Hamburger (14)
Projected Openings: 2
Areas of Operation: AZ, OR, WA
Type of Foodservice: Fast Casual (14)

Key Personnel
MARK MCCRARY - Partner; General Buyer
TJ SOUTHARD - Partner
BOB SPENCER - CFO
ZACK GLESMANN - Senior Manager Training

Laughing Planet Cafe LLC
2120 NE Oregon St
Portland, OR 97232

Telephone: (503) 546-2972
Internet Homepage: laughingplanet.com
Type of Business: Chain Restaurant Operator
Total Units: 6
Trade Names: Laughing Planet Cafe (6)
Company-Owned Units: 6
Primary Menu: American (6)
Areas of Operation: OR
Type of Foodservice: Quick Serve (6)

Key Personnel
FRANZ SPIELVOGEL - CEO
SHERRI GRIFFIN - Director Human Resources

McMenamins Pubs & Breweries
430 N Killingsworth St
Portland, OR 97217-2441

Telephone: (503) 223-0109
Fax Number: (503) 294-0837
Internet Homepage: mcmenamins.com
Company Email: general@mcmenamins.com
Type of Business: Chain Restaurant Operator
Year Founded: 1974
Total Sales: $208,420,000 (e)
Alcohol Sales: 35%
Number of Employees: 1,960
Average Check: Breakfast(10); Lunch(14); Dinner(24)
Foodservice Sales: $135,473,000 (e)
Internet Order Processing: Yes
Internet Sales: 2.00%
Total Units: 67
Trade Names: 23rd Avenue Bottle Shop (1); Anderson School (1); Back Stage Bar (1); Bagdad Cafe and Theater (1); Barley Mill Pub (1); Black Rabbit Restaurant (1); Blue Moon Tavern and Grill (1); Boon's Treasury (1); Broadway Pub (1); Cedar Hills (1); Chapel Pub (1); Cornelius Pass Road House and Brewery (1); Corvallis Pub (1); Courtyard Restaurant (1); Crystal Hotel (1); East 19th Street Cafe (1); East Vancouver (1); Edgefield Manor (1); Elks Temple (1); Fulton Pub and Brewery (1); Gearhart Hotel (1); Grand Lodge (1); Greater Trumps (1); Greenway Pub (1); High Street Brewery & Pub (1); Highland Pub and Brewery (1); Hillsdale Brewery and Public House (1); Hotel Oregon (1); Ironwork Grill (1); John Barleycorn's Restaurant and Brewery (1); Kalama Harbor Lodge (1); Kennedy School (1); Lighthouse Brewpub (1); Mall 205 (1); Market Street Pub (1); McMenamins Murray & Allen (1); McMenamins on Monroe (1); McMenamins on the Columbia (1); Mill Creek (1); Mission Theater and Pub (1); Murray & Allen (1); North Bank (1); Oak Hills Brewpub (1); Old St. Francis School (1); Olympic Club Pub (1); Oregon City (1); Power Station Pub (1); Queen Anne (1); Raleigh Hills Pub (1); Rams Head (1); Ringlers (1); Rock CreekTavern (1); Roseburg Station Pub & Brewery (1); Sand Trap Pub (1); Sherwood (1); Six Arms Brewpub (1); Spar Cafe (1); St. John's Theater & Pub (1);Sunnyside (1); Tavern & Pool (1); Tavern On The Square (1); The White Eagle (1); Thompson Brewery and Public House (1); West Linn (1); Wilsonville Old Church & Pub (1); Zeus Cafe (1)
Company-Owned Units: 67
Preferred Square Footage: 5,500; 6,000
Preferred Location Types: Community Mall; Downtown; Freestanding; Hotel/Motel; Regional Mall; Strip Mall
Alcohol Served: Beer, Wine, Liquor
Primary Menu: American (66)
Areas of Operation: OR, WA
Type of Foodservice: Casual Dining (66)
Primary Distributors: (Full Line) SYSCO Food Services of Portland Inc., WILSONVILLE, OR
Notes: The company derives approximately 35% of its revenue from hotel operations, retail sales of beer, wine, & other operations.

Key Personnel
LARRY DORTMUND - CFO
RICK SMITH - COO
SARA NORTHRUP - Controller
KARA GARCIA - Director; Assistant Sales
OWEN CRAIG - Director Operations
LYNN SMITH - Director
CATHERINE PAPPAS - Director Operations
RENEE RANK - Director Marketing
RENEE RANK IGNACIO - Director Marketing
BRITTNY SALVI - Manager Restaurant Operations
JESS SYPAL - Manager Catering
BECKY WILKERSON - Manager Restaurant Operations
LISA KINSLEY - Manager Human Resources
MATT KORONA - Manager Technology, Digital
GINA NIESL - Manager Food and Beverage
JOE FRAZIER - Manager Information Systems
SEAN OSAKI - Corporate Director Sales, Catering

Micah Camden Restaurant Group
3753 N Mississippi Ave
Portland, OR 97227

Telephone: (971) 254-4575
Internet Homepage: bluestardonuts.com; boxerramen.com; sonofabiscuit.com
Company Email: info@bluestardonuts.com
Type of Business: Chain Restaurant Operator
Total Sales: $8,949,000 (e)
Total Units: 10
Trade Names: Blue Star Donuts (8); Boxer Ramen (1); Son Of A Biscuit (1)
Company-Owned Units: 10
Primary Menu: Asian (1); Chicken (1); Snacks (8)
Areas of Operation: OR
Foreign Countries: JAPAN
Type of Foodservice: Casual Dining (1); Fast Casual (9)

Key Personnel
KATIE POPPE - CEO; Partner
MICAH CAMDEN - Partner; Executive Chef; General Buyer
MATT LYNCH - General Manager

Mio Sushi International
2250 NW 22nd Ave Ste 406
Portland, OR 97210

Telephone: (503) 219-9762
Fax Number: (971) 888-5046
Internet Homepage: miosushi.com
Company Email: info@miofranchising.com
Type of Business: Chain Restaurant Operator
Year Founded: 1995
Total Units: 13
Trade Names: Mio Sushi (13)
Units Franchised To: 13
Preferred Location Types: Strip Mall
Alcohol Served: Beer, Wine, Liquor
Primary Menu: Japanese (13)
Areas of Operation: OR, WA
Type of Foodservice: Casual Dining (13)
Catering Services: Yes

Key Personnel
SONNY KIM - Partner; General Buyer
JOON KIM - Partner

Mohr & Mohr Inc
10713 SE 82nd Ave
Portland, OR 97086-7601

Telephone: (503) 654-0191
Type of Business: Chain Restaurant Operator
Total Sales: $1,822,000 (c)
Total Units: 3
Trade Names: Subway (3)
Units Franchised From: 3
Primary Menu: Sandwiches/Deli (3)
Areas of Operation: OR
Type of Foodservice: Quick Serve (3)
Franchise Affiliation: Doctor's Associates Inc., MILFORD, CT

Key Personnel
JENNIFER SCHWAB - President; General Buyer

North Pacific Management Inc.
1905 SE 10th Ave
Portland, OR 97214-4659

Telephone: (503) 425-1500
Internet Homepage: hudsonsbarandgrill.com; southparkseafood.com; northp.com
Company Email: info@northp.com
Type of Business: Chain Restaurant Operator
Year Founded: 1988
Total Sales: $19,189,000 (e)
Alcohol Sales: 10%
Number of Employees: 250
Average Check: Breakfast(14); Lunch(18); Dinner(26)
Total Units: 4
Trade Names: Hudson's Bar & Grill (1); Lakeside Cafe (1); River Lodge Grill (1); Southpark Seafood Grill & Wine (1)
Company-Owned Units: 4
Preferred Location Types: Freestanding; Hotel/Motel
Alcohol Served: Beer, Wine, Liquor
Primary Menu: American (4)
Areas of Operation: OR, WA
Type of Foodservice: Casual Dining (4)
Catering Services: Yes
Primary Distributors: (Food) SYSCO Food Services of Portland Inc., WILSONVILLE, OR

Key Personnel
BRETT WILKERSON - President
DEX MACQUARRIE - VP Human Resources
CHRIS ALFSON - Director Information Technology
STEVE HEBNER - Director Engineering
DAINA GALSTER - Director Sales
HAROLD COLLINS - Assistant Director Facility/Maintenance
CINDY SCHAFFER - Manager Sales

Ocean Restaurant Corp
9100 SE Powell Blvd
Portland, OR 97266-1943

Telephone: (503) 775-0339
Type of Business: Chain Restaurant Operator
Total Sales: $14,897,000 (e)
Total Units: 3
Trade Names: McDonald's (3)
Units Franchised From: 3
Preferred Location Types: Freestanding
Primary Menu: Hamburger (3)
Areas of Operation: OR
Type of Foodservice: Quick Serve (3)
Franchise Affiliation: McDonald's Corporation, CHICAGO, IL

Key Personnel
JAMES DOTSON - President; General Buyer

OSF International, Inc
715 S Bancroft St Ste 300
Portland, OR 97239-4299

Telephone: (503) 225-0433
Fax Number: (503) 226-6214
Internet Homepage: osf.com
Company Email: info@osf.com
Type of Business: Chain Restaurant Operator
Year Founded: 1969
Systemwide Sales: $150,454,000 (e)
Total Sales: $155,830,000 (e)
Alcohol Sales: 10%
Number of Employees: 2,735
Average Check: Lunch(10); Dinner(18)
Internet Order Processing: Yes
Total Units: 41
Trade Names: The Old Spaghetti Factory (41)
Company-Owned Units: 41
Preferred Square Footage: 10,000; 12,000
Preferred Location Types: Community Mall; Freestanding
Alcohol Served: Beer, Wine, Liquor
Primary Menu: Italian (42)
Areas of Operation: AZ, CA, CO, GA, HI, ID, IN, KY, MN, MO, OH, OR, TN, UT, WA
Type of Foodservice: Casual Dining (42)
Primary Distributors: (Full Line) SYSCO Food Services of Portland Inc., WILSONVILLE, OR

Key Personnel
CHRIS DUSSIN - Chairman
ROBERT MARTIN - VP Construction, Business Development
RIC HOLDERBAUM - Director Real Estate
SONJA ERVIN - Administrator POS/Scanning

Papa John's Distribution Center
15011 N Lombard St
Portland, OR 97203-6809

Telephone: (503) 289-5000
Fax Number: (503) 289-0501
Listing Type: Distribution Center
Type of Business: Chain Restaurant Operator
Areas of Operation: CA, ID, MT, OR, WA
Parent Company: Papa Johns International Inc., LOUISVILLE, KY

Key Personnel
PETER WINNING - General Manager

Papa Restaurant Management
3330 NE 82nd Ave
Portland, OR 97220-5230

Telephone: (503) 254-5349
Type of Business: Chain Restaurant Operator
Total Sales: $10,251,000 (e)
Total Units: 2
Trade Names: McDonald's (2)
Units Franchised From: 2
Preferred Location Types: Freestanding
Primary Menu: Hamburger (2)
Areas of Operation: OR
Type of Foodservice: Quick Serve (2)
Franchise Affiliation: McDonald's Corporation, CHICAGO, IL

Key Personnel
KAREN FITZGERALD - Owner; General Buyer

Pizzicato Gourmet Pizza
121 S Bancroft St
Portland, OR 97239-4051

Telephone: (503) 274-0375
Fax Number: (503) 274-0473
Internet Homepage: pizzicatopizza.com
Company Email: reception@pizzicatopizza.com
Type of Business: Chain Restaurant Operator
Year Founded: 1989
Total Sales: $16,110,000 (e)
Alcohol Sales: 25%
Number of Employees: 225
Average Check: Lunch(10); Dinner(14)
Internet Order Processing: Yes
Total Units: 11
Trade Names: Pizzicato Gourmet Pizza (11)
Company-Owned Units: 11
Preferred Square Footage: 1,500
Preferred Location Types: Freestanding; Lifestyle Center; Strip Mall
Alcohol Served: Beer, Wine
Primary Menu: Pizza (11)
Areas of Operation: CA, OR
Type of Foodservice: Casual Dining (11)
Catering Services: Yes
Primary Distributors: (Food) US Foods, WOODBURN, OR; (Supplies) US Foods, WOODBURN, OR

Key Personnel
FELIX RIPPEL - CEO
MAT WAER - Executive Chef
JOHN PAULUS - Director Operations
CHRISTIE BUI - Director Human Resources
SEAN THORNTON - District Manager
JADE LENNON - Manager Marketing;

Supervisor

Portland Foods Inc.
5949 NE M L King Blvd
Portland, OR 97211-3119

Telephone: (503) 286-4489
Type of Business: Chain Restaurant Operator
Total Sales: $5,494,000 (e)
Number of Employees: 10
Average Check: Lunch(8); Dinner(12)
Total Units: 2
Trade Names: Popeyes Louisiana Kitchen (2)
Units Franchised From: 2
Primary Menu: Chicken (2)
Areas of Operation: OR
Type of Foodservice: Quick Serve (2)
Franchise Affiliation: Popeyes Louisiana Kitchen Inc., ATLANTA, GA
Primary Distributors: (Full Line) McLane/Tualatin, TUALATIN, OR

Key Personnel
GREG HOBROCK - President; General Manager; General Buyer

RingSide Steakhouse - Uptown
2165 W Burnside St
Portland, OR 97210-3540

Telephone: (503) 223-1513
Fax Number: (503) 223-6908
Internet Homepage: ringsidesteakhouse.com
Company Email: admin@ringsidehg.com
Type of Business: Chain Restaurant Operator
Year Founded: 1944
Total Sales: $2,781,000 (e)
Alcohol Sales: 30%
Number of Employees: 106
Average Check: Breakfast(8); Lunch(10); Dinner(24)
Total Units: 1
Trade Names: Ringside Steakhouse Uptown (1)
Company-Owned Units: 1
Preferred Location Types: Freestanding
Alcohol Served: Beer, Wine, Liquor
Primary Menu: Steak/Seafood (1)
Areas of Operation: OR
Type of Foodservice: Fine Dining (1)

Key Personnel
CRAIG PETERSON - Partner; General Buyer
SCOTT PETERSON - Partner; General Buyer
BEAU CARR - Executive Chef; General Buyer

Salt & Straw
110 SE 2nd Ave
Portland, OR 97214

Telephone: (503) 206-8071
Internet Homepage: saltandstraw.com
Company Email: human@saltandstraw.com
Type of Business: Chain Restaurant Operator
Year Founded: 2011
Total Sales: $27,290,000 (e)
Total Units: 21
Trade Names: Salt & Straw (20); Wiz Bang Bar (1)
Company-Owned Units: 21
Primary Menu: Snacks (21)
Areas of Operation: CA, OR, WA
Type of Foodservice: Quick Serve (21)

Key Personnel
KIM MALEK - Co-Founder; General Manager
TYLER MALEK - Co-Founder; General Manager
STEVE BRINK - CFO
TODD WOODRUFF - Chief People Officer
ERIC EMERY - Chief Development Officer
CASEY MILLIGAN - Director Operations
NIKKI YOERG - Director Brand Marketing
LOGAN MILLER - Director Logistics
MICHAEL BEAMER - Director Sales

Salty's Seafood Grill
3839 NE Marine Dr
Portland, OR 97211-2129

Telephone: (503) 288-4444
Fax Number: (503) 288-3426
Internet Homepage: saltys.com
Company Email: columbia@saltys.com
Type of Business: Chain Restaurant Operator
Year Founded: 1987
Total Sales: $6,121,000 (e)
Alcohol Sales: 5%
Internet Order Processing: Yes
Total Units: 3
Trade Names: Alki Beach (1); Columbia River (1); Redondo Beach (1)
Company-Owned Units: 3
Alcohol Served: Beer, Wine, Liquor
Primary Menu: Steak/Seafood (3)
Areas of Operation: OR, WA
Type of Foodservice: Casual Dining (3)
Catering Services: Yes

Key Personnel
GERRY KINGEN - Founder; Owner; General Buyer
LAURA REEDER - General Manager; General Buyer
JOSH THORBURN - Executive Chef; General Buyer
JEREMY MCLACHLAN - Executive Chef;

General Buyer

Shilo Management Co.
11707 NE Airport Way
Portland, OR 97220

Telephone: (503) 641-6565
Fax Number: (503) 419-1750
Internet Homepage: shiloinns.com
Company Email: info@shiloinns.com
Type of Business: Foodservice Operations - Hotel/Motels
Year Founded: 1973
Total Sales: $344,252,000 (e)
Alcohol Sales: 15%
Number of Employees: 2,331
Total Units: 21
Restaurants in Hotels: 21
Trade Names: Shilo Inn (21)
Company-Owned Units: 9
Alcohol Served: Beer, Wine, Liquor
Areas of Operation: OR, TX, WA
Type of Foodservice: Casual Dining (9)
Primary Distributors: (Food) US Foods, WOODBURN, OR
Notes: The company derives approximately 80% of its revenue from hotel operations.

Key Personnel
MARK HEMSTREET - Founder

Sizzle Pie
624 E Burnside St
Portland, OR 97214-1217

Telephone: (503) 234-7437
Internet Homepage: sizzlepie.com
Company Email: info@sizzlepie.com
Type of Business: Chain Restaurant Operator
Total Units: 8
Trade Names: Quality Bar (1); Sizzle Pie (7)
Company-Owned Units: 8
Primary Menu: Pizza (8)
Projected Openings: 1
Areas of Operation: OR, WA
Type of Foodservice: Casual Dining (8)

Key Personnel
MATT JACOBSON - Partner; Executive Chef; General Buyer
MIKEY MCKENNEDY - Partner
BOB PEYTON - Director Operations

Stumptown Coffee Roasters
100 SE Salmon St
Portland, OR 97214

Telephone: (855) 711-3385
Internet Homepage: stumptowncoffee.com

Company Email: info@stumptowncoffee.com
Type of Business: Chain Restaurant Operator
Year Founded: 1999
Total Units: 15
Trade Names: Stumptown (15)
Company-Owned Units: 15
Primary Menu: Coffee (15)
Areas of Operation: CA, IL, LA, NY, OR, WA
Type of Foodservice: Quick Serve (15)
Parent Company: Peet's Coffee & Tea Inc., EMERYVILLE, CA

Key Personnel
KRISTEN HAND - CFO
JIM KELSO - VP Quality Assurance
SHAUNA ALEXANDER - VP Sustainability, Coffee/Tea
JON PERRY - VP Restaurant Operations
JORDAN COBURN - Senior Manager Sales

Sustainable Restaurant Group
850 NW 13th Ave
Portland, OR 97209

Telephone: (503) 232-5255
Internet Homepage: kristoforlofgren.com; sustainablerestaurantgroup.com
Company Email: info@sustainablerestaurantgroup.com
Type of Business: Chain Restaurant Operator
Year Founded: 2008
Total Units: 6
Trade Names: Bamboo Sushi (5); QuickFish (1)
Company-Owned Units: 6
Primary Menu: Japanese (5); Seafood (1)
Projected Openings: 3
Areas of Operation: CO, OR
Type of Foodservice: Casual Dining (5); Fast Casual (1)
Parent Company: Sortis Holdings, PORTLAND, OR

Key Personnel
MATTHEW PARK - CEO; President
ASHLEY CINTAS - Director Operations, Division
ANDY ADAMS - Director Beverages

The Cinnamon Bums Inc.
7800 SW Durham Rd Ste 900
Portland, OR 97224-7596

Telephone: (503) 639-2747
Fax Number: (503) 639-2744
Type of Business: Chain Restaurant Operator
Total Sales: $23,610,000 (e)
Average Check: Dinner(8)
Total Units: 25
Trade Names: Cinnabon (3); Jamba Juice (22)
Units Franchised From: 25
Preferred Square Footage: 1,200
Preferred Location Types: Downtown; Freestanding
Primary Menu: Health Foods (22); Snacks (3)
Areas of Operation: OR, WA
Type of Foodservice: Quick Serve (25)
Franchise Affiliation: Cinnabon Inc., ATLANTA, GA; Jamba Inc., FRISCO, TX

Key Personnel
JOHN WHITTAKER - President; Partner
JAN FOLTZ - Partner
STEVE FOLTZ - Partner
DEBRA DISTANTS - Manager Human Resources

The Original Pancake House Franchising Inc.
8601 SW 24th Ave
Portland, OR 97219-4034

Telephone: (503) 246-1049
Fax Number: (503) 245-2396
Internet Homepage: originalpancakehouse.com
Company Email: oph@teleport.com
Type of Business: Chain Restaurant Operator
Year Founded: 1953
Systemwide Sales: $277,604,000 (e)
Total Sales: $6,170,000 (e)
Number of Employees: 4,488
Average Check: Breakfast(8); Lunch(8); Dinner(8)
Total Units: 132
Trade Names: The Original Pancake House (132)
Company-Owned Units: 1
Units Franchised To: 131
Preferred Square Footage: 4,000
Preferred Location Types: Freestanding; Strip Mall
Primary Menu: American (132)
Projected Openings: 7
Areas of Operation: AL, AZ, CA, CO, FL, GA, HI, ID, IL, IN, MD, MI, MN, MO, NC, NJ, NV, NY, OH, OR, PA, SC, SD, TX, UT, VA, WA, WI
Type of Foodservice: Family Restaurant (132)
Primary Distributors: (Full Line) SYSCO Food Services of Portland Inc., WILSONVILLE, OR
Notes: The company derives approximately 9% of its total revenue from franchise merchandise sales.

Key Personnel
RONALD T. HIGHET - President; Director Real Estate, Franchising, Menu Development
ELIZABETH HIGHET - CIO; Treasurer; Director Finance, Operations, Purchasing, Marketing, Menu Development
ELINOR G. HIGHET - Exec VP
JONATHAN LISS - General Counsel; Executive Chef; General Buyer
EDWARD PEREZ - Director
COLLEEN BRASHEAR - Director Operations

Von Ebert Brewing LLC
131 NW 13th Ave
Portland, OR 97209

Telephone: (503) 820-7721
Internet Homepage: vonebertbrewing.com
Company Email: tscook@vonebertbrewing.com
Type of Business: Chain Restaurant Operator
Year Founded: 2018
Total Units: 2
Trade Names: Von Ebert Brewing (2)
Company-Owned Units: 2
Preferred Location Types: Downtown; Freestanding
Primary Menu: American (2)
Areas of Operation: OR
Type of Foodservice: Casual Dining (2)

Key Personnel
SEAN BURKE - Director Alcoholic Beverages

Voodoo Doughnut LLC
828 SW 1st Ave Ste 300
Portland, OR 97204

Telephone: (503) 546-9666
Internet Homepage: voodoodoughnut.com
Type of Business: Chain Restaurant Operator
Year Founded: 2003
Total Units: 7
Trade Names: Voodoo Doughnut (7)
Company-Owned Units: 7
Primary Menu: Snacks (7)
Areas of Operation: CA, CO, FL, OR, TX
Type of Foodservice: Quick Serve (7)

Key Personnel
KENNETH POGSON - Co-Founder; Partner
TRES SHANNON - Co-Founder; Partner
CHRIS SCHULTZ - CEO

Domino's Franchisee
1604 S Highway 97
Redmond, OR 97756-8420

Telephone: (541) 504-5577
Type of Business: Chain Restaurant Operator
Total Sales: $4,024,000 (e)
Total Units: 2
Trade Names: Domino's (2)
Units Franchised From: 2
Primary Menu: Pizza (2)
Areas of Operation: OR
Type of Foodservice: Quick Serve (2)
Franchise Affiliation: Domino's Pizza Inc, ANN

ARBOR, MI

Key Personnel
CHRIS DROEGE - Owner; General Buyer

Taylor Enterprises, Inc.
1604 S Highway 97 Ste 2-368
Redmond, OR 97756-8420

Telephone: (541) 923-0908
Type of Business: Chain Restaurant Operator
Total Sales: $23,540,000 (e)
Total Units: 5
Trade Names: McDonald's (5)
Units Franchised From: 5
Primary Menu: Hamburger (5)
Areas of Operation: OR
Type of Foodservice: Quick Serve (5)
Franchise Affiliation: McDonald's Corporation, CHICAGO, IL

Key Personnel
PAUL RODBY - President; General Buyer
ROY TAYLOR - President
CHERYL TAYLOR - Owner

Domino's Franchisee
2012 Columbia Blvd
Saint Helens, OR 97051-1737

Telephone: (503) 397-3030
Type of Business: Chain Restaurant Operator
Total Sales: $4,097,000 (e)
Total Units: 2
Trade Names: Domino's (2)
Units Franchised From: 2
Primary Menu: Pizza (2)
Areas of Operation: OR
Type of Foodservice: Quick Serve (2)
Franchise Affiliation: Domino's Pizza Inc, ANN ARBOR, MI

Key Personnel
DAVID E. ORR - Owner; General Buyer

Chick Inc.
3175 Broadway St NE
Salem, OR 97303-5041

Telephone: (503) 304-1019
Type of Business: Chain Restaurant Operator
Year Founded: 1966
Total Sales: $15,800,000 (e)
Number of Employees: 180
Average Check: Lunch(10); Dinner(10)
Total Units: 9
Trade Names: A&W All American Food (2); KFC (6); Taco Bell (1)
Units Franchised From: 9
Preferred Square Footage: 3,000
Preferred Location Types: Freestanding
Primary Menu: American (2); Chicken (6); Taco (1)
Areas of Operation: OR
Type of Foodservice: Quick Serve (9)
Franchise Affiliation: A&W Restaurants Inc., LEXINGTON, KY; KFC Corporation, LOUISVILLE, KY; Taco Bell Corp., IRVINE, CA
Primary Distributors: (Full Line) The SYGMA Network Inc. - Portland, CLACKAMAS, OR

Key Personnel
DAVID HERBER - President; CFO; Director Finance, Operations, Purchasing, Facility/Maintenance, Information Systems, Supply Chain, Ethnic Marketing, Real Estate, Design, Human Resources, Store Fixtures, Store Planning, Catering; General Buyer

Figaro's Italian Pizza Inc.
1500 Liberty St SE Ste 160
Salem, OR 97302-4386

Telephone: (503) 371-9318
Fax Number: (503) 363-5364
Internet Homepage: figaros.com; nicknwillys.com; schmizza.com
Company Email: figaros@figaros.com
Type of Business: Chain Restaurant Operator
Year Founded: 1981
Total Sales: $1,108,000 (e)
Number of Employees: 20
Average Check: Dinner(28)
Internet Order Processing: Yes
Total Units: 56
Trade Names: Figaro's Pizza (31); Nick 'N' Willy's (3); Pizza Schmizza (22)
Company-Owned Units: 2
Units Franchised To: 54
Preferred Square Footage: 1,500; 1,800
Preferred Location Types: Community Mall; Freestanding; Strip Mall
Primary Menu: Pizza (56)
Areas of Operation: AZ, CA, CO, FL, IL, MN, MT, OH, OR, SC, WA, WI
Foreign Countries: CYPRUS; UNITED ARAB EMIRATES
Type of Foodservice: Family Restaurant (31); Quick Serve (25)
Foodservice Management Venues: Schools
Catering Services: Yes
Primary Distributors: (Full Line) SYSCO Food Services of Portland Inc., WILSONVILLE, OR

Key Personnel
RON BERGER - Chairman; CEO
RICHARD S. GLENN - President
KELLY KIMSEY - Controller
HOLLY EARLE-SCHULTZE - Senior Director Sales, Training, Catering
RAY STONEBACK - Director Franchise Operations, Store Development

Hueneke, Inc.
4685 Portland Rd NE
Salem, OR 97305-1662

Telephone: (503) 588-1700
Fax Number: (503) 588-3254
Type of Business: Chain Restaurant Operator
Total Sales: $5,422,000 (e)
Total Units: 2
Trade Names: The Original Pancake House (2)
Units Franchised From: 2
Primary Menu: American (2)
Areas of Operation: OR
Type of Foodservice: Family Restaurant (2)
Franchise Affiliation: The Original Pancake House Franchising Inc., PORTLAND, OR

Key Personnel
RICK BURNS - Owner; General Buyer

Jak Pizza
3402 Commercial St SE
Salem, OR 97302-4635

Telephone: (503) 364-8875
Type of Business: Chain Restaurant Operator
Total Sales: $12,517,000 (e)
Total Units: 6
Trade Names: Domino's (6)
Units Franchised From: 6
Primary Menu: Pizza (6)
Areas of Operation: OR
Type of Foodservice: Quick Serve (6)
Franchise Affiliation: Domino's Pizza Inc, ANN ARBOR, MI

Key Personnel
TIMOTHY R. HAMMER - Owner; General Buyer

McGrath's Fish House Inc.
1935 Davcor St SE
Salem, OR 97302-1146

Telephone: (503) 399-8456
Fax Number: (503) 391-2846
Internet Homepage: mcgrathsfishhouse.com
Type of Business: Chain Restaurant Operator
Year Founded: 1980
Total Sales: $28,950,000 (e)
Alcohol Sales: 15%
Number of Employees: 925
Average Check: Lunch(10); Dinner(22)
Internet Order Processing: Yes
Internet Sales: 1.00%
Total Units: 7
Trade Names: McGrath's Fish House (7)
Company-Owned Units: 7

Preferred Square Footage: 7,500
Preferred Location Types: Freestanding; Regional Mall
Alcohol Served: Beer, Wine, Liquor
Primary Menu: Seafood (7)
Areas of Operation: ID, OR, UT, WA
Type of Foodservice: Casual Dining (7)
Primary Distributors: (Food) Pacific Seafood Group, CLACKAMAS, OR

Key Personnel
JOHN MCGRATH - President; General Buyer

Rawza, Inc.
478 Lancaster Dr NE
Salem, OR 97301-4784

Telephone: (503) 378-7272
Fax Number: (503) 281-8466
Type of Business: Chain Restaurant Operator
Total Sales: $21,400,000 (e)
Total Units: 24
Trade Names: Papa Murphy's Take 'N' Bake Pizza (24)
Units Franchised From: 24
Primary Menu: Pizza (24)
Areas of Operation: KS, MO, OR, WA
Type of Foodservice: Quick Serve (24)
Franchise Affiliation: Papa Murphy's International Inc., VANCOUVER, WA

Key Personnel
CHRIS COPP - President
SHAUNA WALKER - VP Operations

Seaman Restaurant Corp
2791 19th St SE
Salem, OR 97302-1503

Telephone: (503) 378-1072
Fax Number: (503) 378-9149
Type of Business: Chain Restaurant Operator
Year Founded: 1975
Total Sales: $92,180,000 (e)
Number of Employees: 633
Average Check: Breakfast(8); Lunch(10); Dinner(12)
Total Units: 19
Trade Names: McDonald's (19)
Units Franchised From: 19
Preferred Square Footage: 2,500
Preferred Location Types: Freestanding
Primary Menu: Hamburger (19)
Areas of Operation: OR
Type of Foodservice: Quick Serve (19)
Franchise Affiliation: McDonald's Corporation, CHICAGO, IL
Primary Distributors: (Food) The Martin-Brower Co., PORTLAND, OR

Key Personnel
JEFF SWARTZ - CEO
MICHAEL SEAMAN - President; Partner; Executive Chef; Director Operations; Manager Purchasing, Information Systems, Real Estate
JILL SEAMAN POLLARD - Partner; VP; Director Operations; Manager Purchasing, Information Systems, Real Estate
SCOTT GIPSON - VP
RAYMOND PACE - VP; General Manager
LORI WELCH - Manager Accounting

Subway
155 Liberty St NE
Salem, OR 97301

Telephone: (503) 391-7623
Internet Homepage: subway.com
Type of Business: Chain Restaurant Operator
Total Units: 2
Trade Names: Subway (2)
Units Franchised From: 2
Primary Menu: Sandwiches/Deli (2)
Areas of Operation: OR
Type of Foodservice: Quick Serve (2)
Franchise Affiliation: Doctor's Associates Inc., MILFORD, CT

Key Personnel
PARVEEN NAGRA - Owner; General Buyer

Bell-Co Enterprises
219 42nd St
Springfield, OR 97478-5937

Mailing Address: PO Box FF, SPRINGFIELD, OR, 97477-0082
Telephone: (541) 726-8628
Fax Number: (541) 726-9065
Type of Business: Chain Restaurant Operator
Year Founded: 1968
Total Sales: $5,903,000 (e)
Number of Employees: 45
Average Check: Lunch(12); Dinner(12)
Total Units: 2
Trade Names: Taco Bell (2)
Units Franchised From: 2
Preferred Square Footage: 3,500; 4,000
Preferred Location Types: Freestanding
Primary Menu: Taco (2)
Areas of Operation: OR
Type of Foodservice: Quick Serve (2)
Franchise Affiliation: Taco Bell Corp., IRVINE, CA
Primary Distributors: (Food) McLane/Tualatin, TUALATIN, OR

Key Personnel
RANDY JEFFERIS - Controller; Director Information Systems, Human Resources; Manager Finance, Loss Prevention

Double S Foods L.L.C.
302 Shelley St Ste 2
Springfield, OR 97477-5903

Telephone: (541) 744-1093
Fax Number: (541) 744-1386
Type of Business: Chain Restaurant Operator
Year Founded: 1978
Total Sales: $30,400,000 (e)
Alcohol Sales: 5%
Number of Employees: 505
Average Check: Lunch(10); Dinner(14)
Total Units: 13
Trade Names: Papa Murphy's Take 'N' Bake Pizza (3); Sizzler (10)
Units Franchised From: 13
Preferred Square Footage: 5,600
Preferred Location Types: Freestanding
Alcohol Served: Beer, Wine
Primary Menu: Pizza (3); Steak (10)
Areas of Operation: OR
Type of Foodservice: Casual Dining (10); Quick Serve (3)
Franchise Affiliation: Sizzler USA Inc., MISSION VIEJO, CA
Primary Distributors: (Full Line) McDonald Wholesale Co., EUGENE, OR

Key Personnel
MURRAY GAST - Partner; Controller; Director Finance, Operations, Supply Chain, Advertising; General Buyer
KATHY JOHNSON - Partner; Director Human Resources
MARY JONES - Manager Accounting

Cafe Today LLC
11095 SW Sage Ter
Tigard, OR 97223

Mailing Address: PO Box 2162, SALEM, OR, 97308
Telephone: (503) 871-5760
Fax Number: (503) 362-2542
Internet Homepage: cafetoday.net
Company Email: info@cafetoday.net
Type of Business: Chain Restaurant Operator
Year Founded: 1998
Total Sales: $4,505,000 (e)
Alcohol Sales: 5%
Number of Employees: 40
Average Check: Breakfast(6); Lunch(8); Dinner(12)
Total Units: 3
Trade Names: Cafe Today (3)
Company-Owned Units: 3
Preferred Square Footage: 3,000
Preferred Location Types: Freestanding
Alcohol Served: Beer, Wine, Liquor

Primary Menu: American (3)
Areas of Operation: OR
Type of Foodservice: Fast Casual (3)

Key Personnel
KEVIN CAMERON - CEO; General Buyer

I C By the Sea, LLC
12288 SW Scholls Ferry Rd Ste 14
Tigard, OR 97223-3354

Telephone: (503) 590-7766
Type of Business: Chain Restaurant Operator
Total Sales: $1,180,000 (e)
Total Units: 2
Trade Names: Cold Stone Creamery (2)
Units Franchised From: 2
Primary Menu: Snacks (2)
Areas of Operation: OR
Type of Foodservice: Quick Serve (2)
Franchise Affiliation: Kahala Brands, SCOTTSDALE, AZ

Key Personnel
MINDY GROVER - Partner
ROY NIFOUSSI - Partner

Northwest Group, Inc.
7150 SW Fir Loop
Tigard, OR 97223

Telephone: (503) 877-1010
Type of Business: Chain Restaurant Operator
Total Sales: $109,990,000 (e)
Total Units: 43
Trade Names: Jack in the Box (43)
Units Franchised From: 43
Primary Menu: Hamburger (43)
Areas of Operation: OR
Type of Foodservice: Quick Serve (43)
Franchise Affiliation: Jack in the Box Restaurants, SAN DIEGO, CA

Key Personnel
JOSEPH MURASHIE - President
RAJEEV GUPTA - Owner; General Buyer
JEFF TENNANT - VP Operations

H&R Restaurants-Oregon, LLC
7698 SW Nyberg St
Tualatin, OR 97062-9427

Telephone: (503) 482-5942
Type of Business: Chain Restaurant Operator
Total Sales: $6,940,000 (e)
Total Units: 5
Trade Names: Jersey Mike's Subs (5)

Units Franchised From: 5
Primary Menu: Sandwiches/Deli (5)
Areas of Operation: OR
Type of Foodservice: Quick Serve (5)
Franchise Affiliation: Jersey Mike's Franchise Systems, MANASQUAN, NJ

Key Personnel
ERIC S. HEIKKALA - Owner; General Buyer

Domino's Franchisee
29955 SW Boones Ferry Rd Ste G
Wilsonville, OR 97070-9228

Telephone: (503) 582-9393
Type of Business: Chain Restaurant Operator
Total Sales: $29,847,000 (e)
Total Units: 15
Trade Names: Domino's (15)
Units Franchised From: 15
Primary Menu: Pizza (15)
Areas of Operation: OR
Type of Foodservice: Quick Serve (15)
Franchise Affiliation: Domino's Pizza Inc, ANN ARBOR, MI

Key Personnel
TROY C. HAMILTON - Owner; General Buyer

Greentree Enterprises Inc.
8655 SW Citizens Dr Ste 201
Wilsonville, OR 97070-7695

Telephone: (503) 685-5002
Fax Number: (503) 682-5998
Type of Business: Chain Restaurant Operator
Year Founded: 1989
Total Sales: $62,670,000 (e)
Number of Employees: 645
Average Check: Breakfast(8); Lunch(10); Dinner(10)
Total Units: 13
Trade Names: McDonald's (13)
Units Franchised From: 13
Preferred Square Footage: 2,500; 3,000
Preferred Location Types: Discount Dept. Stores; Freestanding
Primary Menu: Hamburger (13)
Areas of Operation: OR
Type of Foodservice: Quick Serve (13)
Franchise Affiliation: McDonald's Corporation, CHICAGO, IL
Primary Distributors: (Food) The Martin-Brower Co., PORTLAND, OR

Key Personnel
MINDY MAYER - Partner; Director Finance, Human Resources; Manager Real Estate
JARED RAY - Partner; Director Operations, Purchasing

RANDI RAY - Partner; Manager Information Systems; General Buyer
JULIE CORDANO - Manager Customer Service

PENNSYLVANIA

Dorney Park & Wildwater Kingdom
3830 Dorney Park Rd
Allentown, PA 18104-5803

Telephone: (610) 395-3724
Fax Number: (610) 391-7685
Company Email: info@dorneypark.com
Listing Type: Divisional Office
Type of Business: Foodservice Operations - Theme Parks
Number of Employees: 2,500
Total Units: 28
Areas of Operation: PA
Parent Company: Cedar Fair LLP, SANDUSKY, OH

Key Personnel
BERNIE BONUCCELLI - VP Marketing, Sales
DAWN REIDENBACH - Director Human Resources
ERIC RHYDER - Manager Information Technology
EDWIN WALTERS - Manager Facility/Maintenance
KRISTEN BARTHOLOMEW - Manager Marketing

Ice Slingers Inc
1918 W Tilghman St
Allentown, PA 18104

Telephone: (610) 435-4501
Type of Business: Chain Restaurant Operator
Total Sales: $1,222,000 (e)
Total Units: 4
Trade Names: Rita's Ice Custard Happiness (4)
Company-Owned Units: 4
Primary Menu: Snacks (4)
Areas of Operation: PA
Type of Foodservice: Quick Serve (4)
Franchise Affiliation: Rita's Franchise Co., TREVOSE, PA

Key Personnel
JACK DARYANI - Owner; General Buyer

Lehigh Valley Restaurant Group
6802 Hamilton Blvd
Allentown, PA 18106-9644

Telephone: (610) 481-0436
Fax Number: (610) 481-0437
Internet Homepage: redrobinpa.com
Type of Business: Chain Restaurant Operator
Year Founded: 1993
Total Sales: $74,810,000 (e)
Alcohol Sales: 15%
Number of Employees: 1,050
Average Check: Lunch(12); Dinner(18)
Total Units: 21
Trade Names: Red Robin Gourmet Burgers & Spirits (21)
Units Franchised From: 21
Preferred Square Footage: 6,500
Preferred Location Types: Freestanding; Strip Mall
Alcohol Served: Beer, Wine
Primary Menu: Hamburger (21)
Areas of Operation: PA
Type of Foodservice: Casual Dining (21)
Franchise Affiliation: Red Robin Gourmet Burgers Inc., ENGLEWOOD, CO
Primary Distributors: (Food) US Foods, ALLENTOWN, PA

Key Personnel
MIKE AXIOTIS - CEO
STEPHEN HANZLIK - President
CHRIS DEFRAIN - CFO
DAVID MORRONE - VP Operations
JODY STETZ - Senior Director Human Resources
ED KRUCZEK - Senior Director Information Technology
GHASSAN MOUSSA - Regional Director Operations
NATALIE SULLIVAN - Senior Manager Human Resources
MEGAN YOUNG - Manager Catering
SHANNON LONGACRE - Manager Training
JAMIE KEEFER - Manager Sales, Catering
NIKKI BLOOM - Manager Accounting
CRAIG WILDFEUER - Supervisor MIS
JENNIFER AQUINO - Specialist Compliance

Sodexo
6081 Hamilton Blvd
Allentown, PA 18106-9767

Telephone: (610) 395-3800
Fax Number: (610) 395-8160
Listing Type: Regional Office
Type of Business: Foodservice Management Operator
Number of Employees: 16,000
Number of Locations Served: 750
Total Foodservice Mgmt Accounts: 500
Areas of Operation: PA
Type of Foodservice: Cafeteria (100); Full-service sit-down dining (100); Mobile units/kiosks (100); Quick Serve (100); Vending machines (100)
Foodservice Management Venues: Business & Industry; College & University; Health Care; Lodging; Other; Parks & Recreation; Prison Feeding; Schools
Parent Company: Sodexo, MONTIGNY-LE-BRETONNEUX, FRA
Headquarters: Sodexo Inc., GAITHERSBURG, MD

Key Personnel
ERICA MILIOS - Senior Director Marketing
HOLLY SMITH - Director Marketing

Sodexo Dining Service
6081 Hamilton Blvd
Allentown, PA 18106-9767

Telephone: (610) 395-3800
Fax Number: (610) 398-1599
Listing Type: Regional Office
Type of Business: Foodservice Management Operator
Number of Employees: 1,300
Number of Locations Served: 105
Total Foodservice Mgmt Accounts: 65
Areas of Operation: NJ
Type of Foodservice: Cafeteria (65)
Foodservice Management Venues: Business & Industry; College & University; Schools
Parent Company: Sodexo Inc., GAITHERSBURG, MD

Key Personnel
ERICA MILIOS - Senior Director Marketing
HOLLY SMITH - Senior Director Marketing
MEGAN NUNAN - Specialist Human Resources

Irvin Enterprises Inc
506 26th St Ste A
Altoona, PA 16602-2027

Telephone: (814) 942-8355
Type of Business: Chain Restaurant Operator
Total Sales: $3,924,000 (e)
Total Units: 2
Trade Names: KFC (2)
Units Franchised From: 2
Primary Menu: Chicken (2)
Areas of Operation: PA
Type of Foodservice: Quick Serve (2)
Franchise Affiliation: KFC Corporation, LOUISVILLE, KY

Key Personnel
FRANK O. IRVIN SR - President
TY IRVIN - President

William Penn Inn Inc.
1017 Dekalb Pike
Amber, PA 19002

Mailing Address: PO Box 6, GWYNEDD, PA, 19436-0006
Telephone: (215) 699-9272
Fax Number: (215) 699-4808
Internet Homepage: williampenninn.com
Company Email: info@williampenninn.com
Type of Business: Foodservice Operations - Hotel/Motels
Year Founded: 1981
Total Sales: $18,468,000 (e)
Alcohol Sales: 10%
Number of Employees: 280
Total Units: 1
Restaurants in Hotels: 3
Trade Names: William Penn Inn (1)
Company-Owned Units: 3
Alcohol Served: Beer, Wine, Liquor
Areas of Operation: PA
Type of Foodservice: Casual Dining (1); Fine Dining (2)
Primary Distributors: (Food) SYSCO Food Services of Pittsburgh Inc., HARMONY, PA
Notes: The company derives approximately 10% of its revenue from hotel operations.

Key Personnel
PETER R. FRIEDRICH - CEO; President; CFO; Controller; Manager Finance, Purchasing, Marketing
GRETCHEN DOWLING - VP Human Resources

Funck's Family Restaurants
1805 N State Route 934
Annville, PA 17003-8424

Telephone: (717) 865-7235
Fax Number: (717) 865-7235
Internet Homepage: funcks.com
Type of Business: Chain Restaurant Operator
Year Founded: 1969
Total Sales: $10,380,000 (e)
Number of Employees: 166
Average Check: Breakfast(10); Lunch(14); Dinner(16)
Total Units: 5
Trade Names: Funck's Family Restaurant (5)
Company-Owned Units: 5
Preferred Location Types: Freestanding
Primary Menu: American (5)
Areas of Operation: PA
Type of Foodservice: Family Restaurant (5)
Primary Distributors: (Equipment) Singer Equipment Co. Inc., ELVERSON, PA; (Food)

Feesers Inc., HARRISBURG, PA; (Supplies)
Singer Equipment Co. Inc., ELVERSON, PA
Notes: The company derives approximately 50% of its revenue from convenience store operations.

Key Personnel
MATTHEW FUNCK - Partner; General Buyer

Chickie's and Pete's
675 Shannondell Blvd
Audubon, PA 19407

Telephone: (610) 631-2530
Internet Homepage: chickiesandpetes.com
Type of Business: Chain Restaurant Operator
Year Founded: 2000
Total Sales: $17,670,000 (e)
Alcohol Sales: 5%
Number of Employees: 861
Average Check: Lunch(8); Dinner(18)
Total Units: 16
Trade Names: Chickie's & Pete's Crab House and Sports Bar (16)
Company-Owned Units: 16
Preferred Square Footage: 7,000; 10,000
Alcohol Served: Beer, Wine, Liquor
Primary Menu: American (16)
Areas of Operation: NJ, PA
Type of Foodservice: Casual Dining (16)
Catering Services: Yes

Key Personnel
ROGER FALLOON - COO
JOE CARPINELLA - VP Operations; General Buyer
BETTY BAECKI - Controller
MICHAEL HUGHES - General Manager

Baden Foods, Inc.
1690 Beaver Rd
Baden, PA 15005

Telephone: (724) 869-1174
Type of Business: Chain Restaurant Operator
Total Sales: $4,885,000 (e)
Total Units: 2
Trade Names: Burger King (2)
Units Franchised From: 2
Preferred Location Types: Freestanding
Primary Menu: Hamburger (2)
Areas of Operation: PA
Type of Foodservice: Quick Serve (2)
Franchise Affiliation: Burger King Worldwide Inc., MIAMI, FL

Key Personnel
CHUCK SPIRK - President; General Buyer

Maggio Corp.
6052 William Flynn Hwy
Bakerstown, PA 15007-9713

Mailing Address: PO Box 334, BAKERSTOWN, PA, 15007-0334
Telephone: (724) 443-3500
Fax Number: (724) 443-7287
Type of Business: Chain Restaurant Operator
Year Founded: 1960
Systemwide Sales: $3,833,000 (e)
Total Sales: $1,093,000 (e)
Number of Employees: 6
Average Check: Breakfast(8); Lunch(8); Dinner(8)
Total Units: 10
Trade Names: The Different Twist Pretzel (10)
Units Franchised To: 10
Preferred Square Footage: 2,500
Preferred Location Types: Community Mall; Regional Mall
Primary Menu: Snacks (10)
Areas of Operation: KY, MI, NJ, NY, OH, OK, PA, PR, WV
Type of Foodservice: Quick Serve (10)
Primary Distributors: (Food) Tova Industries, LOUISVILLE, KY

Key Personnel
AUGUST MAGGIO - President; Partner; CFO; Director Franchise Development, Menu Development; Manager Real Estate, Business Development; General Buyer
JOAN MAGGIO - Partner
PETER MAGGIO - Partner

Al Dar Inc.
281 Montgomery Ave
Bala Cynwyd, PA 19004-2814

Telephone: (610) 667-1245
Fax Number: (610) 667-7239
Internet Homepage: evvivarestaurant.com; aldarrestaurant.com; murraysdeli.com
Company Email: info@evvivarestaurant.com
Type of Business: Chain Restaurant Operator
Total Sales: $8,507,000 (e)
Alcohol Sales: 30%
Number of Employees: 78
Average Check: Lunch(20); Dinner(36)
Total Units: 3
Trade Names: Al Dar Bistro (1); Evviva Bistro (1); Murray's Deli (1)
Company-Owned Units: 3
Preferred Location Types: Freestanding
Alcohol Served: Beer, Wine, Liquor
Primary Menu: French/Continental (1); Middle Eastern (1); Sandwiches/Deli (1)
Areas of Operation: PA
Type of Foodservice: Fine Dining (2); Quick Serve (1)
Catering Services: Yes
Primary Distributors: (Full Line) US Foods, ALLENTOWN, PA

Key Personnel
GEORGE WAKIM - Partner
JOSEPH WAKIM - Partner; General Manager; Executive Chef; General Buyer
MICHAEL WAKIM - Partner
WALID ASSAF - General Manager

Bruster's Real Ice Cream
730 Mulberry St
Beaver, PA 15009-3024

Telephone: (724) 774-4250
Fax Number: (724) 774-0666
Internet Homepage: brusters.com
Company Email: customerservice@brusters.com
Type of Business: Chain Restaurant Operator
Year Founded: 1989
Systemwide Sales: $45,707,000 (e)
Total Sales: $10,610,000 (e)
Number of Employees: 160
Average Check: Breakfast(8); Lunch(8); Dinner(8)
Total Units: 170
Trade Names: Bruster's Real Ice Cream (178)
Company-Owned Units: 3
Units Franchised To: 175
Preferred Square Footage: 988; 1,200
Preferred Location Types: Freestanding; Strip Mall
Primary Menu: Snacks (178)
Projected Openings: 12
Areas of Operation: AL, DE, FL, GA, IN, KY, MD, MS, NC, NH, NJ, NY, OH, PA, SC, TN, TX, VA
Foreign Countries: GUYANA
Type of Foodservice: Quick Serve (178)
Primary Distributors: (Full Line) Performance Foodservice - Milton's, OAKWOOD, GA

Key Personnel
JIM SAHENE - CEO
JENNIFER BRINKER - VP Marketing, Product Development
MARCIE CHONG - VP Operations
GREGG MCMILLAN - VP Finance, Purchasing, Menu Development
KRISTIE BONETTI - VP Marketing
GINA NEGLEY - Creative Director
MARK OLDAKER - Director Operations
KRISTIE BONETTI - Director Marketing
LORI MOLNAR - Director Franchise Development

H.D.S. of Beaver Falls Inc.
300 S Walnut Ln Ste 400
Beaver, PA 15009-1738

Telephone: (724) 775-9070
Fax Number: (724) 775-9074
Internet Homepage:
  brightonhotdogshoppes.com
Type of Business: Chain Restaurant Operator
Year Founded: 1959
Total Sales: $13,730,000 (e)
Number of Employees: 109
Average Check: Lunch(8); Dinner(8)
Total Units: 12
Trade Names: Brighton Hot Dog Shoppe (12)
Company-Owned Units: 12
Preferred Square Footage: 900
Preferred Location Types: Freestanding; Strip Mall
Primary Menu: Hot Dogs (12)
Areas of Operation: OH, PA
Type of Foodservice: Quick Serve (12)
Primary Distributors: (Food) Youngstown Wholesale Grocery Inc., YOUNGSTOWN, OH

Key Personnel
FRANK G. PAPA - President; General Manager; Director Facility/Maintenance, Real Estate, Design, Human Resources, Menu Development; General Buyer

Wooden Angel
308 Leopard Ln
Beaver, PA 15009-3057

Telephone: (724) 774-7880
Fax Number: (724) 775-7994
Internet Homepage: bertswoodenindian.com; wooden-angel.com
Company Email: info@bertswoodenindian.com
Type of Business: Chain Restaurant Operator
Year Founded: 1968
Total Sales: $4,619,000 (e)
Alcohol Sales: 15%
Number of Employees: 70
Average Check: Lunch(12); Dinner(36)
Total Units: 2
Trade Names: Wooden Angel (1); Wooden Indian (1)
Company-Owned Units: 2
Preferred Location Types: Freestanding
Alcohol Served: Beer, Wine, Liquor
Primary Menu: American (2)
Areas of Operation: PA
Type of Foodservice: Casual Dining (1); Fine Dining (1)
Catering Services: Yes
Primary Distributors: (Full Line) SYSCO Food Services of Philadelphia LLC, PHILADELPHIA, PA

Key Personnel
ALEX SEBASTIAN - Partner; General Manager; General Buyer
DAVID SEBASTIAN - Partner; General Buyer
BRIAN BURGESS - Executive Chef; General Buyer

Timoney & Borrelli Enterprises Inc
8752 Lincoln Hwy
Bedford, PA 15522-9720

Mailing Address: PO Box 608, BEDFORD, PA, 15522-0608
Telephone: (814) 623-2559
Fax Number: (814) 623-2559
Type of Business: Chain Restaurant Operator
Total Sales: $15,950,000 (e)
Average Check: Dinner(12)
Total Units: 7
Trade Names: Burger King (7)
Units Franchised From: 7
Primary Menu: Hamburger (7)
Areas of Operation: PA
Type of Foodservice: Quick Serve (7)
Franchise Affiliation: Burger King Worldwide Inc., MIAMI, FL

Key Personnel
CRAIG J. TIMONEY - President; General Buyer
MARTY FLEENER - General Manager

Auntie Anne's Franchise
100 Sara Way
Belle Vernon, PA 15012-1963

Telephone: (724) 929-4257
Type of Business: Chain Restaurant Operator
Total Sales: $1,541,000 (e)
Total Units: 2
Trade Names: Auntie Anne's Hand-Rolled Soft Pretzels (2)
Units Franchised From: 2
Primary Menu: Snacks (2)
Areas of Operation: PA
Type of Foodservice: Quick Serve (2)
Franchise Affiliation: Auntie Anne's Inc., LANCASTER, PA

Key Personnel
LORI ANN PODLOGAR - Owner; General Buyer

Soft Pretzel Franchise Systems, Inc.
1525 Ford Rd
Bensalem, PA 19020

Telephone: (215) 338-4606
Fax Number: (215) 437-6830
Internet Homepage: phillypretzelfactory.com
Company Email: info@spfsinc.com
Type of Business: Chain Restaurant Operator
Year Founded: 1998
Total Units: 156
Trade Names: Philly Pretzel Factory (156)
Units Franchised To: 156
Preferred Location Types: Community Mall; Discount Dept. Stores; Downtown; Freestanding; Institution (college/hospital); Kiosk; Parks; Stadiums; Strip Mall
Primary Menu: Snacks (156)
Projected Openings: 10
Areas of Operation: DE, FL, GA, IN, MD, NC, NJ, NY, OH, PA, SC, TN, TX, VA
Type of Foodservice: Quick Serve (156)

Key Personnel
DAN DIZIO - Co-Founder; CEO
LEN LEHMAN - Co-Founder
MARTY FERRILL - President

V and K Retail, Inc.
656 Neshaminy Mall
Bensalem, PA 19020-1612

Telephone: (215) 357-2201
Type of Business: Chain Restaurant Operator
Total Sales: $1,190,000 (e)
Total Units: 2
Trade Names: Cold Stone Creamery (2)
Units Franchised From: 2
Primary Menu: Snacks (2)
Areas of Operation: PA
Type of Foodservice: Quick Serve (2)
Franchise Affiliation: Kahala Brands, SCOTTSDALE, AZ

Key Personnel
RAJIV PATEL - Owner

Domino's Franchisee
908 Market St
Berwick, PA 18603-3128

Telephone: (570) 759-3100
Type of Business: Chain Restaurant Operator
Total Sales: $4,144,000 (e)
Total Units: 2
Trade Names: Domino's (2)
Units Franchised From: 2
Primary Menu: Pizza (2)
Areas of Operation: PA
Type of Foodservice: Quick Serve (2)
Franchise Affiliation: Domino's Pizza Inc, ANN ARBOR, MI

Key Personnel
MELISSA S. KRAMER - Owner; General Buyer

Domino's Franchisee
1353 Easton Ave
Bethlehem, PA 18018-2624

Telephone: (610) 865-2700
Type of Business: Chain Restaurant Operator
Total Sales: $6,253,000 (e)
Total Units: 3
Trade Names: Domino's (3)
Units Franchised From: 3
Primary Menu: Pizza (3)
Areas of Operation: PA
Type of Foodservice: Quick Serve (3)
Franchise Affiliation: Domino's Pizza Inc, ANN ARBOR, MI

Key Personnel
WILLIAM R. MORRIS - Owner; General Buyer

JDK Management Co. L.P.
1388 State Route 487
Bloomsburg, PA 17815-8953

Telephone: (570) 784-0111
Fax Number: (570) 784-4785
Internet Homepage: jdkmgt.com
Company Email: tkishbau@jdkmgt.com
Type of Business: Chain Restaurant Operator
Year Founded: 1988
Total Sales: $189,330,000 (e)
Number of Employees: 2,590
Average Check: Breakfast(10); Lunch(14); Dinner(18)
Total Units: 83
Trade Names: Perkins Restaurant & Bakery (40); Quaker Steak and Lube (43)
Units Franchised From: 83
Preferred Square Footage: 1,400
Preferred Location Types: Freestanding
Primary Menu: American (83)
Projected Openings: 10
Areas of Operation: KY, MD, NJ, OH, PA
Type of Foodservice: Casual Dining (43); Family Restaurant (40)
Franchise Affiliation: Perkins Restaurant & Bakery, MEMPHIS, TN
Parent Company: JDK Management Co. Inc., BLOOMSBURG, PA

Key Personnel
BRIAN KLINGERMAN - CEO
BRITTANY MYLET - Partner Human Resources
CODY CONCINI - Partner Human Resources
JEFFREY GUEISS - CFO
BRIAN THOMPSON - Senior VP Store Operations
ANGIE KLINGERMAN - VP Operations
MICHELLE POLACHEK - Director Personnel-Training
RYAN TROUP - Director Human Resources
DAVID HAVRILLA - Regional Director
BARRY HORNER - Regional Director
TAMMY CHAPIN - Manager Business Development

The Simple Greek
794 Penllyn Blue Bell Pike Ste. 219
Blue Bell, PA 19422

Telephone: (844) 576-6695
Internet Homepage: thesimplegreek.com; linkedin.com/company/the-simple-greek
Company Email: info@thesimplegreek.com
Type of Business: Chain Restaurant Operator
Year Founded: 2015
Total Sales: $56,830,000 (e)
Total Units: 32
Trade Names: The Simple Greek (32)
Company-Owned Units: 1
Units Franchised To: 33
Primary Menu: Greek/Mediterranean (32)
Projected Openings: 3
Areas of Operation: AL, CA, CO, CT, FL, GA, IA, IL, KY, LA, MA, NC, NJ, OH, PA, RI, TX, VA
Type of Foodservice: Fast Casual (32)
Parent Company: WOWorks, CONSHOHOCKEN, PA

Key Personnel
MARCUS LEMONIS - Founder
MARIA GJONI - General Manager

US Restaurants Inc.
1780 Swede Rd
Blue Bell, PA 19422-3522

Telephone: (610) 277-4200
Fax Number: (610) 277-6527
Company Email: info@usrinc.com
Type of Business: Chain Restaurant Operator
Year Founded: 1985
Total Sales: $68,020,000 (e)
Number of Employees: 1,065
Average Check: Breakfast(6); Lunch(8); Dinner(8)
Total Units: 30
Trade Names: Burger King (30)
Units Franchised From: 30
Preferred Square Footage: 2,500; 7,000
Preferred Location Types: Freestanding
Primary Menu: Hamburger (30)
Areas of Operation: NJ, PA
Type of Foodservice: Quick Serve (30)
Franchise Affiliation: Burger King Worldwide Inc., MIAMI, FL
Primary Distributors: (Full Line) Maines Paper & Food Service Inc., CONKLIN, NY

Key Personnel
STEVEN M. LEWIS - CEO; President
MICHAEL KADELSKI - CFO; CIO; VP Finance, Information Systems, Loss Prevention; Director Real Estate
GREG WINANS - VP Operations, Construction, Store Planning, Division; Director Purchasing

Isaac's Deli Inc.
1104 Fernwood Ave St. 401
Camp Hill, PA 17011

Telephone: (717) 394-0623
Fax Number: (717) 393-0955
Internet Homepage: isaacsrestaurants.com
Type of Business: Chain Restaurant Operator
Year Founded: 1983
Total Sales: $13,890,000 (e)
Total Units: 14
Trade Names: Isaac's Famous Grilled Sandwiches (14)
Company-Owned Units: 14
Preferred Location Types: Downtown; Lifestyle Center; Regional Mall
Primary Menu: Sandwiches/Deli (14)
Areas of Operation: PA
Type of Foodservice: Fast Casual (14)

Key Personnel
MICHAEL WEAVER - CEO; President; General Buyer
JOHNNY ROBERTS - Director Marketing
DORRIE COUROGEN - Senior Manager Restaurant Operations
MATTHEW PASCIUTA - Senior Manager Operations

Cura Hospitality
2400 Ansys Dr Suite 404
Canonsburg, PA 15317

Telephone: (724) 416-7676
Fax Number: (724) 416-7528
Internet Homepage: curahospitality.com
Company Email: info@curahospitality.com
Type of Business: Foodservice Management Operator
Year Founded: 1995
Total Sales: $14,694,000 (e)
Number of Employees: 300
Number of Locations Served: 50
Total Foodservice Mgmt Accounts: 50
Internet Order Processing: Yes
Areas of Operation: PA
Type of Foodservice: Full-service sit-down dining (50)
Foodservice Management Venues: Health Care
Primary Distributors: (Food) Feesers Inc., HARRISBURG, PA
Parent Company: TrustHouse Services Group,

CHARLOTTE, NC

Key Personnel
TRISH SPELLMAN - President
ROBBIE WASHINGTON - Director Food
SHARON KONECSNI - Director Food
SUTTER MEINKE - Director
TOREHN WINDT - Area Manager
LYNNETTE MCNEIL - District Manager
LARRY NEEDLE - Manager Operations
ZACHARY REA - Manager Operations

Delamor Enterprises, Inc
1520 Lincoln Way E
Chambersburg, PA 17202-3314

Telephone: (717) 263-5641
Fax Number: (717) 261-0552
Type of Business: Chain Restaurant Operator
Year Founded: 1992
Total Sales: $47,840,000 (e)
Number of Employees: 500
Average Check: Breakfast(8); Lunch(10); Dinner(10)
Total Units: 10
Trade Names: McDonald's (10)
Units Franchised From: 10
Preferred Square Footage: 2,500; 3,000
Preferred Location Types: Convenience Store/Gas Station; Freestanding
Primary Menu: Hamburger (10)
Areas of Operation: PA
Type of Foodservice: Quick Serve (10)
Franchise Affiliation: McDonald's Corporation, CHICAGO, IL

Key Personnel
STEVEN DELAMATER - President; Director Finance, Supply Chain, Real Estate; General Buyer
SHARI NEADY - Director Operations, Purchasing, Facility/Maintenance

Eurest Dining Services
1500 Liberty Ridge Dr
Chesterbrook, PA 19087-5564

Telephone: (800) 447-4476
Internet Homepage: compass-usa.com; eurest-usa.com; eurestservices.us
Company Email: sales@eurestservices.us
Type of Business: Foodservice Management Operator
Year Founded: 1929
Total Sales: $2,164,087,000 (e)
Number of Employees: 15,500
Number of Locations Served: 1,500
Total Foodservice Mgmt Accounts: 1,500
Areas of Operation: NY
Type of Foodservice: Cafeteria (2,200)
Foodservice Management Venues: Business & Industry
Parent Company: Compass Group PLC, LONDON, ENG
Headquarters: Compass Group The Americas, CHARLOTTE, NC
Divisional Offices: Eurest Dining Services, FORT WASHINGTON, PA
Regional Offices: Eurest Dining Services, NORMAL, IL
Notes: Eurest is a $1.4 billion food and vending organization with 1935 locations and more than 15,500 associates throughout the US. Eurest serves more than 705,000 customers daily and is a division of NC-based Compass Group North America.

Key Personnel
TONY MCDONALD - CEO
ED MUGNANI - President West Division
JIM KALLAS - President Division
MARK MALONEY - President East Division
DAVID HOGLAND - President
TOM TEVES - President Division
CHRISTOPHER IVENS-BROWN - Senior VP Culinary Development; Executive Chef
JEFF BOGGS - VP Region
JON HARRIS - VP Information Systems, Security Systems
DAVID SPATARO - VP Division
R. DOUGLASS SNOOK - Director Business Development

Subway Franchise
36 S 8th Ave
Clarion, PA 16214-1535

Telephone: (814) 226-7131
Internet Homepage: subway.com
Type of Business: Chain Restaurant Operator
Total Sales: $3,932,000 (e)
Total Units: 6
Trade Names: Subway (6)
Units Franchised From: 6
Primary Menu: Sandwiches/Deli (6)
Areas of Operation: PA
Type of Foodservice: Quick Serve (6)
Franchise Affiliation: Doctor's Associates Inc., MILFORD, CT

Key Personnel
TIM MURRAY - President; Owner

Albert & Carol Mueller Inc.
104 S State St
Clarks Summit, PA 18411-1696

Telephone: (570) 586-2255
Fax Number: (570) 586-3096
Type of Business: Chain Restaurant Operator
Year Founded: 1972
Total Sales: $37,580,000 (e)
Number of Employees: 535
Average Check: Breakfast(8); Lunch(8); Dinner(8)
Total Units: 8
Trade Names: McDonald's (8)
Units Franchised From: 8
Preferred Square Footage: 2,500; 3,000
Preferred Location Types: Freestanding
Primary Menu: Hamburger (8)
Areas of Operation: PA
Type of Foodservice: Quick Serve (8)
Franchise Affiliation: McDonald's Corporation, CHICAGO, IL

Key Personnel
ALBERT MUELLER - Partner; Director Operations, Facility/Maintenance, Information Systems, Real Estate; General Buyer
CAROL MUELLER - Partner; Director Operations, Facility/Maintenance, Information Systems, Real Estate; General Buyer
HENRY WESLOWSKI - Director Operations, Purchasing, Supply Chain
JOE BENITA - Director Information Technology

Domino's Franchisee
318 Chestnut St
Columbia, PA 17512-1156

Telephone: (717) 684-3006
Type of Business: Chain Restaurant Operator
Total Sales: $9,985,000 (e)
Total Units: 5
Trade Names: Domino's (5)
Units Franchised From: 5
Primary Menu: Pizza (5)
Projected Openings: 2
Areas of Operation: PA
Type of Foodservice: Quick Serve (5)
Franchise Affiliation: Domino's Pizza Inc, ANN ARBOR, MI

Key Personnel
COURTNERY MILNE - Owner; General Buyer
ADAM ALTLAND - General Manager

IKEA North America
420 Alan Wood Rd
Conshohocken, PA 19428-1141

Telephone: (610) 834-0180
Fax Number: (610) 834-0872
Internet Homepage: ikea.com
Company Email: info@ikea.com
Type of Business: Nontraditional Foodservice Operator
Year Founded: 1943
Total Sales: $12,555,527,000 (e)
Number of Employees: 193,800
Average Check: Breakfast(5); Lunch(6); Dinner(10)

Foodservice Sales: $564,998,000 (e)
Internet Order Processing: Yes
Total Units: 52
Trade Names: IKEA Restaurant Cafe (52)
Company-Owned Units: 52
Preferred Location Types: Freestanding
Primary Menu: Miscellaneous (52)
Projected Openings: 1
Areas of Operation: AZ, CA, CO, CT, FL, GA, IL, KS, MA, MD, MI, MN, NC, NJ, NV, NY, OH, OR, PA, TN, TX, UT, VA, WA, AB, BC, MB, ON, QC
Foreign Countries: CANADA
Type of Foodservice: In-Store Feeder (52)
Parent Company: Inter IKEA Systems B.V., , NLD
Notes: The company derives approximately 95% of its revenue from retail furniture store operations.

Key Personnel
JESPER BRODIN - CEO
BRIAN DROZD - President Financial Planning
MARK FOUTCH - CFO
ROB OLSON - CFO; Director Purchasing, Supply Chain; General Buyer
MICHAEL HARRIGAN - VP Operations, Information Technology
PAM ANDREWS - VP Logistics
NELE BOUCHIER - Director Communications
TIMOTHY EMBRETSON - Director Digital
MICHAEL CAVALIERE - Director Compliance
AMY HAGGBLOM - Director Talent
RICH PIECHOWSKI - Director Tax
JAVIER QUINONES - Manager Retail Operations
KJELD RASMUSSEN - Manager
AMY SINGER - Manager Design
TERRI DIEROLF - Manager Logistics
KRISTA BOYER - Manager Menu Development
ANNIE BOECKMAN - Manager Loyalty Program
MATTHEW HOBBS - Manager Operations, Fulfillment
MICHAEL HAWK - Analyst Information Systems

Pizzeria Cinque, Inc.
1009 W Ridge Pike
Conshohocken, PA 19428-1015

Telephone: (610) 825-3050
Company Email: gpkeenan@gmail.com
Type of Business: Chain Restaurant Operator
Total Sales: $6,854,000 (e)
Average Check: Dinner(8)
Total Units: 2
Trade Names: Uno Chicago Grill (2)
Units Franchised From: 2
Primary Menu: Pizza (2)
Areas of Operation: NY, PA
Type of Foodservice: Casual Dining (2)
Franchise Affiliation: Uno Restaurants, LLC, NORWOOD, MA

Key Personnel
GREG KEENAN - President; General Buyer

Saladworks Inc.
1001 Conshohocken State Rd 100 Four Falls Bldg, Suite 600
Conshohocken, PA 19428

Telephone: (610) 825-3080
Fax Number: (610) 825-3280
Internet Homepage: saladworks.com
Type of Business: Chain Restaurant Operator
Year Founded: 1986
Systemwide Sales: $101,903,000 (e)
Total Sales: $11,950,000 (e)
Number of Employees: 86
Average Check: Lunch(10); Dinner(10)
Internet Order Processing: Yes
Total Units: 100
Trade Names: Saladworks (100)
Company-Owned Units: 1
Units Franchised To: 99
Preferred Square Footage: 3,000
Preferred Location Types: Freestanding; Regional Mall; Strip Mall
Primary Menu: American (100)
Projected Openings: 90
Areas of Operation: DE, GA, IL, KY, MD, NC, NJ, NY, PA, TN, TX, VA, WV
Foreign Countries: CANADA; QATAR; SINGAPORE; UNITED ARAB EMIRATES
Type of Foodservice: Fast Casual (100)
Foodservice Management Venues: Business & Industry; College & University
Catering Services: Yes
Primary Distributors: (Full Line) US Foods, GREENSBURG, PA
Parent Company: WOWorks, CONSHOHOCKEN, PA

Key Personnel
KELLY RODDY - CEO
BRIAN FARRIS - Chief Development Officer
LAURIENA BORSTEIN - VP Operations
ADAM TERRANOVA - Director Marketing
CLIFF WOOD - Director Store Operations

SAVOR...
300 Conshohocken State Rd Ste 770
Conshohocken, PA 19428-3804

Telephone: (610) 729-7900
Fax Number: (610) 729-1590
Internet Homepage: savorsmg.com
Company Email: Savorthemoment@asmglobal.com
Type of Business: Foodservice Management Operator
Year Founded: 1983
Number of Locations Served: 101
Total Foodservice Mgmt Accounts: 101
Areas of Operation: AK, CA, FL, GA, HI, IA, IN, KS, KY, LA, MA, MI, MS, NC, NE, NJ, NM, NY, OK, PA, PR, RI, SC, SD, TN, TX, UT, VA, WA, WV, ON
Foreign Countries: CANADA; ENGLAND; GERMANY
Type of Foodservice: Full-service sit-down dining; Mobile units/kiosks; Quick Serve
Foodservice Management Venues: Other; Parks & Recreation; Sports Venues
Catering Services: Yes
Parent Company: American Capital Ltd, BETHESDA, MD
Headquarters: SMG Holdings Inc., WEST CONSHOHOCKEN, PA

Key Personnel
WES WESTLEY - CEO; President
JENNIFER LEMOS - CEO
SHAUN BEARD - Senior VP Operations, Food and Beverage
JAMIE PARKS - VP East Region
CHRIS BENEVENTO - VP Region
MURAT ESKICIOGLU - General Manager Region
VERONICA QUINTERO - General Manager Region
T. J. HEININGER - Director Finance
MACK GILLENWATER - Director Midwest Region
SCOTT MONTEVERDE - Director Southeast Region
BEATRIZ VALENZUELA - Director Food
THOMAS ROBERTS - Director Food
STEVEN PHASON - Director Operations

Summerwood Corporation
14 Balligomingo Rd
Conshohocken, PA 19428-2725

Mailing Address: PO Box 429, CONSHOHOCKEN, PA, 19428-0429
Telephone: (610) 260-1500
Fax Number: (610) 260-1510
Internet Homepage: summerwood.biz
Company Email: info@summerwood.biz
Type of Business: Chain Restaurant Operator
Year Founded: 1980
Total Sales: $163,840,000 (e)
Number of Employees: 2,682
Average Check: Breakfast(6); Lunch(12); Dinner(12)
Total Units: 109
Trade Names: KFC (0); KFC/Taco Bell (0); Taco Bell (0); Taco Bell/Long John Silver's (0); Taco Bell/Pizza Hut (0)
Units Franchised From: 109
Preferred Square Footage: 2,000
Preferred Location Types: Community Mall; Freestanding; Regional Mall; Strip Mall
Primary Menu: Chicken (0); Pizza (0); Seafood (0); Taco (0)
Areas of Operation: DE, NJ, PA

Type of Foodservice: Quick Serve (109)
Franchise Affiliation: KFC Corporation, LOUISVILLE, KY; Pizza Hut Inc., PLANO, TX; Taco Bell Corp., IRVINE, CA
Primary Distributors: (Full Line) McLane Foodservice, CARROLLTON, TX

Key Personnel
JAMES F. NASUTI - Chairman; CEO
MATT DOEL - President; Partner
JOHN MARSELLA JR - Partner
CELESTE NASUTI - CFO; Exec VP; Director Finance
JIM FULLAM - COO; VP Operations, Marketing; General Buyer
BRET BAEVSKY - COO
KATHY MULLANE - Chief People Officer
TERRY WALKER - CTO; VP Information Technology
JOHN GROOMES - Controller
DENISE BRANCA - Director Facility/Maintenance, Construction
CHRIS WENSTRUP - Director Information Technology
PEGGY KONTRA - Manager Loss Prevention, Risk Management
LORI GROSSMAN - Manager Marketing

Freedom Square Diner
1185 Freedom Rd
Cranberry Township, PA 16066

Telephone: (724) 591-5080
Internet Homepage: freedomsquarediner.com
Company Email: tomcross1429@gmail.com
Type of Business: Chain Restaurant Operator
Year Founded: 2008
Total Units: 4
Trade Names: Freedom Square Diner (4)
Company-Owned Units: 3
Units Franchised To: 1
Primary Menu: American (4)
Projected Openings: 1
Areas of Operation: PA
Type of Foodservice: Casual Dining (4)

Key Personnel
TOM CROSS - Owner; General Buyer
CHRIS CHRIS - Owner

McDonald's Tri-County Management
10 National Way
Cranberry Township, PA 16066-7544

Telephone: (724) 776-6440
Fax Number: (724) 776-4950
Internet Homepage: tricountymanagement.com
Type of Business: Chain Restaurant Operator
Year Founded: 1976
Total Sales: $85,200,000 (e)
Number of Employees: 820
Average Check: Breakfast(8); Lunch(8); Dinner(10)
Total Units: 18
Trade Names: McDonald's (18)
Units Franchised From: 18
Preferred Square Footage: 2,500
Preferred Location Types: Discount Dept. Stores; Freestanding
Primary Menu: Hamburger (18)
Areas of Operation: PA
Type of Foodservice: Quick Serve (18)
Franchise Affiliation: McDonald's Corporation, CHICAGO, IL
Primary Distributors: (Full Line) The Martin-Brower Co., CONROE, TX

Key Personnel
PAUL SWEENEY - President; Partner; Director Purchasing, Real Estate, Design; General Buyer
MEGHAN SWEENEY - Partner; Manager Finance, Human Resources; General Buyer
PAUL CHAUVIN - CFO; Controller
JENNIFER CHRISTY - General Manager
KATHLEEN LIVINGSTON - General Manager
BRENDAN VARGA - General Manager
ANDY GRANDINETTI - Director Operations

The Coffee Village
240 Executive Dr. Unit 1842
Cranberry Twp, PA 16066

Telephone: (412) 356-5127
Internet Homepage: crazymocha.com
Company Email: info@coffeevillages.com
Type of Business: Chain Restaurant Operator
Year Founded: 2000
Total Sales: $4,946,000 (e)
Total Units: 5
Trade Names: The Coffee Village (5)
Company-Owned Units: 5
Primary Menu: Coffee (5)
Areas of Operation: PA
Type of Foodservice: Quick Serve (5)

Key Personnel
ED WETHLI - Founder; Owner
REE MITRA - Manager Operations

Metz Culinary Management
2 Woodland Dr
Dallas, PA 18612-9159

Telephone: (570) 675-8100
Fax Number: (570) 675-0919
Internet Homepage: metzculinary.com
Company Email: bgurdock@metzcorp.com
Type of Business: Foodservice Management Operator
Year Founded: 1994
Total Sales: $117,009,000 (e)
Number of Employees: 3,400
Number of Locations Served: 150
Total Foodservice Mgmt Accounts: 150
Total Units: 26
Trade Names: Lucky's Craft Food & Drink (3); Marlows Tavern (11); Ruth's Chris Steak House (1); T.G.I. Friday's (11)
Company-Owned Units: 14
Units Franchised From: 12
Areas of Operation: PA
Type of Foodservice: Cafeteria (150)
Foodservice Management Venues: Business & Industry; College & University; Health Care; Schools
Franchise Affiliation: T.G.I. Friday's Inc., DALLAS, TX
Primary Distributors: (Full Line) US Foods, ALLENTOWN, PA
Parent Company: Metz Enterprises, DALLAS, PA

Key Personnel
JOHN C. METZ - Executive Chairman
JEFFREY C. METZ - CEO; President
MAUREEN METZ - Exec VP
JAMES DICKSON - Senior VP Operations, Division
CRAIG SOLOMON - Senior VP Operations, Division
BRIAN BACHMAN - VP Purchasing
GREG POLK - VP Finance
JOHN GERONIMO - VP Sales
CHERYL MCCANN - VP Human Resources
MIKE CRAMTON - Controller
WESLEY EPSTEIN - General Manager
MIKE GALLAGHER - Director Information Technology
STEVE DALANSKY - Director Safety, Loss Prevention
MELISSA SWIDA - Director Purchasing
VANESSA WEAVER - Director Marketing, Sales

Metz Culinary Management
2 Woodland Dr
Dallas, PA 18612-9159

Telephone: (570) 675-8100
Fax Number: (570) 675-0919
Internet Homepage: metzcorp.com
Type of Business: Chain Restaurant Operator
Year Founded: 1994
Total Sales: $126,080,000 (e)
Alcohol Sales: 25%
Number of Employees: 1,625
Average Check: Lunch(18); Dinner(30)
Total Units: 34
Trade Names: Lucky's Craft Food & Drink (3); Marlow's Tavern (19); Ruth's Chris Steak House (1); T.G.I. Friday's (11)
Company-Owned Units: 20

Units Franchised From: 14
Preferred Square Footage: 5,600; 6,800
Preferred Location Types: Freestanding; Strip Mall
Alcohol Served: Beer, Wine, Liquor
Primary Menu: American (33); Steak (1)
Areas of Operation: NJ, PA
Type of Foodservice: Casual Dining (33); Fine Dining (1)
Foodservice Management Venues: Schools
Franchise Affiliation: Ruth's Hospitality Group Inc., WINTER PARK, FL; T.G.I. Friday's Inc., DALLAS, TX
Primary Distributors: (Full Line) Performance Food Group, RICHMOND, VA

Key Personnel
JOHN METZ - Executive Chairman
JEFF METZ - CEO; President
GREG POLK - COO; VP Finance, Administration
CORY COCHRAN - CIO
CHRISTOPHER LINDBERG - Chief Growth Officer
JOHN GERONIMO - VP Sales
MATT HENNEY - VP Sales
TOM DIFFILY - VP Business Development
BRIAN BACHMAN - VP Purchasing
KIM BRENKUS - VP
DON REDMOND - VP Business Development
CHAD ROCKOVITS - VP Division
CHERYL MCCANN - VP Human Resources
MAUREEN METZ - VP Marketing
JEFFREY OSBORN - Executive Chef Foodservice; Director
DANIEL PRICHARD - Director Catering
FRANK NOVITSKI - Director Facility/Maintenance
JEFF ROLEN - Director
BRUCE RUBINO - Director Food
JOHN SELICK - Director Culinary Operations
RODNEY SMITH - Director
GREG VITALE - Director Food
VANESSA WEAVER - Director Marketing, Sales
JAY WILLIAMS - Director Foodservice
EUGENIA CAPOBIANCO - Director Foodservice
MIKE GALLAGHER - Director Information Technology
JEFFREY KWOLEK - Director Foodservice
REBECCA MARSTON - Manager Catering

Kavlick Enterprises
436 N Hunter Hwy
Drums, PA 18222-2143

Telephone: (570) 788-7904
Fax Number: (570) 788-7834
Type of Business: Chain Restaurant Operator
Total Sales: $42,610,000 (e)
Total Units: 9
Trade Names: McDonald's (9)
Units Franchised From: 9
Primary Menu: Hamburger (9)
Areas of Operation: PA
Type of Foodservice: Quick Serve (9)
Franchise Affiliation: McDonald's Corporation, CHICAGO, IL

Key Personnel
SCOTT KAVLICK - President; General Buyer

Buck's Pizza Franchising Inc.
53 Industrial Dr
Du Bois, PA 15801-3841

Mailing Address: PO Box 405, DU BOIS, PA, 15801-0405
Telephone: (814) 371-3076
Internet Homepage: buckspizza.com
Type of Business: Chain Restaurant Operator
Year Founded: 1994
Systemwide Sales: $22,489,000 (e)
Total Sales: $958,000 (e)
Alcohol Sales: 10%
Number of Employees: 32
Average Check: Lunch(12); Dinner(16)
Internet Order Processing: Yes
Total Units: 16
Trade Names: Buck's Pizza (16)
Company-Owned Units: 1
Units Franchised To: 15
Preferred Square Footage: 1,200; 5,000
Preferred Location Types: Downtown; Freestanding; Strip Mall
Alcohol Served: Beer, Wine, Liquor
Primary Menu: Pizza (16)
Areas of Operation: GA, MN, NC, NY, PA, SC, TX, WI
Type of Foodservice: Quick Serve (16)
Catering Services: Yes
Primary Distributors: (Food) Performance Foodservice, SPRINGFIELD, MO

Key Personnel
JOSH BENTON - CEO; President; Partner; General Buyer
NATHAN BENTON - Partner; Director Training; Consultant
LANCE BENTON - Director Facility/Maintenance

Domino's Franchisee
177 Glimcher Dr
Duncansville, PA 16635-9415

Telephone: (814) 696-9300
Type of Business: Chain Restaurant Operator
Total Sales: $3,983,000 (e)
Total Units: 2
Trade Names: Domino's (2)
Units Franchised From: 2
Primary Menu: Pizza (2)
Areas of Operation: PA
Type of Foodservice: Quick Serve (2)
Franchise Affiliation: Domino's Pizza Inc, ANN ARBOR, MI

Key Personnel
SHELDON R. PORT - Owner; General Buyer

Hoss's Steak & Sea House Inc.
170 Patchway Rd
Duncansville, PA 16635-8431

Telephone: (814) 695-7600
Fax Number: (814) 695-3865
Internet Homepage: hosss.com; marzonis.com
Company Email: comments@hosscorp.com
Type of Business: Chain Restaurant Operator
Year Founded: 1983
Total Sales: $123,640,000 (e)
Number of Employees: 3,080
Average Check: Lunch(12); Dinner(12)
Internet Order Processing: Yes
Total Units: 34
Trade Names: Hoss's Steak & Sea House (30); Marzoni's (4)
Company-Owned Units: 34
Preferred Square Footage: 9,400
Preferred Location Types: Freestanding
Primary Menu: Pizza (5); Steak/Seafood (30)
Areas of Operation: PA, WV
Type of Foodservice: Casual Dining (5); Family Restaurant (30)
Distribution Centers: CLAYSBURG, PA
Primary Distributors: (Food) Reinhart FoodService, MARSHALL, MN

Key Personnel
CARL RAUP - CFO
PHIL SUKENIK - VP Restaurant Operations
PATRICIA MARKS - Controller
JOE HIRSCH - General Manager
ERIK LINDBERG - General Manager
BILLIE JO WALLS - Director Marketing
DON IMLER - Director Human Resources
TAMI CHADICK - District Manager
CHIP GAPSHES - Manager District
DANIEL MUTTER - Manager
BRENDA OAKES - Manager Benefits
TOM PHILBIN - Manager Information Technology

Meadows Original Frozen Custard
1393 Old Route 220 N
Duncansville, PA 16635

Telephone: (814) 695-0035
Internet Homepage: meadowsfrozencustard.com
Type of Business: Chain Restaurant Operator

Year Founded: 1950
Total Sales: $20,060,000 (e)
Total Units: 30
Trade Names: Meadows Original Frozen Custard (30)
Units Franchised To: 30
Primary Menu: Snacks (30)
Areas of Operation: MD, NC, NJ, PA
Type of Foodservice: Quick Serve (30)

Key Personnel
RICHARD MEADOWS - President; Partner; VP Purchasing, Marketing, Research & Development; General Buyer
JAY MEADOWS - Partner; VP
JOEL MEADOWS - Partner

Domino's Franchisee
900 Business Dr Ste 101
East Stroudsburg, PA 18302-9101

Telephone: (570) 223-5050
Type of Business: Chain Restaurant Operator
Total Sales: $39,955,000 (e)
Total Units: 20
Trade Names: Domino's (20)
Units Franchised From: 20
Primary Menu: Pizza (20)
Areas of Operation: PA
Type of Foodservice: Quick Serve (20)
Franchise Affiliation: Domino's Pizza Inc, ANN ARBOR, MI

Key Personnel
KHUSHMINDER S. BHULLAR - Owner; General Buyer

Don Juan Mex Grill
2600 William Penn Hwy
Easton, PA 18045

Mailing Address: P.O. Box 1064, Easton, PA, 18042
Telephone: (610) 438-5661
Internet Homepage: donjuanmexgrill.com
Company Email: info@donjuanmexgrill.com
Type of Business: Chain Restaurant Operator
Year Founded: 2010
Total Units: 5
Trade Names: Don Juan Mex Grill (4); Don Juan Mex Grill & Cantina (1)
Company-Owned Units: 5
Preferred Location Types: Freestanding; Strip Mall
Primary Menu: Mexican (5)
Areas of Operation: PA
Type of Foodservice: Casual Dining (1); Family Restaurant (4)

Key Personnel
JUAN MARTINEZ - Co-Founder; Partner

Subway Franchise
135 S Market St
Elizabethtown, PA 17022-2308

Telephone: (717) 367-8585
Internet Homepage: subway.com
Type of Business: Chain Restaurant Operator
Total Sales: $2,509,000 (e)
Total Units: 4
Trade Names: Subway (4)
Units Franchised From: 4
Primary Menu: Sandwiches/Deli (4)
Areas of Operation: PA
Type of Foodservice: Quick Serve (4)
Franchise Affiliation: Doctor's Associates Inc., MILFORD, CT

Key Personnel
SHARON PLANK - President

T.J. Rockwell's American Grill & Tavern
800 Mount Gretna Rd
Elizabethtown, PA 17022-1333

Telephone: (717) 367-5544
Fax Number: (717) 367-1992
Internet Homepage: tjrockwells.com
Company Email: info@tjrockwells.com
Type of Business: Chain Restaurant Operator
Year Founded: 1997
Total Sales: $7,800,000 (e)
Alcohol Sales: 15%
Number of Employees: 190
Average Check: Lunch(10); Dinner(16)
Internet Order Processing: Yes
Total Units: 2
Trade Names: TJ Rockwell's American Grill & Tavern (2)
Company-Owned Units: 2
Preferred Location Types: Freestanding; Strip Mall
Alcohol Served: Beer, Wine, Liquor
Primary Menu: American (2)
Areas of Operation: PA
Type of Foodservice: Casual Dining (2)

Key Personnel
JEFF HECKMAN - Partner

Yocco's Hot Dog King
16 E Minor St
Emmaus, PA 18049-4104

Telephone: (610) 928-3100
Fax Number: (610) 928-3200
Internet Homepage: yoccos.com
Type of Business: Chain Restaurant Operator
Year Founded: 1922
Total Sales: $2,167,000 (e)
Alcohol Sales: 0.50%
Number of Employees: 110
Average Check: Lunch(10); Dinner(10)
Total Units: 6
Trade Names: Yocco's Hot Dog King (6)
Company-Owned Units: 6
Preferred Square Footage: 2,000; 3,000
Preferred Location Types: Freestanding; Strip Mall
Alcohol Served: Beer
Primary Menu: Hot Dogs (6)
Areas of Operation: PA
Type of Foodservice: Quick Serve (6)

Key Personnel
GARY IACOCCA - President; General Manager; General Buyer
CHRISTOPHER IACOCCA - VP Operations; Manager
PAM GEHRINGER - Controller

Domino's Franchisee
1101 Peninsula Dr Ste 214
Erie, PA 16505-4169

Telephone: (814) 833-5600
Type of Business: Chain Restaurant Operator
Total Sales: $8,027,000 (e)
Total Units: 4
Trade Names: Domino's (4)
Units Franchised From: 4
Primary Menu: Pizza (4)
Areas of Operation: PA
Type of Foodservice: Quick Serve (4)
Franchise Affiliation: Domino's Pizza Inc, ANN ARBOR, MI

Key Personnel
PAUL M. MOHTASHEMI - Owner; General Buyer

Lyndal Enterprises Inc.
3939 W Ridge Rd Ste B42
Erie, PA 16506-1888

Telephone: (814) 833-8880
Fax Number: (814) 833-8848
Internet Homepage: fengshuichi.wixsite.com/littlecaesars
Type of Business: Chain Restaurant Operator
Total Sales: $23,470,000 (e)
Number of Employees: 240
Average Check: Dinner(16)
Total Units: 19
Trade Names: Little Caesars Pizza (19)
Units Franchised From: 19

Preferred Square Footage: 1,600; 3,000
Preferred Location Types: Strip Mall
Primary Menu: Pizza (19)
Areas of Operation: OH, PA
Type of Foodservice: Quick Serve (19)
Franchise Affiliation: Little Caesar Enterprises Inc., DETROIT, MI

Key Personnel
LYNN MCBRIER - President; Owner; General Buyer
DALE MCBRIER - VP
JUSTIN BORRERO - Director Operations
TRACY WORTH - Manager Administration

Patterson-Erie Corp.
1250 Tower Ln Ste 1
Erie, PA 16505-2533

Telephone: (814) 455-8031
Fax Number: (814) 453-5553
Type of Business: Chain Restaurant Operator
Year Founded: 1988
Total Sales: $42,760,000 (e)
Number of Employees: 1,360
Average Check: Breakfast(8); Lunch(10); Dinner(12)
Total Units: 19
Trade Names: Burger King (19)
Units Franchised From: 19
Preferred Square Footage: 2,500
Preferred Location Types: Freestanding
Primary Menu: Hamburger (19)
Projected Openings: 3
Areas of Operation: OH, PA
Type of Foodservice: Quick Serve (19)
Franchise Affiliation: Burger King Worldwide Inc., MIAMI, FL
Primary Distributors: (Full Line) Maines Paper & Food Services Ohio, OAKWOOD VILLAGE, OH

Key Personnel
WILLIAM L. PATTERSON JR - President; Director Real Estate
CAMERON MCCORMICK - CFO
KEITH EGYED - Director Operations, Purchasing, Information Systems, Supply Chain
PATRICIA LOCKE - Director Human Resources

Scott's Apple, Inc.
2225 Downs Dr Fl 6
Erie, PA 16509-4793

Telephone: (814) 868-9500
Internet Homepage: visitscott.com
Type of Business: Chain Restaurant Operator
Total Sales: $33,410,000 (e)
Total Units: 10
Trade Names: Applebee's Neighborhood Grill & Bar (5); Hooch & Blotto's (1); IHOP (2); Quaker Steak & Lube (1); Safari Grille (1)
Units Franchised From: 10
Alcohol Served: Beer, Wine, Liquor
Primary Menu: American (10)
Areas of Operation: PA
Type of Foodservice: Casual Dining (10)
Franchise Affiliation: Applebee's Services Inc., KANSAS CITY, MO

Key Personnel
NICHOLAS C. SCOTT - President
NICK SCOTT JR - VP
CHRIS SCOTT - VP

Thomel Enterprises, Inc.
2645 W 25th St
Erie, PA 16506-3011

Mailing Address: PO BOX 8288, ERIE, PA, 16505
Telephone: (814) 835-3546
Fax Number: (814) 836-9994
Company Email: bkducharme@gmail.com
Type of Business: Chain Restaurant Operator
Total Sales: $23,440,000 (e)
Total Units: 5
Trade Names: McDonald's (5)
Units Franchised From: 5
Preferred Location Types: Freestanding
Primary Menu: Hamburger (5)
Areas of Operation: PA
Type of Foodservice: Quick Serve (5)
Franchise Affiliation: McDonald's Corporation, CHICAGO, IL

Key Personnel
THOMAS DUCHARME JR - President; General Buyer

Iron Hill Brewery, LLC
260 Eagleview Blvd
Exton, PA 19341

Telephone: (302) 472-2739
Fax Number: (302) 652-4115
Internet Homepage: ironhillbrewery.com
Company Email: geninfo@ironhillbrewery.com
Type of Business: Chain Restaurant Operator
Year Founded: 1996
Total Sales: $53,820,000 (e)
Alcohol Sales: 30%
Number of Employees: 900
Average Check: Lunch(14); Dinner(20)
Total Units: 21
Trade Names: Iron Hill Brewery and Restaurant (21)
Company-Owned Units: 21
Preferred Square Footage: 5,500; 6,000
Preferred Location Types: Freestanding; Strip Mall
Alcohol Served: Beer, Wine, Liquor
Primary Menu: American (21)
Projected Openings: 2
Areas of Operation: DE, NJ, PA
Type of Foodservice: Casual Dining (21)
Primary Distributors: (Full Line) SYSCO Food Services of Philadelphia LLC, PHILADELPHIA, PA

Key Personnel
KEVIN FINN - Chairman; Partner; Director Marketing
KEVIN DAVIES - Partner; Director Finance, Purchasing, Supply Chain, Food and Beverage
MARK EDELSON - Partner; Director Manufacturing-Alcoholic Beverages

Rockham 5G DE/NJ/PA LLC
PO Box 1437
Exton, PA 19341-0106

Telephone: (703) 869-8483
Internet Homepage: rockham.com
Type of Business: Chain Restaurant Operator
Total Sales: $44,710,000 (e)
Number of Employees: 460
Total Units: 23
Trade Names: Five Guys Burgers and Fries (23); Melt Shop
Units Franchised From: 23
Preferred Square Footage: 3,000
Primary Menu: Hamburger (23)
Projected Openings: 1
Areas of Operation: DE, NJ, PA
Type of Foodservice: Fast Casual (23)
Franchise Affiliation: Aurify Brands LLC, NEW YORK, NY; Five Guys Holdings Inc., LORTON, VA

Key Personnel
DREW SMITH - President; General Buyer

The Drafting Room Inc.
540 Wellington Sq
Exton, PA 19341

Telephone: (610) 321-1600
Internet Homepage: bricksidegrille.com
Company Email: taproom@msn.com
Type of Business: Chain Restaurant Operator
Year Founded: 1994
Total Sales: $1,520,000 (e)
Alcohol Sales: 10%
Number of Employees: 60
Average Check: Lunch(12); Dinner(24)
Total Units: 1
Trade Names: Brickside Grille (1)
Company-Owned Units: 1
Preferred Location Types: Freestanding
Alcohol Served: Beer, Wine, Liquor

Primary Menu: American (1)
Areas of Operation: PA
Type of Foodservice: Casual Dining (1)
Catering Services: Yes
Primary Distributors: (Full Line) SYSCO Food Services of Central Pennsylvania LLC, HARRISBURG, PA

Key Personnel
ANDREW WEINTRAUB - Owner; General Buyer

Kosmart Enterprises Inc.
420 Scranton Carbondale Hwy
Eynon, PA 18403

Telephone: (570) 876-5277
Type of Business: Chain Restaurant Operator
Total Sales: $3,884,000 (e)
Alcohol Sales: 3%
Number of Employees: 200
Average Check: Lunch(14); Dinner(14)
Total Units: 3
Trade Names: Pizza Hut (3)
Units Franchised From: 3
Preferred Square Footage: 2,500; 3,200
Preferred Location Types: Freestanding
Alcohol Served: Beer
Primary Menu: Pizza (3)
Areas of Operation: PA
Type of Foodservice: Quick Serve (3)
Franchise Affiliation: Pizza Hut Inc., PLANO, TX
Primary Distributors: (Food) McLane/Burlington, BURLINGTON, NJ

Key Personnel
BOB KENNEDY - President; General Buyer

Management Associates
1900 Macdade Blvd
Folsom, PA 19033-1316

Telephone: (610) 583-6911
Fax Number: (610) 586-5150
Internet Homepage: niftyfiftys.com
Company Email: comments@niftyfiftys.com
Type of Business: Chain Restaurant Operator
Year Founded: 1987
Total Sales: $5,871,000 (e)
Number of Employees: 150
Average Check: Breakfast(10); Lunch(12); Dinner(16)
Total Units: 3
Trade Names: Nifty Fifty's (3)
Company-Owned Units: 3
Preferred Location Types: Freestanding
Primary Menu: American (3)
Areas of Operation: NJ, PA
Type of Foodservice: Family Restaurant (3)
Primary Distributors: (Food) Cedar Farms Co.

Inc., PHILADELPHIA, PA

Key Personnel
DONNA MCGLYNN - Owner; Executive Chef; Director Real Estate, Menu Development; General Buyer
DOUG YOUNG - CFO

Eurest Dining Services
220 Commerce Dr Ste 330
Fort Washington, PA 19034-2419

Telephone: (215) 361-2700
Fax Number: (215) 361-7169
Listing Type: Divisional Office
Type of Business: Foodservice Management Operator
Number of Employees: 1,000
Number of Locations Served: 100
Total Foodservice Mgmt Accounts: 100
Type of Foodservice: Cafeteria (100)
Foodservice Management Venues: Business & Industry
Primary Distributors: (Equipment) Bunzl - Mid-Atlantic Region, PHILADELPHIA, PA; (Food) Performance Food Group, RICHMOND, VA; (Supplies) Bunzl - Mid-Atlantic Region, PHILADELPHIA, PA
Parent Company: Compass Group The Americas, CHARLOTTE, NC
Headquarters: Eurest Dining Services, CHESTERBROOK, PA

Key Personnel
CRISTA WIZEMAN - Regional Director

Papa John's Distribution Center
2513 Lovi Rd
Freedom, PA 15042-9395

Telephone: (724) 770-9100
Fax Number: (724) 770-9190
Listing Type: Distribution Center
Type of Business: Foodservice Operations - Bowling Alley
Areas of Operation: MI, OH, PA, VA, WV
Parent Company: Papa Johns International Inc., LOUISVILLE, KY

Key Personnel
CORY D'ANGELO - General Manager

Auntie Anne's Franchise
1863 Gettysburg Village Dr Ste 1090
Gettysburg, PA 17325-6708

Telephone: (717) 337-3760

Type of Business: Chain Restaurant Operator
Total Sales: $3,163,000 (e)
Total Units: 4
Trade Names: Auntie Anne's Hand-Rolled Soft Pretzels (4)
Units Franchised From: 4
Primary Menu: Snacks (4)
Areas of Operation: PA
Type of Foodservice: Quick Serve (4)
Franchise Affiliation: Auntie Anne's Inc., LANCASTER, PA

Key Personnel
AMIT SHEGLE - Owner; General Buyer

Caplan Industries
1015 E Philadelphia Ave
Gilbertsville, PA 19525-9516

Telephone: (610) 367-1490
Fax Number: (610) 367-1491
Type of Business: Chain Restaurant Operator
Year Founded: 1978
Total Sales: $42,690,000 (e)
Number of Employees: 400
Average Check: Breakfast(6); Lunch(8); Dinner(10)
Total Units: 9
Trade Names: McDonald's (9)
Units Franchised From: 9
Preferred Square Footage: 2,500; 3,000
Preferred Location Types: Freestanding
Primary Menu: Hamburger (9)
Areas of Operation: PA
Type of Foodservice: Quick Serve (9)
Franchise Affiliation: McDonald's Corporation, CHICAGO, IL

Key Personnel
DOUG CAPLAN - Owner; General Buyer

Concordville Inn
780 Baltimore Pike
Glen Mills, PA 19342-1040

Mailing Address: PO Box 607, CONCORDVILLE, PA, 19331-0607
Telephone: (610) 358-9400
Fax Number: (610) 358-9381
Internet Homepage: concordvilleinn.com; mendenhallinn.com
Company Email: info@station52pizza.com
Type of Business: Chain Restaurant Operator
Year Founded: 1968
Total Sales: $6,098,000 (e)
Alcohol Sales: 20%
Number of Employees: 125
Average Check: Lunch(26); Dinner(36)
Internet Order Processing: Yes
Internet Sales: 0.50%
Total Units: 2

Trade Names: Concordville Inn (1); Mendenhall Inn (1)
Company-Owned Units: 2
Preferred Location Types: Freestanding
Alcohol Served: Beer, Wine, Liquor
Primary Menu: American (2)
Areas of Operation: PA
Type of Foodservice: Fine Dining (2)
Catering Services: Yes
Primary Distributors: (Full Line) SYSCO Food Services of Albany, HALFMOON, NY

Key Personnel
STEVE ANGELINE - Director Operations
JUAN BUSTOS - Manager

Domino's Franchisee
1012 Baltimore St
Hanover, PA 17331-4401

Telephone: (717) 633-9411
Type of Business: Chain Restaurant Operator
Total Sales: $3,992,000 (e)
Total Units: 2
Trade Names: Domino's (2)
Units Franchised From: 2
Primary Menu: Pizza (2)
Areas of Operation: PA
Type of Foodservice: Quick Serve (2)
Franchise Affiliation: Domino's Pizza Inc, ANN ARBOR, MI

Key Personnel
JAY WARREN - Owner; General Buyer

Pretzels Plus Inc.
255 Penn St
Hanover, PA 17331

Telephone: (717) 633-7927
Fax Number: (717) 633-5078
Internet Homepage: pretzelsplus.com
Company Email: pretzelsplus@pretzelsplus.com
Type of Business: Chain Restaurant Operator
Year Founded: 1991
Systemwide Sales: $2,407,000 (e)
Total Sales: $779,000 (e)
Number of Employees: 4
Average Check: Breakfast(8); Lunch(8); Dinner(8)
Total Units: 8
Trade Names: Pretzels Plus (8)
Company-Owned Units: 2
Units Franchised To: 6
Preferred Square Footage: 450; 1,200; 2,000
Preferred Location Types: Convenience Store/Gas Station; Downtown; Outlet Mall; Regional Mall
Primary Menu: Snacks (8)
Areas of Operation: PA, VA
Type of Foodservice: Quick Serve (8)
Distribution Centers: HANOVER, PA
On-site Distribution Center: Yes
Primary Distributors: (Full Line) Feesers Inc., HARRISBURG, PA

Key Personnel
BRAD ELINE - President; Director Operations, Real Estate, Franchise Development, Menu Development; General Buyer
MISSY ARIANO - Manager Marketing, Promotion
DIANE BREIGHNER - Manager Accounting, Information Systems, Human Resources

Arooga's Grille House & Sports Bar
1591 S 19th St
Harrisburg, PA 17104-3225

Telephone: (717) 238-9464
Internet Homepage: aroogas.com
Type of Business: Chain Restaurant Operator
Year Founded: 2008
Systemwide Sales: $61,712,000 (e)
Total Sales: $41,340,000 (e)
Internet Order Processing: Yes
Total Units: 18
Trade Names: Arooga's Grille House & Sports Bar (18)
Company-Owned Units: 10
Units Franchised To: 8
Alcohol Served: Beer, Wine, Liquor
Primary Menu: American (18)
Projected Openings: 1
Areas of Operation: CT, FL, MA, NJ, NY, PA, RI
Type of Foodservice: Casual Dining (18)
Catering Services: Yes

Key Personnel
GARY HUETHER JR - Co-Founder; President
TONY DAWOOD - Executive Chef
KEITH SWADE - Director Franchise Development
TANYA SCANNELLI - Manager Catering
BRIAN SCANNELLI - Manager District, Culinary Development

Auntie Anne's Franchise
31A Colonial Park Mall
Harrisburg, PA 17109

Telephone: (717) 540-1990
Internet Homepage: auntieannesfranchising.com
Type of Business: Chain Restaurant Operator
Total Sales: $14,470,000 (e)
Total Units: 20
Trade Names: Auntie Anne's Hand-Rolled Soft Pretzels (20)
Units Franchised From: 20
Primary Menu: Snacks (20)
Areas of Operation: PA
Type of Foodservice: Quick Serve (20)
Franchise Affiliation: Auntie Anne's Inc., LANCASTER, PA

Key Personnel
SAN ROMANO - Owner; General Buyer

Hersha Hospitality Trust
44 Hersha Dr Fl 2
Harrisburg, PA 17102-2241

Telephone: (717) 236-4400
Fax Number: (717) 774-7383
Internet Homepage: hersha.com; hershahotels.com
Type of Business: Foodservice Operations - Hotel/Motels
Year Founded: 1998
Publicly Held: Yes
Total Sales: $279,490,000 (e)
Alcohol Sales: 16%
Number of Employees: 49
Total Units: 38
Restaurants in Hotels: 38
Trade Names: Blue Moon (1); Cadillac Hotel & Beach Club (1); Courtyard by Marriott (4); Duane Street Hotel (1); Gate Hotel (1); Hampton Inn (3); Hilton Garden Inn (4); Holiday Inn Express & Suites (2); Hyatt (1); Hyatt House (1); Marriott (1); Nu Hotel (1); Parrot Key Hotel & Villas (1); Residence Inn Miami Coconut Grove (1); Rittenhouse Hotel (1); Sheraton (1); The Ambrose Hotel (1); The Boxer (1); The Capitol Hill Hotel (1); The Envoy (1); The Hotel Milo (1); The Pan Pacific Hotel Seattle (1); The Ritz-Carlton (2); The Sanctuary Beach Resort (1); The St. Gregory Hotel (1); TownePlace Suites (1); Westin (1); Winter Haven (1)
Company-Owned Units: 38
Alcohol Served: Beer, Wine, Liquor
Areas of Operation: AZ, CA, CT, DC, DE, FL, MA, MD, NJ, NY, PA, VA
Primary Distributors: (Food) SYSCO Food Services of Philadelphia LLC, PHILADELPHIA, PA
Notes: Hersha Hospitality Trust derives approximately 89% of its revenue from the operation of hotels. The company also operates a number of limited-service hotels/motels without restaurants; the list of trade names includes these operations and revenue from these locations are included in total sales. The total number of locations also includes joint-venture properties.

Key Personnel
HASU P. SHAH - Chairman
JAY H. SHAH - CEO

NAVEEN KAKARLA - CEO Group; President Group
NEIL H. SHAH - President; COO
ASHISH R. PARIKH - CFO
MICHAEL R. GILLESPIE - Chief Accounting Officer
MICHAEL W. MURRAY - COO
GREGORY ADE - Exec VP Operations
WILLIAM J. WALSH - Senior VP Asset Protection, Strategic Planning
DAVID L. DESFOR - Treasurer; Corporate Secretary
KIRAN P. PATEL - Corporate Secretary
BRETT SHADE CPA - Manager Tax

● ▲
Hazel-Wen, Inc.
61 N Cedar St
Hazleton, PA 18201-6037

Mailing Address: PO Box 2241, HAZLETON, PA, 18201-0380
Telephone: (570) 459-1424
Fax Number: (570) 459-3468
Type of Business: Chain Restaurant Operator
Total Sales: $11,770,000 (e)
Total Units: 4
Trade Names: Wendy's Old Fashioned Hamburgers (4)
Units Franchised From: 4
Primary Menu: Hamburger (4)
Areas of Operation: PA
Type of Foodservice: Quick Serve (4)
Franchise Affiliation: The Wendy's Company, DUBLIN, OH

Key Personnel
MARY ELIZABETH HAYDEN - Owner; General Buyer
TERRI STRAUCH - General Manager

●
M&N Foods, LLC
1367 N Church St
Hazleton, PA 18202

Telephone: (570) 401-2755
Type of Business: Chain Restaurant Operator
Total Sales: $11,480,000 (e)
Total Units: 5
Trade Names: Burger King (4); The Halal Guys (1)
Units Franchised From: 5
Primary Menu: Hamburger (4); Middle Eastern (1)
Projected Openings: 1
Areas of Operation: PA
Type of Foodservice: Quick Serve (5)
Franchise Affiliation: Burger King Worldwide Inc., MIAMI, FL; The Halal Guys Inc., ASTORIA, NY

Key Personnel
NAVEEN MOHIUDDIN - President; Director Operations; General Buyer
MICHAEL BORCHARD - President
ALMA JARA - Director Communications

● ▲
McIntyre Management
654 Front St
Hellertown, PA 18055-1770

Telephone: (610) 838-4995
Fax Number: (610) 838-4989
Type of Business: Chain Restaurant Operator
Total Sales: $15,119,000 (e)
Total Units: 3
Trade Names: McDonald's (3)
Units Franchised From: 3
Preferred Location Types: Freestanding
Primary Menu: Hamburger (3)
Areas of Operation: PA
Type of Foodservice: Quick Serve (3)
Franchise Affiliation: McDonald's Corporation, CHICAGO, IL

Key Personnel
CHARLES MCINTYRE - President; General Buyer

‡
Hershey Entertainment & Resort Co.
27 W Chocolate Ave Ste 100
Hershey, PA 17033-1672

Telephone: (717) 534-3131
Internet Homepage: hersheypa.com
Company Email: info@hersheypa.com
Type of Business: Foodservice Operations - Hotel/Motels
Year Founded: 1927
Total Sales: $72,172,000 (e)
Alcohol Sales: 20%
Number of Employees: 3,000
Total Units: 2
Restaurants in Hotels: 11
Trade Names: Hershey Lodge (1); The Hotel Hershey (1)
Company-Owned Units: 11
Alcohol Served: Beer, Wine, Liquor
Areas of Operation: PA
Type of Foodservice: Casual Dining (10); Fast Casual (1)
Primary Distributors: (Food) US Foods Philadelphia Metro, BRIDGEPORT, NJ
Notes: The company derives approximately 70% of its revenue from hotel operations.

Key Personnel
JOHN LAWN - Chairman; CEO; President
DAVID LAVERY - CFO; VP
LESLIE A. FERRARO - Chief Marketing Officer; VP
GARRETT GALLIA - VP Communications, Corporate Affairs
ANDREW HELMER - VP Human Resources
GREG KLOPP - VP Information Technology
JANE W. LAFRANCHI - VP; Corporate Secretary; General Counsel
WENDY MCCLINTOCK - VP Finance; Treasurer
REBECCA A. PRICE - Controller
BRIAN O'DAY - General Manager Division
RONALD SUSKI - Director Procurement
KATHLEEN MCGRAW - Director Communications
JOHN DALY - Director Food and Beverage

▲
Kazi Foods
134 W Chocolate Ave
Hershey, PA 17033-1527

Telephone: (717) 534-2422
Fax Number: (717) 534-2239
Company Email: info@kazifoods.com
Listing Type: Regional Office
Type of Business: Chain Restaurant Operator
Year Founded: 1993
Number of Employees: 3,300
Average Check: Breakfast(6); Lunch(8); Dinner(8)
Total Units: 13
Trade Names: KFC (13)
Units Franchised From: 13
Preferred Square Footage: 2,500
Primary Menu: Chicken (13)
Areas of Operation: CA, CO, MD, PA
Parent Company: Kazi Foods Inc., STUDIO CITY, CA
Notes: This office serves as the Information Technology center for Kazi Foods.

Key Personnel
SHAMBHU ACHARYA - CFO

● ▲
Domino's Franchisee
503 Fox Chase Rd
Hollywood, PA 19046-4436

Telephone: (215) 379-0800
Type of Business: Chain Restaurant Operator
Total Sales: $24,200,000 (e)
Total Units: 12
Trade Names: Domino's (12)
Units Franchised From: 12
Primary Menu: Pizza (12)
Areas of Operation: PA
Type of Foodservice: Quick Serve (12)
Franchise Affiliation: Domino's Pizza Inc, ANN ARBOR, MI

Key Personnel
MURAT COSKUN - Owner; General Buyer

Eat'n Park Hospitality Group Inc.
285 E Waterfront Dr Ste 200
Homestead, PA 15120-5017

Telephone: (412) 461-2000
Fax Number: (412) 461-6000
Internet Homepage: eatnpark.com; enphospitality.com; hellobistro.com; sixpennkitchen.com; smileycookie.com; theporchatschenley.com
Company Email: comments@eatnpark.com
Type of Business: Chain Restaurant Operator
Year Founded: 1949
Systemwide Sales: $300,905,000 (e)
Total Sales: $609,900,000 (e)
Alcohol Sales: 1%
Number of Employees: 7,500
Average Check: Breakfast(6); Lunch(10); Dinner(12)
Foodservice Sales: $347,643,000 (e)
Internet Order Processing: Yes
Internet Sales: 10.00%
Total Units: 69
Trade Names: Eat'n Park Restaurant (57); Hello Bistro (10); The Porch at Schenley (2)
Company-Owned Units: 69
Preferred Square Footage: 6,500; 7,400
Preferred Location Types: Freestanding; Institution (college/hospital); Outlet Mall; Regional Mall; Strip Mall
Alcohol Served: Beer, Wine, Liquor
Primary Menu: American (69)
Projected Openings: 2
Areas of Operation: FL, OH, PA, WV
Type of Foodservice: Casual Dining (12); Family Restaurant (57)
Foodservice Management Venues: Business & Industry; College & University; Health Care
Distribution Centers: PITTSBURGH, PA
Subsidiaries: Parkhurst Dining Services, HOMESTEAD, PA
Primary Distributors: (Food) US Foods, GREENSBURG, PA
Notes: The company also operates Parkhurst Dining Services & Cura Hospitality. The company derives approximately 43% of its revenue from these operations. Systemwide sales reflect operation of the Eat 'n Park restaurants only.

Key Personnel
JAMES S. BROADHURST - Chairman
DAN WILSON - CFO
MERCY SENCHUR - COO
E. ANDREW DUNMIRE - VP Construction, Design
JULIA BROCHETTI - VP Accounting; Controller
JULIE BROCHETTI - VP Accounting; Controller
ANDY DUNMIRE - VP Construction, Design
BROOKS BROADHURST - VP; Transformation
MARK BROADHURST - VP Development
TONY PANAIIA - Director Recruitment
AMANDA GIACOBBI - Director Marketing
NICHOLE SCHWABENBAUER-DUDA - Director Strategic Planning
PATRICE MICHEALS - Director Development, Training
SHANNON MARSHALL - Director Human Resources
TRINA DEMARCO - Director Communications
JESSE STOCK - Director Design
ERIN STOUGHTON - Director Technology
NICOLE SCHWABENBAUER - Director Strategic Planning
COURTNEY CAPRARA - Director Omnichannel, Marketing; Manager Omnichannel, Marketing
TONY WHITE - Director
CINDY SIMAK - Director Marketing
JOHN FRICK - Director Menu Development
MICHELLE SCHOY - Director Loyalty Program
DANIELLE WEBER - Assistant Director Accounting
DOMENIC FRICIONI - District Manager
JANINE JOHNSON - Manager Marketing
CAITLIN IRION SCHWEIGHARDT - Manager
MICHAEL MIHALCO - Manager Operations, Information Technology
CHARLES MORRISON - Manager Sales
CRISTIN YODER - Designer Graphic Design
JACLYN LOVE - Designer Graphic Design

Parkhurst Dining Services
285 E Waterfront Dr Ste 200
Homestead, PA 15120-5017

Telephone: (412) 464-3000
Fax Number: (412) 464-0600
Internet Homepage: enphospitality.com; parkhurstdining.com
Company Email: dine@parkhurstdining.com
Listing Type: Subsidiary
Type of Business: Foodservice Management Operator
Year Founded: 1949
Total Sales: $24,652,000 (e)
Number of Employees: 1,500
Number of Locations Served: 110
Total Foodservice Mgmt Accounts: 30
Total Units: 40
Trade Names: Eat'n Park (60); Parkhurst Dining (40)
Company-Owned Units: 40
Areas of Operation: DE, MD, OH, PA, VA, WV
Type of Foodservice: Cafeteria (40)
Foodservice Management Venues: Business & Industry; College & University
Primary Distributors: (Full Line) US Foods, ALTOONA, PA
Parent Company: Eat'n Park Hospitality Group Inc., HOMESTEAD, PA

Key Personnel
JEFF BROADHURST - CEO; President
DAN WILSON - CFO
MARK BROADHURST - COO
SUZIE LACHUT - Director Marketing
AMY B. MOORE - Director Business Development
JAMIE MOORE - Director Sustainability, Sourcing
NELSON PRAY - Director Retail Operations
NASHE SCOTT - Director Business Development
DAN TOKAREK - Director Operations

ASHA Corporation
810 Welsh Rd Ste A
Horsham, PA 19044-1011

Telephone: (267) 626-3336
Type of Business: Chain Restaurant Operator
Total Sales: $5,074,000 (e)
Average Check: Dinner(8)
Total Units: 3
Trade Names: Dunkin' Donuts (3)
Units Franchised From: 3
Preferred Location Types: Freestanding
Primary Menu: Snacks (3)
Areas of Operation: PA
Type of Foodservice: Quick Serve (3)
Franchise Affiliation: DD IP Holder, CANTON, MA

Key Personnel
HARSHAD PATEL - President; General Buyer

BRYN and DANE's
400 Privet Rd
Horsham, PA 19044

Telephone: (215) 675-1599
Internet Homepage: brynanddanes.com; linkedin.com/company/bryn-and-danes/about
Type of Business: Chain Restaurant Operator
Year Founded: 2010
Total Units: 4
Trade Names: BRYN and DANE's (4)
Company-Owned Units: 4
Primary Menu: Health Foods (4)
Projected Openings: 2
Areas of Operation: PA
Foreign Countries: UGANDA
Type of Foodservice: Fast Casual (4)

Key Personnel
CRAIG WILLIAMS - Director Culinary Development

McDonald's Franchise
1510 Oakland Ave
Indiana, PA 15701-2494

Telephone: (724) 465-8570
Type of Business: Chain Restaurant Operator

Total Sales: $14,716,000 (e)
Average Check: Breakfast(12); Lunch(12); Dinner(12)
Total Units: 3
Trade Names: McDonald's (3)
Units Franchised From: 3
Primary Menu: Hamburger (3)
Areas of Operation: PA
Type of Foodservice: Quick Serve (3)
Franchise Affiliation: McDonald's Corporation, CHICAGO, IL

Key Personnel
JASON TEAL - President; General Buyer

Nutrition Management Services Co.
2071 Kimberton Rd
Kimberton, PA 19442

Mailing Address: PO Box 725, KIMBERTON, PA, 19442-0725
Telephone: (610) 935-2050
Fax Number: (610) 917-3629
Internet Homepage: nmsc.com
Company Email: bfioravanti@nmsc.com
Type of Business: Foodservice Management Operator
Year Founded: 1979
Total Sales: $35,989,000 (e)
Number of Employees: 1,500
Number of Locations Served: 75
Total Foodservice Mgmt Accounts: 75
Areas of Operation: PA
Type of Foodservice: Quick Serve (75)
Foodservice Management Venues: Health Care
Notes: The company derives approximately 2% of its revenue from training/conference center operations.

Key Personnel
JOSEPH V. ROBERTS - Chairman; CEO; CFO
KATHLEEN A. HILL - President; COO
KATE HILL - President
JOSEPH MAZZONI - VP
PAUL ST BERNARD - General Manager Food
NANCY RAPISARDI - General Manager
KERRIAN MERSOLA - Director
LISA SEGELBACHER - Director Food
ANDREW JENKINS - Director Food
LIGIA CARDENAS - Director Food
ANGELA STATON - Manager Food
MICHAEL CARLIN - Manager Operations

Bower Management
271 Joseph Dr
Kingston, PA 18704-5357

Telephone: (570) 287-6216

Type of Business: Chain Restaurant Operator
Year Founded: 1996
Total Sales: $10,860,000 (e)
Number of Employees: 460
Average Check: Breakfast(12); Lunch(8); Dinner(10)
Total Units: 6
Trade Names: KFC (6)
Units Franchised From: 6
Preferred Square Footage: 2,500; 3,200
Preferred Location Types: Freestanding
Primary Menu: Chicken (6)
Areas of Operation: PA
Type of Foodservice: Quick Serve (6)
Franchise Affiliation: KFC Corporation, LOUISVILLE, KY

Key Personnel
RICHARD BOWER - President; Director Information Systems; Manager Real Estate; General Buyer
ANDREA BOWER - Executive Director

Domino's Franchisee
15100 Kutztown Rd Ste 4
Kutztown, PA 19530-9214

Telephone: (610) 894-4444
Type of Business: Chain Restaurant Operator
Total Sales: $3,965,000 (e)
Total Units: 2
Trade Names: Domino's (2)
Units Franchised From: 2
Primary Menu: Pizza (2)
Areas of Operation: PA
Type of Foodservice: Quick Serve (2)
Franchise Affiliation: Domino's Pizza Inc, ANN ARBOR, MI

Key Personnel
JOHN M. BOWER - Owner; General Buyer

Auntie Anne's Inc.
48-50 W Chestnut St Ste 200
Lancaster, PA 17603-3791

Telephone: (717) 435-1435
Fax Number: (717) 435-1436
Internet Homepage: auntieannes.com
Type of Business: Chain Restaurant Operator
Year Founded: 1988
Systemwide Sales: $1,075,045,000 (e)
Total Sales: $120,360,000 (e)
Number of Employees: 250
Average Check: Lunch(8); Dinner(8)
Internet Order Processing: Yes
Internet Sales: 2.00%
Total Units: 1,920
Trade Names: Auntie Anne's Hand-Rolled Soft Pretzels (1,920)
Units Franchised To: 1,920
Preferred Square Footage: 77; 300; 450; 600
Preferred Location Types: Airports; Community Mall; Discount Dept. Stores; Downtown; Institution (college/hospital); Kiosk; Lifestyle Center; Mobile Unit; Outlet Mall; Parks; Regional Mall; Strip Mall; Travel Plazas
Primary Menu: Snacks (1,920)
Projected Openings: 110
Areas of Operation: AL, AR, AZ, CA, CO, CT, DC, DE, FL, GA, IA, IL, IN, KS, KY, LA, MA, MD, MI, MN, MO, MS, NC, ND, NE, NH, NJ, NM, NV, NY, OH, OK, OR, PA, RI, SC, SD, TN, TX, UT, VA, VT, WA, WI, WV
Foreign Countries: ARUBA; BAHAMAS; BAHRAIN; BRUNEI; CHINA; GREAT BRITAIN; GREECE; GUATEMALA; HONDURAS; HONG KONG; INDIA; INDONESIA; ISRAEL; JAMAICA; JAPAN; KUWAIT; MALAYSIA; SAUDI ARABIA; SINGAPORE; SOUTH KOREA; TAIWAN; THAILAND; THE PHILIPPINES; TURKEY; UNITED ARAB EMIRATES; VENEZUELA; VIETNAM
Type of Foodservice: Quick Serve (1,920)
Primary Distributors: (Full Line) Vistar Rocky Mountain, DENVER, CO
Parent Company: GoTo Foods, ATLANTA, GA

Key Personnel
JIM HOLTHOUSER - CEO
JACKIE GEISEL - VP Operations
TIM GOODMAN - VP Franchise Operations
KATHY SCANLON - Director Mid-Atlantic Region
TARA WISE - Director Franchise Operations
BRIAN KUJAK - Director Operations
SAVANNAH HARPER - Director Operations
JOAN SCHMIDT - Manager Quality Assurance

Brown & Patterson
1755 Columbia Ave
Lancaster, PA 17603-4530

Telephone: (717) 397-5112
Fax Number: (717) 397-3893
Type of Business: Chain Restaurant Operator
Total Sales: $15,352,000 (e)
Total Units: 3
Trade Names: McDonald's (3)
Units Franchised From: 3
Preferred Location Types: Freestanding
Primary Menu: Hamburger (3)
Areas of Operation: PA
Type of Foodservice: Quick Serve (3)
Franchise Affiliation: McDonald's Corporation, CHICAGO, IL

Key Personnel
WILLIAM BROWN - President; General Buyer

Domino's Franchisee
1611 Manheim Pike
Lancaster, PA 17601-3027

Telephone: (717) 581-5200
Type of Business: Chain Restaurant Operator
Total Sales: $4,065,000 (e)
Total Units: 2
Trade Names: Domino's (2)
Units Franchised From: 2
Primary Menu: Pizza (2)
Areas of Operation: PA
Type of Foodservice: Quick Serve (2)
Franchise Affiliation: Domino's Pizza Inc, ANN ARBOR, MI

Key Personnel
MICHAEL M. MIKHAIL - Owner; General Buyer

Eden Resort & Suites
222 Eden Rd
Lancaster, PA 17601-4216

Telephone: (717) 569-6444
Fax Number: (717) 569-5920
Internet Homepage: edenresort.com
Company Email: garfields@edenresort.com
Type of Business: Chain Restaurant Operator
Year Founded: 1978
Total Sales: $5,658,000 (e)
Alcohol Sales: 25%
Number of Employees: 55
Average Check: Breakfast(14); Lunch(18); Dinner(36)
Total Units: 3
Trade Names: Arthur's Restaurant (1); Encore Lounge (1); Garfield's Restaurant (1)
Company-Owned Units: 3
Preferred Location Types: Hotel/Motel
Alcohol Served: Beer, Wine, Liquor
Primary Menu: American (3)
Areas of Operation: PA
Type of Foodservice: Casual Dining (2); Fine Dining (1)
Notes: Located at the Eden Resort.

Key Personnel
DON TRIPPLE - Executive Chef
NICOLE AQUILINI - Assistant Director Food
DARIAN BRENNER - Manager Event Planning, Sales
RICK TRIPPLE - Manager Food and Beverage
MEGHAN YOUNG - Manager Purchasing
BRYAN SEIDLE - Project Manager Facility/Maintenance

GTM Restaurant Corp.
2173 Embassy Dr
Lancaster, PA 17603-2387

Telephone: (717) 397-5464
Fax Number: (717) 431-2014
Type of Business: Chain Restaurant Operator
Year Founded: 1979
Total Sales: $4,770,000 (e)
Number of Employees: 150
Average Check: Breakfast(6); Lunch(8); Dinner(8)
Total Units: 2
Trade Names: Burger King (2)
Units Franchised From: 2
Preferred Square Footage: 2,500; 4,000
Preferred Location Types: Freestanding
Primary Menu: Hamburger (2)
Areas of Operation: PA
Type of Foodservice: Quick Serve (2)
Franchise Affiliation: Burger King Worldwide Inc., MIAMI, FL
Primary Distributors: (Food) The SYGMA Network Inc. - Pennsylvania, HARRISBURG, PA

Key Personnel
MIKE ALIOTTA - President; General Buyer

Mel-Lin Enterprises
2030 Wynfield Dr
Lancaster, PA 17601-4969

Telephone: (717) 435-6575
Type of Business: Chain Restaurant Operator
Total Sales: $10,048,000 (e)
Total Units: 2
Trade Names: McDonald's (2)
Units Franchised From: 2
Preferred Location Types: Freestanding
Primary Menu: Hamburger (2)
Areas of Operation: PA
Type of Foodservice: Quick Serve (2)
Franchise Affiliation: McDonald's Corporation, CHICAGO, IL

Key Personnel
GLEN MATTOX - President; General Buyer

Sesame Place
100 Sesame Rd
Langhorne, PA 19047-1821

Mailing Address: PO Box L579, LANGHORNE, PA, 19047-0579
Telephone: (215) 752-7070
Fax Number: (215) 741-5307
Listing Type: Divisional Office
Type of Business: Foodservice Operations - Theme Parks
Total Units: 9
Areas of Operation: PA
Parent Company: SeaWorld Entertainment Inc., ORLANDO, FL

Key Personnel
CATHY VALERIANO - President; Exec VP; General Manager
HENRY BACHSTEIN - VP Facility/Maintenance
CARMEN ANTHONY - VP Culinary Operations
BOB POTTEBAUM - Director Information Technology
GREINER SHAWN - Director Culinary Operations
PAM NUZZO - Director Marketing
JESSICA FINUCANE - Director Operations
DANA RYAN - Manager Public Relations

PSI Pizza Inc.
548 E State St
Larksville, PA 18651-1422

Telephone: (570) 779-3370
Fax Number: (570) 779-3375
Type of Business: Chain Restaurant Operator
Year Founded: 1987
Total Sales: $22,715,000 (e)
Number of Employees: 120
Average Check: Lunch(16); Dinner(22)
Total Units: 11
Trade Names: Domino's (11)
Units Franchised From: 11
Preferred Square Footage: 1,000; 1,300
Preferred Location Types: Strip Mall
Primary Menu: Pizza (11)
Areas of Operation: PA
Type of Foodservice: Quick Serve (11)
Foodservice Management Venues: Schools
Franchise Affiliation: Domino's Pizza Inc, ANN ARBOR, MI
Primary Distributors: (Full Line) SYSCO Food Services of Pittsburgh Inc., HARMONY, PA

Key Personnel
SETH GOLLHARDT - President; Director Operations; Manager Information Systems; Real Estate; General Buyer

Valley Dairy
1562 Mission Rd
Latrobe, PA 15650-2845

Telephone: (724) 537-7111
Fax Number: (724) 537-7249
Internet Homepage: valleydairy.net
Company Email: icecreamjoe@valleydairy.net
Type of Business: Chain Restaurant Operator
Year Founded: 1938
Total Sales: $12,860,000 (e)
Number of Employees: 408

Average Check: Breakfast(5); Lunch(8); Dinner(12)
Total Units: 12
Trade Names: Valley Dairy Restaurants (12)
Company-Owned Units: 12
Preferred Square Footage: 3,500; 4,200
Preferred Location Types: Freestanding; Regional Mall; Strip Mall
Primary Menu: American (12)
Areas of Operation: PA
Type of Foodservice: Family Restaurant (12)
Primary Distributors: (Food) Gordon Food Service, SPRINGFIELD, OH; (Full Line) Reinhart FoodService, MOUNT PLEASANT, PA

Key Personnel
TOM WEBB - Director Operations
RHONDA HAZLETT - Manager Human Resources

McDonald's Franchise
PO Box 526
Lawrence, PA 15055-0526

Telephone: (724) 941-8282
Fax Number: (724) 941-8585
Type of Business: Chain Restaurant Operator
Total Sales: $60,640,000 (e)
Total Units: 13
Trade Names: McDonald's (13)
Units Franchised From: 13
Preferred Location Types: Freestanding; Grocery Stores
Primary Menu: Hamburger (13)
Areas of Operation: PA
Type of Foodservice: Quick Serve (13)
Franchise Affiliation: McDonald's Corporation, CHICAGO, IL

Key Personnel
RONALD GALIANO - President; General Buyer
CHRIS CZAJKOWSKI - General Manager

Circle C Corporation
931 Market St
Lemoyne, PA 17043-1412

Telephone: (717) 214-7272
Fax Number: (717) 214-7273
Type of Business: Chain Restaurant Operator
Year Founded: 1981
Total Sales: $9,545,000 (e)
Number of Employees: 250
Average Check: Lunch(26); Dinner(26)
Total Units: 7
Trade Names: Papa John's Pizza (7)
Units Franchised From: 7
Preferred Square Footage: 1,100; 1,500
Preferred Location Types: Freestanding; Strip Mall
Primary Menu: Pizza (7)
Areas of Operation: PA
Type of Foodservice: Quick Serve (7)
Franchise Affiliation: Papa Johns International Inc., LOUISVILLE, KY
Primary Distributors: (Full Line) Papa John's Distribution Center, FREEDOM, PA

Key Personnel
LEE CARROLL - President; CFO; General Buyer
BARBARA JUNKER - Administrative Assistant

Leakas Quality Food Inc.
629 N Derr Dr
Lewisburg, PA 17837-1003

Telephone: (570) 524-0469
Fax Number: (570) 523-9279
Type of Business: Chain Restaurant Operator
Total Sales: $24,220,000 (e)
Number of Employees: 160
Average Check: Lunch(8); Dinner(8)
Total Units: 9
Trade Names: Wendy's Old Fashioned Hamburgers (9)
Units Franchised From: 9
Preferred Square Footage: 2,100; 2,900
Preferred Location Types: Freestanding
Primary Menu: Hamburger (9)
Areas of Operation: PA
Type of Foodservice: Quick Serve (9)
Franchise Affiliation: The Wendy's Company, DUBLIN, OH
Primary Distributors: (Food) The SYGMA Network Inc. - Pennsylvania, HARRISBURG, PA

Key Personnel
CHRIS EVANGELOU - CEO; President; General Buyer
MISTY JOHNSON - General Manager

Amsher Enterprises Inc
19 Olde Mill Ct
Lititz, PA 17543

Telephone: (717) 560-8734
Internet Homepage: auntieannesfranchising.com
Type of Business: Chain Restaurant Operator
Total Sales: $2,321,000 (e)
Total Units: 3
Trade Names: Auntie Anne's Hand-Rolled Soft Pretzels (3)
Units Franchised From: 3
Primary Menu: Snacks (3)
Areas of Operation: MD
Type of Foodservice: Quick Serve (3)
Franchise Affiliation: Auntie Anne's Inc., LANCASTER, PA

Key Personnel
GARY KOGON - Owner; General Buyer

Domino's Franchisee
203 N Jay St
Lock Haven, PA 17745-2026

Telephone: (570) 748-3100
Type of Business: Chain Restaurant Operator
Total Sales: $8,238,000 (e)
Total Units: 4
Trade Names: Domino's (4)
Units Franchised From: 4
Primary Menu: Pizza (4)
Areas of Operation: PA
Type of Foodservice: Quick Serve (4)
Franchise Affiliation: Domino's Pizza Inc, ANN ARBOR, MI

Key Personnel
JAMES N. GREGORY - Owner; General Buyer

Brock & Co. Inc.
257 Great Valley Pkwy
Malvern, PA 19355-1308

Telephone: (610) 647-5656
Fax Number: (610) 647-0867
Internet Homepage: brockco.com
Company Email: info@brockco.com
Type of Business: Foodservice Management Operator
Year Founded: 1927
Total Sales: $62,977,000 (e)
Number of Employees: 550
Number of Locations Served: 70
Total Foodservice Mgmt Accounts: 70
Areas of Operation: PA
Type of Foodservice: Cafeteria (70)
Foodservice Management Venues: Business & Industry; Schools
Primary Distributors: (Full Line) Sysco Eastern Maryland Inc., POCOMOKE CITY, MD

Key Personnel
CLAUDIE BROCK - Chairman
LYNMAR BROCK JR - Vice Chairman
ANDREW BROCK - CEO; President
BRIAN HEISS - VP Purchasing
JAMES BRANT - Manager District
ERCU ERKUT - Manager Information Systems

Sadaza Management
210 Lancaster Ave
Malvern, PA 19355-1802

Telephone: (610) 722-5717

Type of Business: Chain Restaurant Operator
Total Sales: $12,350,000 (e)
Number of Employees: 114
Average Check: Dinner(8)
Total Units: 8
Trade Names: Dunkin' Donuts (8)
Units Franchised From: 8
Preferred Square Footage: 1,500; 2,200
Preferred Location Types: Freestanding; Strip Mall
Primary Menu: Snacks (8)
Areas of Operation: PA
Type of Foodservice: Quick Serve (8)
Franchise Affiliation: DD IP Holder, CANTON, MA

Key Personnel
EYAD TAKIEDINE - President; General Buyer

Duck Donuts Franchising Company
1215 Manor Dr
Mechanicsburg, PA 17055

Telephone: (717) 691-1005
Internet Homepage: duckdonuts.com
Company Email: franchising@duckdonuts.com
Type of Business: Chain Restaurant Operator
Year Founded: 2006
Total Sales: $80,230,000 (e)
Total Units: 106
Trade Names: Duck Donuts (106)
Units Franchised To: 106
Primary Menu: Snacks (106)
Projected Openings: 10
Areas of Operation: FL, GA, KS, MD, NC, NJ, NY, OH, PA, SC, TN, TX, VA
Type of Foodservice: Quick Serve (106)

Key Personnel
RUSS DIGILIO - Founder; CEO
BETSY HAMM - CEO
MARISSA DIGILIO - Director Operations, Training
BRIGID BINK - Director Digital Marketing
TOM PERELLA - Director Technology

Keystone Apple Inc.
4940 Ritter Rd Ste 104
Mechanicsburg, PA 17055-6920

Mailing Address: PO Box 2055, MECHANICSBURG, PA, 17055-0749
Telephone: (717) 790-9744
Fax Number: (717) 790-9130
Internet Homepage: keystoneapple.com
Company Email: info@keystoneapple.com
Type of Business: Chain Restaurant Operator
Year Founded: 1914
Total Sales: $32,310,000 (e)
Alcohol Sales: 20%
Number of Employees: 500
Average Check: Lunch(14); Dinner(24)
Total Units: 8
Trade Names: Applebee's Neighborhood Grill & Bar (8)
Units Franchised From: 8
Preferred Square Footage: 5,000; 6,700
Preferred Location Types: Freestanding
Alcohol Served: Beer, Wine, Liquor
Primary Menu: American (8)
Areas of Operation: PA
Type of Foodservice: Casual Dining (8)
Franchise Affiliation: Applebee's Services Inc., KANSAS CITY, MO
Primary Distributors: (Full Line) Maines Paper & Food Service New York Metro, FARMINGDALE, NY

Key Personnel
STEPHEN DAVENPORT - President; Director Information Systems; General Buyer
GREG SARABOK - CFO; Director Purchasing, Supply Chain, Real Estate
R.D. FRYE - Area Director; VP
TIM DAVENPORT - VP; General Manager
LARRY GOODLING - Director Area

Seven Hills Restaurant Group Inc
5010 Lenker St Ste 100
Mechanicsburg, PA 17050-3205

Telephone: (717) 909-0580
Fax Number: (717) 909-0582
Type of Business: Chain Restaurant Operator
Total Sales: $43,350,000 (e)
Total Units: 47
Trade Names: Sbarro (47)
Units Franchised From: 47
Primary Menu: Italian (47)
Areas of Operation: PA
Type of Foodservice: Quick Serve (47)
Franchise Affiliation: Sbarro Holdings LLC, COLUMBUS, OH

Key Personnel
RAGHU TADAVARTHY - President

Springfield Restaurant Group
1553 Perry Hwy
Mercer, PA 16137-3931

Telephone: (724) 748-4666
Fax Number: (724) 748-5056
Internet Homepage: springfields.com
Company Email: comments@springfields.com
Type of Business: Chain Restaurant Operator
Year Founded: 1979
Total Sales: $17,220,000 (e)
Number of Employees: 350
Average Check: Lunch(22); Dinner(36)
Internet Order Processing: Yes
Total Units: 8
Trade Names: Hickory Bar & Grille (1); Iron Bridge Inn (1); Log Cabin Inn (1); Rachel's Roadhouse (3); Springfield Grille (2)
Company-Owned Units: 8
Preferred Square Footage: 5,500; 6,000
Preferred Location Types: Freestanding
Alcohol Served: Beer, Wine, Liquor
Primary Menu: American (8)
Areas of Operation: OH, PA
Type of Foodservice: Casual Dining (8)
Primary Distributors: (Full Line) US Foods, ALLENTOWN, PA

Key Personnel
TARRI SHAY - President; CFO; Controller
JOHN MCKINLEY - Owner; COO; Director Information Systems, Real Estate, Design; General Buyer
DOUG ALLEN - General Manager
KAREN MONG - Director Food
SHEILA NUTH - Director Training
JESSICA COOPER - Manager Marketing

Pizza Fusion Holdings
322 Mall Blvd Ste 149
Monroeville, PA 15146

Telephone: (888) 534-6662
Internet Homepage: pizzafusion.com
Company Email: info@pizzafusion.com
Listing Type: Subsidiary
Type of Business: Chain Restaurant Operator
Year Founded: 2006
Systemwide Sales: $15,712,000 (e)
Total Sales: $2,944,000 (e)
Alcohol Sales: 5%
Number of Employees: 207
Average Check: Dinner(32)
Internet Order Processing: Yes
Total Units: 17
Trade Names: Pizza Fusion (17)
Units Franchised To: 17
Preferred Location Types: Downtown; Freestanding; Office Complex; Strip Mall
Alcohol Served: Beer, Wine
Primary Menu: Pizza (17)
Areas of Operation: FL, NJ, VA, FC
Foreign Countries: SAUDI ARABIA; UNITED ARAB EMIRATES
Type of Foodservice: Fast Casual (17)
Catering Services: Yes

Key Personnel
RANDY G. ROMANO - President

Domino's Franchisee
803 Horsham Rd Unit B
Montgomeryville, PA 18936-9639

Telephone: (215) 362-7660
Type of Business: Chain Restaurant Operator
Total Sales: $6,211,000 (e)
Total Units: 3
Trade Names: Domino's (3)
Units Franchised From: 3
Primary Menu: Pizza (3)
Areas of Operation: PA
Type of Foodservice: Quick Serve (3)
Franchise Affiliation: Domino's Pizza Inc, ANN ARBOR, MI

Key Personnel
BASHKIM REXHA - Owner; General Buyer

Big Plan Investments, LLC
305 Blue Spruce Way
Murrysville, PA 15668-8060

Telephone: (724) 919-4004
Type of Business: Chain Restaurant Operator
Total Sales: $14,740,000 (e)
Total Units: 9
Trade Names: Moe's Southwest Grill (9)
Units Franchised From: 9
Primary Menu: Southwest/Tex-Mex (9)
Areas of Operation: PA
Type of Foodservice: Fast Casual (9)
Franchise Affiliation: Moe's Southwest Grill LLC, ATLANTA, GA

Key Personnel
MICHAEL GEIGER - Owner; General Buyer

KCS Management
1000 Jacks Run Rd
N Versailles, PA 15137-2744

Telephone: (412) 751-0700
Fax Number: (412) 751-9008
Internet Homepage: kingsfamily.com
Type of Business: Chain Restaurant Operator
Year Founded: 1967
Total Sales: $57,610,000 (e)
Number of Employees: 1,650
Average Check: Breakfast(8); Lunch(8); Dinner(10)
Total Units: 22
Trade Names: Kings Family Restaurant (22)
Company-Owned Units: 22
Preferred Square Footage: 6,800
Preferred Location Types: Freestanding
Alcohol Served: Beer, Wine, Liquor
Primary Menu: American (22)
Projected Remodelings: 4

Areas of Operation: OH, PA
Type of Foodservice: Family Restaurant (22)

Key Personnel
MICHAEL KELLY - Owner; General Buyer
CHRIS WHALEN - CFO
ANTHONY EGIZIO - Director Purchasing, Food and Beverage
BARBARA DUNLAY - Coordinator Marketing

Bill's Sandwich Shops
2425 Wilmington Rd
New Castle, PA 16105-1953

Telephone: (724) 654-7573
Fax Number: (724) 654-5352
Type of Business: Chain Restaurant Operator
Year Founded: 1971
Total Sales: $1,841,000 (e)
Number of Employees: 35
Average Check: Lunch(12); Dinner(12)
Total Units: 2
Trade Names: Bill's Sandwich Shop (2)
Company-Owned Units: 1
Units Franchised To: 1
Preferred Location Types: Downtown; Mixed-use Center; Office Complex
Primary Menu: Sandwiches/Deli (2)
Areas of Operation: PA
Type of Foodservice: Quick Serve (2)
Primary Distributors: (Equipment) Tri-State Equipment Co., BEAVER FALLS, PA; (Food) US Foods, GREENSBURG, PA; (Supplies) US Foods, GREENSBURG, PA

Key Personnel
SPIROS KARDAMDIKIS - Owner; General Buyer

Classico Foods/Pizza Joe's
275 Commerce Ave
New Castle, PA 16101-7625

Telephone: (724) 658-1716
Fax Number: (724) 658-6063
Internet Homepage: pizzajoes.com
Company Email: comments@pizzajoes.com
Type of Business: Chain Restaurant Operator
Year Founded: 1980
Systemwide Sales: $20,535,000 (e)
Total Sales: $3,777,000 (e)
Number of Employees: 504
Average Check: Lunch(16); Dinner(22)
Internet Order Processing: Yes
Total Units: 42
Trade Names: Pizza Joe's (42)
Company-Owned Units: 2
Units Franchised To: 40
Preferred Square Footage: 2,000
Preferred Location Types: Freestanding; Regional Mall; Strip Mall

Primary Menu: Pizza (42)
Projected Openings: 2
Areas of Operation: OH, PA
Type of Foodservice: Quick Serve (42)
Foodservice Management Venues: Schools
Catering Services: Yes
On-site Distribution Center: Yes
Primary Distributors: (Full Line) SYSCO Food Services of Philadelphia LLC, PHILADELPHIA, PA

Key Personnel
JOE SEMINARA - Founder; President; Manager Retail Operations, Purchasing, Distribution, Advertising, Real Estate, Design, Training, Franchising, Store Fixtures, Store Planning, Menu Development, Catering

Golden Star Theaters
2000 W State St
New Castle, PA 16101

Telephone: (724) 652-9072
Internet Homepage: goldenstartheaters.com; moviescoop.com
Type of Business: Foodservice Operations - Movie Theatre
Total Sales: $6,833,000 (e)
Average Check: Dinner(12)
Total Units: 4
Trade Names: Century Square Luxury Cinemas (1); Country Club Mall Cinemas (1); Shenango Valley Cinemas (1); Westgate Cinemas (1)
Company-Owned Units: 4
Primary Menu: Snacks (4)
Areas of Operation: MD, PA
Type of Foodservice: In-Store Feeder (4)

Key Personnel
FRANK MOSES - President
JOE RETHEGE - Manager Operations; General Buyer

Marsha Brown Enterprises
15 S Main St
New Hope, PA 18938-1320

Telephone: (215) 862-7044
Fax Number: (215) 862-7077
Internet Homepage: marshabrownrestaurant.com
Company Email: info@marshabrownrestaurant.com
Type of Business: Chain Restaurant Operator
Total Sales: $9,242,000 (e)
Alcohol Sales: 20%
Number of Employees: 160
Average Check: Dinner(84)
Internet Order Processing: Yes
Total Units: 4
Trade Names: Marsha Brown Creole Kitchen

(1); Ruth's Chris Steak House (3)
Company-Owned Units: 1
Units Franchised From: 3
Preferred Location Types: Downtown; Office Complex; Other
Alcohol Served: Beer, Wine, Liquor
Primary Menu: Cajun/Creole (1); Steak (3)
Areas of Operation: NY, PA
Type of Foodservice: Fine Dining (4)
Franchise Affiliation: Ruth's Hospitality Group Inc., WINTER PARK, FL
Primary Distributors: (Supplies) US Foods, GREENSBURG, PA

Key Personnel
MARSHA BROWN - President; Director Operations; General Buyer

The Cock 'n Bull Inc.
5800 Upper York Rd
New Hope, PA 18938

Mailing Address: PO Box 218, LAHASKA, PA, 18931-0218
Telephone: (215) 794-4010
Fax Number: (215) 794-4001
Internet Homepage: peddlersvillage.com
Company Email: info@peddlersvillage.com
Type of Business: Chain Restaurant Operator
Year Founded: 1962
Total Sales: $18,740,000 (e)
Alcohol Sales: 10%
Number of Employees: 200
Average Check: Breakfast(8); Lunch(14); Dinner(36)
Internet Order Processing: Yes
Internet Sales: 1.00%
Total Units: 8
Trade Names: Button Wood (1); Cock 'n Bull (1); Earl's New American (1); Hart's Tavern (1); Murder Mystery Dinner Theater (1); Nancy's Village Cafe (1); Painted Pony (1); Peddler's Pub (1)
Company-Owned Units: 8
Preferred Square Footage: 6,000; 9,000
Preferred Location Types: Freestanding
Alcohol Served: Beer, Wine, Liquor
Primary Menu: American (7); Hamburger (1)
Areas of Operation: PA
Type of Foodservice: Casual Dining (8)
Primary Distributors: (Full Line) US Foods, ALLENTOWN, PA
Parent Company: Peddler's Village, LAHASKA, PA

Key Personnel
DONNA JAMISON - President
TERRY S. WARD - COO
JIM PERILLO - Director Operations, Facility/Maintenance, Design, Store Fixtures
SUSAN TOBIAS - Manager Human Resources
SHARON SCHMIDT - Manager Marketing
EVE GELMAN - Manager Public Relations, Social Media

Don Mc Entire
305 Greensburg Rd
New Kensington, PA 15068-3917

Telephone: (724) 337-3370
Type of Business: Chain Restaurant Operator
Total Sales: $5,838,000 (e)
Average Check: Dinner(12)
Total Units: 4
Trade Names: Dairy Queen (4)
Units Franchised From: 4
Primary Menu: American (4)
Areas of Operation: PA
Type of Foodservice: Quick Serve (4)
Franchise Affiliation: International Dairy Queen Inc., BLOOMINGTON, MN

Key Personnel
DON MCENTIRE - Owner; General Buyer

Plaza Azteca Mexican Restaurant
12099 Jefferson Ave
Newport News Va, PA 23606

Telephone: (757) 969-1621
Internet Homepage: plazaazteca.com
Type of Business: Chain Restaurant Operator
Year Founded: 1996
Average Check: Lunch(12); Dinner(24)
Total Units: 40
Trade Names: Plaza Azteca Mexican Restaurant (40)
Company-Owned Units: 40
Primary Menu: Mexican (40)
Areas of Operation: CT, MA, MD, NC, NJ, PA, VA
Type of Foodservice: Casual Dining (40)
Catering Services: Yes

Key Personnel
MIGUEL LOPEZ - Co-Founder
JESUS TORRES - Co-Founder
ARES MELCHOR - Manager Marketing

The Rose Group
29 Friends Ln
Newtown, PA 18940-1803

Telephone: (215) 579-9220
Fax Number: (215) 579-9226
Internet Homepage: therosegroup.com
Company Email: 411info@therosegroup.com
Type of Business: Chain Restaurant Operator
Year Founded: 1985
Total Sales: $209,630,000 (e)
Alcohol Sales: 25%
Number of Employees: 4,480
Average Check: Lunch(14); Dinner(24)
Total Units: 53
Trade Names: Applebee's Neighborhood Grill & Bar (51); Shannon Rose (2)
Company-Owned Units: 2
Units Franchised From: 51
Preferred Square Footage: 2,800; 3,000; 5,600
Preferred Location Types: Community Mall; Freestanding; Strip Mall
Alcohol Served: Beer, Wine, Liquor
Primary Menu: American (54); Miscellaneous (2)
Areas of Operation: DE, MD, NJ, PA
Type of Foodservice: Casual Dining (56)
Franchise Affiliation: Applebee's Services Inc., KANSAS CITY, MO
Primary Distributors: (Full Line) Maines Paper & Food Service New York Metro, FARMINGDALE, NY
Notes: The Applebee's restaurants operate as Delaware Valley Rose LP.

Key Personnel
P. JEFFREY WARDEN - CEO; President
CHRISTOPHER J. TOBIA - CFO; VP
BONNIE LIPPINCOTT - COO; VP Operations, Inventory, Quality Assurance, Menu Development, Food Safety; General Buyer
DINA MARIE MORGAN - Area Director
TODD CUMMINGS - Area Director Operations
JOSH BRITTON - Area Director
CATHERINE CHUCK - VP Marketing, Public Relations
PAUL ROCKELMANN - VP Loss Prevention, Risk Management, Human Resources
JASON ROSE - VP Real Estate
CATHI CHUCK - VP Marketing, Public Relations
KIMBERLY GRAHAM - Director Legal
BOB WERNIK - Manager Recruitment
LARRY ROSE - Principal

Delmac Management Corp
18 Clover Ln
Newtown Square, PA 19073-4103

Telephone: (610) 356-8775
Fax Number: (610) 353-8161
Internet Homepage: mcdonalds-doane.com
Company Email: doane.cares@gmail.com
Type of Business: Chain Restaurant Operator
Year Founded: 1974
Total Sales: $70,810,000 (e)
Number of Employees: 581
Average Check: Breakfast(8); Lunch(8); Dinner(10)
Total Units: 15
Trade Names: McDonald's (15)
Units Franchised From: 15
Preferred Square Footage: 2,500; 3,000
Preferred Location Types: Freestanding
Primary Menu: Hamburger (15)

Areas of Operation: PA
Type of Foodservice: Quick Serve (15)
Franchise Affiliation: McDonald's Corporation, CHICAGO, IL

Key Personnel
RICH DOANE - President; General Buyer

Insomnia Cookies
10 Campus Blvd
Newtown Square, PA 19073-3200

Telephone: (877) 632-6654
Internet Homepage: insomniacookies.com
Company Email: customerservice@insomniacookies.com
Type of Business: Chain Restaurant Operator
Total Sales: $61,810,000 (e)
Internet Order Processing: Yes
Total Units: 165
Trade Names: Insomnia Cookies (165)
Company-Owned Units: 165
Primary Menu: Snacks (165)
Projected Openings: 15
Areas of Operation: AL, CO, CT, DC, DE, FL, GA, IA, IL, IN, KS, KY, LA, MA, MD, MI, MN, MO, MS, NC, ND, NH, NJ, OH, OK, RI, SC, TN, TX, VA, VT, WI, WV
Type of Foodservice: Quick Serve (165)
Parent Company: JAB Holding Company, LUDWIGSHAFEN, GER
Headquarters: Krispy Kreme Doughnut Corporation, CHARLOTTE, NC

Key Personnel
SETH BERKOWITZ - Founder; President
TOM CARUSONA - Chief Marketing Officer
DAVID SALAMA - VP Digital Media

Grady's Bar-B-Q
1000 Jacks Run Rd
North Versailles, PA 15137

Telephone: (412) 751-9005
Internet Homepage: gradysbbq.com
Type of Business: Chain Restaurant Operator
Total Units: 5
Trade Names: Grady's Bar-B-Q (5)
Company-Owned Units: 5
Primary Menu: Bar-B-Q (5)
Areas of Operation: TX
Type of Foodservice: Casual Dining (5)
Parent Company: Kelly Companies, SAN DIEGO, CA

Key Personnel
MICHAEL KELLY - Owner

Jade Management Inc
314 E 21st St
Northampton, PA 18067-1206

Mailing Address: PO Box 269, NORTHAMPTON, PA, 18067-0269
Telephone: (610) 262-2010
Type of Business: Chain Restaurant Operator
Year Founded: 1983
Total Sales: $13,660,000 (e)
Number of Employees: 260
Average Check: Breakfast(8); Lunch(10); Dinner(12)
Total Units: 6
Trade Names: Burger King (6)
Units Franchised From: 6
Preferred Square Footage: 2,500
Preferred Location Types: Freestanding
Primary Menu: Hamburger (6)
Areas of Operation: PA
Type of Foodservice: Quick Serve (6)
Franchise Affiliation: Burger King Worldwide Inc., MIAMI, FL
Primary Distributors: (Full Line) Maines Paper & Food Service Inc., CONKLIN, NY

Key Personnel
JOHN P. BARTO JR - President; Director Finance, Operations, Facility/Maintenance, Supply Chain, Real Estate, Store Fixtures; General Buyer
DESIREE BARTO - Manager Information Systems, Marketing, Design, Human Resources

Chelsea Grille
515 Allegheny Ave
Oakmont, PA 15139-2002

Telephone: (412) 828-7572
Fax Number: (412) 828-0336
Internet Homepage: chelseagriloak.com; hoffstots.com
Company Email: contact@chelseagrilloakmont.com
Type of Business: Chain Restaurant Operator
Year Founded: 1992
Total Sales: $12,215,000 (e)
Alcohol Sales: 25%
Number of Employees: 100
Average Check: Lunch(10); Dinner(20)
Total Units: 2
Trade Names: Chelsea Grille (1); Hoffstot's Cafe Monaco (1)
Company-Owned Units: 2
Alcohol Served: Beer, Wine, Liquor
Primary Menu: Italian (1); Steak/Seafood (1)
Areas of Operation: PA
Type of Foodservice: Fine Dining (1)
Catering Services: Yes
Primary Distributors: (Food) US Foods,

ALTOONA, PA; (Supplies) Penn Fixture & Supply Co. Inc., PITTSBURGH, PA

Key Personnel
TOM MONACO - Partner; General Manager
BRIAN LERI - Executive Chef
NICOLE SHELESTAK - Office Manager

Crescent Vending Company
1446 Ulmer Ave
Oreland, PA 19075-1712

Telephone: (215) 884-4290
Fax Number: (215) 884-4317
Internet Homepage: crescentvending.com
Company Email: geocres@aol.com
Type of Business: Foodservice Management Operator
Year Founded: 1967
Total Sales: $3,594,000 (e)
Number of Employees: 25
Number of Locations Served: 70
Total Foodservice Mgmt Accounts: 1
Areas of Operation: PA
Type of Foodservice: Vending machines (1)
Foodservice Management Venues: Business & Industry
Primary Distributors: (Full Line) Feesers Inc., HARRISBURG, PA

Key Personnel
MARK D. CRANEY - VP; Manager Finance, Business Development
TRUDY CRANEY - Controller; Director Human Resources

Aramark
2400 Market St Fl 20
Philadelphia, PA 19103

Telephone: (215) 238-3000
Internet Homepage: aramark.com
Type of Business: Foodservice Management Operator
Year Founded: 1959
Publicly Held: Yes
Total Sales: $22,411,488,000 (e)
Number of Employees: 270,000
Number of Locations Served: 59,000
Total Foodservice Mgmt Accounts: 59,000
Trade Names: Chili's Grill & Bar (3); Denny's (1); Dunkin' Donuts (1); IHOP Restaurant (1); Jamba Juice (3); Moe's Southwest Grill (11); Papa John's Pizza (1); Quiznos (4); Wendy's Old Fashioned Hamburgers (4)
Areas of Operation: PA
Type of Foodservice: Cafeteria; Full-service sit-down dining; Mobile units/kiosks; Quick Serve; Vending machines
Foodservice Management Venues: Business & Industry; College & University; Health Care;

Other; Parks & Recreation; Prison Feeding; Schools; Sports Venues

Primary Distributors: (Full Line) SYSCO Corporation, HOUSTON, TX

Divisional Offices: ARAMARK Business Services, PHILADELPHIA, PA; ARAMARK Canada, TORONTO, ON CANADA; ARAMARK Conference Centers Management, PHILADELPHIA, PA; ARAMARK Higher Education, PHILADELPHIA, PA; ARAMARK International Services, PHILADELPHIA, PA; ARAMARK School Support Services, PHILADELPHIA, PA; ARAMARK Sports & Entertainment Group, PHILADELPHIA, PA

Regional Offices: ARAMARK, DOWNERS GROVE, IL; ARAMARK Business Services, DOWNERS GROVE, IL; ARAMARK Business Services, PHILADELPHIA, PA; ARAMARK Campus Services(HIGHER EDUCATION), WAKEFIELD, MA; ARAMARK Education, COPPELL, TX; ARAMARK Healthcare Support Services, PHILADELPHIA, PA; ARAMARK Higher Education, CARY, NC; ARAMARK Higher Education, DALLAS, TX; ARAMARK Higher Education, DOWNERS GROVE, IL

Notes: Industry sales includes some support services revenue, but excludes uniform & career apparel sales, which accounts for approximately 10% of total revenue.

Key Personnel

JOHN ZILLMER - CEO
BRUCE W. FEARS - President Division
TOM ORDROF - CFO; Exec VP
TOM ONDROF - CFO; Exec VP
TIM O'SHAUGHNESSY - CFO; VP Finance
MARC BRUNO - COO Division
CARL MITTLEMAN - COO International
ROGER FRANKE - CIO; VP
RON IORI - Senior VP Communications, Public Relations
JOHN RYAN - Senior VP
LAUREN HARRINGTON - Senior VP; General Counsel
ANN MARIE SOLOMON - VP Marketing, Business Development, Strategic Planning
IAN M. BAILEY JR - VP Investor Relations
ALLAN FERNANDES - VP Safety, Risk Management
DOUG MARTINIDES - VP Culinary Development
RON MESAROS - VP Facility/Maintenance
BARBARA SHILOWICH - VP Human Resources
MIHIR PRASAD - VP Information Technology
BRIAN WASHINGTON - VP Talent
ROBERT DEITZ - VP Tax
JIM BROKER - VP
AUTUMN BAYLES - VP Global Development
GORDON CAMPBELL - VP Sourcing
JORDAN GLAZIER - VP Human Resources
RICH SAXE - Assistant VP Information Technology, Enterprise Solutions, Retail Information Systems
BLASE IACONELLI - Assistant VP; General Counsel
TAMSIN NEWMAN - Assistant VP; General Counsel
GERARD KANE - Assistant VP Benefits
GEORGE SMITH - Assistant VP Foodservice
JESSICA PHILLIPS - Assistant VP Information Technology
STEVE KAUFMAN - Assistant VP Labor Relations
BOB BARR - Assistant VP Operations
BOB EULE - Assistant VP Procurement
ANDREW GRIBBIN - Assistant VP Procurement
DAN WAINFAN - Assistant VP HBC
JESSICA DUNNING - General Manager
GENE DONATO - General Manager
ARIC FERRELL - General Manager
DARAND GARNER - General Manager
JOHNNY HARRIS - General Manager
GERALD KULA - General Manager
MARIE QUINN - General Manager
MICHAEL RYAN - General Manager
KEVIN TEDESCO - General Manager
RICK WHITE - General Manager
JIM PIANO - Executive Chef; Director Foodservice
INDRISO BRANDON - Executive Chef; Manager
MARIA FUNCHEZ - Executive Chef; Manager
BRIAN DUNN JR - Executive Chef
PAUL CARR - Senior Director Group, Foodservice, Menu Development
MEETA ADVANI - Senior Director Technology, Digital
MATTHEW JUDGE - Senior Director Business Development
STEVEN BRUSH - Senior Director Development
BRUCE ALPERIN LEED, AP - Senior Director Marketing
ELLEN WILSON-GHEE - Senior Director Member Services
KAREN MACHOL PIRAINO - Senior Director Talent
NORA FOLK - Senior Director Catering
RYAN COLLINGS - Senior Director Marketing
RYAN SELLARS - Director Tax
DAVID BASIN - Director Information Technology, Applications, Labor Relations
STACY CELLMAN - Director Development-Beverages, Development-Food
TIM SPENCER - Director Operations, Supply Chain
GREGORY LENNOX - Director Digital, Visual Merchandising
STEVE EPSTEIN - Director Accounting
BRINKLEY JOANN - Director Accounting
DAVE PELLEGRINO - Director Administration
SAMANTHA KATZ - Director Brand Marketing
KAREN MCGEEHAN - Director Business Development
JERRY O'CONNOR - Director Business Development
KEVIN KEBEA - Director Category Management-Beverages
KELLY LEWIS - Director Catering
SCOTT J. ZAHREN - Director Culinary Development
FRANCESCO ESPOSITO - Director Culinary Operations
MIKE HAWKINS - Director Finance
NIRAV SHAH - Director Finance
SCOTT UNTERBRINK - Director Finance
CHRISTOPHER VOLOSIN - Director Finance
CHRIS ANSARDI - Director Foodservice
JOE ANTAL - Director Foodservice
DEREK BRAY - Director Foodservice
CEE BROWN - Director Foodservice
MEGHAN CLINE - Director Foodservice
WADE GROSWITH - Director Foodservice
KIMMIE HITCHENS - Director Foodservice
SULAIMAN MANSARAY - Director Foodservice
ALLISON THOMAS - Director Foodservice
STEPHEN WANCZYK - Director Foodservice
EMILY WILSON - Director Foodservice
DREW O'DONNELL - Director Global Development
LISA STONER - Director HRIS
PATRICIA GIORDANO - Director Human Resources
DANIELLE WARK - Director Human Resources
D. MATT MILES - Director Information Technology
DOUG TRAHER - Director Information Technology
ROBERT GOULD - Director Labor Relations
DAVID LANE - Director Operations
BRANDON WRIGHT - Director Operations
PATRICK MAYHEW - Director Procurement
WILLIAM MILLER - Director Procurement
GLORIA O'BRIEN PMP - Director Development
RON BENNETT - Director Retail Operations
JIM GONSIOREK - Director Retail Operations
MICHAEL PETTINELLI - Director Risk Management
PAUL STAB - Director Sales
DUANE BEDLEY - Director Security
DUANE N. BEDLEY SR - Director Security
CARALYN DANKS - Director Strategic Planning
BRIAN LEE - Director Strategic Planning
ELIZABETH PEARSON - Director Talent
SCOTT BOOTH - Director Tax
MICHAEL BENEDETTI - Director
MAUREEN CASE - Director
BARRY HALLIDAY - Director
FRED MAAHS - Director
JEREMIAH HISER - Director Business Development
MICHELLE TUHOWSKI - Director Human Resources
JOHN DRELICH - Director Information Technology
BRANDON INDRISO - Assistant Director Foodservice
KIM MARTIN-GOODMAN - Assistant Director Foodservice
FRANCIS WINKEY - Senior Manager Merchandising
ERIN NOSS - Senior Manager Communications
EDWARD JONES - Senior Manager Culinary Development
JANINE LIEBEL - Senior Manager Marketing
LEAH BERRY - Senior Manager Sales

DALTON DANIELLE - Senior Manager Sales
DAVIS MARCIA - Senior Manager Training
HEATHER NOLAND - Business Manager Accounting
THOMAS DUNN - Regional Manager Distribution
NATILY SANTOS MBA - Regional Manager Purchasing
CHRIS SCHILLING - Regional Manager Purchasing
BRIAN DATTE - District Manager Facility/Maintenance
RYAN BOYER MBA - District Manager Marketing
GARY DONNELLY - District Manager
JIM ZANZINGER - District Manager
LACEY PETERMAN - Manager Finance
JEN BLOOM - Manager Finance, Operations
LISA FULLER - Manager Accounting
VINCENT GOAN - Manager Accounting
DEB FETSCHER - Manager Administration
MICHELE HEINEMAN - Manager Administration
MRZBOTZ SHIELDS - Manager Branch
LISA BUSH - Manager Branding
JEFF HICKMAN - Manager Branding
BRIANNA MURPHY - Manager Business Development
TONYA BUTLER - Manager Catering
TRISH DUDAS - Manager Catering
BRIONNA FRENCH - Manager Catering
ANNE HORSTMANN - Manager Catering
PAM LYONS - Manager Content Marketing
TERRI DAWICKI - Manager Customer Service
KIM ROSSITER - Manager Development
TONY GIANGIORDANO - Manager Distribution
GEORGEEN BUTZ - Manager Employee Benefits
AMY DEMARCO - Manager Employee Development
JENNIFER MILLER - Manager Event Planning
PATRICK DOLAN - Manager Facility/Maintenance
EDWARD ORNER - Manager Facility/Maintenance
BRIAN WEBB - Manager Facility/Maintenance
NICHOLAS CAPUTO - Manager Finance
LARRY MCLAUGHLIN - Manager Finance
MUHAMMAD MILLER - Manager Food and Beverage
EBONEY GILLIAM - Manager Foodservice
JOE HUBER - Manager Foodservice
MICHAEL LUMER - Manager Foodservice
ROB MCCABE - Manager Foodservice
ROSEANN RIEDMILLER - Manager Foodservice
SANDY WILLIAMSON - Manager Foodservice
BETH GENTHER - Manager Human Resources
NAKISHIA BAILEY - Manager Human Resources
LISA NARDI - Manager Human Resources
RIOS YARITZA - Manager Human Resources
ERIC ADAMS - Manager Information Technology
KEITH ALBRIGHT - Manager Information Technology
SEAN FITZGERALD - Manager Information Technology
R. ALEX LOPEZ - Manager Information Technology
DAVE MESSIER - Manager Information Technology
WON-SHIK OH - Manager Information Technology
BRETT WARMAN - Manager Information Technology
MICHAEL DOUGHTY - Manager Investor Relations
ROSE POMIDORO - Manager Labor Relations
MICHELE BROWN - Manager Licensing
GOLDBERG JESSICA - Manager Marketing
STEVE MALACKEY - Manager Marketing
KAREN BRIGHTCLIFFE - Manager Operations
BRUCE NORMAN CPMM - Manager Operations
JANET STANISZEWSKI - Manager Operations
DENNIS BRODERICK - Manager Payroll
THERESA PRICE - Manager Production
BRIAN WILCOX - Manager Public Relations
BOB KRUSE - Manager Purchasing
TERI HOPWOOD - Manager Restaurant Operations
BERNARD CARPENTER - Manager Sales
BILL GITHENS - Manager Sales
JEFF STEFANO - Manager Sales
JOSHUA STERN - Manager Sales
RICK WASHER - Manager Sales
BRIAN WEBER - Manager Sales
HAROLD GUYTON - Manager Security
CINDY THOMAS - Manager Strategic Planning
BRYAN BERZINS - Manager Talent
GREG BURKE - Manager Warehouse
KENNETH LEY - Manager Warehouse
BILL LUBECK - Manager Alcoholic Beverages
BRUCE BOGDANOFF - Manager
MICHAEL BRENNAN - Manager
BRIAN BURCH - Manager
ANGELA DIBELLA - Manager
RICKY MASTER - Manager
CHANEL MCCOY - Manager
JEFFERY PRESSLEY - Manager
ARLENE RICHARDSON - Manager
GREGORY ZARCONE - Manager
TRACY BROWN - Manager Training
MEGAN WHALEN - Manager Communications
JACQULINE WHITFIELD - Manager Marketing
JENNIFER MUNNS - Manager Event Planning
THOMAS BROCKMEYER - Manager Information Technology
TRACY STYF - Brand Manager Development
DANIEL DIMONTE - Supervisor Payroll
WALTER HENDERSON - Supervisor Retail Operations
SAMSON CHAN - Project Manager Information Technology
YVETTE SCOTT - Project Manager Information Technology
CLAYTON GARLOCK - Project Manager
CHRISTINE LEPRE - Project Manager
JIM MCGINNISS - Project Manager
PAT ROONEY - Project Manager
INGRID TROMMER - Project Manager
MARK LAUBSCHER - Senior Analyst Risk Management
PETER LUU - Analyst Quality Assurance
PETER COMMANDER - Analyst Information Technology

† ARAMARK Business Services

2400 Market St
Philadelphia, PA 19103

Telephone: (215) 238-3000
Fax Number: (215) 238-8178
Listing Type: Divisional Office
Type of Business: Foodservice Management Operator
Year Founded: 1959
Number of Employees: 1,300
Number of Locations Served: 1,500
Total Foodservice Mgmt Accounts: 1,500
Areas of Operation: PA
Type of Foodservice: Cafeteria (1,500)
Foodservice Management Venues: Business & Industry
Primary Distributors: (Full Line) SYSCO Food Services of Chicago Inc., DES PLAINES, IL
Parent Company: Aramark, PHILADELPHIA, PA
Regional Offices: ARAMARK Business Services, DOWNERS GROVE, IL; ARAMARK Business Services, PHILADELPHIA, PA

Key Personnel
SANDRA DEMAS - VP Supply Chain
JOSEPH STEMME - Senior Analyst Finance

† ARAMARK Business Services

1101 Market St
Philadelphia, PA 19107-2934

Telephone: (215) 238-3000
Fax Number: (215) 409-7952
Listing Type: Regional Office
Type of Business: Foodservice Management Operator
Year Founded: 1959
Number of Employees: 2,000
Number of Locations Served: 1,350
Total Foodservice Mgmt Accounts: 1,350
Areas of Operation: PA
Type of Foodservice: Cafeteria (1,350)
Foodservice Management Venues: Business & Industry
Primary Distributors: (Full Line) SYSCO Food Services of Philadelphia LLC, PHILADELPHIA, PA
Parent Company: Aramark, PHILADELPHIA, PA
Headquarters: ARAMARK Business Services,

PHILADELPHIA, PA

Key Personnel
MARC BRUNO - COO
SCOTT UNTERBRINK - General Manager; Director Operations, Purchasing, Human Resources, Region

ARAMARK Conference Centers Management
1101 Market St
Philadelphia, PA 19107

Telephone: (215) 238-3000
Fax Number: (215) 409-7940
Listing Type: Divisional Office
Type of Business: Foodservice Management Operator
Year Founded: 1959
Number of Employees: 4,000
Number of Locations Served: 45
Total Foodservice Mgmt Accounts: 45
Areas of Operation: CA, DC, IL, MA, MD, MI, MO, MS, NJ, PA, TX, VA, WI, WV, ON
Type of Foodservice: Full-service sit-down dining (45)
Foodservice Management Venues: Other
Primary Distributors: (Full Line) SYSCO Food Services of Philadelphia LLC, PHILADELPHIA, PA
Parent Company: Aramark, PHILADELPHIA, PA

Key Personnel
MARC BRUNO - COO

ARAMARK Healthcare Support Services
1101 Market St
Philadelphia, PA 19107-2934

Telephone: (215) 238-3000
Fax Number: (215) 409-7955
Listing Type: Regional Office
Type of Business: Foodservice Management Operator
Year Founded: 1959
Number of Employees: 50
Number of Locations Served: 70
Total Foodservice Mgmt Accounts: 70
Areas of Operation: PA
Type of Foodservice: Cafeteria (70)
Foodservice Management Venues: Health Care
Primary Distributors: (Full Line) SYSCO Food Services of Philadelphia LLC, PHILADELPHIA, PA
Parent Company: Aramark, PHILADELPHIA, PA
Headquarters: ARAMARK Healthcare,

PHILADELPHIA, PA

Key Personnel
EVIN WOOD - Senior Director Digital, Innovation
ALASSANE DANTE - Director

ARAMARK Higher Education
1101 Market St
Philadelphia, PA 19107

Telephone: (215) 238-3000
Fax Number: (215) 238-4088
Listing Type: Divisional Office
Type of Business: Foodservice Management Operator
Year Founded: 1959
Number of Employees: 2,000
Number of Locations Served: 500
Total Foodservice Mgmt Accounts: 500
Areas of Operation: PA
Type of Foodservice: Cafeteria (500)
Foodservice Management Venues: College & University
Primary Distributors: (Full Line) SYSCO Food Services of Philadelphia LLC, PHILADELPHIA, PA
Parent Company: Aramark, PHILADELPHIA, PA
Regional Offices: ARAMARK Campus Services(HIGHER EDUCATION), WAKEFIELD, MA; ARAMARK Higher Education, CARY, NC; ARAMARK Higher Education, DALLAS, TX; ARAMARK Higher Education, DOWNERS GROVE, IL

Key Personnel
BRENT FRANKS - COO
CHRIS AUGUSTIN - Director Information Technology
ANDREA GALLANT - Regional Director Marketing

ARAMARK International Services
1101 Market St
Philadelphia, PA 19107-2934

Telephone: (215) 238-3000
Listing Type: Divisional Office
Type of Business: Foodservice Management Operator
Year Founded: 1959
Number of Employees: 1,000
Number of Locations Served: 2,000
Total Foodservice Mgmt Accounts: 2,000
Areas of Operation: PA
Type of Foodservice: Quick Serve (2,000)
Foodservice Management Venues: Other
Primary Distributors: (Full Line) SYSCO Food

Services of Philadelphia LLC, PHILADELPHIA, PA
Parent Company: Aramark, PHILADELPHIA, PA

Key Personnel
SANDRA DEMAS - VP Finance

ARAMARK School Support Services
2400 Market St
Philadelphia, PA 19103

Telephone: (215) 238-3000
Fax Number: (215) 238-8169
Listing Type: Divisional Office
Type of Business: Foodservice Management Operator
Year Founded: 1959
Number of Employees: 10,000
Number of Locations Served: 200
Total Foodservice Mgmt Accounts: 200
Areas of Operation: PA
Type of Foodservice: Cafeteria (200)
Foodservice Management Venues: Schools
Primary Distributors: (Full Line) SYSCO Food Services of Chicago Inc., DES PLAINES, IL
Parent Company: Aramark, PHILADELPHIA, PA
Regional Offices: ARAMARK, DOWNERS GROVE, IL; ARAMARK Education, COPPELL, TX

Key Personnel
QUENTEN WENTWORTH - President Group

ARAMARK Sports & Entertainment Group
2400 Market St
Philadelphia, PA 19103

Telephone: (215) 238-3000
Listing Type: Divisional Office
Type of Business: Foodservice Management Operator
Year Founded: 1959
Number of Employees: 1,500
Number of Locations Served: 300
Total Foodservice Mgmt Accounts: 300
Areas of Operation: MA, PA
Type of Foodservice: Cafeteria (300)
Foodservice Management Venues: Other; Parks & Recreation; Sports Venues
Primary Distributors: (Full Line) SYSCO Food Services of Chicago Inc., DES PLAINES, IL
Parent Company: Aramark, PHILADELPHIA, PA

Key Personnel
BRUCE FEARS - President Group

MARC BRUNO - COO

Auntie Anne's Franchise
1455 Franklin Mills Cir
Philadelphia, PA 19154-3131

Telephone: (215) 281-1225
Internet Homepage: auntieannesfranchising.com
Type of Business: Chain Restaurant Operator
Total Sales: $8,640,000 (e)
Total Units: 12
Trade Names: Auntie Anne's Hand-Rolled Soft Pretzels (12)
Units Franchised From: 12
Primary Menu: Snacks (12)
Areas of Operation: PA
Type of Foodservice: Quick Serve (12)
Franchise Affiliation: Auntie Anne's Inc., LANCASTER, PA

Key Personnel
NIRAV PATEL - Owner; General Buyer

Auntie Anne's Franchise
8500 Essington Ave
Philadelphia, PA 19153-3755

Telephone: (215) 492-5537
Type of Business: Chain Restaurant Operator
Total Sales: $2,385,000 (e)
Total Units: 3
Trade Names: Auntie Anne's Hand-Rolled Soft Pretzels (3)
Units Franchised From: 3
Primary Menu: Snacks (3)
Areas of Operation: PA
Type of Foodservice: Quick Serve (3)
Franchise Affiliation: Auntie Anne's Inc., LANCASTER, PA

Key Personnel
ELIZABETH ROBERTSON - Owner; General Buyer

CinCin Inc.
7838 Germantown Ave
Philadelphia, PA 19118-3527

Telephone: (215) 242-8800
Fax Number: (215) 242-3548
Internet Homepage: nectarphilly.com; cincinrestaurant.com; yangmingrestaurant.com
Type of Business: Chain Restaurant Operator
Year Founded: 1996
Total Sales: $5,325,000 (e)
Alcohol Sales: 20%
Number of Employees: 80
Average Check: Lunch(10); Dinner(18)
Total Units: 3
Trade Names: Cin Cin (1); Nectar (1); Yang Ming (1)
Company-Owned Units: 3
Preferred Location Types: Freestanding
Alcohol Served: Beer, Wine, Liquor
Primary Menu: Chinese (2); French/Continental (1)
Areas of Operation: PA
Type of Foodservice: Casual Dining (2); Fine Dining (1)
Primary Distributors: (Food) SYSCO Food Services of Central Pennsylvania LLC, HARRISBURG, PA

Key Personnel
MICHAEL WEI - President; General Buyer
HENRY LEE - General Manager

CookNSolo, Inc.
237 Saint James Pl
Philadelphia, PA 19106-3936

Telephone: (215) 625-8800
Internet Homepage: cooknsolo.com
Company Email: info@cooknsolo.com
Type of Business: Chain Restaurant Operator
Year Founded: 2008
Total Units: 11
Trade Names: Abe Fisher (1); Dizengoff (1); Federal Donuts (6); Goldie (1); Rooster Soup Co (1); Zahav (1)
Company-Owned Units: 11
Primary Menu: American (2); Chicken (6); Middle Eastern (2); Snacks (1)
Areas of Operation: PA
Type of Foodservice: Casual Dining (9); Quick Serve (2)

Key Personnel
MIKE SOLOMONOV - Partner; Executive Chef
STEVE COOK - Partner

Fez Fine Moroccan Cuisine
620 S 2nd St
Philadelphia, PA 19147-2418

Telephone: (215) 925-5367
Internet Homepage: cedarslebanesecuisine.com; byblosrestaurantandhookahbar.com; fezrestaurant.com; vangoloungeandskybar.com
Type of Business: Chain Restaurant Operator
Year Founded: 1991
Total Sales: $5,736,000 (e)
Alcohol Sales: 35%
Number of Employees: 30
Average Check: Lunch(30); Dinner(42)
Total Units: 4
Trade Names: Byblos (1); Cedars Restaurant (1); Fez Moroccan Cuisine (1); Vango Lounge and Sky Bar (1)
Company-Owned Units: 4
Preferred Location Types: Downtown; Freestanding
Alcohol Served: Beer, Wine, Liquor
Primary Menu: French/Continental (1); Greek/Mediterranean (1); Middle Eastern (2)
Areas of Operation: PA
Type of Foodservice: Fine Dining (4)
Catering Services: Yes
Primary Distributors: (Full Line) Jetro Cash & Carry, PHILADELPHIA, PA

Key Personnel
DIAA SAWAN - Partner; General Manager
GEORGE SAWAN - Partner; General Buyer
GHASSAN SAWAN - Partner
MICHAEL SAWAN - Partner
TONY SAWAN - Partner; General Manager; Executive Chef; Director Catering

Garces Restaurant Group Inc. LLC
2401 Walnut St Ste 300
Philadelphia, PA 19103-4219

Telephone: (215) 625-2506
Internet Homepage: garcesgroup.com
Type of Business: Chain Restaurant Operator
Year Founded: 2005
Total Sales: $50,480,000 (e)
Alcohol Sales: 15%
Number of Employees: 1,820
Total Units: 14
Trade Names: Amada (2); Buena Onda (1); Distrito Taqueria (2); J G Domestic (1); Okatshe (1); Olon (1); Ortzi (1); Stella (1); The Olde Bar (1); Tinto (1); Village Whiskey (1); Volver (1)
Company-Owned Units: 14
Preferred Location Types: Downtown; Hotel/Motel; Mobile Unit
Alcohol Served: Beer, Wine, Liquor
Primary Menu: American (3); Japanese (1); Mexican (3); Miscellaneous (4); Seafood (1); Spanish (3)
Areas of Operation: NJ, NY, PA
Type of Foodservice: Casual Dining (12); Fine Dining (2)
Catering Services: Yes
Parent Company: Ballard Brands LLC, MANDEVILLE, LA

Key Personnel
JOSE GARCES - Chairman; Executive Chef
CAROLINE GUTSHALL - Senior Manager Marketing, Sales

Guest Counts Hospitality
1 Reed St Ste 200
Philadelphia, PA 19147

Telephone: (215) 922-3200
Fax Number: (215) 922-7429
Internet Homepage: cubalibrerestaurant.com; guestcounts.com
Company Email: INFO@CUBALIBRERESTAURANT.COM
Type of Business: Chain Restaurant Operator
Total Sales: $5,054,000 (e)
Internet Order Processing: Yes
Total Units: 4
Trade Names: Cuba Libre (4)
Company-Owned Units: 4
Alcohol Served: Beer, Wine, Liquor
Primary Menu: Latin American/Cuban (4)
Areas of Operation: DC, FL, NJ, PA
Type of Foodservice: Casual Dining (4)
Catering Services: Yes

Key Personnel
GUILLERMO PERNOT - Partner; Executive Chef; General Buyer
BARRY GUTIN - Partner
LARRY COHEN - Partner
JOE MISUNAS - Director Catering

Han Dynasty
123 Chestnut St
Philadelphia, PA 19106

Telephone: (215) 922-1888
Internet Homepage: handynasty.net
Company Email: info@handynasty.net
Type of Business: Chain Restaurant Operator
Year Founded: 2006
Total Units: 9
Trade Names: Han Dynasty (9)
Company-Owned Units: 9
Primary Menu: Chinese (9)
Areas of Operation: NY, PA
Type of Foodservice: Casual Dining (9)

Key Personnel
HAN CHIANG - Founder; President
MARK ALLAN - Director Operations
CHRISTOPHER SLAUGHTER - Director Operations

Hibachi Steakhouse
325 N Columbus Blvd
Philadelphia, PA 19106-1416

Telephone: (215) 592-7100
Internet Homepage: hibachidining.com
Type of Business: Chain Restaurant Operator
Year Founded: 1988
Total Sales: $7,305,000 (e)
Alcohol Sales: 10%
Number of Employees: 540
Average Check: Dinner(30)
Total Units: 8
Trade Names: Hibachi Steakhouse (8)
Company-Owned Units: 8
Preferred Square Footage: 5,500; 6,000
Preferred Location Types: Community Mall; Freestanding
Alcohol Served: Beer, Wine, Liquor
Primary Menu: Japanese (8)
Areas of Operation: DE, PA
Type of Foodservice: Casual Dining (8)
Primary Distributors: (Full Line) US Foods, ALLENTOWN, PA

Key Personnel
WAI CHAN - President; Executive Chef; Director Facility/Maintenance, Supply Chain; General Buyer
DUNCAN NGUYEN - General Manager; Director Information Systems, Real Estate, Design

Honeygrow
110 S 16th St
Philadelphia, PA 19102-2802

Telephone: (215) 545-1206
Internet Homepage: honeygrow.com
Company Email: ComeTogether@honeygrow.com
Type of Business: Chain Restaurant Operator
Year Founded: 2012
Total Sales: $58,350,000 (e)
Average Check: Lunch(12); Dinner(14)
Total Units: 25
Trade Names: honeygrow (25)
Company-Owned Units: 25
Preferred Square Footage: 2,100
Primary Menu: Asian (25)
Areas of Operation: DC, DE, MA, MD, NJ, NY, PA
Type of Foodservice: Fast Casual (25)

Key Personnel
JUSTIN ROSENBERG - Co-Founder; CEO
JOHN THOMAS - VP Operations
ED BUCKLEY - General Manager
AMY BARKASY DEPAOLI - Director Marketing
LIZ FIFIS - Director Human Resources
RACHEL SCHOFIELD - Regional Director
MIKE MAZER - District Manager

La Colombe Torrefaction, Inc.
2620 E Tioga St
Philadelphia, PA 19134-5415

Telephone: (215) 426-2011
Internet Homepage: lacolombe.com
Company Email: help@lacolombe.net
Type of Business: Chain Restaurant Operator
Year Founded: 1994
Total Units: 30
Trade Names: La Colombe Coffee Roasters (30)
Company-Owned Units: 30
Primary Menu: Coffee (30)
Areas of Operation: CA, DC, IL, MA, NY, PA
Type of Foodservice: Quick Serve (30)

Key Personnel
TODD CARMICHAEL - Co-Founder; CEO
JP IBERTI - Co-Founder; President
HAMDI ULUKAYA - Owner
KATHRYN O'CONNOR - Director Marketing, Merchandising
NICOLAS O'CONNELL - Director Sales

Marathon Restaurants
1818 Market St
Philadelphia, PA 19103-3638

Telephone: (215) 561-1818
Fax Number: (215) 561-2275
Internet Homepage: eatmarathon.com
Company Email: marketing@marathongrill.com
Type of Business: Chain Restaurant Operator
Year Founded: 1979
Total Sales: $9,861,000 (e)
Alcohol Sales: 20%
Number of Employees: 250
Average Check: Breakfast(14); Lunch(18); Dinner(28)
Internet Order Processing: Yes
Total Units: 3
Trade Names: Marathon on the Square (1); The Marathon Grill (2)
Company-Owned Units: 3
Preferred Square Footage: 5,500; 6,000
Preferred Location Types: Downtown; Freestanding; Lifestyle Center; Office Complex
Alcohol Served: Beer, Wine, Liquor
Primary Menu: American (3)
Areas of Operation: PA
Type of Foodservice: Casual Dining (3)
Catering Services: Yes
Primary Distributors: (Full Line) US Foods, PITTSTON, PA

Key Personnel
JON BORISH - General Manager
KEVIN KONG - General Manager; Director Marketing
SHERYL BORISH - Director Quality Assurance, Customer Service
VICKIE IZZO - Director Operations; General Buyer

Marquis & Co
127 S 18th St
Philadelphia, PA 19103-5246

Telephone: (215) 278-7605
Internet Homepage: barbombon.com; charliewasasinner.com; hipcityveg.com
Company Email: hello@hipcityveg.com
Type of Business: Chain Restaurant Operator
Year Founded: 2012
Total Units: 7
Trade Names: Bar Bombon (1); Charlie Was A Sinner (1); HipCityVeg (5)
Company-Owned Units: 7
Primary Menu: American (1); Latin American/Cuban (1); Sandwiches/Deli (5)
Projected Openings: 2
Areas of Operation: DC, PA
Type of Foodservice: Casual Dining (2); Fast Casual (5)

Key Personnel
NICOLE MARQUIS - Owner; General Buyer
MICHAEL SANTORO - Executive Chef
MICHELLE SODA - Director Operations

Northeast Donut Shop Management Inc
5201 Darrah St
Philadelphia, PA 19124-1317

Telephone: (215) 288-3407
Fax Number: (800) 351-1337
Type of Business: Chain Restaurant Operator
Year Founded: 1989
Total Sales: $46,450,000 (e)
Average Check: Lunch(6); Dinner(8)
Total Units: 30
Trade Names: Dunkin' Donuts (30)
Units Franchised From: 30
Preferred Square Footage: 1,500; 2,200
Preferred Location Types: Freestanding
Primary Menu: Snacks (30)
Areas of Operation: PA
Type of Foodservice: Quick Serve (30)
Franchise Affiliation: DD IP Holder, CANTON, MA

Key Personnel
BILLY HONG - President; General Buyer
KHIM CHIM - VP

Real Food Eatery
207 S 16th St
Philadelphia, PA 19102

Telephone: (215) 608-8941
Internet Homepage: realfoodeatery.com
Company Email: info@realfoodeatery.com
Type of Business: Chain Restaurant Operator
Year Founded: 2016
Total Units: 4
Trade Names: Real Food Eatery (4)
Company-Owned Units: 4
Preferred Location Types: Downtown
Primary Menu: Health Foods (4)
Areas of Operation: PA
Type of Foodservice: Fast Casual (4)

Key Personnel
MIKE MANGOLD - Co-Founder

Saxbys Coffee, LLC
2300 Chestnut St Ste 310
Philadelphia, PA 19103-4362

Telephone: (215) 853-6140
Fax Number: (610) 397-1672
Internet Homepage: saxbyscoffee.com
Company Email: info@saxbyscoffee.com
Type of Business: Chain Restaurant Operator
Year Founded: 2004
Systemwide Sales: $15,419,000 (e)
Total Sales: $3,055,000 (e)
Number of Employees: 242
Average Check: Breakfast(8); Lunch(12);
Internet Order Processing: Yes
Internet Sales: 2.00%
Total Units: 26
Trade Names: Saxbys Coffee (26)
Company-Owned Units: 2
Units Franchised To: 24
Preferred Square Footage: 600; 1,100; 1,500
Preferred Location Types: Community Mall; Freestanding; Lifestyle Center; Regional Mall; Strip Mall
Primary Menu: Coffee (26)
Projected Openings: 9
Areas of Operation: DC, DE, GA, KY, NC, NJ, OH, PA, VA
Type of Foodservice: Quick Serve (26)
Primary Distributors: (Full Line) SYSCO Food Services of Philadelphia LLC, PHILADELPHIA, PA; (Full Line) Dairyland, The Chefs' Warehouse, BRONX, NY
Parent Company: MVP Capital Partners, RADNOR, PA

Key Personnel
NICK BAYER - CEO; President; COO; Treasurer
RICHARD ROLLIER - VP Operations
HALEY SAMSI - VP Operations
RUSS WILKIN - VP Marketing

SNAP Cutom Pizza & Salads
1504 Sansom St
Philadelphia, PA 19102

Telephone: (484) 380-2054
Internet Homepage: snapcustompizza.com
Company Email: snappizzacustomerservice@gmail.com
Type of Business: Chain Restaurant Operator
Year Founded: 1998
Total Units: 8
Trade Names: SNAP Custom Pizza & Salads (8)
Company-Owned Units: 8
Primary Menu: Pizza (8)
Areas of Operation: PA
Type of Foodservice: Fast Casual (8)

Key Personnel
PETER HOWEY - Co-Founder
AARON NOCKS - Co-Founder

Starr Restaurant Group
134 Market St
Philadelphia, PA 19106-3015

Telephone: (215) 923-4838
Fax Number: (215) 923-2955
Internet Homepage: starr-restaurant.com
Company Email: starr.info@starr-restaurant.com
Type of Business: Chain Restaurant Operator
Year Founded: 1995
Total Sales: $325,000,000 (e)
Alcohol Sales: 10%
Number of Employees: 1,850
Average Check: Lunch(32); Dinner(46)
Total Units: 36
Trade Names: Alma de Cuba (1); Barclay Prime (1); Buddakan (2); Butcher and Singer (1); Caffe Storico (1); Chezla Vieille (1); Continental Midtown (1); El Rey (1); El Vez (3); Electric Lemon (1); Fette Sau (1); Frankford Hall (1); Jones (1); La Mercerie (1); Le Coucou (1); Le Diplomate (1); Le Zoo (1); Makoto (1); Morimoto (1); Parc (1); Pastis (1); Pizzeria Stella (1); Pod (1); Serpico (1); St Anselm (1); Steak 954 (1); Talula's Daily (1); Talula's Garden (1); The Clock Tower(1); The Continental (2); The Dandelion Pub (1); Upland (1)
Company-Owned Units: 36
Preferred Square Footage: 5,500; 6,000
Preferred Location Types: Freestanding; Office Complex
Alcohol Served: Beer, Wine, Liquor
Primary Menu: American (10); Asian (6); Bar-B-Q (1); French/Continental (7); Hamburger (1); Italian (1); Japanese (2); Latin American/Cuban (1); Mexican (4); Pizza (1); Seafood (1); Steak (3)
Areas of Operation: DC, FL, NJ, NY, PA
Type of Foodservice: Casual Dining (35); Quick Serve (1)
Primary Distributors: (Food) SYSCO Food Services of Central Pennsylvania LLC, HARRISBURG, PA

Key Personnel
STEPHEN STARR - President; Director Purchasing
DAVID ROBKIN - Chief Development Officer
JOSHUA LEVINE - VP Operations
JASON MILLER - VP Information Technology
JULIA AURITT - Senior Director Loyalty Program
MICHELLE YIANOLATOS - Senior Director Human Resources, Talent
RACHEL OSSAKOW - Director
RANDI SIRKIN - Director Display
JENNA VELELLA - Director Strategy, Sales
ALIX BELL - Senior Project Manager Licensing
JASON IVEY - Project Manager Information Technology

The Irish Pub
2007 Walnut St
Philadelphia, PA 19103-4403

Telephone: (215) 568-5603
Fax Number: (215) 568-2944
Internet Homepage: irishpubphilly.com
Type of Business: Chain Restaurant Operator
Year Founded: 1972
Total Sales: $7,884,000 (e)
Alcohol Sales: 30%
Number of Employees: 110
Average Check: Lunch(8); Dinner(18)
Total Units: 3
Trade Names: Irish Pub (3)
Company-Owned Units: 3
Preferred Square Footage: 4,000
Preferred Location Types: Downtown; Freestanding
Alcohol Served: Beer, Wine, Liquor
Primary Menu: American (3)
Areas of Operation: NJ, PA
Type of Foodservice: Casual Dining (3)
Primary Distributors: (Equipment) Edward Don & Co., WESTAMPTON, NJ; (Food) US Foods Philadelphia Metro, BRIDGEPORT, NJ; (Supplies) Edward Don & Co., WESTAMPTON, NJ

Key Personnel
RICHARD BURKE SR - President; CFO; Manager Quality Assurance, Human Resources, Research & Development, Business Development, Store Planning, Food Safety
CATHERINE BURKE - VP; Director Information Systems, Marketing, Advertising
MARK O'CONNOR - VP Operations
RICHARD BURKE JR - General Manager; Executive Chef; General Buyer

The Restaurant School
4207 Walnut St
Philadelphia, PA 19104-5238

Telephone: (215) 222-4200
Fax Number: (215) 222-4219
Internet Homepage: walnuthillcollege.edu
Company Email: info@walnuthillcollege.edu
Type of Business: Chain Restaurant Operator
Year Founded: 1974
Total Sales: $6,991,000 (e)
Alcohol Sales: 10%
Number of Employees: 50
Average Check: Breakfast(6); Lunch(12); Dinner(54)
Total Units: 5
Trade Names: Bistro Perrier (1); Pastry Shop (1); The American Heartland (1); The Great Chefs of Philadelphia (1); The Italian Trattoria (1)
Company-Owned Units: 5
Preferred Location Types: Institution (college/hospital)
Alcohol Served: Beer, Wine, Liquor
Primary Menu: American (4); Eastern European (1)
Areas of Operation: PA
Type of Foodservice: Casual Dining (2); Fast Casual (2); Fine Dining (1)
Primary Distributors: (Food) SYSCO Food Services of Philadelphia LLC, PHILADELPHIA, PA

Key Personnel
DANIEL LIBERATOSCIOLI - President
DENNIS LIBERATI - VP Operations; General Buyer
PEGGY LIBERATOSCIOLI - Director Human Resources
VALERIE SNISARENKO - Director Marketing
GARY TREVISANI - Director Culinary Development

Tiffin Indian Cuisine
710 W Girard Ave
Philadelphia, PA 19123

Telephone: (215) 922-1297
Internet Homepage: tiffin.com
Company Email: franchise@tiffin.com
Type of Business: Chain Restaurant Operator
Year Founded: 2006
Total Sales: $8,423,000 (e)
Total Units: 9
Trade Names: Tiffin (9)
Company-Owned Units: 9
Primary Menu: Indian (9)
Areas of Operation: NJ, PA
Type of Foodservice: Fast Casual (9)

Key Personnel
MUNISH NARULA - President; General Buyer

Vetri Family
412 S 13th St
Philadelphia, PA 19147

Telephone: (215) 732-2647
Internet Homepage: amisphilly.com; pizzeriavetri.com; vetrifamily.com
Company Email: info@vetrifamily
Type of Business: Chain Restaurant Operator
Year Founded: 2013
Total Units: 7
Trade Names: Amis Trattoria (3); Bar Amis (1); Pizzeria Vetri (3)
Company-Owned Units: 8
Primary Menu: Italian (4); Pizza (3)
Projected Openings: 1
Areas of Operation: DC, PA, TX
Type of Foodservice: Casual Dining (7)
Parent Company: Urban Outfitters Inc., PHILADELPHIA, PA

Key Personnel
BRAD SPENCE - Executive Chef; Director Culinary Development
OONA MCCULLOUGH - Director Investor Relations
CARLA NORELLI - Director Culinary Operations
SUZANNE ROSSINI - Manager Event Planning, Sales
BRANDON COHILL - Manager Beverages

H. James Rippon Enterprises
427 Suedberg Rd
Pine Grove, PA 17963

Mailing Address: PO Box 327, PINE GROVE, PA, 17963-0327
Telephone: (570) 345-6400
Fax Number: (570) 345-2435
Type of Business: Chain Restaurant Operator
Year Founded: 1984
Total Sales: $23,640,000 (e)
Number of Employees: 190
Average Check: Breakfast(8); Lunch(12); Dinner(12)
Total Units: 5
Trade Names: McDonald's (5)
Units Franchised From: 5
Preferred Square Footage: 2,500; 3,000
Preferred Location Types: Freestanding
Primary Menu: Hamburger (5)
Areas of Operation: PA
Type of Foodservice: Quick Serve (5)
Franchise Affiliation: McDonald's Corporation, CHICAGO, IL

Key Personnel
H. JAMES RIPPON - Owner; General Manager;

General Buyer
MILTON GREEN - Director Operations

Kokolas Inc
120 E Chestnut St
Pine Grove Mills, PA 16868

Mailing Address: P O Box 627, Pine Grove Mills, PA, 16868
Telephone: (814) 237-1622
Fax Number: (814) 237-1633
Type of Business: Chain Restaurant Operator
Total Sales: $14,420,000 (e)
Total Units: 8
Trade Names: KFC (8)
Units Franchised From: 8
Primary Menu: Chicken (8)
Areas of Operation: PA
Type of Foodservice: Quick Serve (8)
Franchise Affiliation: KFC Corporation, LOUISVILLE, KY

Key Personnel
KEITH COLE - President; General Buyer

Big Burrito Restaurant Group
5740 Baum Blvd Ste 1
Pittsburgh, PA 15206-3775

Telephone: (412) 361-3272
Fax Number: (412) 361-4318
Internet Homepage: bigburrito.com; madmex.com
Company Email: info@bigburrito.com
Type of Business: Chain Restaurant Operator
Year Founded: 1994
Total Sales: $20,300,000 (e)
Alcohol Sales: 33%
Number of Employees: 900
Average Check: Breakfast(10); Lunch(12); Dinner(22)
Internet Order Processing: Yes
Total Units: 18
Trade Names: Casbah (1); Eleven (1); Kaya (1); Mad Mex (13); Soba (1); Umi (1)
Company-Owned Units: 18
Preferred Square Footage: 8,500
Preferred Location Types: Freestanding
Alcohol Served: Beer, Wine, Liquor
Primary Menu: American (1); Asian (1); Caribbean (1); Japanese (1); Mexican (13); Middle Eastern (1)
Areas of Operation: OH, PA
Type of Foodservice: Casual Dining (18)
Catering Services: Yes
Primary Distributors: (Full Line) SYSCO Food Services of Pittsburgh Inc., HARMONY, PA

Key Personnel
CARY KLEIN - CEO
GLORIA SCIARAPPA - VP Operations
WILLIAM FULLER - Executive Chef; General Buyer
COREY LECHAT - Director Marketing
JEN LOVE - Director Operations
RACHEL YAMADA - Director Human Resources
JOSHUA KLEIN - Regional Manager
STEPHANIE MCCULLOUGH - Manager Restaurant Operations
SUSAN OMALLEY - Manager Catering
SHERI HARTMAN - Manager Payroll
TAUSHA ADAMS - Manager Accounting
MAX BARON - Manager Information Systems; Systems Analyst

Burgatory
932 Freeport Rd
Pittsburgh, PA 15238

Telephone: (412) 781-1456
Internet Homepage: burgatorybar.com; unclesamssubs.com
Company Email: wehearya@burgatorybar.com
Type of Business: Chain Restaurant Operator
Total Sales: $15,760,000 (e)
Total Units: 12
Trade Names: Burgatory (9); Uncle Sam's Sandwich Bar (3)
Company-Owned Units: 12
Preferred Location Types: Community Mall; Stadiums; Strip Mall
Primary Menu: Hamburger (9); Sandwiches/Deli (3)
Areas of Operation: PA
Type of Foodservice: Casual Dining (9); Fast Casual (3)

Key Personnel
JERRY DILEMBO - Partner; General Buyer
MIKE HANLEY - Partner
BRAD KOHUT - Director Foodservice

Eric Drake
39 Walsh Rd
Pittsburgh, PA 15205-2336

Mailing Address: PO Box 44014, PITTSBURGH, PA, 15205-0214
Telephone: (412) 921-5099
Type of Business: Chain Restaurant Operator
Total Sales: $2,107,000 (e)
Total Units: 3
Trade Names: Subway (3)
Units Franchised From: 3
Primary Menu: Sandwiches/Deli (3)
Areas of Operation: PA
Type of Foodservice: Quick Serve (3)
Franchise Affiliation: Doctor's Associates Inc., MILFORD, CT

Key Personnel
ERIC DRAKE - Owner; General Buyer

g3 Restaurant Group
393 N Shore Dr
Pittsburgh, PA 15212

Telephone: (412) 224-6287
Internet Homepage: g3restaurants.com; eddiegeorgesgrille27.g3restaurants.com; jeromebettisgrille36.g3restaurants.com
Type of Business: Chain Restaurant Operator
Total Units: 2
Trade Names: Eddie George's Grille 27 (1); Jerome Bettis' Grille 36 (1)
Company-Owned Units: 2
Primary Menu: American (2)
Areas of Operation: OH, PA
Type of Foodservice: Casual Dining (2)

Key Personnel
HOWARD SHILLER - President
DAVE STAMPO - General Manager; General Buyer

Heartland Restaurant Group LLC
40 24th St Fl 3
Pittsburgh, PA 15222-4656

Telephone: (412) 321-0313
Fax Number: (412) 321-0314
Internet Homepage: heartlandrestaurantgroup.com
Type of Business: Chain Restaurant Operator
Total Sales: $72,610,000 (e)
Total Units: 46
Trade Names: Dunkin' Donuts (46)
Units Franchised From: 46
Preferred Square Footage: 800; 1,500; 2,000; 2,400
Primary Menu: Snacks (46)
Areas of Operation: PA, WV
Type of Foodservice: Quick Serve (46)
Catering Services: Yes
Franchise Affiliation: DD IP Holder, CANTON, MA

Key Personnel
THOMAS BROWNE - CEO; President
EDWARD J. JATEN - President
ANTHONY BRAUN - Owner; CFO; COO
MICHAEL ORIE - VP Real Estate
AMY BYARS - Regional Director Operations
MIKE ZAPPONE - Manager Marketing, Recruitment
CHELSEA HALKER - Manager Marketing

Laurel Foodsystems
4590 Campbells Run Rd
Pittsburgh, PA 15205-1314

Telephone: (412) 494-4400
Fax Number: (412) 787-2275
Internet Homepage: laurelfoodsystems.com
Company Email: info@laurelfoodsystems.com
Type of Business: Foodservice Management Operator
Year Founded: 1974
Total Sales: $42,640,000 (e)
Number of Employees: 225
Number of Locations Served: 38
Total Foodservice Mgmt Accounts: 38
Areas of Operation: PA
Type of Foodservice: Cafeteria (38)
Foodservice Management Venues: Business & Industry; College & University
Primary Distributors: (Full Line) US Foods, GREENSBURG, PA

Key Personnel
TOM DIFFENDAL JR - President; Manager Operations, Human Resources
DON DIFFENDAL - CFO; Executive Chef; Manager Finance, Information Systems, Risk Management, Menu Development, Food Safety, Food and Beverage
RICHARD DIFFENDAL - VP Purchasing; General Buyer
AL SCHROTH - VP Sales
JIM JORDAN - Manager Branch
MARIA SCHWAB - Manager Sales

M & J Management Corp
1366 Old Freeport Rd
Pittsburgh, PA 15238

Telephone: (412) 963-6550
Fax Number: (412) 963-6557
Type of Business: Chain Restaurant Operator
Year Founded: 1957
Total Sales: $80,440,000 (e)
Number of Employees: 9,947
Average Check: Breakfast(8); Lunch(10); Dinner(12)
Total Units: 17
Trade Names: McDonald's (17)
Units Franchised From: 17
Preferred Square Footage: 2,500; 3,000
Preferred Location Types: Discount Dept. Stores; Freestanding
Primary Menu: Hamburger (17)
Areas of Operation: PA
Type of Foodservice: Quick Serve (17)
Franchise Affiliation: McDonald's Corporation, CHICAGO, IL

Key Personnel
DAN DELLIGATTI - CEO; Partner
MICHAEL J. DELLIGATTI - President; Partner; Manager Information Systems, Supply Chain, Real Estate, Design; General Buyer
SCOTT MASCILLI - CFO
DEE SUMMERS - Manager Human Resources
HOLLY LASITIS - Manager Accounting

Mario's South Side Saloon
1514 E Carson St
Pittsburgh, PA 15203-1702

Telephone: (412) 381-5610
Fax Number: (412) 381-8138
Internet Homepage: mariospgh.com; mariospgh.com/eastside
Company Email: info@mariospgh.com
Type of Business: Chain Restaurant Operator
Year Founded: 1981
Total Sales: $3,806,000 (e)
Alcohol Sales: 60%
Number of Employees: 40
Average Check: Lunch(14); Dinner(24)
Total Units: 2
Trade Names: Mario's East side Saloon (1); Mario's South Side Saloon (1)
Company-Owned Units: 2
Preferred Location Types: Downtown; Freestanding
Alcohol Served: Beer, Wine, Liquor
Primary Menu: American (2)
Areas of Operation: PA
Type of Foodservice: Casual Dining (2)
Primary Distributors: (Full Line) Curtze Food Service, ERIE, PA

Key Personnel
MICHAEL BECK - President; General Manager; General Buyer
MICHAEL PERUCCI - Executive Chef; General Buyer

Monte Cello's Italian Restaurants Inc.
3650 Babcock Blvd
Pittsburgh, PA 15209

Telephone: (412) 366-8938
Fax Number: (412) 821-8177
Internet Homepage: montecellos.com
Company Email: info@montecellos.com
Type of Business: Chain Restaurant Operator
Year Founded: 1980
Systemwide Sales: $13,407,000 (e)
Total Sales: $1,944,000 (e)
Alcohol Sales: 20%
Number of Employees: 110
Average Check: Lunch(14); Dinner(14)
Total Units: 5
Trade Names: Monte Cello's Italian Restaurant (5)
Company-Owned Units: 2
Units Franchised To: 3
Preferred Square Footage: 3,500
Preferred Location Types: Community Mall; Freestanding; Strip Mall
Alcohol Served: Beer, Wine, Liquor
Primary Menu: Italian (5)
Areas of Operation: PA
Type of Foodservice: Casual Dining (5)
Catering Services: Yes
On-site Distribution Center: Yes
Primary Distributors: (Full Line) US Foods, GREENSBURG, PA

Key Personnel
JOSEPH WADLOW - President; Partner; CFO; Director Operations, Purchasing, Facility/Maintenance, Risk Management, Real Estate, Design, Human Resources, Store Fixtures, Menu Development, Food Safety, Catering
DOMENIC RICCI - Partner; VP Construction, Store Planning; Director Franchising
GREG WADLOW - General Manager; Director Supply Chain

P & G
1711 Murray Ave
Pittsburgh, PA 15217-1603

Telephone: (412) 422-9457
Internet Homepage: pamelasdiner.com
Type of Business: Chain Restaurant Operator
Year Founded: 1985
Total Sales: $6,232,000 (e)
Number of Employees: 75
Average Check: Breakfast(14); Lunch(16);
Total Units: 6
Trade Names: Pamela's P & G Diner (6)
Company-Owned Units: 4
Units Franchised To: 2
Preferred Square Footage: 5,500; 6,000
Preferred Location Types: Freestanding
Primary Menu: American (6)
Areas of Operation: PA
Type of Foodservice: Family Restaurant (6)
Primary Distributors: (Full Line) Reinhart FoodService, MOUNT PLEASANT, PA

Key Personnel
PAM COHEN - Partner; General Manager; Executive Chef; Director Real Estate, Design
GAIL KLINGENSMITH - Partner; General Manager; Director Supply Chain; General Buyer

Peppi's Inc.
1721 Penn Ave
Pittsburgh, PA 15222-4320

Telephone: (412) 562-0125
Internet Homepage: peppisubs.com

Type of Business: Chain Restaurant Operator
Year Founded: 1983
Total Sales: $3,191,000 (e)
Number of Employees: 40
Average Check: Lunch(12); Dinner(16)
Total Units: 4
Trade Names: Peppi's (4)
Company-Owned Units: 4
Preferred Location Types: Downtown; Mixed-use Center; Strip Mall
Primary Menu: Sandwiches/Deli (4)
Areas of Operation: PA
Type of Foodservice: Quick Serve (4)
Primary Distributors: (Full Line) SYSCO Food Services of Philadelphia LLC, PHILADELPHIA, PA

Key Personnel
LOU BOSSER - Partner; General Manager; General Buyer
JEFF TREBAC - Partner; General Manager

Pizza Roma Corp.
8350 Perry Hwy
Pittsburgh, PA 15237-5251

Telephone: (412) 367-7677
Fax Number: (412) 367-1898
Internet Homepage: pizzaromarest.com
Company Email: pizzaromarest@yahoo.com
Type of Business: Chain Restaurant Operator
Year Founded: 1972
Systemwide Sales: $10,007,000 (e)
Total Sales: $1,043,000 (e)
Alcohol Sales: 25%
Number of Employees: 195
Average Check: Lunch(12); Dinner(16)
Total Units: 9
Trade Names: Chippawa Roma (1); Pizza Roma (7); Roma Restaurant (1)
Company-Owned Units: 1
Units Franchised To: 8
Preferred Square Footage: 1,200; 3,500
Preferred Location Types: Freestanding
Alcohol Served: Beer, Wine, Liquor
Primary Menu: Italian (2); Pizza (7)
Areas of Operation: PA
Type of Foodservice: Casual Dining (9)
Primary Distributors: (Full Line) Nappie's Food Service Co., OAKDALE, PA

Key Personnel
ADOLFO D'ACHILLE - President; CFO; General Manager Human Resources; Executive Chef; General Buyer
TOM PAPPALARDO - Manager Operations, Information Systems

Primanti Bros.
2100 Wharton St Ste 720
Pittsburgh, PA 15203-1942

Telephone: (412) 325-2455
Internet Homepage: primantibros.com
Company Email: info@PrimantiBros.com
Type of Business: Chain Restaurant Operator
Year Founded: 1934
Total Sales: $51,730,000 (e)
Alcohol Sales: 2%
Internet Order Processing: Yes
Total Units: 44
Trade Names: Primanti Bros. Restaurant & Bar (44)
Company-Owned Units: 37
Units Franchised To: 7
Preferred Location Types: Freestanding; Stadiums; Strip Mall
Alcohol Served: Beer, Wine, Liquor
Primary Menu: Sandwiches/Deli (44)
Projected Openings: 3
Areas of Operation: FL, IN, MD, MI, OH, PA, WV
Type of Foodservice: Casual Dining (44)

Key Personnel
ADAM GOLOMB - Chief Marketing Officer
MORGHAN MCLAUGHLIN - Director Operations
MIKE MITCHAM - Director Operations
JEROME BITZ - Director Information Technology
CHERYL L. DOMITROVIC - Director Human Resources
GREG DUBOIS - Director Operations
MICHAEL PURPURA - Director Operations
STAN WEINSTEIN - Director Operations
MATTHEW WITHEROW - Director Operations
WILL BOWKER - Regional Director Operations
PAMELA PREISACH - Manager Payroll
JIM PREZIOSO - Manager Marketing

Restaurant Holdings
115 Federal St Ste 230
Pittsburgh, PA 15212-5724

Telephone: (412) 325-0550
Fax Number: (412) 325-0551
Internet Homepage: atrias.com; ditkasrestaurants.com; junipergrill.com
Company Email: feedback@atrias.com
Type of Business: Chain Restaurant Operator
Year Founded: 1998
Total Sales: $35,390,000 (e)
Alcohol Sales: 25%
Number of Employees: 949
Average Check: Lunch(18); Dinner(36)
Internet Order Processing: Yes
Internet Sales: 2.00%
Total Units: 15
Trade Names: Atria's Restaurant & Tavern (8); Grill 89 (1); Juniper Grill (3); Mike Ditka's Iron Mike's Grill (3)
Company-Owned Units: 15
Preferred Square Footage: 5,500; 6,000
Preferred Location Types: Downtown; Freestanding; Strip Mall
Alcohol Served: Beer, Wine, Liquor
Primary Menu: American (12); Steak (3)
Areas of Operation: AZ, IL, PA
Type of Foodservice: Casual Dining (15)
Catering Services: Yes
Primary Distributors: (Full Line) SYSCO Food Services of Pittsburgh Inc., HARMONY, PA

Key Personnel
PAT MCDONNELL - CEO; President; General Manager; Director Operations, Information Systems; General Buyer
DAVID STANCHAK - Director Facility/Maintenance, Real Estate

Rice Enterprises
5415 Clairton Blvd
Pittsburgh, PA 15236-2714

Telephone: (412) 831-3784
Fax Number: (412) 831-3855
Type of Business: Chain Restaurant Operator
Year Founded: 2000
Total Sales: $28,080,000 (e)
Number of Employees: 200
Average Check: Breakfast(8); Lunch(8); Dinner(8)
Total Units: 6
Trade Names: McDonald's (6)
Units Franchised From: 6
Preferred Square Footage: 2,500; 3,000
Preferred Location Types: Freestanding; Regional Mall
Primary Menu: Hamburger (6)
Areas of Operation: PA
Type of Foodservice: Quick Serve (6)
Franchise Affiliation: McDonald's Corporation, CHICAGO, IL

Key Personnel
MICHELLE RICE - CEO; General Buyer

Sesame Inn
715 Washington Rd
Pittsburgh, PA 15228-2001

Telephone: (412) 341-2555
Fax Number: (412) 341-6887
Internet Homepage: sesameinn.com
Type of Business: Chain Restaurant Operator
Year Founded: 1987
Total Sales: $4,507,000 (e)
Alcohol Sales: 25%
Number of Employees: 80

Average Check: Lunch(10); Dinner(18)
Total Units: 3
Trade Names: Sesame Inn (3)
Company-Owned Units: 3
Preferred Location Types: Freestanding; Strip Mall
Alcohol Served: Beer, Wine, Liquor
Primary Menu: Chinese (3)
Areas of Operation: PA
Type of Foodservice: Casual Dining (3)
Catering Services: Yes
Primary Distributors: (Food) SYSCO Food Services of Philadelphia LLC, PHILADELPHIA, PA

Key Personnel
GEORGE LEE - President; Partner; Controller; Manager Operations, Purchasing, Marketing, Menu Development, Catering; Buyer Food
JENNIFER LEE - Partner; Manager Human Resources, Catering; General Buyer
CHEF HO - Executive Chef

Shah Ventures LLC
5800 Forbes Ave
Pittsburgh, PA 15217-1602

Telephone: (412) 422-2291
Company Email: coldstonesqhill@gmail.com
Type of Business: Chain Restaurant Operator
Total Sales: $1,890,000 (e)
Total Units: 3
Trade Names: Cold Stone Creamery (3)
Units Franchised From: 3
Primary Menu: Snacks (3)
Areas of Operation: PA
Type of Foodservice: Quick Serve (3)
Franchise Affiliation: Kahala Brands, SCOTTSDALE, AZ

Key Personnel
NUMAAN SHAH - Partner
MANSOORA SHAH - Partner
MUBARIK SHAH - Partner

The PIPA Group
503 Martindale St
Pittsburgh, PA 15212-5746

Telephone: (412) 231-5720
Fax Number: (412) 231-5700
Internet Homepage: thepipagroup.com/clarkbar; thepipagroup.com
Type of Business: Chain Restaurant Operator
Year Founded: 1989
Total Sales: $4,647,000 (e)
Alcohol Sales: 20%
Number of Employees: 60
Average Check: Lunch(14); Dinner(30)
Total Units: 2
Trade Names: Bistecca Steakhouse & Wine Bar (1); Clarks Bar & Grill (1)
Company-Owned Units: 2
Preferred Location Types: Regional Mall
Alcohol Served: Beer, Wine, Liquor
Primary Menu: American (1); Steak (1)
Areas of Operation: PA
Type of Foodservice: Casual Dining (2)
Catering Services: Yes
Primary Distributors: (Food) Reinhart FoodService, MOUNT PLEASANT, PA

Key Personnel
DAVID LAMATRICE - President; General Manager; Executive Chef
JOE LAMATRICE - VP

Vocelli Pizza
1005 S Bee St
Pittsburgh, PA 15220-3406

Telephone: (412) 919-2100
Fax Number: (412) 937-9204
Internet Homepage: rocknjoe.com; vocellipizza.com
Type of Business: Chain Restaurant Operator
Year Founded: 1988
Systemwide Sales: $46,079,000 (e)
Total Sales: $23,740,000 (e)
Number of Employees: 2,000
Average Check: Lunch(22); Dinner(22)
Internet Order Processing: Yes
Internet Sales: 1.00%
Total Units: 88
Trade Names: Rockn' Joe Coffeehouse and Bistro (7); Vocelli Pizza (88)
Company-Owned Units: 7
Units Franchised To: 88
Preferred Square Footage: 1,200; 1,500
Preferred Location Types: Community Mall; Freestanding; Strip Mall
Primary Menu: Coffee (7); Pizza (88)
Areas of Operation: AL, FL, MD, OH, PA, VA, WV
Type of Foodservice: Quick Serve (95)
Foodservice Management Venues: Business & Industry; Parks & Recreation; Transportation
Catering Services: Yes
Primary Distributors: (Food) Reinhart FoodService, MARQUETTE, MI
Parent Company: Ablak Holdings, PITTSBURGH, PA

Key Personnel
VAROL ABLAK - Chairman; President
KAMILA MIRZA - Owner; General Manager
AMAR PAUL - General Manager
JOSEPH BARSOTTINI - General Manager
STEVE MACESIC - Director Information Technology
DAN MCSWEENEY - Director Operations
JOHN TORCH - Director
AARON HUTCHINS - Senior Manager Marketing
JOE BUTTON - Manager Construction
LAURA SABLE - Manager Accounting
AMY MYERS - Senior Designer

Wholesome International LLC
180 Fort Couch Rd Ste 150
Pittsburgh, PA 15241-1046

Telephone: (888) 394-5326
Internet Homepage: choolaah.com; eatwholesome.com
Company Email: info@eatwholesome.com
Type of Business: Chain Restaurant Operator
Year Founded: 2004
Number of Employees: 594
Total Units: 27
Trade Names: Choolaah (14); Five Guys Burgers and Fries (13)
Company-Owned Units: 14
Units Franchised From: 13
Areas of Operation: OH, PA, VA

Key Personnel
RANDHIR SETHI - Co-CEO
RAJI SANKAR - Co-CEO
JAY NESBITT - Chief Creative Officer
TONY LOFRESO - VP
MICHELE NICHOLLS - VP Division

Pama's Subs & Salads Inc
170 Laurel Plz
Pittston, PA 18640-3546

Telephone: (570) 655-7257
Fax Number: (570) 655-7257
Type of Business: Chain Restaurant Operator
Total Sales: $3,019,000 (e)
Total Units: 5
Trade Names: Subway (5)
Units Franchised From: 5
Primary Menu: Sandwiches/Deli (5)
Areas of Operation: PA
Type of Foodservice: Quick Serve (5)
Franchise Affiliation: Doctor's Associates Inc., MILFORD, CT

Key Personnel
ROSEMARY D. SANTO - President

Auntie Anne's Franchise
233 Shoemaker Rd
Pottstown, PA 19464-6441

Telephone: (610) 323-5050
Type of Business: Chain Restaurant Operator
Total Sales: $2,350,000 (e)
Total Units: 3
Trade Names: Auntie Anne's Hand-Rolled Soft

Pretzels (3)
Units Franchised From: 3
Primary Menu: Snacks (3)
Areas of Operation: PA
Type of Foodservice: Quick Serve (3)
Franchise Affiliation: Auntie Anne's Inc., LANCASTER, PA

Key Personnel
VISHAL PATEL - Owner; General Buyer

Graham Management
1618 Potter Dr
Pottstown, PA 19464-2977

Telephone: (610) 327-9669
Fax Number: (610) 327-3147
Type of Business: Chain Restaurant Operator
Total Sales: $47,050,000 (e)
Total Units: 10
Trade Names: McDonald's (10)
Units Franchised From: 10
Primary Menu: Hamburger (10)
Areas of Operation: PA
Type of Foodservice: Quick Serve (10)
Franchise Affiliation: McDonald's Corporation, CHICAGO, IL

Key Personnel
MARCIA GRAHAM - President; General Buyer
TRACY GRAHAM - President
DESAREE PROKOS - Manager
REBECCA ROQUE - Manager Accounting
MARY ZARAGOZA - Manager

Domino's Franchisee
300 Terry Reiley Way
Pottsville, PA 17901-2523

Telephone: (570) 628-4400
Internet Homepage: pbjpizza.com
Company Email: CustService@PBJPizza.Com
Type of Business: Chain Restaurant Operator
Total Sales: $4,018,000 (e)
Internet Order Processing: Yes
Total Units: 2
Trade Names: Domino's (2)
Units Franchised From: 2
Primary Menu: Pizza (2)
Areas of Operation: PA
Type of Foodservice: Quick Serve (2)
Franchise Affiliation: Domino's Pizza Inc, ANN ARBOR, MI

Key Personnel
MIKE KAHN - Owner; General Buyer

Domino's Franchisee
109 Indiana St
Punxsutawney, PA 15767-1957

Telephone: (814) 938-3900
Type of Business: Chain Restaurant Operator
Total Sales: $12,405,000 (e)
Total Units: 6
Trade Names: Domino's (6)
Units Franchised From: 6
Primary Menu: Pizza (6)
Areas of Operation: PA
Type of Foodservice: Quick Serve (6)
Franchise Affiliation: Domino's Pizza Inc, ANN ARBOR, MI

Key Personnel
BEAU J. HILL - Owner; General Buyer

Goodman Vending & Food Service
1000 Commons Blvd
Reading, PA 19605-3332

Telephone: (610) 926-8363
Fax Number: (610) 926-0795
Internet Homepage: goodmanvending.com
Company Email: info@goodmanvending.com
Type of Business: Foodservice Management Operator
Year Founded: 1946
Total Sales: $23,592,000 (e)
Number of Employees: 68
Number of Locations Served: 270
Total Foodservice Mgmt Accounts: 140
Areas of Operation: PA
Type of Foodservice: Quick Serve (140); Vending machines (130)
Foodservice Management Venues: College & University; Health Care
Primary Distributors: (Full Line) Performance Foodservice, SWEDESBORO, NJ

Key Personnel
TONY BUCKHOLZ - CEO; President; Director Purchasing, Information Systems
DEBBY MARRERO - Director Finance, Administration
DEB HECKMAN - Director Finance, Administration

Domino's Franchisee
102 W Madison St
Rochester, PA 15074-2251

Telephone: (724) 770-9090
Type of Business: Chain Restaurant Operator
Total Sales: $7,920,000 (e)
Total Units: 4

Trade Names: Domino's (4)
Units Franchised From: 4
Primary Menu: Pizza (4)
Areas of Operation: PA
Type of Foodservice: Quick Serve (4)
Franchise Affiliation: Domino's Pizza Inc, ANN ARBOR, MI

Key Personnel
RAJA M. KHURRAM - Owner; General Buyer

Thomas E. Strauss Inc.
2811 Lincoln Hwy E
Ronks, PA 17572-9608

Telephone: (717) 687-8480
Fax Number: (717) 687-8557
Internet Homepage: millerssmorgasbord.com; plainandfancyfarm.com
Type of Business: Chain Restaurant Operator
Year Founded: 1940
Total Sales: $7,656,000 (e)
Number of Employees: 120
Average Check: Breakfast(10); Lunch(22); Dinner(22)
Total Units: 2
Trade Names: Miller's Smorgasbord (1); Smokehouse BBQ and Brews at Plain & Fancy Farm (1)
Company-Owned Units: 2
Preferred Location Types: Freestanding
Alcohol Served: Beer, Wine, Liquor
Primary Menu: American (1); Bar-B-Q (1)
Areas of Operation: PA
Type of Foodservice: Casual Dining (1); Family Restaurant (1)
Primary Distributors: (Food) Ettline Foods Corp., YORK, PA; (Supplies) Veritiv, LEMOYNE, PA

Key Personnel
DANIEL STRAUSS - President; Owner
STEVE GAINER - Executive Chef; General Buyer

GDK Development Inc.
43 N 4th St Ste 45
Shamokin, PA 17872-5205

Telephone: (570) 648-8634
Fax Number: (570) 648-3132
Type of Business: Chain Restaurant Operator
Year Founded: 1982
Total Sales: $36,490,000 (e)
Number of Employees: 730
Average Check: Breakfast(8); Lunch(8); Dinner(12)
Total Units: 16
Trade Names: Burger King (16)
Units Franchised From: 16
Preferred Square Footage: 2,500; 3,000

Preferred Location Types: Freestanding
Primary Menu: Hamburger (16)
Areas of Operation: PA
Type of Foodservice: Quick Serve (16)
Franchise Affiliation: Burger King Worldwide Inc., MIAMI, FL
Primary Distributors: (Full Line) SYSCO Food Services of Philadelphia LLC, PHILADELPHIA, PA

Key Personnel
GENE WELSH - President; Partner
DENISE WELSH - Partner; Controller; Director Finance, Human Resources
MICHAEL MAZER - Director Operations, Loss Prevention, Food Safety
JIM BACKES - Director Operations, Real Estate; Manager Purchasing, Marketing
DEBBIE MAZER - Manager Administration, Facility/Maintenance, Information Systems

PDM Foods Company LLC.
185 Ferguson Ave
Shavertown, PA 18708-1114

Telephone: (570) 675-3636
Fax Number: (570) 675-0361
Type of Business: Chain Restaurant Operator
Year Founded: 1972
Total Sales: $34,310,000 (e)
Number of Employees: 1,000
Average Check: Breakfast(5); Lunch(8); Dinner(8)
Total Units: 15
Trade Names: Burger King (15)
Units Franchised From: 15
Preferred Square Footage: 2,500
Preferred Location Types: Freestanding
Primary Menu: Hamburger (15)
Areas of Operation: PA
Type of Foodservice: Quick Serve (15)
Franchise Affiliation: Burger King Worldwide Inc., MIAMI, FL
Primary Distributors: (Full Line) Maines Paper & Food Service Inc., CONKLIN, NY

Key Personnel
STEPHEN MORRIS - CEO; President; Director Finance, Loss Prevention, Real Estate
JAY MEYER - Controller; Director Information Systems
GINI SCAVONE - Director Human Resources
JOE STEININGER - Director Operations
DEBBIE ZIMMERMAN - Manager Accounting

Restaurant Management Corp.
22 E King St
Shippensburg, PA 17257-1308

Telephone: (717) 267-0727
Fax Number: (717) 477-2427
Company Email: restmgmt@comcast.net
Type of Business: Chain Restaurant Operator
Year Founded: 1989
Total Sales: $25,000,000 (e)
Number of Employees: 450
Average Check: Breakfast(8); Lunch(10); Dinner(12)
Total Units: 14
Trade Names: Hardee's (14)
Units Franchised From: 14
Preferred Square Footage: 4,000
Preferred Location Types: Freestanding
Primary Menu: Hamburger (14)
Areas of Operation: MD, PA
Type of Foodservice: Quick Serve (14)
Franchise Affiliation: Hardee's Food Systems Inc., FRANKLIN, TN
Primary Distributors: (Full Line) McLane/Rocky Mount, ROCKY MOUNT, NC

Key Personnel
BRYAN HOGGE - President; Director Finance, Information Systems
DONNA HOLLENBAUGH - Director Accounting, Human Resources
MIKE SIPES - Director Risk Management, Marketing, Real Estate; General Buyer
JERRY STOTTLEMYER - Director Operations
SHARON YUN EBERSOLE - District Manager
MIKE FLANAGAN - Manager District
BRIAN FUNDANISH - Manager Facility/Maintenance, Store Fixtures

Maak Alamo LLC
1590 N Center Ave Ste 112
Somerset, PA 15501-7019

Telephone: (814) 701-2463
Fax Number: (814) 701-2465
Type of Business: Chain Restaurant Operator
Total Sales: $28,030,000 (e)
Total Units: 6
Trade Names: McDonald's (6)
Units Franchised From: 6
Primary Menu: Hamburger (6)
Areas of Operation: PA
Type of Foodservice: Quick Serve (6)
Franchise Affiliation: McDonald's Corporation, CHICAGO, IL

Key Personnel
ART ALAMO - Owner; General Buyer

Lee's Hoagie House Restaurants
26 2nd Street Pike
Southampton, PA 18966-3807

Telephone: (215) 322-2500
Fax Number: (215) 322-2537
Internet Homepage: leeshoagiehouse.com
Company Email: leessouth@aol.com
Type of Business: Chain Restaurant Operator
Year Founded: 1953
Systemwide Sales: $6,700,000 (e)
Total Sales: $2,854,000 (e)
Number of Employees: 12
Average Check: Lunch(12); Dinner(12)
Internet Order Processing: Yes
Total Units: 18
Trade Names: Lee's Hoagie House (18)
Company-Owned Units: 3
Units Franchised To: 15
Preferred Square Footage: 1,500
Preferred Location Types: Community Mall; Freestanding; Strip Mall
Primary Menu: Sandwiches/Deli (18)
Areas of Operation: NJ, PA
Type of Foodservice: Quick Serve (18)
Catering Services: Yes
Primary Distributors: (Food) US Foods, ALTOONA, PA

Key Personnel
JOHN CONNELL - Co-Founder; President; Director Finance, Facility/Maintenance, Real Estate, Human Resources, Menu Development
AL LEWIN - Co-Founder; CEO; Director Purchasing, Security, Inventory, Loss Prevention, Risk Management, Quality Assurance, Supply Chain, Food Safety, Catering; General Buyer
JON WAXMAN - VP; Director Operations
ROBIN CONNELL - Treasurer; Director Information Systems

Dante's Restaurant Inc.
138 Moses Thompson Ln
State College, PA 16801-6840

Telephone: (814) 234-1344
Fax Number: (814) 237-2925
Internet Homepage: dantesinc.com
Company Email: info@dantesinc.com
Type of Business: Chain Restaurant Operator
Year Founded: 1963
Total Sales: $14,730,000 (e)
Alcohol Sales: 16%
Number of Employees: 45
Average Check: Lunch(18); Dinner(24)
Internet Order Processing: Yes
Internet Sales: 2.00%
Total Units: 6

Trade Names: Bar Bleu (1); Hi-Way Pizza (1); Inferno (1); Liberty Craft House (1); The Deli & Z-Bar (1); The Saloon (1)
Company-Owned Units: 6
Preferred Square Footage: 2,500
Preferred Location Types: Freestanding; Strip Mall
Alcohol Served: Beer, Wine, Liquor
Primary Menu: American (3); Bar-B-Q (1); Pizza (2)
Areas of Operation: PA
Type of Foodservice: Casual Dining (6)
Primary Distributors: (Full Line) US Foods, ALTOONA, PA

Key Personnel
ANDY ZANGRILLI - President; Executive Chef; Director Quality Assurance, Real Estate
JENNIFER ZANGRILLI - Director Operations
MARK DELORENZO - Manager

Shaner Hotel Group Ltd.
1965 Waddle Rd
State College, PA 16803-1639

Telephone: (814) 234-4460
Fax Number: (814) 278-7295
Internet Homepage: shanercorp.com
Company Email: info@shanercorp.com
Type of Business: Foodservice Operations - Hotel/Motels
Year Founded: 1970
Total Sales: $801,640,000 (e)
Alcohol Sales: 20%
Number of Employees: 3,080
Total Units: 55
Restaurants in Hotels: 24
Trade Names: Art Ovation Hotel (1); Comfort Inn & Suites (1); Courtyard (12); Fairfield Inn & Suites (12); French Leave Resort (1); Hampton Inn & Suites (2); Holiday Inn Express (3); Home2 Suites (1); Marriott (4); Moxy Short North (1); Pine Barn Inn (1); Playa Largo Resort & Spa (1); Renaissance Tuscany Il Ciocco Resort & Spa (1); Residence Inn (3); Seven Sebring Raceway Hotel (1); Sleep Inn & Suites (1); Southbridge Hotel (1); SpringHill Suites State College (2); The Daytona (1); The Newport Harbor Hotel & Marina (1); Toftrees Golf Resort (1); Towneplace Suites (3)
Company-Owned Units: 24
Alcohol Served: Beer, Wine, Liquor
Projected Openings: 3
Areas of Operation: CT, FL, GA, IA, LA, MA, MN, NC, NJ, PA, RI, TN, WV, FC
Type of Foodservice: Casual Dining (24)
Primary Distributors: (Food) US Foods, ALLENTOWN, PA; (Specialty Foods) US Foods, ALLENTOWN, PA
Notes: The company derives approximately 75% of its revenue from hotel operations.

Key Personnel
LANCE T. SHANER - Chairman; CEO
PLATO GHINOS - President
PATRICK LANDY - CFO; Senior VP
STEVE SHALA - CIO
GEORGE WOLFE - Senior VP
DERRICK SKILLINGS - VP Finance, Development
WILLIAM HOY - VP Construction, Design

State College Subs, LLC
2009 N Atherton St Ste 100
State College, PA 16803-1525

Telephone: (814) 954-4179
Type of Business: Chain Restaurant Operator
Total Sales: $9,601,000 (e)
Total Units: 7
Trade Names: Jersey Mike's Subs (7)
Units Franchised From: 7
Primary Menu: Sandwiches/Deli (7)
Areas of Operation: PA
Type of Foodservice: Quick Serve (7)
Franchise Affiliation: Jersey Mike's Franchise Systems, MANASQUAN, NJ

Key Personnel
DAVID M. PATTERSON - Owner; General Buyer

Toftrees Resort
1 Country Club Ln
State College, PA 16803-2001

Telephone: (814) 234-8000
Fax Number: (814) 238-4404
Internet Homepage: shanercorp.com; toftrees.com
Company Email: info@toftrees.com
Type of Business: Foodservice Operations - Hotel/Motels
Year Founded: 1975
Total Sales: $5,525,000 (e)
Alcohol Sales: 25%
Number of Employees: 50
Average Check: Breakfast(12); Lunch(14); Dinner(30)
Total Units: 1
Trade Names: The Field Burger and Tap (1)
Company-Owned Units: 1
Preferred Location Types: Hotel/Motel
Alcohol Served: Beer, Wine, Liquor
Primary Menu: American (1)
Areas of Operation: PA
Type of Foodservice: Casual Dining (1)
Catering Services: Yes
Primary Distributors: (Full Line) US Foods, ALLENTOWN, PA

Key Personnel
LANCE T. SHANER - Chairman; CEO
PLATO GHINOS - President
STEFAN CHERINK - General Manager; General Buyer
TRACI MANNINO - Director Food and Beverage

Two Guys Pizza
1100 N Atherton St
State College, PA 16803-2926

Telephone: (814) 237-8991
Fax Number: (814) 238-5305
Type of Business: Chain Restaurant Operator
Year Founded: 1980
Total Sales: $4,164,000 (e)
Number of Employees: 45
Average Check: Lunch(22); Dinner(34)
Total Units: 2
Trade Names: Domino's (2)
Units Franchised From: 2
Preferred Square Footage: 1,000; 1,300
Preferred Location Types: Strip Mall
Primary Menu: Pizza (2)
Areas of Operation: PA
Type of Foodservice: Quick Serve (2)
Franchise Affiliation: Domino's Pizza Inc, ANN ARBOR, MI
Primary Distributors: (Food) Domino's Distribution Center, ANN ARBOR, MI

Key Personnel
CURT SPALSBURY - Owner; Director Operations, Purchasing, Facility/Maintenance, Information Systems, Supply Chain, Human Resources, Store Fixtures; General Buyer

GRP Management Inc.
18588 Route 322
Strattanville, PA 16258-2904

Telephone: (814) 764-6071
Type of Business: Chain Restaurant Operator
Total Sales: $23,480,000 (e)
Number of Employees: 200
Average Check: Breakfast(8); Lunch(8); Dinner(12)
Total Units: 5
Trade Names: McDonald's (5)
Units Franchised From: 5
Preferred Location Types: Freestanding
Primary Menu: Hamburger (5)
Areas of Operation: PA
Type of Foodservice: Quick Serve (5)
Franchise Affiliation: McDonald's Corporation, CHICAGO, IL
Primary Distributors: (Full Line) SYSCO Food Services of Central Pennsylvania LLC, HARRISBURG, PA

Key Personnel
EUGENE PUSKASH - President; General Buyer

Rita's Franchise Co.
1210 Northbrook Dr Ste 310
Trevose, PA 19053-8426

Telephone: (215) 876-9300
Fax Number: (866) 448-9067
Internet Homepage: ritasice.com
Company Email: feedback@ritascorp.com
Type of Business: Chain Restaurant Operator
Year Founded: 1984
Systemwide Sales: $226,442,000 (e)
Total Sales: $50,130,000 (e)
Number of Employees: 2,535
Average Check: Lunch(8); Dinner(12)
Internet Order Processing: Yes
Internet Sales: 1.00%
Total Units: 498
Trade Names: Rita's Ice Custard Happiness (520)
Company-Owned Units: 1
Units Franchised To: 519
Preferred Square Footage: 600; 800; 1,000; 1,200
Preferred Location Types: Community Mall; Convenience Store/Gas Station; Freestanding; Mobile Unit; Regional Mall; Stadiums; Strip Mall
Primary Menu: Snacks (520)
Projected Openings: 11
Areas of Operation: AL, AR, AZ, CA, CO, CT, DC, DE, FL, GA, HI, IA, IL, IN, KS, LA, MA, MD, MI, MN, NC, NE, NJ, NM, NV, NY, OH, PA, SC, TN, TX, UT, VA
Foreign Countries: CHINA
Type of Foodservice: Quick Serve (520)
On-site Distribution Center: Yes
Primary Distributors: (Food) Stanley Marvel Inc., BENSALEM, PA
Parent Company: Argosy Private Equity, ,
Notes: Rita's derives approximately 65% of total revenue from product sales to franchisees.

Key Personnel
KIRK GRISWOLD - Chairman
LINDA CHADWICK - CEO; President
JOHN DOMBROSKI - CFO; VP
PHYLLIS SAVAR LEVY - Chief Marketing Officer
GERRY WELLS - Chief Compliance Officer; General Counsel
PETER JURTA - Senior VP Operations
MARK JENKINS - VP Marketing
KATHLEEN DEAL - Senior Director Operations, Training
LORI SHAFFRON - Senior Director Franchise Sales
MADALYN WEINTRAUB - Director Brand Marketing
BRIANNE BARKET - Director Quality Assurance, Product Development
JOYCE LIBERATORE - Senior Manager Human Resources

Revere Restaurant Group
7532 Hamilton Blvd
Trexlertown, PA 18087

Mailing Address: PO Box 57, TREXLERTOWN, PA, 18087-0057
Telephone: (610) 351-1193
Fax Number: (610) 351-2461
Company Email: radmin4u@rcn.com
Type of Business: Chain Restaurant Operator
Year Founded: 2001
Total Sales: $8,028,000 (e)
Number of Employees: 325
Average Check: Breakfast(5); Lunch(8); Dinner(10)
Total Units: 5
Trade Names: Friendly's (5)
Units Franchised From: 5
Preferred Square Footage: 5,500; 6,000
Preferred Location Types: Freestanding; Strip Mall
Primary Menu: American (6)
Areas of Operation: PA
Type of Foodservice: Family Restaurant (5)
Franchise Affiliation: FIC Restaurants, WILBRAHAM, MA
Primary Distributors: (Full Line) US Foods, ALLENTOWN, PA

Key Personnel
BOB BENDER - President; CFO; General Buyer

Walsh Management, Inc.
4279 Covered Bridge Rd
Ulster, PA 18850-7797

Telephone: (570) 265-2928
Type of Business: Chain Restaurant Operator
Total Sales: $20,114,000 (e)
Total Units: 4
Trade Names: McDonald's (4)
Units Franchised From: 4
Preferred Location Types: Freestanding
Primary Menu: Hamburger (4)
Areas of Operation: PA
Type of Foodservice: Quick Serve (4)
Franchise Affiliation: McDonald's Corporation, CHICAGO, IL

Key Personnel
ROBERT WALSH - President; General Buyer

Domino's Franchisee
3266 Chichester Ave Ste 7
Upper Chichester, PA 19061-3250

Telephone: (610) 485-7070
Type of Business: Chain Restaurant Operator
Total Sales: $5,954,000 (e)
Total Units: 3
Trade Names: Domino's (3)
Units Franchised From: 3
Primary Menu: Pizza (3)
Areas of Operation: PA
Type of Foodservice: Quick Serve (3)
Franchise Affiliation: Domino's Pizza Inc, ANN ARBOR, MI

Key Personnel
JOHN C. PRAIZNER - Owner; General Buyer

Four Star Pizza Inc
860 Jefferson Ave
Washington, PA 15301-3823

Mailing Address: PO Box W, CLAYSVILLE, PA, 15323-0520
Telephone: (724) 484-9263
Internet Homepage: fourstarpizza.com
Type of Business: Chain Restaurant Operator
Total Units: 7
Trade Names: Four Star Pizza (7)
Company-Owned Units: 7
Primary Menu: Pizza (7)
Areas of Operation: OH, PA
Type of Foodservice: Quick Serve (7)

Key Personnel
DAVID RODERICK - President; Owner

Georgine's Restaurant
1320 Newport Rd
West Bristol, PA 19007-6530

Telephone: (215) 785-0446
Internet Homepage: comedyworksbristol.com; georgines.com; georgines.com/jrs.html
Company Email: info@georgines.com
Type of Business: Chain Restaurant Operator
Year Founded: 1976
Total Sales: $9,349,000 (e)
Alcohol Sales: 18%
Number of Employees: 60
Average Check: Lunch(16); Dinner(32)
Total Units: 4
Trade Names: Georgine's Juniors (1); Georgine's Restaurant & Lounge (1); The Comedy Works (1); The Market Place (1)
Company-Owned Units: 4
Preferred Location Types: Freestanding; Strip Mall
Alcohol Served: Beer, Wine, Liquor
Primary Menu: American (1); Miscellaneous (1); Sandwiches/Deli (1); Steak/Seafood (1)
Areas of Operation: PA
Type of Foodservice: Casual Dining (2); Quick Serve (2)
Catering Services: Yes
Primary Distributors: (Full Line) SYSCO Food Services of Philadelphia LLC,

PHILADELPHIA, PA

Key Personnel
RAY GEPHART - CFO
KIM NAGLE - Manager Accounting

Dave Magrogan Group
21 W Washington St
West Chester, PA 19380

Telephone: (610) 431-2485
Fax Number: (610) 431-7021
Internet Homepage: davemagrogangroup.com; harvestseasonalgrill.com
Company Email: info@davemagrogangroup.com
Type of Business: Chain Restaurant Operator
Total Sales: $43,970,000 (e)
Alcohol Sales: 10%
Number of Employees: 670
Total Units: 12
Trade Names: Barosa (1); Harvest Seasonal Grill & Wine Bar (9); Kildare's Irish Pub (1); Red Star Craft House (1)
Company-Owned Units: 12
Preferred Location Types: Downtown; Freestanding; Strip Mall
Alcohol Served: Beer, Wine, Liquor
Primary Menu: American (1); Italian (1); Miscellaneous (10)
Areas of Operation: DE, PA
Type of Foodservice: Casual Dining (12)

Key Personnel
DAVE MAGROGAN - CEO; President; General Buyer
PATRICK MCBRIDE - Director Product Development
ADAM GOTTLIEB - Director Operations
CHRISTOPHER CREBS - Director Operations

DMG Group
21 W Washington St
West Chester, PA 19380-2670

Telephone: (610) 431-2485
Fax Number: (610) 431-7021
Internet Homepage: davemagrogangroup.com; harvestseasonalgrill.com
Company Email: info@davemagrogangroup.com
Type of Business: Chain Restaurant Operator
Total Sales: $35,270,000 (e)
Number of Employees: 551
Internet Order Processing: Yes
Total Units: 9
Trade Names: Harvest Seasonal Grill & Wine Bar (9)
Company-Owned Units: 9
Alcohol Served: Beer, Wine, Liquor
Primary Menu: Miscellaneous (9)
Projected Openings: 2
Areas of Operation: DE, FL, PA
Type of Foodservice: Casual Dining (9)

Key Personnel
DAVE MAGROGAN - CEO; Owner; General Manager; General Buyer
DEBBI ANDERS - CFO

Lehigh Valley Ice Cream Factory, Inc
178 Lehigh Valley Mall
Whitehall, PA 18052-5718

Telephone: (610) 264-4985
Type of Business: Chain Restaurant Operator
Total Sales: $1,184,000 (e)
Total Units: 2
Trade Names: Cold Stone Creamery (2)
Units Franchised From: 2
Primary Menu: Snacks (2)
Areas of Operation: PA
Type of Foodservice: Quick Serve (2)
Franchise Affiliation: Kahala Brands, SCOTTSDALE, AZ

Key Personnel
DAN BROWN - Owner

Queen City Pizza
155 Mickley Rd Ste 1
Whitehall, PA 18052-6208

Telephone: (610) 439-7040
Fax Number: (610) 439-7044
Type of Business: Chain Restaurant Operator
Year Founded: 1981
Total Sales: $14,511,000 (e)
Number of Employees: 280
Average Check: Lunch(16); Dinner(30)
Total Units: 7
Trade Names: Domino's (7)
Units Franchised From: 7
Preferred Square Footage: 1,000; 1,300
Preferred Location Types: Strip Mall
Primary Menu: Pizza (8)
Areas of Operation: PA
Type of Foodservice: Quick Serve (7)
Franchise Affiliation: Domino's Pizza Inc, ANN ARBOR, MI

Key Personnel
TOM BOLGER - President; Director Purchasing, Information Systems, Real Estate, Design; General Buyer
CHRIS BURNS - General Manager
GREG LAPP - Director Operations, Facility/Maintenance, Store Fixtures; Manager Area
ELISE SPAYD - Director Finance, Human Resources

Auntie Anne's Franchise
2150 Wilkes Barre Twnsp Mktpl
Wilkes Barre, PA 18702

Telephone: (570) 825-5112
Type of Business: Chain Restaurant Operator
Total Sales: $3,096,000 (e)
Total Units: 4
Trade Names: Auntie Anne's Hand-Rolled Soft Pretzels (4)
Units Franchised From: 4
Primary Menu: Snacks (4)
Areas of Operation: PA
Type of Foodservice: Quick Serve (4)
Franchise Affiliation: Auntie Anne's Inc., LANCASTER, PA

Key Personnel
JOSEPH MAZZARELLA - Owner; General Buyer

Penn National Gaming Inc.
825 Berkshire Blvd Ste 200
Wyomissing, PA 19610-1247

Telephone: (610) 373-2400
Fax Number: (610) 373-4966
Internet Homepage: pngaming.com
Type of Business: Foodservice Operations - Casinos
Year Founded: 1972
Publicly Held: Yes
Total Sales: $6,115,599,000 (e)
Alcohol Sales: 20%
Number of Employees: 25,750
Foodservice Sales: $1,070,230,000 (e)
Total Units: 44
Trade Names: 1st Jackpot Casino Tunica (1); Ameristar Black Hawk Black Hawk (1); Ameristar Council Bluffs Council Bluffs (1); Ameristar East Chicago (1); Argosy Casino Alton (1); Argosy Casino Riverside (1); Boomtown Biloxi (1); Boomtown Bossier City (1); Boomtown New Orleans (1); Cactus Petes and Horseshu Jackpot (1); Freehold Raceway (1); Greektown Casino (1); Hollywood Casino at Kansas Speedway (1); Hollywood Casino at Penn National Race Course (1); Hollywood Casino at Perryville (1); Hollywood Casino Aurora (1); Hollywood Casino Bangor (1); Hollywood Casino Columbus (1); Hollywood Casino Gulf Coast (1); Hollywood Casino Joliet (1); Hollywood Casino Kansas Speedway; Hollywood Casino Lawrenceburg (1); Hollywood Casino Morgantown (1);Hollywood Casino St. Louis (1); Hollywood Casino Toledo (1); Hollywood Casino Tunica (1); Hollywood Casino York (1); Hollywood Gaming at Dayton Raceway (1); L'Auberge

Baton Rouge (1); L'Auberge Lake Charles (1); M Resort Spa Casino (1); Margaritaville Resort Casino Bossier City (1); Marquee (1); Meadows Racetrack and Casino (1); Plainridge Park Casino (1); Prairie State Gaming (1); Retama Park Racetrack Selma (1); River City Casino St. Louis (1); SamHouston Race Park (1); Sanford Orlando Kennel Club (1); The M Resort Spa Casino (1); Tropicana Las Vegas (1); Valley Race Park (1); Zia Park Casino (1)
Company-Owned Units: 44
Preferred Square Footage: 3,000; 5,500; 6,000
Preferred Location Types: Other
Alcohol Served: Beer, Wine, Liquor
Primary Menu: Miscellaneous (43)
Areas of Operation: FL, IL, IN, KS, MA, MD, ME, MO, MS, NJ, NM, NV, OH, PA, TX, WV, ON
Foreign Countries: CANADA
Type of Foodservice: Casual Dining; Fast Casual; Fine Dining; Quick Serve
Subsidiaries: 1st Jackpot Casino, ROBINSONVILLE, MS
Primary Distributors: (Food) US Foods Holding Corp., ROSEMONT, IL
Notes: Penn National derives approximately 82% of its revenue from casino & gaming/racing operations.

Key Personnel
JAY SNOWDEN - President; COO
SAUL REIBSTEIN - CFO; VP Finance; Treasurer
WILLIAM J. FAIR - CFO; Exec VP; Treasurer
FELICIA HENDRIX - CFO; VP
CHRISTINE LABOMBARD - Chief Accounting Officer; Senior VP
RICHARD PRIMUS - CIO; Senior VP
JENNIFER WEISSMAN - Chief Marketing Officer; Senior VP Marketing
MICHAEL WEST - Chief Compliance Officer
CHRISTOPHER SORIANO - Chief Compliance Officer; VP
RAFAEL VERDE - Senior VP Operations, Region
D. ERIC SCHIPPERS - Senior VP Communications
CHRIS ROGERS - Senior VP Development
AMEET PATEL - Senior VP Operations, Central Region
TODD GEORGE - Senior VP Operations, Region
ERIN CHAMBERLIN - Senior VP Operations, Region
GENE P. CLARK - Senior VP Human Resources
CHRIS BRUNO - VP Finance
LISA BURTON - VP Human Resources
CARLOS FIGUEROA - VP Information Technology, Infrastructure
SUSAN FOSTER - VP Operations
LANCE GEORGE - VP; General Manager Division
CHRISTINA HERRERA - VP Operations
RYAN HINTHORNE - VP Operations
DREW MISHER - VP Procurement
HUSSAIN MAHROUS - VP Division; General Manager Division
SCOTT SAUNDERS - VP; General Manager Division
KATE WHITE - VP Business Development
MARK J YOURKAWITCH - VP Tax
BRAD HIRSCH - General Manager Division
DAVID LINGENFELTER - Director Information/Data Security
MIKE FOLEY - Director Digital Marketing
DAVID B. CHA - Director Quality Assurance
TOM DENNIS - Director Information Technology
DEAN MINIACCI - Director Operations
JASON GITTLE - Regional Director Information Technology, Northeast Region

Domino's Franchisee
3921 E Market St
York, PA 17402-2779

Telephone: (717) 840-4446
Type of Business: Chain Restaurant Operator
Total Sales: $10,285,000 (e)
Total Units: 5
Trade Names: Domino's (5)
Units Franchised From: 5
Primary Menu: Pizza (5)
Areas of Operation: PA
Type of Foodservice: Quick Serve (5)
Franchise Affiliation: Domino's Pizza Inc, ANN ARBOR, MI

Key Personnel
TODD O. BARRICK - Owner; General Buyer

Latshaw & Menditto Inc
2650 S Queen St
York, PA 17402-4952

Telephone: (717) 741-9648
Type of Business: Chain Restaurant Operator
Total Sales: $7,802,000 (e)
Total Units: 4
Trade Names: KFC (4)
Units Franchised From: 4
Primary Menu: Chicken (4)
Areas of Operation: PA
Type of Foodservice: Quick Serve (4)
Franchise Affiliation: KFC Corporation, LOUISVILLE, KY

Key Personnel
HARRY LATSHAW - President; General Buyer

Starbucks Distribution Center
3000 Espresso Way
York, PA 17406-6035

Telephone: (717) 266-4500
Fax Number: (717) 472-4409
Listing Type: Distribution Center
Type of Business: Chain Restaurant Operator
Number of Employees: 575
Areas of Operation: CT, DC, FL, GA, KY, MA, MD, NC, NH, NJ, NY, PA, RI, SC, TN, VA, ON
Foreign Countries: CANADA
Parent Company: Starbucks Corporation, SEATTLE, WA

Key Personnel
RYAN WHITE - Manager Operations

PUERTO RICO

BMJ Foods P.R. Inc.
100 Rio Canas Industrial Park
Caguas, PR 00725

Mailing Address: PO Box 4963, CAGUAS, PR, 00726-4963
Telephone: (787) 286-7040
Fax Number: (787) 286-7055
Internet Homepage: ponderosapr.com
Company Email: finance@bmjfoodspr.com
Type of Business: Chain Restaurant Operator
Year Founded: 1984
Total Sales: $66,300,000 (e)
Alcohol Sales: 8%
Number of Employees: 1,070
Average Check: Breakfast(14); Lunch(14); Dinner(20)
Total Units: 25
Trade Names: Ponderosa Express (1); Ponderosa Steakhouse (24)
Units Franchised From: 25
Preferred Square Footage: 4,500; 6,700; 8,200; 10,000
Preferred Location Types: Freestanding; Regional Mall
Alcohol Served: Beer, Wine
Primary Menu: Steak (25)
Areas of Operation: PR
Type of Foodservice: Casual Dining (24); Quick Serve (1)
Distribution Centers: CAGUAS, PR
On-site Distribution Center: Yes
Franchise Affiliation: Fat Brands, Inc., BEVERLY HILLS, CA
Primary Distributors: (Food) SYSCO Central Florida Inc., OCOEE, FL

Key Personnel
SAMUEL H. JOVE - President; Director

Facility/Maintenance, Real Estate
SAMMY JOVE - VP Operations; Director Purchasing
JOSE ALICEA - Manager Information Technology
MAYRA RIVERA - Manager Business Development

Marpor Corporation
Gautier Benitez Ave Ste A-6
Consolidated Mall
Caguas, PR 00725

Mailing Address: PO Box 4952 PMB 316, CAGUAS, PR, 00726
Telephone: (787) 653-6262
Fax Number: (787) 653-6266
Company Email: r_g@dennyspr.com
Type of Business: Chain Restaurant Operator
Year Founded: 1987
Total Sales: $37,040,000 (e)
Number of Employees: 758
Average Check: Breakfast(8); Lunch(8); Dinner(10)
Total Units: 13
Trade Names: Denny's (13)
Units Franchised From: 13
Preferred Square Footage: 5,000
Preferred Location Types: Community Mall; Freestanding
Primary Menu: American (13)
Areas of Operation: PR
Type of Foodservice: Family Restaurant (13)
Franchise Affiliation: Denny's Corporation, SPARTANBURG, SC
Primary Distributors: (Full Line) McLane/Orlando, ORLANDO, FL

Key Personnel
RICARDO GONZALEZ - VP; General Manager; General Buyer

R & C Creamery, Inc.
52 Ave Puerto Rico
Caguas, PR 00727

Telephone: (787) 286-1770
Type of Business: Chain Restaurant Operator
Total Sales: $1,755,000 (e)
Total Units: 3
Trade Names: Cold Stone Creamery (3)
Units Franchised From: 3
Primary Menu: Snacks (3)
Areas of Operation: PR
Type of Foodservice: Quick Serve (3)
Franchise Affiliation: Kahala Brands, SCOTTSDALE, AZ

Key Personnel
MIGUEL PEREZ - Partner
LOURDES PEREZ - Partner

Enigma Investments Inc.
655 Marginal Del Parque
Carolina, PR 00987-2502

Telephone: (787) 253-0200
Fax Number: (787) 253-0211
Internet Homepage: dominospr.com
Type of Business: Chain Restaurant Operator
Year Founded: 1986
Total Sales: $76,982,000 (e)
Number of Employees: 516
Average Check: Lunch(8); Dinner(8)
Total Units: 37
Trade Names: Domino's (37)
Units Franchised From: 37
Preferred Square Footage: 1,200
Preferred Location Types: Downtown; Freestanding; Strip Mall
Primary Menu: Pizza (37)
Projected Openings: 10
Areas of Operation: PR
Type of Foodservice: Quick Serve (37)
Franchise Affiliation: Domino's Pizza Inc, ANN ARBOR, MI

Key Personnel
EDWARD LIEBERMAN - President; General Buyer
ALBERTO NARVAEZ - COO
JOSE ROMAN - Director Operations

Caribbean Restaurants LLC
Puerto Nuevo Distribution Center, Bldg 1, Hwy 5
Catano, PR 00962

Mailing Address: PO Box 366999, SAN JUAN, PR, 00936-6999
Telephone: (787) 474-7777
Fax Number: (787) 275-7808
Internet Homepage: burgerkingpr.com
Type of Business: Chain Restaurant Operator
Year Founded: 1963
Total Sales: $359,253,000 (e)
Number of Employees: 6,000
Average Check: Breakfast(5); Lunch(6); Dinner(6)
Total Units: 184
Trade Names: Burger King (171); Firehouse Subs (13)
Units Franchised From: 184
Preferred Square Footage: 2,500
Preferred Location Types: Convenience Store/Gas Station; Freestanding; Regional Mall; Strip Mall
Primary Menu: Hamburger (171); Sandwiches/Deli (13)
Projected Openings: 3
Areas of Operation: PR
Type of Foodservice: Fast Casual (13); Quick Serve (171)
Distribution Centers: CATANO, PR
Franchise Affiliation: Burger King Worldwide Inc., MIAMI, FL
Parent Company: Castle Harlan Inc., NEW YORK, NY

Key Personnel
CARLOS MORELL - President
DANIEL PÉREZ DEL VALLE - VP Marketing
TANIA SUAREZ - Director Public Relations
RAUL MARTINEZ - Regional Director
ARELIS CARRASQUILLO - Specialist Human Resources
MIRNALY BURGOS - Buyer
BIANCA N. MARTINEZ RIVERA - Coordinator Marketing, Social Media

International Restaurant Services Inc.
Calle Emma Lot #23
Guaynabo, PR 00968

Mailing Address: Call Box 51990, TOA BAJA, PR, 00950-1990
Telephone: (787) 273-3131
Fax Number: (787) 273-3141
Internet Homepage: chilispr.com
Company Email: operations@irsipr.com
Type of Business: Chain Restaurant Operator
Year Founded: 1993
Total Sales: $62,550,000 (e)
Alcohol Sales: 20%
Number of Employees: 3,450
Average Check: Lunch(10); Dinner(10)
Total Units: 22
Trade Names: Chili's Grill & Bar (22)
Units Franchised From: 22
Preferred Square Footage: 4,200; 5,600
Preferred Location Types: Community Mall; Freestanding; Regional Mall; Strip Mall
Alcohol Served: Beer, Wine, Liquor
Primary Menu: American (22)
Areas of Operation: PR
Type of Foodservice: Casual Dining (22)
Franchise Affiliation: Chili's Grill & Bar, DALLAS, TX; Dividend Restaurant Group, DENVER, CO; On The Border LLC, IRVING, TX
Primary Distributors: (Full Line) SYSCO Food Services of Southeast Florida LLC, RIVIERA BEACH, FL

Key Personnel
ARTUR J. JOTIC - President
RAMON LEAL - Senior VP
OSWALDO TORRES - VP Operations
JEANETTE AGUILAR - Director Human Resources
ALINA GIRON - Director Information Systems
SARAHI LUGO - Director Purchasing

HACTOR PANTOJA - Manager Purchasing, Construction

South American Restaurants Corp.
Amelia Ind Park Diana St Lote 35
Guaynavo, PR 00968

Telephone: (787) 788-8811
Fax Number: (787) 788-8855
Internet Homepage: churchspr.net
Type of Business: Chain Restaurant Operator
Total Sales: $222,480,000 (e)
Number of Employees: 2,116
Average Check: Lunch(10); Dinner(10)
Total Units: 125
Trade Names: Church's Chicken (101); Krispy Kreme Donuts (4); Pollo Tropical (20)
Units Franchised From: 125
Preferred Square Footage: 1,850
Preferred Location Types: Freestanding; Strip Mall
Primary Menu: Chicken (125)
Areas of Operation: PR
Type of Foodservice: Quick Serve (125)
Franchise Affiliation: Church's Chicken, ATLANTA, GA; Pollo Tropical Operations Inc., MIAMI, FL

Key Personnel
GERARDO LARREA - CEO
JUAN A. LARREA - President; Director Operations; General Buyer
IVELISSE BORRERO - VP Human Resources
JOAQUIN CAMARGO - VP Finance
FLELIPE FLORES - VP Marketing
CARLOS TORRES - Director Information Technology
JORGE ROS - Analyst

El Meson de Felipe Inc.
Calle Manuel Pirallo #263 Esquina
Calle Aduana
Mayaguez, PR 00680

Mailing Address: PO Box 3067, MAYAGUEZ, PR, 00681-3067
Telephone: (787) 833-1239
Fax Number: (787) 265-1988
Internet Homepage: elmesonsandwiches.com; mesonsandwiches.com
Company Email: elmesonero@elmesonsandwiches.com
Type of Business: Chain Restaurant Operator
Year Founded: 1972
Systemwide Sales: $118,858,000 (e)
Total Sales: $112,250,000 (e)
Number of Employees: 1,950
Average Check: Breakfast(12); Lunch(12); Dinner(12)
Total Units: 40
Trade Names: Meson Sandwiches (40)
Company-Owned Units: 40
Preferred Square Footage: 750; 2,500
Preferred Location Types: Airports; Community Mall; Convenience Store/Gas Station; Downtown; Freestanding; Outlet Mall; Regional Mall; Strip Mall
Primary Menu: Sandwiches/Deli (40)
Projected Openings: 1
Areas of Operation: FL, PR
Type of Foodservice: Quick Serve (40)

Key Personnel
FELIPE PEREZ GRAJALES JR - CEO; President; General Buyer
GIL PEREZ - Exec VP
HECTOR JIMENEZ - VP Marketing

The Creamery Shop Corporation
1046 Ave Hostos Ste 100
Ponce, PR 00716-1119

Telephone: (787) 290-3400
Type of Business: Chain Restaurant Operator
Total Sales: $1,493,000 (e)
Total Units: 2
Trade Names: Cold Stone Creamery (2)
Units Franchised From: 2
Primary Menu: Snacks (2)
Areas of Operation: PR
Type of Foodservice: Quick Serve (2)
Franchise Affiliation: Cold Stone Creamery Inc., SCOTTSDALE, AZ

Key Personnel
JOHN TORRES - President

Caribbean Cinemas
1512 Ave Fernandez Juncos
San Juan, PR 00909-2743

Telephone: (787) 727-7137
Fax Number: (787) 982-0336
Internet Homepage: caribbeancinemas.com
Company Email: customerservice@caribbeancinemas.com
Type of Business: Foodservice Operations - Movie Theatre
Year Founded: 1965
Total Sales: $74,240,000 (e)
Alcohol Sales: 4%
Number of Employees: 75
Total Units: 30
Trade Names: Caribbean Cinema (30)
Company-Owned Units: 30
Preferred Square Footage: 2,500
Preferred Location Types: Freestanding; Regional Mall; Strip Mall
Alcohol Served: Beer, Wine
Primary Menu: Snacks (60)
Areas of Operation: PR, VI
Foreign Countries: ANTIGUA; SAINT MARTIN; TRINIDAD & TOBAGO
Type of Foodservice: In-Store Feeder (60)

Key Personnel
ROBERT CARRADY - CEO; President
SILVINA CAMPOS - CFO; Director Finance
JUAN ORTEGA - District Manager
GABRIEL ALICEA - Specialist Information Technology

Colon Gerena Group
1155 Ave Ponce De Leon PH 4
San Juan, PR 00907-3803

Mailing Address: PO Box 366308, SAN JUAN, PR, 00936-6308
Telephone: (787) 792-2001
Fax Number: (787) 273-0523
Company Email: rvavquez@gcg.pr
Type of Business: Chain Restaurant Operator
Year Founded: 1983
Total Sales: $226,740,000 (e)
Number of Employees: 100
Total Units: 81
Trade Names: Applebee's Neighborhood Grill & Bar (5); Wendy's Old Fashioned Hamburgers (76)
Units Franchised From: 81
Preferred Square Footage: 2,100; 2,900
Preferred Location Types: Freestanding; Strip Mall
Alcohol Served: Beer, Wine, Liquor
Primary Menu: American (5); Hamburger (76)
Projected Openings: 10
Areas of Operation: PR
Type of Foodservice: Casual Dining (5); Quick Serve (76)
Franchise Affiliation: Applebee's Services Inc., KANSAS CITY, MO; The Wendy's Company, DUBLIN, OH
Notes: The Wendy's restaurants operate as Wendco of Puerto Rico, Inc.

Key Personnel
JORGE COLON GERENA - CEO; President; General Buyer
CARLOS GARCIA - Chief Administrative Officer
MICHAEL SNODDY - VP Operations
LISELLE LUE QUI - Director Operations

Fast Food Management, Inc.
1519 Ave Ponce De Leon Ste 507
San Juan, PR 00909-1715

Telephone: (787) 725-1814
Fax Number: (787) 725-1859
Internet Homepage: thehotpotato.com
Company Email: info@thehotpotato.com

Type of Business: Chain Restaurant Operator
Year Founded: 1979
Total Sales: $13,880,000 (e)
Number of Employees: 264
Average Check: Breakfast(5); Lunch(8); Dinner(8)
Total Units: 15
Trade Names: Hot Potato (9); Reggio Pizza (3); Top Potato (3)
Company-Owned Units: 15
Preferred Location Types: Community Mall
Primary Menu: Miscellaneous (12); Pizza (3)
Areas of Operation: PR
Type of Foodservice: Quick Serve (15)
Primary Distributors: (Full Line) Jose Santiago Inc., BAYAMON, PR

Key Personnel
JOHN A. REGIS JR - CEO
JAY REGIS - President; VP Menu Development; General Buyer
LILLIBET COLON - Controller
IVAN CRUZ - Manager District

Ital Americas Foods Corp.
312 Calle De La Fortaleza
San Juan, PR 00901-1718

Mailing Address: PO Box 9024030, SAN JUAN, PR, 00902-4030
Telephone: (787) 723-2627
Fax Number: (787) 729-2963
Company Email: sbarropr@hotmail.com
Type of Business: Chain Restaurant Operator
Year Founded: 1979
Total Sales: $2,883,000 (e)
Number of Employees: 66
Average Check: Lunch(12); Dinner(14)
Total Units: 2
Trade Names: Sbarro (2)
Units Franchised From: 2
Preferred Square Footage: 900
Preferred Location Types: Community Mall; Freestanding
Primary Menu: Italian (2)
Areas of Operation: PR
Type of Foodservice: Quick Serve (2)
Franchise Affiliation: Sbarro Holdings LLC, COLUMBUS, OH
Primary Distributors: (Equipment) HED Foodservice Equipment, ROCKY MOUNT, NC; (Food) Jose Santiago Inc., BAYAMON, PR; (Supplies) Jose Santiago Inc., BAYAMON, PR

Key Personnel
ELISABETH SALDANA-SCHMIER - President; General Manager; Manager Human Resources; General Buyer
PEDRO JUARBE - CFO; Controller; Director Real Estate, Design

JR Acquisition Corp
Condominio Reina De Castilla
San Juan, PR 00901

Telephone: (787) 721-2653
Type of Business: Chain Restaurant Operator
Total Sales: $2,365,000 (e)
Total Units: 4
Trade Names: Cold Stone Creamery (4)
Units Franchised From: 4
Primary Menu: Snacks (4)
Areas of Operation: PR
Type of Foodservice: Quick Serve (4)
Franchise Affiliation: Kahala Brands, SCOTTSDALE, AZ

Key Personnel
JOSE E. RAMOS - Partner
JOSE A. RAMOSE - Partner

Multisystem Restaurants Inc.
1155 Ave Ponce De Leon
San Juan, PR 00907-3803

Mailing Address: PO BOX 366308, San Juan, PR, 00936
Telephone: (787) 273-3180
Fax Number: (787) 273-6965
Type of Business: Chain Restaurant Operator
Total Sales: $68,220,000 (e)
Alcohol Sales: 5%
Number of Employees: 1,800
Average Check: Lunch(12); Dinner(22)
Total Units: 26
Trade Names: LongHorn Steakhouse (9); Olive Garden (4); Sizzler (13)
Units Franchised From: 26
Preferred Square Footage: 5,000; 6,000
Preferred Location Types: Freestanding; Strip Mall
Alcohol Served: Beer, Wine, Liquor
Primary Menu: Italian (4); Steak (22)
Areas of Operation: PR
Type of Foodservice: Casual Dining (26)
Franchise Affiliation: LongHorn Steakhouse, ORLANDO, FL; Olive Garden, ORLANDO, FL; Sizzler USA Inc., MISSION VIEJO, CA
Primary Distributors: (Full Line) US Foods Holding Corp., ROSEMONT, IL

Key Personnel
JORGE COLON GERENA - President
ELENA ERAZO - General Manager

The Taco Maker Inc.
1055 Marginal Ave Jf Kennedy
San Juan, PR 00920

Mailing Address: PO Box 362888, San Juan, PR, 00936-2888
Telephone: (787) 273-3160
Fax Number: (787) 793-3130
Internet Homepage: tacomaker.com
Company Email: sales@fransglobal.com
Type of Business: Chain Restaurant Operator
Year Founded: 1978
Systemwide Sales: $303,641,000 (e)
Total Sales: $13,330,000 (e)
Number of Employees: 75
Average Check: Breakfast(8); Lunch(12); Dinner(12)
Total Units: 100
Trade Names: The Taco Maker (100)
Company-Owned Units: 8
Units Franchised To: 92
Preferred Square Footage: 800; 1,500; 2,500
Preferred Location Types: Community Mall; Convenience Store/Gas Station; Downtown; Freestanding; Outlet Mall; Strip Mall
Primary Menu: Taco (100)
Projected Openings: 2
Areas of Operation: CA, DC, FL, NV, PA, PR, UT, VA, WA
Foreign Countries: RUSSIA; VENEZUELA
Type of Foodservice: Quick Serve (100)
Primary Distributors: (Full Line) US Foods, OGDEN, UT
Notes: Hi-Noon Petroleum & The Taco Maker have announced an agreement to install a variety of licensed Taco Maker locations into multiple travel & convenience centers.

Key Personnel
CARLOS M. BUDET - President; COO; Exec VP Purchasing, Marketing
ANGEL RIVERA - CFO; Controller
JOSE SOHO - Exec VP
RICARDO RIVERA - Senior VP Operations; Director Training

RHODE ISLAND

Del's Lemonade & Refreshments
1260 Oaklawn Ave
Cranston, RI 02920-2628

Telephone: (401) 463-6190
Fax Number: (401) 463-7931
Internet Homepage: dels.com
Company Email: dels@dels.com
Type of Business: Chain Restaurant Operator
Year Founded: 1948
Systemwide Sales: $16,286,000 (e)
Total Sales: $4,793,000 (e)
Alcohol Sales: 1%
Number of Employees: 60
Average Check: Breakfast(5); Lunch(8); Dinner(14)
Internet Order Processing: Yes
Internet Sales: 1.00%

Total Units: 33
Trade Names: Del's Lemonade (30); Dorthy Cox's Chocolates (2); Tom & Jimmy's Ice Cream (1)
Company-Owned Units: 4
Units Franchised To: 29
Preferred Square Footage: 1,000
Preferred Location Types: Community Mall; Freestanding; Strip Mall
Primary Menu: Snacks (33)
Areas of Operation: CA, CT, FL, KY, MA, NH, NJ, NV, NY, PA, RI, UT, WI
Type of Foodservice: Quick Serve (33)
Catering Services: Yes

Key Personnel
BRUCE DELUCIA - CEO; President; Executive Chef; Director Finance, Facility/Maintenance, Real Estate, Design, Human Resources, Catering
JOE PADULA - VP Operations, Purchasing, Information Systems, Loss Prevention, Supply Chain, Franchising

Pergom Inc.
680 Reservoir Ave
Cranston, RI 02910-3226

Telephone: (401) 785-2530
Internet Homepage: waltsroastbeef.net
Company Email: info@waltsinternational.com
Type of Business: Chain Restaurant Operator
Year Founded: 1957
Systemwide Sales: $6,473,000 (e)
Total Sales: $4,631,000 (e)
Number of Employees: 100
Average Check: Dinner(14)
Total Units: 5
Trade Names: Walt's Roast Beef (5)
Units Franchised To: 5
Preferred Square Footage: 1,800
Preferred Location Types: Freestanding
Primary Menu: Sandwiches/Deli (5)
Areas of Operation: RI
Type of Foodservice: Quick Serve (5)
Primary Distributors: (Supplies) Gordon Food Service, TAUNTON, MA

Key Personnel
RAYMOND PERROTTA - President; General Manager; Director Finance, Purchasing, Information Systems, Supply Chain, Real Estate, Design, Human Resources, Menu Development; General Buyer

The Jan Companies
35 Sockanosset Cross Rd
Cranston, RI 02920-5535

Mailing Address: PO Box 8819, CRANSTON, RI, 02920-0819

Telephone: (401) 946-4000
Fax Number: (401) 946-4392
Internet Homepage: jancompanies.com
Type of Business: Chain Restaurant Operator
Year Founded: 1969
Total Sales: $202,210,000 (e)
Alcohol Sales: 5%
Number of Employees: 4,459
Average Check: Breakfast(8); Lunch(22); Dinner(28)
Total Units: 96
Trade Names: Burger King (82); Krispy Kreme Doughnuts (4); Newport Creamery (10)
Company-Owned Units: 10
Units Franchised From: 86
Preferred Square Footage: 4,500
Preferred Location Types: Downtown; Freestanding; Regional Mall
Alcohol Served: Beer, Wine, Liquor
Primary Menu: Hamburger (82); Snacks (14)
Areas of Operation: CA, CT, DE, FL, GA, MA, MD, NY, RI, TX, VT
Type of Foodservice: Quick Serve (96)
Franchise Affiliation: Burger King Worldwide Inc., MIAMI, FL; CoreLife Eatery, LLC, VESTAL, NY; Krispy Kreme Doughnut Corporation, CHARLOTTE, NC; Popeyes Louisiana Kitchen Inc., ATLANTA, GA
Primary Distributors: (Equipment) SYSCO of Boston, PLYMPTON, MA; (Food) Maines Paper & Food Services Ohio, OAKWOOD VILLAGE, OH; (Supplies) Maines Paper & Food Services Ohio, OAKWOOD VILLAGE, OH
Notes: The company derives approximately 19% of its revenue from country club operations.

Key Personnel
WILLIAM N. JANIKIES - President; COO; VP
JANICE MATHEWS - VP Administration
JONATHAN JANIKIES - VP Operations
DANIEL LETT - VP Operations
CYNTHIA JANIKIES-SIMONSON - Treasurer; Controller; Director Finance
GREG GULINO - Director Real Estate

Chelo's Restaurant
1725 Mendon Rd Unit 209
Cumberland, RI 02864-4340

Telephone: (401) 312-6500
Fax Number: (401) 312-6501
Internet Homepage: chelos.com
Type of Business: Chain Restaurant Operator
Year Founded: 1955
Total Sales: $36,350,000 (e)
Alcohol Sales: 10%
Number of Employees: 1,000
Average Check: Lunch(18); Dinner(24)
Internet Order Processing: Yes
Total Units: 8
Trade Names: Chelo's Hometown Bar & Grille (8)
Company-Owned Units: 8
Preferred Square Footage: 7,000
Preferred Location Types: Community Mall; Freestanding
Alcohol Served: Beer, Wine, Liquor
Primary Menu: American (8)
Areas of Operation: RI
Type of Foodservice: Casual Dining (8)
Catering Services: Yes
Distribution Centers: WARWICK, RI
Primary Distributors: (Full Line) SYSCO Food Services of Northern New England Inc., WESTBROOK, ME; (Full Line) Performance Foodservice - Springfield, SPRINGFIELD, MA

Key Personnel
GARY CHELO - President; Partner; Controller; General Manager; General Buyer
RANDY CHELO - Partner; Director Advertising; General Buyer
CRAIG CHELO - Partner; CFO; Director Finance, Purchasing, Menu Development
BARBARA CASWELL - Director Human Resources
LORI RODGER - Manager Accounting
JAROD CHELO - Manager Operations, Marketing

Gregg's Restaurants Inc.
214 Main St # B
East Greenwich, RI 02818-3828

Telephone: (401) 886-5700
Fax Number: (401) 336-3990
Internet Homepage: greggsusa.com
Company Email: customercare@greggsusa.com
Type of Business: Chain Restaurant Operator
Year Founded: 1972
Total Sales: $27,387,000 (e)
Alcohol Sales: 15%
Number of Employees: 510
Average Check: Lunch(14); Dinner(22)
Internet Order Processing: Yes
Internet Sales: 1.00%
Total Units: 4
Trade Names: Gregg's Restaurant & Pub (4)
Company-Owned Units: 4
Preferred Location Types: Freestanding
Alcohol Served: Beer, Wine, Liquor
Primary Menu: American (4)
Areas of Operation: RI
Type of Foodservice: Casual Dining (4)
Primary Distributors: (Full Line) SYSCO of Boston, PLYMPTON, MA

Key Personnel
ROBERT BACON - President
PATTY MCGUIRE - Controller
TONY OLIVERA - General Manager
JEN COOKE - General Manager

ADAM COLE - General Manager; General Buyer

ADJ Management
499 Warren Ave
East Providence, RI 02914-2810

Telephone: (401) 751-6688
Type of Business: Chain Restaurant Operator
Year Founded: 1990
Total Sales: $29,960,000 (e)
Number of Employees: 140
Average Check: Breakfast(8); Lunch(8); Dinner(10)
Total Units: 19
Trade Names: Dunkin' Donuts (19)
Units Franchised From: 19
Preferred Square Footage: 1,500; 2,200
Preferred Location Types: Freestanding; Strip Mall
Primary Menu: Snacks (19)
Areas of Operation: MA, RI
Type of Foodservice: Quick Serve (19)
Franchise Affiliation: DD IP Holder, CANTON, MA

Key Personnel
JOSE DUTRA - Partner

Davenport's Restaurant Corp.
1925 Pawtucket Ave
East Providence, RI 02914-1642

Telephone: (401) 438-3381
Fax Number: (401) 435-8064
Internet Homepage: davenportsri.com
Type of Business: Chain Restaurant Operator
Year Founded: 1995
Total Sales: $8,403,000 (e)
Alcohol Sales: 25%
Number of Employees: 55
Average Check: Lunch(18); Dinner(34)
Internet Order Processing: Yes
Internet Sales: 4.00%
Total Units: 2
Trade Names: Davenport's Restaurant (2)
Company-Owned Units: 2
Preferred Location Types: Freestanding
Alcohol Served: Beer, Wine, Liquor
Primary Menu: American (2)
Areas of Operation: RI
Type of Foodservice: Casual Dining (2)
Catering Services: Yes
Primary Distributors: (Food) SYSCO of Boston, PLYMPTON, MA

Key Personnel
GREGG DAVENPORT - President; Partner

Howley Bread Group, Ltd
640 George Washington Hwy Ste 100
Lincoln, RI 02865

Telephone: (401) 333-1542
Fax Number: (401) 333-1543
Internet Homepage: howleybread.com
Type of Business: Chain Restaurant Operator
Year Founded: 1999
Total Sales: $130,370,000 (e)
Number of Employees: 100
Average Check: Breakfast(6); Lunch(6); Dinner(10)
Total Units: 28
Trade Names: Panera Bread (28)
Units Franchised From: 28
Preferred Square Footage: 4,500; 4,800
Preferred Location Types: Freestanding; Strip Mall
Primary Menu: Sandwiches/Deli (28)
Areas of Operation: CT, MA, RI
Type of Foodservice: Fast Casual (28)
Franchise Affiliation: Panera Bread Company, SAINT LOUIS, MO
Primary Distributors: (Full Line) US Foods, SEABROOK, NH

Key Personnel
LEE HOWLEY - President; Partner
TOM HOWLEY - Partner; Director Real Estate
MARK DRAPEAU - Area Director
DAVID BEAUREGARD - VP Operations
LEANNE SMITH - VP Human Resources
MARK LAPLACA - Director Training

Ronzio Management Inc.
111 John St Ste 2
Lincoln, RI 02865-1708

Telephone: (401) 334-9750
Fax Number: (401) 312-0378
Internet Homepage: ronziopizza.com
Company Email: mic.gandhi@ronziopizza.com
Type of Business: Chain Restaurant Operator
Year Founded: 1987
Systemwide Sales: $1,923,000 (e)
Total Sales: $285,000 (e)
Alcohol Sales: 0.50%
Number of Employees: 9
Average Check: Lunch(12); Dinner(20)
Internet Order Processing: Yes
Internet Sales: 1.00%
Total Units: 6
Trade Names: Ronzio Pizza & Subs (6)
Units Franchised To: 6
Preferred Square Footage: 900; 1,200
Preferred Location Types: Institution (college/hospital); Strip Mall
Alcohol Served: Beer, Wine
Primary Menu: Pizza (6)
Areas of Operation: MA, RI
Type of Foodservice: Quick Serve (6)
Foodservice Management Venues: Parks & Recreation; Schools
Catering Services: Yes

Key Personnel
MICK GUNDY - President; Executive Chef; Director Facility/Maintenance, Real Estate, Design
FERNANDO SOUSA - VP Operations, Supply Chain, Human Resources, Menu Development, Food Safety; General Buyer

Kenneth Byam
238 E Main Rd Unit 3
Middletown, RI 02842-7221

Telephone: (401) 847-7670
Fax Number: (401) 847-7340
Type of Business: Chain Restaurant Operator
Total Sales: $1,542,000 (e)
Total Units: 2
Trade Names: Subway (2)
Units Franchised From: 2
Primary Menu: Sandwiches/Deli (2)
Areas of Operation: RI
Type of Foodservice: Quick Serve (2)
Franchise Affiliation: Doctor's Associates Inc., MILFORD, CT

Key Personnel
KENNETH BYAM - President; General Buyer

Domino's Franchisee
5953 Post Rd
North Kingstown, RI 02852-1301

Telephone: (401) 884-8546
Type of Business: Chain Restaurant Operator
Total Sales: $3,967,000 (e)
Total Units: 2
Trade Names: Domino's (2)
Units Franchised From: 2
Primary Menu: Pizza (2)
Areas of Operation: RI
Type of Foodservice: Quick Serve (2)
Franchise Affiliation: Domino's Pizza Inc, ANN ARBOR, MI

Key Personnel
GREGORY S. LYONS - Owner; General Buyer

Dunkin' Donuts Franchise
421 Broadway
Pawtucket, RI 02860

Telephone: (401) 724-1800
Internet Homepage: dunkindonuts.com
Type of Business: Chain Restaurant Operator

Total Sales: $7,898,000 (e)
Average Check: Lunch(6); Dinner(8)
Total Units: 5
Trade Names: Dunkin' Donuts (5)
Units Franchised From: 5
Preferred Square Footage: 1,500; 2,200
Preferred Location Types: Freestanding
Primary Menu: Snacks (5)
Areas of Operation: RI
Type of Foodservice: Quick Serve (5)
Franchise Affiliation: DD IP Holder, CANTON, MA

Key Personnel
ALFREDO ANDRADE - President; General Buyer

Newport Ave Donuts Inc
81 Newport Ave
Pawtucket, RI 02861-4107

Telephone: (401) 724-2458
Fax Number: (401) 724-2458
Type of Business: Chain Restaurant Operator
Total Sales: $7,673,000 (e)
Number of Employees: 100
Average Check: Dinner(8)
Total Units: 5
Trade Names: Dunkin' Donuts (5)
Units Franchised From: 5
Preferred Square Footage: 1,500; 2,200
Preferred Location Types: Freestanding
Primary Menu: Snacks (5)
Areas of Operation: RI
Type of Foodservice: Quick Serve (5)
Franchise Affiliation: DD IP Holder, CANTON, MA

Key Personnel
FERNANDO J. VIERA - President; General Buyer

Chow Fun Food Group
1345 Westminster St
Providence, RI 02909-1412

Telephone: (401) 453-2077
Fax Number: (401) 453-9918
Internet Homepage: chowfunfoodgroup.com; luxeburgerbar.com; ricksroadhouseri.com; tenprimesteakandsushi.com; xocafe.com
Company Email: info@cffgri.com
Type of Business: Chain Restaurant Operator
Year Founded: 1998
Total Sales: $20,230,000 (e)
Alcohol Sales: 10%
Number of Employees: 292
Average Check: Breakfast(12); Lunch(24); Dinner(54)
Internet Order Processing: Yes
Internet Sales: 10.00%
Total Units: 4
Trade Names: Harry's Bar & Burger (2); Ten Prime Steak and Sushi (1); Xaco Taco (1)
Company-Owned Units: 4
Preferred Square Footage: 5,000
Preferred Location Types: Freestanding
Alcohol Served: Beer, Wine, Liquor
Primary Menu: American (0); Hamburger (2); Steak/Seafood (1); Taco (1)
Areas of Operation: RI
Type of Foodservice: Casual Dining (4)
Catering Services: Yes

Key Personnel
JOHN ELKHAY - President; Director Facility/Maintenance, Information Systems, Supply Chain, Real Estate, Design, Store Fixtures
MICHAEL CAPOLUPO - Manager Social Media

Domino's Franchisee
1010 Chalkstone Ave
Providence, RI 02908-4238

Telephone: (401) 861-9800
Type of Business: Chain Restaurant Operator
Total Sales: $6,152,000 (e)
Total Units: 3
Trade Names: Domino's (3)
Units Franchised From: 3
Primary Menu: Pizza (3)
Areas of Operation: RI
Type of Foodservice: Quick Serve (3)
Franchise Affiliation: Domino's Pizza Inc, ANN ARBOR, MI

Key Personnel
JOHN D. ENO - Owner; General Buyer

Johnson & Wales University Providence Campus
8 Abbott Park Pl
Providence, RI 02903-3703

Telephone: (401) 598-1000
Fax Number: (401) 538-2948
Internet Homepage: jwu.edu/providence
Company Email: pvd@admissions.jwu.edu
Type of Business: Culinary Schools
Areas of Operation: RI

Key Personnel
MIM RUNEY - Chairman

Rhode Rockets Inc./ROCACONN Inc.
115 Pratt St Ste A
Providence, RI 02906-1412

Mailing Address: PO Box 2504, PROVIDENCE, RI, 02912-2504
Telephone: (401) 419-3803
Company Email: jrocket1@aol.com
Type of Business: Chain Restaurant Operator
Year Founded: 2000
Total Sales: $46,450,000 (e)
Number of Employees: 1,096
Average Check: Breakfast(10); Lunch(12); Dinner(14)
Total Units: 30
Trade Names: Johnny Rockets (30)
Units Franchised From: 30
Preferred Square Footage: 1,800
Preferred Location Types: Freestanding; Regional Mall
Primary Menu: Hamburger (30)
Areas of Operation: CA, CT, MA, MN, NY, PA, RI
Type of Foodservice: Fast Casual (30)
Franchise Affiliation: The Johnny Rockets Group Inc., LAKE FOREST, CA
Primary Distributors: (Food) Reinhart Agar Supply Inc., TAUNTON, MA

Key Personnel
LLOYD SUGARMAN - President; Partner; General Manager; Director Information Systems, Real Estate; General Buyer
RHONA SUGARMAN - Partner
JASON SUGARMAN - Partner; VP Operations

Domino's Franchisee
1086 Willett Ave
Riverside, RI 02915-2067

Telephone: (401) 433-0200
Type of Business: Chain Restaurant Operator
Total Sales: $6,139,000 (e)
Total Units: 3
Trade Names: Domino's (3)
Units Franchised From: 3
Primary Menu: Pizza (3)
Areas of Operation: RI
Type of Foodservice: Quick Serve (3)
Franchise Affiliation: Domino's Pizza Inc, ANN ARBOR, MI

Key Personnel
JOE ZONFRILLI - Owner

Domino's Franchisee
375 Putnam Pike Ste 25
Smithfield, RI 02917-2455

Telephone: (401) 233-8966
Type of Business: Chain Restaurant Operator
Total Sales: $8,074,000 (e)
Total Units: 4
Trade Names: Domino's (4)
Units Franchised From: 4
Primary Menu: Pizza (4)
Areas of Operation: RI
Type of Foodservice: Quick Serve (4)
Franchise Affiliation: Domino's Pizza Inc, ANN ARBOR, MI

Key Personnel
WILLIAM J. CHRISTINA - Owner; General Buyer

Domino's Franchisee
2757 Post Rd
Warwick, RI 02886-3042

Telephone: (401) 732-5770
Type of Business: Chain Restaurant Operator
Total Sales: $8,097,000 (e)
Total Units: 4
Trade Names: Domino's (4)
Units Franchised From: 4
Primary Menu: Pizza (4)
Areas of Operation: RI
Type of Foodservice: Quick Serve (4)
Franchise Affiliation: Domino's Pizza Inc, ANN ARBOR, MI

Key Personnel
JAMES A. PARDY - Owner; General Buyer

Newport Harbor Corp
300 Metro Center Blvd Ste 100
Warwick, RI 02886-1763

Telephone: (401) 848-7010
Fax Number: (401) 847-0560
Internet Homepage: 22bowens.com; mooringrestaurant.com; newportharbor.com; smokehousecafe.com; watermangrille.com
Type of Business: Chain Restaurant Operator
Year Founded: 1981
Total Sales: $11,040,000 (e)
Alcohol Sales: 19%
Number of Employees: 845
Average Check: Lunch(18); Dinner(36)
Internet Order Processing: Yes
Internet Sales: 3.00%
Total Units: 11
Trade Names: 22 Bowen's (1); Castle Hill Inn & Restaurant (1); Hemenway's Seafood Grille (1); Papa Razzi Restaurant (3); Smoke House Cafe (1); The Boathouse (1); The Mooring (1); Trio (1); Waterman Grille (1)
Company-Owned Units: 11
Preferred Square Footage: 5,500; 6,000
Preferred Location Types: Freestanding
Alcohol Served: Beer, Wine, Liquor
Primary Menu: American (2); Bar-B-Q (1); Italian (3); Seafood (3); Steak/Seafood (2)
Areas of Operation: RI
Type of Foodservice: Casual Dining (6); Fine Dining (5)
Primary Distributors: (Equipment) SYSCO of Boston, PLYMPTON, MA

Key Personnel
PAUL O'REILLY - CEO; President; Director Finance, Purchasing
CASEY RILEY - COO; VP
CORRINE SYLVIA - Controller
JOSHUA BROWN - Director Content Development
KEN CUSSON - Director Business Development

Uncle Tony's USA Inc.
1800 Post Rd Ste 17G
Warwick, RI 02886-1534

Telephone: (401) 738-1322
Fax Number: (401) 732-1936
Internet Homepage: uncletonys.net
Type of Business: Chain Restaurant Operator
Year Founded: 1970
Systemwide Sales: $31,075,000 (e)
Total Sales: $5,826,000 (e)
Alcohol Sales: 20%
Number of Employees: 25
Average Check: Lunch(8); Dinner(14)
Internet Sales: 20.00%
Total Units: 3
Trade Names: Uncle Tony's Pizza & Pasta Restaurant (3)
Units Franchised To: 3
Preferred Square Footage: 6,000
Preferred Location Types: Freestanding
Alcohol Served: Beer, Wine
Primary Menu: Italian (3)
Areas of Operation: RI
Type of Foodservice: Casual Dining (3)
Catering Services: Yes
Primary Distributors: (Equipment) Paramount Restaurant Supply Corp., FARMINGDALE, NY; (Food) Allstate Restaurant Supply Inc., PAWTUCKET, RI;(Supplies) Paramount Restaurant Supply Corp., FARMINGDALE, NY

Key Personnel
EDWARD A. CAROSI - President; Executive Chef; Director Advertising, Menu Development, Catering; General Buyer
DAVID BRADBURY - CFO; Director Finance

SOUTH CAROLINA

Domino's Franchisee
1006 N Main St
Anderson, SC 29621-4841

Telephone: (864) 226-9393
Type of Business: Chain Restaurant Operator
Total Sales: $3,959,000 (e)
Total Units: 2
Trade Names: Domino's (2)
Units Franchised From: 2
Primary Menu: Pizza (2)
Areas of Operation: SC
Type of Foodservice: Quick Serve (2)
Franchise Affiliation: Domino's Pizza Inc, ANN ARBOR, MI

Key Personnel
CATHERINE A. SMITH - Owner; General Buyer

Hankins Development Corp
4120 Clemson Blvd Ste D
Anderson, SC 29621-1176

Telephone: (864) 226-5080
Fax Number: (864) 224-3341
Internet Homepage: sonicdrivein.com
Type of Business: Chain Restaurant Operator
Total Sales: $4,494,000 (e)
Total Units: 2
Trade Names: Sonic America's Drive-In (2)
Units Franchised From: 2
Primary Menu: Hamburger (2)
Areas of Operation: SC
Type of Foodservice: Quick Serve (2)
Franchise Affiliation: Sonic Corp., OKLAHOMA CITY, OK

Key Personnel
ANDY HANKINS - Owner; General Buyer

Domino's Franchisee
11381 Dunbarton Blvd
Barnwell, SC 29812-3033

Telephone: (803) 541-8646
Type of Business: Chain Restaurant Operator
Total Sales: $8,140,000 (e)
Total Units: 4
Trade Names: Domino's (4)
Units Franchised From: 4
Primary Menu: Pizza (4)
Areas of Operation: SC
Type of Foodservice: Quick Serve (4)
Franchise Affiliation: Domino's Pizza Inc, ANN ARBOR, MI

Key Personnel
HIMANSHU B. PATEL - Owner; General Buyer

Island Subway Inc
10 Sams Point Rd Unit B6
Beaufort, SC 29907-2099

Telephone: (843) 522-1300
Type of Business: Chain Restaurant Operator
Total Sales: $6,352,000 (e)
Total Units: 11
Trade Names: Subway (11)
Units Franchised From: 11
Primary Menu: Sandwiches/Deli (11)
Areas of Operation: SC
Type of Foodservice: Quick Serve (11)
Franchise Affiliation: Doctor's Associates Inc., MILFORD, CT

Key Personnel
JOHN REMEGI - President; Partner; General Buyer
KARLA REMEGI - Partner

The Anchor Group, LLC
5846 Guilford Pl
Bluffton, SC 29910

Telephone: (843) 815-6536
Fax Number: (843) 815-6537
Company Email: jimsaba@hargray.com
Type of Business: Chain Restaurant Operator
Total Sales: $3,719,000 (e)
Total Units: 3
Trade Names: Captain D's Seafood Kitchen (3)
Units Franchised From: 3
Primary Menu: Seafood (3)
Areas of Operation: GA
Type of Foodservice: Quick Serve (3)
Franchise Affiliation: Captain D's LLC, NASHVILLE, TN

Key Personnel
JAMES SABA - President; General Buyer
BRTINI KIDWELL - CFO

Outlaw Enterprises, Inc.
816 Mill St
Camden, SC 29020-4417

Telephone: (803) 432-4305
Fax Number: (803) 432-7606
Company Email: j_outlaw@bellsouth.net
Type of Business: Chain Restaurant Operator
Year Founded: 1965
Total Sales: $28,810,000 (e)
Number of Employees: 406
Average Check: Lunch(8); Dinner(10)
Total Units: 14

Trade Names: KFC (11); Taco Bell (3)
Units Franchised From: 14
Preferred Square Footage: 2,500; 3,200
Preferred Location Types: Freestanding
Primary Menu: Chicken (11); Taco (3)
Areas of Operation: SC
Type of Foodservice: Quick Serve (14)
Catering Services: Yes
Franchise Affiliation: KFC Corporation, LOUISVILLE, KY; Taco Bell Corp., IRVINE, CA

Key Personnel
JOHNNY OUTLAW - President
ASHLEY PAGE - Director Operations; General Buyer

CentraArchy Restaurant Management Co.
236 Albemarle Rd
Charleston, SC 29407-7522

Telephone: (843) 571-0096
Fax Number: (843) 571-0336
Internet Homepage: centraarchy.com
Company Email: customerrelations@centraarchy.com
Type of Business: Chain Restaurant Operator
Year Founded: 1984
Total Sales: $70,960,000 (e)
Alcohol Sales: 17%
Number of Employees: 1,700
Total Units: 14
Trade Names: California Dreaming (8); Carolina Roadhouse (1); Chophouse 47 (1); Chophouse New Orleans (1); Gulfstream Cafe (1); Joey D's Oak Room(1); New York Prime (1)
Company-Owned Units: 14
Preferred Square Footage: 5,000; 7,000
Preferred Location Types: Freestanding
Alcohol Served: Beer, Wine, Liquor
Primary Menu: American (11); Steak (4)
Areas of Operation: AL, FL, GA, LA, NC, SC
Type of Foodservice: Casual Dining (11); Fine Dining (5)

Key Personnel
GREGORY GREENBAUM - CEO; President; Partner; Executive Chef
VINCE VAN BRUNT - CEO
JULIE SMITH - CFO; Director Store Fixtures
STEPHANIE LONDON - Controller
ROBERT KINSELLA - Director Purchasing, Menu Development
KAREN HALL - Director Operations
MEGAN WALLACE - Director Recruitment
AMBER STEWART - Director Marketing
MARK BALDWIN - Director
LUKE L'HEUREUX - Director Operations
DON SCHARER - Manager Facility/Maintenance

ALEX ZENGOTITA - Manager

Charleston Crab House
145 Wappoo Creek Dr
Charleston, SC 29412-2119

Telephone: (843) 795-1963
Fax Number: (843) 762-4866
Internet Homepage: charlestoncrabhouse.com
Company Email: comments@charlestoncrabhouse.com
Type of Business: Chain Restaurant Operator
Year Founded: 1991
Total Sales: $23,379,000 (e)
Alcohol Sales: 20%
Number of Employees: 240
Average Check: Lunch(16); Dinner(36)
Total Units: 3
Trade Names: Charleston Crab House (2); Oyster House (1)
Company-Owned Units: 3
Preferred Square Footage: 800; 5,500; 6,000; 9,000
Preferred Location Types: Downtown; Freestanding
Alcohol Served: Beer, Wine, Liquor
Primary Menu: Seafood (3)
Areas of Operation: SC
Type of Foodservice: Casual Dining (3)
Primary Distributors: (Full Line) SYSCO Atlanta LLC, COLLEGE PARK, GA

Key Personnel
JOHN KEENER - President; General Manager; Executive Chef; General Buyer
SCOTT LARYMORE - General Manager
KIM JACKSON - Director Finance; Manager Operations
KATELYN MERRYMAN - Manager Restaurant Operations

Charleston Sports Pub
1124 Sam Rittenberg Blvd
Charleston, SC 29407

Telephone: (843) 203-3329
Internet Homepage: charlestonsportspub.com
Company Email: Charlestonsportspub@gmail.com
Type of Business: Chain Restaurant Operator
Year Founded: 2015
Total Units: 6
Trade Names: Charleston Sports Pub (6)
Company-Owned Units: 6
Preferred Square Footage: 15,000
Primary Menu: American (6)
Areas of Operation: SC
Type of Foodservice: Casual Dining (6)

Key Personnel
PERRY FREEMAN - Owner

ADAM LAROCHE - Director Foodservice

Chesapeake Bay Subs, LLC
1479 Tobias Gadson Blvd
Charleston, SC 29407-4794

Telephone: (843) 402-0710
Fax Number: (843) 402-0716
Type of Business: Chain Restaurant Operator
Total Sales: $7,193,000 (e)
Total Units: 7
Trade Names: Jersey Mike's Subs (7)
Units Franchised From: 7
Preferred Square Footage: 1,100; 1,500; 2,200; 2,400
Preferred Location Types: Freestanding; Strip Mall
Primary Menu: American (7)
Areas of Operation: FL, GA, LA, MS, NC, SC, TN
Type of Foodservice: Fast Casual (7)
Franchise Affiliation: Papa Johns International Inc., LOUISVILLE, KY

Key Personnel
PHILIP L. HORN JR - President; General Buyer
PEGGY HUNT - CFO
GINGER ANDERSON - Director Human Resources

Dining Group South
141 E Bay St
Charleston, SC 29401-2104

Telephone: (843) 720-1950
Fax Number: (843) 720-1951
Internet Homepage: colasrestaurant.com; ansonrestaurant.com; garibaldisavannah.com
Company Email: info@ansonrestaurant.com
Type of Business: Chain Restaurant Operator
Year Founded: 1976
Total Sales: $9,214,000 (e)
Alcohol Sales: 25%
Number of Employees: 360
Average Check: Dinner(42)
Total Units: 4
Trade Names: Anson (1); Cola (1); Garibaldi's (1); The Old Pink House (1)
Company-Owned Units: 4
Preferred Square Footage: 1,500; 4,000
Preferred Location Types: Downtown
Alcohol Served: Beer, Wine, Liquor
Primary Menu: American (1); French/Continental (1); Seafood (2)
Areas of Operation: GA, SC
Type of Foodservice: Casual Dining (1); Fine Dining (3)
Primary Distributors: (Equipment) Atlanta Fixture & Sales Co., ATLANTA, GA; (Food) US Foods, FORT MILL, SC; (Supplies) Atlanta Fixture & Sales Co., ATLANTA, GA

Key Personnel
CHIARA BARNETT - Partner
DONNA BALISH - Partner
JEFF BALISH - Partner
ERIC RICHARDS - Director Operations; General Buyer

Holy City Hospitality
39 John St
Charleston, SC 29403-6432

Mailing Address: PO Box 21506, Charleston, SC, 29413
Telephone: (843) 725-5959
Fax Number: (843) 722-8835
Internet Homepage: coastbarandgrill.com; 39ruedejean.com; goodfoodcatering.net; holycityhospitality.com; virginiasonking.com
Company Email: comments@holycityhospitality.com
Type of Business: Chain Restaurant Operator
Year Founded: 1999
Total Sales: $5,798,000 (e)
Alcohol Sales: 12%
Average Check: Lunch(18); Dinner(48)
Total Units: 7
Trade Names: 39 Rue de Jean (2); Coast Seafood (1); Michael's on the Alley (1); Victor Social Club (1); Vincent Chicco's (1); Virginia's on King (1)
Company-Owned Units: 7
Preferred Location Types: Downtown; Freestanding
Alcohol Served: Beer, Wine, Liquor
Primary Menu: French/Continental (1); Seafood (2); Southern (1); Steak/Seafood (1)
Areas of Operation: SC
Type of Foodservice: Casual Dining (4); Fine Dining (3)
Catering Services: Yes
Notes: HCH also operates Good Food Catering. and Historic Rice Mill special event venue

Key Personnel
DARREN WOLFE - President; Executive Chef
TRISTAN WHITE - Director Catering; General Buyer
AMANDA GRANT - Manager Human Resources
CARLA MERRILL - Manager Accounting; General Buyer
KINSEY ROGERS - Manager Marketing
KARLA CRISP - Administrator Operations

Home Grown Hospitality
1177 Southgate Dr
Charleston, SC 29407-4209

Telephone: (843) 769-0350
Fax Number: (843) 766-4358
Internet Homepage: hghosp.com
Company Email: comments@hghosp.com
Type of Business: Chain Restaurant Operator
Year Founded: 1985
Total Sales: $53,840,000 (e)
Alcohol Sales: 20%
Number of Employees: 1,314
Average Check: Lunch(12); Dinner(24)
Internet Order Processing: Yes
Total Units: 24
Trade Names: Flying Fish (1); Kaminsky's Dessert Cafe (3); Liberty Brewery & Grill (2); Liberty Tap Room & Grill (6); Pearlz Oyster Bar (4); Rioz Brazilian Steakhouse (3); T-Bonz Gill & Grill (5)
Company-Owned Units: 24
Preferred Square Footage: 4,000; 5,000
Preferred Location Types: Freestanding; Strip Mall
Alcohol Served: Beer, Wine, Liquor
Primary Menu: American (6); Seafood (1); Snacks (3); Steak (3); Steak/Seafood (11)
Areas of Operation: GA, NC, SC
Type of Foodservice: Casual Dining (24)
Catering Services: Yes
Primary Distributors: (Full Line) SYSCO Food Services of Columbia, COLUMBIA, SC

Key Personnel
JERRY SCHEER - President; Partner; Director Finance, Operations, Purchasing, Design, Menu Development
MARK CUMINS - Partner; VP; Director Real Estate
CHRIS PLATT - Director Information Technology
EMMY SCOTT - Director Marketing

Home Management Group
211 King St Suite 320
Charleston, SC 29401

Telephone: (843) 724-3808
Fax Number: (843) 203-4821
Internet Homepage: highcottoncharleston.com; snobcharleston.com; mavericksouthernkitchens.com; hallmanagementgroup.com
Type of Business: Chain Restaurant Operator
Year Founded: 1989
Total Sales: $24,840,000 (e)
Alcohol Sales: 25%
Number of Employees: 396
Average Check: Lunch(24); Dinner(90)
Total Units: 7
Trade Names: Hall's Chophouse (4); High Cotton (1); Rita's Seaside Grill (1); Slightly North of Broad (1)
Company-Owned Units: 7
Preferred Location Types: Downtown
Alcohol Served: Beer, Wine, Liquor
Primary Menu: American (2); Southern (1); Steak (4)

Areas of Operation: SC
Type of Foodservice: Casual Dining (1); Fine Dining (6)
Primary Distributors: (Food) SYSCO Food Services of Virginia LLC, HARRISONBURG, VA
Notes: The company operates three Charleston Cooks! retail/teaching stores and derives approximately 25% of its revenue from these operations.

Key Personnel
DEBORAH RETALIS - CFO
JOE MELOY - VP Operations; Director Operations; General Buyer
MATTHEW NIESSNER - Executive Chef; General Buyer

Hospitality Management Group Inc.
185 E Bay St
Charleston, SC 29401-2126

Telephone: (843) 577-7771
Fax Number: (843) 722-0035
Internet Homepage: blossomcharleston.com; magnoliascharleston.com
Company Email: info@hmgi.net
Type of Business: Chain Restaurant Operator
Year Founded: 1990
Total Sales: $5,884,000 (e)
Alcohol Sales: 10%
Number of Employees: 100
Average Check: Lunch(18); Dinner(48)
Internet Order Processing: Yes
Internet Sales: 1.00%
Total Units: 2
Trade Names: Blossom (1); Magnolias (1)
Company-Owned Units: 2
Preferred Location Types: Freestanding
Alcohol Served: Beer, Wine, Liquor
Primary Menu: Asian (1); Southern (1)
Areas of Operation: SC
Type of Foodservice: Fine Dining (2)

Key Personnel
DIANE HOWARD - General Manager
JAMES SIMMONS - Executive Chef
MICHAEL NICKELL - Director Operations
BARBARA NATALE - Manager Accounting

JEM Restaurant Group
2 Wharfside St Ste 2O
Charleston, SC 29401-1658

Mailing Address: PO Box 22246, CHARLESTON, SC, 29413-2246
Telephone: (843) 958-8660
Fax Number: (843) 958-8455
Company Email: jemflorida@msn.com
Type of Business: Chain Restaurant Operator
Year Founded: 1998
Total Sales: $96,230,000 (e)
Alcohol Sales: 3%
Number of Employees: 4,000
Average Check: Lunch(8); Dinner(10)
Total Units: 35
Trade Names: Taco Bell (35)
Units Franchised From: 35
Preferred Square Footage: 2,500; 3,200
Preferred Location Types: Freestanding; Regional Mall; Strip Mall
Alcohol Served: Beer, Wine
Primary Menu: Taco (35)
Projected Openings: 2
Projected Remodelings: 8
Areas of Operation: FL, SC
Type of Foodservice: Quick Serve (35)
Franchise Affiliation: KFC Corporation, LOUISVILLE, KY; Pizza Hut Inc., PLANO, TX; Taco Bell Corp., IRVINE, CA
Primary Distributors: (Food) McLane/Concord, CONCORD, NC

Key Personnel
JOHN MCGRATH - CEO; General Buyer
WARREN NELSON - President; CFO
ALLEN WOOD - CFO
VIRGINIA RIVALAIN - Controller
MELISSA BENSON - Director Human Resources
MIKE BUSS - Director Operations, Facility/Maintenance, Information Systems
JONATHAN GONZALEZ - Director Operations; Coach
KAJ BECK-ANDERSEN - Manager Operations
KELLY FRAZIER - Coordinator Accounting

Palas Hospitality
2008 Savannah Hwy
Charleston, SC 29407-6286

Telephone: (843) 571-1000
Fax Number: (843) 766-9444
Internet Homepage: grill225.com; palashospitality.com; thetownandcountryinn.com
Company Email: contactus@palashospitality.com
Type of Business: Chain Restaurant Operator
Year Founded: 1991
Total Sales: $7,528,000 (e)
Alcohol Sales: 25%
Number of Employees: 250
Average Check: Lunch(10); Dinner(16)
Total Units: 4
Trade Names: Grill 225 (1); Key West Grill Broadway at the Beach (1); Pavilion Bar & Cafe (1); Trotters Restaurant (1)
Company-Owned Units: 4
Preferred Location Types: Freestanding
Alcohol Served: Beer, Wine, Liquor
Primary Menu: American (4)
Areas of Operation: SC
Type of Foodservice: Casual Dining (4)
Catering Services: Yes
Primary Distributors: (Full Line) US Foods, LEXINGTON, SC

Key Personnel
JIM PALASSIS - CEO; Owner; Executive Chef; General Buyer
THERESA FRENCH - Controller
PETER REID - General Manager
STEVEN CLARK - Director Sales
ELAINA ENGLAND - Director Operations, Catering
JOHN MOORE - Manager Food and Beverage
RONNIE SILVA - Manager Food and Beverage; Buyer Beverages

Rodney Scott's Whole Hog Barbecue
1011 King St
Charleston, SC 29403

Telephone: (843) 990-9535
Internet Homepage: rodneyscottsbbq.com
Type of Business: Chain Restaurant Operator
Year Founded: 2017
Total Sales: $4,881,000 (e)
Total Units: 5
Trade Names: Rodney Scott's Whole Hog Barbecue (5)
Company-Owned Units: 5
Primary Menu: Bar-B-Q (5)
Areas of Operation: AL, GA, SC, TN
Type of Foodservice: Casual Dining (5)

Key Personnel
NICK PIHAKIS - Founder
RODNEY SCOTT - Founder; CEO; Partner
TYLER ASHTON - Partner; COO

Calhoun Management Corporation
108 Elm St
Clemson, SC 29631 1013

Mailing Address: PO Box 1767, CLEMSON, SC, 29633-1767
Telephone: (864) 624-9962
Fax Number: (864) 624-9963
Type of Business: Chain Restaurant Operator
Total Sales: $81,540,000 (e)
Total Units: 30
Trade Names: Wendy's Old Fashioned Hamburgers (30)
Units Franchised From: 30
Primary Menu: Hamburger (30)
Areas of Operation: GA, NC, SC
Type of Foodservice: Quick Serve (30)
Franchise Affiliation: The Wendy's Company,

DUBLIN, OH

Key Personnel
PICKENS M. LINDSAY - President; General Buyer
SHERMAN CHRISTENSEN - CFO
TIM BAUMAN - District Manager
TERESA WELDON - Manager

Estimated Profit, LLC
391 College Ave
Clemson, SC 29631-2929

Telephone: (864) 654-6630
Type of Business: Chain Restaurant Operator
Total Sales: $13,290,000 (e)
Total Units: 8
Trade Names: Moe's Southwest Grill (8)
Units Franchised From: 8
Primary Menu: Southwest/Tex-Mex (8)
Areas of Operation: SC
Type of Foodservice: Fast Casual (8)
Franchise Affiliation: Moe's Southwest Grill LLC, ATLANTA, GA

Key Personnel
STEVE SMITH - Owner; General Buyer

Groucho's Franchise System, LLC
611 Harden St
Columbia, SC 29205-2214

Telephone: (803) 799-9867
Fax Number: (803) 799-2297
Internet Homepage: grouchos.com
Company Email: info@grouchos.com
Type of Business: Chain Restaurant Operator
Year Founded: 1941
Total Sales: $20,000,000 (e)
Average Check: Dinner(12)
Internet Order Processing: Yes
Total Units: 32
Trade Names: Groucho's Deli (32)
Company-Owned Units: 32
Primary Menu: Sandwiches/Deli (32)
Projected Openings: 1
Areas of Operation: NC, SC
Type of Foodservice: Quick Serve (32)
Catering Services: Yes

Key Personnel
BRUCE MILLER - President; Owner; Executive Chef; General Buyer
CINDY SUTTON - Director Franchise Development

J-Ray, Inc
107 Burmaster Dr
Columbia, SC 29229-4352

Telephone: (803) 462-6103
Fax Number: (803) 462-6160
Type of Business: Chain Restaurant Operator
Total Sales: $116,150,000 (e)
Total Units: 25
Trade Names: McDonald's (25)
Units Franchised From: 25
Primary Menu: Hamburger (25)
Areas of Operation: SC
Type of Foodservice: Quick Serve (25)
Franchise Affiliation: McDonald's Corporation, CHICAGO, IL

Key Personnel
ROBERT VALDES - President; General Buyer

Lizard's Thicket Inc.
1036 Market St
Columbia, SC 29201-4741

Telephone: (803) 799-5016
Fax Number: (803) 799-2512
Internet Homepage: lizardsthicket.com
Company Email: customerservice@lizardsthicket.com
Type of Business: Chain Restaurant Operator
Year Founded: 1977
Total Sales: $41,935,000 (e)
Number of Employees: 700
Average Check: Breakfast(6); Lunch(8); Dinner(8)
Internet Order Processing: Yes
Total Units: 15
Trade Names: Lizard's Thicket (15)
Company-Owned Units: 15
Preferred Square Footage: 6,000
Preferred Location Types: Freestanding
Primary Menu: Southern (15)
Areas of Operation: SC
Type of Foodservice: Family Restaurant (15)
Catering Services: Yes
Primary Distributors: (Full Line) SYSCO Food Services of Columbia, COLUMBIA, SC

Key Personnel
JOHN WILLIAMS - Exec VP
SARA WENTZ-KRISNOW - Manager Communications

Sensor Enterprises, Inc.
3924 Forest Dr Ste 12
Columbia, SC 29204-4148

Telephone: (803) 787-6647
Fax Number: (803) 787-7245
Internet Homepage: sensorenterprises.com
Type of Business: Chain Restaurant Operator
Total Sales: $65,520,000 (e)
Number of Employees: 323
Total Units: 14
Trade Names: McDonald's (14)
Units Franchised From: 14
Preferred Square Footage: 2,500
Preferred Location Types: Freestanding
Primary Menu: Hamburger (14)
Areas of Operation: SC
Type of Foodservice: Quick Serve (14)
Franchise Affiliation: McDonald's Corporation, CHICAGO, IL

Key Personnel
GEORGE SENSOR - President; General Buyer
LAURIE BUNN - Controller
ROLAND TUCKER - Director Human Resources; Manager Accounting
MIKE PIPPIN - Supervisor Operations

Sonic Irons Group
5623 Fairfield Rd
Columbia, SC 29203-3304

Telephone: (803) 714-9888
Fax Number: (803) 714-7849
Type of Business: Chain Restaurant Operator
Year Founded: 1990
Total Sales: $180,170,000 (e)
Number of Employees: 2,750
Average Check: Lunch(8); Dinner(10)
Total Units: 84
Trade Names: Sonic Drive Inn (84)
Units Franchised From: 84
Preferred Square Footage: 1,100
Preferred Location Types: Freestanding
Primary Menu: Hamburger (84)
Projected Openings: 20
Areas of Operation: AL, GA, SC
Type of Foodservice: Quick Serve (84)
Primary Distributors: (Full Line) US Foods, FORT MILL, SC

Key Personnel
MIKE IRONS - President; COO
BARBARA IRONS - Corporate Secretary
ELI MASSEY - Controller
SUTTON SHAW - Director Marketing
BECCA MILLS - Director Accounting
DEBI WILBURN - Manager Accounting

Sub Station II Inc.
1237 Gadsden St Ste 100
Columbia, SC 29201

Telephone: (803) 831-3007
Internet Homepage: substationii.com
Company Email: info@substationii.com
Type of Business: Chain Restaurant Operator

Year Founded: 1975
Systemwide Sales: $55,728,000 (e)
Total Sales: $1,087,000 (e)
Alcohol Sales: 1%
Number of Employees: 500
Average Check: Lunch(14); Dinner(14)
Internet Order Processing: Yes
Total Units: 43
Trade Names: Sub Station II (43)
Company-Owned Units: 1
Units Franchised To: 42
Preferred Square Footage: 1,500
Preferred Location Types: Freestanding; Strip Mall
Primary Menu: Sandwiches/Deli (43)
Projected Openings: 2
Projected Remodelings: 2
Areas of Operation: GA, KY, NC, SC, TN, VA
Type of Foodservice: Quick Serve (43)
Catering Services: Yes

Key Personnel
SANDRA CORBETT - President; Director Human Resources; Manager Marketing, Catering
SUSAN R. OWENS - VP Purchasing
TRIPP CRAVER - Director Operations
ALISON CORBETT - Director Development

Subway Franchisee
9153 Two Notch Rd
Columbia, SC 29223-5852

Telephone: (803) 788-8514
Type of Business: Chain Restaurant Operator
Total Sales: $1,406,000 (e)
Total Units: 2
Trade Names: Subway (2)
Units Franchised From: 2
Areas of Operation: SC
Franchise Affiliation: Doctor's Associates Inc., MILFORD, CT

Key Personnel
SWETANG PATEL - Owner; General Buyer

Yamato Steak House of Japan
360 Columbiana Dr
Columbia, SC 29212-2252

Telephone: (803) 407-0033
Fax Number: (803) 407-8024
Internet Homepage: yamatoinc.com
Company Email: cola@yamatoinc.com
Type of Business: Chain Restaurant Operator
Year Founded: 1975
Total Sales: $4,535,000 (e)
Alcohol Sales: 20%
Number of Employees: 125
Average Check: Lunch(14); Dinner(22)
Total Units: 2
Trade Names: Yamato Seafood Steak and Sushi (2)
Company-Owned Units: 2
Preferred Location Types: Freestanding; Lifestyle Center
Alcohol Served: Beer, Wine, Liquor
Primary Menu: Steak/Seafood (2)
Areas of Operation: SC
Type of Foodservice: Casual Dining (2)
Primary Distributors: (Food) US Foods, LEXINGTON, SC

Key Personnel
SOOKIE HARRIS - President; Director Food and Beverage; General Buyer
SOO KNOESTER - General Manager; General Buyer

Two Lads, Inc.
2676 Church St Unit B
Conway, SC 29526-4471

Telephone: (843) 365-6453
Type of Business: Chain Restaurant Operator
Total Sales: $5,782,000 (e)
Total Units: 4
Trade Names: Jersey Mike's Subs (4)
Units Franchised From: 4
Primary Menu: Sandwiches/Deli (4)
Areas of Operation: SC
Type of Foodservice: Quick Serve (4)
Franchise Affiliation: Jersey Mike's Franchise Systems, MANASQUAN, NJ

Key Personnel
J. KEVIN SATTERFIELD - Owner; General Buyer

Amin Taha
700 E Main St
Duncan, SC 29334-9149

Telephone: (864) 439-7305
Type of Business: Chain Restaurant Operator
Total Sales: $1,674,000 (e)
Total Units: 3
Trade Names: Subway (3)
Units Franchised From: 3
Primary Menu: Sandwiches/Deli (3)
Areas of Operation: SC
Type of Foodservice: Quick Serve (3)
Franchise Affiliation: Doctor's Associates Inc., MILFORD, CT

Key Personnel
AMIN TAHA - President; Owner; General Buyer

The Butcher-The Baker Management Co. Inc.
160 Congress Blvd Ste C
Duncan, SC 29334-8890

Telephone: (864) 433-0345
Fax Number: (864) 433-0452
Internet Homepage: myfuddruckers.com
Type of Business: Chain Restaurant Operator
Total Sales: $16,320,000 (e)
Alcohol Sales: 10%
Number of Employees: 168
Average Check: Lunch(10); Dinner(14)
Internet Order Processing: Yes
Total Units: 8
Trade Names: Fuddruckers (8)
Units Franchised From: 8
Preferred Square Footage: 500; 4,200; 9,000
Preferred Location Types: Downtown; Freestanding; Strip Mall
Alcohol Served: Beer, Wine
Primary Menu: Hamburger (8)
Areas of Operation: NC, SC, TN
Type of Foodservice: Casual Dining (8)
Franchise Affiliation: Fuddruckers Restaurants LLC, HOUSTON, TX
Primary Distributors: (Full Line) US Foods, FORT MILL, SC

Key Personnel
ALLEN JOHNSTON - Partner; General Manager; Director Menu Development; General Buyer
LEE ANN JOHNSTON - Partner; Manager Operations, Marketing

Goecker Enterprises Inc
1304 E Main St Ste B
Easley, SC 29640-4204

Telephone: (864) 855-4521
Fax Number: (864) 855-5881
Type of Business: Chain Restaurant Operator
Total Sales: $19,939,000 (e)
Total Units: 4
Trade Names: McDonald's (4)
Units Franchised From: 4
Preferred Location Types: Convenience Store/Gas Station; Freestanding
Primary Menu: Hamburger (4)
Projected Remodelings: 1
Areas of Operation: SC
Type of Foodservice: Quick Serve (4)
Franchise Affiliation: McDonald's Corporation, CHICAGO, IL

Key Personnel
LOUIS GOECKER - President; General Buyer

CTK Pizza, LLC
1415 Jackson Ave
Florence, SC 29501-4522

Telephone: (843) 260-5574
Type of Business: Chain Restaurant Operator
Total Sales: $7,377,000 (e)
Total Units: 6
Trade Names: Little Caesars Pizza (6)
Units Franchised From: 6
Primary Menu: Pizza (6)
Areas of Operation: SC
Type of Foodservice: Quick Serve (6)
Franchise Affiliation: Little Caesar Enterprises Inc., DETROIT, MI

Key Personnel
OTIS KELLY - Owner; General Buyer

Domino's Franchisee
500 Pamplico Hwy Ste E
Florence, SC 29505-6051

Telephone: (843) 292-0499
Type of Business: Chain Restaurant Operator
Total Sales: $56,173,000 (e)
Total Units: 28
Trade Names: Domino's (28)
Units Franchised From: 28
Primary Menu: Pizza (28)
Projected Openings: 2
Areas of Operation: SC, TN
Type of Foodservice: Quick Serve (28)
Franchise Affiliation: Domino's Pizza Inc, ANN ARBOR, MI

Key Personnel
AARON A. FOX - Owner; General Buyer

Hoff Enterprises
2014 S Irby St
Florence, SC 29505

Telephone: (843) 662-3545
Type of Business: Chain Restaurant Operator
Total Sales: $33,250,000 (e)
Total Units: 7
Trade Names: McDonald's (7)
Units Franchised From: 7
Primary Menu: Hamburger (7)
Areas of Operation: SC
Type of Foodservice: Quick Serve (7)
Franchise Affiliation: McDonald's Corporation, CHICAGO, IL

Key Personnel
KURT FREIDHOFF - President
RICHARD HOFF - Owner; General Buyer

JAYANN CHRISTIANA - CFO

JB Restaurants Inc.
1816 Wall St
Florence, SC 29501-6902

Telephone: (843) 662-0728
Type of Business: Chain Restaurant Operator
Total Sales: $63,630,000 (e)
Average Check: Dinner(12)
Total Units: 18
Trade Names: Zaxby's (18)
Units Franchised From: 18
Primary Menu: Chicken (18)
Areas of Operation: SC
Type of Foodservice: Fast Casual (18)
Franchise Affiliation: Zaxby's Franchising Inc., ATHENS, GA

Key Personnel
BRITT T. POSTON - President; General Buyer

JBC Inc.
1816 Wall St
Florence, SC 29501-6902

Telephone: (843) 662-0728
Type of Business: Chain Restaurant Operator
Total Sales: $7,584,000 (e)
Total Units: 2
Trade Names: Zaxby's (2)
Units Franchised From: 2
Primary Menu: Chicken (2)
Areas of Operation: SC
Type of Foodservice: Fast Casual (2)
Franchise Affiliation: Zaxby's Franchising Inc., ATHENS, GA

Key Personnel
BRITT T. POSTON - President
RACHEL VIEIRA - VP
JACKIE PIAZZA - VP Talent, Talent Acquisitions
SAMANTHA MASSA FARBER - VP Talent
TARA GIANNOLLA - VP Talent, Talent Acquisitions
LUCILLE WILLIAMS - Senior Director
ERICA ZUCKER - Senior Director Talent, Talent Acquisitions
LAURA BURNS - Director Talent
LAURA PARKER - Associate Director Business Development
PAHOLA DE SOUZA DAY - Senior Manager Talent, Talent Acquisitions
KATHERINE SAVARESE - Manager Sales
SOPHIE HUTCHINSON - Manager Marketing, Social Media
JANIL BRAVO - Manager Talent, Talent Acquisitions
JORDAN STRAUSS - Manager Talent
MICHAEL MEADE - Manager Talent, Talent

Acquisitions

Motel Associates Inc.
2004 W Lucas St
Florence, SC 29501-1203

Mailing Address: PO Box 1031, FLORENCE, SC, 29503-1031
Telephone: (843) 669-3232
Fax Number: (843) 667-8198
Internet Homepage: thunderbirdgolf.com
Company Email: mail@thunderbirdgolf.com
Type of Business: Foodservice Operations - Hotel/Motels
Year Founded: 1964
Total Sales: $13,170,000 (e)
Alcohol Sales: 20%
Number of Employees: 175
Total Units: 1
Restaurants in Hotels: 2
Trade Names: Thunderbird Inn (1)
Company-Owned Units: 2
Alcohol Served: Beer, Wine, Liquor
Areas of Operation: SC
Type of Foodservice: Casual Dining (1); Family Restaurant (1)
Primary Distributors: (Food) SYSCO Food Services of Louisville, LOUISVILLE, KY
Notes: The company derives approximately 80% of its revenue from hotel operations.

Key Personnel
FRANK M. ROGERS IV - CEO; President; Director Finance, Real Estate, Menu Development

Bill Mason Enterprises
844 Chesnee Hwy
Gaffney, SC 29341-3410

Mailing Address: PO Box 66, GAFFNEY, SC, 29342-0066
Telephone: (864) 489-3900
Type of Business: Chain Restaurant Operator
Total Sales: $15,028,000 (e)
Total Units: 3
Trade Names: McDonald's (3)
Units Franchised From: 3
Preferred Square Footage: 2,500
Primary Menu: Hamburger (3)
Areas of Operation: SC
Type of Foodservice: Quick Serve (3)
Franchise Affiliation: McDonald's Corporation, CHICAGO, IL

Key Personnel
SHERRY WRIGHT - President; General Buyer

Alex's Restaurants Inc.
132 Saint James Ave
Goose Creek, SC 29445

Telephone: (843) 553-3325
Internet Homepage: alexsrestaurants.com
Type of Business: Chain Restaurant Operator
Year Founded: 1973
Total Sales: $5,359,000 (e)
Number of Employees: 160
Average Check: Breakfast(8); Lunch(10); Dinner(14)
Total Units: 2
Trade Names: Alex's of Summerville (1); Alex's Restaurant (1)
Company-Owned Units: 2
Preferred Square Footage: 3,000; 6,000
Preferred Location Types: Freestanding; Office Complex; Strip Mall
Primary Menu: American (2)
Areas of Operation: SC
Type of Foodservice: Family Restaurant (2)
Distribution Centers: MOUNT PLEASANT, SC
Primary Distributors: (Full Line) US Foods, LEXINGTON, SC

Key Personnel
CAROLYN BILLIPS - President; Controller; Executive Chef; Director Purchasing, Supply Chain, Real Estate, Design, Store Planning; General Buyer

† Canteen Vending Services
205 Woods Lake Rd
Greenville, SC 29607-2739

Telephone: (864) 288-1133
Fax Number: (864) 288-9863
Listing Type: Regional Office
Type of Business: Foodservice Management Operator
Year Founded: 1929
Number of Employees: 800
Number of Locations Served: 173
Total Foodservice Mgmt Accounts: 508
Areas of Operation: SC
Type of Foodservice: Cafeteria (108); Vending machines (400)
Foodservice Management Venues: Business & Industry; College & University; Health Care; Lodging; Schools; Transportation
Parent Company: Compass Group The Americas, CHARLOTTE, NC
Headquarters: Canteen Vending Services, CHARLOTTE, NC

Key Personnel
MIKE SEXTON - Director Purchasing; Manager Warehouse

Culinary Institute of the Carolinas At Greenville
8109 White Horse Rd
Greenville, SC 29617-1835

Telephone: (864) 250-3671
Fax Number: (864) 246-7534
Internet Homepage: gvltec.edu
Type of Business: Culinary Schools
Areas of Operation: SC

Key Personnel
KEITH MILLER - President; General Buyer
ALAN J. SCHEIDHAUER - Executive Chef

●▲ Esbenshade, Inc
700 Haywood Rd Spc 2020A
Greenville, SC 29607-2781

Telephone: (864) 284-0577
Type of Business: Chain Restaurant Operator
Total Sales: $1,549,000 (e)
Total Units: 2
Trade Names: Auntie Anne's Hand-Rolled Soft Pretzels (2)
Units Franchised From: 2
Primary Menu: Snacks (2)
Areas of Operation: SC
Type of Foodservice: Quick Serve (2)
Franchise Affiliation: Auntie Anne's Inc., LANCASTER, PA

Key Personnel
GREGORY ESBENSHADE - Owner; General Buyer

●▲ F F & A
939 N Pleasantburg Dr
Greenville, SC 29607-1626

Telephone: (864) 235-4224
Type of Business: Chain Restaurant Operator
Total Sales: $1,525,000 (e)
Average Check: Dinner(14)
Total Units: 2
Trade Names: Subway (2)
Units Franchised From: 2
Primary Menu: Sandwiches/Deli (2)
Areas of Operation: SC
Type of Foodservice: Quick Serve (2)
Franchise Affiliation: Doctor's Associates Inc., MILFORD, CT

Key Personnel
DAVOOD BAGHEROS - President; General Buyer

●▲ Goldsmith Development, Inc.
PO Box 8757
Greenville, SC 29604-8757

Telephone: (864) 363-5620
Type of Business: Chain Restaurant Operator
Total Sales: $5,728,000 (e)
Number of Employees: 80
Total Units: 5
Trade Names: Firehouse Subs (5)
Units Franchised From: 5
Preferred Square Footage: 1,500
Preferred Location Types: Strip Mall
Primary Menu: Sandwiches/Deli (5)
Areas of Operation: SC
Type of Foodservice: Fast Casual (5)
Franchise Affiliation: Firehouse Restaurant Group Inc., JACKSONVILLE, FL

Key Personnel
ELLIOTT GOLDSMITH - President; General Buyer

●▲ Perfect Delivery Inc.
401 Vardry St
Greenville, SC 29601-3307

Telephone: (864) 627-7272
Fax Number: (864) 987-7272
Internet Homepage: papajohns.com
Type of Business: Chain Restaurant Operator
Year Founded: 1992
Total Sales: $20,510,000 (e)
Number of Employees: 450
Average Check: Lunch(16); Dinner(26)
Internet Order Processing: Yes
Total Units: 15
Trade Names: Papa John's Pizza (15)
Units Franchised From: 15
Preferred Square Footage: 1,100; 1,500
Preferred Location Types: Convenience Store/Gas Station; Strip Mall
Primary Menu: Pizza (15)
Areas of Operation: NC, SC
Type of Foodservice: Quick Serve (15)
Foodservice Management Venues: Business & Industry; College & University; Schools
Catering Services: Yes
Franchise Affiliation: Papa Johns International Inc., LOUISVILLE, KY

Key Personnel
RENEE FAUCETTE - Controller
CARMEN HARDY - General Manager
DAVID KUCINSKI - Manager
ANNA BLAIR CAMERON - Manager Marketing
DANA PEACE - Head Pharmacist Purchasing

Sasaki Sogyo USA Inc.
533 Haywood Rd
Greenville, SC 29607-2710

Telephone: (864) 234-0334
Fax Number: (864) 234-0165
Internet Homepage: kanpaioftokyo.com
Type of Business: Chain Restaurant Operator
Year Founded: 1990
Total Sales: $2,704,000 (e)
Alcohol Sales: 5%
Number of Employees: 200
Average Check: Dinner(26)
Total Units: 3
Trade Names: Kanpai of Tokyo (3)
Company-Owned Units: 3
Preferred Square Footage: 1,200
Preferred Location Types: Freestanding
Alcohol Served: Beer, Wine, Liquor
Primary Menu: Japanese (3)
Areas of Operation: SC
Type of Foodservice: Casual Dining (3)

Key Personnel
SATOSHI POWELL - President; General Manager; Executive Chef; Manager Operations, Purchasing, Facility/Maintenance, Supply Chain, Human Resources; General Buyer

Southeast Jack, Inc.
1106 N Pleasantburg Dr
Greenville, SC 29607-1223

Telephone: (864) 609-0019
Type of Business: Chain Restaurant Operator
Total Sales: $74,360,000 (e)
Total Units: 29
Trade Names: Jack in the Box (29)
Units Franchised From: 29
Primary Menu: Hamburger (29)
Areas of Operation: SC
Type of Foodservice: Quick Serve (29)
Franchise Affiliation: Jack in the Box Restaurants, SAN DIEGO, CA

Key Personnel
WASEEM KHAN - Owner; General Buyer

Table 301
207 S Main St
Greenville, SC 29601-2831

Telephone: (864) 232-7007
Fax Number: (864) 232-5282
Internet Homepage:
southernpressedjuicery.com; sobys.com; table301.com
Company Email: contact@sobys.com
Type of Business: Chain Restaurant Operator
Total Sales: $17,090,000 (e)
Alcohol Sales: 20%
Number of Employees: 70
Average Check: Breakfast(8); Lunch(10); Dinner(32)
Total Units: 7
Trade Names: Jianna (1); Passerelle (1); Soby's (1); Table 301 (1); The Lazy Goat (1); The Nose Dive (1); The Southern Pressed Juicery (1)
Company-Owned Units: 8
Preferred Location Types: Freestanding
Alcohol Served: Beer, Wine, Liquor
Primary Menu: American (2); French/Continental (1); Greek/Mediterranean (1); Italian (1); Miscellaneous (1); Southern (1)
Areas of Operation: SC
Type of Foodservice: Casual Dining (5); Fine Dining (1); Quick Serve (1)
Catering Services: Yes

Key Personnel
CARL SOBOCINSKI - President; Partner
RODNEY FRIEDANK - Partner; Corporate Chef; General Buyer
STEVE SEITZ - COO Operations; VP
PAM FALVEY - General Manager
JORGE BARALLES JR - General Manager
GINA BOULWARE - Director Marketing, Public Relations
ANGIE CORTNEY - Manager Customer Service
SHERRY DEES-MILLER - Manager Event Planning
KATIE GUPTILL-THOMPSON - Manager Marketing; Web Developer
EMILY MURRAY - Manager Event Planning
AVERY PORTER - Manager Sales
ANGIE FRANK - Manager Accounting
ANGELA TOTH - Manager Sales

Domino's Franchisee
217 W Wade Hampton Blvd Ste A
Greer, SC 29650-1667

Telephone: (864) 879-0111
Type of Business: Chain Restaurant Operator
Total Sales: $5,982,000 (e)
Total Units: 3
Trade Names: Domino's (3)
Units Franchised From: 3
Primary Menu: Pizza (3)
Areas of Operation: SC
Type of Foodservice: Quick Serve (3)
Franchise Affiliation: Domino's Pizza Inc, ANN ARBOR, MI

Key Personnel
EASAB SAEED - Owner; General Buyer

Sema Inc.
50 Parkway Commons Way
Greer, SC 29650-5213

Telephone: (864) 848-4150
Fax Number: (864) 848-9034
Type of Business: Chain Restaurant Operator
Year Founded: 1963
Total Sales: $16,180,000 (e)
Number of Employees: 190
Average Check: Breakfast(8); Lunch(8); Dinner(10)
Total Units: 7
Trade Names: Burger King (7)
Units Franchised From: 7
Preferred Square Footage: 2,500
Preferred Location Types: Freestanding
Primary Menu: Hamburger (7)
Areas of Operation: SC
Type of Foodservice: Quick Serve (7)
Franchise Affiliation: Burger King Worldwide Inc., MIAMI, FL
Primary Distributors: (Food) Reinhart FoodService, AUSTELL, GA

Key Personnel
LAWRENCE D. STOKES - President; Controller; Director Purchasing, Supply Chain, Real Estate
PERRY KELLETT - VP Operations, Information Systems, Risk Management, Marketing, Food Safety; General Buyer

Main Waters Enterprises
1505 Crescent Moon Cv
Hanahan, SC 29410-8579

Telephone: (843) 572-8989
Fax Number: (843) 820-9737
Type of Business: Chain Restaurant Operator
Year Founded: 1992
Total Sales: $14,724,000 (e)
Number of Employees: 180
Average Check: Breakfast(8); Lunch(8); Dinner(8)
Total Units: 3
Trade Names: McDonald's (3)
Units Franchised From: 3
Preferred Square Footage: 2,500; 3,000
Preferred Location Types: Freestanding
Primary Menu: Hamburger (3)
Areas of Operation: SC
Type of Foodservice: Quick Serve (3)
Franchise Affiliation: McDonald's Corporation, CHICAGO, IL
Primary Distributors: (Full Line) The Martin-Brower Co., LEXINGTON, SC

Key Personnel
EMORY MAIN - Partner; Manager Real Estate; General Buyer

DEWALL WATERS - Partner; Manager Information Systems; General Buyer

WBIsland, Inc.
430 William Hilton Pkwy STE 201
Hilton Head, SC 29926

Telephone: (843) 341-6800
Type of Business: Chain Restaurant Operator
Total Sales: $4,309,000 (e)
Total Units: 3
Trade Names: Jersey Mike's Subs (3)
Units Franchised From: 3
Primary Menu: Sandwiches/Deli (3)
Areas of Operation: SC
Type of Foodservice: Quick Serve (3)
Franchise Affiliation: Jersey Mike's Franchise Systems, MANASQUAN, NJ

Key Personnel
WILLIAM C. BROWN - Owner; General Buyer

Crazy Crab Associates
10 Office Way Ste 222
Hilton Head Island, SC 29928-4646

Telephone: (843) 686-6500
Fax Number: (843) 686-3041
Internet Homepage: thecrazycrab.com
Type of Business: Chain Restaurant Operator
Year Founded: 1980
Total Sales: $11,035,000 (e)
Alcohol Sales: 15%
Number of Employees: 220
Average Check: Lunch(16); Dinner(30)
Internet Order Processing: Yes
Total Units: 2
Trade Names: Crazy Crab (2)
Company-Owned Units: 2
Preferred Location Types: Community Mall; Freestanding
Alcohol Served: Beer, Wine, Liquor
Primary Menu: Seafood (2)
Areas of Operation: SC
Type of Foodservice: Casual Dining (2)
Primary Distributors: (Equipment) Restaurant Equipment Co. of Savannah, SAVANNAH, GA; (Supplies) Restaurant Equipment Co. of Savannah, SAVANNAH, GA

Key Personnel
PETER KENNEWEG - President; Partner; Executive Chef; Manager Operations; General Buyer
COURTNEY KENNEWEG - Partner; CFO
CHUCK LARSON - General Manager

SERG Restaurant Group
9 Hunter Rd Ste A
Hilton Head Island, SC 29926-3791

Mailing Address: PO Box 22851, Hilton Head Island, SC, 29925
Telephone: (843) 715-0344
Internet Homepage: serggroup.com
Company Email: serg@serggroup.com
Type of Business: Chain Restaurant Operator
Year Founded: 1984
Total Units: 13
Trade Names: Frankie Bones (1); Giuseppi's Pizza & Pasta (2); Marley's Island Grill (1); Marleys Shrimp Shack (1); One Hot Mama's (1); Poseidon (1); Rooftop Bar (1); Skull Creek Boathouse (1); Skull Ctreek Dockside (1); The Black Marlin (1); The Lodge (1); Wise Guys (1)
Company-Owned Units: 13
Primary Menu: American (2); Bar-B-Q (1); Hamburger (2); Italian (2); Seafood (4); Steak (1); Steak/Seafood (1)
Projected Openings: 1
Areas of Operation: SC

Key Personnel
STEVE CARB - President; Partner
PHILLIP LECLAIRE - Partner
JORDAN NORRIS - Manager Operations
CARY WELKER - Manager Operations

The Old Oyster Factory
101 Marshland Rd
Hilton Head Island, SC 29926-2306

Mailing Address: PO BOX 7547, Hilton Head Island, SC, 29938-2306
Telephone: (843) 342-2762
Fax Number: (843) 681-6418
Internet Homepage: oldoysterfactory.com; redfishofhiltonhead.com
Type of Business: Chain Restaurant Operator
Year Founded: 1979
Total Sales: $12,441,000 (e)
Alcohol Sales: 20%
Number of Employees: 200
Average Check: Lunch(42); Dinner(50)
Total Units: 2
Trade Names: Old Oyster Factory (1); The Red Fish (1)
Company-Owned Units: 2
Preferred Location Types: Freestanding
Alcohol Served: Beer, Wine, Liquor
Primary Menu: Seafood (2)
Areas of Operation: SC
Type of Foodservice: Casual Dining (2)
Primary Distributors: (Food) SYSCO Food Services of Columbia, COLUMBIA, SC

Key Personnel
RICK PETERSON - Partner; General Manager

DeVille Foods Inc.
1042 Lake Murray Blvd
Irmo, SC 29063-2821

Telephone: (803) 732-0011
Fax Number: (803) 732-1366
Type of Business: Chain Restaurant Operator
Year Founded: 2000
Total Sales: $10,902,000 (e)
Number of Employees: 100
Average Check: Lunch(10); Dinner(12)
Total Units: 3
Trade Names: Zaxby's (3)
Units Franchised From: 3
Preferred Location Types: Freestanding
Primary Menu: Chicken (3)
Areas of Operation: SC
Type of Foodservice: Fast Casual (3)
Franchise Affiliation: Zaxby's Franchising Inc., ATHENS, GA
Primary Distributors: (Full Line) PFG - Customized South Carolina, ROCK HILL, SC

Key Personnel
JOE TURBVILLE - President; General Buyer
TINA PUSHIT - General Manager
CHRIS CHAIF - Manager Plant

Gilligan's Management Co.
160 Main Rd Ste A
Johns Island, SC 29455-3402

Telephone: (843) 763-2244
Fax Number: (843) 556-2244
Internet Homepage: gilligans.net
Company Email: marketing@gilligans.net
Type of Business: Chain Restaurant Operator
Year Founded: 1991
Total Sales: $11,490,000 (e)
Alcohol Sales: 15%
Number of Employees: 117
Average Check: Lunch(10); Dinner(18)
Internet Order Processing: Yes
Total Units: 6
Trade Names: Gilligan's Steamer and Raw Bar (6)
Company-Owned Units: 6
Preferred Location Types: Freestanding; Strip Mall
Alcohol Served: Beer, Wine, Liquor
Primary Menu: Seafood (6)
Areas of Operation: SC
Type of Foodservice: Casual Dining (6)

Key Personnel
DAN TOLBERT - General Manager

TASHA EADY - Director Marketing, Advertising

Kiawah Island Golf Resort
1 Sanctuary Beach Dr
Kiawah Island, SC 29455-5434

Telephone: (843) 768-2121
Fax Number: (843) 768-6054
Internet Homepage: kiawahresort.com
Company Email:
 reservation@kiawahresort.com
Type of Business: Foodservice Operations - Hotel/Motels
Year Founded: 1974
Total Sales: $66,671,000 (e)
Alcohol Sales: 20%
Number of Employees: 1,350
Total Units: 1
Restaurants in Hotels: 15
Trade Names: Kiawah Island Golf Resort (1)
Company-Owned Units: 15
Alcohol Served: Beer, Wine, Liquor
Areas of Operation: SC
Type of Foodservice: Casual Dining (14); Fine Dining (1)
Primary Distributors: (Food) SYSCO Food Services of Columbia, COLUMBIA, SC
Notes: The company derives approximately 65% of its revenue from hotel operations.

Key Personnel
BILL GOODWIN - Chairman; CEO
ROGER WARREN - President
BILL LACEY - General Manager
BOB HIRSCH - Director Facility/Maintenance
BARBARA STEELE - Director Operations
ROY BARTH - Director Group
JASON HASENBERG - Director
JERILYN KUTHE - Director
TERRY TREUTING - Director Catering
BRYAN HUNTER - Director Public Relations
YVONNE JOHNSON - Director Security, Safety
SARAH MORGAN - Director Human Resources

H and R Family Foods Inc
1145 Highway 9 Byp W
Lancaster, SC 29720

Telephone: (803) 283-8871
Type of Business: Chain Restaurant Operator
Total Sales: $4,054,000 (e)
Total Units: 6
Trade Names: Huddle House (6)
Units Franchised From: 6
Primary Menu: American (6)
Areas of Operation: SC
Type of Foodservice: Family Restaurant (6)
Franchise Affiliation: Huddle House Inc., ATLANTA, GA

Key Personnel
BILL WILKERSON - President; General Buyer

Fire Brigade Restaurant Group, Inc.
450 Ashley Oaks Dr
Moore, SC 29369-8705

Telephone: (864) 357-8952
Type of Business: Chain Restaurant Operator
Total Sales: $3,706,000 (e)
Total Units: 3
Trade Names: Firehouse Subs (3)
Units Franchised From: 3
Preferred Square Footage: 1,500
Primary Menu: Sandwiches/Deli (3)
Areas of Operation: SC
Type of Foodservice: Fast Casual (3)
Franchise Affiliation: Firehouse Restaurant Group Inc., JACKSONVILLE, FL

Key Personnel
IRAJ (OMAR) GHORBANI - Owner; General Buyer

Dog & Duck Family Pubs
624 Long Point Rd Unit A
Mount Pleasant, SC 29464-8283

Telephone: (843) 881-3056
Fax Number: (843) 881-2647
Internet Homepage: dogandduckfamilypubs.com
Company Email: dogduckmtp@yahoo.com
Type of Business: Chain Restaurant Operator
Year Founded: 2001
Total Sales: $3,149,000 (e)
Alcohol Sales: 42%
Number of Employees: 100
Average Check: Dinner(12)
Total Units: 2
Trade Names: Dog & Duck Food & Spirits (2)
Company-Owned Units: 2
Alcohol Served: Beer, Wine, Liquor
Primary Menu: American (2)
Areas of Operation: SC
Type of Foodservice: Casual Dining (2)
Catering Services: Yes
Primary Distributors: (Full Line) SYSCO Food Services of Columbia, COLUMBIA, SC

Key Personnel
ROD BRADLEY - Partner; General Buyer
ANDREW REED - Partner; Executive Chef

RPM Management Co.
1459 Stuart Engals Blvd Unit 202
Mount Pleasant, SC 29464-3600

Telephone: (843) 284-0257
Fax Number: (843) 284-0258
Internet Homepage: kickinchicken.com
Company Email: david@thekickinchicken.com
Type of Business: Chain Restaurant Operator
Year Founded: 1997
Total Sales: $4,498,000 (e)
Alcohol Sales: 3%
Number of Employees: 250
Average Check: Dinner(12)
Internet Order Processing: Yes
Internet Sales: 3.00%
Total Units: 6
Trade Names: The Kickin' Chicken (6)
Company-Owned Units: 6
Preferred Location Types: Freestanding; Strip Mall
Alcohol Served: Beer, Wine, Liquor
Primary Menu: Chicken (6)
Areas of Operation: SC
Type of Foodservice: Casual Dining (6)

Key Personnel
DAVID MILLER - Partner
BOBBY PERRY - Partner
CHIP ROBERTS - Partner; General Buyer
SYDNEY FERRARA - Director Marketing

The Bloomin Apple, LLC
1127 Queensborough Blvd Ste 201
Mount Pleasant, SC 29464-4589

Telephone: (843) 849-1877
Fax Number: (843) 849-1395
Company Email: jd@bloominapple.com
Type of Business: Chain Restaurant Operator
Year Founded: 2002
Total Sales: $78,760,000 (e)
Alcohol Sales: 10%
Number of Employees: 888
Average Check: Lunch(12); Dinner(16)
Internet Sales: 2.00%
Total Units: 20
Trade Names: Applebee's Neighborhood Grill & Bar (20)
Units Franchised From: 20
Preferred Square Footage: 5,000
Preferred Location Types: Freestanding
Alcohol Served: Beer, Wine, Liquor
Primary Menu: American (20)
Areas of Operation: IA, IL
Type of Foodservice: Casual Dining (20)
Franchise Affiliation: Applebee's Services Inc., KANSAS CITY, MO
Primary Distributors: (Food) US Foods, LEXINGTON, SC; (Food) Maines Paper & Food Service Maryland, SAVAGE, MD

Notes: The company also operates as The Bloomin' Apple LLC and Heartland Apple Inc.; total units reflects stores operated by all companies.

Key Personnel
KEVIN ALLARDICE - President; Director Facility/Maintenance, Real Estate, Store Fixtures
MARIANNE ALLARDICE - Partner; Controller; Manager Finance, Information Systems, Risk Management
MIKE BRENNAN - General Manager
JOANNE DRY - Director Marketing
KEVIN FREEPORT - Manager

King Street Grille
1136 Hungryneck Blvd
Mt Pleasant, SC 29464-3427

Telephone: (843) 216-7272
Internet Homepage: thekingstreetgrille.com
Type of Business: Chain Restaurant Operator
Year Founded: 2002
Total Sales: $4,932,000 (e)
Alcohol Sales: 15%
Number of Employees: 815
Average Check: Dinner(20)
Total Units: 4
Trade Names: King Street Grille (4)
Company-Owned Units: 4
Preferred Location Types: Freestanding; Strip Mall
Alcohol Served: Beer, Wine, Liquor
Primary Menu: American (4)
Areas of Operation: SC
Type of Foodservice: Casual Dining (4)
Primary Distributors: (Full Line) SYSCO Food Services of Columbia, COLUMBIA, SC

Key Personnel
SCOTT KIER - President; General Buyer

Sticky Fingers
311 Johnnie Dodds Blvd Ste 131
Mt Pleasant, SC 29464

Telephone: (843) 849-8495
Fax Number: (336) 714-1520
Internet Homepage: stickyfingers.com
Type of Business: Chain Restaurant Operator
Year Founded: 1992
Total Sales: $53,400,000 (e)
Alcohol Sales: 12%
Number of Employees: 1,065
Average Check: Lunch(10); Dinner(18)
Internet Order Processing: Yes
Internet Sales: 1.00%
Total Units: 12
Trade Names: Sticky Fingers Ribhouse (12)
Company-Owned Units: 12
Preferred Square Footage: 6,100
Preferred Location Types: Downtown; Freestanding
Alcohol Served: Beer, Wine, Liquor
Primary Menu: Bar-B-Q (12)
Areas of Operation: FL, NC, SC, TN
Type of Foodservice: Casual Dining (12)
Catering Services: Yes
Primary Distributors: (Food) US Foods, LEXINGTON, SC; (Supplies) US Foods, LEXINGTON, SC
Parent Company: RJD Management, WINSTON SALEM, NC
Notes: The company derives approximately 5% of its revenue from retail sales of its BBQ sauce.

Key Personnel
TODD EISCHEID - Partner; CFO
ANNA CARROLL - Manager Human Resources

Vicious Biscuit
409 W Coleman Blvd
Mt Pleasant, SC 29464

Telephone: (843) 388-7362
Internet Homepage: viciousbiscuit.com
Company Email: aparker@viciousbiscuit.com
Type of Business: Chain Restaurant Operator
Year Founded: 2018
Total Sales: $6,008,000 (e)
Total Units: 9
Trade Names: Vicious Biscuit (9)
Company-Owned Units: 9
Primary Menu: American (9)
Projected Openings: 5
Areas of Operation: FL, NC, SC
Type of Foodservice: Fast Casual (9)

Key Personnel
MICHAEL GREELEY - Co-Founder; Partner
GEORGE MCLAUGHLIN - Co-Founder; Partner
CAMERON CUMMINS - Director Franchising

Captain Johnny's
4037 Highway 17 Business
Murrells Inlet, SC 29576

Telephone: (843) 651-5850
Fax Number: (843) 651-8915
Internet Homepage: bubbasloveshak.com; catfishjohnnys.com; jpetersgrill.com
Type of Business: Chain Restaurant Operator
Year Founded: 1974
Total Sales: $15,960,000 (e)
Alcohol Sales: 15%
Number of Employees: 40
Average Check: Lunch(12); Dinner(22)
Total Units: 11
Trade Names: Bubba's Love Shak (1); Catfish Johnny's (2); J Peters Grill & Bar (8)
Company-Owned Units: 15
Preferred Location Types: Freestanding
Alcohol Served: Beer, Wine, Liquor
Primary Menu: American (8); Seafood (3)
Areas of Operation: SC
Type of Foodservice: Casual Dining (11)
Catering Services: Yes
Primary Distributors: (Food) US Foods, FORT MILL, SC

Key Personnel
JON ANGELL - Partner; General Buyer
RUSSELL GREEN - General Manager
ASHLEY JUSTICE - Manager Catering
PAMELA ANDERSON - Manager Finance

Divine Dining Group
2504 S Kings Hwy
Myrtle Beach, SC 29577-4814

Telephone: (843) 238-9381
Fax Number: (843) 238-5580
Internet Homepage: divinedininggroup.com
Company Email: info@divinedininggroup.com
Type of Business: Chain Restaurant Operator
Year Founded: 1989
Total Sales: $50,610,000 (e)
Alcohol Sales: 25%
Number of Employees: 890
Average Check: Lunch(22); Dinner(42)
Total Units: 17
Trade Names: Bubba's Fish Shack (1); Nacho Hippo Cantina (2); Pawley's Raw Bar (1); River City Cafe (7); Ultimate California Pizza (6)
Company-Owned Units: 17
Preferred Square Footage: 5,000
Preferred Location Types: Freestanding; Other; Strip Mall
Alcohol Served: Beer, Wine, Liquor
Primary Menu: American (8); Pizza (6); Seafood (1); Southwest/Tex-Mex (2)
Areas of Operation: SC
Type of Foodservice: Casual Dining (17)
Catering Services: Yes
Primary Distributors: (Food) US Foods, LEXINGTON, SC; (Supplies) US Foods, LEXINGTON, SC

Key Personnel
JACK S. DIVINE IV - President; Director Real Estate, Design
NATE ANDERSON - Senior VP; Director Purchasing, Design
JULIE DANIELS - Controller; Director Finance
DARREN LEIGH - General Manager
LUIZ NASCIMENTO - General Manager
APRIL BUFFKIN - Director Information Systems
THOMAS BASTIAN - Manager Restaurant Operations
TODD VAN GELUWE - Manager Area

Fireside Restaurant Company
1211 38th Ave N
Myrtle Beach, SC 29577-1313

Mailing Address: P.O. Box 50820, MYRTLE BEACH, SC, 29579-0014
Telephone: (843) 626-9111
Type of Business: Chain Restaurant Operator
Total Sales: $3,639,000 (e)
Total Units: 3
Trade Names: Firehouse Subs (3)
Units Franchised From: 3
Preferred Location Types: Strip Mall
Primary Menu: Sandwiches/Deli (3)
Areas of Operation: SC
Type of Foodservice: Fast Casual (3)
Franchise Affiliation: Firehouse Restaurant Group Inc., JACKSONVILLE, FL

Key Personnel
STEVEN DUNCAN - President; General Buyer

J & L Services
171 McDonald Ct
Myrtle Beach, SC 29588-6181

Telephone: (843) 293-3245
Fax Number: (843) 293-3411
Type of Business: Chain Restaurant Operator
Year Founded: 1985
Total Sales: $57,040,000 (e)
Number of Employees: 455
Average Check: Breakfast(8); Lunch(10); Dinner(10)
Total Units: 12
Trade Names: McDonald's (12)
Units Franchised From: 12
Preferred Square Footage: 3,000
Preferred Location Types: Freestanding
Primary Menu: Hamburger (12)
Areas of Operation: SC
Type of Foodservice: Quick Serve (12)
Franchise Affiliation: McDonald's Corporation, CHICAGO, IL
Primary Distributors: (Full Line) The Martin-Brower Co., LEXINGTON, SC

Key Personnel
JOEL PELLICCI SR - President; Partner; Director Finance, Operations, Information Systems, Real Estate
JOEL PELLICCI JR - Partner; General Manager; Director Facility/Maintenance, Human Resources; General Buyer
CARLON HAMADE - Director Operations
CHRISTY PELLICCI - Manager Accounting, Branch

J R of M B Inc
1216 Celebrity Cir
Myrtle Beach, SC 29577-7420

Mailing Address: PO Box 70339, MYRTLE BEACH, SC, 29572-0024
Telephone: (843) 448-8575
Type of Business: Chain Restaurant Operator
Total Sales: $3,637,000 (e)
Total Units: 2
Trade Names: Johnny Rockets (2)
Units Franchised From: 2
Primary Menu: Hamburger (2)
Areas of Operation: SC
Type of Foodservice: Family Restaurant (2)
Franchise Affiliation: The Johnny Rockets Group Inc., LAKE FOREST, CA

Key Personnel
DAVID SPANGLER - President; Partner; General Buyer
DAVID MACKENZIE - Partner
MIKE FELIPIC - Partner

Myrtle Beach Friends LLC
4705 N Kings Hwy
Myrtle Beach, SC 29577-2501

Telephone: (843) 497-6665
Fax Number: (843) 249-6775
Company Email: mbf.7319@gmail.com
Type of Business: Chain Restaurant Operator
Total Sales: $5,171,000 (e)
Total Units: 3
Trade Names: Friendly's (3)
Units Franchised From: 3
Primary Menu: American (3)
Areas of Operation: SC
Type of Foodservice: Family Restaurant (3)
Franchise Affiliation: FIC Restaurants, WILBRAHAM, MA

Key Personnel
JAMES SAKALIAN JR - Owner; General Buyer

Pellegrino & Sons LLC
1130 Celebrity Cir Unit 322E
Myrtle Beach, SC 29577-7422

Telephone: (843) 626-7801
Type of Business: Chain Restaurant Operator
Total Sales: $1,197,000 (e)
Total Units: 3
Trade Names: Cold Stone Creamery (3)
Units Franchised From: 3
Primary Menu: Snacks (3)
Areas of Operation: SC
Type of Foodservice: Quick Serve (3)
Franchise Affiliation: Kahala Brands, SCOTTSDALE, AZ

Key Personnel
DAVID PELLEGRINO - Partner
ELIZABETH PELLEGRINO - Partner

SA Restaurants Group, Inc.
102 Loyola Dr Ste B
Myrtle Beach, SC 29588-7736

Telephone: (843) 215-7880
Type of Business: Chain Restaurant Operator
Total Sales: $4,336,000 (e)
Total Units: 3
Trade Names: Jersey Mike's Subs (3)
Units Franchised From: 3
Primary Menu: Sandwiches/Deli (3)
Areas of Operation: SC
Type of Foodservice: Quick Serve (3)
Franchise Affiliation: Jersey Mike's Franchise Systems, MANASQUAN, NJ

Key Personnel
PHILIPPE SAAD - Owner; General Buyer

Southeast Restaurants Corp.
1621 Executive Ave
Myrtle Beach, SC 29577-6501

Mailing Address: PO Box 3677, MYRTLE BEACH, SC, 29578-3677
Telephone: (843) 448-2646
Fax Number: (843) 626-8613
Type of Business: Chain Restaurant Operator
Year Founded: 1988
Total Sales: $48,170,000 (e)
Alcohol Sales: 1%
Number of Employees: 1,300
Average Check: Lunch(16); Dinner(16)
Total Units: 39
Trade Names: Pizza Hut (39)
Units Franchised From: 39
Preferred Square Footage: 2,500
Preferred Location Types: Freestanding
Alcohol Served: Beer
Primary Menu: Pizza (39)
Areas of Operation: SC
Type of Foodservice: Quick Serve (39)
Franchise Affiliation: Pizza Hut Inc., PLANO, TX
Primary Distributors: (Equipment) QualServ Corporation, FORT SMITH, AR; (Food) McLane/Carolina, BATTLEBORO, NC; (Supplies) QualServ Corporation, FORT SMITH, AR

Key Personnel
RICK SEAGROVES - CEO; President
MIRANDIA BAXLEY - General Manager

Restaurant Operations

D & G Management
PO Box 6217
North Augusta, SC 29861-6217

Telephone: (803) 279-2820
Type of Business: Chain Restaurant Operator
Total Sales: $10,011,000 (e)
Number of Employees: 40
Total Units: 2
Trade Names: McDonald's (2)
Units Franchised From: 2
Preferred Square Footage: 2,500
Primary Menu: Hamburger (2)
Areas of Operation: GA, SC
Type of Foodservice: Quick Serve (2)
Franchise Affiliation: McDonald's Corporation, CHICAGO, IL

Key Personnel
DELORES CRAWFORD - President; General Buyer

Wife Saver Inc.
414 E Martintown Rd
North Augusta, SC 29841-4263

Telephone: (803) 279-1446
Internet Homepage: wifesaverrestaurants.com
Type of Business: Chain Restaurant Operator
Year Founded: 1965
Systemwide Sales: $8,708,000 (e)
Total Sales: $703,000 (e)
Number of Employees: 80
Average Check: Lunch(8); Dinner(10)
Total Units: 5
Trade Names: Fury's Ferry (1); Wife Saver (4)
Units Franchised To: 5
Preferred Square Footage: 3,000
Preferred Location Types: Freestanding
Primary Menu: Chicken (5)
Areas of Operation: GA, SC
Type of Foodservice: Family Restaurant (5)
Catering Services: Yes
Primary Distributors: (Equipment) Norvell Fixture & Equipment Co. Inc., GROVETOWN, GA; (Supplies) Norvell Fixture & Equipment Co. Inc., GROVETOWN, GA

Key Personnel
CHRIS CUNNINGHAM - President; Owner; Controller; Executive Chef; Director Information Systems, Real Estate, Design, Catering; General Buyer
TED GODFREY - Owner

Capital Fast Foods, Ltd
3875 Faber Place Dr Ste 201
North Charleston, SC 29405-8558

Telephone: (843) 202-0033
Fax Number: (800) 878-5081
Type of Business: Chain Restaurant Operator
Total Sales: $58,140,000 (e)
Total Units: 26
Trade Names: Burger King (26)
Units Franchised From: 26
Primary Menu: Hamburger (26)
Areas of Operation: TX
Type of Foodservice: Quick Serve (26)
Franchise Affiliation: Burger King Worldwide Inc., MIAMI, FL

Key Personnel
DARRYL BERRY - CEO
NANCY RITCHIE - General Manager
DAVID ALLEN - General Manager

Culinary Institute of Charleston
7000 Rivers Ave
North Charleston, SC 29406-4607

Telephone: (843) 574-6111
Internet Homepage: tridenttech.edu
Type of Business: Culinary Schools
Areas of Operation: SC

Key Personnel
MARY THORNLEY - President; General Buyer
MICHAEL CARMEL - Director Culinary Operations

Ochlocknee Ventures, LLC
7800 Rivers Ave Ste 1020
North Charleston, SC 29406-4055

Telephone: (843) 569-0688
Type of Business: Chain Restaurant Operator
Total Sales: $9,950,000 (e)
Total Units: 6
Trade Names: Moe's Southwest Grill (6)
Units Franchised From: 6
Primary Menu: Southwest/Tex-Mex (6)
Areas of Operation: SC
Type of Foodservice: Fast Casual (6)
Franchise Affiliation: Moe's Southwest Grill LLC, ATLANTA, GA

Key Personnel
CARY CHASTAIN - Owner; General Buyer

Second Alarm Restaurant Group, Inc.
7250 Rivers Ave
North Charleston, SC 29406-4625

Telephone: (843) 532-1516
Type of Business: Chain Restaurant Operator
Total Sales: $3,745,000 (e)
Total Units: 3
Trade Names: Firehouse Subs (3)
Company-Owned Units: 3
Preferred Square Footage: 1,500
Preferred Location Types: Freestanding; Strip Mall
Primary Menu: Sandwiches/Deli (3)
Areas of Operation: SC
Type of Foodservice: Fast Casual (3)
Franchise Affiliation: Firehouse Restaurant Group Inc., JACKSONVILLE, FL

Key Personnel
KEVIN HATTON - President; General Buyer

Eggs Up Grill
115 Willbrook Blvd Unit L
Pawleys Island, SC 29585-6542

Telephone: (864) 310-2400
Internet Homepage: eggsupgrill.com
Company Email: info@eggsupgrill.com
Type of Business: Chain Restaurant Operator
Year Founded: 1997
Systemwide Sales: $37,019,000 (e)
Total Sales: $20,500,000 (e)
Number of Employees: 56
Average Check: Breakfast(8); Lunch(8);
Total Units: 42
Trade Names: Eggs Up Grill (42)
Units Franchised To: 42
Preferred Location Types: Freestanding
Primary Menu: American (42)
Projected Openings: 9
Areas of Operation: AL, FL, GA, KY, LA, MS, NC, SC, TN
Type of Foodservice: Family Restaurant (42)
Catering Services: Yes
Primary Distributors: (Full Line) SYSCO Food Services of Columbia, COLUMBIA, SC

Key Personnel
RICKY RICHARDSON - CEO
TIM EATON - Senior Director Development
CHRISTOPHER BAILEY - Director Franchise Development

Domino's Franchisee
102 E Main St
Pickens, SC 29671-2320

Telephone: (864) 878-0833
Type of Business: Chain Restaurant Operator
Total Sales: $4,132,000 (e)
Total Units: 2
Trade Names: Domino's (2)
Units Franchised From: 2
Primary Menu: Pizza (2)
Areas of Operation: SC
Type of Foodservice: Quick Serve (2)
Franchise Affiliation: Domino's Pizza Inc, ANN ARBOR, MI

Key Personnel
JOHN P. DERHAM - Partner; General Buyer
ALLEN DERHAM - Partner; General Buyer

First Sun Management
127 Kiowa Ln
Piedmont, SC 29673-6751

Telephone: (864) 626-3227
Fax Number: (864) 263-7037
Internet Homepage: wendysfsmc.com
Type of Business: Chain Restaurant Operator
Year Founded: 1989
Total Sales: $46,590,000 (e)
Number of Employees: 756
Average Check: Lunch(8); Dinner(12)
Total Units: 17
Trade Names: Wendy's Old Fashioned Hamburgers (17)
Units Franchised From: 17
Preferred Square Footage: 3,500
Preferred Location Types: Freestanding
Primary Menu: Hamburger (17)
Projected Openings: 3
Areas of Operation: GA, SC
Type of Foodservice: Quick Serve (17)
Franchise Affiliation: The Wendy's Company, DUBLIN, OH
Primary Distributors: (Full Line) The SYGMA Network Inc. - Carolina, CHARLOTTE, NC

Key Personnel
JOE TURNER - CEO; Owner; Director Facility/Maintenance, Real Estate, Store Fixtures
JACKSON TURNER - CEO; VP Operations; General Buyer
CLARK MIZELL - CFO; Controller
ERIC ODOM - Director Marketing
JEFF GRACE - Director Operations

Clover Foods Inc
684 Waterford Glen Way
Rock Hill, SC 29730-8012

Telephone: (803) 366-7092
Type of Business: Chain Restaurant Operator
Total Sales: $2,786,000 (e)
Total Units: 4
Trade Names: Subway (4)
Units Franchised From: 4
Primary Menu: Sandwiches/Deli (4)
Areas of Operation: SC
Type of Foodservice: Quick Serve (4)
Franchise Affiliation: Doctor's Associates Inc., MILFORD, CT

Key Personnel
DONALD HYATT - President; General Buyer

Vance H Houston
2550 Main St W Ste 125
Rock Hill, SC 29732-9828

Telephone: (803) 328-5445
Type of Business: Chain Restaurant Operator
Total Sales: $8,564,000 (e)
Total Units: 15
Trade Names: Subway (15)
Units Franchised From: 15
Primary Menu: Sandwiches/Deli (15)
Areas of Operation: SC
Type of Foodservice: Quick Serve (15)
Franchise Affiliation: Doctor's Associates Inc., MILFORD, CT

Key Personnel
VANCE HOUSTON - President

Cravco III, LLC
300 Carter St
Seneca, SC 29672

Telephone: (864) 882-4348
Type of Business: Chain Restaurant Operator
Total Sales: $19,814,000 (e)
Total Units: 4
Trade Names: McDonald's (4)
Units Franchised From: 4
Preferred Location Types: Discount Dept. Stores; Freestanding
Primary Menu: Hamburger (4)
Areas of Operation: SC
Type of Foodservice: Quick Serve (4)
Franchise Affiliation: McDonald's Corporation, CHICAGO, IL

Key Personnel
JAMES PARTRIDGE - President; General Buyer

Denny's Corporation
203 E Main St
Spartanburg, SC 29319-0001

Telephone: (864) 597-8000
Fax Number: (864) 597-7708
Internet Homepage: dennysfranchising.com; thedenbydennys.com; dennys.com
Type of Business: Chain Restaurant Operator
Year Founded: 1953
Systemwide Sales: $5,016,265,000 (e)
Publicly Held: Yes
Total Sales: $489,433,000 (e)
Number of Employees: 12,000
Average Check: Breakfast(8); Lunch(8); Dinner(10)
Internet Order Processing: Yes
Internet Sales: 0.50%
Total Units: 1,558
Trade Names: Denny's (1,568); Keke's Breakfast Cafe (58); The Den (5)
Company-Owned Units: 73
Units Franchised To: 1,558
Preferred Square Footage: 2,955; 3,480; 3,520; 4,000; 4,605; 4,800; 4,950; 5,085
Preferred Location Types: Airports; Freestanding; Institution (college/hospital); Strip Mall; Travel Plazas
Alcohol Served: Beer, Wine, Liquor
Primary Menu: American (1,631)
Projected Openings: 35
Areas of Operation: AK, AL, AR, AZ, CA, CO, CT, DC, DE, FL, GA, GU, HI, IA, ID, IL, IN, KS, KY, LA, MA, MD, ME, MI, MN, MO, MS, MT, NC, ND, NE, NH, NJ, NM, NV, NY, OH, OK, OR, PA, PR, RI, SC, SD, TN, TX, UT, VA, VT, WA, WI, WV, AB, BC, MB, ON, SK
Foreign Countries: CANADA; CHILE; COSTA RICA; DOMINICAN REPUBLIC; EL SALVADOR; GUATEMALA; HONDURAS; MEXICO; NEW ZEALAND; THE PHILIPPINES; UNITED ARAB EMIRATES
Type of Foodservice: Casual Dining (58); Family Restaurant (1,568); Fast Casual (5)
Primary Distributors: (Food) McLane/Rocky Mount, ROCKY MOUNT, NC; (Supplies) McLane/Rocky Mount, ROCKY MOUNT, NC

Key Personnel
BRENDA J. LAUDERBACK - Chairman
KELLI VALADE - CEO
F. MARK WOLFINGER - President
DAVID SCHMIDT - President Division
ROBERT P. VEROSTEK - CFO; Exec VP
JAY C. GILMORE - Chief Accounting Officer; VP; Controller
STEPHEN C. DUNN - Chief Development Officer; Senior VP
GAIL SHARPS MYERS - Chief Legal Officer
MIKE STARNES - Exec VP Food Safety; VP Quality Assurance
R. GREGORY LINFORD - VP Purchasing
FASIKA MELAKU-PETERSON - VP Training

RAMON TORRES - VP Operations
SCOTT SMALLEY - VP Human Resources
KRISTEN ZUCKS DIDIER - VP Marketing
JIM BATCHLER-SMITH - Senior Director Technology
DEANNA BANISTER - Senior Director Human Resources
MARK GRAY - Senior Director Distribution, Logistics
SHARON LYKINS - Senior Director Product Development
MICHELLE CHAMPION - Senior Director Product Development
JANICE BRADY - Senior Director Quality Assurance, Compliance
TIM SEIBER - Senior Director Information Systems
LAURA GRACE - Director Real Estate Development
APRIL KELLY-DRUMMOND - Director Diversity
MICHELLE THOMPSON - Director Technology, Food and Beverage
JOEY FOWLER - Director Information Technology
MOLLY LARSON - Director Training
ANDREA WILCOX - Director Internal Audit
KIM RAWLINGS - Director Employee Development
MATT REID - Director Technology
TANYA WATERS - Director Safety, Loss Prevention, Risk Management
GENE HARRIS - Senior Manager Purchasing
GLEN MARTIN - Senior Manager Real Estate Development
TRACY KELLER - Senior Manager Real Estate
GABRIEL MONTAUTI - Senior Manager Product Development, International
MICHAEL SULLIVAN - Senior Manager Financial Planning, Investor Relations
APRIL CRANDALL - Senior Manager Inventory
MIKE LAWSON - Senior Manager Information Technology
GLENN COX - Manager Purchasing
DORY DJERF - Manager Franchise Development
MEGHAN TURNER - Manager Information Technology
GERALD DIXON - Manager POS/Scanning, Applications
DAN ELDRIDGE - Manager Development
OZZIE HUTSON - Manager Development
DORI HUMMEL - Manager Employee Benefits
SUSAN CARR - Project Manager
TERRY WICKS - Administrator Data Security
ELIZABETH MCABEE - Coordinator Franchise Development
PAT GUDELL - Executive Assistant

●▲
Delman, Inc.
310 Azalea Square Blvd Ste 11
Summerville, SC 29483-7362

Telephone: (843) 875-3480

Type of Business: Chain Restaurant Operator
Total Sales: $19,350,000 (e)
Total Units: 14
Trade Names: Jersey Mike's Subs (14)
Units Franchised From: 14
Primary Menu: Sandwiches/Deli (14)
Areas of Operation: SC
Type of Foodservice: Quick Serve (14)
Franchise Affiliation: Jersey Mike's Franchise Systems, MANASQUAN, NJ

Key Personnel
RYAN DELMAN - Owner; General Buyer

●▲
Lottsa Cheese Inc
1504 Azalea Dr Ste 601
Surfside Beach, SC 29575-5232

Mailing Address: PO Box 15988, SURFSIDE BEACH, SC, 29587-5988
Telephone: (843) 828-0669
Fax Number: (843) 828-0835
Type of Business: Chain Restaurant Operator
Total Sales: $13,610,000 (e)
Number of Employees: 230
Total Units: 10
Trade Names: Papa John's Pizza (10)
Units Franchised From: 10
Primary Menu: Pizza (10)
Areas of Operation: SC
Type of Foodservice: Quick Serve (10)
Franchise Affiliation: Papa Johns International Inc., LOUISVILLE, KY

Key Personnel
JUDY KEENER - President; General Buyer
CINDY HOPKINS - COO
CHRIS EDGE - Director Operations

Maurice's Piggie Park BBQ
1600 Charleston Hwy
West Columbia, SC 29169-5050

Mailing Address: PO Box 6847, WEST COLUMBIA, SC, 29171-6847
Telephone: (803) 791-5887
Fax Number: (803) 791-8707
Internet Homepage: piggiepark.com
Company Email: mail@piggiepark.com
Type of Business: Chain Restaurant Operator
Year Founded: 1953
Total Sales: $9,657,000 (e)
Number of Employees: 220
Average Check: Lunch(8); Dinner(12)
Internet Order Processing: Yes
Internet Sales: 4.00%
Total Units: 10
Trade Names: Maurice's Piggie Park (10)
Company-Owned Units: 10
Preferred Square Footage: 3,500
Preferred Location Types: Freestanding
Primary Menu: Bar-B-Q (10)
Areas of Operation: SC
Type of Foodservice: Family Restaurant (10)
Catering Services: Yes
On-site Distribution Center: Yes
Primary Distributors: (Supplies) Veritiv, COLUMBIA, SC

Key Personnel
LLOYD BESSINGER - CEO; Partner; VP Real Estate; General Buyer
PAUL BESSINGER - Partner; VP Purchasing, Facility/Maintenance, Real Estate
PAT CLOUGH - Manager Information Systems, Human Resources
LINDA TOTTEN - Manager Accounting

Rush's Food Systems Inc.
2332 Sunset Blvd
West Columbia, SC 29169-4716

Telephone: (803) 796-5034
Fax Number: (803) 796-1326
Internet Homepage: rushs.net
Company Email: info@rushs.net
Type of Business: Chain Restaurant Operator
Year Founded: 1940
Total Sales: $25,003,000 (e)
Number of Employees: 360
Average Check: Lunch(10); Dinner(10)
Total Units: 10
Trade Names: Rush's (10)
Company-Owned Units: 10
Preferred Square Footage: 3,300
Preferred Location Types: Freestanding
Primary Menu: Hamburger (10)
Areas of Operation: SC
Type of Foodservice: Quick Serve (10)
Primary Distributors: (Full Line) US Foods, LEXINGTON, SC

Key Personnel
DON ALCORN - President; CFO; VP Purchasing; Director Information Systems, Human Resources
MEAGAN BURKETT - Treasurer
DEN HEVIA - General Manager Operations, Manager Real Estate
BILL RADEMACHER - Director Operations; Manager Design, Menu Development

●▲
Sylvan Food Systems Inc.
1245 Boston Ave
West Columbia, SC 29170-2123

Telephone: (803) 796-1421
Fax Number: (803) 796-2461
Type of Business: Chain Restaurant Operator
Year Founded: 1960
Total Sales: $36,960,000 (e)
Number of Employees: 350

Average Check: Lunch(8); Dinner(8)
Total Units: 20
Trade Names: KFC (20)
Units Franchised From: 20
Preferred Square Footage: 4,000
Preferred Location Types: Freestanding
Primary Menu: Chicken (20); Seafood (20)
Areas of Operation: SC
Type of Foodservice: Quick Serve (20)
Catering Services: Yes
Franchise Affiliation: KFC Corporation, LOUISVILLE, KY
Primary Distributors: (Full Line) US Foods, LEXINGTON, SC

Key Personnel
CHIP PRYOR - President
DONNA P. STURKIE - Partner; General Buyer
CLIFFORD H. PRYOR JR - Partner; Director Supply Chain, Real Estate
CHARLES PRYOR - Partner; Director Real Estate, Design
TIM WILSON - VP Operations; Director Purchasing; Manager Finance

SOUTH DAKOTA

M.J. Salem Corp.
1601 S 1st St
Aberdeen, SD 57401

Mailing Address: PO Box 1299, ABERDEEN, SD, 57402-1299
Telephone: (605) 226-3242
Type of Business: Chain Restaurant Operator
Total Sales: $9,930,000 (e)
Total Units: 2
Trade Names: McDonald's (2)
Units Franchised From: 2
Preferred Location Types: Freestanding
Primary Menu: Hamburger (2)
Areas of Operation: SD
Type of Foodservice: Quick Serve (2)
Franchise Affiliation: McDonald's Corporation, CHICAGO, IL

Key Personnel
MICHAEL SALEM - President; General Buyer

Pentax Restaurant Group
14 2nd Ave SE Ste 1
Aberdeen, SD 57401-4246

Mailing Address: PO Box 60, ABERDEEN, SD, 57402-0060
Telephone: (605) 229-2005
Fax Number: (605) 225-0172
Internet Homepage: pentexrg.com
Company Email: info@pentexmanagement.com

Type of Business: Chain Restaurant Operator
Total Sales: $29,630,000 (e)
Total Units: 27
Trade Names: Hu Hot (4); Taco John's (23)
Units Franchised From: 27
Primary Menu: Asian (4); Mexican (23)
Areas of Operation: SD
Type of Foodservice: Fast Casual (27)

Key Personnel
BRYON ITTERMAN - CEO; President; General Buyer; Advisor Company Operations
BRETT ITTERMAN - CEO
DAMIEN VARELA - CFO
BILLIE MCGINNIS - Manager Human Resources

Kenway Foods Inc
1835 6th St
Brookings, SD 57006-1606

Telephone: (605) 692-8442
Type of Business: Chain Restaurant Operator
Total Sales: $2,050,000 (e)
Total Units: 3
Trade Names: Subway (3)
Units Franchised From: 3
Primary Menu: Sandwiches/Deli (3)
Areas of Operation: SD
Type of Foodservice: Quick Serve (3)
Franchise Affiliation: Doctor's Associates Inc., MILFORD, CT

Key Personnel
KIRK WILES - President; General Buyer

McDonald's of Mitchell
1704 N Main St
Mitchell, SD 57301-1119

Telephone: (605) 996-6200
Fax Number: (605) 996-0812
Type of Business: Chain Restaurant Operator
Year Founded: 1974
Total Sales: $46,169,000 (e)
Number of Employees: 400
Average Check: Breakfast(8); Lunch(8); Dinner(8)
Total Units: 9
Trade Names: McDonald's (9)
Units Franchised From: 9
Preferred Square Footage: 2,500
Preferred Location Types: Freestanding
Primary Menu: Hamburger (9)
Areas of Operation: MN, NE, SD
Type of Foodservice: Quick Serve (9)
Franchise Affiliation: McDonald's Corporation, CHICAGO, IL

Key Personnel
DEBBIE SHANNON - Controller

United Vending & Food Services
509 River Dr
North Sioux City, SD 57049-3008

Telephone: (605) 422-4166
Fax Number: (605) 422-1803
Type of Business: Foodservice Management Operator
Year Founded: 1980
Total Sales: $21,296,000 (e)
Number of Employees: 500
Number of Locations Served: 19
Total Foodservice Mgmt Accounts: 19
Areas of Operation: AR, CO, DE, IA, IL, IN, MN
Type of Foodservice: Cafeteria (19)
Foodservice Management Venues: Business & Industry; College & University

Key Personnel
SCOTT WILCOX - President; Partner; General Buyer
JOE RICHTER - Partner; CFO
PATTY POJAR - Director Risk Management, Quality Assurance, Human Resources, Personnel, Food Safety; Manager Payroll

Jak Inc
720 Cleveland St
Rapid City, SD 57701-5463

Telephone: (605) 343-6984
Fax Number: (605) 343-6984
Type of Business: Chain Restaurant Operator
Total Sales: $23,260,000 (e)
Total Units: 5
Trade Names: McDonald's (5)
Units Franchised From: 5
Primary Menu: Hamburger (5)
Areas of Operation: SD
Type of Foodservice: Quick Serve (5)
Franchise Affiliation: McDonald's Corporation, CHICAGO, IL

Key Personnel
WENDY WALLA - Owner; General Buyer

Papa Murphy's Take 'N' Bake Pizza Franchise
606 E North St
Rapid City, SD 57701-1687

Telephone: (605) 341-3252
Fax Number: (605) 341-3492

Type of Business: Chain Restaurant Operator
Total Sales: $1,885,000 (e)
Total Units: 2
Trade Names: Papa Murphy's Take 'N' Bake Pizza (2)
Units Franchised From: 2
Primary Menu: Pizza (2)
Areas of Operation: SD
Type of Foodservice: Quick Serve (2)
Franchise Affiliation: Papa Murphy's International Inc., VANCOUVER, WA

Key Personnel
DOUG CHRISTENSON - Owner; General Buyer

American Roast Beef, Inc.
4615 W Homefield Dr Ste 101
Sioux Falls, SD 57106-3512

Telephone: (605) 373-9444
Fax Number: (605) 373-9150
Type of Business: Chain Restaurant Operator
Year Founded: 1987
Total Sales: $22,470,000 (e)
Number of Employees: 436
Average Check: Lunch(10); Dinner(12)
Total Units: 12
Trade Names: Arby's (12)
Units Franchised From: 12
Preferred Square Footage: 2,500; 3,000
Preferred Location Types: Freestanding
Primary Menu: Sandwiches/Deli (12)
Areas of Operation: SD
Type of Foodservice: Quick Serve (12)
Franchise Affiliation: Arby's Restaurant Group, ATLANTA, GA

Key Personnel
MIKE WALZ - CEO
JOE JAMES - President; COO; General Buyer

B&G Milkyway
2410 W 12th St
Sioux Falls, SD 57104

Telephone: (605) 338-9501
Internet Homepage: bandgmilkyway.com
Type of Business: Chain Restaurant Operator
Year Founded: 1954
Total Sales: $7,045,000 (e)
Trade Names: B&G Milkyway (6)
Company-Owned Units: 6
Primary Menu: American (6)
Type of Foodservice: Quick Serve (6)

Key Personnel
BRUCE BETTMENG - Partner
PAM BETTMENG - Partner

J B Enterprises Inc
5120 S Western Ave Ste 102
Sioux Falls, SD 57108-2664

Telephone: (605) 334-3750
Fax Number: (800) 673-5360
Internet Homepage: jbperkins.net
Type of Business: Chain Restaurant Operator
Total Sales: $19,730,000 (e)
Total Units: 9
Trade Names: Perkins (9)
Units Franchised From: 9
Areas of Operation: SD
Type of Foodservice: Family Restaurant (9)
Franchise Affiliation: Perkins Restaurant & Bakery, MEMPHIS, TN

Key Personnel
ROBERT L. MILLER - President

K & K Management
738 W 10th St
Sioux Falls, SD 57104-3516

Telephone: (605) 361-7804
Internet Homepage: frynpan.net
Company Email: CorporateHeadquarters@frynpan.net
Type of Business: Chain Restaurant Operator
Year Founded: 1975
Total Sales: $16,040,000 (e)
Number of Employees: 375
Average Check: Lunch(10); Dinner(14)
Total Units: 7
Trade Names: Fryn' Pan Family Restaurant (7)
Company-Owned Units: 7
Preferred Square Footage: 3,000
Preferred Location Types: Freestanding
Primary Menu: American (7)
Areas of Operation: MN, ND, SD
Type of Foodservice: Family Restaurant (7)
Primary Distributors: (Equipment) Culinex, FARGO, ND; (Food) Reinhart FoodService, MARSHALL, MN; (Supplies) Culinex, FARGO, ND

Key Personnel
MARK OREN - Partner

Regency Hotel Management, LLC
3211 W Sencore Dr
Sioux Falls, SD 57107-0728

Telephone: (605) 334-2371
Fax Number: (605) 334-8480
Internet Homepage: regency-mgmt.com
Company Email: info@regency-mgmt.com
Type of Business: Foodservice Operations - Hotel/Motels
Year Founded: 1965
Total Sales: $171,180,000 (e)
Alcohol Sales: 20%
Number of Employees: 3,200
Internet Order Processing: Yes
Total Units: 32
Restaurants in Hotels: 32
Trade Names: Arrowwood Resort & Conference Center (3); Best Western (8); Bridges Bay Resort (1); Club House (5); Crown Plaza (1); Custer State Park Resorts (4); Grand Lake Lodge (1); Hilton Garden Inn (1); Marina Inn (1); Ohio Properties (3); Park Place (1); Radisson (1); Rock Crest Lodge (1); The Lodge at Deadwood (1)
Company-Owned Units: 27
Units Franchised From: 5
Alcohol Served: Beer, Wine, Liquor
Areas of Operation: AR, GA, IA, IL, KS, MI, MN, MO, ND, NE, NM, OK, SD, WY
Type of Foodservice: Casual Dining (7); Fine Dining (25)
Primary Distributors: (Food) SYSCO Food Services of Minnesota Inc., MOUNDSVIEW, MN
Notes: The company derives approximately 80% of its revenue from hotel operations.

Key Personnel
DAVID R. SWEET - Chairman
TOM BIEGLER - CEO; President
KYLE SCHOLTEN - CFO
GLORIANN KUETER - Director Marketing, Sales

WR Restaurants Management LLC
3211 W Sencore Dr
Sioux Falls, SD 57107-0728

Telephone: (605) 334-2371
Fax Number: (605) 334-8480
Internet Homepage: wrrestaurants.com
Company Email: marketing@wrrestaurants.com
Type of Business: Chain Restaurant Operator
Year Founded: 1994
Total Sales: $39,450,000 (e)
Alcohol Sales: 15%
Number of Employees: 1,092
Average Check: Lunch(18); Dinner(30)
Total Units: 17
Trade Names: 22Ten Kitchen Cocktails (1); All Day Cafe (1); Buglin' Bull (1); Deadwood Grille (1); Kahill's Chophouse (1); Minervas Restaurant & Bar (8); Oggie's Sports Bar (1); Redrossa Italian Grille (1); Taphouse 41 (1); The Phillips Avenue Diner (1)
Company-Owned Units: 17
Preferred Square Footage: 3,000; 5,500; 6,000
Preferred Location Types: Freestanding;

Hotel/Motel
Alcohol Served: Beer, Wine, Liquor
Primary Menu: American (7); Californian (0); Caribbean (0); Hamburger (0); Italian (2); Mexican (0); Seafood (0); Steak (8); Steak/Seafood (0)
Areas of Operation: IA, MI, MN, ND, NE, SD
Type of Foodservice: Casual Dining (4); Fine Dining (13)
Primary Distributors: (Full Line) US Foods, PLYMOUTH, MN

Key Personnel
DON ANDERSON - President
JIM TUSCHEN - Controller
JOAN HYLAND - Director Marketing
RUSS OGDEN - Manager Region
TERRY VAN DE WALLE - Manager Human Resources, Training, Region

Yotes Two, Inc
2101 W 41st St
Sioux Falls, SD 57105-6102

Telephone: (605) 339-4772
Type of Business: Chain Restaurant Operator
Total Sales: $4,402,000 (e)
Total Units: 5
Trade Names: Papa Murphy's Take 'N' Bake Pizza (5)
Units Franchised From: 5
Primary Menu: Pizza (5)
Areas of Operation: SD
Type of Foodservice: Quick Serve (5)
Franchise Affiliation: Papa Murphy's International Inc., VANCOUVER, WA

Key Personnel
TOM HENDERSON - Owner

M. C. Hartshorn, Inc.
701 3rd St SE
Watertown, SD 57201-4804

Mailing Address: PO Box 167, WATERTOWN, SD, 57201-0167
Telephone: (605) 882-6948
Fax Number: (605) 882-6949
Type of Business: Chain Restaurant Operator
Total Sales: $32,280,000 (e)
Total Units: 7
Trade Names: McDonald's (7)
Units Franchised From: 7
Preferred Location Types: Freestanding
Primary Menu: Hamburger (7)
Areas of Operation: SD
Type of Foodservice: Quick Serve (7)
Franchise Affiliation: McDonald's Corporation, CHICAGO, IL

Key Personnel
MICHAEL HARTSHORN - President; General Buyer

TENNESSEE

Fat Mo's
6525 Wildgrove Dr
Antioch, TN 37013-5669

Telephone: (615) 482-4205
Internet Homepage: fatmos.com
Company Email: info@fatmos.com
Type of Business: Chain Restaurant Operator
Year Founded: 1991
Systemwide Sales: $23,642,000 (e)
Total Sales: $3,556,000 (e)
Number of Employees: 4
Average Check: Lunch(12); Dinner(12)
Total Units: 13
Trade Names: Fat Mo's (13)
Units Franchised To: 13
Preferred Square Footage: 5,500; 6,000
Preferred Location Types: Freestanding; Strip Mall
Primary Menu: Hamburger (13)
Areas of Operation: TN
Type of Foodservice: Quick Serve (13)
Primary Distributors: (Food) US Foods, MEMPHIS, TN

Key Personnel
SHIVA KARIMY - President; Partner; Director Purchasing, Marketing, Franchising
MOHAMMAD "MO" KARIMY - Partner; Director Information Systems, Menu Development

Pizza Plus Inc.
299 Franklin Dr
Blountville, TN 37617-4543

Mailing Address: PO Box 629, BLOUNTVILLE, TN, 37618
Telephone: (423) 279-9335
Fax Number: (423) 279-0532
Internet Homepage: pizzaplusinc.com
Company Email: office@pizzaplusinc.com
Type of Business: Chain Restaurant Operator
Year Founded: 1982
Systemwide Sales: $78,989,000 (e)
Total Sales: $73,250,000 (e)
Number of Employees: 978
Average Check: Lunch(14); Dinner(18)
Internet Order Processing: Yes
Total Units: 59
Trade Names: Steph & Andy's Pizza Plus (59)
Company-Owned Units: 48
Units Franchised To: 11
Preferred Square Footage: 4,000
Preferred Location Types: Downtown; Freestanding; Strip Mall
Primary Menu: Pizza (59)
Areas of Operation: KY, TN, VA
Type of Foodservice: Casual Dining (59)
Foodservice Management Venues: Schools
Primary Distributors: (Full Line) Reinhart FoodService, LOUISVILLE, TN

Key Personnel
DANIEL MORRISON - President; CFO; Manager Purchasing, Real Estate, Design, Research & Development, Franchising, Menu Development, Food and Beverage
JIM DUNCAN - CIO; Director Information Systems
CHERYL MORRISON - VP Risk Management, Human Resources
KEVIN LAYELL - Director Operations, Supply Chain
SANDY KESTNER - Director Marketing
ROBERT GALASTRO - Director Franchise Development; Senior Manager Operations

Bar-B-Cutie Franchise Systems Inc.
5120 Virginia Way Ste B23
Brentwood, TN 37027-7594

Telephone: (615) 372-0707
Fax Number: (615) 372-0705
Internet Homepage: bar-b-cutie.com
Company Email: inquiry@bar-b-cutie.com
Type of Business: Chain Restaurant Operator
Year Founded: 1950
Systemwide Sales: $23,822,000 (e)
Total Sales: $7,053,000 (e)
Alcohol Sales: 0.30%
Number of Employees: 59
Average Check: Lunch(8); Dinner(12)
Internet Order Processing: Yes
Total Units: 11
Trade Names: Bar-B-Cutie (11)
Company-Owned Units: 2
Units Franchised To: 9
Preferred Square Footage: 5,500; 6,000
Preferred Location Types: Convenience Store/Gas Station; Freestanding; Strip Mall; Travel Plazas
Alcohol Served: Beer
Primary Menu: Bar-B-Q (11)
Projected Openings: 2
Areas of Operation: GA, OH, TN, TX
Type of Foodservice: Fast Casual (11)
Catering Services: Yes
Primary Distributors: (Food) Sysco Food Services of Nashville, NASHVILLE, TN

Key Personnel
RONNIE MCFARLAND - CEO; President; Executive Chef; Manager Menu Development; General Buyer
BRETT MCFARLAND - COO

CHRISTIE MCFARLAND - Director Marketing; Manager Branding
ANNIE MCFARLAND - Manager Finance, Human Resources
LYNN LUNN - Administrative Assistant

Blue Coast Burrito Inc.
7003 Chadwick Dr Ste 151
Brentwood, TN 37027-3288

Telephone: (615) 373-9090
Fax Number: (615) 373-9977
Internet Homepage: bluecoastburrito.com
Company Email: getinfo@bluecoastburrito.com
Type of Business: Chain Restaurant Operator
Systemwide Sales: $7,577,000 (e)
Total Sales: $3,572,000 (e)
Alcohol Sales: 5%
Average Check: Dinner(10)
Internet Order Processing: Yes
Total Units: 13
Trade Names: Blue Coast Burrito (9); Blue Coast Burrito Express (4)
Company-Owned Units: 10
Units Franchised To: 3
Alcohol Served: Beer
Primary Menu: Mexican (13)
Areas of Operation: AL, AR, TN
Type of Foodservice: Fast Casual (13)
Catering Services: Yes

Key Personnel
BOB SPECK - CEO; President; Director Menu Development; General Buyer
BEVERLY DONAHUE - Director Franchising
KRISTI KNIERIM - Director Marketing

Go Green Subs, Llc
101 Creekside Xing
Brentwood, TN 37027-1062

Telephone: (615) 730-6249
Type of Business: Chain Restaurant Operator
Total Sales: $2,675,000 (e)
Total Units: 2
Trade Names: Jimmy John's Gourmet Sandwich Shop (2)
Units Franchised From: 2
Areas of Operation: TN
Franchise Affiliation: Jimmy John's Franchise LLC, CHAMPAIGN, IL

Key Personnel
ADAM OLESZKOWICZ - Partner
WILLIAM CROZER - Partner

Management Resources Co.
1728 General George Patton Dr Ste 200
Brentwood, TN 37027-2861

Telephone: (615) 377-3100
Fax Number: (615) 377-3551
Type of Business: Chain Restaurant Operator
Year Founded: 1971
Total Sales: $105,020,000 (e)
Number of Employees: 2,485
Average Check: Lunch(8); Dinner(8)
Total Units: 37
Trade Names: KFC (2); Taco Bell (35)
Units Franchised From: 37
Preferred Square Footage: 2,500
Preferred Location Types: Freestanding; Regional Mall
Primary Menu: Chicken (2); Taco (35)
Projected Openings: 2
Areas of Operation: KY, TN
Foreign Countries: DOMINICAN REPUBLIC
Type of Foodservice: Quick Serve (37)
Franchise Affiliation: KFC Corporation, LOUISVILLE, KY; Taco Bell Corp., IRVINE, CA
Primary Distributors: (Full Line) McLane/Memphis, MEMPHIS, TN

Key Personnel
FARZIN FERDOWSI - President
MICHAEL SHAHSAVARI - CFO; Director Facility/Maintenance, Information Systems, Real Estate, Design
HOMAYOUN AMINMADANI - VP
JOHN MILJANICH - VP Operations, Supply Chain; General Buyer
KYLE ROUHANI-FARD - VP Operations, Purchasing, Store Fixtures, Food Safety
DONNA NEVELS - Controller
SHABNAM AMIN-MADANI - Director Human Resources

Yolo Food Systems, LLC
833 Pipers Ln
Brentwood, TN 37027-8745

Telephone: (615) 585-1996
Internet Homepage: firehousesubs.com/locations/tn/brentwood
Type of Business: Chain Restaurant Operator
Total Sales: $3,688,000 (e)
Total Units: 3
Trade Names: Firehouse Subs (3)
Units Franchised From: 3
Primary Menu: Sandwiches/Deli (3)
Areas of Operation: TN
Type of Foodservice: Fast Casual (3)
Catering Services: Yes
Franchise Affiliation: Firehouse Restaurant Group Inc., JACKSONVILLE, FL

Key Personnel
MARK GAMBOA - President; General Buyer

Arbico East LLC
1135 Volunteer Pkwy Ste 16A
Bristol, TN 37620-4658

Telephone: (423) 968-2729
Fax Number: (423) 968-2728
Internet Homepage: arbicoeast.com; arbys.com
Type of Business: Chain Restaurant Operator
Year Founded: 1982
Total Sales: $22,500,000 (e)
Number of Employees: 220
Average Check: Breakfast(8); Lunch(10); Dinner(12)
Total Units: 12
Trade Names: Arby's (12)
Units Franchised From: 12
Preferred Square Footage: 5,000
Preferred Location Types: Freestanding; Office Complex
Primary Menu: Sandwiches/Deli (12)
Areas of Operation: TN, VA
Type of Foodservice: Quick Serve (12)
Franchise Affiliation: Arby's Restaurant Group, ATLANTA, GA
Primary Distributors: (Full Line) McLane/Rocky Mount, ROCKY MOUNT, NC

Key Personnel
JEFF SHAWL - President; General Buyer
RUDY JOHNSON - Controller; Manager Finance

JMS Associates, LLC
1430 Volunteer Pkwy Ste 9
Bristol, TN 37620-6062

Telephone: (423) 968-2838
Type of Business: Chain Restaurant Operator
Total Sales: $6,793,000 (e)
Total Units: 5
Trade Names: Jersey Mike's Subs (5)
Units Franchised From: 5
Primary Menu: Sandwiches/Deli (5)
Areas of Operation: TN
Type of Foodservice: Quick Serve (5)
Franchise Affiliation: Jersey Mike's Franchise Systems, MANASQUAN, NJ

Key Personnel
DAVID WAMPLER - Owner; General Buyer

Lynn-Ja Inc.
1145 Volunteer Pkwy Ste 1
Bristol, TN 37620-4652

Telephone: (423) 844-0621

Fax Number: (423) 844-0533
Type of Business: Chain Restaurant Operator
Total Sales: $41,400,000 (e)
Number of Employees: 450
Total Units: 9
Trade Names: McDonald's (9)
Units Franchised From: 9
Preferred Square Footage: 2,500
Primary Menu: Hamburger (9)
Areas of Operation: TN
Type of Foodservice: Quick Serve (9)
Franchise Affiliation: McDonald's Corporation, CHICAGO, IL

Key Personnel
JESSIE CARTER - President; General Buyer

Subco East, Inc
2409 Volunteer Pkwy Ste A
Bristol, TN 37620-6807

Telephone: (423) 764-8382
Type of Business: Chain Restaurant Operator
Total Sales: $15,250,000 (e)
Total Units: 25
Trade Names: Subway (25)
Units Franchised From: 25
Primary Menu: Sandwiches/Deli (25)
Areas of Operation: TN, VA
Type of Foodservice: Quick Serve (25)
Franchise Affiliation: Doctor's Associates Inc., MILFORD, CT

Key Personnel
MICKEY BAKER - President; Partner
KEN VANCE - Partner
BRENDA STILTNER - Director Operations
WESLEY BOOHER - Administrative Assistant

Top Dining Inc.
1501 Bluff City Hwy
Bristol, TN 37620-6018

Mailing Address: PO Box 3292, BRISTOL, TN, 37625-3292
Telephone: (423) 764-1916
Fax Number: (423) 764-2455
Type of Business: Chain Restaurant Operator
Year Founded: 1984
Total Sales: $11,300,000 (e)
Number of Employees: 100
Average Check: Breakfast(8); Lunch(8); Dinner(8)
Total Units: 6
Trade Names: Arby's (6)
Units Franchised From: 6
Preferred Square Footage: 3,000
Preferred Location Types: Freestanding
Primary Menu: Sandwiches/Deli (6)
Areas of Operation: NC
Type of Foodservice: Quick Serve (6)
Franchise Affiliation: Arby's Restaurant Group, ATLANTA, GA
Primary Distributors: (Food) McLane/Lagrange, LAGRANGE, GA

Key Personnel
BEN FRIZZELL - President; Director Facility/Maintenance, Real Estate; General Buyer
DOUG BRIGGS - Manager Operations, Quality Assurance, Human Resources

Trident Holdings LLC
2815 W State St
Bristol, TN 37620-1716

Telephone: (423) 968-7878
Internet Homepage: tridentholdingsllc.com
Type of Business: Chain Restaurant Operator
Total Sales: $47,510,000 (e)
Number of Employees: 132
Average Check: Lunch(12); Dinner(16)
Total Units: 33
Trade Names: Captain D's Seafood (33)
Units Franchised From: 33
Preferred Location Types: Freestanding
Primary Menu: Seafood (33)
Projected Openings: 3
Areas of Operation: AL, GA, MS, TN, VA
Type of Foodservice: Quick Serve (33)
Catering Services: Yes
Franchise Affiliation: Captain D's LLC, NASHVILLE, TN
Primary Distributors: (Full Line) McLane/Rocky Mount, ROCKY MOUNT, NC

Key Personnel
CHRIS BENNER - President; Partner; General Buyer
ED STOKES - Partner

Domino's Franchisee
4640 Nashville Hwy Ste D
Chapel Hill, TN 37034-2126

Telephone: (931) 364-5775
Type of Business: Chain Restaurant Operator
Total Sales: $7,968,000 (e)
Total Units: 4
Trade Names: Domino's (4)
Units Franchised From: 4
Primary Menu: Pizza (4)
Areas of Operation: TN
Type of Foodservice: Quick Serve (4)
Franchise Affiliation: Domino's Pizza Inc, ANN ARBOR, MI

Key Personnel
JOHN M. GORDON - Owner; General Buyer

Chattanooga Billiard Club Inc.
110 Jordan Dr
Chattanooga, TN 37421-6731

Telephone: (423) 499-3883
Fax Number: (423) 499-0816
Internet Homepage: cbcburns.com
Company Email: cbcburns@cbcburns.com
Type of Business: Chain Restaurant Operator
Year Founded: 1982
Total Sales: $6,176,000 (e)
Alcohol Sales: 28%
Number of Employees: 35
Average Check: Lunch(10); Dinner(16)
Total Units: 2
Trade Names: Chattanooga Billard Club Downtown (1); Chattanooga Billiard Club East (1)
Company-Owned Units: 2
Preferred Location Types: Freestanding
Alcohol Served: Beer, Wine, Liquor
Primary Menu: American (2)
Areas of Operation: TN
Type of Foodservice: Casual Dining (2)
Catering Services: Yes
Primary Distributors: (Full Line) US Foods, MEMPHIS, TN

Key Personnel
PHIL WINDHAM - President; General Buyer
MICHELLE GREENLEAF - General Manager
RYANNE JOHNSON - Manager

Cici's Pizza Franchise
2288 Gunbarrel Rd Ste 186
Chattanooga, TN 37421-3895

Telephone: (423) 485-0900
Fax Number: (423) 485-0904
Type of Business: Chain Restaurant Operator
Total Sales: $3,779,000 (e)
Average Check: Dinner(10)
Total Units: 3
Trade Names: Cici's Pizza (3)
Units Franchised From: 3
Primary Menu: Pizza (3)
Areas of Operation: TN
Type of Foodservice: Family Restaurant (3)
Franchise Affiliation: CiCi Enterprises L.P., COPPELL, TX

Key Personnel
STEVE POTTS - President; General Buyer

Debo's Diners, Inc.
7625 Hamilton Park Dr Ste 26
Chattanooga, TN 37421-1188

Telephone: (423) 855-4650
Fax Number: (423) 855-8836
Internet Homepage: debosdiners.com
Company Email: info@debosdiners.com
Type of Business: Chain Restaurant Operator
Year Founded: 1994
Total Sales: $13,400,000 (e)
Number of Employees: 490
Total Units: 7
Trade Names: Steak 'n Shake (7)
Units Franchised From: 7
Primary Menu: Hamburger (7)
Areas of Operation: GA, TN
Type of Foodservice: Family Restaurant (7)
Franchise Affiliation: The Steak n Shake Operations Inc., INDIANAPOLIS, IN

Key Personnel
DEBBIE RICHMAN - President; General Buyer
MICHAEL RICHMAN - CFO; VP
MIKE RICHMAN - VP

Domino's Franchisee
1150 Hixson Pike
Chattanooga, TN 37405-3107

Telephone: (423) 267-3000
Type of Business: Chain Restaurant Operator
Total Sales: $16,635,000 (e)
Total Units: 8
Trade Names: Domino's (8)
Units Franchised From: 8
Primary Menu: Pizza (8)
Areas of Operation: TN
Type of Foodservice: Quick Serve (8)
Franchise Affiliation: Domino's Pizza Inc, ANN ARBOR, MI

Key Personnel
RONALD C. HAMILTON - Owner; General Buyer

Domino's Franchisee
8644 E Brainerd Rd
Chattanooga, TN 37421-8325

Telephone: (423) 899-3030
Type of Business: Chain Restaurant Operator
Total Sales: $7,927,000 (e)
Total Units: 4
Trade Names: Domino's (4)
Units Franchised From: 4
Primary Menu: Pizza (4)
Areas of Operation: TN
Type of Foodservice: Quick Serve (4)
Franchise Affiliation: Domino's Pizza Inc, ANN ARBOR, MI

Key Personnel
RANDY S. SPENCER - Owner; General Buyer

Five Star Foodservice Inc.
6005 Century Oaks Dr Ste 100
Chattanooga, TN 37416-3677

Telephone: (423) 643-2600
Fax Number: (423) 643-2633
Internet Homepage: fivestar-food.com
Type of Business: Foodservice Management Operator
Year Founded: 1993
Total Sales: $457,231,000 (e)
Number of Employees: 1,200
Number of Locations Served: 9,300
Total Foodservice Mgmt Accounts: 6,100
Trade Names: Five Star Foodservices
Areas of Operation: TN
Type of Foodservice: Cafeteria (150); Quick Serve (150); Vending machines (5,800)
Foodservice Management Venues: Business & Industry; College & University; Other; Prison Feeding; Schools
Primary Distributors: (Full Line) SYSCO Food Services of South Florida Inc., MEDLEY, FL

Key Personnel
ALAN RECHER - CEO; President
RICHARD KENNEDY - COO
GREGORY MCCALL - Senior VP Marketing, Sales
MARK STEPHANOS - Senior VP
BRUCE GARNER - VP Information Systems
PEGGY RUSSELL - VP Human Resources
PAT BARGER - VP Sales
MIKE LAURER - VP
BUDDY DUKE - Regional VP

JAK Foods Inc
2401 Broad St Ste 201
Chattanooga, TN 37408-2922

Telephone: (423) 894-3881
Fax Number: (423) 894-3991
Type of Business: Chain Restaurant Operator
Total Sales: $18,280,000 (e)
Number of Employees: 285
Average Check: Lunch(10); Dinner(14)
Total Units: 13
Trade Names: A&W All American Food (1); Jimmy John's Gourmet Sandwich Shop (2); KFC (6); Long John Silver's (4)
Units Franchised From: 13
Preferred Square Footage: 2,500; 3,200
Preferred Location Types: Freestanding
Primary Menu: American (1); Chicken (6); Sandwiches/Deli (2); Seafood (4)
Areas of Operation: GA, NC, TN
Type of Foodservice: Quick Serve (13)
Franchise Affiliation: A&W Restaurants Inc., LEXINGTON, KY; KFC Corporation, LOUISVILLE, KY; Long John Silver's Inc., LOUISVILLE, KY

Key Personnel
JOHN KLEBAN - Owner; General Buyer

Robert Dreesch
1820 Gunbarrel Rd
Chattanooga, TN 37421-7179

Telephone: (423) 553-6930
Type of Business: Chain Restaurant Operator
Total Sales: $5,236,000 (e)
Total Units: 3
Trade Names: Moe's Southwest Grill (3)
Units Franchised From: 3
Primary Menu: Southwest/Tex-Mex (3)
Areas of Operation: TN
Type of Foodservice: Fast Casual (3)
Franchise Affiliation: Moe's Southwest Grill LLC, ATLANTA, GA

Key Personnel
ROBERT DREESCH - Owner; General Buyer

Bluegrass Subs, LLC
2808 Wilma Rudolph Blvd
Clarksville, TN 37040-5032

Telephone: (931) 245-0961
Type of Business: Chain Restaurant Operator
Total Sales: $6,013,000 (e)
Total Units: 4
Trade Names: Jersey Mike's Subs (4)
Units Franchised From: 4
Primary Menu: Sandwiches/Deli (4)
Areas of Operation: TN
Type of Foodservice: Quick Serve (4)
Franchise Affiliation: Jersey Mike's Franchise Systems, MANASQUAN, NJ

Key Personnel
JEFFREY L. HORN - Owner

Domino's Franchisee
1803 Madison St
Clarksville, TN 37043-8058

Telephone: (931) 552-0030
Type of Business: Chain Restaurant Operator
Total Sales: $8,007,000 (e)
Total Units: 4
Trade Names: Domino's (4)
Units Franchised From: 4
Primary Menu: Pizza (4)

Areas of Operation: TN
Type of Foodservice: Quick Serve (4)
Franchise Affiliation: Domino's Pizza Inc, ANN ARBOR, MI

Key Personnel
ANTONIO C. MURGAS - Owner; General Buyer

Fresh Subs & Salads Inc
1620 Fort Campbell Blvd
Clarksville, TN 37042-3554

Telephone: (931) 648-9270
Fax Number: (931) 906-0178
Type of Business: Chain Restaurant Operator
Total Sales: $6,086,000 (e)
Total Units: 10
Trade Names: Subway (10)
Units Franchised From: 10
Primary Menu: Sandwiches/Deli (10)
Areas of Operation: TN
Type of Foodservice: Quick Serve (10)
Franchise Affiliation: Doctor's Associates Inc., MILFORD, CT

Key Personnel
RICK PATEL - President

J & S Restaurants Inc.
2060 Candies Ln NW
Cleveland, TN 37312-2615

Mailing Address: PO Box 2428, CLEVELAND, TN, 37320-2428
Telephone: (423) 478-0003
Fax Number: (423) 614-4247
Internet Homepage: jandshardees.com
Type of Business: Chain Restaurant Operator
Year Founded: 1967
Total Sales: $77,349,000 (e)
Number of Employees: 1,130
Average Check: Breakfast(8); Lunch(8); Dinner(8)
Total Units: 41
Trade Names: Hardee's (41)
Units Franchised From: 41
Preferred Square Footage: 2,500
Preferred Location Types: Freestanding
Primary Menu: Hamburger (41)
Areas of Operation: GA, TN
Type of Foodservice: Quick Serve (41)
Franchise Affiliation: Hardee's Food Systems Inc., FRANKLIN, TN
Primary Distributors: (Full Line) McLane/Rocky Mount, ROCKY MOUNT, NC

Key Personnel
MARK JOHNSON - Chairman; CEO
JULIA SCOGGINS - President; COO; Director Finance

TAMMY BIVENS - VP Finance; Controller; Director Accounting, Information Systems, Design, Human Resources, Franchising

Miza Foods Inc
PO Box 5660
Cleveland, TN 37320-5660

Telephone: (423) 478-1321
Type of Business: Chain Restaurant Operator
Total Sales: $9,627,000 (e)
Total Units: 8
Trade Names: Little Caesars Pizza (8)
Units Franchised From: 8
Primary Menu: Pizza (8)
Areas of Operation: TN
Type of Foodservice: Quick Serve (8)
Franchise Affiliation: Little Caesar Enterprises Inc., DETROIT, MI

Key Personnel
NATHAN NAPIER - President; Director Operations; General Buyer

Smith Family Restaurants
4385 Ocoee St N
Cleveland, TN 37312-4832

Telephone: (423) 478-5661
Fax Number: (423) 479-5535
Type of Business: Chain Restaurant Operator
Total Sales: $42,320,000 (e)
Number of Employees: 900
Total Units: 9
Trade Names: McDonald's (9)
Units Franchised From: 9
Preferred Square Footage: 2,500
Primary Menu: Hamburger (9)
Areas of Operation: TN
Type of Foodservice: Quick Serve (9)
Franchise Affiliation: McDonald's Corporation, CHICAGO, IL

Key Personnel
HENRY SMITH - President; General Buyer
GREG WHITE - Director Operations
MARK SMITH - General Buyer

StarrChex LLC
2401 Keith St NW
Cleveland, TN 37311-1310

Mailing Address: PO BOX 5019, MARIETTA, GA, 30061
Telephone: (423) 478-5238
Internet Homepage: starrchexllc.weebly.com
Company Email: hbdixon@bellsouth.net
Type of Business: Chain Restaurant Operator
Total Sales: $14,690,000 (e)

Total Units: 10
Trade Names: Checkers (10)
Units Franchised From: 10
Primary Menu: Hamburger (10)
Areas of Operation: GA, LA
Type of Foodservice: Quick Serve (10)
Franchise Affiliation: Checkers Drive-In Restaurants Inc., TAMPA, FL

Key Personnel
DANNY LINDERMAN - President; Partner
HAL B. DIXON - Partner

Faris Properties LLC
2237 N Charles G Seivers Blvd
Clinton, TN 37716

Telephone: (865) 463-9500
Company Email: vsfraker@bellsouth.net
Type of Business: Chain Restaurant Operator
Year Founded: 1985
Total Sales: $224,250,000 (e)
Number of Employees: 1,634
Average Check: Breakfast(8); Lunch(8); Dinner(10)
Total Units: 47
Trade Names: McDonald's (47)
Units Franchised From: 47
Preferred Square Footage: 2,500
Preferred Location Types: Discount Dept. Stores; Freestanding
Primary Menu: Hamburger (47)
Projected Openings: 2
Areas of Operation: TN
Type of Foodservice: Quick Serve (47)
Franchise Affiliation: McDonald's Corporation, CHICAGO, IL
Primary Distributors: (Food) The Martin-Brower Co., DICKSON, TN

Key Personnel
JOHN JUDE FARIS - President; Director Finance, Operations, Facility/Maintenance, Information Systems, Real Estate, Design, Human Resources; General Buyer
JACK SULLIVAN - Director Operations
KRIS KING - Regional Manager
RYCHARD DAMEWOOD - Manager Operations
SUE FRAKER - Manager Branch

Hart's Ventures, LLC
3660 S Houston Levee Rd Ste 106
Collierville, TN 38017-9146

Telephone: (901) 457-7227
Type of Business: Chain Restaurant Operator
Total Sales: $8,342,000 (e)
Total Units: 5
Trade Names: Moe's Southwest Grill (5)
Units Franchised From: 5
Primary Menu: Southwest/Tex-Mex (5)

Areas of Operation: TN
Type of Foodservice: Fast Casual (5)
Franchise Affiliation: Moe's Southwest Grill LLC, ATLANTA, GA

Key Personnel
MATTHEW ZUFALL - Owner; General Buyer

Radiant Group of Companies
384 Distribution Pkwy
Collierville, TN 38017-3910

Telephone: (901) 853-0709
Fax Number: (901) 853-6141
Internet Homepage: radiantgroup.us
Company Email: info@radiantgroup.us
Type of Business: Chain Restaurant Operator
Total Sales: $20,740,000 (e)
Total Units: 14
Trade Names: Checkers (14)
Units Franchised From: 14
Primary Menu: Hamburger (14)
Areas of Operation: TN
Type of Foodservice: Quick Serve (14)
Franchise Affiliation: Checkers Drive-In Restaurants Inc., TAMPA, FL

Key Personnel
ANWAR AMAN - CEO; President
BADRUDDIN KHERAJ - CFO
RAFIQ DEVJI - COO
SARDAR AMAN - Chief Investment Officer

JRN Inc.
209 W 7th St
Columbia, TN 38401-3233

Mailing Address: 209 W 7th St, COLUMBIA, TN, 38401-3233
Telephone: (931) 381-3000
Fax Number: (931) 490-4801
Type of Business: Chain Restaurant Operator
Year Founded: 1970
Total Sales: $310,240,000 (e)
Number of Employees: 3,875
Average Check: Lunch(10); Dinner(10)
Total Units: 168
Trade Names: KFC (154); Long John Silver's (2); Taco Bell (12)
Units Franchised From: 168
Preferred Square Footage: 4,200
Preferred Location Types: Freestanding
Primary Menu: Chicken (154); Seafood (2); Taco (12)
Projected Openings: 15
Areas of Operation: AL, FL, GA, IL, IN, KY, MO, NC, SC, TN, VA
Type of Foodservice: Quick Serve (168)
Franchise Affiliation: KFC Corporation, LOUISVILLE, KY; Taco Bell Corp., IRVINE, CA
Primary Distributors: (Full Line) US Foods,

MEMPHIS, TN

Key Personnel
CLAY NEAL - Partner; VP Real Estate
DAVID G. NEAL - Partner; Senior VP Operations; Director Purchasing
STEPHEN DEARING - VP Construction, Design
JOE KENDALL - VP Operations; Controller; Director Finance
ANDREW SAMPSEL - General Manager
SHELLY SYKES - General Manager
KASEY KELLY - General Manager Area-Training; Manager
CLAIRE MOYE - Director Human Resources
HEATH HARRISON - Director Loss Prevention
TERRY JENNINGS - Director Operations
PAM NORWOOD - Manager Area

Wolfe Enterprises
807 Nashville Hwy Ste 12
Columbia, TN 38401-2418

Telephone: (931) 388-0701
Fax Number: (931) 388-0448
Company Email: happymealoffice@aol.com
Type of Business: Chain Restaurant Operator
Year Founded: 1988
Total Sales: $23,440,000 (e)
Number of Employees: 278
Average Check: Breakfast(8); Lunch(8); Dinner(8)
Total Units: 5
Trade Names: McDonald's (5)
Units Franchised From: 5
Preferred Square Footage: 1,600
Preferred Location Types: Discount Dept. Stores; Freestanding
Primary Menu: Hamburger (5)
Areas of Operation: TN
Type of Foodservice: Quick Serve (5)
Franchise Affiliation: McDonald's Corporation, CHICAGO, IL
Primary Distributors: (Food) The Martin-Brower Co., DICKSON, TN

Key Personnel
BRIAN WOLFE - President
TONY WOLFE - President; General Manager; Director Information Systems, Real Estate; General Buyer
KRIS TURNER - Manager Facility/Maintenance, District
KIYOMI KIHARA - Office Manager

Domino's Franchisee
512 N Willow Ave
Cookeville, TN 38501-1759

Telephone: (931) 520-3333
Type of Business: Chain Restaurant Operator
Total Sales: $4,046,000 (e)

Total Units: 2
Trade Names: Domino's (2)
Units Franchised From: 2
Primary Menu: Pizza (2)
Areas of Operation: TN
Type of Foodservice: Quick Serve (2)
Franchise Affiliation: Domino's Pizza Inc, ANN ARBOR, MI

Key Personnel
JOHN M. POWERS - Owner; General Buyer

L & E Management Comapny Inc
830 Herbert Rd Ste 101
Cordova, TN 38018-2276

Telephone: (901) 375-9477
Type of Business: Chain Restaurant Operator
Total Units: 3
Trade Names: Perkins (3)
Units Franchised From: 3
Primary Menu: American (3)
Areas of Operation: TN
Type of Foodservice: Family Restaurant (3)
Franchise Affiliation: Perkins Restaurant & Bakery, MEMPHIS, TN

Key Personnel
LARRY WALKER - President; General Buyer

Pyro's Fire Fresh Pizza
65 Germantown Ct Ste 420
Cordova, TN 38018-4484

Telephone: (901) 379-8294
Internet Homepage: pyrospizza.com
Company Email: info@pyrospizza.com
Type of Business: Chain Restaurant Operator
Year Founded: 2013
Total Units: 8
Trade Names: Pyro's Fire Fresh Pizza (8)
Company-Owned Units: 8
Primary Menu: Pizza (8)
Projected Openings: 2
Areas of Operation: AL, MS, TN
Type of Foodservice: Fast Casual (8)
Notes: Contact Note: Address is corporate HQ. Phone is original location on Ridgeway Rd.

Key Personnel
KIRK COTHAM - Co-Founder; Partner
CHAD FORMAN - Co-Founder; Partner
MARTY MORGAN - CFO
DEANA SPANGLER - Manager Sales, Catering
STEVEN GEYER - Manager Human Resources

Wright Investment Properties Inc.
277 German Oak Dr
Cordova, TN 38018-7221

Telephone: (901) 755-9501
Fax Number: (901) 755-8230
Internet Homepage: wrightinvestments.com
Type of Business: Foodservice Operations - Hotel/Motels
Year Founded: 1982
Total Sales: $116,290,000 (e)
Alcohol Sales: 15%
Number of Employees: 890
Total Units: 17
Restaurants in Hotels: 17
Trade Names: Comfort Inn (3); Courtyard by Marriott (4); DoubleTree by Hilton (1); Hilton (1); Holiday Inn (6); Radisson (1); Residence Inn (1)
Company-Owned Units: 17
Alcohol Served: Beer, Wine, Liquor
Areas of Operation: FL, GA, LA, MS, NC, TN, TX
Type of Foodservice: Casual Dining (13); Fine Dining (2); Quick Serve (2)
Primary Distributors: (Food) SYSCO Food Services of Indianapolis LLC, INDIANAPOLIS, IN; (Specialty Foods) SYSCO Food Services of Indianapolis LLC, INDIANAPOLIS, IN
Notes: The company derives approximately 75% of its revenue from hotel operations.

Key Personnel
LARRY F. WRIGHT SR - Chairman
LARRY F. WRIGHT JR - CEO; President
ROY STEPHENSON - CFO; Controller
BRANDON T. BIRKHEAD - VP Construction
GARY TIGGES - Regional VP Operations

Subway Franchise
639 N Main St
Crossville, TN 38555-5641

Telephone: (931) 484-6090
Fax Number: (931) 484-6090
Internet Homepage: subway.com
Type of Business: Chain Restaurant Operator
Total Sales: $47,080,000 (e)
Total Units: 80
Trade Names: Subway (80)
Units Franchised From: 80
Primary Menu: Sandwiches/Deli (80)
Areas of Operation: TN
Type of Foodservice: Quick Serve (80)
Franchise Affiliation: Doctor's Associates Inc., MILFORD, CT

Key Personnel
JOHN BOIKI - President; General Buyer

Bad Bob's Barbeque Restaurant
1979 Saint John Ave Ste D
Dyersburg, TN 38024

Telephone: (731) 285-3026
Internet Homepage: badbobs.net
Company Email: badbobsllc@badbobs.net
Type of Business: Chain Restaurant Operator
Year Founded: 2001
Total Sales: $6,843,000 (e)
Number of Employees: 75
Average Check: Lunch(10); Dinner(14)
Internet Order Processing: Yes
Total Units: 5
Trade Names: Bad Bob's Barbeque Restaurant (5)
Units Franchised To: 5
Preferred Location Types: Freestanding; Strip Mall
Primary Menu: Bar-B-Q (5)
Areas of Operation: KY, TN
Type of Foodservice: Family Restaurant (5)
Catering Services: Yes

Key Personnel
SHARON GROOMS - Owner; Executive Chef; General Buyer
BILLY GREER - Director Information Technology
BOBBY GROOMS - Director Product Development, Franchising, Menu Development
ERIC LUMMUS - Manager Sales

D & B Properties
1045 Vendall Rd
Dyersburg, TN 38024-1622

Mailing Address: PO Box 427, DYERSBURG, TN, 38025-0427
Telephone: (731) 286-0744
Fax Number: (731) 286-2354
Type of Business: Chain Restaurant Operator
Year Founded: 1975
Total Sales: $61,490,000 (e)
Number of Employees: 1,196
Average Check: Breakfast(8); Lunch(8); Dinner(10)
Total Units: 29
Trade Names: Sonic America's Drive-In (29)
Units Franchised From: 29
Preferred Square Footage: 1,320
Preferred Location Types: Freestanding
Primary Menu: Hamburger (29)
Areas of Operation: IL, KY, MO, TN
Type of Foodservice: Quick Serve (28)
Franchise Affiliation: Sonic Corp., OKLAHOMA CITY, OK
Primary Distributors: (Equipment) The Wasserstrom Co., COLUMBUS, OH; (Food) US Foods, ALCOA, TN; (Supplies) The Wasserstrom Co., COLUMBUS, OH

Key Personnel
PENNY GUTHRIE - CEO; Director Finance
CINDY GOLDEN - Owner
BARBARA WHITE - Owner
MARK ROBERSON - Director Operations, Inventory, Loss Prevention, Risk Management, Quality Assurance, Supply Chain, Food Safety; General Buyer

D.L. Sells Inc.
575 Mall Blvd Ste M
Dyersburg, TN 38024-1690

Telephone: (731) 285-0032
Fax Number: (731) 285-5417
Company Email: marla@sisbromgmt.com
Type of Business: Chain Restaurant Operator
Year Founded: 1976
Total Sales: $55,470,000 (e)
Number of Employees: 400
Average Check: Breakfast(8); Lunch(8); Dinner(10)
Total Units: 12
Trade Names: McDonald's (12)
Units Franchised From: 12
Preferred Square Footage: 3,000
Preferred Location Types: Convenience Store/Gas Station; Discount Dept. Stores; Freestanding
Primary Menu: Hamburger (12)
Areas of Operation: AR, MO, TN
Type of Foodservice: Quick Serve (12)
Franchise Affiliation: McDonald's Corporation, CHICAGO, IL
Primary Distributors: (Full Line) The Martin-Brower Co., DICKSON, TN

Key Personnel
DARREN SELLS - Partner; Director Advertising; Manager Finance
DANA QUERTERMOUS - Partner; General Manager
BRIAN SHIPLEY - Director Operations, Information Systems

Sonic Drive-In
1906 Saint John Ave
Dyersburg, TN 38024

Telephone: (731) 285-4155
Internet Homepage: sonicdrivein.com
Type of Business: Chain Restaurant Operator
Total Sales: $19,600,000 (e)
Total Units: 9
Trade Names: Sonic America's Drive-In (9)
Units Franchised From: 9

Primary Menu: Hamburger (9)
Areas of Operation: TN
Type of Foodservice: Quick Serve (9)
Franchise Affiliation: Sonic Corp., OKLAHOMA CITY, OK

Key Personnel
SHIRLEY DEWITT - Owner; General Buyer
PENNY GUTHRIE - Owner

Carl's Jr.
6700 Tower Cir Ste 1000
Franklin, TN 37067

Telephone: (615) 538-9400
Fax Number: (714) 780-6315
Internet Homepage: carlsjr.com; ckefranchise.com
Company Email: info@carlsjr.com
Type of Business: Chain Restaurant Operator
Year Founded: 1941
Systemwide Sales: $2,871,851,000 (e)
Total Sales: $568,477,000 (e)
Number of Employees: 13,000
Average Check: Lunch(8); Dinner(10)
Total Units: 1,652
Trade Names: Carl's Jr. (1,313); Carl's Jr/Green Burrito (339)
Company-Owned Units: 49
Units Franchised To: 1,603
Preferred Square Footage: 2,450; 2,831; 3,212
Preferred Location Types: Airports; Community Mall; Convenience Store/Gas Station; Downtown; Freestanding; Institution (college/hospital); Mobile Unit; Regional Mall; Stadiums; Strip Mall; Travel Plazas
Primary Menu: Hamburger (1,652)
Projected Openings: 35
Areas of Operation: AK, AZ, CA, CO, HI, ID, NM, NV, OK, OR, TX, UT, WA, WY
Foreign Countries: AMERICAN SAMOA; AUSTRALIA; BELARUS; CAMBODIA; CANADA; CHILE; CHINA; COLOMBIA; COSTA RICA; DENMARK; ECUADOR; FRANCE; GUATEMALA; HONDURAS; INDIA; INDONESIA; JAPAN; MALAYSIA; MEXICO; NEW ZEALAND; NICARAGUA; PANAMA; RUSSIA;SINGAPORE; SPAIN; THAILAND; TURKEY
Type of Foodservice: Quick Serve (1,652)
Primary Distributors: (Full Line) McLane/Rocky Mount, ROCKY MOUNT, NC
Parent Company: CKE Restaurants Inc., FRANKLIN, TN
Regional Offices: Carl's Jr. Region 2, FRANKLIN, TN

Key Personnel
MICHAEL WOIDA - President International
JUSTIN FALCIOLA - CTO; Chief Growth Officer
DAVID ANDRECHUK - VP Procurement
KIM CABADA - VP Applications
MIKE DARGER - VP Facility/Maintenance
BRIAN VOSS - VP Operations
RON WENNERBERG - VP Quality Assurance
EDDIE KEEN - Director Franchise Operations
EMILY KING - Director Field Marketing
MEREDITH MARTIN - Director Marketing, Advertising
DAVE MCDIVETT - Director Construction
AUDREY BALDWIN - Senior Manager Product Development
DONNA DANIELS - Manager Human Resources
MARTY STEELMAN - Manager Event Planning

Carl's Jr. Region 2
6700 Tower Cir Ste 1000
Franklin, TN 37067

Telephone: (805) 745-7500
Listing Type: Regional Office
Type of Business: Chain Restaurant Operator
Total Units: 32
Areas of Operation: TN
Parent Company: CKE Restaurants Inc., FRANKLIN, TN
Headquarters: Carl's Jr., FRANKLIN, TN

Key Personnel
ROBIN MORROW - Director Region

CKE Restaurants Inc.
6700 Tower Cir Ste 100
Franklin, TN 37067-1476

Telephone: (615) 538-9400
Fax Number: (714) 780-6315
Internet Homepage: carlsjr.com; ckefranchise.com; ckr.com; hardees.com
Company Email: thorth@cke.com
Listing Type: Corporate Office
Type of Business: Chain Restaurant Operator
Year Founded: 1941
Total Sales: $995,983,000 (e)
Number of Employees: 31,000
Total Units: 3,431
Trade Names: Carl's Jr. (1,063); Carl's Jr/Green Burrito (339); Hardee's (1,734); Hardee's/Red Burrito (295)
Company-Owned Units: 168
Units Franchised To: 3,263
Preferred Location Types: Airports; Community Mall; Convenience Store/Gas Station; Downtown; Freestanding; Institution (college/hospital); Mobile Unit; Outlet Mall; Regional Mall; Stadiums; Strip Mall
Primary Menu: Hamburger (2,797)
Projected Openings: 100
Areas of Operation: AK, AL, AR, AZ, CA, CO, DE, FL, GA, HI, IA, ID, IL, IN, KS, KY, LA, MD, MI, MN, MO, MS, MT, NC, ND, NE, NM, NV, OH, OK, OR, PA, SC, SD, TN, TX, UT, VA, WA, WI, WV, WY
Foreign Countries: BRAZIL; CANADA; CHINA; COLOMBIA; DENMARK; ECUADOR; EGYPT; INDIA; INDONESIA; IRAQ; KAZAKHSTAN; MEXICO; OMAN; PAKISTAN; RUSSIA; SAUDI ARABIA; THAILAND; TURKEY; VIETNAM
Type of Foodservice: Quick Serve (3,431)
Catering Services: Yes
Franchise Affiliation: Murphy's Star, Inc., BANNING, CA
Primary Distributors: (Food) SYSCO Corporation, HOUSTON, TX; (Food) Systems Services of America, MILPITAS, CA
Parent Company: Roark Capital Group, ATLANTA, GA
Headquarter Offices: Carl's Jr., FRANKLIN, TN; Hardee's Food Systems Inc., FRANKLIN, TN
Regional Offices: Carl's Jr. Region 2, FRANKLIN, TN

Key Personnel
SARAH SPIEGEL - CEO Interim
MICHAEL MURPHY - President
MICHAEL WOIDA - President International
CHRISTOPHER BODE - President
ANDREW ROBINSON - Chief Human Resources Officer
JUSTIN FALCIOLA - CTO; Chief Growth Officer
ARTURO PEREZ CALVO - Chief Marketing Officer
MATTHEW WELLS - Chief Development Officer Global
KERRY OLSON - Chief Legal Officer; Corporate Secretary; General Counsel
JACK WILLINGHAM - Senior VP Construction, Design
TODD HUETINCK - Senior VP Supply Chain
REGINA SCHNEIDER - Senior VP Marketing
RON WENNERBERG - VP Quality Assurance
MIKE DARGER - VP Facility/Maintenance
VICKI EGIDI - VP Franchise Operations
DAN HOGAN - VP Construction
STEVEN SMELTZER - VP Operations
MICHELE RUSHING - VP Supply Chain, International
TIM WEIGEL - VP Field Marketing
DAVID ANDRECHUK - VP Procurement
ANTHONY NGUYEN - VP Brand Marketing
ANDRE STRYDOM - VP Supply Chain, International
MIKE DENSON - VP Loyalty Program
BRACKEN GARDNER - VP Franchising
RYAN HANAWALT - Senior Director Operations
RAMEZ GUIRGUIS - Senior Director Franchise Operations, International
SEAN DEWITT - Senior Director Accounting
DON JONES - Director Construction, Design
TIM MESSENGALE - Director Internal Audit
MELISSA ALVIS - Director Technology, Information Technology
ADAM ROBBINS - Director Operations
JOHN MAYES - Director Franchise Development
KATHY JOHNSON - Director Brand Marketing

EMILY KING - Director Field Marketing
CHARON ALEXANDER - Director Human Resources
MAUREEN BROWN - Director Marketing, International
JIM SHERADIN - Senior Manager Facility/Maintenance
JAMES MANESS - Senior Manager Information Technology
MARK ROMAGNO - District Manager
JAMES A. BIGGS - Manager Purchasing
SUSAN COCHRANE - Manager Human Resources
PATTI LEATHERMAN - Manager Recruitment
BETTY LOMAX - Manager HRIS
TOM MERINO - Manager Supply Chain
STEVEN WALKER - Manager Information Systems
ANDREW BROWN - Manager Supply Chain, International
ETHAN HIGHERS CFI - Manager Asset Protection
ANGELA BROWN - Manager Real Estate
JEFF PURDY - Project Manager Facility/Maintenance
TINA SLAY - Administrator Franchise Sales
KAYLA WELLS - Specialist Marketing
STEVEN BARKER-BALL - Analyst Systems
BRANDI FALLS - Analyst
DEANNA STEELE - Generalist Human Resources

Famous Five Dining Inc.
227 Polk Place Dr
Franklin, TN 37064-5765

Telephone: (615) 794-0858
Fax Number: (615) 591-5265
Internet Homepage: homeofthebigslab.com
Company Email: info@homeofthebigslab.com
Type of Business: Chain Restaurant Operator
Year Founded: 2001
Total Sales: $9,307,000 (e)
Alcohol Sales: 20%
Number of Employees: 350
Average Check: Lunch(8); Dinner(8)
Total Units: 5
Trade Names: Famous Dave's (5)
Units Franchised From: 5
Preferred Square Footage: 6,000
Preferred Location Types: Freestanding
Alcohol Served: Beer, Wine, Liquor
Primary Menu: Bar-B-Q (5)
Areas of Operation: TN
Type of Foodservice: Casual Dining (5)
Franchise Affiliation: BBQ Holdings, Inc., MINNETONKA, MN
Primary Distributors: (Food) Reinhart FoodService, LOUISVILLE, TN; (Full Line) Reinhart FoodService, LOUISVILLE, TN

Key Personnel
MIKE LISTER - President; Partner; General Buyer
TAMARA LISTER - Partner; General Buyer
DOUG RENEGAR - Partner; General Buyer
LAUREL RENEGAR - Partner; General Buyer

Hardee's Food Systems Inc.
6700 Tower Cir Ste 1000
Franklin, TN 37067

Telephone: (615) 538-9400
Fax Number: (314) 259-6258
Internet Homepage: hardees.com
Company Email: info@hardees.com
Type of Business: Chain Restaurant Operator
Year Founded: 1960
Systemwide Sales: $3,679,015,000 (e)
Total Sales: $509,669,000 (e)
Number of Employees: 17,500
Average Check: Breakfast(8); Lunch(8); Dinner(8)
Total Units: 2,233
Trade Names: Hardee's (1,938); Hardee's/Red Burrito (295)
Company-Owned Units: 119
Units Franchised To: 2,114
Preferred Square Footage: 3,000; 3,500
Preferred Location Types: Community Mall; Downtown; Freestanding; Regional Mall; Stadiums; Travel Plazas
Primary Menu: Hamburger (2,233)
Projected Openings: 20
Areas of Operation: AL, AR, DE, FL, GA, IA, IL, IN, KS, KY, LA, MD, MI, MN, MO, MS, MT, NC, ND, NE, OH, OK, PA, SC, SD, TN, VA, WI, WV, WY
Foreign Countries: BAHRAIN; EGYPT; IRAQ; JORDAN; KAZAKHSTAN; KENYA; KUWAIT; OMAN; PAKISTAN; QATAR; SAUDI ARABIA
Type of Foodservice: Quick Serve (2,233)
Primary Distributors: (Full Line) McLane/Rocky Mount, ROCKY MOUNT, NC
Parent Company: CKE Restaurants Inc., FRANKLIN, TN

Key Personnel
JUSTIN FALCIOLA - CTO; Chief Growth Officer
CHRISTOPHER NORTON - Chief Sales Officer
MIKE DARGER - VP Facility/Maintenance
KIM TROOK - VP Restaurant Operations
ANN KISTLER - Senior Manager Quality Assurance
DEBBIE MANS - District Manager
JEREMY HOWELL - District Manager
BRENDA UTT - Manager Development, Training
MARK KOESTNER - Manager Purchasing
KIM WACKER - Consultant Franchising

Jonathan's Grille
7135 S Springs Dr
Franklin, TN 37067-1616

Telephone: (615) 771-0355
Internet Homepage: jonathansgrille.com
Company Email: heather@jonathansgrill.com
Type of Business: Chain Restaurant Operator
Total Units: 7
Trade Names: Jonathan's Grille (7)
Company-Owned Units: 7
Primary Menu: American (7)
Projected Openings: 1
Areas of Operation: TN
Type of Foodservice: Casual Dining (7)

Key Personnel
MASON REVELETTE - CEO; Partner; General Buyer
CURT REVELETTE - Partner

Southern Rock Restaurants LLC
1881 General George Patton Dr Ste 107
Franklin, TN 37067-4610

Telephone: (615) 656-7250
Fax Number: (615) 656-7255
Internet Homepage: southernrockrestaurants.com
Type of Business: Chain Restaurant Operator
Year Founded: 2011
Total Sales: $125,790,000 (e)
Number of Employees: 3,000
Average Check: Lunch(8); Dinner(10)
Total Units: 93
Trade Names: McAlister's Deli (93)
Units Franchised From: 93
Preferred Location Types: Regional Mall; Strip Mall
Primary Menu: Sandwiches/Deli (93)
Projected Openings: 30
Areas of Operation: IL, IN, KY, MO, MS, TN
Type of Foodservice: Fast Casual (93)
Franchise Affiliation: McAlister's Corporation, ATLANTA, GA

Key Personnel
DAVID R. BLACKBURN - CEO; COO
MAX PIET - CEO
LISA MATHIS - CFO
KITO CODY - COO
MARK RUSS - Area Director
SCOTT MORRIS - Area Director
BRITTANY MILLER - Area Director
KAT ANAGNOS - Area Director
GUY WHITLEY - VP Operations
BARRY FORTNER - VP Operations
CARRIE SPENCER - Director Marketing
THOM PANNULLO - Director Operations

STACEY WILLIAMS - Director Operations
TIFFANI STEELE - Manager Human Resources
BOB CASSADY - Supervisor Operations, District
RYAN OLDHAM - Supervisor Area
EDDIE MARR - Supervisor Area

Sweet CeCe's Franchising, LLC
500 W Main St
Franklin, TN 37064-2722

Telephone: (615) 807-1412
Internet Homepage: sweetceces.com
Type of Business: Chain Restaurant Operator
Year Founded: 2009
Total Sales: $5,487,000 (e)
Total Units: 10
Trade Names: Sweet Cece's Frozen Yogurt & Treats (10)
Units Franchised To: 10
Primary Menu: Snacks (16)
Areas of Operation: IL, KY, NM, OH, TN, TX
Type of Foodservice: Fast Casual (10)

Key Personnel
MIKE HISSONG - Partner; General Buyer
STACEY HISSONG - Partner

The Good Food Group
109 Holiday Ct Ste C5
Franklin, TN 37067-3084

Telephone: (615) 591-2862
Fax Number: (615) 791-1394
Type of Business: Chain Restaurant Operator
Year Founded: 2001
Total Sales: $43,140,000 (e)
Number of Employees: 400
Average Check: Breakfast(8); Lunch(8); Dinner(10)
Total Units: 9
Trade Names: McDonald's (9)
Units Franchised From: 9
Preferred Square Footage: 2,500; 3,000
Preferred Location Types: Freestanding
Primary Menu: Hamburger (9)
Areas of Operation: TN
Type of Foodservice: Quick Serve (9)
Franchise Affiliation: McDonald's Corporation, CHICAGO, IL
Primary Distributors: (Food) The Martin-Brower Co., DICKSON, TN

Key Personnel
JEMOND DAUGHTRY - Owner; Director Real Estate, Business Development; General Buyer
KEN TURNER - Director Operations, Facility/Maintenance, District

LEA MOSLEY - Manager Business Development
DAVID PARKS - Supervisor Region

England Foods
976 Parkway Ste 9
Gatlinburg, TN 37738-3104

Mailing Address: P O BOX 610, GATLINBURG, TN, 37738-0610
Telephone: (865) 436-5300
Internet Homepage: bestitalian.com
Company Email: info@bestitalian.com
Type of Business: Chain Restaurant Operator
Year Founded: 1993
Total Sales: $5,928,000 (e)
Alcohol Sales: 20%
Number of Employees: 120
Average Check: Breakfast(10); Lunch(18); Dinner(36)
Total Units: 3
Trade Names: Howard's Restaurant (1); The Best Italian Restaurant (2)
Company-Owned Units: 3
Preferred Location Types: Downtown; Freestanding; Mixed-use Center; Strip Mall
Alcohol Served: Beer, Wine, Liquor
Primary Menu: Italian (2); Steak/Seafood (1)
Areas of Operation: TN
Type of Foodservice: Casual Dining (3)
Catering Services: Yes
Primary Distributors: (Full Line) Performance Foodservice - Lester, LEBANON, TN

Key Personnel
MEREDITH MCDOWELL - Manager Accounting

The Peddler Steakhouse
820 River Rd
Gatlinburg, TN 37738-3133

Mailing Address: 1110 Parkway, GATLINBURG, TN, 37738-3100
Telephone: (865) 436-3800
Fax Number: (865) 436-2836
Internet Homepage: peddlergatlinburg.com; peddlerparkgrill.com
Type of Business: Chain Restaurant Operator
Year Founded: 1976
Total Sales: $9,173,000 (e)
Alcohol Sales: 18%
Number of Employees: 75
Average Check: Dinner(36)
Internet Order Processing: Yes
Internet Sales: 0.50%
Total Units: 2
Trade Names: The Park Grill (1); The Peddler Steak House (1)
Company-Owned Units: 2
Preferred Location Types: Downtown; Freestanding

Alcohol Served: Beer, Wine, Liquor
Primary Menu: American (1); Steak (1)
Areas of Operation: TN
Type of Foodservice: Casual Dining (2)
Primary Distributors: (Full Line) Sysco Food Services of Nashville, NASHVILLE, TN

Key Personnel
GEOFFREY WOLPERT - Partner; Executive Chef; Director Menu Development; General Buyer
PAT WOLPERT - Partner
DALE BRIGHT - Director Operations

Gus's Franchisor, LLC
2636 Lockesley Cv N
Germantown, TN 38139

Telephone: (901) 527-4877
Internet Homepage: gusfriedchicken.com
Company Email: communications@gusfriedchicken.com
Type of Business: Chain Restaurant Operator
Year Founded: 2013
Total Sales: $27,660,000 (e)
Total Units: 34
Trade Names: Gus's World Famous Fried Chicken (34)
Company-Owned Units: 2
Units Franchised To: 32
Primary Menu: Chicken (34)
Projected Openings: 3
Areas of Operation: AR, CA, GA, IL, KS, MD, MI, MO, MS, TN, TX
Type of Foodservice: Casual Dining (34)

Key Personnel
WENDY MCCRORY - President
BRAD TURNER - CFO
EDDIE LAPLANTE - Exec VP
TRIP DAY - Manager Operations

GPR Hospitality, LLC/FG Oaks, LLC
5928 Hixson Pike Ste A305
Hixson, TN 37343-4838

Telephone: (423) 605-1253
Company Email: jimrichards5guys@gprhospitalityllc.com
Type of Business: Chain Restaurant Operator
Total Sales: $13,570,000 (e)
Total Units: 7
Trade Names: Five Guys Burgers and Fries (7)
Units Franchised From: 7
Preferred Square Footage: 3,000
Primary Menu: Hamburger (7)
Areas of Operation: GA, TN
Type of Foodservice: Fast Casual (7)
Franchise Affiliation: Five Guys Holdings Inc.,

LORTON, VA

Key Personnel
JAMES RICHARDS - President; General Buyer

Investors of West Tennessee Inc
200 S Royal St
Jackson, TN 38301-6334

Mailing Address: PO Box 11926, JACKSON, TN, 38308-0132
Telephone: (731) 422-5566
Fax Number: (731) 422-5567
Type of Business: Chain Restaurant Operator
Total Sales: $10,757,000 (e)
Total Units: 4
Trade Names: Popeyes Louisiana Kitchen (4)
Units Franchised From: 4
Primary Menu: Chicken (4)
Areas of Operation: TN
Type of Foodservice: Quick Serve (4)
Franchise Affiliation: Popeyes Louisiana Kitchen Inc., ATLANTA, GA

Key Personnel
DON AGNEW - President

Subway Carriage House Inc
660 Carriage House Dr
Jackson, TN 38305-4253

Telephone: (731) 668-1678
Type of Business: Chain Restaurant Operator
Total Sales: $2,216,000 (e)
Total Units: 3
Trade Names: Subway (3)
Units Franchised From: 3
Primary Menu: Sandwiches/Deli (3)
Areas of Operation: TN
Type of Foodservice: Quick Serve (3)
Franchise Affiliation: Doctor's Associates Inc., MILFORD, CT

Key Personnel
PAUL PATEL - Owner; General Buyer

J S H Enterprises Inc
2503 Avondale Dr
Johnson City, TN 37604-2406

Telephone: (423) 929-1221
Type of Business: Chain Restaurant Operator
Total Sales: $3,011,000 (e)
Total Units: 2
Trade Names: Jersey Mike's Subs (2)
Units Franchised From: 2
Primary Menu: Sandwiches/Deli (2)
Areas of Operation: TN
Type of Foodservice: Quick Serve (2)
Franchise Affiliation: Jersey Mike's Franchise Systems, MANASQUAN, NJ

Key Personnel
JIM HUDSON - President; General Buyer

JSH Enterprises, Inc.
1805 W State of Franklin Rd Ste 100
Johnson City, TN 37604-8802

Telephone: (423) 929-1221
Type of Business: Chain Restaurant Operator
Total Sales: $2,910,000 (e)
Total Units: 2
Trade Names: Jersey Mike's Subs (2)
Units Franchised From: 2
Primary Menu: Sandwiches/Deli (2)
Areas of Operation: TN
Type of Foodservice: Quick Serve (2)
Franchise Affiliation: Jersey Mike's Franchise Systems, MANASQUAN, NJ

Key Personnel
JIM HUDSON - Owner; General Buyer

Pal's Sudden Service
1001 Konnarock Rd
Kingsport, TN 37664

Telephone: (423) 926-9494
Internet Homepage: palsweb.com
Type of Business: Chain Restaurant Operator
Total Units: 30
Trade Names: Pal's Sudden Service (30)
Company-Owned Units: 30
Primary Menu: Hamburger (30)
Areas of Operation: TN, VA
Type of Foodservice: Quick Serve (30)

Key Personnel
THOM CROSBY - President

Pal's Sudden Service Inc.
1001 Konnarock Rd
Kingsport, TN 37664-3720

Telephone: (423) 247-3501
Fax Number: (423) 247-3502
Internet Homepage: palsweb.com
Company Email: info@palsweb.com
Type of Business: Chain Restaurant Operator
Year Founded: 1955
Total Sales: $44,210,000 (e)
Number of Employees: 1,100
Average Check: Breakfast(8); Lunch(8); Dinner(8)
Total Units: 29

Trade Names: Pal's (29)
Company-Owned Units: 29
Preferred Square Footage: 1,100; 3,000
Preferred Location Types: Freestanding
Primary Menu: Hamburger (29)
Areas of Operation: TN, VA
Type of Foodservice: Quick Serve (29)
Primary Distributors: (Full Line) SYSCO Corporation, HOUSTON, TX

Key Personnel
FRED BARGER - Chairman; Director Facility/Maintenance, Real Estate, Design
THOM CROSBY - CEO; President; COO; Manager Finance, Operations, Information Systems, Risk Management, Human Resources; General Buyer
RICK BARGER - Partner; VP Advertising; Director Menu Development; Manager Food Safety
CHRIS BARGER - Partner; VP Store Planning
ROB THOMPSON - CIO

Palace Vending Inc.
1820 N Eastman Rd
Kingsport, TN 37664-2312

Telephone: (423) 247-9181
Fax Number: (888) 329-2784
Internet Homepage: palacevending.com
Company Email: palaceoffice@palacevending.com
Type of Business: Foodservice Management Operator
Year Founded: 1952
Total Sales: $14,197,000 (e)
Number of Employees: 60
Number of Locations Served: 150
Total Foodservice Mgmt Accounts: 150
Areas of Operation: NC, TN, VA
Type of Foodservice: Vending machines (150)
Foodservice Management Venues: Business & Industry; Health Care
Primary Distributors: (Full Line) Reinhart Foodservice, JOHNSON CITY, TN

Key Personnel
P. T. NOTTINGHAM - President; Controller; Director Operations, Purchasing, Information Technology, Human Resources
JOHN O. NOTTINGHAM - VP Finance
MARTHA GILLENWATER - General Manager
SANDY FIELDS - Manager Administration

RMG LC, LLC
113 Regional Park Dr
Kingsport, TN 37660-7455

Telephone: (423) 349-6204
Fax Number: (423) 349-6721
Internet Homepage: rmgrestaurants.com

Type of Business: Chain Restaurant Operator
Total Sales: $78,820,000 (e)
Number of Employees: 1,259
Average Check: Dinner(16)
Total Units: 63
Trade Names: Little Caesars Pizza (63)
Units Franchised From: 63
Preferred Square Footage: 1,600; 3,000
Preferred Location Types: Downtown; Freestanding; Strip Mall
Primary Menu: Pizza (63)
Areas of Operation: FL, GA, NC, SC, TN, VA
Type of Foodservice: Quick Serve (63)
Franchise Affiliation: Little Caesar Enterprises Inc., DETROIT, MI

Key Personnel
PIERRE BOURSSE - Owner
CRAIG MCCLURE - CFO; General Buyer
JOSHUA BRYANT - General Manager
KIM COLE - Director Human Resources

Shamrock LLC
4924 Fort Henry Dr Ste A
Kingsport, TN 37663-3386

Telephone: (423) 239-1896
Fax Number: (423) 239-1892
Type of Business: Chain Restaurant Operator
Total Sales: $37,770,000 (e)
Number of Employees: 185
Total Units: 8
Trade Names: McDonald's (8)
Units Franchised From: 8
Preferred Square Footage: 2,500
Primary Menu: Hamburger (8)
Areas of Operation: TN
Type of Foodservice: Quick Serve (8)
Franchise Affiliation: McDonald's Corporation, CHICAGO, IL

Key Personnel
DIANE WASHBURN - President; General Buyer

Vanmar Inc.
2505 S Wilcox Dr Ste 1
Kingsport, TN 37660-7472

Telephone: (423) 343-8020
Type of Business: Chain Restaurant Operator
Year Founded: 1970
Total Sales: $13,360,000 (e)
Number of Employees: 275
Average Check: Breakfast(8); Lunch(10); Dinner(10)
Total Units: 6
Trade Names: Burger King (6)
Units Franchised From: 6
Preferred Square Footage: 2,500
Preferred Location Types: Freestanding
Primary Menu: Hamburger (6)
Areas of Operation: TN
Type of Foodservice: Quick Serve (6)
Franchise Affiliation: Burger King Worldwide Inc., MIAMI, FL
Primary Distributors: (Equipment) QualServ Corporation, FORT SMITH, AR; (Supplies) QualServ Corporation, FORT SMITH, AR

Key Personnel
DIANE CLAYTON - President; Controller; Director Facility/Maintenance, Real Estate, Design
MARY MCREYNOLDS - Director Operations; General Buyer

Aubrey's Inc.
5401 Kingston Pike Ste 280
Knoxville, TN 37919-5073

Mailing Address: PO Box 11564, Knoxville, Tn, 37939
Telephone: (865) 584-7779
Fax Number: (865) 584-7786
Internet Homepage: aubreysrestaurants.com
Company Email: info@aubreysrestaurants.com
Type of Business: Chain Restaurant Operator
Year Founded: 1992
Total Sales: $15,360,000 (e)
Alcohol Sales: 8%
Number of Employees: 1,392
Average Check: Lunch(18); Dinner(36)
Total Units: 22
Trade Names: Aubrey's Restaurant (13); Barley's Taproom & Pizzeria (2); Bistro by the Tracks (1); Crown & Goose (1); Drink (1); Field House Social (1); Stefano's Pizza (2); Sunspot (1)
Company-Owned Units: 22
Preferred Square Footage: 5,500; 6,000
Preferred Location Types: Freestanding
Alcohol Served: Beer, Wine, Liquor
Primary Menu: American (16); Miscellaneous (1); Pizza (4); Snacks (1)
Projected Openings: 3
Areas of Operation: TN
Type of Foodservice: Casual Dining (22)
Primary Distributors: (Food) Reinhart FoodService, LOUISVILLE, TN

Key Personnel
RANDY BURLESON - Owner; General Manager; Director Real Estate, Design, Human Resources; General Buyer
DAVID BELCHER - CFO; Controller
CRAIG KRAUSE - Director Communications, Human Resources

Audubon Inc
107 Westfield Rd
Knoxville, TN 37919-4820

Telephone: (865) 588-2875
Type of Business: Chain Restaurant Operator
Total Sales: $28,360,000 (e)
Number of Employees: 420
Total Units: 21
Trade Names: Papa John's Pizza (21)
Units Franchised From: 21
Preferred Location Types: Freestanding; Strip Mall
Primary Menu: Pizza (21)
Areas of Operation: AL, GA, SC
Type of Foodservice: Quick Serve (21)
Franchise Affiliation: Papa Johns International Inc., LOUISVILLE, KY

Key Personnel
DOUGLAS HARRIS - Owner
JEFF WEBER - CFO; Controller
ROBERTO ZAYAS - VP Finance

B Squared Enterprises, LLC
8853 Town and Country Cir
Knoxville, TN 37923-4905

Telephone: (865) 531-2303
Fax Number: (865) 531-2304
Type of Business: Chain Restaurant Operator
Total Sales: $10,450,000 (e)
Total Units: 9
Trade Names: Firehouse Subs (9)
Units Franchised From: 9
Preferred Square Footage: 1,500
Primary Menu: Sandwiches/Deli (9)
Areas of Operation: TN
Type of Foodservice: Fast Casual (9)
Franchise Affiliation: Firehouse Restaurant Group Inc., JACKSONVILLE, FL

Key Personnel
JAMES BLAKE - President; General Buyer
ROBBIE CARROLL - Manager District

Bros. Management Inc.
2501 E Magnolia Ave
Knoxville, TN 37914-5311

Telephone: (865) 523-2157
Fax Number: (865) 523-0367
Type of Business: Chain Restaurant Operator
Year Founded: 1965
Total Sales: $109,180,000 (e)
Number of Employees: 378
Average Check: Breakfast(8); Lunch(8); Dinner(10)
Total Units: 23

Trade Names: McDonald's (23)
Units Franchised From: 23
Preferred Square Footage: 1,500; 3,000
Preferred Location Types: Convenience Store/Gas Station; Discount Dept. Stores; Freestanding; Regional Mall
Primary Menu: Hamburger (23)
Areas of Operation: TN
Type of Foodservice: Quick Serve (23)
Franchise Affiliation: McDonald's Corporation, CHICAGO, IL

Key Personnel
TOM COCHRAN - CEO; President; Director Operations
GARY MAGEE - CFO; Controller; Manager Finance, Purchasing, Risk Management
JOANNE HUDDLESTON - VP Marketing, Advertising
JACK DICKINSON - Director Human Resources; Manager Facility/Maintenance

Buddy's bar-b-q
5806 Kingston Pike
Knoxville, TN 37919-6339

Telephone: (865) 588-0051
Fax Number: (865) 588-7211
Internet Homepage: buddysbarbq.com
Company Email: markl@buddysbarbq.com
Type of Business: Chain Restaurant Operator
Year Founded: 1972
Systemwide Sales: $36,176,000 (e)
Total Sales: $20,320,000 (e)
Alcohol Sales: 1%
Number of Employees: 428
Average Check: Breakfast(10); Lunch(12); Dinner(14)
Internet Order Processing: Yes
Total Units: 16
Trade Names: Buddy's bar-b-q (16)
Company-Owned Units: 11
Units Franchised To: 5
Preferred Square Footage: 3,000
Preferred Location Types: Freestanding
Primary Menu: Bar-B-Q (16)
Areas of Operation: TN
Type of Foodservice: Casual Dining (16)
Catering Services: Yes
Primary Distributors: (Full Line) US Foods, ALCOA, TN

Key Personnel
MARK SMOTHERS - CEO; President; Director Real Estate, Design
MARK LEMONCELLI - CEO; President
ALLEN GRADY - CFO; Controller
REED LINDSEY - VP Operations, Purchasing, Loss Prevention, Supply Chain, Human Resources; General Buyer
VIRGINIA SMOTHERS - Corporate Secretary
CLAYTON DAMATO - General Manager

SUZANNE LINDSEY - Director Marketing

Connor Concepts
10911 Turkey Dr
Knoxville, TN 37934-1970

Telephone: (865) 777-2677
Fax Number: (865) 671-1977
Internet Homepage: connorconcepts.com; connorsrestaurant.com; thechophouse.com
Company Email: comments@thechophouse.com
Type of Business: Chain Restaurant Operator
Year Founded: 1991
Total Sales: $59,750,000 (e)
Alcohol Sales: 26%
Number of Employees: 1,136
Average Check: Lunch(24); Dinner(46)
Internet Order Processing: Yes
Internet Sales: 3.00%
Total Units: 17
Trade Names: Connor's Steak & Seafood (5); The Chop House (12)
Company-Owned Units: 17
Preferred Square Footage: 7,000
Preferred Location Types: Freestanding
Alcohol Served: Beer, Wine, Liquor
Primary Menu: Steak (12); Steak/Seafood (5)
Areas of Operation: AL, FL, GA, KY, OH, TN
Type of Foodservice: Casual Dining (17)
Primary Distributors: (Equipment) Trimark Strategic, KNOXVILLE, TN; (Supplies) Trimark Strategic, KNOXVILLE, TN

Key Personnel
MIKE CONNOR - CEO; President; Manager Finance, Real Estate, Design, Human Resources
BRIAN KEYES - Partner; VP Operations; Director Operations, Purchasing, Facility/Maintenance, Risk Management, Supply Chain, Marketing, Store Fixtures, Internet Development
TONY WATSON - Partner; VP Purchasing; Director Information Systems, Research & Development
NICKI DAWSON - CFO
ANGELA HAWKINS - Controller
MARK DAVIS - Corporate Chef

Copper Cellar Corporation
3001 Industrial Pkwy E
Knoxville, TN 37921-1711

Mailing Address: PO Box 50370, KNOXVILLE, TN, 37950-0370
Telephone: (865) 522-3500
Fax Number: (865) 522-8526
Internet Homepage: copperfoods.com; calhouns.com; cherokeegrill.com; chesapeakes.com; coppercellar.com; smoky-mtn-brewery.com
Company Email: info@coppercellar.com
Type of Business: Chain Restaurant Operator
Year Founded: 1975
Total Sales: $126,900,000 (e)
Alcohol Sales: 10%
Number of Employees: 1,358
Average Check: Lunch(24); Dinner(32)
Internet Order Processing: Yes
Internet Sales: 1.00%
Total Units: 22
Trade Names: Calhoun's (9); Cappuccino's (1); Cherokee Grill (1); Chesapeake's (3); Copper Cellar Restaurant (3); Corner 16 (1); Smoky Mountain Brewery(4)
Company-Owned Units: 22
Preferred Square Footage: 10,000
Preferred Location Types: Freestanding; Strip Mall
Alcohol Served: Beer, Wine, Liquor
Primary Menu: American (18); Italian (1); Seafood (3)
Areas of Operation: TN
Type of Foodservice: Casual Dining (19); Fine Dining (3)
Catering Services: Yes
On-site Distribution Center: Yes
Primary Distributors: (Full Line) US Foods, ALCOA, TN

Key Personnel
MICHAEL D. CHASE - President; Director Real Estate, Construction, Store Planning
MIKE GASTON - Director Information Systems

Denton's Family Foods
6920 Kingston Pike
Knoxville, TN 37919

Telephone: (865) 558-8676
Internet Homepage: dentonfoods.com
Company Email: info@dentonfoods.com
Type of Business: Chain Restaurant Operator
Year Founded: 1946
Total Units: 4
Trade Names: Denton's (1); Wishbones (3)
Company-Owned Units: 4
Preferred Location Types: Freestanding
Primary Menu: American (1); Chicken (3)
Areas of Operation: TN
Type of Foodservice: Family Restaurant (1); Fast Casual (3)

Key Personnel
DOC DENTON - Partner
BRAD DENTON - Partner

Diverse Concepts
7100 Kingston Pike Ste B
Knoxville, TN 37919-5709

Telephone: (865) 584-4245
Fax Number: (865) 584-4284
Internet Homepage: dclfood.com
Type of Business: Chain Restaurant Operator
Year Founded: 1919
Total Sales: $9,247,000 (e)
Alcohol Sales: 30%
Number of Employees: 1,055
Average Check: Lunch(12); Dinner(22)
Total Units: 9
Trade Names: Blue Moose Burgers and Wings (1); Bullfish (1); Carino's Italian (1); Harrison's (1); Lakeside Tavern (1); Liberty Grill (1); Mellow Mushroom (1); Parkside Grill (1); Timberwood Grill (1)
Company-Owned Units: 2
Units Franchised From: 7
Preferred Location Types: Freestanding
Alcohol Served: Beer, Wine, Liquor
Primary Menu: American (7); Italian (1); Pizza (1)
Areas of Operation: TN
Type of Foodservice: Casual Dining (9)
Catering Services: Yes
Primary Distributors: (Food) Reinhart FoodService, LOUISVILLE, TN

Key Personnel
BOB MCMANUS - President; General Buyer
BETH MARTIN - General Counsel
PAUL DELAHUNT - Director Operations
MARTHA YARNELL - Manager Special Projects

Home Run Inc.
1819 Lake Ave
Knoxville, TN 37916-3007

Telephone: (865) 584-7190
Fax Number: (865) 588-8034
Internet Homepage: Papajohns.com; homeruninc.com
Type of Business: Chain Restaurant Operator
Year Founded: 1991
Total Sales: $14,940,000 (e)
Number of Employees: 330
Average Check: Lunch(16); Dinner(22)
Total Units: 11
Trade Names: Papa John's Pizza (11)
Units Franchised From: 11
Preferred Square Footage: 1,100; 1,500
Preferred Location Types: Strip Mall
Primary Menu: Pizza (11)
Areas of Operation: TN
Type of Foodservice: Quick Serve (11)
Franchise Affiliation: Papa Johns International Inc., LOUISVILLE, KY
Primary Distributors: (Food) Papa John's Distribution Center, LOUISVILLE, KY

Key Personnel
DAVID PEARCE - CEO; Partner
LEE STINSON JR - Partner; Director Finance, Purchasing, Real Estate
CHRIS COFFEY - VP Operations

Nixon Deli Franchises, LLC
508 Merchant Dr
Knoxville, TN 37912-3851

Telephone: (865) 332-4686
Fax Number: (865) 219-9669
Internet Homepage: nixonsdeli.com
Company Email: contact@nixonsdeli.com
Type of Business: Chain Restaurant Operator
Year Founded: 1976
Total Sales: $4,795,000 (e)
Number of Employees: 60
Average Check: Lunch(10); Dinner(10)
Total Units: 5
Trade Names: Nixon's Deli (5)
Company-Owned Units: 5
Preferred Square Footage: 1,500
Preferred Location Types: Downtown; Office Complex; Strip Mall
Primary Menu: Sandwiches/Deli (5)
Areas of Operation: TN
Type of Foodservice: Family Restaurant (5)
Catering Services: Yes
Primary Distributors: (Full Line) PFG - Customized Support Services, LEBANON, TN

Key Personnel
BILL BROOKS - President; Partner; Executive Chef; Manager Finance, Operations, Purchasing, Facility/Maintenance, Real Estate, Design
MATTHEW BROOKS - Partner; Director Operations, Information Systems
MICHELLE FUERST - Director Catering

Phoenix Theatres LLC
9111 Cross Park Dr Ste E275
Knoxville, TN 37923-4532

Telephone: (865) 692-4061
Fax Number: (865) 692-4065
Internet Homepage: phoenixtheatres.com
Company Email: info@phoenixtheatres.com
Type of Business: Foodservice Operations - Movie Theatre
Year Founded: 2000
Total Sales: $14,670,000 (e)
Alcohol Sales: 25%
Number of Employees: 375
Average Check: Breakfast(5); Lunch(5); Dinner(5)
Internet Order Processing: Yes
Internet Sales: 1.00%
Total Units: 12
Trade Names: Capitol 3 (1); Chartiers Valley Stadium 18 (1); Cherokee (1); Lake Worth 8 (1); Laughlin Stadium 9 Cinemas (1); Main Gate Movies 10 (1); Marlow Cinema 6 (1); North Versailles Stadium 10 (1); Peninsula Movie Bistro (1); Phoenix The Edge 12 (1); Phoenix Theaters The Edge 8 (1); The Forge Cinemas 5 (1)
Company-Owned Units: 12
Preferred Square Footage: 35,000; 60,000
Preferred Location Types: Freestanding; Lifestyle Center; Regional Mall
Alcohol Served: Beer, Wine
Primary Menu: Snacks (12)
Areas of Operation: CA, FL, GA, IL, KS, MD, NC, NJ, NV, NY, PA, TN, VA
Type of Foodservice: In-Store Feeder (12)
Notes: The company derives approximately 80% of its revenue from admissions and other retail operations.

Key Personnel
PHIL ZACHERETTI - President; General Buyer

Pilot Flying J
5508 Lonas Dr
Knoxville, TN 37909-3221

Mailing Address: PO Box 10146, KNOXVILLE, TN, 37939-0146
Telephone: (865) 588-7488
Fax Number: (865) 450-2830
Internet Homepage: pilotflyingJ.com
Company Email: customerservice@pilottravelcenters.com
Type of Business: Nontraditional Foodservice Operator
Year Founded: 1958
Total Sales: $48,235,402,000 (e)
Number of Employees: 29,000
Average Check: Breakfast(8); Lunch(14); Dinner(14)
Total Units: 736
Trade Names: Arby's; Auntie Anne's; Chester's Chicken; Cinnabon; Dairy Queen; Denny's; Huddle House; KFC; Mama DeLuca's; McDonald's; Moe's Southwest Grill; Pizza Hut; Subway; Taco Bell; Wendy's Old Fashioned Hamburgers
Company-Owned Units: 736
Preferred Square Footage: 1,500; 2,000; 2,500; 3,000
Preferred Location Types: Travel Plazas
Primary Menu: Chinese (0); Hot Dogs (0); Mexican (0); Miscellaneous (-56); Seafood (0); Steak (0); Steak (187)
Areas of Operation: AL, AR, AZ, CA, CO, CT, FL, GA, IA, ID, IL, IN, KS, KY, LA, MA, MD, ME, MI, MN, MO, MS, MT, NC, ND, NE, NH, NJ, NM, NV, NY, OH, OK, OR, PA, SC, SD, TN, TX, UT, VA, WA, WI, WV, WY, AB, BC, MB, ON, QC, SK

Foreign Countries: CANADA
Type of Foodservice: Casual Dining; Family Restaurant; Fast Casual; Quick Serve
Franchise Affiliation: A&W Restaurants Inc., LEXINGTON, KY; Arby's Restaurant Group, ATLANTA, GA; Burger King Worldwide Inc., MIAMI, FL; Chester's International LLC, MOUNTAIN BRK, AL; Cinnabon Inc., ATLANTA, GA; DD IP Holder, CANTON, MA; Denny's Corporation, SPARTANBURG, SC; Doctor's Associates Inc., MILFORD, CT; Golden Corral Corp., RALEIGH, NC; Huddle House Inc., ATLANTA, GA; IHOP Restaurant System, GLENDALE, CA; International Dairy Queen Inc., BLOOMINGTON, MN; KFC Corporation, LOUISVILLE, KY; Legacy Franchise Group, MIDDLETON, WI; Long John Silver's Inc., LOUISVILLE, KY; McDonald's Corporation, CHICAGO, IL; Moe's Southwest Grill LLC, ATLANTA, GA; Noble Roman's Inc., INDIANAPOLIS, IN; Orion Food Systems LLC, SIOUX FALLS, SD; Pizza Hut Inc., PLANO, TX; Taco Bell Corp., IRVINE, CA; The Quiznos Master LLC, DENVER, CO; The Wendy's Company, DUBLIN, OH
Primary Distributors: (Full Line) McLane Foodservice, CARROLLTON, TX
Notes: The company derives approximately 90% of its revenue from operating travel centers & convenience stores. Pilot Travel Centers named Denny's its full-service restaurant operator of choice for approximately 130 travel plazas in the US.

Key Personnel
JAMES A. HASLAM II - Chairman
JAMES A. HASLAM III - Chairman
SHAMEEK KONAR - CEO
KEVIN WILLS - CFO
MIKE RODGERS - CIO; Chief Strategy Officer; Senior VP
KRISTIN SEABROOK - Chief Legal Officer; VP; Corporate Secretary
DAVID HUGHES - Senior VP Sales
DAVE LATIMER - VP Strategy
JOSH BIRDWELL - Senior Director Systems
KIMBERLY BILLINGS - Director Merchandising
DON GRAHAM - Senior Manager Loss Prevention, Risk Management
DENNIS EDWARDS - Manager Facility/Maintenance

Regal Entertainment Group
7132 Regal Ln
Knoxville, TN 37918-5803

Telephone: (865) 922-1123
Fax Number: (865) 922-3188
Internet Homepage: regalcinemas.com; regmovies.com
Company Email: comments@regalcinemas.com
Type of Business: Foodservice Operations - Movie Theatre
Year Founded: 1989
Total Sales: $5,248,338,000 (e)
Number of Employees: 23,000
Average Check: Lunch(5); Dinner(5)
Foodservice Sales: $1,574,501,000 (e)
Internet Order Processing: Yes
Total Units: 522
Trade Names: Consolidated Theatres (6); Regal Cinemas (431)
Company-Owned Units: 437
Preferred Location Types: Downtown; Freestanding; Lifestyle Center; Other; Regional Mall; Strip Mall
Areas of Operation: AK, AL, AR, CA, CO, CT, DC, DE, FL, GA, GU, HI, ID, IL, IN, KY, LA, MA, MD, ME, MI, MN, MO, MS, NC, NH, NJ, NM, NV, NY, OH, OR, PA, SC, TN, TX, VA, WA, WV
Foreign Countries: AMERICAN SAMOA
Type of Foodservice: In-Store Feeder
Primary Distributors: (Full Line) Sysco Food Services of Nashville, NASHVILLE, TN
Notes: The company derives approximately 71% of its revenue from movie theatre admissions, on-screen advertising, & other operations.

Key Personnel
NISAN COHEN - CEO
MOSHE GREIDINGER - CEO
TAL SOUDRY - CFO; VP Finance
JOHN CURRY - Senior VP Foodservice; General Buyer
TODD BORUFF - Senior VP Real Estate
LISA BYRNES - VP Risk Management
JAKE BISHOP - VP Culinary Development
CHRIS FRYE - VP Tax
KELLY HAWKINS - VP Loyalty Program
BARRY STEINBERG - VP
BRANDON STROUD - VP Operations, Information Technology
CHRIS SYLVIA - VP Media
ANDREW TURNER - VP Media
ROB WESTERLING - VP
CAROLE MALEK - VP Operations
WAVERLY MAPLES - VP Real Estate
JOSEPH MARLOWE - VP Payroll
KELLY PALMER - VP Administration, Systems
ROBBIE POPE - General Counsel; Director Real Estate
DAVID JONES - General Manager
JOHN DURLIAT - Senior Director
DEAN DUNCAN - Director Inventory
JONATHAN DOUGLAS - Director Media
JUSTIN CAMPBELL - Director Operations
STEVE ALLEN - Director Technology, West Region
JERRY BERG - Director
ANGIE BERRY - Director Construction, Design
JENNIFER JONES - Director Human Resources
GARY HEBEBRAND - Director Loss Prevention
STEPHEN HILL - Director Information Technology
TIM HINSON - Director Operations
RICHARD GROVER - Director Marketing
TED HATFIELD - Director Marketing
JEAN FOX - Director Benefits
LEEANN PANNELL - Director Security, Quality Assurance
TOM O'ROURKE - Director Foodservice
PAUL ONEILL - Director Security
AUDREY MAY - Director Finance
TOM MANNING - Director Operations
MICHAEL LEWIS - Director Legal
JOHN LIVIGNI - Director Procurement
GINGER WHITED - Director Quality Assurance
KATRINA WILSON - Director Real Estate
COURTNEY SPIRES - Director Cloud Computing
JESSICA STANFORD - Director Internal Audit
ABEL PEREZ - Regional Director
MELODY GOODWIN - Senior Manager Human Resources
SHANE MONGAR - District Manager
ANTHONY SCARPACI - District Manager
WILLIAM SEAY - Manager Procurement
THOMAS O'ROURKE - Manager Foodservice
JEFFREY PENDLETON - Manager Data Production
JACK FORD - Manager Purchasing
TIMOTHY BIRD - Manager Web Design
ELIZABETH ALBERT - Manager Email Marketing
TIM BORUFF - Project Manager
GLEN MOUNGER - Project Manager
STEVE MASSEY - Project Manager
DAVID ROE - Administrator Tax
LAURA SKIBINSKI - Administrator Software
RUBI THOMAS - Specialist Benefits
MISTY WOLFE - Specialist Payroll
JANICE ENIX - Specialist Human Resources
JUDY KARNES - Coordinator
CHRIS FOWLKES - Systems Analyst
TREY FRANKLIN - Analyst Information Technology
SCOTT DUMMITT - Analyst Information/Data Security
TJ GOODEN - Engineer Network
KEITH KOCHER - Engineer Network

Shoney's of Knoxville Inc.
9720 Parkside Dr
Knoxville, TN 37922-2203

Telephone: (865) 690-6331
Fax Number: (865) 690-0620
Internet Homepage: shoneysknox.com
Company Email: info@shoneysknox.com
Type of Business: Chain Restaurant Operator
Year Founded: 1962
Total Sales: $41,780,000 (e)
Total Units: 18
Trade Names: Shoney's (18)
Units Franchised From: 18
Preferred Square Footage: 5,500
Preferred Location Types: Freestanding
Primary Menu: American (18)

Areas of Operation: TN
Type of Foodservice: Family Restaurant (18)
Franchise Affiliation: Shoney's North America Corp., NASHVILLE, TN

Key Personnel
ROY LESLIE - CEO; President; General Buyer
MARY EMBLER - CFO
ROBERT LAGUERRE - Senior VP Operations

Sullivan's Fine Food at Rocky Hill
7545 S Northshore Dr
Knoxville, TN 37919-8002

Telephone: (865) 694-9696
Fax Number: (865) 693-4922
Internet Homepage: sullivansfinefoods.com
Type of Business: Chain Restaurant Operator
Year Founded: 1982
Total Sales: $4,658,000 (e)
Alcohol Sales: 15%
Number of Employees: 60
Average Check: Dinner(18)
Total Units: 2
Trade Names: Sullivan's Fine Food (2)
Company-Owned Units: 2
Preferred Location Types: Downtown; Freestanding
Alcohol Served: Beer, Wine, Liquor
Primary Menu: American (2)
Areas of Operation: TN
Type of Foodservice: Casual Dining (2)
Primary Distributors: (Food) Sysco Food Services of Nashville, NASHVILLE, TN

Key Personnel
CHARLES IRVINE JR - President; General Manager
JOHNATHON ROBERTS - General Manager
ALEJANDRO BILLEGAS - Executive Chef; General Buyer

The Great TN Pizza Company Inc
6661 Maynardville Pike
Knoxville, TN 37918-4863

Telephone: (865) 925-2151
Type of Business: Chain Restaurant Operator
Total Sales: $67,477,000 (e)
Total Units: 33
Trade Names: Domino's (33)
Units Franchised From: 33
Primary Menu: Pizza (33)
Areas of Operation: TN
Type of Foodservice: Quick Serve (33)
Franchise Affiliation: Domino's Pizza Inc, ANN ARBOR, MI

Key Personnel
PETER P. D'ANDREA - Owner; General Buyer

X2L Inc.
9104 US Highway 64
Lakeland, TN 38002-9765

Mailing Address: PO Box 1181, Collierville, TN, 38027-1181
Telephone: (901) 386-9683
Fax Number: (901) 386-9824
Type of Business: Chain Restaurant Operator
Total Sales: $28,190,000 (e)
Number of Employees: 50
Average Check: Lunch(10); Dinner(14)
Total Units: 8
Trade Names: Zaxby's (8)
Units Franchised From: 8
Preferred Location Types: Freestanding
Primary Menu: Chicken (8)
Areas of Operation: TN
Type of Foodservice: Fast Casual (8)
Franchise Affiliation: Zaxby's Franchising Inc., ATHENS, GA
Primary Distributors: (Full Line) Sysco Food Services of Memphis, MEMPHIS, TN

Key Personnel
JEREMY GATTI - President; General Buyer

Bush Management
1215 N Locust Ave
Lawrenceburg, TN 38464-2710

Mailing Address: PO Box 1025, LAWRENCEBURG, TN, 38464-1025
Telephone: (931) 762-3400
Fax Number: (931) 762-3561
Type of Business: Chain Restaurant Operator
Year Founded: 1986
Total Sales: $20,256,000 (e)
Number of Employees: 300
Average Check: Breakfast(0); Lunch(8); Dinner(10)
Total Units: 4
Trade Names: McDonald's (4)
Units Franchised From: 4
Preferred Square Footage: 2,000
Preferred Location Types: Discount Dept. Stores; Freestanding
Primary Menu: Hamburger (4)
Areas of Operation: AL, TN
Type of Foodservice: Quick Serve (4)
Franchise Affiliation: McDonald's Corporation, CHICAGO, IL
Primary Distributors: (Full Line) The Martin-Brower Co. LLC, ROSEMONT, IL

Key Personnel
BETTY BUSH - President; Manager Finance, Purchasing, Facility/Maintenance, Supply Chain, Real Estate, Design
KRIS QUILLEN - Manager Real Estate, Human Resources
CAROL MURRAY - Manager Operations, Information Systems, Marketing

Rising Sun Corp.
2220 Wo Smith Dr
Lawrenceburg, TN 38464-7373

Telephone: (931) 762-8134
Fax Number: (931) 766-2222
Internet Homepage: legendssteakhouse.com
Company Email: info@legendssteakhouse.com
Type of Business: Chain Restaurant Operator
Year Founded: 1993
Total Sales: $13,190,000 (e)
Alcohol Sales: 25%
Number of Employees: 252
Average Check: Lunch(20); Dinner(32)
Total Units: 6
Trade Names: Brass Lantern Road House Grill (1); Legends Restaurant (5)
Company-Owned Units: 7
Preferred Square Footage: 5,500; 6,000
Preferred Location Types: Downtown; Office Complex; Strip Mall
Alcohol Served: Beer, Wine, Liquor
Primary Menu: Steak (6)
Areas of Operation: AL, TN
Type of Foodservice: Casual Dining (5); Quick Serve (1)
Primary Distributors: (Full Line) PFG - Customized Support Services, LEBANON, TN
Notes: Operates as Sundowner Management Group.

Key Personnel
JOHNNY FLEEMAN - Owner; Corporate Chef; Director Real Estate
JACLYN SEXTON - Corporate Secretary
BILL OSBORN - General Manager; General Buyer; Coordinator Information Systems

Cracker Barrel Distribution Center
900 Hutchinson Pl
Lebanon, TN 37090-0786

Telephone: (615) 443-9738
Fax Number: (615) 443-9636
Listing Type: Distribution Center
Type of Business: Chain Restaurant Operator
Areas of Operation: AL, AR, AZ, CO, CT, DE, FL, GA, IA, ID, IL, IN, KS, KY, LA, MA, MD, ME, MI, MN, MO, MS, MT, NC, ND, NE, NH, NJ, NM, NY, OH, OK, PA, RI, SC, SD, TN, TX, UT, VA, VT, WI, WV
Parent Company: Cracker Barrel Old Country

Store Inc., LEBANON, TN

Key Personnel
MADEANNA ADAMS - Manager Logistics

Cracker Barrel Old Country Store Inc.
305 S Hartmann Dr
Lebanon, TN 37087-4779

Mailing Address: PO Box 787, LEBANON, TN, 37088-0787
Telephone: (615) 444-5533
Fax Number: (615) 443-9818
Internet Homepage: holleranddash.com; crackerbarrel.com
Company Email: guestrelations@crackerbarrel.com
Type of Business: Chain Restaurant Operator
Year Founded: 1969
Systemwide Sales: $3,374,978,000 (e)
Publicly Held: Yes
Total Sales: $3,586,235,000 (e)
Number of Employees: 77,000
Average Check: Breakfast(10); Lunch(10); Dinner(10)
Internet Order Processing: Yes
Internet Sales: 5.00%
Total Units: 720
Trade Names: Cracker Barrel Old Country Store (661); Maple Street Biscuit Company (59)
Company-Owned Units: 714
Units Franchised To: 6
Preferred Square Footage: 8,900; 10,000
Preferred Location Types: Freestanding
Primary Menu: American (720)
Projected Openings: 12
Areas of Operation: AL, AR, AZ, CO, CT, DE, FL, GA, IA, ID, IL, IN, KS, KY, LA, MA, MD, ME, MI, MN, MO, MS, MT, NC, ND, NE, NH, NJ, NM, NV, NY, OH, OK, OR, PA, RI, SC, SD, TN, TX, UT, VA, WI, WV
Type of Foodservice: Casual Dining (59); Family Restaurant (661)
Distribution Centers: LEBANON, TN
Subsidiaries: Maple Street Biscuit Company, ORANGE PARK, FL
Primary Distributors: (Full Line) PFG - Customized Support Services, LEBANON, TN
Notes: The company derives approximately 20% of its revenue from retail sales.

Key Personnel
JAMES W. BRADFORD - Chairman
JULIE FELSS - CEO
CHRISTIE HALE - President Internal Audit, Loss Prevention
SHERRI MOORE - President Operations
DOUG COUVILLION - CFO Interim; Senior VP Sourcing, Supply Chain
CRAIG POMMELLS - CFO; Senior VP

DONNA ROBERTS - Chief Human Resources Officer
SARAH MOORE - Chief Marketing Officer
RICH WOLFSON - Senior VP; Corporate Secretary; General Counsel
SCOTT GARDNER - VP Distribution, Logistics
CAMMIE SPILLYARDS-SCHAEFER - VP Culinary Development
ROBERT ROBERGE - Regional VP
MATT SCHAEFER - Senior Director Operations, Innovation
JESSICA HAZEL - Senior Director Investor Relations
DREW A. GERMAIN - Director Purchasing
CINDY OVERTON - Director Retail Information Systems
JIMMIE ALVIS - Director Supply Chain
ROB BEHNKE - Director Risk Management
PENNY CARROLL - Director
SAM GOODSON - Director Systems, Human Resources
AMY HOHIMER - Director Quality Assurance
BILL KINTZLER - Director Product Development
MARK WILLIAMSON - Director Strategy
JULIE CRAIG - Senior Manager Marketing
SYD PHILLIPS - Senior Manager Information Systems, Business Development
HEATHER ASHLEY - Senior Manager
JULIE CRAIG ULMER - Senior Manager Marketing
JASON KARSTEN - Senior Manager Development
DIANNA WINFREE - Senior Manager
JACKIE CATO - Senior Manager Loss Prevention
LARRY SINGLETON - Manager Warehouse
JODY GORE - Manager Strategic Sourcing
MADEANNA ADAMS - Manager Logistics
ANGELA BUEHLER - Manager Marketing
MICHELLE CARLISLE - Manager District
TAJUANA GARVIN - Manager Quality Assurance, Safety-Food
MARY GREEN - Manager Information Systems, Security, Compliance
JASON MARSHALL - Manager Development
SHEILA STANTON - Manager
JESSIE THURSTON - Manager
KAREN WALKER - Manager Information Systems, Quality Assurance
EFRAIN GONZALEZ - Manager Logistics
REGINA BOGLE - Manager Information Technology
TIFFANY COOK - Manager
CAREY THOMPSON - Project Manager
MARYBETH TOME - Senior Buyer
SARAH ALLISON - Senior Buyer
JESSICA GANT - Buyer Strategic Sourcing
TREY HECKMAN - Buyer Foodservice Equip/Supplies

Nashville JM, LLC
1315 W Main St Ste E
Lebanon, TN 37087-3276

Telephone: (615) 444-9886
Type of Business: Chain Restaurant Operator
Total Sales: $9,546,000 (e)
Total Units: 7
Trade Names: Jersey Mike's Subs (7)
Units Franchised From: 7
Primary Menu: Sandwiches/Deli (7)
Areas of Operation: TN
Type of Foodservice: Quick Serve (7)
Franchise Affiliation: Jersey Mike's Franchise Systems, MANASQUAN, NJ

Key Personnel
DHARMESH PATEL - Owner; General Buyer

Domino's Franchisee
131 Kelsey Ln
Lenoir City, TN 37772-6444

Telephone: (865) 988-7777
Type of Business: Chain Restaurant Operator
Total Sales: $7,917,000 (e)
Total Units: 4
Trade Names: Domino's (4)
Units Franchised From: 4
Primary Menu: Pizza (4)
Areas of Operation: TN
Type of Foodservice: Quick Serve (4)
Franchise Affiliation: Domino's Pizza Inc, ANN ARBOR, MI

Key Personnel
DOMINIC N. PITARRO - Owner; General Buyer

York Enterprises of Millington Tennessee LLC
675 W Church St Ste C
Lexington, TN 38351-1711

Telephone: (731) 968-4889
Internet Homepage: archpowered.com/yorkmcd
Type of Business: Chain Restaurant Operator
Total Sales: $33,550,000 (e)
Total Units: 7
Trade Names: McDonald's (7)
Units Franchised From: 7
Primary Menu: Hamburger (7)
Areas of Operation: TN
Type of Foodservice: Quick Serve (7)
Franchise Affiliation: McDonald's Corporation, CHICAGO, IL

Key Personnel
SCOTT YORK - Owner; General Buyer

SPFS Inc.
1309 Briarville Rd Ste 201
Madison, TN 37115-5132

Mailing Address: P O Box 1537, MADISON, TN, 37116
Telephone: (615) 860-2592
Fax Number: (615) 860-2591
Type of Business: Chain Restaurant Operator
Year Founded: 1976
Total Sales: $25,680,000 (e)
Number of Employees: 500
Average Check: Lunch(12); Dinner(20)
Total Units: 18
Trade Names: Captain D's Seafood (18)
Units Franchised From: 18
Preferred Square Footage: 800; 2,000; 3,000
Preferred Location Types: Freestanding
Primary Menu: Seafood (18)
Areas of Operation: GA, KY, MS
Type of Foodservice: Fast Casual (18)
Franchise Affiliation: Captain D's LLC, NASHVILLE, TN
Primary Distributors: (Food) Sysco Food Services of Nashville, NASHVILLE, TN

Key Personnel
DAVID SIMMONS - President
MIKE TIDWELL - CFO; Director Operations, Purchasing, Supply Chain, Real Estate

J.R. Young Enterprises Inc.
1820 McArthur St Ste C
Manchester, TN 37355-2683

Telephone: (931) 723-4476
Fax Number: (931) 723-0924
Type of Business: Chain Restaurant Operator
Year Founded: 1981
Total Sales: $63,530,000 (e)
Number of Employees: 1,670
Average Check: Breakfast(8); Lunch(8); Dinner(8)
Total Units: 30
Trade Names: Sonic America's Drive-In (30)
Units Franchised From: 30
Preferred Square Footage: 1,200
Preferred Location Types: Freestanding
Primary Menu: Hamburger (30)
Areas of Operation: AL, GA, TN
Type of Foodservice: Quick Serve (30)
Franchise Affiliation: Sonic Corp., OKLAHOMA CITY, OK
Primary Distributors: (Full Line) Reinhart Foodservice, JOHNSON CITY, TN

Key Personnel
JOHNNY YOUNG - President; CFO; General Manager; Director Finance, Operations, Purchasing, Facility/Maintenance, Supply Chain, Real Estate, Store Fixtures
LEANN USELTON - Director Human Resources

Ruby Tuesday Inc.
216 E Church Ave
Maryville, TN 37804

Telephone: (865) 379-5700
Fax Number: (865) 379-6817
Internet Homepage: rubytuesday.com
Company Email: info@rubytuesday.com
Type of Business: Chain Restaurant Operator
Year Founded: 1972
Systemwide Sales: $592,814,000 (e)
Total Sales: $458,750,000 (e)
Alcohol Sales: 11%
Number of Employees: 12,500
Average Check: Lunch(14); Dinner(16)
Internet Order Processing: Yes
Internet Sales: 15.00%
Total Units: 209
Trade Names: Ruby Tuesday (209)
Company-Owned Units: 195
Units Franchised To: 14
Preferred Square Footage: 4,600; 5,400
Preferred Location Types: Airports; Freestanding; Lifestyle Center; Regional Mall; Strip Mall
Alcohol Served: Beer, Wine, Liquor
Primary Menu: American (209)
Areas of Operation: AL, AR, AZ, CO, CT, DC, DE, FL, GA, GU, HI, IA, ID, IN, KS, KY, LA, MA, MD, ME, MI, MN, MO, MS, NC, ND, NE, NH, NJ, NM, NV, NY, OH, OK, OR, PA, RI, SC, SD, TN, TX, UT, VA, WI, WV, ON
Foreign Countries: CANADA; CHILE; EL SALVADOR; HONDURAS; HONG KONG; KUWAIT; PANAMA; ROMANIA; TRINIDAD & TOBAGO
Type of Foodservice: Casual Dining (209)
Catering Services: Yes
Primary Distributors: (Food) PFG - Customized Support Services, LEBANON, TN
Parent Company: NRD Capital Management II LLC, BROOKHAVEN, GA

Key Personnel
RHONDA J. PARISH - Chief Legal Officer
ELLEN CLARRY - Chief Supply Chain Officer
GEORGE EVANS - VP Operations
ROD MASON - VP Operations
LIBBY TUFFILE - Director Culinary Development
DEBBIE WINDHAM - Director Real Estate
CHUCK MCGUFF - Director Human Resources
JAMIE PEARSON - Director Training
BEN RENBERG - Director Operations
JOSH HARVEY - Director Operations
KIMBERLY KNEIER - Director Development
PATRICK BEARDEN - Manager Information Technology
MARCUS RICHEY - Manager POS/Scanning
CRAIG WILSON - Manager
JAMEY HILL - Project Manager Procurement

Subway Franchise
612 N Chancery St
Mcminnville, TN 37110-2054

Telephone: (931) 473-3094
Fax Number: (931) 486-0002
Internet Homepage: subway.com
Type of Business: Chain Restaurant Operator
Total Sales: $1,553,000 (e)
Total Units: 2
Trade Names: Subway (2)
Units Franchised From: 2
Primary Menu: Sandwiches/Deli (2)
Areas of Operation: TN
Type of Foodservice: Quick Serve (2)
Franchise Affiliation: Doctor's Associates Inc., MILFORD, CT

Key Personnel
PARESH PATEL - President; Partner; General Buyer
DARMISH PATEL - Partner

Auntie Anne's Franchise
2760 N Germantown Pkwy Ste 240
Memphis, TN 38133-8166

Telephone: (901) 373-7107
Type of Business: Chain Restaurant Operator
Total Sales: $8,780,000 (e)
Total Units: 12
Trade Names: Auntie Anne's Hand-Rolled Soft Pretzels (12)
Units Franchised From: 12
Primary Menu: Snacks (12)
Areas of Operation: TN
Type of Foodservice: Quick Serve (12)
Franchise Affiliation: Auntie Anne's Inc., LANCASTER, PA

Key Personnel
SARAH MAZZOCCO - Owner; General Buyer

Canteen Vending Services
4339 S Mendenhall Rd
Memphis, TN 38141-6714

Telephone: (901) 383-9393
Fax Number: (901) 375-1018
Listing Type: Branch Office
Type of Business: Foodservice Management Operator
Year Founded: 1929
Number of Employees: 70
Number of Locations Served: 140

Total Foodservice Mgmt Accounts: 140
Areas of Operation: AR, MS, TN
Type of Foodservice: Cafeteria (4); Vending machines (136)
Foodservice Management Venues: Business & Industry; College & University; Health Care; Schools
Primary Distributors: (Food) Vistar Tennessee, MEMPHIS, TN
Parent Company: Compass Group The Americas, CHARLOTTE, NC
Headquarters: Canteen Vending Services, CHARLOTTE, NC

Key Personnel
MIKE JAKUBIK - General Manager

Carlisle Corporation
263 Wagner Pl
Memphis, TN 38103-3808

Telephone: (901) 271-2500
Fax Number: (901) 271-2564
Internet Homepage: carlislecorp.com
Type of Business: Chain Restaurant Operator
Year Founded: 1982
Total Sales: $443,800,000 (e)
Number of Employees: 3,800
Average Check: Lunch(8); Dinner(10)
Total Units: 161
Trade Names: Wendy's Old Fashioned Hamburgers (161)
Units Franchised From: 161
Preferred Square Footage: 2,100; 2,900
Preferred Location Types: Freestanding; Regional Mall
Primary Menu: Hamburger (161)
Areas of Operation: AL, AR, CA, CO, IL, LA, MS, NV, TN, TX
Type of Foodservice: Quick Serve (161)
Franchise Affiliation: The Wendy's Company, DUBLIN, OH
Primary Distributors: (Full Line) Maines Paper & Food Service Inc., CONKLIN, NY

Key Personnel
CHANCE CARLISLE - President Group; COO Group
LOUIS JEHL - CFO
KAREN CARLISLE - Chief Marketing Officer; Exec VP
STEVEN BINNIE - Senior VP
GREG JONES - VP Operations, Division
DON NICHOLS - VP Facility/Maintenance, Real Estate
MATT PEARSON - VP Global sales
BRIAN MCDANIEL - VP Operations, Division
JAMES WARD - Senior Director Marketing
YUJIA WANG - Director Operations, Global
ILLYA SPIECKER - Director Inventory, Production
LUCY RIOS - Director Marketing
ROBBY LOYED - Director Information Technology
JEANNIE BURRIS - Director Human Resources
KORA SANCHEZ - Regional Manager
SHAWN SCHLUSSER - Manager Infrastructure, Network, Global
JEREMY STUBBLEFIELD - Manager Supply Chain
LISA MILLER - Manager
BOB CONVERSE - Manager Business Development
ASHTON H - Manager Information Technology

Cooper Companies
1661 Aaron Brenner Dr Ste 200
Memphis, TN 38120-1466

Telephone: (901) 322-1400
Fax Number: (901) 322-1403
Internet Homepage: cooperhotels.com
Type of Business: Foodservice Operations - Hotel/Motels
Year Founded: 1961
Total Sales: $115,780,000 (e)
Alcohol Sales: 20%
Number of Employees: 425
Total Units: 17
Restaurants in Hotels: 17
Trade Names: Best Western Plus (1); Crowne Plaza (1); DoubleTree by Hilton (6); Embassy Suites (1); Hampton Inn (1); Hilton (5); Homewood Suites (2)
Company-Owned Units: 17
Alcohol Served: Beer, Wine, Liquor
Areas of Operation: AL, FL, MI, NY, TN
Type of Foodservice: Casual Dining (17)
Primary Distributors: (Food) Sysco Food Services of Memphis, MEMPHIS, TN
Notes: The company derives approximately 80% of its revenue from hotel operations.

Key Personnel
PACE COOPER - CEO; President
DAVID KRUEGER - CFO; VP Accounting
DAVID COOPER - Exec VP
LAURIE COOPER - VP; General Counsel
BRIAN CARNEY - VP Operations
ALAN RUFFIN - Controller Division
ANDY LAUBSCHER - Executive Chef; Director Food and Beverage
PAMELA LITTLE - Director Sales, Region
GINGER BROWN - Director Purchasing
HUGH LADD - Director Information Technology
ALAN JARRETT - Director Operations, Region

Corky's Old Fashioned Bar-B-Q
5259 Poplar Ave
Memphis, TN 38119-3513

Telephone: (901) 685-9744
Fax Number: (901) 685-9088
Internet Homepage: corkysbbq.com
Type of Business: Chain Restaurant Operator
Year Founded: 1984
Systemwide Sales: $13,500,000 (e)
Total Sales: $8,240,000 (e)
Alcohol Sales: 2%
Number of Employees: 137
Average Check: Lunch(12); Dinner(12)
Internet Order Processing: Yes
Internet Sales: 5.00%
Total Units: 11
Trade Names: Corky's Ribs & BBQ (11)
Company-Owned Units: 4
Units Franchised To: 7
Preferred Square Footage: 4,000
Preferred Location Types: Freestanding
Alcohol Served: Beer
Primary Menu: Bar-B-Q (11)
Areas of Operation: AR, MS, TN
Type of Foodservice: Casual Dining (11)
Catering Services: Yes
Primary Distributors: (Full Line) SYSCO Atlanta LLC, COLLEGE PARK, GA
Notes: The company derives approximately 25% of its revenue from retail operations.

Key Personnel
ANDY WOODMAN - Partner; CFO; Director Facility/Maintenance, Real Estate, Design, Store Fixtures; Manager Franchise Development

Exline Inc.
2935 Old Austin Peay Hwy
Memphis, TN 38128-5648

Telephone: (901) 388-3044
Fax Number: (901) 383-2039
Internet Homepage: exlinespizza.com
Company Email: info@exlinespizza.com
Type of Business: Chain Restaurant Operator
Year Founded: 1974
Systemwide Sales: $3,424,000 (e)
Total Sales: $2,415,000 (e)
Alcohol Sales: 2%
Number of Employees: 48
Average Check: Lunch(8); Dinner(18)
Total Units: 4
Trade Names: Exline Best Pizza In Town (4)
Company-Owned Units: 4
Preferred Square Footage: 2,300; 4,200
Preferred Location Types: Freestanding; Strip Mall
Alcohol Served: Beer
Primary Menu: Pizza (4)
Areas of Operation: MS, TN
Type of Foodservice: Casual Dining (4)
On-site Distribution Center: Yes
Primary Distributors: (Food) Gordon Food Service, SPRINGFIELD, OH

Key Personnel
BRET HIGHTOWER - President; Chief

Commercial Officer
KEVIN KOOCHEL - Senior VP Marketing, Sales, Business Development
JANET BAKER - VP
WILL EXLINE - VP Operations
VIOLET EXLINE - Treasurer; Manager Marketing
KEVIN EINHAUS - Division Manager
MIKE BLAIR - Division Manager Operations
LAURIE KNIGHT - Manager Purchasing
ELIAS LUCERO - Manager Sales
JACOB VOGEL - Manager Sales

Half Shell
688 S Mendenhall Rd
Memphis, TN 38117-5213

Telephone: (901) 682-4038
Fax Number: (901) 682-3926
Internet Homepage: halfshell-memphis.com
Company Email: halfshellmendenhall@comcast.net
Type of Business: Chain Restaurant Operator
Year Founded: 1972
Total Sales: $3,119,000 (e)
Alcohol Sales: 11%
Number of Employees: 65
Average Check: Lunch(8); Dinner(14)
Total Units: 2
Trade Names: Half Shell (2)
Company-Owned Units: 2
Preferred Location Types: Freestanding; Strip Mall
Alcohol Served: Beer, Wine, Liquor
Primary Menu: Seafood (2)
Areas of Operation: TN
Type of Foodservice: Casual Dining (2)
Primary Distributors: (Food) US Foods, MEMPHIS, TN

Key Personnel
DANNY SUMRALL - President; General Buyer
STEPHEN TWOMBLY - General Manager
DARRELL SMITH - Executive Chef; Director Menu Development
SHARON SUMRALL - Manager Administration

Happy Mexican
385 S 2nd St
Memphis, TN 38103-4324

Mailing Address: PO Box 11704, Memphis, TN, 38111
Telephone: (901) 529-9991
Fax Number: (901) 529-9915
Internet Homepage: happymexican.com
Type of Business: Chain Restaurant Operator
Year Founded: 2006
Total Sales: $3,423,000 (e)
Total Units: 3
Trade Names: Happy Mexican (3)
Company-Owned Units: 3
Preferred Location Types: Community Mall; Downtown; Freestanding
Alcohol Served: Beer, Wine, Liquor
Primary Menu: Mexican (3)
Areas of Operation: TN
Type of Foodservice: Casual Dining (3)

Key Personnel
RAFAEL RAMIREZ - President; General Buyer

Huey's Inc.
1910 Madison Ave
Memphis, TN 38104-2620

Telephone: (901) 726-9693
Internet Homepage: hueyburger.com
Company Email: comments@hueyburger.com
Type of Business: Chain Restaurant Operator
Year Founded: 1970
Total Sales: $14,050,000 (e)
Alcohol Sales: 25%
Number of Employees: 285
Average Check: Lunch(18); Dinner(18)
Internet Order Processing: Yes
Internet Sales: 2.00%
Total Units: 9
Trade Names: Huey's (9)
Company-Owned Units: 9
Preferred Square Footage: 4,000
Preferred Location Types: Downtown; Freestanding; Strip Mall
Alcohol Served: Beer, Wine, Liquor
Primary Menu: Hamburger (9)
Areas of Operation: MS, TN
Type of Foodservice: Casual Dining (9)
Primary Distributors: (Food) US Foods, MEMPHIS, TN; (Full Line) Sysco Food Services of Memphis, MEMPHIS, TN

Key Personnel
LAUREN MCHUGH ROBINSON - CEO; President; Controller; General Manager; Director Purchasing, Facility/Maintenance, Information Systems, Supply Chain, Store Fixtures
ASHLEY BOGGS ROBILIO - COO; VP; Director Real Estate
STEVE VOSS - VP Operations
NEIL JOHNSON - Senior Director Information Systems
SAMANTHA DEAN - Coordinator Marketing

J 3L Enterprises, Inc.
7505 US Highway 64
Memphis, TN 38133-8947

Telephone: (901) 373-9200
Type of Business: Chain Restaurant Operator
Total Sales: $2,472,000 (e)
Total Units: 2
Trade Names: Firehouse Subs (2)
Units Franchised From: 2
Preferred Location Types: Strip Mall
Primary Menu: Sandwiches/Deli (2)
Areas of Operation: TN
Type of Foodservice: Fast Casual (2)
Franchise Affiliation: Firehouse Restaurant Group Inc., JACKSONVILLE, FL

Key Personnel
JOHN PARISH - President; General Buyer

Jack Pirtle Inc.
1687 Shelby Oaks Dr N Ste 4
Memphis, TN 38134-7421

Telephone: (901) 372-9897
Fax Number: (901) 387-1101
Internet Homepage: jackpirtleschicken.com
Company Email: customer2jackpirtles@gmail.com
Type of Business: Chain Restaurant Operator
Year Founded: 1957
Total Sales: $8,567,000 (e)
Number of Employees: 112
Average Check: Lunch(12); Dinner(14)
Total Units: 8
Trade Names: Jack Pirtle's Fried Chicken (8)
Company-Owned Units: 8
Preferred Square Footage: 2,500
Preferred Location Types: Freestanding
Primary Menu: Chicken (8)
Projected Openings: 1
Areas of Operation: TN
Type of Foodservice: Quick Serve (8)
Primary Distributors: (Full Line) US Foods, MEMPHIS, TN

Key Personnel
CORDELL I. PIRTLE - President; Partner; Executive Chef; Director Facility/Maintenance, Real Estate, Design

Jordan Enterprises
5885 Ridgeway Center Pkwy Ste 110
Memphis, TN 38120-4011

Telephone: (901) 755-8103
Fax Number: (901) 767-0199
Internet Homepage: holidaydeli.com
Company Email: office@jordanco.cc
Type of Business: Chain Restaurant Operator
Year Founded: 1993
Total Sales: $4,869,000 (e)
Number of Employees: 125
Average Check: Lunch(12); Dinner(12)
Internet Order Processing: Yes
Total Units: 4
Trade Names: Holiday Deli & Ham (4)
Company-Owned Units: 4
Preferred Location Types: Freestanding; Strip

Mall
Primary Menu: Sandwiches/Deli (4)
Areas of Operation: TN
Type of Foodservice: Quick Serve (4)
Catering Services: Yes

Key Personnel
TREY JORDAN - President; Executive Chef; General Buyer

Ken Kel Management
1785 Winchester Rd
Memphis, TN 38116-3650

Telephone: (901) 257-1747
Fax Number: (901) 257-1750
Internet Homepage: kenkelmanagement.com
Company Email: kenkeloffice@gmail.com
Type of Business: Chain Restaurant Operator
Total Sales: $20,408,000 (e)
Number of Employees: 83
Total Units: 4
Trade Names: McDonald's (4)
Units Franchised From: 4
Preferred Square Footage: 2,500
Primary Menu: Hamburger (4)
Areas of Operation: TN
Type of Foodservice: Quick Serve (4)
Franchise Affiliation: McDonald's Corporation, CHICAGO, IL

Key Personnel
GEORGE JONES - President; Partner; General Buyer
JANE JONES - Partner
KENT JONES - Partner
CAROL HUTCHINSON - Director Operations

Lenny's Franchise Systems, LLC
8295 Tournament Dr Ste 200
Memphis, TN 38125-8902

Telephone: (901) 753-4002
Fax Number: (901) 753-4395
Internet Homepage: lennys.com
Company Email: info@lennys.com
Type of Business: Chain Restaurant Operator
Year Founded: 1998
Systemwide Sales: $67,007,000 (e)
Total Sales: $4,267,000 (e)
Number of Employees: 20
Average Check: Lunch(8); Dinner(8)
Internet Order Processing: Yes
Total Units: 74
Trade Names: Lenny's Grill & Subs (80)
Units Franchised To: 80
Preferred Square Footage: 3,000
Preferred Location Types: Airports; Downtown; Freestanding; Strip Mall
Primary Menu: Sandwiches/Deli (80)
Areas of Operation: AL, AR, FL, GA, KS, KY, MI, MS, NC, OK, TN, TX
Type of Foodservice: Fast Casual (80)
Catering Services: Yes
Primary Distributors: (Food) Reinhart FoodService, LOUISVILLE, TN

Key Personnel
RICK JOHNSON - Chairman; Chief Concept Officer
AMANDA JOHNSTON - Owner; General Manager
BILLY PARENT - Owner
JOHN F. CAMERON - VP Operations
ANITA HOWALD - Senior Director Information Technology
RANEE HUFF - Manager Marketing, Communications

Malco Theatres Inc.
5851 Ridgeway Center Pkwy
Memphis, TN 38120-4003

Telephone: (901) 761-3480
Fax Number: (901) 681-2044
Internet Homepage: malco.com
Type of Business: Foodservice Operations - Movie Theatre
Year Founded: 1915
Total Sales: $155,130,000 (e)
Alcohol Sales: 1%
Number of Employees: 1,245
Average Check: Lunch(6); Dinner(6)
Internet Order Processing: Yes
Internet Sales: 2.00%
Total Units: 41
Trade Names: Malco Theatre (36); Premier Lanes (5)
Company-Owned Units: 41
Preferred Square Footage: 30,000
Preferred Location Types: Freestanding; Regional Mall
Alcohol Served: Beer, Wine
Primary Menu: Miscellaneous (5); Snacks (36)
Projected Openings: 2
Areas of Operation: AR, KY, MO, MS, TN
Type of Foodservice: Casual Dining (5); In-Store Feeder (36)
Notes: The company derives approximately 85% of its revenue from theater admissions, on-screen advertising, & other sales.

Key Personnel
DAVID TASHIE - President; COO
JOHN TASHIE - CIO; CTO; Director Information Technology, POS/Scanning, Loss Prevention, E-Commerce, Internet Development
JAMES TASHIE - Exec VP Operations, Facility/Maintenance, Design; Director Information Technology
LARRY ETTER - Senior VP Foodservice
ROBERT HARRINGTON - VP Finance, Accounting; Controller
DONALD TERRY - VP Operations
NANCY KEOUGH - Director Human Resources
KAREN SCOTT - Director Marketing

Pancho's Mexican Foods Inc.
2855 Lamb Pl
Memphis, TN 38118-1518

Telephone: (901) 362-9691
Fax Number: (901) 362-8487
Internet Homepage: panchoscheesedip.com
Type of Business: Chain Restaurant Operator
Year Founded: 1956
Total Sales: $9,256,000 (e)
Alcohol Sales: 10%
Number of Employees: 125
Average Check: Lunch(10); Dinner(12)
Total Units: 2
Trade Names: Pancho's Restaurant (2)
Company-Owned Units: 2
Preferred Location Types: Freestanding; Strip Mall
Alcohol Served: Beer, Wine, Liquor
Primary Menu: Mexican (2)
Areas of Operation: TN
Type of Foodservice: Casual Dining (2)
On-site Distribution Center: Yes
Primary Distributors: (Full Line) US Foods, MEMPHIS, TN
Parent Company: Pancho's Restaurants Inc., AUSTIN, TX
Notes: The company derives approximately 23% of its revenue from retail groceries.

Key Personnel
BRENDA O'BRIEN - CEO; President; Manager Operations, Marketing, Human Resources
STEVEN O'BRIEN - COO; Executive Chef
TIM WALLACE - VP Purchasing; General Manager; Manager Warehouse, Transportation, Food Safety; General Buyer

Perkins Restaurant & Bakery
6075 Poplar Ave Ste 800
Memphis, TN 38119-4717

Telephone: (901) 766-6400
Fax Number: (901) 766-6482
Internet Homepage: perkinsrestaurants.com
Company Email: perkins@perkinsrestaurants.com
Listing Type: Subsidiary
Type of Business: Chain Restaurant Operator
Year Founded: 1958
Systemwide Sales: $840,100,000 (e)
Total Sales: $319,760,000 (e)
Number of Employees: 9,800
Average Check: Breakfast(8); Lunch(10); Dinner(10)
Total Units: 371

Trade Names: Perkins Restaurant & Bakery (371)
Company-Owned Units: 132
Units Franchised To: 246
Preferred Square Footage: 5,000
Preferred Location Types: Freestanding; Hotel/Motel; Strip Mall; Travel Plazas
Primary Menu: American (371)
Areas of Operation: AR, AZ, CO, DE, FL, GA, IA, ID, IL, IN, KS, MD, MI, MN, MO, MT, NC, ND, NE, NJ, NY, OH, OK, PA, SC, SD, TN, UT, VA, WA, WI, WV, WY, AB, BC, MB, ON, SK
Foreign Countries: CANADA
Type of Foodservice: Family Restaurant (371)
Primary Distributors: (Full Line) US Foods Holding Corp., ROSEMONT, IL
Parent Company: Huddle House Inc., ATLANTA, GA

Key Personnel
ROBERT HESS - CIO
JAMES PRITCHARD - Senior VP Marketing
DONNA HERBEL - VP Talent Training
DAVID BLOUIN - VP Franchise Operations
KIMBERLY BEAN - VP Marketing
KATIE T. COACH - General Manager
MARCUS HEWITT - Senior Director Finance
DENISE BUCKNER - Senior Manager Operations

RGT Management, Inc.
6389 N Quail Hollow Rd Ste 101
Memphis, TN 38120-1427

Telephone: (901) 881-9684
Fax Number: (901) 762-0625
Internet Homepage: rxtcareers.com
Company Email: info@rgtfoods.com
Type of Business: Chain Restaurant Operator
Year Founded: 1971
Total Sales: $21,860,000 (e)
Number of Employees: 2,200
Average Check: Lunch(12); Dinner(12)
Total Units: 8
Trade Names: Taco Bell (8)
Units Franchised From: 8
Preferred Square Footage: 1,800; 2,100
Preferred Location Types: Freestanding
Primary Menu: Taco (8)
Areas of Operation: FL
Type of Foodservice: Quick Serve (8)
Franchise Affiliation: Taco Bell Corp., IRVINE, CA

Key Personnel
SEAN TUOHY - President; Partner; Director Real Estate
TIM MCCLAIN - CFO
STANFORD ROBERTS - VP Marketing, Advertising, Business Development
RALPH BURNS - Director Human Resources
KENDALL LOGSDEN - Director Operations
KIM WIMBERLY - Business Manager

KAYLA TRUITT - Manager Human Resources
KIM MCCLAIN - Manager Finance
TERESA CHADWICK - Manager Human Resources
MEGGEN VALLE - Manager
BOB SAUNDERS - Coach Area

Sekisui
6696 Poplar Ave
Memphis, TN 38138-3625

Telephone: (901) 747-0003
Internet Homepage: sekisuiusa.com
Type of Business: Chain Restaurant Operator
Year Founded: 1989
Systemwide Sales: $7,540,000 (e)
Total Sales: $4,704,000 (e)
Alcohol Sales: 15%
Number of Employees: 90
Average Check: Lunch(18); Dinner(24)
Internet Order Processing: Yes
Total Units: 5
Trade Names: Sekisui (5)
Company-Owned Units: 5
Preferred Square Footage: 5,500; 6,000
Preferred Location Types: Downtown; Freestanding; Office Complex; Regional Mall; Strip Mall
Alcohol Served: Beer, Wine, Liquor
Primary Menu: Japanese (5)
Areas of Operation: TN
Type of Foodservice: Casual Dining (5)
Catering Services: Yes
Primary Distributors: (Food) Sysco Food Services of Memphis, MEMPHIS, TN

Key Personnel
JIMMY ISHII - President; Director Menu Development, Catering; General Buyer
IAN MORAN - President
NORITAKE YOSHIMIZU - VP Finance, Accounting
DAVID LINDSEY - Director Operations, Facility/Maintenance

Tops Bar-B-Q Inc.
5720 Mount Moriah Rd
Memphis, TN 38115-1623

Telephone: (901) 363-4007
Fax Number: (901) 363-8365
Internet Homepage: topsbarbq.com
Type of Business: Chain Restaurant Operator
Year Founded: 1952
Total Sales: $11,830,000 (e)
Number of Employees: 135
Average Check: Lunch(12); Dinner(14)
Total Units: 15
Trade Names: Tops Bar-B-Q (15)
Company-Owned Units: 15
Preferred Square Footage: 1,500; 2,000

Preferred Location Types: Freestanding; Strip Mall
Primary Menu: Bar-B-Q (15)
Projected Remodelings: 5
Areas of Operation: AR, MS, TN
Type of Foodservice: Quick Serve (15)
Catering Services: Yes
Primary Distributors: (Full Line) US Foods, PLYMOUTH, MN

Key Personnel
RANDY HOUGH - CEO
BOBBIE BENDER - Manager

Charter Foods, Inc
1111 Gateway Service Park Rd
Morristown, TN 37813-2512

Mailing Address: PO Box 430, TALBOTT, TN, 37877-0430
Telephone: (423) 587-0690
Fax Number: (423) 586-6076
Company Email: hr@chatrterfoods.net
Type of Business: Chain Restaurant Operator
Year Founded: 1998
Total Sales: $150,630,000 (e)
Number of Employees: 4,000
Average Check: Lunch(12); Dinner(16)
Total Units: 229
Trade Names: A&W All American Food (6); KFC (8); Long John Silver's (57); Taco Bell (158)
Units Franchised From: 229
Preferred Square Footage: 2,500; 3,200
Preferred Location Types: Freestanding; Regional Mall; Strip Mall
Primary Menu: American (6); Chicken (8); Mexican (158); Seafood (57)
Areas of Operation: AL, GA, KY, MA, NC, NH, OH, PA, TN, VA, WV
Type of Foodservice: Quick Serve (229)
Franchise Affiliation: KFC Franchise, EL MONTE, CA; Long John Silver's Inc., LOUISVILLE, KY; Pizza Hut of Arizona Inc., TUCSON, AZ; Taco Bell Corp., IRVINE, CA

Key Personnel
NATHAN BUCHANAN - CFO
JOHN RANKIN - Senior Director Operations
TOM DONNELLY - Director Operations
BETH MARTAUS - Director Marketing
ASHTON RICHARDSON - District Manager
DEBRA WILLIAMS - District Manager
LEAH TAYLOR - Manager Human Resources
CAROL TROUP - Manager Accounting
JAMIE REGAN - Manager Facility/Maintenance, Safety
JOSH BROOKS - Manager Restaurant Operations
JOE NAILL - Manager Recruitment
BROOKE MOYERS - Generalist Human

American Family Foods, LLC
2678 S Church St
Murfreesboro, TN 37127-6370

Telephone: (615) 895-5133
Type of Business: Chain Restaurant Operator
Total Sales: $11,214,000 (e)
Total Units: 3
Trade Names: Zaxby's (3)
Units Franchised From: 3
Primary Menu: Chicken (3)
Areas of Operation: NE, TN
Type of Foodservice: Fast Casual (3)
Franchise Affiliation: Zaxby's Franchising Inc., ATHENS, GA

Key Personnel
CHAD MARTIN - Owner
JASMINE JACKSON - General Manager; General Buyer

Brentwood Subs Inc.
2910 S Church St Ste E
Murfreesboro, TN 37127-7149

Telephone: (615) 494-1311
Type of Business: Chain Restaurant Operator
Total Sales: $26,750,000 (e)
Total Units: 20
Trade Names: Jersey Mike's Subs (20)
Units Franchised From: 20
Primary Menu: Sandwiches/Deli (20)
Areas of Operation: TN
Type of Foodservice: Quick Serve (20)
Franchise Affiliation: Jersey Mike's Franchise Systems, MANASQUAN, NJ

Key Personnel
WILLIAM C. BROWN - Owner; General Buyer

Demos' Steak and Spaghetti House
503 N Maney Ave
Murfreesboro, TN 37130-2922

Telephone: (615) 848-1777
Fax Number: (615) 848-0902
Internet Homepage: demosrestaurants.com
Company Email: peter@demosrestaurants.com
Type of Business: Chain Restaurant Operator
Year Founded: 1989
Total Sales: $17,272,000 (e)
Alcohol Sales: 20%
Number of Employees: 400
Average Check: Lunch(14); Dinner(20)
Internet Sales: 0.50%
Total Units: 4
Trade Names: Demos' Steak and Spaghetti House (4)
Company-Owned Units: 4
Preferred Location Types: Freestanding
Alcohol Served: Beer, Wine, Liquor
Primary Menu: Steak (4)
Areas of Operation: TN
Type of Foodservice: Casual Dining (4)
Primary Distributors: (Food) PFG - Customized Support Services, LEBANON, TN

Key Personnel
PETER DEMOS - CEO; President; Partner; General Manager; Executive Chef
JIM DEMOS - Partner; Executive Chef
JOHN O'KAIN - Director Information Technology

Fortner Foods
830 Old Salem Rd
Murfreesboro, TN 37129-4943

Telephone: (615) 896-9660
Fax Number: (615) 896-9660
Internet Homepage: sirpizzatenn.com
Company Email: info@sirpizzatenn.com
Type of Business: Chain Restaurant Operator
Year Founded: 1966
Systemwide Sales: $22,843,000 (e)
Total Sales: $10,675,000 (e)
Alcohol Sales: 5%
Number of Employees: 220
Average Check: Lunch(8); Dinner(8)
Total Units: 11
Trade Names: Sir Pizza (11)
Company-Owned Units: 3
Units Franchised To: 8
Preferred Square Footage: 4,000; 6,000
Preferred Location Types: Freestanding; Strip Mall
Alcohol Served: Beer
Primary Menu: Pizza (11)
Areas of Operation: TN
Type of Foodservice: Casual Dining (11)
On-site Distribution Center: Yes
Primary Distributors: (Food) Sysco Food Services of Nashville, NASHVILLE, TN

Key Personnel
LEIGHANNE POOLE - Owner; General Buyer

McQuire Management Group
3979 Berry Ford Rd
Murfreesboro, TN 37130

Telephone: (615) 904-9496
Internet Homepage: mcguiremanagement.com
Company Email: office@mcguiremanagement.com
Type of Business: Chain Restaurant Operator
Total Sales: $89,160,000 (e)
Total Units: 19
Trade Names: McDonald's (19)
Units Franchised From: 19
Preferred Square Footage: 2,500
Primary Menu: Hamburger (19)
Areas of Operation: TN
Type of Foodservice: Quick Serve (19)
Franchise Affiliation: McDonald's Corporation, CHICAGO, IL

Key Personnel
ANTHONY MCGUIRE - President; Partner; General Buyer
JONATHON MCGUIRE - Partner

Middle Tennessee Pizza Inc.
421 E Vine St
Murfreesboro, TN 37130-4226

Telephone: (615) 893-0078
Fax Number: (615) 890-2315
Type of Business: Chain Restaurant Operator
Year Founded: 1979
Total Sales: $22,821,000 (e)
Number of Employees: 280
Average Check: Lunch(22); Dinner(34)
Total Units: 11
Trade Names: Domino's (11)
Units Franchised From: 11
Preferred Square Footage: 1,400; 1,800
Preferred Location Types: Strip Mall
Primary Menu: Pizza (11)
Areas of Operation: TN
Type of Foodservice: Quick Serve (11)
Foodservice Management Venues: College & University
Franchise Affiliation: Domino's Pizza Inc, ANN ARBOR, MI
Primary Distributors: (Food) Domino's Distribution Center, KENNESAW, GA

Key Personnel
PAT HOUSEMAN - President; Treasurer; Manager Finance, Human Resources

Thermal Vision Investments, Inc
412 Golden Bear Ct
Murfreesboro, TN 37128-5514

Telephone: (615) 893-4439
Fax Number: (615) 410-4719
Type of Business: Chain Restaurant Operator
Total Sales: $3,883,000 (e)
Average Check: Lunch(22); Dinner(22)
Total Units: 3
Trade Names: Little Caesars Pizza (3)
Units Franchised From: 3
Primary Menu: Pizza (3)
Areas of Operation: TN

Type of Foodservice: Quick Serve (3)
Franchise Affiliation: Little Caesar Enterprises Inc., DETROIT, MI

Key Personnel
DEWAYNE SADLER - President; General Buyer

Townsend Foods, Inc.
239 Cason Ln
Murfreesboro, TN 37128-4857

Telephone: (615) 907-0727
Type of Business: Chain Restaurant Operator
Total Sales: $6,894,000 (e)
Total Units: 6
Trade Names: Captain D's Seafood Kitchen (6)
Units Franchised From: 6
Primary Menu: Seafood (6)
Areas of Operation: AL, FL, TN
Type of Foodservice: Quick Serve (6)
Franchise Affiliation: Captain D's LLC, NASHVILLE, TN

Key Personnel
BILL TOWNSEND - President; General Buyer

4Top Hospitality
1922 W End Ave
Nashville, TN 37203

Telephone: (615) 321-6024
Internet Homepage: 4tophospitality.com; linkedin.com/company/4tophospitality
Company Email: office@amerigo.net
Type of Business: Chain Restaurant Operator
Year Founded: 2009
Total Sales: $13,740,000 (e)
Total Units: 16
Trade Names: Amerigo an Italian Restaurant (5); Anjou Restaurant (1); Char Restaurant (4); etc. (1); Etch (1); Jaspers (1); Saltine (1); Sombra Mexican Kitchen (1)
Company-Owned Units: 15
Primary Menu: American (6); French/Continental (1); Italian (5); Mexican (1); Southern (1); Steak/Seafood (1)
Areas of Operation: AL, MS, TN
Type of Foodservice: Casual Dining (10); Fine Dining (5)

Key Personnel
DOUG HOGREFE - Partner
PAUL SCHRAMKOWSKI - Partner
DAVID CONN - Partner
BEN BROCK - Partner
ALI GENSERT - Director Marketing

Back Yard Burgers Inc.
500 Church St Ste 200
Nashville, TN 37219-2339

Telephone: (615) 620-2300
Fax Number: (615) 620-2301
Internet Homepage: backyardburgers.com
Type of Business: Chain Restaurant Operator
Year Founded: 1987
Systemwide Sales: $107,191,000 (e)
Total Sales: $45,770,000 (e)
Number of Employees: 569
Average Check: Lunch(10); Dinner(10)
Total Units: 43
Trade Names: Back Yard Burgers (48)
Company-Owned Units: 28
Units Franchised To: 20
Preferred Square Footage: 820; 2,400; 4,000
Preferred Location Types: Convenience Store/Gas Station; Freestanding
Primary Menu: Hamburger (48)
Areas of Operation: AL, AR, FL, GA, IL, KS, KY, LA, MO, MS, NC, NE, OK, PA, SC, TN
Type of Foodservice: Quick Serve (48)
Catering Services: Yes
Primary Distributors: (Equipment) Dykes Restaurant Supply Inc., HUNTSVILLE, AL; (Food) Ben E. Keith Foods, NORTH LITTLE ROCK, AR; (Supplies) Ben E. Keith Foods, NORTH LITTLE ROCK, AR
Parent Company: Axum Capital Partners, CHARLOTTE, NC

Key Personnel
TERESA SINGLETON - VP Operations, Supply Chain
WADE BREAUX - VP Marketing

Best American Hospitality Inc.
1717 Elm Hill Pike Ste B1
Nashville, TN 37210-3628

Telephone: (615) 610-3142
Fax Number: (615) 231-2779
Internet Homepage: bahinc.com
Company Email: bahcontact@shoneys.com
Type of Business: Chain Restaurant Operator
Year Founded: 1996
Total Sales: $123,600,000 (e)
Number of Employees: 3,500
Average Check: Lunch(10); Dinner(12)
Total Units: 98
Trade Names: Church's Chicken (98)
Units Franchised From: 98
Preferred Square Footage: 2,500
Preferred Location Types: Community Mall; Freestanding; Strip Mall
Primary Menu: Chicken (98)
Areas of Operation: AZ, CA, TX
Type of Foodservice: Quick Serve (98)
Catering Services: Yes
Franchise Affiliation: Church's Chicken, ATLANTA, GA
Primary Distributors: (Full Line) Performance Foodservice - Victoria, VICTORIA, TX
Parent Company: Royal Capital Corp., ATLANTA, GA

Key Personnel
DAVID DAVOUDPOUR - Chairman; CEO
STEVE NEUROTH - CFO
GILL C. DUFF - Chief Marketing Officer
ROBERT FULLER - Director Supply Chain
DEBBIE CAMPA - Director Human Resources
CLIFF MOEN - Manager Facility/Maintenance, Information Systems, Real Estate, Business Development, Store Fixtures

Burger Republic
6900 Lenox Village Dr
Nashville, TN 37211

Internet Homepage: burgerrepublic.com
Company Email: eat@burgerrepublic.net
Type of Business: Chain Restaurant Operator
Year Founded: 2012
Number of Employees: 150
Total Units: 4
Trade Names: Burger Republic (4)
Company-Owned Units: 4
Primary Menu: Hamburger (4)
Areas of Operation: TN
Type of Foodservice: Casual Dining (4)

Key Personnel
DREW JACKMAN - Partner

Cannon Restaurant Management, LLC
2909 Poston Ave Ste 100
Nashville, TN 37203-6319

Telephone: (615) 383-8993
Company Email: MoesWestEnd@gmail.com
Type of Business: Chain Restaurant Operator
Total Sales: $16,710,000 (e)
Total Units: 10
Trade Names: Moe's Southwest Grill (10)
Units Franchised From: 10
Primary Menu: Southwest/Tex-Mex (10)
Areas of Operation: TN
Type of Foodservice: Fast Casual (10)
Franchise Affiliation: Moe's Southwest Grill LLC, ATLANTA, GA

Key Personnel
SCOTT PORTIS - Owner; General Buyer
DEBBIE TIDWELL - Director Company Operations

KRIS GERNENTZ - Director Operations

Captain D's LLC
624 Grassmere Park Ste 30
Nashville, TN 37211-3671

Telephone: (615) 391-5461
Fax Number: (615) 231-2309
Internet Homepage: captainds.com; grandys.com
Company Email: dscomments@captainds.com
Type of Business: Chain Restaurant Operator
Year Founded: 1969
Systemwide Sales: $797,396,000 (e)
Total Sales: $445,000,000 (e)
Number of Employees: 5,600
Average Check: Lunch(8); Dinner(8)
Internet Order Processing: Yes
Total Units: 540
Trade Names: Captain D's Seafood Kitchen (540); Grandy's (27)
Company-Owned Units: 258
Units Franchised To: 309
Preferred Square Footage: 2,500; 3,500
Preferred Location Types: Convenience Store/Gas Station; Freestanding; Other; Strip Mall
Primary Menu: American (27); Seafood (540)
Projected Openings: 29
Areas of Operation: AL, AR, CO, FL, GA, IL, IN, KS, KY, LA, MO, MS, NC, NM, OH, OK, SC, TN, TX, VA, WI, WV
Type of Foodservice: Quick Serve (567)
Primary Distributors: (Full Line) McLane/Rocky Mount, ROCKY MOUNT, NC

Key Personnel
PHILIP M. GREIFELD - Chairman; CEO; President
DEBBIE LOCKE - President Accounting
KORI WALKER - President Training
JEFF WILSON - CFO
NANCY WARD - COO
SEAN MCANALLY - CIO
BINDI MENON - Chief Marketing Officer
BRAD REED - Chief Development Officer
BRAD CLARK - Chief Supply Chain Officer
MICHAEL T. FOLKS - Senior VP; Corporate Secretary; General Counsel
LARRY JONES - VP Operations, Construction
PHIL RUSSO - VP Real Estate
MARK EARNEST - VP Quality Assurance
ROBERT JONES - VP Franchise Operations
ANN SIZEMORE - VP Human Resources
STEVE BIELEWICZ - Senior Director Franchise Development
KEITH CANSECO - Director Marketing, National
JEN DISMUKES - Director Training
JESSICA TUCKER - Director Finance
SCOTT WILSON - Director Operations-Training
SAM BRENNER - Senior Manager Brand Marketing
JANA PARKER - Senior Manager Accounting

LOUIS LECOCKE - Senior Manager Purchasing
MARIE BURKE - Manager

DLR Restaurants LLC
611 Commerce St Ste 2911
Nashville, TN 37203-3747

Telephone: (615) 254-5844
Fax Number: (615) 254-5843
Internet Homepage: dickslastresort.com
Company Email: dlrmc@dickslastresort.com
Type of Business: Chain Restaurant Operator
Year Founded: 1985
Total Sales: $51,060,000 (e)
Alcohol Sales: 40%
Number of Employees: 570
Average Check: Breakfast(5); Lunch(10); Dinner(24)
Internet Order Processing: Yes
Internet Sales: 1.00%
Total Units: 13
Trade Names: Dick's Last Resort (13)
Company-Owned Units: 1
Units Franchised To: 12
Preferred Square Footage: 10,000; 12,000
Preferred Location Types: Downtown; Freestanding
Alcohol Served: Beer, Wine, Liquor
Primary Menu: American (13)
Areas of Operation: CA, FL, IL, MA, MD, NV, SC, TN, TX, VA
Type of Foodservice: Casual Dining (13)
Primary Distributors: (Equipment) Ford Hotel Supply Co., SAINT LOUIS, MO; (Food) SYSCO Food Services of Houston Inc., HOUSTON, TX; (Supplies) Ford Hotel Supply Co., SAINT LOUIS, MO
Parent Company: Triton Pacific Capital Partners LLC, LOS ANGELES, CA

Key Personnel
SHANE SPARKS - CFO
AMANDA RAY - Consultant

Edley's Bar-B-Que
2706 12th Ave S
Nashville, TN 37204

Telephone: (615) 953-2951
Internet Homepage: edleysbbq.com
Company Email: newman@edleysbbq.com
Type of Business: Chain Restaurant Operator
Year Founded: 2011
Total Units: 5
Trade Names: Edley's Bar-B-Que (5)
Company-Owned Units: 5
Preferred Location Types: Downtown; Freestanding
Primary Menu: Bar-B-Q (5)
Areas of Operation: KY, TN

Type of Foodservice: Casual Dining (5)

Key Personnel
WILL NEWMAN - Co-Founder; Partner
CATHARINE NEWMAN - Co-Founder; Partner
CHRIS BECKLER - VP Operations
BILL DUBUC - General Manager
KATIE LARSON - Director Catering
JON PARKER - Regional Manager

Fresh Hospitality LLC
631 2nd Ave
Nashville, TN 37210-2074

Mailing Address: PO Box 331272, NASHVILLE, TN, 37203
Telephone: (615) 823-3713
Internet Homepage: freshhospitality.net; ilovejuicebar.com; jimnnicks.com; martinsbbqjoint.com; octanecoffee.com; paninipetes.com; tazikiscafe.com; tellinis.com; thelittledonkey.com
Type of Business: Chain Restaurant Operator
Year Founded: 2008
Total Sales: $166,690,000 (e)
Total Units: 194
Trade Names: 'Za (1); 55 South (3); Big Bad Breakfast (9); Biscuit Love (3); City Silo (1); Count Porkula BBQ (1); Greko (1); Hugh Baby's BBQ and Burger Shop (3); I Love Juice Bar (30); Martin's BBQ Joint (10); MARY MAC'S TEA ROOM (1); Taco Mac (28); Tacos Aurora (1); Tazikis Mediterranean Cafe (93); The Grilled Cheeserie (1); Tomacco (1); Vui's Kitchen (3); Waldo's Chicken & Beer (4)
Company-Owned Units: 194
Primary Menu: American (41); Asian (3); Bar-B-Q (11); Chicken (5); Greek/Mediterranean (94); Health Foods (30); Italian (0); Latin American/Cuban (0); Pizza (1); Sandwiches/Deli (1); Southern (6); Taco (2)
Projected Openings: 15
Areas of Operation: AL, AR, CA, CO, FL, GA, IN, KY, MO, MS, NC, OK, SC, TN, TX, VA, WV
Type of Foodservice: Casual Dining (45); Fast Casual (148); Quick Serve (1)
Headquarter Offices: I Love Juice Bar, NASHVILLE, TN; Martin's BBQ Joint, NASHVILLE, TN; Taco Mac Restaurant Group, ALPHARETTA, GA; Taziki's Cafe, VESTAVIA, AL
Notes: When Fresh Hospitality buys an existing concept/business it purchases majority equity in about 90 percent of such instances. However, It leaves the majority of the decision-making to the concepts' original owners. The company's structure is unstructured. Close to a dozen partners govern its affairs, with a small group of core partners more involved in day-to-day operations than others.

Key Personnel
J M. BODNER - Chairman; Partner

JOHN CURRENCE - Founder
KEITH RICHARDS - Founder; Chief Development Officer
COLE BODNER - CEO
MATT BODNAR - Partner
MIKE TIDWELL - Partner
DAVID GILBERT - Partner
JOHN MICHAEL BODNER - Partner
DOUG VAN SCOY - Partner
ERIC S. DEEMS - Partner
HAROLD MARTIN - Partner
JESS LIBERMAN - Partner
NICHOLAS CESNIK - Partner
TODD MORMAN - CFO
RUSTY RUSHTON - COO
TIM MULLEN - COO; CIO
SHAUN SHANKEL - CTO
CASSANDRA PRESLEY - General Manager; Executive Chef; Assistant
CHRIS MEYER - Director Information Technology
RUSSELL CAMPBELL - Director Design
DREW MAYNARD - Manager
TOBY RUMBARGER - Advisor Construction

Hattie B's Hot Chicken
112 19th Ave S
Nashville, TN 37203-2716

Telephone: (615) 678-4794
Internet Homepage: hattieb.com
Company Email: info@hattieb.com
Type of Business: Chain Restaurant Operator
Internet Order Processing: Yes
Total Units: 7
Trade Names: Hattie B's Hot Chicken (7)
Company-Owned Units: 7
Primary Menu: Chicken (7)
Projected Openings: 1
Areas of Operation: TN
Type of Foodservice: Casual Dining (7)

Key Personnel
NICK BISHOP - President; Owner; General Buyer
JONATHAN CAROTHERS - VP Operations
JOHN LASATER - Executive Chef
SUSAN LOLA CONWAY - Director Human Resources

I Love Juice Bar
631 2nd Ave Ste 3R
Nashville, TN 37210

Telephone: (615) 241-8847
Internet Homepage: ilovejuicebar.com; vuiskitchen.com
Company Email: info@ilovejuicebar.com
Type of Business: Chain Restaurant Operator
Total Sales: $22,700,000 (e)
Total Units: 33
Trade Names: I Love Juice Bar (30); Vui's Kitchen (3)
Company-Owned Units: 33
Primary Menu: Asian (3); Health Foods (30)
Areas of Operation: AL, AR, CA, FL, GA, IN, KY, MO, MS, NC, SC, TN, TX, WV
Type of Foodservice: Fast Casual (33)
Parent Company: Fresh Hospitality LLC, NASHVILLE, TN

Key Personnel
MATTHEW HAJACOS - General Manager

Jack Cawthon's Bar-B-Que Inc.
310 McMillin St
Nashville, TN 37203-2915

Telephone: (615) 228-4600
Fax Number: (615) 228-4700
Internet Homepage: jacksbarbque.com
Type of Business: Chain Restaurant Operator
Year Founded: 1989
Total Units: 3
Company-Owned Units: 3
Primary Menu: Bar-B-Q (3)
Areas of Operation: TN
Type of Foodservice: Casual Dining (3)

Key Personnel
JACK CAWTHON - Founder; President

Las Palmas Mexican Restaurants Inc.
1905 Hayes St
Nashville, TN 37203-2316

Telephone: (615) 322-9588
Fax Number: (615) 322-9588
Internet Homepage: laspalmasnashville.com
Type of Business: Chain Restaurant Operator
Year Founded: 1990
Total Sales: $11,240,000 (e)
Alcohol Sales: 10%
Number of Employees: 385
Average Check: Lunch(10); Dinner(16)
Total Units: 9
Trade Names: Las Palmas Mexican Restaurant (9)
Company-Owned Units: 9
Preferred Square Footage: 5,500; 6,000
Preferred Location Types: Freestanding; Strip Mall
Alcohol Served: Beer, Wine, Liquor
Primary Menu: Mexican (9)
Areas of Operation: TN
Type of Foodservice: Casual Dining (9)
Primary Distributors: (Food) Sysco Food Services of Nashville, NASHVILLE, TN

Key Personnel
JOSE AYALA - Partner; Executive Chef; Director Information Systems, Supply Chain, Real Estate, Design; General Buyer
LUIS AYALA - Partner; Executive Chef; General Buyer
QUIRINO ONATE - Partner; Executive Chef; General Buyer

Martin's BBQ Joint
3108 Belmont Blvd
Nashville, TN 37212-6004

Telephone: (615) 200-1181
Internet Homepage: martinsbbqjoint.com; hughbabys.com
Company Email: catering@martinsbbqjoint.com
Type of Business: Chain Restaurant Operator
Year Founded: 2006
Total Units: 9
Trade Names: Hugh Baby's BBQ and Burger Shop (2); Martin's BBQ Joint (7)
Company-Owned Units: 9
Primary Menu: American (2); Bar-B-Q (7)
Areas of Operation: KY, TN, WV
Type of Foodservice: Fast Casual (9)
Parent Company: Fresh Hospitality LLC, NASHVILLE, TN

Key Personnel
PAT MARTIN - Founder; President; Executive Chef; General Buyer
ANDREW BRACE - General Manager; Supervisor Art

McDonald's Management Co.
152 McGavock Pike
Nashville, TN 37214-2144

Telephone: (615) 885-3209
Fax Number: (615) 885-9858
Type of Business: Chain Restaurant Operator
Year Founded: 1985
Total Sales: $115,480,000 (e)
Number of Employees: 1,080
Average Check: Breakfast(8); Lunch(8); Dinner(10)
Total Units: 30
Trade Names: McDonald's (30)
Units Franchised From: 30
Preferred Square Footage: 2,500
Preferred Location Types: Freestanding; Regional Mall
Primary Menu: Hamburger (30)
Projected Remodelings: 4
Areas of Operation: TN
Type of Foodservice: Quick Serve (30)
Franchise Affiliation: McDonald's Corporation, CHICAGO, IL
Primary Distributors: (Full Line) The Martin-

Brower Co., DICKSON, TN

Key Personnel
CHRIS KEMPCZINSKI - CEO; President
PHIL GRAY - Partner; General Manager; Director Purchasing, Real Estate; General Buyer
VICKI GRAY - Partner; General Buyer
NATHANIEL JACOBSON - Director Marketing

Midtown Cafe
102 19th Ave S
Nashville, TN 37203-2716

Telephone: (615) 320-7176
Fax Number: (615) 320-0920
Internet Homepage: cabananashville.com; midtowncafe.com
Company Email: comments@midtowncafe.com
Type of Business: Chain Restaurant Operator
Year Founded: 1987
Total Sales: $6,367,000 (e)
Alcohol Sales: 25%
Number of Employees: 140
Average Check: Lunch(18); Dinner(48)
Internet Sales: 0.50%
Total Units: 2
Trade Names: Cabana (1); Midtown Cafe (1)
Company-Owned Units: 2
Preferred Location Types: Freestanding
Alcohol Served: Beer, Wine, Liquor
Primary Menu: American (2)
Areas of Operation: TN
Type of Foodservice: Casual Dining (1); Fine Dining (1)
Primary Distributors: (Food) SYSCO Food Services of Arkansas LLC, LITTLE ROCK, AR

Key Personnel
RANDY RAYBURN - President; General Manager
ROBIN MCGUIGAN - Owner
MAX PASTOR - Executive Chef; General Buyer

Monell's Dining & Catering
1235 6th Ave N
Nashville, TN 37208-2601

Telephone: (615) 248-4747
Fax Number: (615) 248-4755
Internet Homepage: monellstn.com
Type of Business: Chain Restaurant Operator
Year Founded: 1995
Total Sales: $4,269,000 (e)
Number of Employees: 25
Average Check: Breakfast(10); Lunch(10); Dinner(16)
Total Units: 3
Trade Names: Monell's Restaurant (3)
Company-Owned Units: 3
Preferred Square Footage: 1,500; 3,000
Preferred Location Types: Freestanding
Primary Menu: Southern (3)
Areas of Operation: TN
Type of Foodservice: Family Restaurant (3)
Catering Services: Yes
Primary Distributors: (Full Line) Sysco Food Services of Nashville, NASHVILLE, TN

Key Personnel
MICHAEL KING - President; General Manager; Executive Chef; Director Finance, Operations, Facility/Maintenance, Information Systems, Real Estate, Design, Human Resources; General Buyer

O'Charley's Restaurants
3038 Sidco Dr
Nashville, TN 37204-4506

Telephone: (615) 256-8500
Fax Number: (615) 782-5000
Internet Homepage: abrholdings.com; ocharleys.com
Company Email: abrhcustomerservice@abrholdings.com
Type of Business: Chain Restaurant Operator
Year Founded: 1983
Systemwide Sales: $552,718,000 (e)
Total Sales: $604,960,000 (e)
Alcohol Sales: 8%
Number of Employees: 17,000
Average Check: Lunch(14); Dinner(14)
Total Units: 156
Trade Names: O'Charley's (156)
Company-Owned Units: 156
Preferred Square Footage: 6,000
Preferred Location Types: Airports; Downtown; Freestanding; Strip Mall
Alcohol Served: Beer, Wine, Liquor
Primary Menu: American (156)
Areas of Operation: AL, AR, FL, IA, IL, IN, KY, LA, MO, MS, NC, OH, PA, SC, TN, VA, WV
Type of Foodservice: Casual Dining (156)
Primary Distributors: (Full Line) Performance Food Group, RICHMOND, VA
Parent Company: Restaurant Growth Services, LLC, NASHVILLE, TN
Headquarters: Restaurant Growth Services, LLC, NASHVILLE, TN

Key Personnel
RANDY HARRIS - Chief Human Resources Officer
IAN GERALDS - VP; Executive Chef
PATRICK DUNNE - Director Operations
KEVIN FORSBERG - Director Retail Sales
STEVE OPITZ - Director Safety, Quality Assurance
MICKI WALSH - Senior Manager Supply Chain
ASHLEY HINTON - Senior Manager Recruitment
PAM KING - Regional Manager Marketing
CARY KUYKENDALL - Manager Loyalty Program
EDWARD ROSE - Manager Financial Planning
DAWN ELLSPERMANN - Manager Human Resources

Provence Breads & Cafe
1705 21st Ave S
Nashville, TN 37217-3034

Telephone: (615) 566-5740
Fax Number: (615) 251-9042
Internet Homepage: provencebreads.com
Type of Business: Chain Restaurant Operator
Year Founded: 1996
Total Sales: $9,405,000 (e)
Number of Employees: 100
Average Check: Breakfast(8); Lunch(8); Dinner(8)
Total Units: 4
Trade Names: Provence Breads & Cafe (4)
Company-Owned Units: 4
Preferred Square Footage: 3,000
Preferred Location Types: Airports; Downtown; Freestanding
Primary Menu: Sandwiches/Deli (4)
Areas of Operation: TN
Type of Foodservice: Fast Casual (4)
Catering Services: Yes
Primary Distributors: (Full Line) Sysco Food Services of Nashville, NASHVILLE, TN
Notes: The company derives approximately 30% of its revenue from wholesale operations.

Key Personnel
TERRY CARR-HALL - President; Director Purchasing, Menu Development, Catering; General Buyer

Restaurant Growth Services, LLC
3038 Sidco Dr
Nashville, TN 37204-4506

Telephone: (615) 256-8500
Fax Number: (615) 782-5043
Internet Homepage: 99restaurants.com; ocharleys.com; restaurantgrowthservices.com
Company Email: info@restgrowthservices.com
Listing Type: Corporate Office
Type of Business: Chain Restaurant Operator
Year Founded: 1958
Total Sales: $1,392,506,000 (e)
Alcohol Sales: 10%
Number of Employees: 32,500
Total Units: 232
Trade Names: 99 Restaurant & Pub (94); O'Charley's (138)
Company-Owned Units: 241
Preferred Location Types: Community Mall; Freestanding; Lifestyle Center; Other

Alcohol Served: Beer, Wine, Liquor
Primary Menu: American (232)
Areas of Operation: AK, AL, AR, AZ, CO, CT, DC, DE, FL, GA, IA, IL, IN, KS, KY, LA, MA, MD, ME, MI, MN, MO, MS, NC, ND, NE, NH, NJ, NM, NY, OH, OK, OR, PA, RI, SC, SD, TN, TX, UT, VA, WA, WI, WV, WY
Type of Foodservice: Casual Dining (94); Family Restaurant (138)
Catering Services: Yes
Distribution Centers: OAK FOREST, IL
Primary Distributors: (Full Line) US Foods, CENTENNIAL, CO
Parent Company: Fidelity National Financial Inc., JACKSONVILLE, FL
Headquarter Offices: O'Charley's Restaurants, NASHVILLE, TN
Notes: The company derives approximately 5% of its revenue from manufacturing operations.

Key Personnel
CRAIG BARBER - CEO
KARA JACOBS - CFO
ZACH HUTTO - Chief Accounting Officer
CLINT LAUTENSCHLEGER - Chief People Officer
ROBERT LANGFORD - Chief Concept Officer Group
DOUG SNYDER - VP Finance
PHILLIP PURCELL - VP; General Counsel
SCOTT BLEAU - VP Infrastructure, Security
KEVIN FORSBERG - VP Retail Operations
MICHELLE DAVIDSON - Senior Director Human Resources
BETSY MARTIN - Senior Director Employee Development
GORDON DAVENPORT - Senior Director Software Engineering
ADAM MARTIN - Senior Director Supply Chain
MONICA MATTHEWS - Director Information Technology
ABBIE BUTLER - Director Accounting
TERRI MCNEILL - Director Information Systems
LEE RATHBUN - Director Human Resources

Shoney's North America Corp.
1717 Elm Hill Pike Ste B1
Nashville, TN 37210-3628

Telephone: (615) 391-5395
Fax Number: (615) 231-2009
Internet Homepage: shoneys.com
Company Email: feedback@shoneys.com
Type of Business: Chain Restaurant Operator
Year Founded: 1947
Systemwide Sales: $211,041,000 (e)
Total Sales: $72,230,000 (e)
Number of Employees: 2,387
Average Check: Breakfast(10); Lunch(12); Dinner(14)
Total Units: 105
Trade Names: Shoney's (105)
Company-Owned Units: 43
Units Franchised To: 62
Preferred Square Footage: 5,500
Preferred Location Types: Downtown; Freestanding
Primary Menu: American (105)
Areas of Operation: AL, AR, FL, GA, KY, LA, MO, MS, NC, NM, OH, SC, TN, TX, VA, WV
Type of Foodservice: Family Restaurant (105)
Catering Services: Yes
Parent Company: Royal Capital Corp., ATLANTA, GA

Key Personnel
DAVID DAVOUDPOUR - Chairman; CEO
KAMRAN HABEEB - President; COO
STEVE NEUROTH - CFO
GILL DUFF - Chief Marketing Officer
CATHERINE HITE - Exec VP; Corporate Secretary; General Counsel
BILL BERTRAM - General Counsel Legal
DEADRICK THAXTON - Director Legal, Human Resources
MAX GOWER - Director Information Technology
WILLIAM STOCK - Manager

Sperry's Restaurant Inc.
5109 Harding Pike
Nashville, TN 37205-2802

Telephone: (615) 353-0809
Internet Homepage: sperrys.com
Type of Business: Chain Restaurant Operator
Year Founded: 1974
Total Sales: $7,884,000 (e)
Alcohol Sales: 5%
Number of Employees: 40
Average Check: Dinner(42)
Total Units: 2
Trade Names: Sperry's Restaurant (2)
Company-Owned Units: 2
Alcohol Served: Beer, Wine, Liquor
Primary Menu: Steak/Seafood (2)
Areas of Operation: TN
Type of Foodservice: Fine Dining (2)

Key Personnel
AL THOMAS - President; General Manager; General Buyer
SCOTT JOHNSON - Manager

TailGate Brewery
7300 Charlotte Pike
Nashville, TN 37209

Telephone: (615) 861-98842
Internet Homepage: tailgatebeer.com
Company Email: social@tailgatebeer.com
Type of Business: Chain Restaurant Operator
Year Founded: 2007
Total Units: 3
Trade Names: Tailgate Brewery East Nashville (1); Tailgate Brewery Music Row (1); Tailgate Brewery West Nashville (1)
Company-Owned Units: 3
Preferred Square Footage: 26,000
Preferred Location Types: Downtown; Freestanding
Primary Menu: Pizza (3)
Areas of Operation: TN
Type of Foodservice: Casual Dining (3)

Key Personnel
WES KEEGAN - Founder; Owner
JESSICA HARDING - Chief of Staff
LIZ TARRY - Manager Marketing, Brand Marketing
SEAN STEELE - Manager Operations
RYAN BRUCHEY - Brand Manager

The Herndon Group, Inc.
211 Union St Ste 106
Nashville, TN 37201-1525

Telephone: (615) 891-3750
Type of Business: Chain Restaurant Operator
Total Sales: $5,958,000 (e)
Total Units: 4
Trade Names: Jersey Mike's Subs (4)
Units Franchised From: 4
Primary Menu: Sandwiches/Deli (4)
Areas of Operation: TN
Type of Foodservice: Quick Serve (4)
Franchise Affiliation: Jersey Mike's Franchise Systems, MANASQUAN, NJ

Key Personnel
CHRIS HERNDON - Owner; General Buyer

TomKats Inc
641 Fogg St
Nashville, TN 37203-4605

Telephone: (615) 256-9596
Internet Homepage: woolworthonfifth.com; tomkats.com
Type of Business: Chain Restaurant Operator
Total Units: 2
Trade Names: Acme Feed and Seed (1); Woolworth on 5th (1)
Company-Owned Units: 2
Primary Menu: American (2)
Areas of Operation: TN
Type of Foodservice: Casual Dining (2)

Key Personnel
KATHERINE MORALES - Owner
ROBYNNE NAPIER - CFO
LAUREN MORALES - COO
MARK FLANDERS - Executive Director
MATT FARLEY - Executive Chef

WBNippers, Inc.
5527 Edmondson Pike
Nashville, TN 37211-5808

Telephone: (615) 315-5555
Type of Business: Chain Restaurant Operator
Total Sales: $6,863,000 (e)
Total Units: 5
Trade Names: Jersey Mike's Subs (5)
Units Franchised From: 5
Primary Menu: Sandwiches/Deli (5)
Areas of Operation: TN
Type of Foodservice: Quick Serve (5)
Franchise Affiliation: Jersey Mike's Franchise Systems, MANASQUAN, NJ

Key Personnel
WILLIAM C. BROWN - Owner; General Buyer

West End Restaurants LLC
200 31st Ave N Ste 100
Nashville, TN 37203-1205

Mailing Address: PO Box 330152, NASHVILLE, TN, 37203
Telephone: (615) 292-0188
Fax Number: (615) 292-0189
Internet Homepage: bricktops.com
Type of Business: Chain Restaurant Operator
Total Sales: $27,460,000 (e)
Alcohol Sales: 15%
Internet Order Processing: Yes
Total Units: 9
Trade Names: Bricktop's (9)
Company-Owned Units: 9
Preferred Square Footage: 7,500
Alcohol Served: Beer, Wine, Liquor
Primary Menu: American (9)
Projected Openings: 1
Areas of Operation: FL, GA, MO, NC, TN
Type of Foodservice: Casual Dining (9)

Key Personnel
JOSEPH B. LEDBETTER - CEO; Partner
TOM BRUNNBERG - President; Partner; COO
AILEEN MCCORMICK - CFO

Whitt's B-B-Q
5211 Alabama Ave
Nashville, TN 37209-3344

Telephone: (615) 385-1553
Internet Homepage: whittsbarbecue.com
Company Email: info@whittsbarbecue.com
Type of Business: Chain Restaurant Operator
Year Founded: 1978
Systemwide Sales: $20,437,000 (e)
Total Sales: $8,614,000 (e)
Number of Employees: 195
Average Check: Lunch(10); Dinner(16)
Total Units: 25
Trade Names: Whitt's B-B-Q (25)
Company-Owned Units: 8
Units Franchised To: 17
Preferred Square Footage: 700; 1,500
Preferred Location Types: Freestanding
Primary Menu: Bar-B-Q (25)
Areas of Operation: KY, TN
Type of Foodservice: Casual Dining (8); Quick Serve (17)
Catering Services: Yes
Primary Distributors: (Full Line) PFG - Customized Support Services, LEBANON, TN

Key Personnel
BILL DEAN - President; Partner
STEVE DUNLAP - Partner; General Manager; Director Information Systems
RENEE DUNLAP - Partner; Controller; Director Finance, Real Estate, Franchising
TONY PIGUE - Partner; Manager Facility/Maintenance, Real Estate, Design, Franchising, Store Fixtures; General Buyer

WTC Ventures
7135 Charlotte Pike Suite 100
Nashville, TN 37209

Telephone: (615) 850-0505
Internet Homepage: wtcventures.com
Company Email: info@wtcventures.com
Type of Business: Chain Restaurant Operator
Total Sales: $87,390,000 (e)
Total Units: 82
Trade Names: Wendy's (82)
Units Franchised From: 82
Primary Menu: Hamburger (82)
Areas of Operation: WA, BC
Foreign Countries: CANADA
Type of Foodservice: Quick Serve (82)

Key Personnel
TITO WISEMANN - Owner
DAVID ANTIS - Senior VP Operations
HANS RASMUSSEN - Senior Director Information Technology

Ed Razban
203 Tyson Ave Ste C
Paris, TN 38242-4588

Telephone: (731) 644-3030
Type of Business: Chain Restaurant Operator
Total Sales: $33,793,000 (e)

CHRISTIAN TODD - Director Beverages
BRITTANY SNOWDEN - Director Human Resources
NICOLE HOWELL - Manager Administration
KRISTIN WALKER - Project Manager

Average Check: Dinner(16)
Total Units: 17
Trade Names: Domino's (17)
Units Franchised From: 17
Primary Menu: Pizza (17)
Areas of Operation: TN
Type of Foodservice: Quick Serve (17)
Franchise Affiliation: Domino's Pizza Inc, ANN ARBOR, MI

Key Personnel
ED RAZBAN - President; General Buyer

McWorth Management
450 Pine Ridge Dr
Paris, TN 38242-4944

Telephone: (731) 642-4506
Fax Number: (731) 642-1962
Type of Business: Chain Restaurant Operator
Year Founded: 1977
Total Sales: $37,220,000 (e)
Number of Employees: 400
Average Check: Breakfast(8); Lunch(12); Dinner(12)
Total Units: 8
Trade Names: McDonald's (8)
Units Franchised From: 8
Preferred Square Footage: 2,500
Preferred Location Types: Freestanding
Primary Menu: Hamburger (8)
Areas of Operation: KY, TN
Type of Foodservice: Quick Serve (8)
Franchise Affiliation: McDonald's Corporation, CHICAGO, IL
Primary Distributors: (Full Line) The Martin-Brower Co. LLC, ROSEMONT, IL

Key Personnel
KRISTINE KENWORTHY - Owner; General Buyer

A S C Corporation
3536 Parkway Ste 8
Pigeon Forge, TN 37863-3836

Telephone: (865) 428-7700
Type of Business: Chain Restaurant Operator
Total Sales: $9,025,000 (e)
Total Units: 16
Trade Names: Subway (16)
Units Franchised From: 16
Primary Menu: Sandwiches/Deli (16)
Areas of Operation: TN
Type of Foodservice: Quick Serve (16)
Franchise Affiliation: Doctor's Associates Inc., MILFORD, CT

The Dollywood Company
2700 Dollywood Parks Blvd
Pigeon Forge, TN 37863-4102

Telephone: (865) 428-9428
Fax Number: (865) 428-9407
Internet Homepage: dollywood.com
Company Email: guestservices@dollywood.com
Type of Business: Foodservice Operations - Theme Parks
Year Founded: 1986
Total Sales: $103,213,000 (e)
Number of Employees: 4,000
Average Check: Lunch(12); Dinner(14)
Total Units: 40
Trade Names: A Foodies Dream (1); Aunt Granny's (1); Berries N Cream (1); Blue Ribbon Cones (1); Country Cookers-Kettle Corn (1); Crossroads Funnel Cakes (1); Dippin Dots (1); DM Pantry (1); Dog House (1); Dog N Taters (1); Front Porch Cafe (1); Grandstand Cafe (1); Granny Ogle's Ham 'n Beans (1);Hickory House BBQ (1); Jukebox Junction Food Truck (1); Lumber Jack's Pizza (1); LumberJack (1); Market Square (1); Midway Market (1); Miss Lillian's BBQ Corner (1); Miss Lillian's Smokehouse (1); Picnic In The Park (1); Pork Rinds (1); Red's Drive In (1); Show Street Concession (5); Sit & Sip (1); SkyView Snacks(1); Song & Hearth (1); Splinter's (1); Spotlight Bakery (1); Sweet Shoppe (1); The Grist Mill (1); The Lounge at Dollywoods (1); Till & Harvest (1); TrailheadTacos (1); Victoria's Pizza (1)
Company-Owned Units: 61
Preferred Square Footage: 2,500; 5,500; 6,000
Preferred Location Types: Freestanding; Kiosk
Primary Menu: American (9); Bar-B-Q (2); Chicken (1); Hot Dogs (1); Mexican (1); Miscellaneous (1); Pizza (3); Sandwiches/Deli (1); Snacks (17); Southern(3); Taco (1)
Areas of Operation: TN
Type of Foodservice: Casual Dining (14); Family Restaurant (1); Fast Casual (21); In-Store Feeder (1); Quick Serve (3)
Primary Distributors: (Full Line) Reinhart FoodService, LOUISVILLE, TN
Parent Company: Herschend Family Entertainment Corporation, NORCROSS, GA
Notes: The company derives approximately 82% of its revenue from admission tickets & retail sales.

Key Personnel
EUGENE NAUGHTON - President
CRAIG ROSS - President
CINDY SMELCER - VP Finance, Information Technology; Controller
AMY OWENBY - VP Marketing
JASON BOOTHE - VP Operations
PATRICE MENDES - VP Culinary Operations
MELISSA WALKER - VP Finance
TED MILLER - General Manager
CORDELIA MORRELL - Director Sales
PETE OWENS - Director Public Relations
TOWANNA STONE - Director Communications, Business Development
JACOB MILLER - Director Finance
JAY MCNEILL - Director Human Resources
ANN BOWERS - Director Finance
STEVE BURRELL - Director Security, Safety
BRAD JUSTICE - Director Customer Service
JOE LINDSEY - Director Foodservice, Food and Beverage
REBECCA MANLEY - Director Human Resources
SAMUEL E. YALLEY - Director Information Technology
AARON BANKS - Director Culinary Operations
BROOKE MCCARTER - Regional Manager Marketing
DIVYA MELWANI - Manager Procurement
BRANDI SALYERS - Manager Sales

Subway of Portland Inc
201 N Broadway
Portland, TN 37148-1111

Telephone: (615) 325-3790
Type of Business: Chain Restaurant Operator
Total Sales: $3,070,000 (e)
Total Units: 5
Trade Names: Subway (5)
Units Franchised From: 5
Primary Menu: Sandwiches/Deli (5)
Areas of Operation: TN
Type of Foodservice: Quick Serve (5)
Franchise Affiliation: Doctor's Associates Inc., MILFORD, CT

Key Personnel
DANNY ELDRIDGE - Partner; General Buyer
ADAM ELDRIDGE - Partner

Domino's Franchisee
291 S Washington St
Ripley, TN 38063-1732

Telephone: (731) 635-3020
Type of Business: Chain Restaurant Operator
Total Sales: $4,044,000 (e)
Total Units: 2
Trade Names: Domino's (2)
Units Franchised From: 2
Primary Menu: Pizza (2)
Areas of Operation: TN
Type of Foodservice: Quick Serve (2)
Franchise Affiliation: Domino's Pizza Inc, ANN ARBOR, MI

Key Personnel
JOSH L. HERRON - Owner; General Buyer

Collier Restaurant Group
473 Old Douglas Dam Rd
Sevierville, TN 37876

Telephone: (865) 774-8004
Internet Homepage: collierrestaurantgroup.com; flapjackspancakes.com
Type of Business: Chain Restaurant Operator
Total Units: 18
Trade Names: Corky's Ribs & BBQ (1); FlapJack's Pancake Cabin (7); Golden Corral Buffet & Grill (2); Old Chicago (1); Quaker Steak & Lube (1); Smoky Mountain Pancake House (1); Smoky's Pancake Cabin (1); T.G.I. Friday's (3); The Melting Pot (1)
Company-Owned Units: 3
Units Franchised From: 15
Primary Menu: American (16); Bar-B-Q (1); Pizza (1)
Areas of Operation: TN
Type of Foodservice: Casual Dining (9); Family Restaurant (9)
Catering Services: Yes

Key Personnel
BRENT COLLIER - Founder
CARY ZIMMERMAN - CEO; General Buyer
LORI COLLIER - Partner
ELISE COLLIER-MASSEY - Partner
ROYCE PRUITT - CFO
AMANDA BARNES - Manager Marketing, Sales

Rel Maples Institute of Culinary Arts
1720 Old Newport Hwy
Sevierville, TN 37876-5100

Telephone: (865) 774-5826
Fax Number: (865) 774-5804
Internet Homepage: ws.edu
Company Email: admissions@ws.edu
Type of Business: Culinary Schools
Areas of Operation: TN

Key Personnel
JOE CAIRNS - Director Culinary Operations

Stokely Hospitality Enterprises
250 Apple Valley Rd
Sevierville, TN 37862-5401

Telephone: (865) 429-5700
Fax Number: (865) 429-5705
Internet Homepage:
  applewoodfarmhouserestaurant.com
Type of Business: Chain Restaurant Operator
Year Founded: 1975
Total Sales: $2,738,000 (e)
Alcohol Sales: 4%
Number of Employees: 250
Average Check: Breakfast(10); Lunch(12); Dinner(16)
Internet Order Processing: Yes
Internet Sales: 0.50%
Total Units: 7
Trade Names: Applewood Farmhouse (2); Baskin-Robbins (5)
Company-Owned Units: 2
Units Franchised From: 5
Preferred Square Footage: 6,000
Preferred Location Types: Downtown; Freestanding
Primary Menu: American (2); Snacks (5)
Areas of Operation: TN
Type of Foodservice: Casual Dining (2); Quick Serve (5)
Franchise Affiliation: BR IP Holder LLC, CANTON, MA; Pool's Restaurant Group, LAWRENCEVILLE, GA
Primary Distributors: (Full Line) Reinhart FoodService, LOUISVILLE, TN

Key Personnel
WILLIAM STOKELY III - Partner; General Manager; Director Facility/Maintenance, Real Estate, Design
TASHA WADE - CTO; VP Human Resources; Controller; Manager Information Systems
LAURA FLYNN - Director Operations, Training, Franchising, Menu Development
SCOTT KING - Director Sales

Hickory Falls Wood-Fired Grille & Bar LLC
999 Industrial Blvd
Smyrna, TN 37167-6815

Telephone: (615) 459-3900
Fax Number: (615) 459-3943
Internet Homepage:
  hickoryfallsrestaurant.com;
  thefranklinchophouse.com
Type of Business: Chain Restaurant Operator
Year Founded: 1990
Total Sales: $7,711,000 (e)
Alcohol Sales: 20%
Number of Employees: 60
Average Check: Lunch(10); Dinner(16)
Total Units: 2
Trade Names: Franklin Chop House (1); Hickory Falls Wood Fired Grill (1)
Company-Owned Units: 2
Preferred Location Types: Freestanding
Alcohol Served: Beer, Wine, Liquor
Primary Menu: American (2)
Areas of Operation: TN
Type of Foodservice: Casual Dining (2)

Key Personnel
PAUL KEHAYES - Partner
PETER KEHAYES - Partner; General Manager; General Buyer
MARK ROBBINS - Partner
MEREDITH CAUDILL - General Manager

Cockrum & Cockrum Inc
782 New Highway 68
Sweetwater, TN 37874

Telephone: (423) 337-7840
Fax Number: (423) 337-2898
Type of Business: Chain Restaurant Operator
Total Sales: $35,730,000 (e)
Total Units: 17
Trade Names: Sonic America's Drive-In (17)
Units Franchised From: 17
Primary Menu: Hamburger (17)
Areas of Operation: TN
Type of Foodservice: Quick Serve (17)
Franchise Affiliation: Sonic Corp., OKLAHOMA CITY, OK

Key Personnel
BOB DEWITT - Owner

TEXAS

Domino's Franchisee
1125 E North 10th St
Abilene, TX 79601-4634

Telephone: (325) 677-3030
Type of Business: Chain Restaurant Operator
Total Sales: $4,120,000 (e)
Total Units: 2
Trade Names: Domino's (2)
Units Franchised From: 2
Primary Menu: Pizza (2)
Areas of Operation: TX
Type of Foodservice: Quick Serve (2)
Franchise Affiliation: Domino's Pizza Inc, ANN ARBOR, MI

Key Personnel
JONATHAN D. SHARP - Owner; General Buyer

Double O Inc. / Exceptional Brands LLC
1902 Industrial Blvd
Abilene, TX 79602-7842

Telephone: (325) 698-2600
Fax Number: (325) 698-2355
Internet Homepage: exceptional-brands.com; miguelsmextexcafe.com
Type of Business: Chain Restaurant Operator
Year Founded: 1973
Total Sales: $41,400,000 (e)
Alcohol Sales: 20%
Number of Employees: 440
Average Check: Lunch(14); Dinner(20)
Total Units: 14
Trade Names: Buffalo Wild Wings (6); Miguel's Tex-Mex (1); Taco Bell (7)
Company-Owned Units: 1
Units Franchised From: 13
Preferred Square Footage: 2,500
Preferred Location Types: Freestanding
Alcohol Served: Beer, Wine, Liquor
Primary Menu: Chicken (6); Southwest/Tex-Mex (1); Taco (7)
Areas of Operation: OK, TX
Type of Foodservice: Casual Dining (7); Quick Serve (7)
Franchise Affiliation: Buffalo Wild Wings Inc., ATLANTA, GA; Taco Bell Corp., IRVINE, CA

Key Personnel
DAVID OHRE - CEO; Partner; Controller; Director Finance, Purchasing, Facility/Maintenance, Information Systems, Loss Prevention, Real Estate, Design, Human Resources, Store Fixtures
MICHAEL BURTON - President; Partner; VP Operations, Food Safety
TRISTA VINCENT - Director Accounting, Administration, Customer Service

HOL-MC Inc.
4427 S 1st St
Abilene, TX 79605

Telephone: (325) 695-1710
Internet Homepage: arbys.com
Type of Business: Chain Restaurant Operator
Total Sales: $3,967,000 (e)
Average Check: Lunch(10); Dinner(10)
Total Units: 2
Trade Names: Arby's (2)
Units Franchised From: 2
Preferred Square Footage: 2,500; 3,000
Preferred Location Types: Freestanding
Primary Menu: Sandwiches/Deli (2)
Areas of Operation: TX
Type of Foodservice: Quick Serve (2)
Franchise Affiliation: Arby's Restaurant Group, ATLANTA, GA

Primary Distributors: (Food) McLane/Fort Worth, FORT WORTH, TX

Key Personnel
DAVE MCDERMOTT - President; Partner; Director Operations, Purchasing; General Buyer
ADAIR MCDERMOTT - Partner; Director Finance
JON GILL - Director Operations, Technology, Systems
HOWARD SOILEAU - Director Operations

BLH Acquisition Co, LLC.
15851 Dallas Pkwy Ste 600
Addison, TX 75001

Telephone: (214) 845-4800
Fax Number: (214) 845-4801
Internet Homepage: barlouie.com
Type of Business: Chain Restaurant Operator
Systemwide Sales: $451,358,000 (e)
Total Sales: $223,780,000 (e)
Alcohol Sales: 50%
Total Units: 72
Trade Names: Bar Louie Tavern & Grill (72)
Company-Owned Units: 72
Preferred Square Footage: 5,000; 6,000
Alcohol Served: Beer, Wine, Liquor
Primary Menu: American (72)
Projected Openings: 3
Areas of Operation: AL, AR, AZ, CA, CO, CT, DC, FL, IA, IL, IN, KY, LA, MA, MD, MI, MO, NC, NJ, NY, OH, PA, RI, SC, TN, TX, VA, WI
Type of Foodservice: Casual Dining (72)

Key Personnel
BRIAN WRIGHT - CEO
BRIAN DEHART - VP Franchise Operations
STEVE CULBERT - VP Administration, Franchise Sales
IAN WELBY - Senior Director Operations

Bone Daddy's
15303 Dallas Pkwy Ste 285
Addison, TX 75001-6733

Telephone: (214) 302-5070
Internet Homepage: bonedaddys.com
Company Email: heydaddy@bonedaddys.com
Type of Business: Chain Restaurant Operator
Total Units: 6
Trade Names: Bone Daddy's (6)
Company-Owned Units: 6
Primary Menu: Bar-B-Q (6)
Areas of Operation: TX
Type of Foodservice: Casual Dining (6)

Key Personnel
MIKE LEATHERWOOD - CEO; President; Owner
MEGAN ELLIOTT - Exec VP

Caesars of DFW, LLC
4203 Beltway Dr Ste 1
Addison, TX 75001

Telephone: (972) 620-0885
Fax Number: (214) 636-0988
Internet Homepage: lcpizzadallas.com
Type of Business: Chain Restaurant Operator
Total Sales: $30,850,000 (e)
Total Units: 25
Trade Names: Little Caesars Pizza (25)
Units Franchised From: 25
Primary Menu: Pizza (25)
Areas of Operation: TX
Type of Foodservice: Quick Serve (25)
Franchise Affiliation: Little Caesar Enterprises Inc., DETROIT, MI

Key Personnel
ERIC SORENSEN - Owner; General Buyer

Ferrari's Italian Villa
14831 Midway Rd
Addison, TX 75001-4956

Telephone: (972) 980-9898
Fax Number: (972) 980-9903
Internet Homepage: ferrarisrestaurant.com
Type of Business: Chain Restaurant Operator
Year Founded: 1983
Total Sales: $3,094,000 (e)
Alcohol Sales: 10%
Number of Employees: 25
Average Check: Lunch(12); Dinner(30)
Total Units: 2
Trade Names: Ferrari's Italian Villa (2)
Company-Owned Units: 2
Preferred Location Types: Freestanding; Strip Mall
Alcohol Served: Beer, Wine, Liquor
Primary Menu: Italian (2)
Areas of Operation: TX
Type of Foodservice: Fine Dining (2)
Catering Services: Yes
Primary Distributors: (Full Line) FreshPoint Dallas, DALLAS, TX

Key Personnel
FRANCESCO SECCHI - President; Partner; General Manager; Executive Chef; General Buyer
JANE SECCHI - Partner; VP Risk Management
PEPE CABRERA - General Manager
TISSITY DESEO - General Manager

Neighborhood Ventures Inc.
14679 Midway Rd Ste 100
Addison, TX 75001-3194

Telephone: (972) 716-3474
Fax Number: (972) 716-4047
Internet Homepage: fishcitygrill.com
Type of Business: Chain Restaurant Operator
Systemwide Sales: $53,595,000 (e)
Total Sales: $27,850,000 (e)
Alcohol Sales: 10%
Number of Employees: 168
Average Check: Lunch(18); Dinner(20)
Total Units: 21
Trade Names: Fish City Grill (19); Half Shells Seafood Grill (2)
Company-Owned Units: 11
Units Franchised To: 10
Preferred Square Footage: 2,400
Preferred Location Types: Downtown; Freestanding; Strip Mall
Alcohol Served: Beer, Wine, Liquor
Primary Menu: Seafood (21)
Projected Openings: 1
Areas of Operation: AR, FL, OK, TX
Type of Foodservice: Casual Dining (21)

Key Personnel
JAMISON MANWARING - Co-Founder; CEO
BILL BAYNE - CEO
DAVE ORENSTEIN - President; COO
LESLIE CHRISTON - COO
PATTY VELASCO - Controller; Director Human Resources
TIM GREEN - Director Operations, Purchasing, Construction, Foodservice
GJE GREENE - Director Marketing

Razzoo's Inc.
14131 Midway Rd Ste 750
Addison, TX 75001

Telephone: (972) 233-6300
Fax Number: (972) 233-1540
Internet Homepage: razzoos.com; trickyfish.com
Company Email: comments@razzoos.com
Type of Business: Chain Restaurant Operator
Year Founded: 1991
Total Sales: $119,850,000 (e)
Alcohol Sales: 10%
Number of Employees: 1,541
Average Check: Lunch(18); Dinner(18)
Internet Order Processing: Yes
Total Units: 25
Trade Names: Razzoo's Cajun Cafe (22); Tricky Fish (3)
Company-Owned Units: 25
Preferred Square Footage: 7,500; 8,300
Preferred Location Types: Freestanding
Alcohol Served: Beer, Wine, Liquor

Primary Menu: Cajun/Creole (22); Seafood (3)
Areas of Operation: NC, TX
Type of Foodservice: Casual Dining (25)
Catering Services: Yes
Primary Distributors: (Food) SYSCO Food Services of North Texas, LEWISVILLE, TX

Key Personnel
JEFF POWELL - CEO; President; Director Real Estate
GARRET BROOKS - COO
TIM COLLINS - Senior Director Information Technology
CRAIG BAYLESS - Director Facility/Maintenance
CORY SHROPSHIRE - Director
DEEDEE TINSLEY - Manager Accounting
SHAENA TUOHY - Manager Marketing
JULIAN BILLINGSLEY - Manager Restaurant Operations

Palio's Pizza Cafe
705 S Custer Rd
Allen, TX 75013

Telephone: (214) 383-9899
Internet Homepage: paliospizzacafe.com
Type of Business: Chain Restaurant Operator
Year Founded: 2007
Total Sales: $42,100,000 (e)
Total Units: 47
Trade Names: Palio's Pizza Cafe (47)
Units Franchised To: 47
Primary Menu: Pizza (47)
Areas of Operation: TX
Type of Foodservice: Casual Dining (47)

Key Personnel
DAVE HOFFMAN - President; Partner
SHARLA HOFFMAN - Partner
HOLDEN BELL - General Manager
SARAH PUZIO - Manager

Chop Chop Rice Co.
6601 W Interstate 40 Ste 2
Amarillo, TX 79106-2628

Telephone: (806) 223-2749
Internet Homepage: chopchoprice.com
Company Email: info@chopchoprice.com
Type of Business: Chain Restaurant Operator
Internet Order Processing: Yes
Total Units: 4
Company-Owned Units: 4
Primary Menu: Chinese (4)
Areas of Operation: TX
Type of Foodservice: Fast Casual (4)

Key Personnel
DAVID TERRY - Co-CEO; Partner
DAVID SMITH - Co-CEO; Partner

HJ Dana Enterprises
7515 SW 45th Ave
Amarillo, TX 79119-6495

Telephone: (806) 358-4845
Fax Number: (806) 355-9196
Type of Business: Chain Restaurant Operator
Year Founded: 1989
Total Sales: $62,620,000 (e)
Number of Employees: 440
Average Check: Breakfast(8); Lunch(8); Dinner(8)
Total Units: 13
Trade Names: McDonald's (13)
Units Franchised From: 13
Preferred Square Footage: 3,000
Preferred Location Types: Discount Dept. Stores; Freestanding
Primary Menu: Hamburger (13)
Areas of Operation: TX
Type of Foodservice: Quick Serve (13)
Franchise Affiliation: McDonald's Corporation, CHICAGO, IL
Primary Distributors: (Full Line) The Martin-Brower Co., GRAND PRAIRIE, TX

Key Personnel
HASSAN DANA - President; Controller; Director Finance, Operations, Purchasing, Facility/Maintenance, Information Systems, Supply Chain, Real Estate, Design; General Buyer
ANNE SARAH - Manager Human Resources

JMTX, LLC
2311 S Georgia St
Amarillo, TX 79109-1836

Telephone: (806) 731-0731
Listing Type: Subsidiary
Type of Business: Chain Restaurant Operator
Total Sales: $2,928,000 (e)
Total Units: 2
Trade Names: Jersey Mike's Subs (2)
Units Franchised From: 2
Primary Menu: Sandwiches/Deli (2)
Areas of Operation: TX
Type of Foodservice: Quick Serve (2)
Franchise Affiliation: Jersey Mike's Franchise Systems, MANASQUAN, NJ
Parent Company: Paradigm Investment Group, LLC, SAN DIEGO, CA

Key Personnel
BRIAN KELLEY - Owner; General Buyer

Leal's Mexican Food, Inc
1619 S Kentucky St
Amarillo, TX 79109

Telephone: (806) 359-5959
Internet Homepage: lealsmexicanfoods.com; myleals.com
Company Email: info@lealsmexicanfoods.com
Type of Business: Chain Restaurant Operator
Year Founded: 1957
Total Sales: $8,734,000 (e)
Average Check: Lunch(10); Dinner(18)
Total Units: 6
Trade Names: Leal's Mexican Restaurant (6)
Company-Owned Units: 6
Preferred Location Types: Freestanding
Alcohol Served: Beer, Liquor
Primary Menu: Mexican (6)
Areas of Operation: NM, TX
Type of Foodservice: Casual Dining (6)
Catering Services: Yes
Notes: Store count reflects restaurant locations only. Leal's Mexican Food, Inc. also manufactures and distributes branded products to retail venues.

Key Personnel
VICTOR LEAL - Chairman
MARCIE LEAL - CEO; President; Owner; General Buyer

R-C Investments
7000 SW 45th Ave Ste 5
Amarillo, TX 79109-5002

Telephone: (806) 354-9660
Fax Number: (806) 354-9554
Listing Type: Divisional Office
Type of Business: Chain Restaurant Operator
Number of Employees: 6
Total Units: 33
Areas of Operation: OK, TX
Parent Company: Castleberry Investments Inc., ELK CITY, OK

Key Personnel
DAVID CASTLEBERRY - Partner
ROGER CASTLEBERRY - Partner; Director Real Estate; General Buyer
JAMES NEWMAN - Director Information Systems
CAMIE BOONE - Director Human Resources

The Donut Stop
3419 S Coulter St Ste 2B
Amarillo, TX 79109-3998

Mailing Address: PO Box 50838, AMARILLO, TX, 79159-0838

Telephone: (806) 355-5774
Fax Number: (806) 355-3831
Internet Homepage: donutstop.com
Company Email: contactthedonutstop.com
Type of Business: Chain Restaurant Operator
Year Founded: 1974
Total Sales: $3,442,000 (e)
Number of Employees: 80
Average Check: Dinner(5)
Total Units: 7
Trade Names: The Donut Stop (7)
Company-Owned Units: 7
Preferred Square Footage: 1,500
Preferred Location Types: Freestanding
Primary Menu: Snacks (7)
Areas of Operation: TX
Type of Foodservice: Quick Serve (7)
Catering Services: Yes
On-site Distribution Center: Yes
Primary Distributors: (Full Line) SYSCO Central Texas Inc., NEW BRAUNFELS, TX

Key Personnel
ERIN DAUER - Partner; General Buyer
RUSSELL DAUER - Partner

Carroll Family Restaurant Group
2340 W Interstate 20 Ste 100
Arlington, TX 76017-7601

Telephone: (817) 467-0505
Fax Number: (817) 467-0506
Internet Homepage: springcreekbarbeque.com
Company Email: contactspringcreek@springcreekbarbeque.com
Type of Business: Chain Restaurant Operator
Year Founded: 1980
Total Sales: $22,470,000 (e)
Alcohol Sales: 5%
Number of Employees: 1,954
Average Check: Lunch(18); Dinner(24)
Internet Order Processing: Yes
Total Units: 43
Trade Names: Mexican Inn (9); Shady Oak Bar & Grill (1); Spring Creek Barbeque (33)
Company-Owned Units: 43
Preferred Square Footage: 5,000
Preferred Location Types: Freestanding; Strip Mall
Alcohol Served: Beer, Wine, Liquor
Primary Menu: American (1); Bar-B-Q (33); Mexican (9)
Areas of Operation: TX
Type of Foodservice: Casual Dining (43)
Catering Services: Yes
Primary Distributors: (Food) Ben E. Keith Foods, FORT WORTH, TX

Key Personnel
CHRIS CARROLL - President; Director
Operations, Purchasing, Facility/Maintenance, Information Systems, Design
GREG LOZIER - Controller
KEITH MEIROSE - Manager Catering
CINDY KARTER - Manager Accounting

Mariano's Mexican Restaurants Inc.
2614 Majesty Dr
Arlington, TX 76011-5322

Telephone: (817) 640-5118
Internet Homepage: laharanch.com
Company Email: mar2@marianosrestaurants.com
Type of Business: Chain Restaurant Operator
Year Founded: 1971
Total Sales: $11,514,000 (e)
Alcohol Sales: 20%
Number of Employees: 100
Average Check: Breakfast(14); Lunch(20); Dinner(26)
Internet Order Processing: Yes
Internet Sales: 1.00%
Total Units: 6
Trade Names: La Hacienda Ranch (4); Mariano's Mexican Restaurant (2)
Company-Owned Units: 6
Preferred Square Footage: 5,500; 6,000
Preferred Location Types: Freestanding
Alcohol Served: Beer, Wine, Liquor
Primary Menu: Mexican (6)
Areas of Operation: TX
Type of Foodservice: Casual Dining (6)
Primary Distributors: (Full Line) US Foods, GARLAND, TX

Key Personnel
MARIANO MARTINEZ - President; Executive Chef; Manager Finance, Operations, Purchasing, Quality Assurance, Supply Chain, Research & Development, Menu Development, Food Safety; General Buyer

Mercado Juarez Cafe Inc.
125 E Interstate 20
Arlington, TX 76018-1117

Telephone: (817) 557-9776
Fax Number: (817) 509-0636
Internet Homepage: mercadojuarez.com
Company Email: mercadojuarez@yahoo.com
Type of Business: Chain Restaurant Operator
Year Founded: 1974
Total Sales: $20,977,000 (e)
Alcohol Sales: 20%
Number of Employees: 425
Average Check: Lunch(14); Dinner(26)
Internet Order Processing: Yes
Total Units: 2
Trade Names: Mercado Juarez (2)
Company-Owned Units: 2
Preferred Location Types: Freestanding
Alcohol Served: Beer, Wine, Liquor
Primary Menu: Mexican (2)
Areas of Operation: TX
Type of Foodservice: Casual Dining (2)
Catering Services: Yes
On-site Distribution Center: Yes
Primary Distributors: (Full Line) US Foods, GARLAND, TX

Key Personnel
DAVE COX - President; General Buyer
MIKE RODRIGUEZ - Store Manager

Hablinski Investments Inc.
419 S Carroll St
Athens, TX 75751-2855

Telephone: (903) 677-9000
Fax Number: (903) 677-3976
Type of Business: Chain Restaurant Operator
Year Founded: 1991
Total Sales: $7,984,000 (e)
Number of Employees: 295
Average Check: Breakfast(8); Lunch(8); Dinner(8)
Total Units: 7
Trade Names: Whataburger (7)
Units Franchised From: 7
Preferred Square Footage: 2,500
Preferred Location Types: Freestanding
Primary Menu: Hamburger (7)
Areas of Operation: TX
Type of Foodservice: Quick Serve (7)
Franchise Affiliation: Whataburger Restaurants LLC, SAN ANTONIO, TX
Primary Distributors: (Equipment) Kirby Restaurant & Chemical Supply Inc., LONGVIEW, TX; (Food) The SYGMA Network Inc.- San Antonio, SAN ANTONIO, TX; (Supplies) SYSCO Central Texas Inc., NEW BRAUNFELS, TX

Key Personnel
BILLY HABLINSKI - CEO; President; Partner; Director Facility/Maintenance, Information Systems, Real Estate, Design; Manager Operations; General Buyer
JACKIE HABLINSKI - Partner; VP; Director Finance, Purchasing, Human Resources
JOSEY VAUGHAN - Administrative Assistant

Lilly Enterprises, Inc
1001 E Tyler St
Athens, TX 75751-2143

Mailing Address: PO Box 2920, ATHENS, TX, 75751-7920
Telephone: (903) 677-4806
Fax Number: (903) 677-8473

Internet Homepage: lillymcd.com
Type of Business: Chain Restaurant Operator
Total Sales: $113,430,000 (e)
Number of Employees: 988
Total Units: 24
Trade Names: McDonald's (24)
Units Franchised From: 24
Preferred Square Footage: 2,500
Primary Menu: Hamburger (24)
Areas of Operation: TX
Type of Foodservice: Quick Serve (24)
Franchise Affiliation: McDonald's Corporation, CHICAGO, IL

Key Personnel
KEVIN LILLY - President; Partner; General Buyer
JEANEANE LILLY - Partner

Alamo Drafthouse
612A E 6th St
Austin, TX 78701

Telephone: (512) 476-1320
Internet Homepage: drafthouse.com
Company Email: venue@originalalamo.com
Type of Business: Foodservice Operations - Movie Theatre
Year Founded: 1997
Systemwide Sales: $9,111,000 (e)
Total Sales: $48,660,000 (e)
Alcohol Sales: 22%
Number of Employees: 2,500
Average Check: Lunch(12); Dinner(18)
Total Units: 25
Trade Names: Alamo Drafthouse Cinema (25)
Company-Owned Units: 18
Units Franchised To: 6
Preferred Location Types: Freestanding
Alcohol Served: Beer, Wine, Liquor
Primary Menu: American (25)
Projected Openings: 1
Areas of Operation: CA, CO, MI, MO, NY, TX, VA, WA
Type of Foodservice: Casual Dining (25)

Key Personnel
MICHAEL KUSTERMANN - CEO
KRISTEN WHEATON - President Customer Service
KARRIE LEAGUE - Partner
MATTHEW VONDERAHE - CFO
CHRIS DRAZBA - Chief Development Officer
MIKE SHERRILL - Chief Creative Officer
ERICA VOGEL - VP Accounting
VIT DOLEZEL - General Manager
JON-MICHAEL ROGERS - General Manager
CHAYA ROSENTHAL - Senior Director Marketing
RACHEL PLETZ - Senior Director Marketing
KAYLA PUGH - Senior Director Strategy
ANDREW MCEATHRON - Director Technology
KELLEY BONDELIE - Director Operations

ALEXANDRA GRIESMER - Director Marketing
JUSTIN ISHMAEL - Director Design
DANA PEARSON - Director Finance
RANDAL WHITE - Director Information Technology
SARAH WILLIAMS - Director Operations
JOHN SMITH - Senior Manager
MATTHEW JEANES - Senior Manager
DENNIS OGAARD - Senior Manager Operations
IAN MCKENZIE - Manager
NATHAN JAMES - Manager Accounting
HEATHER LEACH - Manager
TERI STEGALL - Manager Training

Amy's Ice Creams
1012 W 6th St
Austin, TX 78703

Telephone: (512) 458-6149
Internet Homepage: amysicecreams.com
Company Email: howdy@amysicecreams.com
Type of Business: Chain Restaurant Operator
Year Founded: 1984
Total Sales: $15,020,000 (e)
Number of Employees: 260
Total Units: 17
Trade Names: Amy's Ice Creams (17)
Company-Owned Units: 17
Preferred Location Types: Downtown; Strip Mall
Primary Menu: Snacks (17)
Areas of Operation: TX
Type of Foodservice: Quick Serve (17)

Key Personnel
AMY SIMMONS - Founder; CEO
MARK A. BANKS - COO
ERIN STANLEY - Director Business Development
JENNIFER SCOTT - Manager Operations

ATX Brands LLC
8500 Shoal Creek Blvd Bldg 3-100
Austin, TX 78757-6882

Telephone: (512) 687-4745
Internet Homepage: atxbrands.com
Company Email: info@atxbrands.com
Type of Business: Chain Restaurant Operator
Year Founded: 2006
Total Sales: $16,960,000 (e)
Alcohol Sales: 25%
Total Units: 8
Trade Names: Bikinis Sports Bar & Grill (1); Gino's East Chicago Pizzeria (6); Pelons (1)
Company-Owned Units: 8
Alcohol Served: Beer, Wine, Liquor
Primary Menu: American (1); Pizza (6); Southwest/Tex-Mex (1)
Areas of Operation: OK, TX
Type of Foodservice: Casual Dining (8)

Notes: Not included in store count and trade names are a number of bar and private event venues also operated by ATX Brands.

Key Personnel
DOUG GULLER - Founder; CEO
JUSTINE SILVA - Coordinator Marketing

Auguste Escoffier School of Culinary Arts
6020 Dillard Cir Ste B
Austin, TX 78752-4438

Telephone: (512) 451-5743
Fax Number: (513) 467-9120
Internet Homepage: escoffier.edu
Type of Business: Culinary Schools
Areas of Operation: TX

Key Personnel
MARCUS MCMELLON - President; General Buyer
CHARLES R. CHRISTOPHERSON - CFO
ROBYN MCARTHUR - Executive Chef
JANE JEPSON - Senior Director Employee Development
MARY REARDON - Director Operations
COY BERNARDO - Director Customer Analytics
CHUCK GIGLIO - Director

Austin Sonic Inc.
4513 Burleson Rd
Austin, TX 78744-1203

Mailing Address: PO Box 17788, AUSTIN, TX, 78760-7788
Telephone: (512) 462-0393
Fax Number: (512) 462-3639
Type of Business: Chain Restaurant Operator
Year Founded: 1959
Total Sales: $118,060,000 (e)
Number of Employees: 3,000
Average Check: Breakfast(8); Lunch(8); Dinner(8)
Total Units: 54
Trade Names: Sonic America's Drive-In (54)
Units Franchised From: 54
Preferred Square Footage: 1,320
Preferred Location Types: Freestanding
Primary Menu: Hamburger (66)
Areas of Operation: TX
Type of Foodservice: Quick Serve (54)
Franchise Affiliation: Sonic Corp., OKLAHOMA CITY, OK

Key Personnel
MACKENZIE GIBSON - VP Culinary Operations
SELINA STANLEY - VP Operations
ADAM SCOTT - VP Operations, Technology
KEVIN KNUTSON - VP Operations-Training

JOSEPH SAPOZNIKOV - Senior Director Operations
JULIE SLOAN - Senior Director Operations
MELINDA ZAMORA - Director Operations

Baby Acapulco Restaurant
1705 S Lakeshore Blvd Ste A
Austin, TX 78741-1259

Telephone: (512) 447-1339
Fax Number: (512) 447-7481
Internet Homepage: babyacapulco.com
Type of Business: Chain Restaurant Operator
Total Sales: $3,051,000 (e)
Alcohol Sales: 5%
Total Units: 4
Trade Names: Baby Acapulco Restaurant (4)
Company-Owned Units: 4
Preferred Location Types: Freestanding; Strip Mall
Primary Menu: Mexican (4)
Areas of Operation: TX
Type of Foodservice: Casual Dining (4)

Key Personnel
JERRY SANCHEZ - President; Executive Chef; General Buyer
CALRITA ACAPULCO - Director Operations

Bao'd Up
1911 Aldrich St
Austin, TX 78723

Telephone: (737) 717-3002
Internet Homepage: baodup.com
Company Email: contact@baodup.com
Type of Business: Chain Restaurant Operator
Total Sales: $6,051,000 (e)
Total Units: 4
Trade Names: Bao'd Up (4)
Company-Owned Units: 4
Primary Menu: Asian (4)
Type of Foodservice: Fast Casual (4)

Key Personnel
ALEX WU - Co-Founder
TING LING - Co-Founder; Owner
JESSICA ALEJOS - Director Human Resources

BNC Food Group LLC
7700 Crackling Creek Dr
Austin, TX 78736-3310

Telephone: (512) 636-9138
Type of Business: Chain Restaurant Operator
Year Founded: 1990
Total Sales: $5,390,000 (e)
Number of Employees: 180
Average Check: Lunch(8); Dinner(10)

Total Units: 5
Trade Names: Long John Silver's (5)
Units Franchised From: 5
Preferred Square Footage: 2,500; 3,200
Preferred Location Types: Freestanding
Primary Menu: Seafood (5)
Areas of Operation: TX
Type of Foodservice: Quick Serve (5)
Franchise Affiliation: Long John Silver's Inc., LOUISVILLE, KY

Key Personnel
CHARLES PENLAND - President; Owner; Director Real Estate; General Buyer
CHRIS JACCARD - Director Operations, Information Systems

Capitol Subs Group, LLC
1000 E 41st St Ste 235
Austin, TX 78751-4857

Telephone: (512) 459-1555
Type of Business: Chain Restaurant Operator
Total Sales: $8,274,000 (e)
Total Units: 6
Trade Names: Jersey Mike's Subs (6)
Units Franchised From: 6
Primary Menu: Sandwiches/Deli (6)
Areas of Operation: TX
Type of Foodservice: Quick Serve (6)
Franchise Affiliation: Jersey Mike's Franchise Systems, MANASQUAN, NJ

Key Personnel
STEVE CULLEN - Partner; General Buyer
YVONNE CULLEN - Partner

Chameleon Group
901 W 9th St Ste 102
Austin, TX 78703

Telephone: (512) 476-2469
Internet Homepage: chameleongp.com
Company Email: info@chameleongp.com
Type of Business: Chain Restaurant Operator
Year Founded: 2009
Total Units: 3
Trade Names: Guild (1); Swift's Attic (1); Wu Chow (1)
Company-Owned Units: 3
Primary Menu: American (1); Chinese (1); Seafood (1)
Areas of Operation: TX
Type of Foodservice: Casual Dining (3)

Key Personnel
STUART THOMAJAN - Founder; CEO; Partner
STERLING RIDINGS - Partner; Executive Chef
CK CHIN - Partner
VINNY BOSSI - COO

GEOFF BOOKER - Director Sales

CHI'LANTRO
823 Congress Ave
Austin, TX 78701-2405

Telephone: (512) 800-9098
Internet Homepage: chilantrobbq.com
Company Email: team@chilantrobbq.com
Type of Business: Chain Restaurant Operator
Year Founded: 2010
Total Units: 7
Trade Names: CHI'LANTRO (7)
Company-Owned Units: 7
Projected Openings: 2
Areas of Operation: TX

Key Personnel
JAE KIM - Founder; Owner; General Buyer
RYAN SUMAGAYSAY - Director Operations
NOELLE FUENTES-LOPEZ - District Manager
CALEB RALEY - Project Manager

Chuy's Holdings Inc.
1623 Toomey Rd
Austin, TX 78704-1032

Telephone: (512) 473-2783
Fax Number: (512) 473-8684
Internet Homepage: chuys.com
Company Email: hey@chuys.com
Type of Business: Chain Restaurant Operator
Year Founded: 1982
Publicly Held: Yes
Total Sales: $565,686,000 (e)
Alcohol Sales: 18.40%
Number of Employees: 6,700
Average Check: Lunch(12); Dinner(16)
Total Units: 96
Trade Names: Chuy's (101)
Company-Owned Units: 101
Preferred Square Footage: 5,300; 12,500
Preferred Location Types: Freestanding
Alcohol Served: Beer, Wine, Liquor
Primary Menu: Mexican (101)
Projected Openings: 5
Areas of Operation: AL, AR, CO, FL, GA, IL, IN, KS, KY, LA, MD, MO, NC, OH, OK, SC, TN, TX, VA
Type of Foodservice: Casual Dining (101)
Primary Distributors: (Full Line) Labatt Food Service, SAN ANTONIO, TX

Key Personnel
STEVE HISLOP - Chairman; CEO; President
JON W. HOWIE - CFO; VP
JOHN MOUNTFORD - COO
MARCIA WILLIAMS - VP Human Resources
MICHAEL HATCHER - VP Real Estate; Manager Operations, Purchasing, Supply Chain, Research & Development, Product

Development, Menu Development
THOMAS LARUE - VP Operations
TRAVIS HUDSON - VP Operations
LISA BRYANT - Director Training
HILARY DELLING - Director Marketing
JOHN BOLLIER - Director Area-Training;
 Supervisor
JOHN HRINKEVICH - Director
TWANNA BLACKWELL - Director Training
MIKE HUDSON - Director Construction
KIANNE HILBURN - Senior Manager Marketing
VICI LACY - Manager Payroll, Human
 Resources
BROOKE COX - Manager
JOSEPH CUMMINS - Manager Information
 Technology
CORBIN GASS - Manager Operations
STEPHANIE KRALIK - Manager Field Marketing
SHARI MORELAND - Manager Payroll
JOEL PECK - Manager Accounting
MATT SANDERS - Manager Information
 Technology
JASON SOLIVAN - Manager
JORDAN COLE - Manager Financial Planning
CANDICE BUI - Manager Administration
HOLLY ROBBINS - Manager Field Marketing,
 Southeast Region
RICHARD BROZDA - Manager Area, Catering
RUSSELL BURNS - Supervisor Area
SONNY MOORE - Assistant Procurement

Conans Pizza Inc.
4107 Medical Pkwy Ste C
Austin, TX 78756-3701

Telephone: (512) 478-5914
Internet Homepage: conanspizza.com
Type of Business: Chain Restaurant Operator
Year Founded: 1976
Total Sales: $2,905,000 (e)
Alcohol Sales: 5%
Number of Employees: 75
Average Check: Lunch(10); Dinner(12)
Total Units: 2
Trade Names: Conans Pizza (2)
Company-Owned Units: 2
Preferred Location Types: Freestanding; Strip
 Mall
Alcohol Served: Beer
Primary Menu: Pizza (2)
Areas of Operation: TX
Type of Foodservice: Casual Dining (2)
Catering Services: Yes
On-site Distribution Center: Yes

Key Personnel
SCOTT LEIST - Partner; Director Operations,
 Advertising; General Buyer
JERRY STRADER - Partner; VP; General
 Manager; Manager Accounting

Domino's Franchisee
719 W William Cannon Dr
Austin, TX 78745-5696

Telephone: (512) 440-8833
Type of Business: Chain Restaurant Operator
Total Sales: $8,270,000 (e)
Total Units: 4
Trade Names: Domino's (4)
Units Franchised From: 4
Primary Menu: Pizza (4)
Areas of Operation: TX
Type of Foodservice: Quick Serve (4)
Franchise Affiliation: Domino's Pizza Inc, ANN
 ARBOR, MI

Key Personnel
FRANK A. FELAND - Owner; General Buyer

DoubleDave's Pizzaworks Systems Inc.
14823 Fitzhugh Rd
Austin, TX 78736

Telephone: (512) 328-3283
Fax Number: (512) 343-0248
Internet Homepage: doubledaves.com
Company Email: christie@doubledaves.com
Type of Business: Chain Restaurant Operator
Year Founded: 1984
Systemwide Sales: $17,000,000 (e)
Total Sales: $3,086,000 (e)
Alcohol Sales: 3%
Number of Employees: 90
Average Check: Lunch(12); Dinner(18)
Internet Order Processing: Yes
Total Units: 41
Trade Names: DoubleDave's (41)
Company-Owned Units: 2
Units Franchised To: 39
Preferred Square Footage: 4,000
Preferred Location Types: Strip Mall
Alcohol Served: Beer, Wine
Primary Menu: Pizza (41)
Areas of Operation: OK, TX
Type of Foodservice: Fast Casual (41)
Foodservice Management Venues: Business
 & Industry; College & University; Health Care;
 Lodging; Military Feeding; Parks & Recreation;
 Schools; Transportation
Catering Services: Yes
Primary Distributors: (Food) Performance
 Foodservice, DALLAS, TX; (Supplies) Labatt
 Food Service, SAN ANTONIO, TX

Key Personnel
CHUCK THORP - CEO; General Buyer
DAVID J. MILLER - President; Director
 Facility/Maintenance, Real Estate, Design,
 Store Fixtures
JOEY W. BRAMWELL - COO; VP Finance,
 Operations, Information Systems, Supply
 Chain, Human Resources; Coordinator Menu
 Development, Catering
CHRISTIE LEWIS - Director Marketing

El Mercado
1702 Lavaca St
Austin, TX 78701-1316

Telephone: (512) 477-7689
Fax Number: (512) 473-8333
Internet Homepage: elmercadorestaurant.com
Type of Business: Chain Restaurant Operator
Year Founded: 1984
Systemwide Sales: $6,180,000 (e)
Total Sales: $5,562,000 (e)
Alcohol Sales: 30%
Number of Employees: 250
Average Check: Breakfast(10); Lunch(16);
 Dinner(20)
Total Units: 3
Trade Names: El Mercado (3)
Company-Owned Units: 3
Preferred Location Types: Freestanding; Strip
 Mall
Alcohol Served: Beer, Wine, Liquor
Primary Menu: Southwest/Tex-Mex (3)
Areas of Operation: TX
Type of Foodservice: Casual Dining (3)
Catering Services: Yes
Primary Distributors: (Equipment) Ace Mart
 Restaurant Supply Co., AUSTIN, TX; (Food)
 SYSCO Corporation, HOUSTON, TX;
 (Supplies) SYSCO Corporation, HOUSTON,
 TX

Key Personnel
TONY VILLEGAS - President; Partner;
 Controller; Executive Chef; Director Finance,
 Purchasing, Supply Chain, Catering; Manager
 Operations
GERALD STONE - Partner; VP; Director
 Facility/Maintenance, Real Estate, Design;
 General Buyer
LUPE MENDOZA - General Manager; Director
 Human Resources

ELM Restaurant Group
1106 W 38th St Ste 200
Austin, TX 78705

Telephone: (512) 467-8776
Internet Homepage: elmrg.com
Company Email: info@elmrg.com
Type of Business: Chain Restaurant Operator
Year Founded: 2009
Total Units: 5
Trade Names: 24 Diner (1); Cookbook Bar &
 Cafe (1); Fareground (1); Irene's (1); Italic (1)
Company-Owned Units: 5
Primary Menu: American (3); Italian (1);

Miscellaneous (1)
Projected Openings: 2
Areas of Operation: TX
Type of Foodservice: Casual Dining (5)

Key Personnel
SCOTT HENTSCHEL - Partner; Director Real Estate, Business Development
ANDREW CURREN - Partner; Executive Chef
MARY CATHERINE CURRENT - Executive Chef
VINCENT ASHWILL - Director Operations
KAYLA FRENCH - Director Event Planning

Engel Management Services
5425 Burnet Rd STE 106
Austin, TX 78756

Telephone: (512) 804-0326
Fax Number: (512) 707-1110
Internet Homepage: skishoresaustin.com; austinjava.com; littlewoodrows.com; texadelphia.com; unclebillys.com
Type of Business: Chain Restaurant Operator
Year Founded: 2006
Systemwide Sales: $60,784,000 (e)
Total Sales: $63,500,000 (e)
Alcohol Sales: 15%
Number of Employees: 1,204
Average Check: Breakfast(8); Lunch(14); Dinner(20)
Total Units: 34
Trade Names: Austin Java (1); Little Woodrow's (19); Ski Shores Cafe (2); Texadelphia (12)
Company-Owned Units: 27
Units Franchised To: 7
Preferred Location Types: Freestanding; Strip Mall
Alcohol Served: Beer, Wine, Liquor
Primary Menu: American (22); Mexican (12)
Areas of Operation: OK, TX
Type of Foodservice: Fast Casual (34)
Primary Distributors: (Full Line) SYSCO Food Services of Houston Inc., HOUSTON, TX

Key Personnel
RICK ENGEL - Partner
MARK TURNER - Partner
SANDRA KASO - Director Information Systems

Fitness Food Holdings Inc.
4616 Triangle Ave
Austin, TX 78751-3504

Telephone: (512) 428-4000
Fax Number: (512) 407-9646
Internet Homepage: snapkitchen.com
Company Email: austininfo@snapkitchen.com
Type of Business: Chain Restaurant Operator
Year Founded: 2010
Average Check: Lunch(22); Dinner(22)

Total Units: 35
Trade Names: Snap Kitchen (35)
Company-Owned Units: 35
Preferred Square Footage: 600; 1,500; 4,000; 5,000
Primary Menu: Health Foods (35)
Areas of Operation: PA, TX
Type of Foodservice: Quick Serve (35)
Catering Services: Yes

Key Personnel
BRADLEY RADOFF - Co-Founder
JOHN CARTER - CEO
DALE EASDON - COO
TARA LANE - VP Foodservice
JASON MAREK - General Manager
MICHAEL SABRIN - Executive Chef
TY DUPREE - Generalist Human Resources

Fixe Restaurant
500 W 5th St
Austin, TX 78701

Telephone: (512) 954-3493
Internet Homepage: fixesouthernhouse.com
Company Email: keith@austinfixe.com
Type of Business: Chain Restaurant Operator
Year Founded: 2013
Total Units: 2
Trade Names: Fixe Southern House (2)
Company-Owned Units: 2
Primary Menu: Southern (2)
Areas of Operation: TX
Type of Foodservice: Casual Dining (2)

Key Personnel
KEITH HOUSE - President; Partner
JAMES ROBERTS - Partner; Executive Chef

Flyrite Chicken Inc.
2129 E 7th St
Austin, TX 78702

Telephone: (512) 284-8014
Internet Homepage: flyritechicken.com
Company Email: customerservice7th@flyritechicken.com
Type of Business: Chain Restaurant Operator
Year Founded: 2014
Total Units: 3
Trade Names: Flyrite Chicken Sandwiches (3)
Company-Owned Units: 3
Preferred Square Footage: 2,300
Preferred Location Types: Airports; Freestanding
Primary Menu: Chicken (3)
Areas of Operation: TX
Type of Foodservice: Fast Casual (3)

Key Personnel
KEVIN WARDEN - Founder; President

Foods Management Group LLC
4501 Springdale Rd
Austin, TX 78723-6031

Telephone: (512) 441-8900
Internet Homepage: torchystacos.com
Company Email: reception@torchystacos.com
Type of Business: Chain Restaurant Operator
Year Founded: 2006
Total Units: 77
Trade Names: Torchy's Tacos (63)
Company-Owned Units: 63
Preferred Location Types: Downtown; Freestanding; Strip Mall
Alcohol Served: Beer, Wine, Liquor
Primary Menu: Taco (63)
Projected Openings: 10
Areas of Operation: CO, OK, TX
Type of Foodservice: Fast Casual (63)

Key Personnel
MICHAEL RYPKA - Chairman; Founder; Chief Innovation Officer
RYAN MOORE - CFO
ELIZABETH BAXTER - Chief People Officer
DANNY RUSSO - Controller
CHERYL DRUMMOND - Director Culinary Development
ZACK WEINBERG - District Manager
MATTHEW GREEN - Project Manager Construction

Freebirds World Burrito
9050 N Capital of Texas Hwy
Austin, TX 78759

Telephone: (512) 428-6802
Internet Homepage: freebirds.com
Company Email: eat@freebirds.com
Listing Type: Subsidiary
Type of Business: Chain Restaurant Operator
Year Founded: 1987
Total Sales: $49,260,000 (e)
Number of Employees: 2,400
Total Units: 73
Trade Names: FREEBIRDS World Burrito (55)
Company-Owned Units: 55
Preferred Location Types: Freestanding; Regional Mall
Primary Menu: Californian (55)
Areas of Operation: CA, OK, TN, TX, UT
Type of Foodservice: Fast Casual (55)
Parent Company: Tavistock Restaurants LLC, ORLANDO, FL

Key Personnel
ALEX EAGLE - CEO; President
KRISTEN ALEXANDER - General Manager
ARMANDO JUAREZ - General Manager Training
MICA WILLOUGHBY - Director Communications, Training
RYAN EARDLEY - Director Finance, Accounting
JT SMITH - Director Information Technology
NICK BUCHHORN - Director Operations
GRADY TAYLOR - Director Construction
ADRIENNE FIRTH - Regional Manager
RYAN BRADSHAW - Regional Manager
BLAIR KANTZ - Regional Manager
CLIFF NAQUIN - Regional Manager
TIM ROBINSON - Manager Finance, Purchasing
KAI LEONG - Manager Information Technology
STACY LOPEZ - Executive Assistant

Ger-Del, LLC
5355 N Interstate 35
Austin, TX 78723-2428

Mailing Address: PO Box 6330, ROUND ROCK, TX, 78683-6330
Telephone: (512) 452-7473
Type of Business: Chain Restaurant Operator
Total Sales: $19,698,000 (e)
Total Units: 4
Trade Names: McDonald's (4)
Units Franchised From: 4
Primary Menu: Hamburger (4)
Areas of Operation: TX
Type of Foodservice: Quick Serve (4)
Franchise Affiliation: McDonald's Corporation, CHICAGO, IL

Key Personnel
GERMAN USTARIZ - President; General Buyer

Hai Hospitality
701 S Lamar Blvd Ste C
Austin, TX 78704-1547

Telephone: (512) 916-4808
Internet Homepage: haihospitality.com; uchirestaurants.com
Company Email: info@haihospitality.com
Type of Business: Chain Restaurant Operator
Total Units: 7
Trade Names: Loro (1); Uchi (4); Uchiba (1); Uchiko (1)
Company-Owned Units: 7
Primary Menu: Asian (1); Japanese (6)
Areas of Operation: TX
Type of Foodservice: Casual Dining (7)

Key Personnel
DARYL KUNIK - Founder
TONY MONTERO - CEO
JOHN BAYDALE - President
TYSON COLE - Owner; Executive Chef
BRIAN MORROW - CFO
TODD REPPERT - Chief Development Officer
AMBER QUIST - Chief Brand Officer
MELISSA JENSEN - General Manager
MIKE ENRIGHT - Director Human Resources
LEO BARRERA - Director Operations
JANET AVALOS - Senior Manager Design
SAM DAVIDSON - Manager Public Relations
STEVEN STANWYCK - Manager Training
ANTHONY HOPKINS - Manager Procurement

Halcyon
218 W 4th St
Austin, TX 78701-3917

Telephone: (512) 472-9637
Internet Homepage: halcyoncoffeebar.com
Type of Business: Chain Restaurant Operator
Year Founded: 2001
Total Units: 6
Trade Names: Halcyon (4); Stella Public House (2)
Company-Owned Units: 6
Primary Menu: American (4); Pizza (2)
Projected Openings: 2
Areas of Operation: CA, TX
Type of Foodservice: Casual Dining (6)

Key Personnel
KRIS HARDY - Co-Founder; Partner
JOHN LONG - Co-Founder; Partner

Hopdoddy Burger Bar Inc.
1401 S Congress Ave
Austin, TX 78704

Telephone: (512) 852-9340
Internet Homepage: hopdoddy.com
Company Email: info@hopdoddy.com
Type of Business: Chain Restaurant Operator
Year Founded: 2010
Total Sales: $113,290,000 (e)
Average Check: Lunch(16); Dinner(18)
Internet Order Processing: Yes
Total Units: 32
Trade Names: Hopdoddy Burger Bar (32)
Company-Owned Units: 32
Preferred Square Footage: 3,800; 4,000
Primary Menu: Hamburger (31)
Areas of Operation: AZ, CA, CO, TN, TX
Type of Foodservice: Casual Dining (31)

Key Personnel
GUY VILLAVASO - Co-Founder
JEFF CHANDLER - CEO
DANIEL SMITH - COO
KENNY JETT - VP Operations
JENNIFER FAREN - VP Marketing
MATT SCHWEITZER - Senior Director Food and Beverage
JAMES B. HOSS - Director Culinary Operations
PURSHOTAM KUMAR - Director Information Technology
VICTOR HOLT - Director Training
KIM EVANS - Regional Director Training
RAY LOZADA - Regional Director Culinary Operations
ROBERT RODER - Regional Director Operations
JASON J. FEINBERG - Regional Director Operations
MARK BUNIM - Regional Director Operations
MICHAEL STEELE - Regional Director Operations
EDDIE JONES - Regional Director Operations
MEKECHNIE MENDOZA - Regional Director Training
AUDREY REED - Regional Director Training
TOM LOCKWOOD - Manager Marketing
TIM HUSSEY - Specialist; Community Relations

JuiceLand
1625 Barton Springs Rd
Austin, TX 78704-1034

Telephone: (512) 363-5760
Internet Homepage: juiceland.com
Company Email: contact@juiceland.com
Type of Business: Chain Restaurant Operator
Year Founded: 2011
Total Units: 30
Trade Names: JuiceLand (30)
Company-Owned Units: 30
Primary Menu: Health Foods (30)
Projected Openings: 2
Areas of Operation: TX
Type of Foodservice: Fast Casual (30)

Key Personnel
MATT SHOOK - Founder; Owner
MAURINE WINKLEY - Director Finance, Operations
JENNIFER CUPID - Director Human Resources

K&N Management
11570 Research Blvd
Austin, TX 78759-4036

Telephone: (512) 418-0444
Fax Number: (512) 418-8992
Internet Homepage: knmanagement.com; mightyfineburgers.com; rudys.com
Type of Business: Chain Restaurant Operator
Year Founded: 1989
Total Sales: $158,180,000 (e)
Alcohol Sales: 5%
Number of Employees: 2,450
Average Check: Breakfast(10); Lunch(12); Dinner(14)
Internet Order Processing: Yes
Internet Sales: 15.00%

Total Units: 46
Trade Names: Rudy's "Country Store" and Bar-B-Q (46)
Units Franchised From: 46
Preferred Square Footage: 5,500; 6,000
Preferred Location Types: Freestanding; Strip Mall
Alcohol Served: Beer
Primary Menu: Bar-B-Q (46)
Areas of Operation: TX
Type of Foodservice: Casual Dining (46)
Catering Services: Yes
Franchise Affiliation: Ford Restaurant Group, LAKEWAY, TX

Key Personnel
BRIAN NOLEN - Partner
KEN SCHILLER - Partner; General Buyer
DAN PEABODY - General Manager
JACK BREWER - General Manager
CHRIS CLEMENTS - General Manager
SARAH HOUSE - Manager Sales, Group
CARL LEBOEUF - Manager Special Projects; Technician
STACY ROSENGREN - Manager Catering
JAY ANDRUK - Manager Facility/Maintenance, Transportation

KT's Austin
5609 Adams Ave
Austin, TX 78756-1101

Telephone: (512) 453-5806
Fax Number: (512) 453-7945
Type of Business: Chain Restaurant Operator
Year Founded: 1950
Total Sales: $18,880,000 (e)
Number of Employees: 350
Average Check: Lunch(8); Dinner(10)
Total Units: 12
Trade Names: Sandy's (1); Short Stop Austin (11)
Company-Owned Units: 12
Preferred Square Footage: 850
Preferred Location Types: Freestanding
Primary Menu: Hamburger (12)
Areas of Operation: TX
Type of Foodservice: Quick Serve (12)

Key Personnel
JEARL LEDBETTER - President; CFO; Director Operations, Purchasing, Facility/Maintenance, Real Estate, Design, Research & Development, Menu Development
SANDY ENDERLIN - Controller; Director Information Systems, Risk Management, Human Resources
ROY GOMEZ - Manager Area

Manuel's
310 Congress Ave
Austin, TX 78701-4024

Telephone: (512) 472-7555
Fax Number: (512) 472-6055
Internet Homepage: changos.com; manuels.com
Type of Business: Chain Restaurant Operator
Year Founded: 1984
Total Sales: $6,016,000 (e)
Alcohol Sales: 10%
Number of Employees: 60
Average Check: Lunch(16); Dinner(20)
Total Units: 3
Trade Names: Changos (1); Manuel's (2)
Company-Owned Units: 3
Preferred Location Types: Freestanding
Alcohol Served: Beer, Wine, Liquor
Primary Menu: Mexican (2); Taco (1)
Areas of Operation: TX
Type of Foodservice: Casual Dining (3)
Primary Distributors: (Full Line) SYSCO Corporation, HOUSTON, TX

Key Personnel
GREG KOURY - CEO; President; Partner
AHMAD MODONI - Partner
HECTOR ZACATULA - Executive Chef; General Buyer

McLiff Vending & Office Coffee Services
204 W Powell Ln Bldg 4
Austin, TX 78753-5938

Telephone: (512) 441-8424
Fax Number: (512) 334-0199
Internet Homepage: mcliff.com
Type of Business: Foodservice Management Operator
Year Founded: 1967
Total Sales: $30,977,000 (e)
Number of Employees: 100
Number of Locations Served: 2,000
Total Foodservice Mgmt Accounts: 15
Areas of Operation: TX
Type of Foodservice: Vending machines (15)
Foodservice Management Venues: Business & Industry
Primary Distributors: (Full Line) Vistar North Texas, ARLINGTON, TX

Key Personnel
KENDYL JAHNS - Controller
MICHAEL FUREY - Director Supply Chain
MARY VILLARREAL - Manager Customer Service

Mesa Rosa Inc.
15509 Ranch Road 620 N
Austin, TX 78717-5206

Telephone: (512) 219-7444
Fax Number: (512) 219-8777
Internet Homepage: mesarosa.com
Type of Business: Chain Restaurant Operator
Year Founded: 1994
Total Sales: $6,271,000 (e)
Alcohol Sales: 15%
Total Units: 2
Trade Names: Mesa Rosa Mexican Restaurant (2)
Company-Owned Units: 2
Alcohol Served: Beer, Wine, Liquor
Primary Menu: Mexican (2)
Areas of Operation: TX
Type of Foodservice: Casual Dining (2)

Key Personnel
HAMID ZARAFSHANI - President; General Buyer

Murphy Adams Restaurant Group
512 E Riverside Dr Ste 250
Austin, TX 78704-1300

Mailing Address: PO Box 200762, Austin, TX, 78720-0762
Telephone: (512) 949-3220
Fax Number: (800) 905-2147
Internet Homepage: austinspizza.com; mamafus.com
Company Email: info@mamafus.com
Type of Business: Chain Restaurant Operator
Systemwide Sales: $75,035,000 (e)
Total Sales: $33,660,000 (e)
Average Check: Dinner(16)
Internet Order Processing: Yes
Total Units: 9
Trade Names: Austin's Pizza (14); Mama Fu's Asian House (15)
Company-Owned Units: 18
Units Franchised To: 24
Preferred Square Footage: 1,300; 1,500; 2,500; 3,000
Preferred Location Types: Freestanding; Outlet Mall; Strip Mall
Alcohol Served: Beer, Wine
Primary Menu: Asian (15); Pizza (14)
Projected Openings: 2
Areas of Operation: AR, FL, TX, FC
Foreign Countries: UNITED ARAB EMIRATES
Type of Foodservice: Casual Dining (14); Fast Casual (15)
Catering Services: Yes

Key Personnel
MARK ADAMS - Partner; Manager

Infrastructure, Systems
MARY ORLANDO - COO
ALLEN R. MCFEATERS - Director Company Operations

P. Terry's
5555 N Lamar Blvd
Austin, TX 78751

Telephone: (512) 419-0670
Internet Homepage: pterrys.com/locations
Company Email: pterry@pterrys.com
Type of Business: Chain Restaurant Operator
Year Founded: 2005
Total Units: 16
Trade Names: P. Terry's (16)
Company-Owned Units: 16
Preferred Square Footage: 950; 2,800
Primary Menu: Hamburger (16)
Projected Openings: 8
Areas of Operation: TX
Type of Foodservice: Quick Serve (16)

Key Personnel
PATRICK TERRY - Founder; Owner
MILLICENT HAWKINS - CFO
MONTY MONTGOMERY - VP Development
LORI NAUERT - VP Finance
CHRIS WILLIAMS - Director Operations
MATT M. MONTGOMERY - Director Facility/Maintenance, Construction

PhoNatic Real Vietamese Cuisine
2525 W Anderson Ln Bldg 3, Suite 280
Austin, TX 78757

Telephone: (512) 458-8889
Internet Homepage: pho-natic.com
Type of Business: Chain Restaurant Operator
Year Founded: 2011
Total Units: 3
Trade Names: PhoNatic Real Vietnamese Food (3)
Company-Owned Units: 3
Preferred Location Types: Downtown; Strip Mall
Primary Menu: Asian (3)
Areas of Operation: TX
Type of Foodservice: Fast Casual (3)

Key Personnel
SARA LEE - Co-Founder; Partner
PAT LEE - Co-Founder; Partner

Picnik
3000 E Cesar Chavez St Ste 100
Austin, TX 78702

Telephone: (737) 226-0644
Internet Homepage: picnikaustin.com
Type of Business: Chain Restaurant Operator
Year Founded: 2013
Total Sales: $3,547,000 (e)
Trade Names: Picnik (2)
Company-Owned Units: 2
Primary Menu: Californian (2)
Type of Foodservice: Fast Casual (2)

Key Personnel
NAOMI SEIFTER - Founder; Owner
CHRISTOPHER SKILLERN - General Manager
JUSTINA KNUTSON - Director Finance

Pluckers Wing Factory & Grill
811 Barton Springs Rd Ste 600
Austin, TX 78704-1164

Telephone: (512) 236-9110
Fax Number: (512) 236-9113
Internet Homepage: pluckers.com
Type of Business: Chain Restaurant Operator
Year Founded: 1995
Total Sales: $48,470,000 (e)
Alcohol Sales: 3%
Number of Employees: 835
Average Check: Lunch(10); Dinner(14)
Internet Order Processing: Yes
Total Units: 24
Trade Names: Pluckers Wing Factory & Grill (24)
Company-Owned Units: 13
Units Franchised To: 11
Preferred Location Types: Freestanding
Alcohol Served: Beer, Wine, Liquor
Primary Menu: Chicken (24)
Areas of Operation: LA, TX
Type of Foodservice: Casual Dining (24)
Catering Services: Yes

Key Personnel
MARK GREENBERG - Partner
SEAN GREENBERG - Partner
DAVID PAUL - Partner; Director Finance, Operations, Purchasing, Menu Development, Catering

Pok-e-Jo's Smokehouse Inc.
12905 Burnet Rd
Austin, TX 78727-3101

Telephone: (512) 833-0212
Fax Number: (512) 833-7114
Internet Homepage: pokejos.com
Company Email: sam@pokejos.com
Type of Business: Chain Restaurant Operator
Year Founded: 1979
Total Sales: $5,006,000 (e)
Alcohol Sales: 0.50%
Number of Employees: 150
Average Check: Lunch(10); Dinner(10)
Internet Order Processing: Yes
Total Units: 5
Trade Names: Pok-e-Jo's Barbeque & Catering (5)
Company-Owned Units: 5
Preferred Location Types: Freestanding; Strip Mall
Alcohol Served: Beer
Primary Menu: Bar-B-Q (5)
Areas of Operation: TX
Type of Foodservice: Fast Casual (5)
Catering Services: Yes
Notes: The company derives approximately 50% of its total revenue from catering.

Key Personnel
DOUG BOHNE - President; Partner; General Buyer
DANNY HABERMAN - Partner; VP; Director Operations

Poke Poke
3100 S Congress Ave
Austin, TX 78704-6427

Telephone: (512) 814-1032
Internet Homepage: poke-poke.com
Company Email: eat@poke-poke.com
Type of Business: Chain Restaurant Operator
Year Founded: 2010
Total Units: 4
Trade Names: Poke Poke (4)
Company-Owned Units: 4
Primary Menu: American (2)
Areas of Operation: CA, TX
Type of Foodservice: Fast Casual (4)

Key Personnel
JASON MCVEARRY - Partner; General Buyer
TRISH MCVEARRY - Partner
JOSEPH GVORA - General Manager
ANDY GONZALES - General Manager

Senior Pizza Inc
13764 N Highway 183
Austin, TX 78750-2287

Telephone: (512) 250-9190
Type of Business: Chain Restaurant Operator
Total Sales: $14,052,000 (e)
Total Units: 7
Trade Names: Domino's (7)
Units Franchised From: 7

Primary Menu: Pizza (7)
Areas of Operation: TX
Type of Foodservice: Quick Serve (7)
Franchise Affiliation: Domino's Pizza Inc, ANN ARBOR, MI

Key Personnel
SHERYLN W. SENIOR - Owner; General Buyer

Taco Shack
6721 Burnet Ln
Austin, TX 78757-2426

Telephone: (512) 451-0075
Internet Homepage: tacoshack.com
Company Email: clerk@tacoshack.com
Type of Business: Chain Restaurant Operator
Year Founded: 1996
Total Sales: $7,511,000 (e)
Total Units: 9
Trade Names: Taco Shack (9)
Company-Owned Units: 9
Primary Menu: Mexican (9)
Projected Openings: 1
Areas of Operation: TX
Type of Foodservice: Quick Serve (9)

Key Personnel
ORLANDO ARRIAGA - Partner
YOLI ARRIAGA - Partner; Executive Chef; General Buyer
CARLOS RIVERA - General Manager

Tacodeli Holdings
4313 Medical Pkwy
Austin, TX 78756

Telephone: (512) 339-1700
Internet Homepage: tacodeli.com
Company Email: feedback@tacodeli.com
Type of Business: Chain Restaurant Operator
Year Founded: 1999
Total Sales: $3,076,000 (e)
Number of Employees: 40
Average Check: Dinner(6)
Total Units: 11
Trade Names: Tacodeli (11)
Company-Owned Units: 8
Preferred Location Types: Strip Mall
Primary Menu: Taco (11)
Areas of Operation: TX
Type of Foodservice: Fast Casual (11)
Catering Services: Yes

Key Personnel
ROBERTO ESPINOSA - Founder; Partner
ERIC WILKERSON - Partner; General Buyer
SCOTT GROSSFELD - CFO; COO
EVA CLARK - VP Talent, People

Tarka Indian Kitchen
1601 Guadalupe St
Austin, TX 78701-1212

Telephone: (512) 322-5131
Internet Homepage: tarkaindiankitchen.com
Company Email: info@tarkaindiankitchen.com
Type of Business: Chain Restaurant Operator
Year Founded: 2009
Total Sales: $18,110,000 (e)
Total Units: 9
Trade Names: Clay Pit (1); Tarka Indian Kitchen (8)
Company-Owned Units: 9
Primary Menu: Indian (9)
Projected Openings: 1
Areas of Operation: TX
Type of Foodservice: Casual Dining (1); Fast Casual (8)
Notes: Sales information does not include the one (1) Clay Pit casual restaurant.

Key Personnel
TINKU SAINI - Co-Founder; CEO; Partner; General Buyer
BALINDER SINGH - Co-Founder; Partner
KAVAL BOMBRA - Co-Founder Finance; COO Strategy
CRAIG BREAUX - COO

Texas Restaurant Group Inc.
1717 W 6th St Ste 270
Austin, TX 78703-4869

Telephone: (512) 347-1400
Type of Business: Chain Restaurant Operator
Total Sales: $74,920,000 (e)
Average Check: Dinner(8)
Total Units: 16
Trade Names: Panera Bread (16)
Units Franchised From: 16
Preferred Square Footage: 1,500; 3,000; 3,200; 4,700
Preferred Location Types: Community Mall; Freestanding; Strip Mall
Primary Menu: Sandwiches/Deli (16)
Areas of Operation: TX
Type of Foodservice: Fast Casual (16)
Franchise Affiliation: Panera Bread Company, SAINT LOUIS, MO
Notes: The Baja Fresh restaurants operate as Dallas Fresh Inc.

Key Personnel
JOHN OUDT - CEO; Partner; General Buyer
RANDAL OUDT - Partner
BOB STEWART - Partner

The County Line Inc.
512 E Riverside Dr Ste 200
Austin, TX 78704-1306

Telephone: (512) 327-1959
Fax Number: (512) 327-2622
Internet Homepage: barribacantina.com; countyline.com
Type of Business: Chain Restaurant Operator
Year Founded: 1975
Systemwide Sales: $37,384,000 (e)
Total Sales: $23,780,000 (e)
Alcohol Sales: 20%
Number of Employees: 490
Average Check: Lunch(12); Dinner(16)
Internet Order Processing: Yes
Internet Sales: 2.00%
Total Units: 7
Trade Names: Barriba Cantina (1); State Line BBQ (1); The County Line Bar-B-Q (5)
Company-Owned Units: 7
Preferred Square Footage: 12,000
Preferred Location Types: Freestanding; Strip Mall
Alcohol Served: Beer, Wine, Liquor
Primary Menu: Bar-B-Q (6); Mexican (1)
Areas of Operation: NM, TX
Type of Foodservice: Casual Dining (7)
Catering Services: Yes

Key Personnel
SKEETER MILLER - President
ED NORTON - CFO

Threadgill's
6416 N Lamar Blvd
Austin, TX 78752-4008

Telephone: (512) 451-5440
Fax Number: (512) 451-5033
Internet Homepage: threadgills.com
Company Email: info@threadgills.com
Type of Business: Chain Restaurant Operator
Year Founded: 1981
Total Sales: $1,514,000 (e)
Alcohol Sales: 15%
Number of Employees: 90
Average Check: Lunch(10); Dinner(12)
Internet Order Processing: Yes
Internet Sales: 5.00%
Total Units: 1
Trade Names: Threadgill's (1)
Company-Owned Units: 1
Preferred Location Types: Freestanding
Alcohol Served: Beer, Wine, Liquor
Primary Menu: Southern (1)
Areas of Operation: TX
Type of Foodservice: Casual Dining (1)
Catering Services: Yes
Primary Distributors: (Full Line) Labatt Food

Service, SAN ANTONIO, TX

Key Personnel
EDWIN O. WILSON - President; Manager Catering; General Buyer
AUGUSTA B. EVANS - Manager Operations
DAVID COTTON - Buyer

ThunderCloud Inc.
203 E Riverside Dr
Austin, TX 78704-1203

Telephone: (512) 474-2363
Fax Number: (512) 474-2989
Internet Homepage: thundercloud.com
Company Email: info@thundercloud.com
Type of Business: Chain Restaurant Operator
Year Founded: 1975
Systemwide Sales: $19,406,000 (e)
Total Sales: $22,340,000 (e)
Alcohol Sales: 1%
Number of Employees: 198
Average Check: Lunch(10); Dinner(12)
Internet Order Processing: Yes
Total Units: 33
Trade Names: ThunderCloud Subs (33)
Company-Owned Units: 14
Units Franchised To: 19
Preferred Square Footage: 1,500
Preferred Location Types: Freestanding; Strip Mall
Primary Menu: Sandwiches/Deli (33)
Projected Openings: 2
Areas of Operation: TX
Type of Foodservice: Quick Serve (33)
Catering Services: Yes

Key Personnel
ANDREW COTTON - Co-Founder; President; Partner; CFO; Director Real Estate, Menu Development; General Buyer
MIKE HAGGERTY - Partner
PATRICIA SUGHRUE - COO; Controller; Director Operations, Purchasing, Information Systems, Advertising, Human Resources, Catering; Manager Finance

Via 313 Pizzeria
1802 East 6th Street
Austin, TX 78702

Internet Homepage: via313.com
Type of Business: Chain Restaurant Operator
Year Founded: 2011
Total Sales: $16,106,000 (e)
Total Units: 13
Trade Names: Via 313 (13)
Company-Owned Units: 13
Primary Menu: Pizza (13)
Areas of Operation: TX

Type of Foodservice: Casual Dining (13)

Key Personnel
KIPLAN WELSCH - President
PETER RAVESIES - Director Operations
JESSIE GALIOTO-GREBE - Director Marketing
HEATHER FIGG - Director Development, Training
ALYSA THORNLEY - Director Beverages
DENISE STEWARD - Director Catering

Waterloo Restaurant Group
1106 W 38th St Ste 200
Austin, TX 78705-1037

Telephone: (512) 467-8776
Fax Number: (512) 467-8804
Internet Homepage: waterlooicehouse.com
Company Email: info@waterlooicehouse.com
Type of Business: Chain Restaurant Operator
Total Sales: $3,086,000 (e)
Total Units: 4
Trade Names: Waterloo Ice House (4)
Company-Owned Units: 4
Alcohol Served: Beer, Wine, Liquor
Primary Menu: American (4)
Areas of Operation: TX
Type of Foodservice: Family Restaurant (4)

Key Personnel
SCOTT HENTSCHEL - Partner; General Manager
STUART HENTSCHEL - Partner; General Buyer
TED KARAM - Partner
JENA KARAM - Director Marketing

Kinney Restaurant Management
496 Highway 71 E
Bastrop, TX 78602-5077

Telephone: (512) 321-4712
Fax Number: (512) 985-5100
Type of Business: Chain Restaurant Operator
Total Sales: $19,634,000 (e)
Total Units: 4
Trade Names: McDonald's (4)
Units Franchised From: 4
Primary Menu: Hamburger (4)
Areas of Operation: TX
Type of Foodservice: Quick Serve (4)
Franchise Affiliation: McDonald's Corporation, CHICAGO, IL

Key Personnel
DANIEL KINNEY - President; General Buyer

Domino's Franchisee
3001 Avenue F
Bay City, TX 77414-7101

Telephone: (979) 244-4775
Type of Business: Chain Restaurant Operator
Total Sales: $3,998,000 (e)
Total Units: 2
Trade Names: Domino's (2)
Units Franchised From: 2
Primary Menu: Pizza (2)
Areas of Operation: TX
Type of Foodservice: Quick Serve (2)
Franchise Affiliation: Domino's Pizza Inc, ANN ARBOR, MI

Key Personnel
MAHMOOD EBRAHIM - Owner; General Buyer

Cinnabon Franchisee
4010 Garth Rd
Baytown, TX 77521-3108

Telephone: (281) 420-1557
Type of Business: Chain Restaurant Operator
Total Sales: $750,000 (e)
Total Units: 2
Trade Names: Cinnabon (2)
Units Franchised From: 2
Primary Menu: Snacks (2)
Areas of Operation: TX
Type of Foodservice: Quick Serve (2)
Franchise Affiliation: Cinnabon Inc., ATLANTA, GA

Key Personnel
JIN HAK KIM - Owner; General Buyer

El-T Mexican Restaurants Inc.
7529 Bayway Dr
Baytown, TX 77520-1309

Telephone: (281) 838-3709
Fax Number: (281) 838-3879
Internet Homepage: eltorotexmex.com
Company Email: info@eltorotexmex.com
Type of Business: Chain Restaurant Operator
Year Founded: 1960
Total Sales: $7,455,000 (e)
Alcohol Sales: 15%
Number of Employees: 180
Average Check: Lunch(12); Dinner(18)
Internet Order Processing: Yes
Total Units: 6
Trade Names: El Toro Mexican Restaurant (6)
Company-Owned Units: 6
Preferred Square Footage: 7,500
Preferred Location Types: Freestanding

Alcohol Served: Beer, Wine, Liquor
Primary Menu: Mexican (6)
Areas of Operation: TX
Type of Foodservice: Casual Dining (6)
Catering Services: Yes
Primary Distributors: (Equipment) Ace Mart Restaurant Supply Co., SAN ANTONIO, TX; (Food) US Foods, HOUSTON, TX; (Supplies) SYSCO Corporation, HOUSTON, TX

Key Personnel
ROLAND YBARRA - Chairman; CEO; Manager Operations; General Buyer
JOHN MAYES - Director Operations; Manager Catering

Burgers of Beaumont
6930 College St
Beaumont, TX 77707-3232

Telephone: (409) 866-2364
Fax Number: (409) 866-7699
Type of Business: Chain Restaurant Operator
Year Founded: 1948
Total Sales: $6,865,000 (e)
Number of Employees: 130
Average Check: Lunch(12); Dinner(14)
Total Units: 10
Trade Names: Whataburger (10)
Units Franchised From: 10
Preferred Square Footage: 2,000
Preferred Location Types: Freestanding
Primary Menu: Hamburger (10)
Areas of Operation: TX
Type of Foodservice: Quick Serve (10)
Franchise Affiliation: Whataburger Restaurants LLC, SAN ANTONIO, TX
Primary Distributors: (Full Line) The SYGMA Network Inc.- San Antonio, SAN ANTONIO, TX

Key Personnel
GILE GIDDINGS - Partner; General Buyer
JIM WATTS - Partner; Director Real Estate
LARRY WOODMAN - Partner; General Buyer
LINDA RANGLEY - Controller
EMILY DANIEL - Manager Human Resources

D & D Ventures, Inc.
8825 Eastex Fwy
Beaumont, TX 77708

Telephone: (409) 835-0338
Company Email: ddavis2136@aol.com
Type of Business: Chain Restaurant Operator
Total Sales: $8,538,000 (e)
Total Units: 7
Trade Names: Little Caesars Pizza (7)
Units Franchised From: 7
Primary Menu: Pizza (7)
Areas of Operation: TX
Type of Foodservice: Quick Serve (7)
Franchise Affiliation: Little Caesar Enterprises Inc., DETROIT, MI

Key Personnel
D DAVIS - President; General Buyer

Deli Management Inc.
2400 Broadway St
Beaumont, TX 77702-1904

Telephone: (409) 838-1976
Fax Number: (409) 838-1906
Internet Homepage: jasonsdeli.com
Type of Business: Chain Restaurant Operator
Year Founded: 1976
Systemwide Sales: $929,643,000 (e)
Total Sales: $624,740,000 (e)
Alcohol Sales: 1%
Number of Employees: 11,000
Average Check: Breakfast(8); Lunch(8); Dinner(8)
Internet Order Processing: Yes
Internet Sales: 1.00%
Total Units: 256
Trade Names: Jason's Deli (256)
Company-Owned Units: 159
Units Franchised To: 97
Preferred Square Footage: 4,500; 5,000
Preferred Location Types: Freestanding; Lifestyle Center; Regional Mall; Strip Mall
Alcohol Served: Beer, Wine
Primary Menu: Sandwiches/Deli (256)
Projected Openings: 10
Areas of Operation: AL, AR, AZ, CO, FL, GA, IA, IL, IN, KS, KY, LA, MD, MN, MO, MS, NC, NE, NM, NV, OH, OK, PA, SC, TN, TX, VA, WI
Type of Foodservice: Fast Casual (256)
Foodservice Management Venues: Schools
Catering Services: Yes
Distribution Centers: GRAND PRAIRIE, TX
Notes: The company derives approximately 15% of total revenue from distribution activities.

Key Personnel
RAGAN EDGERLY - President
JAY TORTORICE - President
KEVIN ALFORD - Partner
GENE LEAL - Partner
BRIAN HEBERT - CFO; Controller
BLAKE PARKER - Exec VP Culinary Development
MICHELE ERVIN - Director Human Resources
AMY SCHUSTER - Director Information Technology
MICHELE KEMPLAY - Director Human Resources
GRACIE PRASANSON - Director Sales
ALEX CONE - Director Talent Acquisitions
FOUAD JOMAA - Director Development
AARON MATER - Director Distribution
KEVIN GRAY - Director Development
MISSY PINT - Director Marketing
PAT HERRING - Director Product Development
LISA TILLMAN - Director Product Development
MARE GIBBS - Director Marketing, Sales
NICK MCLAUGHLIN - Manager Real Estate
KEVIN LAIRD - Manager POS/Scanning
JENNIFER STEPHENSON - Manager Human Resources
CLIFF JONES - Manager
ERICA LA ROCCA - Manager
AMANDA O'BRIEN - Manager Sales
MARI PARHAM - Manager Customer Service

Subway Franchise
1125 S 11th St
Beaumont, TX 77701-4742

Telephone: (409) 832-8251
Internet Homepage: subway.com
Type of Business: Chain Restaurant Operator
Total Sales: $1,505,000 (e)
Total Units: 2
Trade Names: Subway (2)
Units Franchised From: 2
Primary Menu: Sandwiches/Deli (2)
Areas of Operation: TX
Type of Foodservice: Quick Serve (2)
Franchise Affiliation: Doctor's Associates Inc., MILFORD, CT

Key Personnel
KIRIT PATEL - President; Owner

The Iron Cactus
12912 Hill Country Blvd Ste F-255
Bee Cave, TX 78738-6477

Telephone: (512) 692-8059
Fax Number: (512) 692-3691
Internet Homepage: ironcactus.com
Type of Business: Chain Restaurant Operator
Year Founded: 1996
Total Sales: $3,737,000 (e)
Alcohol Sales: 4%
Number of Employees: 120
Average Check: Lunch(16); Dinner(22)
Total Units: 3
Trade Names: The Iron Cactus (3)
Company-Owned Units: 3
Preferred Square Footage: 5,500; 6,000
Preferred Location Types: Freestanding
Alcohol Served: Beer, Wine, Liquor
Primary Menu: Southwest/Tex-Mex (3)
Areas of Operation: TX
Type of Foodservice: Casual Dining (3)
Catering Services: Yes

Key Personnel
GARY MANLEY - President; Partner; Director Operations, Purchasing
MICHAEL POTTORFF - Partner; Director Menu

Development; General Buyer
JASON CLAUNCH - Director Operations

Emerald Foods Inc
6300 West Loop S Ste 275
Bellaire, TX 77401-2903

Telephone: (713) 791-9167
Fax Number: (713) 790-1927
Type of Business: Chain Restaurant Operator
Year Founded: 1991
Total Sales: $31,810,000 (e)
Average Check: Lunch(8); Dinner(10)
Total Units: 12
Trade Names: Wendy's Old Fashioned Hamburgers (12)
Units Franchised From: 12
Preferred Square Footage: 2,100; 2,900
Primary Menu: Hamburger (12)
Areas of Operation: LA, TX
Type of Foodservice: Quick Serve (12)
Franchise Affiliation: The Wendy's Company, DUBLIN, OH

Key Personnel
DONALD L. FEINSTEIN - Chairman
MARK J. GEORGE - President
BRIAN HARPER - VP; Manager Facility/Maintenance, Human Resources

GR8 Plate Hospitality
6510 S Rice Ave
Bellaire, TX 77401

Telephone: (713) 668-6029
Internet Homepage: gr8plate.com
Company Email: info@gr8plate.com
Type of Business: Chain Restaurant Operator
Year Founded: 2010
Total Units: 7
Trade Names: Jax Grill (2); The Union Kitchen (5)
Company-Owned Units: 7
Primary Menu: American (7)
Areas of Operation: TX
Type of Foodservice: Casual Dining (5); Family Restaurant (2)

Key Personnel
PAUL MILLER - Founder; Partner
DORIS MILLER - Partner
DOUGLAS WILSON - COO
JEANNETTE KELLER-CUEVAS - Creative Director

McDonald's Franchise
101 S Expressway 83
Brownsville, TX 78520-8049

Telephone: (956) 541-1031
Fax Number: (956) 550-8106
Type of Business: Chain Restaurant Operator
Total Sales: $33,030,000 (e)
Total Units: 7
Trade Names: McDonald's (7)
Units Franchised From: 7
Preferred Square Footage: 2,500
Primary Menu: Hamburger (7)
Areas of Operation: TX
Type of Foodservice: Quick Serve (7)
Franchise Affiliation: McDonald's Corporation, CHICAGO, IL

Key Personnel
ANNA OQUIN - President; General Buyer

VZS Concessions
500 E Ringgold St
Brownsville, TX 78520-7918

Telephone: (956) 546-0050
Fax Number: (956) 541-4940
Internet Homepage: gpz.org
Type of Business: Foodservice Operations - Theme Parks
Year Founded: 1971
Total Sales: $7,875,000 (e)
Number of Employees: 30
Average Check: Lunch(12); Dinner(16)
Total Units: 5
Trade Names: Coyote Cafe (1); Lion's Pride (1); The Asian Grill (1); The Eagle Nest (1); The Oasis (1)
Company-Owned Units: 5
Preferred Location Types: Freestanding
Alcohol Served: Beer
Primary Menu: American (4); Sandwiches/Deli (1)
Areas of Operation: TX
Type of Foodservice: Quick Serve (5)
Catering Services: Yes
On-site Distribution Center: Yes
Primary Distributors: (Food) SYSCO Food Services of Houston Inc., HOUSTON, TX; (Supplies) SYSCO Food Services of Houston Inc., HOUSTON, TX

Key Personnel
JUANITA RENDON - General Manager

GBB Hospitality Group, LLC
3740 Copperfield Dr
Bryan, TX 77802-5932

Telephone: (214) 876-2054
Internet Homepage: grubburgerbar.com
Company Email: inquiry@grubburgerbar.com
Type of Business: Chain Restaurant Operator
Total Units: 23
Trade Names: Grub Burger Bar (23)
Company-Owned Units: 23
Primary Menu: Hamburger (23)
Areas of Operation: CA, DE, FL, GA, LA, PA, TX
Type of Foodservice: Casual Dining (23)

Key Personnel
TOM KENNEY - Co-Founder

Smith Dairy Queens Ltd.
161 N Earl Rudder Fwy
Bryan, TX 77802-5004

Telephone: (979) 846-2222
Fax Number: (979) 846-8618
Internet Homepage: smithdq.com
Type of Business: Chain Restaurant Operator
Year Founded: 1953
Total Sales: $53,730,000 (e)
Number of Employees: 575
Average Check: Lunch(8); Dinner(8)
Total Units: 39
Trade Names: Dairy Queen (39)
Units Franchised From: 39
Preferred Square Footage: 2,600
Preferred Location Types: Freestanding
Primary Menu: American (39)
Areas of Operation: TX
Type of Foodservice: Quick Serve (39)
Franchise Affiliation: International Dairy Queen Inc., BLOOMINGTON, MN

Key Personnel
KAREN SMITH - President; CFO; Manager Advertising, Real Estate, Design; General Buyer
DOUGLAS WOHL - Director Operations
TIFFANY SNIDER - Director Human Resources
ALEXIS ALEXANDER - Manager Human Resources

Posados Cafe Inc.
PO Box 1018
Bullard, TX 75757-1018

Telephone: (903) 894-3106
Fax Number: (903) 894-6805
Internet Homepage: happysfishhouse.com; posados.com

Type of Business: Chain Restaurant Operator
Year Founded: 1987
Total Sales: $43,340,000 (e)
Alcohol Sales: 10%
Number of Employees: 1,059
Average Check: Lunch(12); Dinner(12)
Internet Order Processing: Yes
Total Units: 15
Trade Names: Happy's Fish House (1); Mercados (1); Posados Cafe (13)
Company-Owned Units: 15
Preferred Square Footage: 5,800; 6,000; 8,000
Preferred Location Types: Freestanding; Strip Mall
Alcohol Served: Beer, Wine, Liquor
Primary Menu: Seafood (1); Southwest/Tex-Mex (14)
Areas of Operation: LA, TX
Type of Foodservice: Casual Dining (15)
Primary Distributors: (Full Line) US Foods, HOUSTON, TX

Key Personnel
ANDY GUGAR - CEO; Owner
PAUL ROSEBERRY - Controller

Cowboy Chicken Inc.
3450 E Hebron Pkwy Ste 100
Carrollton, TX 75010-4479

Telephone: (972) 267-2000
Fax Number: (972) 267-2004
Internet Homepage: cowboychicken.com
Type of Business: Chain Restaurant Operator
Year Founded: 1981
Systemwide Sales: $13,398,000 (e)
Total Sales: $36,940,000 (e)
Number of Employees: 259
Internet Order Processing: Yes
Total Units: 16
Trade Names: Cowboy Chicken (16)
Company-Owned Units: 8
Units Franchised To: 8
Preferred Location Types: Strip Mall
Primary Menu: Chicken (16)
Projected Openings: 1
Areas of Operation: AL, CA, GA, IA, KS, LA, NE, OK, TX
Type of Foodservice: Fast Casual (16)
Catering Services: Yes
Primary Distributors: (Full Line) Ben E. Keith Foods, FORT WORTH, TX

Key Personnel
SEAN KENNEDY - CEO; President; Owner
KIP KOLOW - Chief Strategy Officer

RDSL Enterprises, LLC
2510 Tarpley Rd Ste 4
Carrollton, TX 75006-2268

Telephone: (972) 418-6622
Internet Homepage: rdslgroup.com
Type of Business: Chain Restaurant Operator
Total Sales: $110,040,000 (e)
Total Units: 43
Trade Names: Jack in the Box (43)
Units Franchised From: 43
Primary Menu: Hamburger (44)
Areas of Operation: TX
Type of Foodservice: Quick Serve (43)
Franchise Affiliation: Jack in the Box Restaurants, SAN DIEGO, CA

Key Personnel
RABINDRANATH VISWANATH - Partner; General Buyer
SHANNON VISWANATH - Partner

Shell Shack, Inc.
3330 Earhart Dr Ste 213
Carrollton, TX 75006-5041

Telephone: (214) 351-0951
Internet Homepage: theshellshack.com
Type of Business: Chain Restaurant Operator
Year Founded: 2013
Systemwide Sales: $21,437,000 (e)
Total Sales: $23,320,000 (e)
Alcohol Sales: 20%
Total Units: 8
Trade Names: Shell Shack (8)
Company-Owned Units: 4
Units Franchised To: 4
Preferred Square Footage: 4,000; 5,000; 6,000
Primary Menu: Seafood (8)
Projected Openings: 1
Areas of Operation: TX
Type of Foodservice: Casual Dining (8)

Key Personnel
ANGELA HALE - CFO

Yogurtland Franchisee
2625 Old Denton Rd Ste 316
Carrollton, TX 75007-5113

Telephone: (214) 483-3553
Type of Business: Chain Restaurant Operator
Total Sales: $3,176,000 (e)
Total Units: 3
Trade Names: Yogurtland (3)
Units Franchised From: 3
Primary Menu: Snacks (3)
Areas of Operation: TX
Type of Foodservice: Quick Serve (3)
Franchise Affiliation: Yogurtland Franchising Inc., FARMERS BRANCH, TX

Key Personnel
GEUN KWON - Owner; General Buyer

White Rhino Coffee
230 W. Belt Line Road
Cedar Hill, TX 75104

Telephone: (972) 293-7361
Internet Homepage: whiterhinocoffee.com
Company Email: marketing@whiterhinocoffee.com
Type of Business: Chain Restaurant Operator
Year Founded: 2007
Total Sales: $12,980,000 (e)
Total Units: 13
Trade Names: White Rhino Coffee (13)
Company-Owned Units: 13
Primary Menu: Coffee (13)
Areas of Operation: TX
Type of Foodservice: Quick Serve (13)

Key Personnel
CHRIS PARVIN - Founder; President; Owner
JOE RESKE - Chief Marketing Officer
JACOB JOLLY - Creative Director
THOMAS DENTON - Director Culinary Operations

Glazing Saddles LLC
1464 E Whitestone Blvd Ste 1201
Cedar Park, TX 78613-9071

Telephone: (512) 744-4000
Fax Number: (512) 744-4040
Internet Homepage: krispykremetexas.com
Type of Business: Chain Restaurant Operator
Year Founded: 2000
Total Sales: $28,470,000 (e)
Number of Employees: 720
Average Check: Breakfast(6); Lunch(6); Dinner(6)
Total Units: 16
Trade Names: Bush's Chicken (3); Krispy Kreme Doughnuts (13)
Units Franchised From: 16
Preferred Square Footage: 2,000; 4,000
Preferred Location Types: Freestanding
Primary Menu: Chicken (3); Snacks (13)
Areas of Operation: TX
Type of Foodservice: Quick Serve (16)
Franchise Affiliation: Krispy Kreme Doughnut Corporation, CHARLOTTE, NC

Key Personnel
TIM SABO - Director Marketing
JASON REYNOLDS - Manager Information

Technology

Two Domer Management, LLC
2000 S Lakeline Blvd
Cedar Park, TX 78613-3667

Telephone: (512) 899-3473
Type of Business: Chain Restaurant Operator
Total Sales: $4,886,000 (e)
Internet Order Processing: Yes
Total Units: 4
Trade Names: Firehouse Subs (4)
Units Franchised From: 4
Primary Menu: Sandwiches/Deli (4)
Type of Foodservice: Fast Casual (4)
Franchise Affiliation: Firehouse Restaurant Group Inc., JACKSONVILLE, FL

Key Personnel
VICKI ECKEL - President; General Buyer

Domino's Franchisee
2750 S Preston Rd Ste 114
Celina, TX 75009-3844

Telephone: (214) 851-2222
Type of Business: Chain Restaurant Operator
Total Sales: $8,159,000 (e)
Total Units: 4
Trade Names: Domino's (4)
Units Franchised From: 4
Primary Menu: Pizza (4)
Areas of Operation: TX
Type of Foodservice: Quick Serve (4)
Franchise Affiliation: Domino's Pizza Inc, ANN ARBOR, MI

Key Personnel
KEVIN P. SEE - Owner; General Buyer

Heavenly Scent Pizza LLC
615 W Henderson St
Cleburne, TX 76033-4847

Telephone: (817) 641-6266
Type of Business: Chain Restaurant Operator
Total Sales: $16,373,000 (e)
Total Units: 8
Trade Names: Domino's (8)
Units Franchised From: 8
Primary Menu: Pizza (8)
Areas of Operation: TX
Type of Foodservice: Quick Serve (8)
Franchise Affiliation: Domino's Pizza Inc, ANN ARBOR, MI

Key Personnel
RONALD L. RUSSEK - Owner; General Buyer

Centex Subway Inc.
2031 Harvey Mitchell Pkwy S
College Station, TX 77840-5102

Mailing Address: PO Box 10161, COLLEGE STATION, TX, 77842-0161
Telephone: (979) 693-3933
Company Email: bcssubway@suddenlinkmail.com
Type of Business: Chain Restaurant Operator
Year Founded: 1981
Total Sales: $10,910,000 (e)
Number of Employees: 265
Average Check: Lunch(12); Dinner(12)
Total Units: 19
Trade Names: Subway (19)
Units Franchised From: 19
Preferred Square Footage: 1,200; 1,800
Preferred Location Types: Convenience Store/Gas Station; Freestanding; Strip Mall
Primary Menu: Sandwiches/Deli (19)
Areas of Operation: TX
Type of Foodservice: Quick Serve (19)
Franchise Affiliation: Doctor's Associates Inc., MILFORD, CT
Primary Distributors: (Food) Performance Foodservice - Temple, TEMPLE, TX; (Supplies) Performance Foodservice - Temple, TEMPLE, TX

Key Personnel
JEAN PEARN - President; Director Real Estate
BERT KELLER - Director Human Resources; Manager Operations, Advertising; General Buyer

Fuego Tortilla Grill
108 Poplar St
College Station, TX 77840-1911

Telephone: (979) 703-1804
Internet Homepage: fuegotortillagrill.com
Type of Business: Chain Restaurant Operator
Year Founded: 2010
Total Units: 3
Trade Names: Fuego Tortilla Grill (3)
Company-Owned Units: 3
Primary Menu: Mexican (3)
Areas of Operation: TX
Type of Foodservice: Fast Casual (3)
Catering Services: Yes

Key Personnel
PAUL MOLER - Co-Founder; Partner
DAVID LOVELACE - Co-Founder; Partner
JERRY MANSERA - Executive Chef

MELISSA AHRENDT - Director Operations

MAC Pizza Management
3106 Texas Ave S
College Station, TX 77845-5050

Telephone: (979) 695-9912
Fax Number: (979) 695-0553
Internet Homepage: macpizzamgmt.com
Type of Business: Chain Restaurant Operator
Year Founded: 1986
Total Sales: $168,048,000 (e)
Number of Employees: 2,200
Average Check: Lunch(16); Dinner(30)
Total Units: 82
Trade Names: Domino's (82)
Units Franchised From: 82
Preferred Square Footage: 1,000; 1,300
Preferred Location Types: Strip Mall
Primary Menu: Pizza (82)
Areas of Operation: TX
Type of Foodservice: Quick Serve (82)
Franchise Affiliation: Domino's Pizza Inc, ANN ARBOR, MI
Primary Distributors: (Food) Domino's Distribution Center, GRAND PRAIRIE, TX

Key Personnel
KEYTH CITIZEN - CEO
MIKE CUNNINGHAM - President; General Buyer
TOM MOYES - President
ASHLEY LEWIS - CFO
ALAN CUNNNINGHAM - VP Information Technology
JESSICA DICKENSON - VP Human Resources
MORGAN KEROLA - Controller
DEVIN HARMAN - Assistant Director Operations, Talent
CHRIS HERD - Manager District
DON LEWIS - Manager Construction
JIMMY WILBANKS - Manager District

Trapani & Trapani
5012 Augusta Cir
College Station, TX 77845

Mailing Address: P O Box 9556, COLLEGE STATION, TX, 77842
Telephone: (979) 774-7974
Type of Business: Chain Restaurant Operator
Total Sales: $7,413,000 (e)
Total Units: 6
Trade Names: Little Caesars Pizza (6)
Units Franchised From: 6
Preferred Location Types: Strip Mall
Primary Menu: Pizza (6)
Areas of Operation: TX
Type of Foodservice: Quick Serve (6)
Franchise Affiliation: Little Caesar Enterprises

Inc., DETROIT, MI

Key Personnel
PHIL TRAPANI - President; General Buyer
BRITTANY TRAPANI - VP Finance

ARAMARK Education
1199 S Belt Line Rd Ste 160
Coppell, TX 75019-4656

Telephone: (972) 462-6014
Fax Number: (972) 462-6053
Listing Type: Regional Office
Type of Business: Foodservice Management Operator
Year Founded: 1959
Number of Employees: 200
Number of Locations Served: 86
Total Foodservice Mgmt Accounts: 86
Areas of Operation: TX
Type of Foodservice: Cafeteria (86)
Foodservice Management Venues: Schools
Primary Distributors: (Full Line) SYSCO Food Services of Houston Inc., HOUSTON, TX
Parent Company: Aramark, PHILADELPHIA, PA
Headquarters: ARAMARK School Support Services, PHILADELPHIA, PA

Key Personnel
BARBARA FLANAGAN - President

CiCi Enterprises L.P.
1080 W Bethel Rd
Coppell, TX 75019-4427

Telephone: (972) 745-4200
Fax Number: (972) 745-4204
Internet Homepage: cicispizza.com
Company Email: GuestServices@cicispizza.com
Type of Business: Chain Restaurant Operator
Year Founded: 1985
Systemwide Sales: $540,124,000 (e)
Total Sales: $45,670,000 (e)
Number of Employees: 400
Average Check: Lunch(6); Dinner(6)
Total Units: 318
Trade Names: CiCi's Pizza (318)
Company-Owned Units: 9
Units Franchised To: 309
Preferred Square Footage: 800; 1,000; 4,200
Preferred Location Types: Community Mall; Freestanding; Strip Mall
Primary Menu: Pizza (318)
Projected Openings: 10
Areas of Operation: AL, AR, AZ, CA, CO, FL, GA, IA, IL, IN, KS, KY, LA, MD, MI, MO, MS, NC, NE, NJ, NM, NV, OH, OK, PA, SC, TN, TX, VA, WI, WV
Type of Foodservice: Family Restaurant (318)

Primary Distributors: (Full Line) JMC Restaurant Distribution LP, COPPELL, TX
Parent Company: Arlon Group LLC, NEW YORK, NY
Headquarter Offices: JMC Restaurant Distribution LP, COPPELL, TX

Key Personnel
WILLIAM MITCHELL - CEO
GINESE SMITH - VP Information Technology
BOB FULKS - Director Purchasing

GMC Enterprises Inc.
125 S Denton Tap Rd
Coppell, TX 75019-3204

Telephone: (972) 514-2073
Fax Number: (972) 462-0620
Internet Homepage: jmcmcdonalds.com
Type of Business: Chain Restaurant Operator
Total Sales: $28,250,000 (e)
Total Units: 6
Trade Names: McDonald's (6)
Units Franchised From: 6
Primary Menu: Hamburger (6)
Areas of Operation: TX
Type of Foodservice: Quick Serve (6)
Franchise Affiliation: McDonald's Corporation, CHICAGO, IL

Key Personnel
CLIFF JOHNSON JR - Owner; General Buyer

Boat N Net Inc.
5657 Old Brownsville Rd
Corpus Christi, TX 78417-9763

Telephone: (361) 852-6947
Fax Number: (361) 852-6986
Internet Homepage: boat-n-net.blogspot.com
Type of Business: Chain Restaurant Operator
Year Founded: 1972
Total Sales: $4,503,000 (e)
Number of Employees: 50
Average Check: Lunch(6); Dinner(6)
Total Units: 5
Trade Names: Boat n' Net Drive-In (5)
Company-Owned Units: 5
Preferred Square Footage: 950
Preferred Location Types: Freestanding
Primary Menu: Seafood (5)
Areas of Operation: TX
Type of Foodservice: Quick Serve (5)
On-site Distribution Center: Yes

Key Personnel
WOO SUNG LEE - Owner; General Buyer

Bowen Enterprises, Inc.
1006 Texas Ave
Corpus Christi, TX 78404-2729

Mailing Address: PO Box 3707, CORPUS CHRISTI, TX, 78463-3707
Telephone: (361) 808-8858
Fax Number: (361) 855-3968
Type of Business: Chain Restaurant Operator
Total Sales: $20,840,000 (e)
Total Units: 15
Trade Names: Dairy Queen (15)
Units Franchised From: 15
Primary Menu: American (15)
Areas of Operation: TX
Type of Foodservice: Quick Serve (15)
Franchise Affiliation: International Dairy Queen Inc., BLOOMINGTON, MN

Key Personnel
JENNIFER J. BOWEN - President; General Buyer
EVEY GARCIA - VP Operations
JB SALINAS - Administrator Safety, Marketing

Coastal Deli Inc.
6000 S Staples St Ste 300
Corpus Christi, TX 78413-2952

Telephone: (361) 854-5446
Fax Number: (361) 854-0565
Internet Homepage: coastaldeliinc.com
Type of Business: Chain Restaurant Operator
Year Founded: 1995
Total Sales: $22,840,000 (e)
Number of Employees: 490
Average Check: Breakfast(10); Lunch(10); Dinner(12)
Total Units: 16
Trade Names: Jason's Deli (16)
Units Franchised From: 16
Preferred Square Footage: 4,800
Preferred Location Types: Freestanding; Strip Mall
Primary Menu: Sandwiches/Deli (16)
Projected Openings: 2
Areas of Operation: NM, TX
Type of Foodservice: Fast Casual (16)
Catering Services: Yes
Franchise Affiliation: Deli Management Inc., BEAUMONT, TX
Primary Distributors: (Full Line) JDD - Jason's Deli Distribution Center, GRAND PRAIRIE, TX

Key Personnel
ROBERT BECQUET - CEO; President; Partner; Director Finance, Facility/Maintenance, Real Estate, Catering
PAT O'BOYLE - Partner; VP; Director Operations, Purchasing, Supply Chain, Design, Human Resources, Store Fixtures

LAUREN FRANCISCO - Manager Information Technology
ANGIE BURK - Administrative Assistant

Dwd Pizza Company Inc
2345 Pollex Ave
Corpus Christi, TX 78415

Telephone: (361) 356-6220
Type of Business: Chain Restaurant Operator
Total Sales: $18,121,000 (e)
Total Units: 9
Trade Names: Domino's (9)
Units Franchised From: 9
Primary Menu: Pizza (9)
Areas of Operation: TX
Type of Foodservice: Quick Serve (9)
Franchise Affiliation: Domino's Pizza Inc, ANN ARBOR, MI

Key Personnel
DANIEL DAIN - President; General Buyer

Hart Restaurant Management, Inc.
108 N Mesquite St
Corpus Christi, TX 78401-2823

Telephone: (361) 882-4100
Fax Number: (361) 882-0708
Company Email: support@texasbk.com
Type of Business: Chain Restaurant Operator
Total Sales: $13,610,000 (e)
Total Units: 6
Trade Names: Burger King (6)
Units Franchised From: 6
Preferred Square Footage: 1,900; 4,300
Primary Menu: Hamburger (6)
Areas of Operation: TX
Type of Foodservice: Quick Serve (6)
Franchise Affiliation: Burger King Worldwide Inc., MIAMI, FL

Key Personnel
ROBERT HART - President
GARY HODGE - Owner

PL Squared Inc
4256 S Alameda St
Corpus Christi, TX 78412

Telephone: (361) 993-7979
Type of Business: Chain Restaurant Operator
Total Sales: $3,442,000 (e)
Total Units: 6
Trade Names: Subway (6)
Units Franchised From: 6
Primary Menu: Sandwiches/Deli (6)
Areas of Operation: TX
Type of Foodservice: Quick Serve (6)
Franchise Affiliation: Doctor's Associates Inc., MILFORD, CT

Key Personnel
J. PATEL - Owner; General Buyer

Taqueria Jalisco
902 S Port Ave
Corpus Christi, TX 78405-2302

Telephone: (361) 881-8739
Internet Homepage: taqueriajalisco.net
Type of Business: Chain Restaurant Operator
Total Sales: $15,210,000 (e)
Alcohol Sales: 3%
Number of Employees: 165
Average Check: Lunch(8); Dinner(10)
Total Units: 21
Trade Names: Taqueria Jalisco (21)
Company-Owned Units: 21
Preferred Location Types: Freestanding
Alcohol Served: Beer
Primary Menu: Southwest/Tex-Mex (21)
Areas of Operation: TX
Type of Foodservice: Casual Dining (21)

Key Personnel
JAIME LEON - Partner; Executive Chef; General Buyer
LUPE LEON - Partner

Water Street Ltd
309 N Water St Ste A
Corpus Christi, TX 78401-2570

Telephone: (361) 882-2211
Fax Number: (361) 882-2835
Internet Homepage: executivesurfclub.com; waterstreetseafood.net
Company Email: corp@waterstreetco.com
Type of Business: Chain Restaurant Operator
Year Founded: 1983
Total Sales: $11,020,000 (e)
Alcohol Sales: 15%
Number of Employees: 150
Average Check: Breakfast(6); Lunch(18); Dinner(24)
Total Units: 3
Trade Names: Executive Surf Club (1); Water Street Oyster Bar (1); Water Street Seafood (1)
Company-Owned Units: 3
Preferred Square Footage: 5,500; 6,000
Preferred Location Types: Freestanding
Alcohol Served: Beer, Wine, Liquor
Primary Menu: Seafood (3)
Areas of Operation: TX
Type of Foodservice: Casual Dining (3)
Catering Services: Yes
Primary Distributors: (Full Line) SYSCO Corporation, HOUSTON, TX

Key Personnel
BRADLEY S. LOMAX - President; Director Finance, Operations, Information Systems, Real Estate, Design, Human Resources, Research & Development, Product Development, Menu Development, Catering; General Buyer
SHERRY HULL - Supervisor Accounting

8.0 Management Inc.
1722 S Harwood St
Dallas, TX 75215-1221

Telephone: (214) 969-9321
Fax Number: (214) 969-0505
Internet Homepage: beerknurd.com; birdinthe.net; flyingfishinthe.net; larkonthepark.com; meddlesomemoth.com; mothinthe.net; mudheninthe.net; rodeogoat.com
Company Email: larry@anotherplanet.com
Type of Business: Chain Restaurant Operator
Year Founded: 1992
Total Sales: $80,520,000 (e)
Alcohol Sales: 15%
Number of Employees: 578
Average Check: Lunch(20); Dinner(32)
Internet Order Processing: Yes
Internet Sales: 1.00%
Total Units: 33
Trade Names: Flying Fish (12); Flying Saucer Draught Emporium (13); Meddlesome Moth (1); Mudhen Meat and Greens (1); Rodeo Goat (6)
Company-Owned Units: 33
Preferred Square Footage: 5,500
Preferred Location Types: Downtown; Freestanding; Office Complex; Strip Mall
Alcohol Served: Beer, Wine, Liquor
Primary Menu: American (14); Hamburger (6); Miscellaneous (1); Seafood (12)
Projected Openings: 2
Areas of Operation: AR, MO, NC, SC, TN, TX
Type of Foodservice: Casual Dining (19); Fine Dining (1); Quick Serve (13)
Primary Distributors: (Full Line) SYSCO Food Services of North Texas, LEWISVILLE, TX

Key Personnel
SHANNON WYNNE - President; Partner; Executive Chef; Manager Real Estate; General Buyer
KEITH SCHLABS - Partner Operations; Director Operations
LARRY RICHARDSON - VP
RAYNOR BEARDEN BRUMFIELD - Director Marketing
ANDREA COAN - Director Training
MARY FETZKO - Manager Information Systems

80/20 Hopsitality
5740 Prospect Ave Ste 2001
Dallas, TX 75206

Telephone: (469) 334-0896
Internet Homepage: gunghodallas.com; herobyhg.com; hgsplyco.com; thestandardservice.com
Company Email: eric@livinghg.com
Type of Business: Chain Restaurant Operator
Year Founded: 2016
Total Units: 6
Trade Names: Gung Ho (1); HERO (1); HG Sply Co. (3); Standard Service (1)
Company-Owned Units: 6
Preferred Location Types: Downtown; Strip Mall
Primary Menu: American (5); Asian (1)
Areas of Operation: TX
Type of Foodservice: Casual Dining (6)

Key Personnel
ELIAS POPE - Founder; President
DANYELE MCPHERSON - Executive Chef

Al Biernat's
4217 Oak Lawn Ave
Dallas, TX 75219-2313

Telephone: (214) 219-2201
Fax Number: (214) 219-2093
Internet Homepage: albiernats.com
Type of Business: Chain Restaurant Operator
Year Founded: 1997
Total Sales: $8,549,000 (e)
Number of Employees: 65
Average Check: Lunch(22); Dinner(66)
Total Units: 2
Trade Names: Al Biernat's (2)
Company-Owned Units: 2
Alcohol Served: Beer, Wine, Liquor
Primary Menu: Steak/Seafood (2)
Areas of Operation: TX
Type of Foodservice: Fine Dining (2)
Primary Distributors: (Food) Ben E. Keith Foods, FORT WORTH, TX

Key Personnel
AL BIERNAT - Owner; General Manager; Executive Chef; General Buyer
DIANE BLACK - Controller
BRAD FULLER - General Manager; Director Operations

Ampex Brands
17774 Preston Rd
Dallas, TX 75252

Telephone: (469) 917-3804
Fax Number: (972) 248-1056
Internet Homepage: ampexbrands.com
Type of Business: Chain Restaurant Operator
Year Founded: 2005
Total Sales: $532,660,000 (e)
Number of Employees: 8,016
Average Check: Dinner(10)
Total Units: 552
Trade Names: A&W All American Food (26); Au Bon Pain (171); KFC (136); Long John Silver's (46); Pizza Hut (106); Taco Bell (15); Tim Hortons (52)
Company-Owned Units: 171
Units Franchised From: 381
Preferred Square Footage: 2,500; 3,200
Preferred Location Types: Freestanding
Primary Menu: American (26); Chicken (136); Pizza (106); Sandwiches/Deli (171); Seafood (46); Snacks (52); Taco (15)
Areas of Operation: CA, IL, OK, TX
Type of Foodservice: Fast Casual (171); Quick Serve (381)
Subsidiaries: ABP Corporation, BOSTON, MA
Franchise Affiliation: A&W Restaurants Inc., LEXINGTON, KY; Long John Silver's Inc., LOUISVILLE, KY; Taco Bell Corp., IRVINE, CA

Key Personnel
TABBASSUM MUMTAZ - CEO
TASHA WALDRON - President Finance, Accounting
ERIC EASTON - CFO
ANN JOHNSON - COO
BETH COLLINS - Chief Marketing Officer
KEVIN FALCONER - Chief Development Officer
OMAR MISLEH - Chief Legal Officer
MARLEE LEBLANC - VP Human Resources
ERIK BEDNAR - VP Operations
SHELBY CARCIO - Creative Director
SANDY BROWN - Director Operations
STEFANY MCCARTNEY - Director Loyalty Program
BRUCE ZUREK - Director Operations
ALAN PRUITT - Director Operations
LANEKA ROGERS - Area Manager Training
BRENDA MORIN - Manager Payroll
FAISAL CHOWDHURY - Manager Marketing
MELISSA MAJDI - Manager Human Resources

ARAMARK Higher Education
2525 McKinnon St Ste 600
Dallas, TX 75201-1543

Telephone: (972) 462-6000
Fax Number: (972) 462-6053
Listing Type: Regional Office
Type of Business: Foodservice Management Operator
Year Founded: 1959
Number of Employees: 500
Number of Locations Served: 60
Total Foodservice Mgmt Accounts: 60
Areas of Operation: TX
Type of Foodservice: Cafeteria (60)
Foodservice Management Venues: College & University
Primary Distributors: (Full Line) SYSCO Food Services of Houston Inc., HOUSTON, TX
Parent Company: Aramark, PHILADELPHIA, PA
Headquarters: ARAMARK Higher Education, PHILADELPHIA, PA

Key Personnel
ERIC WARE - Director Operations

Army & Air Force Exchange Service (AAFES)
3911 S Walton Walker Blvd
Dallas, TX 75236-1509

Mailing Address: PO Box 660202, DALLAS, TX, 75266
Telephone: (214) 312-2011
Fax Number: (214) 312-6697
Internet Homepage: aafes.com
Type of Business: Nontraditional Foodservice Operator
Total Sales: $20,611,961,000 (e)
Foodservice Sales: $3,091,793,000 (e)
Total Units: 2,266
Trade Names: American Eatery; Anthony's Pizza; Arby's; Baskin-Robbins; BLIMPIE; Boston Market; Burger King; Captain D's Seafood; Charley's Grilled Subs; Church's Chicken; Cinnabon; Domino's Pizza; Dunkin' Donuts; Einstein Bros. Bagels; Frank's Franks; Freshens Fresh Food Studio; Froots; Godfather's Pizza; Krispy Kreme Doughnuts; Manchu Wok; Muscle Maker Grill; Panda Express; Pizza Hut/Wing Street; Popeyes Louisiana Kitchen; Qdoba Mexican Grill; Robin Hood Sandwich Shoppe; Seattle's Best Coffee; Starbucks Coffee; Subway; Taco Bell; Taco John's; Wasabi; Wing Zone
Units Franchised From: 2,266
Areas of Operation: AK, AL, AR, AZ, CA, CO, DE, FL, GA, GU, HI, ID, IL, IN, KS, KY, LA, MA, MD, MI, MN, MO, MS, MT, NC, ND, NE, NJ, NM, NV, NY, OH, OK, PA, PR, SC, SD, TX, VA, WA, WI, WV, WY
Type of Foodservice: Quick Serve
Franchise Affiliation: Arby's Restaurant Group, ATLANTA, GA; BR IP Holder LLC, CANTON, MA; Burger King Worldwide Inc., MIAMI, FL; Captain D's LLC, NASHVILLE, TN; Church's Chicken, ATLANTA, GA; Cinnabon Inc., ATLANTA, GA; Coffee & Bagel Brands, LAKEWOOD, CO; DD IP Holder, CANTON, MA; Doctor's Associates Inc., MILFORD, CT; Froots Franchising Companies Inc., DAVIE, FL; Godfather's Pizza, Inc., OMAHA, NE; Gosh Enterprises Inc., COLUMBUS, OH; Kahala Brands, SCOTTSDALE, AZ; MTY Food Group Inc., SAINT-LAURENT, QC; Pizza Hut Inc., PLANO, TX; Popeyes Louisiana

KitchenInc., ATLANTA, GA; Starbucks Corporation, SEATTLE, WA; Taco Bell Corp., IRVINE, CA; Wing Zone Franchise Corp., ATLANTA, GA

Notes: Facilities include main stores, Military Clothing stores, convenience stores, specialty stores that carry furniture and outdoor living merchandise and movie theaters. The Exchange also runs quick-serve restaurants under licenses such as Subway, Boston Market and Starbucks, and oversees retail concessions operations. Restaurant counts include only those operated by The Exchange and excludes concessionaires.

Key Personnel
THOMAS C. SHULL - CEO; Director
ANA MIDDLETON - President; Chief Merchandising Officer
JAMES JORDAN - CFO; Exec VP
DAVID NELSON - COO
LEIGH ROOP - Chief Human Resources Officer
MICKEY BRADFORD - Chief Administrative Officer
JASON ROSENBERG - Senior VP
THOMAS OCKENFELS - VP Administration; Director
MORGAN MEEKS - VP Transportation
JESUS SAUTO - VP Payment Methods
PATRICK OLDENBURGH JR - VP Human Resources
JEFF XIA - VP
TIMOTHY KELLY - VP Information Technology, Development, Innovation
DEBRA ZARSK - VP Operations, Information Technology
MARISSA CARPENTER - VP Merchandising
CHARLES HATTON - Director Art
SHANE BINION - Director Marketing, E-Commerce
BARBARA FORKAPA - Director Operations, Information Technology
RENA ARNOLD - Director Leasing, National
QIANA LEONARD - Regional Manager Branding
EDWARD CHRISTIAN - Area Manager Sales
DAVID DRYSDALE - Manager Employee Development
MELISSA MORSE - Manager Human Resources
MORRY BAIER - Manager Loss Prevention
KALAN BROWN - Manager Recruitment
DOUG COLE - Manager Talent
ELIONOR LOUIS - Manager Sales, Merchandising
TIM SULLIVAN - Manager Financial Planning
TINA CHEN - Manager Consumer Insights
RON PIMENTAL - Manager Loss Prevention
MONTE DANGERFIELD - Manager Data Security
THOMAS JONES - Project Manager Real Estate
KEVIN MCLAREN - Project Manager West Region
DAN DICKINSON - Project Manager Construction

Asian Mint Restaurant Group
11617 N Central Expy Ste 135
Dallas, TX 75243

Telephone: (214) 363-6655
Internet Homepage: asianmint.com
Company Email: catering@asianmint.com
Type of Business: Chain Restaurant Operator
Year Founded: 2004
Total Units: 3
Trade Names: Asian Mint (3)
Company-Owned Units: 3
Primary Menu: Asian (3)
Projected Openings: 1
Areas of Operation: TX
Type of Foodservice: Casual Dining (3)

Key Personnel
NIKKY PHINYAWATANA - Partner; Executive Chef; General Buyer
TAN NOISIRI - Partner

BB Franchising Inc.
5500 Greenville Ave Ste 1102
Dallas, TX 75206

Telephone: (216) 966-6030
Internet Homepage: bakerbrosdeli.com
Company Email: Info@bakerbrosdeli.com
Type of Business: Chain Restaurant Operator
Year Founded: 1999
Systemwide Sales: $12,069,000 (e)
Total Sales: $6,789,000 (e)
Alcohol Sales: 1%
Number of Employees: 90
Average Check: Lunch(8); Dinner(10)
Total Units: 3
Trade Names: Baker Bros. American Deli (3)
Units Franchised To: 3
Preferred Square Footage: 4,000
Preferred Location Types: Freestanding; Strip Mall
Alcohol Served: Beer, Wine
Primary Menu: Sandwiches/Deli (3)
Projected Openings: 1
Areas of Operation: TX
Type of Foodservice: Fast Casual (3)
Catering Services: Yes
Parent Company: Fgr Food Corporation, DALLAS, TX

Key Personnel
KEN REIMER - CEO
TOM DAHL - President
ROB GOLDBLATT - COO

Bent Tree Country Club Inc.
5201 Westgrove Dr
Dallas, TX 75248-2044

Telephone: (972) 931-7326
Fax Number: (972) 250-3780
Internet Homepage: benttreecc.org
Company Email: linda@benttreecc.org
Type of Business: Chain Restaurant Operator
Year Founded: 1974
Total Sales: $10,585,000 (e)
Alcohol Sales: 25%
Number of Employees: 120
Average Check: Breakfast(8); Lunch(22); Dinner(38)
Total Units: 4
Trade Names: Charlie's Grill (1); Ladies' 19th Hole (1); Men's 19th Hole (1); The Lakeview Lounge (1)
Company-Owned Units: 4
Preferred Square Footage: 5,500; 6,000
Preferred Location Types: Freestanding; Other
Alcohol Served: Beer, Wine, Liquor
Primary Menu: American (4)
Areas of Operation: TX
Type of Foodservice: Casual Dining (4)
Primary Distributors: (Food) SYSCO Food Services of North Texas, LEWISVILLE, TX
Notes: The company derives approximately 50% of its revenue from country club operations.

Key Personnel
KENT HERNDON - President
DAN BURKETT - COO; General Manager; General Buyer
LANCE WARREN - Executive Chef; Director Purchasing

Bob's Steak & Chop House
4300 Lemmon Ave
Dallas, TX 75219-2705

Telephone: (214) 528-9446
Fax Number: (214) 526-8159
Internet Homepage: bobs-steakandchop.com
Type of Business: Chain Restaurant Operator
Year Founded: 1993
Total Sales: $41,590,000 (e)
Alcohol Sales: 15%
Number of Employees: 186
Average Check: Dinner(90)
Total Units: 16
Trade Names: Bob's Steak & Chop House (16)
Company-Owned Units: 16
Preferred Location Types: Freestanding
Alcohol Served: Beer, Wine, Liquor
Primary Menu: Steak (16)
Projected Openings: 2
Areas of Operation: AZ, CA, TN, TX

Type of Foodservice: Fine Dining (16)

Key Personnel
SILVIO CARBONE - General Manager
DAN MARTINEZ - General Manager
SEAN NEWSOM - Director Alcoholic Beverages
BRYAN HANTES - Director Operations
CARRIE WATSON - Director Sales
STEVE CLEMENS - Regional Director
AUDREY PETROSS - Manager Restaurant Operations

Bonchon Franchise LLC
15660 Dallas Pkwy
Dallas, TX 15660

Internet Homepage: bonchon.com
Company Email: bonchon@bonchon.com
Type of Business: Chain Restaurant Operator
Year Founded: 2006
Total Sales: $826,980,000 (e)
Total Units: 159
Trade Names: BonChon (159)
Company-Owned Units: 2
Units Franchised To: 157
Primary Menu: Asian (159)
Projected Openings: 15
Areas of Operation: AL, AZ, CA, CO, CT, DC, FL, GA, IL, MA, MD, MN, NC, NJ, NV, NY, OH, OR, PA, TN, TX, VA, WA
Type of Foodservice: Casual Dining (159)
Notes: Korean fried chicken concept.

Key Personnel
BRYAN SHIN - CEO International; CFO Group
SUZIE TSAI - CEO United States
HONG T. KIM - COO
KATE WRIGHT - Director Marketing
JEDD LEVITSKY - Manager Operations
CHRISTOPHER PARK - Specialist Franchise Development
JOOREE KIM - Specialist Information Technology
ELIZABETH COZZI - Designer
MONICA LEE - Developer Franchising

Boston's Restaurant & Sports Bar
14850 Quorum Dr Ste 201
Dallas, TX 75254

Telephone: (972) 484-9022
Fax Number: (972) 484-7630
Internet Homepage: bostons.com
Company Email: contact@bostons.com
Type of Business: Chain Restaurant Operator
Systemwide Sales: $97,016,000 (e)
Total Sales: $9,097,000 (e)
Alcohol Sales: 20%
Internet Order Processing: Yes
Total Units: 22
Trade Names: Boston's The Gourmet Pizza Restaurant & Sports Bar (23)
Company-Owned Units: 2
Units Franchised To: 21
Preferred Location Types: Freestanding; Lifestyle Center; Strip Mall
Alcohol Served: Beer, Wine, Liquor
Primary Menu: Pizza (23)
Projected Openings: 1
Areas of Operation: AR, AZ, CA, CO, CT, FL, IL, IN, MD, MI, MN, MT, OH, PA, SD, TX, UT, VA, WA
Foreign Countries: MEXICO
Type of Foodservice: Casual Dining (23)
Parent Company: Boston Pizza International Inc., RICHMOND, BC CANADA

Key Personnel
GEORGE MELVILLE - Chairman; Partner
WALTER J. TRELIVING - Chairman; Partner
JEFF MELNICK - President
RICHARD LAURO - CFO
RICK LAURO - VP Finance
BRAD BEVILL - VP Marketing
MO BOUTARA - VP Development, Franchise Sales
MOE BOUTARA - VP Franchise Development
DERYCK PHIMISTER - Director Operations
RYAN TOMANIK - Director Operations
JULIE SCHAFFNER - Senior Manager Marketing
MANAN PARIKH - Manager Finance
MICHAEL VELASCO - Project Manager Construction

Bread Winners Cafe & Bakery
7205 Envoy Ct
Dallas, TX 75247

Telephone: (214) 754-0099
Internet Homepage: breadwinnerscafe.com; quarterbardallas.com
Company Email: info@breadwinnerscafe.com
Type of Business: Chain Restaurant Operator
Total Units: 8
Trade Names: Bread Winners Cafe and Bakery (6); The Quarter Bar (2)
Company-Owned Units: 8
Primary Menu: American (8)
Areas of Operation: TX
Type of Foodservice: Casual Dining (8)

Key Personnel
JIM HUGHES - Partner
CINDY HUGHES - Partner
CHERYL TIBERGHIEN - Director Human Resources

Bread Zeppelin Salads Elevated
1300 Main St
Dallas, TX 75202

Telephone: (214) 666-6065
Internet Homepage: breadzeppelin.com
Company Email: feedback@breadzeppelinsalads.com
Type of Business: Chain Restaurant Operator
Year Founded: 2010
Average Check: Lunch(10); Dinner(14)
Total Units: 6
Trade Names: Bread Zeppelin Salads Elevated (6)
Company-Owned Units: 6
Primary Menu: Health Foods (6)
Areas of Operation: TX
Type of Foodservice: Fast Casual (6)
Catering Services: Yes

Key Personnel
ANDREW SCHOELLKOPF - Co-Founder
TROY CHARHON - Co-Founder
VINCENT GINATTA - VP Franchising

Brinker International Inc.
3000 Olympus Blvd
Dallas, TX 75019

Telephone: (972) 980-9917
Fax Number: (972) 770-9593
Internet Homepage: brinker.com
Listing Type: Corporate Office
Type of Business: Chain Restaurant Operator
Year Founded: 1975
Publicly Held: Yes
Total Sales: $4,409,173,000 (e)
Number of Employees: 53,000
Internet Order Processing: Yes
Total Units: 1,657
Trade Names: Chili's Grill & Bar (1,605); Maggiano's Little Italy (52)
Company-Owned Units: 1,185
Units Franchised To: 472
Preferred Square Footage: 4,300; 6,000; 8,000; 24,800
Preferred Location Types: Airports; Community Mall; Downtown; Freestanding; Institution (college/hospital); Lifestyle Center; Office Complex; Outlet Mall; Regional Mall; Strip Mall
Alcohol Served: Beer, Wine, Liquor
Primary Menu: Italian (52); Southwest/Tex-Mex (1,605)
Areas of Operation: AK, AL, AR, AZ, CA, CO, CT, DC, DE, FL, GA, GU, HI, IA, ID, IL, IN, KS, KY, LA, MA, MD, ME, MI, MN, MO, MS, NC, ND, NE, NH, NJ, NM, NV, NY, OH, OK, OR, PA, PR, RI, SC, SD, TN, TX, UT, VA, VT, WA, WI, WV, WY, AB, ON, QC

Foreign Countries: BAHRAIN; CANADA; COLOMBIA; COSTA RICA; DOMINICAN REPUBLIC; ECUADOR; EGYPT; EL SALVADOR; GERMANY; GUATEMALA; HONDURAS; INDIA; INDONESIA; JAPAN; JORDAN; KUWAIT; LEBANON; MALAYSIA; MEXICO; OMAN; PERU; QATAR; SAUDI ARABIA; SINGAPORE; SOUTH KOREA; TAIWAN; UNITED ARAB EMIRATES; VENEZUELA
Type of Foodservice: Casual Dining (1,657)
Catering Services: Yes
Distribution Centers: CARROLLTON, TX
On-site Distribution Center: Yes
Primary Distributors: (Full Line) US Foods, GARLAND, TX
Headquarter Offices: Chili's Grill & Bar, DALLAS, TX; Maggiano's Little Italy, DALLAS, TX

Key Personnel
KEVIN HOCHMAN - CEO
DOMINIQUE BERTOLONE - President Division
JOSEPH G. TAYLOR - CFO; Senior VP
LARRY KONECNY - Chief Brand Officer Group
MIKA WARE - VP Finance, Investor Relations
JESSE JOHNSON - VP Marketing
SANELLA HADZOVIC WERTZ - Treasurer; Analyst
TAMMY JONES-STILL - Senior Director Diversity
M.J. SHULT - Senior Director Quality Assurance, Food Safety
MIKE STONE - Senior Director Construction
RICHARD BENEFIELD - Senior Director Systems Engineering
LARRY HENDREN - Director
TRACY T. LUIGS - Director
KATY WILKINSON - Director Operations
JJ JAMADAR - Director Development
JASON NOORIAN - Director Business Development
CATHY LEFFINGWELL - Director Supply Chain
LARRY LYSEK - Director Real Estate
JOHN MANNING - Director Business Development
CHAD COLLINS - Director Operations
ANTHONY DEVESCOVI - Director Operations
ADAM DINGMAN - Director Operations
SHERIF ELBEDEIWY - Director Operations
EVA LYDIA LINDENBERGER - Director Operations
OBI NWACHUKWU - Director Operations
DHARAM RAMPERSAD - Director Operations
AMANDA TORRENCE - Director Operations
CHAD WOOD - Director Operations
BRAD HERRON - Director Procurement-Food
JESSICA BOWLES - Director Human Resources
MARGARET SUAREZ - Director Strategic Planning
STEPHEN PILANT - Senior Manager Loss Prevention
JIM SMITH - Senior Manager Facility/Maintenance
CLAY THURMAN - Senior Manager Facility/Maintenance
TARA JACKSON - Senior Manager Information Technology
JARED MILLER - Senior Manager Financial Planning
CARRIE RUFF - Senior Manager Operations
LUZ BICKERT - Senior Manager Marketing
ANDREA LANGUS - Senior Manager Branding
RANDY REID - Manager Compensation
JOHN TUREK - Manager Facility/Maintenance
LISA DIXON - Manager Systems, Quality Assurance
CAMI JONES - Manager Marketing
SUSAN LUTSINGER - Manager Quality Assurance
MELANIE REESE - Manager
AURORA ROSAS - Manager Human Resources
DAVID HAVIS - Manager Data Warehouse; Engineer Database
SCOTT ROBERSON - Project Manager Global Development
KAREN FISHER - Project Manager Information Technology
JIM SWANSON - Senior Category Manager
NYLE BRANDENBURG - Senior Engineer Network

Bruegger's Enterprises Inc.
12201 Merit Dr Ste 900
Dallas, TX 75251-3139

Telephone: (888) 822-5379
Internet Homepage: brueggers.com
Company Email: info@brueggers.com
Listing Type: Subsidiary
Type of Business: Chain Restaurant Operator
Year Founded: 1983
Systemwide Sales: $221,080,000 (e)
Total Sales: $129,030,000 (e)
Number of Employees: 6,634
Average Check: Breakfast(6); Lunch(6); Dinner(6)
Total Units: 214
Trade Names: Bruegger's Bagel Bakery (214)
Company-Owned Units: 114
Units Franchised To: 100
Preferred Square Footage: 1,200; 1,500; 2,200; 2,500
Preferred Location Types: Community Mall; Downtown; Freestanding; Grocery Stores; Institution (college/hospital); Kiosk; Regional Mall; Strip Mall
Primary Menu: Bagels (214)
Areas of Operation: AK, AL, AZ, CA, CO, CT, FL, IA, KY, MA, MI, MN, NC, NE, NV, NY, OH, PA, SC, TN, VA, VT, WI
Foreign Countries: CANADA
Type of Foodservice: Fast Casual (214)
Parent Company: JAB Holding Company, LUDWIGSHAFEN, GER
Headquarters: Coffee & Bagel Brands, LAKEWOOD, CO

Key Personnel
MERCEDES RESTEGHINI - Senior Manager Purchasing
VIRGINIA KARAKHANIAN - Senior Manager Sales, Catering
BOB GRIGLAK - Manager Sales, Region

Burger House Franchising, L.P.
6248 E Mockingbird Ln
Dallas, TX 75214-2619

Telephone: (214) 828-2732
Internet Homepage: burgerhouse.com
Company Email: mail@burgerhouse.com
Type of Business: Chain Restaurant Operator
Total Sales: $5,144,000 (e)
Number of Employees: 60
Internet Order Processing: Yes
Total Units: 3
Trade Names: Burger House Hamburgers (3)
Units Franchised To: 3
Preferred Square Footage: 2,800
Preferred Location Types: Freestanding; Institution (college/hospital)
Primary Menu: American (4); Hamburger (3)
Areas of Operation: TX
Type of Foodservice: Family Restaurant (4); Quick Serve (3)

Key Personnel
ANGELO S. CHANTILIS SR - Chairman
STEVE G. CANELLOS - President; General Buyer

Burguesa Burger Franchise LLC
1412 Main St Ste 2000
Dallas, TX 75202-4087

Telephone: (214) 747-9424
Fax Number: (214) 744-4329
Internet Homepage: burguesa.com
Company Email: info@burguesa.com
Type of Business: Chain Restaurant Operator
Total Sales: $2,527,000 (e)
Number of Employees: 18
Total Units: 2
Trade Names: Burguesa Burger (2)
Units Franchised To: 2
Preferred Location Types: Freestanding; Office Complex; Strip Mall
Alcohol Served: Beer
Primary Menu: Hamburger (2)
Areas of Operation: TX
Type of Foodservice: Fast Casual (2)
Parent Company: Sinelli Concepts, Inc., ,

Key Personnel
JEFF SINELLI - CEO; President; General Buyer

Cafe Brazil LLC
3851 Cedar Springs Rd
Dallas, TX 75219

Telephone: (214) 461-8762
Company Email: mail@cafebrazil.com
Type of Business: Chain Restaurant Operator
Year Founded: 1998
Total Units: 7
Trade Names: Cafe Brazil (7)
Company-Owned Units: 7
Primary Menu: American (7)
Areas of Operation: TX
Type of Foodservice: Casual Dining (7)

Key Personnel
BRANT WOOD - CEO
KEVIN PULTZ - VP; Director Operations

Campero USA
12404 Park Central Dr Ste 250
Dallas, TX 75251-1803

Telephone: (972) 770-2800
Fax Number: (972) 770-2801
Internet Homepage: campero.com
Type of Business: Chain Restaurant Operator
Year Founded: 2007
Systemwide Sales: $111,997,000 (e)
Total Sales: $50,080,000 (e)
Alcohol Sales: 5%
Number of Employees: 842
Average Check: Lunch(8); Dinner(8)
Total Units: 80
Trade Names: Pollo Campero (77)
Company-Owned Units: 28
Units Franchised To: 49
Preferred Square Footage: 2,700; 2,830
Preferred Location Types: Freestanding; Strip Mall
Alcohol Served: Beer, Wine, Liquor
Primary Menu: Chicken (77)
Projected Openings: 15
Areas of Operation: DC, FL, IL, MD, NJ, NY, TX, VA
Type of Foodservice: Quick Serve (77)
Notes: Campero USA has licensing rights for all of the U.S. except AZ, CA, NM, NV, OR and WA; rights for these states are held by ADIR Restaurant Corp.

Key Personnel
ALVARO MORALES - President
LUIS JAVIER RODAS - COO; Director; General Buyer
BLAS ESCARCEGA - VP Accounting
FERNANDO PALAREA - Director Operations

REBECCA KHAN - Brand Manager

Campisi's Restaurants
5520 Lyndon B Johnson Fwy Ste 580
Dallas, TX 75240-6253

Telephone: (972) 789-1919
Fax Number: (972) 789-1055
Internet Homepage: campisis.us
Company Email: comments@campisis.us
Type of Business: Chain Restaurant Operator
Total Sales: $24,450,000 (e)
Alcohol Sales: 10%
Number of Employees: 68
Total Units: 9
Trade Names: Campisi's (9)
Company-Owned Units: 9
Preferred Location Types: Freestanding; Strip Mall
Alcohol Served: Beer, Wine, Liquor
Primary Menu: Italian (9)
Areas of Operation: TX
Type of Foodservice: Casual Dining (11)

Key Personnel
DAVID CAMPISI - CEO; General Manager
KENNY PENN - President; Director Operations; General Buyer

Cane Rosso
2612 Commerce St
Dallas, TX 75226

Telephone: (214) 741-1188
Internet Homepage: canerosso.com; zolispizza.com
Company Email: jobs@canerosso.com
Type of Business: Chain Restaurant Operator
Year Founded: 2009
Total Units: 9
Trade Names: Cane Rosso (8); Zoli's (1)
Company-Owned Units: 9
Primary Menu: Italian (1); Pizza (8)
Areas of Operation: TX
Type of Foodservice: Casual Dining (9)

Key Personnel
JAY JERRIER - Owner
STEVEN SMULLEN - CFO
TODD GARTON - Director Operations
JESSICA FRANKLIN - Director Human Resources
JEFF AMADOR - Manager Marketing

Canteen Vending Services
4301 N Beltwood Pkwy
Dallas, TX 75244-3214

Telephone: (972) 392-1665

Listing Type: Divisional Office
Type of Business: Foodservice Management Operator
Year Founded: 1929
Number of Employees: 160
Number of Locations Served: 1,500
Total Foodservice Mgmt Accounts: 1,500
Areas of Operation: TX
Type of Foodservice: Vending machines (1,500)
Foodservice Management Venues: Business & Industry; College & University; Health Care; Lodging; Military Feeding; Parks & Recreation; Prison Feeding; Schools; Transportation
Primary Distributors: (Food) Vistar North Texas, ARLINGTON, TX
Parent Company: Compass Group The Americas, CHARLOTTE, NC
Headquarters: Canteen Vending Services, CHARLOTTE, NC

Key Personnel
WEST HYATT - President Central Division
GREG SNODGRASS - Controller; Director Operations, Southwest Region

CBC Restaurant Corp.
12700 Park Central Dr Ste 1300
Dallas, TX 75251-1523

Telephone: (972) 619-4100
Fax Number: (972) 788-5038
Internet Homepage: cornerbakerycafe.com
Company Email: guestrelations@cornerbakerycafe.com
Type of Business: Chain Restaurant Operator
Year Founded: 1991
Systemwide Sales: $495,753,000 (e)
Total Sales: $308,200,000 (e)
Number of Employees: 5,711
Average Check: Breakfast(10); Lunch(10); Dinner(10)
Internet Order Processing: Yes
Internet Sales: 1.00%
Total Units: 230
Trade Names: Corner Bakery Cafe (230)
Company-Owned Units: 103
Units Franchised To: 127
Preferred Square Footage: 2,000; 5,300
Preferred Location Types: Airports; Downtown; Lifestyle Center; Office Complex; Regional Mall; Strip Mall
Primary Menu: American (230)
Areas of Operation: AZ, CA, CO, DC, FL, GA, ID, IL, IN, KS, KY, MD, MS, NJ, NM, NV, OH, OK, OR, PA, RI, TX, UT, VA, WA, WI
Type of Foodservice: Fast Casual (230)
Catering Services: Yes
Primary Distributors: (Full Line) SYSCO Corporation, HOUSTON, TX
Parent Company: Rohan Group of Companies, FEASTERVILLE TREVOSE, PA
Headquarters: Il Fornaio Corporation, CORTE

MADERA, CA

Key Personnel
DONNA JOSEPHSON - Chief Marketing Officer; Senior VP
DAN HIGH - Area Director
DENISE K. CLEMENS - Senior VP Human Resources
RACHEL WATSON - VP Marketing
DIANA BURNS - Director Operations, Administration
BRAD RAYBURN - Director Information Technology, Security

CHI Management LLC
1700 Pacific Ave Ste 1840
Dallas, TX 75201

Telephone: (214) 219-5858
Fax Number: (214) 219-6868
Company Email: sferguson@chitexas.com
Type of Business: Chain Restaurant Operator
Year Founded: 1998
Total Sales: $20,350,000 (e)
Number of Employees: 210
Average Check: Lunch(12); Dinner(20)
Total Units: 11
Trade Names: Arby's (11)
Units Franchised From: 11
Preferred Square Footage: 2,000
Preferred Location Types: Freestanding; Strip Mall
Primary Menu: Sandwiches/Deli (11)
Areas of Operation: TX
Type of Foodservice: Quick Serve (11)
Catering Services: Yes
Franchise Affiliation: Arby's Restaurant Group, ATLANTA, GA

Key Personnel
DENNIS WELLS - President; General Buyer
JIM KELLUM - VP Operations, Purchasing, Facility/Maintenance, Real Estate, Design, Business Development, Store Fixtures

Chili's Grill & Bar
3000 Olympus Blvd
Dallas, TX 75019

Telephone: (972) 980-9917
Internet Homepage: chilis.com
Type of Business: Chain Restaurant Operator
Year Founded: 1975
Systemwide Sales: $6,255,395,000 (e)
Publicly Held: Yes
Total Sales: $3,692,733,000 (e)
Alcohol Sales: 14%
Number of Employees: 52,000
Average Check: Lunch(16); Dinner(18)
Internet Order Processing: Yes
Internet Sales: 0.50%
Total Units: 1,605
Trade Names: Chili's Grill & Bar (1,605)
Company-Owned Units: 1,135
Units Franchised To: 470
Preferred Square Footage: 4,200; 5,450; 6,000
Preferred Location Types: Airports; Community Mall; Downtown; Freestanding; Regional Mall; Strip Mall
Alcohol Served: Beer, Wine, Liquor
Primary Menu: Southwest/Tex-Mex (1,605)
Areas of Operation: AK, AL, AR, AZ, CA, CO, CT, DC, DE, FL, GA, GU, HI, IA, ID, IL, IN, KS, KY, LA, MA, MD, ME, MI, MN, MO, MS, MT, NC, ND, NE, NH, NJ, NM, NV, NY, OH, OK, OR, PA, PR, RI, SC, SD, TN, TX, UT, VA, VT, WA, WI, WV, WY, AB, ON, SK
Foreign Countries: BAHRAIN; BRAZIL; CANADA; COLOMBIA; COSTA RICA; DOMINICAN REPUBLIC; ECUADOR; EGYPT; EL SALVADOR; GERMANY; GUATEMALA; HONDURAS; INDIA; INDONESIA; JAPAN; JORDAN; KUWAIT; LEBANON; MALAYSIA; MEXICO; OMAN; PERU; QATAR; RUSSIA; SAUDI ARABIA; SINGAPORE; SOUTH KOREA; SYRIA; TAIWAN; THE PHILIPPINES; UNITED ARAB EMIRATES; VENEZUELA
Type of Foodservice: Casual Dining (1,605)
Primary Distributors: (Food) US Foods, GARLAND, TX; (Supplies) The Wasserstrom Co., COLUMBUS, OH
Parent Company: Brinker International Inc., DALLAS, TX

Key Personnel
KEVIN HOCHMAN - CEO
DOUG COMINGS - COO; Senior VP
GEORGE FELIX - Chief Marketing Officer
JESSE JOHNSON - VP Marketing
ALAN KAPLAN - General Manager
MIKE STONE - Senior Director Construction
ROBIN THOMAS - Director Media
BRIAN ADKINS - Director Operations
PATRICK PARKER - Manager Security

Coal Vines
2404 Cedar Springs Rd
Dallas, TX 75201-1408

Telephone: (214) 855-4999
Internet Homepage: coalvines.com
Company Email: info@coalvines.com
Type of Business: Chain Restaurant Operator
Year Founded: 2006
Total Sales: $3,781,000 (e)
Total Units: 3
Trade Names: Coal Vines (3)
Company-Owned Units: 4
Units Franchised To: 3
Primary Menu: Pizza (3)
Areas of Operation: TX
Type of Foodservice: Casual Dining (3)

Key Personnel
JOSEPH PALLADINO - Founder; Owner
BEN DARROW - General Manager

Colter's Bar-B-Q
3904 W Camp Wisdom Rd
Dallas, TX 75237-2425

Telephone: (972) 298-3335
Fax Number: (972) 709-7482
Internet Homepage: coltersbbq.com
Type of Business: Chain Restaurant Operator
Year Founded: 1980
Systemwide Sales: $2,001,000 (e)
Total Sales: $461,000 (e)
Number of Employees: 60
Average Check: Lunch(8); Dinner(14)
Total Units: 3
Trade Names: Colter's Bar-B-Q (3)
Units Franchised To: 3
Preferred Square Footage: 5,500; 6,000
Preferred Location Types: Community Mall; Freestanding; Kiosk; Strip Mall
Primary Menu: Bar-B-Q (3)
Areas of Operation: TX
Type of Foodservice: Family Restaurant (3)

Key Personnel
PAYTON CULLUM - Owner
JIM KUNKLE - General Manager

Consolidated Restaurant Operations, Inc.
12200 N Stemmons Fwy Ste 100
Dallas, TX 75234-5877

Telephone: (972) 241-5500
Fax Number: (972) 888-8198
Internet Homepage: blackoakgrill.com; cantinalaredo.com; coolrivercafe.com; croinc.com; elchico.com; iiiforks.com; silverfoxcafe.com
Company Email: cro_contact@croinc.com
Type of Business: Chain Restaurant Operator
Year Founded: 1998
Systemwide Sales: $335,509,000 (e)
Total Sales: $186,700,000 (e)
Alcohol Sales: 15%
Number of Employees: 5,680
Average Check: Lunch(18); Dinner(30)
Internet Order Processing: Yes
Internet Sales: 1.00%
Total Units: 52
Trade Names: Black Oak Grill (1); Cantina Laredo (22); Cool River Cafe Steakhouse & Southwestern Grill (2); El Chico Cafe (20); III Forks (4); Lucky's Cafe(1); Silver Fox Steakhouse (2)
Company-Owned Units: 68
Units Franchised To: 12
Preferred Location Types: Airports;

Community Mall; Downtown; Freestanding; Lifestyle Center; Regional Mall; Strip Mall
Alcohol Served: Beer, Wine, Liquor
Primary Menu: American (2); Mexican (42); Steak (8)
Areas of Operation: AL, AR, CA, CO, FL, IL, KY, LA, MO, NE, NY, OH, OK, PA, SC, TN, TX
Foreign Countries: EGYPT; SAUDI ARABIA; UNITED ARAB EMIRATES
Type of Foodservice: Casual Dining (44); Fine Dining (8)
Catering Services: Yes

Key Personnel
JOHN HARKEY JR - CEO
DON DUNGY - President Division
MARK LAMM - President; COO
CURTIS OSMOND - President
WENDY HACKEMACK - CFO
JOETTE COX - VP Purchasing, Supply Chain, Distribution; General Buyer
MARK CZAUS - VP Catering
DAVID WIERMAN - VP Operations
JOHN SULAK - Controller
CLINT VIEHMAN - General Manager
MIKE CABALLERO - Senior Director Operations, Menu Development
KERRY KREITZER - Director Design
ERIC RASMUSSEN - Director Acquisitions, Mergers
JUDY SPIVA - Regional Manager
PAULA BERCHER - Manager Accounting
ALLISON TAYLOR - Manager Marketing
MALLORY SCUDDER - Manager Marketing
KANDY SHELTON - Manager Event Planning
PAULA SHIPMAN - Project Manager Construction
THERESA PARRISH - Administrator Real Estate
BRUCE COX - Coordinator Fulfillment
MICHELLE CZAUS - Coordinator Sales, Catering
DEBBIE MALAER - Analyst

Culinaire International Co.
8303 Elmbrook Dr
Dallas, TX 75247-4011

Telephone: (214) 754-1880
Fax Number: (214) 754-1891
Internet Homepage: culinaireintl.com
Type of Business: Foodservice Management Operator
Year Founded: 1993
Total Sales: $81,286,000 (e)
Number of Employees: 2,000
Number of Locations Served: 35
Total Foodservice Mgmt Accounts: 35
Total Units: 29
Trade Names: Culinaire International (35)
Company-Owned Units: 35
Areas of Operation: AZ, CA, FL, MN, NJ, TN, TX
Type of Foodservice: Full-service sit-down dining (35)
Foodservice Management Venues: College & University; Health Care; Lodging; Other
Primary Distributors: (Food) Merchant's Mart - Houston, HOUSTON, TX

Key Personnel
RICHARD N. GUSSONI - Founder; CEO
BILL THOMPSON - President; COO
CHARLES LAFRANO - CFO; Manager Risk Management
JAMES MUNOZ - CIO; VP Information Systems
SCOTT THOMPSON - VP
KIMBERLY LARSEN - VP Human Resources
WILLIAM LENOIR - VP Purchasing
JOHAN VERMEIR - Manager Information Systems, POS/Scanning, E-Commerce, Internet Development

Dave & Buster's Inc.
2481 Manana Dr
Dallas, TX 75220-1203

Telephone: (214) 357-9588
Fax Number: (214) 357-1536
Internet Homepage: daveandbusters.com
Listing Type: Corporate Office
Type of Business: Chain Restaurant Operator
Year Founded: 1982
Systemwide Sales: $1,136,723,000 (e)
Publicly Held: Yes
Total Sales: $2,205,300,000 (e)
Alcohol Sales: 31%
Number of Employees: 16,100
Average Check: Lunch(10); Dinner(18)
Foodservice Sales: $727,749,000 (e)
Internet Order Processing: Yes
Total Units: 220
Trade Names: Dave & Buster's (162); Main Event (58)
Company-Owned Units: 220
Preferred Square Footage: 17,000; 28,000; 47,000; 52,000; 68,000
Preferred Location Types: Downtown; Freestanding; Regional Mall, Strip Mall
Alcohol Served: Beer, Wine, Liquor
Primary Menu: American (220)
Areas of Operation: AK, AL, AR, AZ, CA, CO, CT, FL, GA, HI, ID, IL, IN, KS, KY, LA, MA, MD, MI, MN, MO, NC, NE, NJ, NM, NV, NY, OH, OK, OR, PA, PR, RI, SC, TN, TX, UT, VA, WA, WI, ON
Foreign Countries: CANADA
Type of Foodservice: Casual Dining (220)
On-site Distribution Center: Yes
Subsidiaries: Main Event Entertainment, LP, PLANO, TX
Primary Distributors: (Equipment) Edward Don & Co., WOODRIDGE, IL; (Food) US Foods Holding Corp., ROSEMONT, IL; (Supplies) Edward Don & Co., WOODRIDGE, IL; (Supplies) US Foods Holding Corp., ROSEMONT, IL
Parent Company: Oak Hill Capital Partners, L.P., NEW YORK, NY
Notes: The company derives approximately 56% of its revenue from amusement & other operations. Systemwide sales are for foodservice revenue only.

Key Personnel
MICHAEL QUARTIERI - CFO
TONY WEHNER - COO
STEVE KLOHN - CIO
JOHN B. MULLEADY - Chief Development Officer
ANTONIO BAUTISTA - Chief Development Officer International
LES LEHNER - Chief Procurement Officer; Director Development
APRIL SPEARMAN - VP Marketing
PETE THORNFIELD - VP Brand Marketing
RYAN NOWICKI - Senior Director Operations
AYOTUNDE GIBBS - Senior Director Technology
REVA AGUILAR - Director Information Technology, Systems
CHRIS SERRA - Director Operations
SARA VON READEN - Director Accounting, Systems
CHRIS WAUGAMAN - Director Operations
DAVID SCHMIDT - Director Tax
ERIC MEYLER - Director Purchasing
CHASE MADSEN - Director Accounting, Operations
GARY PASSARDI - Regional Director New Store Development
KERRI WALTERS - Manager HRIS

Del Sur Restaurant Group
3317 McKinney Ave Ste 201
Dallas, TX 75204

Telephone: (214) 272-7619
Company Email: info@dinedsrg.com
Type of Business: Chain Restaurant Operator
Year Founded: 2009
Total Units: 5
Trade Names: Hook Line & Sinker (2); Hookline (1); Urban Taco (2)
Company-Owned Units: 5
Primary Menu: Seafood (3); Taco (2)
Areas of Operation: TX
Type of Foodservice: Casual Dining (3); Fast Casual (2)

Key Personnel
JOHN TUMA - Co-Founder; Partner
AARON NELSON - Executive Chef
JOSHUA ROMERO - Manager Marketing

Desperados Mexican Restaurant
4818 Greenville Ave
Dallas, TX 75206-4120

Telephone: (214) 363-1850
Fax Number: (214) 373-0752
Internet Homepage: desperadosrestaurant.com
Company Email: desperadouno@sbcglobal.net
Type of Business: Chain Restaurant Operator
Year Founded: 1976
Total Sales: $4,696,000 (e)
Alcohol Sales: 25%
Number of Employees: 85
Average Check: Breakfast(8); Lunch(8); Dinner(16)
Total Units: 2
Trade Names: Desperados Mexican Restaurant (2)
Company-Owned Units: 2
Preferred Location Types: Freestanding
Alcohol Served: Beer, Wine, Liquor
Primary Menu: Mexican (2)
Areas of Operation: TX
Type of Foodservice: Casual Dining (2)
Catering Services: Yes

Key Personnel
JORGE LEVY - President; General Buyer
MICHAEL LEVY - General Manager; Director Operations
JAKE LEVY - General Manager; Director Marketing; General Buyer
ENRIQUE HERNANDEZ - Executive Chef; General Buyer
AMEET SOMANEY - Director Catering

Dickey's Barbecue Restaurants Inc.
4514 Cole Ave Ste 1015
Dallas, TX 75205-5449

Telephone: (972) 248-9899
Fax Number: (972) 248-8667
Internet Homepage: dickeys.com
Company Email: contactus@dickeys.com
Type of Business: Chain Restaurant Operator
Year Founded: 1941
Systemwide Sales: $622,342,000 (e)
Total Sales: $38,900,000 (e)
Alcohol Sales: 4%
Number of Employees: 1,012
Average Check: Breakfast(8); Lunch(12); Dinner(12)
Internet Order Processing: Yes
Total Units: 507
Trade Names: Dickey's Barbecue Pit (507)
Company-Owned Units: 11
Units Franchised To: 496
Preferred Square Footage: 1,800; 3,000
Preferred Location Types: Airports; Downtown; Freestanding; Outlet Mall; Strip Mall; Travel Plazas
Alcohol Served: Beer, Wine
Primary Menu: Bar-B-Q (507)
Projected Openings: 50
Areas of Operation: AR, AZ, CA, CO, CT, FL, GA, IA, ID, IL, IN, KS, KY, LA, MA, MD, ME, MI, MN, MO, MS, NC, ND, NE, NJ, NM, NV, NY, OH, OK, OR, PA, SC, SD, TX, UT, VA, WA, WI, WV, WY
Foreign Countries: BRAZIL; JAPAN; PAKISTAN
Type of Foodservice: Fast Casual (507)
Catering Services: Yes
Primary Distributors: (Full Line) SYSCO Corporation, HOUSTON, TX
Parent Company: Dickey's Capital Group Inc., ,

Key Personnel
ROLAND R. DICKEY SR - Chairman
ROLAND R. DICKEY JR - CEO
LAURA REA DICKEY - CEO
RENEE ROOZEN - President
ED HERMAN - Senior VP Operations
ALEXANDER UY - VP Operations
SHAYLA PARTUSCH - VP Purchasing
DEBORAH L - VP Franchise Development
MAURINE DICKEY - VP
KURTIS GALYEN - VP New Store Development, Construction
J ACKLEY - VP Technology, Development
SHANNON BULLOCK - VP Operations; Senior Director Finance
OWEN EDWARDS - Director Purchasing
MATT BURTON - Director Research & Development

Domino's Franchisee
3720 Walnut Hill Ln Ste 105
Dallas, TX 75229-6171

Telephone: (972) 620-7444
Type of Business: Chain Restaurant Operator
Total Sales: $6,041,000 (e)
Total Units: 3
Trade Names: Domino's (3)
Units Franchised From: 3
Primary Menu: Pizza (3)
Areas of Operation: TX
Type of Foodservice: Quick Serve (3)
Franchise Affiliation: Domino's Pizza Inc, ANN ARBOR, MI

Key Personnel
HENG LI - Owner; General Buyer

DRG Concepts
1717 Main St Ste 5630
Dallas, TX 75201-7337

Telephone: (214) 231-3432
Internet Homepage: drgconcepts.com
Company Email: info@drgconcepts.com
Type of Business: Chain Restaurant Operator
Year Founded: 2005
Total Units: 8
Trade Names: Chop House Burgers (3); Dallas Chop House (1); Dallas Fish Market (1); Wild Salsa (3)
Company-Owned Units: 8
Preferred Location Types: Downtown
Alcohol Served: Beer, Wine, Liquor
Primary Menu: American (3); Mexican (3); Seafood (1); Steak (1)
Areas of Operation: TX
Type of Foodservice: Casual Dining (8)
Catering Services: Yes

Key Personnel
NAFEES ALAM - CEO; Partner
MIKE HOQUE - Partner
AJ JOGLEKAR - Corporate Chef; General Buyer
MANUEL DE MARTINO - Director Operations
KENDRA AVERITT - Manager Marketing, Sales
KELLY STUDLEY - Engineer

Dunston's Prime Steak House
8526 Harry Hines Blvd
Dallas, TX 75235-3013

Telephone: (214) 637-3513
Fax Number: (214) 637-3514
Internet Homepage: dunstonssteakhouse.com
Company Email: info@dunstonssteakhouse.com
Type of Business: Chain Restaurant Operator
Year Founded: 1956
Total Sales: $6,441,000 (e)
Alcohol Sales: 37%
Number of Employees: 110
Average Check: Lunch(14); Dinner(26)
Total Units: 2
Trade Names: Dunston's Prime Steakhouse (1); Dunston's Steakhouse & Bar (1)
Company-Owned Units: 2
Preferred Location Types: Freestanding
Alcohol Served: Beer, Wine, Liquor
Primary Menu: Steak (2)
Areas of Operation: TX
Type of Foodservice: Casual Dining (2)
Primary Distributors: (Supplies) SYSCO Food Services of North Texas, LEWISVILLE, TX

Key Personnel
GENE DUNSTON - President; Controller; Executive Chef; Manager Operations,

Advertising; General Buyer
MARY HAVENS - Manager Purchasing, Risk Management, Human Resources, Food Safety

East Hampton Sandwich Co.
3888 Oak Lawn Ave Ste 100
Dallas, TX 75219-4457

Telephone: (214) 443-7925
Internet Homepage: ehsandwich.com
Company Email: contact@ehsandwich.com
Type of Business: Chain Restaurant Operator
Total Units: 8
Trade Names: East Hampton Sandwich Co. (8)
Company-Owned Units: 8
Primary Menu: Sandwiches/Deli (8)
Projected Openings: 2
Areas of Operation: TX
Type of Foodservice: Fast Casual (8)

Key Personnel
HUNTER POND - Founder; CEO
WES FREEMAN - Director Operations

Eatzi's Market & Bakery
3403 Oak Lawn Ave
Dallas, TX 75219-4215

Telephone: (214) 526-1515
Internet Homepage: eatzis.com
Type of Business: Chain Restaurant Operator
Year Founded: 1996
Total Sales: $7,626,000 (e)
Total Units: 6
Trade Names: Eatzi's Market & Bakery (6)
Company-Owned Units: 6
Primary Menu: American (6)
Areas of Operation: TX
Type of Foodservice: Fast Casual (6)

Key Personnel
PHILIP ROMANO - Founder; Owner
ADAM ROMO - CEO
JAY VALLEY - President; General Buyer
BRIAN SNOW - CFO; VP Finance

El Pollo Loco Holdings, Inc.
14800 Landmark Blvd Ste 500
Dallas, TX 75254-7013

Telephone: (972) 702-9300
Internet Homepage: frgi.com
Company Email: contact@frgi.com
Listing Type: Corporate Office
Type of Business: Chain Restaurant Operator
Year Founded: 2012
Publicly Held: Yes
Total Sales: $518,304,000 (e)
Alcohol Sales: 4%
Number of Employees: 4,480
Total Units: 495
Trade Names: Pollo Tropical (495)
Company-Owned Units: 172
Units Franchised To: 323
Preferred Location Types: Downtown; Freestanding; Institution (college/hospital); Strip Mall
Alcohol Served: Beer, Liquor
Primary Menu: Chicken (495); Mexican (0)
Projected Openings: 3
Areas of Operation: AZ, CA, CO, LA, NV, TX, UT
Foreign Countries: BAHAMAS; GUYANA; PANAMA
Type of Foodservice: Fast Casual (495)
Primary Distributors: (Food) Performance Food Group, RICHMOND, VA
Headquarter Offices: Pollo Tropical Operations Inc., MIAMI, FL

Key Personnel
DIRK MONTGOMERY - CEO
TYLER YOESTING - Chief Accounting Officer
JOHN DOYLE - CIO
HOPE DIAZ - Chief Marketing Officer
ADAM HLAVATY - Chief Development Officer
LOUIS DIPIETRO - Senior VP; Corporate Secretary; General Counsel
ILLANSY RUIZ - VP; Executive Chef
ANTHONY SANDERFER - Director Accounting
ANN SHERER - Director Digital Solutions
MARK NAPLES - Director Applications
KAREN EHART - Director Product Development
DIEGO CABRERA - Director Administration, Employee Benefits
RYAN NOYES - Director Accounting
DAVID SMYTH - Director Facility/Maintenance
ROBERT ZIMMERMANN - Director Operations
ANTHONY TONY SANDERFER - Director Accounting
MAXIMILIANO MOLL - Regional Director Operations
SHARON RUSSELL - Manager Payroll
DEBORAH CZERWINSKI - Manager
DAVID LUSK - Manager Information Technology, Security
LATISHA BILLINGS - Manager Accounting
BIANCA MUENZBERG - Specialist Talent Acquisitions

Enchiladas Restaurant & Catering Corp.
7050 Greenville Ave
Dallas, TX 75231

Telephone: (214) 363-1100
Fax Number: (214) 265-7956
Internet Homepage: enchiladasrestaurants.com
Company Email: eat@enchiladasrestaurants.com
Type of Business: Chain Restaurant Operator
Year Founded: 1979
Total Sales: $3,640,000 (e)
Alcohol Sales: 10%
Number of Employees: 120
Average Check: Lunch(14); Dinner(18)
Total Units: 2
Trade Names: Enchiladas (2)
Company-Owned Units: 2
Preferred Location Types: Downtown; Freestanding
Alcohol Served: Beer, Wine, Liquor
Primary Menu: Mexican (2)
Areas of Operation: TX
Type of Foodservice: Casual Dining (2)
Catering Services: Yes
Primary Distributors: (Food) Ben E. Keith Foods, FORT WORTH, TX

Key Personnel
TONY WALDROP - President; Executive Chef; General Buyer
CINDY WALDROP - CFO; VP

Encore Restaurants
5005 Lyndon B Johnson Fwy Ste 1200
Dallas, TX 75244-6100

Telephone: (214) 259-7000
Fax Number: (214) 259-7001
Internet Homepage: encore.bz/restaurants
Type of Business: Chain Restaurant Operator
Year Founded: 2014
Total Units: 24
Trade Names: Five Guys Burgers and Fries (20); IHOP (4)
Units Franchised From: 24
Primary Menu: American (4); Hamburger (20)
Projected Openings: 8
Areas of Operation: CA, MS, OK
Type of Foodservice: Family Restaurant (4); Fast Casual (20)

Key Personnel
DALE DOERHOFF - President
TONY WOODRUFF - Director Human Resources
TIM BIRDWELL - District Manager
MIKE ULMER - Manager Region

Entertainment Properties Group, Inc
12400 Coit Rd Ste 800
Dallas, TX 75251-2067

Telephone: (214) 751-8300
Fax Number: (214) 271-4138
Internet Homepage: pinstackbowl.com; itzusa.com
Company Email: info@itzusa.com

Type of Business: Foodservice Operations - Bowling Alley
Year Founded: 2006
Total Sales: $11,890,000 (e)
Alcohol Sales: 5%
Number of Employees: 40
Average Check: Dinner(22)
Total Units: 6
Trade Names: IT'Z (3); Pinstack (3)
Company-Owned Units: 6
Preferred Square Footage: 55,000
Preferred Location Types: Freestanding; Strip Mall
Alcohol Served: Beer, Wine
Primary Menu: American (3); Italian (3)
Areas of Operation: TX
Type of Foodservice: Casual Dining (6)
Catering Services: Yes
Primary Distributors: (Food) Ben E. Keith Foods, ALBUQUERQUE, NM; (Food) Shamrock Liquors, COLORADO SPRINGS, CO

Key Personnel
MARK MOORE - President; General Buyer
BRIAN COHEN - VP Operations
LEIGH ANN HATCHETT - Director Marketing

FB Society
5151 Belt Line Rd Ste 1200
Dallas, TX 75254

Telephone: (972) 941-3150
Internet Homepage: foodhallco.com; frontburnergroupdining.com
Company Email: info@foodhallco.com
Listing Type: Corporate Office
Type of Business: Chain Restaurant Operator
Year Founded: 1994
Total Sales: $70,950,000 (e)
Total Units: 25
Trade Names: Haywire (1); Ida Claire (1); Legacy Hall (Food Hall) (1); Mexican Sugar (1); Nashville Food Hall (1); Sixty Vines (2); The Keeper (1); The Ranch(1); Velvet Taco (10); Whiskey Cake (6)
Company-Owned Units: 25
Primary Menu: American (11); Miscellaneous (2); Southern (1); Southwest/Tex-Mex (1); Taco (10)
Areas of Operation: IL, OK, TX
Type of Foodservice: Casual Dining (13); Fast Casual (12)
Headquarter Offices: Velvet Taco, DALLAS, TX
Notes: Subsidiary The Food Hall Co.operated by Front Burner.

Key Personnel
RANDY DEWITT - Chairman
JACK GIBBONS - CEO; President
BRAD LEIST - CFO
TODD EBERT - Chief Marketing Officer
RAE PHILLIPS-LUTHER - Chief Brand Officer
TIM TIMBS - Senior VP Supply Chain
JOSH SMITH - General Manager

Firebird Restaurant Group
1845 Woodall Rodgers Fwy Ste 1100
Dallas, TX 75201-2239

Telephone: (972) 241-2171
Fax Number: (972) 241-3031
Internet Homepage: firebirdrg.com; mesomaya.com; taquerialaventana.com; elfenix.com; snuffers.com
Company Email: comments@firebirdrg.com
Type of Business: Chain Restaurant Operator
Year Founded: 1918
Systemwide Sales: $230,898,000 (e)
Total Sales: $291,480,000 (e)
Alcohol Sales: 8%
Number of Employees: 1,809
Average Check: Lunch(12); Dinner(14)
Internet Order Processing: Yes
Internet Sales: 1.00%
Total Units: 54
Trade Names: El Fenix Restaurant (16); Meso Maya (6); Snuffer's Burgers (9); Taqueria La Ventana (4); Tortaco (1); Twisted Root Burger Co. (13); Village Burger Bar (4); Wok Star (1)
Company-Owned Units: 54
Preferred Square Footage: 6,500
Preferred Location Types: Freestanding; Strip Mall
Alcohol Served: Beer, Wine, Liquor
Primary Menu: Chinese (1); Hamburger (26); Mexican (10); Southwest/Tex-Mex (16); Taco (1)
Areas of Operation: TX
Type of Foodservice: Casual Dining (54)
Primary Distributors: (Equipment) SYSCO Food Services of North Texas, LEWISVILLE, TX; (Food) Patterson Food Processors, DALLAS, TX; (Food) Nogales Produce Inc., DALLAS, TX
Parent Company: Firebird Restaurant Group LLC, DALLAS, TX

Key Personnel
NICO SANCHEZ - Executive Chef
STEVE CHAMBERS - Director Operations

Fox & Hound Restaurant Group
19111 Dallas Pkwy Ste 370
Dallas, TX 75287-6819

Telephone: (972) 581-1171
Fax Number: (708) 564-2282
Internet Homepage: champps.com; foxandhound.com; baileyssportsgrille.com
Type of Business: Chain Restaurant Operator
Year Founded: 1989
Total Sales: $39,810,000 (e)
Alcohol Sales: 55%
Number of Employees: 6,448
Average Check: Lunch(18); Dinner(30)
Internet Order Processing: Yes
Internet Sales: 0.50%
Total Units: 15
Trade Names: Champps Kitchen & Bar (4); Fox and Hound Bar & Grill (11)
Company-Owned Units: 15
Preferred Square Footage: 7,000; 9,000; 9,600
Preferred Location Types: Freestanding; Strip Mall
Alcohol Served: Beer, Wine, Liquor
Primary Menu: American (15)
Areas of Operation: IL, KS, MI, MN, MS, NC, NJ, NY, OH, TN, TX
Type of Foodservice: Casual Dining (15)
Primary Distributors: (Full Line) Reinhart FoodService, LOUISVILLE, TN
Parent Company: Kelly Companies, SAN DIEGO, CA
Notes: The company derives approximately 5% of its revenue from billiards & other amusement fees.

Key Personnel
STEVE JOHNSON - CEO
KEVIN GARRISON - District Manager
ERIC SMITH - Manager

FreeRange Concepts
8084 Park Ln Ste 145
Dallas, TX 75231-6047

Telephone: (214) 363-2695
Internet Homepage: bowlandbarrel.com
Type of Business: Chain Restaurant Operator
Year Founded: 2012
Total Sales: $7,209,000 (e)
Number of Employees: 250
Total Units: 15
Trade Names: Bowl & Barrel (3); Mutts Canine Cantina (9); The General Public (2); The Rustic (1)
Company-Owned Units: 8
Units Franchised To: 7
Primary Menu: American (15)
Projected Openings: 3
Areas of Operation: CO, TX
Type of Foodservice: Casual Dining (15)

Key Personnel
PETER WHITE - President; COO
JOSHUA SEPKOWITZ - Partner
KYLE NOONAN - Partner
KELLEE BASCHER - VP Marketing
JESSICA SEPKOWITZ - Director Technology
DANIEL MENCHACA - Director Culinary Operations
KARA RAYMOND-COOK - Director Food and Beverage

MITCH MAHAN - Director Finance, Accounting
RICHARD GRAY - Director Technology
WADE HOLDEN - Director Training
KRISTINA BONTRAGER - Regional Director Sales
IRENE PARK - Art Director
INGRID LYNCH - Manager Event Planning
MICHELLE MORRIS - Specialist Human Resources

Gloria's Latin Cuisine
600 N Bishop Ave
Dallas, TX 75208-4358

Mailing Address: 16816 DALLAS PKWY, Dallas, TX, 75248
Telephone: (214) 948-3672
Internet Homepage: gloriascuisine.com
Type of Business: Chain Restaurant Operator
Year Founded: 1986
Total Units: 21
Trade Names: Gloria's Latin Cuisine (21)
Company-Owned Units: 21
Primary Menu: Latin American/Cuban (21)
Projected Openings: 1
Areas of Operation: TX
Type of Foodservice: Casual Dining (21)

Key Personnel
GLORIA FUENTES - Co-Founder; Partner
JOSE FUENTES - Co-Founder; Partner
CARLOS RIVEROLL - Manager Operations; General Buyer

Gloria's Restaurants
5100 Belt Line Rd Ste 864
Dallas, TX 75254-7040

Telephone: (972) 387-8442
Fax Number: (972) 387-8488
Internet Homepage: gloriasrestaurants.com; gloriascuisine.com
Type of Business: Chain Restaurant Operator
Year Founded: 1998
Total Sales: $3,602,000 (e)
Alcohol Sales: 5%
Number of Employees: 143
Average Check: Lunch(18); Dinner(20)
Internet Order Processing: Yes
Total Units: 19
Trade Names: Gloria's (19)
Company-Owned Units: 19
Preferred Location Types: Freestanding
Alcohol Served: Beer, Wine, Liquor
Primary Menu: Mexican (19)
Areas of Operation: TX
Type of Foodservice: Casual Dining (19)
Catering Services: Yes
Primary Distributors: (Full Line) US Foods, LUBBOCK, TX

Key Personnel
JOSE FUENTES - Owner; Executive Chef; General Buyer
BRIAN PENROD - VP Marketing, Communications
CARLOS RIVEROLL - Director Human Resources

H B Restaurants, Inc.
11127 Shady Trl Ste 108
Dallas, TX 75229-4630

Telephone: (972) 554-7270
Fax Number: (972) 554-8528
Internet Homepage: hoffbrausteaks.com
Type of Business: Chain Restaurant Operator
Year Founded: 1990
Total Sales: $13,629,000 (e)
Alcohol Sales: 20%
Number of Employees: 160
Average Check: Lunch(14); Dinner(22)
Total Units: 4
Trade Names: Hoffbrau Steaks (4)
Company-Owned Units: 4
Preferred Square Footage: 5,500; 6,000
Preferred Location Types: Freestanding; Strip Mall
Alcohol Served: Beer, Wine, Liquor
Primary Menu: Steak (4)
Areas of Operation: TX
Type of Foodservice: Casual Dining (4)
Catering Services: Yes
Primary Distributors: (Full Line) US Foods, HOUSTON, TX

Key Personnel
RAINEY FOGIEL - Director Ethnic Marketing, Human Resources

Halal Guys Franchisee Dallas
5444 Lemmon Ave
Dallas, TX 75209-6240

Telephone: (469) 729-9929
Type of Business: Chain Restaurant Operator
Total Units: 3
Trade Names: The Halal Guys (3)
Units Franchised From: 3
Primary Menu: Middle Eastern (3)
Projected Openings: 1
Areas of Operation: TX
Type of Foodservice: Quick Serve (3)
Franchise Affiliation: The Halal Guys Inc., ASTORIA, NY

Key Personnel
DANNY BUI - Owner

Hospitality Management Corp.
17950 Preston Rd Ste 710
Dallas, TX 75252-5637

Telephone: (972) 934-2040
Fax Number: (972) 934-2070
Internet Homepage: hospitalitymgt.com
Type of Business: Foodservice Operations - Hotel/Motels
Year Founded: 1971
Total Sales: $121,610,000 (e)
Alcohol Sales: 20%
Number of Employees: 544
Total Units: 17
Restaurants in Hotels: 17
Trade Names: Best Western (1); Candlewood Suites (1); Crowne Plaza (1); Fredericksburg Inn (1); Hawthorne Suites (2); Holiday Inn Express (1); LaQuinta Inn (2); Microtel (4); Oberlin Inn (1); Premiere Suites (1); Radisson (1); Sheraton (1)
Company-Owned Units: 3
Units Franchised From: 16
Alcohol Served: Beer, Wine, Liquor
Projected Remodelings: 2
Areas of Operation: FL, OH, OK, PA, TX
Type of Foodservice: Casual Dining (17)
Primary Distributors: (Food) SYSCO Food Services of North Texas, LEWISVILLE, TX
Notes: The company derives approximately 80% of its revenue from hotel operations.

Key Personnel
LEO SPRIGGS - CEO; President; General Manager; Executive Chef
BILL SULLIVAN - CFO; Director Information Systems, Menu Development, Food and Beverage; General Buyer
JOHN O'CONNOR - COO
BRADY ARMSTRONG - Area Director Sales
JOE LUCK - Senior VP Development
CHAD COBB - VP Accounting
DEL ROBINETTE - VP Marketing, Sales
RUTHIE JAVIER-PETTIGREW - Director
TYLER CUNNINGHAM - Regional Director Marketing, Sales
JORGE VILLASENOR - Regional Manager Operations

J&F and Sons, LLC
11404 Garland Rd
Dallas, TX 75218-2516

Telephone: (214) 327-8363
Type of Business: Chain Restaurant Operator
Total Sales: $43,100,000 (e)
Total Units: 17
Trade Names: Jack in the Box (17)
Units Franchised From: 17
Primary Menu: Hamburger (17)

Areas of Operation: TX
Type of Foodservice: Quick Serve (17)
Franchise Affiliation: Jack in the Box Restaurants, SAN DIEGO, CA

Key Personnel
CHRISTOPHER ASLAM - Owner; General Buyer

JSP Management LLC
12900 Preston Rd Ste 1111
Dallas, TX 75230-1327

Telephone: (972) 233-0861
Fax Number: (972) 233-9333
Company Email: info@jsp-mcd.com
Type of Business: Chain Restaurant Operator
Year Founded: 1973
Total Sales: $105,790,000 (e)
Number of Employees: 900
Average Check: Breakfast(8); Lunch(8); Dinner(8)
Total Units: 22
Trade Names: McDonald's (22)
Units Franchised From: 22
Preferred Square Footage: 2,500
Preferred Location Types: Discount Dept. Stores; Freestanding
Primary Menu: Hamburger (22)
Areas of Operation: TX
Type of Foodservice: Quick Serve (22)
Franchise Affiliation: McDonald's Corporation, CHICAGO, IL
Primary Distributors: (Food) The Martin-Brower Co., CONROE, TX

Key Personnel
SANDY PHILLIPS - Owner
BRAD SEELEY - Director Operations

La Calle Doce
415 W 12th St
Dallas, TX 75208-6507

Mailing Address: PO Box 4207, DALLAS, TX, 75208-0207
Telephone: (214) 941-4304
Internet Homepage: elranchito-dallas.com; lacalledoce-dallas.com
Company Email: lacalledoce-dallas.com
Type of Business: Chain Restaurant Operator
Year Founded: 1981
Total Sales: $6,090,000 (e)
Alcohol Sales: 35%
Number of Employees: 150
Average Check: Breakfast(10); Lunch(14); Dinner(16)
Total Units: 4
Trade Names: El Ranchito Cafe & Club (2); La Calle Doce (2)
Company-Owned Units: 4

Preferred Location Types: Freestanding
Alcohol Served: Beer, Wine, Liquor
Primary Menu: Mexican (4)
Areas of Operation: TX
Type of Foodservice: Casual Dining (4)
Catering Services: Yes
Primary Distributors: (Full Line) SYSCO Food Services of North Texas, LEWISVILLE, TX

Key Personnel
LAURA SANCHEZ - President; General Buyer
ALMA RUBIO - General Manager

La Madeleine Inc.
12201 Merit Dr Ste 900
Dallas, TX 75251-3139

Telephone: (214) 696-6962
Fax Number: (214) 696-0485
Internet Homepage: lamadeleine.com
Company Email: guestrelations@lamadeleine.com
Type of Business: Chain Restaurant Operator
Year Founded: 1983
Systemwide Sales: $289,848,000 (e)
Total Sales: $166,207,000 (e)
Alcohol Sales: 2%
Number of Employees: 2,300
Average Check: Breakfast(10); Lunch(12); Dinner(14)
Internet Order Processing: Yes
Internet Sales: 10.00%
Total Units: 83
Trade Names: la Madeleine Bakery, Cafe & Bistro (83)
Company-Owned Units: 33
Units Franchised To: 50
Preferred Square Footage: 2,000; 4,000
Preferred Location Types: Downtown; Freestanding; Office Complex; Regional Mall; Strip Mall
Alcohol Served: Beer, Wine
Primary Menu: French/Continental (83)
Areas of Operation: AR, DC, FL, GA, KY, LA, MD, OK, TX, VA
Type of Foodservice: Fast Casual (83)
Catering Services: Yes
Primary Distributors: (Full Line) SYSCO Corporation, HOUSTON, TX
Parent Company: Groupe Le Duff SA, PARIS, FRA
Headquarters: Le Duff America Inc., DALLAS, TX

Key Personnel
JOHN DILLON - President
CHRISTINE JOHNSON - COO
KERRI MCLEROY - Senior Director Marketing
MARK RAMAGE - Senior Director Franchise Development
MIKE LASCOLA - Director Operations
JEFF ERTS - Director Human Resources
CHELSEA FRISBY - Director Operations-Training

Legendary Restaurant Brands LLC
5151 Belt Line Rd Ste 300
Dallas, TX 75254-1456

Telephone: (469) 248-4419
Fax Number: (469) 248-4433
Internet Homepage: bennigans.com
Company Email: info@lrbllc.com
Type of Business: Chain Restaurant Operator
Year Founded: 1976
Systemwide Sales: $188,069,000 (e)
Total Sales: $1,949,000 (e)
Alcohol Sales: 20%
Number of Employees: 1,785
Average Check: Lunch(14); Dinner(20)
Total Units: 13
Trade Names: Bennigan's (10); Bennigan's On The Fly (3)
Company-Owned Units: 5
Units Franchised To: 8
Preferred Square Footage: 1,500; 5,000; 7,000
Preferred Location Types: Airports; Downtown; Freestanding; Hotel/Motel; Regional Mall
Alcohol Served: Beer, Wine, Liquor
Primary Menu: American (13)
Areas of Operation: CA, FL, IA, IL, IN, MD, MI, NJ, OH, TX, VA
Foreign Countries: BAHRAIN; CYPRUS; EL SALVADOR; MEXICO; QATAR; UNITED ARAB EMIRATES
Type of Foodservice: Casual Dining (10); Quick Serve (3)
Parent Company: Legendary Restaurant Brands, DALLAS, TX

Key Personnel
PAUL M. MANGIAMELE - CEO; President; Partner
GWEN MANGIAMELE - Partner; Director Operations
SHAWN FINN - Senior VP Operations
LUCAS DUDLEY - Manager Franchise Operations
YEDID DUDLEY - Manager Training

Liberty Burger Inc.
1904 Abrams Pkwy
Dallas, TX 75214

Telephone: (214) 887-9999
Internet Homepage: givemelibertyburger.com
Company Email: info@givemelibertyburger.com
Type of Business: Chain Restaurant Operator
Year Founded: 2011
Total Units: 6

Trade Names: Liberty Burger (6)
Company-Owned Units: 5
Units Franchised To: 1
Primary Menu: Hamburger (6)
Areas of Operation: TX, WY
Type of Foodservice: Casual Dining (6)

Key Personnel
MARIEL STREET - Owner; General Buyer

Lombardi's Family Concepts
3100 Monticello Ave Ste 325
Dallas, TX 75205-3477

Telephone: (214) 748-5566
Fax Number: (214) 748-6204
Internet Homepage: lombardifamilyconcepts.com
Type of Business: Chain Restaurant Operator
Year Founded: 1979
Total Sales: $52,000,000 (e)
Alcohol Sales: 35%
Number of Employees: 700
Average Check: Lunch(20); Dinner(36)
Internet Order Processing: Yes
Total Units: 15
Trade Names: Bistro 31 (1); KAI (1); Lombardi's Romagna Mia (1); Lounge 31 (1); Penne Pomodoro (3); Taverna (6); Toulouse Cafe and Bar (2)
Company-Owned Units: 15
Preferred Square Footage: 3,000
Preferred Location Types: Community Mall; Freestanding
Alcohol Served: Beer, Wine, Liquor
Primary Menu: Asian (1); French/Continental (2); Italian (7); Japanese (1); Miscellaneous (1); Spanish (2)
Projected Openings: 2
Areas of Operation: CA, NV, TX, FC
Type of Foodservice: Casual Dining (12); Fine Dining (3)
Catering Services: Yes
Primary Distributors: (Full Line) SYSCO Food Services of North Texas, LEWISVILLE, TX

Key Personnel
ALBERTO LOMBARDI - President; Director Supply Chain, Real Estate, Design, Research & Development, Franchising, Store Planning
VIVIAN ESCOBAR-LOMBARDI - Exec VP; Manager Operations, Purchasing, Quality Assurance, Marketing, Training, Product Development, Menu Development
EMMANUEL HODENCQ - Executive Chef

●▲
Maggiano's Little Italy
3000 Olympus Blvd
Dallas, TX 75019

Telephone: (972) 980-9917
Internet Homepage: maggianos.com
Type of Business: Chain Restaurant Operator
Year Founded: 1990
Systemwide Sales: $652,780,000 (e)
Publicly Held: Yes
Total Sales: $505,931,000 (e)
Alcohol Sales: 15%
Number of Employees: 3,000
Average Check: Lunch(32); Dinner(34)
Internet Order Processing: Yes
Internet Sales: 1.00%
Total Units: 52
Trade Names: Maggiano's Little Italy (52)
Company-Owned Units: 50
Units Franchised To: 2
Preferred Square Footage: 7,700; 12,000; 17,000; 24,000
Preferred Location Types: Downtown; Freestanding; Regional Mall
Alcohol Served: Beer, Wine, Liquor
Primary Menu: Italian (52)
Areas of Operation: AZ, CA, CO, DC, FL, GA, IL, IN, MA, MI, MO, NC, NJ, NV, OH, PA, TN, TX, VA, WA, WI
Type of Foodservice: Casual Dining (52)
Catering Services: Yes
Franchise Affiliation: Maggiano's Little Italy, DALLAS, TX
Primary Distributors: (Food) US Foods, GARLAND, TX; (Supplies) The Wasserstrom Co., COLUMBUS, OH
Parent Company: Brinker International Inc., DALLAS, TX

Key Personnel
DOMINIQUE BERTOLONE - President
LARRY KONECNY - Chief Concept Officer; VP
RON RYAN - VP Operations
DAVID DURON - Executive Chef
BROOKE STADTMILLER - Senior Director Human Resources
STACEY HUNTER - Director Finance
BROOKE BURGIEL - Director Human Resources
BETTY CRITES - Manager Marketing
SHERRI BRAST - Manager Talent
ERIN LEWIS - Manager Development
TASHA MULLEN - Manager Sales
MARISA AMMENDOLA - Manager Communications

●▲
McKaren Industries Inc.
4131 N Central Expy Ste 640
Dallas, TX 75204-2117

Telephone: (214) 520-2596
Fax Number: (214) 520-2598
Company Email: mckarenind-mba@yahoo.com
Type of Business: Chain Restaurant Operator
Year Founded: 1995
Total Sales: $72,920,000 (e)
Number of Employees: 660
Average Check: Breakfast(8); Lunch(12); Dinner(12)
Total Units: 15
Trade Names: McDonald's (15)
Units Franchised From: 15
Preferred Square Footage: 2,500; 3,000
Preferred Location Types: Freestanding; Office Complex
Primary Menu: Hamburger (15)
Areas of Operation: TX
Type of Foodservice: Quick Serve (15)
Franchise Affiliation: McDonald's Corporation, CHICAGO, IL
Primary Distributors: (Food) The Martin-Brower Co., CONROE, TX

Key Personnel
KAREN SKINNER - Partner; General Buyer
CRAIG YORK - Partner; VP; General Buyer
TERRI TAYLOR - Controller; Director Finance, Human Resources

Mesa SW Restaurants
14866 Montfort Dr
Dallas, TX 75254

Telephone: (972) 934-0165
Internet Homepage: tacosandtequilatnt.com; bluemesagrill.com
Company Email: info@bluemesagrill.com
Type of Business: Chain Restaurant Operator
Year Founded: 1988
Total Sales: $20,543,000 (e)
Alcohol Sales: 15%
Number of Employees: 177
Average Check: Breakfast(12); Lunch(18); Dinner(24)
Internet Order Processing: Yes
Internet Sales: 1.00%
Total Units: 4
Trade Names: Blue Mesa Grill (3); Taco's & Tequila Grill (1)
Company-Owned Units: 4
Preferred Square Footage: 5,500; 6,000
Preferred Location Types: Freestanding; Strip Mall
Alcohol Served: Beer, Wine, Liquor
Primary Menu: Southwest/Tex-Mex (4)
Areas of Operation: TX
Type of Foodservice: Casual Dining (4)
Catering Services: Yes
Primary Distributors: (Full Line) US Foods, HOUSTON, TX

Key Personnel
JIM BARON - CEO; President; Director Menu Development
LIZ BARON - VP; Director Marketing, Menu Development; Buyer Foodservice Equip/Supplies
CHRISTINA PEW - Manager Accounting

ZAK BARON - Manager

Mike Terry Enterprises
5950 Berkshire Ln Ste 400
Dallas, TX 75225

Telephone: (214) 368-1550
Fax Number: (713) 977-9519
Internet Homepage: mterryenterprises.com; cafe-express.com
Company Email: cafe_comments@cafe-express.com
Type of Business: Chain Restaurant Operator
Year Founded: 1979
Total Sales: $11,880,000 (e)
Alcohol Sales: 10%
Number of Employees: 283
Average Check: Lunch(12); Dinner(12)
Internet Order Processing: Yes
Total Units: 6
Trade Names: Cafe Express (6)
Company-Owned Units: 6
Preferred Square Footage: 4,700; 6,000
Preferred Location Types: Freestanding; Other; Strip Mall
Alcohol Served: Beer, Wine
Primary Menu: American (6)
Areas of Operation: TX
Type of Foodservice: Fast Casual (6)

Key Personnel
MIKE TERRY - CEO; President
PATTY MUNSON - Chief of Staff
KEVIN TRAE TOOKER - VP Finance, Operations
MICHAEL TERRY JR - Director Real Estate

Milkshake Concepts
4000 Elm St
Dallas, TX 75226

Telephone: (469) 708-9892
Internet Homepage: milkshakeconcepts.com
Type of Business: Chain Restaurant Operator
Total Units: 10
Trade Names: Dirty Bones (1); Harper's (1); Layer Cake (1); Serious Pizza (2); Stirr (2); The Finch (1); Vidorra (2)
Company-Owned Units: 10
Primary Menu: American (5); Mexican (2); Pizza (2); Seafood (1)
Areas of Operation: TN, TX
Type of Foodservice: Casual Dining (8); Fast Casual (2)

Key Personnel
JAMES FALLER - Founder; Partner; COO
ASIM SHEIKH - Founder; Partner
IMRAN SHEIKH - Founder; CEO; Partner
BRYAN MCVAY - CFO

MATT SMITH - Chief Marketing Officer

NL Group
1234 Cedar Springs Rd
Dallas, TX 75202

Telephone: (214) 663-4317
Internet Homepage: nlgroup-dallas.com
Company Email: tmceneny@nlgroup-dallas.com
Type of Business: Chain Restaurant Operator
Total Units: 8
Trade Names: Cedar Grove (1); Dakota's Steakhouse (1); DISH (1); Dragonfly (1); Lift (1); obar (1); One Dallas Center Lounge (1); The Front Room (1)
Company-Owned Units: 8
Primary Menu: American (4); Miscellaneous (3); Steak (1)
Areas of Operation: TX
Type of Foodservice: Casual Dining (7); Fine Dining (1)

Key Personnel
TIM MCENENY - Owner; General Buyer

Omni Hotels & Resorts
4001 Maple Ave Ste 500
Dallas, TX 75219-3241

Telephone: (972) 871-5600
Fax Number: (972) 871-5665
Internet Homepage: omnihotels.com
Company Email: info@omnihotels.com
Type of Business: Foodservice Operations - Hotel/Motels
Year Founded: 1958
Total Sales: $95,510,000 (e)
Alcohol Sales: 15%
Number of Employees: 10,560
Total Units: 55
Restaurants in Hotels: 55
Trade Names: Omni Hotel (55)
Company-Owned Units: 55
Alcohol Served: Beer, Wine, Liquor
Projected Remodelings: 5
Areas of Operation: AZ, CA, CO, CT, DC, FL, GA, IL, IN, LA, MA, MO, NC, NH, NY, PA, RI, SC, TN, TX, VA, ON, QC
Foreign Countries: CANADA; MEXICO
Type of Foodservice: Casual Dining (55)
Primary Distributors: (Food) SYSCO Food Services of Houston Inc., HOUSTON, TX
Parent Company: TRT Holdings, IRVING, TX
Notes: The company derives approximately 80% of its revenue from hotel operations.

Key Personnel
JOY ROTHSCHILD - Chief Human Resources Officer
STEPHEN ROSENSTOCK - Senior VP

Business Development, Food and Beverage
RUSTY WALLACE - Regional VP Operations
JENNIE BLAIR - Director Finance
AMBER BUFKIN - Manager Marketing
AMANDA DISORBO - Manager Catering
PAULA DRUMMOND - Manager Sales
PATRICK KENT - Manager Information Systems

Paciugo Franchising L.P.
1215 Viceroy Dr
Dallas, TX 75247-3908

Telephone: (214) 631-2663
Fax Number: (214) 654-9991
Internet Homepage: paciugo.com
Company Email: info@paciugo.com
Type of Business: Chain Restaurant Operator
Year Founded: 2000
Systemwide Sales: $12,603,000 (e)
Total Sales: $3,942,000 (e)
Number of Employees: 153
Average Check: Breakfast(14); Lunch(14); Dinner(14)
Total Units: 32
Trade Names: Paciugo (32)
Units Franchised To: 32
Preferred Square Footage: 800; 1,200
Preferred Location Types: Lifestyle Center; Regional Mall; Strip Mall
Primary Menu: Snacks (32)
Areas of Operation: CA, CO, FL, IL, KS, MA, MD, MN, MT, NV, NY, OH, OK, PA, TX, WA
Type of Foodservice: Quick Serve (32)
Parent Company: Sinelli Concepts, Inc., ,
Notes: The Paciugo Chioso stores are smaller sized and most are co-located in other retail stores.

Key Personnel
JEREMY COOK - VP

Parrish Foods
400 S Zang Blvd Ste 1203
Dallas, TX 75208-6624

Telephone: (214) 941-9172
Fax Number: (214) 941-9280
Company Email: mcd.comments@att.net
Type of Business: Chain Restaurant Operator
Year Founded: 1989
Total Sales: $94,000,000 (e)
Number of Employees: 980
Average Check: Breakfast(8); Lunch(8); Dinner(10)
Total Units: 20
Trade Names: McDonald's (20)
Units Franchised From: 20
Preferred Square Footage: 2,500; 3,000
Preferred Location Types: Freestanding
Primary Menu: Hamburger (20)
Areas of Operation: TX

Type of Foodservice: Quick Serve (20)
Franchise Affiliation: McDonald's Corporation, CHICAGO, IL
Primary Distributors: (Full Line) The Martin-Brower Co. LLC, ROSEMONT, IL

Key Personnel
ROLAND PARRISH - President; Partner; Director Finance, Real Estate; General Buyer
JEWEL PARRISH - Partner
DAWN MARTIN - Director Operations; Manager Information Systems

Pizza Patron Inc.
10999 Petal St Ste 200
Dallas, TX 75238-2424

Telephone: (972) 613-8000
Fax Number: (972) 613-8014
Internet Homepage: pizzapatron.com
Company Email: info@pizzapatron.com
Type of Business: Chain Restaurant Operator
Year Founded: 1986
Systemwide Sales: $64,963,000 (e)
Total Sales: $21,210,000 (e)
Number of Employees: 739
Average Check: Lunch(22); Dinner(28)
Internet Order Processing: Yes
Total Units: 93
Trade Names: Pizza Patron (93)
Company-Owned Units: 11
Units Franchised To: 82
Preferred Square Footage: 800; 900; 1,100; 1,400
Preferred Location Types: Freestanding; Strip Mall
Primary Menu: Pizza (93)
Areas of Operation: AZ, CA, CO, TX
Type of Foodservice: Quick Serve (93)
Foodservice Management Venues: Schools
Catering Services: Yes
Primary Distributors: (Food) Performance Foodservice, DALLAS, TX

Key Personnel
CHARLES M. LOFLIN - CEO; Owner
CHRISTOPHER PARTYKA - President
CHARLOTTE HARGROVE - Controller; Manager Finance, Supply Chain, Human Resources
ERNESTO HERNANDEZ - Director Operations
LOURDES RIVERA - Director Training

Quorum Hotels & Resorts
5429 Lyndon B Johnson Fwy Ste 625
Dallas, TX 75240-2628

Telephone: (972) 458-7265
Fax Number: (972) 991-5647
Internet Homepage: quorumhotels.com
Company Email: admin@quorumhotels.com
Type of Business: Foodservice Operations - Hotel/Motels
Year Founded: 1987
Total Sales: $147,370,000 (e)
Alcohol Sales: 12%
Number of Employees: 750
Total Units: 10
Restaurants in Hotels: 8
Trade Names: Brown Palace (5); Hilton Pavillion (1); Holiday Inn (2); Radisson (1); The Quorum Hotel (1)
Company-Owned Units: 8
Alcohol Served: Beer, Wine, Liquor
Areas of Operation: AZ, CO, FL, TX, VA
Type of Foodservice: Casual Dining (8)
Primary Distributors: (Food) SYSCO Food Services of North Texas, LEWISVILLE, TX; (Specialty Foods) SYSCO Food Services of North Texas, LEWISVILLE, TX
Notes: The company derives approximately 51% of its revenue from hotel operations.

Key Personnel
TONY FARRIS - Chairman; CEO
TED MOSLEY - President; COO; Director Information Systems, Risk Management, Quality Assurance, Recruitment, Food Safety
ROB DRAWBRIDGE - Exec VP Asset Management
PAM MACRAE - VP Human Resources, Training, Recruitment
LINDSAY HOLDER - Regional Director Operations

Red Mango FC LLC
2811 McKinney Ave Ste 354
Dallas, TX 75204-8504

Telephone: (214) 302-5910
Fax Number: (214) 302-5980
Internet Homepage: redmangofranchising.com; redmangousa.com
Company Email: info@redmangousa.com
Type of Business: Chain Restaurant Operator
Systemwide Sales: $29,728,000 (e)
Total Sales: $3,603,000 (e)
Total Units: 53
Trade Names: Red Mango (121)
Units Franchised To: 121
Preferred Square Footage: 600; 1,000; 1,200
Preferred Location Types: Institution (college/hospital); Lifestyle Center; Regional Mall; Stadiums; Strip Mall
Primary Menu: Snacks (121)
Areas of Operation: AL, AR, AZ, CA, CO, CT, FL, GA, IL, IN, KY, LA, MA, MD, MN, MO, MS, NC, NE, NJ, NV, NY, OK, PA, SD, TN, TX, UT, VA, WA, WI
Foreign Countries: MEXICO; URUGUAY
Type of Foodservice: Quick Serve (121)
Parent Company: BRIX Holdings LLC, DALLAS, TX

Key Personnel
BILL CHINN - Owner
RICHARD JENSRUD - CFO
JIM NOTARNICOLA - Chief Marketing Officer; VP Franchise Sales
MITZI BROWN - Chief Legal Officer; Corporate Secretary
YVETTE MARTINEZ - VP Operations
ADRIAN LOMIBAO - General Manager
MOLLY DANIEL - General Manager
LINDSAY CARREKER - Director Design; Manager Branding
RUSS MUSHRO - Director Licensing
CANDY JAMES - Director Quality Assurance, Product Development
JOHNNY TELLEZ - Manager Franchise Development
RYAN WESTERFIELD - Manager Training
MANDY GRIBBLE - Coordinator Franchising

RedBrick Pizza Worldwide, Inc.
2811 McKinney Ave Ste 354
Dallas, TX 75204-8504

Telephone: (214) 302-5912
Internet Homepage: redbrickpizza.com
Company Email: general@redbrickpizza.com
Type of Business: Chain Restaurant Operator
Year Founded: 2001
Systemwide Sales: $10,792,000 (e)
Total Sales: $420,000 (e)
Alcohol Sales: 10%
Number of Employees: 8
Average Check: Lunch(14); Dinner(20)
Total Units: 7
Trade Names: RedBrick Pizza (7)
Units Franchised To: 7
Preferred Square Footage: 1,500
Preferred Location Types: Downtown; Strip Mall
Primary Menu: Pizza (7)
Projected Openings: 25
Areas of Operation: AL, CA, FL, IL, KY, MD, MO, NE, NM, TX
Type of Foodservice: Fast Casual (7)
Catering Services: Yes
Parent Company: BRIX Holdings LLC, DALLAS, TX

Key Personnel
MIGUEL FOEGAL - President; General Buyer
ARNOLDO RESENDEZ - Owner

Rem Inc.
16610 Dallas Pkwy Ste 1200
Dallas, TX 75248-6803

Telephone: (972) 458-0800
Fax Number: (972) 458-0965
Internet Homepage: sambucarestaurant.com

Type of Business: Chain Restaurant Operator
Year Founded: 1991
Total Sales: $18,842,000 (e)
Alcohol Sales: 5%
Number of Employees: 200
Average Check: Lunch(24); Dinner(36)
Internet Order Processing: Yes
Total Units: 3
Trade Names: Sambuca Restaurant (3)
Company-Owned Units: 3
Preferred Square Footage: 5,500; 6,000
Preferred Location Types: Freestanding
Alcohol Served: Beer, Wine, Liquor
Primary Menu: Greek/Mediterranean (3)
Areas of Operation: TN, TX
Type of Foodservice: Fine Dining (3)
Primary Distributors: (Full Line) SYSCO Food Services of North Texas, LEWISVILLE, TX

Key Personnel
KIM FORSYTHE - President; Director Operations, Menu Development; General Buyer
DEBBIE BARBER - CFO
VICKY COLEMAN - Manager Human Resources

Remington Hotel Corp.
14185 Dallas Pkwy Ste 1150
Dallas, TX 75254-4309

Telephone: (972) 980-2700
Fax Number: (972) 980-2705
Internet Homepage: remingtonhotels.com
Company Email: info@remingtonhotels.com
Type of Business: Foodservice Operations - Hotel/Motels
Year Founded: 1968
Total Sales: $463,620,000 (e)
Alcohol Sales: 15%
Number of Employees: 1,350
Total Units: 87
Restaurants in Hotels: 87
Trade Names: Courtyard (7); Crowne Plaza (1); Embassy Suites (10); Fairfield Inn (1); Hampton Inn (8); Hilton (12); Hilton Garden Inn (4); Homewood Suites(1); Hyatt (1); Independents (8); Indigo (1); La Podada De Santa Fe (1); Luxury (5); Marriott (8); One Ocean (1); Renaissance (1); Residence Inn (6); Sheraton(6); Spring Hill Inn & Suites (4); Westin (1)
Company-Owned Units: 87
Alcohol Served: Beer, Wine, Liquor
Areas of Operation: CA, FL, GA, IN, KY, MA, MD, MN, MO, NJ, NV, NY, TX, VA
Type of Foodservice: Casual Dining (87)
Primary Distributors: (Food) SYSCO Corporation, HOUSTON, TX
Notes: The company derives approximately 80% of its revenue from hotel operations.

Key Personnel
ARCHIE BENNETT JR - Chairman
MARK A. SHARKEY - President
SLOAN DEAN - COO
JARRAD J. EVANS - Chief Investment Officer
STAN KENNEDY - Senior VP Operations
ROBERT KING - Senior VP Accounting
HASSAN MAJD - Senior VP Operations
SONNY SRA - Senior VP Marketing, Business Development
BENJAMIN VEGA - Senior VP Optimization
HOMAN CULL - VP Finance
KEITH NEWBY - Controller
JIM COWEN - General Counsel

Remington Hotels
14185 Dallas Pkwy Ste 1100
Dallas, TX 75254-4308

Telephone: (972) 980-2700
Fax Number: (972) 991-6365
Internet Homepage: ahtreit.com
Company Email: info@remingtonhotels.com
Type of Business: Foodservice Operations - Hotel/Motels
Year Founded: 2003
Publicly Held: Yes
Total Sales: $807,670,000 (e)
Alcohol Sales: 15%
Number of Employees: 116
Total Units: 119
Restaurants in Hotels: 119
Trade Names: Courtyard (20); Crowne Plaza (2); Embassy Suites (13); Fairfield Inn (1); Hampton Inn (8); Hilton (9); Hilton Garden Inn (5); Historic Inns of Annapolis (8); Homewood Suites (1); Hyatt (3); Marriott (11); One Ocean (1); Renaissance (2); Residence Inn (13); Ritz Carlton (1); Sheraton (6); Silversmith(1); SpringHill Suites (8); The Churchill (1); The Melrose (1); TownePlace Suites (1); Westin (1); WorldQuest Resort (2)
Company-Owned Units: 119
Alcohol Served: Beer, Wine, Liquor
Projected Remodelings: 3
Areas of Operation: AK, AL, AZ, CA, CO, CT, DC, FL, GA, IL, IN, KS, KY, MA, MD, MN, NC, NE, NJ, NM, NV, NY, OR, PA, TN, TX, UT, VA
Type of Foodservice: Casual Dining; Fine Dining
Headquarter Offices: The Pier House Resort & Caribbean Spa, KEY WEST, FL
Notes: Included in the list of properties are a large number of limited-service hotels & inns. Total sales reflects revenue from hotel operations and excludes revenue from advisory services and other operations. The company derives approximately 84% of its revenue from rooms & other hotel-related operations.

Key Personnel
MONTY J. BENNETT - Chairman
DERIC EUBANKS - CFO
MARK L. NUNNELEY - Chief Accounting Officer
AL GRANHOLM - Senior VP Facility/Maintenance, Loss Prevention
ROBERT KING - Senior VP Accounting
AMY MCDANIEL - Senior VP Administration, Strategic Planning

Rosewood Hotels & Resorts Inc.
500 Crescent Ct Ste 300
Dallas, TX 75201-7861

Telephone: (214) 880-4200
Fax Number: (214) 880-2468
Internet Homepage: rosewoodhotels.com
Company Email: rosewood@rosewood-hotels.com
Type of Business: Foodservice Operations - Hotel/Motels
Year Founded: 1979
Total Sales: $421,250,000 (e)
Alcohol Sales: 5%
Number of Employees: 4,000
Total Units: 19
Restaurants in Hotels: 19
Trade Names: Acqualina, A Rosewood Hotel (2); Caneel Bay, A Rosewood Hotel (1); Cordevalle (2); Georgia, A Rosewood Hotel (1); Hotel Crescent Court, A Rosewood Hotel (2); Inn of the Anasazi (1); King Pacific Lodge (1); Las Ventanas Al Paraiso, A Rosewood Hotel (2); Rosewood Mansion on Peach Tree (1); Rosewood Mansion on Turtle Creek (1); San Miguel (1); San Ysidro Ranch, A Rosewood Hotel (2); Sand Hill, A Rosewood Hotel (1); The Carlyle, A RosewoodHotel (1)
Company-Owned Units: 19
Alcohol Served: Beer, Wine, Liquor
Areas of Operation: CA, FL, NM, NY, TX, VI, BC
Foreign Countries: ANTIGUA; BRITISH VIRGIN ISLANDS; CANADA; JAPAN; MEXICO; SAUDI ARABIA
Type of Foodservice: Fine Dining (19)
Primary Distributors: (Food) SYSCO Food Services of North Texas, LEWISVILLE, TX
Parent Company: Rosewood Corp., DALLAS, TX
Notes: The company derives approximately 80% of its revenue from hotel operations.

Key Personnel
SONIA CHENG - CEO
RADHA ARORA - President
SUSAN ALDRIDGE - Senior VP; General Counsel
PAUL ARNOLD - VP Business Development
FRANCIS LING - VP Finance
IVAN SUARDI - VP Food and Beverage
KIP TOWNSEND - VP Information Technology

TONY MOSCA - Director Food and Beverage

Roy's
13355 Noel Rd Ste 1645
Dallas, TX 75240-6835

Telephone: (949) 261-2424
Fax Number: (972) 644-9490
Internet Homepage: royshawaii.com
Company Email: roysguestservices@roysrestaurant.com
Type of Business: Chain Restaurant Operator
Year Founded: 1988
Systemwide Sales: $25,718,000 (e)
Total Sales: $20,894,000 (e)
Alcohol Sales: 28%
Number of Employees: 375
Average Check: Lunch(36); Dinner(54)
Total Units: 4
Trade Names: Roy's (12)
Company-Owned Units: 12
Preferred Square Footage: 6,000; 7,500
Preferred Location Types: Freestanding; Hotel/Motel; Office Complex; Strip Mall
Alcohol Served: Beer, Wine, Liquor
Primary Menu: Miscellaneous (12)
Areas of Operation: AZ, CA, FL, GU, HI, IL, MD, NV, PA, TX, FC
Type of Foodservice: Fine Dining (12)
Catering Services: Yes
Primary Distributors: (Food) SYSCO Newport Meat Company, IRVINE, CA

Key Personnel
SUNIL DHAROD - CEO; President
JOHN CRAWFORD - COO

Smoothie King Franchises Inc.
9797 Rombauer Rd
Dallas, TX 75019

Telephone: (985) 635-6973
Fax Number: (985) 635-6987
Internet Homepage: smoothieking.com
Company Email: info@smoothieking.com
Type of Business: Chain Restaurant Operator
Year Founded: 1973
Systemwide Sales: $709,274,000 (e)
Total Sales: $34,960,000 (e)
Number of Employees: 60
Average Check: Breakfast(8); Lunch(8); Dinner(8)
Total Units: 1,347
Trade Names: Smoothie King (1,347)
Company-Owned Units: 30
Units Franchised To: 1,317
Preferred Square Footage: 800; 1,200; 1,600
Preferred Location Types: Airports; Community Mall; Downtown; Freestanding; Lifestyle Center; Office Complex; Other; Regional Mall; Strip Mall
Primary Menu: Health Foods (1,347)
Projected Openings: 150
Areas of Operation: AL, AR, AZ, CA, CO, DC, FL, GA, IA, IL, IN, KS, KY, LA, MA, MD, MI, MO, MS, NC, NJ, NM, NV, NY, OH, OK, RI, SC, SD, TN, TX, VA, WI
Foreign Countries: CAYMAN ISLANDS; SINGAPORE; SOUTH KOREA
Type of Foodservice: Quick Serve (1,347)
Foodservice Management Venues: Health Care; Military Feeding; Schools
Catering Services: Yes
Primary Distributors: (Food) Vistar Rocky Mountain, DENVER, CO; (Supplies) Vistar Rocky Mountain, DENVER, CO

Key Personnel
WAN KIM - Chairman; CEO
THOMAS KIM - CFO
GAVIN FELDER - CFO
CAMILLE HYMES - COO
LAURA SCAVONE - Chief People Officer
JYOTI LYNCH - CIO
MARIANNE RADLEY - Chief Marketing Officer
JOSH NICOSIA - Chief Legal Officer
MIKE POWERS - Exec VP Business Development
KATHERINE MEARIMAN - VP Human Resources, Training
ROCKY GETTYS - VP Product Development
BARBARA MAYRAND - VP Purchasing, Supply Chain
MATT KAFKA - VP Operations
SHAWN CARIC - VP Franchise Development
ROBBIE BANKSTON - Director Training
ANDREA WITT - Director Real Estate
JESSICA ROQUES - Director Development
LORI PRIMAVERA - Director Marketing
CHRIS DE WOLFF - Director Real Estate
CYNTHIA TURNER - Regional Director Franchise Operations
ALEXANDRIA SNYDER - Manager Purchasing, Logistics
JAN KELLY - Manager
JEFFERSON DUNN - Manager Construction

Sonny Bryan's Smoke House
12720 Hillcrest Rd Ste 910
Dallas, TX 75230-7103

Telephone: (214) 350-1800
Fax Number: (214) 350-3738
Internet Homepage: sonnybryans.com
Type of Business: Chain Restaurant Operator
Year Founded: 1910
Total Sales: $6,035,000 (e)
Alcohol Sales: 2%
Number of Employees: 117
Average Check: Lunch(20); Dinner(24)
Internet Order Processing: Yes
Internet Sales: 2.00%
Total Units: 5
Trade Names: Sonny Bryan's Smoke House (5)
Company-Owned Units: 5
Preferred Square Footage: 750; 5,000
Preferred Location Types: Freestanding; Strip Mall
Alcohol Served: Beer, Wine, Liquor
Primary Menu: Bar-B-Q (5)
Areas of Operation: TX
Type of Foodservice: Casual Dining (5)
Catering Services: Yes
Primary Distributors: (Food) Ben E. Keith Foods, FORT WORTH, TX

Key Personnel
WALKER G. HARMAN SR - Chairman
BRENT E. HARMAN - CEO; President; Director Purchasing, Menu Development
TOMMY ZAPATA - Senior VP Operations; Director Operations, Training, Catering
BETH SQUIRE - Executive Assistant

Souper Salad Inc.
2811 McKinney Ave Ste 354
Dallas, TX 75204-8504

Telephone: (214) 302-5920
Internet Homepage: brixholdings.com; soupersalad.com
Type of Business: Chain Restaurant Operator
Year Founded: 1978
Total Sales: $12,320,000 (e)
Number of Employees: 882
Average Check: Breakfast(6); Lunch(8); Dinner(8)
Internet Order Processing: Yes
Total Units: 10
Trade Names: Souper Salad (18)
Company-Owned Units: 7
Units Franchised To: 11
Preferred Square Footage: 3,800; 4,200; 5,000
Preferred Location Types: Community Mall; Convenience Store/Gas Station; Freestanding; Lifestyle Center; Office Complex; Outlet Mall; Strip Mall
Primary Menu: American (18)
Areas of Operation: AZ, CO, ID, NC, NM, TX
Type of Foodservice: Fast Casual (18)
Catering Services: Yes
Primary Distributors: (Full Line) Labatt Food Service, SAN ANTONIO, TX
Parent Company: BRIX Holdings LLC, DALLAS, TX

Key Personnel
CRAIG ERLICH - CEO; President
JIM NOTARNICOLA - Chief Marketing Officer; VP Franchise Sales
MITZI BROWN - Chief Legal Officer
YVETTE MARTINEZ - VP Operations
MICHELLE VELEZ - Director Purchasing

Spaghetti Warehouse Restaurants Inc.
1815 N Market St
Dallas, TX 75202-1809

Telephone: (972) 536-2002
Internet Homepage: meatballs.com
Company Email: info@meatballs.com
Listing Type: Subsidiary
Type of Business: Chain Restaurant Operator
Year Founded: 1972
Systemwide Sales: $39,563,000 (e)
Total Sales: $40,020,000 (e)
Alcohol Sales: 8%
Number of Employees: 1,065
Average Check: Lunch(8); Dinner(14)
Internet Order Processing: Yes
Total Units: 8
Trade Names: The Spaghetti Warehouse (8)
Company-Owned Units: 8
Preferred Square Footage: 5,500; 6,000
Preferred Location Types: Downtown; Freestanding
Alcohol Served: Beer, Wine, Liquor
Primary Menu: Italian (8)
Areas of Operation: NY, OH, OK, PA, TN, TX
Type of Foodservice: Casual Dining (8)
Catering Services: Yes
Primary Distributors: (Full Line) SYSCO Central Texas Inc., NEW BRAUNFELS, TX
Parent Company: BLD Brands, NEWPORT BEACH, CA

Key Personnel
DOUG PAK - CEO; General Buyer
SHAWN RICHARDS - Manager Operations, Information Technology

SSCP Management
13355 Noel Rd Ste 1645
Dallas, TX 75240-6835

Telephone: (972) 644-9494
Fax Number: (972) 644-9490
Internet Homepage: sscpmanagement.com; roysrestaurant.com
Company Email: info@cspsinc.com
Type of Business: Chain Restaurant Operator
Year Founded: 1993
Total Sales: $329,050,000 (e)
Alcohol Sales: 10%
Number of Employees: 4,834
Total Units: 122
Trade Names: Applebees (70); Roy's (5); Sonic America's Drive-In (47)
Company-Owned Units: 5
Units Franchised From: 117
Preferred Square Footage: 2,500; 4,000; 4,700; 5,500
Preferred Location Types: Freestanding
Alcohol Served: Beer, Wine, Liquor
Primary Menu: American (0); American (-29); Miscellaneous (75)
Areas of Operation: TX
Type of Foodservice: Casual Dining (70); Fine Dining (5); Quick Serve (47)
Franchise Affiliation: Applebee's Services Inc., KANSAS CITY, MO; Sonic Corp., OKLAHOMA CITY, OK
Primary Distributors: (Full Line) McLane/Fort Worth, FORT WORTH, TX

Key Personnel
CHRIS DHAROD - President
DAN PATEL - CFO
MELANIE BARICHIVICH - Senior VP Marketing
CHERYL GREEN - VP Human Resources
KERRY NORTON - VP Operations
BLAKE ROE - Senior Director Marketing
THOMAS HOOKE - Director Real Estate
KERRY ASSA - Director Real Estate
KRISTA DORSETT - Manager
PUJA DHAROD - Specialist Marketing

St. Martin's Wine Bistro
3020 Greenville Ave
Dallas, TX 75206-6030

Telephone: (214) 826-0940
Fax Number: (214) 826-1229
Internet Homepage: arthursdallas.com; stmartinswinebistro.com
Type of Business: Chain Restaurant Operator
Year Founded: 1948
Total Sales: $8,106,000 (e)
Alcohol Sales: 20%
Number of Employees: 90
Average Check: Dinner(60)
Total Units: 2
Trade Names: Arthur's Prime Steaks & Seafood (1); St. Martin's Wine Bistro (1)
Company-Owned Units: 2
Preferred Location Types: Freestanding
Alcohol Served: Beer, Wine, Liquor
Primary Menu: French/Continental (1); Steak/Seafood (1)
Areas of Operation: TX
Type of Foodservice: Fine Dining (2)
Primary Distributors: (Full Line) FreshPoint Dallas, DALLAS, TX

Key Personnel
MOHSEN HEIDARI - President; General Manager; General Buyer
ALFREDO SANTAMARIA - Executive Chef; General Buyer

Star Concessions
7929 Brookriver Dr Ste 200
Dallas, TX 75247-4945

Telephone: (214) 353-3959
Fax Number: (214) 353-3963
Internet Homepage: starcons.com
Company Email: info@starcons.com
Type of Business: Foodservice Management Operator
Year Founded: 1995
Total Sales: $38,138,000 (e)
Number of Employees: 600
Number of Locations Served: 60
Total Foodservice Mgmt Accounts: 20
Trade Names: Campisi's Italian Restauran; Cantina Laredo; Chili's too; Cinnabon; Cool River Cafe; Pizza Hut; Taco Bell; Whataburger
Areas of Operation: TX
Type of Foodservice: Quick Serve (20)
Foodservice Management Venues: Transportation
Franchise Affiliation: Chili's Grill & Bar, DALLAS, TX; Pizza Hut Inc., PLANO, TX; Taco Bell Corp., IRVINE, CA

Key Personnel
GILBERT ARANZA - CEO; President; General Buyer
MOLLIE STANDRIDGE - VP; Manager Human Resources
TERRI VAN HOOSER - Controller
DARLENE LANDER - Manager Human Resources

Stephan Pyles Concepts
2330 Flora St
Dallas, TX 75201

Telephone: (214) 580-7000
Internet Homepage: stampede66.com; stephanpyles.com
Company Email: info@stephanpyles.com
Type of Business: Chain Restaurant Operator
Average Check: Lunch(36); Dinner(60)
Total Units: 2
Trade Names: Floral Street Cafe (1); Stampede 66 (1)
Company-Owned Units: 2
Preferred Location Types: Freestanding; Strip Mall
Alcohol Served: Beer, Wine, Liquor
Primary Menu: Miscellaneous (1); Southwest/Tex-Mex (1)
Areas of Operation: TX
Type of Foodservice: Fine Dining (2)
Catering Services: Yes

Key Personnel
STEPHAN PYLES - Partner; Executive Chef; General Buyer
GEORGE MAJDALANI - Partner; General Buyer

Stock In Trade Restaurant Group
7034 Irongate Ln
Dallas, TX 75214

Telephone: (817) 410-7444
Internet Homepage: stockintraderg.com
Company Email: hello@stockintraderg.com
Type of Business: Chain Restaurant Operator
Year Founded: 2015
Total Units: 4
Trade Names: Unleavened Fresh Kitchen (4)
Company-Owned Units: 4
Primary Menu: American (4)
Areas of Operation: TX
Type of Foodservice: Casual Dining (4)

Key Personnel
TOM DYNAN - Partner

Studio Movie Grill
12404 Park Central Dr Ste 400n
Dallas, TX 75251

Telephone: (469) 405-8529
Fax Number: (214) 751-3980
Internet Homepage: studiomoviegrill.com
Company Email: info@studiomoviegrill.com
Type of Business: Foodservice Operations - Movie Theatre
Year Founded: 1999
Total Sales: $19,980,000 (e)
Number of Employees: 132
Average Check: Dinner(6)
Total Units: 33
Trade Names: Studio Movie Grill (33)
Company-Owned Units: 33
Preferred Square Footage: 41,300
Preferred Location Types: Downtown; Freestanding; Strip Mall
Alcohol Served: Beer, Wine, Liquor
Primary Menu: American (33)
Projected Openings: 3
Areas of Operation: AZ, CA, FL, GA, IL, IN, NC, OH, PA, TX
Type of Foodservice: Casual Dining (33)

Key Personnel
BRIAN HOOD - COO
JUSTIN CATES - Area Director
CHRISTOPHER ROBERSON - Senior VP Information Technology
TED LOW - VP Marketing
THAD KELLEY - Executive Chef; Director Food and Beverage
SHERI LAWRENCE - Senior Director
RICK MANRIQUEZ - Director Security
KAREN SIBLEY - Manager Operations
DAWN STANLEY - Manager Sales
ELIZABETH KEELER - Project Manager

Information Technology

Subway Franchise
6760 Abrams Rd Ste 109
Dallas, TX 75231

Telephone: (214) 553-9300
Internet Homepage: subway.com
Type of Business: Chain Restaurant Operator
Total Sales: $2,194,000 (e)
Total Units: 3
Trade Names: Subway (3)
Units Franchised From: 3
Primary Menu: Sandwiches/Deli (3)
Areas of Operation: TX
Type of Foodservice: Quick Serve (3)
Franchise Affiliation: Doctor's Associates Inc., MILFORD, CT

Key Personnel
PANKAJ PATEL - Owner; General Buyer

Sun Holdings LLC
4055 Valley View Ln Ste 500
Dallas, TX 75244-5048

Telephone: (972) 620-2287
Internet Homepage: sunholdings.net
Listing Type: Corporate Office
Type of Business: Chain Restaurant Operator
Year Founded: 1997
Total Sales: $1,933,753,000 (e)
Alcohol Sales: 2%
Number of Employees: 12,290
Average Check: Breakfast(10); Lunch(14); Dinner(16)
Total Units: 1,175
Trade Names: Applebee's Neighborhood Grill & Bar (132); Arby's (229); Burger King (141); Cici's Pizza (32); Golden Corral Buffet & Grill (6); IHOP Restaurant (36); Krispy Kreme Doughnuts (18); McAlister's Deli (73); Papa Johns (218); Popeyes Louisiana Kitchen (160); Taco Bueno (130)
Company-Owned Units: 5
Units Franchised From: 1,170
Preferred Square Footage: 2,000; 2,500; 3,000; 4,000; 5,000; 7,800; 10,300; 11,500
Preferred Location Types: Airports; Freestanding
Alcohol Served: Beer, Wine, Liquor
Primary Menu: American (174); Bagels (0); Bar-B-Q (0); Chicken (160); French/Continental (0); Hamburger (141); Mexican (0); Pizza (250); Sandwiches/Deli (302); Snacks (18); Taco (130)
Areas of Operation: AL, FL, GA, IN, OK, TN, TX
Type of Foodservice: Casual Dining (132); Family Restaurant (74); Fast Casual (73); Quick Serve (896)

Catering Services: Yes
Franchise Affiliation: Arby's Restaurant Group, ATLANTA, GA; Burger King Worldwide Inc., MIAMI, FL; CiCi Enterprises L.P., COPPELL, TX; Golden Corral Corp., RALEIGH, NC; Krispy Kreme Doughnut Corporation, CHARLOTTE, NC; Popeyes Louisiana Kitchen Inc., ATLANTA, GA
Primary Distributors: (Full Line) McLane/Fort Worth, FORT WORTH, TX
Headquarter Offices: RMH Franchise, ATLANTA, GA; Taco Bueno Restaurants LP, FARMERS BRANCH, TX
Notes: The Arby's restaurants operate as Turbo Restaurants LLC. Krispy Kreme restaurants operate as Dulce Restaurants LLC.

Key Personnel
GUILLERMO PERALES - CEO; President; CFO; VP Purchasing
FREDERICK DREIBHOLZ - CFO
COLLIN THOMPSON - CFO
DAVID FABIAN - Chief Development Officer
TIMOTHY COMER - Chief Legal Officer
JIMMY DANG - VP Information Technology
TIM EMERSON - VP Finance
DIONNA JEFFREY - VP Operations, Division
JOSE REYES - VP Operations, Division
ANTHONY SCHLEMMER - VP Operations, Division
SARAHI PADILLA - Controller
RAFAEL RAMOS - Director Operations
OMAR SANTIAGO - Director Risk Management, Employee Benefits
LAURA MCLAND - Director Human Resources
HEATHER NORTON - Director Sales
TOPPER SEIFERTH - District Manager
JEFF WOOD - District Manager
PALOMA MACIAS - Manager Accounting
JULIE FARR - Manager Construction
ERNESTO PEREZ - Project Manager

SWH Mimi's Cafe Holding Company Inc.
12201 Merit Dr Ste 900
Dallas, TX 75251-3122

Telephone: (866) 926-6636
Internet Homepage: mimiscafe.com
Company Email: mail@mimiscafe.com
Type of Business: Chain Restaurant Operator
Year Founded: 1978
Systemwide Sales: $177,082,000 (e)
Total Sales: $194,860,000 (e)
Alcohol Sales: 4%
Number of Employees: 8,800
Average Check: Breakfast(12); Lunch(12); Dinner(14)
Internet Order Processing: Yes
Internet Sales: 15.00%
Total Units: 43
Trade Names: Mimi's Bistro + Bakery (43)
Company-Owned Units: 43

Preferred Square Footage: 6,000; 6,475; 7,000
Preferred Location Types: Freestanding; Lifestyle Center
Alcohol Served: Beer, Wine, Liquor
Primary Menu: American (43)
Areas of Operation: AR, AZ, CA, CO, FL, GA, KY, MO, NC, NM, NV, OH, TN, TX, UT, VA
Type of Foodservice: Casual Dining (43)
Distribution Centers: IRVINE, CA
On-site Distribution Center: Yes
Primary Distributors: (Full Line) PFG - Customized California, SHAFTER, CA
Parent Company: Le Duff America Inc., DALLAS, TX

Key Personnel
MARINA DANIELS - VP Operations
ERIC HERNANDEZ - Manager

T.G.I. Friday's Inc.
19111 Dallas Pkwy Ste 165
Dallas, TX 75287-3199

Telephone: (972) 662-5400
Fax Number: (972) 662-5505
Internet Homepage: fridays.com
Company Email: internetmail@fridays.com
Type of Business: Chain Restaurant Operator
Year Founded: 1965
Systemwide Sales: $2,267,907,000 (e)
Total Sales: $1,671,090,000 (e)
Alcohol Sales: 20%
Number of Employees: 24,800
Total Units: 164
Trade Names: T.G.I. Friday's (164)
Company-Owned Units: 65
Units Franchised To: 99
Preferred Square Footage: 5,500; 7,000; 7,600
Preferred Location Types: Airports; Community Mall; Downtown; Freestanding; Hotel/Motel; Lifestyle Center; Mobile Unit; Parks; Regional Mall; Stadiums; Strip Mall
Alcohol Served: Beer, Wine, Liquor
Primary Menu: American (164)
Areas of Operation: AK, AL, AR, AZ, CA, CO, CT, DC, DE, FL, GA, GU, IA, ID, IL, IN, KS, KY, MA, MD, ME, MI, MN, MO, MS, NC, ND, NE, NH, NJ, NM, NV, NY, OH, OK, OR, PA, PR, RI, SC, SD, TN, TX, UT, VA, VT, WA, WI, WV, BC, NS, ON
Foreign Countries: AFGHANISTAN; ARGENTINA; ARUBA; AUSTRALIA; AUSTRIA; BAHRAIN; BARBADOS; BELARUS; CANADA; CHILE; CHINA; COLOMBIA; COSTA RICA; CYPRUS; CZECH REPUBLIC; DOMINICAN REPUBLIC; ECUADOR; EGYPT; EL SALVADOR; ENGLAND; GREECE; GUATEMALA; HONDURAS; HONG KONG; HUNGARY; ICELAND; INDIA; INDONESIA; IRELAND; JAMAICA; JAPAN; JORDAN; KUWAIT; LATVIA; LEBANON; MALAYSIA; MEXICO; NICARAGUA; NORWAY; OMAN; PANAMA; PARAGUAY; PERU; POLAND; QATAR; RUSSIA; SAUDI ARABIA; SCOTLAND; SINGAPORE; SOUTH KOREA; SPAIN; SWEDEN; TAIWAN; THE PHILIPPINES; TRINIDAD & TOBAGO; UKRAINE; UNITED ARAB EMIRATES; VENEZUELA; WALES
Type of Foodservice: Casual Dining (164)
Foodservice Management Venues: Schools
Catering Services: Yes
Primary Distributors: (Full Line) Performance Foodservice - Victoria, VICTORIA, TX
Parent Company: Sentinel Capital Holdings, NEW YORK, NY

Key Personnel
KATIE KNIGHT - Chief Revenue Officer
ROHIT MANOCHA - Chairman; CEO Interim
WELDON SPANGLER - CEO
RAY RISLEY - President United States; COO
NIK RUPP - President International; CFO
BILL ALEXANDER - Chief Development Officer; Senior VP
CHRIS DEVLIN - Chief Development Officer
KATHLEEN SCHLOTH - VP Supply Chain
SAMMY LANGLEY - VP Information Technology
JAY HORNACEK - VP; Global Operations
JEFF MORAN - VP Accounting
TRES WHITLEY - VP Licensing
ANDRES TREJO - VP Finance; Corporate Controller
LEANNE STENDELL - General Counsel
CHIP BUNDICK - General Counsel International
CHRIS HANSEN - Senior Director Digital
JEFF HUMPHREY - Senior Director Financial Planning
DENNY GUERRERO - Senior Director Finance, International
KATHY MCINTYRE-PETO - Director Innovation
ROBERT FREEMAN - Director Marketing
SILVIA FLORES - Director Marketing
RYAN GOODMAN - Director Accounting
TANYA STEARNS - Director Marketing
ROBERT TIJERINA - Director Supply Chain, Global
REGINALD EVERS - Director Operations
COREY DAY - Director Operations
KEVIN MURTAGH - Director Operations
JENI BAILEY - Director Operations
RAY SCHOLLMEYER - Director Operations
RYAN MCLAUGHLIN - Director Operations
VINODH KAMARAJ - Director Software Development
YVETTE ENCALADA - Senior Manager Digital Marketing
CHRISTINA DAVENPORT - Manager Real Estate
RYAN ANZALDUA - Manager Operations, Development
JENNIFER CLAYBAUGH - Manager Digital Marketing, Media
KATHLEEN SIMPSON - Manager Safety, Global-Food
CHRISTOPHER THARP - Manager

Texas de Brazil
2952 N Stemmons Fwy
Dallas, TX 75247-6113

Telephone: (214) 615-2184
Fax Number: (214) 720-3854
Internet Homepage: texasdebrazil.com
Company Email: customerrelations@texasdebrazil.com
Type of Business: Chain Restaurant Operator
Year Founded: 1998
Total Sales: $19,350,000 (e)
Alcohol Sales: 15%
Number of Employees: 707
Average Check: Breakfast(36); Lunch(36); Dinner(66)
Total Units: 62
Trade Names: Texas de Brazil Churrascaria (62)
Company-Owned Units: 62
Preferred Square Footage: 2,500
Preferred Location Types: Freestanding
Alcohol Served: Beer, Wine, Liquor
Primary Menu: Steak (62)
Projected Openings: 2
Areas of Operation: CA, CO, FL, IL, KY, LA, MI, MO, NV, NY, OH, OK, PA, PR, TN, TX, UT, VA, WA, FC
Foreign Countries: ARUBA; MEXICO; SOUTH KOREA; SPAIN; TRINIDAD & TOBAGO; UNITED ARAB EMIRATES
Type of Foodservice: Casual Dining (62)
Primary Distributors: (Full Line) SYSCO Food Services of North Texas, LEWISVILLE, TX

Key Personnel
SALAH IZZEDIN - Chairman; CEO
LEILA IZZEDIN - President
SALIM ASRAWI - COO
JAD IZZEDIN - Executive Director
ED RIFKIN - Controller; Manager Finance
ANIL SEKHRI - Director Operations
HANNAH T - Director Marketing, Public Relations
HANNAH THOMPSON - Director Public Relations
DANIELLE GOODGION - Director Human Resources

The International Culinary School Dallas
8080 Park Ln Ste 100
Dallas, TX 75231-5900

Telephone: (214) 692-8080
Internet Homepage: artinstitutes.edu/dallas
Company Email: aidadm@aii.edu
Type of Business: Culinary Schools

Areas of Operation: TX

Key Personnel
GINA QUINN - President

The Saxton Group
7859 Walnut Hill Ln Ste 375
Dallas, TX 75230-5632

Telephone: (214) 373-3400
Fax Number: (214) 373-3403
Internet Homepage: thesaxtongroup.com
Type of Business: Chain Restaurant Operator
Year Founded: 1982
Total Sales: $33,460,000 (e)
Number of Employees: 3,600
Average Check: Lunch(10); Dinner(10)
Total Units: 67
Trade Names: McAlister's Deli (67)
Units Franchised From: 67
Preferred Square Footage: 3,000; 3,800
Preferred Location Types: Freestanding; Strip Mall
Primary Menu: Sandwiches/Deli (67)
Projected Openings: 40
Areas of Operation: KS, MO, OK, TX
Type of Foodservice: Fast Casual (67)
Catering Services: Yes
Franchise Affiliation: McAlister's Corporation, ATLANTA, GA
Primary Distributors: (Full Line) McLane/Rocky Mount, ROCKY MOUNT, NC

Key Personnel
KELLY SAXTON - Chairman; President
MATT SAXTON - Co-CEO
ADAM SAXTON - Co-CEO
MICHAEL BAMBACH - VP Information Technology
MATT HESTON - VP People
MAX JODRY - VP Finance
STEPHEN LEE - VP
ADDISON MCALISTERS - General Manager
CHRIS FAHRNEY - General Manager
PHILLIP PANTLEO - General Manager
JOEL OONK - Director Region
SEAN ADAMS - Regional Director Operations
WAYNE ANDERSEN - Regional Director Operations
CHASE KELLY - Regional Director Operations
EMILY OLIVE - Area Manager Catering
CHRIS GUERRERO - Manager Recruitment

The Smoothie Factory Inc.
2811 McKinney Ave Ste 354
Dallas, TX 75204-8504

Telephone: (214) 302-5979
Internet Homepage: smoothiefactory.com
Company Email: info@smoothiefactory.com
Type of Business: Chain Restaurant Operator
Year Founded: 1996
Total Sales: $15,480,000 (e)
Total Units: 28
Trade Names: Smoothie Factory (28)
Company-Owned Units: 28
Primary Menu: Snacks (28)
Areas of Operation: AZ, CO, FL, GA, IL, LA, MO, NJ, TX, NL
Foreign Countries: CANADA; CHINA; INDIA; SAUDI ARABIA; VIETNAM
Type of Foodservice: Quick Serve (28)
Parent Company: BRIX Holdings LLC, DALLAS, TX

Key Personnel
JOHN ANTICOCO - Chairman
MIGUEL FOEGAL - President

TopGolf International, Inc.
8750 N Central Expy Ste 1200
Dallas, TX 75231-6430

Telephone: (214) 377-0615
Internet Homepage: topgolf.com
Type of Business: Nontraditional Foodservice Operator
Year Founded: 2000
Publicly Held: Yes
Total Sales: $2,635,796,000 (e)
Total Units: 89
Trade Names: TopGolf (89)
Company-Owned Units: 89
Preferred Location Types: Freestanding; Hotel/Motel
Alcohol Served: Beer, Wine, Liquor
Primary Menu: American (89)
Projected Openings: 10
Areas of Operation: AL, AZ, CA, CO, FL, GA, IL, IN, KS, LA, MI, MN, MO, NC, NJ, NV, OH, OK, OR, PA, TN, TX, UT, VA
Foreign Countries: AUSTRALIA; ENGLAND
Type of Foodservice: Casual Dining (89)

Key Personnel
ERIK J. ANDERSON - Co-Chairman
ARTIE STARRS - CEO
BEN SHARPE - President Division
GENIFER GRAY - COO
KRISTI MAYNOR - Chief People Officer
MARYAM MORSE - Chief People Officer
GEOFF COTTRILL - Chief Marketing Officer
J. C. CALLAWAY - Chief Development Officer
RODNEY FERRELL - VP Strategic Planning
KEVIN MINER - VP Construction, Design
LLOYD CARMACK - VP Supply Chain
MYNOR GONZALEZ - VP Finance
DAN GIBBONS - Director Facility/Maintenance
RACHEL RYPEL - Director Sales
ROSS BEATON - Director International
DANIELLE DEFALCO - Director Operations
MATT SMITH - Director Real Estate
SHAUN SINNOTT - Director Digital Marketing
AMY STEVENS - Director Technology, Innovation
BRANDON GABAY - Senior Manager Marketing
MIKE ZVOLANEK - Manager Infrastructure

Twin Restaurant Holding LLC
5151 Belt Line Rd Ste 1200
Dallas, TX 75254-7858

Telephone: (972) 941-3150
Internet Homepage: twinpeaksrestaurant.com
Company Email: info@twinpeaksmerch.com
Listing Type: Subsidiary
Type of Business: Chain Restaurant Operator
Year Founded: 2005
Systemwide Sales: $378,732,000 (e)
Total Sales: $171,620,000 (e)
Alcohol Sales: 48%
Internet Order Processing: Yes
Total Units: 91
Trade Names: Twin Peaks Restaurant (91)
Company-Owned Units: 30
Units Franchised To: 61
Preferred Square Footage: 5,000; 6,500; 8,000
Alcohol Served: Beer, Liquor
Primary Menu: American (91)
Projected Openings: 2
Areas of Operation: AL, AR, AZ, CA, CO, FL, GA, IA, ID, IL, KS, LA, MI, MO, MS, NC, NE, NM, NV, OK, SC, TN, TX, WA, FC
Foreign Countries: RUSSIA
Type of Foodservice: Casual Dining (91)
Parent Company: Fat Brands, Inc., BEVERLY HILLS, CA

Key Personnel
JOE HUMMEL - CEO
SCOTT GRAY - CFO
ROGER GONDEK - COO
MIKE LOCEY - Chief Development Officer
CLAY MINGUS - Chief Legal Officer
GLENN MOON - VP Franchise Development
TOM WEISHEYER - VP Operations
ALEX SADOWSKY - Executive Chef
PAUL STEVENS - Senior Director Development, Design
JERRY YUHASZ - Senior Director Information Technology
PATRICK ROSO - Senior Director Purchasing-Food
LEXI BURNS - Director Training
MARK RAMAGE - Director Franchise Development, Franchise Sales
MEGHAN COLLUM - Manager Marketing

Vandelay Hospitality Group
3838 Oak Lawn Ave
Dallas, TX 75219

Telephone: (469) 567-3125
Internet Homepage: vandelayhospitality.com

Type of Business: Chain Restaurant Operator
Year Founded: 2012
Total Units: 14
Trade Names: Brentwood (1); D.L. Mack's (3); Drake's Hollywood (3); Hudson House (7)
Company-Owned Units: 14
Primary Menu: American (14)
Type of Foodservice: Casual Dining (3); Fine Dining (11)

Key Personnel
JAMES DOUGLAS - Chief Culinary Officer
HUNTER POND - Founder; CEO
KYLE BROOKS - Founder; Partner
MATT MCCLAIN - Partner; Director Real Estate
RICK DUNLAP - Partner; Director
WES FREEMAN - Partner; VP Construction
KENDALL HELFENBEIN - CFO
ANGELA BAIRD - VP Human Resources
CHRISSIE NEMETH - VP
MARC MESSINA - Director Operations
DIMPLE PATEL - Director Finance

Velvet Taco
5151 Belt Line Rd Ste 1200
Dallas, TX 75254

Telephone: (972) 941-3150
Internet Homepage: velvettaco.com
Company Email: recruiting@velvettaco.com
Type of Business: Chain Restaurant Operator
Year Founded: 2011
Total Sales: $30,640,000 (e)
Total Units: 35
Trade Names: Velvet Taco (35)
Company-Owned Units: 35
Primary Menu: Taco (35)
Projected Openings: 1
Areas of Operation: IL, TX
Type of Foodservice: Fast Casual (35)
Parent Company: FB Society, DALLAS, TX

Key Personnel
CLAY DOVER - CEO
WILLIAM DAVENPORT - CFO
MICHAEL PEREIRA - COO
HEATHER MCINTOSH - VP Talent, People
STEPHEN WALL - VP Development, Construction
BROOKE PERRY - VP Marketing
CASSIE COOPER - Director Marketing
DIANA HERNANDEZ - Regional Manager People; Manager People
SARA WALKER - Manager Training
TONY A. WILSON JR - Manager Operations
JESSE WORTHINGTON - Manager Digital Marketing

Waugh Enterprises
10903 Alder Cir
Dallas, TX 75238-1354

Telephone: (214) 349-9600
Fax Number: (214) 349-9427
Internet Homepage: burgerstreet.com
Company Email: customerservice@burgerstreet.com
Type of Business: Chain Restaurant Operator
Year Founded: 1985
Total Sales: $36,648,000 (e)
Number of Employees: 200
Average Check: Lunch(14); Dinner(14)
Total Units: 19
Trade Names: Burger Street (19)
Company-Owned Units: 19
Preferred Square Footage: 2,500
Preferred Location Types: Freestanding
Primary Menu: Hamburger (19)
Areas of Operation: OK, TX
Type of Foodservice: Quick Serve (19)
Catering Services: Yes
Primary Distributors: (Full Line) SYSCO Food Services of North Texas, LEWISVILLE, TX

Key Personnel
LIWEI WAUGH - CEO; President; General Buyer
JEREMIAS REBEL - Director Operations

Which Wich Inc.
1412 Main St Ste 2000
Dallas, TX 75202-4087

Telephone: (214) 747-9424
Fax Number: (214) 242-4329
Internet Homepage: whichwich.com
Company Email: info@whichwich.com
Type of Business: Chain Restaurant Operator
Year Founded: 2003
Systemwide Sales: $81,290,000 (e)
Total Sales: $15,870,000 (e)
Number of Employees: 873
Average Check: Breakfast(8); Lunch(8); Dinner(8)
Internet Order Processing: Yes
Total Units: 157
Trade Names: Which Wich Superior Sandwiches (438)
Company-Owned Units: 3
Units Franchised To: 435
Preferred Square Footage: 500; 2,700
Preferred Location Types: Downtown; Freestanding; Institution (college/hospital); Lifestyle Center; Regional Mall; Strip Mall
Primary Menu: Sandwiches/Deli (438)
Areas of Operation: AL, AR, AZ, CA, CO, CT, DC, FL, GA, IA, IL, IN, KS, KY, LA, MA, MD, MI, MN, MO, MS, NC, NE, NJ, NM, NV, NY, OH, OK, SC, TN, TX, UT, VA, WA, WI
Foreign Countries: BAHRAIN; GUATEMALA; KUWAIT; MEXICO; PANAMA; QATAR; SAUDI ARABIA; UNITED ARAB EMIRATES
Type of Foodservice: Fast Casual (438)
Catering Services: Yes
Primary Distributors: (Full Line) SYSCO Corporation, HOUSTON, TX
Parent Company: Sinelli Concepts, Inc., ,

Key Personnel
JEFFREY P. SINELLI - Founder; CEO
SARA RIVERA - Chief Administrative Officer
HALA HABAL - Chief Communications Officer; VP Communications
COURTNEY SINELLI - Exec VP
JOHN LOONEY - Regional VP Operations
JAIME HORDGE - General Manager
CASSANDRA MUELLNER - Director Marketing
BARBARA SCHENKER - Director Development, Logistics
HECTOR CONTRERAS - Area Manager
KIELAND HORNSBY - Manager Technology

Williams Fried Chicken Inc.
2831 E Ledbetter Dr
Dallas, TX 75216-7515

Telephone: (214) 371-1430
Fax Number: (214) 372-4231
Internet Homepage: williamschicken.net
Type of Business: Chain Restaurant Operator
Year Founded: 1987
Systemwide Sales: $26,798,000 (e)
Total Sales: $36,660,000 (e)
Number of Employees: 388
Average Check: Lunch(8); Dinner(12)
Total Units: 37
Trade Names: Williams Chicken (37)
Company-Owned Units: 10
Units Franchised To: 27
Preferred Square Footage: 2,500
Preferred Location Types: Convenience Store/Gas Station; Freestanding; Strip Mall
Primary Menu: Chicken (37)
Areas of Operation: TX
Type of Foodservice: Quick Serve (37)

Key Personnel
HIAWATHA WILLIAMS - CEO; President; VP Purchasing, Marketing
VERNA BRYANT - Director Accounting

Wingstop Restaurants Inc.
5501 Lyndon B Johnson Fwy 5th Floor
Dallas, TX 75240-2348

Telephone: (972) 686-6500
Fax Number: (972) 686-6502
Internet Homepage: wingstop.com; wingstop.com.mx; wingstopfranchise.com
Type of Business: Chain Restaurant Operator

Year Founded: 1994
Systemwide Sales: $3,136,733,000 (e)
Publicly Held: Yes
Total Sales: $414,393,000 (e)
Alcohol Sales: 5%
Number of Employees: 890
Average Check: Lunch(20); Dinner(24)
Internet Order Processing: Yes
Internet Sales: 24.00%
Total Units: 1,926
Trade Names: Wingstop (1,926)
Company-Owned Units: 49
Units Franchised To: 1,877
Preferred Square Footage: 1,200; 1,500
Preferred Location Types: Downtown; Strip Mall
Alcohol Served: Beer, Wine
Primary Menu: Chicken (1,926)
Projected Openings: 300
Areas of Operation: AK, AL, AR, AZ, CA, CO, CT, FL, GA, GU, HI, IA, ID, IL, IN, KS, KY, LA, MD, MI, MN, MO, MS, NC, NE, NJ, NM, NV, NY, OH, OK, OR, PA, SC, SD, TN, TX, UT, VA, WA, WI, FC
Foreign Countries: COLOMBIA; INDONESIA; MALAYSIA; MEXICO; PANAMA; SAUDI ARABIA; SINGAPORE; THE PHILIPPINES; UNITED ARAB EMIRATES
Type of Foodservice: Quick Serve (1,926)
Catering Services: Yes
Primary Distributors: (Full Line) US Foods, TOPEKA, KS
Notes: The company has plans to relocate their headquarters from Dallas, Texas to Addison, Texas by the end of 2019.

Key Personnel
MICHAEL SKIPWORTH - CEO; President; CFO
RAJ KAPOOR - President International; Senior VP
DONNIE UPSHAW - Chief People Officer
CHRIS FALLON - CIO
MARISA CARONA - Chief Growth Officer; Senior VP
ANNE FISCHER - Chief Growth Officer
KEVIN FISH - Senior VP Digital
KELLEY HARTLEY - VP; Controller
JOHN FINCH - VP Development
SAMIR RAY - VP Corporate Development
JOE SCHECHINGER - VP Global
THOMAS KAMOWSKI - Regional VP Operations
RUSBEL SANUDO - General Manager
LISA ROSTOV - Senior Director Global Marketing
CHRISTOPHER LILES - Senior Director Security
TODD BRIN - Senior Director Construction, Design
ATHENA THOMAS - Senior Director Brand Marketing
APRIL STEWART - Director Operations
JEFF BURNS - Director Operations
PATRICK CAMPBELL - Director Training
JASON CATALINE - Director Infrastructure
PENNY CESAK - Director Franchise Operations
HAYLEY DAWSON-OWENS - Director Strategy, Consumer Insights, Innovation
NICK DISTASI - Director Real Estate, Northeast Division
LARRY BELLAH - Director Culinary Development
JENNIFER HUBBARD-MORGAN - Director Purchasing
BRIAN MANNIS - Director Operations
EMILIA LARA - Director Marketing, International
ZACHARY SCHERMER - Director Marketing
BRANDY ROTHDEUTSCH - Regional Director Marketing
LISA SPOONER-WHYTE - Senior Manager Field Marketing
CAMERON MILAM - Manager Restaurant Operations
QING NILLAA - Manager Food and Beverage
BETSY PETERS - Manager Finance
SAMANTHA KERICK - Manager Customer Service
LINDA HIGGINS - Manager Real Estate
KHUYEN NGUYEN - Senior Product Manager
ANDY GARCIA-KRUPSKI - Project Manager Construction
APRIL PRICE - Administrator Information Technology, POS/Scanning
RICHARD RAY - Engineer Software
CORIE MORRIS - Executive Assistant Legal

Yumilicious Franchise LLC
1807 E Levee St
Dallas, TX 75207

Telephone: (214) 730-6601
Internet Homepage: yumilicious.co
Company Email: Info@Yumilicious.co
Type of Business: Chain Restaurant Operator
Year Founded: 2008
Total Units: 11
Trade Names: Yumilicious Frozen Yogurt (11)
Company-Owned Units: 2
Units Franchised To: 9
Primary Menu: Snacks (11)
Areas of Operation: TX
Type of Foodservice: Quick Serve (11)

Key Personnel
CHRISTIAN LE - President; Owner

Domino's Franchisee
3415 W FM 120
Denison, TX 75020-1506

Telephone: (903) 463-4444
Type of Business: Chain Restaurant Operator
Total Sales: $14,424,000 (e)
Total Units: 7
Trade Names: Domino's (7)
Units Franchised From: 7
Primary Menu: Pizza (7)
Projected Openings: 1
Areas of Operation: TX
Type of Foodservice: Quick Serve (7)
Franchise Affiliation: Domino's Pizza Inc, ANN ARBOR, MI

Key Personnel
STEVE T. PALMER - Owner; General Buyer

Seven Mile Cafe
2123 Sadau Ct
Denton, TX 76210

Telephone: (940) 808-0200
Internet Homepage: sevenmilecafe.com
Company Email: INFO@SEVENMILECAFE.COM
Type of Business: Chain Restaurant Operator
Year Founded: 2011
Total Sales: $1,191,000 (e)
Total Units: 6
Trade Names: Seven Mile Cafe (6)
Company-Owned Units: 6
Primary Menu: American (6)
Areas of Operation: TX
Type of Foodservice: Casual Dining (6)

Key Personnel
KEVIN KLINGELE - Founder; Partner
JOSI KLINGELE - Founder; Partner

Sonic Drive-In of Denton
624 W University Dr
Denton, TX 76201-1889

Telephone: (940) 591-8009
Fax Number: (940) 484-6217
Company Email: sonicoffice@verizon.net
Type of Business: Chain Restaurant Operator
Year Founded: 1986
Total Sales: $64,890,000 (e)
Number of Employees: 900
Average Check: Breakfast(10); Lunch(12); Dinner(12)
Total Units: 30
Trade Names: Sonic America's Drive-In (30)
Units Franchised From: 30
Preferred Square Footage: 1,320
Preferred Location Types: Freestanding
Primary Menu: Hamburger (30)
Areas of Operation: TX
Type of Foodservice: Quick Serve (30)
Foodservice Management Venues: Schools
Franchise Affiliation: Sonic Corp., OKLAHOMA CITY, OK
Primary Distributors: (Full Line) Gordon Food Service, HOUSTON, TX

Wen Den Inc
2516 Lillian Miller Pkwy Ste 100
Denton, TX 76202

Mailing Address: PO Box 2162, DENTON, TX, 76202-2162
Telephone: (940) 383-0998
Fax Number: (940) 381-9059
Internet Homepage: wendeninc.com
Type of Business: Chain Restaurant Operator
Total Sales: $11,701,000 (e)
Total Units: 4
Trade Names: Wendy's Old Fashioned Hamburgers (4)
Units Franchised From: 4
Primary Menu: Hamburger (4)
Areas of Operation: TX
Type of Foodservice: Quick Serve (4)
Franchise Affiliation: The Wendy's Company, DUBLIN, OH

Key Personnel
RON REINKE - President; General Buyer

EPSI Inc.
1510 N Hampton Rd Ste 240
Desoto, TX 75115-8301

Telephone: (972) 722-2073
Fax Number: (972) 224-5717
Type of Business: Chain Restaurant Operator
Total Sales: $72,269,000 (e)
Number of Employees: 366
Total Units: 36
Trade Names: Domino's (36)
Units Franchised From: 36
Preferred Square Footage: 1,000
Primary Menu: Pizza (36)
Areas of Operation: TX
Type of Foodservice: Quick Serve (36)
Franchise Affiliation: Domino's Pizza Inc, ANN ARBOR, MI

Key Personnel
MAC MEKONNEN - Owner; Director Operations

Salt Lick BBQ
17900 FM 1826
Driftwood, TX 78619-4202

Mailing Address: PO Box 311, DRIFTWOOD, TX, 78619-0311

Key Personnel
GENE GUMFORY - Owner; General Manager; Director Finance, Operations, Facility/Maintenance, Information Systems, Supply Chain, Real Estate, Design, Human Resources, Store Fixtures; General Buyer

Telephone: (512) 829-5285
Fax Number: (512) 858-2038
Internet Homepage: saltlickbbq.com
Company Email: saltlick@saltlickbbq.com
Type of Business: Chain Restaurant Operator
Year Founded: 1969
Total Sales: $5,381,000 (e)
Number of Employees: 200
Average Check: Lunch(20); Dinner(24)
Internet Order Processing: Yes
Total Units: 4
Trade Names: Salt Lick BBQ (4)
Company-Owned Units: 4
Preferred Location Types: Airports; Freestanding
Alcohol Served: Beer, Wine, Liquor
Primary Menu: Bar-B-Q (4)
Areas of Operation: TX
Type of Foodservice: Family Restaurant (4)
Catering Services: Yes
Primary Distributors: (Food) Ben E. Keith Foods, FORT WORTH, TX
Notes: The restaurant can accommodate up to 2,000 people with its various indoor and outdoor facilities.

Key Personnel
SUSAN GOFF - President
SCOTT ROBERTS - Owner; Executive Chef; General Buyer
JARRED ANCELET - Manager Fulfillment
ADAM GLANDT - Manager Restaurant Operations

Domino's Franchisee
300 E 19th St Ste 300
Dumas, TX 79029-6110

Telephone: (806) 934-0030
Type of Business: Chain Restaurant Operator
Total Sales: $26,871,000 (e)
Total Units: 13
Trade Names: Domino's (13)
Units Franchised From: 13
Primary Menu: Pizza (13)
Areas of Operation: TX
Type of Foodservice: Quick Serve (13)
Franchise Affiliation: Domino's Pizza Inc, ANN ARBOR, MI

Key Personnel
LAWRENCE A. VIGIL - Owner; General Buyer

Auntie Anne's Franchise
2522 W Freddy Gonzalez Dr
Edinburg, TX 78539-7339

Telephone: (956) 618-3663
Type of Business: Chain Restaurant Operator
Total Sales: $7,472,000 (e)
Total Units: 10

Trade Names: Auntie Anne's Hand-Rolled Soft Pretzels (10)
Units Franchised From: 10
Primary Menu: Snacks (10)
Areas of Operation: TX
Type of Foodservice: Quick Serve (10)
Franchise Affiliation: Auntie Anne's Inc., LANCASTER, PA

Key Personnel
HICKMAN CHOW - Owner; General Buyer

Boss Tenders, Dogs & Custard
1830 Joe Battle Blvd
El Paso, TX 79936

Telephone: (915) 271-4148
Internet Homepage: bosschicken.com
Type of Business: Chain Restaurant Operator
Year Founded: 2017
Total Sales: $11,210,000 (e)
Total Units: 6
Trade Names: Boss Tenders, Dogs & Custard (6)
Company-Owned Units: 6
Primary Menu: Chicken (6)
Type of Foodservice: Fast Casual (6)

Key Personnel
KIRK ROBISON - Founder; CEO; Owner
JOHN GESKE - Founder; President; Owner

Castro Enterprises Inc.
3332 Wedgewood Dr
El Paso, TX 79925-2834

Telephone: (915) 599-2982
Fax Number: (915) 599-2570
Type of Business: Chain Restaurant Operator
Year Founded: 1999
Total Sales: $57,910,000 (e)
Number of Employees: 955
Average Check: Breakfast(8); Lunch(8); Dinner(8)
Total Units: 25
Trade Names: McDonald's (25)
Units Franchised From: 25
Preferred Square Footage: 2,500; 3,000
Preferred Location Types: Community Mall; Freestanding
Primary Menu: Hamburger (25)
Projected Openings: 1
Areas of Operation: TX
Type of Foodservice: Quick Serve (25)
Franchise Affiliation: McDonald's Corporation, CHICAGO, IL
Primary Distributors: (Food) The Martin-Brower Co., GRAND PRAIRIE, TX

Key Personnel
RICHARD A. CASTRO - President; Director Operations, Purchasing, Facility/Maintenance, Supply Chain, Real Estate
REGINA PAYTON - Director Finance, Information Systems, Human Resources

Chico's Tacos
1365 George Dieter Dr
El Paso, TX 79936-7410

Telephone: (915) 592-8484
Internet Homepage: chicostacosbuenos.weebly.com
Type of Business: Chain Restaurant Operator
Year Founded: 1953
Total Sales: $2,807,000 (e)
Number of Employees: 115
Total Units: 4
Trade Names: Chico's Tacos (4)
Company-Owned Units: 4
Preferred Location Types: Freestanding
Primary Menu: Taco (4)
Areas of Operation: TX
Type of Foodservice: Quick Serve (4)

Key Personnel
WILLIAM MORA - Partner; General Manager
BERNIE MORA - Partner; General Manager

Domino's Franchisee
12420 Edgemere Blvd Ste 108
El Paso, TX 79938-4534

Telephone: (915) 855-4555
Type of Business: Chain Restaurant Operator
Total Sales: $6,189,000 (e)
Total Units: 3
Trade Names: Domino's (3)
Units Franchised From: 3
Primary Menu: Pizza (3)
Areas of Operation: TX
Type of Foodservice: Quick Serve (3)
Franchise Affiliation: Domino's Pizza Inc, ANN ARBOR, MI

Key Personnel
RICARDO ALVARADO - Owner; General Buyer

El Taco Tote Franchise Systems Ltd.
600 Sunland Park Dr Bldg 500
El Paso, TX 79912-5115

Telephone: (915) 838-6000
Fax Number: (915) 838-7755
Internet Homepage: tacotote.com
Company Email: info@tacotote.com
Type of Business: Chain Restaurant Operator
Year Founded: 1988
Systemwide Sales: $40,620,000 (e)
Total Sales: $30,850,000 (e)
Alcohol Sales: 2%
Number of Employees: 302
Average Check: Lunch(8); Dinner(8)
Total Units: 22
Trade Names: El Taco Tote Real! Mexican Grill (22)
Company-Owned Units: 11
Units Franchised To: 11
Preferred Square Footage: 5,000
Preferred Location Types: Freestanding
Alcohol Served: Beer, Wine
Primary Menu: Mexican (22)
Areas of Operation: AZ, NM, TX, FC
Foreign Countries: MEXICO
Type of Foodservice: Fast Casual (22)
Catering Services: Yes
Primary Distributors: (Full Line) Shamrock Foods Co., PHOENIX, AZ

Key Personnel
PACIFICO J. HERAS - Chairman
HECTOR HERAS SR - President
JORGE HERAS - VP
MARCO HERAS - VP
SERGIO HERAS - VP
EDUARDO HERAS - VP Real Estate, Design

L.C.I. Enterprises Inc
1119 N Virginia St Ste A
El Paso, TX 79902-4410

Telephone: (915) 533-2233
Type of Business: Chain Restaurant Operator
Total Sales: $3,419,000 (e)
Total Units: 6
Trade Names: Subway (6)
Units Franchised From: 6
Primary Menu: Sandwiches/Deli (6)
Areas of Operation: TX
Type of Foodservice: Quick Serve (6)
Franchise Affiliation: Doctor's Associates Inc., MILFORD, CT

Key Personnel
SAM D. ARNEY - President

Lone Star Apple, LLC
4445 N Mesa St Ste 100
El Paso, TX 79902

Telephone: (915) 544-8565
Fax Number: (915) 581-6244
Type of Business: Chain Restaurant Operator
Year Founded: 1994
Total Sales: $35,580,000 (e)
Alcohol Sales: 10%
Number of Employees: 700
Average Check: Lunch(12); Dinner(22)
Total Units: 9
Trade Names: Applebee's Neighborhood Grill & Bar (9)
Units Franchised From: 9
Preferred Square Footage: 3,600; 5,000
Preferred Location Types: Freestanding
Alcohol Served: Beer, Wine, Liquor
Primary Menu: American (9)
Areas of Operation: NM, TX
Type of Foodservice: Casual Dining (9)
Franchise Affiliation: Applebee's Services Inc., KANSAS CITY, MO
Primary Distributors: (Food) The SYGMA Network Inc.- San Antonio, SAN ANTONIO, TX

Key Personnel
KIRK ROBISON - Chairman; CEO
JOHN HJALMQUIST - President; COO

Odessa Enterprises, Inc
5017 Conley Rd Ste B
El Paso, TX 79932-1741

Telephone: (915) 533-7327
Fax Number: (915) 533-3908
Type of Business: Chain Restaurant Operator
Total Sales: $33,500,000 (e)
Total Units: 13
Trade Names: Jack in the Box (13)
Units Franchised From: 13
Primary Menu: Hamburger (13)
Areas of Operation: NM, TX
Type of Foodservice: Quick Serve (13)
Franchise Affiliation: Jack in the Box Restaurants, SAN DIEGO, CA

Key Personnel
FREDRICK NORWICH JR - President; General Buyer
MICHAEL ESCAJEDA - Director Operations

Pizza Properties, Inc
4445 N Mesa St Ste 100
El Paso, TX 79902-1109

Telephone: (915) 544-8565
Fax Number: (915) 544-8586
Internet Homepage: peterpiperpizza.com
Type of Business: Chain Restaurant Operator
Year Founded: 1982
Total Sales: $112,650,000 (e)
Alcohol Sales: 2%
Number of Employees: 2,650
Average Check: Breakfast(5); Lunch(8); Dinner(10)
Internet Order Processing: Yes
Total Units: 46
Trade Names: Peter Piper Pizza (46)
Units Franchised From: 46

Preferred Square Footage: 2,800; 4,000; 10,000
Preferred Location Types: Freestanding; Hotel/Motel; Strip Mall
Alcohol Served: Beer
Primary Menu: Pizza (46)
Projected Openings: 3
Areas of Operation: NM, TX
Type of Foodservice: Casual Dining (46)
Franchise Affiliation: CEC Entertainment Inc., IRVING, TX
Primary Distributors: (Equipment) National Restaurant Supply Co., EL PASO, TX; (Food) Performance Foodservice, DALLAS, TX; (Supplies) National Restaurant Supply Co., EL PASO, TX

Key Personnel
JOHN HJALMQUIST - President; COO
SHARON VOELZ - VP Risk Management, Human Resources
WILLIAM TEPSICK - Director Real Estate, Construction
ROB ROUSSEAU - Director
MAURICE OSTOS - Director Information Technology
JOE ABLES - Director Training

Sasnak, LLC
7040 N Mesa St Ste B3
El Paso, TX 79912-3667

Telephone: (915) 581-3993
Type of Business: Chain Restaurant Operator
Total Sales: $1,766,000 (e)
Total Units: 3
Trade Names: Cold Stone Creamery (3)
Units Franchised From: 3
Primary Menu: Snacks (3)
Areas of Operation: TX
Type of Foodservice: Quick Serve (3)
Franchise Affiliation: Kahala Brands, SCOTTSDALE, AZ

Key Personnel
GREG CROPP - Owner

Mr. Jim's Pizza Inc.
2521 Pepperwood St
Farmers Branch, TX 75234-6148

Telephone: (972) 267-5467
Fax Number: (972) 241-8590
Internet Homepage: mrjims.pizza
Type of Business: Chain Restaurant Operator
Year Founded: 1975
Systemwide Sales: $31,761,000 (e)
Total Sales: $2,641,000 (e)
Number of Employees: 6
Average Check: Lunch(6); Dinner(8)
Internet Order Processing: Yes
Internet Sales: 1.00%
Total Units: 47
Trade Names: Mr. Jim's Pizza (47)
Units Franchised To: 47
Preferred Square Footage: 1,200
Preferred Location Types: Freestanding; Strip Mall
Primary Menu: Pizza (47)
Areas of Operation: LA, NC, NV, TX, WY
Type of Foodservice: Quick Serve (47)
Foodservice Management Venues: Schools
Primary Distributors: (Full Line) Performance Foodservice, DALLAS, TX

Key Personnel
SCOTT SEWELL - VP Purchasing; Director Purchasing, Loss Prevention, Risk Management, Quality Assurance, Food Safety
LINDA CHAMBERS - Controller; Director Finance
MIKE CHRISTIAN - Director Marketing

Taco Bueno Restaurants LP
1605 Lyndon B Johnson Fwy Ste 800
Farmers Branch, TX 75234-6099

Telephone: (972) 919-4800
Fax Number: (972) 919-4811
Internet Homepage: tacobueno.com
Type of Business: Chain Restaurant Operator
Year Founded: 1967
Systemwide Sales: $286,265,000 (e)
Total Sales: $223,960,000 (e)
Number of Employees: 2,902
Average Check: Breakfast(6); Lunch(8); Dinner(12)
Total Units: 132
Trade Names: Taco Bueno (148)
Company-Owned Units: 148
Preferred Square Footage: 2,600
Preferred Location Types: Freestanding; Mobile Unit
Primary Menu: Taco (148)
Projected Openings: 15
Areas of Operation: AR, KS, LA, MO, OK, TX
Type of Foodservice: Quick Serve (148)
Primary Distributors: (Food) The SYGMA Network Inc.- San Antonio, SAN ANTONIO, TX
Parent Company: Sun Holdings LLC, DALLAS, TX

Key Personnel
CHRIS HASSELSCHWERT - Area Director
STEPHANIE LIPSCOMB - Area Director
ANNA SIGALA - Area Director
ROY WOOD - Area Director
REX POURSOLTANI - VP Operations
JOHN BARTEL - Executive Chef
DANNY MORELOS - Regional Manager Training
GARY WINNER - Regional Manager Training
JAMES RODRIGUEZ - Manager Sales
BRENDA DAVENPORT - Specialist Payroll

Yogurtland Franchising Inc.
2100 Valley View Lane Suite 101
Farmers Branch, TX 75234

Telephone: (949) 265-8000
Fax Number: (949) 496-4878
Internet Homepage: yogurt-land.com
Company Email: info@yogurtland.com
Type of Business: Chain Restaurant Operator
Systemwide Sales: $240,666,000 (e)
Total Sales: $24,170,000 (e)
Number of Employees: 640
Total Units: 260
Trade Names: Yogurtland (260)
Company-Owned Units: 20
Units Franchised To: 240
Preferred Location Types: Community Mall; Freestanding; Lifestyle Center; Regional Mall; Strip Mall
Primary Menu: Snacks (260)
Projected Openings: 10
Areas of Operation: AK, AZ, CA, CO, FL, GA, GU, HI, LA, MA, MO, NJ, NM, NV, NY, OR, PA, TX, UT, WA
Foreign Countries: AUSTRALIA; INDONESIA; MEXICO; THAILAND; VENEZUELA
Type of Foodservice: Quick Serve (260)

Key Personnel
PHILLIP CHANG - Chairman; Treasurer; Corporate Secretary
JAIME MIRO - Director Operations

Weachter & Associates, LLC
2701 Cross Timbers Rd Ste 202
Flower Mound, TX 75028-2779

Telephone: (972) 906-1066
Type of Business: Chain Restaurant Operator
Total Sales: $4,402,000 (e)
Total Units: 3
Trade Names: Jersey Mike's Subs (3)
Units Franchised From: 3
Primary Menu: Sandwiches/Deli (3)
Areas of Operation: TX
Type of Foodservice: Quick Serve (3)
Franchise Affiliation: Jersey Mike's Franchise Systems, MANASQUAN, NJ

Key Personnel
PHILLIP WEACHTER - Owner

Bobby Cox Companies Inc.
5000 Overton Plz Ste 300
Fort Worth, TX 76109-4441

Telephone: (817) 377-6200

Fax Number: (817) 377-6201
Internet Homepage: bobbycox.com
Company Email: inquiries@bobbycox.com
Type of Business: Chain Restaurant Operator
Year Founded: 1961
Total Sales: $94,280,000 (e)
Alcohol Sales: 3%
Number of Employees: 2,309
Average Check: Breakfast(8); Lunch(10); Dinner(12)
Total Units: 70
Trade Names: Rosa's Cafe (46); Taco Villa (17); Texas Burger (7)
Company-Owned Units: 70
Preferred Square Footage: 2,700; 5,000
Preferred Location Types: Freestanding; Strip Mall
Alcohol Served: Beer, Liquor
Primary Menu: Hamburger (7); Taco (63)
Areas of Operation: CA, NM, TX
Type of Foodservice: Fast Casual (46); Quick Serve (24)
Catering Services: Yes
Distribution Centers: MIDLAND, TX
Primary Distributors: (Full Line) SYSCO Food Services of North Texas, LEWISVILLE, TX
Parent Company: Bobby Cox Companies, FORT WORTH, TX

Key Personnel
BOBBY COX - President
RONNY JORDAN - CFO; Exec VP Finance, Real Estate
MIKE WHELAN - CFO
STEVE CARROLL - CIO; Controller
KAREN HOPKINS - Director Purchasing, Loss Prevention, Risk Management, Menu Development, Food Safety, Catering; General Buyer
KENT DEAN - Director Marketing; Specialist
ANTHONY VILLALOBOZ - Director Quality Assurance
BRUCE BLUMENTRITT - Regional Manager
CHRIS BALL - Manager Customer Analytics
GLENDA ETHERIDGE - Manager Human Resources
ROBERT NOWLIN - Manager POS/Scanning
CRAIG SCHMOKER - Engineer

CKMS McDonald's Inc
PO Box 821260
Fort Worth, TX 76182-1260

Telephone: (817) 428-7808
Type of Business: Chain Restaurant Operator
Total Sales: $42,880,000 (e)
Number of Employees: 225
Total Units: 9
Trade Names: McDonald's (9)
Units Franchised From: 9
Preferred Square Footage: 2,500
Preferred Location Types: Airports; Freestanding; Institution (college/hospital)
Primary Menu: Hamburger (9)
Areas of Operation: TX
Type of Foodservice: Quick Serve (9)
Franchise Affiliation: McDonald's Corporation, CHICAGO, IL

Key Personnel
KAREN LOPEZ-MCWILLIAMS - President; General Buyer

Deli Partners of Oklahoma Lp
1608 Rogers Rd
Fort Worth, TX 76107-6514

Telephone: (817) 738-9355
Fax Number: (817) 738-8716
Type of Business: Chain Restaurant Operator
Total Sales: $25,790,000 (e)
Total Units: 8
Trade Names: Jason's Deli (8)
Units Franchised From: 8
Primary Menu: Sandwiches/Deli (8)
Areas of Operation: AR, MN, MO, OK, TX
Type of Foodservice: Fast Casual (8)
Franchise Affiliation: Deli Management Inc., BEAUMONT, TX

Key Personnel
BOURKE HARVEY - President; General Buyer

Jasper Holdings
3505 Reagan Dr
Fort Worth, TX 76116-7044

Telephone: (817) 293-4633
Fax Number: (817) 293-4750
Type of Business: Chain Restaurant Operator
Year Founded: 1996
Total Sales: $103,790,000 (e)
Number of Employees: 950
Average Check: Breakfast(8); Lunch(8); Dinner(8)
Total Units: 22
Trade Names: McDonald's (22)
Units Franchised From: 22
Preferred Square Footage: 2,500; 3,000
Preferred Location Types: Freestanding
Primary Menu: Hamburger (22)
Projected Openings: 2
Areas of Operation: TX
Type of Foodservice: Quick Serve (22)
Franchise Affiliation: McDonald's Corporation, CHICAGO, IL
Primary Distributors: (Food) The Martin-Brower Co., CONROE, TX

Key Personnel
JOE JASPER - Owner; Director Finance, Real Estate; General Buyer
RANDY BAUER - VP
JASON NORD - VP People
DENNIS BODAK - Regional VP
DARIN DAMRON - Regional VP
STEPHEN LUBBEHUSEN - Regional Manager Operations
KAREN JASPER - Manager Operations, Purchasing, Information Systems, Supply Chain, Ethnic Marketing, Design, Human Resources, Store Fixtures

Kenney Trousdale Inc.
7200 South Fwy
Fort Worth, TX 76134-5403

Telephone: (817) 551-1027
Fax Number: (817) 568-0577
Type of Business: Chain Restaurant Operator
Year Founded: 1970
Total Sales: $10,510,000 (e)
Number of Employees: 264
Average Check: Breakfast(6); Lunch(12); Dinner(14)
Total Units: 11
Trade Names: Whataburger (11)
Units Franchised From: 11
Preferred Square Footage: 1,400; 1,800
Preferred Location Types: Freestanding
Primary Menu: Hamburger (11)
Areas of Operation: TX
Type of Foodservice: Quick Serve (11)
Franchise Affiliation: Whataburger Restaurants LLC, SAN ANTONIO, TX
Primary Distributors: (Full Line) The SYGMA Network, Inc., DUBLIN, OH

Key Personnel
KENNEY TROUSDALE - CEO; President; CFO; Director Design
SHELL HALL - Director Operations; General Buyer
GARRICK HUGHES - Supervisor Area

Lonesome Dove Western Bistro
2406 N Main St
Fort Worth, TX 76164-8519

Telephone: (817) 740-8810
Fax Number: (817) 740-8632
Internet Homepage: cheftimlove.com; lonesomedovebistro.com
Type of Business: Chain Restaurant Operator
Year Founded: 2000
Total Sales: $16,880,000 (e)
Alcohol Sales: 20%
Number of Employees: 72
Average Check: Lunch(24); Dinner(90)
Internet Order Processing: Yes
Internet Sales: 5.00%
Total Units: 9

Trade Names: Genelle (1); Queenie's Steakhouse (1); The Lonesome Dove Western Bistro (3); The Love Shack (2); White Elephant Saloon (1); Woodshed Smokehouse (1)
Company-Owned Units: 9
Preferred Location Types: Strip Mall
Alcohol Served: Beer, Wine, Liquor
Primary Menu: Hamburger (2); Miscellaneous (1); Pizza (1); Southwest/Tex-Mex (4); Steak (1)
Areas of Operation: TX
Type of Foodservice: Casual Dining (8); Fine Dining (1)
Catering Services: Yes
Primary Distributors: (Food) Ben E. Keith Foods, FORT WORTH, TX

Key Personnel
TIM LOVE - President; Executive Chef; General Buyer

McCan's Sonic Group
7404 Calmont Ave
Fort Worth, TX 76116-4007

Telephone: (817) 696-9800
Fax Number: (817) 696-9807
Internet Homepage: mccanssonicgroup.net
Company Email: office@mccanssonicoffice.net
Type of Business: Chain Restaurant Operator
Year Founded: 1986
Total Sales: $74,320,000 (e)
Number of Employees: 1,266
Average Check: Breakfast(10); Lunch(10); Dinner(10)
Total Units: 35
Trade Names: Sonic America's Drive-In (35)
Units Franchised From: 35
Preferred Square Footage: 1,320
Preferred Location Types: Freestanding
Primary Menu: Hamburger (35)
Projected Openings: 1
Areas of Operation: FL, GA, TX
Type of Foodservice: Quick Serve (35)
Franchise Affiliation: Sonic Corp., OKLAHOMA CITY, OK

Key Personnel
BILL MCCANS SR - CEO; Director Facility/Maintenance, Real Estate, Design, Store Fixtures
STEVE MCCANS - President; General Buyer
KERRY MCCONATHY - CFO; Controller; Manager Finance, Risk Management, Marketing, Human Resources
BILL MCCANS JR - Director Operations
DANNY JOHNSON - Director Operations

Moriarty Creamery, LLC
2948 Texas Sage Trl
Fort Worth, TX 76177-8209

Telephone: (817) 741-9007
Type of Business: Chain Restaurant Operator
Total Sales: $1,163,000 (e)
Total Units: 2
Trade Names: Cold Stone Creamery (2)
Units Franchised From: 2
Primary Menu: Snacks (2)
Areas of Operation: TX
Type of Foodservice: Quick Serve (2)
Franchise Affiliation: Kahala Brands, SCOTTSDALE, AZ

Key Personnel
TIM MORIARTY - Partner
KATHLEEN MORIARTY - Partner

Mr. Gatti's Inc.
550 Bailey Ave Ste 650
Fort Worth, TX 76107-2162

Telephone: (817) 546-3500
Fax Number: (817) 735-4183
Internet Homepage: gattispizza.com
Type of Business: Chain Restaurant Operator
Year Founded: 1968
Systemwide Sales: $212,978,000 (e)
Total Sales: $29,175,000 (e)
Alcohol Sales: 1%
Number of Employees: 400
Average Check: Lunch(8); Dinner(24)
Internet Order Processing: Yes
Total Units: 68
Trade Names: Gatti's Pizza Buffet (64); Gatti's Pizza Carryout (21); GattiTown (25)
Company-Owned Units: 7
Units Franchised To: 103
Preferred Square Footage: 1,100
Preferred Location Types: Airports; Freestanding; Strip Mall
Primary Menu: Pizza (110)
Areas of Operation: IN, KY, LA, MS, NC, SC, TN, TX, VA, WV
Type of Foodservice: Casual Dining (110)
Primary Distributors: (Full Line) Labatt Food Service, SAN ANTONIO, TX
Parent Company: FundCorp Inc, FORT WORTH, TX

Key Personnel
TRAVIS SMITH - VP Marketing
MARY LEWIS - Controller

Pulido Associates Inc.
4924 Old Benbrook Rd
Fort Worth, TX 76116-8923

Telephone: (817) 731-4241
Fax Number: (817) 731-4244
Internet Homepage: pulidosrestaurant.com
Company Email: pulidotf@sbcglobal.net
Type of Business: Chain Restaurant Operator
Year Founded: 1966
Total Sales: $36,900,000 (e)
Alcohol Sales: 15%
Number of Employees: 300
Average Check: Breakfast(6); Lunch(14); Dinner(24)
Total Units: 10
Trade Names: Cafe Pulido (1); Pulido's (9)
Company-Owned Units: 10
Preferred Square Footage: 4,000; 6,500
Preferred Location Types: Freestanding
Alcohol Served: Beer, Wine, Liquor
Primary Menu: Mexican (10)
Areas of Operation: TX
Type of Foodservice: Casual Dining (10)
Catering Services: Yes
Distribution Centers: FORT WORTH, TX
Primary Distributors: (Food) US Foods, GARLAND, TX

Key Personnel
ROBERT PULIDO SR - Chairman; CEO; President; Controller; Director Finance, Facility/Maintenance, Information Systems, Real Estate
ROSIE REYES - Director Human Resources

Reata
310 Houston St
Fort Worth, TX 76102-7404

Telephone: (817) 336-1009
Fax Number: (817) 336-0267
Internet Homepage: reata.net
Company Email: krsm@reata.net
Type of Business: Chain Restaurant Operator
Year Founded: 1996
Total Sales: $7,095,000 (e)
Alcohol Sales: 25%
Number of Employees: 225
Average Check: Lunch(14); Dinner(26)
Internet Order Processing: Yes
Total Units: 2
Trade Names: Reata (2)
Company-Owned Units: 2
Preferred Square Footage: 2,000; 4,500; 30,000
Preferred Location Types: Freestanding
Alcohol Served: Beer, Wine, Liquor
Primary Menu: Southwest/Tex-Mex (2)
Areas of Operation: TX
Type of Foodservice: Casual Dining (2)

Catering Services: Yes
Primary Distributors: (Food) Ben E. Keith Foods, FORT WORTH, TX

Key Personnel
MIKE MICALLEF - President; Partner
MARIAH BROOKS - General Manager; General Buyer
JANE CONLON-WERNER - Senior Director Quality Assurance
VALERIE GUST-BRITO - Senior Director Procurement
LAUREN MILLER - Director Restaurant Operations
JON LE CULPEPPER - Director Information Technology
MISTI CALLICOTT - Director Sales, Catering
ERICA ANDRLE - Manager Retail Operations

Taco Casa
133 Aviator Dr
Fort Worth, TX 76179-5412

Telephone: (817) 439-2277
Internet Homepage: tacocasatexas.com
Type of Business: Chain Restaurant Operator
Total Units: 86
Trade Names: Taco Casa (86)
Company-Owned Units: 86
Primary Menu: Taco (86)
Projected Openings: 3
Areas of Operation: OK, TX
Type of Foodservice: Quick Serve (86)

Key Personnel
ROY UPSHAW - Founder; CEO
BRETT WILKIN - VP
BEN WILKIN - VP Marketing

Texas Subs Inc
3575 Lone Star Cir Ste 303
Fort Worth, TX 76177-8908

Telephone: (682) 831-0800
Fax Number: (682) 831-0806
Internet Homepage: texassubs.com
Type of Business: Chain Restaurant Operator
Total Sales: $36,940,000 (e)
Total Units: 40
Trade Names: Mooyah (1); Subway (39)
Units Franchised From: 40
Primary Menu: Hamburger (1); Sandwiches/Deli (39)
Areas of Operation: TX
Type of Foodservice: Fast Casual (1); Quick Serve (39)
Franchise Affiliation: Doctor's Associates Inc., MILFORD, CT

Key Personnel
ERIC J. WERNER - CEO; President; General Buyer
JESSICA ELASMAR - Specialist Training

William G. Hall & Co.
2600 8th Ave Unit 12069
Fort Worth, TX 76110-6945

Telephone: (817) 371-1177
Fax Number: (817) 921-5499
Internet Homepage: wghall.com
Company Email: bill@wghall.com
Type of Business: Chain Restaurant Operator
Year Founded: 1979
Total Sales: $5,918,000 (e)
Number of Employees: 120
Average Check: Breakfast(8); Lunch(10); Dinner(10)
Total Units: 4
Trade Names: Dairy Queen (4)
Units Franchised From: 4
Preferred Square Footage: 2,000; 3,000
Preferred Location Types: Freestanding; Strip Mall
Primary Menu: American (4)
Areas of Operation: TX
Type of Foodservice: Quick Serve (4)
Franchise Affiliation: International Dairy Queen Inc., BLOOMINGTON, MN
Primary Distributors: (Full Line) Labatt Food Service, SAN ANTONIO, TX

Key Personnel
WILLIAM G. HALL - Chairman; CEO; General Buyer

RTPJ Inc
611 E Main St
Fredericksburg, TX 78624-4641

Telephone: (512) 589-4795
Type of Business: Chain Restaurant Operator
Total Sales: $23,630,000 (e)
Number of Employees: 160
Total Units: 5
Trade Names: McDonald's (5)
Units Franchised From: 5
Preferred Square Footage: 2,500
Preferred Location Types: Convenience Store/Gas Station; Discount Dept. Stores; Freestanding
Primary Menu: Hamburger (5)
Areas of Operation: TX
Type of Foodservice: Quick Serve (5)
Franchise Affiliation: McDonald's Corporation, CHICAGO, IL

Key Personnel
RONALD J. YOUNG - President; Owner; General Buyer

DREAM ROLLS, LLC
500 Baybrook Mall
Friendswood, TX 77546-2796

Telephone: (281) 286-2276
Type of Business: Chain Restaurant Operator
Total Sales: $734,000 (e)
Total Units: 2
Trade Names: Cinnabon (2)
Units Franchised From: 2
Primary Menu: Snacks (2)
Areas of Operation: TX
Type of Foodservice: Quick Serve
Franchise Affiliation: Cinnabon Inc., ATLANTA, GA

Key Personnel
SHANE HANSEN - Owner; General Buyer

Fiyi Development, Inc.
109 E Parkwood Ave
Friendswood, TX 77546-5177

Telephone: (281) 996-5483
Type of Business: Chain Restaurant Operator
Total Sales: $1,104,000 (e)
Total Units: 3
Trade Names: Cinnabon (2); Schlotzsky's (1)
Units Franchised From: 3
Primary Menu: Sandwiches/Deli (1); Snacks (2)
Areas of Operation: TX
Type of Foodservice: Quick Serve (3)
Franchise Affiliation: Cinnabon Inc., ATLANTA, GA; Schlotzsky's Ltd., ATLANTA, GA

Key Personnel
JIMMY LEUNG - Owner; General Buyer

Qsr's of Texas Inc
PO Box 1387
Friendswood, TX 77549-1387

Telephone: (281) 557-0737
Fax Number: (281) 557-8274
Company Email: mcdonflo@sbcglobal.net
Type of Business: Chain Restaurant Operator
Total Sales: $66,860,000 (e)
Number of Employees: 300
Total Units: 14
Trade Names: McDonald's (14)
Units Franchised From: 14
Preferred Square Footage: 2,500
Primary Menu: Hamburger (14)
Areas of Operation: TX
Type of Foodservice: Quick Serve (14)

Franchise Affiliation: McDonald's Corporation, CHICAGO, IL

Key Personnel
ROBERT FLORES - President; General Buyer

Auntie Anne's Franchise
2601 Preston Rd Ste 110
Frisco, TX 75034-9468

Telephone: (214) 705-1653
Type of Business: Chain Restaurant Operator
Total Sales: $5,062,000 (e)
Total Units: 7
Trade Names: Auntie Anne's Hand-Rolled Soft Pretzels (7)
Units Franchised From: 7
Primary Menu: Snacks (7)
Areas of Operation: TX
Type of Foodservice: Quick Serve (7)
Franchise Affiliation: Auntie Anne's Inc., LANCASTER, PA

Key Personnel
RANDY LABOSCO - Owner; General Buyer

Burning Rice
3930 Preston Rd Ste 100
Frisco, TX 75034

Telephone: (214) 601-0464
Internet Homepage: burningrice.com
Type of Business: Chain Restaurant Operator
Year Founded: 2016

Key Personnel
MICHELLE CHOI - Partner

Jamba Inc.
3001 Dallas Pkwy Ste 700
Frisco, TX 75034-8048

Telephone: (469) 294-9600
Fax Number: (510) 653-0484
Internet Homepage: jamba.com; jambajuice.com
Company Email: franchiseeinfo@jambajuice.com
Type of Business: Chain Restaurant Operator
Year Founded: 1990
Systemwide Sales: $730,228,000 (e)
Total Sales: $116,660,000 (e)
Number of Employees: 4,200
Average Check: Lunch(8); Dinner(8)
Total Units: 783
Trade Names: Jamba (837)
Units Franchised To: 837
Preferred Square Footage: 1,200
Preferred Location Types: Airports; Community Mall; Convenience Store/Gas Station; Downtown; Freestanding; Grocery Stores; Institution (college/hospital); Lifestyle Center; Office Complex; Regional Mall; Strip Mall; Travel Plazas
Primary Menu: Health Foods (837)
Projected Openings: 21
Areas of Operation: AZ, CA, CO, CT, DC, FL, GA, HI, ID, IL, IN, KY, LA, MA, MD, MN, MO, NC, NJ, NV, NY, OH, OK, OR, PA, TN, TX, UT, VA, WA, WI, FC, ON
Foreign Countries: CANADA; MEXICO; SOUTH KOREA; THE PHILIPPINES; UNITED ARAB EMIRATES
Type of Foodservice: Quick Serve (837)
Primary Distributors: (Full Line) Systems Services of America, MILPITAS, CA
Parent Company: GoTo Foods, ATLANTA, GA

Key Personnel
JIM HOLTHOUSER - CEO
DAVE MIKITA - President; Senior VP
KRISTEN HARTMAN - President
FRANK SHAIKH - Owner
MIKE DIXON - CFO
SARAH POWELL - Exec VP; Corporate Secretary; General Counsel
ROBERT RUIZ - General Manager; Assistant
JANICE DUIS - Senior Director Communications

1859 Historic Hotels Ltd
2302 Post Office St Ste 500
Galveston, TX 77550-1936

Mailing Address: PO Box 59, GALVESTON, TX, 77553-0059
Telephone: (409) 763-8536
Fax Number: (409) 763-5304
Internet Homepage: 1859historichotels.com
Company Email: info@gal-tex.com
Type of Business: Foodservice Operations - Hotel/Motels
Year Founded: 1940
Total Sales: $98,140,000 (e)
Alcohol Sales: 15%
Number of Employees: 15,000
Total Units: 11
Restaurants in Hotels: 14
Trade Names: Cliff House (1); DoubleTree by Hilton Houston Airport (1); Fredericksburg Hospitality House (1); Inn at the Water Park (1); Inn of the Hills (1); Menger Hotel (1); Overton Hotel & Conference Center (1); South Shore Harbor Hotel & Conference Center (1); The Brown Hotel (1); The Crockett Hotel (1);Y.O. Hotel (1)
Company-Owned Units: 14
Alcohol Served: Beer, Wine, Liquor
Areas of Operation: KY, TX, VA
Type of Foodservice: Casual Dining (14)
Primary Distributors: (Food) SYSCO Food Services of North Texas, LEWISVILLE, TX
Parent Company: Moody Foundation, GALVESTON, TX
Notes: The company derives approximately 75% of its revenue from hotel operations.

Key Personnel
EUGENE LUCAS - CEO; President; Director Real Estate
LOU SANFORD - Treasurer; Corporate Secretary; Controller; Director Finance, Information Systems

Clean Plate Restaurants Inc.
1715 Church St
Galveston, TX 77550

Telephone: (409) 974-4642
Internet Homepage: cleanplaterestaurants.com
Type of Business: Chain Restaurant Operator
Year Founded: 2013
Total Sales: $40,260,000 (e)
Total Units: 14
Trade Names: Carmine's Pie House (1); Doc's Fish Camp & Grill (1); Hamburger Inn Diner (1); Joe's Italian Pizza, Pasta & Caffe (1); Lola's Burger & Tequila Bar (1); Lola's Burrito & Burger Joint (1); Malibu Beach Grill (1); MarketPlace Grill (2); Monterey Grill (1); Moon Dog Pie House (1); Noca (1); Sono (1); Zest (1)
Company-Owned Units: 14
Primary Menu: American (4); Californian (1); Hamburger (2); Japanese (1); Mexican (1); Pizza (2); Seafood (2); Steak/Seafood (1)
Areas of Operation: AL, AR, FL, GA, NC, OH, TX
Type of Foodservice: Casual Dining (13)

Key Personnel
TONY KAMIN - Executive Chairman
WOOD CHATHAM - CEO; President
MICHAEL NICHOLAS - CFO
VIRGIL MORAR - General Manager
MUCAHIT ORHAN - General Manager
KATHRYN BRODERICK - Director Marketing

Food Franchise Corporation of America, LLC
2705 61st St Ste H
Galveston, TX 77551-1865

Telephone: (832) 582-8854
Type of Business: Chain Restaurant Operator
Total Sales: $2,785,000 (e)
Total Units: 8
Trade Names: Cinnabon (8)
Units Franchised From: 8
Primary Menu: Snacks (8)
Areas of Operation: NM, TX
Type of Foodservice: Quick Serve (8)
Franchise Affiliation: Cinnabon Inc.,

ATLANTA, GA

Key Personnel
GORAV JAIN - President
RICKY JAIN - Owner; General Buyer

Gaido's of Galveston Inc.
3828 Seawall Blvd
Galveston, TX 77550-8848

Mailing Address: PO Box 3130, GALVESTON, TX, 77552-0130
Telephone: (409) 762-9625
Fax Number: (409) 761-5518
Internet Homepage: gaidos.com; nicksgalveston.com
Company Email: info@nicksgalveston.com
Type of Business: Chain Restaurant Operator
Year Founded: 1911
Total Sales: $6,056,000 (e)
Alcohol Sales: 25%
Number of Employees: 300
Average Check: Lunch(12); Dinner(18)
Total Units: 2
Trade Names: Gaido's Seafood Restaurant (1); Nick's Kitchen and Beach Bar (1)
Company-Owned Units: 2
Preferred Location Types: Freestanding; Hotel/Motel
Alcohol Served: Beer, Wine, Liquor
Primary Menu: Steak/Seafood (2)
Areas of Operation: TX
Type of Foodservice: Casual Dining (1); Fine Dining (1)
Primary Distributors: (Food) SYSCO Corporation, HOUSTON, TX

Key Personnel
NICK GAIDO - President; General Manager; General Buyer
KEVIN JOHNSON - General Manager
NANCY KITCHEL - Director Accounting
MARY BASS - Director Accounting

TriBox, LLC
PO Box 106630
Garland, TX 75049-6539

Telephone: (972) 240-5225
Type of Business: Chain Restaurant Operator
Total Sales: $58,070,000 (e)
Total Units: 23
Trade Names: Jack in the Box (23)
Units Franchised From: 23
Primary Menu: Hamburger (23)
Areas of Operation: TX
Type of Foodservice: Quick Serve (23)
Franchise Affiliation: Jack in the Box Restaurants, SAN DIEGO, CA

Key Personnel
CRAIG DETWILER - President; Owner
YASIN CHOUDRY - Owner; General Buyer

Yadarr, Inc.
335 S Garland Ave
Garland, TX 75040-6150

Telephone: (972) 276-7643
Type of Business: Chain Restaurant Operator
Total Sales: $5,384,000 (e)
Total Units: 2
Trade Names: Jack in the Box (2)
Units Franchised From: 2
Primary Menu: Hamburger (2)
Areas of Operation: TX
Type of Foodservice: Quick Serve (2)
Franchise Affiliation: Jack in the Box Restaurants, SAN DIEGO, CA

Key Personnel
MANUEL ARRUDA - Owner; General Buyer

Meyer Enterprises
102 Dawana Ln
Georgetown, TX 78628-1217

Telephone: (512) 863-8334
Fax Number: (512) 868-1064
Type of Business: Chain Restaurant Operator
Total Sales: $20,451,000 (e)
Number of Employees: 115
Total Units: 4
Trade Names: McDonald's (4)
Units Franchised From: 4
Preferred Square Footage: 2,500
Primary Menu: Hamburger (4)
Projected Remodelings: 1
Areas of Operation: TX
Type of Foodservice: Quick Serve (4)
Franchise Affiliation: McDonald's Corporation, CHICAGO, IL

Key Personnel
DENNIS MEYER - Partner; General Buyer
JOANN MEYER - Partner; General Buyer

D Q Richeson Group
1711 State Highway 16 S
Graham, TX 76450-4607

Mailing Address: PO Box 1299, GRAHAM, TX, 76450-1299
Telephone: (940) 549-5041
Fax Number: (940) 549-6106
Internet Homepage: richesondq.com
Type of Business: Chain Restaurant Operator
Total Sales: $54,440,000 (e)
Total Units: 39
Trade Names: DQ Grill & Chill (39)
Units Franchised From: 39
Primary Menu: American (39)
Areas of Operation: TX
Type of Foodservice: Quick Serve (39)
Franchise Affiliation: International Dairy Queen Inc., BLOOMINGTON, MN

Key Personnel
DORIS RICHESON - Owner; General Buyer

Bassam Odeh, Inc.
1915 Pine St
Grand Prairie, TX 75050-6157

Telephone: (469) 865-1300
Type of Business: Chain Restaurant Operator
Total Sales: $8,303,000 (e)
Total Units: 3
Trade Names: Jack in the Box (3)
Units Franchised From: 3
Primary Menu: Hamburger (3)
Areas of Operation: TX
Type of Foodservice: Quick Serve (3)
Franchise Affiliation: Jack in the Box Restaurants, SAN DIEGO, CA

Key Personnel
BASSAM ODEH - Owner; General Buyer

JDD - Jason's Deli Distribution Center
2103 W Interstate 20
Grand Prairie, TX 75052-1005

Telephone: (972) 602-4305
Fax Number: (972) 606-2406
Internet Homepage: jasonsdeli.com
Listing Type: Distribution Center
Type of Business: Chain Restaurant Operator
Number of Employees: 100
Areas of Operation: AR, AZ, CO, FL, GA, IA, KS, LA, NC, NV, OK, TN, TX
Parent Company: Deli Management Inc., BEAUMONT, TX

Key Personnel
CHRIS NORTHRUP - General Manager

Odeh Premier - B Operational Enterprises, L.P.
1915 Pine St
Grand Prairie, TX 75050

Telephone: (469) 733-1863
Type of Business: Chain Restaurant Operator
Total Sales: $64,230,000 (e)
Total Units: 27

Trade Names: Bleu Med Bar (2); Chick-Fil-A (1); Jack in the Box (17); Qdoba (7)
Units Franchised From: 27
Primary Menu: American (2); Chicken (1); Hamburger (17); Mexican (7)
Areas of Operation: TX
Type of Foodservice: Casual Dining (10); Quick Serve (17)
Franchise Affiliation: Jack in the Box Restaurants, SAN DIEGO, CA

Key Personnel
BASSAM ODEH - Owner; General Buyer

Six Flags Entertainment Corp. (Food Service)
924 E Avenue J
Grand Prairie, TX 75050-2622

Telephone: (972) 595-5000
Fax Number: (972) 641-0323
Internet Homepage: sixflags.com
Company Email: guestrelations@sftp.com
Type of Business: Foodservice Operations - Theme Parks
Year Founded: 1961
Publicly Held: Yes
Total Sales: $612,818,000 (e)
Alcohol Sales: 1%
Number of Employees: 42,500
Foodservice Sales: $147,076,000 (e)
Internet Order Processing: Yes
Total Units: 24
Trade Names: Frontier City (1); La Ronde (1); Six Flags America (1); Six Flags Darien Lake (1); Six Flags Discovery Kingdom (1); Six Flags Fiesta (1); Six Flags Great Adventure & Wild Safari (1); Six Flags Great America (1); Six Flags Great Escape Lodge & Indoor Water Park (1); Six Flags Hurricane Harbor (8); Six Flags Magic Mountain (1); Six Flags New England (1); Six Flags Over Georgia (1); Six Flags Over Texas (1); Six Flags Saint Louis (1); Six Flags White Water (1); The Great Escape & Splashwater Kingdom (1)
Company-Owned Units: 24
Preferred Square Footage: 300; 1,200; 2,000
Preferred Location Types: Parks
Alcohol Served: Beer, Wine, Liquor
Primary Menu: Miscellaneous (24)
Projected Openings: 2
Areas of Operation: AZ, CA, GA, IL, MA, MD, MO, NJ, NY, OK, TX, QC
Foreign Countries: CANADA; CHINA; MEXICO; SAUDI ARABIA
Type of Foodservice: Cafeteria; Casual Dining; Family Restaurant; Fast Casual; Fine Dining; In-Store Feeder; Quick Serve
On-site Distribution Center: Yes
Primary Distributors: (Full Line) SYSCO Food Services of North Texas, LEWISVILLE, TX
Notes: The company operates more than 1,200 foodservice units and derives approximately 76% of its revenue from theme-park admissions and retail sales of merchandise.

Key Personnel
KYLE BRADSHAW - President Finance
BRIAN MACHAMER - President Division
DAVE AUSTIN - Chief Information Security Officer; Senior VP Information Systems
JOHN BEMENT - Senior VP
NANCY HAMLIN - Senior VP Accounting
STEPHANIE JESSOP BORGES - VP Marketing, Strategic Planning
MARK KUPFERMAN - VP Marketing, Digital Media, Consumer Insights
CHRISTOPHER NEUMANN - VP Legal
JEFF HARRIS - Senior Director Finance
BONNIE BOE - Director Operations
BRIAN BOTTINI - Director E-Commerce
PAUL AMBROSE - Manager Information Systems
JILL HOWARD - Manager Employee Benefits
JENSEN PARRA - Manager Accounting
STEPHANIE NANCE - Corporate Manager Financial Planning
JENNIFER GARCIA - Corporate Manager
ROBERT BUSTLE - Corporate Director Games
STEPHEN WRIGHT - Corporate Director Operations, Network

Tandy Pizza LLC
2724 Vela
Grand Prairie, TX 75054-5537

Telephone: (817) 896-7258
Company Email: rvankawana@yahoo.com
Type of Business: Chain Restaurant Operator
Total Sales: $17,050,000 (e)
Total Units: 14
Trade Names: Little Caesars Pizza (14)
Units Franchised From: 14
Primary Menu: Pizza (14)
Projected Openings: 1
Areas of Operation: FL, TX
Type of Foodservice: Quick Serve (14)
Franchise Affiliation: Little Caesar Enterprises Inc., DETROIT, MI

Key Personnel
RAJENDRA VANKAWALA - Owner; General Buyer

Boi Na Braza Churrascaria
4025 William D Tate Ave
Grapevine, TX 76051-7111

Telephone: (817) 329-5514
Fax Number: (817) 416-7451
Internet Homepage: boinabraza.com
Company Email: boinabraza.dfw@boinabraza.com
Type of Business: Chain Restaurant Operator
Year Founded: 2000
Total Sales: $2,998,000 (e)
Alcohol Sales: 2%
Number of Employees: 70
Average Check: Dinner(58)
Internet Order Processing: Yes
Total Units: 3
Trade Names: Boi Na Braza Churrascaria (3)
Company-Owned Units: 3
Preferred Location Types: Freestanding
Alcohol Served: Beer, Wine, Liquor
Primary Menu: Steak (3)
Projected Openings: 1
Areas of Operation: OH, TX
Type of Foodservice: Casual Dining (3)
Primary Distributors: (Full Line) SYSCO Food Services of North Texas, LEWISVILLE, TX

Key Personnel
JULIO MATHEUS - CEO; Owner; General Buyer
NEIMAR HENSEL - General Manager; General Buyer
WENDEL SILVA - Manager Sales; Planner
RAFAELA SOZIM - Manager Accounting

Cotton Patch Cafe Inc.
600 E Dallas Rd Ste 300
Grapevine, TX 76051-4191

Telephone: (972) 929-2806
Fax Number: (817) 865-6396
Internet Homepage: cottonpatch.com
Company Email: comments@cottonpatch.com
Type of Business: Chain Restaurant Operator
Year Founded: 1989
Systemwide Sales: $90,272,000 (e)
Total Sales: $100,480,000 (e)
Alcohol Sales: 2%
Number of Employees: 1,527
Average Check: Lunch(18); Dinner(18)
Total Units: 52
Trade Names: Cotton Patch Cafe (52)
Company-Owned Units: 52
Preferred Square Footage: 4,000
Preferred Location Types: Freestanding; Strip Mall
Alcohol Served: Beer, Wine, Liquor
Primary Menu: American (52)
Areas of Operation: AR, NM, OK, TX
Type of Foodservice: Casual Dining (52)
Catering Services: Yes
Primary Distributors: (Full Line) Ben E. Keith Foods, FORT WORTH, TX
Parent Company: Altamont Capital Partners, PALO ALTO, CA

Key Personnel
KATHY NELSON - CEO; General Buyer
STEPHANIE CALLIHAN - CFO
JUSTIN MARSHALL - Area Director
VICTOR RIOS - Area Director
CANDICE BROOKE RAUCH - Creative Director
LISA CASE - Director Marketing

BRANDON KEATING - Director Technology

D.L. Rogers Corporation
1225 S Main St
Grapevine, TX 76051-5585

Telephone: (817) 428-2077
Fax Number: (817) 428-7254
Type of Business: Chain Restaurant Operator
Year Founded: 1962
Total Sales: $508,710,000 (e)
Number of Employees: 5,500
Average Check: Breakfast(6); Lunch(8); Dinner(8)
Total Units: 237
Trade Names: Sonic America's Drive-In (237)
Units Franchised From: 237
Preferred Square Footage: 2,400; 3,500
Preferred Location Types: Freestanding
Primary Menu: Hamburger (237)
Areas of Operation: AR, KS, LA, MO, NC, OK, SC, TN, TX
Type of Foodservice: Quick Serve (237)
Franchise Affiliation: Sonic Corp., OKLAHOMA CITY, OK

Key Personnel
DARRELL ROGERS - Chairman
SHAWN CATHER - CEO; President
JAMES JUNKIN - COO
CHRIS ROGERS - VP
CHRIS LOCKE - VP Accounting
TRACY KELLER - Treasurer
JIM SIMONS - Director Operations, Midwest Region
JAMY SLOAN - Director Operations, Central Region
JONATHAN PRESTON - Director Operations
JIM PEOPLES - Regional Director Operations
REBECCA SWINK - Manager Communications
KEVIN WHITE - Supervisor Area

Encore Restaurants Inc.
1705 W Northwest Hwy Ste 260
Grapevine, TX 76051-8125

Telephone: (817) 329-7343
Fax Number: (817) 481-1544
Type of Business: Chain Restaurant Operator
Year Founded: 1992
Total Sales: $79,700,000 (e)
Number of Employees: 1,655
Average Check: Breakfast(12); Lunch(14); Dinner(14)
Total Units: 37
Trade Names: Sonic America's Drive-In (37)
Units Franchised From: 37
Preferred Square Footage: 1,300; 3,000
Preferred Location Types: Freestanding
Primary Menu: American (37)
Areas of Operation: TX

Type of Foodservice: Quick Serve (37)
Franchise Affiliation: Sonic Corp., OKLAHOMA CITY, OK
Primary Distributors: (Equipment) The Wasserstrom Co., COLUMBUS, OH

Key Personnel
DENNIS CLARK - Owner; Director Finance, Operations, Information Systems, Real Estate; General Buyer
LINDA CLARK - CFO; VP; Controller; Manager Risk Management, Human Resources
MICHAEL CLARK - Director Operations

Auntie Anne's Franchise
7401 Interstate Highway 30
Greenville, TX 75402-7121

Telephone: (972) 978-7160
Type of Business: Chain Restaurant Operator
Total Sales: $1,539,000 (e)
Total Units: 2
Trade Names: Auntie Anne's Hand-Rolled Soft Pretzels (2)
Units Franchised From: 2
Areas of Operation: TX
Type of Foodservice: Quick Serve
Franchise Affiliation: Auntie Anne's Inc., LANCASTER, PA

Key Personnel
DEAN STOLTZFUS - Owner; General Buyer

Domino's Franchisee
713 N 77 Sunshine Strip
Harlingen, TX 78550-8847

Telephone: (956) 428-6296
Type of Business: Chain Restaurant Operator
Total Sales: $6,001,000 (e)
Total Units: 3
Trade Names: Domino's (3)
Units Franchised From: 3
Primary Menu: Pizza (3)
Areas of Operation: TX
Type of Foodservice: Quick Serve (3)
Franchise Affiliation: Domino's Pizza Inc, ANN ARBOR, MI

Key Personnel
MITCHEL A. MCCORMICK - Owner; General Buyer

D&P Ice Cream, L.L.C.
11851 Bandera Rd Ste 114
Helotes, TX 78023-4513

Telephone: (210) 372-9730
Company Email: csc857@yahoo.com

Type of Business: Chain Restaurant Operator
Total Sales: $1,233,000 (e)
Total Units: 2
Trade Names: Cold Stone Creamery (2)
Units Franchised From: 2
Primary Menu: Snacks (2)
Areas of Operation: TX
Type of Foodservice: Quick Serve (2)
Franchise Affiliation: Kahala Brands, SCOTTSDALE, AZ

Key Personnel
PAUL DEININGER - Partner
DEBBIE DEININGER - Partner

Reno Ltd
PO Box 777
Hewitt, TX 76643-0777

Telephone: (254) 709-3058
Fax Number: (254) 666-6174
Type of Business: Chain Restaurant Operator
Total Sales: $2,648,000 (e)
Total Units: 4
Trade Names: Little Caesars Pizza (4)
Units Franchised From: 4
Primary Menu: Pizza (4)
Areas of Operation: TX
Type of Foodservice: Quick Serve (4)
Franchise Affiliation: Little Caesar Enterprises Inc., DETROIT, MI

Key Personnel
J. NIEOLICH - Partner; General Buyer
KEVIN FOSTER - Partner; General Buyer

Domino's Franchisee
701 N International Blvd Ste 108
Hidalgo, TX 78557-2583

Telephone: (956) 843-8899
Type of Business: Chain Restaurant Operator
Total Sales: $7,958,000 (e)
Total Units: 4
Trade Names: Domino's (4)
Units Franchised From: 4
Primary Menu: Pizza (4)
Areas of Operation: TX
Type of Foodservice: Quick Serve (4)
Franchise Affiliation: Domino's Pizza Inc, ANN ARBOR, MI

Key Personnel
THOMAS R. BENEVENTE - Owner; General Buyer

Hielan Management LLC
2280 Highland Village Rd Ste 150
Highland Village, TX 75077-7184

Telephone: (972) 966-2221
Fax Number: (972) 534-1345
Type of Business: Chain Restaurant Operator
Total Sales: $168,250,000 (e)
Alcohol Sales: 5%
Number of Employees: 5,375
Average Check: Dinner(18)
Total Units: 42
Trade Names: Chili's Grill & Bar (42)
Units Franchised From: 42
Preferred Square Footage: 3,900; 5,500
Preferred Location Types: Freestanding
Alcohol Served: Beer, Wine, Liquor
Primary Menu: Southwest/Tex-Mex (42)
Areas of Operation: GA, SC
Type of Foodservice: Casual Dining (42)
Franchise Affiliation: Chili's Grill & Bar, DALLAS, TX

Key Personnel
GREG CYRIER - CEO; President; General Manager; General Buyer
KEITH MENKING - CEO; President
JODI ALDRIDGE - Area Director
TREY BUTTERFIELD - Area Director Operations
BOB HOOVER - Senior Director Information Technology
BILL WILES - Director Finance
ELAINA CANTRELL - Director Operations
JIM GILLILAN - Director

Catalina Restaurant Group Inc.
120 Chula Vis
Hollywood Park, TX 78232-2234

Telephone: (210) 403-3725
Fax Number: (760) 476-5141
Internet Homepage: carrows.com; cocosbakery.com; foodmps.com
Type of Business: Chain Restaurant Operator
Year Founded: 2002
Total Sales: $128,790,000 (e)
Alcohol Sales: 15%
Number of Employees: 4,576
Average Check: Breakfast(12); Lunch(16); Dinner(18)
Internet Order Processing: Yes
Internet Sales: 1.00%
Total Units: 39
Trade Names: Carrows (6); Coco's Bakery Restaurant (33)
Company-Owned Units: 33
Units Franchised To: 6
Preferred Location Types: Downtown; Freestanding; Strip Mall

Alcohol Served: Beer, Wine, Liquor
Primary Menu: American (39)
Projected Openings: 3
Areas of Operation: AZ, CA, NV
Type of Foodservice: Casual Dining (39)
Parent Company: Shari's Management Corporation, BEAVERTON, OR

Key Personnel
ALLEN JONES - CEO; President
JASON KEMP - CFO
NORMAN STEVENS - Area Director Operations
PETER DONBAVAND - VP Real Estate, Business Development
GARY GRAHAM - VP Real Estate; Director Research & Development
BILL RUNYON - Director Operations
RAMIRO SILVA - Regional Director Operations

Adcock QSR Group, LLC
7117 Belgold St Ste C
Houston, TX 77066-1027

Telephone: (281) 440-5131
Fax Number: (281) 605-1789
Internet Homepage: adcockqsrgroup.com
Type of Business: Chain Restaurant Operator
Total Sales: $37,820,000 (e)
Total Units: 8
Trade Names: McDonald's (8)
Units Franchised From: 8
Primary Menu: Hamburger (8)
Areas of Operation: TX
Type of Foodservice: Quick Serve (8)
Franchise Affiliation: McDonald's Corporation, CHICAGO, IL

Key Personnel
DOUG ADCOCK - President; Partner; General Buyer
BRAD ADCOCK - Partner; General Buyer

Agricole Hosplitality
550 Heights Blvd
Houston, TX 77007-2533

Telephone: (713) 880-8463
Internet Homepage: agricolehospitality.com
Company Email: info@revivalmarket.com
Type of Business: Chain Restaurant Operator
Total Units: 7
Trade Names: Coltivare (1); Eight Row Flint (1); Indianola (1); Miss Carousel (1); Night Heron (1); Revival Market (1); Vinny's (1)
Company-Owned Units: 7
Primary Menu: American (3); Italian (1); Pizza (1); Snacks (1); Taco (1)
Projected Openings: 1
Areas of Operation: TX
Type of Foodservice: Casual Dining (7)

Key Personnel
RYAN PERA - Partner; Executive Chef
MORGAN WEBER - Partner; Director Beverages
CHRISTINA RAMEY - General Manager
VINCENT HUYNH - Director Culinary Operations
BRYAN DAVIS - Director Operations

Annieyi Inc
14510 Memorial Dr
Houston, TX 77079-5408

Telephone: (281) 493-9778
Type of Business: Chain Restaurant Operator
Total Sales: $3,121,000 (e)
Average Check: Dinner(10)
Total Units: 2
Trade Names: Schlotzsky's Deli/Cinnabon (2)
Units Franchised From: 2
Primary Menu: Sandwiches/Deli (2); Snacks (2)
Areas of Operation: TX
Type of Foodservice: Fast Casual (2)
Franchise Affiliation: Cinnabon Inc., ATLANTA, GA; Schlotzsky's Ltd., ATLANTA, GA

Key Personnel
DOUGLAS YI - President

Arandas Franchise
2525 North Loop W Ste 610
Houston, TX 77008-1094

Telephone: (713) 691-3373
Fax Number: (713) 691-3442
Internet Homepage: taqueriasarandas.com
Type of Business: Chain Restaurant Operator
Systemwide Sales: $69,352,000 (e)
Total Units: 28
Trade Names: Ostioneria Arandas Seafood (1); Taquerias Arandas (27)
Units Franchised To: 28
Primary Menu: Seafood (1); Taco (27)
Areas of Operation: TX
Type of Foodservice: Casual Dining (1); Quick Serve (27)
Notes: The company also operates four bakeries, dba Arandas Bakery.

Key Personnel
JUDY CAMARENA - Chairman; CEO; President; Exec VP Finance, Purchasing, Marketing, Human Resources, Menu Development

Auntie Anne's Franchise
303 Memorial City Ste 574
Houston, TX 77024-2691

Telephone: (832) 358-8888
Internet Homepage: auntieannesfranchising.com
Type of Business: Chain Restaurant Operator
Total Sales: $8,669,000 (e)
Total Units: 12
Trade Names: Auntie Anne's Hand-Rolled Soft Pretzels (12)
Units Franchised From: 12
Primary Menu: Snacks (12)
Areas of Operation: TX
Type of Foodservice: Quick Serve (12)
Franchise Affiliation: Auntie Anne's Inc., LANCASTER, PA

Key Personnel
DAVID INGENITO - Owner; General Buyer

AYG Food Services
3821 Farnham St
Houston, TX 77098

Telephone: (713) 681-5465
Type of Business: Chain Restaurant Operator
Year Founded: 2014
Total Units: 2
Trade Names: The Halal Guys (2)
Units Franchised From: 2
Primary Menu: Middle Eastern (2)
Projected Openings: 1
Areas of Operation: TX
Type of Foodservice: Quick Serve (2)
Franchise Affiliation: The Halal Guys Inc., ASTORIA, NY

Key Personnel
GEOFFREY HERBERT - President
MASROOR FATANY - Owner; Director

Azuma Restaurant Group
4820 Washington Ave
Houston, TX 77007

Telephone: (713) 861-2726
Internet Homepage: azumarestaurant.com; katarobata.com; somasushi.com; theazumagroup.com
Company Email: events@theazumagroup.com
Type of Business: Chain Restaurant Operator
Total Units: 5
Trade Names: Azuma (3); Kata Robata (1); Soma (1)
Company-Owned Units: 5
Primary Menu: Japanese (5)
Areas of Operation: TX

Type of Foodservice: Casual Dining (5)

Key Personnel
YUN CHENG - Owner; General Buyer

Becks Prime
115 W 19th St
Houston, TX 77008-4007

Telephone: (713) 470-1176
Internet Homepage: becksprime.com
Type of Business: Chain Restaurant Operator
Year Founded: 1985
Total Sales: $11,050,000 (e)
Alcohol Sales: 2%
Number of Employees: 162
Average Check: Lunch(10); Dinner(10)
Internet Order Processing: Yes
Total Units: 14
Trade Names: Becks Prime (14)
Company-Owned Units: 14
Preferred Square Footage: 2,000
Preferred Location Types: Downtown; Freestanding
Alcohol Served: Beer, Wine
Primary Menu: American (14)
Areas of Operation: TX
Type of Foodservice: Fast Casual (14)
Catering Services: Yes
Primary Distributors: (Food) SYSCO Food Services of Houston Inc., HOUSTON, TX

Key Personnel
WINFIELD CAMPBELL - CEO; Partner; Director Information Systems, Real Estate
MOLLY VOORHEES - President; General Buyer
JOHN STORMS - Partner; CFO
MIKE KNAPP - Partner; COO; Director Finance, Operations, Facility/Maintenance, Information Systems, Real Estate, Design, Menu Development, Catering; General Buyer
MICHEAL GEISZLER - VP Operations
MIKE GEISZLER - VP Operations
JULIE KNAPP - VP Human Resources
LIONEL COLLINS - General Manager
MICHAEL KOEPPLINGER - General Manager
JIM KRAFKA - General Manager
LAVERNE ROBERTSON - General Manager
CHRIS SUAREZ - General Manager
RAY ASLI - General Manager
ALAN UNDERWOOD - Regional Manager Operations
LEE SCARPINATO - Project Manager

Bella Restaurants Group
4708 Lillian St
Houston, TX 77007

Telephone: (346) 444-6888
Company Email: ddonovan@bellarestaurants.com

Type of Business: Chain Restaurant Operator
Year Founded: 1998
Total Sales: $9,947,000 (e)
Total Units: 13
Trade Names: Zoa Moroccan Kitchen (2); Coco Crepes, Waffles & Coffee (9); Mia Bella Trattoria (2)
Company-Owned Units: 13
Primary Menu: Coffee (9); Italian (2); Spanish (2)
Areas of Operation: TX
Type of Foodservice: Casual Dining (4); Fast Casual (9)

Key Personnel
YOUSSEF NAFAA - CEO
RYLEE MARTIN - Director Marketing

Bellagreen Holdings LLC
2305 W Alabama St R2
Houston, TX 77098

Telephone: (713) 533-0777
Fax Number: (713) 533-0043
Internet Homepage: bellagreen.com
Type of Business: Chain Restaurant Operator
Year Founded: 2008
Total Units: 8
Trade Names: Bellagreen (8)
Company-Owned Units: 8
Primary Menu: American (8)
Projected Openings: 2
Areas of Operation: TX
Type of Foodservice: Fast Casual (8)
Catering Services: Yes
Parent Company: Hargett Hunter Capital Partners, RALEIGH, NC

Key Personnel
JEFF BROCK - Partner

Berryhill Baja Grill
4205 San Felipe St Ste 200
Houston, TX 77027-2915

Telephone: (713) 850-7949
Internet Homepage: berryhillbajagrill.com
Company Email: information@berryhillbajagrill.com
Type of Business: Chain Restaurant Operator
Year Founded: 1992
Systemwide Sales: $54,936,000 (e)
Total Sales: $16,300,000 (e)
Alcohol Sales: 12%
Number of Employees: 294
Average Check: Breakfast(8); Lunch(10); Dinner(14)
Total Units: 10
Trade Names: Berryhill Baja Grill (10)
Company-Owned Units: 5
Units Franchised To: 5

Preferred Square Footage: 3,500
Preferred Location Types: Freestanding; Strip Mall
Alcohol Served: Beer, Wine, Liquor
Primary Menu: Mexican (10)
Areas of Operation: TX
Foreign Countries: MEXICO
Type of Foodservice: Fast Casual (10)
Catering Services: Yes
Primary Distributors: (Full Line) SYSCO Food Services of Houston Inc., HOUSTON, TX

Key Personnel
JEFF ANON - CEO; President; Director Facility/Maintenance, Information Systems, Real Estate, Human Resources; General Buyer
NICOLE BLANCHARD - VP Operations
KRISTINE TROGER - VP
LAURA MAY - Director Human Resources
LEAH ROGERS - Manager Catering
JOELYN SOLANA - Manager Catering

BMB Franchising
10737 Cutten Rd
Houston, TX 77066-5007

Telephone: (281) 397-6730
Internet Homepage: 4bombshells.com; bombshellsfranchise.com
Company Email: ir@ricks.com
Type of Business: Chain Restaurant Operator
Year Founded: 2013
Total Units: 7
Trade Names: Bombshells (7)
Company-Owned Units: 7
Primary Menu: American (7)
Projected Openings: 2
Areas of Operation: TX
Type of Foodservice: Casual Dining (7)
Parent Company: RCI Hospitality Holdings Inc, HOUSTON, TX

Key Personnel
ERIC LANGAN - CEO
DAVID SIMMONS - Director Operations

Clark Cooper Concepts
2525 Robinhood St
Houston, TX 77005-2573

Telephone: (832) 523-1777
Internet Homepage: brasserie19.com; clarkcooperconcepts.com; coppaosteriahouston.com; ibizafoodandwinebar.com; mobilemug.com; punkssimplesouthernfood.com; thedunlavy.com
Type of Business: Chain Restaurant Operator
Total Units: 6
Trade Names: Brasserie 19 (1); Coppa Osteria (1); Ibiza Food & Wine Bar (1); Punk's Simple Southern Food (1); The Dunlavy (1); The Kitchen at the Dunlavy(1)
Company-Owned Units: 6
Primary Menu: American (1); French/Continental (1); Greek/Mediterranean (1); Italian (1); Miscellaneous (1); Southern (1)
Areas of Operation: TX
Type of Foodservice: Casual Dining (4); Fast Casual (1); Fine Dining (1)

Key Personnel
GRANT COOPER - President; Partner
CHARLES CLARK - Partner; Executive Chef
MARC CANTU - Senior Director Operations

Continental Superior Management Group
12011 Westbrae Pkwy
Houston, TX 77031-3814

Telephone: (713) 266-8799
Fax Number: (713) 266-2703
Type of Business: Chain Restaurant Operator
Year Founded: 1984
Total Sales: $91,800,000 (e)
Number of Employees: 480
Average Check: Lunch(12); Dinner(16)
Total Units: 35
Trade Names: Popeyes Louisiana Kitchen (35)
Units Franchised From: 35
Preferred Square Footage: 2,000
Preferred Location Types: Freestanding
Primary Menu: Chicken (35)
Areas of Operation: TX
Type of Foodservice: Quick Serve (35)
Franchise Affiliation: Popeyes Louisiana Kitchen Inc., ATLANTA, GA
Primary Distributors: (Equipment) The Wasserstrom Co., COLUMBUS, OH; (Food) Performance Foodservice - Victoria, VICTORIA, TX; (Supplies) The Wasserstrom Co., COLUMBUS, OH

Key Personnel
ALI LAKHANY - CEO; President; CFO; General Buyer
EMAD LAKHANY - VP; Director
NATE ATTAIE - Director Operations
MARIE SERRANO - Manager Human Resources

Cordua Restaurants LP
3300 S Gessner Rd Ste 270
Houston, TX 77063-5197

Telephone: (713) 355-6281
Fax Number: (832) 922-6232
Internet Homepage: americasrestaurant.com; churrascos.com
Company Email: corporate@cordua.com
Type of Business: Chain Restaurant Operator
Year Founded: 1993
Total Sales: $34,260,000 (e)
Alcohol Sales: 25%
Number of Employees: 395
Average Check: Lunch(36); Dinner(72)
Internet Order Processing: Yes
Total Units: 9
Trade Names: Amazon Grille (1); Americas (1); Artista (1); Churrascos (6)
Company-Owned Units: 9
Preferred Square Footage: 5,500; 6,000
Preferred Location Types: Freestanding
Alcohol Served: Beer, Wine, Liquor
Primary Menu: Latin American/Cuban (9)
Areas of Operation: TX
Type of Foodservice: Casual Dining (1); Fine Dining (8)
Catering Services: Yes
Primary Distributors: (Full Line) SYSCO Corporation, HOUSTON, TX

Key Personnel
HORLANDO DUQUE - General Manager

Culinary Institute LeNotre
7070 Allensby St
Houston, TX 77022-4322

Telephone: (713) 692-0077
Fax Number: (713) 692-7399
Internet Homepage: culinaryinstitute.edu
Type of Business: Culinary Schools
Areas of Operation: TX

Key Personnel
JANE SMITH - Manager Finance

Da Marco
1520 Westheimer Rd
Houston, TX 77006-3736

Telephone: (713) 807-8857
Fax Number: (713) 807-8301
Internet Homepage: dolcevitahouston.com; poscolhouston.com; damarcohouston.com
Type of Business: Chain Restaurant Operator
Year Founded: 2000
Total Sales: $2,915,000 (e)
Alcohol Sales: 40%
Number of Employees: 30
Average Check: Lunch(24); Dinner(42)
Total Units: 3
Trade Names: Da Marco (1); Dolce Vita Pizzeria (1); Vinoteca Poscol (1)
Units Franchised To: 3
Preferred Location Types: Freestanding
Alcohol Served: Beer, Wine, Liquor
Primary Menu: Italian (3)
Areas of Operation: TX

Type of Foodservice: Casual Dining (2); Fine Dining (1)
Primary Distributors: (Food) SYSCO Food Services of Houston Inc., HOUSTON, TX

Key Personnel
GLORIA WILES - President
MARCO WILES - President; General Manager; Executive Chef; General Buyer
NICHOLAS NIKIC - General Manager

David Moss Management
10638 W Bellfort Ave
Houston, TX 77099-4747

Telephone: (281) 313-4191
Type of Business: Chain Restaurant Operator
Total Sales: $32,520,000 (e)
Total Units: 7
Trade Names: McDonald's (7)
Units Franchised From: 7
Preferred Location Types: Freestanding
Primary Menu: Hamburger (7)
Areas of Operation: TX
Type of Foodservice: Quick Serve (7)
Franchise Affiliation: McDonald's Corporation, CHICAGO, IL

Key Personnel
DAVE MOSS JR - President; General Buyer
ANERESA GREEN - Supervisor Area

Delicious Concepts Restaurant Group
1102 Yale St Ste 300
Houston, TX 77008

Telephone: (832) 767-1380
Internet Homepage: deliciousconcepts.com
Company Email: info@deliciousconcepts.com
Type of Business: Chain Restaurant Operator
Total Sales: $9,748,000 (e)
Total Units: 11
Trade Names: Blackbird Izakaya (1); Lola Diner (1); Pinks Pizza (7); Ritual (1); Shepherd Park (1)
Company-Owned Units: 11
Primary Menu: American (3); Asian (1); Pizza (7)
Areas of Operation: TX
Type of Foodservice: Casual Dining (4); Quick Serve (7)

Key Personnel
KEN BRIDGE - CEO; Owner; General Buyer

Demeris Barbecue
2911 S Shepherd Dr
Houston, TX 77098-1537

Telephone: (713) 529-7326
Fax Number: (713) 529-2682
Internet Homepage: demeris.com
Company Email: yonny@demeris.com
Type of Business: Chain Restaurant Operator
Year Founded: 1963
Total Sales: $7,386,000 (e)
Alcohol Sales: 1%
Number of Employees: 30
Average Check: Lunch(12); Dinner(14)
Total Units: 2
Trade Names: Demeris Barbecue (2)
Company-Owned Units: 2
Preferred Location Types: Freestanding; Strip Mall
Alcohol Served: Beer
Primary Menu: Bar-B-Q (2)
Areas of Operation: TX
Type of Foodservice: Quick Serve (2)
Catering Services: Yes
On-site Distribution Center: Yes
Primary Distributors: (Full Line) SYSCO Corporation, HOUSTON, TX

Key Personnel
GEORGE DEMERIS - Executive Chef; Director Food Safety, Catering

Denny's Astrodome Restaurant Inc
3332 South Loop W
Houston, TX 77025-5203

Telephone: (713) 666-0999
Fax Number: (713) 666-5657
Type of Business: Chain Restaurant Operator
Total Sales: $54,324,000 (e)
Average Check: Dinner(10)
Total Units: 10
Trade Names: Denny's (18)
Units Franchised From: 18
Primary Menu: American (18)
Areas of Operation: TX
Type of Foodservice: Family Restaurant (18)
Franchise Affiliation: Denny's Corporation, SPARTANBURG, SC

Key Personnel
GIOVANI GARCIA - District Manager

Dish Society
5740 San Felipe St
Houston, TX 77057-3282

Telephone: (832) 538-1060
Internet Homepage: dishsociety.com
Company Email: hello@dishsociety.com
Type of Business: Chain Restaurant Operator
Internet Order Processing: Yes
Total Units: 3
Trade Names: Dish Society (3)
Company-Owned Units: 3

Key Personnel
AARON LYONS - Partner; General Buyer
TRENT PATTERSON - Partner; General Buyer
ERICA BURNS - Director Human Resources

Domino's Franchisee
14520 Memorial Dr Ste J
Houston, TX 77079-5427

Telephone: (281) 497-3977
Type of Business: Chain Restaurant Operator
Total Sales: $3,986,000 (e)
Total Units: 2
Trade Names: Domino's (2)
Units Franchised From: 2
Primary Menu: Pizza (2)
Areas of Operation: TX
Type of Foodservice: Quick Serve (2)
Franchise Affiliation: Domino's Pizza Inc, ANN ARBOR, MI

Key Personnel
WAHID I. DHEDHI - Owner; General Buyer

Domino's Franchisee
14705 Woodforest Blvd Ste 4
Houston, TX 77015-3259

Telephone: (281) 457-1400
Type of Business: Chain Restaurant Operator
Total Sales: $8,170,000 (e)
Total Units: 4
Trade Names: Domino's (4)
Units Franchised From: 4
Primary Menu: Pizza (4)
Areas of Operation: TX
Type of Foodservice: Quick Serve (4)
Franchise Affiliation: Domino's Pizza Inc, ANN ARBOR, MI

Key Personnel
BRIAN K. DENNIS - Owner; General Buyer

El Tiempo Cantina
602 Sawyer St Ste 110
Houston, TX 77007-7510

Telephone: (713) 807-8100
Fax Number: (713) 492-2079
Internet Homepage: eltiempocantina.com
Type of Business: Chain Restaurant Operator

Total Sales: $6,314,000 (e)
Alcohol Sales: 5%
Number of Employees: 530
Internet Order Processing: Yes
Total Units: 12
Trade Names: El Tiempo Cantina (11); Laurenzo's Restaurant (1)
Company-Owned Units: 12
Preferred Location Types: Freestanding
Alcohol Served: Beer, Wine, Liquor
Primary Menu: Mexican (11); Steak (1)
Areas of Operation: TX
Type of Foodservice: Casual Dining (12)

Key Personnel
BLANCA LAURENZO - Partner
DOMENIC LAURENZO - Partner; Executive Chef
LAURENZO ROLLAND - Partner; Executive Chef; General Buyer
KEN JAMAIL - CTO
SHERRY KINSEY - General Manager
PAMELA (PK) HENNIGAN - Manager Catering
MARIA MACHADO - Manager
ANGEL MARTINEZ - Specialist Event Planning
JAMIE DYE - Representative Sales, Catering

Escalante's Mexican Restaurant
5311 Kirby Dr Ste 111
Houston, TX 77005-1317

Telephone: (713) 975-1100
Internet Homepage: escalantes.net
Company Email: julia@escalantes.net
Type of Business: Chain Restaurant Operator
Total Units: 6
Trade Names: Escalante's (6)
Company-Owned Units: 6
Primary Menu: Mexican (6)
Areas of Operation: TX
Type of Foodservice: Casual Dining (6)

Key Personnel
PATRICK TORRES - President; Owner
CYNTHIA HERNANDEZ - Director Catering

Fajita Pete's
6719 Weslayan St
Houston, TX 77005

Telephone: (713) 723-8100
Internet Homepage: fajitapetes.com
Company Email: fajitapetes@bellaire.com
Type of Business: Chain Restaurant Operator
Year Founded: 2002
Total Sales: $13,630,000 (e)
Total Units: 16
Trade Names: Fajita Pete's (16)
Company-Owned Units: 16
Primary Menu: Mexican (16)
Projected Openings: 2
Areas of Operation: TX
Type of Foodservice: Casual Dining (13); Fast Casual (16)

Key Personnel
PEDRO MORA - Owner; General Buyer
DAVID DEANDA - VP Operations
MARK CARRUBA - Director Marketing
RYAN KAUL - Director Operations
PATTY BROWNE - Director Training
ANA SOFIA POCATERRA - Director Operations

Fuddruckers Restaurants LLC
13111 Northwest Fwy Ste 600
Houston, TX 77040-6392

Telephone: (713) 329-6800
Internet Homepage: fuddruckers.com; lubys.com
Company Email: feedback@fuddruckers.com
Type of Business: Chain Restaurant Operator
Year Founded: 1980
Systemwide Sales: $376,134,000 (e)
Total Sales: $93,830,000 (e)
Alcohol Sales: 2%
Number of Employees: 2,560
Average Check: Lunch(10); Dinner(12)
Internet Order Processing: Yes
Internet Sales: 1.00%
Total Units: 85
Trade Names: Fuddruckers (85)
Company-Owned Units: 85
Preferred Square Footage: 500; 800; 2,500; 4,200; 5,500; 6,100; 9,000
Preferred Location Types: Airports; Community Mall; Downtown; Freestanding; Other; Regional Mall; Strip Mall
Alcohol Served: Beer, Wine
Primary Menu: Hamburger (85)
Projected Openings: 10
Areas of Operation: AZ, CA, CT, DC, DE, FL, GA, IA, ID, IL, KS, LA, MA, MD, ME, MI, MN, MO, MS, MT, NC, ND, NE, NJ, NM, NV, NY, OH, OK, OR, PA, PR, SC, SD, TN, TX, UT, VA, WI, FC, SK
Foreign Countries: CANADA; CHILE; COLOMBIA; DOMINICAN REPUBLIC; ITALY; MEXICO; PANAMA; POLAND
Type of Foodservice: Fast Casual (85)
Catering Services: Yes
Primary Distributors: (Equipment) The Wasserstrom Co., COLUMBUS, OH; (Food) US Foods, HOUSTON, TX; (Supplies) The Wasserstrom Co., COLUMBUS, OH
Parent Company: Black Titan Franchise Systems, DALLAS, TX

Key Personnel
NICHOLAS PERKINS - CEO; President
BENJAMIN T. COUTEE - COO
WIMMER JOEY - Area Director
STEVE GOODWEATHER - VP Finance, Communications, Investor Relations
BILL GORDON - VP Real Estate
TRENT TAYLOR - VP Operations
MICHAEL ROKAS - Executive Director Facility/Maintenance, Construction
PETER TROPOLI - Corporate Secretary; General Counsel
KEITH HOOPER - Director Operations, Region
MICHAEL PAUL - Director Internal Audit
DANA ROGERS - Director Marketing
NICK WORLEY - Director Brand Marketing
RICHARD MASON - Director Administration, Design
CINDY RIOJAS - Manager Human Resources

Golden Dream
5861 W 34th St
Houston, TX 77092-6401

Telephone: (713) 655-8989
Fax Number: (832) 201-8827
Internet Homepage: workmcd.com
Type of Business: Chain Restaurant Operator
Total Sales: $23,300,000 (e)
Number of Employees: 300
Average Check: Lunch(8); Dinner(8)
Total Units: 5
Trade Names: McDonald's (5)
Units Franchised From: 5
Preferred Square Footage: 2,500
Preferred Location Types: Convenience Store/Gas Station; Freestanding; Regional Mall
Primary Menu: Hamburger (5)
Areas of Operation: TX
Type of Foodservice: Quick Serve (5)
Franchise Affiliation: McDonald's Corporation, CHICAGO, IL

Key Personnel
CARLA MOORE - Partner
KEVIN MOORE - Partner; General Buyer

Goode Co. Restaurants
2422 Bartlett St Ste 1
Houston, TX 77098-5130

Telephone: (713) 529-4616
Fax Number: (713) 529-6042
Internet Homepage: goodecompany.com
Company Email: information@goodecompany.com
Type of Business: Chain Restaurant Operator
Year Founded: 1977
Total Sales: $12,960,000 (e)
Alcohol Sales: 13%
Number of Employees: 357
Average Check: Breakfast(8); Lunch(10);

Dinner(18)
Internet Order Processing: Yes
Internet Sales: 10.00%
Total Units: 10
Trade Names: Armadillo Palace (1); Goode Co. Kitchen & Cantina (2); Goode Co. Taqueria & Hamburgers (1); Goode Co. Texas Barbeque (4); Goode Co. Texas Seafood (2)
Company-Owned Units: 10
Preferred Square Footage: 5,500; 6,000
Preferred Location Types: Freestanding
Alcohol Served: Beer, Wine, Liquor
Primary Menu: American (1); Bar-B-Q (4); Mexican (1); Seafood (2); Southwest/Tex-Mex (2)
Areas of Operation: TX
Type of Foodservice: Casual Dining (10)
Catering Services: Yes
On-site Distribution Center: Yes
Primary Distributors: (Food) SYSCO Food Services of Houston Inc., HOUSTON, TX; (Specialty Foods) Gordon Food Service, HOUSTON, TX
Notes: The company derives approximately 10% of its revenue from retail operations.

Key Personnel
LEVI GOODE - President
RUDY FERNANDEZ - CFO; Manager Operations, Purchasing, Human Resources
TAYLOR CLARK - Director E-Commerce

H Town Restaurant Group
1103 S Shepherd Dr
Houston, TX 77019

Telephone: (713) 521-2239
Internet Homepage: htownrestaurantgroup.com
Company Email: jobs@htownrestaurantgroup.com
Type of Business: Chain Restaurant Operator
Year Founded: 1983
Total Units: 5
Trade Names: Backstreet Cafe (1); Caracol (1); Hugo's (1); Origen (1); Xochi (1)
Company-Owned Units: 5
Primary Menu: American (1); Mexican (4)
Areas of Operation: TX, FC
Type of Foodservice: Casual Dining (3); Fine Dining (2)

Key Personnel
TRACY VAUGHT - Partner
HUGO ORTEGA - Partner; Executive Chef
RUBEN ORTEGA - Corporate Chef
CARLOS NERI - Director Operations

Harris County Smokehouse
19811 Northwest Fwy
Houston, TX 77065

Telephone: (281) 890-5735
Internet Homepage: harriscountysmokehouse.com
Type of Business: Chain Restaurant Operator
Year Founded: 1998
Total Units: 3
Trade Names: Harris County Smokehouse (3)
Company-Owned Units: 3
Primary Menu: Bar-B-Q (3)
Areas of Operation: TX
Type of Foodservice: Family Restaurant (3)

Key Personnel
HARRY CHAMBERS - Owner
TAMMY CHAMBERS - VP

Houston Pizza Venture LP
13131 Champions Dr Ste 110
Houston, TX 77069-3220

Telephone: (281) 580-6088
Fax Number: (281) 580-8489
Internet Homepage: pjhouston.com
Type of Business: Chain Restaurant Operator
Year Founded: 1994
Total Sales: $74,320,000 (e)
Number of Employees: 2,000
Average Check: Lunch(16); Dinner(30)
Total Units: 55
Trade Names: Papa John's Pizza (55)
Units Franchised From: 55
Preferred Square Footage: 1,400
Preferred Location Types: Downtown; Freestanding; Strip Mall
Primary Menu: Pizza (55)
Areas of Operation: CA, HI, KS, MO, TX
Type of Foodservice: Quick Serve (55)
Foodservice Management Venues: Parks & Recreation, Schools
Catering Services: Yes
Franchise Affiliation: Papa Johns International Inc., LOUISVILLE, KY
Primary Distributors: (Food) US Foods, HOUSTON, TX

Key Personnel
KEITH SULLINS - President; COO
BILLY ROBINETT - VP Communications

Houston Restaurant Group, LLC
12149 FM 1960 Rd W Ste A
Houston, TX 77065-5477

Telephone: (281) 807-0005

Type of Business: Chain Restaurant Operator
Total Sales: $2,543,000 (e)
Total Units: 2
Trade Names: Firehouse Subs (2)
Units Franchised From: 2
Primary Menu: Sandwiches/Deli (2)
Areas of Operation: TX
Type of Foodservice: Fast Casual (2)
Franchise Affiliation: Firehouse Restaurant Group Inc., JACKSONVILLE, FL

Key Personnel
KEVIN KELLY - Partner; General Manager

Hugo's
1600 Westheimer Rd
Houston, TX 77006-3728

Telephone: (713) 524-7744
Fax Number: (713) 524-7719
Internet Homepage: htownrestaurantgroup.com; hugosrestaurant.net
Type of Business: Chain Restaurant Operator
Total Sales: $20,310,000 (e)
Alcohol Sales: 10%
Number of Employees: 280
Average Check: Lunch(14); Dinner(20)
Total Units: 7
Trade Names: Back Street Cafe (1); Caracol (1); Hugo's (1); Origen (1); Prego's (1); Third Coast (1); Xochi (1)
Company-Owned Units: 7
Preferred Location Types: Freestanding
Alcohol Served: Beer, Wine, Liquor
Primary Menu: American (1); Italian (2); Mexican (2); Miscellaneous (2)
Areas of Operation: TX
Type of Foodservice: Casual Dining (3); Fine Dining (4)
Catering Services: Yes
Primary Distributors: (Full Line) SYSCO Corporation, HOUSTON, TX

Key Personnel
HUGO ORTEGA - Partner; Executive Chef; General Buyer
TRACY VAUGHT - Partner
RUBEN ORTEGA - Executive Chef
TAJ WALKER - Director Information Technology, Human Resources
CARLOS NERI - Director Operations

JCJ Tex Mex/Wings LLC
12703 Eastex Fwy
Houston, TX 77039

Telephone: (281) 570-4395
Internet Homepage: bigcitywings.com
Company Email: info@bigcitywings.com
Type of Business: Chain Restaurant Operator

Year Founded: 2015
Total Units: 9
Trade Names: Big City Wings (7); La Finca (2)
Company-Owned Units: 9
Primary Menu: Chicken (7); Mexican (2)
Projected Openings: 2
Areas of Operation: TX
Type of Foodservice: Casual Dining (9)

Key Personnel
SAM ELSAADI - Director Operations

K-Bob's USA Inc.
4119 Montrose Blvd
Houston, TX 77006

Telephone: (713) 355-4300
Fax Number: (505) 982-3468
Internet Homepage: k-bobs.com
Company Email: CustomerService@K-Bobs.com
Type of Business: Chain Restaurant Operator
Year Founded: 1966
Systemwide Sales: $18,569,000 (e)
Total Sales: $9,721,000 (e)
Alcohol Sales: 2%
Number of Employees: 172
Average Check: Lunch(10); Dinner(16)
Internet Order Processing: Yes
Internet Sales: 1.00%
Total Units: 9
Trade Names: K-Bob's Steakhouse (9)
Company-Owned Units: 9
Preferred Square Footage: 6,300
Preferred Location Types: Freestanding
Alcohol Served: Beer, Wine
Primary Menu: Steak (9)
Areas of Operation: CO, NM, TX
Type of Foodservice: Casual Dining (9)
Catering Services: Yes

Key Personnel
MORGAN BOOTH - Partner

Kim Son Inc.
10603 Bellaire Blvd
Houston, TX 777072

Telephone: (281) 598-1777
Internet Homepage: kimson.com
Company Email: info@kimson.com
Type of Business: Chain Restaurant Operator
Year Founded: 1983
Total Sales: $15,710,000 (e)
Alcohol Sales: 5%
Number of Employees: 113
Average Check: Dinner(10)
Internet Order Processing: Yes
Total Units: 6
Trade Names: Kim Son (3); Kim Son Cafe (1); Nam Noodles and More (2)

Company-Owned Units: 6
Preferred Location Types: Downtown; Freestanding; Hotel/Motel
Alcohol Served: Beer, Wine, Liquor
Primary Menu: Asian (6)
Areas of Operation: TX
Type of Foodservice: Casual Dining (2); Family Restaurant (4)
Catering Services: Yes
On-site Distribution Center: Yes
Primary Distributors: (Food) SYSCO Food Services of Houston Inc., HOUSTON, TX

Key Personnel
TRI MINH LA - Partner; VP Finance
KIM SU TRAN LA - Partner
THERESA VO - Manager Operations

LA Crawfish
8207 Hazen St
Houston, TX 77036

Telephone: (713) 461-8808
Internet Homepage: thelacrawfish.com
Company Email: thelacrawfish@hotmail.com
Type of Business: Chain Restaurant Operator
Year Founded: 2011
Systemwide Sales: $63,334,000 (e)
Total Sales: $16,230,000 (e)
Total Units: 25
Trade Names: LA Crawfish (25)
Company-Owned Units: 2
Units Franchised To: 23
Primary Menu: Cajun/Creole (25)
Areas of Operation: CA, TX
Type of Foodservice: Fast Casual (25)

Key Personnel
MINSON NGO - President; General Buyer

Landry's Distribution Center
7310 Old Katy Rd Ste B
Houston, TX 77024-2116

Telephone: (713) 680-1185
Fax Number: (713) 683-0747
Listing Type: Distribution Center
Type of Business: Chain Restaurant Operator
Number of Employees: 20
Areas of Operation: AL, AZ, CA, CO, CT, FL, GA, ID, IL, IN, KS, KY, LA, MA, MD, MI, MN, MO, MS, NC, NJ, NM, NV, NY, OH, OK, OR, PA, TX, ON
Foreign Countries: CANADA
Parent Company: Landry's Restaurants Inc., HOUSTON, TX

Key Personnel
JANIE GUTIERREZ - General Manager;

Director Operations; Manager Warehouse

Landry's Restaurants Inc.
1510 West Loop S
Houston, TX 77027-9505

Telephone: (713) 850-1010
Fax Number: (713) 850-7205
Internet Homepage: aquariumrestaurants.com; babinsseafood.com; besolasvegas.com; brennerssteakhouse.com; cadillacbar.com; camerons-steakhouse.com; chart-house.com; claimjumper.com; crabhouseseafood.com; flyingdutchmankemah.com; grottohouston.com; harlowsrestaurants.com;kemahboardwalk.com; lagrigliarestaurant.com; landrysinc.com; landrysseafoodhouse.com; mastrosrestaurants.com; mccormickandschmicks.com;mitchellsfishmarket.com; mortons.com; muer.com; pescehouston.com; rainforestcafe.com; red-sushi.com; rustypelican.com; saltgrass.com;simmssteakhouse.com; theoceanaire.com; trexcafe.com; vicandanthonys.com; williegs.com; yakandyetirestaurant.com
Listing Type: Corporate Office
Type of Business: Chain Restaurant Operator
Year Founded: 1980
Total Sales: $4,721,533,000 (e)
Alcohol Sales: 20%
Number of Employees: 40,000
Internet Order Processing: Yes
Internet Sales: 0.50%
Total Units: 611
Trade Names: Aquarium (4); Babin's Seafood House (2); Bill's Bar & Burger (5); Bloom & Bee (1); Blue Fin (1); Bouchee Patisserie (1); Brenner's Steakhouse(3); Brick House Tavern + Tap (20); Bristol (4); Bubba Gump Shrimp Co. (38); Cadillac Bar Restaurant (3); Chart House (24); Claim Jumper (29); Clinkerdagger (1); Columbus Fish Market (8); Craft F&B (1); Cutters Crabhouse (1); Del Frisco's Double Eagle Steak House (18); Del Frisco's Grille (15); Devon (3); DosCaminos (4); Fish Tales (1); Fisherman's Wharf (1); Gandy Dancer (1); Gandy Dancer Saloon (1); Grand Concourse (1); Grotto (5); Henry's Tavern: AmericanBar & Grill (2); Horatio's Restaurant (1); Houlihan's (39); J. Gilbert's (6); Jake's Famous Crawfish (1); Jake's Grill (1); Joe's Crab Shack (46); Kincaid's Fish, Chop & Steak House (4); King Ranch (1); La Griglia (1); Landry's Seafood House (14); Lillie's (4); Maggie Bluffs (1); Mai Tai Bar (2); Manzana Rotisserie Grill (1); Mastro's Ocean Club (6); Mastro's Penthouse (1); Mastro's Steakhouse (22); McCormick & Schmick's Seafood & Steaks (27); Mitchell's Fish Market (8); Mitchell's Steakhouse (2); Morton's Grille (1); Morton's The Steakhouse (56); Palisade (1); Palm Restaurant (18);

Peohe's (1); Portland City Grill (1); Rainforest Cafe (18); River Crab (1); Rusty Pelican (1); Saltgrass Steak House (91); Scott's Bar & Grill (1); Simms Steakhouse (1); Simons & Seafort's (1); Skates on the Bay (1); Stanford's Restaurant & Bar (1); Stanley & Seafort's (1); Strip House (4); T-Rex Cafe (1); The Boathouse (5); The Flying Dutchman (1); The Oceanaire(9); The Pizza Oven (1); Trevi (1); Troy (1); Vic & Anthony's Steakhouse (4); Willie G's Seafood & Steak House (2); Yak & Yeti (1)
Company-Owned Units: 611
Preferred Location Types: Community Mall; Downtown; Freestanding; Hotel/Motel; Lifestyle Center; Outlet Mall; Regional Mall; Strip Mall
Alcohol Served: Beer, Wine, Liquor
Primary Menu: American (86); Asian (5); Chicken (18); Hamburger (5); Italian (7); Mexican (7); Pizza (1); Seafood (152); Steak (262); Steak/Seafood (67)
Areas of Operation: AK, AL, AZ, CA, CO, CT, DC, FL, GA, HI, IL, IN, KS, KY, LA, MA, MD, MI, MN, MO, NC, NJ, NM, NV, NY, OH, OK, OR, PA, PR, SC, TN, TX, VA, WA, ON
Foreign Countries: CANADA; CHINA; ENGLAND; FRANCE; HONG KONG; INDONESIA; JAPAN; MACAO; MALAYSIA; MEXICO; SINGAPORE; THE PHILIPPINES; UNITED ARAB EMIRATES
Type of Foodservice: Casual Dining (411); Fine Dining (200)
Catering Services: Yes
Distribution Centers: HOUSTON, TX
Primary Distributors: (Full Line) SYSCO Corporation, HOUSTON, TX
Parent Company: Fertitta Holdings Inc., HOUSTON, TX
Headquarter Offices: Del Frisco's Restaurant Group Inc., SOUTH HOUSTON, TX; Restaurants Unlimited Inc., SEATTLE, WA; Golden Nugget Inc., LAS VEGAS, NV
Notes: The company derives approximately 10% of its revenue from hotel and gaming operations at its casinos.

Key Personnel
TILMAN J. FERTITTA - Chairman; CEO; President
JOE LEAHEY - President Purchasing
RICHARD H. LIEM - CFO; Exec VP
K. KELLY ROBERTS - Chief Administrative Officer Gaming/Entertainment, Division
LORI KITTLE - CIO
JEFFREY L. CANTWELL - Chief Development Officer; Exec VP
NICKI KEENAN - Senior VP Sales
JULIE LIEBELT - VP Human Resources
JAMES KRAMER - VP Operations-Beverages
BILL STORY - VP Training
ARTHUR MOORADIAN - VP Operations
MELISSA RADOVICH - VP Marketing
JILL W. HUMPHREY - VP Business Development
DASH KOHLHAUSEN - General Counsel
WILL CARRIGAN - Senior Director Technology
JILL KLEPSER - Director Recruitment
SCOTT TARWATER - Director Event Planning, Alcoholic Beverages
MIKE SIFFORD - Director Operations, Information Technology
LOREN RAPP - Director Information Technology
AUTUMN MECHLER CHILD - Director Marketing
CHRISTOPHER MCCOMAS - Director Facility/Maintenance
CYNTHIA COFFIELD - Director Marketing
BRIAN JEPPESEN - Director Operations
STEVE SALMON - Director Operations
CESAR BRACAMONTES - Regional Director
CHRIS BRUDER - Regional Director
REBECCA WICKES - Senior Manager Strategy, Digital Marketing
RICHARD BRINSON - Manager Operations, Information Technology
BENJAMIN LOPEZ - Manager
TIMOTHY HOFFMAN - Manager Purchasing
KRIS GUTHRIE - Consultant Marketing
CYNTHIA HARTMANN - Analyst Finance

Lasco Enterprises, LLC
7026 Old Katy Rd Ste 250
Houston, TX 77024-2135

Telephone: (713) 622-4003
Fax Number: (713) 523-1523
Internet Homepage: boilerhousesa.com; lascoenterprises.com; maxswinedive.com; tastingroomwines.com
Company Email: info@lascoenterprises.com
Type of Business: Chain Restaurant Operator
Year Founded: 2006
Total Sales: $22,350,000 (e)
Alcohol Sales: 50%
Average Check: Lunch(36); Dinner(42)
Total Units: 8
Trade Names: Boiler House Texas Grill & Wine Bar (1); Max's Wine Dive (5); The Tasting Room (2)
Company-Owned Units: 11
Alcohol Served: Beer, Wine
Primary Menu: American (8)
Projected Openings: 2
Areas of Operation: CO, GA, IL, TX
Type of Foodservice: Casual Dining (8)

Key Personnel
JERRY LASCO - CEO; Partner
LAURA LASCO - Partner; VP; General Counsel
JACOB FAIRCHILD - Manager Sales

Legacy Restaurants
1050 N Post Oak Rd Ste 200
Houston, TX 77055-7233

Telephone: (832) 494-2670
Fax Number: (832) 484-2675
Internet Homepage: legacyrestaurants.com
Company Email: info@legacyrestaurants.com
Type of Business: Chain Restaurant Operator
Year Founded: 1962
Total Sales: $3,899,000 (e)
Alcohol Sales: 2%
Number of Employees: 200
Average Check: Lunch(10); Dinner(10)
Total Units: 3
Trade Names: Antone's Famous Po' Boys (2); The Original Ninfa's (1)
Company-Owned Units: 3
Preferred Square Footage: 2,000; 3,000
Preferred Location Types: Freestanding
Alcohol Served: Beer, Wine, Liquor
Primary Menu: Mexican (1); Sandwiches/Deli (2)
Areas of Operation: TX
Type of Foodservice: Casual Dining (1); Quick Serve (2)
On-site Distribution Center: Yes
Primary Distributors: (Full Line) SYSCO Corporation, HOUSTON, TX

Key Personnel
NIEL MORGAN - Owner; General Buyer
ALEX PADILLA - Corporate Chef; General Buyer
MARK MAVRANPONIS - Director Food and Beverage

Logan's Roadhouse Inc.
19219 Katy Fwy
Houston, TX 77094

Telephone: (346) 440-0772
Fax Number: (615) 346-6333
Internet Homepage: logansroadhouse.com
Type of Business: Chain Restaurant Operator
Year Founded: 1991
Systemwide Sales: $398,158,000 (e)
Total Sales: $584,510,000 (e)
Alcohol Sales: 8%
Number of Employees: 15,000
Average Check: Lunch(12); Dinner(16)
Total Units: 136
Trade Names: Logan's Roadhouse (136)
Company-Owned Units: 113
Units Franchised To: 23
Preferred Square Footage: 6,500; 8,000; 8,200
Preferred Location Types: Freestanding
Alcohol Served: Beer, Wine, Liquor
Primary Menu: Steak (136)
Areas of Operation: AL, AR, CA, FL, GA, IL, IN, KS, KY, LA, MI, MO, MS, NC, OH, OK, PA,

SC, TN, TX, VA, WV
Type of Foodservice: Casual Dining (136)
Primary Distributors: (Food) PFG - Customized Support Services, LEBANON, TN
Parent Company: SPB Hospitality, HOUSTON, TX

Key Personnel
CAM CAMPBELL - Senior VP Operations
MARIA DAWSON - Director Talent Acquisitions
LUIS HARO - Director Culinary Operations
KRISTEN HOHL - Director Marketing
MICHAEL MATOS - Director Store Operations
WILLIAM MURPHY - Director Operations
GREGORY SWAFFORD - Senior Manager Purchasing
RALEIGH MORRIS - Manager
JAMIE LANE - Manager Supply Chain

Luby's Inc.
13111 Northwest Fwy Ste 600
Houston, TX 77040-6392

Telephone: (713) 329-6800
Fax Number: (713) 329-6909
Internet Homepage: cheeseburgerinparadise.com; fuddruckers.com; lubys.com
Listing Type: Corporate Office
Type of Business: Chain Restaurant Operator
Year Founded: 1947
Total Sales: $346,540,000 (e)
Alcohol Sales: 1%
Number of Employees: 8,700
Average Check: Lunch(10); Dinner(12)
Foodservice Sales: $301,490,000 (e)
Internet Order Processing: Yes
Internet Sales: 2.00%
Total Units: 38
Trade Names: Luby's Cafeteria (38)
Company-Owned Units: 38
Units Franchised From: 4
Preferred Square Footage: 8,000; 10,500
Preferred Location Types: Community Mall; Downtown; Freestanding; Institution (college/hospital); Regional Mall; Strip Mall
Alcohol Served: Beer, Wine, Liquor
Primary Menu: American (38); Hamburger (0)
Areas of Operation: AR, AZ, CA, CT, DC, DE, FL, GA, IA, ID, IL, IN, KS, LA, MA, MD, MI, MN, MO, MS, MT, NC, NE, NJ, NM, NV, NY, OH, OK, OR, PA, PR, SC, SD, TN, TX, VA, WI, SK
Foreign Countries: CANADA; COLOMBIA; MEXICO; PANAMA
Type of Foodservice: Cafeteria (38); Fast Casual (0)
Foodservice Management Venues: College & University; Health Care
Catering Services: Yes
Primary Distributors: (Food) Shamrock Foods Co., PHOENIX, AZ; (Supplies) Ben E. Keith Foods, SAN ANTONIO, TX

Notes: The company derives approximately 5% of its total revenue from culinary contract services and vending operations.

Key Personnel
JOE C. MCKINNEY - Vice Chairman
JOHN GARILLI - CEO; President
PHILIP RIDER - President Accounting
TODD COUTEE - COO
PAULETTE GERUKOS - VP Human Resources
TRENT TAYLOR - VP Operations
STEVE GOODWEATHER - VP Financial Planning
JOHN HOLZEM - VP Information Technology
BILL DEVLIN - Executive Director Information Technology
ROY CAMBERG - Corporate Secretary; General Counsel
ARTHUR RAMIREZ - Executive Chef; Associate Manager
JAMILLE BOND - Senior Director
BRYANT WILKINS - Director Infrastructure
KRISTEN FLORES - Director
CHRISTINA GARZA - Director
LANI ORDONE - Director Procurement-Inventory Control
DANA ROGERS-YATES - Director Marketing
IRENE SIMOTAS - Director Operations
JESSICA AMOS - Senior Manager Applications
ROGER GONZALES - Regional Manager
CHRISTINE MARTIN - Manager Financial Planning
ANNA SKINNER - Manager Engineering
NICHOLAS VROULIS - Manager Sales, Catering
KEVIN WHITE - Manager
SUE ANN XUAN NGU - Manager

Lupe Tortillas Mexican Restaurants
10333 Richmond Ave Ste 210
Houston, TX 77042-4244

Telephone: (832) 772-6301
Fax Number: (281) 829-2303
Internet Homepage: lupetortilla.com
Company Email: comments@lupetortilla.com
Type of Business: Chain Restaurant Operator
Year Founded: 1983
Total Sales: $178,840,000 (e)
Alcohol Sales: 10%
Number of Employees: 1,537
Average Check: Lunch(10); Dinner(20)
Internet Order Processing: Yes
Total Units: 27
Trade Names: Lupe Tortillas (27)
Company-Owned Units: 27
Preferred Square Footage: 5,500; 6,000
Preferred Location Types: Freestanding
Alcohol Served: Beer, Wine, Liquor
Primary Menu: Mexican (26)
Areas of Operation: TX
Type of Foodservice: Casual Dining (26)

Catering Services: Yes
Primary Distributors: (Equipment) Ace Mart Restaurant Supply Co., HOUSTON, TX; (Food) US Foods, HOUSTON, TX

Key Personnel
PAUL MCELROY - Chairman
JUDSON HOLT - CEO; Partner; Director Operations; General Buyer
PETER HOLT - Partner
SAMANTHA JAMESON - Director Purchasing
SCOTT LEACH - Director Construction
CORRINE MARTINEZ - Director Marketing
PATRICK THOMPSON - Manager Training
EDWARD BRENS - Manager Restaurant Operations

Mambo Seafood Restaurants
6101 Airline Dr
Houston, TX 77076

Telephone: (713) 691-9700
Internet Homepage: mamboseafood.com
Company Email: eat@mamborestaurants.com
Type of Business: Chain Restaurant Operator
Year Founded: 1996
Total Sales: $8,287,000 (e)
Total Units: 11
Trade Names: Mambo Seafood (11)
Company-Owned Units: 11
Primary Menu: Seafood (11)
Projected Openings: 1
Areas of Operation: TX
Type of Foodservice: Casual Dining (11)

Key Personnel
ROBERT MCKINLEY - CEO
MICHAEL HO - President
ENRIQUE ZARAGOZA - Controller
MANOLO ARROYO - Director Business Development

MAS Restaurant Group
10600 Shadow Wood Dr Ste 600
Houston, TX 77043-2838

Telephone: (713) 980-2860
Fax Number: (713) 980-3099
Internet Homepage: kormexinc.com
Type of Business: Chain Restaurant Operator
Year Founded: 2000
Total Sales: $177,480,000 (e)
Number of Employees: 1,480
Average Check: Lunch(8); Dinner(8)
Total Units: 72
Trade Names: KFC/Taco Bell (2); Taco Bell (70)
Units Franchised From: 72
Preferred Square Footage: 2,500; 3,200
Preferred Location Types: Freestanding
Primary Menu: Chicken (2); Taco (70)
Areas of Operation: TX

Type of Foodservice: Quick Serve (72)
Franchise Affiliation: Taco Bell Corp., IRVINE, CA

Key Personnel
CHAD MOTSINGER - CEO
PHILLIP S. RHEE - President; Director Real Estate; General Buyer
BEN WALSH - CFO
CASEY STEPHENSON - Area Director
CASSANDRA JARRETT - Area Director
ROMAN KARABANOV - Area Director
STEVE SULA - Senior VP Operations
ALEJANDRO LIMAS - VP Operations
MELISSA BURTON - VP Operations
SHONDA GUERIN - Executive Director Administration
OSCAR LEON - General Manager
ANA BUSTILLO - General Manager
MANNY CHAVEZ - Director Information Technology
MANUEL CHAVEZ - Director Information Technology
CHUCK NEW - Director Development
LUIS TALAMANTES - Manager Training
VINH TU - Manager Information Technology
AMY GUILE - Manager Human Resources

McDonald's USA LLC
3707 Cypress Creek Pkwy Ste 300
Houston, TX 77068-3525

Telephone: (281) 580-3322
Fax Number: (281) 587-7368
Listing Type: Regional Office
Type of Business: Chain Restaurant Operator
Number of Employees: 60
Total Units: 779
Areas of Operation: TX
Parent Company: McDonald's Corporation, CHICAGO, IL

Key Personnel
TODD JACKSON - Director Finance
KEITH BOTKIN - Manager Construction
CHANDRA GREGOIRE - Manager Purchasing

Molina's Enterprises Inc.
3737 Crossview Dr
Houston, TX 77063-5708

Telephone: (713) 266-2042
Fax Number: (713) 266-2153
Internet Homepage: molinasrestaurants.com
Company Email: molinas@molinasrestaurants.com
Type of Business: Chain Restaurant Operator
Total Sales: $3,841,000 (e)
Alcohol Sales: 10%
Number of Employees: 60
Average Check: Lunch(22); Dinner(26)
Total Units: 2
Trade Names: Molina's Cantina (2)
Company-Owned Units: 2
Preferred Location Types: Freestanding
Alcohol Served: Beer, Wine, Liquor
Primary Menu: Mexican (2)
Areas of Operation: TX
Type of Foodservice: Casual Dining (2)

Key Personnel
RAUL MOLINA III - Partner; Director Menu Development
RICARDO MOLINA - Partner; Manager Advertising
ROBERTO MOLINA - Partner; General Buyer

Murphy's Deli Franchising Inc.
1704 Townhurst Dr
Houston, TX 77043-2811

Telephone: (713) 827-8881
Fax Number: (713) 827-8810
Internet Homepage: murphysdeli.com
Company Email: mr_murphy@murphysdeli.com
Type of Business: Chain Restaurant Operator
Year Founded: 1993
Total Sales: $6,340,000 (e)
Number of Employees: 8
Average Check: Dinner(10)
Total Units: 60
Trade Names: Murphy's Deli (60)
Units Franchised To: 60
Preferred Location Types: Downtown; Institution (college/hospital); Lifestyle Center; Office Complex; Regional Mall
Primary Menu: Sandwiches/Deli (60)
Areas of Operation: CA, FL, TX
Type of Foodservice: Fast Casual (60)
Catering Services: Yes

Key Personnel
LAURA WATTS - CEO
KARIM VIRANI - President

MZK Enterprise, LLC
1120 Nasa Pkwy
Houston, TX 77058-3320

Telephone: (281) 549-4361
Fax Number: (832) 864-3475
Type of Business: Chain Restaurant Operator
Total Sales: $42,790,000 (e)
Total Units: 17
Trade Names: Jack in the Box (17)
Units Franchised From: 17
Primary Menu: Hamburger (17)
Areas of Operation: TX
Type of Foodservice: Quick Serve (17)
Franchise Affiliation: Jack in the Box Restaurants, SAN DIEGO, CA

Key Personnel
KHALID KAHN - Director Operations

Pak Foods LLC
17154 Butte Creek Rd Ste 200
Houston, TX 77090-2332

Telephone: (281) 569-4640
Fax Number: (281) 569-4638
Type of Business: Chain Restaurant Operator
Total Sales: $241,390,000 (e)
Average Check: Lunch(8); Dinner(10)
Total Units: 149
Trade Names: KFC (80); Long John Silver's (5); Pizza Hut (51); Taco Bell (13)
Units Franchised From: 149
Preferred Square Footage: 2,500; 3,200
Preferred Location Types: Freestanding
Primary Menu: Chicken (80); Pizza (51); Seafood (5); Taco (13)
Areas of Operation: AZ, TX
Type of Foodservice: Quick Serve (149)
Franchise Affiliation: KFC Corporation, LOUISVILLE, KY; Long John Silver's Inc., LOUISVILLE, KY; Taco Bell Corp., IRVINE, CA
Notes: Holds Pizza Hut locations through ITL Foods, L.P.

Key Personnel
TANWEER AHMED - President; General Buyer
DAVID WEHRMAN - COO
HASSAN RASHID - District Manager
NAJEE WASHINGTON - District Manager

Pappa Genos' Steak & Cheese
9930 Katy Fwy
Houston, TX 77055

Telephone: (281) 501-1617
Internet Homepage: pappagenos.com
Company Email: pappagenos@gmail.com
Type of Business: Chain Restaurant Operator
Number of Employees: 50
Total Units: 6
Trade Names: Pappa Genos' Steak & Cheese (6)
Company-Owned Units: 6
Primary Menu: American (6)
Areas of Operation: TX
Type of Foodservice: Fast Casual (6)

Key Personnel
PAUL MITCHELL - Owner

Pappas Restaurants, Inc
13939 Northwest Fwy
Houston, TX 77040-5115

Mailing Address: PO Box 41567, HOUSTON, TX, 77241
Telephone: (713) 869-0151
Internet Homepage: pappadeaux.com; pappas.com; pappasbbq.com; pappasbros.com; pappasburger.com; pappasitos.com; pappasseafood.com; yiayiamarys.com
Company Email: info@pappas.com
Type of Business: Chain Restaurant Operator
Year Founded: 1976
Total Sales: $923,930,000 (e)
Alcohol Sales: 15%
Number of Employees: 6,234
Average Check: Breakfast(8); Lunch(14); Dinner(22)
Internet Order Processing: Yes
Internet Sales: 1.00%
Total Units: 89
Trade Names: Dot Coffee Shop (1); Pappadeaux Seafood Kitchen (32); Pappas Bar-B-Q (17); Pappas Bros. Steakhouse (3); Pappas Burger (2); Pappas Delta Blues Smokehouse (2); Pappas Seafood House (5); Pappasito's Cantina (25); Yia Yia Marys Pappas Greek Kitchen (2)
Company-Owned Units: 89
Preferred Square Footage: 10,000; 12,000
Preferred Location Types: Airports; Freestanding; Office Complex
Alcohol Served: Beer, Wine, Liquor
Primary Menu: American (1); Bar-B-Q (19); Greek/Mediterranean (2); Hamburger (2); Mexican (25); Seafood (37); Steak (3)
Projected Openings: 3
Areas of Operation: AL, AZ, CO, GA, IL, NM, OH, TX
Type of Foodservice: Casual Dining (89)
Catering Services: Yes
Distribution Centers: HOUSTON, TX
Primary Distributors: (Food) SYSCO Corporation, HOUSTON, TX

Key Personnel
HARRIS J. PAPPAS - CEO; President; Partner
CHRISTOPHER J. PAPPAS - Partner; COO; Director Real Estate
ERNEST PEKMEZARIS - CFO; Treasurer
WILLIAM HOISAGER - Chief Information Security Officer; Architect
CALEB MARUTZKY - VP Finance, Strategy
NEIL HILL - General Manager Operations
MICHAEL VELARDI - Corporate Chef
BRYAN WOODS - Director Information Technology
LESLIE DRAGNA - Director Operations
STACEY SMITH - Director Beverages
CHRISTINA PAPPAS - Director Marketing
KATIE STEIN - Director Human Resources
BETH CASWELL STEPHENS - Director Recruitment
ERIC SWANSON - Director Finance
SUSAN AWALT - Director Risk Management
MELISSA RECH - Director Compensation
DANIELLE GANTT - Director Human Resources
EVY PAPPAS - Director Design
MICHELLE HORNES - Director Operations
D DOCKERY - Senior Manager
MARK KAHANEK - Manager Information Technology, Infrastructure
MARVIN JOHNSON - Manager Applications
SHERAZ ISLAM - Manager Systems
APRIL NELSON LOZANO - Manager Information Technology
RITA JOSEPHSON - Coordinator Customer Care
TERRY RITZMAN - Engineer Software

Pepi Corporation
1210 W Clay St Ste 17
Houston, TX 77019-4190

Telephone: (713) 528-7000
Fax Number: (713) 528-7333
Internet Homepage: alonti.com
Company Email: info@alonti.com
Type of Business: Chain Restaurant Operator
Year Founded: 1974
Total Sales: $39,105,000 (e)
Alcohol Sales: 2%
Number of Employees: 400
Average Check: Breakfast(8); Lunch(14);
Internet Order Processing: Yes
Internet Sales: 12.00%
Total Units: 28
Trade Names: Alonti Cafe & Catering (28)
Company-Owned Units: 28
Preferred Square Footage: 2,500
Preferred Location Types: Office Complex
Primary Menu: American (28)
Areas of Operation: CA, IL, TX
Type of Foodservice: Fast Casual (28)
Catering Services: Yes
Primary Distributors: (Food) SYSCO Corporation, HOUSTON, TX; (Supplies) SYSCO Corporation, HOUSTON, TX

Key Personnel
DAVID KORMAN - Controller

Perry's Restaurant Corp.
9805 Katy Fwy
Houston, TX 77024

Telephone: (281) 480-3337
Fax Number: (281) 480-5455
Internet Homepage: perrysrestaurants.com
Company Email: receptionist@perrysrestaurants.com
Type of Business: Chain Restaurant Operator
Year Founded: 1979
Total Sales: $18,000,000 (e)
Alcohol Sales: 10%
Number of Employees: 455
Average Check: Lunch(24); Dinner(42)
Total Units: 22
Trade Names: Perry & Sons Market & Grille (2); Perry's Steakhouse & Grille (20)
Company-Owned Units: 22
Preferred Square Footage: 5,500; 6,000
Preferred Location Types: Freestanding; Strip Mall
Alcohol Served: Beer, Wine, Liquor
Primary Menu: American (2); Steak (20)
Areas of Operation: AL, CO, FL, IL, NC, TN, TX
Type of Foodservice: Casual Dining (22)
Catering Services: Yes
Primary Distributors: (Full Line) McLane/Arlington, ARLINGTON, TX

Key Personnel
CHRIS PERRY - CEO; President; General Buyer
RICK HENDERSON - COO; VP
DAVID FREEMAN - Senior VP Operations; Director Operations
DEREK PEARSON - VP Operations; Controller
GRANT HUNTER - Corporate Chef

Prince Food Systems Inc.
11001 S Wilcrest Dr Ste 200
Houston, TX 77099-4329

Telephone: (281) 568-3131
Fax Number: (281) 568-2323
Internet Homepage: princefoodsystems.com
Company Email: information@princefoodsystems.com
Type of Business: Foodservice Management Operator
Year Founded: 1929
Total Sales: $44,176,000 (e)
Number of Employees: 450
Number of Locations Served: 35
Total Foodservice Mgmt Accounts: 35
Areas of Operation: TX
Type of Foodservice: Cafeteria (35)
Foodservice Management Venues: Business & Industry; Health Care
Primary Distributors: (Full Line) SYSCO Corporation, HOUSTON, TX

Key Personnel
CHARLES E. PRINCE SR - President
STEVE CAUDLE - COO; Exec VP Purchasing, Foodservice; Director Operations
JAMIE YEW - Controller
SUZANNE MASSOTH - Representative Marketing, Sales

Ragin Cajun
4302 Richmond Ave
Houston, TX 77027-6723

Telephone: (713) 623-6321
Fax Number: (713) 960-5015
Internet Homepage: ragin-cajun.com
Type of Business: Chain Restaurant Operator
Total Sales: $6,004,000 (e)
Alcohol Sales: 15%
Total Units: 2
Trade Names: Ragin Cajun (2)
Company-Owned Units: 2
Alcohol Served: Beer, Wine, Liquor
Primary Menu: Cajun/Creole (2)
Areas of Operation: TX
Type of Foodservice: Casual Dining (2)
Catering Services: Yes

Key Personnel
DOMINIC B. MANDOLA - President; Executive Chef; General Buyer
SCOTT HIGHTOWER - Director Catering
MICHAEL GITTESS - Coordinator Catering

RamRock LLC
3101 N Shepherd Dr
Houston, TX 77018-8333

Mailing Address: PO Box 1308, RICHMOND, TX, 77406
Telephone: (713) 864-5049
Internet Homepage: gabbysbbq.com; spankyspizza.net
Type of Business: Chain Restaurant Operator
Year Founded: 1979
Total Sales: $15,626,000 (e)
Alcohol Sales: 16%
Number of Employees: 150
Average Check: Lunch(6); Dinner(10)
Total Units: 3
Trade Names: Gabby's Barbeque (1); Spanky's Pizza Parlor (2)
Company-Owned Units: 3
Preferred Location Types: Freestanding; Strip Mall
Alcohol Served: Beer, Wine, Liquor
Primary Menu: Bar-B-Q (1); Pizza (2)
Areas of Operation: TX
Type of Foodservice: Casual Dining (3)
Catering Services: Yes
Primary Distributors: (Full Line) SYSCO Corporation, HOUSTON, TX

Key Personnel
FRANK ROCHE - Partner; CFO; Controller
HOLLY WATERS - Partner
NICOLE BENAVIDEZ - Manager Catering
PAUL WENGENROTH - Manager

Russo's Restaurants
5847 San Felipe St Ste 1730
Houston, TX 77057-3437

Telephone: (713) 821-1322
Fax Number: (832) 251-8718
Internet Homepage: nypizzeria.com; russoscoalfired.com
Company Email: anthony@nypizzeria.com
Type of Business: Chain Restaurant Operator
Year Founded: 1978
Systemwide Sales: $57,709,000 (e)
Total Sales: $4,055,000 (e)
Alcohol Sales: 15%
Number of Employees: 65
Average Check: Lunch(10); Dinner(10)
Internet Order Processing: Yes
Total Units: 58
Trade Names: Russo's Coal-Fired Italian Kitchen (38); Russo's New York Pizzeria (20)
Company-Owned Units: 11
Units Franchised To: 47
Preferred Square Footage: 5,500; 6,000
Preferred Location Types: Freestanding; Mixed-use Center; Strip Mall
Alcohol Served: Beer, Wine
Primary Menu: Pizza (58)
Areas of Operation: AR, FL, HI, OK, TN, TX, FC
Foreign Countries: UNITED ARAB EMIRATES
Type of Foodservice: Casual Dining (58)
Catering Services: Yes

Key Personnel
ANTHONY RUSSO - CEO; Owner; Executive Chef; General Buyer
ENZO LAVECCHIA - Corporate Chef
JIM CARR - Director Franchise Development
SUSAN SCOTT - Director Marketing, Public Relations

S & S Related Companies
11626 Meadowchase Dr
Houston, TX 77065-4903

Telephone: (281) 955-7352
Fax Number: (281) 807-0083
Type of Business: Chain Restaurant Operator
Year Founded: 1992
Total Sales: $52,990,000 (e)
Number of Employees: 500
Average Check: Breakfast(8); Lunch(8); Dinner(8)
Total Units: 41
Trade Names: Church's Chicken (31); Little Caesars Pizza (10)
Units Franchised From: 41
Preferred Square Footage: 1,800
Preferred Location Types: Freestanding
Primary Menu: Chicken (31); Pizza (10)
Areas of Operation: FL, TX
Type of Foodservice: Quick Serve (41)
Franchise Affiliation: Church's Chicken, ATLANTA, GA; Little Caesar Enterprises Inc., DETROIT, MI
Primary Distributors: (Supplies) Performance Foodservice - Temple, TEMPLE, TX

Key Personnel
SUKHWINDER SINGH - President; Controller; Director Facility/Maintenance, Information Systems, Supply Chain, Real Estate, Design; Manager Operations, Purchasing; General Buyer
RAMINDER KAUR - VP Human Resources
JAMES HENDER - Director
AUSTIN WATKINS - Senior Manager

Salata Inc.
16720 Park Row Dr
Houston, TX 77084

Telephone: (713) 739-0101
Fax Number: (281) 945-8892
Internet Homepage: salata.com
Company Email: contact@salata.com
Type of Business: Chain Restaurant Operator
Year Founded: 2005
Systemwide Sales: $128,226,000 (e)
Total Sales: $25,980,000 (e)
Total Units: 87
Trade Names: Salata (87)
Company-Owned Units: 17
Units Franchised To: 70
Alcohol Served: Wine
Primary Menu: Miscellaneous (87)
Projected Openings: 10
Areas of Operation: CA, FL, GA, IL, LA, OK, TX
Type of Foodservice: Fast Casual (87)

Key Personnel
BERGE SIMONIAN - Co-Founder; CEO; President
TONY KYOUMJIAN - Co-Founder; VP

Shahir Bros., Inc.
8607 Southwest Fwy
Houston, TX 77074-1501

Telephone: (713) 779-4467
Company Email: ihopgessener@gmail.com
Type of Business: Chain Restaurant Operator
Total Sales: $16,060,000 (e)
Total Units: 5
Trade Names: IHOP (5)
Units Franchised From: 5
Primary Menu: American (5)
Areas of Operation: TX
Type of Foodservice: Family Restaurant (5)
Franchise Affiliation: IHOP Restaurant

System, GLENDALE, CA

Key Personnel
MUHAMID AMIN - President

Shipley Do-Nuts
5200 N Main St
Houston, TX 77009-3665

Telephone: (713) 869-4636
Fax Number: (713) 863-9623
Internet Homepage: shipleydonuts.com
Company Email:
  marketing@shipleydonuts.com
Type of Business: Chain Restaurant Operator
Year Founded: 1936
Total Sales: $30,880,000 (e)
Average Check: Dinner(6)
Total Units: 321
Trade Names: Shipley Do-Nuts (321)
Company-Owned Units: 15
Units Franchised To: 306
Primary Menu: Snacks (321)
Projected Openings: 57
Areas of Operation: AL, AR, LA, MS, TN, TX
Type of Foodservice: Quick Serve (321)
Catering Services: Yes

Key Personnel
CLIFTON RUTLEDGE - CEO
GARY M. ESTACIO - CFO
HANK SIMPSON - COO
DONNA JOSEPHSON - Chief Marketing Officer
JIM FISHER - Senior VP Supply Chain
KERRY LEO - VP Technology
LUKE B. MANDOLA - VP Development, Franchise Sales
STACEY MICHEL - Director Marketing
SHELLY KAY - Director Field Marketing
JESSICA LAWSON - Director Marketing

SPB Hospitality
19219 Katy Fwy Suite 500
Houston, TX 77094

Telephone: (346) 440-0772
Internet Homepage: a1aaleworks.com;
  bigrivergrille.com; bluewaterchattanooga.com;
  chophouse.com; logansroadhouse.com;
  oldchicago.com; ragtimetavern.com;
  rockbottom.com; singsing.com
Listing Type: Corporate Office
Type of Business: Chain Restaurant Operator
Year Founded: 2010
Total Sales: $483,340,000 (e)
Total Units: 560
Trade Names: A1A Ale Works (1); Big River Grille & Brewing Works (3); Chophouse & Brewery (1); Ember Smoked BBQ (19); Gordon Biersch Brewery Restaurant (7); J. Alexander's (25); Leo's Italian Kitchen (46); Logan's Roadhouse (139); Merus Grill (1); Old Chicago Pizza & Taproom (81); Ragtime Tavern (1); Redlands Grill (9); Roadies Sliders (17); Rock Bottom Restaurant & Brewery (17); Seven Bridges Grille (1); Stoney River (13); Twisted Tenders (179)
Company-Owned Units: 460
Units Franchised To: 100
Preferred Location Types: Airports; Downtown; Freestanding; Hotel/Motel; Lifestyle Center
Primary Menu: American (81); Bar-B-Q (19); Chicken (179); Italian (46); Pizza (81); Steak (153); Steak/Seafood (1)
Projected Openings: 10
Areas of Operation: AL, AR, AZ, CA, CO, DC, FL, GA, HI, IA, ID, IL, IN, KS, KY, LA, MD, MI, MN, MO, MS, MT, NC, ND, NE, NV, NY, OH, OK, OR, PA, SC, TN, TX, UT, VA, WA, WI, WV, WY
Type of Foodservice: Casual Dining (331); Fast Casual (215); Fine Dining (14)
Headquarter Offices: Logan's Roadhouse Inc., HOUSTON, TX
Notes: 2nd Corporate HQ Location:
  Chattanooga
  201 W. Main St., Ste. 301
  Chattanooga, TN 37408
  423.424.2000

Key Personnel
JOSH KERN - CEO
JIM LEBS - CFO
JESSICA HAGLER - CFO
MICHAEL CASEY - Chief Development Officer
ELLEN ROCKWELL - Exec VP People
CAM CAMPBELL - Senior VP Operations
CHRIS CONLON - Senior VP Operations
ERIC PHILLIPS - Senior VP People
SCOTT ADAMS - VP Supply Chain
KRISTEN HOHL - VP Marketing
TOM PETSKA - VP Franchise Sales
JASON MURRAY - VP Facility/Maintenance, Construction
NICHOLAS TZOMPANAKIS - VP Culinary Operations
AMANDA HYDE - VP Operations
BROOKE TRAUGER - VP Tax
NICHOLAS MASON - Senior Director Finance
RACHAEL MOSELEY - Senior Director Employee Development
LUIS HARO - Senior Director Culinary Development
JEFF KOWAL - Senior Director Operations
MIKE IBIS - Senior Director Supply Chain
BRIAN SHANER - Director Operations
MAREN MARTINSON - Director Real Estate
SCOTT WORKMAN - Director Information Systems
MICHAEL MATOS - Director Store Operations
JESSICA AMOS - Director Restaurant Operations
RAY WILMETTI - Director Operations
BRIAN DUKES - Director Supply Chain
RYAN RUSSELL - Director Marketing, Communications
MATTHEW POFFEL - Director Alcoholic Beverages
BETH KEATING - Director Operations
SHANNON GLACKEN - Director Operations
JEREMY UNDERHILL - Director Operations
FELIX CHEATHAM - Director Operations
KRISTINA NEWTON - Director Operations
MEGHAN IRWIN - Director Digital
KEVEN PETERSEN - Senior Manager Applications
JAMIE LANE - Manager Supply Chain
SARAH JORANDBY - Manager Operations
MICCAH MATARAZZO - Manager Sales

Submarina Inc.
4801 Woodway Dr Ste 300E
Houston, TX 77056-1888

Telephone: (713) 963-8125
Fax Number: (760) 471-3387
Internet Homepage: submarina.com
Company Email:
  customerservice@submarina.com
Type of Business: Chain Restaurant Operator
Year Founded: 1977
Systemwide Sales: $25,043,000 (e)
Total Sales: $1,284,000 (e)
Number of Employees: 5
Average Check: Lunch(12); Dinner(12)
Total Units: 19
Trade Names: Submarina Better Built Subs (19)
Units Franchised To: 19
Preferred Square Footage: 1,500
Preferred Location Types: Strip Mall
Primary Menu: Sandwiches/Deli (19)
Projected Openings: 2
Projected Remodelings: 3
Areas of Operation: AZ, CA, FL, GU, MI, NV, TN, TX
Type of Foodservice: Quick Serve (19)
Catering Services: Yes
Primary Distributors: (Full Line) US Foods - San Diego, VISTA, CA

Key Personnel
BRUCE ROSENTHAL - Chairman; CEO; President
JEFF WARFIELD - CEO

The Toasted Yolk Cafe
12151 Westheimer Rd
Houston, TX 77077

Telephone: (281) 617-7458
Internet Homepage: thetoastedyolk.com
Type of Business: Chain Restaurant Operator
Year Founded: 2010
Total Sales: $24,980,000 (e)
Total Units: 17

Trade Names: The Toasted Yolk Cafe (17)
Company-Owned Units: 17
Alcohol Served: Beer, Wine, Liquor
Primary Menu: American (17)
Projected Openings: 19
Type of Foodservice: Casual Dining (17)

Key Personnel
CHRIS MILTON - Co-Founder; Partner
MATHEW DEMOTT - Co-Founder; Partner
DONNIE MIXON - VP Franchising
JAMES GRAY - Regional VP Operations
SCOTT RAINES - Director Training

TLG Restaurants, LLC
13250 FM 1960 Rd W
Houston, TX 77065-4005

Telephone: (281) 894-1252
Type of Business: Chain Restaurant Operator
Total Sales: $100,440,000 (e)
Total Units: 39
Trade Names: Jack in the Box (39)
Units Franchised From: 39
Primary Menu: Hamburger (39)
Areas of Operation: TX
Type of Foodservice: Quick Serve (39)
Franchise Affiliation: Jack in the Box Restaurants, SAN DIEGO, CA

Key Personnel
SHERMAN LEWIS III - President; Partner; General Buyer

Tony's Restaurant, Inc
3755 Richmond Ave
Houston, TX 77046-3703

Telephone: (713) 622-6779
Fax Number: (713) 626-1232
Internet Homepage: tonyshouston.com; ciaobellohouston.com
Type of Business: Chain Restaurant Operator
Total Sales: $21,353,000 (e)
Total Units: 3
Trade Names: Ciao Bello (1); Tony's (1); Vallone's (1)
Company-Owned Units: 3
Alcohol Served: Beer, Wine, Liquor
Primary Menu: Italian (2); Steak (1)
Areas of Operation: TX
Type of Foodservice: Fine Dining (3)

Key Personnel
TONY VALLONE - President; General Buyer

Treebeards
315 Travis St
Houston, TX 77002-1812

Telephone: (713) 225-2160
Fax Number: (713) 228-2649
Internet Homepage: treebeards.com
Type of Business: Chain Restaurant Operator
Year Founded: 1978
Total Sales: $5,871,000 (e)
Alcohol Sales: 1%
Number of Employees: 45
Average Check: Lunch(8);
Internet Order Processing: Yes
Total Units: 5
Trade Names: Treebeards (5)
Company-Owned Units: 5
Preferred Location Types: Freestanding; Other
Alcohol Served: Wine
Primary Menu: Southern (5)
Areas of Operation: TX
Type of Foodservice: Casual Dining (5)
Catering Services: Yes
Primary Distributors: (Full Line) US Foods, HOUSTON, TX

Key Personnel
JOLIE STINNEFORD - President; Partner; General Manager; General Buyer
CHARLES STINEFORD - Partner
LISA POLLARO - General Manager

Truluck's Restaurant Group
9601 Katy Fwy Ste 210
Houston, TX 77024-1332

Telephone: (832) 358-2900
Fax Number: (832) 358-2901
Internet Homepage: trulucks.com
Type of Business: Chain Restaurant Operator
Total Sales: $24,960,000 (e)
Alcohol Sales: 10%
Number of Employees: 575
Average Check: Lunch(54); Dinner(90)
Internet Order Processing: Yes
Total Units: 12
Trade Names: Truluck's Seafood, Steak, Crab House (12)
Company-Owned Units: 12
Preferred Square Footage: 7,000
Preferred Location Types: Freestanding
Alcohol Served: Beer, Wine, Liquor
Primary Menu: Steak/Seafood (12)
Projected Openings: 1
Areas of Operation: CA, FL, TX
Type of Foodservice: Fine Dining (12)
Catering Services: Yes
Primary Distributors: (Full Line) SYSCO Food Services of North Texas, LEWISVILLE, TX

Key Personnel
STUART SARGENT - Founder; Owner; Controller
ANDREA GENTRY - General Manager
DAVE MATTERN - Director Category Management-Beverages

Vibe Restaurants
6804 Bintliff Dr
Houston, TX 77074-3516

Telephone: (888) 427-0554
Internet Homepage: viberestaurants.com
Company Email: marketing@viberestaurants.com
Type of Business: Chain Restaurant Operator
Total Sales: $73,240,000 (e)
Number of Employees: 858
Total Units: 59
Trade Names: Little Caesars Pizza (59)
Units Franchised From: 59
Preferred Location Types: Freestanding; Strip Mall
Primary Menu: Pizza (59)
Areas of Operation: AR, KS, LA, MD, OK, TX, VA
Type of Foodservice: Quick Serve (59)
Franchise Affiliation: Little Caesar Enterprises Inc., DETROIT, MI; Which Wich Inc., DALLAS, TX

Key Personnel
IRFAAN LALANI - CEO
JEREMY VILLERE - CFO
MICHAEL TRIFARI - COO
FAISAL LALANI - Chief Development Officer
SHALIN PATEL - Chief Investment Officer
JOE MACRI - VP Operations
JOSEPH MACRI - VP Operations
JEAN SAINTVIL - Senior Director Operations
SHANE GREEN - Director Training
JOHN POLCHINSKI - Director Operations

Vincent Mandola Family Restaurants
2817 W Dallas St
Houston, TX 77019-4006

Telephone: (713) 522-5120
Fax Number: (713) 528-1008
Internet Homepage: ninos-vincents.com
Type of Business: Chain Restaurant Operator
Year Founded: 1977
Total Sales: $14,110,000 (e)
Alcohol Sales: 10%
Number of Employees: 142
Average Check: Lunch(34); Dinner(72)
Total Units: 5
Trade Names: Grappino di Nino (1); Nino's Restaurant & Bar (1); Pronto Cucinino (2); Vincent's Restaurant (1)

Company-Owned Units: 5
Preferred Location Types: Freestanding
Alcohol Served: Beer, Wine, Liquor
Primary Menu: Italian (5)
Areas of Operation: TX
Type of Foodservice: Casual Dining (5)
Primary Distributors: (Full Line) Martin Preferred Foods, HOUSTON, TX

Key Personnel
MARY MANDOLA - Partner
VINCENT MANDOLA - Partner; Executive Chef; General Buyer
DANA MANDOLA-CORBETT - General Manager
VINCEANNE MANDOLA-GREEN - General Manager

Westmont Hospitality Group
5847 San Felipe St Ste 4650
Houston, TX 77057-3277

Telephone: (713) 782-9100
Fax Number: (713) 782-9600
Internet Homepage: whg.com
Type of Business: Foodservice Operations - Hotel/Motels
Year Founded: 1975
Total Sales: $426,640,000 (e)
Alcohol Sales: 20%
Number of Employees: 4,200
Total Units: 71
Restaurants in Hotels: 71
Trade Names: Agatha & Ernstein's (1); Alexander's (1); Alfredo's (1); Assorted (9); Backporch Grill & Piano Bar (1); Bari's Restaurant (1); Best Western (2); Bibelots (1); Brasserie (1); Bridges (1); Cafe Bellevue (1); Cafe Creole (1); Cafe du Jardin (1); Cafe du Moulin (1); Cafe Flou (1); Cafe Lascombe (1); Cafe Riva (1); Cafe Toulouse (1); Charlie's (1); Chelsea's (1); Chestnut Tree (1); Chez Chine (1); Clarion Hotel & Suites (1); Club B 52 (1); Courtyard Cafe (1); Embassy (1); Franco's Cafe (1); Graffiti's Italian Eatery (5); Hanson Inn (1); Harper's (1); Holiday Inn (6); Howard Johnson (1); Jonathan's (1); Knights Inn (1); L'Habitant (1); Le Marche (1); Le Trianon (1); Lorenzo's (1); Max & Waldo's (1); Maxwell's Riverside (1); Mr. Abernathy's (1); Parkway (1); Quality Inn (1); Radisson Inn (2); Ramada Inn (2); Rodeway Inn (1); Roof Garden (1); Tattinger's (1); The Park Lane Cafe (1); Travelodge (1); Willow's (1)
Company-Owned Units: 71
Alcohol Served: Beer, Wine, Liquor
Areas of Operation: CA, CO, FL, IL, IN, KS, MI, MO, NY, PA, TX, AB, NS, ON, QC, SK
Foreign Countries: CANADA
Type of Foodservice: Casual Dining; Fine Dining
Subsidiaries: Boykin Lodging Company, HUNTERSVILLE, NC

Primary Distributors: (Food) SYSCO Central Florida Inc., OCOEE, FL
Notes: The company derives approximately 80% of its revenue from hotel operations.

Key Personnel
A. MAJID MANGALJI - CEO; President
MOEZ MANGALJI - Owner; VP Risk Management
JERRY BURRELL - CFO
MOHAMED THOWFEEK - Executive Director
KENNETH OCASIO - General Manager Area
LAWRENCE YATES - Director Business Development
GREG BINGAMAN - Director
PENNY BROWN - Director Operations
DORRAINE LALLANI - Director
HECTOR QUESADA - Regional Director Operations
ANTHONY SANDERS - Senior Manager District
ELMER GARCIA - Regional Manager
BRANDON CROSBY - Area Manager
ROBERT MAYO - Manager Operations
BRANDON LAWN - Coordinator Information Technology

Willie's Restaurants
10627 Tower Oaks Blvd
Houston, TX 77070-5926

Telephone: (281) 807-5200
Fax Number: (281) 807-0666
Internet Homepage: williesrestaurants.com
Type of Business: Chain Restaurant Operator
Year Founded: 1982
Total Sales: $38,120,000 (e)
Alcohol Sales: 20%
Number of Employees: 645
Average Check: Lunch(14); Dinner(20)
Total Units: 18
Trade Names: Fajita Willie's Cafe & Cantina (1); Willie's Grill & Icehouse (17)
Company-Owned Units: 18
Preferred Location Types: Freestanding; Strip Mall
Alcohol Served: Beer, Wine, Liquor
Primary Menu: American (17); Southwest/Tex-Mex (1)
Areas of Operation: TX
Type of Foodservice: Fast Casual (18)
Catering Services: Yes

Key Personnel
GREGORY LIPPERT - CEO; President
MALORI CALLAHAN - CFO; VP Finance
SCOTT CHLEBOS - VP Human Resources, Talent
JUSTIN SCHULTZ - VP Operations
MARTY WADSWORTH - VP Marketing
JOSH HILL - VP Operations
BRANDON JOHNSON - Director Operations
FAY CADE - Director Finance, Human Resources, Catering; Manager Administration

VINCENT BALSAMO - Manager
JAMES COLBY - Manager Facility/Maintenance
PAUL LAMBERT - Manager

Williston Holding Company
12000 Aerospace Ave Ste 400
Houston, TX 77034-5576

Telephone: (832) 300-5858
Fax Number: (832) 300-5859
Internet Homepage: whcbrands.com
Type of Business: Chain Restaurant Operator
Year Founded: 2012
Total Sales: $72,240,000 (e)
Alcohol Sales: 10%
Number of Employees: 1,754
Average Check: Lunch(14); Dinner(24)
Total Units: 39
Trade Names: Casa Ole Restaurant & Cantina (25); Crazy Jose's (1); Monterey's Little Mexico (9); Tortuga Coastal Cantina (1); Uberrito Mexican Grill (3)
Company-Owned Units: 27
Units Franchised To: 12
Preferred Square Footage: 8,000; 20,000
Preferred Location Types: Community Mall; Freestanding; Strip Mall
Alcohol Served: Beer, Wine, Liquor
Primary Menu: Mexican (39)
Areas of Operation: LA, OK, TX
Type of Foodservice: Casual Dining (36); Fast Casual (3)
Catering Services: Yes
Primary Distributors: (Full Line) Ben E. Keith Foods, SAN ANTONIO, TX

Key Personnel
MARCUS JUNDT - Co-Founder; CEO
DENNIS PACIFICO - Co-Founder; VP Operations
NANCY CROSS - Chief People Officer
BRIAN INGRAM - Chief Development Officer
DANA HAMILTON - Controller
RUBEN CORTEZ - Director Operations, Group
TWE HOPKINS - Director Information Technology
CRISTIAN GAXIOLA - Manager
JENNIFER PARRETT - Supervisor Area
MELANIE BARNES - Coordinator Recruitment
JOHNNY GUZMAN - Designer Graphic Design

Wymer Management
13711 FM 529 Rd
Houston, TX 77041-2522

Telephone: (713) 937-6108
Fax Number: (713) 856-8014
Type of Business: Chain Restaurant Operator
Total Sales: $56,750,000 (e)
Total Units: 12
Trade Names: McDonald's (12)

Units Franchised From: 12
Preferred Square Footage: 2,500
Primary Menu: Hamburger (12)
Areas of Operation: TX
Type of Foodservice: Quick Serve (12)
Franchise Affiliation: McDonald's Corporation, CHICAGO, IL

Key Personnel
HOWARD CARNICLE - Director Operations
SALENA FUENTEVILLA - Administrative Assistant

Yogurtland Franchisee
5901 Westheimer Rd Ste V
Houston, TX 77057-7651

Telephone: (713) 952-8880
Type of Business: Chain Restaurant Operator
Total Sales: $2,091,000 (e)
Total Units: 2
Trade Names: Yogurtland (2)
Units Franchised From: 2
Primary Menu: Snacks (2)
Areas of Operation: TX
Type of Foodservice: Quick Serve (2)
Franchise Affiliation: Yogurtland Franchising Inc., FARMERS BRANCH, TX

Key Personnel
MATTHEW PHU - Owner; General Buyer

Fairground Foods LLC
1914 E 1st
Hughes Springs, TX 75656-3645

Mailing Address: PO Box 907, HUGHES SPRINGS, TX, 75656-0907
Telephone: (903) 639-3575
Type of Business: Chain Restaurant Operator
Year Founded: 1991
Systemwide Sales: $2,756,000 (e)
Total Sales: $213,000 (c)
Number of Employees: 36
Average Check: Dinner(8)
Total Units: 4
Trade Names: Corn Dog 7 (4)
Company-Owned Units: 4
Preferred Square Footage: 600
Preferred Location Types: Community Mall; Regional Mall
Primary Menu: American (4)
Areas of Operation: GA, LA, MS, OK, TX
Type of Foodservice: Quick Serve (4)
Primary Distributors: (Full Line) Vistar North Texas, ARLINGTON, TX

Key Personnel
STEPHEN MCKINNEY - Chairman; President; CFO; Director Facility/Maintenance, Information Systems, Real Estate, Design; Manager Risk Management, Human Resources, Business Development

Great American Food Corporation
3684 FM 161 N
Hughes Springs, TX 75656-6487

Telephone: (903) 639-1482
Fax Number: (866) 356-4232
Internet Homepage: davidbeards.com
Company Email: office@davidbeards.com
Type of Business: Chain Restaurant Operator
Year Founded: 1981
Systemwide Sales: $26,446,000 (e)
Total Sales: $25,870,000 (e)
Number of Employees: 355
Average Check: Lunch(8); Dinner(14)
Total Units: 15
Trade Names: Catfish King (11); Catfish Village Restaurant (3); David Beards (1)
Company-Owned Units: 13
Units Franchised To: 2
Preferred Square Footage: 2,500; 5,500; 6,000
Preferred Location Types: Freestanding
Primary Menu: Seafood (15)
Areas of Operation: LA, OK, TX
Type of Foodservice: Family Restaurant (3); Quick Serve (12)

Key Personnel
DAVID BEARD - President; General Buyer

Mark of Excellence
1808 Harwood Ct
Hurst, TX 76054-3190

Telephone: (817) 632-2222
Type of Business: Chain Restaurant Operator
Total Sales: $97,856,000 (e)
Total Units: 48
Trade Names: Domino's (48)
Units Franchised From: 48
Primary Menu: Pizza (48)
Areas of Operation: TX
Type of Foodservice: Quick Serve (48)
Franchise Affiliation: Domino's Pizza Inc, ANN ARBOR, MI

Key Personnel
JERALD POSTEN - President
DENNIS L. MAYHALL - Owner; General Buyer
MATT BENTON - CFO
NYX NAVA - Director Human Resources
CARLOS CISNEROS - District Manager

Tracs Food Inc
969 Melbourne Rd
Hurst, TX 76053-4632

Telephone: (817) 946-8091
Type of Business: Chain Restaurant Operator
Total Sales: $2,876,000 (e)
Total Units: 5
Trade Names: Subway (5)
Units Franchised From: 5
Primary Menu: Sandwiches/Deli (5)
Areas of Operation: TX
Type of Foodservice: Quick Serve (5)
Franchise Affiliation: Doctor's Associates Inc., MILFORD, CT

Key Personnel
ELIZABETH CORNELL - President; General Buyer

Albert Restaurant Group
1600 Corporate Ct Ste 150
Irving, TX 75038

Telephone: (972) 241-2165
Internet Homepage: albertenterprises.com
Type of Business: Chain Restaurant Operator
Total Sales: $50,380,000 (e)
Total Units: 35
Trade Names: Dairy Queen Restaurant (2); Schlotzsky's Deli (33)
Units Franchised From: 35
Primary Menu: Sandwiches/Deli (33); Snacks (2)
Areas of Operation: TX
Type of Foodservice: Fast Casual (33)
Franchise Affiliation: International Dairy Queen Inc., BLOOMINGTON, MN; Schlotzsky's Ltd., ATLANTA, GA

Key Personnel
CARY ALBERT - President; Partner; General Buyer
JACKIE ALBERT - Partner
ROBERT VEGA - Senior VP Operations
DAVID HELGESON - Controller
KIRK SHARP - Director Construction
STEVE GUIDROZ - Director Catering
JOSH WANDER - Director Operations
FRED VEGA - Director Operations
JAVIER BENETIZ - District Manager Central Region
RICARDO ARAUJO - District Manager
ZACH SEEFELDT - Assistant Accounting, Marketing

BD's Mongolian Grill
8200 Springwood Dr
Irving, TX 75063

Telephone: (888) 436-4447
Internet Homepage: bdsgrill.com
Listing Type: Subsidiary
Type of Business: Chain Restaurant Operator
Year Founded: 1992
Systemwide Sales: $101,026,000 (e)
Total Sales: $19,130,000 (e)
Alcohol Sales: 25%
Number of Employees: 1,305
Average Check: Lunch(18); Dinner(18)
Internet Order Processing: Yes
Total Units: 28
Trade Names: bd's Mongolian Grill (21); Flat Top Grill (7)
Company-Owned Units: 17
Units Franchised To: 11
Preferred Square Footage: 5,000
Preferred Location Types: Downtown; Freestanding
Alcohol Served: Beer, Wine, Liquor
Primary Menu: Asian (28)
Areas of Operation: CO, FL, IL, IN, KS, KY, MD, MI, MO, OH, VA, WI, FC
Foreign Countries: MONGOLIA
Type of Foodservice: Casual Dining (21); Fast Casual (7)
Primary Distributors: (Food) Reinhart Foodservice, WARREN, MI
Parent Company: Mongolian Concepts LLC, IRVING, TX

Key Personnel
PATRICK COLEMAN - General Manager
DEBBIE PHRANER - Director Marketing
MARK NOVAK - Regional Director

CEC Entertainment Inc.
1707 Market Place Blvd
Irving, TX 75063

Mailing Address: PO Box 152077, IRVING, TX, 75015-2077
Telephone: (972) 258-8507
Fax Number: (972) 258-5524
Internet Homepage: chuckecheese.com; peterpiperfranchise.com; peterpiperpizza.com
Company Email: guestrelations@cecentertainment.com
Type of Business: Chain Restaurant Operator
Year Founded: 1980
Systemwide Sales: $598,799,000 (e)
Total Sales: $1,216,700,000 (e)
Alcohol Sales: 0.50%
Foodservice Sales: $535,348,000 (e)
Internet Order Processing: Yes
Internet Sales: 0.50%
Total Units: 594
Trade Names: Chuck E. Cheese's (498); Peter Piper Pizza (96)
Company-Owned Units: 418
Units Franchised To: 176
Preferred Location Types: Community Mall; Freestanding; Regional Mall; Strip Mall
Alcohol Served: Beer, Wine
Primary Menu: Pizza (594)
Areas of Operation: AK, AL, AR, AZ, CA, CO, CT, DE, FL, GA, GU, HI, IA, ID, IL, IN, KS, KY, LA, MA, MD, ME, MI, MN, MO, MS, MT, NC, ND, NE, NH, NJ, NM, NV, NY, OH, OK, OR, PA, PR, SC, SD, TN, TX, UT, VA, WA, WI, WV, AB, BC, ON, SK
Foreign Countries: CANADA; CHILE; COLOMBIA; COSTA RICA; GUATEMALA; HONDURAS; MEXICO; PANAMA; PERU; SAUDI ARABIA; TRINIDAD & TOBAGO; UNITED ARAB EMIRATES
Type of Foodservice: Casual Dining (594)
Primary Distributors: (Food) McLane Company, Inc., TEMPLE, TX; (Food) Vistar North Texas, ARLINGTON, TX
Parent Company: Apollo Global Management LLC, NEW YORK, NY

Key Personnel
SCOTT DRAKE - CFO
TONY HOWARD - Chief Accounting Officer; VP; Controller
GENARO PEREX - Chief Marketing Officer
DAVID DECK - Chief Compliance Officer; General Counsel
TROY V WATRING - Area Director Operations
YURI PENA - Area Director
PETER PANUNZI - Area Director
DAN BESSEMER - Area Director
RANDY FORSYTHE - Exec VP; Director Operations
CHRIS KELLY - VP Operations, Central Region
BLAKE HUGGINS - VP Tax
JAY SPEARS - VP Information Technology
MELISSA MCLEANAS - VP Media, Licensing
JIM BRAWLEY - VP Operations, Region
COLTON PEARSON - VP Real Estate
DEB HALLMARK - Senior Director Talent Acquisitions
JEREMY WEINER - Senior Director Operations; Manager
JANET MICHELS - Senior Director Supply Chain
KELLY HANSEN POWERS - Senior Director Marketing
ANTONIO BARRON - Senior Director Strategy, Innovation
JUSTIN LEE - Director Construction
GINA DARTY - Director Facility/Maintenance
MICAH HARDT - Director Development
NANCY HARRIS - Director Human Resources
BARBARA JENNESS - Director Payroll
ADAM SULLIVAN - Director
CORY LORIA - Director Finance
ADRIENNE GONZALEZ - Director Marketing, Franchising, International
RYAN RIDDER - Director Information Technology
DEBRA HENRY - Director Marketing
DEANDREA BEAN - Director Operations
SCOTT GLASSMAN - Director Talent Acquisitions
MATT DANIEL - Director Operations
NICK LOEFFLER - Senior Manager Store Systems
MINDY BROWN - Regional Manager Human Resources
JUAN GARZA - Manager Operations
CHERYL TOMLINSON - Manager Payroll, Operations
BRENDA HOLLOWAY - Manager Marketing
PEDRO SANCHEZ - Manager
JOHN BRUCE - Manager
TAMMY WADE - Manager Technology
MARCO MOLINARI - Manager Technology
RICK RAISON - Sr Merchant

Coury Hospitality
400 East Las Colinas Boulevard Suite 660
Irving, TX 75039

Telephone: (817) 796-9696
Internet Homepage: couryhospitality.com
Type of Business: Chain Restaurant Operator
Year Founded: 1986
Total Sales: $48,821,000 (e)
Total Units: 26
Trade Names: Adagio Lounge (1); Aravalli (1); Bacchus Kitchen and Bar (1); CaveSociety (1); Dockum Bar (1); Feinstein's at Hotel Carmichael (1); Flint Restaurant (1); Harvest Hall (1); Lonnie's Reno Club (1); Magnum Speakeasy (1); Nebu (1); O Bar (1); Oggie's Restaurant (1); One Bar (1); ParamountRecreation Club (1); Puffer Fish (1); Rioja Terrace (1); Siena Tuscan Steakhouse (1); Supper Club (1); The American Reserve (1); The Chalkboard Kitchen and Bar (1); Third Rail Lounge (1); Toscana Italian Steakhouse (1); Vast Restaurant (1); Vivante Restaurant and Bar (1); WineYard Grille and Bar (1)
Company-Owned Units: 26
Primary Menu: American (17); Coffee (1); French/Continental (1); Greek/Mediterranean (1); Miscellaneous (1); Seafood (1); Snacks (1); Steak (1); Steak/Seafood (2)
Areas of Operation: IN, KS, MO, OK, TX, WI
Type of Foodservice: Casual Dining (10); Fine Dining (16)

Key Personnel
PAUL COURY - Founder; CEO
ANDREW CASPERSON - COO
TODD M. RABURN - VP Operations
HEATHER CARRASCO - VP Procurement
MATTHEW RODRIGUEZ - Director Engineering

Dallas Jersey Mike's, LP
6550 N MacArthur Blvd Ste 140
Irving, TX 75039-2825

Telephone: (972) 556-0900
Type of Business: Chain Restaurant Operator
Total Sales: $12,400,000 (e)
Total Units: 9
Trade Names: Jersey Mike's Subs (9)
Units Franchised From: 9
Primary Menu: Sandwiches/Deli (9)
Areas of Operation: TX
Type of Foodservice: Quick Serve (9)
Franchise Affiliation: Jersey Mike's Franchise Systems, MANASQUAN, NJ

Key Personnel
DALTON STEWART - Partner; General Buyer
JOEY FLUETTE - Partner

Fuzzy's Taco Shop
4200 Regent Blvd Ste C-210
Irving, TX 75063

Telephone: (817) 624-8226
Internet Homepage: fuzzystacoshop.com
Company Email: fuzzy@fuzzystacoshop.com
Type of Business: Chain Restaurant Operator
Year Founded: 2003
Systemwide Sales: $291,440,000 (e)
Total Sales: $29,238,000 (e)
Number of Employees: 291
Total Units: 131
Trade Names: Fuzzy's Taco Shop (131)
Company-Owned Units: 1
Units Franchised To: 130
Preferred Location Types: Freestanding; Strip Mall
Alcohol Served: Beer, Wine, Liquor
Primary Menu: Taco (131)
Projected Openings: 25
Areas of Operation: AZ, CO, FL, GA, KS, LA, MO, NC, NE, NV, OK, TN, TX
Type of Foodservice: Fast Casual (131)
Parent Company: Dine Brands Global, Inc., PASADENA, CA

Key Personnel
PAUL DAMICO - CEO
PATRICK KIRK - President; Chief Marketing Officer
SCOTT SHOTTER - COO
MARSHALL CLAYCAMP - COO
LEO AGUILAR - VP Technology
LAURA PURSER - VP Marketing
EDUARDO JIMINEZ - General Manager
BRANDON PHILLIPS - General Manager
CARLOS CRUZ - General Manager
GREGORY SALMON - Director Research & Development
NIKKI RASMUSSEN - Director Digital Marketing
JOSH DIEKMAN - Director Culinary Operations
KELLIE KNOTTS - Director Operations
KARINA MARTINEZ - Manager Franchise Operations
ALEXANDER OAKES - Manager Training
ANDIE SMIRL - Manager Franchise Sales
JILL KNIGHT - Manager Development, Construction
DOUG BOWEN - Consultant Franchise Operations
TOM JUDD - Consultant Operations

Ibrahim Investment Corporation
1915 Westridge Dr
Irving, TX 75038-2902

Telephone: (972) 550-1282
Type of Business: Chain Restaurant Operator
Total Sales: $98,820,000 (e)
Total Units: 38
Trade Names: Jack in the Box (38)
Units Franchised From: 38
Primary Menu: Hamburger (38)
Areas of Operation: TX
Type of Foodservice: Quick Serve (38)
Franchise Affiliation: Jack in the Box Restaurants, SAN DIEGO, CA

Key Personnel
UMAR IBRAHIM - Owner; General Buyer

M Crowd Restaurant Group
350 E Royal Ln Bldg 4
Irving, TX 75039-3538

Telephone: (214) 217-3000
Fax Number: (214) 217-0212
Internet Homepage: mcrowd.com
Company Email: kbooth@mcrowd.com
Type of Business: Chain Restaurant Operator
Year Founded: 1990
Total Sales: $95,550,000 (e)
Alcohol Sales: 8%
Number of Employees: 1,765
Average Check: Lunch(30); Dinner(30)
Total Units: 27
Trade Names: Mi Cocina (22); Taco Diner (4); The Mercury Grill (1)
Company-Owned Units: 27
Preferred Square Footage: 5,500; 6,000
Preferred Location Types: Freestanding
Alcohol Served: Beer, Wine, Liquor
Primary Menu: American (1); Southwest/Tex-Mex (22); Taco (7)
Areas of Operation: GA, OK, TX
Type of Foodservice: Casual Dining (30)
Primary Distributors: (Food) FreshPoint Dallas, DALLAS, TX

Key Personnel
EDGAR GUEVARA - CEO; President
JONATHAN DUBROC - CFO
JOHN DRUMMOND - VP Human Resources-Training
GIOVANNI N. GIOVANINI - VP Strategy, Supply Chain
CHRIS WARD - Executive Chef; Manager Purchasing, Supply Chain, Food Safety
FERNANDO GALLEGOS-VELASQUEZ - Director Restaurant Operations
DINA REED - Manager Human Resources
RAQUEL VIAFRANCO - Manager Restaurant Operations
ALEJANDRO VICENTE - Manager Culinary Development

Medieval Times Management Inc.
5020 Riverside Dr Ste 400
Irving, TX 75039

Telephone: (214) 596-7600
Fax Number: (214) 596-7601
Internet Homepage: medievaltimes.com
Company Email: communications@medievaltimes.com
Type of Business: Chain Restaurant Operator
Year Founded: 1983
Total Sales: $13,850,000 (e)
Alcohol Sales: 20%
Number of Employees: 888
Average Check: Dinner(60)
Total Units: 10
Trade Names: Medieval Times Dinner & Tournament (10)
Company-Owned Units: 9
Preferred Square Footage: 20,000
Preferred Location Types: Freestanding
Alcohol Served: Beer, Wine, Liquor
Primary Menu: American (10)
Areas of Operation: AZ, CA, FL, GA, IL, MD, NJ, SC, TX, ON
Foreign Countries: CANADA
Type of Foodservice: Casual Dining (10)
Primary Distributors: (Equipment) Edward Don & Co., MIRAMAR, FL; (Food) SYSCO Central Florida Inc., OCOEE, FL; (Supplies) Edward Don & Co., MIRAMAR, FL

Key Personnel
P MONTANER - President; General Buyer
DANIEL KIM - VP
CELESTE LANUZA - VP Marketing, Sales

Mongolian Concepts LLC
8200 Springwood Dr Ste 230
Irving, TX 75063

Telephone: (214) 774-4240
Fax Number: (214) 774-4243

Internet Homepage: flattopgrill.com; genghisgrill.com; gomongo.com
Company Email: info@genghisgrill.com
Type of Business: Chain Restaurant Operator
Year Founded: 1998
Systemwide Sales: $65,735,000 (e)
Total Sales: $43,310,000 (e)
Alcohol Sales: 5%
Number of Employees: 557
Average Check: Lunch(14); Dinner(18)
Internet Order Processing: Yes
Total Units: 79
Trade Names: bd's Mongolian Grill (21); Flat Top Grill (7); Genghis Grill (51)
Company-Owned Units: 59
Units Franchised To: 18
Preferred Square Footage: 3,000; 3,500
Preferred Location Types: Downtown; Freestanding; Lifestyle Center
Alcohol Served: Beer, Wine, Liquor
Primary Menu: Asian (49)
Areas of Operation: AR, AZ, CO, FL, GA, MD, MN, NC, NM, NV, OK, SC, TN, TX, VA
Type of Foodservice: Fast Casual (49)
Catering Services: Yes
Subsidiaries: BD's Mongolian Grill, IRVING, TX
Parent Company: The Chalak Group, DALLAS, TX

Key Personnel
GREGG MAJEWSKI - CEO
CASSIE SCHOLTENS - Senior Director Training
SAMANTHA KEARNS - Creative Director
ERNIE BIGHAUS - Director Construction
WILL COLLINS - Director Operations
AMANDA BOYD - Regional Director
DOUG NOLAN - Regional Director
JUSTIN HOKE - Assistant Director Area
JEFF JONES - Manager Training

On The Border LLC
2201 W Royal Ln Ste 240
Irving, TX 75063-3208

Telephone: (972) 499-3000
Internet Homepage: ontheborder.com
Company Email: info@ontheborder.com
Type of Business: Chain Restaurant Operator
Year Founded: 1990
Systemwide Sales: $762,942,000 (e)
Total Sales: $466,226,000 (e)
Alcohol Sales: 10%
Number of Employees: 5,200
Average Check: Lunch(16); Dinner(16)
Internet Order Processing: Yes
Internet Sales: 5.00%
Total Units: 127
Trade Names: On The Border Mexican Grill & Cantina (127)
Company-Owned Units: 111
Units Franchised To: 15
Preferred Square Footage: 5,700; 6,200
Preferred Location Types: Community Mall; Downtown; Freestanding; Lifestyle Center; Regional Mall; Strip Mall
Alcohol Served: Beer, Wine, Liquor
Primary Menu: Mexican (127)
Areas of Operation: AR, AZ, CA, CO, CT, FL, GA, IA, ID, IL, IN, KS, LA, MA, MD, ME, MI, MO, MS, NC, NJ, NV, NY, OH, OK, PA, PR, SC, TN, TX, VA
Foreign Countries: SOUTH KOREA
Type of Foodservice: Casual Dining (127)
Catering Services: Yes
Primary Distributors: (Food) US Foods, GARLAND, TX
Parent Company: Argonne Capital Group LLC, ATLANTA, GA

Key Personnel
BILL MCMILLAN - CIO
MIKE WOOD - Chief Real Estate Officer
JEFF HAWKINS - Area Director
CODY SHIPPEY - Area Director
SHELLY PIERCE - Director Development, Training
STEPHANIE VARGHESE - Director Benefits, Compensation
WAYNE NGUYEN - Director Architecture
ALEX STUCKY - Senior Manager Digital Marketing
ROBERT LEWIS - Area Manager
LAUREN CASSADY - Area Manager Sales
DEB LAWTON - Manager Human Resources
LACY MORGANTI - Specialist Catering

Pei Wei Asian Diner
6191 N State Highway 161
Irving, TX 75038

Telephone: (480) 888-3000
Fax Number: (480) 888-3001
Internet Homepage: peiwei.com
Type of Business: Chain Restaurant Operator
Year Founded: 1993
Systemwide Sales: $263,291,000 (e)
Total Sales: $299,100,000 (e)
Alcohol Sales: 2%
Number of Employees: 8,328
Average Check: Lunch(10); Dinner(12)
Internet Order Processing: Yes
Internet Sales: 15.00%
Total Units: 120
Trade Names: Pei Wei Asian Diner (120)
Company-Owned Units: 120
Preferred Square Footage: 2,800; 3,000; 3,400
Preferred Location Types: Airports; Community Mall; Downtown; Freestanding; Institution (college/hospital); Lifestyle Center; Regional Mall; Strip Mall
Alcohol Served: Beer, Wine, Liquor
Primary Menu: Asian (120)
Projected Openings: 10
Areas of Operation: AR, AZ, CA, CO, FL, MD, MI, MN, MO, NC, NM, NV, OK, PA, TN, TX, UT, VA
Foreign Countries: KUWAIT; UNITED ARAB EMIRATES
Type of Foodservice: Fast Casual (120)
Primary Distributors: (Full Line) US Foods-Los Angeles, LA MIRADA, CA
Parent Company: West Coast Capital, SHERMAN OAKS, CA

Key Personnel
LINDA NELSON - COO
MATTHEW RUNKLE - VP Supply Chain
MICHAEL COON - Director Applications
SEAN FITZPATRICK - Regional Director Operations
TAMMIE MONTGOMERY - Senior Manager Technology
ALFREDO PINON - Manager Culinary Operations
GINA WILSON - Specialist Facility/Maintenance

Uncle Julio's Corp
1101 N Union Bower Rd Ste 160
Irving, TX 75061-5850

Telephone: (972) 554-6886
Fax Number: (972) 554-6888
Internet Homepage: unclejulios.com
Company Email: info@unclejulios.com
Type of Business: Chain Restaurant Operator
Year Founded: 1986
Total Sales: $48,990,000 (e)
Alcohol Sales: 10%
Number of Employees: 2,641
Average Check: Lunch(14); Dinner(24)
Total Units: 47
Trade Names: Elways Steak House (4); Hacienda Colorado (6); Uncle Julio's (36); Uncle Julio's-Hacienda Colorado (1)
Company-Owned Units: 47
Preferred Square Footage: 4,500
Preferred Location Types: Freestanding; Office Complex
Alcohol Served: Beer, Wine, Liquor
Primary Menu: Mexican (43); Steak (4)
Projected Openings: 1
Areas of Operation: FL, GA, IL, MD, TN, TX, VA
Type of Foodservice: Casual Dining (43); Fine Dining (4)
Catering Services: Yes
Primary Distributors: (Food) SYSCO Food Services of Arkansas LLC, LITTLE ROCK, AR; (Food) SYSCO Food Services of Jacksonville Inc., JACKSONVILLE, FL; (Food) SYSCO Atlanta LLC, COLLEGE PARK, GA; (Food) SYSCO Food Services of Chicago Inc., DES PLAINES, IL; (Food) SYSCO Food Services of Baltimore, JESSUP, MD; (Food) SYSCO Food Services of North Texas, LEWISVILLE, TX; (Food) SYSCO Food Services of Houston Inc., HOUSTON, TX; (Food) SYSCO Food Services of Virginia LLC, HARRISONBURG,

VA; (Food) SYSCO Food Services of West Coast Florida Inc., PALMETTO, FL
Parent Company: L Catterton, GREENWICH, CT
Headquarter Offices: Hacienda Colorado, DENVER, CO

Key Personnel
TOM VOGEL - CEO; President
STEVE BRATTON - CFO
HARPER CARON - COO
DAN WHEELER - Chief Marketing Officer
HILLARY SHAHBABIAN - VP Human Resources
SREEDHAR VEMIREDDY - VP Information Technology
CHARLES BANKS - VP Information Technology
MARY BATSON - VP
NANCY WEST - Executive Director Administration
KATIE KAFER - Senior Director Training
RICK ROBERTS - Senior Director Purchasing
JOHN JOHNSON - Director Operations
ORIO LODAL - Senior Manager
TREY HARPER - Senior Manager
VALERIE VOGES - Senior Manager Marketing, Graphic Design

Whataburger Inc.
8201 Ridgepoint Dr
Irving, TX 75063-3160

Telephone: (972) 756-0096
Fax Number: (972) 756-2960
Listing Type: Regional Office
Type of Business: Chain Restaurant Operator
Total Units: 700
Areas of Operation: AL, AZ, FL, LA, MS, NM, OK, TX
Parent Company: Whataburger Restaurants LLC, SAN ANTONIO, TX

Key Personnel
LESLIE MATTINGLY - Director Human Resources
JEFF WEINSTEIN - Manager Human Resources

Southern Multifoods Inc.
101 E Cherokee St
Jacksonville, TX 75766-4807

Telephone: (903) 586-1524
Fax Number: (903) 586-9644
Internet Homepage: smi-tex.com
Type of Business: Chain Restaurant Operator
Year Founded: 1976
Total Sales: $282,410,000 (e)
Number of Employees: 1,975
Average Check: Lunch(12); Dinner(14)
Total Units: 105
Trade Names: KFC/Taco Bell (2); Long John Silver's/A&W All American Food (1); Taco Bell (97); Taco Bell/Long John Silver's (5)
Units Franchised From: 105
Preferred Square Footage: 2,500
Preferred Location Types: Convenience Store/Gas Station; Downtown; Freestanding
Primary Menu: American (1); Chicken (4); Seafood (5); Taco (87)
Areas of Operation: TX
Type of Foodservice: Quick Serve (97)
Franchise Affiliation: A&W Restaurants Inc., LEXINGTON, KY; KFC Corporation, LOUISVILLE, KY; Long John Silver's Inc., LOUISVILLE, KY; Taco Bell Corp., IRVINE, CA

Key Personnel
ROBERT CUDD - CFO; Director Finance, Purchasing, Information Systems, Supply Chain
TOMMY POLLARD - Regional Director

Domino's Franchisee
4950 Katy Gaston Rd Ste A
Katy, TX 77494-7361

Telephone: (281) 574-2070
Type of Business: Chain Restaurant Operator
Total Sales: $6,189,000 (e)
Total Units: 3
Trade Names: Domino's (3)
Units Franchised From: 3
Primary Menu: Pizza (3)
Areas of Operation: TX
Type of Foodservice: Quick Serve (3)
Franchise Affiliation: Domino's Pizza Inc, ANN ARBOR, MI

Key Personnel
THOMAS F. MOUCH - Owner; General Buyer

Gas Investments Corporation
25112 Market Place Dr
Katy, TX 77494-1130

Telephone: (281) 644-4433
Type of Business: Chain Restaurant Operator
Total Sales: $5,672,000 (e)
Total Units: 3
Trade Names: A&W All American Food (1); KFC (2)
Units Franchised From: 3
Areas of Operation: TX
Type of Foodservice: Quick Serve (3)
Franchise Affiliation: A&W Restaurants Inc., LEXINGTON, KY; KFC Corporation, LOUISVILLE, KY

Key Personnel
SYED ALI KAMAL - President; General Buyer

Hasta la Pasta Italian Grill
5705 4th St
Katy, TX 77493

Telephone: (281) 398-8300
Fax Number: (281) 398-1780
Internet Homepage: hastalapasta.com; lasagnahouse.com
Company Email: info@lasagnahouseIII.com
Type of Business: Chain Restaurant Operator
Total Sales: $6,180,000 (e)
Number of Employees: 280
Average Check: Dinner(20)
Total Units: 4
Trade Names: Hasta la Pasta Champions (1); Hasta la Pasta KATY (1); Lasagna House (2)
Company-Owned Units: 4
Preferred Location Types: Strip Mall
Alcohol Served: Beer, Wine, Liquor
Primary Menu: Italian (4)
Areas of Operation: TX
Type of Foodservice: Casual Dining (4)
Catering Services: Yes
Primary Distributors: (Food) Martin Preferred Foods, HOUSTON, TX; (Food) SYSCO Food Services of Houston Inc., HOUSTON, TX

Key Personnel
ALAN SMITH - Partner; General Buyer
JEFF SMITH - Partner; COO

Kolache Factory Inc.
23240 Westheimer Pkwy Ste A
Katy, TX 77494-3621

Telephone: (281) 829-6188
Fax Number: (281) 829-6813
Internet Homepage: kolachefactory.com
Type of Business: Chain Restaurant Operator
Year Founded: 1982
Systemwide Sales: $70,399,000 (e)
Total Sales: $32,950,000 (e)
Alcohol Sales: 1%
Number of Employees: 165
Average Check: Breakfast(12); Lunch(12);
Internet Order Processing: Yes
Internet Sales: 1.00%
Total Units: 58
Trade Names: Kolache Factory (58)
Company-Owned Units: 27
Units Franchised To: 31
Preferred Square Footage: 1,500; 1,800
Preferred Location Types: Freestanding; Strip Mall
Primary Menu: Eastern European (58)
Projected Openings: 5
Areas of Operation: CA, IN, KS, MO, OH, TX, VA

Type of Foodservice: Quick Serve (58)
Catering Services: Yes
Primary Distributors: (Full Line) Ben E. Keith Foods, FORT WORTH, TX

Key Personnel
JOHN BANKS - President; Partner; Director Menu Development, Catering; General Buyer
DAWN NIELSEN - Partner; COO
AARON NIELSEN - Chief Development Officer; Director Franchise Sales
TONY KOZEL - VP Information Technology; Director Operations
VICKI KOZEL - VP Administration, Human Resources
MIRNA VELASQUEZ - Manager District
HERMAN GRUEBLER - Manager District
SAM HERRARA - Manager Facility/Maintenance, Information Technology
SONIA HERRERA - Manager District

Domino's Franchisee
100 Old Rail Rd Ste C
Kaufman, TX 75142-2651

Telephone: (469) 376-8001
Type of Business: Chain Restaurant Operator
Total Sales: $8,283,000 (e)
Total Units: 4
Trade Names: Domino's (4)
Units Franchised From: 4
Primary Menu: Pizza (4)
Areas of Operation: TX
Type of Foodservice: Quick Serve (4)
Franchise Affiliation: Domino's Pizza Inc, ANN ARBOR, MI

Key Personnel
RICHARD P. CUNNINGHAM - Owner; General Buyer

DJ Clark
601 10th St
Kemah, TX 77565-2933

Telephone: (281) 334-6575
Fax Number: (281) 538-3347
Type of Business: Chain Restaurant Operator
Total Sales: $10,179,000 (e)
Number of Employees: 95
Total Units: 2
Trade Names: McDonald's (2)
Units Franchised From: 2
Preferred Square Footage: 2,500
Primary Menu: Hamburger (2)
Projected Remodelings: 1
Areas of Operation: TX
Type of Foodservice: Quick Serve (2)
Franchise Affiliation: McDonald's Corporation, CHICAGO, IL

Key Personnel
DENNIS DARLING - VP Operations

R.J. Bowen Inc.
313 Schreiner St
Kerrville, TX 78028-4464

Telephone: (830) 257-3133
Fax Number: (830) 257-2420
Company Email: bowen@ktc.com
Type of Business: Chain Restaurant Operator
Year Founded: 1993
Total Sales: $7,503,000 (e)
Number of Employees: 110
Average Check: Lunch(8); Dinner(8)
Total Units: 6
Trade Names: Church's Chicken (6)
Units Franchised From: 6
Preferred Square Footage: 1,500; 2,000
Preferred Location Types: Convenience Store/Gas Station; Freestanding
Primary Menu: Chicken (6)
Areas of Operation: TX
Type of Foodservice: Quick Serve (6)
Franchise Affiliation: Church's Chicken, ATLANTA, GA
Primary Distributors: (Equipment) The Wasserstrom Co., COLUMBUS, OH; (Food) Performance Foodservice - Temple, TEMPLE, TX; (Supplies) The Wasserstrom Co., COLUMBUS, OH

Key Personnel
JANICE BOWEN - President; Controller; Director Operations, Purchasing, Food Safety; General Buyer

Auntie Anne's Franchise
2100 S W S Young Dr Ste 1334
Killeen, TX 76543-5359

Telephone: (254) 200-0090
Type of Business: Chain Restaurant Operator
Total Sales: $3,164,000 (e)
Total Units: 4
Trade Names: Auntie Anne's Hand-Rolled Soft Pretzels (4)
Units Franchised From: 4
Primary Menu: Snacks (4)
Areas of Operation: TX
Type of Foodservice: Quick Serve (4)
Franchise Affiliation: Auntie Anne's Inc., LANCASTER, PA

Key Personnel
MICHAEL BOTTOM - Owner; General Buyer

Domino's Franchisee
609 E King Ave
Kingsville, TX 78363-5780

Telephone: (361) 595-5591
Type of Business: Chain Restaurant Operator
Total Sales: $3,967,000 (e)
Total Units: 2
Trade Names: Domino's (2)
Units Franchised From: 2
Primary Menu: Pizza (2)
Areas of Operation: TX
Type of Foodservice: Quick Serve (2)
Franchise Affiliation: Domino's Pizza Inc, ANN ARBOR, MI

Key Personnel
HENRY MOLINA - Owner; General Buyer

King-A Inc
511 S 11th St
Kingsville, TX 78363-5705

Mailing Address: PO Box 1455, KINGSVILLE, TX, 78364-1455
Telephone: (361) 592-2911
Fax Number: (361) 592-9252
Company Email: dale.raabe@partners.mcd.com
Type of Business: Chain Restaurant Operator
Total Sales: $52,780,000 (e)
Total Units: 11
Trade Names: McDonald's (11)
Units Franchised From: 11
Primary Menu: Hamburger (11)
Areas of Operation: TX
Type of Foodservice: Quick Serve (11)
Franchise Affiliation: McDonald's Corporation, CHICAGO, IL

Key Personnel
DALE RAABE - President; General Buyer

LaTrelle's Management Corp.
2131 Green Oak Dr
Kingwood, TX 77339-2073

Telephone: (281) 359-9959
Fax Number: (281) 359-9966
Internet Homepage: latrelles.com
Type of Business: Chain Restaurant Operator
Year Founded: 1988
Total Sales: $47,940,000 (e)
Number of Employees: 884
Average Check: Lunch(8); Dinner(8)
Total Units: 30
Trade Names: Buffalo Wild Wings (1); Bullritos (1); Hubcap (1); Peet's Coffee (9); Pick Up Stix (1); Pinks Pizza (1); Potbelly (1); Stumptown

Coffee Roasters(1); Subway (1); Wendy's Old Fashioned Hamburgers (13)
Units Franchised From: 30
Preferred Square Footage: 2,500
Preferred Location Types: Airports; Freestanding
Alcohol Served: Beer, Wine, Liquor
Primary Menu: Asian (1); Bar-B-Q (1); Coffee (10); Hamburger (14); Pizza (1); Sandwiches/Deli (1); Southwest/Tex-Mex (1)
Areas of Operation: TX, WA
Type of Foodservice: Quick Serve (30)
Franchise Affiliation: Buffalo Wild Wings Inc., ATLANTA, GA; Doctor's Associates Inc., MILFORD, CT; The Wendy's Company, DUBLIN, OH

Key Personnel
WALLY JAMES - Partner; COO; Director Information Systems, Real Estate, Design; General Buyer
KENNETH JAMES - Partner; CFO; Director Facility/Maintenance, Supply Chain; General Buyer
LATRELLE D. JAMES - VP; Director Human Resources
CYNTHIA JAMES - VP
HOLLY MADDEN - Senior Director Financial Planning
MARK MCGOWAN - Director Operations
VICKYE PECK - Director

Domino's Franchisee
101 Hall Professional Ctr Ste D
Kyle, TX 78640-8862

Telephone: (512) 268-5883
Company Email: dominos6742@yahoo.com
Type of Business: Chain Restaurant Operator
Total Sales: $6,193,000 (e)
Total Units: 3
Trade Names: Domino's (3)
Units Franchised From: 3
Primary Menu: Pizza (3)
Areas of Operation: TX
Type of Foodservice: Quick Serve (3)
Franchise Affiliation: Domino's Pizza Inc, ANN ARBOR, MI

Key Personnel
RORY L. BUCKNER - Owner; General Buyer

Gringo's Mexican Kitchen
2601 Underwood Rd
La Porte, TX 77571-9477

Telephone: (281) 470-7900
Fax Number: (281) 470-7799
Internet Homepage: freshmexfun.com; gringostexmex.com
Company Email: feedback@freshmexfun.com

Type of Business: Chain Restaurant Operator
Year Founded: 1993
Total Sales: $36,310,000 (e)
Alcohol Sales: 15%
Number of Employees: 771
Average Check: Lunch(12); Dinner(14)
Total Units: 17
Trade Names: Gringo's Mexican Kitchen (13); Jimmy Changas (4)
Company-Owned Units: 17
Preferred Location Types: Freestanding
Alcohol Served: Beer, Wine, Liquor
Primary Menu: Mexican (17)
Areas of Operation: TX
Type of Foodservice: Casual Dining (17)
Catering Services: Yes
Primary Distributors: (Food) SYSCO Corporation, HOUSTON, TX

Key Personnel
RUSSELL YBARRA - CEO; Owner
BRIAN JENNINGS III - CFO
JONATHAN KIM - COO; Senior VP Restaurant Operations
HEATHER L. MCKEON - Chief Marketing Officer; VP Marketing
JOHN FERNANDEZ - Senior VP Operations
STEVE YBARRA - VP Real Estate
DANNY HANKS - VP Operations
AL FLORES - General Counsel

Domino's Franchisee
900 Ranch Road 620 S
Lakeway, TX 78734-5615

Telephone: (512) 402-9444
Type of Business: Chain Restaurant Operator
Total Sales: $4,125,000 (e)
Total Units: 2
Trade Names: Domino's (2)
Units Franchised From: 2
Primary Menu: Pizza (2)
Areas of Operation: TX
Type of Foodservice: Quick Serve (2)
Franchise Affiliation: Domino's Pizza Inc, ANN ARBOR, MI

Key Personnel
CHRIS PALLAGI - Owner; General Buyer

Ford Restaurant Group
1514 Ranch Road 620 S
Lakeway, TX 78734-6210

Telephone: (512) 263-0929
Fax Number: (512) 263-1942
Internet Homepage: getluckyrestaurants.com; rudys.com
Type of Business: Chain Restaurant Operator
Year Founded: 1997
Total Sales: $124,230,000 (e)
Alcohol Sales: 15%
Number of Employees: 1,880
Average Check: Breakfast(5); Lunch(10); Dinner(20)
Internet Order Processing: Yes
Total Units: 49
Trade Names: Ozona Grill and Bar (1); Rudy's "Country Store" and Bar-B-Q (48)
Company-Owned Units: 49
Preferred Square Footage: 5,500; 6,000
Preferred Location Types: Freestanding
Alcohol Served: Beer, Wine, Liquor
Primary Menu: American (1); Bar-B-Q (48)
Areas of Operation: AZ, CO, NM, OK, TX
Type of Foodservice: Casual Dining (49)
Catering Services: Yes
Primary Distributors: (Full Line) Ben E. Keith Foods, AMARILLO, TX

Key Personnel
CREED FORD III - Partner; General Buyer
LYNN FORD - Partner; General Buyer
CORY WAUSON - Area Director
PETE BASSETT - VP Operations
HARPER FORD REHME - Director
SEAN POWER - Director Information Technology
CREED FORD IV - Director

B.P. Newman Investments
2801 E Montgomery St
Laredo, TX 78043-1402

Telephone: (956) 722-8021
Fax Number: (956) 724-2441
Company Email: cmolina@bpnic.com
Type of Business: Chain Restaurant Operator
Year Founded: 1962
Total Sales: $30,490,000 (e)
Number of Employees: 1,010
Average Check: Lunch(8); Dinner(8)
Total Units: 52
Trade Names: Church's Chicken (33); Popeyes Louisiana Kitchen (19)
Units Franchised From: 52
Preferred Square Footage: 2,450
Preferred Location Types: Freestanding
Primary Menu: Chicken (52)
Projected Remodelings: 4
Areas of Operation: AR, LA, NM, TX
Type of Foodservice: Quick Serve (52)
Distribution Centers: EL PASO, TX
Franchise Affiliation: Church's Chicken, ATLANTA, GA; Popeyes Louisiana Kitchen Inc., ATLANTA, GA
Primary Distributors: (Food) Performance Foodservice - Temple, TEMPLE, TX

Key Personnel
JAVIER DE-ANDA - Partner; VP; General Buyer
PEGGY NEWMAN - Partner; General Buyer
FRANK AGUILAR - Director Information Systems

FERNANDO MENDIOLA - Manager Security, Inventory, Loss Prevention, Risk Management, Quality Assurance, Human Resources, Food Safety; General Buyer

Dairy Queens of Laredo Inc
4205 San Bernardo Ave
Laredo, TX 78041-4446

Telephone: (956) 724-3355
Fax Number: (956) 724-1019
Type of Business: Chain Restaurant Operator
Total Sales: $2,988,000 (e)
Average Check: Dinner(12)
Total Units: 2
Trade Names: Dairy Queen (2)
Units Franchised From: 2
Primary Menu: American (2)
Areas of Operation: TX
Type of Foodservice: Quick Serve (2)
Franchise Affiliation: International Dairy Queen Inc., BLOOMINGTON, MN

Key Personnel
MIKE LERMA - President; General Buyer

Palenque Group
4515 San Bernardo Ave
Laredo, TX 78041

Telephone: (866) 233-8226
Internet Homepage: palenquegrill.com; palenquegroup.com; tacopalenque.com
Company Email: tacopfeedback@palenquegroup.com
Type of Business: Chain Restaurant Operator
Year Founded: 1987
Number of Employees: 600
Total Units: 40
Trade Names: Palenque Grill (5); Taco Palenque Fresh Mex (35)
Company-Owned Units: 40
Primary Menu: Mexican (40)
Areas of Operation: TX
Type of Foodservice: Casual Dining (40)

Key Personnel
FRANCISCO OCHOA JR - CEO Group
ALEJANDRO GUTIERREZ HEREDIA - Director Operations
JOAQUIN LLAMAS JR - Director Information Technology

South-Wen Inc.
5201 Tesoro Plz
Laredo, TX 78041-5752

Telephone: (956) 722-8921
Fax Number: (956) 722-8922
Company Email: elopez@tesoroservices.com
Type of Business: Chain Restaurant Operator
Total Sales: $40,750,000 (e)
Total Units: 15
Trade Names: Wendy's Old Fashioned Hamburgers (15)
Units Franchised From: 15
Primary Menu: Hamburger (15)
Areas of Operation: TX
Type of Foodservice: Quick Serve (15)
Franchise Affiliation: The Wendy's Company, DUBLIN, OH
Notes: Also operates as Exelco Inc.

Key Personnel
HUGO CHAPARRO - President
RON EICHORST - CFO; VP

C4 Pizza
175 W Southwest Pkwy Ste C
Lewisville, TX 75067-7768

Telephone: (972) 219-1717
Fax Number: (972) 219-1717
Type of Business: Chain Restaurant Operator
Total Sales: $18,715,000 (e)
Total Units: 9
Trade Names: Domino's (9)
Units Franchised From: 9
Preferred Square Footage: 1,200
Primary Menu: Pizza (9)
Areas of Operation: TX
Type of Foodservice: Quick Serve (9)
Franchise Affiliation: Domino's Pizza Inc, ANN ARBOR, MI

Key Personnel
COREY MCKANNA - General Buyer

Cristina's Fine Mexican Restaurant
297 W Round Grove Rd Ste 110
Lewisville, TX 75067-8148

Telephone: (972) 315-8859
Internet Homepage: cristinasmex.com
Company Email: contact@cristinasmex.com
Type of Business: Chain Restaurant Operator
Year Founded: 1989
Total Sales: $5,503,000 (e)
Internet Order Processing: Yes
Total Units: 13
Trade Names: Cristina's Fine Mexican Restaurant (13)
Company-Owned Units: 13
Primary Menu: Mexican (13)
Areas of Operation: TX
Type of Foodservice: Casual Dining (13)
Catering Services: Yes

Key Personnel
ARTURO VARGAS - President; Partner; General Buyer
AGLAE MEJIA - Director Catering

Hobeau Inc
2301 S State Highway 121
Lewisville, TX 75067-8130

Telephone: (972) 691-5875
Fax Number: (972) 315-2882
Internet Homepage: mcmassey.com
Company Email: 7014@mcmassey.com
Type of Business: Chain Restaurant Operator
Total Sales: $66,080,000 (e)
Total Units: 14
Trade Names: McDonald's (14)
Units Franchised From: 14
Primary Menu: Hamburger (14)
Areas of Operation: TX
Type of Foodservice: Quick Serve (14)
Franchise Affiliation: McDonald's Corporation, CHICAGO, IL

Key Personnel
BILL MASSEY - President; General Buyer

Domino's Franchisee
2301 N Main St Ste A
Liberty, TX 77575-3901

Telephone: (936) 336-1900
Type of Business: Chain Restaurant Operator
Total Sales: $10,251,000 (e)
Total Units: 5
Trade Names: Domino's (5)
Units Franchised From: 5
Primary Menu: Pizza (5)
Areas of Operation: TX
Type of Foodservice: Quick Serve (5)
Franchise Affiliation: Domino's Pizza Inc, ANN ARBOR, MI

Key Personnel
DANISH W. DHEDHI - Owner; General Buyer

Dalton Howell Inc
4400 W Marshall Ave
Longview, TX 75604-4811

Telephone: (903) 291-8370
Fax Number: (903) 291-8370
Type of Business: Chain Restaurant Operator
Total Sales: $2,749,000 (e)
Total Units: 4
Trade Names: Subway (4)
Units Franchised From: 4
Primary Menu: Sandwiches/Deli (4)
Areas of Operation: TX

Type of Foodservice: Quick Serve (4)
Franchise Affiliation: Doctor's Associates Inc., MILFORD, CT

Key Personnel
RICK HOWELL - Partner
PAMELA HOWELL - Partner; General Buyer

JMET, LLC
3312 4th St Ste 100
Longview, TX 75605-7954

Telephone: (903) 663-3362
Type of Business: Chain Restaurant Operator
Total Sales: $4,316,000 (e)
Total Units: 3
Trade Names: Jersey Mike's Subs (3)
Units Franchised From: 3
Primary Menu: Sandwiches/Deli (3)
Areas of Operation: TX
Type of Foodservice: Quick Serve (3)
Franchise Affiliation: Jersey Mike's Franchise Systems, MANASQUAN, NJ

Key Personnel
BRYAN SELDEN - Owner; General Buyer

Langseth-Wofford Inc
1121 Judson Rd Ste 151
Longview, TX 75601-5119

Telephone: (903) 753-9051
Type of Business: Chain Restaurant Operator
Total Sales: $70,250,000 (e)
Total Units: 15
Trade Names: McDonald's (15)
Units Franchised From: 15
Preferred Square Footage: 2,500
Primary Menu: Hamburger (15)
Areas of Operation: TX
Type of Foodservice: Quick Serve (15)
Franchise Affiliation: McDonald's Corporation, CHICAGO, IL

Key Personnel
CAROLYN WOFFORD-LANGSETH - President; General Buyer

Little Caesar's
1809 W Loop 281
Longview, TX 75604

Telephone: (903) 295-0111
Fax Number: (903) 295-0673
Internet Homepage: littlecaesars.com
Type of Business: Chain Restaurant Operator
Total Sales: $3,879,000 (e)
Total Units: 6
Trade Names: Little Caesars Pizza (6)
Units Franchised From: 6
Primary Menu: Pizza (6)
Areas of Operation: TX
Type of Foodservice: Quick Serve (6)
Franchise Affiliation: Little Caesar Enterprises Inc., DETROIT, MI

Key Personnel
RICK CARR - President; General Buyer

Sertex of Longview, Inc
101 W Hawkins Pkwy Ste 1
Longview, TX 75605-1833

Mailing Address: PO Box 9215, LONGVIEW, TX, 75608-9215
Telephone: (903) 663-6790
Fax Number: (903) 663-5569
Type of Business: Chain Restaurant Operator
Total Sales: $11,350,000 (e)
Total Units: 5
Trade Names: Burger King (5)
Units Franchised From: 5
Preferred Square Footage: 2,500
Preferred Location Types: Convenience Store/Gas Station; Freestanding
Primary Menu: Hamburger (5)
Areas of Operation: TX
Type of Foodservice: Quick Serve (5)
Franchise Affiliation: Burger King Worldwide Inc., MIAMI, FL

Key Personnel
PAUL FRENCH - President; General Buyer

Whataburger of East Texas
1 Pegues Pl
Longview, TX 75601-4601

Telephone: (903) 236-8775
Fax Number: (903) 236-7866
Internet Homepage: whataburgerofeasttexas.com
Type of Business: Chain Restaurant Operator
Year Founded: 1965
Total Sales: $23,230,000 (e)
Number of Employees: 110
Average Check: Breakfast(6); Lunch(6); Dinner(6)
Total Units: 10
Trade Names: Whataburger (10)
Units Franchised From: 10
Preferred Square Footage: 1,800
Preferred Location Types: Freestanding
Primary Menu: Hamburger (10)
Areas of Operation: TX
Type of Foodservice: Quick Serve (10)
Franchise Affiliation: Whataburger Restaurants LLC, SAN ANTONIO, TX
Primary Distributors: (Full Line) The SYGMA Network Inc.- San Antonio, SAN ANTONIO, TX

Key Personnel
DOUG EDWARDS - Director Operations, Human Resources, Food Safety
ELIZ HEIMAN - Manager Operations

Bubba's & Babe's Restaurants
107 Hillside Dr Ste 101
Louisville, TX 75057

Telephone: (469) 552-9725
Fax Number: (972) 245-7079
Internet Homepage: bubbasdallas.com; babeschicken.com; sweetiepiesribeyes.com
Type of Business: Chain Restaurant Operator
Year Founded: 1993
Total Sales: $11,270,000 (e)
Number of Employees: 2,061
Average Check: Lunch(8); Dinner(8)
Total Units: 12
Trade Names: Babe's Chicken Dinner House (10); Bubba's Cooks Country (1); Sweetie Pies Ribeyes (1)
Company-Owned Units: 11
Units Franchised From: 1
Preferred Location Types: Freestanding; Strip Mall
Alcohol Served: Beer, Wine, Liquor
Primary Menu: Bar-B-Q (1); Chicken (10); Steak (1)
Areas of Operation: TX
Type of Foodservice: Casual Dining (1); Family Restaurant (11)
Catering Services: Yes

Key Personnel
PAUL VINYARD - President; Partner; General Buyer
TIFFANY WHEELESS - Partner; Director Catering; General Buyer
JOEL VINYARD - Partner

Bahama Buck's Franchise Corporation
5741 50th St
Lubbock, TX 79424-1134

Telephone: (806) 771-2189
Fax Number: (806) 771-2190
Internet Homepage: bahamabucks.com
Type of Business: Chain Restaurant Operator
Year Founded: 1990
Total Sales: $27,130,000 (e)
Average Check: Lunch(8); Dinner(8)
Internet Order Processing: Yes
Total Units: 113
Trade Names: Bahama Buck's (113)
Units Franchised To: 113

Preferred Location Types: Freestanding; Strip Mall
Primary Menu: Snacks (113)
Projected Openings: 94
Areas of Operation: AL, AZ, CA, FL, GA, KY, MO, NM, NV, OK, PR, TX, UT
Type of Foodservice: Quick Serve (113)

Key Personnel
BLAKE BUCHANAN - President; General Buyer
BALEY POLLARD - General Manager
JESSICA GUTIERREZ - General Manager
LAURA EWING - Director Franchising
INGRAM RICH - Director Operations
KYLIE BRASHEAR - Manager Design
MATT EWING - Specialist Finance
KOLTEN KNOX - Coordinator Training
CALLEY BRAKE - Designer Graphic Design

Best Bunz, Inc.
3715 19th St
Lubbock, TX 79410-1204

Telephone: (806) 793-5542
Fax Number: (806) 796-1541
Type of Business: Chain Restaurant Operator
Year Founded: 1978
Total Sales: $4,521,000 (e)
Number of Employees: 35
Average Check: Lunch(8); Dinner(8)
Total Units: 3
Trade Names: Schlotzsky's Deli (2); Schlotzsky's Deli/Cinnabon (1)
Units Franchised From: 3
Preferred Location Types: Freestanding; Strip Mall
Primary Menu: Sandwiches/Deli (3); Snacks (1)
Areas of Operation: TX
Type of Foodservice: Fast Casual (3)
Catering Services: Yes
Franchise Affiliation: Cinnabon Inc., ATLANTA, GA; Schlotzsky's Ltd., ATLANTA, GA

Key Personnel
CHRIS LONNGREN - Director Operations; General Buyer

Brady's Dairy Queen Inc.
1001 Main St Ste 801
Lubbock, TX 79401-3322

Telephone: (806) 792-0037
Fax Number: (806) 792-9990
Type of Business: Chain Restaurant Operator
Year Founded: 1983
Total Sales: $16,900,000 (e)
Number of Employees: 243
Average Check: Breakfast(8); Lunch(8); Dinner(8)
Total Units: 12
Trade Names: Dairy Queen (12)
Units Franchised From: 12
Preferred Square Footage: 2,000
Preferred Location Types: Freestanding
Primary Menu: American (12)
Areas of Operation: NM, TX
Type of Foodservice: Quick Serve (12)
Franchise Affiliation: International Dairy Queen Inc., BLOOMINGTON, MN
Primary Distributors: (Full Line) Labatt Food Service, SAN ANTONIO, TX

Key Personnel
COURTNEY SIMMS - Manager Risk Management, Human Resources

Cafe Venture Company
8008 Slide Rd Ste 3
Lubbock, TX 79424-2828

Mailing Address: PO Box 54200, LUBBOCK, TX, 79453-4200
Telephone: (806) 745-3833
Fax Number: (806) 785-3855
Internet Homepage: cafeventure.com
Company Email: catering@cafeventure.com
Type of Business: Chain Restaurant Operator
Total Sales: $23,490,000 (e)
Total Units: 12
Trade Names: Fuddruckers (12)
Units Franchised From: 12
Primary Menu: Hamburger (12)
Areas of Operation: NM, OK, TX
Type of Foodservice: Fast Casual (12)
Franchise Affiliation: Fuddruckers Restaurants LLC, HOUSTON, TX

Key Personnel
MICKEY ROGERS - President; General Buyer
DANIEL STANTON - Partner
STACEY ROGERS - Partner
TOM HARDIN - Director Information Technology
TAMARA LUDWIG - Coordinator Marketing, Business Development

Campiza Foods
4418 74th St Ste 65
Lubbock, TX 79424-2336

Telephone: (806) 785-5300
Fax Number: (806) 473-0199
Type of Business: Chain Restaurant Operator
Year Founded: 1987
Total Sales: $11,160,000 (e)
Alcohol Sales: 0.50%
Number of Employees: 705
Average Check: Lunch(8); Dinner(8)
Total Units: 9
Trade Names: Pizza Hut (9)
Units Franchised From: 9
Preferred Square Footage: 2,500; 3,500
Preferred Location Types: Freestanding; Strip Mall
Alcohol Served: Beer
Primary Menu: Pizza (9)
Projected Remodelings: 3
Areas of Operation: KS, OK, TX
Type of Foodservice: Casual Dining (9)
Franchise Affiliation: Pizza Hut Inc., PLANO, TX
Primary Distributors: (Full Line) McLane Foodservice, CARROLLTON, TX

Key Personnel
JOHN CAMP - CEO; President; Director Real Estate; General Buyer
MATTHEW CAMP - Partner; Director Operations, Facility/Maintenance, Information Systems, Risk Management, Quality Assurance, Food Safety
PATRICK CAMP - Partner; Director Operations, Purchasing
SANDI BARTCH - Controller; Director Human Resources, Recruitment
JEFF GAGE - Manager Operations
GORDON SANDERCOX - Manager Operations

DTH Enterprises
3318 83rd St Ste 300
Lubbock, TX 79423-2812

Telephone: (806) 795-1283
Type of Business: Chain Restaurant Operator
Total Sales: $1,350,000 (e)
Average Check: Dinner(14)
Total Units: 6
Trade Names: Fazoli's (6)
Units Franchised From: 6
Preferred Square Footage: 2,100; 3,200
Preferred Location Types: Downtown; Freestanding
Primary Menu: American (6)
Areas of Operation: TX
Type of Foodservice: Fast Casual (6)
Franchise Affiliation: Fazoli's Restaurant LLC, LEXINGTON, KY

Key Personnel
PAUL HOLLABAUGH - Owner; General Buyer
CHRIS KHATSHWA - Manager Business Development

Food Concepts International LLP
4413 82nd St
Lubbock, TX 79424

Telephone: (806) 785-8686
Fax Number: (806) 785-8866
Internet Homepage: abuelos.com

Type of Business: Chain Restaurant Operator
Year Founded: 1989
Total Sales: $79,780,000 (e)
Alcohol Sales: 15%
Number of Employees: 4,875
Average Check: Lunch(10); Dinner(14)
Internet Order Processing: Yes
Internet Sales: 1.00%
Total Units: 28
Trade Names: Abuelo's Mexican Restaurant (28)
Company-Owned Units: 28
Preferred Square Footage: 7,500; 8,100
Preferred Location Types: Freestanding; Strip Mall
Alcohol Served: Beer, Wine, Liquor
Primary Menu: Mexican (28)
Areas of Operation: AR, AZ, FL, IN, KS, KY, LA, MI, MN, MO, OH, OK, SC, TN, TX, VA, WI
Type of Foodservice: Casual Dining (28)
Primary Distributors: (Full Line) Ben E. Keith Foods, FORT WORTH, TX

Key Personnel
ROBERT "BOB" LIN - President
BRIAN BELL - Chief Marketing Officer Marketing; VP Merchandising
DICKIE OVERSTREET - VP Real Estate
MARGARET YOUNG - Treasurer
LUIS SANCHEZ - Executive Chef
MELANIE CARROLL - Director Marketing, Communications
SARAH MCDUFF - Manager Human Resources

Jazz
3703 19th St Ste C
Lubbock, TX 79410-1221

Telephone: (806) 799-2124
Fax Number: (806) 799-7870
Internet Homepage: jazzkitchen.com
Company Email: tbrown@jazzkitchen.com
Type of Business: Chain Restaurant Operator
Year Founded: 1986
Total Sales: $4,940,000 (e)
Alcohol Sales: 12%
Number of Employees: 100
Average Check: Dinner(12)
Total Units: 6
Trade Names: Jazz - A Louisiana Kitchen (6)
Company-Owned Units: 6
Preferred Square Footage: 5,500; 6,000
Preferred Location Types: Freestanding
Alcohol Served: Beer, Wine, Liquor
Primary Menu: Cajun/Creole (6)
Areas of Operation: KS, MO, TX
Type of Foodservice: Casual Dining (6)
Primary Distributors: (Food) US Foods, LUBBOCK, TX

Key Personnel
TRACEE HOFFMAN-BROWN - Executive Chef; Director Finance, Operations, Site Selection; General Buyer
BABAR AHMAD - Director Digital, Marketing

Junior Senior Inc.
601 E Slaton Rd
Lubbock, TX 79404-5821

Telephone: (806) 748-7827
Fax Number: (806) 748-7830
Type of Business: Chain Restaurant Operator
Year Founded: 1988
Total Sales: $15,450,000 (e)
Number of Employees: 290
Average Check: Breakfast(6); Lunch(6); Dinner(10)
Total Units: 29
Trade Names: IHOP Restaurant (1); Subway (28)
Units Franchised From: 29
Preferred Square Footage: 2,000
Preferred Location Types: Freestanding; Strip Mall
Primary Menu: American (1); Sandwiches/Deli (28)
Areas of Operation: TX
Type of Foodservice: Family Restaurant (1); Quick Serve (28)
Franchise Affiliation: Doctor's Associates Inc., MILFORD, CT
Primary Distributors: (Full Line) Performance Foodservice - Victoria, VICTORIA, TX

Key Personnel
BILL BUTLER - CEO; President; Manager Purchasing, Facility/Maintenance, Loss Prevention, Risk Management, Quality Assurance, Real Estate, Design, Food Safety
COLLEEN BUTLER - VP Finance, Supply Chain
WILBERT HARDWELL - Controller; Manager Operations, Marketing; General Buyer

Patch Management Inc.
3415 73rd St
Lubbock, TX 79423-1101

Telephone: (866) 785-0507
Fax Number: (806) 785-0579
Internet Homepage: tacovillaonline.com
Type of Business: Chain Restaurant Operator
Year Founded: 1968
Total Sales: $26,110,000 (e)
Number of Employees: 630
Average Check: Breakfast(10); Lunch(14); Dinner(18)
Total Units: 21
Trade Names: Pizza Hut (11); Taco Villa (10)
Company-Owned Units: 10
Units Franchised From: 11
Preferred Square Footage: 2,500; 3,200
Preferred Location Types: Freestanding; Strip Mall
Primary Menu: Pizza (11); Taco (10)
Areas of Operation: NM, TX
Type of Foodservice: Fast Casual (11); Quick Serve (10)
Franchise Affiliation: Pizza Hut Inc., PLANO, TX
Primary Distributors: (Full Line) McLane/Arlington, ARLINGTON, TX

Key Personnel
GREG BLANKENSHIP - President; Director Facility/Maintenance, Information Systems, Real Estate; Manager Site Selection; General Buyer
STEVEN COMPO - VP Marketing, Sales
JEFFREY FIGUEROA - Director Operations

Bonafide QSR, LTD
2606 Daniel McCall Dr
Lufkin, TX 75904-7133

Telephone: (936) 632-6222
Fax Number: (936) 632-6285
Type of Business: Chain Restaurant Operator
Total Sales: $44,100,000 (e)
Total Units: 17
Trade Names: Popeyes Louisiana Kitchen (17)
Units Franchised From: 17
Primary Menu: Chicken (17)
Areas of Operation: TX
Type of Foodservice: Quick Serve (17)
Franchise Affiliation: Popeyes Louisiana Kitchen Inc., ATLANTA, GA

Key Personnel
TODD STAFFORD - President; Partner; General Buyer
HARRY STAFFORD - Partner; General Buyer

G.V.C.S.
421 N Timberland Dr
Lufkin, TX 75901-4061

Telephone: (936) 632-4827
Fax Number: (936) 632-7061
Internet Homepage: gvcs.com
Type of Business: Chain Restaurant Operator
Year Founded: 1985
Total Sales: $7,174,000 (e)
Number of Employees: 300
Average Check: Lunch(8); Dinner(12)
Total Units: 12
Trade Names: Whataburger (12)
Units Franchised From: 12
Preferred Square Footage: 1,800; 3,400
Preferred Location Types: Freestanding
Primary Menu: Hamburger (12)
Areas of Operation: TX
Type of Foodservice: Quick Serve (12)
Franchise Affiliation: Whataburger Restaurants LLC, SAN ANTONIO, TX

Primary Distributors: (Full Line) The SYGMA Network Inc.- San Antonio, SAN ANTONIO, TX

Key Personnel
GLENN JOHNSON - President; CFO; General Manager; General Buyer
COURTNEY KING - General Manager
MACY DOVER - Director Marketing
DARLENE SCHMIDT - Office Manager

Carter Enterprises
102 N Madison St
Madisonville, TX 77864-1508

Mailing Address: PO Box 429, MADISONVILLE, TX, 77864-0429
Telephone: (936) 348-3703
Fax Number: (936) 348-5907
Internet Homepage: spoonsyogurt.com; txburger.com; carter.enterprises
Type of Business: Chain Restaurant Operator
Year Founded: 1972
Total Sales: $31,080,000 (e)
Number of Employees: 320
Average Check: Lunch(14); Dinner(22)
Total Units: 31
Trade Names: Church's Chicken (1); Pizza Hut (18); Subway (12)
Units Franchised From: 31
Preferred Square Footage: 2,500
Preferred Location Types: Freestanding
Primary Menu: Chicken (1); Pizza (18); Sandwiches/Deli (12)
Areas of Operation: TX
Type of Foodservice: Quick Serve (31)
Franchise Affiliation: Church's Chicken, ATLANTA, GA; Doctor's Associates Inc., MILFORD, CT; Pizza Hut Inc., PLANO, TX
Primary Distributors: (Food) Performance Foodservice - Temple, TEMPLE, TX

Key Personnel
JAMES CARTER - President; CFO; Director Finance, Purchasing, Facility/Maintenance, Information Systems, Real Estate, Human Resources, Franchise Development, Menu Development
MARIO VERA - Manager District
ELIZABETH CABREA - Manager Human Resources

Domino's Franchisee
11211 US Highway 290 E Ste 400
Manor, TX 78653-9703

Telephone: (512) 272-8888
Type of Business: Chain Restaurant Operator
Total Sales: $12,011,000 (e)
Total Units: 6
Trade Names: Domino's (6)
Units Franchised From: 6
Primary Menu: Pizza (6)
Areas of Operation: TX
Type of Foodservice: Quick Serve (6)
Franchise Affiliation: Domino's Pizza Inc, ANN ARBOR, MI

Key Personnel
SELBY M. MARSHALL - Owner; General Buyer

D W Reed Enterprises Inc
1510 N US Highway 281 Ste 101
Marble Falls, TX 78654-4563

Telephone: (830) 693-9595
Type of Business: Chain Restaurant Operator
Total Sales: $3,472,000 (e)
Number of Employees: 30
Total Units: 5
Trade Names: Subway (5)
Units Franchised From: 5
Primary Menu: Sandwiches/Deli (5)
Areas of Operation: TX
Type of Foodservice: Quick Serve (5)
Franchise Affiliation: Doctor's Associates Inc., MILFORD, CT

Key Personnel
DENNIS REED - President; General Buyer

Domino's Franchisee
2508 N US Highway 281 Ste 110
Marble Falls, TX 78654-3985

Telephone: (830) 798-8080
Type of Business: Chain Restaurant Operator
Total Sales: $18,408,000 (e)
Total Units: 9
Trade Names: Domino's (9)
Units Franchised From: 9
Primary Menu: Pizza (9)
Areas of Operation: TX
Type of Foodservice: Quick Serve (9)
Franchise Affiliation: Domino's Pizza Inc, ANN ARBOR, MI

Key Personnel
DAIN F. FUNDERBURG - Owner; General Buyer

Messick Properties LLC
2905 S Washington Ave
Marshall, TX 75672-7769

Mailing Address: PO Box 187, MARSHALL, TX, 75671
Telephone: (903) 938-7745
Fax Number: (903) 938-6906
Type of Business: Chain Restaurant Operator
Total Sales: $33,940,000 (e)
Total Units: 7
Trade Names: McDonald's (7)
Units Franchised From: 7
Preferred Square Footage: 2,500
Primary Menu: Hamburger (7)
Areas of Operation: LA, TX
Type of Foodservice: Quick Serve (7)
Franchise Affiliation: McDonald's Corporation, CHICAGO, IL

Key Personnel
RORY MESSICK - President; General Buyer

Tarrant Millican of Texas, Inc.
2130 Bear Creek Xing
Mc Gregor, TX 76657-3448

Telephone: (254) 848-2506
Type of Business: Chain Restaurant Operator
Total Sales: $769,000 (e)
Total Units: 2
Trade Names: Cinnabon (2)
Units Franchised From: 2
Primary Menu: Snacks (2)
Areas of Operation: TX
Type of Foodservice: Quick Serve (2)
Franchise Affiliation: Cinnabon Inc., ATLANTA, GA

Key Personnel
MICHAEL POOL - Owner; General Buyer

Richworth Properties
1835 W Louisiana St
Mc Kinney, TX 75069-7859

Telephone: (972) 542-0480
Fax Number: (903) 977-1291
Internet Homepage: herschels.com
Company Email: dqtxmckinney@hotmail.com
Type of Business: Chain Restaurant Operator
Year Founded: 1963
Total Sales: $9,768,000 (e)
Number of Employees: 140
Average Check: Breakfast(10); Lunch(10); Dinner(10)
Total Units: 7
Trade Names: Dairy Queen (7); Herschel's Family Restaurant (7)
Company-Owned Units: 3
Units Franchised From: 7
Preferred Square Footage: 2,400
Preferred Location Types: Freestanding
Primary Menu: American (7); Southern (7)
Areas of Operation: TX
Type of Foodservice: Family Restaurant (7); Quick Serve (7)
Franchise Affiliation: International Dairy Queen Inc., BLOOMINGTON, MN
Primary Distributors: (Equipment) Kirby

Restaurant & Chemical Supply Inc., LONGVIEW, TX; (Full Line) Labatt Food Service, SAN ANTONIO, TX

Key Personnel
RICHARD WITHERSPOON - CEO; President; Executive Chef; Director Real Estate; General Buyer
THOMAS HALFORD - COO; VP; Director Finance, Operations, Purchasing, Facility/Maintenance, Information Systems, Supply Chain, Design, Human Resources

Mannat Food Inc.
1825 W University Dr
Mckinney, TX 75069-3222

Telephone: (972) 562-5625
Fax Number: (972) 562-5625
Type of Business: Chain Restaurant Operator
Total Sales: $38,420,000 (e)
Total Units: 15
Trade Names: Jack in the Box (15)
Units Franchised From: 15
Primary Menu: Hamburger (15)
Areas of Operation: TX
Type of Foodservice: Quick Serve (15)
Franchise Affiliation: Jack in the Box Restaurants, SAN DIEGO, CA

Key Personnel
MANNU METHA - President; Owner
JUAN REYNA - Director Operations
C PATEL - Manager Accounting

Pizza Partners, Inc.
321 N Central Expy Ste 360
Mckinney, TX 75070-3552

Mailing Address: 2785 Virginia Pkwy, McKinney, 75071
Telephone: (972) 540-5554
Fax Number: (972) 540-5540
Type of Business: Chain Restaurant Operator
Year Founded: 1990
Total Sales: $42,530,000 (e)
Alcohol Sales: 9%
Number of Employees: 960
Average Check: Lunch(16); Dinner(28)
Total Units: 35
Trade Names: Pizza Hut (35)
Units Franchised From: 35
Preferred Square Footage: 2,500
Preferred Location Types: Freestanding
Alcohol Served: Beer
Primary Menu: Pizza (35)
Areas of Operation: TX
Type of Foodservice: Quick Serve (35)
Franchise Affiliation: Pizza Hut Inc., PLANO, TX
Notes: Pizza Partners, Inc. hold Pizza Hut properties under Progressive Pizza Partners LP, San Angelo Pizza Partners LP, and Tumbleweed Pizza Partners.

Key Personnel
MIKE BAIRD - President; CFO; Director Operations, Facility/Maintenance, Supply Chain, Real Estate; General Buyer
PEGGY BAIRD - VP; Director Finance, Information Systems, Marketing, Design
NANCY LEBLANC - Manager Human Resources

Barton Group
4200 Gus Thomasson Rd Ste 111
Mesquite, TX 75150-7009

Telephone: (972) 270-8296
Fax Number: (972) 613-8866
Company Email: stephanie@bartonsonics.com
Type of Business: Chain Restaurant Operator
Year Founded: 1958
Total Sales: $27,670,000 (e)
Number of Employees: 425
Average Check: Breakfast(5); Lunch(10); Dinner(10)
Total Units: 13
Trade Names: Sonic America's Drive-In (13)
Units Franchised From: 13
Preferred Square Footage: 2,500
Preferred Location Types: Freestanding
Primary Menu: Hamburger (13)
Areas of Operation: TX
Type of Foodservice: Quick Serve (13)
Franchise Affiliation: Sonic Corp., OKLAHOMA CITY, OK
Primary Distributors: (Equipment) The Wasserstrom Co., COLUMBUS, OH; (Supplies) The Wasserstrom Co., COLUMBUS, OH

Key Personnel
THELMA BARTON - CEO; President; Director Finance; General Buyer

Great Outdoor Sub Shop Inc.
3910 Interstate 30
Mesquite, TX 75150-2022

Telephone: (972) 698-7505
Fax Number: (972) 698-7545
Internet Homepage: greatoutdoorsubs.com
Company Email: gail@greatoutdoorsubs.com
Type of Business: Chain Restaurant Operator
Year Founded: 1973
Systemwide Sales: $8,036,000 (e)
Total Sales: $7,625,000 (e)
Alcohol Sales: 2%
Number of Employees: 140
Average Check: Breakfast(6); Lunch(6); Dinner(8)
Total Units: 7
Trade Names: Great Outdoor Sub Shop (7)
Company-Owned Units: 6
Units Franchised To: 1
Preferred Square Footage: 2,300; 2,500
Preferred Location Types: Freestanding; Strip Mall
Primary Menu: Sandwiches/Deli (7)
Areas of Operation: TX
Type of Foodservice: Quick Serve (7)
Catering Services: Yes
On-site Distribution Center: Yes
Primary Distributors: (Full Line) Ben E. Keith Foods, FORT WORTH, TX

Key Personnel
GAIL VOELCKER - VP Operations, Purchasing, Real Estate; Director Finance, Store Fixtures; Manager Franchising
TAMMY KNOTT - Controller; Manager Human Resources

Roger Clark
1600 N Town East Blvd
Mesquite, TX 75150-4106

Telephone: (972) 686-0067
Type of Business: Chain Restaurant Operator
Total Sales: $27,788,000 (e)
Total Units: 3
Trade Names: Chick-fil-A (3)
Units Franchised From: 3
Primary Menu: Chicken (3)
Areas of Operation: TX
Type of Foodservice: Quick Serve (3)
Franchise Affiliation: Chick-fil-A Inc., ATLANTA, GA

Key Personnel
ROGER CLARK - President; General Buyer

SLI Enterprises
4180 Interstate 30
Mesquite, TX 75150-2069

Mailing Address: PO Box 153248, IRVING, TX, 75015-3248
Telephone: (972) 252-8509
Fax Number: (214) 324-1359
Company Email: mcdsli@aol.com
Type of Business: Chain Restaurant Operator
Year Founded: 1987
Total Sales: $65,120,000 (e)
Number of Employees: 470
Average Check: Breakfast(8); Lunch(8); Dinner(10)
Total Units: 14
Trade Names: McDonald's (14)
Units Franchised From: 14
Preferred Square Footage: 2,500; 3,000
Preferred Location Types: Community Mall;

Discount Dept. Stores; Freestanding
Primary Menu: Hamburger (14)
Areas of Operation: TX
Type of Foodservice: Quick Serve (14)
Franchise Affiliation: McDonald's Corporation, CHICAGO, IL
Primary Distributors: (Full Line) The Martin-Brower Co., GRAND PRAIRIE, TX

Key Personnel
DAVID FLOYD - Partner; Director Operations, Facility/Maintenance
LAWRENCE INGRAM - Partner; Director Finance, Supply Chain; General Buyer
SUE INGRAM - Partner; Director Information Systems, Real Estate, Human Resources

Whataburger of Mesquite Inc.
3200 N Town East Blvd
Mesquite, TX 75150-3923

Telephone: (972) 270-3400
Fax Number: (972) 613-0508
Internet Homepage: womtx.com
Company Email: info@womtx.com
Type of Business: Chain Restaurant Operator
Year Founded: 1950
Total Sales: $22,090,000 (e)
Number of Employees: 500
Average Check: Lunch(12); Dinner(12)
Total Units: 17
Trade Names: Whataburger (17)
Units Franchised From: 17
Preferred Square Footage: 2,800
Preferred Location Types: Freestanding
Primary Menu: Hamburger (17)
Areas of Operation: TX
Type of Foodservice: Quick Serve (17)
Franchise Affiliation: Whataburger Restaurants LLC, SAN ANTONIO, TX
Primary Distributors: (Full Line) The SYGMA Network Inc.- San Antonio, SAN ANTONIO, TX

Key Personnel
JOHN L. HEIMAN JR - President; Director Real Estate, Design
BOB POTTER - CFO; VP Operations
RANDALL KIRK - VP; Manager Facility/Maintenance
ZAK HEIMAN - VP Information Technology
MICHAEL GARVEY - Director Operations
JASON KIRK - Director Operations
WENDEL BROWN - Area Manager

Elite Team LP
4519 N Garfield St Ste 17
Midland, TX 79705-3421

Telephone: (432) 570-1990
Fax Number: (432) 683-2632
Type of Business: Chain Restaurant Operator
Total Sales: $36,406,000 (e)
Number of Employees: 310
Total Units: 18
Trade Names: Domino's (18)
Units Franchised From: 18
Preferred Square Footage: 1,000
Preferred Location Types: Strip Mall
Primary Menu: Pizza (18)
Areas of Operation: TX
Type of Foodservice: Quick Serve (18)
Franchise Affiliation: Domino's Pizza Inc, ANN ARBOR, MI

Key Personnel
JIM GERETY - Owner; General Buyer

JumBurrito Inc.
1701 N Big Spring St
Midland, TX 79701-2623

Mailing Address: PO Box 50607, MIDLAND, TX, 79710-0607
Telephone: (432) 520-3529
Internet Homepage: jumburrito.com
Company Email: info@jumburrito.com
Type of Business: Chain Restaurant Operator
Total Sales: $4,301,000 (e)
Number of Employees: 100
Average Check: Dinner(14)
Total Units: 6
Trade Names: JumBurrito (6)
Company-Owned Units: 6
Preferred Location Types: Freestanding; Strip Mall
Primary Menu: Mexican (6)
Areas of Operation: TX
Type of Foodservice: Fast Casual (6)

Key Personnel
DIANE CUEVAS - Partner; General Manager; General Buyer
JOSE CUEVAS - Partner; General Manager; General Buyer

K A J Subway
610 N Big Spring St
Midland, TX 79701-4329

Telephone: (432) 682-4816
Type of Business: Chain Restaurant Operator
Total Sales: $2,929,000 (e)
Total Units: 5
Trade Names: Subway (5)
Units Franchised From: 5
Primary Menu: Sandwiches/Deli (5)
Areas of Operation: TX
Type of Foodservice: Quick Serve (5)
Franchise Affiliation: Doctor's Associates Inc., MILFORD, CT

Key Personnel
TERRY IVES - President

Thomas Distributing, Inc.
5211 W Wadley Ave
Midland, TX 79707-5127

Telephone: (432) 689-0373
Type of Business: Chain Restaurant Operator
Total Sales: $3,061,000 (e)
Total Units: 2
Trade Names: Schlotzsky's/Cinnabon (2)
Units Franchised From: 2
Primary Menu: Sandwiches/Deli (2); Snacks (2)
Areas of Operation: TX
Type of Foodservice: Quick Serve (2)
Franchise Affiliation: Cinnabon Inc., ATLANTA, GA; Schlotzsky's Deli, MIDLAND, TX

Key Personnel
CHUCK WOOD - Owner; General Buyer

Chicken Express
100 SE 25th Ave
Mineral Wells, TX 76067-5716

Mailing Address: PO Box 1309, MINERAL WELLS, TX, 76068-1309
Telephone: (817) 594-9300
Fax Number: (817) 594-9302
Internet Homepage: chickene.com
Company Email: mineralwells@chickenefs.com
Type of Business: Chain Restaurant Operator
Year Founded: 1988
Systemwide Sales: $109,691,000 (e)
Total Sales: $13,280,000 (e)
Number of Employees: 40
Average Check: Lunch(8); Dinner(16)
Total Units: 247
Trade Names: Chicken Express (256)
Company-Owned Units: 1
Units Franchised To: 255
Preferred Square Footage: 2,200
Preferred Location Types: Freestanding
Primary Menu: Chicken (256)
Projected Openings: 8
Areas of Operation: AR, LA, OK, TX
Type of Foodservice: Quick Serve (256)
Catering Services: Yes
Distribution Centers: FORTH WORTH, TX

On-site Distribution Center: Yes

Key Personnel
RICHARD STUART - President; Director Operations, Real Estate, Design; Manager Finance, Franchise Development
NANCY STUART - VP Information Systems; General Manager; Executive Chef; Director Purchasing, Marketing, Human Resources, Catering; General Buyer
RICHARD STUART II - General Manager; Director Facility/Maintenance, Supply Chain, Franchising
TINA HIGH - District Manager
EDDIE HOLYFIELD - Manager Information Technology

Licon Enterprises, Inc.
1800 E Business Highway 83
Mission, TX 78572-9202

Telephone: (956) 581-8523
Fax Number: (956) 581-8668
Internet Homepage: casadeltacorgv.com
Company Email: lacasadeltaco@aol.com
Type of Business: Chain Restaurant Operator
Total Sales: $3,163,000 (e)
Average Check: Dinner(8)
Total Units: 4
Trade Names: La Casa Del Taco Restaurants (4)
Company-Owned Units: 4
Primary Menu: Taco (4)
Areas of Operation: TX
Type of Foodservice: Quick Serve (4)

Key Personnel
SANDRA LICON - VP

Domino's Franchisee
10424 Interstate 10 E
Mont Belvieu, TX 77523-1200

Telephone: (281) 573-3333
Type of Business: Chain Restaurant Operator
Total Sales: $21,947,000 (e)
Total Units: 11
Trade Names: Domino's (11)
Units Franchised From: 11
Primary Menu: Pizza (11)
Areas of Operation: TX
Type of Foodservice: Quick Serve (11)
Franchise Affiliation: Domino's Pizza Inc, ANN ARBOR, MI

Key Personnel
RANDY L. BROWN - Owner; General Buyer

Rand Knotts Enterprises Inc.
209 W 18th St
Mount Pleasant, TX 75455-2311

Mailing Address: PO Box 1623, MOUNT PLEASANT, TX, 75456-1623
Telephone: (903) 572-5380
Fax Number: (903) 577-1208
Type of Business: Chain Restaurant Operator
Year Founded: 1985
Total Sales: $15,427,000 (e)
Number of Employees: 80
Average Check: Breakfast(5); Lunch(8); Dinner(8)
Total Units: 3
Trade Names: McDonald's (3)
Units Franchised From: 3
Preferred Square Footage: 2,500; 3,000
Preferred Location Types: Freestanding
Primary Menu: Hamburger (3)
Areas of Operation: TX
Type of Foodservice: Quick Serve (3)
Franchise Affiliation: McDonald's Corporation, CHICAGO, IL

Key Personnel
RAND KNOTTS - Partner; General Manager; General Buyer
SHERYL KNOTTS - Partner

Domino's Franchisee
2403 North St
Nacogdoches, TX 75965-3517

Telephone: (936) 569-2121
Type of Business: Chain Restaurant Operator
Total Sales: $8,324,000 (e)
Total Units: 4
Trade Names: Domino's (4)
Units Franchised From: 4
Primary Menu: Pizza (4)
Areas of Operation: TX
Type of Foodservice: Quick Serve (4)
Franchise Affiliation: Domino's Pizza Inc, ANN ARBOR, MI

Key Personnel
GREGORY A. RANDOLPH - Owner; General Buyer

Great Texas Foods
8568 S US Highway 59
Nacogdoches, TX 75964-8390

Telephone: (936) 564-5757
Fax Number: (936) 564-0816
Internet Homepage: cafedelrio.net; ralphandkacoos.com; greattexasfoods.com
Company Email: greattexasfoods@att.net
Type of Business: Chain Restaurant Operator
Year Founded: 1992
Total Sales: $28,030,000 (e)
Alcohol Sales: 25%
Number of Employees: 159
Total Units: 11
Trade Names: Bistro Mezzaluna (1); Cafe Del Rio (5); Ralph & Kacoos (5)
Company-Owned Units: 11
Preferred Square Footage: 4,000
Preferred Location Types: Freestanding
Alcohol Served: Beer, Wine, Liquor
Primary Menu: Italian (1); Mexican (5); Seafood (5)
Areas of Operation: FL, LA, TX
Type of Foodservice: Casual Dining (10)
Primary Distributors: (Full Line) SYSCO Food Services of North Texas, LEWISVILLE, TX

Key Personnel
DON DAVIS - CEO; Owner
WARREN HUTSON - President

Jivan Foods Inc.
1145 Interstate 35 S
New Braunfels, TX 78130-5916

Telephone: (830) 629-2030
Fax Number: (830) 624-1756
Type of Business: Chain Restaurant Operator
Year Founded: 1986
Total Sales: $8,071,000 (e)
Number of Employees: 100
Average Check: Lunch(12); Dinner(14)
Total Units: 3
Trade Names: Popeyes Louisiana Kitchen (3)
Units Franchised From: 3
Preferred Square Footage: 2,000
Preferred Location Types: Freestanding
Primary Menu: Chicken (3)
Areas of Operation: TX
Type of Foodservice: Quick Serve (3)
Franchise Affiliation: Popeyes Louisiana Kitchen Inc., ATLANTA, GA
Primary Distributors: (Full Line) SYSCO Central Texas Inc., NEW BRAUNFELS, TX

Key Personnel
VEDO KEMRAJ - President; General Buyer
JAISHREE KEMRAJ - Manager Accounting

Los Cucos Mexican Cafe
1310 E Common St
New Braunfels, TX 78130

Telephone: (830) 624-8770
Internet Homepage: loscucos.com
Company Email: loscucosnb@loscucos.com
Type of Business: Chain Restaurant Operator
Year Founded: 1991
Total Sales: $17,860,000 (e)

Total Units: 19
Trade Names: Los Cucos Mexican Cafe (19)
Company-Owned Units: 19
Primary Menu: Mexican (19)
Areas of Operation: TX, UT
Type of Foodservice: Casual Dining (19)

Key Personnel
SERGIO CABRERA JR - Owner
MANUEL CABRERA JR - Owner; Director Purchasing; General Buyer
SERGIO PINEDA - Director Operations

R & S Dairy Queens Inc.
1555 E Common St
New Braunfels, TX 78130-3154

Telephone: (830) 606-2063
Fax Number: (830) 609-4814
Internet Homepage: randsdairyqueens.com
Company Email: jackie@randsdairyqueens.com
Type of Business: Chain Restaurant Operator
Year Founded: 1979
Total Sales: $26,420,000 (e)
Number of Employees: 400
Average Check: Lunch(8); Dinner(8)
Total Units: 19
Trade Names: Dairy Queen (19)
Units Franchised From: 19
Preferred Square Footage: 1,700; 2,000
Preferred Location Types: Freestanding; Strip Mall
Primary Menu: American (19)
Areas of Operation: TX
Type of Foodservice: Quick Serve (19)
Franchise Affiliation: International Dairy Queen Inc., BLOOMINGTON, MN
Primary Distributors: (Food) Labatt Food Service, SAN ANTONIO, TX

Key Personnel
SHANNON THAYER - President; Partner
CINDY THAYER - Partner
MELBA LUMPKINS - Director Operations; General Buyer; Buyer Food, Foodservice Equip/Supplies
ERIN TORRES - Administrator Payroll, Human Resources

Subway of New Braunfels
1081 Interstate 35 S
New Braunfels, TX 78130-5914

Telephone: (830) 608-1472
Type of Business: Chain Restaurant Operator
Total Sales: $3,609,000 (e)
Total Units: 6
Trade Names: Subway (6)
Units Franchised From: 6
Primary Menu: Sandwiches/Deli (6)
Areas of Operation: TX
Type of Foodservice: Quick Serve (6)
Franchise Affiliation: Doctor's Associates Inc., MILFORD, CT

Key Personnel
RICK . - Owner

Twoshoes, Inc.
1691 State Highway 46 W Ste 300
New Braunfels, TX 78132-2924

Telephone: (830) 387-4610
Type of Business: Chain Restaurant Operator
Total Sales: $6,861,000 (e)
Total Units: 5
Trade Names: Jersey Mike's Subs (5)
Units Franchised From: 5
Primary Menu: Sandwiches/Deli (5)
Areas of Operation: TX
Type of Foodservice: Quick Serve (5)
Franchise Affiliation: Jersey Mike's Franchise Systems, MANASQUAN, NJ

Key Personnel
JASON ODOM - Owner; General Buyer

David Turner Co Inc.
2512 N Grandview Ave
Odessa, TX 79761-1606

Telephone: (432) 580-3434
Fax Number: (432) 580-5562
Type of Business: Chain Restaurant Operator
Total Sales: $5,683,000 (e)
Total Units: 10
Trade Names: Subway (10)
Units Franchised From: 10
Primary Menu: Sandwiches/Deli (10)
Areas of Operation: TX
Type of Foodservice: Quick Serve (10)
Franchise Affiliation: Doctor's Associates Inc., MILFORD, CT

Key Personnel
DAVID TURNER - President; General Buyer

MAS Sandwiches, LLC
7270 E Highway 191 Ste 214
Odessa, TX 79765-8657

Telephone: (432) 563-5656
Type of Business: Chain Restaurant Operator
Total Sales: $2,981,000 (e)
Total Units: 2
Trade Names: Jersey Mike's Subs (2)
Units Franchised From: 2
Primary Menu: Sandwiches/Deli (2)
Areas of Operation: TX
Type of Foodservice: Quick Serve (2)
Franchise Affiliation: Jersey Mike's Franchise Systems, MANASQUAN, NJ

Key Personnel
WAYLAN MICHAELS - Owner; General Buyer

McDonald's Franchise
2304 W Pioneer Pkwy Ste 7
Pantego, TX 76013-6051

Telephone: (817) 265-5702
Fax Number: (817) 265-5735
Type of Business: Chain Restaurant Operator
Total Sales: $67,070,000 (e)
Total Units: 14
Trade Names: McDonald's (14)
Units Franchised From: 14
Preferred Square Footage: 2,500
Primary Menu: Hamburger (14)
Areas of Operation: TX
Type of Foodservice: Quick Serve (14)
Franchise Affiliation: McDonald's Corporation, CHICAGO, IL

Key Personnel
MICHAEL VANECEK - President; General Buyer

West Cassell Enterprises
2504 W Park Row Dr Ste B7
Pantego, TX 76013-2274

Telephone: (817) 460-2021
Type of Business: Chain Restaurant Operator
Total Sales: $1,195,000 (e)
Total Units: 2
Trade Names: Subway (2)
Units Franchised From: 2
Primary Menu: Sandwiches/Deli (2)
Areas of Operation: TX
Type of Foodservice: Quick Serve (2)
Franchise Affiliation: Doctor's Associates Inc., MILFORD, CT

Key Personnel
CLIFF CASSELL - President; General Buyer

Kades Corporation
5621 Red Bluff Rd
Pasadena, TX 77505-2638

Telephone: (281) 479-4700
Fax Number: (281) 479-7568
Internet Homepage: kadescorp.com
Type of Business: Chain Restaurant Operator
Year Founded: 1992
Total Sales: $178,170,000 (e)
Number of Employees: 3,000
Average Check: Breakfast(8); Lunch(8);

Dinner(10)
Total Units: 53
Trade Names: McDonald's (53)
Units Franchised From: 53
Preferred Square Footage: 2,500; 3,000
Preferred Location Types: Discount Dept. Stores; Freestanding
Primary Menu: Hamburger (53)
Areas of Operation: TX
Type of Foodservice: Quick Serve (53)
Franchise Affiliation: McDonald's Corporation, CHICAGO, IL

Key Personnel
KENNETH KADES - President; General Manager; Director Finance, Real Estate; General Buyer
MELANIE REGAN - Director Marketing
ROBERT BOWIE - Director Operations, Facility/Maintenance, Information Systems, Personnel
OMAR CASTRO - Director

Q Mar, Inc.
5021 Fairmont Pkwy
Pasadena, TX 77505-3725

Telephone: (713) 944-0003
Fax Number: (713) 944-0090
Type of Business: Chain Restaurant Operator
Total Sales: $120,660,000 (e)
Total Units: 26
Trade Names: McDonald's (26)
Units Franchised From: 26
Preferred Square Footage: 2,500
Primary Menu: Hamburger (26)
Areas of Operation: TX
Type of Foodservice: Quick Serve (26)
Franchise Affiliation: McDonald's Corporation, CHICAGO, IL

Key Personnel
NELLY QUIJANO - President; General Buyer

Southeast Corporation
3525 Preston Ave
Pasadena, TX 77505-2008

Telephone: (281) 487-0292
Internet Homepage: dqpasadena.com
Company Email: marketing@dqpasadena.com
Type of Business: Chain Restaurant Operator
Total Sales: $15,070,000 (e)
Internet Order Processing: Yes
Total Units: 11
Trade Names: Dairy Queen (11)
Units Franchised From: 11
Primary Menu: Snacks (11)
Areas of Operation: TX
Type of Foodservice: Quick Serve (11)
Franchise Affiliation: International Dairy Queen Inc., BLOOMINGTON, MN

Key Personnel
WESLEY R. HOWARD - President; General Buyer

R & L LOZANO OPERATING LTD
208 N Cage Blvd
Pharr, TX 78577-3906

Telephone: (956) 787-8770
Fax Number: (956) 787-8749
Internet Homepage: thedqteam.com
Type of Business: Chain Restaurant Operator
Total Sales: $56,530,000 (e)
Total Units: 41
Trade Names: Dairy Queen (41)
Units Franchised From: 41
Primary Menu: American (41)
Areas of Operation: TX
Type of Foodservice: Quick Serve (41)
Franchise Affiliation: International Dairy Queen Inc., BLOOMINGTON, MN

Key Personnel
ROBERT LOZANO - President; General Buyer

Bailey's Sports Grille
1111 Jupiter Rd Ste 110B
Plano, TX 75074

Telephone: (214) 556-0967
Fax Number: (708) 564-2282
Internet Homepage: baileyssportsgrille.com
Type of Business: Chain Restaurant Operator
Year Founded: 1989
Total Units: 4
Trade Names: Bailey's Sports Grille (4)
Company-Owned Units: 4
Preferred Square Footage: 4,000
Alcohol Served: Beer, Wine, Liquor
Primary Menu: American (4)
Areas of Operation: NC, TN
Type of Foodservice: Casual Dining (4)

Key Personnel
BRIAN JAMES - District Manager

Cinemark Holdings Inc.
3900 Dallas Pkwy Ste 500
Plano, TX 75093-7871

Telephone: (972) 665-1000
Fax Number: (972) 665-1400
Internet Homepage: cinemark.com
Type of Business: Foodservice Operations - Movie Theatre
Year Founded: 1987
Publicly Held: Yes
Total Sales: $5,003,435,000 (e)
Number of Employees: 20,000
Average Check: Lunch(6); Dinner(6)
Foodservice Sales: $1,751,202,000 (e)
Total Units: 309
Trade Names: Cinemark Theater (309)
Company-Owned Units: 309
Preferred Square Footage: 50,000
Preferred Location Types: Community Mall; Freestanding; Lifestyle Center; Regional Mall
Alcohol Served: Beer, Wine, Liquor
Primary Menu: Snacks (309)
Areas of Operation: AK, AL, AR, AZ, CA, CO, CT, DE, FL, GA, IA, IL, IN, KS, KY, LA, MA, MD, MI, MN, MO, MS, MT, NC, NJ, NM, NV, NY, OH, OK, OR, PA, SC, SD, TN, TX, UT, VA, WA, WI, WV
Foreign Countries: ARGENTINA; BOLIVIA; BRAZIL; CHILE; COLOMBIA; COSTA RICA; CURACAO; ECUADOR; EL SALVADOR; GUATEMALA; HONDURAS; NICARAGUA; PANAMA; PARAGUAY; PERU
Type of Foodservice: In-Store Feeder (309)
Primary Distributors: (Food) SYSCO Corporation, HOUSTON, TX
Parent Company: Madison Dearborn Partners Inc., CHICAGO, IL
Notes: The company derives approximately 65% of its revenue from theater admissions, management fees & other operations.

Key Personnel
LEE ROY MITCHELL - Executive Chairman
MARK ZORADI - CEO
VALMIR FERNANDES - President International Division
SEAN GAMBLE - CFO; COO; Exec VP
DOUG FAY - CTO
MICHAEL CAVALIER - Exec VP; Corporate Secretary; General Counsel
JUSTIN MCDANIEL - Senior VP Strategy, Global
AGUSTIN VIOLA-PRIOLI - Senior VP Operations
JAY JOSTRAND - Senior VP Real Estate
GREG MUSE - Senior VP Information Systems
JEFF ROSENFELD - Senior VP Digital, Customer Care
MIKE ZAPKA - VP Supply Chain
ALAN BENJAMIN - VP Real Estate
CHANDA BRASHEARS - VP Public Relations, Investor Relations
SHARLA JONES - VP Talent, Global
DON HARTON - VP Construction, Design
DAVID HAYWOOD - VP
LENSEY MORRIS - Creative Director
STEVE KAUZLARIC - Director Real Estate
JAIME LESSER - Director Promotions
KATHLEEN SPINA - Director Human Resources
RAYMOND VALENCIA - Director Digital
BRANDON HOBBY - Director HRIS
JIMMY CARRERA - Director Purchasing, International

JEANINE BLAIR - Director Information Technology
LANCE CLARK - Director Information/Data Security
LISA COOK - Director Finance
LETHA CREAMER - Director Payroll
CAITLIN PIPER - Senior Manager Communications, Public Relations
HARVEY HERNANDEZ - Manager Purchasing
ALTON BROWN - Administrator Networking

Cookies by Design, Inc
1865 Summit Ave Ste 605
Plano, TX 75074-8185

Telephone: (972) 398-9536
Fax Number: (972) 398-9542
Internet Homepage: cookiesbydesign.com
Company Email: customerservice@cookiesbydesign.com
Type of Business: Chain Restaurant Operator
Systemwide Sales: $22,991,000 (e)
Total Sales: $1,411,000 (e)
Number of Employees: 80
Internet Order Processing: Yes
Internet Sales: 50.00%
Total Units: 54
Trade Names: Cookies By Design (58)
Company-Owned Units: 1
Units Franchised To: 57
Preferred Location Types: Community Mall; Downtown; Freestanding; Strip Mall
Primary Menu: Snacks (58)
Areas of Operation: AL, AZ, CA, CO, FL, GA, HI, IA, IL, IN, KS, KY, LA, MA, MD, MI, MN, MO, NC, NE, NH, NJ, NM, NV, NY, OH, OK, OR, PA, TN, TX, UT, VA, WA, WI
Type of Foodservice: Quick Serve (58)
Primary Distributors: (Full Line) US Foods-Los Angeles, LA MIRADA, CA

Key Personnel
GWEN GILLIAM - Founder
JACK LONG - CEO; President
OLIVIA LONG - Corporate Manager

Dillas Quesadillas, LLC
2008 Midway Rd
Plano, TX 75093

Telephone: (972) 808-6981
Internet Homepage: dillas.com
Company Email: office@dillas.com
Type of Business: Chain Restaurant Operator
Year Founded: 2013
Total Sales: $4,717,000 (e)
Number of Employees: 100
Total Units: 4
Trade Names: Dillas Quesadillas (4)
Company-Owned Units: 4
Primary Menu: Mexican (4)
Areas of Operation: LA, TX
Type of Foodservice: Fast Casual (4)

Key Personnel
KYLE GORDON - Owner
MAGGIE GORDON - Owner; Manager Marketing, Human Resources
MICHAEL PIACENTE - General Manager

Domino's Franchisee
3509 E Park Blvd Ste 170
Plano, TX 75074-3199

Telephone: (972) 424-4561
Type of Business: Chain Restaurant Operator
Total Sales: $17,884,000 (e)
Total Units: 9
Trade Names: Domino's (9)
Units Franchised From: 9
Primary Menu: Pizza (9)
Areas of Operation: TX
Type of Foodservice: Quick Serve (9)
Franchise Affiliation: Domino's Pizza Inc, ANN ARBOR, MI

Key Personnel
DONALD H. GARMAN - Owner; General Buyer

Fogo de Chao Inc.
5908 Headquarters Dr Ste K150
Plano, TX 75024

Telephone: (972) 960-9533
Fax Number: (972) 960-9877
Internet Homepage: fogodechao.com
Type of Business: Chain Restaurant Operator
Year Founded: 1979
Total Sales: $558,830,000 (e)
Alcohol Sales: 16%
Number of Employees: 822
Average Check: Lunch(54); Dinner(90)
Total Units: 65
Trade Names: Fogo De Chao (65)
Company-Owned Units: 65
Preferred Square Footage: 5,500; 6,000; 12,000
Preferred Location Types: Freestanding
Alcohol Served: Beer, Wine, Liquor
Primary Menu: Steak (65)
Projected Openings: 2
Areas of Operation: AZ, CA, CO, DC, FL, GA, IL, IN, MA, MD, MN, MO, NV, NY, OR, PA, PR, TX, FC
Foreign Countries: BRAZIL; MEXICO; SAUDI ARABIA; UNITED ARAB EMIRATES
Type of Foodservice: Fine Dining (65)
Primary Distributors: (Food) SYSCO Food Services of North Texas, LEWISVILLE, TX; (Supplies) Edward Don & Co., THE COLONY, TX

Parent Company: Rhône Capital, ,

Key Personnel
BARRY MCGOWAN - CEO
ANDREW FELDMANN - President International
TONY LADAY - CFO
SELMA OLIVEIRA - Chief People Officer; Chief Culture Officer
JANET GIESELMAN - Chief Marketing Officer
JOSEPH PASQUESI - Area Director
STUART RACKHAM - VP Supply Chain, Innovation
HILMA HERNANDEZ - VP Human Resources
RICHARD LENDERMAN - VP Operations
HIGINIO ORDONEZ - Executive Chef
JENNIFER CAIN - Senior Director Operations; Director Operations
GRANT RICE - Director Human Resources
BRYAN ROBERTS - Director Financial Planning
ROSANGELA SOUZA - Director
ALICIA HESS - Director Global
NERI GIACHINI - Regional Director Operations
VALERIE OLVERA - Senior Manager Accounting
ASHLEY YOUNG - Senior Manager Marketing
KATHERINE VALENTINE - Manager Marketing

Kent Rathbun Concepts
8100 Dallas Pkwy Ste 110
Plano, TX 75024-4010

Telephone: (214) 619-3510
Internet Homepage: abacus-restaurant.com; kentrathbun.com
Type of Business: Chain Restaurant Operator
Total Sales: $12,847,000 (e)
Alcohol Sales: 12%
Number of Employees: 35
Average Check: Lunch(20); Dinner(42)
Total Units: 4
Trade Names: Jasper's (4)
Company-Owned Units: 4
Preferred Location Types: Freestanding
Alcohol Served: Beer, Wine, Liquor
Primary Menu: American (4)
Areas of Operation: TX
Type of Foodservice: Fine Dining (4)
Catering Services: Yes
Primary Distributors: (Food) FreshPoint Dallas, DALLAS, TX

Key Personnel
BRIAN GRINDEM - Controller
RICK OTTO - Controller
JON-MICHAEL ROGERS - General Manager Division
JEFF MOSCHETTI - Executive Chef
CHARLOTTE GANNON - Director Catering

Main Event Entertainment, LP
5445 Legacy Dr #400
Plano, TX 75024

Telephone: (469) 661-2695
Internet Homepage: mainevent.com
Company Email: feedback@mainevent.com
Listing Type: Subsidiary
Type of Business: Chain Restaurant Operator
Year Founded: 1998
Total Sales: $22,240,000 (e)
Number of Employees: 4,605
Total Units: 44
Trade Names: Main Event (44)
Company-Owned Units: 44
Preferred Square Footage: 45,000; 55,000; 75,000
Preferred Location Types: Freestanding
Primary Menu: American (44)
Projected Openings: 2
Areas of Operation: AZ, CO, DE, FL, GA, IL, IN, KS, KY, LA, MD, MO, NM, OH, OK, PA, TN, TX
Type of Foodservice: Casual Dining (44)
Parent Company: Dave & Buster's Inc., DALLAS, TX

Key Personnel
CHRIS MORRIS - CEO; President
TONY WEHNER - COO
LES L. LEHNER - Chief Development Officer; Chief Procurement Officer; Exec VP
ROBERT JENKINS - VP Sales
MIKE GRAY - Senior Director Architecture, Design
LOUIS LAROCCO - Director Operations
MATT WELCH - Director Construction
LAURIE BETH JENSEN - Director Human Resources
MIKE MANLEY - Director Information Technology, Systems
WILLIAM HARBOUR - Regional Director Operations
KD HAMILTON - District Manager Sales
AYA MURADOVNA - Manager Talent Acquisitions
WENDI LUCAS - Manager Sales
ASIA WHETSTINE - Manager Operations
LETHA HENDRIX - Manager Benefits
ANTHONY SILVA - Manager Operations
APRIL ROWLETTE - Coordinator Event Planning

Mama's Daughters' Diner
6509 W Park Blvd Ste 400
Plano, TX 75093

Telephone: (972) 473-8877
Internet Homepage: mamasdaughtersdiner.com
Company Email: catering@mamasdaughtersdiner.com
Type of Business: Chain Restaurant Operator
Year Founded: 1988
Total Units: 5
Trade Names: Mama's Daughters' Diner (5)
Company-Owned Units: 5
Primary Menu: American (5)
Areas of Operation: TX
Type of Foodservice: Family Restaurant (5)

Key Personnel
NANCY PROCACCINI - President; Owner; General Buyer

Mitra QSR KNE, LLC
7250 Dallas Pkwy 8th Floor Ste 800
Plano, TX 75024

Telephone: (214) 774-4240
Fax Number: (214) 774-4243
Internet Homepage: mitraqsr.com
Company Email: info@mitraqsr.com
Type of Business: Chain Restaurant Operator
Total Sales: $331,620,000 (e)
Total Units: 223
Trade Names: KFC; KFC/Long John Silver's; KFC/Taco Bell
Units Franchised From: 223
Areas of Operation: DE, IL, KS, MD, MO, NJ, OK, PA, TX, VA, WV
Type of Foodservice: Quick Serve (223)
Franchise Affiliation: KFC Corporation, LOUISVILLE, KY; Long John Silver's Inc., LOUISVILLE, KY; Taco Bell Corp., IRVINE, CA
Parent Company: The Chalak Group, DALLAS, TX

Key Personnel
COLLIN THOMPSON - CFO
LADI OLUWOLE - COO
JASON HIMBER - Chief Strategy Officer
HOMER HUNT - Senior VP Operations
JITEN PATEL - VP
TOM PETRECCA - VP Operations
DARREN MUIRHEID - VP Finance
KHALED HABASH - VP Operations
SCOTT SCHULTZ - Director Operations
TOYIN FAWEHINMI - Director Loss Prevention
RUDY EDGHILL - Director Facility/Maintenance
AMANDA STINETTE - Director Training
MICHELLE EVANS - Director Operations
TRENT SHAW - Manager
BRETT MCINTYRE - Manager
EMILIA MBONU - Manager
RAKESH RAMDASS - Manager

MOOYAH Franchise LLC
6865 Windcrest Dr Ste 400
Plano, TX 75024-4229

Telephone: (214) 310-0768
Internet Homepage: mooyah.com
Type of Business: Chain Restaurant Operator
Year Founded: 2007
Systemwide Sales: $104,568,000 (e)
Total Sales: $5,235,000 (e)
Average Check: Dinner(10)
Internet Order Processing: Yes
Total Units: 81
Trade Names: MooYah Burgers & Fries (81)
Company-Owned Units: 4
Units Franchised To: 77
Primary Menu: Hamburger (81)
Projected Openings: 49
Areas of Operation: AL, AR, CA, CO, CT, FL, IL, LA, MA, MT, NC, NH, NJ, NY, OH, PA, RI, TN, TX, UT, VA, WI, FC
Foreign Countries: BAHRAIN; CANADA; OMAN; QATAR; SAUDI ARABIA; UNITED ARAB EMIRATES
Type of Foodservice: Fast Casual (81)

Key Personnel
DOUG WILLMARTH - President
NOAH GLASS - Partner
SARAH BEDDOE - VP Marketing

O'Reilly Group
3400 Silverstone Dr Ste 118
Plano, TX 75023-7843

Telephone: (972) 985-9675
Fax Number: (972) 985-8624
Internet Homepage: oreillymcd.com
Type of Business: Chain Restaurant Operator
Year Founded: 2003
Total Sales: $98,700,000 (e)
Number of Employees: 840
Average Check: Breakfast(8), Lunch(8), Dinner(10)
Total Units: 21
Trade Names: McDonald's (21)
Units Franchised From: 21
Preferred Square Footage: 2,500
Preferred Location Types: Freestanding
Primary Menu: Hamburger (21)
Areas of Operation: TX
Type of Foodservice: Quick Serve (21)
Franchise Affiliation: McDonald's Corporation, CHICAGO, IL
Primary Distributors: (Food) The Martin-Brower Co., CONROE, TX

Key Personnel
HENRY C. O'REILLY III - President; Partner; CFO; General Manager; Manager Information Systems, Real Estate; General Buyer

JULIE O'REILLY - Partner
ALLISON GILLESPIE - VP Marketing
SCOTT PATERSON - VP
PHILLIP HUNTER - Senior Director Product Development
MAMTA PATEL - Director Operations, Facility/Maintenance, Human Resources
JEFF POWELL - Director Internal Audit
SASHA DIVITKINA - Director Communications

PhaseNext Hospitality
6141 Palomino Dr
Plano, TX 75024-6036

Telephone: (855) 639-2041
Internet Homepage: phasenexthospitality.com
Company Email: inquiries@phasenexthospitality.com
Type of Business: Chain Restaurant Operator
Year Founded: 2009
Total Sales: $24,330,000 (e)
Total Units: 8
Trade Names: Blaze Fast-Fire'd Pizza (1); Buffalo Wild Wings (3); Corner Bakery Cafe (1); Smashburger (2); The Italian Kitchen by Wolfgang Puck (1)
Units Franchised From: 8
Alcohol Served: Beer, Wine
Primary Menu: American (1); Chicken (3); Hamburger (2); Italian (1); Pizza (1)
Areas of Operation: GA, MN, TX
Type of Foodservice: Casual Dining (3); Fast Casual (4); Fine Dining (1)
Franchise Affiliation: Blaze Pizza LLC, PASADENA, CA; Buffalo Wild Wings Inc., ATLANTA, GA; CBC Restaurant Corp., DALLAS, TX; Smashburger Master LLC, DENVER, CO; Wolfgang Puck Inc., LAS VEGAS, NV

Key Personnel
ROZ MALLET - CEO; President
RYAN VALLEJO - Manager Finance

Pizza Hut Inc.
7100 Corporate Dr
Plano, TX 75024-4100

Telephone: (972) 338-7700
Fax Number: (972) 338-7689
Internet Homepage: pizzahut.com; PizzaHutFranchise.com; wingstreet.com
Company Email: comments@yum.com
Type of Business: Chain Restaurant Operator
Year Founded: 1958
Systemwide Sales: $13,643,340,000 (e)
Publicly Held: Yes
Total Sales: $1,044,128,000 (e)
Alcohol Sales: 1%
Number of Employees: 6,000
Average Check: Lunch(12); Dinner(14)
Internet Order Processing: Yes
Total Units: 19,866
Trade Names: Pizza Hut (19,866)
Company-Owned Units: 199
Units Franchised To: 19,667
Preferred Square Footage: 1,400; 1,800; 2,500; 3,200; 4,000; 4,500
Preferred Location Types: Airports; Community Mall; Downtown; Freestanding; Hotel/Motel; Institution (college/hospital); Kiosk; Mobile Unit; Office Complex; Regional Mall; Stadiums; Strip Mall; Travel Plazas
Alcohol Served: Beer, Wine
Primary Menu: Pizza (19,866)
Areas of Operation: AK, AL, AR, AZ, CA, CO, CT, DC, DE, FL, GA, HI, IA, ID, IL, IN, KS, KY, LA, MA, MD, ME, MI, MN, MO, MS, MT, NC, ND, NE, NH, NJ, NM, NV, NY, OH, OK, OR, PA, PR, RI, SC, SD, TN, TX, UT, VA, VT, WA, WI, WV, WY, AB, BC, MB, NB, NL, NS, NT, ON, PE, QC, SK, YT
Foreign Countries: AFGHANISTAN; AMERICAN SAMOA; ARMENIA; AUSTRALIA; AZERBAIJAN; BAHRAIN; BANGLADESH; BELGIUM; BRAZIL; CANADA; CHINA; COLOMBIA; COSTA RICA; CYPRUS; DENMARK; DOMINICAN REPUBLIC; ECUADOR; EGYPT; EL SALVADOR; ENGLAND; FIJI; FINLAND;FRANCE; GERMANY; GIBRALTAR; GREECE; GUATEMALA; GUYANA; HONDURAS; HONG KONG; HUNGARY; ICELAND; INDIA; INDONESIA; IRAQ;IRELAND; ISRAEL; JAMAICA; JAPAN; JORDAN; KUWAIT; LEBANON; LITHUANIA; LUXEMBOURG; MALAYSIA; MALTA; MAURITIUS; MEXICO; MOROCCO; NEPAL; NEW ZEALAND; NICARAGUA; NORTHERN IRELAND; NORWAY; OMAN; PAKISTAN; PANAMA; PARAGUAY; PERU; POLAND; PORTUGAL; QATAR; ROMANIA; RUSSIA; SAINT MAARTEN; SAINT MARTIN; SAUDI ARABIA; SCOTLAND; SINGAPORE; SLOVAKIA; SOUTH AFRICA; SOUTH KOREA; SPAIN; SRI LANKA; SURINAME; SWEDEN; TAIWAN; THAILAND; THE NETHERLANDS; THE PHILIPPINES; TRINIDAD & TOBAGO;TUNISIA; TURKEY; UKRAINE; UNITED ARAB EMIRATES; VENEZUELA; VIETNAM
Type of Foodservice: Quick Serve (19,866)
Catering Services: Yes
Primary Distributors: (Full Line) McLane Foodservice, CARROLLTON, TX
Parent Company: YUM! Brands Inc., LOUISVILLE, KY

Key Personnel
AARON POWELL - CEO
PAT MCCONAUGHEY - President
CARL LOREDO - President United States
JUERGEN SCHROEDL - CFO Digital; Director Strategy, Technology
CHARLIE SHORT - CFO Interim
LYNNE BROAD - CFO
NICOLAS BURQUIER - COO; Chief Customer Officer
KAMIL HILMI - COO
JAMES WATTS - Chief Human Resources Officer International
MELISSA FRIEBE - Chief Marketing Officer United States
DAVID GRAVES - Chief Brand Officer; General Manager
KALEN THORNTON - Chief Brand Officer Global
ROBERT W. MILLEN - Senior VP; Corporate Secretary; General Counsel
VARUN AGASTI - VP E-Commerce
BRIAN M MULLIS - Regional VP
RYAN HOLOMSHEK - Senior Director Compliance
RACHEL LORRAINE - Director Strategic Services
PATRICK BRANLEY - Director Technology
TALYTHA COLLINS - Director Operations
MAURICIO DAVILA - Director Operations
CHRIS DELRE - Director Operations
PETER GRAHAM - Director Operations
GAYLE KIRBY - Director Operations
ALEX KNIGHT - Director
TED MILLER - Director Operations
DOUG SCOTT - Director Restaurant Operations
ALLAN THOMPSON - Director Operations
AMY GINGERICH - Director Human Resources
OSCAR PELAEZ - Director Innovation, Global
BETH KENNEDY - Director Supply Chain
CHANTEL CHEATHAM - Director Legal
STEVE VOELS - Senior Manager Operations, Development
SCOTT WEBERG - Senior Manager Technology
KAREN WHITE - Senior Manager Innovation, Product Development
ARNEL CORTUNA - Manager Operations
HAIM EDRI - Manager Information Technology
DON ERIC ROMARATE - Manager Operations
MCQUELLA FERNANDER - Manager Operations
FAISAL KP - Manager Engineering
MATT MCLELLAND - Manager
BILLY NIETERT - Manager Operations, Strategy
REGU RAMEN - Manager Operations
KEVIN SMITH - Manager Operations
ERIC WALTON - Manager Engineering
JOHN WELLS - Manager Engineering
YVETTE SEXTON - Manager Information Systems
SUMEER SHARMA - Manager Marketing

Press Waffle Company
7800 Windrose Ave
Plano, TX 75024

Telephone: (972) 850-0189
Internet Homepage: presswaffleco.com
Company Email: eat@presswaffleco.com
Type of Business: Chain Restaurant Operator
Year Founded: 2016

Total Units: 4
Trade Names: Press Waffle Co. (4)
Company-Owned Units: 4
Preferred Location Types: Community Mall; Mixed-use Center
Primary Menu: Snacks (4)
Areas of Operation: OK, TX
Type of Foodservice: Quick Serve (4)

Key Personnel
BRYAN LEWIS - Founder; Partner
NATHAN LEWIS - Partner
LEAH F. EWING - General Manager

The Biscuit Bar
5880 TX-121 Suite 102B
Plano, TX 75024

Telephone: (469) 238-2227
Internet Homepage: thebiscuit.bar
Company Email: boardwalk@thebiscuit.bar
Type of Business: Chain Restaurant Operator
Year Founded: 2018
Total Units: 2
Trade Names: The Biscuit Bar (2)
Company-Owned Units: 2
Preferred Square Footage: 2,500
Preferred Location Types: Strip Mall
Primary Menu: American (2)
Projected Openings: 3
Areas of Operation: TX
Type of Foodservice: Casual Dining (2)

Key Personnel
JANIE BURKETT - Co-Founder
JAKE BURKETT - Co-Founder; CEO
REIF CHRON - President

ZaLat Pizza
7224 Independence Pkwy Ste 316
Plano, TX 75025

Telephone: (972) 208-2371
Internet Homepage: zalatpizza.com
Type of Business: Chain Restaurant Operator
Year Founded: 2015
Total Sales: $21,040,000 (e)
Number of Employees: 80
Total Units: 18
Trade Names: ZaLat Pizza (18)
Company-Owned Units: 18
Primary Menu: Pizza (18)
Type of Foodservice: Quick Serve (18)

Key Personnel
KHANH NGUYEN - Founder; Owner

Zeigler Direct, LLC
1881 N Central Expy Ste 100
Plano, TX 75075-6974

Telephone: (972) 509-1881
Type of Business: Chain Restaurant Operator
Total Sales: $6,756,000 (e)
Total Units: 5
Trade Names: Jersey Mike's Subs (5)
Units Franchised From: 5
Primary Menu: Sandwiches/Deli (5)
Areas of Operation: TX
Type of Foodservice: Quick Serve (5)
Franchise Affiliation: Jersey Mike's Franchise Systems, MANASQUAN, NJ

Key Personnel
STEVEN J. ZEIGLER - Owner; General Buyer

South Texas Dairy Queen Inc.
823 Austin St
Portland, TX 78374-2007

Mailing Address: PO Box 1326, PORTLAND, TX, 78374-1185
Telephone: (361) 643-5993
Fax Number: (361) 643-1397
Internet Homepage: southtexasdq.com
Type of Business: Chain Restaurant Operator
Year Founded: 1974
Total Sales: $48,870,000 (e)
Number of Employees: 300
Average Check: Lunch(8); Dinner(8)
Total Units: 35
Trade Names: Dairy Queen (35)
Units Franchised From: 35
Preferred Square Footage: 3,000
Preferred Location Types: Freestanding
Primary Menu: American (35)
Areas of Operation: TX
Type of Foodservice: Quick Serve (35)
Franchise Affiliation: International Dairy Queen Inc., BLOOMINGTON, MN
Primary Distributors: (Full Line) Performance Foodservice - Victoria, VICTORIA, TX

Key Personnel
JIM WEST - President; General Buyer
SUE WEST - Exec VP Loss Prevention, Risk Management, Supply Chain, Advertising, Human Resources
LISA GONZALEZ - Director Finance, Operations, Information Systems, Real Estate, Store Fixtures

Learco Restaurant Management, LLC
291 E Ovilla Rd
Red Oak, TX 75154-2619

Telephone: (972) 576-0123
Type of Business: Chain Restaurant Operator
Total Sales: $6,762,000 (e)
Total Units: 3
Trade Names: Sonic America's Drive-In (3)
Units Franchised From: 3
Primary Menu: Hamburger (3)
Areas of Operation: TX
Type of Foodservice: Quick Serve (3)
Franchise Affiliation: Sonic Corp., OKLAHOMA CITY, OK

Key Personnel
PATRICK LEAR - Owner; General Buyer

A.C.G. Texas
1778 N Plano Rd Ste 100
Richardson, TX 75081-1962

Telephone: (972) 861-5757
Fax Number: (972) 861-5788
Internet Homepage: acgtexas.com
Company Email: info@acgtexas.com
Type of Business: Chain Restaurant Operator
Year Founded: 1986
Total Sales: $243,180,000 (e)
Number of Employees: 4,350
Average Check: Breakfast(14); Lunch(18); Dinner(18)
Total Units: 77
Trade Names: IHOP Restaurant (77)
Units Franchised From: 77
Preferred Square Footage: 4,400; 5,000
Preferred Location Types: Freestanding
Alcohol Served: Beer, Wine, Liquor
Primary Menu: American (75)
Projected Openings: 10
Areas of Operation: TX
Type of Foodservice: Family Restaurant (75)
Franchise Affiliation: IHOP Restaurant System, GLENDALE, CA
Parent Company: Argonne Capital Group LLC, ATLANTA, GA
Headquarters: Summit Restaurant Group LLC, ATLANTA, GA
Notes: The Applebee's restaurants operate as Neighborhood Restaurant Partners LLC.

Key Personnel
MIKE EVANS - CEO; President
MIKE AMORE - Area Director
JULIO DOMINGUEZ - Area Director
HISHAM JADA - Area Director
SCOT THOMAS - Area Director
DARYLANN SYLKATIS - Controller
JOSHUA PATTERSON - General Manager

PATRICIA MARTINEZ - Director Information Systems, Human Resources
PAUL PLUTAE - Director Information Systems
MIKE WALDEN - Director Development, Construction
WENDELL PATTERSON - Regional Director Operations
MARCUS MESSERLIE - Manager Training
YUSUF FATANI - Manager
NICK HYSAW - Manager Information Technology

Crest Foods Inc.
101 W Renner Rd Ste 240
Richardson, TX 75082-2002

Telephone: (214) 495-9533
Fax Number: (214) 239-3091
Internet Homepage: nestlecafe.com
Company Email: info@nestlecafe.com
Type of Business: Chain Restaurant Operator
Year Founded: 1998
Systemwide Sales: $73,701,000 (e)
Total Sales: $10,070,000 (e)
Number of Employees: 668
Average Check: Breakfast(8); Lunch(8); Dinner(8)
Internet Order Processing: Yes
Total Units: 76
Trade Names: Nestle Toll House Cafe by Chip (162)
Units Franchised To: 162
Preferred Square Footage: 2,200
Preferred Location Types: Airports; Community Mall; Institution (college/hospital); Other; Regional Mall; Strip Mall
Primary Menu: Snacks (162)
Projected Openings: 15
Areas of Operation: CA, FL, GA, IL, LA, MD, MI, MN, MO, NC, NH, NV, NY, OH, OK, OR, PA, SC, TX, UT, VA, BC, ON
Foreign Countries: CANADA; QATAR; SAUDI ARABIA
Type of Foodservice: Quick Serve (162)
Catering Services: Yes
Primary Distributors: (Food) Vistar Rocky Mountain, DENVER, CO

Key Personnel
ZIAD S. DALAL - Founder; CEO; President
TODD PANCHUK - Senior Manager Construction

Golden Franchising Corp.
1131 Rockingham Dr Ste 250
Richardson, TX 75080-4326

Telephone: (972) 831-0911
Fax Number: (972) 831-0401
Internet Homepage: goldenchick.com
Company Email: gfcinfo@goldenchick.com
Type of Business: Chain Restaurant Operator
Year Founded: 1967
Systemwide Sales: $273,499,000 (e)
Total Sales: $18,630,000 (e)
Number of Employees: 70
Average Check: Lunch(12); Dinner(14)
Total Units: 221
Trade Names: Golden Chick (221)
Company-Owned Units: 14
Units Franchised To: 207
Preferred Square Footage: 1,800; 2,000
Preferred Location Types: Convenience Store/Gas Station; Freestanding; Strip Mall
Primary Menu: Chicken (221)
Projected Openings: 35
Areas of Operation: FL, GA, OK, SC, TX
Type of Foodservice: Quick Serve (221)
Catering Services: Yes
Primary Distributors: (Full Line) Performance Foodservice - Victoria, VICTORIA, TX

Key Personnel
DAVE RUTKOWSKI - CFO; Treasurer; Director Information Systems, Loss Prevention
BRIAN LOESCHER - COO
MICHAEL JENSEN - Senior VP; VP Operations; Director Purchasing, Product Development, Menu Development, Food Safety, Catering
MONTY WHITEHURST - Senior VP Real Estate Development
SCOTT STEVENSON - VP Development, Construction
CYNTHIA ANNA LOESCHER - VP Information Technology
LINDSEY ORENSTEIN - Director Brand Marketing

Griff's of America Inc.
1202 Richardson Dr Ste 312
Richardson, TX 75080-4678

Mailing Address: PO Box 830459, RICHARDSON, TX, 75083-0459
Telephone: (972) 238-9561
Fax Number: (972) 238-9564
Internet Homepage: griffshamburgers.com
Company Email: griffsofam@sbcglobal.net
Type of Business: Chain Restaurant Operator
Year Founded: 1960
Total Sales: $14,480,000 (e)
Number of Employees: 240
Average Check: Lunch(8); Dinner(8)
Total Units: 12
Trade Names: Griff's Hamburgers (12)
Company-Owned Units: 12
Preferred Square Footage: 4,000
Preferred Location Types: Freestanding
Primary Menu: Hamburger (12)
Areas of Operation: LA, NM, TX
Type of Foodservice: Quick Serve (12)
Primary Distributors: (Full Line) SYSCO Food Services of North Texas, LEWISVILLE, TX

Key Personnel
HARVEY FATTIG - President; Director Operations, Facility/Maintenance, Menu Development; General Buyer
MICHAEL PRESCOTT - Director Operations; General Buyer
BROOKE LIVELY - Manager Operations

Jalapeno Tree Holdings LLC
1131 Rockingham Dr Ste 250
Richardson, TX 75080-4326

Telephone: (972) 831-0911
Fax Number: (972) 831-0401
Internet Homepage: jalapenotree.com
Company Email: info@jalapenotree.com
Type of Business: Chain Restaurant Operator
Year Founded: 1980
Total Sales: $7,526,000 (e)
Alcohol Sales: 10%
Number of Employees: 177
Average Check: Lunch(12); Dinner(12)
Total Units: 14
Trade Names: The Jalapeno Tree Mexican Restaurant (14)
Company-Owned Units: 14
Preferred Square Footage: 5,500; 6,000
Preferred Location Types: Freestanding
Alcohol Served: Beer, Wine, Liquor
Primary Menu: Mexican (14)
Areas of Operation: TX
Type of Foodservice: Casual Dining (14)
Catering Services: Yes
Primary Distributors: (Food) Performance Foodservice - Victoria, VICTORIA, TX
Notes: Chairman Mark Parmerlee is also chairman of the Golden Chick restaurant chain; Golden Chick will be providing support services to Jalapeno Tree, including accounting and payroll.

Key Personnel
MARK PARMERLEE - Chairman; Partner; Director Supply Chain, Real Estate, Design
PAUL BAMBREY - CEO; President; Partner; General Manager; Director Information Systems, Menu Development, Catering; General Buyer

Rockfish Seafood Grill Inc.
275 W Campbell Rd Ste 115
Richardson, TX 75080

Telephone: (214) 887-9400
Fax Number: (214) 821-0138
Internet Homepage: rockfish.com
Company Email: guestrelations@rockfish.com
Type of Business: Chain Restaurant Operator
Year Founded: 1994
Total Sales: $46,600,000 (e)
Alcohol Sales: 18%

Number of Employees: 768
Average Check: Lunch(22); Dinner(30)
Internet Order Processing: Yes
Total Units: 10
Trade Names: Rockfish Seafood Grill (10)
Company-Owned Units: 10
Preferred Square Footage: 3,000; 4,500
Preferred Location Types: Freestanding; Lifestyle Center
Alcohol Served: Beer, Wine, Liquor
Primary Menu: Seafood (10)
Areas of Operation: TX
Type of Foodservice: Casual Dining (10)
Primary Distributors: (Food) Ocean Beauty Seafood Inc, CARROLLTON, TX

Key Personnel
TINA LIMSKY - Controller; Director
CLARISSA DANIEL - Director Operations

McDonald's Franchise
2006 Thompson Rd Ste 100
Richmond, TX 77469-4947

Telephone: (281) 342-8602
Fax Number: (832) 595-0814
Type of Business: Chain Restaurant Operator
Total Sales: $33,190,000 (e)
Total Units: 7
Trade Names: McDonald's (7)
Units Franchised From: 7
Preferred Square Footage: 2,500
Primary Menu: Hamburger (7)
Areas of Operation: TX
Type of Foodservice: Quick Serve (7)
Franchise Affiliation: McDonald's Corporation, CHICAGO, IL

Key Personnel
MICHAEL SCHMID - President; Partner; General Buyer
MARK SCHMID - Partner

MSK Enterprises Inc.
5015 FM 723 Rd
Richmond, TX 77406-8707

Telephone: (281) 232-2300
Fax Number: (281) 232-2324
Type of Business: Chain Restaurant Operator
Year Founded: 1992
Total Sales: $39,220,000 (e)
Number of Employees: 915
Average Check: Lunch(8); Dinner(10)
Total Units: 32
Trade Names: Church's Chicken (32)
Units Franchised From: 32
Preferred Square Footage: 2,300
Preferred Location Types: Freestanding
Primary Menu: Chicken (32)
Areas of Operation: AR, TX
Type of Foodservice: Quick Serve (32)
Catering Services: Yes
Franchise Affiliation: Church's Chicken, ATLANTA, GA
Primary Distributors: (Food) Performance Foodservice - Temple, TEMPLE, TX

Key Personnel
MICHAEL KNOBELOCK - President; Partner; General Manager; Director Finance, Facility/Maintenance, Real Estate; General Buyer
PATTY KNOBELOCK - Partner; VP
JJ VILAFRANCA - COO
CARLOS ROMERO - Supervisor Operations

BC Restaurants, Ltd.
15449 Northwest Blvd
Robstown, TX 78380-5927

Telephone: (361) 248-4740
Fax Number: (361) 248-4738
Type of Business: Chain Restaurant Operator
Total Sales: $6,102,000 (e)
Average Check: Dinner(8)
Total Units: 5
Trade Names: Church's Chicken (5)
Units Franchised From: 5
Preferred Square Footage: 1,850
Preferred Location Types: Freestanding
Primary Menu: Chicken (5)
Areas of Operation: TX
Type of Foodservice: Quick Serve (5)
Franchise Affiliation: Church's Chicken, ATLANTA, GA

Key Personnel
JOHN TRASK - CEO; President; General Buyer

Domino's Franchisee
1927 Highway 35 N Ste 1927
Rockport, TX 78382-3344

Telephone: (361) 729-4700
Type of Business: Chain Restaurant Operator
Total Sales: $5,967,000 (e)
Total Units: 3
Trade Names: Domino's (3)
Units Franchised From: 3
Primary Menu: Pizza (3)
Areas of Operation: TX
Type of Foodservice: Quick Serve (3)
Franchise Affiliation: Domino's Pizza Inc, ANN ARBOR, MI

Key Personnel
DAVID E. HENDERSON - Owner; General Buyer

R & D Foods Inc
935 W Ralph Hall Pkwy Ste 101
Rockwall, TX 75032-8707

Telephone: (469) 402-0100
Fax Number: (469) 402-0666
Type of Business: Chain Restaurant Operator
Total Sales: $37,840,000 (e)
Number of Employees: 200
Total Units: 8
Trade Names: McDonald's (8)
Units Franchised From: 8
Preferred Location Types: Freestanding
Primary Menu: Hamburger (8)
Areas of Operation: TX
Type of Foodservice: Quick Serve (8)
Franchise Affiliation: McDonald's Corporation, CHICAGO, IL

Key Personnel
LISA DRIBBEN - Partner

Hammock Restaurants, LLC
1410 Round Rock Ave
Round Rock, TX 78681-4950

Telephone: (512) 246-0343
Internet Homepage: bushschicken.com
Company Email: info@bushschicken.com
Type of Business: Chain Restaurant Operator
Year Founded: 2005
Total Units: 86
Trade Names: Bush's Chicken (86)
Company-Owned Units: 3
Units Franchised To: 83
Preferred Location Types: Freestanding
Primary Menu: Chicken (86)
Projected Openings: 3
Areas of Operation: AZ, TX
Type of Foodservice: Quick Serve (86)
Catering Services: Yes

Key Personnel
JIM HAMMOCK - Chairman
JEFF HAMMOCK - President; General Buyer

HMR Pretzel LLC
4 Ridge Run
Round Rock, TX 78664-9632

Telephone: (512) 716-0342
Type of Business: Chain Restaurant Operator
Total Sales: $8,848,000 (e)
Total Units: 12
Trade Names: Auntie Anne's Hand-Rolled Soft Pretzels (12); Auntie Anne's Hand-Rolled Soft Pretzels/Cinnabon (12)
Units Franchised From: 12
Primary Menu: Snacks (12)

Areas of Operation: TX
Type of Foodservice: Quick Serve (12)
Franchise Affiliation: Auntie Anne's Inc., LANCASTER, PA; Cinnabon Inc., ATLANTA, GA

Key Personnel
STEVEN GRIGSBY - Owner; General Buyer
JONATHAN GRIGSBY - Owner

Stockade Companies LLC
1611 Chisholm Trail Rd
Round Rock, TX 78681

Telephone: (512) 352-5030
Fax Number: (512) 297-2578
Internet Homepage: stockadecompanies.com; sirloinstockade.mx
Company Email: office@stockadecompanies.com
Type of Business: Chain Restaurant Operator
Year Founded: 1984
Systemwide Sales: $16,301,000 (e)
Total Sales: $2,268,000 (e)
Alcohol Sales: 3%
Number of Employees: 60
Average Check: Lunch(24); Dinner(40)
Total Units: 72
Trade Names: Coyote Canyon (1); Montana Mike's (14); Sirloin Stockade (57)
Company-Owned Units: 1
Units Franchised To: 71
Preferred Square Footage: 6,500; 8,300; 10,300
Preferred Location Types: Freestanding
Alcohol Served: Beer, Wine, Liquor
Primary Menu: Steak (72)
Areas of Operation: IA, IL, IN, KS, KY, MO, ND, OK, TX
Foreign Countries: MEXICO
Type of Foodservice: Casual Dining (15); Family Restaurant (57)
Catering Services: Yes
Primary Distributors: (Full Line) McLane/Rocky Mount, ROCKY MOUNT, NC

Key Personnel
DOUG FRIELING - Owner
LEWIS BRYAN - CFO; Senior VP Finance, Operations, Facility/Maintenance, Information Systems, Real Estate, Human Resources, Franchising
RICK PASTOREK - COO
ACE CHANNELL - VP Purchasing, Supply Chain, Menu Development; General Buyer

Soulman's Bar-B-Que
818 E Interstate 30
Royce City, TX 75189

Telephone: (972) 636-0000
Internet Homepage: soulmans.com
Type of Business: Chain Restaurant Operator
Year Founded: 1974
Total Sales: $14,900,000 (e)
Total Units: 17
Trade Names: Soulman's Bar-B-Que (17)
Company-Owned Units: 6
Units Franchised To: 11
Primary Menu: Bar-B-Q (17)
Projected Openings: 2
Areas of Operation: TX
Type of Foodservice: Casual Dining (17)
Notes: Family owned and operated business. Don Randle, Founder; son, Brett Randle CEO; daughter, Amber Polk Catering.

Key Personnel
DON RANDLE - Founder
BRETT RANDLE - CEO; General Buyer
RANDALL MCGEE - COO; VP Franchising
AMBER POLK - Director Catering

Jobren Inc
30 W Beauregard Ave Ste 100
San Angelo, TX 76903-5851

Telephone: (325) 944-3135
Type of Business: Chain Restaurant Operator
Total Sales: $20,578,000 (e)
Number of Employees: 250
Total Units: 4
Trade Names: McDonald's (4)
Units Franchised From: 4
Preferred Square Footage: 2,500
Primary Menu: Hamburger (4)
Areas of Operation: TX
Type of Foodservice: Quick Serve (4)
Franchise Affiliation: McDonald's Corporation, CHICAGO, IL

Key Personnel
ERIC WILSON - President; General Buyer

Acosta Inc.
5815 Callaghan Rd Ste 100
San Antonio, TX 78228-1111

Telephone: (210) 227-5004
Fax Number: (210) 227-1910
Internet Homepage: mcdonaldssa.com
Company Email: mcdonaldssa@satx.rr.com
Type of Business: Chain Restaurant Operator
Total Sales: $182,930,000 (e)
Number of Employees: 1,404
Average Check: Breakfast(8); Lunch(8); Dinner(10)
Total Units: 39
Trade Names: McDonald's (39)
Units Franchised From: 39
Preferred Square Footage: 2,500; 3,000
Preferred Location Types: Convenience Store/Gas Station; Discount Dept. Stores; Freestanding
Primary Menu: Hamburger (39)
Areas of Operation: TX
Type of Foodservice: Quick Serve (39)
Franchise Affiliation: McDonald's Corporation, CHICAGO, IL

Key Personnel
CELIA ACOSTA - Partner; VP
MICHAEL VAN AKEN - Chief Human Resources Officer
TODD JOHNSON - Chief Legal Officer
LISA KOTH - Chief Strategy Officer
JOHN CARROLL - Chief Growth Officer
ASHLEY ROEHM - Chief Sales Officer
DAWN SHIRLEY - VP Operations
DANNY ODOM - VP Operations
SONYA RICHBURG - VP Compliance
PALLABEE BERA - VP; Transformation
CHRISTINE BELL - General Counsel
BEAU HARRIS - Senior Director Sales, West Region
JENNIFER ABEL - Director Customer Analytics
THOMAS KLINKENBERG - Director Customer Analytics
TIM FOLEY - Director Strategy
MELANIE FRANTZ - Director
LUIS ACOSTA - Director Finance
JOE BALL - Director; Transformation Strategy
JOHN CURLETT - Director
AMIT DABHOLKAR - Director Architecture
MANNY RODRIGUEZ - Director Sales
MICHAEL STORTECKY - Director Retail Operations
KATIE LARNEY - Director Research & Development
CHRIS LAURY - Director Digital Marketing
MICHAEL MCSWEGIN - Director Sales
SKIPPER NELSON - Senior Manager
RYAN THAYER - Business Manager
KEVIN EBERWEIN - Business Manager
JASON BIROS - Business Manager
JEREMY BENEDICT - Transformation Strategy

Alamo Cafe
14250 San Pedro Ave
San Antonio, TX 78232-4342

Mailing Address: PO Box 790721, SAN ANTONIO, TX, 78279-0721
Telephone: (210) 341-1336
Internet Homepage: alamocafe.com
Type of Business: Chain Restaurant Operator
Year Founded: 1981
Total Sales: $9,417,000 (e)
Alcohol Sales: 10%
Number of Employees: 300
Average Check: Lunch(12); Dinner(12)
Total Units: 2
Trade Names: Alamo Cafe (2)
Company-Owned Units: 2
Preferred Location Types: Freestanding

Alcohol Served: Beer, Wine, Liquor
Primary Menu: Southwest/Tex-Mex (2)
Areas of Operation: TX
Type of Foodservice: Casual Dining (2)
Catering Services: Yes
Primary Distributors: (Full Line) Labatt Food Service, SAN ANTONIO, TX

Key Personnel
PAT HANLON - President; General Buyer
ROBERT VELASQUEZ - General Manager; Director Foodservice, Menu Development, Food and Beverage; General Buyer
GREG AUSTIN - General Manager

Auntie Anne's Franchise
15900 La Cantera Pkwy Ste 8801
San Antonio, TX 78256-2430

Telephone: (210) 399-1604
Internet Homepage: auntieannes.com
Type of Business: Chain Restaurant Operator
Total Sales: $3,105,000 (e)
Total Units: 4
Trade Names: Auntie Anne's Hand-Rolled Soft Pretzels (4); Cinnabon (4)
Units Franchised From: 4
Primary Menu: Snacks (4)
Areas of Operation: TX
Type of Foodservice: Quick Serve (4)
Franchise Affiliation: Auntie Anne's Inc., LANCASTER, PA

Key Personnel
LISA FULLERTON - Owner; General Buyer

Barreras Entities
12500 Network Blvd Ste 410
San Antonio, TX 78249-3308

Telephone: (210) 499-5309
Fax Number: (210) 499-5307
Type of Business: Chain Restaurant Operator
Year Founded: 1998
Total Sales: $6,034,000 (e)
Number of Employees: 90
Average Check: Breakfast(8); Lunch(14); Dinner(16)
Total Units: 3
Trade Names: Denny's (1); Wiener Schnitzel (2)
Units Franchised From: 3
Preferred Square Footage: 3,000; 5,000
Preferred Location Types: Freestanding
Primary Menu: American (1); Hot Dogs (2)
Areas of Operation: TX
Type of Foodservice: Family Restaurant (1); Quick Serve (2)
Franchise Affiliation: Denny's Corporation, SPARTANBURG, SC
Primary Distributors: (Food) McLane/Fort Worth, FORT WORTH, TX

Key Personnel
JUDITH BARRERAS - President; General Buyer

Biglari Holdings Inc.
17802 W Interstate 10 Ste 400
San Antonio, TX 78257-2509

Telephone: (210) 344-3400
Internet Homepage: biglariholdings.com
Listing Type: Corporate Office
Type of Business: Chain Restaurant Operator
Publicly Held: Yes
Total Sales: $532,085,000 (e)
Number of Employees: 10,906
Total Units: 492
Trade Names: Steak 'n Shake (457); WesterN SizzliN Steak & More (35)
Company-Owned Units: 364
Units Franchised To: 128
Primary Menu: Hamburger (457); Steak (35)
Areas of Operation: AL, AR, AZ, CA, CO, FL, GA, IA, IL, IN, KS, KY, LA, MD, MI, MO, MS, MT, NC, NJ, NV, NY, OH, OK, PA, SC, TN, TX, VA, WV
Foreign Countries: FRANCE; SPAIN; UNITED ARAB EMIRATES
Type of Foodservice: Family Restaurant (492)
Headquarter Offices: The Steak n Shake Operations Inc., INDIANAPOLIS, IN; The Western Sizzlin Corp., ROANOKE, VA
Notes: Total sales reflects restaurant operations only and excludes revenue derived from investment management.

Key Personnel
SARDAR BIGLARI - Chairman; CEO; President
PHILIP L. COOLEY - Vice Chairman
BRUCE LEWIS - Controller
KRISTIN TREDEMEYER - Director Tax
KELLY PETERSON - Manager Restaurant Operations
SARAH KING - Manager Accounting

Bill Miller Bar-B-Q Enterprise LTD
430 S Santa Rosa
San Antonio, TX 78207-4551

Mailing Address: PO Box 839925, SAN ANTONIO, TX, 78283-3925
Telephone: (210) 225-4461
Fax Number: (210) 302-1533
Internet Homepage: lagunamadreseafood.com; billmillerbbq.com
Company Email: hq@billmillerbbq.com
Type of Business: Chain Restaurant Operator
Year Founded: 1953
Total Sales: $108,500,000 (e)
Number of Employees: 4,212
Average Check: Breakfast(5); Lunch(8); Dinner(8)
Internet Order Processing: Yes
Total Units: 81
Trade Names: Bill Miller Bar-B-Q (75); Bill Miller's Laguna Madre Seafood Company (6)
Company-Owned Units: 81
Preferred Square Footage: 4,000
Preferred Location Types: Freestanding
Primary Menu: Bar-B-Q (75); Seafood (6)
Projected Openings: 3
Areas of Operation: TX
Type of Foodservice: Family Restaurant (81)
Catering Services: Yes
On-site Distribution Center: Yes

Key Personnel
JIM GUY EGBERT - CEO; President
BARBARA NEWMAN - Treasurer; Director Finance, Information Systems

C-Ck's , Inc.
1819 S New Braunfels Ave
San Antonio, TX 78210-3013

Mailing Address: PO Box 8335, SAN ANTONIO, TX, 78208-0335
Telephone: (210) 534-9200
Type of Business: Chain Restaurant Operator
Total Sales: $19,830,000 (e)
Total Units: 4
Trade Names: McDonald's (4)
Units Franchised From: 4
Preferred Location Types: Freestanding
Primary Menu: Hamburger (4)
Projected Remodelings: 1
Areas of Operation: TX
Type of Foodservice: Quick Serve (4)
Franchise Affiliation: McDonald's Corporation, CHICAGO, IL

Key Personnel
KATHERINE SHIELDS - President; General Buyer

Canteen Vending Services
3410 Steen St
San Antonio, TX 78219-2332

Telephone: (210) 658-7419
Fax Number: (210) 658-1638
Listing Type: Branch Office
Type of Business: Foodservice Management Operator
Year Founded: 1929
Number of Employees: 18
Number of Locations Served: 130
Total Foodservice Mgmt Accounts: 130
Areas of Operation: TX
Type of Foodservice: Vending machines (130)

Foodservice Management Venues: Business & Industry; College & University; Health Care; Schools; Travel Plazas
Parent Company: Compass Group The Americas, CHARLOTTE, NC
Headquarters: Canteen Vending Services, CHARLOTTE, NC

Key Personnel
AARON PENA - District Manager

Casa Rio Mexican Foods
430 E Commerce St
San Antonio, TX 78205-2629

Telephone: (210) 229-1646
Fax Number: (210) 225-2216
Internet Homepage: schilos.com; casa-rio.com
Company Email: info@casa-rio.com
Type of Business: Chain Restaurant Operator
Year Founded: 1946
Total Sales: $10,582,000 (e)
Alcohol Sales: 25%
Number of Employees: 125
Average Check: Breakfast(10); Lunch(14); Dinner(18)
Total Units: 2
Trade Names: Casa Rio Mexican Foods (1); Schilo's (1)
Company-Owned Units: 2
Preferred Location Types: Other
Alcohol Served: Beer, Wine, Liquor
Primary Menu: German (1); Mexican (1)
Areas of Operation: TX
Type of Foodservice: Casual Dining (2)
Primary Distributors: (Food) SYSCO Central Texas Inc., NEW BRAUNFELS, TX

Key Personnel
WILLIAM J. LYONS - President
TERESA AKKOLA - CFO
FRANK MUNOZ - Manager; General Buyer

Curmac Inc
11000 NE Loop 410
San Antonio, TX 78209

Telephone: (210) 930-4674
Fax Number: (210) 930-3743
Type of Business: Chain Restaurant Operator
Total Sales: $34,580,000 (e)
Total Units: 16
Trade Names: Sonic America's Drive-In (16)
Units Franchised From: 16
Primary Menu: Hamburger (16)
Areas of Operation: TX
Type of Foodservice: Quick Serve (16)
Franchise Affiliation: Sonic Corp., OKLAHOMA CITY, OK

Key Personnel
TOM CURTIS - President; General Buyer

Den-Tex Central Inc.
5839 Sebastian Pl Ste 102
San Antonio, TX 78249-2262

Mailing Address: PO Box 690730, SAN ANTONIO, TX, 78269-0730
Telephone: (210) 694-0707
Fax Number: (210) 694-0400
Type of Business: Chain Restaurant Operator
Year Founded: 1986
Total Sales: $170,670,000 (e)
Number of Employees: 1,886
Average Check: Breakfast(8); Lunch(10); Dinner(12)
Total Units: 82
Trade Names: Denny's (81); Judy's Cookhouse (1)
Company-Owned Units: 1
Units Franchised From: 81
Preferred Square Footage: 9,000; 17,000
Preferred Location Types: Freestanding; Strip Mall
Primary Menu: American (82)
Areas of Operation: AR, IL, KS, MO, OK, TX
Type of Foodservice: Family Restaurant (82)
Franchise Affiliation: Denny's Corporation, SPARTANBURG, SC
Primary Distributors: (Full Line) McLane/Fort Worth, FORT WORTH, TX

Key Personnel
DAWN LAFREEDA - CEO; President; Director Real Estate
LORI MACKAY - CFO; Controller; Director Finance, Purchasing
LUPITA CORBEIL - VP Human Resources
HOLLY PIETZ - Director Operations, Facility/Maintenance, Security, Inventory, Loss Prevention, Risk Management, Quality Assurance, Training, Menu Development, Food Safety; General Buyer

Dough Nation Headquarters LLC
4 Dominion Dr Ste 200
San Antonio, TX 78257

Telephone: (210) 495-6666
Internet Homepage: urbanbrickspizza.com
Company Email: customerservice@urbanbrickspizza.com
Type of Business: Chain Restaurant Operator
Year Founded: 2015
Total Units: 17
Trade Names: Urban Bricks Pizza (17)
Company-Owned Units: 1
Units Franchised To: 16
Preferred Location Types: Institution (college/hospital); Strip Mall
Primary Menu: Pizza (17)
Projected Openings: 8
Areas of Operation: CO, FL, IL, KY, NC, TX, ON
Foreign Countries: CANADA
Type of Foodservice: Fast Casual (17)

Key Personnel
SAMMY ALDEEB - Founder; CEO; Owner
ASHLEY VILLARREAL - Director Marketing
CARLA HOLT - Manager Training
PAUL LOOTS - Manager Construction, Design

Earth Burger
818 NW Loop 410
San Antonio, TX 78216

Telephone: (210) 524-1086
Internet Homepage: eatearthburger.com
Type of Business: Chain Restaurant Operator
Year Founded: 2014
Total Sales: $6,215,000 (e)
Total Units: 3
Trade Names: Earth Burger (3)
Company-Owned Units: 3
Primary Menu: American (3)
Areas of Operation: TX
Type of Foodservice: Fast Casual (3)

Key Personnel
MIKE BEHREND - Owner

Fred's Fish Fry Inc.
1621 Somerset Rd
San Antonio, TX 78211-3043

Telephone: (210) 924-5679
Fax Number: (210) 923-1291
Company Email: fredsfish@att.net
Type of Business: Chain Restaurant Operator
Year Founded: 1991
Total Sales: $17,210,000 (e)
Number of Employees: 450
Average Check: Lunch(14); Dinner(16)
Total Units: 16
Trade Names: Fred's Fish Fry (16)
Company-Owned Units: 16
Preferred Square Footage: 2,500
Preferred Location Types: Freestanding
Primary Menu: Seafood (16)
Areas of Operation: TX
Type of Foodservice: Quick Serve (16)

Key Personnel
ALFRED CASTELLANO JR - Owner; General Manager

Frontier Enterprises
8520 Crownhill Blvd
San Antonio, TX 78209-1119

Telephone: (210) 828-1493
Fax Number: (210) 822-8606
Internet Homepage: jimsrestaurants.com; magictimemachine.com
Company Email: info@jimsrestaurants.com
Type of Business: Chain Restaurant Operator
Year Founded: 1948
Total Sales: $56,160,000 (e)
Alcohol Sales: 1%
Number of Employees: 1,080
Average Check: Breakfast(10); Lunch(10); Dinner(10)
Internet Order Processing: Yes
Total Units: 20
Trade Names: Jim's Coffee Shop (18); Magic Time Machines (2)
Company-Owned Units: 20
Preferred Square Footage: 4,500; 5,000
Preferred Location Types: Freestanding; Office Complex; Strip Mall
Alcohol Served: Beer, Wine, Liquor
Primary Menu: American (20)
Areas of Operation: TX
Type of Foodservice: Casual Dining (18); Fine Dining (2)
Primary Distributors: (Full Line) SYSCO Corporation, HOUSTON, TX
Parent Company: Hasslocher Enterprises, SAN ANTONIO, TX

Key Personnel
JAMES RIEMENSCHNEIDER - CEO
RICHARD OPPELT - General Manager Restaurant Operations
JEFF MORROW - Director Operations
VICTOR ABREGO - Director Employee Development
GARY JOHNSON - Director Operations
SAM ECKE - Associate Manager
DON HOHENSEE - Specialist Payroll
MARY FOWLER - Coordinator Benefits

Haljohn San Antonio Inc.
7300 Blanco Rd Ste 302
San Antonio, TX 78216-4939

Telephone: (210) 344-9707
Fax Number: (210) 349-4820
Type of Business: Chain Restaurant Operator
Year Founded: 1963
Total Sales: $94,260,000 (e)
Number of Employees: 668
Average Check: Breakfast(5); Lunch(8); Dinner(8)
Total Units: 20
Trade Names: McDonald's (20)
Units Franchised From: 20
Preferred Square Footage: 2,500
Preferred Location Types: Freestanding
Primary Menu: Hamburger (20)
Areas of Operation: TX
Type of Foodservice: Quick Serve (20)
Franchise Affiliation: McDonald's Corporation, CHICAGO, IL
Primary Distributors: (Full Line) The Martin-Brower Co., CONROE, TX

Key Personnel
JOHN V. BOHLING - President
TOM LIBBEY - Director Operations, Purchasing, Supply Chain
WANDA LIBBEY - Director Marketing
JIMMY SANCHEZ - Director Operations

Jubile Holdings JM
7970 Fredericksburg Rd Ste 102
San Antonio, TX 78229-3891

Telephone: (210) 254-9618
Type of Business: Chain Restaurant Operator
Total Sales: $6,925,000 (e)
Total Units: 5
Trade Names: Jersey Mike's Subs (5)
Units Franchised From: 5
Primary Menu: Sandwiches/Deli (5)
Areas of Operation: TX
Type of Foodservice: Quick Serve (5)
Franchise Affiliation: Jersey Mike's Franchise Systems, MANASQUAN, NJ

Key Personnel
DEREK MURPH - Partner; General Buyer
MICHELLE MURPH - Partner

Kirby's Prime Steakhouse
123 N Loop 1604 E
San Antonio, TX 78232

Telephone: (210) 404-2221
Fax Number: (210) 404-2225
Internet Homepage: kirbyssteakhouse.com
Company Email: sanantonio@kirbyssteakhouse.com
Type of Business: Chain Restaurant Operator
Year Founded: 1954
Total Units: 5
Trade Names: Kirby's Prime Steakhouse (4); Mickey Mantle's Steakhouse (1)
Company-Owned Units: 5
Preferred Location Types: Downtown; Freestanding; Hotel/Motel
Primary Menu: Steak (5)
Areas of Operation: OK, TX
Type of Foodservice: Fine Dining (5)

Key Personnel
MONTE HOUGH - Partner
CLARENCE ALEXANDER - Corporate Chef

La Familia Cortez Restaurants
800 Dolorosa Ste 204
San Antonio, TX 78207-4561

Telephone: (210) 225-3955
Fax Number: (210) 222-8566
Internet Homepage: lafamiliacortez.com; lamargarita.com; mitierracafe.com; picodegallo.com; vivavillatacos.com
Company Email: info@mitierracafe.com
Type of Business: Chain Restaurant Operator
Total Sales: $15,020,000 (e)
Alcohol Sales: 12%
Internet Order Processing: Yes
Total Units: 5
Trade Names: La Margarita Restaurant and Oyster Bar (1); Mi Familia (1); Mi Tierra Cafe (1); Pico de Gallo (1); Viva Villa (1)
Company-Owned Units: 5
Alcohol Served: Beer, Wine, Liquor
Primary Menu: Mexican (5)
Areas of Operation: TX
Type of Foodservice: Casual Dining (4); Fine Dining (1)

Key Personnel
JORGE CORTEZ - Partner; General Buyer
DAVID CORTEZ - Partner
RUBEN CORTEZ - Partner
ROSA LINDA CORTEZ - Partner
MANUEL MORENO - General Manager
CARINO CORTEZ - Executive Chef; Project Manager
MARIA TIJERINA - Director Human Resources
BIANCA PELAYO - Coordinator Human Resources

Las Palapas
503 Med Ct
San Antonio, TX 78258

Telephone: (210) 471-2101
Internet Homepage: laspalapas.com
Type of Business: Chain Restaurant Operator
Year Founded: 1981
Total Sales: $29,590,000 (e)
Trade Names: Las Palapas (21)
Company-Owned Units: 21
Primary Menu: Mexican (21)
Areas of Operation: TX
Type of Foodservice: Fast Casual (21)

Key Personnel
RON ACOSTA - CEO; Owner

Leon Springs Gas Ltd.
24152 W Interstate 10
San Antonio, TX 78257-1156

Telephone: (210) 698-2840
Fax Number: (210) 698-0995
Internet Homepage: rudysbbq.com
Type of Business: Chain Restaurant Operator
Year Founded: 1987
Total Sales: $24,610,000 (e)
Alcohol Sales: 2%
Number of Employees: 100
Average Check: Lunch(10); Dinner(10)
Total Units: 49
Trade Names: The Original Rudy's Country Store & BBQ (49)
Company-Owned Units: 49
Preferred Location Types: Freestanding
Alcohol Served: Beer
Primary Menu: Bar-B-Q (49)
Areas of Operation: AZ, CO, NM, OK, TX
Type of Foodservice: Casual Dining (45); Fast Casual (49)
Catering Services: Yes
Primary Distributors: (Food) SYSCO Central Texas Inc., NEW BRAUNFELS, TX
Parent Company: Leon Springs Gas Co., SAN ANTONIO, TX

Key Personnel
RICH LUDERS - CEO
MIKE BARKER - President; General Manager; Executive Chef; Director Catering; General Buyer
TIM LOUTON - Exec VP
RANDY KENNA - Director Operations
LAUREN TRAHAN - Director Franchise Operations

Longhorn Cafe
17625 Blanco Rd
San Antonio, TX 78232

Telephone: (210) 492-0301
Internet Homepage: thelonghorncafe.com
Type of Business: Chain Restaurant Operator
Year Founded: 1995
Total Units: 8
Trade Names: Longhorn Cafe (8)
Company-Owned Units: 8
Primary Menu: American (8)
Areas of Operation: TX
Type of Foodservice: Casual Dining (8)

Key Personnel
PAUL WEIR - Partner; General Buyer
DAVID WYNN - Partner

Los Barrios Mexican Restaurant
4223 Blanco Rd
San Antonio, TX 78212-1107

Telephone: (210) 732-6017
Fax Number: (210) 732-9720
Internet Homepage: lahaciendabarrios.com; losbarrios1.com; violasventanas.com
Company Email: manager@losbarrios1.com
Type of Business: Chain Restaurant Operator
Total Sales: $5,134,000 (e)
Number of Employees: 95
Average Check: Breakfast(10); Lunch(12); Dinner(22)
Total Units: 3
Trade Names: La Hacienda De Los Barrios (1); Los Barrios Mexican Restaurant (1); Viola's Ventanas (1)
Company-Owned Units: 3
Preferred Square Footage: 4,500
Preferred Location Types: Freestanding
Alcohol Served: Beer, Wine, Liquor
Primary Menu: Mexican (3)
Areas of Operation: TX
Type of Foodservice: Casual Dining (3)
Catering Services: Yes
Primary Distributors: (Full Line) Labatt Food Service, SAN ANTONIO, TX

Key Personnel
LOUIS BARRIOS - CEO; President; Executive Chef
JOSH RILEY - VP Operations; General Manager
ROLAND TREVINO - Director Operations; General Buyer
DIANA BARRIOS - Director Menu Development

Luciano Management
1870 W Bitters Rd Ste 101
San Antonio, TX 78248-1827

Telephone: (210) 349-9404
Fax Number: (210) 349-3972
Internet Homepage: lucianorestaurants.com
Company Email: info@lucianorestaurants.com
Type of Business: Chain Restaurant Operator
Year Founded: 1973
Total Sales: $23,290,000 (e)
Alcohol Sales: 10%
Number of Employees: 300
Average Check: Breakfast(5); Lunch(22); Dinner(40)
Total Units: 15
Trade Names: Luciano Express (12); Luciano Family Pizzeria (1); Luciano Neighborhood Pizzeria (2)
Company-Owned Units: 15
Preferred Square Footage: 700; 4,000
Preferred Location Types: Community Mall; Freestanding; Regional Mall
Alcohol Served: Beer, Wine, Liquor
Primary Menu: Italian (12); Pizza (3)
Areas of Operation: NC, OK, TX, FC
Foreign Countries: MEXICO
Type of Foodservice: Casual Dining (3); Fast Casual (12)
Catering Services: Yes
Primary Distributors: (Full Line) SYSCO Corporation, HOUSTON, TX

Key Personnel
GENNARO CENTOFANTI - CEO; President; CFO
LUCIANO CENTOFANTI - VP; Controller; Director Purchasing, Facility/Maintenance, Marketing, Ethnic Marketing, Design
RANDY HOLLINSHEAD - Controller
SALVATORE CENTOFANTI - Executive Chef; Director Operations, Information Systems, Loss Prevention, Real Estate, Human Resources, Catering; General Buyer
DANIELA AVILAS - Director Marketing

Newton Associates Inc
1009 Austin Hwy
San Antonio, TX 78209-4729

Telephone: (210) 826-9507
Type of Business: Chain Restaurant Operator
Total Sales: $44,827,000 (e)
Number of Employees: 840
Average Check: Lunch(10); Dinner(16)
Total Units: 34
Trade Names: Pizza Hut (34)
Units Franchised From: 34
Preferred Square Footage: 1,400; 4,500
Preferred Location Types: Freestanding; Strip Mall
Alcohol Served: Beer
Primary Menu: Pizza (34)
Areas of Operation: TX
Type of Foodservice: Casual Dining (29); Quick Serve (5)
Franchise Affiliation: Pizza Hut Inc., PLANO, TX

Key Personnel
LAURA GRAVES - VP; General Buyer
GREG WALRAFEN - Manager Accounting

Paesano Di San Antonio Inc.
1121 Patricia
San Antonio, TX 78213-1332

Telephone: (210) 828-4525
Fax Number: (210) 828-6329
Internet Homepage: riorioriverwalk.com; paesanos1604.com
Type of Business: Chain Restaurant Operator
Year Founded: 1969
Total Sales: $18,173,000 (e)

Alcohol Sales: 30%
Number of Employees: 295
Average Check: Breakfast(14); Lunch(18); Dinner(24)
Internet Order Processing: Yes
Internet Sales: 2.00%
Total Units: 4
Trade Names: Paesanos 1604 (1); Paesanos Lincoln Heights (1); Paesanos River Walk (1); Rio Rio Cantina (1)
Company-Owned Units: 4
Preferred Square Footage: 9,000
Preferred Location Types: Freestanding
Alcohol Served: Beer, Wine, Liquor
Primary Menu: Italian (3); Mexican (1)
Areas of Operation: TX
Type of Foodservice: Casual Dining (4)
Catering Services: Yes
Primary Distributors: (Full Line) Ben E. Keith Foods, FORT WORTH, TX

Key Personnel
PATRICK JENNINGS - VP; Controller; Manager Information Systems, Risk Management, Marketing, Human Resources
TIMOTHY BIEKER - General Manager
LINDA ALDERSON - Manager Human Resources

River Sub Ltd
2124 Jackson Keller Rd
San Antonio, TX 78213-2722

Telephone: (210) 375-2412
Type of Business: Chain Restaurant Operator
Total Units: 13
Trade Names: Subway (13)
Units Franchised From: 13
Primary Menu: Sandwiches/Deli (13)
Areas of Operation: TX
Type of Foodservice: Quick Serve (13)
Franchise Affiliation: Doctor's Associates Inc., MILFORD, CT

Key Personnel
PAT PATEL - President; General Buyer
LYDIA RIVERSUB - Director Operations

Rivera Dairy Queen
600 Fair Ave
San Antonio, TX 78223-1304

Mailing Address: PO Box 157, CONVERSE, TX, 78109-0157
Telephone: (210) 532-4030
Type of Business: Chain Restaurant Operator
Total Sales: $7,028,000 (e)
Average Check: Dinner(14)
Total Units: 5
Trade Names: Dairy Queen (5)
Units Franchised From: 5

Primary Menu: Snacks (5)
Areas of Operation: TX
Type of Foodservice: Quick Serve (5)
Franchise Affiliation: International Dairy Queen Inc., BLOOMINGTON, MN

Key Personnel
ROSA RIVERA - President; General Buyer

Sea Island Shrimp House
10010 San Pedro Ave Ste E
San Antonio, TX 78216-3862

Telephone: (210) 342-2800
Fax Number: (210) 348-0199
Internet Homepage: shrimphouse.com
Company Email: contactus@shrimphouse.com
Type of Business: Chain Restaurant Operator
Year Founded: 1965
Total Sales: $35,530,000 (e)
Alcohol Sales: 5%
Number of Employees: 20
Average Check: Lunch(12); Dinner(24)
Internet Order Processing: Yes
Total Units: 7
Trade Names: Sea Island Shrimp House (7)
Company-Owned Units: 7
Preferred Square Footage: 6,500
Preferred Location Types: Freestanding
Alcohol Served: Beer, Wine
Primary Menu: Seafood (7)
Areas of Operation: TX
Type of Foodservice: Casual Dining (7)

Key Personnel
CHRISSY ANTHONY - Founder
BARCLAY ANTHONY - CEO; President; Partner
CURT WINKLER - Partner
MIKE MILHOLN - Area Director
ROBERT GORMLEY - General Manager
STEVE PARMA - Director Human Resources
MEAGAN VINCENT - Director Marketing
VINCENT ALVARADO - Director Accounting
KACY SUMRALL - Director Purchasing
DEDORAH GUERRERO - Business Manager Accounting
SIMMONS ALLISON - Area Manager
MIKE MILLHOLLEN - Manager Area
DENNIS VASQUEZ - Manager Training

Selrico Services Inc.
717 W Ashby Pl
San Antonio, TX 78212-3808

Telephone: (210) 737-8220
Fax Number: (210) 737-7994
Internet Homepage: selricoservices.com
Company Email: info@selricoservices.com
Type of Business: Foodservice Management Operator
Year Founded: 1989

Total Sales: $50,499,000 (e)
Number of Employees: 1,000
Number of Locations Served: 26
Total Foodservice Mgmt Accounts: 26
Areas of Operation: TX
Type of Foodservice: Cafeteria; Mobile units/kiosks; Vending machines
Foodservice Management Venues: Business & Industry; College & University; Military Feeding; Other; Prison Feeding
Primary Distributors: (Full Line) SYSCO Central Texas Inc., NEW BRAUNFELS, TX

Key Personnel
JOHN R. ALEMAN - CEO; President; Owner
RICK ALEMAN - President
DEEDEE MARTINHO - Director Human Resources

St. Juste Management Corp.
11911 Warfield St
San Antonio, TX 78216-3216

Telephone: (210) 366-9900
Fax Number: (210) 366-9901
Type of Business: Chain Restaurant Operator
Year Founded: 1990
Total Sales: $22,050,000 (e)
Number of Employees: 160
Average Check: Breakfast(10); Lunch(10); Dinner(10)
Total Units: 10
Trade Names: Burger King (10)
Units Franchised From: 10
Preferred Square Footage: 8,000
Preferred Location Types: Freestanding
Primary Menu: Hamburger (10)
Areas of Operation: TX
Type of Foodservice: Quick Serve (10)
Franchise Affiliation: Burger King Worldwide Inc., MIAMI, FL
Primary Distributors: (Food) The SYGMA Network Inc.- San Antonio, SAN ANTONIO, TX

Key Personnel
ROBESPIERRE ST. JUSTE - President; General Manager; General Buyer
LAURA GLANCY - Project Manager

Stagg Restaurant Partnership
8507 Speedway Dr
San Antonio, TX 78230-5330

Telephone: (210) 375-7100
Fax Number: (210) 375-7109
Company Email: office@staggrp.com
Type of Business: Chain Restaurant Operator
Year Founded: 1993

Total Sales: $161,710,000 (e)
Number of Employees: 1,300
Average Check: Breakfast(8); Lunch(8); Dinner(10)
Total Units: 34
Trade Names: McDonald's (34)
Units Franchised From: 34
Preferred Square Footage: 2,500; 3,000
Preferred Location Types: Community Mall; Discount Dept. Stores; Freestanding
Primary Menu: Hamburger (34)
Areas of Operation: TX
Type of Foodservice: Quick Serve (34)
Franchise Affiliation: McDonald's Corporation, CHICAGO, IL
Primary Distributors: (Food) The Martin-Brower Co., CONROE, TX

Key Personnel
NEDRICK STAGG - President; General Manager; General Buyer
REBECCA CALDERON - Administrator Payroll

Sushi Zushi Inc
4730 Shavano Oak Ste 201
San Antonio, TX 78249-4029

Telephone: (210) 492-5100
Fax Number: (210) 492-5104
Internet Homepage: sushizushi.com
Company Email: comments@sushizushi.com
Type of Business: Chain Restaurant Operator
Total Sales: $6,479,000 (e)
Alcohol Sales: 5%
Number of Employees: 400
Average Check: Lunch(16); Dinner(20)
Internet Order Processing: Yes
Total Units: 7
Trade Names: Sushi Zushi (7)
Company-Owned Units: 7
Preferred Location Types: Downtown; Strip Mall
Alcohol Served: Beer, Wine, Liquor
Primary Menu: Japanese (7)
Projected Openings: 1
Areas of Operation: TX
Type of Foodservice: Casual Dining (7)
Catering Services: Yes
Parent Company: VitaNova Brands, SAN ANTONIO, TX

Key Personnel
AL TOMITA - CEO; President; Owner; General Manager; General Buyer

Taco Cabana Inc.
1077 Central Pkwy S Ste 600
San Antonio, TX 78232

Telephone: (210) 804-0990
Fax Number: (210) 804-1970
Internet Homepage: tacocabana.com
Company Email: info@tacocabana.com
Type of Business: Chain Restaurant Operator
Year Founded: 1978
Systemwide Sales: $403,212,000 (e)
Total Sales: $386,190,000 (e)
Alcohol Sales: 2%
Number of Employees: 4,500
Average Check: Breakfast(6); Lunch(10); Dinner(10)
Internet Order Processing: Yes
Internet Sales: 1.00%
Total Units: 141
Trade Names: Taco Cabana (141)
Company-Owned Units: 135
Units Franchised To: 6
Preferred Square Footage: 3,200
Preferred Location Types: Freestanding; Regional Mall
Alcohol Served: Beer, Liquor
Primary Menu: Mexican (141)
Projected Openings: 2
Areas of Operation: NM, TX
Type of Foodservice: Fast Casual (141)
Catering Services: Yes
Primary Distributors: (Food) Performance Food Group, RICHMOND, VA
Parent Company: Yadav Enterprises, Inc., FREMONT, CA

Key Personnel
DEAN KIMBALL - CIO
TONY DINKINS - Senior VP Human Resources
LOUIS DIPIETRO - Senior VP Gaming/Entertainment
SANDY SALINAS - VP Strategy, Communications
ROBERTO LOPEZ - VP Culinary Development
ULYSES CAMACHO - VP Operations
MARK CRAMER - Senior Director Real Estate Development, Construction
MARK FISHER - Director Human Resources
FRANK SOLIS - Director Marketing
DEBORAH HOOD - Director Development, Training
ARMANDO FLORES - Director Procurement
JOHN RAMSAY - Director Franchise Development, Franchise Sales
MIKE VELA - Regional Director Operations
BEN BOYD - Regional Director
RAYMOND COMBE - District Manager
RYAN HAWTHORNE - Manager Talent
REGINA HAYNES - Manager Accounting

The Art Institute of San Antonio
10000 W Interstate 10 Ste 200
San Antonio, TX 78230-2242

Telephone: (210) 338-7320
Fax Number: (210) 338-7321
Internet Homepage: artinstitutes.edu/san-antonio
Type of Business: Culinary Schools
Areas of Operation: TX

Key Personnel
JEMENTE L. - Assistant Director Administration

Triple M Industries
7035 Bandera Rd
San Antonio, TX 78238-1266

Telephone: (210) 520-8086
Type of Business: Chain Restaurant Operator
Total Units: 12
Trade Names: Subway (12)
Units Franchised From: 12
Primary Menu: Sandwiches/Deli (12)
Areas of Operation: TX
Type of Foodservice: Quick Serve (12)
Franchise Affiliation: Doctor's Associates Inc., MILFORD, CT

Key Personnel
MICHAEL MCCOY - President; General Buyer

VitaNova Brands
2338 N Loop 1604 W #350
San Antonio, TX 78248

Telephone: (210) 403-3725
Internet Homepage: vitanovabrands.com
Listing Type: Corporate Office
Type of Business: Chain Restaurant Operator
Total Sales: $32,776,000 (e)
Total Units: 96
Trade Names: Furr's Marketplace (16); HomeTown AYCE Marketplace (28); Old Country AYCE Marketplace (18); Ryan's AYCE Marketplace (15); Sushi Zushi (8); Zio's Italian Kitchen (11)
Company-Owned Units: 96
Headquarter Offices: Sushi Zushi Inc, SAN ANTONIO, TX

Key Personnel
DANIEL GARGARO - Executive Chef; Manager Development

Whataburger Restaurants LLC
300 Concord Plaza Dr
San Antonio, TX 78216-6903

Mailing Address: PO Box 791990, San Antonio, TX, 78279
Telephone: (210) 476-6000
Fax Number: (210) 476-6973
Internet Homepage: whataburger.com
Type of Business: Chain Restaurant Operator

Year Founded: 1950
Systemwide Sales: $4,222,693,000 (e)
Total Sales: $3,570,581,000 (e)
Number of Employees: 27,000
Average Check: Lunch(8); Dinner(8)
Internet Order Processing: Yes
Internet Sales: 0.50%
Total Units: 1,043
Trade Names: Whataburger (1,043)
Company-Owned Units: 832
Units Franchised To: 211
Preferred Square Footage: 1,800; 3,400
Preferred Location Types: Community Mall; Convenience Store/Gas Station; Freestanding; Regional Mall; Stadiums
Primary Menu: Hamburger (1,043)
Projected Openings: 3
Areas of Operation: AL, AR, AZ, FL, GA, LA, MS, NM, OK, TX
Type of Foodservice: Quick Serve (1,043)
Primary Distributors: (Full Line) The SYGMA Network Inc.- San Antonio, SAN ANTONIO, TX
Parent Company: BDT Capital Partners, CHICAGO, IL
Regional Offices: Whataburger Inc., IRVING, TX

Key Personnel
TOM DOBSON - Chairman
ED NELSON - CEO; President
JANELLE SYKES - CFO
LEONARD MAZZOCCO - COO; Senior VP
DEBBIE STROUD - COO; Exec VP
JOE SHANNON - CIO
JAMES TURCOTTE - Chief Development Officer; Senior VP Real Estate
ELENA KRAUS - Chief Legal Officer; Exec VP
TODD HUETINCK - Chief Supply Chain Officer
PAM COX - VP Communications, Human Resources
MAZZOCCO LEONARD - VP Operations
ALEXANDER IVANNIKOV - VP Supply Chain
VICTOR CASTILLO - Treasurer
SANDY WERENSKJOLD - Director Finance
MARK FEENEY - Director Digital, Strategic Planning
JEFF AIMONE - Director Strategy, Human Resources
TROY MEYER - Director Information Technology, Infrastructure
T. ALEXANDER DUNN - Director Talent Training
JAMEY MOLSBEE - Director Enterprise Solutions
JOE JAYNES - Director Real Estate
CHARLES SCUETZ - Director Infrastructure
KAREN ALEX - Director Human Resources
DAVID BLADEL - Director Operations
JERRY PHILLIPS - Director Technology, Digital
SCOTT PHILLIPS - Director Operations
JOHN MCLELLAN - Director Digital Experience, Customer Loyalty
BROOKS BOENIG - Director Marketing, Advertising, Media
PETE VALADEZ - Director
ANDY DOSS - Director
MICHAEL MILLER - Director Operations
THEODORE PAYNE - Director Strategic Planning
TOM WILLET - Director Operations
CHRIS SZEMAN - Senior Manager Digital Marketing
TRESA WELLS - Senior Manager Design
JUSTIN STRICKLAND - Business Manager; Manager Real Estate
NICKI KELLER - Division Manager Talent Acquisitions
CHRIS POWELL - Regional Manager Marketing
MARCELA CORREA - Manager Marketing
JOY PAUL - Manager
AMANDA ROMEU - Manager Marketing, Innovation
MEGAN WATSON - Manager
PETER MAZZOCCO - Manager Distribution
JILL BAYS - Manager Field Marketing
ALYSSA FRASER - Manager Finance
DARREN LABRUZZO - Manager Logistics
REBECCA RODRIGUEZ - Manager Marketing
CAITLYN CAMERON - Manager New Store Development
THAYS FERNANDES - Coordinator Field Marketing
MONIKA HAMM - Designer
JEFFREY YOUNG - Analyst Customer Service
MARCO MUNIZ - Developer
ANDREW COULS - Senior Engineer

Liepman Restaurants Inc.
PO Box 770
San Augustine, TX 75972-0770

Telephone: (903) 277-7226
Type of Business: Chain Restaurant Operator
Total Sales: $23,810,000 (e)
Number of Employees: 400
Total Units: 17
Trade Names: Dairy Queen (2); Dairy Queen Brazier (7); DQ Grill & Chill (8)
Units Franchised From: 17
Preferred Location Types: Freestanding
Primary Menu: American (17)
Areas of Operation: AR, LA, OK, TX
Type of Foodservice: Quick Serve (17)
Franchise Affiliation: International Dairy Queen Inc., BLOOMINGTON, MN

Key Personnel
MARK LIEPMAN - Owner; General Buyer
LORIE MCCULLOUGH - Director Food and Beverage

Texas Subs Inc
202 University Dr Ste A
San Marcos, TX 78666-5754

Telephone: (512) 353-7500
Internet Homepage: texassubs.com
Type of Business: Chain Restaurant Operator
Total Sales: $39,390,000 (e)
Average Check: Dinner(12)
Total Units: 61
Trade Names: Mooyah (1); Subway (60)
Units Franchised From: 61
Primary Menu: Hamburger (1); Sandwiches/Deli (60)
Areas of Operation: TX
Type of Foodservice: Quick Serve (60)
Franchise Affiliation: Doctor's Associates Inc., MILFORD, CT

Key Personnel
SHANE FRASIER - President; General Buyer
ERICA JOSLEN - CFO
MICHAEL EBERS - COO

Mcclanahan Management Inc
601 E Sinton St
Sinton, TX 78387-2801

Mailing Address: PO Box 1076, SINTON, TX, 78387-1076
Telephone: (361) 364-3002
Fax Number: (361) 729-8299
Type of Business: Chain Restaurant Operator
Total Units: 2
Trade Names: Good-N-Crisp (2)
Company-Owned Units: 2
Primary Menu: Chicken (2)
Areas of Operation: TX
Type of Foodservice: Fast Casual (2)

Key Personnel
JACK G. MCCLANAHAN - President

Tc4 & Co.
3555 Ranch Road 620 S
South Austin, TX 78738

Telephone: (823) 824-3663
Internet Homepage: mightyfineburgers.com; tonycs.com; tonycsbeergarden.com; tc4.co, leaguekitchen.com
Type of Business: Chain Restaurant Operator
Total Sales: $15,800,000 (e)
Total Units: 13
Trade Names: Mighty Fine Burgers, Fries & Shakes (5); The League Kitchen & Tavern (4); Tony C's Coal Fired Pizza (2); Tony C's Pizza & Beer Garden (2)
Company-Owned Units: 13
Primary Menu: American (4); Hamburger (5); Pizza (4)
Areas of Operation: TX
Type of Foodservice: Casual Dining (8); Quick Serve (5)

Key Personnel
TONY CIOLA - Co-CEO; COO
CREED FORD - Co-CEO; CFO
BRETT OLDHAM - VP Operations
KEVIN YEAGER - Director Branding
MICHAEL SCOTT - Director Culinary Development
TERI HATHAWAY - Director Training
MEG MOODY - Director Marketing

Del Frisco's Restaurant Group Inc.
1510 West Loop S
South Houston, TX 77027

Telephone: (713) 224-9115
Internet Homepage: dfrg.com
Type of Business: Chain Restaurant Operator
Year Founded: 1981
Total Sales: $287,090,000 (e)
Alcohol Sales: 35%
Number of Employees: 5,000
Average Check: Dinner(74)
Total Units: 40
Trade Names: Del Frisco's Double Eagle Steakhouse (16); Del Frisco's Grille (24)
Company-Owned Units: 40
Preferred Square Footage: 6,500; 8,000; 8,500; 9,000; 12,000; 16,000
Preferred Location Types: Downtown; Freestanding
Alcohol Served: Beer, Wine, Liquor
Primary Menu: American (24); Steak (16)
Areas of Operation: CO, CT, DC, FL, GA, IL, MA, NC, NY, PA, TN, TX, VA, WI
Type of Foodservice: Casual Dining (24); Fine Dining (16)
Primary Distributors: (Food) US Foods Holding Corp., ROSEMONT, IL
Parent Company: Landry's Restaurants Inc., HOUSTON, TX
Notes: The average dinner check shown is for Sullivan's; the average check for Del Frisco's is $110 and for the Grille restaurants is between $45-55.

Key Personnel
IAN R. CARTER - Chairman
ADAM HALBERG - President Group
MIA MEACHEM - Chief Marketing Officer
THOMAS G. DRITSAS - Senior VP Culinary Development; Corporate Chef
JAMES W. KIRKPATRICK - VP Real Estate
SABRINA SCULLY - VP Operations
BRIAN CHRISTMAN - Executive Chef
ORLANDO SANTANA - Regional Director
ERICA OLSEN - Senior Manager Talent Acquisitions
ALECIA PULMAN - Manager Media Relations
MICHELLE KAPIN - Manager National
DEBBI ANDREWS - Manager Sales
NATALIE BAILIFF - Manager Sales

DAVID TARAFA - Manager Restaurant Operations

Durango Restaurants, LLC
1401 Monarch Way
Southlake, TX 76092-9617

Telephone: (817) 288-3010
Type of Business: Chain Restaurant Operator
Total Sales: $13,410,000 (e)
Total Units: 11
Trade Names: Little Caesars Pizza (11)
Units Franchised From: 11
Preferred Location Types: Freestanding; Strip Mall
Primary Menu: Pizza (11)
Areas of Operation: TX
Type of Foodservice: Quick Serve (11)
Franchise Affiliation: Little Caesar Enterprises Inc., DETROIT, MI

Key Personnel
GAYLE MEADOWS - President
ROBERT DRURY - VP Development
PATSY LITTLE - Treasurer; Corporate Secretary; General Buyer

JMFW, LLC
2645 E Southlake Blvd Ste 120
Southlake, TX 76092-6836

Telephone: (817) 421-5300
Type of Business: Chain Restaurant Operator
Total Sales: $11,020,000 (e)
Total Units: 8
Trade Names: Jersey Mike's Subs (8)
Units Franchised From: 8
Primary Menu: Sandwiches/Deli (8)
Areas of Operation: TX
Type of Foodservice: Quick Serve (8)
Franchise Affiliation: Jersey Mike's Franchise Systems, MANASQUAN, NJ

Key Personnel
JEFF WORTHEN - Partner; General Buyer
CHAD HUFFINS - Partner

Cain Group
25003 Pitkin Rd Ste B100
Spring, TX 77386-1472

Telephone: (832) 663-9787
Fax Number: (866) 315-4582
Company Email: thecaingroup@hotmail.com
Type of Business: Chain Restaurant Operator
Year Founded: 2002
Total Sales: $91,070,000 (e)
Number of Employees: 1,140
Average Check: Breakfast(8); Lunch(12); Dinner(14)
Total Units: 20
Trade Names: Panera Bread (20)
Units Franchised From: 20
Preferred Square Footage: 1,100; 1,200; 1,350; 2,500; 3,200; 4,480
Preferred Location Types: Freestanding; Regional Mall
Primary Menu: Sandwiches/Deli (20)
Projected Openings: 1
Areas of Operation: TX
Type of Foodservice: Fast Casual (20)
Franchise Affiliation: Panera Bread Company, SAINT LOUIS, MO

Key Personnel
PAUL CAIN - CEO
CHUCK CAIN - President; Partner; Director Real Estate, Design
ANDRIA CAIN - Partner; General Buyer
ROBERT DRISALDI - Partner; VP Operations, Facility/Maintenance; General Manager
KEVIN SCHULTZ - Manager District

D R Scholz Inc
8718 Spring Cypress Rd
Spring, TX 77379-3135

Telephone: (281) 550-4033
Type of Business: Chain Restaurant Operator
Total Sales: $27,990,000 (e)
Total Units: 6
Trade Names: McDonald's (6)
Units Franchised From: 6
Primary Menu: Hamburger (6)
Areas of Operation: TX
Type of Foodservice: Quick Serve (6)
Franchise Affiliation: McDonald's Corporation, CHICAGO, IL

Key Personnel
LAURIE GLASER - President; General Buyer

Hartz Franchise Restaurants Ltd
16670 Stuebner Airline Rd
Spring, TX 77379-7373

Telephone: (281) 257-8822
Fax Number: (281) 257-8830
Internet Homepage: hartz-chicken.com
Company Email: hartz@hartz-chicken.com
Type of Business: Chain Restaurant Operator
Year Founded: 1972
Systemwide Sales: $40,562,000 (e)
Total Sales: $5,284,000 (e)
Number of Employees: 10
Average Check: Lunch(10); Dinner(16)
Total Units: 62
Trade Names: Hartz Chicken Buffet (61); Hartz

Krispy Chicken 'N' Rolls (1)
Units Franchised To: 62
Preferred Square Footage: 2,000
Preferred Location Types: Convenience Store/Gas Station; Freestanding; Strip Mall
Primary Menu: Chicken (62)
Projected Openings: 5
Areas of Operation: TX
Foreign Countries: INDONESIA; MALAYSIA
Type of Foodservice: Quick Serve (62)

Key Personnel
LEVAN VU - CEO; President; Partner; Director Facility/Maintenance, Real Estate, Design
LAN VU - Partner; COO
QUAN VU - CFO; Director Purchasing, Supply Chain

Rafiq Enterprises Inc
18431 Bivens Bnd
Spring, TX 77379-7037

Telephone: (832) 524-5909
Fax Number: (281) 257-0519
Company Email: rafiq4974@sbcglobal.net
Type of Business: Chain Restaurant Operator
Total Sales: $23,140,000 (e)
Total Units: 5
Trade Names: McDonald's (5)
Units Franchised From: 5
Preferred Location Types: Freestanding; Other
Primary Menu: Hamburger (5)
Areas of Operation: TX
Type of Foodservice: Quick Serve (5)
Franchise Affiliation: McDonald's Corporation, CHICAGO, IL

Key Personnel
MOHAMMED SOUDAGAR - President; General Buyer

BreWingZ Sports Bar & Grill
12660 S Kirkwood Rd
Stafford, TX 77477-2915

Telephone: (281) 265-9464
Internet Homepage: brewingz.com
Company Email: marketing@brewingz.com
Type of Business: Chain Restaurant Operator
Year Founded: 2013
Total Units: 23
Trade Names: BreWingZ on the Fly (6); BreWingZ Sports Bar & Grill (17)
Company-Owned Units: 23
Primary Menu: American (23)
Areas of Operation: TX
Type of Foodservice: Casual Dining (17); Quick Serve (6)

Key Personnel
MANISH AGRAWAL - President; General Buyer
TINA LAFAVE - Area Director
LARRY KOLTUN - Area Director
JEREMY HORNE - Director Operations

GS Beaumont Enterprise
12660 S Kirkwood Rd
Stafford, TX 77477-2915

Telephone: (281) 565-9779
Type of Business: Chain Restaurant Operator
Total Sales: $17,690,000 (e)
Total Units: 23
Trade Names: Subway (19); The Fish Place (4)
Units Franchised From: 23
Primary Menu: Cajun/Creole (4); Sandwiches/Deli (19)
Areas of Operation: LA, TX
Type of Foodservice: Casual Dining (4); Quick Serve (19)
Franchise Affiliation: Doctor's Associates Inc., MILFORD, CT

Key Personnel
SANJAY JAIN - President; General Buyer

Pepperoni's Inc
12807 Royal Dr Ste 106
Stafford, TX 77477-4222

Telephone: (281) 240-1020
Fax Number: (281) 240-1347
Internet Homepage: pepperonis.net
Company Email: pizza@pepperonis.net
Type of Business: Chain Restaurant Operator
Total Sales: $10,130,000 (e)
Total Units: 14
Trade Names: Pepperonis (14)
Company-Owned Units: 12
Units Franchised To: 2
Primary Menu: Pizza (14)
Projected Openings: 1
Areas of Operation: TX
Type of Foodservice: Quick Serve (14)

Key Personnel
RAY SALTI - Owner; General Buyer
JORGE SANCHEZ - General Manager
ADINA CASTELLI - Administrative Assistant

HZ LM CASUAL FOODS, LLC
4415 Highway 6
Sugar Land, TX 77478-4476

Telephone: (281) 201-2700
Type of Business: Chain Restaurant Operator
Year Founded: 2017
Total Units: 26
Trade Names: La Madeleine Bakery Cafe (26)
Units Franchised From: 26
Primary Menu: French/Continental (26)
Areas of Operation: LA, TX
Type of Foodservice: Fast Casual (26)
Franchise Affiliation: La Madeleine Inc., DALLAS, TX
Parent Company: Dhanani Group, ,

Key Personnel
AMIN DHANANI - President; General Buyer

Nee Mee Corp
11549 S Highway 6
Sugar Land, TX 77498-4932

Telephone: (281) 980-8161
Type of Business: Chain Restaurant Operator
Total Sales: $2,954,000 (e)
Total Units: 5
Trade Names: Subway (5)
Units Franchised From: 5
Primary Menu: Sandwiches/Deli (5)
Areas of Operation: TX
Type of Foodservice: Quick Serve (5)
Franchise Affiliation: Doctor's Associates Inc., MILFORD, CT

Key Personnel
MUKULESH N. SHAH - President; General Buyer

VKC Group
322 Julie Rivers Dr
Sugar Land, TX 77478-3179

Telephone: (281) 340-3000
Fax Number: (281) 277-4190
Internet Homepage: vkcgrp.com
Company Email: info@vkcgrp.com
Type of Business: Chain Restaurant Operator
Trade Names: Great American Cookies; Pretzelmaker; Subway; TCBY
Areas of Operation: TX
Type of Foodservice: Quick Serve
Franchise Affiliation: Doctor's Associates Inc., MILFORD, CT; Great American Cookies, NORCROSS, GA; TCBY Systems LLC, BROOMFIELD, CO

Key Personnel
SUNITA AGRAWAL - President; Partner
BRIJ AGRAWAL - Partner

Z & H Foods, Inc.
4415 Highway 6
Sugar Land, TX 77478-4476

Telephone: (281) 201-2700

Fax Number: (281) 201-2798
Company Email: aisha@gulshaninc.com
Type of Business: Chain Restaurant Operator
Total Sales: $619,330,000 (e)
Total Units: 260
Trade Names: Burger King (2); Popeyes Louisiana Kitchen (258)
Units Franchised From: 260
Preferred Square Footage: 1,900; 4,300
Preferred Location Types: Freestanding
Primary Menu: Chicken (258); Hamburger (2)
Areas of Operation: AZ, CO, IL, MO, OH, TX, UT
Type of Foodservice: Quick Serve (260)
Franchise Affiliation: Burger King Worldwide Inc., MIAMI, FL
Parent Company: Dhanani Group, ,

Key Personnel
AMIN DHANANI - Partner
MARK SPENCE - VP Operations
BRIAN THATCHER - VP Development
MARK FISHER - Director Human Resources
ARMANDO CLARK - Director Operations

D & B Pizza Inc
305 E Moore Ave
Terrell, TX 75160-3209

Telephone: (972) 563-0511
Type of Business: Chain Restaurant Operator
Total Sales: $6,215,000 (e)
Total Units: 3
Trade Names: Domino's (3)
Units Franchised From: 3
Primary Menu: Pizza (3)
Areas of Operation: TX
Type of Foodservice: Quick Serve (3)
Franchise Affiliation: Domino's Pizza Inc, ANN ARBOR, MI

Key Personnel
DAVID INGRAM - President; Owner

Abbott & Avard LLC
3444 Summerhill Rd
Texarkana, TX 75503-3560

Telephone: (903) 794-9111
Type of Business: Chain Restaurant Operator
Total Sales: $7,246,000 (e)
Average Check: Dinner(12)
Total Units: 3
Trade Names: Burger King (3)
Units Franchised From: 3
Preferred Location Types: Freestanding
Primary Menu: Hamburger (3)
Areas of Operation: AR
Type of Foodservice: Quick Serve (3)
Franchise Affiliation: Burger King Worldwide Inc., MIAMI, FL

Key Personnel
NATHAN D. AVARD - President; General Buyer

Apple Arkansas, Inc
5120 Summerhill Rd
Texarkana, TX 75503-1824

Telephone: (903) 794-3743
Fax Number: (903) 793-1414
Type of Business: Chain Restaurant Operator
Year Founded: 1976
Total Sales: $39,820,000 (e)
Alcohol Sales: 5%
Number of Employees: 750
Average Check: Lunch(12); Dinner(16)
Total Units: 10
Trade Names: Applebee's Neighborhood Grill & Bar (10)
Units Franchised From: 10
Preferred Square Footage: 6,000
Preferred Location Types: Community Mall; Freestanding; Strip Mall
Alcohol Served: Beer, Wine, Liquor
Primary Menu: American (10)
Areas of Operation: AR, LA, TX
Type of Foodservice: Casual Dining (13)
Franchise Affiliation: Applebee's Services Inc., KANSAS CITY, MO

Key Personnel
ALAN SMITH - Partner; Director Facility/Maintenance, Information Systems, Real Estate, Design, Human Resources, Franchising, Store Fixtures
JASON THOMSON - Partner
GWENDOLYN DEAN - Corporate Secretary
GINA GINA - Manager Marketing
DEBBIE CROUCH - Manager Marketing

TaMolly's of America Ltd.
5940 Summerhill Rd
Texarkana, TX 75503-1639

Telephone: (903) 792-0732
Fax Number: (903) 792-9786
Internet Homepage: tamollys.com
Company Email: comments@tamollys.com
Type of Business: Chain Restaurant Operator
Total Sales: $12,790,000 (e)
Average Check: Dinner(14)
Total Units: 11
Trade Names: TaMolly's Mexican Kitchen (11)
Company-Owned Units: 11
Preferred Location Types: Freestanding; Strip Mall
Alcohol Served: Beer, Wine, Liquor
Primary Menu: Mexican (11)
Areas of Operation: AR, LA, TX
Type of Foodservice: Casual Dining (11)

Key Personnel
BOB STRAIGHT - COO; Director Store Operations; Manager Facility/Maintenance
VAL DE LA GARZA - Director Human Resources
KATIE HILL - Director Marketing

RAVE Restaurant Group Inc.
3551 Plano Pkwy
The Colony, TX 75056-5245

Telephone: (469) 384-5000
Fax Number: (469) 384-5058
Internet Homepage: piefivepizza.com; pizzainn.com
Type of Business: Chain Restaurant Operator
Year Founded: 1958
Systemwide Sales: $110,203,000 (e)
Publicly Held: Yes
Total Sales: $11,480,000 (e)
Alcohol Sales: 20%
Number of Employees: 557
Average Check: Lunch(14); Dinner(18)
Foodservice Sales: $3,214,000 (e)
Internet Order Processing: Yes
Total Units: 168
Trade Names: Pie Five Pizza (33); Pizza Inn (135)
Units Franchised To: 168
Preferred Square Footage: 200; 400; 1,200; 2,100; 4,500; 5,000
Preferred Location Types: Airports; Community Mall; Convenience Store/Gas Station; Downtown; Freestanding; Institution (college/hospital); Kiosk; Office Complex; Regional Mall; Stadiums; Strip Mall
Alcohol Served: Beer, Wine
Primary Menu: Pizza (168)
Projected Openings: 11
Areas of Operation: AL, AR, AZ, CO, DE, FL, GA, IL, IN, KS, KY, LA, MD, MO, MS, NC, NE, NJ, NM, OK, PA, SC, SD, TN, TX, VA
Foreign Countries: BANGLADESH; CHINA; CYPRUS; GUATEMALA; HONDURAS; IRAQ; KUWAIT; OMAN; QATAR; ROMANIA; SAUDI ARABIA; UNITED ARAB EMIRATES
Type of Foodservice: Casual Dining (135); Fast Casual (33)
Foodservice Management Venues: Schools
Catering Services: Yes
On-site Distribution Center: Yes
Primary Distributors: (Full Line) Reinhart FoodService, LOUISVILLE, TN; (Full Line) Roma Food Enterprises Inc., RICHMOND, VA
Notes: The company derives approximately 72% of its total revenue from food & supply sales to its franchisees.

Key Personnel
MARK E. SCHWARZ - Chairman; Director
RAMON D. PHILLIPS - Vice Chairman; Director
BRANDON L. SOLANO - CEO

JAY ROONEY - CFO
CHRISTINA COY - VP Marketing
DAVID ROBERTS - VP Information Technology
ZACK VILJOEN - VP Operations; General Manager Division
DENISE WILSON - Assistant VP Supply Chain
JUSTIN SMITH - Senior Director Operations, Division
CLINTON COLEMAN - Director
DARREN WEBB - Director Development
CARLOS COJULUN - Director Marketing
LIAM FINN - Director Franchise Development
ROGER MAGNUM - Director Operations, Training
CYNTHIA NELSON - Manager Operations, Construction, Design
AARON FOUST - Manager Facility/Maintenance, Construction
PAMELA ROBINSON-MARTIN - Specialist Accounting
DION FIROOZNIA - Consultant Franchise Development

Black Forest Ventures
24 Waterway Ave Suite 225
The Woodlands, TX 77380

Telephone: (832) 813-7373
Internet Homepage: blackforestventures.com; blackwalnutcafe.com; hubbellandhudson.com
Company Email: hr@hubbellandhudson.com
Type of Business: Chain Restaurant Operator
Total Sales: $12,890,000 (e)
Total Units: 13
Trade Names: Black Walnut Cafe (11); Cureight (1); The Kitchen (1)
Company-Owned Units: 13
Alcohol Served: Beer, Wine, Liquor
Primary Menu: American (12); Miscellaneous (1)
Areas of Operation: TX
Type of Foodservice: Casual Dining (1); Fast Casual (11); Fine Dining (1)
Catering Services: Yes
Notes: In addition to its hospitality operations, Black Forest Ventures also specializes in commercial real estate, aviation, and technology investments.

Key Personnel
DIRK LAUKIEN - Founder; President
JONATHAN HITCHCOCK - CFO
SEAN QUINN - Senior VP Real Estate
AUSTIN SIMMONS - Executive Chef
HAYDAR KUSTU - Director Marketing, Business Development

GDK GO INC
14057 FM 2920 Rd
Tomball, TX 77377-5501

Telephone: (281) 351-0030
Type of Business: Chain Restaurant Operator
Total Sales: $26,407,000 (e)
Total Units: 13
Trade Names: Domino's (13)
Units Franchised From: 13
Primary Menu: Pizza (13)
Areas of Operation: TX
Type of Foodservice: Quick Serve (13)
Franchise Affiliation: Domino's Pizza Inc, ANN ARBOR, MI

Key Personnel
ELSADIG M. ABDELMOTAL - Owner; General Buyer

Dairy Queen of Tyler Inc.
106 E Heritage Dr Ofc
Tyler, TX 75703-5175

Telephone: (903) 561-4018
Fax Number: (903) 561-4668
Internet Homepage: dqtyler.com
Type of Business: Chain Restaurant Operator
Year Founded: 1980
Total Sales: $22,318,000 (e)
Number of Employees: 350
Average Check: Lunch(10); Dinner(10)
Total Units: 15
Trade Names: Dairy Queen (15)
Units Franchised From: 15
Preferred Square Footage: 3,000
Preferred Location Types: Freestanding; Strip Mall
Primary Menu: American (15)
Projected Openings: 1
Areas of Operation: TX
Type of Foodservice: Quick Serve (15)
Franchise Affiliation: International Dairy Queen Inc., BLOOMINGTON, MN

Key Personnel
TERRY GILES - President; Partner; Controller; Director Operations, Purchasing, Marketing, Advertising
DARRELL FORSTER - Partner; VP Construction, Store Planning; Controller
BRYAN KELLY - Manager District
JULIE JOHNSON - Manager District

US Merit Inc.
11406 State Highway 64 E
Tyler, TX 75707-3445

Telephone: (903) 566-4900
Fax Number: (903) 566-4907
Internet Homepage: usmerit.net
Company Email: monica@usmerit.net
Type of Business: Chain Restaurant Operator
Year Founded: 1991
Total Sales: $43,500,000 (e)
Number of Employees: 440
Average Check: Breakfast(6); Lunch(8); Dinner(8)
Total Units: 21
Trade Names: Burger King (17); Taco Bueno (4)
Units Franchised From: 21
Preferred Square Footage: 2,500
Preferred Location Types: Freestanding
Primary Menu: Hamburger (17); Taco (4)
Areas of Operation: TX
Type of Foodservice: Quick Serve (21)
Franchise Affiliation: Burger King Worldwide Inc., MIAMI, FL
Primary Distributors: (Full Line) McLane/Fort Worth, FORT WORTH, TX

Key Personnel
TERRY DAVIS - President; Director Real Estate
LYNNE DAVIS - VP
LEE CHADICK - Director Operations, Supply Chain; Manager Purchasing, Marketing
TONY HARRIS - Director Operations

C & C Food Co, Inc
2222 E Main St
Uvalde, TX 78801-4947

Telephone: (830) 278-6124
Fax Number: (830) 278-6138
Type of Business: Chain Restaurant Operator
Total Sales: $4,360,000 (e)
Average Check: Dinner(14)
Total Units: 3
Trade Names: Dairy Queen (3)
Units Franchised From: 3
Primary Menu: American (3)
Areas of Operation: TX
Type of Foodservice: Quick Serve (3)
Franchise Affiliation: International Dairy Queen Inc., BLOOMINGTON, MN

Key Personnel
CLISS REED - Owner

Rainbow Pizza, LLC
243 W Main St
Uvalde, TX 78801-5505

Telephone: (830) 591-1020
Type of Business: Chain Restaurant Operator
Total Sales: $49,128,000 (e)
Total Units: 24
Trade Names: Domino's (24)
Units Franchised From: 24

Primary Menu: Pizza (24)
Areas of Operation: TX
Type of Foodservice: Quick Serve (24)
Franchise Affiliation: Domino's Pizza Inc, ANN ARBOR, MI

Key Personnel
FERNANDO SALIDO - Owner; General Buyer

Texcellent
2007 N Laurent St
Victoria, TX 77901-5414

Telephone: (361) 576-4156
Fax Number: (361) 582-0088
Type of Business: Chain Restaurant Operator
Total Sales: $6,256,000 (e)
Total Units: 3
Trade Names: Domino's (3)
Units Franchised From: 3
Primary Menu: Pizza (3)
Areas of Operation: TX
Type of Foodservice: Quick Serve (3)
Franchise Affiliation: Domino's Pizza Inc, ANN ARBOR, MI

Key Personnel
JAMES ROISE - President; Partner
TIM MCBRIDE - Partner; General Buyer
PREETI THAKORE - Chief Administrative Officer

Uncle Dan's Rib House
1001 Lake Air Dr
Waco, TX 76710-4550

Telephone: (254) 772-3532
Fax Number: (254) 776-7206
Internet Homepage: uncledansbbq.com
Company Email: uncledans@hot.rr.com
Type of Business: Chain Restaurant Operator
Year Founded: 1977
Total Sales: $2,844,000 (e)
Alcohol Sales: 1%
Number of Employees: 40
Average Check: Lunch(10); Dinner(10)
Total Units: 2
Trade Names: Uncle Dan's Rib House (2)
Company-Owned Units: 2
Preferred Location Types: Freestanding
Alcohol Served: Beer
Primary Menu: Bar-B-Q (2)
Areas of Operation: TX
Type of Foodservice: Casual Dining (2)
Catering Services: Yes

Key Personnel
DAN HENDERSON SR - Owner; Director Finance, Catering
GREG BEHM - General Manager; General Buyer

Domino's Franchisee
602 Redwater Rd
Wake Village, TX 75501-6007

Telephone: (903) 838-3030
Type of Business: Chain Restaurant Operator
Total Sales: $6,066,000 (e)
Total Units: 3
Trade Names: Domino's (3)
Units Franchised From: 3
Primary Menu: Pizza (3)
Areas of Operation: TX
Type of Foodservice: Quick Serve (3)
Franchise Affiliation: Domino's Pizza Inc, ANN ARBOR, MI

Key Personnel
KENNETH M. SCHROEPFER - Owner; General Buyer

Hat Creek Burger Company
4407 Bee Caves Rd
West Lake Hills, TX 78746

Telephone: (512) 732-2025
Internet Homepage: hatcreekburgers.com
Type of Business: Chain Restaurant Operator
Total Sales: $23,280,000 (e)
Total Units: 27
Trade Names: Hat Creek Burger Company (27)
Company-Owned Units: 27
Primary Menu: Hamburger (27)
Projected Openings: 5
Areas of Operation: TX
Type of Foodservice: Fast Casual (27)

Key Personnel
DREW GRESSET - President; General Buyer
DAVID HOWELL - CFO; Controller
RYAN SIMPSON - Director Human Resources
LUCAS LEE - Director Business Development
SCOTT BROWN - Director Construction
BRANDON HARRIS - Manager Area

Falcon Holdings Management LLC
1301 Solana Blvd Ste 2300
Westlake, TX 76262-1676

Telephone: (817) 693-5151
Fax Number: (888) 580-3963
Internet Homepage: falconholdings.com
Type of Business: Chain Restaurant Operator
Year Founded: 1999
Total Sales: $327,790,000 (e)
Number of Employees: 6,815
Average Check: Lunch(8); Dinner(10)
Total Units: 305
Trade Names: A&W All American Food; Carls Jr; Church's Chicken; FATZ; Hardee's; Long John Silver's; Piccadilly Cafeteria
Units Franchised From: 305
Preferred Square Footage: 2,500
Preferred Location Types: Freestanding
Areas of Operation: IL, IN, MI, OH, VA
Type of Foodservice: Quick Serve (305)
Franchise Affiliation: A&W Restaurants Inc., LEXINGTON, KY; Church's Chicken, ATLANTA, GA; Hardee's Food Systems Inc., FRANKLIN, TN; Long John Silver's Inc., LOUISVILLE, KY
Primary Distributors: (Food) SYSCO Food Services of Chicago Inc., DES PLAINES, IL

Key Personnel
ASLAM KHAN - Chairman
GIOVANNA KONING - CFO
NAZAR SYED - COO
FRED OTILLIO - VP Information Technology
SYED IMRAN - VP Operations; Regional VP Operations
JORIE SEXTON - VP Business Development
JILL FILIPAK - VP Finance
JILL FILIPIAK - VP Finance
SERGIO FLORES - Controller
LOU BOEMIA - Director Development, Real Estate
BRANDON MCCANN - Director Operations
NASAR MIR - Director Development
DEANNA HAMILTON - District Manager
VICKI BLANCETT - Manager Human Resources
NANCY DIMAS - Manager Accounting
HECTOR FLORES - Manager Accounting
KAITLYN MOORE - Manager Risk Management
SARAH RHOADES - Supervisor Payroll
KARRAR HAIDER - Specialist Human Resources

Diamondback Pizza, Inc
4114 Old Burkburnett Rd
Wichita Falls, TX 76306

Telephone: (940) 855-8110
Type of Business: Chain Restaurant Operator
Total Sales: $22,596,000 (e)
Total Units: 11
Trade Names: Domino's (11)
Units Franchised From: 11
Primary Menu: Pizza (11)
Areas of Operation: TX
Type of Foodservice: Quick Serve (11)
Franchise Affiliation: Domino's Pizza Inc, ANN ARBOR, MI

Key Personnel
JOHN MEKLER - President; General Buyer

R.A.C.M., Inc.
1510 15th St
Wichita Falls, TX 76301-5117

Telephone: (940) 767-1339
Fax Number: (940) 767-3514
Type of Business: Chain Restaurant Operator
Total Sales: $20,662,000 (e)
Total Units: 4
Trade Names: McDonald's (4)
Units Franchised From: 4
Preferred Location Types: Freestanding
Primary Menu: Hamburger (4)
Areas of Operation: TX
Type of Foodservice: Quick Serve (4)
Franchise Affiliation: McDonald's Corporation, CHICAGO, IL

Key Personnel
RICHARD BOONE - President; General Buyer

Cedar Creek Food Group, Inc.
402 W North Commerce St
Wills Point, TX 75169

Mailing Address: PO Box 573, WILLS POINT, TX, 75169-0573
Telephone: (903) 873-2573
Fax Number: (903) 873-5346
Type of Business: Chain Restaurant Operator
Total Sales: $4,492,000 (e)
Total Units: 3
Trade Names: Dairy Queen (3)
Units Franchised From: 3
Primary Menu: American (3)
Areas of Operation: TX
Type of Foodservice: Quick Serve (3)
Franchise Affiliation: International Dairy Queen Inc., BLOOMINGTON, MN

Key Personnel
JEFF PENNINGTON - President; General Buyer

South Texas Pizza Inc.
5496 Walzem Rd
Windcrest, TX 78218-2125

Telephone: (210) 657-2431
Internet Homepage: sapizza.com
Type of Business: Chain Restaurant Operator
Total Sales: $144,917,000 (e)
Average Check: Dinner(16)
Internet Order Processing: Yes
Total Units: 73
Trade Names: Domino's (73)
Units Franchised From: 73
Preferred Square Footage: 1,000; 1,300
Preferred Location Types: Downtown; Freestanding; Strip Mall
Primary Menu: Pizza (73)
Areas of Operation: TX
Type of Foodservice: Quick Serve (73)
Franchise Affiliation: Domino's Pizza Inc, ANN ARBOR, MI

Key Personnel
ALAN MURPH - President; General Buyer
MICHAEL BERNAL - COO; Director Operations
LUCIANO LOZANO - Director Human Resources
PATRICK VANDIERENDONK - District Manager
GARRETT MOLENDA - Manager Construction

UTAH

Abundant Brands
551 E State Rd Ste 201
American Fork, UT 84003-2225

Telephone: (801) 492-4344
Fax Number: (801) 492-3804
Type of Business: Chain Restaurant Operator
Year Founded: 1984
Total Sales: $32,010,000 (e)
Number of Employees: 645
Average Check: Lunch(10); Dinner(14)
Total Units: 43
Trade Names: Costa Vida Mexican Grill (16); Roxberry Juice Co. (9); Subway (18)
Units Franchised To: 9
Units Franchised From: 34
Preferred Square Footage: 1,000
Preferred Location Types: Convenience Store/Gas Station; Regional Mall; Strip Mall
Primary Menu: Mexican (16); Sandwiches/Deli (18); Snacks (16)
Areas of Operation: NV, UT, WY
Type of Foodservice: Casual Dining (16); Quick Serve (27)
Foodservice Management Venues: College & University
Franchise Affiliation: Doctor's Associates Inc., MILFORD, CT
Primary Distributors: (Full Line) Nicholas & Co. Inc., SALT LAKE CITY, UT

Key Personnel
LOGAN HUNTER - CEO; Partner; Director Purchasing, Facility/Maintenance, Supply Chain
SHAWN COOK - Partner; VP
LIZ HUNTER - Partner; Controller; Director Real Estate, Human Resources
GEOFFREY ALTER - Executive Chef

Nielsen's Frozen Custard
570 W 2600 S
Bountiful, UT 84010-7718

Telephone: (801) 292-7479
Internet Homepage: nielsensfrozencustardut.com
Company Email: info@nielsensfrozencustardut.com
Type of Business: Chain Restaurant Operator
Year Founded: 1981
Total Sales: $1,433,000 (e)
Number of Employees: 23
Average Check: Lunch(8); Dinner(8)
Total Units: 6
Trade Names: Nielsen's Frozen Custard (6)
Company-Owned Units: 3
Units Franchised To: 5
Preferred Location Types: Freestanding
Primary Menu: Snacks (6)
Areas of Operation: UT
Type of Foodservice: Quick Serve (6)
Primary Distributors: (Full Line) SYSCO Intermountain Food Services Inc., WEST JORDAN, UT

Key Personnel
STEVE NIELSEN - Owner; General Manager

Yogurtland Franchisee
234 S 500 W Ste 107
Bountiful, UT 84010-8700

Telephone: (801) 335-7252
Type of Business: Chain Restaurant Operator
Total Sales: $2,994,000 (e)
Total Units: 3
Trade Names: Yogurtland (3)
Units Franchised From: 3
Primary Menu: Snacks (3)
Areas of Operation: UT
Type of Foodservice: Quick Serve (3)
Franchise Affiliation: Yogurtland Franchising Inc., FARMERS BRANCH, TX

Key Personnel
JOSHUA FELLER - Partner; General Buyer
AMBER FELLER - Partner; General Buyer

Iceberg Drive Inn Inc.
438 W 12300 S Ste 104
Draper, UT 84020

Mailing Address: P.O. Box 1065, DRAPER, UT, 84020
Telephone: (801) 424-5400
Fax Number: (801) 542-8655
Internet Homepage: icebergdriveinn.com
Company Email: info@icebergdriveinn.com

Type of Business: Chain Restaurant Operator
Year Founded: 1960
Systemwide Sales: $20,070,000 (e)
Total Sales: $3,865,000 (e)
Number of Employees: 597
Average Check: Breakfast(8); Lunch(8); Dinner(8)
Internet Order Processing: Yes
Internet Sales: 0.50%
Total Units: 14
Trade Names: Iceberg Drive Inn (14)
Company-Owned Units: 6
Units Franchised To: 8
Preferred Square Footage: 2,000
Preferred Location Types: Convenience Store/Gas Station; Freestanding
Primary Menu: American (14)
Areas of Operation: AZ, CA, UT
Type of Foodservice: Quick Serve (14)
Primary Distributors: (Full Line) Nicholas & Co. Inc., SALT LAKE CITY, UT

Key Personnel
F. KELLY CHRISTENSEN - President; Director Finance, Human Resources
REED R - President

Mountain West Wendy's
76 W13775 S ste 2
Draper, UT 84020

Telephone: (208) 336-7400
Type of Business: Chain Restaurant Operator
Total Sales: $51,870,000 (e)
Average Check: Dinner(8)
Total Units: 19
Trade Names: Wendy's Old Fashioned Hamburgers (19)
Units Franchised From: 19
Primary Menu: Hamburger (19)
Areas of Operation: ID
Type of Foodservice: Quick Serve (19)
Franchise Affiliation: The Wendy's Company, DUBLIN, OH

Key Personnel
JIM TAGGART - Owner; General Buyer
JEFF RICH - Director Operations
KEVIN MORGAN - District Manager

DJ Management
PO Box 713
Ephraim, UT 84627-0713

Telephone: (435) 283-5272
Fax Number: (435) 565-6488
Type of Business: Chain Restaurant Operator
Total Sales: $42,690,000 (e)
Number of Employees: 720
Total Units: 9
Trade Names: McDonald's (9)
Units Franchised From: 9
Preferred Square Footage: 2,500
Preferred Location Types: Discount Dept. Stores; Freestanding
Primary Menu: Hamburger (9)
Areas of Operation: UT
Type of Foodservice: Quick Serve (9)
Franchise Affiliation: McDonald's Corporation, CHICAGO, IL

Key Personnel
DAVID PARRISH - President; General Buyer
MARK PARISH - Owner
JUDY PARRISH - VP
MAYRA HERBERT - Director Operations, Sales

Blue Lemon
11073 N Alpine Hwy Ste 101
Highland, UT 84003-8933

Telephone: (801) 756-5855
Internet Homepage: bluelemon.com
Type of Business: Chain Restaurant Operator
Year Founded: 2009
Total Sales: $11,550,000 (e)
Internet Order Processing: Yes
Total Units: 5
Trade Names: Blue Lemon (5)
Company-Owned Units: 5
Preferred Location Types: Community Mall; Regional Mall; Strip Mall
Primary Menu: American (5)
Projected Openings: 1
Areas of Operation: AZ, UT
Type of Foodservice: Fast Casual (5)
Catering Services: Yes

Key Personnel
LYCHELLE DAY - Partner

Snowbird Ski & Summer Resort
3165 E Millrock Dr Ste 190
Holladay, UT 84121-5571

Mailing Address: PO Box 929000, SNOWBIRD, UT, 84092-9000
Telephone: (801) 742-2222
Fax Number: (801) 933-2187
Internet Homepage: snowbird.com
Company Email: info@snowbird.com
Type of Business: Foodservice Operations - Hotel/Motels
Year Founded: 1971
Total Sales: $33,073,000 (e)
Alcohol Sales: 20%
Number of Employees: 667
Total Units: 3
Restaurants in Hotels: 16
Trade Names: The Inn (1); The Iron Blosam (1); The Lodge at Snowbird (1)
Company-Owned Units: 16
Alcohol Served: Beer, Wine, Liquor
Areas of Operation: UT
Type of Foodservice: Casual Dining (9); Fine Dining (7)
Primary Distributors: (Food) SYSCO Intermountain Food Services Inc., WEST JORDAN, UT
Notes: The company derives approximately 75% of its revenue from hotel/resort operations.

Key Personnel
DAVE FIELDS - President; General Manager
TESS HOBBS - Director Marketing
WENDY ADAMSON - Senior Manager Sales
CECILE BUSE - Specialist Human Resources
LAUREN HILL - Specialist Human Resources

Hokulia Shave Ice
872 Heritage Park Blvd
Layton, UT 84041-5714

Telephone: (801) 478-4646
Internet Homepage: hokuliashaveice.com
Type of Business: Chain Restaurant Operator
Total Units: 54
Trade Names: Hokulia Shave Ice (54)
Units Franchised To: 54
Primary Menu: Snacks (54)
Projected Openings: 1
Areas of Operation: AK, CA, CO, FL, GA, ID, IN, KS, LA, NE, NV, OH, TX, UT
Type of Foodservice: Quick Serve (54)
Catering Services: Yes

Key Personnel
CLINT SEVERSON - Exec VP

Costa Vida Management
3451 N Triumph Blvd Ste 105
Lehi, UT 84043

Telephone: (801) 797-2374
Internet Homepage: costavida.com
Company Email: info@costavida.com
Type of Business: Chain Restaurant Operator
Year Founded: 2003
Systemwide Sales: $102,835,000 (e)
Total Sales: $38,010,000 (e)
Alcohol Sales: 5%
Number of Employees: 1,724
Average Check: Dinner(14)
Internet Order Processing: Yes
Total Units: 93
Trade Names: Costa Vida Fresh Mexican Grill (99)
Company-Owned Units: 11
Units Franchised To: 88
Preferred Square Footage: 3,200

Preferred Location Types: Freestanding; Regional Mall; Strip Mall
Primary Menu: Mexican (99)
Projected Openings: 10
Areas of Operation: AZ, CA, CO, FL, ID, IL, MO, NM, NV, TX, UT, WA, AB
Foreign Countries: CANADA
Type of Foodservice: Fast Casual (99)
Catering Services: Yes
Primary Distributors: (Full Line) SYSCO Intermountain Food Services Inc., WEST JORDAN, UT

Key Personnel
SEAN COLLINS - Chairman; Partner
MISTI LARSEN - CEO; Executive Assistant
DAVE RUTTER - CEO; President; Partner
MARC BEYNON - Director Training
KIP PRESTWICH - Director Operations
JEREMY ERNI - Director Marketing
TONY GRECO - Senior Manager Information Technology
AARON WALLICK - Manager District

Su Casa
6878 S State St
Midvale, UT 84047-1260

Telephone: (801) 255-1042
Internet Homepage: fredricospizza.com; saltcityburgerco.com
Company Email: info@saltcityburgerco.com
Type of Business: Chain Restaurant Operator
Year Founded: 1958
Total Sales: $5,372,000 (e)
Number of Employees: 200
Average Check: Lunch(12); Dinner(12)
Total Units: 4
Trade Names: Frederico's Pizza and Salads (1); Salt City Burger (1); Su Casa Mexican Restaurant (2)
Company-Owned Units: 4
Preferred Location Types: Freestanding
Primary Menu: Hamburger (1); Mexican (2); Pizza (1)
Areas of Operation: UT
Type of Foodservice: Family Restaurant (4)
Primary Distributors: (Full Line) SYSCO Intermountain Food Services Inc., WEST JORDAN, UT

Key Personnel
RICK OSTERLOH - CEO; Partner; Executive Chef; Director Facility/Maintenance, Loss Prevention, Real Estate, Design; General Buyer
CRAIG OSTERLOH - Partner; CFO; Treasurer; Director Information Systems, Human Resources; General Buyer

Harman Management Corp.
5544 S Green St
Murray, UT 84123-5798

Telephone: (801) 313-8000
Fax Number: (801) 313-9795
Listing Type: Regional Office
Type of Business: Chain Restaurant Operator
Number of Employees: 209
Total Units: 44
Areas of Operation: CA, CO, UT, WA
Parent Company: Harman Management Corp., LOS ALTOS, CA

Key Personnel
CLAY BARTON - Manager Training

Sizzling Platter LLC
348 E Winchester St Ste 200
Murray, UT 84107-8518

Mailing Address: PO Box 572408, SALT LAKE CITY, UT, 84157-2408
Telephone: (801) 268-3400
Fax Number: (801) 263-9595
Internet Homepage: redrobin.com; sizzler.com; sizzlingplatter.com; splat.com
Company Email: corporatecontact@splat.com
Type of Business: Chain Restaurant Operator
Year Founded: 1963
Total Sales: $870,600,000 (e)
Alcohol Sales: 2%
Number of Employees: 4,000
Total Units: 480
Trade Names: Dunkin' Donuts (23); Little Caesars Pizza (387); Red Robin Gourmet Burgers & Spirits (6); Sizzler (12); Wingstop (52)
Units Franchised From: 480
Preferred Square Footage: 3,000; 5,000
Preferred Location Types: Community Mall; Downtown; Freestanding; Regional Mall; Strip Mall
Alcohol Served: Beer, Wine, Liquor
Primary Menu: Chicken (52); Hamburger (6); Pizza (387); Snacks (23); Steak (12)
Areas of Operation: CA, CO, FL, ID, IN, LA, MD, MS, NM, OH, TX, UT, VA, WA
Foreign Countries: MEXICO
Type of Foodservice: Casual Dining (18); Quick Serve (462)
Catering Services: Yes
Franchise Affiliation: DD IP Holder, CANTON, MA; Little Caesar Enterprises Inc., DETROIT, MI; Red Robin Gourmet Burgers Inc., ENGLEWOOD, CO; Sizzler USA Inc., MISSION VIEJO, CA; Wingstop Restaurants Inc., DALLAS, TX
Primary Distributors: (Full Line) US Foods, OGDEN, UT
Parent Company: Valor Equity Partners, CHICAGO, IL

Key Personnel
JIM BALIS - CEO
JAMES HENDERSHOTT - Owner; Manager; Project Manager Quality Assurance
CHRIS MYLES - Area Director Operations
JANET SMITH - VP Development
MARK HOWE - VP Operations
DAVE MOODY - VP Finance
ISAAC MORTON - VP Information Technology
NATHAN GARN - VP Business Development; General Counsel
KRIS COX - Controller
STEVEN PACK - Controller
BRAD WALLACE - Senior Director Facility/Maintenance, Construction
DAVID TRESKO - Director Marketing
MORGAN WALKENHORST - Director Finance
JEREMY SANCHEZ - Director Human Resources
RAMON SEGURA - Director Information Technology
RUSS SHURTLEFF - Director Operations; Manager Construction
ALEX GLANTZIS - Director Construction
ENRIQUE CERVANTES - Director Real Estate
KISHA CHRISTENSEN - Director Operations
RANDY MILLET - Director Development
DEBBIE HOPKINS - Director Accounting
JESUS IBARRA HERNANDEZ - Manager Information Technology
GUILLERMO W. LOPEZ-NEGRETE - Manager
TONY AVERY - Manager Information Technology
ANNAALISA BURBIDGE - Manager Promotion; Brand Manager Marketing
ADAM FERRERO - Manager Information Technology
DOROTHY TOLMAN - Manager Software Development
JEANNIE PAULOVICH - Manager Catering
CARMEN O'BRIGHT - Manager Operations

DST Enterprises
860 W Riverdale Rd Ste B7
Ogden, UT 84405-3760

Telephone: (801) 392-4656
Fax Number: (801) 392-4654
Type of Business: Chain Restaurant Operator
Total Sales: $89,550,000 (e)
Total Units: 19
Trade Names: McDonald's (19)
Units Franchised From: 19
Primary Menu: Hamburger (19)
Areas of Operation: UT
Type of Foodservice: Quick Serve (19)
Franchise Affiliation: McDonald's Corporation, CHICAGO, IL

Key Personnel
DARRELL TROESTER - President; General

Buyer

Grounds for Coffee
3005 Harrison Blvd
Ogden, UT 84403

Telephone: (801) 621-3014
Internet Homepage: groundsforcoffee.com
Type of Business: Chain Restaurant Operator
Year Founded: 1991
Total Sales: $10,670,000 (e)
Total Units: 11
Trade Names: Grounds for Coffee (11)
Company-Owned Units: 11
Primary Menu: Coffee (11)
Areas of Operation: UT
Type of Foodservice: Quick Serve (11)

Key Personnel
DAN DAILEY - Owner
SUZY DAILEY - Owner

5Buck Pizza
93 S State St
Orem, UT 84058-5417

Telephone: (801) 225-1185
Internet Homepage: 5buckpizza.com
Company Email: corporate@5buckpizza.com
Type of Business: Chain Restaurant Operator
Total Sales: $2,438,000 (e)
Alcohol Sales: 5%
Internet Order Processing: Yes
Total Units: 4
Trade Names: 5Buck Pizza (4)
Company-Owned Units: 4
Preferred Square Footage: 1,500
Alcohol Served: Beer
Primary Menu: Pizza (2)
Areas of Operation: ID, UT
Type of Foodservice: Quick Serve (2)

Key Personnel
DAVID JUDD - CEO; President; VP Purchasing, Marketing, Menu Development

Crumbl Cookies
160 E University Pkwy
Orem, UT 84058

Telephone: (801) 939-0433
Internet Homepage: crumblcookies.com
Type of Business: Chain Restaurant Operator
Systemwide Sales: $39,267,000 (e)
Total Sales: $33,060,000 (e)
Total Units: 96
Trade Names: Crumbl Cookies (96)
Company-Owned Units: 81
Units Franchised To: 15
Primary Menu: Snacks (96)
Areas of Operation: AL, AZ, CA, CO, FL, GA, ID, KS, MT, NC, NV, OR, TN, TX, UT
Type of Foodservice: Quick Serve (96)

Key Personnel
SAWYER HEMSLEY - Co-Founder; COO
JASON MCGOWAN - Co-Founder; CEO
BRYCE REDD - CTO
MICHAEL CARD - Controller
AMY BARKER - Senior Director Human Resources
ANDREW YEAGER - Director Customer Communications
EMILY WALKER - Director Quality Assurance
TAYLOR MORSE - Director Social Media
DEREK SARAIVA - Manager Digital Marketing

GCW Corporation
1980 N State St
Orem, UT 84057-2029

Telephone: (801) 221-7064
Fax Number: (801) 228-2584
Internet Homepage: kneaders.com
Company Email: info@kneaders.com
Type of Business: Chain Restaurant Operator
Year Founded: 1997
Total Sales: $36,450,000 (e)
Number of Employees: 45
Average Check: Breakfast(6); Lunch(8); Dinner(8)
Total Units: 59
Trade Names: Kneaders Bakery & Cafe (59)
Company-Owned Units: 10
Units Franchised To: 49
Preferred Square Footage: 1,800
Preferred Location Types: Freestanding
Primary Menu: Sandwiches/Deli (59)
Areas of Operation: AZ, CO, ID, KS, MO, NV, TX, UT
Type of Foodservice: Fast Casual (59)
On-site Distribution Center: Yes
Notes: The company derives approximately 15% of its revenue from retail operations.

Key Personnel
JAMES WORTHINGTON - CEO
DAVID VINCENT - President; CFO; General Buyer
COLLEEN WORTHINGTON - Partner
GARY WORTHINGTON - Partner

Deer Valley Ski Resort
2250 Deer Valley Dr
Park City, UT 84060

Mailing Address: PO Box 889, PARK CITY, UT, 84060-0889
Telephone: (435) 649-1000
Fax Number: (435) 649-1910
Internet Homepage: deervalley.com
Company Email: info@deervalley.com
Type of Business: Foodservice Operations - Hotel/Motels
Year Founded: 1981
Total Sales: $33,164,000 (e)
Alcohol Sales: 15%
Number of Employees: 250
Total Units: 20
Restaurants in Hotels: 20
Trade Names: Bald Mountain Pizza (1); Cushing's Cabin (1); Deer Valley Bakery (1); Deer Valley Etc. (1); Deer Valley Grocery~Cafe (1); Dining To Go (1); EBS Lounge (1); Empire Canyon Grille (1); Fireside Dining (1); Goldener Hirsch Restaurant (1); Mariposa (1); Quincy's Frozen Yogurt (1); Seafood Buffet (1); Silver Lake Restaurant (1); Silver Lake Snack Shack (1); Snow Park (1); Snow Park Bakery (1); Snowshoe Tommy's (1); The Brass Tag (1); The Royal Street Cafe (1)
Company-Owned Units: 20
Alcohol Served: Beer, Wine, Liquor
Projected Remodelings: 2
Areas of Operation: UT
Type of Foodservice: Fine Dining (2)
Primary Distributors: (Food) SYSCO Intermountain Food Services Inc., WEST JORDAN, UT
Notes: The company derives approximately 70% of its revenue from hotel operations.

Key Personnel
RYAN LLOYD - Executive Chef; Manager Menu Development
DIRK BEAL - Director Sales
EMILY SUMMERS - Senior Manager Communications
STACY TAYLOR - Manager Human Resources
RYAN MAYFIELD - Manager Social Media

White Restaurant Group
1918 Prospector Ave
Park City, UT 84060-4410

Mailing Address: PO Box 3537, PARK CITY, UT, 84060-3537
Telephone: (435) 647-2908
Fax Number: (435) 615-1149
Internet Homepage: billwhiterestaurantgroup.com; billyblancos.com; chimayorestaurant.com; ghidottis.com; grapparestaurant.com; wahso.com; windyridgefoods.com
Company Email: comments@billwhiteenterprises.com
Type of Business: Chain Restaurant Operator
Year Founded: 1996
Total Sales: $13,480,000 (e)
Alcohol Sales: 10%
Number of Employees: 400
Average Check: Breakfast(14); Lunch(26);

Dinner(50)
Total Units: 8
Trade Names: Billy Blanco's (1); Chimayo (1); Ghidottis (1); Grappa Italian (1); Sushi Blue (1); Wahso (1); Windy Ridge Bakery (1); Windy Ridge Cafe (1)
Company-Owned Units: 8
Preferred Square Footage: 5,500; 6,000
Preferred Location Types: Freestanding
Alcohol Served: Beer, Wine, Liquor
Primary Menu: American (2); Asian (1); Italian (1); Japanese (1); Miscellaneous (2); Southwest/Tex-Mex (1)
Areas of Operation: UT
Type of Foodservice: Casual Dining (3); Fast Casual (1); Fine Dining (4)
Primary Distributors: (Food) US Foods, OGDEN, UT

Key Personnel
BILL WHITE - Owner; General Buyer

Domino's Franchisee
725 W 1200 S Ste C
Perry, UT 84302-5592

Telephone: (435) 734-9200
Type of Business: Chain Restaurant Operator
Total Sales: $8,095,000 (e)
Total Units: 4
Trade Names: Domino's (4)
Units Franchised From: 4
Primary Menu: Pizza (4)
Areas of Operation: UT
Type of Foodservice: Quick Serve (4)
Franchise Affiliation: Domino's Pizza Inc, ANN ARBOR, MI

Key Personnel
JONATHON G. BEADLES - Owner; General Buyer

Swig
2102 W Grove Pkwy Ste 220
Pleasant Grove, UT 84062

Telephone: (801) 642-3800
Internet Homepage: swigsweets.com
Type of Business: Chain Restaurant Operator
Total Sales: $34,810,000 (e)
Total Units: 37
Trade Names: Swig (37)
Company-Owned Units: 37
Primary Menu: Snacks (37)
Type of Foodservice: Fast Casual (37)

Key Personnel
NICOLE TANNER - Founder; Owner
ALEX DUNN - CEO Interim
BILL AYERS - CFO

DANIEL BATTY - Chief Development Officer
JORDAN HILL - Senior Director Facility/Maintenance, Development
ANGELA KAVANAUGH - Director People

Brick Oven Restaurant
111 E 800 N
Provo, UT 84606-1713

Telephone: (801) 374-8800
Fax Number: (801) 370-9044
Internet Homepage: brickovenrestaurants.com
Type of Business: Chain Restaurant Operator
Year Founded: 1956
Total Sales: $7,808,000 (e)
Number of Employees: 200
Average Check: Lunch(14); Dinner(18)
Internet Order Processing: Yes
Total Units: 3
Trade Names: Brick Oven Restaurant (3)
Company-Owned Units: 3
Primary Menu: Italian (3)
Areas of Operation: UT
Type of Foodservice: Family Restaurant (3)
Catering Services: Yes
Primary Distributors: (Food) Nicholas & Co. Inc., SALT LAKE CITY, UT

Key Personnel
DANE BLACK - Partner; General Manager; General Buyer
SCOTT CARNAGIE - General Manager; General Buyer
DAVID GEORGE - General Manager
STUART CHENEY - Manager Accounting

Malawi's Pizza
4833 N Edgewood Dr
Provo, UT 84604-6170

Telephone: (801) 960-1130
Internet Homepage: malawispizza.com
Type of Business: Chain Restaurant Operator
Total Units: 4
Trade Names: Malawi's Pizza (4)
Company-Owned Units: 4
Primary Menu: Pizza (4)
Projected Openings: 1
Areas of Operation: TX, UT, VA
Type of Foodservice: Fast Casual (4)

Key Personnel
BLAKE RONEY - Founder
KENT ANDERSEN - CEO; President

Sodalicious
1331 S State St
Provo, UT 84606

Telephone: (801) 717-5330
Internet Homepage: mysodalicious.com
Type of Business: Chain Restaurant Operator
Total Sales: $23,870,000 (e)
Total Units: 25
Trade Names: Sodalicious (25)
Company-Owned Units: 25
Primary Menu: Snacks (25)
Type of Foodservice: Fast Casual (25)

Key Personnel
KEVIN AUERNIG - Founder; CEO

Sub Zero Ice Cream
62 W Center St
Provo, UT 84601-4417

Telephone: (801) 494-0960
Internet Homepage: subzeroicecream.com
Company Email: info@subzeroicecream.com
Type of Business: Chain Restaurant Operator
Year Founded: 2004
Total Sales: $23,630,000 (e)
Number of Employees: 455
Total Units: 47
Trade Names: Sub Zero Ice Cream & Yogurt (47)
Company-Owned Units: 3
Units Franchised To: 44
Primary Menu: Snacks (47)
Projected Openings: 2
Areas of Operation: AZ, CA, FL, ID, IN, LA, MI, MN, NC, NH, OR, PA, SC, TX, UT, WA
Foreign Countries: CHINA; UNITED ARAB EMIRATES
Type of Foodservice: Quick Serve (47)

Key Personnel
JERRY HANCOCK - Co-Founder; President
NAOMI HANCOCK - Co-Founder; Executive Director

Subzero Nitrogen Ice Cream
1718 N University Pkwy
Provo, UT 84604

Telephone: (385) 208-4353
Internet Homepage: subzeroicecream.com
Type of Business: Chain Restaurant Operator
Year Founded: 2004
Systemwide Sales: $40,853,000 (e)
Total Sales: $15,190,000 (e)
Total Units: 42
Trade Names: Subzero Nitrogen Ice Cream (43)

Company-Owned Units: 2
Units Franchised To: 41
Primary Menu: Ice Cream (43)
Type of Foodservice: Fast Casual (43)

Key Personnel
JERRY HANCOCK - Co-Founder; CEO
NAOMI HANCOCK - Co-Founder; Corporate Secretary

Fiiz
2339 S River Rd
Saint George, UT 84790

Telephone: (435) 656-4349
Internet Homepage: fiizdrinks.com
Type of Business: Chain Restaurant Operator
Total Sales: $37,180,000 (e)
Total Units: 39
Trade Names: Fiiz (39)
Company-Owned Units: 1
Units Franchised To: 38
Primary Menu: Snacks (39)
Type of Foodservice: Fast Casual (39)

Key Personnel
JOEL MORGAN - Founder; Owner

New Start, LC
1185 S Main St
Saint George, UT 84770-5239

Telephone: (435) 628-2101
Fax Number: (435) 673-1668
Type of Business: Chain Restaurant Operator
Year Founded: 2000
Total Sales: $13,440,000 (e)
Number of Employees: 272
Average Check: Breakfast(10); Lunch(10); Dinner(10)
Total Units: 6
Trade Names: Burger King (6)
Units Franchised From: 6
Preferred Square Footage: 2,500
Preferred Location Types: Convenience Store/Gas Station; Freestanding
Primary Menu: Hamburger (6)
Areas of Operation: AZ, UT
Type of Foodservice: Quick Serve (6)
Franchise Affiliation: Burger King Worldwide Inc., MIAMI, FL
Primary Distributors: (Full Line) Nicholas & Co. Inc., SALT LAKE CITY, UT

Key Personnel
JAMES GULLO - President; General Manager; Director Finance, Operations, Purchasing, Facility/Maintenance, Information Systems, Supply Chain, Real Estate, Human Resources, Store Fixtures; General Buyer

Apollo Burger
940 W 1700 S
Salt Lake City, UT 84104-2200

Telephone: (801) 975-4052
Internet Homepage: apolloburgers.com
Company Email: michael@apolloburgers.com
Type of Business: Chain Restaurant Operator
Total Sales: $1,862,000 (e)
Number of Employees: 171
Average Check: Lunch(12); Dinner(22)
Total Units: 11
Trade Names: Apollo Burger (11)
Company-Owned Units: 11
Preferred Square Footage: 2,000
Preferred Location Types: Freestanding
Primary Menu: Hamburger (11)
Projected Openings: 1
Areas of Operation: UT
Type of Foodservice: Quick Serve (11)
Distribution Centers: SALT LAKE CITY, UT

Key Personnel
DENO PRISKOS - Partner
MICHAEL ZIOURAS - Partner; Executive Chef; Director Operations; General Buyer
PAIGE JOCOBSON - Director Marketing

Apple Spice Junction
2235 S 1300 W Ste A
Salt Lake City, UT 84119-7244

Telephone: (801) 359-8821
Fax Number: (801) 433-3030
Internet Homepage: applespice.com
Company Email: asjhq@applespice.com
Type of Business: Chain Restaurant Operator
Year Founded: 1988
Total Sales: $67,070,000 (e)
Total Units: 52
Trade Names: Apple Spice Junction (52)
Company-Owned Units: 36
Units Franchised To: 16
Preferred Location Types: Office Complex
Primary Menu: Sandwiches/Deli (52)
Projected Openings: 19
Areas of Operation: AR, CA, FL, IN, MA, MD, NC, NJ, OH, PA, UT, VA, WA
Type of Foodservice: Quick Serve (52)

Key Personnel
RANDY CLEGG - Partner; VP Menu Development; General Buyer
WAYNE CURTIS - Partner; VP Marketing; General Buyer
MARK D. PETERSEN - VP Marketing
LUCY THOMPSON - Director Marketing
ALISON AINGE - Director Operations, Training
CHRIS GYGI - Director Marketing, Sales

Bad Ass Coffee Company of Hawaii
155 W Malvern Ave Ste A
Salt Lake City, UT 84115-3070

Telephone: (801) 463-1966
Fax Number: (801) 463-2606
Internet Homepage: badasscoffeestore.com
Company Email: info@badasscoffee.com
Type of Business: Chain Restaurant Operator
Year Founded: 1997
Systemwide Sales: $29,151,000 (e)
Total Sales: $2,572,000 (e)
Number of Employees: 7
Average Check: Breakfast(8); Lunch(8); Dinner(8)
Internet Order Processing: Yes
Internet Sales: 1.00%
Total Units: 24
Trade Names: Bad Ass Coffee (24)
Units Franchised To: 29
Preferred Square Footage: 1,500
Preferred Location Types: Downtown; Freestanding; Kiosk; Strip Mall
Primary Menu: Coffee (24)
Areas of Operation: CA, FL, GA, HI, IL, LA, MT, NM, NV, NY, OR, PR, TX, UT, VA, VI, FC
Foreign Countries: JAPAN; MALAYSIA
Type of Foodservice: Quick Serve (29)
On-site Distribution Center: Yes
Primary Distributors: (Food) US Foods, OGDEN, UT

Key Personnel
GREGG KOFFLER - Chief Development Officer
STEVE MEEKER - VP Operations, Supply Chain, Store Fixtures, Menu Development
MISTY PETERSEN - Specialist Customer Service

Beans & Brews Coffee House
8619 Sandy Parkway Ste. 110
Salt Lake City, UT 84070

Telephone: (801) 561-5241
Internet Homepage: beansandbrews.com
Type of Business: Chain Restaurant Operator
Year Founded: 1993
Systemwide Sales: $80,150,000 (e)
Total Sales: $47,882,000 (e)
Total Units: 81
Trade Names: Beans & Brews Coffee House (81)
Company-Owned Units: 10
Units Franchised To: 71
Primary Menu: Coffee (81)
Areas of Operation: AZ, CA, ID, NV, TX, UT

Type of Foodservice: Quick Serve (81)

Key Personnel
DOUG WILLMARTH - CEO
SARAH ANDERSON - Senior VP Operations
CARRIE MONGOLD - VP Marketing
MELANIE SPENCER - VP Finance
PAUL SPIERS - VP Construction, Design
SONJA LEIGH - Director Training
MINDY VOSE - Director Franchise Operations
JULIE HANSEN - Director Human Resources
DANIELLE DEJONG - Director Operations

Cafe Rio Inc.
215 N Admiral Byrd Rd Ste 100
Salt Lake City, UT 84116-3780

Telephone: (801) 441-5000
Fax Number: (801) 441-5100
Internet Homepage: caferio.com
Company Email: Questions@CafeRio.com
Type of Business: Chain Restaurant Operator
Year Founded: 1997
Total Sales: $473,330,000 (e)
Number of Employees: 880
Average Check: Lunch(8); Dinner(10)
Total Units: 144
Trade Names: Cafe Rio Mexican Grill (144)
Company-Owned Units: 144
Preferred Square Footage: 2,500
Preferred Location Types: Airports; Freestanding
Primary Menu: Mexican (144)
Areas of Operation: AZ, CA, CO, ID, MD, MT, NV, UT, VA, WA, WY
Type of Foodservice: Fast Casual (144)
Catering Services: Yes
Primary Distributors: (Full Line) SYSCO Intermountain Food Services Inc., WEST JORDAN, UT
Parent Company: Freeman Spogli & Co., NEW YORK, NY

Key Personnel
STEVE VAUGHAN - CEO; President
SHEA BODET - CFO
ABE HOLLANDS - COO
CORTNEY WORLE - Chief People Officer
TODD SMITH - Chief Concept Officer
REMO MELUCCI - VP Operations
CHRIS READING - Senior Director Operations
BRANDAN BIEKER - Director Information Technology
CATHY KNOWLSON - Director Marketing
RANDY LOFASO - Director
AARON MANGUM - Director
STACY YOUNG - Director Marketing; Community Relations

Chuck-A-Rama Buffet Inc.
744 E 400 S
Salt Lake City, UT 84102-2902

Telephone: (801) 433-3663
Internet Homepage: chuck-a-rama.com
Company Email: randy@chuck-a-rama.com
Type of Business: Chain Restaurant Operator
Year Founded: 1966
Total Sales: $38,910,000 (e)
Number of Employees: 840
Average Check: Lunch(10); Dinner(12)
Internet Order Processing: Yes
Total Units: 12
Trade Names: Chuck-A-Rama Buffet (12)
Company-Owned Units: 12
Preferred Square Footage: 8,400
Preferred Location Types: Freestanding
Primary Menu: American (12)
Areas of Operation: ID, UT
Type of Foodservice: Family Restaurant (12)
Primary Distributors: (Equipment) Restaurant & Store Equipment Inc., SALT LAKE CITY, UT; (Food) Nicholas & Co. Inc., SALT LAKE CITY, UT; (Supplies) Bintz Restaurant Supply Co., SALT LAKE CITY, UT

Key Personnel
RENE SCHUURMAN - Director Operations, Purchasing, Loss Prevention, Quality Assurance, Menu Development, Food Safety; Buyer Beverages, Food

CMK Enterprises
1877 E Murray Holladay Rd
Salt Lake City, UT 84117-5110

Telephone: (801) 523-8960
Fax Number: (801) 272-9234
Company Email: conny.kramer@cmkmcd.us
Type of Business: Chain Restaurant Operator
Total Sales: $32,870,000 (e)
Number of Employees: 210
Total Units: 7
Trade Names: McDonald's (7)
Units Franchised From: 7
Preferred Square Footage: 2,500
Primary Menu: Hamburger (7)
Areas of Operation: UT
Type of Foodservice: Quick Serve (7)
Franchise Affiliation: McDonald's Corporation, CHICAGO, IL

Key Personnel
CORNELIA KRAMER - President; General Buyer

Gastronomy Inc.
48 W Market St Ste 250
Salt Lake City, UT 84101-2147

Telephone: (801) 239-2400
Fax Number: (801) 539-8758
Internet Homepage: ginc.com
Company Email: comments@ginc.com
Type of Business: Chain Restaurant Operator
Year Founded: 1977
Total Sales: $32,010,000 (e)
Alcohol Sales: 10%
Number of Employees: 562
Average Check: Breakfast(18); Lunch(30); Dinner(36)
Internet Order Processing: Yes
Internet Sales: 1.00%
Total Units: 6
Trade Names: Market Street Grill (3); Market Street Oyster Bar (3)
Company-Owned Units: 6
Preferred Square Footage: 10,000
Preferred Location Types: Downtown; Freestanding; Office Complex
Alcohol Served: Beer, Wine, Liquor
Primary Menu: American (3); Seafood (3)
Areas of Operation: UT
Type of Foodservice: Casual Dining (6)
Primary Distributors: (Full Line) US Foods, OGDEN, UT

Key Personnel
PATRICIA G. STEVENSON - VP Real Estate
ROBERT HALLADAY - General Manager
MARYANNE FARRIER - Director Marketing
JUDY REESE - Director Communications
NICHO ALMY - Coordinator Training

H.B. Boy's LLC
2280 S Main St
Salt Lake City, UT 84115-2629

Telephone: (801) 486-6777
Fax Number: (801) 487-8304
Internet Homepage: hbboys.com
Type of Business: Chain Restaurant Operator
Year Founded: 1984
Total Sales: $119,230,000 (e)
Number of Employees: 1,950
Average Check: Breakfast(8); Lunch(8); Dinner(8)
Total Units: 78
Trade Names: Beans and Brews (6); Burger King (63); Costa Vita (6); Subway (3)
Units Franchised From: 78
Preferred Square Footage: 3,500; 4,500
Preferred Location Types: Convenience Store/Gas Station; Freestanding
Primary Menu: Coffee (6); Hamburger (57); Hamburger (63); Mexican (6); Sandwiches/Deli (3)

Areas of Operation: ID, NV, UT, WY
Type of Foodservice: Quick Serve (78)
Franchise Affiliation: Burger King Worldwide Inc., MIAMI, FL; Doctor's Associates Inc., MILFORD, CT
Primary Distributors: (Food) Nicholas & Co. Inc., SALT LAKE CITY, UT

Key Personnel
DAVID WILLIAMS - President; Director Finance, Real Estate
GARY MOORE - VP Operations, Purchasing, Food Safety; General Manager
MELISSA DEMPSEY - General Manager
CHRISTA WILKINS - Director Marketing
EMILY HARDING - Manager Human Resources

Johnny Appleseed Inc.
308 E 4500 S Ste 210
Salt Lake City, UT 84107-3997

Telephone: (801) 532-5108
Internet Homepage: restaurants.applebees.com/ak
Type of Business: Chain Restaurant Operator
Total Sales: $35,110,000 (e)
Alcohol Sales: 5%
Number of Employees: 27
Average Check: Lunch(18); Dinner(18)
Total Units: 9
Trade Names: Applebee's Neighborhood Grill & Bar (9)
Units Franchised From: 9
Preferred Square Footage: 3,600; 5,000
Preferred Location Types: Freestanding
Alcohol Served: Beer, Wine, Liquor
Primary Menu: American (9)
Areas of Operation: AR, KS, OK
Type of Foodservice: Casual Dining (9)
Franchise Affiliation: Applebee's Services Inc., KANSAS CITY, MO
Primary Distributors: (Full Line) US Foods, ANCHORAGE, AK

Key Personnel
JOHN PRINCE - President; Director Operations; General Buyer
JEFF MYERS - VP; Director Menu Development

MJM 5G LLC
125 W Burton Ave Ste 2
Salt Lake City, UT 84115-2610

Telephone: (801) 231-6101
Type of Business: Chain Restaurant Operator
Total Sales: $85,120,000 (e)
Total Units: 43
Trade Names: Five Guys Burgers and Fries (43)
Units Franchised From: 43
Primary Menu: Hamburger (43)
Areas of Operation: UT
Type of Foodservice: Fast Casual (43)
Franchise Affiliation: Five Guys Holdings Inc., LORTON, VA

Key Personnel
JEFFREY HOWES - Partner; General Buyer
MICHAEL B. CUMMINGS - Partner
RYAN HOWES - Partner

Pub Inc.
1414 S Foothill Dr Ste C
Salt Lake City, UT 84108-2347

Telephone: (801) 581-9498
Fax Number: (801) 582-0631
Internet Homepage: martinecafe.com; desertedgebrewery.com; stellagrill.com; theredbuttecafe.com
Type of Business: Chain Restaurant Operator
Year Founded: 1970
Total Sales: $6,004,000 (e)
Alcohol Sales: 5%
Number of Employees: 100
Average Check: Dinner(22)
Total Units: 4
Trade Names: Desert Edge Pub & Brewery (1); Martine Cafe (1); Red Butte Cafe (1); Stella Grille (1)
Company-Owned Units: 4
Preferred Location Types: Freestanding
Alcohol Served: Beer, Wine, Liquor
Primary Menu: American (1); Southwest/Tex-Mex (2); Spanish (1)
Areas of Operation: UT
Type of Foodservice: Casual Dining (3); Fine Dining (1)
Primary Distributors: (Full Line) Nicholas & Co. Inc., SALT LAKE CITY, UT

Key Personnel
SCOTT HALE - Partner; General Buyer
MARK MURPHY - Partner; General Manager; Buyer Beverages
RICH PARRENT - Partner; Executive Chef

R&R BBQ
307 W 600 S
Salt Lake City, UT 84101-2732

Telephone: (801) 364-0443
Internet Homepage: randrbbq.net
Company Email: slc@randrbbq.com
Type of Business: Chain Restaurant Operator
Total Units: 8
Trade Names: R&R BBQ (8)
Company-Owned Units: 8
Primary Menu: Bar-B-Q (8)
Areas of Operation: UT
Type of Foodservice: Fast Casual (8)

Key Personnel
ROD LIVINGSTON - Co-Founder; General Buyer
ROGER LIVINGSTON - Co-Founder
NEIL HARFERT - President
WILLIAM SINGLETARY - Area Manager

Ronda Foods LLC
1168 S Legacy View St
Salt Lake City, UT 84104-6500

Telephone: (801) 571-9841
Fax Number: (801) 571-9883
Type of Business: Chain Restaurant Operator
Year Founded: 1975
Total Sales: $6,869,000 (e)
Number of Employees: 180
Average Check: Lunch(8); Dinner(10)
Total Units: 8
Trade Names: Taco Time (8)
Units Franchised From: 8
Preferred Square Footage: 2,500
Preferred Location Types: Freestanding
Primary Menu: Taco (8)
Areas of Operation: UT
Type of Foodservice: Quick Serve (8)
Franchise Affiliation: Kahala Brands, SCOTTSDALE, AZ
Primary Distributors: (Full Line) Nicholas & Co. Inc., SALT LAKE CITY, UT

Key Personnel
RON LARSEN - President; Director Finance, Real Estate
BARBARA HOWARD - Controller
KEVIN WALL - General Manager; Director Facility/Maintenance, Information Systems, Design, Human Resources; General Buyer
KIMBERLY SUNDBERG - Manager Accounting

Rumbi Holdings LLC
3865 S Wasatch Blvd Ste 300
Salt Lake City, UT 84109-3865

Telephone: (801) 545-0232
Internet Homepage: rumbi.com
Company Email: info@rumbi.com
Type of Business: Chain Restaurant Operator
Year Founded: 2000
Systemwide Sales: $34,837,000 (e)
Total Sales: $27,960,000 (e)
Total Units: 22
Trade Names: Rumbi Island Grill (22)
Company-Owned Units: 22
Preferred Square Footage: 1,500; 1,800; 3,500
Preferred Location Types: Community Mall; Freestanding; Strip Mall
Primary Menu: Miscellaneous (22)
Areas of Operation: AZ, ID, UT
Type of Foodservice: Fast Casual (22)

Primary Distributors: (Food) SYSCO Intermountain Food Services Inc., WEST JORDAN, UT

Key Personnel
KAITLYN WOODS - General Manager
KATIE WOODS - District Manager

Salt Lake Brewing Co.
147 W Broadway
Salt Lake City, UT 84101-1914

Telephone: (801) 328-2329
Fax Number: (801) 924-0380
Internet Homepage: squatters.com
Company Email: beer@squatters.com
Type of Business: Chain Restaurant Operator
Year Founded: 1989
Total Sales: $7,099,000 (e)
Alcohol Sales: 30%
Number of Employees: 267
Average Check: Breakfast(18); Lunch(18); Dinner(24)
Internet Order Processing: Yes
Internet Sales: 1.00%
Total Units: 3
Trade Names: Squatters Airport Pub (1); Squatters Downtown Pub (1); Wasatch Brew Pub Park City (1)
Company-Owned Units: 3
Preferred Location Types: Airports; Downtown; Freestanding; Mixed-use Center
Alcohol Served: Beer, Wine, Liquor
Primary Menu: American (3)
Areas of Operation: UT
Type of Foodservice: Casual Dining (3)
Catering Services: Yes

Key Personnel
MICHAEL DRENNAN - Manager Sales

Super Chix, Inc.
7135 S Highland Dr Ste 200
Salt Lake City, UT 84121

Telephone: (801) 277-1011
Internet Homepage: superchix.com
Company Email: customersupport@superchix.com
Type of Business: Chain Restaurant Operator
Year Founded: 2014
Average Check: Lunch(10); Dinner(10)
Total Units: 5
Trade Names: Super Chix Chicken & Custard (5)
Company-Owned Units: 4
Units Franchised To: 1
Primary Menu: Chicken (5)
Projected Openings: 2
Areas of Operation: AL, TX, UT

Type of Foodservice: Fast Casual (5)

Key Personnel
NICK OUIMET - CEO

Western States Foods
230 E South Temple
Salt Lake City, UT 84111-1205

Telephone: (801) 478-0183
Fax Number: (801) 487-8564
Type of Business: Chain Restaurant Operator
Year Founded: 1983
Total Sales: $17,760,000 (e)
Number of Employees: 250
Average Check: Breakfast(8); Lunch(6); Dinner(14)
Total Units: 20
Trade Names: Edo Japan (1); Great Stakes (4); Karmelkorn Shoppe (1); Mario's Pizza (5); Orange Julius (9)
Company-Owned Units: 4
Units Franchised From: 16
Preferred Square Footage: 600
Preferred Location Types: Regional Mall
Primary Menu: Japanese (1); Pizza (5); Sandwiches/Deli (4); Snacks (10)
Areas of Operation: ID, OR, UT, WA
Type of Foodservice: Quick Serve (20)
Primary Distributors: (Full Line) SYSCO Intermountain Food Services Inc., WEST JORDAN, UT

Key Personnel
STEVEN PRICE - President; Manager Facility/Maintenance, Real Estate, Design
PHILLIP ODEKIRK - Exec VP; Manager Finance, Operations, Information Systems, Loss Prevention, Marketing, Human Resources, Menu Development, Food Safety; General Buyer
KELLY SMITH PETERSON - Controller

Cafe Zupas LLC
460 W Universal Cir
Sandy, UT 84070-2573

Telephone: (801) 878-4536
Fax Number: (801) 878-4537
Internet Homepage: cafezupas.com
Company Email: info@cafezupas.com
Type of Business: Chain Restaurant Operator
Year Founded: 2005
Total Sales: $66,720,000 (e)
Number of Employees: 1,500
Average Check: Lunch(14); Dinner(14)
Total Units: 59
Trade Names: Cafe Zupas (59)
Company-Owned Units: 59
Preferred Location Types: Strip Mall
Primary Menu: American (59)

Projected Openings: 2
Areas of Operation: AZ, ID, IL, MN, NV, OH, UT, WI
Type of Foodservice: Quick Serve (58)
Catering Services: Yes
Parent Company: KarpReilly LLC, GREENWICH, CT

Key Personnel
DUSTIN SCHULTHIES - Partner
ROBERT SEELEY - Partner; General Buyer
PAUL KILLPACK - CFO
WESTLEY BEAMAN - CIO
CHRIS L - VP Operations
TRAVIS LARSEN - VP Construction
CHRIS LUDLOW - VP Operations
LAUREN AAMODT - VP Marketing
LAURA RIDGEWAY - Senior Director Purchasing
KEVIN STOKER - Director Business Development, Catering
BRANDON PFUNDER - Art Director Design
JORDAN LARSEN - Manager Strategy
KATIE DALLEY - Manager Catering

Jim's Family Restaurants
10640 S Holladay Park Dr
Sandy, UT 84070

Telephone: (801) 553-8100
Fax Number: (801) 553-8430
Internet Homepage: jimsfamilyrestaurant.com
Type of Business: Chain Restaurant Operator
Year Founded: 1988
Total Sales: $9,105,000 (e)
Number of Employees: 250
Average Check: Breakfast(10); Lunch(12); Dinner(14)
Total Units: 6
Trade Names: Jim's Family Restaurant (6)
Company-Owned Units: 3
Units Franchised To: 3
Preferred Location Types: Freestanding
Alcohol Served: Beer
Primary Menu: American (6)
Areas of Operation: UT
Type of Foodservice: Family Restaurant (6)

Key Personnel
JIM FUSKANDRAKIS - Partner; General Buyer
MIKE FUSKANDRAKIS - Partner; Corporate Secretary

Peak Restaurant Group, LLC
10815 S State St
Sandy, UT 84070-4104

Telephone: (801) 523-8613
Internet Homepage: prpihop.com
Type of Business: Chain Restaurant Operator
Total Sales: $86,370,000 (e)

Total Units: 28
Trade Names: IHOP (28)
Units Franchised From: 28
Primary Menu: American (28)
Areas of Operation: UT
Type of Foodservice: Family Restaurant (28)
Franchise Affiliation: IHOP Restaurant System, GLENDALE, CA

Key Personnel
ROBERT TOMLINSON - President
GREG PAGE - Area Director
TIM BIHUN - Area Director
AMBER BULLOCK - Area Director
ROBIN BRONSON - Director Human Resources
PATRICIA MARTINEZ - Director Human Resources
JEDYDYAH ALLRED - Director Strategic Services
STEVE MILLER - Regional Manager Marketing
MIKE ANDRUS - Manager Facility/Maintenance

The Phoenix Restaurant Group
9829 S 1300 E Ste 302
Sandy, UT 84094-4056

Telephone: (801) 567-0500
Fax Number: (801) 567-0501
Internet Homepage: rodiziogrill.com
Company Email: info@rodiziogrill.com
Type of Business: Chain Restaurant Operator
Total Sales: $14,650,000 (e)
Alcohol Sales: 18%
Average Check: Lunch(24); Dinner(32)
Internet Order Processing: Yes
Total Units: 21
Trade Names: Rodizio Grill (21)
Company-Owned Units: 3
Units Franchised To: 18
Preferred Location Types: Downtown; Freestanding
Alcohol Served: Beer, Wine, Liquor
Primary Menu: Steak (21)
Projected Openings: 1
Areas of Operation: AZ, CO, FL, IN, MN, NJ, OH, PA, TN, TX, UT, WI
Type of Foodservice: Casual Dining (21)
Catering Services: Yes
Primary Distributors: (Full Line) SYSCO Intermountain Food Services Inc., WEST JORDAN, UT

Key Personnel
IVAN UTRERA - Founder; President
WLADIMIR RIBEIRO - CFO
EDUARDO GOURLART - Executive Chef; Director Operations, Menu Development
ASHLEE HILLE - Director Marketing
GREG PEREIRA - Manager Information Systems

Meridian Restaurant Unlimited LLC
5929 Fashion Point Dr Ste 501
South Ogden, UT 84403

Telephone: (801) 621-0905
Fax Number: (801) 621-6764
Internet Homepage: meridianrestaurantsunlimited.com
Type of Business: Chain Restaurant Operator
Year Founded: 1978
Total Sales: $312,890,000 (e)
Number of Employees: 4,000
Average Check: Breakfast(8); Lunch(8); Dinner(8)
Total Units: 125
Trade Names: Burger King (118); Chili's (7)
Units Franchised From: 125
Preferred Square Footage: 2,500
Preferred Location Types: Freestanding
Primary Menu: Hamburger (118)
Areas of Operation: AZ, ID, MN, MT, ND, UT, WY
Type of Foodservice: Quick Serve (118)
Franchise Affiliation: Burger King Worldwide Inc., MIAMI, FL
Primary Distributors: (Food) Nicholas & Co. Inc., SALT LAKE CITY, UT
Headquarter Offices: PLM Restaurants, L.C., OGDEN, UT
Notes: Meridian Restaurant Unlimited LLC is also a franchisee of El Pollo Loco (organized under PLM Restaurants, L.C.) and Chili's (organized under Paradigm Restaurants).

Key Personnel
DAVID HARPER - President; Partner; General Buyer
GARRETT CAZIER - CFO
STUART DUKE - Chief Business Development Officer
JASON WOLFF - VP Operations
STAYSEE WOLFF - Director Human Resources
DWIGHT SCHLEGEL - Director Operations
KEN KENNEDY - Director Operations
WALTER WHITED - Regional Director Operations
THOMAS PINKERTON - Manager District

Auntie Anne's Franchise
660 S 1750 W
Springville, UT 84663-3071

Telephone: (801) 853-1310
Type of Business: Chain Restaurant Operator
Total Sales: $3,125,000 (e)
Total Units: 4
Trade Names: Auntie Anne's Hand-Rolled Soft Pretzels (4)
Units Franchised From: 4
Primary Menu: Snacks (4)
Areas of Operation: UT
Type of Foodservice: Quick Serve (4)
Franchise Affiliation: Auntie Anne's Inc., LANCASTER, PA

Key Personnel
JACK BICKMORE - Owner; General Buyer

Rjss Corporation
987 S Bluff St
St George, UT 84770-7309

Telephone: (435) 229-8991
Type of Business: Chain Restaurant Operator
Total Sales: $10,103,000 (e)
Total Units: 5
Trade Names: Domino's (5)
Units Franchised From: 5
Primary Menu: Pizza (5)
Areas of Operation: NV, UT
Type of Foodservice: Quick Serve (5)
Franchise Affiliation: Domino's Pizza Inc, ANN ARBOR, MI

Key Personnel
RANDY SNOW - President; General Buyer

Sundance Partners Ltd.
8841 N Alpine Loop Rd
Sundance, UT 84604-5538

Mailing Address: 8841 N Alpine Loop Rd, SUNDANCE, UT, 84604
Telephone: (801) 225-4107
Fax Number: (801) 226-1937
Internet Homepage: sundanceresort.com
Company Email: info@sundanceresort.com
Type of Business: Chain Restaurant Operator
Year Founded: 1969
Total Sales: $15,516,000 (e)
Alcohol Sales: 25%
Number of Employees: 110
Average Check: Breakfast(24); Lunch(32); Dinner(66)
Total Units: 4
Trade Names: Bearclaw Cabin (1); Foundry Grill (1); Sundance Deli (1); Tree Room (1)
Company-Owned Units: 4
Preferred Location Types: Freestanding; Hotel/Motel
Alcohol Served: Beer, Wine, Liquor
Primary Menu: American (3); Sandwiches/Deli (1)
Areas of Operation: UT
Type of Foodservice: Casual Dining (2); Fine Dining (1); Quick Serve (1)
Catering Services: Yes
Primary Distributors: (Full Line) SYSCO Intermountain Food Services Inc., WEST JORDAN, UT

Key Personnel
ROBERT REDFORD - Owner
SAMANTHA VARGA - Manager Human Resources
ROY MCCLUSKEY - Manager Purchasing

MP2 Enterprises
2303 N Coral Canyon Blvd Ste 99
Washington, UT 84780-2509

Telephone: (435) 986-1220
Fax Number: (435) 304-0212
Internet Homepage: mp2pizza.com
Company Email: bryant.peterson@mp2pizza.com
Type of Business: Chain Restaurant Operator
Year Founded: 2006
Total Sales: $20,820,000 (e)
Alcohol Sales: 7%
Number of Employees: 330
Average Check: Lunch(10); Dinner(14)
Total Units: 17
Trade Names: Pizza Hut (17)
Units Franchised From: 17
Preferred Square Footage: 1,400; 4,500
Preferred Location Types: Freestanding; Strip Mall
Alcohol Served: Beer
Primary Menu: Pizza (17)
Areas of Operation: AZ, NV, UT
Type of Foodservice: Casual Dining (17); Quick Serve (17)
Franchise Affiliation: Pizza Hut Inc., PLANO, TX

Key Personnel
BRYANT PETERSON - President; General Buyer

Arctic Circle Restaurants Inc.
4214 W 8370 S
West Jordan, UT 84088

Mailing Address: PO Box 517, West Jordan, UT, 84084
Telephone: (801) 561-3620
Internet Homepage: arcticcirclerest.com
Type of Business: Chain Restaurant Operator
Year Founded: 1950
Systemwide Sales: $60,193,000 (e)
Total Sales: $23,740,000 (e)
Number of Employees: 630
Average Check: Lunch(8); Dinner(8)
Total Units: 63
Trade Names: Arctic Circle Restaurant (63)
Company-Owned Units: 32
Units Franchised To: 31
Preferred Square Footage: 3,000
Preferred Location Types: Community Mall; Freestanding

Primary Menu: Hamburger (63)
Areas of Operation: ID, MT, OR, UT, WA, WY
Type of Foodservice: Quick Serve (63)
Primary Distributors: (Full Line) Nicholas & Co. Inc., SALT LAKE CITY, UT

Key Personnel
FRANK CHRISTENSON - CFO; VP; Treasurer

Cima Group Inc.
7650 S Redwood Rd Ste F
West Jordan, UT 84084-5631

Telephone: (801) 566-1112
Fax Number: (801) 566-1552
Type of Business: Chain Restaurant Operator
Total Sales: $24,970,000 (e)
Number of Employees: 100
Average Check: Lunch(8); Dinner(8)
Total Units: 44
Trade Names: Auntie Anne's Cinnabon Cafe (1); Auntie Anne's Hand-rolled Soft Pretzels (1); Subway (42)
Units Franchised From: 44
Preferred Square Footage: 300; 1,200; 2,000
Preferred Location Types: Convenience Store/Gas Station; Discount Dept. Stores; Strip Mall
Primary Menu: Sandwiches/Deli (42); Snacks (2)
Areas of Operation: UT
Type of Foodservice: Quick Serve (44)
Franchise Affiliation: Doctor's Associates Inc., MILFORD, CT
Primary Distributors: (Food) Nicholas & Co. Inc., SALT LAKE CITY, UT

Key Personnel
JACK BICKMORE - President; General Manager; General Buyer

VIRGINIA

Be Fish
631 King St
Alexandria, VA 22314-3105

Telephone: (877) 234-7490
Internet Homepage: bumblefishsushi.com; be.fish
Company Email: sales@be.fish
Type of Business: Chain Restaurant Operator
Year Founded: 2003
Total Sales: $2,646,000 (e)
Number of Employees: 50
Total Units: 3
Trade Names: Be Fish (3)
Company-Owned Units: 3
Primary Menu: Asian (3)
Areas of Operation: MD, MS, PA

Type of Foodservice: Fast Casual (3)

Key Personnel
JOHN STOJ - Chief of Staff; VP Business Development

Bowl America Inc.
6446 Edsall Rd
Alexandria, VA 22312-6410

Mailing Address: PO Box 1288, SPRINGFIELD, VA, 22151-0288
Telephone: (703) 941-6300
Fax Number: (703) 256-2430
Internet Homepage: bowl-america.com
Company Email: administrator@bowl-america.com
Type of Business: Foodservice Operations - Bowling Alley
Year Founded: 1958
Total Sales: $28,730,000 (e)
Alcohol Sales: 20%
Number of Employees: 500
Average Check: Breakfast(5); Lunch(8); Dinner(8)
Total Units: 18
Trade Names: Bowl America (18)
Company-Owned Units: 18
Preferred Square Footage: 3,000
Preferred Location Types: Freestanding
Alcohol Served: Beer, Wine, Liquor
Primary Menu: American (18)
Areas of Operation: DC, FL, MD, VA
Type of Foodservice: In-Store Feeder (18)
Primary Distributors: (Equipment) Lancaster Colony Corporation, COLUMBUS, OH; (Food) US Foods, MANASSAS, VA; (Supplies) Leonard Paper Co., BALTIMORE, MD
Notes: The company derives approximately 71% of its revenue from bowling center operations.

Key Personnel
LESLIE H. GOLDBERG - CEO; President; COO
CHERYL A. DRAGOO - CFO; Senior VP; Controller
RUTH E. MACKLIN - Senior VP; Treasurer; Corporate Secretary
RICHARD DAVIS - Director Facility/Maintenance
ERIC GREEN - Director Purchasing, Supply Chain
MICHAEL DICK - Director Risk Management
MIKE GOTTLIEB - Director Food and Beverage

Bread & Chocolate
1033 W Glebe Rd
Alexandria, VA 22305-1458

Telephone: (703) 549-7524
Fax Number: (703) 836-7021
Internet Homepage: breadandchocolate.net

Type of Business: Chain Restaurant Operator
Year Founded: 1980
Total Sales: $11,750,000 (e)
Alcohol Sales: 1%
Number of Employees: 175
Average Check: Breakfast(10); Lunch(12); Dinner(18)
Total Units: 3
Trade Names: Bread & Chocolate (3)
Company-Owned Units: 3
Preferred Square Footage: 2,500
Preferred Location Types: Downtown
Alcohol Served: Beer, Wine
Primary Menu: French/Continental (3)
Areas of Operation: DC, VA
Type of Foodservice: Casual Dining (3)
Foodservice Management Venues: College & University; Health Care; Lodging; Military Feeding
Catering Services: Yes
On-site Distribution Center: Yes
Primary Distributors: (Equipment) Adams-Burch Inc., LANDOVER, MD; (Food) US Foods, MANASSAS, VA; (Supplies) Adams-Burch Inc., LANDOVER, MD

Key Personnel
THEODORE MANOUSAKIS - CEO; President; Director Finance, Purchasing, Design, Menu Development, Catering

Cheesetique
2411 Mount Vernon Ave
Alexandria, VA 22301-1352

Telephone: (703) 706-5300
Internet Homepage: cheesetique.com
Company Email: delray@cheesetique.com
Type of Business: Chain Restaurant Operator
Year Founded: 2004
Total Sales: $1,432,000 (e)
Alcohol Sales: 1%
Internet Order Processing: Yes
Internet Sales: 1.00%
Total Units: 2
Trade Names: Cheesetique Cheese & Wine Bar (2)
Company-Owned Units: 2
Alcohol Served: Beer, Wine
Primary Menu: Miscellaneous (2)
Areas of Operation: VA
Type of Foodservice: Casual Dining (2)

Key Personnel
JILL ERBER - Owner; General Buyer
KATE MILLER - General Manager

Firenza Pizza Franchise LLC
7001 Manchester Blvd
Alexandria, VA 22310-3212

Telephone: (571) 551-6438
Internet Homepage: firenzapizza.com; myfirenza.com
Company Email: info@firenzapizza.com
Type of Business: Chain Restaurant Operator
Total Units: 19
Trade Names: Firenza (19)
Company-Owned Units: 15
Units Franchised From: 4
Primary Menu: Pizza (19)
Projected Openings: 14
Areas of Operation: CA, GA, IL, KY, MO, NC, OR, SC, TX, VA, WI
Type of Foodservice: Fast Casual (19)

Key Personnel
DAVE WOOD - Co-Founder; CEO
STEVE SCHREIBER - Director Operations; General Buyer

Stratford University
2900 Eisenhower Ave
Alexandria, VA 22314-5202

Telephone: (571) 699-3200
Internet Homepage: stratford.edu; stratford.edu/campus-home/alexandria
Company Email: alexandriaadmissions@stratford.edu
Type of Business: Culinary Schools
Areas of Operation: VA

Key Personnel
RICHARD R. SHURTZ II - CEO; President; General Buyer
MARY ANN SHURTZ - VP

Bartaco
671 N Glebe Rd Suite 600
Arlington, VA 97008

Telephone: (203) 629-4901
Internet Homepage: bartaco.com
Type of Business: Chain Restaurant Operator
Total Sales: $32,200,000 (e)
Total Units: 32
Trade Names: Bartaco (32)
Company-Owned Units: 32
Primary Menu: Mexican (32)
Areas of Operation: CO, CT, DC, FL, GA, IL, MA, NC, NY, PA, SC, TN, VA, WI
Type of Foodservice: Fast Casual (32)

Key Personnel
SCOTT LAWTON - Co-Founder; CEO
ANTHONY VALLETTA - President
LEVI MARTIN - CFO
LISA BASSILIOS MOSBY - Chief People Officer
BRADLEY SANDERS - Chief Development Officer
KELLY MCCARDLE - VP Information Technology
JUSTINE FISHER - VP Marketing
BECKY HOLLER - VP Development
ELISSA PABLO - Regional VP Operations
CHRIS MESSINA - Regional VP Operations
KYLE WITTER - Senior Director Branding, Talent
JARED BENNETT - Senior Director Culinary Operations
ANNA GREENBERG - Director Marketing
SAM MENDAL - Director Purchasing
NIA BROOKER - Director Employee Development
LINDSAY CRASNICK - Director Digital, E-Commerce
NIC STOYER - Director Facility/Maintenance, Foodservice Equip/Supplies
JAVIER GONZALEZ - Regional Director
JAMIE CRAIG - Regional Director
SHERI ZIPPO - Senior Manager Recruitment
LAUREN SWANSON - Senior Manager Digital Marketing
SCOTT RODNEY - Manager Payroll, Benefits

D.C. Ben & Jerry's Ice Cream
2701 S Oakland St Ste C
Arlington, VA 22206-2349

Telephone: (202) 842-5882
Fax Number: (202) 318-4271
Internet Homepage: dcbenjerry.com
Company Email: catering@dcbenjerry.com
Type of Business: Chain Restaurant Operator
Total Sales: $3,413,000 (e)
Average Check: Dinner(8)
Total Units: 5
Trade Names: Ben & Jerry's (5)
Units Franchised From: 5
Primary Menu: Snacks (5)
Areas of Operation: DC, MD, VA
Type of Foodservice: Quick Serve (5)
Franchise Affiliation: Ben & Jerry's Franchising Inc., SOUTH BURLINGTON, VT

Key Personnel
KAREN MORSE - President; General Buyer

Interstate Hotels & Resorts Inc.
4501 Fairfax Dr Ste 700
Arlington, VA 22203-1659

Telephone: (703) 387-3100
Fax Number: (703) 387-3101
Internet Homepage: interstatehotels.com

Company Email: info@interstatehotels.com
Type of Business: Foodservice Operations - Hotel/Motels
Year Founded: 1988
Total Sales: $1,399,700,000 (e)
Alcohol Sales: 4%
Number of Employees: 35,000
Total Units: 430
Restaurants in Hotels: 382
Trade Names: Aloft; Baymont Inns & Suites; Best Western; Comfort Inn; Country Inn & Suites; Courtyard by Marriott; Crowne Plaza; Days Inn; Doubletree by Hilton; Embassy Suites; Fairfield Inn; Four Points; Hampton Inn; Hilton; Hilton Garden Inn; Holiday Inn; Holiday Inn Express; Homewood Suites; Hotel Indigo; Hyatt; Hyatt House; Hyatt Place; Independent; Marriott; Quality Inn; Radisson; Renaissance Hotel; Residence Inn; Sheraton; SpringHill Suites; Staybridge; TownePlace Suites; Westin; Wingate; Wyndham; Wyndham Garden
Company-Owned Units: 430
Alcohol Served: Beer, Wine, Liquor
Projected Openings: 5
Areas of Operation: AZ, CA, CO, CT, DC, FL, GA, IA, ID, IL, IN, KS, KY, LA, MA, MD, MI, MN, MO, NC, NE, NJ, NV, NY, OH, OK, OR, PA, SC, TX, UT, VA, VT, WA, WI, WV
Foreign Countries: BELGIUM; CANADA; CHINA; ENGLAND; HUNGARY; INDIA; IRELAND; RUSSIA; THE NETHERLANDS
Type of Foodservice: Casual Dining; Fine Dining
Primary Distributors: (Food) US Foods, BENSENVILLE, IL
Parent Company: Hotel Acquisition Company LLC, ANNAPOLIS, MD
Notes: The company derives approximately 75% of its revenue from hotel operations, management fees, & other related activities; not all of the hotels listed operate on-site foodservice.

Key Personnel
JANE BLAKE - Chief Human Resources Officer; Exec VP
LARRY SHUPNICK - Senior VP Real Estate, Business Development
JENNY ZHAN - Senior VP; Controller

Latin Concepts LLC
2039 Wilson Blvd
Arlington, VA 22201-3006

Telephone: (703) 528-1500
Internet Homepage: latinconcepts.com
Company Email: lc@latinconcepts.com
Type of Business: Chain Restaurant Operator
Year Founded: 2002
Total Sales: $11,709,000 (e)
Alcohol Sales: 22%
Number of Employees: 225
Average Check: Lunch(20); Dinner(42)
Total Units: 3
Trade Names: Chi-Cha Lounge (1); Mate (1); Susheria (1)
Company-Owned Units: 3
Preferred Square Footage: 5,500; 6,000
Preferred Location Types: Freestanding
Alcohol Served: Beer, Wine, Liquor
Primary Menu: Latin American/Cuban (1); Miscellaneous (1); Southern (1)
Areas of Operation: DC, VA
Type of Foodservice: Casual Dining (3)
Primary Distributors: (Full Line) SYSCO Food Services of Hampton Roads Inc., SUFFOLK, VA

Key Personnel
MAURICIO FRAGA-ROSENFELD - President; Director Operations, Purchasing, Menu Development; General Buyer

Lebanese Taverna Inc.
4400 Langston Blvd
Arlington, VA 22207-3310

Telephone: (703) 841-1501
Fax Number: (703) 841-1504
Internet Homepage: lebanesetaverna.com
Company Email: info@lebanesetaverna.com
Type of Business: Chain Restaurant Operator
Year Founded: 1979
Total Sales: $14,560,000 (e)
Alcohol Sales: 15%
Number of Employees: 363
Average Check: Lunch(18); Dinner(32)
Internet Order Processing: Yes
Total Units: 10
Trade Names: Lebanese Taverna (5); Lebanese Taverna Cafe (4); Lebanese Taverna Market (1)
Company-Owned Units: 10
Preferred Square Footage: 5,500; 6,000
Preferred Location Types: Freestanding
Alcohol Served: Beer, Wine, Liquor
Primary Menu: Middle Eastern (10)
Areas of Operation: DC, MD, VA
Type of Foodservice: Casual Dining (10)
Catering Services: Yes
Primary Distributors: (Full Line) US Foods, MANASSAS, VA

Key Personnel
DANY ABI-NAJM - President; General Manager; Director Purchasing, Facility/Maintenance, Real Estate
GRACE SHEA - VP; Director Operations
KHALIL IBRAHIM - Director Human Resources

Buffalo Wing Factory
43761 Parkhurst Plz #100
Ashburn, VA 20147

Telephone: (703) 729-4200
Internet Homepage: buffalowingfactory.com
Company Email: info@buffalowingfactory.com
Type of Business: Chain Restaurant Operator
Year Founded: 1996
Total Units: 4
Trade Names: Buffalo Wing Factory (4)
Company-Owned Units: 4
Preferred Location Types: Strip Mall
Primary Menu: Chicken (4)
Areas of Operation: VA
Type of Foodservice: Casual Dining (4)

Key Personnel
DAN TUFTS - VP
STEPHEN BEECH - General Manager
NIKKI SICILIAN - Director Customer Service
ALI CHOI - Director Training

Auntie Anne's Franchise
145 Hill Carter Pkwy
Ashland, VA 23005-2327

Telephone: (804) 798-5366
Type of Business: Chain Restaurant Operator
Total Sales: $1,524,000 (e)
Total Units: 2
Trade Names: Auntie Anne's Hand-Rolled Soft Pretzels (2)
Units Franchised From: 2
Primary Menu: Snacks (2)
Areas of Operation: VA
Type of Foodservice: Quick Serve (2)
Franchise Affiliation: Auntie Anne's Inc., LANCASTER, PA

Key Personnel
CHAITANYA PATEL - Owner; General Buyer

Triple C Pizza LLC
109 N Bridge St
Bedford, VA 24523-1923

Telephone: (540) 587-5555
Type of Business: Chain Restaurant Operator
Total Sales: $55,424,000 (e)
Total Units: 28
Trade Names: Domino's (28)
Units Franchised From: 28
Primary Menu: Pizza (28)
Areas of Operation: VA
Type of Foodservice: Quick Serve (28)
Franchise Affiliation: Domino's Pizza Inc, ANN ARBOR, MI

Key Personnel
KENNETH L. COBBS - Owner; General Buyer

GSW Inc
Saint 20121 Germain Dr
Centreville, VA 20121

Telephone: (703) 815-5570
Fax Number: (703) 815-5573
Company Email: gswsubway@verizon.net
Type of Business: Chain Restaurant Operator
Total Sales: $11,880,000 (e)
Number of Employees: 50
Average Check: Lunch(8); Dinner(8)
Total Units: 21
Trade Names: Subway (21)
Units Franchised From: 21
Primary Menu: Sandwiches/Deli (21)
Areas of Operation: MD
Type of Foodservice: Quick Serve (21)
Franchise Affiliation: Doctor's Associates Inc., MILFORD, CT

Key Personnel
JACK MCGUIN - President; Executive Chef; General Buyer

Capital Restaurant Group
4465 Brookfield Corporate Dr Ste 202
Chantilly, VA 20151-2107

Telephone: (703) 378-1500
Internet Homepage: bellapizzava.com; paisanospizza.com; spinfirepizza.com
Company Email: office@pizzapaisanos.com
Type of Business: Chain Restaurant Operator
Year Founded: 1997
Total Sales: $36,470,000 (e)
Total Units: 39
Trade Names: Bella Pizza (1); Paisano's (37); SpinFire (1)
Company-Owned Units: 39
Primary Menu: Pizza (39)
Areas of Operation: DC, MD, VA
Type of Foodservice: Casual Dining (1); Fast Casual (1); Quick Serve (37)

Key Personnel
FOUAD QREITEM - CEO; President

Firehook Bakery & Coffeehouse
14701 Flint Lee Rd Ste C
Chantilly, VA 20151-1505

Telephone: (703) 263-2253
Fax Number: (703) 263-9328
Internet Homepage: firehook.com
Company Email: info@firehook.com
Type of Business: Chain Restaurant Operator
Year Founded: 1992
Total Sales: $18,780,000 (e)
Number of Employees: 140
Average Check: Breakfast(14); Lunch(14); Dinner(14)
Internet Order Processing: Yes
Internet Sales: 4.00%
Total Units: 8
Trade Names: Firehook Bakery & Coffeehouse (8)
Company-Owned Units: 8
Preferred Square Footage: 1,500; 2,000
Preferred Location Types: Downtown; Freestanding
Primary Menu: Miscellaneous (8)
Areas of Operation: DC, VA
Type of Foodservice: Family Restaurant (8)
On-site Distribution Center: Yes
Notes: The company derives approximately 30% of its revenue from wholesale bakery operations.

Key Personnel
PIERRE ABUSHACARA - CEO; Director Finance, Operations, Facility/Maintenance, Information Systems, Supply Chain, Real Estate, Design; General Buyer
NORMA RIVERA - Director Distribution, Production

Auntie Anne's Franchise
1547 Rio Rd E
Charlottesville, VA 22901-1402

Telephone: (434) 974-7532
Type of Business: Chain Restaurant Operator
Total Sales: $2,371,000 (e)
Total Units: 3
Trade Names: Auntie Anne's Hand-Rolled Soft Pretzels (3)
Units Franchised From: 3
Primary Menu: Snacks (3)
Areas of Operation: VA
Type of Foodservice: Quick Serve (3)
Franchise Affiliation: Auntie Anne's Inc., LANCASTER, PA

Key Personnel
BRIAN COWAN - Owner; General Buyer

Domino's Franchisee
325 Four Leaf Ln Ste 5
Charlottesville, VA 22903-9203

Telephone: (434) 823-7752
Type of Business: Chain Restaurant Operator
Total Sales: $8,086,000 (e)
Total Units: 4
Trade Names: Domino's (4)
Units Franchised From: 4
Primary Menu: Pizza (4)
Areas of Operation: VA
Type of Foodservice: Quick Serve (4)
Franchise Affiliation: Domino's Pizza Inc, ANN ARBOR, MI

Key Personnel
STEPHEN J. AMBROSI - Owner; General Buyer

Greenberry's Coffee & Tea Company
1610 Quail Run
Charlottesville, VA 22911-9011

Telephone: (434) 984-0151
Fax Number: (434) 984-0153
Internet Homepage: greenberrys.com
Company Email: contact@greenberrys.com
Type of Business: Chain Restaurant Operator
Year Founded: 1992
Systemwide Sales: $10,868,000 (e)
Total Sales: $5,007,000 (e)
Number of Employees: 24
Average Check: Breakfast(6); Lunch(6); Dinner(6)
Internet Order Processing: Yes
Internet Sales: 3.00%
Total Units: 12
Trade Names: Greenberry's Coffee & Tea Company (12)
Company-Owned Units: 2
Units Franchised To: 10
Preferred Square Footage: 1,500
Preferred Location Types: Institution (college/hospital); Strip Mall
Primary Menu: Coffee (12)
Areas of Operation: DC, LA, VA, FC
Type of Foodservice: Quick Serve (12)
Distribution Centers: CHARLOTTESVILLE, VA
Primary Distributors: (Full Line) SYSCO Food Services of Virginia LLC, HARRISONBURG, VA

Key Personnel
SEAN SIMMONS - CEO; Partner; Manager Menu Development; General Buyer
ROXANNE SIMMONS - President; Partner; CFO

Kohr Bros. Franchise Systems Inc.
2151 Richmond Rd Ste 200
Charlottesville, VA 22911-3636

Telephone: (434) 975-1500
Fax Number: (434) 975-1505
Internet Homepage: kohrbros.com
Company Email: operations@kohrbros.com

Type of Business: Chain Restaurant Operator
Year Founded: 1919
Systemwide Sales: $16,428,000 (e)
Total Sales: $14,690,000 (e)
Number of Employees: 300
Average Check: Lunch(8); Dinner(8)
Internet Order Processing: Yes
Internet Sales: 1.00%
Total Units: 27
Trade Names: Kohr Brothers Frozen Custard (27)
Company-Owned Units: 27
Preferred Square Footage: 150; 500
Preferred Location Types: Community Mall; Freestanding; Kiosk; Strip Mall
Primary Menu: Snacks (27)
Areas of Operation: DE, MD, NJ, VA
Type of Foodservice: Quick Serve (27)
Primary Distributors: (Food) Performance Foodservice, DALLAS, TX

Key Personnel
RANDOLPH L. KOHR - Chairman; Executive Director Operations, Purchasing, Inventory, Loss Prevention, Quality Assurance, Supply Chain, Franchising, Menu Development, Food Safety; General Manager; General Buyer
RANDOLPH KOHR II - CEO; President; Partner; Manager Information Technology
GREG KOHR - Partner
LISA MANN - CFO; Controller; Manager Accounting, Risk Management, Human Resources

Atlantic Food Group, LLC
516 Innovation Dr Ste 202
Chesapeake, VA 23320-3866

Telephone: (252) 689-6255
Internet Homepage: atlanticfoodgroup.com
Type of Business: Chain Restaurant Operator
Total Sales: $20,680,000 (e)
Total Units: 15
Trade Names: Jersey Mike's Subs (15)
Units Franchised From: 15
Primary Menu: Sandwiches/Deli (15)
Areas of Operation: VA
Type of Foodservice: Quick Serve (15)
Franchise Affiliation: Jersey Mike's Franchise Systems, MANASQUAN, NJ

Key Personnel
MARTIN ANDERSON - Partner; General Buyer
CLARK STALLINGS - Partner
MIKE STEMLER - Director Operations

Auntie Anne's Franchise
1401 Greenbrier Pkwy
Chesapeake, VA 23320-2830

Telephone: (757) 420-0485
Type of Business: Chain Restaurant Operator
Total Sales: $2,365,000 (e)
Total Units: 3
Trade Names: Auntie Anne's Hand-Rolled Soft Pretzels (3)
Units Franchised From: 3
Primary Menu: Snacks (3)
Areas of Operation: VA
Type of Foodservice: Quick Serve (3)
Franchise Affiliation: Auntie Anne's Inc., LANCASTER, PA

Key Personnel
DAYNA COOPER - Owner; General Buyer

J S & J Restaurants Inc.
3937 Portsmouth Blvd
Chesapeake, VA 23321-3624

Mailing Address: Po Box 4061, Portsmouth, VA, 23701
Telephone: (757) 271-4589
Fax Number: (757) 271-4590
Type of Business: Chain Restaurant Operator
Total Sales: $20,462,000 (e)
Total Units: 4
Trade Names: McDonald's (4)
Units Franchised From: 4
Primary Menu: Hamburger (4)
Areas of Operation: VA
Type of Foodservice: Quick Serve (4)
Franchise Affiliation: McDonald's Corporation, CHICAGO, IL

Key Personnel
JOHN MAYER - President; General Buyer
SHOWANDA MAYER - Owner

Lionheart, Ltd.
808 Live Oak Dr Ste 122
Chesapeake, VA 23320-2622

Telephone: (757) 366-0307
Fax Number: (757) 523-6178
Type of Business: Chain Restaurant Operator
Total Sales: $13,490,000 (e)
Number of Employees: 165
Total Units: 6
Trade Names: Burger King (6)
Units Franchised From: 6
Preferred Square Footage: 2,500
Primary Menu: Hamburger (6)
Areas of Operation: NC, VA
Type of Foodservice: Quick Serve (6)
Franchise Affiliation: Burger King Worldwide Inc., MIAMI, FL

Key Personnel
TED STOVALL - CEO
SAL DABIERO - President; General Buyer
RICHARD RUBERTI - Creative Director Communications; Principal Marketing; Specialist

MGC Enterprises
644 Independence Pkwy Ste 300
Chesapeake, VA 23320-5212

Telephone: (757) 410-4478
Fax Number: (757) 410-4479
Type of Business: Chain Restaurant Operator
Year Founded: 1985
Total Sales: $23,810,000 (e)
Number of Employees: 225
Average Check: Breakfast(8); Lunch(8); Dinner(10)
Total Units: 5
Trade Names: McDonald's (5)
Units Franchised From: 5
Preferred Square Footage: 2,400; 3,000
Preferred Location Types: Freestanding
Primary Menu: Hamburger (5)
Areas of Operation: VA
Type of Foodservice: Quick Serve (5)
Franchise Affiliation: McDonald's Corporation, CHICAGO, IL
Primary Distributors: (Full Line) SYSCO Food Services of Virginia LLC, HARRISONBURG, VA

Key Personnel
MICHAEL CUSTER - President; Director Information Systems, Real Estate; General Buyer

SKS, LLC
836 Eden Way N Ste 141
Chesapeake, VA 23320-0202

Telephone: (757) 353-3222
Type of Business: Chain Restaurant Operator
Total Sales: $1,229,000 (e)
Total Units: 2
Trade Names: Cold Stone Creamery (2)
Units Franchised From: 2
Primary Menu: Snacks (2)
Areas of Operation: VA
Type of Foodservice: Quick Serve (2)
Franchise Affiliation: Kahala Brands, SCOTTSDALE, AZ

Key Personnel
SANJAY KAPOOR - Partner
KEVEL SHAH - Partner
SANJAY PATEL - Partner

Domino's Franchisee
700 McKinney Blvd Ste 900
Colonial Beach, VA 22443-1934

Telephone: (804) 224-2334
Type of Business: Chain Restaurant Operator
Total Sales: $11,947,000 (e)
Total Units: 6
Trade Names: Domino's (6)
Units Franchised From: 6
Primary Menu: Pizza (6)
Areas of Operation: VA
Type of Foodservice: Quick Serve (6)
Franchise Affiliation: Domino's Pizza Inc, ANN ARBOR, MI

Key Personnel
CHRISTINA S. PALMERI - Owner; General Buyer

Bacon Enterprises
2259 N Main St
Danville, VA 24540-2415

Telephone: (434) 836-9531
Fax Number: (434) 836-1244
Company Email: baconent@comcast.net
Type of Business: Chain Restaurant Operator
Total Sales: $22,080,000 (e)
Number of Employees: 240
Average Check: Breakfast(6); Lunch(12); Dinner(12)
Total Units: 12
Trade Names: KFC (9); KFC/Long John Silver's (1); KFC/Taco Bell (2)
Units Franchised From: 12
Preferred Square Footage: 2,500; 3,200
Preferred Location Types: Freestanding; Strip Mall
Primary Menu: Chicken (11); Seafood (1); Taco (2)
Areas of Operation: NC, VA
Type of Foodservice: Quick Serve (12)
Franchise Affiliation: KFC Corporation, LOUISVILLE, KY; Long John Silver's Inc., LOUISVILLE, KY; Taco Bell Corp., IRVINE, CA

Key Personnel
BILL SHELTON - President; General Buyer
MARCUS SHELTON - Owner
BONNY SHELTON - CFO
JACKIE SLAUGHTER - Director Information Systems
TRISH CARSON - Manager Human Resources

Auntie Anne's Franchise
21100 Dulles Town Cir Ste 262
Dulles, VA 20166-2489

Telephone: (571) 926-8322
Type of Business: Chain Restaurant Operator
Total Sales: $1,591,000 (e)
Total Units: 2
Trade Names: Auntie Anne's Hand-Rolled Soft Pretzels (2)
Units Franchised From: 2
Primary Menu: Snacks (2)
Areas of Operation: VA
Type of Foodservice: Quick Serve (2)
Franchise Affiliation: Auntie Anne's Inc., LANCASTER, PA

Key Personnel
THOMAS HURSON - Owner; General Buyer

Crestline Hotels & Resorts
3950 University Dr Ste 301
Fairfax, VA 22030-2566

Telephone: (571) 529-6100
Fax Number: (571) 529-6095
Internet Homepage: crestlinehotels.com
Company Email: info@crestlinehotels.com
Type of Business: Foodservice Operations - Hotel/Motels
Year Founded: 2000
Total Sales: $809,960,000 (e)
Alcohol Sales: 20%
Number of Employees: 6,095
Total Units: 115
Restaurants in Hotels: 100
Trade Names: Courtyard by Marriott (21); Crowne Plaza (1); Embassy Suites (2); Fairfield Inn (7); Hampton Inn (14); Hilton (4); Hilton Garden Inn (9); Homewood Suites (8); Hotel Indigo (1); Hyatt (18); Independent (5); Marriott (3); Residence Inn (10); Springhill Suites (7); Starwood (1); TownePlace Suites (1); Westin (3)
Company-Owned Units: 100
Alcohol Served: Beer, Wine, Liquor
Projected Remodelings: 10
Areas of Operation: AL, AZ, CA, CT, DC, DE, FL, GA, IL, IN, KS, KY, LA, MA, MD, MI, MN, NC, NJ, NM, NV, OH, OR, RI, SC, TN, TX, VA, WA
Type of Foodservice: Casual Dining; Fine Dining; Quick Serve
Parent Company: Barcelo Crestline Corporation, BETHESDA, MD
Notes: The company derives approximately 96% of its revenue from hotel operations.

Key Personnel
JAMES CARROLL - CEO; President
BRUCE NELKER - Senior VP Operations
TERRI RYAN - VP Operations
JERRY GALINDO - VP Information Technology
DEANNE JOHNSON-ANDERSON - VP Human Resources
CAROLEE ETTLINE MOORE - VP Marketing, Sales
CRAIG ROBACK - Director Operations
CAROL SIMON - Manager Operations, Region

Great American Restaurants
8280 Willow Oaks Corporate Dr Ste 700
Fairfax, VA 22031-4519

Telephone: (703) 645-0700
Fax Number: (703) 876-6082
Internet Homepage: greatamericanrestaurants.com
Type of Business: Chain Restaurant Operator
Year Founded: 1974
Total Sales: $53,710,000 (e)
Alcohol Sales: 15%
Number of Employees: 996
Average Check: Breakfast(8); Lunch(12); Dinner(24)
Internet Order Processing: Yes
Total Units: 17
Trade Names: Artie's (1); Best Buns (2); Carlyle (1); Coastal Flats (3); Good Eats Emporium (1); Jackson's (1); Mike's American Grill (1); Ozzie (1); Patsy's American (1); Randy's Prime Seafood & Steaks (1); Silverado (1); Sweetwater Tavern (3)
Company-Owned Units: 12
Preferred Square Footage: 4,500; 13,000
Preferred Location Types: Freestanding; Strip Mall
Alcohol Served: Beer, Wine, Liquor
Primary Menu: American (13); Seafood (1); Snacks (2); Steak/Seafood (1)
Areas of Operation: MD, VA
Type of Foodservice: Casual Dining (15); Fast Casual (2)
Primary Distributors: (Full Line) SYSCO Food Services of Virginia LLC, HARRISONBURG, VA

Key Personnel
RANDY NORTON - Chairman; CEO; Director Finance
MIKE RANNEY - Co-Founder
JAMES FARLEY - Co-Founder
JON NORTON - CEO
MEGAN DILLARD - Partner
KRISTIN SHURR - Partner
JILL NORTON - Chief People Officer; VP Construction, Design
PAUL TRAUB - VP Operations
DANIEL CALCANO - General Manager
JEFF GAIKO - Director Operations
ERICA MORGAN - Director Marketing
CHRIS OSBORNE - Manager Purchasing, Supply Chain; General Buyer
JULIA GAJEWSKI - Manager Customer Service

PAUL VETTERICK - Manager Restaurant Operations
JOHN TABLANTE - Manager Operations
KATIE FULLER - Manager Operations
IRYNA IUKHNEI - Supervisor Restaurant Operations
MACON WALKER - Supervisor Restaurant Operations

Guest Services Inc.
3055 Prosperity Ave
Fairfax, VA 22031-2216

Telephone: (703) 849-9300
Fax Number: (703) 641-4690
Internet Homepage: guestservices.com
Company Email: info@guestservices.com
Type of Business: Foodservice Management Operator
Year Founded: 1917
Total Sales: $518,635,000 (e)
Number of Employees: 2,541
Number of Locations Served: 250
Total Foodservice Mgmt Accounts: 92
Trade Names: Guest Services Inc.; Guest Services of Virginia
Areas of Operation: VA
Type of Foodservice: Cafeteria (77); Full-service sit-down dining (7); Quick Serve (1); Vending machines (17)
Foodservice Management Venues: Business & Industry; College & University; Health Care; Lodging; Military Feeding; Other; Parks & Recreation; Schools
Primary Distributors: (Full Line) US Foods, SALEM, VA
Headquarter Offices: Lancaster Foods, JESSUP, MD
Notes: The company derives approximately 15% of its revenue from retail operations.

Key Personnel
GERARD T. GABRYS - CEO
NICO FORIS - COO; VP
DOUG VERNER - VP; Corporate Secretary, General Counsel
ROBERT DOUGLAS - Senior Director Purchasing
KEN LOPEZ - Senior Manager Business Development

JM Team NoVa, LLC
11199 Lee Hwy Ste C
Fairfax, VA 22030-5040

Telephone: (703) 865-7722
Type of Business: Chain Restaurant Operator
Total Sales: $5,820,000 (e)
Total Units: 4
Trade Names: Jersey Mike's Subs (4)
Units Franchised From: 4
Primary Menu: Sandwiches/Deli (4)
Areas of Operation: VA
Type of Foodservice: Quick Serve (4)
Franchise Affiliation: Jersey Mike's Franchise Systems, MANASQUAN, NJ

Key Personnel
JOSEPH P. WHITE - Owner

Bland Management
5671 Columbia Pike Ste 200
Falls Church, VA 22041-2885

Telephone: (703) 379-2266
Fax Number: (703) 379-2267
Internet Homepage: blandmanagement.com
Company Email: blandmgmt@aol.com
Type of Business: Chain Restaurant Operator
Total Sales: $14,966,000 (e)
Number of Employees: 100
Total Units: 3
Trade Names: McDonald's (3)
Units Franchised From: 3
Preferred Square Footage: 2,500
Preferred Location Types: Freestanding; Regional Mall
Primary Menu: Hamburger (3)
Areas of Operation: VA
Type of Foodservice: Quick Serve (3)
Franchise Affiliation: McDonald's Corporation, CHICAGO, IL

Key Personnel
ANNE BLAND - CEO; President; Partner; General Buyer
MICHAEL BLAND - Partner
CARLOS MARRERO - General Manager; Manager Training
DAVID MENGISTAB - Director Operations
JASON BLAND - Director

District Taco
2828 Fallfax Dr
Falls Church, VA 22042

Internet Homepage: districttaco.com
Company Email: taco@districttaco.com
Type of Business: Chain Restaurant Operator
Year Founded: 2009
Total Sales: $16,330,000 (e)
Number of Employees: 300
Total Units: 15
Trade Names: District Taco (15)
Company-Owned Units: 15
Primary Menu: Mexican (15)
Projected Openings: 1
Areas of Operation: DC, MD, PA, VA
Type of Foodservice: Fast Casual (15)

Key Personnel
MARC WALLACE - Chairman; Co-Founder
OSIRIS HOIL - Co-Founder; CEO
KELLY SEXTON - Partner
CHRIS MEDHURST - VP Finance, Operations
MARCELO BUTRON ARNEZ - VP Operations
STEPHAN LALKA - Director Operations
DANIEL PIERCE - Manager Operations

Little Dipper Hot Pot House
3000 Annandale Rd
Falls Church, VA 22042

Telephone: (703) 237-1888
Internet Homepage: littledipperhotpot.com
Company Email: connect@littledipperhotpot.com
Type of Business: Chain Restaurant Operator
Year Founded: 2016
Total Units: 3
Trade Names: Little Dipper Hot Pot House (3)
Company-Owned Units: 3
Preferred Location Types: Community Mall; Downtown; Strip Mall
Primary Menu: Asian (3)
Areas of Operation: MD, VA
Type of Foodservice: Casual Dining (3)

Key Personnel
MELINDA ZHANG - Owner

Metropolitan Restaurant Management Company
7245 Arlington Blvd Ste 314
Falls Church, VA 22042-3217

Telephone: (703) 207-0577
Fax Number: (703) 698-0117
Type of Business: Chain Restaurant Operator
Year Founded: 1987
Total Sales: $11,012,000 (e)
Number of Employees: 400
Average Check: Lunch(8); Dinner(10)
Total Units: 4
Trade Names: Popeyes Louisiana Kitchen (4)
Units Franchised From: 4
Preferred Square Footage: 2,500
Preferred Location Types: Freestanding; Strip Mall
Primary Menu: Chicken (4)
Areas of Operation: DC, MD, VA
Type of Foodservice: Quick Serve (4)
Franchise Affiliation: Popeyes Louisiana Kitchen Inc., ATLANTA, GA

Key Personnel
DAVID J. ROSENSTEIN - President; Director Finance, Real Estate
CHRIS GOBIE - Director Operations, Purchasing, Facility/Maintenance, Information

Systems, Supply Chain, Store Fixtures, Food Safety; Manager Human Resources

Sharp Holding Inc.
6655 Arlington Blvd
Falls Church, VA 22042-3002

Mailing Address: PO Box 3440, OAKTON, VA, 22124-9440
Telephone: (540) 659-4467
Fax Number: (540) 659-0203
Internet Homepage: sharprestaurants.com
Company Email: info@sharpholdinginc.com
Type of Business: Chain Restaurant Operator
Year Founded: 1996
Total Sales: $46,530,000 (e)
Number of Employees: 357
Average Check: Breakfast(16); Lunch(18); Dinner(22)
Total Units: 15
Trade Names: IHOP Restaurant (15)
Units Franchised From: 15
Preferred Square Footage: 4,400; 5,000
Preferred Location Types: Freestanding
Primary Menu: American (15)
Areas of Operation: KY, MD, NJ, VA, WV
Type of Foodservice: Family Restaurant (15)
Franchise Affiliation: IHOP Restaurant System, GLENDALE, CA
Primary Distributors: (Full Line) PFG - Customized Distribution Maryland, ELKTON, MD

Key Personnel
BOB SHARP - President; General Buyer
TOMMY TSITOURIS - VP Operations
TERI LIGUORI - Director Training

Shyam Creamery, LLC
8190 Strawberry Ln Ste 7
Falls Church, VA 22042-1030

Telephone: (703) 992-9805
Type of Business: Chain Restaurant Operator
Total Sales: $1,198,000 (e)
Total Units: 2
Trade Names: Cold Stone Creamery (2)
Units Franchised From: 2
Areas of Operation: VA
Type of Foodservice: Quick Serve (2)
Franchise Affiliation: Kahala Brands, SCOTTSDALE, AZ

Key Personnel
NIRAJ HEMRAJANI - Partner
RAJEN HEMRAJANI - Partner
GOPAL PARDASANI - Partner

Taco Bamba Taqueria
2190 Pimmit Dr
Falls Church, VA 22043

Telephone: (703) 639-0505
Internet Homepage: tacobamba.com
Company Email: bamba@tacobambarestaurant.com
Type of Business: Chain Restaurant Operator
Year Founded: 2013
Total Units: 5
Trade Names: Taco Bamba Taqueria (5)
Company-Owned Units: 5
Preferred Location Types: Downtown; Strip Mall
Primary Menu: Mexican (5)
Areas of Operation: DC, VA
Type of Foodservice: Casual Dining (5)

Key Personnel
VICTOR ALBISU - Founder; Corporate Chef

Russell Enterprises
106 N Bridge St
Farmville, VA 23901-1518

Telephone: (434) 392-8733
Type of Business: Chain Restaurant Operator
Total Sales: $15,498,000 (e)
Total Units: 3
Trade Names: McDonald's (3)
Units Franchised From: 3
Primary Menu: Hamburger (3)
Areas of Operation: VA
Type of Foodservice: Quick Serve (3)
Franchise Affiliation: McDonald's Corporation, CHICAGO, IL

Key Personnel
FRED E. RUSSELL - President; General Buyer
ANGIE CALLAWAY - Specialist Human Resources

Biggar Enterprises Inc
4211 Plank Rd Ste D
Fredericksburg, VA 22407-0122

Telephone: (540) 786-8188
Fax Number: (540) 786-4121
Type of Business: Chain Restaurant Operator
Total Sales: $10,180,000 (e)
Total Units: 5
Trade Names: Domino's (5)
Units Franchised From: 5
Primary Menu: Pizza (5)
Areas of Operation: VA
Type of Foodservice: Quick Serve (5)
Franchise Affiliation: Domino's Pizza Inc, ANN ARBOR, MI

Key Personnel
SHAWN BIGGAR - President; General Buyer

4 Alarm, LLC
4028 Cox Rd Ste K
Glen Allen, VA 23060-6702

Telephone: (804) 270-4242
Type of Business: Chain Restaurant Operator
Total Sales: $5,934,000 (e)
Total Units: 5
Trade Names: Firehouse Subs (5)
Units Franchised From: 5
Primary Menu: Sandwiches/Deli (5)
Areas of Operation: VA
Type of Foodservice: Fast Casual (5)
Catering Services: Yes
Franchise Affiliation: Firehouse Restaurant Group Inc., JACKSONVILLE, FL

Key Personnel
RANDY EVANS - President; General Buyer

Padow's Hams and Deli Inc.
4120 Cox Rd Ste C
Glen Allen, VA 23060-3443

Telephone: (804) 965-6262
Fax Number: (804) 965-9888
Internet Homepage: padows.com
Company Email: sidney@padows.com
Type of Business: Nontraditional Foodservice Operator
Year Founded: 1988
Systemwide Sales: $3,352,000 (e)
Total Sales: $1,799,000 (e)
Number of Employees: 12
Internet Order Processing: Yes
Internet Sales: 1.00%
Total Units: 5
Trade Names: Padow's Hams and Deli (5)
Company-Owned Units: 1
Units Franchised To: 4
Alcohol Served: Beer, Wine
Primary Menu: Sandwiches/Deli (5)
Areas of Operation: VA
Type of Foodservice: Family Restaurant (5)

Key Personnel
SIDNEY PADOW - President; General Buyer

United Restaurant Group LP
4701 Cox Rd Ste 345
Glen Allen, VA 23060-6802

Telephone: (804) 747-5050
Fax Number: (804) 747-3784

Internet Homepage: urglp.com
Company Email: info@urglp.com
Type of Business: Chain Restaurant Operator
Year Founded: 1992
Total Sales: $102,150,000 (e)
Alcohol Sales: 30%
Number of Employees: 1,960
Average Check: Lunch(14); Dinner(22)
Total Units: 24
Trade Names: T.G.I. Friday's (24)
Units Franchised From: 24
Preferred Square Footage: 6,000; 10,000
Preferred Location Types: Freestanding; Office Complex; Regional Mall
Alcohol Served: Beer, Wine, Liquor
Primary Menu: American (24)
Areas of Operation: DE, NC, SC, TN, VA
Type of Foodservice: Casual Dining (24)
Franchise Affiliation: T.G.I. Friday's Inc., DALLAS, TX
Primary Distributors: (Food) PFG - Customized Support Services, LEBANON, TN
Notes: The company also operates as Atlantic Coast Dining Inc.

Key Personnel
TONY GRILLO - President; Director Finance, Operations, Facility/Maintenance, Information Systems, Human Resources
LOUIS QUARTOCHI - VP; General Buyer
VICKI SIMPKISS - Director Human Resources

Walcorp, Inc.
11444 W Broad St
Glen Allen, VA 23060-5821

Telephone: (804) 364-3711
Type of Business: Chain Restaurant Operator
Total Sales: $12,640,000 (e)
Total Units: 9
Trade Names: Jersey Mike's Subs (9)
Units Franchised From: 9
Primary Menu: Sandwiches/Deli (9)
Areas of Operation: VA
Type of Foodservice: Quick Serve (9)
Franchise Affiliation: Jersey Mike's Franchise Systems, MANASQUAN, NJ

Key Personnel
G. ROBERT WALDROP IV - Owner; General Buyer

Virginia Wings Inc.
4410 Claiborne Sq E Ste 334
Hampton, VA 23666-2074

Telephone: (757) 251-3857
Internet Homepage: hootersofhamptonroads.com
Type of Business: Chain Restaurant Operator
Year Founded: 1983
Total Sales: $47,530,000 (e)
Alcohol Sales: 15%
Number of Employees: 292
Average Check: Lunch(30); Dinner(30)
Total Units: 5
Trade Names: Hooters (5)
Units Franchised From: 5
Preferred Square Footage: 4,400; 5,500
Preferred Location Types: Freestanding; Regional Mall; Strip Mall
Alcohol Served: Beer, Wine, Liquor
Primary Menu: American (5)
Areas of Operation: VA
Type of Foodservice: Casual Dining (5)
Franchise Affiliation: HOA Restaurant Group LLC, ATLANTA, GA

Key Personnel
GREG KNOX - President; General Buyer
PAUL PHELPS - Director Operations

APB Management, Inc.
530 Neff Ave
Harrisonburg, VA 22801-3491

Telephone: (540) 432-9383
Fax Number: (540) 433-0459
Type of Business: Chain Restaurant Operator
Total Sales: $51,590,000 (e)
Number of Employees: 400
Total Units: 11
Trade Names: McDonald's (11)
Units Franchised From: 11
Preferred Square Footage: 2,500
Preferred Location Types: Discount Dept. Stores; Freestanding
Primary Menu: Hamburger (11)
Areas of Operation: VA
Type of Foodservice: Quick Serve (11)
Franchise Affiliation: McDonald's Corporation, CHICAGO, IL

Key Personnel
PRICE BOXLEY - President; Owner; General Buyer
BRIANNA PROCHASKA - General Manager

Subco Inc
2421 S Main St
Harrisonburg, VA 22801-2610

Telephone: (540) 433-9866
Type of Business: Chain Restaurant Operator
Total Sales: $6,946,000 (e)
Total Units: 12
Trade Names: Subway (12)
Units Franchised From: 12
Primary Menu: Sandwiches/Deli (12)
Areas of Operation: VA
Type of Foodservice: Quick Serve (12)
Franchise Affiliation: Doctor's Associates Inc., MILFORD, CT

Key Personnel
SCOTT HILLYARD - President; General Buyer

Foster's Grille Inc.
4432 Costello Way
Haymarket, VA 20169-2996

Telephone: (703) 754-6220
Fax Number: (703) 754-6140
Internet Homepage: fostersgrille.com
Company Email: hq@fostersgrille.com
Type of Business: Chain Restaurant Operator
Year Founded: 1999
Systemwide Sales: $37,137,000 (e)
Total Sales: $25,550,000 (e)
Alcohol Sales: 1%
Number of Employees: 194
Average Check: Lunch(12); Dinner(12)
Internet Order Processing: Yes
Internet Sales: 0.50%
Total Units: 12
Trade Names: Foster's Grille (12)
Company-Owned Units: 8
Units Franchised To: 4
Preferred Square Footage: 2,400; 3,000
Preferred Location Types: Freestanding; Strip Mall
Alcohol Served: Beer, Wine
Primary Menu: Hamburger (12)
Areas of Operation: FL, MD, NC, VA
Type of Foodservice: Fast Casual (12)
Primary Distributors: (Full Line) US Foods, MANASSAS, VA

Key Personnel
MIKE CERNY - President; General Buyer
SCOTT LINKOW - Director Operations

Amphora Group
1141 Elden St Ste 224
Herndon, VA 20170-5572

Telephone: (703) 766-4220
Fax Number: (703) 938-1720
Internet Homepage: amphoragroup.com
Company Email: customerservice@amphoragroup.com
Type of Business: Chain Restaurant Operator
Year Founded: 1962
Total Sales: $13,624,000 (e)
Alcohol Sales: 8%
Number of Employees: 180
Average Check: Breakfast(8); Lunch(10); Dinner(14)
Total Units: 4
Trade Names: Amphora Bakery (2); Amphora Diner Deluxe (1); Amphora Restaurant (1)
Company-Owned Units: 4
Preferred Square Footage: 4,000

Preferred Location Types: Freestanding
Alcohol Served: Beer, Wine, Liquor
Primary Menu: American (4)
Projected Remodelings: 1
Areas of Operation: VA
Type of Foodservice: Casual Dining (2); Quick Serve (2)
Catering Services: Yes
Primary Distributors: (Food) SYSCO Food Services of Baltimore, JESSUP, MD; (Food) US Foods, MANASSAS, VA

Key Personnel
GEORGE CHOLAKIS - CEO; President; Partner; CFO; Executive Chef; Manager Marketing, Real Estate
STEVE BILIDAS - Partner; VP Finance, Operations, Information Systems; General Buyer
MARIA CHOLAKIS - Partner

Potomac Family Dining Group
13873 Park Center Rd Ste 316S
Herndon, VA 20171-3247

Telephone: (240) 752-7565
Fax Number: (703) 787-6550
Internet Homepage: potomacdining.com
Company Email: info@potomacdining.com
Type of Business: Chain Restaurant Operator
Total Sales: $195,870,000 (e)
Total Units: 50
Trade Names: Applebee's Neighborhood Grill & Bar (50)
Units Franchised From: 50
Primary Menu: American (59)
Areas of Operation: MD, NC, PA, VA, WV
Type of Foodservice: Casual Dining (59)
Franchise Affiliation: Applebee's Services Inc., KANSAS CITY, MO

Key Personnel
DENNIS BENSON - CEO; President
CYRUS COMMISSARIAT - CFO
THOMAS BRANTLEY - Area Director
CHRIS ANNIS - Area Director Operations
MICHAEL SPENCE - Area Director
SCOTT RIDGWAY - Regional VP Operations
JULIE HEIMER - Controller Finance
KRISTIN LAGERSTROM - General Manager Training
SHANNON LEA - General Manager Training
SHANNON LONG - Director Training
MICHAEL CLAPP - Director Area
HEATHER HUDSON - Director Training
ZHEER ROSTAM - Senior Manager Information Technology
RON MCADOO - Manager Information Technology
NICOLE HOBLIN - Manager Human Resources

The Omni Homestead Resort
1766 Homestead Dr
Hot Springs, VA 24445-2910

Mailing Address: PO Box 2000, HOT SPRINGS, VA, 24445-2000
Telephone: (540) 839-1766
Fax Number: (540) 839-7670
Internet Homepage: thehomestead.com
Company Email: stay@theomnihotels.com
Type of Business: Foodservice Operations - Hotel/Motels
Year Founded: 1993
Total Sales: $33,572,000 (e)
Alcohol Sales: 15%
Number of Employees: 1,000
Total Units: 1
Restaurants in Hotels: 7
Trade Names: The Omni Homestead Resort (1)
Company-Owned Units: 7
Alcohol Served: Beer, Wine, Liquor
Areas of Operation: VA
Type of Foodservice: Casual Dining (6); Quick Serve (1)
Primary Distributors: (Food) SYSCO Food Services of Virginia LLC, HARRISONBURG, VA; (Specialty Foods) Carlisle Food System Inc., ASHLAND, VA
Parent Company: KSL Capital Partners, DENVER, CO
Headquarters: ClubCorp Inc., DALLAS, TX
Notes: The company derives approximately 80% of its revenue from hotel operations.

Key Personnel
LEEN KIM - Executive Chef
DOUG MCLAURIN - Director Information Technology
SEVERIN NUNN - Director Food and Beverage
LYNN SWANN - Director Marketing, Communications
KATHY WOODZELL - Assistant Director Human Resources
MICHAEL BOTKIN - Assistant Director Finance
EILEEN JUDAH - Manager Marketing
SARAH SUTTON - Manager

SSP America
19465 Deerfield Ave Ste 105
Lansdowne, VA 20176-1702

Telephone: (703) 729-2333
Fax Number: (703) 729-4414
Internet Homepage: foodtravelexperts.com
Type of Business: Foodservice Management Operator
Year Founded: 1989
Total Sales: $177,829,000 (e)
Number of Employees: 2,500
Number of Locations Served: 180
Total Foodservice Mgmt Accounts: 45
Total Units: 63
Trade Names: A&W All American Food; Anchor Brewing; Au Bon Pain; Ben & Jerry's; Bill Bateman's Bistro; Blue Note Cafe; Brooklyn Jazz Bar; Burger King; Caffe Ritazza; Camden food co.; Carolina Wings & Rib House; Charley's Grilled Subs; Chick-fil-A; Delux Burger; Dunkin' Donuts; Famous Famiglia; Four Peaks Brewery; Freshens Smoothie Company; Hardee's; Humble Pie; Jamaican Bobsled; KFC; Lola Coffee; Nocawich Express; Panda Express; Peet's; Pei Wei; Pizza Hut; Qdoba Mexican Grill; Quiznos; Rams Head Live!; Red Mango; Red Stripe; Samuel Adams; Sbarro; Starbucks Coffee; UrbanCrave
Units Franchised From: 63
Areas of Operation: CA
Type of Foodservice: Full-service sit-down dining (45); Quick Serve (45)
Foodservice Management Venues: Transportation
Franchise Affiliation: A&W Restaurants Inc., LEXINGTON, KY; ABP Corporation, BOSTON, MA; Ben & Jerry's Franchising Inc., SOUTH BURLINGTON, VT; Burger King Worldwide Inc., MIAMI, FL; Chick-fil-A Inc., ATLANTA, GA; DD IP Holder, CANTON, MA; Famiglia - DeBartolo, LLC, WHITE PLAINS, NY; Freshens Quality Brands, ATLANTA, GA; Gosh Enterprises Inc., COLUMBUS, OH; Hardee's Food Systems Inc., FRANKLIN, TN; KFC Corporation, LOUISVILLE, KY; Panda Restaurant Group Inc., ROSEMEAD, CA; Peet's Coffee & Tea Inc., EMERYVILLE, CA; Pei Wei Asian Diner, IRVING, TX; Pizza HutInc., PLANO, TX; Qdoba Mexican Eats, SAN DIEGO, CA; Red Mango FC LLC, DALLAS, TX; Sbarro Holdings LLC, COLUMBUS, OH; Starbucks Corporation, SEATTLE, WA; T.G.I. Friday's Inc., DALLAS, TX; The Quiznos Master LLC, DENVER, CO
Primary Distributors: (Full Line) SYSCO Food Services of Los Angeles Inc., WALNUT, CA
Parent Company: SSP Group Ltd, SURREY, ENG
Notes: Formerly known as Creative Host Services Inc., the company also provides in-flight catering to certain national airlines in addition to operating concessions in airports. The company derives approximately 5% of its revenue from concessions.

Key Personnel
MICHAEL SVAGDIS - CEO; President
GOERGE MBOYA - CFO
PAT MURRAY - Exec VP
LANA CRAMER - VP Marketing, Communications
LIESKE RENZ - VP Human Resources
JAGPREET SINGH - General Counsel

Five Guys Holdings Inc.
10718 Richmond Hwy
Lorton, VA 22079-2622

Telephone: (703) 339-9500
Fax Number: (703) 339-9501
Internet Homepage: fiveguys.com
Company Email: info@fiveguys.com
Type of Business: Chain Restaurant Operator
Year Founded: 1986
Systemwide Sales: $2,296,276,000 (e)
Total Sales: $833,010,000 (e)
Alcohol Sales: 3%
Number of Employees: 2,210
Average Check: Lunch(10); Dinner(10)
Internet Order Processing: Yes
Internet Sales: 1.00%
Total Units: 1,401
Trade Names: Five Guys Burgers and Fries (1,401)
Company-Owned Units: 273
Units Franchised To: 1,128
Preferred Square Footage: 2,000; 3,000; 5,500; 6,000
Preferred Location Types: Airports; Freestanding; Institution (college/hospital); Regional Mall; Stadiums; Strip Mall
Primary Menu: Hamburger (1,401)
Projected Openings: 7
Areas of Operation: AL, AR, AZ, CA, CO, CT, DC, DE, FL, GA, HI, IA, ID, IL, IN, KS, KY, LA, MA, MD, ME, MI, MN, MO, MS, MT, NC, ND, NE, NH, NJ, NM, NV, NY, OH, OK, OR, PA, RI, SC, SD, TN, TX, UT, VA, VT, WA, WI, WV, WY, AB, BC, MB, ON, QC, SK
Foreign Countries: BAHRAIN; BELGIUM; CANADA; ENGLAND; FRANCE; GERMANY; HONG KONG; IRELAND; ITALY; KUWAIT; LUXEMBOURG; OMAN; QATAR; SAUDI ARABIA; SPAIN; SWITZERLAND; THE NETHERLANDS; UNITED ARAB EMIRATES
Type of Foodservice: Fast Casual (1,401)
Primary Distributors: (Full Line) US Foods, MANASSAS, VA
Notes: The company derives approximately 10% of total revenue from bakery sales.

Key Personnel
JANIE MURRELL - Co-Founder; President
JERRY MURRELL - Co-Founder; CEO
PETER HANSON - CFO
SAM CHAMBERLAIN - COO; Director Operations
CARL NAPIWOCKI - Global VP Supply Chain
RALPH ORTIZ - VP Strategic Services
ZERRICK PEARSON - VP Information Technology
MATTHEW DEMERS - VP Operations
JP ASMEN - VP Operations, Global
MOLLY CATALANO - VP Marketing, Communications
JAMES J. MURRELL - VP
JEFF RUBINO - VP Real Estate
ROBERT TOOMEY - VP Franchise Operations
LARRY HART - Controller
DALE THOMPSON - General Counsel
STEVE TELLER - Director Technology
ANGELA THOMPSON - Director Franchise Operations
REBECCA GOLDSTEIN - Director Operations
CASEY RAY - Director Construction
SARAH BATES - Director
HONEY BELACHEW - Director Human Resources
CHRIS DUNCAN - Director Payroll
MIKE DUNN - Director Safety, Supply Chain
ADAM MONTONATI - District Manager
MARK MOSELEY - Manager Franchise Development
KARL FERTIG - Manager Construction
THERESE FELA - Office Manager

Chick-fil-A Franchise
3405 Candlers Mountain Rd Ste FC6
Lynchburg, VA 24502-2218

Telephone: (434) 237-5231
Internet Homepage: chick-fil-a.com
Company Email: cfamobileexpres@gmail.com
Type of Business: Chain Restaurant Operator
Total Sales: $18,334,000 (e)
Average Check: Dinner(14)
Total Units: 2
Trade Names: Chick-fil-A (2)
Units Franchised From: 2
Primary Menu: Chicken (2)
Areas of Operation: VA
Type of Foodservice: Quick Serve (2)
Franchise Affiliation: Chick-fil-A Inc., ATLANTA, GA

Key Personnel
YENTL WEAVER - Director Operations
TIM PREUSSER - Director Operations
BRIAN ELLIS - Director Operations
JONATHAN KABOLETE - Director Information Technology
MICHAEL MORANO - Director Operations

S. Buckner, Inc.
3919 Wards Rd Ste D
Lynchburg, VA 24502-4042

Telephone: (434) 582-1300
Type of Business: Chain Restaurant Operator
Total Sales: $4,472,000 (e)
Total Units: 3
Trade Names: Jersey Mike's Subs (3)
Units Franchised From: 3
Primary Menu: Sandwiches/Deli (3)
Areas of Operation: VA
Type of Foodservice: Quick Serve (3)
Franchise Affiliation: Jersey Mike's Franchise Systems, MANASQUAN, NJ

Key Personnel
LUTHER S. BUCKNER - Owner; General Buyer

Shakers Restaurant Corporation
106 Goldenrod Pl
Lynchburg, VA 24502-3452

Telephone: (434) 385-1990
Fax Number: (434) 385-1994
Internet Homepage: shakers.com
Company Email: Lynchburg@Shakers.com
Type of Business: Chain Restaurant Operator
Year Founded: 1985
Total Sales: $18,400,000 (e)
Alcohol Sales: 18%
Number of Employees: 400
Average Check: Lunch(8); Dinner(12)
Total Units: 2
Trade Names: Shakers (2)
Company-Owned Units: 2
Preferred Square Footage: 6,500
Preferred Location Types: Freestanding
Alcohol Served: Beer, Wine, Liquor
Primary Menu: American (2)
Areas of Operation: VA
Type of Foodservice: Casual Dining (2)
Catering Services: Yes
Primary Distributors: (Full Line) US Foods, SALEM, VA

Key Personnel
JOHN BUCKLES - President; Director Facility/Maintenance, Real Estate, Design, Store Fixtures
DONNA MANLEY - Controller
BOB PLUNKETT - Director Operations, Purchasing, Marketing, Human Resources, Menu Development, Catering; General Buyer

TCR Enterprises
21 Timberoak Ct Ste B2
Lynchburg, VA 24502-4567

Telephone: (434) 239-8782
Fax Number: (434) 239-6877
Type of Business: Chain Restaurant Operator
Year Founded: 1989
Total Sales: $28,170,000 (e)
Number of Employees: 250
Average Check: Breakfast(8); Lunch(10); Dinner(10)
Total Units: 6
Trade Names: McDonald's (6)
Units Franchised From: 6
Preferred Square Footage: 2,500; 3,000
Preferred Location Types: Convenience Store/Gas Station; Freestanding

Primary Menu: Hamburger (6)
Areas of Operation: VA
Type of Foodservice: Quick Serve (6)
Franchise Affiliation: McDonald's Corporation, CHICAGO, IL

Key Personnel
THOMAS ROCK - President; Partner; Director Finance; General Buyer
DAVID BURNS - Partner; Director Facility/Maintenance, Information Systems, Human Resources, Store Fixtures
BRIAN ROCK - Controller; Director Operations, Supply Chain, Real Estate
LENORA BIGGIO - Manager Accounting, Branch

●▲
SYDLEY International, LLC
8113 Sudley Rd
Manassas, VA 20109-8035

Telephone: (703) 330-7722
Type of Business: Chain Restaurant Operator
Total Sales: $1,259,000 (e)
Total Units: 2
Trade Names: Cold Stone Creamery (2)
Units Franchised From: 2
Primary Menu: Snacks (2)
Areas of Operation: VA
Type of Foodservice: Quick Serve (2)
Franchise Affiliation: Kahala Brands, SCOTTSDALE, AZ

Key Personnel
MICHAEL MCGINNIS - Owner; General Buyer

●▲
Domino's Franchisee
730 E Church St Ste 10
Martinsville, VA 24112-3151

Telephone: (276) 634-5050
Type of Business: Chain Restaurant Operator
Total Sales: $12,490,000 (e)
Total Units: 6
Trade Names: Domino's (6)
Units Franchised From: 6
Primary Menu: Pizza (6)
Areas of Operation: VA
Type of Foodservice: Quick Serve (6)
Franchise Affiliation: Domino's Pizza Inc, ANN ARBOR, MI

Key Personnel
ZACHARY D. BARRETT - Owner; General Buyer

●▲
Subway of Martinsville
2444 Greensboro Rd
Martinsville, VA 24112-8100

Telephone: (276) 638-3433
Type of Business: Chain Restaurant Operator
Total Sales: $9,290,000 (e)
Total Units: 16
Trade Names: Subway (16)
Units Franchised From: 16
Primary Menu: Sandwiches/Deli (16)
Areas of Operation: VA
Type of Foodservice: Quick Serve (16)
Franchise Affiliation: Doctor's Associates Inc., MILFORD, CT

Key Personnel
CARL BRENNER - President
JESSIE MCGRADY - Director Operations

‡
Hilton Worldwide Holdings Inc.
7930 Jones Branch Dr Ste 1100
Mclean, VA 22102-3313

Telephone: (703) 883-1000
Internet Homepage: hiltonfranchise.com; hiltonworldwide.com
Company Email: info@hilton.com
Type of Business: Foodservice Operations - Hotel/Motels
Year Founded: 1919
Publicly Held: Yes
Total Sales: $7,065,400,000 (e)
Alcohol Sales: 30%
Number of Employees: 169,000
Total Units: 6,464
Restaurants in Hotels: 6464
Trade Names: Canopy by Hilton (27); Conrad Hotels & Resorts (39); Curio (96); DoubleTree by Hilton (616); Embassy Suites (258); Hampton (2,661); Hilton(580); Hilton Garden Inn (899); Home2 Suites (463); Homewood Suites (511); Motto by Hilton (1); Other (56); Tapestry by Hilton (46); The Waldorf - Astoria Collection (33); Tru by Hilton (178)
Company-Owned Units: 6,464
Alcohol Served: Beer, Wine, Liquor
Projected Remodelings: 3
Areas of Operation: AK, AL, AR, AZ, CA, CO, CT, DC, DE, FL, GA, GU, HI, IA, ID, IL, IN, KS, KY, LA, MA, MD, ME, MI, MN, MO, MS, MT, NC, ND, NE, NH, NJ, NM, NV, NY, OH, OK, OR, PA, PR, RI, SC, SD, TN, TX, UT, VA, VT, WA, WI, WV, WY, AB, BC, MB, NB, NS, ON, QC, SK
Foreign Countries: ALGERIA; ARGENTINA; AUSTRALIA; AUSTRIA; BAHAMAS; BARBADOS; BELGIUM; BRAZIL; BULGARIA; CAMEROON; CANADA; CHINA; COLOMBIA; COSTA RICA; CROATIA; CURACAO; CYPRUS; CZECH REPUBLIC; DENMARK; DOMINICAN REPUBLIC; ECUADOR; EGYPT; EL SALVADOR; ENGLAND; ETHIOPIA; FIJI; FINLAND; FRANCE; GERMANY; GREECE; HONDURAS; HUNGARY; ICELAND; INDIA; INDONESIA; IRELAND;ISRAEL; ITALY; JAMAICA; JAPAN; KENYA; KUWAIT; LUXEMBOURG; MALAYSIA; MALTA; MAURITIUS; MEXICO; NEW ZEALAND; NICARAGUA; NIGERIA; NORWAY; OMAN; PANAMA; PERU; POLAND; PORTUGAL; ROMANIA; RUSSIA; SAUDI ARABIA; SCOTLAND; SEYCHELLES; SINGAPORE; SLOVAKIA; SOUTH AFRICA; SOUTH KOREA; SPAIN; SRI LANKA; SWEDEN; SWITZERLAND; TANZANIA; THAILAND; THE NETHERLANDS; THE PHILIPPINES;TRINIDAD & TOBAGO; TURKEY; UNITED ARAB EMIRATES; URUGUAY; VENEZUELA; VIETNAM; WALES
Type of Foodservice: Casual Dining; Fine Dining; Quick Serve
Subsidiaries: Hilton Canada, MISSISSAUGA, ON CANADA
Primary Distributors: (Food) SYSCO Corporation, HOUSTON, TX
Parent Company: The Blackstone Group, NEW YORK, NY
Headquarters: Hilton Worldwide, MCLEAN, VA
Notes: Total sales excludes revenues derived from timeshare operations. Company-owned units include leased, managed & joint venture properties as well as units owned and operated by Hilton Worldwide. The list of trade names includes limited-service hotels. The company derives approximately 70% of its revenue from hotel operations.

Key Personnel
JONATHAN D. GRAY - Chairman
CHRISTOPHER J. NASSETTA - CEO; President
MARK D. WANG - CEO; President Group
SIMON VINCENT - President International Division
MATT RICHARDSON - President Real Estate, Construction, Design, International Division
DANNY HUGHES - President
ALAN WATTS - President
KEVIN J. JACOBS - CFO; Exec VP
MICHAEL W. DUFFY - Chief Accounting Officer; Senior VP
MATTHEW W. SCHUYLER - Chief Human Resources Officer; Exec VP
JOHN ROGERS - Chief Brand Officer; Senior VP Global Development
CHRIS SILCOCK - Chief Commercial Officer; Exec VP
RANDY GAINES - Exec VP Operations, Sales
JAMES E. HOLTHOUSER - Exec VP Marketing
PATRICK FITZGIBBON - Senior VP Real Estate Development, Business Development, Division
WILLIAM FORTIER - Senior VP Business Development

PHIL CORDELL - Senior VP
KAREN SATTERLEE - Senior VP; General Counsel
W. STEVEN STANDEFER - Senior VP Tax
TED R. RATCLIFF - Senior VP Operations, Northeast Region
PETE TWYMAN - VP Finance
CONRAD WANGEMAN - VP Operations, Northeast Region
ROB SCYPINSKI - VP Marketing, Sales
AARON C. RADELET - VP Communications
ALAN ROBERTS - VP Marketing
MARYBELLE ARNETT - VP Franchise Development, Central Region
CARLOS BARUKI - VP Marketing, Sales, International Division
JUDY CHRISTA-CATHEY - VP Marketing
GREGORY L. FRANCOIS - VP Franchise Development, West Region
CRAIG MANCE - VP Franchise Development
CHRISTOPHER PERRY - Regional VP Marketing, Sales, Mid-Atlantic Division
TIMOTHY POWELL - Senior Director Franchise Development
DEBRA WILSON - Senior Director Sales
LISA COLE - Director Communications, Southeast Region
CARNITA CHOPIN - Director Ethnic Marketing, Sales
CATHY DIEM - Director Sales
GINA FARRIS - Director Sales
KARLA VISCONTI - Director Communications, International Division
DAVID TRUMBLE - Director Communications, West Region

Bowlmor AMF
7313 Bell Creek Rd
Mechanicsville, VA 23111-3551

Telephone: (804) 730 4000
Fax Number: (804) 730-6601
Internet Homepage: amf.com; bowlerocorp.com
Type of Business: Foodservice Operations - Bowling Alley
Year Founded: 1900
Total Sales: $754,990,000 (e)
Alcohol Sales: 25%
Number of Employees: 10,465
Average Check: Breakfast(6); Lunch(6); Dinner(8)
Foodservice Sales: $188,748,000 (e)
Internet Order Processing: Yes
Total Units: 296
Trade Names: AMF Bowling (132); Bowlero (151); Bowlmor (11); Garage Billiards and Bowl (1); Revel & Roll (1)
Company-Owned Units: 296
Preferred Square Footage: 1,500
Preferred Location Types: Freestanding; Strip Mall
Alcohol Served: Beer, Wine, Liquor
Primary Menu: American (295)
Areas of Operation: AL, AZ, CA, CO, CT, DE, FL, GA, IA, IL, IN, KS, KY, LA, MA, MD, MI, MN, MO, NC, NJ, NV, NY, OH, OK, OR, PA, PR, RI, SC, TN, TX, UT, VA, WA, WI
Foreign Countries: MEXICO
Type of Foodservice: In-Store Feeder (295)
Primary Distributors: (Full Line) US Foods, MANASSAS, VA
Parent Company: Code Hennessy & Simmons LLC, CHICAGO, IL
Notes: Total sales reflect revenue from the company's bowling centers only; bowling fees, shoe rental, pro shops, & other activities account for 72% of bowling center sales.

Key Personnel
TOM SHANNON - Chairman; CEO; President
BRETT PARKER - Vice Chairman; CFO; Exec VP
JEFF KOSTELNI - Chief Accounting Officer; Corporate Controller
THOMAS MACKAY - VP Information Technology
ANDRES RESTREPO - VP Development
JAY LIETMAN - VP
KIM ESTEP - Manager Information Technology
BRIAN DACIER - Senior Project Manager

TCB Management Co
11061 Millpond Ln
Mechanicsville, VA 23116-4803

Telephone: (804) 746-4064
Internet Homepage: tcbmcd.com
Company Email: tcbmcdonalds@yahoo.com
Type of Business: Chain Restaurant Operator
Total Sales: $23,590,000 (e)
Total Units: 5
Trade Names: McDonald's (5)
Units Franchised From: 5
Preferred Square Footage: 2,500
Primary Menu: Hamburger (5)
Areas of Operation: VA
Type of Foodservice: Quick Serve (5)
Franchise Affiliation: McDonald's Corporation, CHICAGO, IL

Key Personnel
THOMAS BISHOP - President; Partner; General Buyer
COLEMAN BISHOP - Partner; General Buyer
JASON WELLS - Director Operations

Catawba Corporation
209 E Washington St
Middleburg, VA 20117

Mailing Address: PO Box 1888, MIDDLEBURG, VA, 20118-1888
Telephone: (540) 687-9790
Fax Number: (540) 687-9791
Internet Homepage: bordercafe.com
Type of Business: Chain Restaurant Operator
Year Founded: 1986
Total Sales: $24,910,000 (e)
Alcohol Sales: 35%
Number of Employees: 300
Average Check: Lunch(10); Dinner(14)
Total Units: 6
Trade Names: Border Cafe (1); Jose Tejas (2); Jose's Border Cafe (3)
Company-Owned Units: 6
Preferred Square Footage: 5,500; 6,000; 7,000
Preferred Location Types: Downtown; Freestanding
Alcohol Served: Beer, Wine, Liquor
Primary Menu: Mexican (6)
Areas of Operation: DE, MA, NJ
Type of Foodservice: Casual Dining (6)
Primary Distributors: (Full Line) US Foods, SEABROOK, NH

Key Personnel
RONNIE BECK - CEO
GARRICK STEELE - President; Director Operations, Purchasing, Facility/Maintenance, Supply Chain, Real Estate, Design, Store Fixtures, Menu Development
MIKE QUICK - CFO; Director Finance

DMT Inc
6007 Harbour Park Dr
Midlothian, VA 23112-2160

Telephone: (804) 739-4774
Fax Number: (804) 739-2880
Company Email: dmtinc1@verizon.net
Type of Business: Chain Restaurant Operator
Total Sales: $47,060,000 (e)
Number of Employees: 450
Total Units: 10
Trade Names: McDonald's (10)
Units Franchised From: 10
Preferred Square Footage: 2,500
Primary Menu: Hamburger (10)
Areas of Operation: VA
Type of Foodservice: Quick Serve (10)
Franchise Affiliation: McDonald's Corporation, CHICAGO, IL

Key Personnel
DAVID TRAUB - President; General Buyer

Peninsula Firehouse, Inc.
12515 Jefferson Ave
Newport News, VA 23602-4386

Telephone: (757) 570-9956
Type of Business: Chain Restaurant Operator
Total Sales: $3,771,000 (e)
Total Units: 3

Trade Names: Firehouse Subs (3)
Units Franchised From: 3
Preferred Location Types: Strip Mall
Primary Menu: Sandwiches/Deli (3)
Areas of Operation: VA
Type of Foodservice: Fast Casual (3)
Franchise Affiliation: Firehouse Restaurant Group Inc., JACKSONVILLE, FL

Key Personnel
WILLIAM TILLEY - President; General Buyer

Catlee Inc.
806 Norview Ave
Norfolk, VA 23509-1541

Mailing Address: PO Box 9748, NORFOLK, VA, 23505-0748
Telephone: (757) 489-8455
Type of Business: Chain Restaurant Operator
Year Founded: 1989
Total Sales: $61,890,000 (e)
Number of Employees: 420
Average Check: Breakfast(10); Lunch(14); Dinner(14)
Total Units: 13
Trade Names: McDonald's (13)
Units Franchised From: 13
Preferred Square Footage: 2,500; 3,000
Preferred Location Types: Freestanding
Primary Menu: Hamburger (13)
Areas of Operation: VA
Type of Foodservice: Quick Serve (13)
Franchise Affiliation: McDonald's Corporation, CHICAGO, IL
Primary Distributors: (Food) The Martin-Brower Co., MANASSAS, VA

Key Personnel
LEON DICKEY - President; Owner; General Manager; Director Finance; General Buyer

Chanello's Pizza Inc.
905 W 21st St
Norfolk, VA 23517-1515

Mailing Address: PO Box 15268, CHESAPEAKE, VA, 23328-5268
Telephone: (877) 517-4992
Fax Number: (757) 963-0411
Internet Homepage: chanellospizza.com
Type of Business: Chain Restaurant Operator
Year Founded: 1987
Total Sales: $24,130,000 (e)
Number of Employees: 310
Internet Order Processing: Yes
Total Units: 30
Trade Names: Chanello's Pizza (31)
Company-Owned Units: 31
Primary Menu: Pizza (31)
Areas of Operation: NC, VA
Type of Foodservice: Quick Serve (31)

Key Personnel
CHIP SHUBERT - CEO; Partner; Director Menu Development; General Buyer
JULIET CHANNELL - President; Partner; VP Purchasing, Marketing

Greater Grinders Inc.
1515 Azalea Garden Rd
Norfolk, VA 23502-1601

Telephone: (757) 855-6370
Fax Number: (757) 855-5134
Internet Homepage: greatergrinderssubmarines.com
Type of Business: Chain Restaurant Operator
Year Founded: 1976
Systemwide Sales: $1,521,000 (e)
Total Sales: $532,000 (e)
Number of Employees: 35
Average Check: Lunch(12); Dinner(12)
Total Units: 2
Trade Names: Greater Grinders (2)
Company-Owned Units: 2
Preferred Square Footage: 1,000; 1,200
Preferred Location Types: Freestanding; Strip Mall
Primary Menu: Sandwiches/Deli (2)
Areas of Operation: VA
Type of Foodservice: Quick Serve (2)

Key Personnel
MARTIN SAUNDERS - President; Executive Chef; Director Finance, Real Estate
BOB BOYD - VP; Director Operations, Facility/Maintenance, Information Systems; General Buyer
NOLA BOYD - Treasurer

Canteen Vending Services
2401 Bellwood Rd
North Chesterfield, VA 23237-1309

Telephone: (804) 271-9441
Fax Number: (804) 271-0371
Listing Type: Branch Office
Type of Business: Foodservice Management Operator
Year Founded: 1929
Number of Employees: 40
Number of Locations Served: 250
Total Foodservice Mgmt Accounts: 250
Areas of Operation: VA
Type of Foodservice: Vending machines (250)
Foodservice Management Venues: Business & Industry; College & University; Health Care; Schools; Travel Plazas
Parent Company: Compass Group The Americas, CHARLOTTE, NC
Headquarters: Canteen Vending Services, CHARLOTTE, NC

Key Personnel
JEFF THWEATT - General Manager; General Buyer

DJB Hospitality LLC
10800 Midlothian Tpke Ste 120
North Chesterfield, VA 23235-4725

Telephone: (804) 545-2498
Internet Homepage: sedonataphouse.com
Company Email: guestlove@sedonataphouse.com
Type of Business: Chain Restaurant Operator
Year Founded: 2011
Total Sales: $22,070,000 (e)
Average Check: Lunch(32); Dinner(44)
Total Units: 16
Trade Names: Sedona Taphouse (16)
Company-Owned Units: 3
Units Franchised To: 13
Primary Menu: American (16)
Areas of Operation: CT, MI, NY, VA
Type of Foodservice: Casual Dining (16)
Catering Services: Yes

Key Personnel
DENNIS BARBARO - CEO; Owner; General Buyer

Domino's Franchisee
9451 Amberdale Dr
North Chesterfield, VA 23236-1249

Telephone: (804) 276-0330
Type of Business: Chain Restaurant Operator
Total Sales: $6,167,000 (e)
Total Units: 3
Trade Names: Domino's (3)
Units Franchised From: 3
Primary Menu: Pizza (3)
Areas of Operation: VA
Type of Foodservice: Quick Serve (3)
Franchise Affiliation: Domino's Pizza Inc, ANN ARBOR, MI

Key Personnel
CHRISTOPHER H. KOCHENSPARGER - Owner; General Buyer

McOffice, LLC
812 Moorefield Park Dr Ste 202
North Chesterfield, VA 23236-3674

Telephone: (804) 320-2296
Company Email: mcdonaldsoffice@aol.com
Type of Business: Chain Restaurant Operator
Year Founded: 1985

Total Sales: $92,380,000 (e)
Number of Employees: 900
Average Check: Breakfast(8); Lunch(8); Dinner(10)
Total Units: 19
Trade Names: McDonald's (19)
Units Franchised From: 19
Preferred Square Footage: 2,500
Preferred Location Types: Freestanding
Primary Menu: Hamburger (19)
Areas of Operation: VA
Type of Foodservice: Quick Serve (19)
Franchise Affiliation: McDonald's Corporation, CHICAGO, IL
Primary Distributors: (Food) The Martin-Brower Co., MANASSAS, VA

Key Personnel
WENDY PERIER - Manager Branch

MBA International Inc.
13036 Park Crescent Cir
Oak Hill, VA 20171-2820

Telephone: (703) 989-6851
Fax Number: (703) 935-0334
Type of Business: Chain Restaurant Operator
Year Founded: 2002
Total Sales: $20,360,000 (e)
Number of Employees: 135
Average Check: Lunch(8); Dinner(12)
Total Units: 8
Trade Names: Popeyes Louisiana Kitchen (8)
Units Franchised From: 8
Preferred Location Types: Freestanding
Primary Menu: Chicken (8)
Areas of Operation: MD, VA
Type of Foodservice: Quick Serve (8)
Franchise Affiliation: Popeyes Louisiana Kitchen Inc., ATLANTA, GA
Primary Distributors: (Full Line) Performance Food Group, RICHMOND, VA

Key Personnel
MANSOOR AWAN - President; General Buyer

HEW Inc.
325 N Madison Rd Ste C
Orange, VA 22960-1129

Mailing Address: PO Box 305, ORANGE, VA, 22960-0177
Telephone: (540) 672-0399
Fax Number: (540) 672-0097
Type of Business: Chain Restaurant Operator
Total Sales: $23,730,000 (e)
Number of Employees: 230
Total Units: 5
Trade Names: McDonald's (5)
Units Franchised From: 5
Preferred Square Footage: 2,500
Primary Menu: Hamburger (5)
Areas of Operation: VA
Type of Foodservice: Quick Serve (5)
Franchise Affiliation: McDonald's Corporation, CHICAGO, IL

Key Personnel
HERBERT WILLIAMS JR - President; General Buyer

Massimo Zanetti Beverage USA
1200 Port St
Portsmouth, VA 23704

Telephone: (757) 215-7300
Fax Number: (757) 215-7447
Internet Homepage: chockfullonuts.com; mzb-usa.com; segafredocafe.com
Company Email: cad@mzb-usa.com
Type of Business: Chain Restaurant Operator
Year Founded: 1932
Systemwide Sales: $16,754,000 (e)
Total Sales: $620,000 (e)
Number of Employees: 66
Average Check: Dinner(5)
Internet Order Processing: Yes
Total Units: 6
Trade Names: Chock full o'Nuts Cafe Express (6)
Units Franchised To: 6
Preferred Square Footage: 800
Preferred Location Types: Convenience Store/Gas Station; Freestanding; Grocery Stores; Other; Strip Mall; Travel Plazas
Primary Menu: Coffee (6)
Areas of Operation: FL, NJ, NY
Type of Foodservice: Quick Serve (6)
Primary Distributors: (Food) SYSCO Food Services of Baltimore, JESSUP, MD

Key Personnel
JOHN E. BOYLE - COO; Senior VP Marketing, Sales
DOUGLAS NESMITH - Senior VP Supply Chain
ERIC VAN DE WAL - Senior VP Marketing, Sales
MIKE RAKOWSKI - VP Sales
CLAY DOCKERY - VP Private Label
BOB ASHFORD - Director Information Technology
BRIDGETT NOTTINGHAM - Director Logistics
MARC HARPIN - Director Operations
NATALIA SUAREZ - Director Information Technology; Senior Manager Applications
JENNIFER WINCHELL - Senior Manager Customer Analytics
DOROTHEA HESCOCK - Senior Manager Safety, Quality Assurance-Food
LIONEL ALVA - Senior Manager Information Technology, Applications
SUZANNE ARY - Senior Manager Communications
TYRONE CHERRY - Senior Manager Distribution
JULIA GIRARD - Division Manager; Regional Manager Sales
KEVIN GOINS - Manager Warehouse
GLENN COOPER - Manager Sales
BOBBY BAUCOM - Manager Facility/Maintenance
SUSAN LAMBERT - Manager Business Development
KELLI SEAL - Manager Purchasing
KELLY W. STOKES - Manager Sales
KELLY WALKER STOKES - Manager Sales
LISA MOSS - Supervisor
RACHEL KIRKPATRICK - Project Manager Product Development

Bullets Hamburgers LLC
4186 Michaux Grant Rd
Powhatan, VA 23139-4119

Telephone: (804) 878-1396
Fax Number: (804) 744-7817
Internet Homepage: bulletshamburgers.com
Company Email: contactus@bulletshamburgers.com
Type of Business: Chain Restaurant Operator
Year Founded: 1991
Systemwide Sales: $32,938,000 (e)
Total Sales: $2,500,000 (e)
Number of Employees: 15
Average Check: Lunch(8); Dinner(12)
Total Units: 35
Trade Names: Bullets Burgers Chicken & More (35)
Units Franchised To: 35
Preferred Square Footage: 1,600
Preferred Location Types: Convenience Store/Gas Station; Freestanding; Strip Mall
Primary Menu: American (35)
Areas of Operation: AL, GA, MS, NC, SC, TX, VA
Type of Foodservice: Quick Serve (35)
Primary Distributors: (Full Line) US Foods, SALEM, VA

Key Personnel
BRIAN MURPHY - President; Owner; General Buyer
PAM SWECKER - Director Human Resources

Gate Gourmet Division Americas
1880 Campus Commons Dr Ste 200
Reston, VA 20191-1503

Telephone: (703) 964-2300
Fax Number: (703) 964-2399
Internet Homepage: gategourmet.com
Company Email:

communications@categourmet.com
Listing Type: Regional Office
Type of Business: Foodservice Management Operator
Year Founded: 1941
Total Sales: $1,896,586,000 (e)
Number of Employees: 11,000
Number of Locations Served: 93
Total Foodservice Mgmt Accounts: 250
Areas of Operation: CA, DC, FL, GA, HI, IL, IN, LA, MI, MO, NJ, NY, VA, WA, AB, BC, MB, NS, ON, SK
Type of Foodservice: Quick Serve (250)
Foodservice Management Venues: Transportation
Primary Distributors: (Full Line) Sysco Food Services of Memphis, MEMPHIS, TN
Parent Company: Gate Gourmet International, ZURICH, CHE

Key Personnel
EDWIN GARCIA - President Division; VP Group
HERMON ANBEEK - President
CHRISTOPHER SCHMITZ - CFO

†

Thompson Hospitality
1741 Business Center Dr Ste 200
Reston, VA 20190-5329

Telephone: (703) 757-5560
Fax Number: (703) 759-1538
Internet Homepage: thompsonhospitality.com
Type of Business: Foodservice Management Operator
Year Founded: 1992
Total Sales: $747,106,000 (e)
Number of Employees: 2,500
Number of Locations Served: 55
Total Foodservice Mgmt Accounts: 55
Trade Names: America's Tap Room (2); Austin Grill (1); Be Right Burger (1); Hen Penny (1); Hen Quarter (3); Matchbox (11); Neapolitan Express (5)
Areas of Operation: AL, AZ, CA, CO, DC, FL, GA, IA, IL, IN, KS, KY, LA, MD, ME, MI, MN, MO, NC, ND, NE, NJ, NM, NY, OH, OK, PA, SC, SD, VA, WA, WI, FC
Type of Foodservice: Cafeteria (35); Quick Serve (20)
Foodservice Management Venues: Business & Industry; College & University
Headquarter Offices: Matchbox Food Group, WASHINGTON, DC

Key Personnel
WARREN M. THOMPSON - Chairman; President
BENITA THOMPSON-BYAS - Vice Chairman; Senior VP
ALI AZIMA - CFO; Exec VP
ALEX BERENTZEN - COO; Senior VP Operations
MAURICE JENOURE - COO

FRED THOMPSON JR - Chief Administrative Officer
RON HALLAGAN - Senior VP Operations, Sales; VP Operations
RODNEY RUFFIN - VP Business Development
MICHAEL FLOOD - VP Business Development

● ▲

F W L & Sons Inc
8210 Brook Rd
Richmond, VA 23227

Telephone: (804) 264-3512
Internet Homepage: fwlandsons.com
Type of Business: Chain Restaurant Operator
Total Sales: $23,890,000 (e)
Total Units: 5
Trade Names: McDonald's (5)
Units Franchised From: 5
Primary Menu: Hamburger (5)
Areas of Operation: VA
Type of Foodservice: Quick Serve (5)
Franchise Affiliation: McDonald's Corporation, CHICAGO, IL

Key Personnel
FREDA THORNTON' - President; General Buyer

Jefferson Hotel
101 W Franklin St
Richmond, VA 23220-5009

Telephone: (804) 788-8000
Fax Number: (804) 649-4400
Internet Homepage: jeffersonhotel.com; lemairerestaurant.com
Type of Business: Chain Restaurant Operator
Total Sales: $6,712,000 (e)
Alcohol Sales: 20%
Number of Employees: 45
Average Check: Breakfast(12); Lunch(30); Dinner(60)
Total Units: 2
Trade Names: Lemaire (1); TJ's Restaurant And Lounge (1)
Company-Owned Units: 2
Preferred Location Types: Freestanding; Hotel/Motel
Alcohol Served: Beer, Wine, Liquor
Primary Menu: American (1); French/Continental (1)
Areas of Operation: VA
Type of Foodservice: Casual Dining (1); Fine Dining (1)
Primary Distributors: (Food) SYSCO Food Services of Virginia LLC, HARRISONBURG, VA

Key Personnel
JOSEPH LONGO - President; General Manager
MOHAMMED SEBTI - Owner
PATRICK WILLIS - Executive Chef; General Buyer
DANNY WORKMAN - Director Facility/Maintenance, Engineering
WALTER ZALEWSKI - Director Information Technology
JAMES RICHTER - Director Finance
CAMERON TRICKEY - Director Alcoholic Beverages
ELLEN WALKER - Director Human Resources
SHAWNE WILLIAMS - Director Training; Coordinator
RICK LUNSFORD - Director Retail Operations
PAT MANNING - Director Food and Beverage
GREG MCGEHEE - Director Food and Beverage
JEANITA HARRIS - Director Customer Service
JIMMY HARRIS - Director Catering
CATHERINE JONES - Manager Sales
KATIE BISHOFF - Manager Customer Service
AMY CLEGG - Manager Finance
KYLE GORENCE - Manager Administration
LISA PHILLIPS - Manager Sales
KELLY TRIPLETT - Manager
VONDELL TOWLES - Manager Catering
RYAN SCHILLING - Manager Sales
DANIELA RINDLER - Assistant Manager

Peking Pavilion
8904 W Broad St Ste F
Richmond, VA 23294

Telephone: (804) 649-8888
Fax Number: (804) 649-8147
Internet Homepage: pekingdining.com
Type of Business: Chain Restaurant Operator
Year Founded: 1984
Total Sales: $6,985,000 (e)
Alcohol Sales: 20%
Number of Employees: 112
Average Check: Lunch(8); Dinner(8)
Internet Order Processing: Yes
Total Units: 4
Trade Names: Peking Restaurant (4)
Company-Owned Units: 4
Preferred Square Footage: 4,000
Preferred Location Types: Downtown; Freestanding; Strip Mall
Alcohol Served: Beer, Wine, Liquor
Primary Menu: Chinese (4)
Areas of Operation: VA
Type of Foodservice: Casual Dining (4)
Catering Services: Yes
Primary Distributors: (Food) Performance Food Group, RICHMOND, VA

Key Personnel
MICHAEL KUO - Co-Founder
CORRINA KUO - Co-Founder
PHILIP CHAN - Partner; Director Finance, Operations, Information Systems, Loss Prevention, Real Estate, Store Planning; General Buyer
RICHARD DU - Partner; Controller; Director

Purchasing, Supply Chain, Design, Human Resources
TONY CHANG - Executive Chef; Manager Menu Development, Food Safety, Catering

Richmond Restaurant Group, Inc.
2934 W Cary St
Richmond, VA 23221-3516

Telephone: (804) 342-8990
Internet Homepage: richmondrestaurantgroup.com
Company Email: contact@richmondrestaurantgroup.com
Type of Business: Chain Restaurant Operator
Total Units: 7
Trade Names: East Coast Provisions (1); Pearl Raw Oyster Bar (1); The Daily Kitchen & Bar (2); The Hard Shell Restaurant (2); The Hill Cafe (1)
Company-Owned Units: 7
Alcohol Served: Beer, Wine, Liquor
Primary Menu: American (4); Seafood (1); Steak/Seafood (3)
Areas of Operation: VA
Type of Foodservice: Casual Dining (7)

Key Personnel
JARED GOLDEN - Partner
MICHELLE WILLIAMS - Partner; Executive Chef
TONY DEYERLE - Partner
TED WALOFF - Partner

S&M Durlak
2807 Ackley Ave
Richmond, VA 23228-2147

Telephone: (804) 273-6954
Fax Number: (804) 273-6691
Type of Business: Chain Restaurant Operator
Total Sales: $42,030,000 (e)
Number of Employees: 400
Total Units: 9
Trade Names: McDonald's (9)
Units Franchised From: 9
Preferred Square Footage: 2,500
Primary Menu: Hamburger (9)
Areas of Operation: VA
Type of Foodservice: Quick Serve (9)
Franchise Affiliation: McDonald's Corporation, CHICAGO, IL

Key Personnel
SUSAN DURLAK - President; General Buyer

Shoney's of Richmond Inc.
7702 Glen Forest Dr Ste 106
Richmond, VA 23226

Telephone: (804) 346-3414
Fax Number: (804) 346-1886
Type of Business: Chain Restaurant Operator
Year Founded: 1958
Total Sales: $49,580,000 (e)
Alcohol Sales: 1%
Number of Employees: 1,050
Average Check: Breakfast(10); Lunch(14); Dinner(14)
Total Units: 26
Trade Names: Captain D's Seafood (19); Shoney's (7)
Units Franchised From: 26
Preferred Square Footage: 7,000
Preferred Location Types: Freestanding; Strip Mall
Alcohol Served: Beer, Wine
Primary Menu: American (7); Seafood (19)
Areas of Operation: NC, VA
Type of Foodservice: Family Restaurant (7); Fast Casual (19)
Franchise Affiliation: Captain D's LLC, NASHVILLE, TN; Shoney's North America Corp., NASHVILLE, TN

Key Personnel
MARK SWEENEY - President; Director Purchasing, Real Estate; General Buyer
ROBERT WEEDON - General Manager; General Buyer
TOM EDENSTROM - General Manager; Director Restaurant Operations; General Buyer
JEFFREY A. NICKLAS - Director Human Resources
JENNIFER FORD - Manager Marketing
WALLACE WHITE - Manager Finance

The Restaurant Company
1132 Hermitage Rd
Richmond, VA 23220-1301

Telephone: (804) 358-2148
Fax Number: (804) 355-8065
Internet Homepage: theburgerbach.com; arbysrva.com; cancanbrasserie.com
Company Email: nbockelman@trcrichmond.com
Type of Business: Chain Restaurant Operator
Year Founded: 1969
Total Sales: $49,810,000 (e)
Alcohol Sales: 3%
Number of Employees: 861
Average Check: Breakfast(8); Lunch(20); Dinner(26)
Total Units: 26
Trade Names: Arby's (20); Burger Bach (5); Can Can (1)
Company-Owned Units: 6
Units Franchised From: 20
Preferred Square Footage: 2,500
Preferred Location Types: Freestanding
Alcohol Served: Beer, Wine, Liquor
Primary Menu: French/Continental (1); Hamburger (5); Sandwiches/Deli (20)
Areas of Operation: VA
Type of Foodservice: Casual Dining (5); Fine Dining (1); Quick Serve (20)
Catering Services: Yes
Franchise Affiliation: Arby's Restaurant Group, ATLANTA, GA

Key Personnel
BILL LOWE - President; General Buyer
JOHN RIPP - Controller
KEITH ACKERMAN - General Manager
JUAN DIOSSA - General Manager
JAMES PADA - General Manager
DAVID WELTY - General Manager
NEL BOCKELMAN - Director Marketing
VINCENT RIPP - Director Marketing
DONALD KNUTH - District Manager
ALBERT NATALINI - Manager Restaurant Operations

Urban Farmhouse
100 Shockoe Slip Lower level
Richmond, VA 23219-4115

Telephone: (804) 447-9028
Internet Homepage: theurbanfarmhouse.net
Company Email: feedback@theurbanfarmhouse.net
Type of Business: Chain Restaurant Operator
Total Units: 5
Trade Names: Urban Farmhouse (5)
Company-Owned Units: 5
Primary Menu: American (5)
Areas of Operation: VA
Type of Foodservice: Casual Dining (5)
Notes: Breakfast and brunch.

Key Personnel
KATHLEEN RICHARDSON - Owner; General Buyer

Bob Childress
4805 Valley View Blvd NW
Roanoke, VA 24012-2018

Telephone: (540) 362-1160
Internet Homepage: cfaofroanoke.com
Type of Business: Chain Restaurant Operator
Total Sales: $17,921,000 (e)
Average Check: Dinner(14)
Total Units: 2
Trade Names: Chick-fil-A (2)
Units Franchised From: 2

Primary Menu: Chicken (2)
Areas of Operation: VA
Type of Foodservice: Quick Serve (2)
Franchise Affiliation: Chick-fil-A Inc., ATLANTA, GA

Key Personnel
BOB CHILDRESS - President; General Buyer

Bondough Inc
7307 Williamson Rd Ste A
Roanoke, VA 24019-4268

Mailing Address: PO Box 7356, ROANOKE, VA, 24019-0356
Telephone: (540) 362-0065
Type of Business: Chain Restaurant Operator
Total Sales: $5,605,000 (e)
Total Units: 10
Trade Names: Subway (10)
Units Franchised From: 10
Primary Menu: Sandwiches/Deli (10)
Areas of Operation: VA
Type of Foodservice: Quick Serve (10)
Franchise Affiliation: Doctor's Associates Inc., MILFORD, CT

Key Personnel
D. L. BONHOTEL - Owner; General Buyer

Country Cookin' Inc.
4335 Brambleton Ave
Roanoke, VA 24018-3404

Telephone: (540) 774-0613
Fax Number: (540) 774-9554
Internet Homepage: countrycookin.com
Company Email: goodfood@countrycookin.com
Type of Business: Chain Restaurant Operator
Year Founded: 1979
Total Sales: $23,260,000 (e)
Number of Employees: 500
Average Check: Breakfast(8); Lunch(10); Dinner(18)
Total Units: 15
Trade Names: Country Cookin' (15)
Company-Owned Units: 15
Preferred Square Footage: 11,000
Preferred Location Types: Freestanding; Regional Mall; Strip Mall
Primary Menu: American (15)
Areas of Operation: VA
Type of Foodservice: Family Restaurant (15)
Catering Services: Yes
Primary Distributors: (Full Line) US Foods, SALEM, VA

Key Personnel
BONNIE WHITE - Director Human Resources
PAUL BAKER - Manager District

Famous Anthony's
4522 Old Cave Spring Rd
Roanoke, VA 24018-3423

Mailing Address: PO Box 21707, ROANOKE, VA, 24018-0585
Telephone: (540) 772-1023
Fax Number: (540) 776-9710
Internet Homepage: famousanthonys.com
Company Email: info@famousanthonys.com
Type of Business: Chain Restaurant Operator
Year Founded: 1986
Systemwide Sales: $12,387,000 (e)
Total Sales: $9,463,000 (e)
Alcohol Sales: 5%
Number of Employees: 355
Average Check: Breakfast(10); Lunch(12); Dinner(14)
Total Units: 7
Trade Names: Famous Anthony's (7)
Company-Owned Units: 7
Preferred Square Footage: 5,500; 6,000
Preferred Location Types: Community Mall; Freestanding; Strip Mall
Alcohol Served: Beer
Primary Menu: American (7)
Areas of Operation: VA
Type of Foodservice: Casual Dining (7)
Primary Distributors: (Full Line) US Foods, MANASSAS, VA

Key Personnel
TONY TRIPLETTE - CEO; Director Facility/Maintenance, Supply Chain, Real Estate, Design; General Buyer
BONNY VIAR - VP Operations

Macado's Inc.
120 Church Ave SW Ste B
Roanoke, VA 24011-1919

Mailing Address: P.O. Box 1911, ROANOKE, VA, 24008
Telephone: (540) 345-8034
Fax Number: (540) 344-7781
Internet Homepage: macados.net
Type of Business: Chain Restaurant Operator
Year Founded: 1978
Total Sales: $30,900,000 (e)
Total Units: 21
Trade Names: Macado's (21)
Company-Owned Units: 21
Alcohol Served: Beer, Wine, Liquor
Primary Menu: Sandwiches/Deli (21)
Areas of Operation: NC, TN, VA, WV
Type of Foodservice: Fast Casual (21)
Catering Services: Yes

Key Personnel
RICHARD MACHER - President; General Buyer

MKG Enterprises, LLC
2800 Electric Rd Ste 101C
Roanoke, VA 24018-3549

Telephone: (540) 989-1707
Fax Number: (540) 989-1751
Type of Business: Chain Restaurant Operator
Year Founded: 1983
Total Sales: $66,890,000 (e)
Number of Employees: 470
Average Check: Breakfast(8); Lunch(8); Dinner(10)
Total Units: 14
Trade Names: McDonald's (14)
Units Franchised From: 14
Preferred Square Footage: 2,500; 3,000
Preferred Location Types: Freestanding; Regional Mall
Primary Menu: Hamburger (14)
Areas of Operation: VA
Type of Foodservice: Quick Serve (14)
Franchise Affiliation: McDonald's Corporation, CHICAGO, IL

Key Personnel
MICHAEL GRIMM - Owner; Director Finance, Information Systems, Real Estate; General Buyer
MICHELLE EWERS - Director Human Resources
SUSAN MCDONALD - Director Customer Service
SALLY SCOTT - Director Marketing
GEORGE TAYLOR - Director Operations, Facility/Maintenance
CRYSTAL HUTCHINSON - Manager Accounting
MATT HUTCHINSON - Manager District
VICKI EARLY - Manager District
HEATHER HOLLAND - Supervisor Accounting

New River Valley Pizza
25 Williamson Rd NE
Roanoke, VA 24016-2009

Telephone: (540) 345-3033
Type of Business: Chain Restaurant Operator
Total Sales: $20,863,000 (e)
Total Units: 10
Trade Names: Domino's (10)
Units Franchised From: 10
Primary Menu: Pizza (10)
Areas of Operation: VA
Type of Foodservice: Quick Serve (10)
Franchise Affiliation: Domino's Pizza Inc, ANN ARBOR, MI

Key Personnel
KEVIN E. SHAW - Owner; General Buyer

The Western Sizzlin Corp.
1545 Lynn Brae Dr NE
Roanoke, VA 24012

Mailing Address: PO Box 12167, ROANOKE, VA, 24023-2167
Telephone: (540) 345-3195
Fax Number: (540) 345-0831
Internet Homepage: western-sizzlin.com; woodgrillbuffet.com
Company Email: contactus@western-sizzlin.com
Type of Business: Chain Restaurant Operator
Year Founded: 1962
Systemwide Sales: $154,090,000 (e)
Total Sales: $21,530,000 (e)
Number of Employees: 248
Average Check: Lunch(10); Dinner(14)
Internet Order Processing: Yes
Internet Sales: 1.00%
Total Units: 59
Trade Names: WesterN SizzliN Steak & More (59)
Company-Owned Units: 4
Units Franchised To: 55
Preferred Square Footage: 7,500; 8,500
Preferred Location Types: Downtown; Freestanding; Strip Mall
Primary Menu: Steak (59)
Areas of Operation: AL, AR, CA, FL, GA, KS, LA, MD, MO, MS, NC, OH, OK, SC, TN, VA, WV
Type of Foodservice: Family Restaurant (59)
Catering Services: Yes
Primary Distributors: (Food) US Foods, SALEM, VA
Parent Company: Biglari Holdings Inc., SAN ANTONIO, TX

Key Personnel
SARDAR BIGLARI - Chairman; CEO; President
BRUCE LEWIS - Controller
THOMAS F. SMITH - Director Franchise Development

Wendy's of Western Virginia
5010 Cell Tower Dr
Roanoke, VA 24018-5000

Telephone: (540) 774-9521
Fax Number: (540) 989-0526
Internet Homepage: wowv.net
Type of Business: Chain Restaurant Operator
Year Founded: 1975
Total Sales: $37,530,000 (e)
Number of Employees: 485
Average Check: Lunch(8); Dinner(8)
Total Units: 14
Trade Names: Wendy's Old Fashioned Hamburgers (14)
Units Franchised From: 14
Preferred Square Footage: 2,500
Preferred Location Types: Freestanding
Primary Menu: Hamburger (14)
Areas of Operation: VA
Type of Foodservice: Quick Serve (14)
Franchise Affiliation: The Wendy's Company, DUBLIN, OH

Key Personnel
SALLY ABSHIRE - President; General Buyer

ACES, LLC
15 Byrd Ln
Rocky Mount, VA 24151

Mailing Address: P.O. Box 2009, Rocky Mount, Va, 24151
Telephone: (540) 489-3434
Internet Homepage: aceslcpizza.com
Type of Business: Chain Restaurant Operator
Year Founded: 2008
Total Sales: $22,970,000 (e)
Number of Employees: 388
Average Check: Lunch(22); Dinner(28)
Total Units: 19
Trade Names: Little Caesars Pizza (19)
Units Franchised From: 19
Preferred Square Footage: 1,600; 3,000
Preferred Location Types: Freestanding; Strip Mall
Primary Menu: Pizza (19)
Areas of Operation: VA
Type of Foodservice: Quick Serve (19)
Franchise Affiliation: Little Caesar Enterprises Inc., DETROIT, MI

Key Personnel
PATRICK O'CONNELL - President; General Buyer
BROOKE SPECK - Area Director Midwest Region; Director Midwest Region
CHRIS BELCHER - Area Director East Region
CHARITY COLE - Area Director West Region
JEFFREY CIBBS - Director Operations
DAVID VAUGHN - Director Administration, Marketing
GENE MARTIN - Manager Facility/Maintenance
KEN WAYBRIGHT - Administrator Information Technology

Arrington Enterprises Inc.
1035 Franklin St Ste 100
Rocky Mount, VA 24151-1280

Telephone: (540) 483-7754
Fax Number: (540) 483-8251
Internet Homepage: arringtonmanagementgroup.com
Company Email: info@amgva.com
Type of Business: Chain Restaurant Operator
Year Founded: 1965
Total Sales: $14,180,000 (e)
Number of Employees: 230
Average Check: Breakfast(5); Lunch(8); Dinner(8)
Total Units: 7
Trade Names: Bojangles' Famous Chicken 'n Biscuits (3); Dairy Queen (4)
Units Franchised From: 7
Preferred Square Footage: 2,000; 2,500; 4,000
Preferred Location Types: Freestanding; Travel Plazas
Primary Menu: American (4); Chicken (3)
Areas of Operation: VA
Type of Foodservice: Quick Serve (7)
Franchise Affiliation: Bojangles Restaurants Inc., CHARLOTTE, NC; International Dairy Queen Inc., BLOOMINGTON, MN

Key Personnel
DAVID ARRINGTON - President
D. RUSSELL - Exec VP
BRIAN ARRINGTON - VP Operations
SUSAN ARRINGTOIN - Manager Accounting
J. MANNING - General Buyer

Bob & Edith's Diner
6316 Springfield Plz
Springfield, VA 22150

Telephone: (703) 854-1401
Fax Number: (703) 920-0634
Internet Homepage: bobandedithsdiner.com/home
Type of Business: Chain Restaurant Operator
Year Founded: 1969
Total Sales: $1,783,000 (e)
Trade Names: Bob & Edith's Diner (4)
Company-Owned Units: 4
Primary Menu: American (4)
Areas of Operation: VA
Type of Foodservice: Casual Dining (4)

Key Personnel
GREG BOLTON - Owner

Domino's Franchisee
6715 Backlick Rd Ste K
Springfield, VA 22150-2708

Telephone: (703) 866-1200
Type of Business: Chain Restaurant Operator
Total Sales: $6,086,000 (e)
Total Units: 3
Trade Names: Domino's (3)
Units Franchised From: 3
Primary Menu: Pizza (3)
Areas of Operation: VA

Type of Foodservice: Quick Serve (3)
Franchise Affiliation: Domino's Pizza Inc, ANN ARBOR, MI

Key Personnel
HADEN ANGULO - Owner; General Buyer

Hard Times Cafe
6362 Springfield Plz
Springfield, VA 22150

Telephone: (703) 913-5600
Fax Number: (703) 913-5605
Internet Homepage: hardtimes.com
Type of Business: Chain Restaurant Operator
Year Founded: 1980
Systemwide Sales: $11,333,000 (e)
Total Sales: $3,057,000 (e)
Alcohol Sales: 25%
Number of Employees: 70
Average Check: Lunch(10); Dinner(18)
Internet Order Processing: Yes
Internet Sales: 0.50%
Total Units: 5
Trade Names: Hard Times Cafe (5)
Company-Owned Units: 3
Units Franchised To: 2
Preferred Square Footage: 10,000
Preferred Location Types: Freestanding; Strip Mall
Alcohol Served: Beer, Wine, Liquor
Primary Menu: American (5)
Areas of Operation: MD, VA
Type of Foodservice: Casual Dining (5)
Catering Services: Yes
Primary Distributors: (Full Line) Saval Foods Corp., ELKRIDGE, MD
Parent Company: F&K Management Inc./HT Acquisition Inc, SPRINGFIELD, VA

Key Personnel
FRED PARKER - Founder; Owner
RICH KELLY - VP
AMELEWORK BEKELE - Controller; Director Finance; Manager Accounting
TRISH ASKEW - Director Marketing

Pile High Subs, Inc.
1495 Stafford Market Pl Ste 119
Stafford, VA 22556-4530

Telephone: (540) 288-5443
Type of Business: Chain Restaurant Operator
Total Sales: $8,364,000 (e)
Total Units: 6
Trade Names: Jersey Mike's Subs (6)
Units Franchised From: 6
Primary Menu: Sandwiches/Deli (6)
Areas of Operation: VA
Type of Foodservice: Quick Serve (6)
Franchise Affiliation: Jersey Mike's Franchise Systems, MANASQUAN, NJ

Key Personnel
KRISTIN TREACY - Partner; General Buyer
PAT FOLEY - Partner

Commonwealth Pizza Inc
204 W Hampton St
Staunton, VA 24401-4600

Telephone: (540) 213-3900
Type of Business: Chain Restaurant Operator
Total Sales: $27,036,000 (e)
Total Units: 13
Trade Names: Domino's (13)
Units Franchised From: 13
Primary Menu: Pizza (13)
Areas of Operation: VA
Type of Foodservice: Quick Serve (13)
Franchise Affiliation: Domino's Pizza Inc, ANN ARBOR, MI

Key Personnel
RAY SELLERS - President; General Buyer
HEATHER SELLERS - Manager Operations-Training

Moseley Partners, LLC
113-5 Founders Way Ste 5
Strasburg, VA 22657-3769

Telephone: (540) 465-2421
Type of Business: Chain Restaurant Operator
Total Sales: $19,820,000 (e)
Total Units: 10
Trade Names: Five Guys Burgers and Fries (10)
Units Franchised From: 10
Preferred Location Types: Freestanding; Strip Mall
Primary Menu: Hamburger (10)
Areas of Operation: VA
Type of Foodservice: Fast Casual (10)
Franchise Affiliation: Five Guys Holdings Inc., LORTON, VA

Key Personnel
MARK MOSELEY - President; Director Franchising; General Buyer

Gary "Chip" Kimnach II
1217 N Main St
Suffolk, VA 23434-4360

Telephone: (757) 925-4405
Type of Business: Chain Restaurant Operator
Total Sales: $3,595,000 (e)
Total Units: 2
Trade Names: Moe's Southwest Grill (2)
Units Franchised From: 2
Primary Menu: Southwest/Tex-Mex (2)
Projected Openings: 2
Areas of Operation: VA
Type of Foodservice: Fast Casual (2)
Franchise Affiliation: Moe's Southwest Grill LLC, ATLANTA, GA

Key Personnel
GARY KIMNACH - Owner; General Buyer

Magnum Enterprises, Inc
1622 Holland Rd # B
Suffolk, VA 23434-6767

Telephone: (757) 934-8641
Fax Number: (757) 809-0507
Company Email: subwayoffice@magnumenterprises.biz
Type of Business: Chain Restaurant Operator
Total Sales: $4,039,000 (e)
Internet Order Processing: Yes
Total Units: 7
Trade Names: Subway (7)
Units Franchised From: 7
Primary Menu: Sandwiches/Deli (7)
Areas of Operation: VA
Type of Foodservice: Quick Serve (7)
Franchise Affiliation: Doctor's Associates Inc., MILFORD, CT

Key Personnel
DOUGLAS EITEL - President; Partner; General Buyer

Domino's Franchisee
1824 Tappahannock Blvd
Tappahannock, VA 22560

Telephone: (804) 443-6585
Type of Business: Chain Restaurant Operator
Total Sales: $4,100,000 (e)
Total Units: 2
Trade Names: Domino's (2)
Units Franchised From: 2
Primary Menu: Pizza (2)
Areas of Operation: VA
Type of Foodservice: Quick Serve (2)
Franchise Affiliation: Domino's Pizza Inc, ANN ARBOR, MI

Key Personnel
BRETT N. SIMMONS - Owner; General Buyer

Eugene Forbes Enterprises
120 McDonalds St
Tazewell, VA 24651-9326

Telephone: (276) 988-2558

Fax Number: (276) 988-3789
Company Email: gfmcdonalds@adelphia.net
Type of Business: Chain Restaurant Operator
Year Founded: 1999
Total Sales: $53,250,000 (e)
Number of Employees: 600
Average Check: Breakfast(8); Lunch(8); Dinner(10)
Total Units: 11
Trade Names: McDonald's (11)
Units Franchised From: 11
Preferred Square Footage: 3,000
Preferred Location Types: Freestanding
Primary Menu: Hamburger (11)
Areas of Operation: VA, WV
Type of Foodservice: Quick Serve (11)
Franchise Affiliation: McDonald's Corporation, CHICAGO, IL

Key Personnel
EUGENE FORBES - President; Director Finance, Information Systems, Real Estate; General Buyer
TIM PLUMLEY - Manager Operations, Facility/Maintenance, Supply Chain, Store Fixtures
JEFF ATWELL - Manager Accounting
TERESA BAKER - Manager Human Resources

Rappahannock Oyster Co.
784 Locklies Creek Rd
Topping, VA 23169

Mailing Address: PO Box 88, TOPPING, VA, 23169
Telephone: (804) 204-1709
Internet Homepage: rroysters.com
Company Email: info@rroysters.com
Type of Business: Chain Restaurant Operator
Year Founded: 2001
Total Units: 6
Trade Names: Merroir (1); Rappahannock (1); Rappahannock Oyster Bar (4)
Company-Owned Units: 6
Primary Menu: Seafood (6)
Projected Openings: 1
Areas of Operation: CA, DC, SC, VA
Type of Foodservice: Casual Dining (6)

Key Personnel
RYAN CROXTON - Partner
TRAVIS CROXTON - Partner
TERRI RIGGS - General Manager
JEAN PAUL SABATIER - General Manager
JESSICA OPPERMAN - Director Restaurant Operations
BRADLEY WALKER - Director Operations
PATRICK OLIVER - Director
JAY JACKSON - Manager Shipping

Team Washington Inc.
1600 Spring Hill Rd Ste 100
Vienna, VA 22182

Telephone: (703) 734-7080
Fax Number: (703) 734-7081
Type of Business: Chain Restaurant Operator
Year Founded: 1983
Total Sales: $172,326,000 (e)
Number of Employees: 1,300
Average Check: Lunch(14); Dinner(14)
Total Units: 83
Trade Names: Domino's (83)
Units Franchised From: 83
Preferred Square Footage: 700; 1,000
Preferred Location Types: Freestanding; Strip Mall
Primary Menu: Pizza (83)
Areas of Operation: DC, MD, VA
Type of Foodservice: Quick Serve (83)
Foodservice Management Venues: Schools
Franchise Affiliation: Domino's Pizza Inc, ANN ARBOR, MI
Primary Distributors: (Food) SYSCO Food Services of Baltimore, JESSUP, MD

Key Personnel
MARY LYNNE CARRAWAY - President; Director Purchasing, Real Estate
KEN SANDERS-SMITH - CFO; Manager Finance, Information Systems, Inventory, Loss Prevention, Risk Management, Quality Assurance, Design, Food Safety
ROBERT DONNER - VP Operations, Supply Chain
MICHAEL BOZARTH - Controller
DEMARCUS RANDLE - Manager Information Technology
LAUREN KIBLER - Manager Marketing
WON JEONG - Manager Training

Vie de France Yamazaki Inc.
2070 Chain Bridge Rd Ste 500
Vienna, VA 22182-2588

Telephone: (703) 442-9205
Fax Number: (703) 821-2695
Internet Homepage: viedefrance.com
Type of Business: Nontraditional Foodservice Operator
Year Founded: 1971
Total Sales: $45,269,000 (e)
Alcohol Sales: 10%
Number of Employees: 532
Total Units: 4
Trade Names: Vie de France Bakery Cafe (4)
Company-Owned Units: 4
Preferred Square Footage: 2,000
Preferred Location Types: Community Mall; Convenience Store/Gas Station; Freestanding; Office Complex; Strip Mall
Alcohol Served: Beer, Wine, Liquor
Primary Menu: French/Continental (4)
Areas of Operation: CA, DC, MD
Type of Foodservice: Casual Dining
Catering Services: Yes
Primary Distributors: (Full Line) SYSCO Food Services of Virginia LLC, HARRISONBURG, VA
Parent Company: Yamazaki Baking Co., JAPAN,
Notes: The company derives approximately 80% of its revenue from wholesale bakery operations.

Key Personnel
FRANK SCHNEIDER - VP Distribution
NOBU SAIKI - Director Construction, Business Development
SUSAN CRAIG - Director Human Resources; Manager Risk Management
SUSAN SALATA - Manager Marketing, Design, Product Development, Catering
CARLA JACKSON - Manager Human Resources
ALICIA PRIETO - Coordinator Information Technology

BurgerBusters Inc.
2242 W Great Neck Rd Ste 201
Virginia Beach, VA 23451-1555

Telephone: (757) 412-0112
Fax Number: (757) 412-0116
Internet Homepage: burgerbusters.com
Company Email: bbi@burgerbusters.com
Type of Business: Chain Restaurant Operator
Year Founded: 1986
Total Sales: $144,800,000 (e)
Number of Employees: 4,791
Average Check: Lunch(8); Dinner(10)
Total Units: 80
Trade Names: Taco Bell (74); Taco bell/KFC (2); Taco Bell/KFC/Pizza Hut (4)
Units Franchised From: 80
Preferred Square Footage: 2,700
Preferred Location Types: Convenience Store/Gas Station; Freestanding; Regional Mall
Primary Menu: Taco (76)
Projected Openings: 2
Areas of Operation: MD, NC, VA, WV
Type of Foodservice: Quick Serve (80)
Franchise Affiliation: KFC Corporation, LOUISVILLE, KY; Pizza Hut Inc., PLANO, TX; Taco Bell Corp., IRVINE, CA
Primary Distributors: (Full Line) McLane/Manassas, MANASSAS, VA

Key Personnel
TASSOS PAPHITES - CEO; President; Partner; Director Information Systems
CHRISTAKIS ACHILLEOS - Partner; Treasurer
MARCUS DRAGAS - Partner; Director Real

Estate; General Buyer
GREGORY ROWLAND - CFO
DAVID LAJOIE - CFO
JOE MANGANO - COO; Director Operations, Facility/Maintenance
JEANETTE JONES - Senior VP Operations
CHRISTOPHER FARWELL - VP Operations
KIRK JESTER - Director Human Resources
YIANNI ACHILLEOS - Director Marketing
ALEXANDROS ACHILLEOS - Director Facility/Maintenance, Loss Prevention
SEAN SMITH - District Manager
DEEDEE SIDES - District Manager
NATALIE FRYE - Specialist Accounting
PATRICK BOWEN - Specialist Loss Prevention

Cal'z Pizza Subs & Chicken Wings
3324 Holland Rd
Virginia Beach, VA 23452-4826

Telephone: (757) 430-2432
Fax Number: (757) 430-2010
Internet Homepage: calzpizza.com
Company Email: calzmain@aol.com
Type of Business: Chain Restaurant Operator
Year Founded: 1982
Total Sales: $7,585,000 (e)
Number of Employees: 170
Average Check: Lunch(14); Dinner(16)
Internet Order Processing: Yes
Internet Sales: 1.00%
Total Units: 9
Trade Names: Cal'z Pizza Subs & Chicken Wings (9)
Company-Owned Units: 9
Preferred Square Footage: 1,500
Preferred Location Types: Freestanding; Strip Mall
Primary Menu: Pizza (9)
Areas of Operation: VA
Type of Foodservice: Quick Serve (9)
Catering Services: Yes

Key Personnel
SEAN CALWAY - CEO; President; Partner; Director Finance, Facility/Maintenance, Supply Chain, Ethnic Marketing, Real Estate, Store Fixtures; Manager Risk Management, Human Resources, Menu Development
BRUCE BREEGER - Owner
DONALD CALWAY - Partner; VP; Manager Purchasing, Information Systems, Design
ELISABETH ZARBO - Partner; Controller; Manager Operations
BEN HERDLEIN - Manager Catering

Capt. George's Seafood Restaurant
1956 Laskin Rd
Virginia Beach, VA 23454-4256

Telephone: (757) 428-3494
Fax Number: (757) 428-8940
Internet Homepage: captaingeorges.com
Company Email: lisa.crain@captaingeorges.com
Type of Business: Chain Restaurant Operator
Year Founded: 1978
Total Sales: $30,371,000 (e)
Alcohol Sales: 4%
Number of Employees: 500
Average Check: Dinner(40)
Internet Order Processing: Yes
Total Units: 4
Trade Names: Captain George's Seafood Restaurant (4)
Company-Owned Units: 4
Preferred Square Footage: 12,000
Preferred Location Types: Freestanding
Alcohol Served: Beer, Wine, Liquor
Primary Menu: Seafood (4)
Areas of Operation: SC, VA
Type of Foodservice: Casual Dining (4)
Catering Services: Yes
Primary Distributors: (Full Line) SYSCO Food Services of Hampton Roads Inc., SUFFOLK, VA

Key Personnel
LISA CRAIN - Director Operations
MIKE JAHN - Director Operations, Purchasing, Supply Chain
MARCY JAHN - Manager Finance
QUENTIN CROCKETT - Coordinator Facility/Maintenance

Dink Inc.
804 Newtown Rd Ste 103
Virginia Beach, VA 23462-1395

Telephone: (757) 497-8761
Fax Number: (757) 497-1356
Type of Business: Chain Restaurant Operator
Year Founded: 1982
Total Sales: $4,480,000 (e)
Number of Employees: 103
Average Check: Lunch(10); Dinner(12)
Total Units: 4
Trade Names: Long John Silver's (4)
Units Franchised From: 4
Preferred Square Footage: 2,200
Preferred Location Types: Freestanding
Primary Menu: Seafood (4)
Areas of Operation: VA
Type of Foodservice: Quick Serve (4)
Franchise Affiliation: Long John Silver's Inc., LOUISVILLE, KY

Primary Distributors: (Food) McLane/Concord, CONCORD, NC

Key Personnel
BILL BREWER - President; Director Real Estate
WANDA BARTON - Director Operations

Dough Boy's California Pizza
2410 Atlantic Ave
Virginia Beach, VA 23451-3204

Telephone: (757) 425-7108
Fax Number: (757) 437-8512
Internet Homepage: doughboyspizza.com
Company Email: info@doughboyspizza.com
Type of Business: Chain Restaurant Operator
Total Sales: $7,329,000 (e)
Alcohol Sales: 20%
Number of Employees: 300
Average Check: Dinner(24)
Total Units: 3
Trade Names: Dough Boy's California Pizza (3)
Company-Owned Units: 3
Preferred Location Types: Freestanding
Alcohol Served: Beer, Wine, Liquor
Primary Menu: Pizza (3)
Areas of Operation: VA
Type of Foodservice: Casual Dining (3)

Key Personnel
GEORGE KOTARIDES - CEO; Director Operations, Menu Development; General Buyer

Food Folks and Fun of Virginia, LLC
1704 Hunt Meet Cir
Virginia Beach, VA 23454-1117

Telephone: (757) 481-3140
Type of Business: Chain Restaurant Operator
Total Sales: $3,426,000 (e)
Total Units: 2
Trade Names: Moe's Southwest Grill (2)
Units Franchised From: 2
Primary Menu: Southwest/Tex-Mex (2)
Areas of Operation: VA
Type of Foodservice: Fast Casual (2)
Franchise Affiliation: Moe's Southwest Grill LLC, ATLANTA, GA

Key Personnel
GARY WEAVER - Owner; General Buyer

Lynn Haven Investors
2720 N Mall Dr
Virginia Beach, VA 23452-7200

Telephone: (757) 463-6700
Type of Business: Chain Restaurant Operator
Total Sales: $4,136,000 (e)
Total Units: 3
Trade Names: Cici's Pizza (3)
Units Franchised From: 3
Primary Menu: Pizza (3)
Areas of Operation: VA
Type of Foodservice: Family Restaurant (3)
Franchise Affiliation: CiCi Enterprises L.P., COPPELL, TX

Key Personnel
CARSON TODD - President; General Buyer
HEATHER BENNETT - General Manager

M.J. Roberts Inc.
2232 Trant Lake Dr
Virginia Beach, VA 23454-2114

Telephone: (757) 305-9791
Fax Number: (757) 313-4078
Internet Homepage: feathernfin.com
Type of Business: Chain Restaurant Operator
Year Founded: 1969
Total Sales: $3,992,000 (e)
Number of Employees: 50
Average Check: Lunch(8); Dinner(14)
Internet Order Processing: Yes
Total Units: 3
Trade Names: Feather 'N' Fin (3)
Company-Owned Units: 3
Preferred Location Types: Freestanding; Strip Mall
Primary Menu: Chicken (3)
Areas of Operation: VA
Type of Foodservice: Quick Serve (3)

Key Personnel
TIM ROBERTS - President; General Buyer

Marx Enterprises, Inc.
5072 Ferrell Pkwy
Virginia Beach, VA 23464-8894

Telephone: (757) 747-2150
Type of Business: Chain Restaurant Operator
Total Sales: $2,100,000 (e)
Total Units: 3
Trade Names: Little Caesars Pizza (3)
Units Franchised From: 3
Primary Menu: Pizza (3)
Areas of Operation: VA
Type of Foodservice: Quick Serve (3)
Franchise Affiliation: Little Caesar Enterprises Inc., DETROIT, MI

Key Personnel
STEVE MARX - President; General Buyer

Newland Management
5741 Cleveland St Ste 180
Virginia Beach, VA 23462-1777

Telephone: (757) 468-6300
Type of Business: Chain Restaurant Operator
Total Sales: $56,830,000 (e)
Total Units: 12
Trade Names: McDonald's (12)
Units Franchised From: 12
Preferred Square Footage: 2,500
Primary Menu: Hamburger (12)
Areas of Operation: VA
Type of Foodservice: Quick Serve (12)
Franchise Affiliation: McDonald's Corporation, CHICAGO, IL

Key Personnel
HUGH FARD - President; General Buyer
TIM DURIE - Senior VP Operations
KIMBERLY BANACH - Director Marketing

Pollard's Enterprises Inc.
2316 Virginia Beach Blvd
Virginia Beach, VA 23454-4008

Telephone: (757) 463-2530
Fax Number: (757) 340-2706
Internet Homepage: pollardscatering.com
Type of Business: Chain Restaurant Operator
Year Founded: 1967
Total Sales: $8,466,000 (e)
Number of Employees: 175
Average Check: Lunch(10); Dinner(10)
Internet Order Processing: Yes
Total Units: 8
Trade Names: Pollard's Chicken & Catering (8)
Company-Owned Units: 8
Preferred Square Footage: 2,000
Preferred Location Types: Freestanding; Strip Mall
Primary Menu: Chicken (8)
Projected Openings: 1
Areas of Operation: VA
Type of Foodservice: Family Restaurant (8)
Catering Services: Yes

Key Personnel
JOHN POLLARD - President; Treasurer; Controller; Executive Chef; Director Finance, Facility/Maintenance, Supply Chain, Real Estate, Design
BETTY POLLARD-GRAVELY - VP Operations, Purchasing, Sales, Catering; General Buyer
MARY GAGNON - Manager Operations

The Art Institute of Virginia Beach
4500 Main St Ste 200
Virginia Beach, VA 23462-3358

Telephone: (877) 437-4428
Internet Homepage: artinstitutes.edu/virginia-beach
Type of Business: Culinary Schools
Areas of Operation: VA

Key Personnel
ERIC WATSON - Director

The Skinny Dip Frozen Yogurt Bar
2589 Kentucky Derby Dr
Virginia Beach, VA 23456-8114

Telephone: (757) 689-3433
Internet Homepage: ilovetheskinnydip.com
Company Email: Fro2Go@theskinnydip.com
Type of Business: Chain Restaurant Operator
Year Founded: 2008
Total Units: 9
Trade Names: The Skinny Dip Frozen Yogurt Bar (9)
Company-Owned Units: 7
Units Franchised To: 2
Primary Menu: Snacks (9)
Areas of Operation: FL, VA
Type of Foodservice: Quick Serve (9)
Notes: Address is owner's home address. Phone number is company-owned store #1.

Key Personnel
CINDY RAUCH - Founder; CEO; General Buyer

Ynot Italian
2102 Great Neck Square Shopping Center
Virginia Beach, VA 23454

Telephone: (757) 496-9111
Internet Homepage: ynotitalian.com
Company Email: tammi@ynotitalian.com
Type of Business: Chain Restaurant Operator
Year Founded: 1993
Total Units: 6
Trade Names: Ynot Italian (6)
Company-Owned Units: 6
Primary Menu: Pizza (6)
Areas of Operation: VA
Type of Foodservice: Fast Casual (6)

Chain Restaurant Operators

Key Personnel
TONY DISILVESTRO - Partner; General Buyer
CYNDI DISILVESTRO - Partner
HARRY DISILVESTRO - Partner

Zero's Mr. Submarine Inc.
576 N Birdneck Rd # 714
Virginia Beach, VA 23451

Telephone: (757) 486-8338
Fax Number: (757) 486-9755
Internet Homepage: zerossubs.com
Company Email: dcarden@zerossubs.com
Type of Business: Chain Restaurant Operator
Year Founded: 1967
Systemwide Sales: $15,374,000 (e)
Total Sales: $10,950,000 (e)
Alcohol Sales: 1%
Number of Employees: 125
Average Check: Breakfast(6); Lunch(10); Dinner(10)
Internet Order Processing: Yes
Total Units: 29
Trade Names: Zero's Subs (29)
Units Franchised To: 29
Preferred Square Footage: 1,000; 1,500
Preferred Location Types: Freestanding; Regional Mall; Strip Mall
Alcohol Served: Beer, Wine, Liquor
Primary Menu: Sandwiches/Deli (29)
Projected Openings: 1
Projected Remodelings: 2
Areas of Operation: NC, TN, VA
Type of Foodservice: Quick Serve (29)
Catering Services: Yes

Key Personnel
LARRY GRAYBILL - CFO Group; Director Finance, Purchasing, Supply Chain; Manager Accounting, Information Systems
DAVE CARDEN - Director Store Development

Mountain Valley Corporation
650 Lew Dewitt Blvd
Waynesboro, VA 22980-1659

Mailing Address: PO Box 1310, WAYNESBORO, VA, 22980-1322
Telephone: (540) 943-1483
Fax Number: (540) 949-7784
Type of Business: Chain Restaurant Operator
Year Founded: 1982
Total Sales: $35,970,000 (e)
Number of Employees: 535
Average Check: Breakfast(8); Lunch(8); Dinner(8)
Total Units: 16
Trade Names: Burger King (16)
Units Franchised From: 16
Preferred Square Footage: 2,600
Preferred Location Types: Convenience Store/Gas Station; Freestanding
Primary Menu: Hamburger (16)
Areas of Operation: VA
Type of Foodservice: Quick Serve (16)
Franchise Affiliation: Burger King Worldwide Inc., MIAMI, FL
Primary Distributors: (Full Line) McLane/Rocky Mount, ROCKY MOUNT, NC

Key Personnel
BRENDA F. WILKINSON - Partner; Treasurer
KEITH A. WRIGHT - Partner; VP; Director Operations, Purchasing, Marketing
CHRISTIAN SIMPKINS - General Manager
AMBER COBB - Director Human Resources
MARTHA WYANT - Director Accounting
TERRIE LAFONTAINE - Manager

RAHE Inc.
1522 Park Rd
Waynesboro, VA 22980-2434

Telephone: (540) 943-3176
Fax Number: (540) 943-5539
Type of Business: Chain Restaurant Operator
Year Founded: 1971
Total Sales: $33,340,000 (e)
Number of Employees: 255
Average Check: Breakfast(8); Lunch(10); Dinner(10)
Total Units: 7
Trade Names: McDonald's (7)
Units Franchised From: 7
Preferred Square Footage: 2,500; 3,000
Preferred Location Types: Discount Dept. Stores; Freestanding
Primary Menu: Hamburger (7)
Areas of Operation: VA
Type of Foodservice: In-Store Feeder (1); Quick Serve (6)
Franchise Affiliation: McDonald's Corporation, CHICAGO, IL
Primary Distributors: (Food) The Martin-Brower Co., MANASSAS, VA

Key Personnel
DIANE HENDRICKS - President; Director Purchasing, Real Estate
SHARON WOOD - Treasurer; Director Finance, Information Systems, Human Resources
JOHN OPSTAD - Director Operations, Facility/Maintenance, Supply Chain; General Buyer
GREG SCHRADER - Supervisor District
RUBY SPROUSE - Supervisor District

Colonial Williamsburg Foundation
134 N Henry St
Williamsburg, VA 23185-4138

Mailing Address: PO Box 1776, WILLIAMSBURG, VA, 23187-1776
Telephone: (757) 229-1000
Fax Number: (757) 220-7797
Internet Homepage: colonialwilliamsburg.com; history.org
Company Email: cwres@cwf.org
Type of Business: Foodservice Operations - Hotel/Motels
Year Founded: 1927
Total Sales: $29,600,000 (e)
Alcohol Sales: 20%
Number of Employees: 210
Total Units: 5
Restaurants in Hotels: 6
Trade Names: Colonial Houses (1); Griffin Hotel (1); Williamsburg Inn (1); Williamsburg Lodge (1); Williamsburg Woodlands Hotel & Suites (1)
Company-Owned Units: 6
Alcohol Served: Beer, Wine, Liquor
Areas of Operation: VA
Type of Foodservice: Casual Dining (5); Family Restaurant (1)
Primary Distributors: (Food) SYSCO Food Services of Virginia LLC, HARRISONBURG, VA; (Specialty Foods) SYSCO Food Services of Virginia LLC, HARRISONBURG, VA
Notes: The company derives approximately 75% of its revenue from hotel operations.

Key Personnel
COLIN CAMPBELL - Chairman
MITCHELL REISS - CEO; President
SAM RUCKER - CIO
TAYLOR ROBERT - Senior VP Finance, Administration
MICHAEL HORNBY - Executive Director Operations
LESLIE NOBLE - General Manager Gaming/Entertainment
GRAZIANO BOB - General Manager
TRACY HAYNES - General Manager
RJHYS LEWIS - Executive Chef
KATHERINE JORDAN - Director Graphic Design
TOM PECK - Director Product Development
RICHARD NICOLL - Director
TORY GUSSMAN - Director Site Selection
CARL CHILDS - Director
KAREN STONE - Director Safety
RENEE CLARK - Senior Manager Sales
BETH KELLY - Senior Manager Area
PAULA PRITCHARD - Senior Manager Sales
DEROSA MICHELE - Senior Manager
DAWN MORRIS - Manager Group
BROOKE MURRAY - Manager Sales
LLOYD JANE - Manager Human Resources

NOREEN GRAZIANO - Manager Customer Service
KOSTA KAPANDELOV - Manager Customer Service
MARY COSTELLO - Manager Customer Service
LEE ANDERSON - Manager Operations
LEROY STOUTINGBERG - Manager Restaurant Operations
DEJAN TERZIEV - Manager Food and Beverage
FELICIA SENSIBA - Manager Restaurant Operations
SUZ SPIRI - Manager Information Systems
MEREDITH SPRINKLE - Manager E-Commerce
KURT REISWEBER - Manager Facility/Maintenance
LEE WHITBY - Supervisor Operations
JOANNE CHAPMAN - Supervisor Operations
RICHARD BUEL - Supervisor Facility/Maintenance
TERRI HARMON - Specialist Operations
RICHELLE TOBIAS - Specialist Administration
LAMBERT BRIAN - Buyer Books
SANDY HOLSTEN - Coordinator
ANNA CORDLE - Coordinator Public Relations
SHAUNDA DAVIS - Agent Information Technology
MOON JOYCE - Agent Purchasing
ELIZABETH EATON - Designer Graphic Design
MIKE BINSFELD - Analyst Information Systems
LEONARD MARY - Analyst HRIS
WAYNE BUHL - Architect
RACHEL WEST - Developer Content Marketing
CAROLE MOORE - Generalist Human Resources

Domino's Franchisee
445 Merrimac Trl Ste D
Williamsburg, VA 23185

Telephone: (757) 220-3770
Type of Business: Chain Restaurant Operator
Total Sales: $10,376,000 (e)
Total Units: 5
Trade Names: Domino's (5)
Units Franchised From: 5
Primary Menu: Pizza (5)
Areas of Operation: VA
Type of Foodservice: Quick Serve (5)
Franchise Affiliation: Domino's Pizza Inc, ANN ARBOR, MI

Key Personnel
SCOTT M. BOYLE - Owner; General Buyer

Fords Colony Country Club
240 Fords Colony Dr
Williamsburg, VA 23188-6412

Telephone: (757) 258-4107
Fax Number: (757) 258-4168
Internet Homepage: clubcorp.com/Clubs/Fords-Colony-Country-Club
Type of Business: Chain Restaurant Operator
Year Founded: 1987
Total Sales: $3,122,000 (e)
Alcohol Sales: 20%
Number of Employees: 50
Average Check: Lunch(16); Dinner(32)
Total Units: 2
Trade Names: Colony Room (1); Murdoch's (1)
Company-Owned Units: 2
Preferred Location Types: Freestanding
Alcohol Served: Beer, Wine, Liquor
Primary Menu: American (2)
Areas of Operation: VA
Type of Foodservice: Casual Dining (2)
Primary Distributors: (Food) Performance Food Group, RICHMOND, VA

Key Personnel
DAVID PILLSBURY - CEO
TIM WESTBY-GIBSON - Director Food and Beverage
JAMIE KEHAYES - Director Restaurant Operations

N & R Dining, Inc.
423 N Boundary St
Williamsburg, VA 23185-3615

Telephone: (757) 564-3175
Fax Number: (757) 564-3179
Company Email: office@nrdining.com
Type of Business: Chain Restaurant Operator
Total Sales: $45,620,000 (e)
Number of Employees: 1,220
Total Units: 20
Trade Names: Burger King (20)
Units Franchised From: 20
Preferred Square Footage: 2,500
Primary Menu: Hamburger (20)
Areas of Operation: VA
Type of Foodservice: Quick Serve (20)
Franchise Affiliation: Burger King Worldwide Inc., MIAMI, FL

Key Personnel
JOSEPH NAPARLO - President; General Buyer

Newport Hospitality Group
4290 New Town Ave
Williamsburg, VA 23188-2681

Telephone: (757) 221-0100
Fax Number: (757) 221-0400
Internet Homepage: nhghotels.com
Company Email: inquiries@nhghotels.com
Type of Business: Foodservice Operations - Hotel/Motels
Year Founded: 1990
Total Sales: $41,140,000 (e)
Alcohol Sales: 15%
Number of Employees: 1,178
Total Units: 38
Restaurants in Hotels: 12
Trade Names: Candlewood Suites (3); Comfort Inn & Suites (1); Courtyard (5); Fairfield Inn (4); Hampton Inn (1); Hilton Garden Inn (3); Holiday Inn (3); Home2 Suites (2); Homewood Suites (2); Hyatt Place (1); Residence Inn (1); Sheraton (2); Sleep Inn & Suites (3); Springhill Suites (2); The Inn (1); The Suites at Yale(1); TownPlace Suites (3)
Company-Owned Units: 38
Alcohol Served: Beer, Wine, Liquor
Projected Openings: 3
Areas of Operation: AL, CT, FL, GA, MD, NC, NJ, NY, RI, SC, VA, WV
Franchise Affiliation: Ruby Tuesday Inc., MARYVILLE, TN
Notes: The company derives approximately 75% of its total revenue from hotel operations.

Key Personnel
SHERI ROUNTREE - Vice Chairman Procurement; VP Purchasing; General Buyer
MICHAEL PLENINGER - President
WAYNE WEST III - COO; Senior VP
ANDY SIMASEK - Exec VP; Director Region
ANDREW CAREY - Exec VP Business Development
FREDERICK TANZER - Senior VP
LIZZ A. CHAMBERS - VP Sales

Sotherly Hotels Inc.
306 S Henry St Ste 100
Williamsburg, VA 23185-4046

Telephone: (757) 229-5648
Fax Number: (757) 564-8801
Internet Homepage: sotherlyhotels.com
Type of Business: Foodservice Operations - Hotel/Motels
Year Founded: 2004
Publicly Held: Yes
Total Sales: $115,900,000 (e)
Alcohol Sales: 10%
Number of Employees: 1,000
Total Units: 12
Trade Names: Crowne Plaza (1); Hilton (1); Hyde Resort & Residences (1); Sheraton (1); The Desoto (1); The Doubletree (5); The Georgian Terrace (1); The Whitehall (1)
Company-Owned Units: 12
Alcohol Served: Beer, Wine, Liquor
Areas of Operation: FL, GA, IN, NC, PA, TX
Primary Distributors: (Food) SYSCO Food Services of Hampton Roads Inc., SUFFOLK, VA
Notes: The company derives approximately 75% of its revenue from hotel operations.

Key Personnel
DREW SIMS - Chairman; CEO

DAVID R. FOLSOM - President; COO
ANTHONY E. DOMALSKI - CFO
SCOTT KUCINSKI - VP Operations
ROBERT KIRKLAND - Director Compliance
ANDREW M. SIMS JR - Brand Manager

Allen Properties Inc.
625 Millwood Ave Ste 1
Winchester, VA 22601-5189

Telephone: (540) 665-0405
Type of Business: Chain Restaurant Operator
Year Founded: 1955
Total Sales: $24,620,000 (e)
Number of Employees: 355
Average Check: Lunch(10); Dinner(12)
Total Units: 13
Trade Names: Arby's (9); KFC (2); Sonic Dine In (2)
Units Franchised From: 13
Preferred Square Footage: 2,500; 3,000; 3,200
Preferred Location Types: Freestanding
Primary Menu: American (2); Chicken (2); Sandwiches/Deli (9)
Areas of Operation: VA, WV
Type of Foodservice: Quick Serve (13)
Franchise Affiliation: Arby's Restaurant Group, ATLANTA, GA; KFC Corporation, LOUISVILLE, KY
Primary Distributors: (Food) McLane/Midwest, DANVILLE, IL

Key Personnel
ERIK BEATLEY - President; Controller; General Manager; Director Real Estate; General Buyer

Anthony's Inc.
2204 Valley Ave
Winchester, VA 22601-2756

Telephone: (540) 667-5660
Fax Number: (540) 868-9322
Internet Homepage: myanthonyspizza.com
Company Email: anthonyspizzawinc@gmail.com
Type of Business: Chain Restaurant Operator
Total Sales: $20,690,000 (e)
Alcohol Sales: 10%
Number of Employees: 115
Average Check: Lunch(8); Dinner(10)
Internet Order Processing: Yes
Total Units: 14
Trade Names: Anthony's Pizza (14)
Company-Owned Units: 14
Preferred Square Footage: 1,000
Preferred Location Types: Freestanding; Strip Mall
Alcohol Served: Beer, Wine
Primary Menu: Pizza (14)
Areas of Operation: VA, WV
Type of Foodservice: Fast Casual (14)
Catering Services: Yes
Primary Distributors: (Full Line) US Foods, HURRICANE, WV

Key Personnel
CLAUDIO BUONO - President; Partner
DEBRA BUONO - Partner; CFO; COO; General Buyer
THOMAS AMORI - Partner

Nerangis Enterprises
177 Kernstown Commons Blvd
Winchester, VA 22602-5364

Telephone: (540) 667-1322
Fax Number: (540) 667-4929
Internet Homepage: nerangismgmt.com
Company Email: lhill@nerangismgmt.com
Type of Business: Chain Restaurant Operator
Year Founded: 1976
Total Sales: $37,620,000 (e)
Number of Employees: 400
Average Check: Breakfast(6); Lunch(8); Dinner(8)
Total Units: 8
Trade Names: McDonald's (8)
Units Franchised From: 8
Preferred Square Footage: 3,000
Preferred Location Types: Discount Dept. Stores; Freestanding
Primary Menu: Hamburger (8)
Areas of Operation: VA, WV
Type of Foodservice: In-Store Feeder (1); Quick Serve (7)
Franchise Affiliation: McDonald's Corporation, CHICAGO, IL
Primary Distributors: (Full Line) The Martin-Brower Co., MANASSAS, VA

Key Personnel
NICHOLAS NERANGIS SR - President; Director Finance, Real Estate, Design
NICHOLAS NERANGIS JR - Director Information Systems, Supply Chain; General Buyer

North Central Virginia Restaurants, Inc
2227 Valley Ave
Winchester, VA 22601-2755

Telephone: (540) 667-4141
Fax Number: (540) 722-4243
Type of Business: Chain Restaurant Operator
Total Sales: $30,900,000 (e)
Total Units: 23
Trade Names: Papa John's Pizza (23)
Units Franchised From: 23
Primary Menu: Pizza (23)
Areas of Operation: VA
Type of Foodservice: Quick Serve (23)
Franchise Affiliation: Papa Johns International Inc., LOUISVILLE, KY

Key Personnel
ROBERT H. MEANS JR - President; Partner; General Buyer
MARYANN EVANS - Partner

Pizza King Wise
308 W Main St
Wise, VA 24293

Telephone: (276) 328-1010
Internet Homepage: pizzakingdelivers.com
Type of Business: Chain Restaurant Operator
Total Units: 2
Trade Names: Pizza King (2)
Units Franchised From: 2
Primary Menu: Pizza (2)
Areas of Operation: VA
Type of Foodservice: Quick Serve (2)
Franchise Affiliation: The Pizza King Inc., LAFAYETTE, IN

Key Personnel
TOM BARNETT - Supervisor Restaurant Operations; General Buyer

Auntie Anne's Franchise
2700 Potomac Mills Cir Ste 168
Woodbridge, VA 22192-4650

Telephone: (703) 497-3127
Internet Homepage: auntieannesfranchising.com
Type of Business: Chain Restaurant Operator
Total Sales: $5,114,000 (e)
Total Units: 7
Trade Names: Auntie Anne's Hand-Rolled Soft Pretzels (7)
Units Franchised From: 7
Primary Menu: Snacks (7)
Areas of Operation: VA
Type of Foodservice: Quick Serve (7)
Franchise Affiliation: Auntie Anne's Inc., LANCASTER, PA

Key Personnel
KATZ JOSEPH - Owner; General Buyer

VERMONT

Domino's Franchisee
322 N Main St
Barre, VT 05641-4122

Telephone: (802) 479-2222
Type of Business: Chain Restaurant Operator
Total Sales: $11,912,000 (e)
Total Units: 6
Trade Names: Domino's (6)
Units Franchised From: 6
Primary Menu: Pizza (6)
Areas of Operation: VT
Type of Foodservice: Quick Serve (6)
Franchise Affiliation: Domino's Pizza Inc, ANN ARBOR, MI

Key Personnel
STEVE C. LITWHILER - Owner; General Buyer

Bartley Management Co.
4518 US Route 5
Derby, VT 05829

Mailing Address: PO Box 310, DERBY, VT, 05829-0310
Telephone: (802) 334-5881
Type of Business: Chain Restaurant Operator
Total Sales: $20,602,000 (e)
Total Units: 4
Trade Names: McDonald's (4)
Units Franchised From: 4
Preferred Square Footage: 2,500
Primary Menu: Hamburger (4)
Areas of Operation: NH, VT
Type of Foodservice: Quick Serve (4)
Franchise Affiliation: McDonald's Corporation, CHICAGO, IL

Key Personnel
JAMES BARTLEY - Owner; General Buyer

The Equinox Resort & Spa
3567 Main St
Manchester, VT 05254

Telephone: (802) 362-4700
Fax Number: (802) 362-4861
Internet Homepage: equinoxresort.com
Type of Business: Foodservice Operations - Hotel/Motels
Total Sales: $21,364,000 (e)
Alcohol Sales: 12%
Number of Employees: 400
Total Units: 1
Restaurants in Hotels: 5
Trade Names: Equinox (1)
Company-Owned Units: 5
Alcohol Served: Beer, Wine, Liquor
Areas of Operation: VT
Type of Foodservice: Casual Dining (3); Fine Dining (2)

Key Personnel
RICK CROSBY - Chief Engineering Officer
MARTY ROSENTHAUL - General Manager
ALEXANDRA ZULLO - Director Marketing, Sales
DPATRICK HUBNER - Director Food and Beverage
JOHN ALEXOUPOLOS - Director Alcoholic Beverages

New England Culinary Institute
7 School St
Montpelier, VT 05602-2911

Telephone: (802) 223-6324
Fax Number: (802) 225-3284
Internet Homepage: neci.edu
Company Email: info@neci.edu
Type of Business: Nontraditional Foodservice Operator
Year Founded: 1980
Total Sales: $24,351,000 (e)
Alcohol Sales: 15%
Number of Employees: 500
Average Check: Breakfast(6); Lunch(10); Dinner(14)
Total Units: 4
Trade Names: La Brioche Bakery (1); National Life Cafeteria (1); NECI on Main (1); VCFA Dewey Cafe (1)
Company-Owned Units: 4
Preferred Square Footage: 4,000; 10,000
Preferred Location Types: Freestanding; Hotel/Motel
Alcohol Served: Beer, Wine, Liquor
Primary Menu: American (2); French/Continental (1); Sandwiches/Deli (1)
Projected Remodelings: 1
Areas of Operation: VT
Type of Foodservice: Cafeteria (1); Casual Dining (2); Fine Dining (1)
Foodservice Management Venues: Business & Industry; College & University
On-site Distribution Center: Yes
Notes: The company derives approximately 60% of its revenue from school tuitions. This is a Culinary School which owns and operates 7 restaurants.

Key Personnel
EMMA CUTLER - Executive Chef
JEAN LOUIS - Executive Chef
WILL COLGAN - Director Facility/Maintenance, Store Planning, Facility/Maintenance-Kitchen Equipment
DAN TABOR - Manager

New England Culinary Institute
7 School St
Montpelier, VT 05602-3115

Telephone: (802) 225-3200
Internet Homepage: neci.edu
Company Email: info@neci.edu
Type of Business: Culinary Schools
Areas of Operation: VT

Key Personnel
MILAN MILASINOVIC - President
ADAM NOE - Executive Chef

Coughlin Inc.
201 Woodstock Ave
Rutland, VT 05701-3317

Telephone: (802) 747-3365
Fax Number: (802) 747-0516
Type of Business: Chain Restaurant Operator
Year Founded: 1971
Total Sales: $47,030,000 (e)
Number of Employees: 440
Average Check: Breakfast(8); Lunch(10); Dinner(12)
Total Units: 10
Trade Names: McDonald's (10)
Units Franchised From: 10
Preferred Square Footage: 2,500; 3,000
Preferred Location Types: Community Mall; Convenience Store/Gas Station; Freestanding
Primary Menu: Hamburger (10)
Areas of Operation: MA, NH, NY, VT
Type of Foodservice: Quick Serve (10)
Franchise Affiliation: McDonald's Corporation, CHICAGO, IL
Primary Distributors: (Full Line) The Martin-Brower Co., ENFIELD, CT

Key Personnel
CHARLES COUGHLIN - President; Partner; Director Operations, Facility/Maintenance, Supply Chain, Real Estate; General Buyer
SHARI HARVEY - Partner; Director Finance, Operations
AMY LARSEN - Director Customer Service
MARY BROWN - Director Human Resources
DEBBIE ACKLEY - Assistant Marketing

Ben & Jerry's Franchising Inc.
30 Community Dr Ste 1
South Burlington, VT 05403-6834

Telephone: (802) 846-1500
Fax Number: (802) 846-1538

Internet Homepage: benjerry.com
Type of Business: Chain Restaurant Operator
Year Founded: 1978
Systemwide Sales: $214,691,000 (e)
Total Sales: $8,972,000 (e)
Number of Employees: 442
Average Check: Lunch(8); Dinner(8)
Internet Order Processing: Yes
Internet Sales: 4.00%
Total Units: 228
Trade Names: Ben & Jerry's (228)
Company-Owned Units: 3
Units Franchised To: 225
Preferred Square Footage: 900; 1,000
Preferred Location Types: Airports; Community Mall; Downtown; Freestanding; Lifestyle Center; Mobile Unit; Office Complex; Parks; Regional Mall; Stadiums; Strip Mall
Primary Menu: Snacks (228)
Areas of Operation: AL, AZ, CA, CO, CT, DC, DE, FL, GA, IL, IN, LA, MA, MD, ME, MI, MN, MO, NC, NH, NJ, NV, NY, OH, OR, PA, RI, SC, TN, TX, UT, VA, VT, WA, AB, ON, QC
Foreign Countries: BAHAMAS; BELGIUM; BRAZIL; CANADA; DENMARK; ENGLAND; FRANCE; GERMANY; ICELAND; IRELAND; ISRAEL; LUXEMBOURG; MALTA; MEXICO; SINGAPORE; SOUTH KOREA; SPAIN; SWEDEN; SWITZERLAND; THE NETHERLANDS
Type of Foodservice: Quick Serve (228)
Foodservice Management Venues: College & University
Catering Services: Yes
On-site Distribution Center: Yes
Primary Distributors: (Full Line) Vistar Rocky Mountain, DENVER, CO
Parent Company: Unilever N.V., ROTTERDAM, NLD
Headquarters: Unilever US, NEW YORK, NY

Key Personnel
DAVID STEVER - Chief Marketing Officer
ELLEN KRESKY - Creative Director
DEBRA HEINTZ - Director Retail Operations
SEAN GREENWOOD - Director Public Relations
MICHAEL GRANING - Director Finance
JAY CURLEY - Director Marketing
EMILY KAYLA SMITH - Director Innovation
REBECCA ROBINSON - Director Marketing
LINDA BLOUIN-ENGLISH - Supervisor Franchise Operations
LINDSAY BUMPS - Assistant Public Relations

Woodstock Inn
14 the Grn
Woodstock, VT 05091-1283

Telephone: (802) 332-6853
Fax Number: (802) 457-6699
Internet Homepage: woodstockinn.com
Company Email: email@woodstockinn.com
Type of Business: Foodservice Operations - Hotel/Motels
Year Founded: 1969
Total Sales: $9,975,000 (e)
Alcohol Sales: 15%
Number of Employees: 300
Average Check: Breakfast(12); Lunch(16); Dinner(20)
Total Units: 1
Restaurants in Hotels: 5
Trade Names: Woodstock Inn & Resort (1)
Company-Owned Units: 5
Alcohol Served: Beer, Wine, Liquor
Areas of Operation: VT
Type of Foodservice: Casual Dining (4); Fine Dining (1)
Primary Distributors: (Food) SYSCO Food Services of Albany, HALFMOON, NY
Notes: The company derives approximately 60% of its revenue from resort/hotel operations.

Key Personnel
JOSEPH MCBETH - Executive Chef
MARY NEARN - Director Food and Beverage
JOHN TOLOSKY - Manager Purchasing
CHRISTINE GOULD - Manager Customer Service

WASHINGTON

Hanner Enterprises
116 W State St
Aberdeen, WA 98520-6229

Telephone: (360) 538-5863
Fax Number: (360) 537-0057
Company Email: rosewood@techline.com
Type of Business: Chain Restaurant Operator
Year Founded: 1991
Total Sales: $28,720,000 (e)
Number of Employees: 200
Average Check: Breakfast(8); Lunch(8); Dinner(8)
Total Units: 6
Trade Names: McDonald's (6)
Units Franchised From: 6
Preferred Square Footage: 2,500
Preferred Location Types: Freestanding
Primary Menu: Hamburger (6)
Areas of Operation: WA
Type of Foodservice: Quick Serve (6)
Franchise Affiliation: McDonald's Corporation, CHICAGO, IL
Primary Distributors: (Food) The Martin-Brower Co., SUMNER, WA

Key Personnel
JULIANNE HANNER - President; General Buyer

Catalyst Six, Inc.
1101 Outlet Collection Dr SW
Auburn, WA 98001-6511

Telephone: (253) 333-8373
Type of Business: Chain Restaurant Operator
Total Sales: $756,000 (e)
Total Units: 2
Trade Names: Cinnabon (2)
Units Franchised From: 2
Primary Menu: Snacks (2)
Areas of Operation: WA
Type of Foodservice: Quick Serve (2)
Franchise Affiliation: Cinnabon Inc., ATLANTA, GA

Key Personnel
JERRY TSAI - Owner

Vince's Enterprises Inc.
116 Clay St NW Ste A3
Auburn, WA 98001-4211

Telephone: (253) 887-9700
Internet Homepage: pulcinellapizza.com; vincesitalian.com
Company Email: comments@vincesitalian.com
Type of Business: Chain Restaurant Operator
Year Founded: 1957
Total Sales: $4,700,000 (e)
Alcohol Sales: 20%
Number of Employees: 250
Average Check: Lunch(14); Dinner(22)
Internet Order Processing: Yes
Internet Sales: 2.00%
Total Units: 5
Trade Names: Pizzaria Pulcinella (1); Via Marina (1); Vince's Italian Restaurant & Pizzeria (3)
Company-Owned Units: 5
Preferred Square Footage: 2,500
Preferred Location Types: Freestanding
Alcohol Served: Beer, Wine, Liquor
Primary Menu: Italian (5)
Areas of Operation: WA
Type of Foodservice: Casual Dining (5)
Distribution Centers: SEATTLE, WA

Key Personnel
VINCENT L. MOTTOLA - CEO; President; Executive Chef; Manager Operations, Purchasing, Risk Management, Menu Development, Food Safety; General Buyer
FRED MARTICHUSKI JR - Exec VP

Farsei Inc
3720 Factoria Blvd SE Ste J
Bellevue, WA 98006-5256

Telephone: (425) 746-9428
Type of Business: Chain Restaurant Operator
Total Units: 3
Trade Names: The Plaza Sandwich Shop (3)
Units Franchised From: 3
Primary Menu: Sandwiches/Deli (3)
Areas of Operation: WA

Key Personnel
ROSIE RAMJEE - President; General Buyer

GIA Enterprises Inc.
1882 136th Pl NE Ste 101
Bellevue, WA 98005-2338

Telephone: (425) 454-3663
Fax Number: (425) 454-7458
Company Email: angelaw@giamcd.com
Type of Business: Chain Restaurant Operator
Year Founded: 1975
Total Sales: $65,270,000 (e)
Number of Employees: 600
Average Check: Breakfast(8); Lunch(8); Dinner(10)
Total Units: 14
Trade Names: McDonald's (14)
Units Franchised From: 14
Preferred Square Footage: 2,500; 3,000
Preferred Location Types: Convenience Store/Gas Station; Discount Dept. Stores; Freestanding
Primary Menu: Hamburger (14)
Areas of Operation: WA
Type of Foodservice: Quick Serve (14)
Franchise Affiliation: McDonald's Corporation, CHICAGO, IL
Primary Distributors: (Full Line) The Martin-Brower Co., SUMNER, WA

Key Personnel
LEONARD GIANNOLA - President; Director Finance, Franchise Development
REBECCA GIANNOLA - Administrative Assistant

John Howie Restaurant Group
205 108th Ave NE Ste 100
Bellevue, WA 98004-5776

Telephone: (425) 456-0010
Internet Homepage: beardsleeph.com; johnhowiesteak.com; plankcooking.com; seastarrestaurant.com; sportrestaurant.com
Type of Business: Chain Restaurant Operator
Internet Order Processing: Yes
Total Units: 4
Trade Names: Beardslee Public House (1); John Howie Steak (1); Seastar Reataurant & Raw Bar (1); Sport Reataurant & Bar (1)
Company-Owned Units: 4
Primary Menu: American (2); Seafood (1); Steak (1)
Areas of Operation: WA
Type of Foodservice: Casual Dining (2); Fine Dining (2)

Key Personnel
JOHN HOWIE - Partner; Executive Chef
ERIK LIEDHOLM - Partner; Director Alcoholic Beverages
ANNIE MEGOFNA - General Manager
JED LAPRADE - Executive Chef
CATHY LALLEY - Director Marketing

MOD Pizza LLC
2035 158th Ct NE Ste 200
Bellevue, WA 98008

Mailing Address: PO Box 53530, BELLEVUE, WA, 98015
Telephone: (888) 770-6637
Internet Homepage: modpizza.com
Company Email: feedback@modpizza.com
Type of Business: Chain Restaurant Operator
Year Founded: 2008
Systemwide Sales: $724,728,000 (e)
Total Sales: $704,550,000 (e)
Number of Employees: 2,430
Total Units: 489
Trade Names: MOD Pizza (489)
Company-Owned Units: 309
Units Franchised To: 180
Preferred Square Footage: 2,200
Preferred Location Types: Airports; Downtown; Strip Mall
Alcohol Served: Beer, Wine
Primary Menu: Pizza (489)
Projected Openings: 54
Areas of Operation: AL, AZ, CA, CO, DE, FL, GA, ID, IL, IN, KS, KY, MD, MI, MO, MT, NC, NJ, NV, OH, OR, PA, SC, TX, UT, VA, WA, WI, FC
Foreign Countries: CANADA; ENGLAND
Type of Foodservice: Fast Casual (489)
Parent Company: The Sienna Group LLC, SEATTLE, WA
Notes: Store counts are US stores only.

Key Personnel
BECKY MULLIGAN - Chief Restaurant Operations Officer
SCOTT SVENSON - Chairman; Co-Founder
ALLY SVENSON - Co-Founder
BETH SCOTT - CEO
DAYNA EBERHARDT - Chief People Officer
JENNIFER ANDERSON - Chief Marketing Officer
STEPHEN BLUM - Chief Development Officer
JERRY KESSELRING - VP Construction, Design
BRAD BAKER - VP Construction, Store Design
ROBIN HAMM - VP Store Operations
ROBERT NOTTE - VP Technology
DEANNE JONES - VP Talent
JASON HALEVA - VP Loyalty Program, Human Resources
CASEY WINCHELL - VP; Controller
BEN COARDE - Regional VP Operations
KIRA DRUYAN - General Counsel
ANDY METZ - Senior Director Construction
MONICA MARTY - Senior Director Real Estate
CHARLOTTE WAYTE - Director Communications, Public Relations
JOANNE REARDON - Director Strategy, Investor Relations
JAN PROSSIN - Director
BEN SADLER - Director Marketing, Loyalty Program
ERIK ANDERSON - Director Operations
JORDAN MUNRO - Director Operations
ERIN DOTY - Director People
ANNELISE CREGGER - Director Store Operations
FRED LINQUI - Regional Director Operations
RACHEL BOYCE - Regional Director Operations
NOEL HERNANDEZ - Manager Information Technology
LISA STAHLER - Manager Training
NICOLETTE SIROTTA - Manager Digital Marketing
LISA HOLFELD - Manager Accounting
JOSE ROMERO - Manager Marketing

Pallino
2020 124th Ave NE Ste C207
Bellevue, WA 98005-2118

Telephone: (206) 838-5466
Fax Number: (206) 238-5488
Internet Homepage: pallino.com
Company Email: info@pallino.com
Type of Business: Chain Restaurant Operator
Year Founded: 1998
Total Sales: $1,809,000 (e)
Alcohol Sales: 20%
Number of Employees: 70
Average Check: Breakfast(10); Lunch(14); Dinner(18)
Internet Order Processing: Yes
Total Units: 1
Trade Names: Pallino Pastaria (1)
Company-Owned Units: 1
Preferred Square Footage: 3,000
Preferred Location Types: Airports; Office Complex; Strip Mall
Alcohol Served: Beer, Wine
Primary Menu: Italian (1)
Areas of Operation: WA
Type of Foodservice: Fast Casual (1)
Primary Distributors: (Full Line) Food Services

of America, KENT, WA

Schwartz Brothers Restaurants
325 118th Ave SE Ste 106
Bellevue, WA 98005-3539

Telephone: (425) 455-3948
Fax Number: (425) 451-3573
Internet Homepage: schwartzbros.com
Company Email: operations@schwartzbros.com
Type of Business: Chain Restaurant Operator
Year Founded: 1970
Total Sales: $35,524,000 (e)
Alcohol Sales: 15%
Number of Employees: 80
Average Check: Lunch(18); Dinner(48)
Total Units: 4
Trade Names: Chandler's Crabhouse (1); Daniel's Broiler (3)
Company-Owned Units: 4
Preferred Square Footage: 4,000
Preferred Location Types: Freestanding; Office Complex
Alcohol Served: Beer, Wine, Liquor
Primary Menu: Seafood (1); Steak (3)
Areas of Operation: WA
Type of Foodservice: Fine Dining (4)
Catering Services: Yes
Primary Distributors: (Equipment) Bargreen-Ellingson Inc., SEATTLE, WA; (Food) SYSCO Food Services of Seattle Inc., KENT, WA; (Supplies) Bargreen-Ellingson Inc., SEATTLE, WA
Notes: The company also operates Gretchen's Shoebox Express, a box-lunch delivery service.

Key Personnel
BILL SCHWARTZ - Chairman
LINDSEY SCHWARTZ - CEO; President; Director Facility/Maintenance, Information Systems, Real Estate, Design, Store Fixtures
BRIAN TEGEN - CFO
MICHAEL SCHWARTZ - VP Purchasing, Supply Chain
BRADLEY MILLER - Director Food
RACHID OUARDI - Director Business Development, Manufacturing
KARMA WICK - Director Marketing

Key Personnel
DAVID MONTANARO - CFO Training; Treasurer Training
JOLENE JEWETT - Director Administration, Human Resources

Timberline Cool Treats, LLC
15600 NE 8th St Ste J2
Bellevue, WA 98008-3917

Telephone: (425) 957-0333
Company Email: coldstone.bellevue@gmail.com
Type of Business: Chain Restaurant Operator
Total Sales: $1,229,000 (e)
Total Units: 2
Trade Names: Cold Stone Creamery (2)
Units Franchised From: 2
Primary Menu: Snacks (2)
Areas of Operation: WA
Type of Foodservice: Quick Serve (2)
Franchise Affiliation: Kahala Brands, SCOTTSDALE, AZ

Key Personnel
JUSTIN KENNEDY - Owner; General Buyer

Torero's Restaurant Inc.
15600 NE 8th St
Bellevue, WA 98008

Telephone: (425) 644-7710
Internet Homepage: toreros-mexicanrestaurants.com
Company Email: Toreros@live.com
Type of Business: Chain Restaurant Operator
Year Founded: 1970
Total Sales: $5,660,000 (e)
Alcohol Sales: 25%
Number of Employees: 100
Average Check: Lunch(10); Dinner(16)
Total Units: 3
Trade Names: The Landing (1); Torero's Taqueria (2)
Company-Owned Units: 3
Preferred Square Footage: 3,200
Preferred Location Types: Community Mall; Freestanding
Alcohol Served: Beer, Wine, Liquor
Primary Menu: Mexican (3)
Areas of Operation: WA
Type of Foodservice: Casual Dining (3)
Catering Services: Yes
Primary Distributors: (Full Line) Food Services of America, KENT, WA

Key Personnel
TED RODRIGUEZ - President; Partner; General Manager; Director Purchasing
MARIA RODRIGUEZ - Partner; CFO
VERONICA MEDINA - Executive Chef; Director Menu Development, Catering; General Buyer

Pioneer Food Service Inc.
3323 Northwest Ave
Bellingham, WA 98225-1208

Telephone: (360) 733-8830
Fax Number: (360) 733-1782
Company Email: mcdonaldsnw@hotmail.com
Type of Business: Chain Restaurant Operator
Year Founded: 1988
Total Sales: $32,470,000 (e)
Number of Employees: 250
Average Check: Breakfast(5); Lunch(8); Dinner(8)
Total Units: 7
Trade Names: McDonald's (7)
Units Franchised From: 7
Preferred Square Footage: 2,500; 3,000
Preferred Location Types: Discount Dept. Stores; Freestanding
Primary Menu: Hamburger (7)
Areas of Operation: WA
Type of Foodservice: Quick Serve (7)
Franchise Affiliation: McDonald's Corporation, CHICAGO, IL
Primary Distributors: (Food) The Martin-Brower Co., SUMNER, WA

Key Personnel
JIM CAMPBELL - President; General Manager; General Buyer
SIMRANPREET KAUR - Manager

Anco Inc
23717 Bothell Everett Hwy
Bothell, WA 98021-9343

Telephone: (425) 485-4123
Fax Number: (425) 483-9314
Type of Business: Chain Restaurant Operator
Total Sales: $2,292,000 (e)
Total Units: 3
Trade Names: Taco Time (3)
Units Franchised From: 3
Primary Menu: Taco (3)
Areas of Operation: WA
Type of Foodservice: Quick Serve (3)
Franchise Affiliation: Kahala Brands, SCOTTSDALE, AZ

Key Personnel
ARNIE J. ANDERSON - President; General Buyer

Cafes Inc.
22620 Bothell Everett Hwy
Bothell, WA 98021

Telephone: (425) 486-7781
Internet Homepage: cafesinc.com

Type of Business: Chain Restaurant Operator
Year Founded: 2010
Total Units: 7
Trade Names: Crystal Creek Cafe (1); Issaquah Cafe (1); Mukilteo's Speedway Cafe (1); Sammamish Cafe (1); Saw Mill Cafe (1); Village Square Cafe (1); Woodinville Cafe (1)
Company-Owned Units: 7
Primary Menu: American (7)
Areas of Operation: WA
Type of Foodservice: Family Restaurant (7)
Notes: Address is owner's home address. Phone is Crystal Creek Cafe, closest location to owner's home.

Key Personnel
RYAN MITCHELL - Owner; General Buyer

Domino's Franchisee
20631 Bothell Everett Hwy Ste J
Bothell, WA 98012-7159

Telephone: (425) 481-4848
Type of Business: Chain Restaurant Operator
Total Sales: $24,274,000 (e)
Total Units: 12
Trade Names: Domino's (12)
Units Franchised From: 12
Primary Menu: Pizza (12)
Areas of Operation: WA
Type of Foodservice: Quick Serve (12)
Franchise Affiliation: Domino's Pizza Inc, ANN ARBOR, MI

Key Personnel
PATRICK D. FARMER - Owner; General Buyer

Mayuri, Inc
20611 Bothell Everett Hwy Ste A
Bothell, WA 98012-7137

Telephone: (425) 481-6900
Internet Homepage: mayuriseattle.com
Company Email: mayuriseattle@yahoo.com
Type of Business: Chain Restaurant Operator
Total Units: 2
Trade Names: Bakery, Chaat & Sweets (1); Mayuri Indian Cuisine (1)
Company-Owned Units: 2
Primary Menu: Indian (2)
Areas of Operation: WA
Type of Foodservice: Casual Dining (1); Quick Serve (1)

Key Personnel
RAMESH BACHALA - Owner; General Buyer

Sound City Foods Inc.
3312 Veska Ave
Bremerton, WA 98310-2148

Telephone: (360) 373-1271
Fax Number: (360) 479-7146
Type of Business: Chain Restaurant Operator
Year Founded: 1986
Total Sales: $19,880,000 (e)
Number of Employees: 250
Average Check: Breakfast(8); Lunch(10); Dinner(12)
Total Units: 9
Trade Names: Burger King (9)
Units Franchised From: 9
Preferred Square Footage: 3,000
Preferred Location Types: Freestanding
Primary Menu: Hamburger (9)
Areas of Operation: WA
Type of Foodservice: Quick Serve (9)
Franchise Affiliation: Burger King Worldwide Inc., MIAMI, FL
Primary Distributors: (Full Line) Systems Services of America, SCOTTSDALE, AZ

Key Personnel
LEE FRITZ - President; General Manager; Director Finance, Facility/Maintenance, Real Estate; General Buyer
JEFF ROSE - Director Operations, Purchasing, Information Systems, Supply Chain, Human Resources

Azteca Restaurant Enterprises Inc.
15735 Ambaum Blvd SW
Burien, WA 98166-2524

Telephone: (206) 243-7021
Fax Number: (206) 246-0429
Internet Homepage: aztecadoro.com; aztecamex.com
Type of Business: Chain Restaurant Operator
Year Founded: 1974
Total Sales: $41,390,000 (e)
Alcohol Sales: 30%
Number of Employees: 943
Average Check: Lunch(12); Dinner(18)
Internet Order Processing: Yes
Total Units: 17
Trade Names: Azteca d"Oro (5); Azteca Mexican Restaurant (18)
Company-Owned Units: 23
Preferred Square Footage: 8,500
Preferred Location Types: Freestanding; Regional Mall; Strip Mall
Alcohol Served: Beer, Wine, Liquor
Primary Menu: Mexican (23)
Areas of Operation: FL, OR, WA
Type of Foodservice: Casual Dining (23)
Catering Services: Yes

Primary Distributors: (Full Line) SYSCO Food Services of Seattle Inc., KENT, WA

Key Personnel
JOSE RAMOS - CEO
JAIME RAMOS - President
HECTOR RAMOS - VP
RANDY THURMAN - Executive Director; Manager Purchasing, Supply Chain, Marketing, Menu Development
SONIA RAMOS - Director Human Resources
STEVE GOSS - Director Facility/Maintenance, Design, Store Fixtures
PAUL SHIPLEY - Specialist Accounting

Domino's Franchisee
1241 Harrison Ave
Centralia, WA 98531-1878

Telephone: (360) 807-6000
Company Email: centraliadominos@live.com
Type of Business: Chain Restaurant Operator
Total Sales: $8,157,000 (e)
Total Units: 4
Trade Names: Domino's (4)
Units Franchised From: 4
Primary Menu: Pizza (4)
Areas of Operation: WA
Type of Foodservice: Quick Serve (4)
Franchise Affiliation: Domino's Pizza Inc, ANN ARBOR, MI

Key Personnel
ELDON R. WALTER - Owner; General Buyer

McDonalds Enterprise of Folsom
971 NW Folsom St
Chehalis, WA 98532-1707

Mailing Address: PO Box 1244, CHEHALIS, WA, 98532-0258
Telephone: (360) 748-0576
Fax Number: (360) 748-0624
Internet Homepage: mcdonalds.com
Type of Business: Chain Restaurant Operator
Year Founded: 1994
Total Sales: $33,630,000 (e)
Number of Employees: 250
Average Check: Breakfast(8); Lunch(8); Dinner(10)
Total Units: 7
Trade Names: McDonald's (7)
Units Franchised From: 7
Preferred Square Footage: 2,500; 3,000
Preferred Location Types: Freestanding
Primary Menu: Hamburger (7)
Areas of Operation: WA
Type of Foodservice: Quick Serve (7)
Franchise Affiliation: McDonald's Corporation,

CHICAGO, IL
Primary Distributors: (Full Line) The Martin-Brower Co., STOCKTON, CA

Key Personnel
SHARI NIXON - President; General Manager; Manager Real Estate; General Buyer
PATTI SHELSTAD - Director Accounting
MIKE FLADAGER - Director Operations, Facility/Maintenance; Manager Human Resources

Domino's Franchisee
1879 1st St
Cheney, WA 99004-1967

Telephone: (509) 235-2000
Type of Business: Chain Restaurant Operator
Total Sales: $22,895,000 (e)
Total Units: 11
Trade Names: Domino's (11)
Units Franchised From: 11
Primary Menu: Pizza (11)
Areas of Operation: WA
Type of Foodservice: Quick Serve (11)
Franchise Affiliation: Domino's Pizza Inc, ANN ARBOR, MI

Key Personnel
SHANE H. ANDERSON - Owner; General Buyer

Auntie Anne's Franchise
306 5th St
Clarkston, WA 99403-1860

Telephone: (509) 758-3462
Type of Business: Chain Restaurant Operator
Total Sales: $1,580,000 (e)
Total Units: 2
Trade Names: Auntie Anne's Hand-Rolled Soft Pretzels (2)
Units Franchised From: 2
Primary Menu: Snacks (2)
Areas of Operation: WA
Type of Foodservice: Quick Serve (2)
Franchise Affiliation: Auntie Anne's Inc., LANCASTER, PA

Key Personnel
GERALD JENSEN - Owner; General Buyer

Kafe Neo Group Inc
21108 Highway 99
Edmonds, WA 98026

Telephone: (425) 672-3476
Internet Homepage: kafeneowoodstonegroup.com
Company Email: terri@kafeneo.net
Type of Business: Chain Restaurant Operator
Year Founded: 1991
Total Units: 7
Trade Names: Demetris Woodstone Taverna (1); Kafe Neo (5); Tablas Woodstone Taverna (1)
Company-Owned Units: 7
Primary Menu: American (2); Greek/Mediterranean (5)
Areas of Operation: WA
Type of Foodservice: Casual Dining (7)
Notes: Address is owner's home. Phone is Edmonds Kafe Neo.

Key Personnel
SOFEEA HUFFMAN - Founder; Partner; General Buyer
KYLE HUFFMAN - Partner
CLARA GUTIERREZ - Partner; Executive Chef

Rusty Pelican Cafe
107 5th Ave N
Edmonds, WA 98020-3211

Telephone: (425) 582-8250
Internet Homepage: rustypelicancafe.com
Type of Business: Chain Restaurant Operator
Year Founded: 2000
Total Units: 2
Trade Names: Rusty Pelican Cafe (2)
Company-Owned Units: 2
Primary Menu: American (2)
Areas of Operation: WA
Type of Foodservice: Casual Dining (2)

Key Personnel
PETER LIMBEROPOULOS - Partner; Executive Chef; General Buyer
MARYLIN LIMBEROPOULOS - Partner

Neltac Inc.
33650 6th Ave S Ste 230
Federal Way, WA 98003-6755

Telephone: (253) 235-5621
Fax Number: (253) 719-8322
Type of Business: Chain Restaurant Operator
Year Founded: 1996
Total Sales: $9,798,000 (e)
Number of Employees: 200
Average Check: Lunch(12); Dinner(12)
Total Units: 11
Trade Names: Taco Time (11)
Units Franchised From: 11
Preferred Square Footage: 2,000
Preferred Location Types: Freestanding
Primary Menu: Taco (11)
Areas of Operation: WA
Type of Foodservice: Quick Serve (11)
Franchise Affiliation: Kahala Brands, SCOTTSDALE, AZ
Primary Distributors: (Full Line) Food Services of America, KENT, WA

Key Personnel
STEPHEN NELSON - CEO; President; Director Operations, Facility/Maintenance, Loss Prevention, Risk Management, Quality Assurance, Real Estate, Human Resources, Training, Recruitment, Food Safety
MICHELLE NELSON - VP; Treasurer; Director Finance, Purchasing, Information Systems, Supply Chain; General Buyer
JESSICA SARGENT - Manager Human Resources

NIK.
28835 Pacific Hwy S
Federal Way, WA 98003-3801

Telephone: (253) 946-4122
Internet Homepage: cliffhousetacoma.com; verrazanos.com
Company Email: verrazanos@gmail.com
Type of Business: Chain Restaurant Operator
Year Founded: 1988
Total Sales: $3,030,000 (e)
Alcohol Sales: 30%
Number of Employees: 100
Average Check: Lunch(32); Dinner(42)
Total Units: 2
Trade Names: Cliff House (1); Verrazano (1)
Company-Owned Units: 2
Preferred Location Types: Freestanding; Lifestyle Center
Alcohol Served: Beer, Wine, Liquor
Primary Menu: Italian (1); Steak/Seafood (1)
Areas of Operation: WA
Type of Foodservice: Fine Dining (2)
Catering Services: Yes
Primary Distributors: (Equipment) Bargreen-Ellingson Inc., SEATTLE, WA; (Food) SYSCO Food Services of Seattle Inc., KENT, WA; (Supplies) Bargreen-Ellingson Inc., SEATTLE, WA

Key Personnel
GIUSEPPE NAPPO - President; Executive Chef; General Buyer
TARA ADAMS - General Manager

Stauros Enterprises, Inc.
2430 S 319th Pl
Federal Way, WA 98003-5017

Telephone: (253) 839-9400
Type of Business: Chain Restaurant Operator
Total Sales: $1,199,000 (e)
Total Units: 2
Trade Names: Cold Stone Creamery (2)
Units Franchised From: 2
Primary Menu: Snacks (2)

Areas of Operation: WA
Type of Foodservice: Quick Serve (2)
Franchise Affiliation: Kahala Brands, SCOTTSDALE, AZ

Key Personnel
TIMOTHY SHELTON - Partner
KAREN SHELTON - Partner

● ▲
AJP Enterprises, LLC
5005 Pacific Hwy E
Fife, WA 98424-2655

Telephone: (253) 353-9867
Type of Business: Chain Restaurant Operator
Total Sales: $108,620,000 (e)
Total Units: 45
Trade Names: Jack in the Box (45)
Units Franchised From: 45
Primary Menu: Hamburger (45)
Projected Openings: 1
Areas of Operation: WA
Type of Foodservice: Quick Serve (45)
Franchise Affiliation: Jack in the Box Restaurants, SAN DIEGO, CA

Key Personnel
STEVE WAZNY - Owner; General Buyer
RIZQ MESID - Director Operations
RON CHARVES - Director Operations
MICHELLE NICLAI - Manager Training

● ▲
NHG Enterprises LLC
5005 Pacific Hwy E Ste 12
Fife, WA 98424-2647

Telephone: (253) 353-9867
Type of Business: Chain Restaurant Operator
Total Sales: $5,358,000 (e)
Total Units: 2
Trade Names: Jack in the Box (2)
Units Franchised From: 2
Primary Menu: Hamburger (2)
Areas of Operation: WA
Type of Foodservice: Quick Serve (2)
Franchise Affiliation: Jack in the Box Restaurants, SAN DIEGO, CA

Key Personnel
STEVEN WAZNY - Owner; General Buyer

Taqueria El Riincosito
2606 70th Ave E Ste 104
Fife, WA 98424-3647

Telephone: (253) 830-3030
Fax Number: (253) 830-5137
Internet Homepage: elantojo.com; elrinconsito.com
Company Email: info@elrinconsito.com
Type of Business: Chain Restaurant Operator
Year Founded: 1997
Total Units: 18
Trade Names: Taqueria El Antojo (3); Taqueria El Rinconsito (15)
Company-Owned Units: 18
Primary Menu: Mexican (18)
Areas of Operation: WA
Type of Foodservice: Fast Casual (18)

Key Personnel
ABEL BRAMBILA - Partner
JOSE GUZMAN - Partner; Executive Chef; General Buyer
JESUS BEDOLLA - Regional Manager
MANUELA FIGUEROA - Manager Marketing

Cutters Point Incorporated
4909 33rd Avenue Ct Ste 201
Gig Harbor, WA 98335-8611

Telephone: (800) 658-9458
Internet Homepage: cutterspoint.com
Type of Business: Chain Restaurant Operator
Year Founded: 1995
Total Units: 12
Trade Names: Cutters Point Coffee Co. (12)
Units Franchised To: 12
Primary Menu: Coffee (12)
Areas of Operation: GA, MA, WA
Type of Foodservice: Quick Serve (12)

Key Personnel
BROOKE PAYNE - Founder; Owner; General Buyer

● ▲
Domino's Franchisee
9805 224th St E Ste E
Graham, WA 98338-5728

Telephone: (253) 847-8393
Type of Business: Chain Restaurant Operator
Total Sales: $6,030,000 (e)
Total Units: 3
Trade Names: Domino's (3)
Units Franchised From: 3
Primary Menu: Pizza (3)
Areas of Operation: WA
Type of Foodservice: Quick Serve (3)
Franchise Affiliation: Domino's Pizza Inc, ANN ARBOR, MI

Key Personnel
STEVEN ALEXANDER - Owner; General Buyer

● ▲
Domino's Franchisee
2605 Simpson Ave
Hoquiam, WA 98550-2928

Telephone: (360) 533-3500
Type of Business: Chain Restaurant Operator
Total Sales: $4,090,000 (e)
Total Units: 2
Trade Names: Domino's (2)
Units Franchised From: 2
Primary Menu: Pizza (2)
Areas of Operation: WA
Type of Foodservice: Quick Serve (2)
Franchise Affiliation: Domino's Pizza Inc, ANN ARBOR, MI

Key Personnel
JEFFREY D. FARMER - Owner; General Buyer

Chan's Places
4592 Klahanie Dr SE
Issaquah, WA 98029

Telephone: (425) 313-8883
Internet Homepage: chansplaces.com
Type of Business: Chain Restaurant Operator
Year Founded: 1980
Total Sales: $5,450,000 (e)
Alcohol Sales: 20%
Average Check: Lunch(14); Dinner(14)
Total Units: 3
Trade Names: Chan's Place (3)
Company-Owned Units: 3
Preferred Location Types: Freestanding
Alcohol Served: Beer, Wine, Liquor
Primary Menu: Chinese (3)
Areas of Operation: WA
Type of Foodservice: Casual Dining (3)

Key Personnel
LOUISA CHAN - Partner; General Buyer
TONY CHAN - Partner; Manager Foodservice, Menu Development; General Buyer

●
Evergreen Burgers
775 NW Gilman Blvd
Issaquah, WA 98027-5374

Telephone: (571) 436-1441
Type of Business: Chain Restaurant Operator
Total Sales: $9,817,000 (e)
Total Units: 5
Trade Names: Five Guys Burgers and Fries (5)
Units Franchised From: 5
Primary Menu: Hamburger (5)
Areas of Operation: WA
Type of Foodservice: Fast Casual (5)
Franchise Affiliation: Five Guys Holdings Inc.,

LORTON, VA

Key Personnel
NABIL ASAD - President; Partner; General Buyer
SAISAL KHALIL - Partner

WildFin American Grill
835 NW Gilman Blvd
Issaquah, WA 98027-5318

Telephone: (425) 427-0127
Internet Homepage: wildfinamericangrill.com
Type of Business: Chain Restaurant Operator
Year Founded: 2011
Total Units: 4
Trade Names: WildFin American Grill (4)
Company-Owned Units: 4
Primary Menu: Seafood (4)
Areas of Operation: WA
Type of Foodservice: Casual Dining (4)

Key Personnel
ATTILA SZABO - President; Partner
BOB ACREE - Partner
CHRIS ANDERSON - Partner
CHRIS BRYANT - Executive Chef

Adams Tri-Cities Enterprises Inc.
6515 W Clearwater Ave Ste 214
Kennewick, WA 99336-6717

Telephone: (509) 735-9311
Fax Number: (509) 735-9225
Company Email: atce@msn.com
Type of Business: Chain Restaurant Operator
Year Founded: 1973
Total Sales: $76,390,000 (e)
Number of Employees: 575
Average Check: Breakfast(8); Lunch(8); Dinner(10)
Total Units: 16
Trade Names: McDonald's (16)
Units Franchised From: 16
Preferred Square Footage: 2,500; 3,000
Preferred Location Types: Freestanding
Primary Menu: Hamburger (16)
Projected Remodelings: 5
Areas of Operation: OR, WA
Type of Foodservice: Quick Serve (16)
Franchise Affiliation: McDonald's Corporation, CHICAGO, IL
Primary Distributors: (Full Line) The Martin-Brower Co., SUMNER, WA

Key Personnel
LEE ADAMS - President; Partner; Director Facility/Maintenance, Real Estate, Design; General Buyer
SCOTT ADAMS - Partner; Director Operations, Human Resources

Cazier Enterprises
2798 Katie Rd
Kennewick, WA 99338-7304

Telephone: (509) 628-8333
Fax Number: (866) 320-9709
Internet Homepage: cazierinc.com; cazierinc.com
Company Email: info@cazierenterprises.com
Type of Business: Chain Restaurant Operator
Total Sales: $14,860,000 (e)
Total Units: 25
Trade Names: Costa Vida (1); Subway (24)
Company-Owned Units: 1
Units Franchised From: 24
Primary Menu: Mexican (1); Sandwiches/Deli (24)
Areas of Operation: WA
Type of Foodservice: Casual Dining (1); Quick Serve (24)
Franchise Affiliation: Doctor's Associates Inc., MILFORD, CT

Key Personnel
RUSSELL CAZIER - President; General Buyer
BOB CAZIER - VP
JENNIFER POLL - Manager Human Resources

Domino's Distribution Center
8005 S 266th St Ste 101
Kent, WA 98032-7518

Telephone: (253) 395-4144
Fax Number: (253) 872-5175
Internet Homepage: dominos.com
Listing Type: Distribution Center
Type of Business: Chain Restaurant Operator
Number of Employees: 60
Areas of Operation: ID, MT, OR, WA, WY
Parent Company: Domino's Pizza Inc, ANN ARBOR, MI

Key Personnel
MICHAEL BLANCHARD - General Manager

Northwest Food Management Group Inc.
221 Central Ave N
Kent, WA 98032-4518

Telephone: (253) 854-2689
Type of Business: Chain Restaurant Operator
Total Sales: $69,170,000 (e)
Total Units: 27
Trade Names: Jack in the Box (27)
Units Franchised From: 27
Primary Menu: Hamburger (27)
Areas of Operation: WA
Type of Foodservice: Quick Serve (27)
Franchise Affiliation: Jack in the Box Restaurants, SAN DIEGO, CA

Key Personnel
ABDULREZA KHAJAVI - Owner; General Buyer

Flatstick Pub
15 Lake St
Kirkland, WA 98033-6167

Telephone: (425) 242-1618
Internet Homepage: flatstickpub.com
Company Email: info@flatstickpub.com
Type of Business: Chain Restaurant Operator
Internet Order Processing: Yes
Total Units: 3
Trade Names: Flatstick Pub (3)
Company-Owned Units: 3
Primary Menu: American (3)
Areas of Operation: WA
Type of Foodservice: Casual Dining (3)
Notes: Craft beer bar with 9-hole indoor miniature golf course.

Key Personnel
SAM LARGENT - Partner; General Buyer
ANDY LARGENT - Partner

Laurier Enterprises
1235 Market St Ste A
Kirkland, WA 98033-5440

Telephone: (425) 822-1055
Fax Number: (425) 739-9899
Company Email: lauriermcd@gmail.com
Type of Business: Chain Restaurant Operator
Year Founded: 1986
Total Sales: $86,880,000 (e)
Number of Employees: 280
Average Check: Breakfast(14); Lunch(10); Dinner(10)
Total Units: 18
Trade Names: McDonald's (18)
Units Franchised From: 18
Preferred Square Footage: 2,500; 3,000
Preferred Location Types: Freestanding
Primary Menu: Hamburger (18)
Areas of Operation: WA
Type of Foodservice: Quick Serve (18)
Franchise Affiliation: McDonald's Corporation, CHICAGO, IL
Primary Distributors: (Full Line) The Martin-Brower Co., SUMNER, WA

Key Personnel
DOUG FENWICK - Director Operations,

Facility/Maintenance

Mad Anthony's Inc.
10502 NE 37th Cir
Kirkland, WA 98033-7920

Mailing Address: PO Box 3805, BELLEVUE, WA, 98009-3805
Telephone: (425) 455-0732
Fax Number: (425) 455-0649
Internet Homepage: anthonys.com
Company Email: feedback@anthonys.com
Type of Business: Chain Restaurant Operator
Year Founded: 1975
Total Sales: $89,020,000 (e)
Alcohol Sales: 15%
Number of Employees: 1,925
Average Check: Dinner(30)
Internet Order Processing: Yes
Internet Sales: 0.50%
Total Units: 30
Trade Names: Anthony's at Cap Sante Boat Haven (1); Anthony's at Columbia Point (1); Anthony's at Gig Harbor (1); Anthony's at Point Defiance (1); Anthony's at Sinclair Inlet (1); Anthony's at Spokane Falls (1); Anthony's at Squalicum Harbor (1); Anthony's at The Old Mill District (1); Anthony's Beach Cafe (1); Anthony's Bell Street Diner (1); Anthony's Boise (1); Anthony's Cabana (1); Anthony's Cap Sante Marina (1); Anthony's Coeur d'Alene (1); Anthony's Fish Bar (1); Anthony's Hearthfire Grill (2); Anthony's HomePort (6); Anthony's Pier 66 (1); Anthony's Seafood Grill (1); Anthony's Woodfire Grill (1); Budd's Broiler(1); Chinook's at Salmon Bay (1); Des Moines Oyster Bar & Grill (1); Harbor Lights (1)
Company-Owned Units: 25
Preferred Square Footage: 4,500
Preferred Location Types: Freestanding
Alcohol Served: Beer, Wine, Liquor
Primary Menu: Seafood (27); Steak/Seafood (3)
Areas of Operation: OR, WA
Type of Foodservice: Casual Dining (6); Fine Dining (18); Quick Serve (1)

Key Personnel
HERBERT GOULD III - Owner; General Buyer
JOE SHMAIT - CFO
PAT DONAHUE - Executive Chef

Noble House Hotels and Resorts
600 6th St S
Kirkland, WA 98033-6716

Telephone: (425) 827-8737
Fax Number: (425) 827-6707
Internet Homepage: noblehousehotels.com
Company Email: info@noblehousehotels.com
Type of Business: Foodservice Operations - Hotel/Motels
Year Founded: 1980
Total Sales: $158,330,000 (e)
Alcohol Sales: 10%
Number of Employees: 2,124
Total Units: 18
Restaurants in Hotels: 18
Trade Names: Argonaut Hotel (1); Gateway Canyons Resort & Spa (1); Hotel Terra Jackson Hole (1); Hotel Zoe Fisherman's Wharf (1); Kona Kai Resort & Spa (1); L'Auberge Del Mar (1); LaPlaya Beach & Golf Resort (1); Little Palm Island Resort & Spa (1); Ocean Key Resort & Spa (1); Pelican Grand BeachResort (1); River Terrace Inn (1); San Diego Mission Bay Resort (1); Sole Miami (1); Teton Mountain Lodge & Spa (1); The Edgewater (1); The Josie Hotel (1); The Portofino Hotel & Yacht Club (1); The Stella Hotel (1)
Company-Owned Units: 18
Alcohol Served: Beer, Wine, Liquor
Areas of Operation: CA, FL, RI, TX, WA
Type of Foodservice: Casual Dining (18)
Primary Distributors: (Food) SYSCO Food Services of Seattle Inc., KENT, WA
Parent Company: Westgroup Partners, SEATTLE, WA
Notes: The company derives approximately 75% of its revenue from hotel operations.

Key Personnel
JOHN DONOGHUE - CEO
SEAN MULLEN - President Store Development
MICHAEL BENECKE - President
PATRICK R. COLEE - President Development
JANETTE AMENT-PIERCE - Chief Accounting Officer
JAMES P. COLEE - Chief Creative Officer
KAREN RANKER - VP Human Resources
THOMAS HAAS - VP Food and Beverage, West Region
DARRELL STARK - VP Distribution
KEVIN FALK - Controller
JAY ROBINSON - Director Information Systems

PARS Group LLC
11411 NE 124th St Ste 170
Kirkland, WA 98034-4322

Telephone: (425) 285-9106
Internet Homepage: parsnw.com
Type of Business: Chain Restaurant Operator
Total Sales: $98,460,000 (e)
Total Units: 39
Trade Names: Jack in the Box (39)
Units Franchised From: 39
Primary Menu: Hamburger (39)
Areas of Operation: WA
Type of Foodservice: Quick Serve (39)
Franchise Affiliation: Jack in the Box Restaurants, SAN DIEGO, CA

Key Personnel
ABDULREZA KHAJAVI - Owner; General Buyer

Urban Coffee Lounge
9744 NE 119th Way
Kirkland, WA 98034-8955

Telephone: (425) 820-7788
Internet Homepage: uclkirkland.squarespace.com
Type of Business: Chain Restaurant Operator
Total Units: 2
Trade Names: Urban Coffee Lounge (2)
Company-Owned Units: 2
Primary Menu: Snacks (2)
Areas of Operation: WA
Type of Foodservice: Fast Casual (2)

Key Personnel
ALICIA MINER - Partner; Executive Chef; General Buyer
JEFF MINER - Partner

Volterra
21 Kirkland Ave
Kirkland, WA 98033

Telephone: (425) 202-7201
Internet Homepage: volterrarestaurant.com
Company Email: info@volterrarestaurant.com
Type of Business: Chain Restaurant Operator
Total Units: 1
Trade Names: Volterra (1)
Company-Owned Units: 1
Primary Menu: Italian (1)
Areas of Operation: WA
Type of Foodservice: Casual Dining (1)

Key Personnel
DON CURTISS - Partner; Executive Chef
MICHELLE QUISENBERRY - Partner; General Buyer

Harman Management Corp.
3010 96th St S
Lakewood, WA 98499-9395

Telephone: (253) 584-1761
Fax Number: (253) 589-2665
Listing Type: Divisional Office
Type of Business: Chain Restaurant Operator
Number of Employees: 300
Total Units: 40
Areas of Operation: WA
Parent Company: Harman Management Corp.,

LOS ALTOS, CA

Key Personnel
CLAYTON PATTERSON - Director Operations, Region

RAM International LLC
10013 59th Ave SW Ste D
Lakewood, WA 98499-2757

Telephone: (253) 588-1788
Fax Number: (253) 588-0713
Internet Homepage: cishenanigans.com; cbpotts.com; theram.com
Company Email: feedback@theram.com
Type of Business: Chain Restaurant Operator
Year Founded: 1971
Total Sales: $127,840,000 (e)
Alcohol Sales: 35%
Number of Employees: 1,932
Average Check: Lunch(24); Dinner(36)
Internet Order Processing: Yes
Internet Sales: 1.00%
Total Units: 13
Trade Names: Ram Restaurant & Brewery (13)
Company-Owned Units: 13
Preferred Square Footage: 7,500
Preferred Location Types: Community Mall; Downtown; Freestanding; Strip Mall
Alcohol Served: Beer, Wine, Liquor
Primary Menu: American (13); Steak/Seafood (0)
Projected Openings: 2
Areas of Operation: CO, ID, IL, IN, OR, WA
Type of Foodservice: Casual Dining (13); Fine Dining (0)
Catering Services: Yes
Primary Distributors: (Full Line) US Foods, FIFE, WA

Key Personnel
JEFF IVERSON JR - CEO; President; Executive Chef; Director Real Estate
KRISTIE WEBB - CFO
RUTH MAC - Chief Strategy Officer; Chief Talent Officer
JAMES CASSIDY - Corporate Chef; Director Purchasing, Supply Chain, Food Safety

D & P Restaurants LLC
PO Box 1696
Longview, WA 98632-8034

Telephone: (360) 574-6279
Fax Number: (360) 574-6292
Type of Business: Chain Restaurant Operator
Total Sales: $15,518,000 (e)
Total Units: 3
Trade Names: McDonald's (3)
Units Franchised From: 3
Preferred Location Types: Freestanding

Primary Menu: Hamburger (3)
Areas of Operation: WA
Type of Foodservice: Quick Serve (3)
Franchise Affiliation: McDonald's Corporation, CHICAGO, IL

Key Personnel
DAVID STOLLER - President; General Buyer

Woods Coffee
191 18th St.
Lynden, WA 98264

Telephone: (360) 933-1855
Internet Homepage: woodscoffee.com
Company Email: info@woodscoffee.com
Type of Business: Chain Restaurant Operator
Year Founded: 2002
Total Sales: $21,038,000 (e)
Total Units: 21
Trade Names: Woods Coffee (21)
Company-Owned Units: 21
Primary Menu: Coffee (21)
Areas of Operation: WA
Type of Foodservice: Quick Serve (21)

Key Personnel
WES HERMAN - Founder; Partner
DIANE HERMAN - Founder; Partner
KELLY SPIKER - President
CARLY BOMBER - CFO
RYAN SPIKER - Director Marketing

Mel Oshiro
13619 Mukilteo Speedway Ste D6
Lynnwood, WA 98087-1672

Telephone: (425) 742-2182
Type of Business: Chain Restaurant Operator
Total Sales: $1,195,000 (e)
Total Units: 2
Trade Names: Subway (2)
Units Franchised From: 2
Primary Menu: Sandwiches/Deli (2)
Areas of Operation: WA
Type of Foodservice: Quick Serve (2)
Franchise Affiliation: Doctor's Associates Inc., MILFORD, CT

Key Personnel
JULIE OSHIRO - Partner; General Buyer
MEL OSHIRO - Partner; General Buyer

Pacific Sliders, LLC
2902 164th St SW
Lynnwood, WA 98087

Telephone: (425) 787-6400
Type of Business: Chain Restaurant Operator

Total Sales: $8,383,000 (e)
Total Units: 4
Trade Names: Five Guys Burgers and Fries (4)
Units Franchised From: 4
Primary Menu: Hamburger (4)
Areas of Operation: WA
Type of Foodservice: Fast Casual (4)
Franchise Affiliation: Five Guys Holdings Inc., LORTON, VA

Key Personnel
WILLIAM BARNETT - Partner; General Buyer
LISA BARNETT - Partner
DAVE DAVIS - Manager District

FOR Northwest LLC
3023 80th Ave SE Ste 200
Mercer Island, WA 98040-6014

Telephone: (206) 233-9727
Fax Number: (206) 233-0539
Internet Homepage: fornorthwest.com
Company Email: forllc@bkfor.com
Type of Business: Chain Restaurant Operator
Year Founded: 1996
Total Sales: $74,380,000 (e)
Number of Employees: 1,116
Average Check: Breakfast(12); Lunch(16); Dinner(22)
Total Units: 33
Trade Names: Burger King (33)
Units Franchised From: 33
Preferred Square Footage: 1,500
Preferred Location Types: Downtown; Office Complex; Strip Mall
Primary Menu: Hamburger (33)
Areas of Operation: AK, WA
Type of Foodservice: Quick Serve (33)
Catering Services: Yes
Franchise Affiliation: Burger King Worldwide Inc., MIAMI, FL
Primary Distributors: (Full Line) SYSCO Food Services of Seattle Inc., KENT, WA
Parent Company: Flynn Industries Inc., SAN FRANCISCO, CA
Notes: The Burger King restaurants operate as Flynn Olympic Restaurants.

Key Personnel
MARK ESCAMILLA - President; COO; Director Facility/Maintenance; Buyer Foodservice Equip/Supplies
PHILLIP DEMARIA - Owner
DANA GRAN - CFO; Controller
BRYAN FRITZ - District Manager
JOE HARTMAN - Manager Special Projects

Blazing Onion Burger Company
15115 Main St
Mill Creek, WA 98012-2066

Telephone: (425) 338-4445
Fax Number: (425) 967-5397
Internet Homepage: blazingonion.com
Type of Business: Chain Restaurant Operator
Year Founded: 2007
Total Sales: $12,400,000 (e)
Alcohol Sales: 10%
Number of Employees: 140
Total Units: 7
Trade Names: Blazing Onion Burger Company (7)
Company-Owned Units: 7
Preferred Square Footage: 4,500
Preferred Location Types: Community Mall; Freestanding; Regional Mall
Alcohol Served: Beer, Wine, Liquor
Primary Menu: Hamburger (7)
Projected Openings: 1
Areas of Operation: WA
Type of Foodservice: Fast Casual (7)

Key Personnel
DAVID JONES - CEO; Partner; General Buyer
LORRI JONES - Partner; CFO
DARIUS HUNTER - VP Operations

Garlic Jim's Franchise Corp.
3922 148th St SE Ste 107
Mill Creek, WA 98012-4752

Telephone: (425) 948-7603
Fax Number: (425) 948-7945
Internet Homepage: garlicjims.com
Type of Business: Chain Restaurant Operator
Year Founded: 2004
Systemwide Sales: $17,419,000 (e)
Total Sales: $3,805,000 (e)
Number of Employees: 85
Average Check: Lunch(14); Dinner(14)
Total Units: 7
Trade Names: Garlic Jim's Famous Gourmet Pizza (7)
Company-Owned Units: 2
Units Franchised To: 5
Preferred Square Footage: 1,200
Preferred Location Types: Freestanding; Regional Mall
Primary Menu: Pizza (7)
Areas of Operation: CO, OR, WA
Type of Foodservice: Fast Casual (7)

Key Personnel
CRAIG ROBERTS - Owner
ROSS MARZOLF - Director Marketing, Public Relations

Buzz Inn Steakhouse Restaurants
18960 State Route 2 Ste 146
Monroe, WA 98272-8998

Telephone: (425) 337-1234
Internet Homepage: buzzinnsteakhouse.com
Company Email: monroe@buzzinnsteakhouse.com
Type of Business: Chain Restaurant Operator
Total Units: 12
Trade Names: Buzz Inn Steakhouse (12)
Company-Owned Units: 12
Primary Menu: Steak (12)
Areas of Operation: WA
Type of Foodservice: Casual Dining (12)

Key Personnel
CRAIG OHM - Owner; General Buyer

Danicia Enterprises
713 N Stratford Rd
Moses Lake, WA 98837-1597

Telephone: (509) 765-0212
Fax Number: (509) 765-0212
Type of Business: Chain Restaurant Operator
Total Sales: $4,904,000 (e)
Total Units: 2
Trade Names: Burger King (2)
Company-Owned Units: 2
Primary Menu: Hamburger (2)
Areas of Operation: WA
Type of Foodservice: Quick Serve (2)
Franchise Affiliation: Burger King Worldwide Inc., MIAMI, FL

Key Personnel
DENAE BOYD - President; General Buyer

Alcan Investments
1701 Freeway Dr
Mount Vernon, WA 98273-5440

Telephone: (360) 428-6611
Fax Number: (360) 424-9666
Type of Business: Chain Restaurant Operator
Total Sales: $7,048,000 (e)
Average Check: Dinner(14)
Total Units: 5
Trade Names: Dairy Queen (5)
Units Franchised From: 5
Primary Menu: Snacks (5)
Areas of Operation: WA
Type of Foodservice: Quick Serve (5)
Franchise Affiliation: International Dairy Queen Inc., BLOOMINGTON, MN

Key Personnel
SCOTT WHITTMAN - President; General Buyer

Jet City Pizza Co.
15969 Mountain View Rd
Mount Vernon, WA 98274-9409

Telephone: (360) 202-6395
Internet Homepage: jetcitypizza.com
Company Email: nfo@jetcitypizza.com
Type of Business: Chain Restaurant Operator
Year Founded: 1994
Systemwide Sales: $4,929,000 (e)
Total Sales: $3,817,000 (e)
Number of Employees: 42
Average Check: Lunch(14); Dinner(16)
Internet Order Processing: Yes
Internet Sales: 1.00%
Total Units: 5
Trade Names: Jet City Pizza (5)
Company-Owned Units: 1
Units Franchised To: 4
Preferred Square Footage: 2,500
Preferred Location Types: Freestanding; Strip Mall
Primary Menu: Pizza (5)
Areas of Operation: WA
Type of Foodservice: Quick Serve (5)
On-site Distribution Center: Yes
Primary Distributors: (Full Line) SYSCO Food Services of Seattle Inc., KENT, WA

Key Personnel
BOBBY SMITH - President
BOB SMITH - Owner; General Buyer
JESSE MOELLER - General Manager

Arnies Restaurants Northwest Inc.
714 2nd St
Mukilteo, WA 98275-1554

Telephone: (425) 293-0319
Internet Homepage: arniesrestaurant.com; cohocafe.com
Company Email: edmonds@arniesrestaurant.com
Type of Business: Chain Restaurant Operator
Year Founded: 1979
Total Sales: $13,991,000 (e)
Alcohol Sales: 15%
Number of Employees: 140
Average Check: Lunch(22); Dinner(32)
Total Units: 4
Trade Names: Arnies Edmonds (1); Arnies Mukilteo (1); Coho Cafe (2)
Company-Owned Units: 4
Preferred Location Types: Freestanding;

Other
Alcohol Served: Beer, Wine, Liquor
Primary Menu: Steak/Seafood (4)
Areas of Operation: WA
Type of Foodservice: Casual Dining (2); Fine Dining (2)
Catering Services: Yes
Primary Distributors: (Equipment) The Wasserstrom Co., COLUMBUS, OH; (Food) Food Services of America, KENT, WA; (Supplies) Food Services of America, KENT, WA

Key Personnel
STEVE PRICE - President; Partner
SCOTT HOWES - Partner; VP Operations
KATHLEEN KAI - Controller
FRANCES LUMM - General Manager
PETER CUMMINGS - General Manager
ROB DAVIS - General Manager
BILL PENNINGTON - Executive Chef
BRUCE NACION - Executive Chef

Emerald City Pizza
12121 Harbour Reach Dr Ste 200
Mukilteo, WA 98275-5314

Telephone: (425) 493-8077
Fax Number: (509) 457-4198
Type of Business: Chain Restaurant Operator
Total Sales: $151,670,000 (e)
Alcohol Sales: 1%
Number of Employees: 700
Average Check: Lunch(16); Dinner(16)
Total Units: 124
Trade Names: Pizza Hut (124)
Units Franchised From: 124
Preferred Square Footage: 2,500; 3,200
Preferred Location Types: Freestanding; Strip Mall
Alcohol Served: Beer, Wine
Primary Menu: Pizza (124)
Areas of Operation: ID, NV, OR, WA
Type of Foodservice: Quick Serve (124)
Foodservice Management Venues: Schools
Franchise Affiliation: Pizza Hut Inc., PLANO, TX
Primary Distributors: (Food) McLane/Tualatin, TUALATIN, OR

Key Personnel
TERRY HOPKINS - CEO; Partner
JOHN NGUYEN - President; Partner; CFO; Controller; Director Operations, Purchasing, Supply Chain, Store Fixtures
SARA PHINNEY - VP Human Resources
KRIS JACKSON - General Manager
CHUCK HENDERSON - Director Facility/Maintenance
ROBERT HERNANDEZ - Manager

MESK Investments
13024 Beverly Park Rd Ste 203
Mukilteo, WA 98275-5857

Telephone: (425) 348-0328
Type of Business: Chain Restaurant Operator
Total Sales: $50,560,000 (e)
Total Units: 16
Trade Names: IHOP (16)
Units Franchised From: 16
Primary Menu: American (16)
Areas of Operation: WA
Type of Foodservice: Family Restaurant (16)
Franchise Affiliation: IHOP Restaurant System, GLENDALE, CA

Key Personnel
MOHAMMED KHADAR - President; Owner

Emerald City Foods, Inc.
31340 State Route 20
Oak Harbor, WA 98277-3170

Telephone: (360) 675-3868
Type of Business: Chain Restaurant Operator
Total Sales: $76,370,000 (e)
Total Units: 34
Trade Names: Burger King (34)
Units Franchised From: 34
Primary Menu: Hamburger (34)
Areas of Operation: WA
Type of Foodservice: Quick Serve (34)
Franchise Affiliation: Burger King Worldwide Inc., MIAMI, FL

Key Personnel
DANIEL GETTEMY - Owner; General Buyer
CHARLES JOHNSON - General Manager

Casa Mia Restaurants
716 Plum St SE
Olympia, WA 98501-1527

Telephone: (360) 352-0440
Fax Number: (360) 753-8526
Internet Homepage: casamiarestaurants.com
Company Email: rknudson@casamiarestaurants.com
Type of Business: Chain Restaurant Operator
Year Founded: 1952
Systemwide Sales: $8,994,000 (e)
Total Sales: $3,965,000 (e)
Alcohol Sales: 8%
Number of Employees: 120
Average Check: Lunch(16); Dinner(24)
Total Units: 7
Trade Names: Casa Mia (7)
Company-Owned Units: 2
Units Franchised To: 5
Preferred Square Footage: 2,500
Preferred Location Types: Freestanding
Alcohol Served: Beer, Wine
Primary Menu: Italian (7)
Areas of Operation: WA
Type of Foodservice: Casual Dining (7)
Catering Services: Yes
Primary Distributors: (Equipment) Bargreen-Ellingson Inc., TACOMA, WA; (Food) Harbor Wholesale Foods, LACEY, WA; (Supplies) Harbor Wholesale Foods, LACEY, WA

Key Personnel
ROBERT KNUDSON - President; VP Operations; Controller; Executive Chef; Manager Finance, Purchasing, Facility/Maintenance, Information Systems, Supply Chain, Marketing, Ethnic Marketing, Real Estate, Design, Human Resources, Store Fixtures, Catering; General Buyer
CHRIS KNUDSON - Owner; General Manager

BigFoot Investment Group LLC
420 Ellingson Rd Ste 200
Pacific, WA 98047-1001

Telephone: (253) 876-7505
Internet Homepage: bigfootjava.com
Type of Business: Chain Restaurant Operator
Year Founded: 1998
Total Sales: $17,240,000 (e)
Number of Employees: 275
Average Check: Breakfast(6); Lunch(6); Dinner(6)
Total Units: 32
Trade Names: BigFoot Java (32)
Company-Owned Units: 32
Preferred Square Footage: 2,500
Preferred Location Types: Freestanding; Strip Mall
Primary Menu: Coffee (32)
Areas of Operation: WA
Foreign Countries: CANADA
Type of Foodservice: Quick Serve (32)

Key Personnel
AL JIWANI - President; Director Finance, Store Fixtures
HAFIZ JIWANI - Exec VP; Director Purchasing, Supply Chain
MINA JIWANI - Director Training
SAM KAJANI - Director Real Estate, Site Selection, Design
JUSTINE WHITMORE - Director Operations, Human Resources; Manager Information Systems

Domino's Franchisee
3802 W Court St
Pasco, WA 99301-2777

Telephone: (509) 547-9999
Type of Business: Chain Restaurant Operator
Total Sales: $8,203,000 (e)
Total Units: 4
Trade Names: Domino's (4)
Units Franchised From: 4
Primary Menu: Pizza (4)
Areas of Operation: WA
Type of Foodservice: Quick Serve (4)
Franchise Affiliation: Domino's Pizza Inc, ANN ARBOR, MI

Key Personnel
TIMOTHY HINES - Owner; General Buyer

Frugals
1527 E 1st St
Port Angeles, WA 98362-4620

Telephone: (360) 417-3598
Fax Number: (360) 417-3056
Internet Homepage: frugalburger.com
Company Email: Frugalfranchise@gmail.com
Type of Business: Chain Restaurant Operator
Total Units: 5
Trade Names: Frugals (5)
Company-Owned Units: 5
Primary Menu: Hamburger (5)
Areas of Operation: WA
Type of Foodservice: Quick Serve (5)

Key Personnel
PETER B. STEWART - Partner
SHEILA STEWART - Partner

Domino's Franchisee
3289 SE Lund Ave Ste 101
Port Orchard, WA 98366-2881

Telephone: (360) 871-9000
Type of Business: Chain Restaurant Operator
Total Sales: $6,179,000 (e)
Total Units: 3
Trade Names: Domino's (3)
Units Franchised From: 3
Primary Menu: Pizza (3)
Areas of Operation: WA
Type of Foodservice: Quick Serve (3)
Franchise Affiliation: Domino's Pizza Inc, ANN ARBOR, MI

Key Personnel
STEVE GAUBE - Owner; General Buyer

Domino's Franchisee
845 NE Monroe St
Pullman, WA 99163-4042

Telephone: (509) 332-1555
Type of Business: Chain Restaurant Operator
Total Sales: $8,343,000 (e)
Total Units: 4
Trade Names: Domino's (4)
Units Franchised From: 4
Primary Menu: Pizza (4)
Areas of Operation: WA
Type of Foodservice: Quick Serve (4)
Franchise Affiliation: Domino's Pizza Inc, ANN ARBOR, MI

Key Personnel
JUSTIN BUONO - Partner
SCOTT BUONO - Partner

Mazatlan Mexican Restaurant
13024 Meridian E
Puyallup, WA 98373-5641

Telephone: (253) 770-8702
Fax Number: (253) 848-8652
Company Email: mazatlan14450@comcast.net
Type of Business: Chain Restaurant Operator
Year Founded: 1975
Total Sales: $12,420,000 (e)
Alcohol Sales: 40%
Number of Employees: 100
Average Check: Lunch(22); Dinner(24)
Total Units: 13
Trade Names: Mazatlan Mexican Restaurant (13)
Company-Owned Units: 13
Preferred Square Footage: 6,000
Preferred Location Types: Community Mall; Freestanding
Alcohol Served: Beer, Wine, Liquor
Primary Menu: Mexican (13)
Areas of Operation: WA
Type of Foodservice: Casual Dining (13)
Catering Services: Yes
Primary Distributors: (Food) SYSCO Detroit LLC, CANTON, MI

Key Personnel
ANDRES CARDENAS - President; CFO; Executive Chef; Manager Finance, Operations, Purchasing, Information Systems, Loss Prevention, Marketing, Real Estate, Design
TERESA CARDENAS-QUIROZ - Exec VP; Manager Human Resources

Berry Investment Group, Ltd.
15230 NE 24th St Ste 1-G
Redmond, WA 98052-5540

Telephone: (425) 641-3969
Type of Business: Chain Restaurant Operator
Total Sales: $5,913,000 (e)
Total Units: 4
Trade Names: Jersey Mike's Subs (4)
Units Franchised From: 4
Primary Menu: Sandwiches/Deli (4)
Areas of Operation: WA
Type of Foodservice: Quick Serve (4)
Franchise Affiliation: Jersey Mike's Franchise Systems, MANASQUAN, NJ

Key Personnel
STEPHEN BERRY JR - Owner

Staples Restaurants LLC
7990 Leary Way NE
Redmond, WA 98052

Telephone: (425) 497-5100
Internet Homepage: quinnspubseattle.com; solerepairshop.com; staplesrestaurantgroup.com; uneedaburger.com
Company Email: info@quinnspubseattle.com
Type of Business: Chain Restaurant Operator
Total Units: 5
Trade Names: Feed Co. Burgers (2); Quinn's Pub (1); Sole Repair Shop (1); Uneeda Burger (1)
Company-Owned Units: 5
Primary Menu: American (2); Hamburger (3)
Areas of Operation: WA
Type of Foodservice: Casual Dining (2); Fast Casual (3)

Key Personnel
HEATHER STAPLES - Partner; COO

Thai Ginger Restaurants Inc.
7430 164th Ave NE Ste B 225
Redmond, WA 98052

Telephone: (425) 558-4044
Internet Homepage: thaiginger.com
Company Email: info@thaiginger.com
Type of Business: Chain Restaurant Operator
Year Founded: 1996
Total Sales: $7,804,000 (e)
Average Check: Lunch(14); Dinner(18)
Total Units: 4
Trade Names: Thai Ginger (4)
Company-Owned Units: 4
Alcohol Served: Beer, Wine, Liquor
Primary Menu: Thai (4)

Areas of Operation: WA
Type of Foodservice: Fine Dining (4)
Catering Services: Yes

Key Personnel
MICHAEL READ - Controller

Taco Time Northwest
3300 Maple Valley Hwy
Renton, WA 98058-2800

Telephone: (425) 226-6656
Fax Number: (425) 228-8226
Internet Homepage: tacotimenw.com
Company Email: info@tacotimenw.com
Type of Business: Chain Restaurant Operator
Year Founded: 1979
Total Sales: $81,940,000 (e)
Number of Employees: 1,642
Total Units: 80
Trade Names: Taco Time (80)
Company-Owned Units: 80
Preferred Location Types: Freestanding
Primary Menu: Taco (80)
Projected Openings: 2
Areas of Operation: WA
Type of Foodservice: Quick Serve (80)
Franchise Affiliation: Kahala Brands, SCOTTSDALE, AZ
Notes: Taco Time Northwest is wholly independent from Taco Time International; It operates and licenses the operation of Taco Time restaurants in Western Washington.

Key Personnel
ROBBY TONKIN - Co-President; General Buyer
CHRIS TONKIN - Co-President; VP
ERNEST CONRADS - VP Finance
GRETCHEN EVEERETT - Director Marketing
GRETCHEN EVERETT - Director Marketing, Advertising
BRANDON PETERSEN - Manager Digital Experience
ALISHA RAMIREZ - Coordinator Recruitment

13 Coins LLC
2107 Elliott Ave Ste 304
Seattle, WA 98121-2159

Telephone: (206) 382-1313
Fax Number: (206) 382-2004
Internet Homepage: 13coins.com
Type of Business: Chain Restaurant Operator
Year Founded: 1967
Total Sales: $18,396,000 (e)
Alcohol Sales: 10%
Number of Employees: 170
Average Check: Breakfast(12); Lunch(24); Dinner(36)
Internet Sales: 2.00%
Total Units: 3
Trade Names: 13 Coins (3)
Company-Owned Units: 3
Preferred Location Types: Freestanding; Strip Mall
Alcohol Served: Beer, Wine, Liquor
Primary Menu: American (3)
Areas of Operation: WA
Type of Foodservice: Fine Dining (3)

Key Personnel
ANN MEI HUIE - Partner
ALBERT MOSCATEL - Partner; General Buyer
JULIE PHAN - Director Human Resources

Belle Epicurean
925 4th Ave
Seattle, WA 98101

Telephone: (206) 262-9306
Internet Homepage: belleepicurean.com
Company Email: info@belleepicurean.com
Type of Business: Chain Restaurant Operator
Total Units: 2
Trade Names: Belle Epicurean (2)
Company-Owned Units: 2
Primary Menu: Snacks (2)
Areas of Operation: WA
Type of Foodservice: Fast Casual (2)

Key Personnel
CAROLYN FERGUSON - Owner; Executive Chef; General Buyer
HOWARD FERGUSON - Owner

Big Mario's New York Style Pizza
1009 E Pike St
Seattle, WA 98122-3818

Telephone: (206) 922-3875
Internet Homepage: bigmariosnewyorkpizza.com
Company Email: contact@bigmariosnewyorkpizza.com
Type of Business: Chain Restaurant Operator
Internet Order Processing: Yes
Total Units: 3
Trade Names: Big Mario's (3)
Company-Owned Units: 3
Primary Menu: Pizza (3)
Areas of Operation: WA
Type of Foodservice: Casual Dining (3)

Key Personnel
JASON LAJEUNESSE - Partner; General Manager; General Buyer
MIKE MCCONNELL - Partner; General Buyer
DAVID MEINERT - Partner; General Buyer

Blue Moon Burgers, Inc.
703 N 34th St
Seattle, WA 98103-8800

Telephone: (206) 547-1907
Internet Homepage: bluemoonburgers.com
Company Email: BOM@bluemoonburgers.com
Type of Business: Chain Restaurant Operator
Year Founded: 2006
Total Units: 3
Trade Names: Blue Moon Burgers (3)
Company-Owned Units: 3
Primary Menu: Hamburger (3)
Areas of Operation: WA
Type of Foodservice: Fast Casual (3)

Key Personnel
CHARLIE OLSON - Owner; General Buyer

Bradford Cafe
3770 SW Alaska St
Seattle, WA 98126

Telephone: (206) 937-8732
Internet Homepage: chacocanyoncafe.com
Company Email: info@chacocanyoncafe.com
Type of Business: Chain Restaurant Operator
Total Units: 2
Trade Names: Chaco Canyon Organic Cafe (2)
Company-Owned Units: 2
Units Franchised To: 2
Primary Menu: American (2)
Areas of Operation: WA
Type of Foodservice: Fast Casual (2)

Key Personnel
MOHAMED YOUSEFF - Owner; General Buyer

Broadcast Coffee Roasters
1918 E Yesler Way
Seattle, WA 98122-5883

Telephone: (206) 322-0807
Internet Homepage: broadcastcoffee.com
Company Email: info@broadcastcoffee.com
Type of Business: Chain Restaurant Operator
Year Founded: 2008
Total Units: 3
Trade Names: Broadcast Coffee Roasters (3)
Company-Owned Units: 3
Primary Menu: Snacks (3)
Areas of Operation: WA
Type of Foodservice: Fast Casual (3)

Key Personnel
BARRY FAUGHT - Owner; General Buyer
NATALIE WALKER - General Manager

Cactus Restaurants
4220 E Madison St
Seattle, WA 98112-3237

Telephone: (206) 324-4140
Internet Homepage: cactusrestaurants.com
Company Email:
 comments@cactusrestaurants.com
Type of Business: Chain Restaurant Operator
Year Founded: 1990
Total Sales: $5,314,000 (e)
Alcohol Sales: 8%
Number of Employees: 50
Average Check: Lunch(10); Dinner(14)
Total Units: 6
Trade Names: Cactus (6)
Company-Owned Units: 6
Preferred Location Types: Freestanding
Alcohol Served: Beer, Wine, Liquor
Primary Menu: Southwest/Tex-Mex (6)
Projected Openings: 1
Areas of Operation: WA
Type of Foodservice: Casual Dining (6)
Catering Services: Yes

Key Personnel
BRET CHATALIS - President; General Manager;
 Executive Chef; General Buyer

Cafe Javasti
8410 5th Ave NE
Seattle, WA 98115-4121

Telephone: (206) 985-9903
Internet Homepage: javasti.com
Company Email: cafejavasi@gmail.com
Type of Business: Chain Restaurant Operator
Year Founded: 2001
Total Units: 2
Trade Names: Cafe Javasti (2)
Company-Owned Units: 2
Primary Menu: Snacks (2)
Areas of Operation: WA
Type of Foodservice: Fast Casual (2)

Key Personnel
SCOTT MORELL - Partner; General Buyer
RYAN SHERIDAN - Partner

Caffe Appassionato
4001 21st Ave W
Seattle, WA 98199-1201

Telephone: (206) 281-8040
Fax Number: (206) 282-5218
Internet Homepage: caffeappassionato.com
Company Email:
 feedback@caffeappassionato.com
Type of Business: Chain Restaurant Operator
Year Founded: 1991
Systemwide Sales: $12,889,000 (e)
Total Sales: $9,875,000 (e)
Number of Employees: 125
Average Check: Lunch(8); Dinner(8)
Internet Order Processing: Yes
Internet Sales: 1.00%
Total Units: 11
Trade Names: Caffe Appassionato (11)
Company-Owned Units: 10
Units Franchised To: 1
Preferred Square Footage: 2,500
Preferred Location Types: Downtown;
 Freestanding
Primary Menu: Coffee (11)
Areas of Operation: WA
Foreign Countries: JAPAN; MALAYSIA;
 SOUTH KOREA; THE PHILIPPINES
Type of Foodservice: Quick Serve (11)
On-site Distribution Center: Yes

Key Personnel
TUCKER MCHUGH - President; Partner;
 Director Finance, Operations,
 Facility/Maintenance, Information Systems,
 Supply Chain, Real Estate, Design, Human
 Resources, Menu Development; General
 Buyer
BARBARA SANCKEN - Partner
PHIL SANCKEN - Partner
KEVIN NORDQUIST - Manager Production

Caffe Ladro
501 2nd Ave W Ste 200
Seattle, WA 98119-3983

Telephone: (206) 634-1356
Fax Number: (206) 634-1357
Internet Homepage: caffeladro.com
Type of Business: Chain Restaurant Operator
Total Units: 16
Trade Names: Caffe Ladro (16)
Company-Owned Units: 16
Primary Menu: Snacks (16)
Areas of Operation: WA
Type of Foodservice: Fast Casual (16)

Key Personnel
JACK KELLY - Founder; CEO; General Buyer
BOB OHLY - CFO; VP
ADRIENNE BLAKE - Manager Branding
HEATHER OHLY - Project Manager

Caffe Vita, Inc.
1005 E Pike St
Seattle, WA 98122-3818

Telephone: (206) 709-4440
Internet Homepage: caffevita.com
Company Email: info@caffevita.com
Type of Business: Chain Restaurant Operator
Year Founded: 1995
Total Units: 10
Trade Names: Caffe Vita (10)
Company-Owned Units: 10
Primary Menu: Snacks (10)
Areas of Operation: CA, NY, OR, WA
Type of Foodservice: Fast Casual (10)
Notes: Founder and owner Michael McConnell
 is also founder and majority owner of the Vita
 Tribunali chain in Seattle.

Key Personnel
SHELLEY GRIFFIN - Director E-Commerce
ERIC FARRUGIA - Director Operations
ERIN FITZPATRICK - Director Wholesale-
 Grocery

CaliBurger, LLC
4509 University Way NE
Seattle, WA 98105-4510

Telephone: (206) 420-8199
Internet Homepage: caliburger.com
Type of Business: Chain Restaurant Operator
Total Units: 41
Trade Names: CaliBurger (41)
Company-Owned Units: 41
Primary Menu: Hamburger (41)
Projected Openings: 2
Areas of Operation: CA, MD, WA, BC, ON
Foreign Countries: BAHRAIN; CANADA;
 CHINA; KUWAIT; MALAYSIA; QATAR; SAUDI
 ARABIA; SPAIN; SWEDEN; TAIWAN; THE
 PHILIPPINES; UNITED ARAB EMIRATES
Type of Foodservice: Fast Casual (41)

Key Personnel
YALE GOLDBERG - VP Business Development
NOEL WILLHITE - General Manager

Cantinetta
3650 Wallingford Ave N
Seattle, WA 98103-8242

Telephone: (206) 632-1000
Internet Homepage: barcantinetta.com;
 mercatostellina.com
Type of Business: Chain Restaurant Operator
Total Units: 5
Trade Names: Bar Cantinetta (1); Cantinetta
 Bellevue (1); Cantinetta Seattle (1); Mercato
 Stellina (2)
Company-Owned Units: 5
Primary Menu: Italian (3); Pizza (2)
Areas of Operation: WA
Type of Foodservice: Casual Dining (5)

Key Personnel
TREVOR GREENWOOD - Partner; General
 Buyer

WADE MOLLER - Partner
RANDY QUARRY - Partner
KATHERINE BOULTER - General Manager

Cherry Street Coffee House
103 Cherry St
Seattle, WA 98104-2205

Telephone: (206) 621-5331
Internet Homepage: cherryst.com
Company Email: info@cherryst.com
Type of Business: Chain Restaurant Operator
Total Units: 12
Trade Names: Cherry Street Coffee House (12)
Company-Owned Units: 12
Primary Menu: Coffee (12)
Projected Openings: 1
Areas of Operation: WA
Type of Foodservice: Quick Serve (12)

Key Personnel
ALI GHAMBARI - Founder; President; General Buyer
LAILA G. WILBUR - Director Food and Beverage

Chow Foods Management
2114 N 45th St
Seattle, WA 98103-6902

Telephone: (206) 322-3421
Fax Number: (206) 322-0435
Internet Homepage: chowfoods.com
Company Email: sales@chowfoods.com
Type of Business: Chain Restaurant Operator
Year Founded: 1987
Total Sales: $20,511,000 (e)
Alcohol Sales: 25%
Number of Employees: 250
Average Check: Breakfast(8); Lunch(14); Dinner(22)
Internet Order Processing: Yes
Total Units: 4
Trade Names: Endolyne Joe's (1); Hi-Life (1); The 5 Spot (1); TNT Taqueria (1)
Company-Owned Units: 4
Preferred Square Footage: 5,500; 6,000
Preferred Location Types: Freestanding
Alcohol Served: Beer, Wine, Liquor
Primary Menu: American (3); Mexican (1)
Areas of Operation: WA
Type of Foodservice: Casual Dining (4)

Key Personnel
PETER LEVY - President; Owner; VP Information Systems; Director Facility/Maintenance; Manager Finance, Operations, Real Estate, Design; General Buyer
MICHELLE GARRARD - CFO; Controller; Director Human Resources

ANTHONY HUBBARD - Executive Chef; Director Purchasing, Supply Chain

Consolidated Restaurants Inc.
820 2nd Ave Ste 300
Seattle, WA 98104-1529

Telephone: (206) 232-9292
Fax Number: (206) 232-7621
Internet Homepage: consolidatedrestaurants.com; e3restaurantgroup.com
Company Email: info@conrests.com
Type of Business: Chain Restaurant Operator
Year Founded: 1951
Total Sales: $34,640,000 (e)
Alcohol Sales: 21%
Number of Employees: 500
Average Check: Lunch(30); Dinner(36)
Internet Order Processing: Yes
Internet Sales: 4.00%
Total Units: 5
Trade Names: Elliott's Oyster House (1); Heartwood Provisions (1); Metropolitan Grill (1); Quincy's Burgers (1); Wing Dome (1)
Company-Owned Units: 5
Preferred Square Footage: 10,000
Preferred Location Types: Freestanding; Regional Mall
Alcohol Served: Beer, Wine, Liquor
Primary Menu: American (2); Hamburger (1); Seafood (1); Steak (1)
Areas of Operation: WA
Type of Foodservice: Casual Dining (2); Fine Dining (3)

Key Personnel
RON COHN - Chairman; Director Design
JAMES ROWE - President; CFO
JEREMY ANDERSON - VP Operations
PAM CASEY - VP Risk Management, Human Resources
GARIN COHN - Director Operations
AARON WOOD-SNYDERMAN - Director
KRISTEN MCCORMACK - Manager Human Resources

Cupcake Royale
1101 34th Ave
Seattle, WA 98122-5138

Telephone: (206) 701-6240
Internet Homepage: cupcakeroyale.com
Company Email: Madrona@cupcakeroyale.com
Type of Business: Chain Restaurant Operator
Year Founded: 2003
Total Units: 6
Trade Names: Cupcake Royale (6)
Company-Owned Units: 6

Primary Menu: Snacks (6)
Areas of Operation: WA
Type of Foodservice: Fast Casual (6)

Key Personnel
JODY HALL - Owner

Dick's Drive In Restaurants
4426 2nd Ave NE
Seattle, WA 98105-6129

Telephone: (206) 634-0300
Fax Number: (206) 632-1165
Internet Homepage: ddir.com
Company Email: mail4ddir@ddir.com
Type of Business: Chain Restaurant Operator
Year Founded: 1954
Total Sales: $6,444,000 (e)
Number of Employees: 200
Average Check: Lunch(8); Dinner(8)
Internet Order Processing: Yes
Total Units: 7
Trade Names: Dick's Drive In (7)
Company-Owned Units: 6
Preferred Square Footage: 3,000
Preferred Location Types: Freestanding
Primary Menu: Hamburger (7)
Areas of Operation: WA
Type of Foodservice: Quick Serve (7)
Primary Distributors: (Equipment) Bargreen-Ellingson Inc., SEATTLE, WA; (Food) US Foods, FIFE, WA; (Supplies) Bargreen-Ellingson Inc., SEATTLE, WA

Key Personnel
JASMINE DONOVAN - CEO; President
KEN FRAZIER - General Manager
STEFAN BENNETT - Director Information Systems
LISSY WARNER - Manager E-Commerce

Diva Espresso
7916 Greenwood Ave N
Seattle, WA 98103-4636

Telephone: (206) 781-8106
Internet Homepage: divaespresso.com
Company Email: info@divaespresso.com
Type of Business: Chain Restaurant Operator
Year Founded: 1992
Total Units: 6
Trade Names: Diva Espresso (6)
Company-Owned Units: 6
Primary Menu: Snacks (6)
Areas of Operation: WA
Type of Foodservice: Family Restaurant (6)

Key Personnel
GREG HAMPER - President; Owner; General Buyer

JESSICA MOSES - COO
AMBER CAMPBELL - General Manager
ROGER DALTRY - Manager Customer Service

Duke's Restaurants
7858 Green Lake Dr N
Seattle, WA 98103-4862

Telephone: (206) 283-8422
Fax Number: (206) 283-8421
Internet Homepage: dukeschowderhouse.com
Company Email:
 duketalk@dukeschowderhouse.com
Type of Business: Chain Restaurant Operator
Year Founded: 1976
Total Sales: $20,290,000 (e)
Alcohol Sales: 20%
Number of Employees: 200
Average Check: Lunch(60); Dinner(60)
Internet Order Processing: Yes
Total Units: 8
Trade Names: Duke's Seafood & Chowder (8)
Company-Owned Units: 8
Preferred Square Footage: 5,500; 6,000
Preferred Location Types: Freestanding
Alcohol Served: Beer, Wine, Liquor
Primary Menu: Seafood (8)
Areas of Operation: WA
Type of Foodservice: Casual Dining (8)
Primary Distributors: (Food) Food Services of America, SCOTTSDALE, AZ

Key Personnel
G. DUKE MOSCRIP - President; Executive Chef; Manager Operations; General Buyer
KRISTINA DICKSON - CFO

El Borracho
1521 1st Ave
Seattle, WA 98101-1523

Telephone: (206) 538-0440
Internet Homepage: elborrachoseattle.com
Type of Business: Chain Restaurant Operator
Year Founded: 2012
Total Units: 3
Trade Names: El Borracho (3)
Company-Owned Units: 3
Primary Menu: Mexican (3)
Areas of Operation: WA
Type of Foodservice: Casual Dining (3)

Key Personnel
KITTIE DAVIDOVICH - Owner; General Buyer

Elemental Pizza LLC
2634 NE University Village St
Seattle, WA 98105-5023

Telephone: (206) 524-4930
Internet Homepage: elementalpizza.com
Type of Business: Chain Restaurant Operator
Year Founded: 2012
Total Units: 2
Trade Names: Elemental Pizza (2)
Company-Owned Units: 2
Primary Menu: Pizza (2)
Areas of Operation: WA
Type of Foodservice: Fast Casual (2)

Key Personnel
JAMES ALLARD - Partner; General Buyer

Eltana Wood-Fired Bagel Cafe
1538 12th Ave
Seattle, WA 98122-3908

Telephone: (206) 724-0660
Internet Homepage: eltana.com
Company Email: stephen@eltana.com
Type of Business: Chain Restaurant Operator
Year Founded: 2010
Total Units: 3
Trade Names: Eltana Wood-Fired Bagel Cafe (3)
Company-Owned Units: 3
Primary Menu: Bagels (3)
Areas of Operation: WA
Type of Foodservice: Fast Casual (3)

Key Personnel
DANIEL LEVIN - Partner Food and Beverage
STEPHEN BROWN - Partner Administration

Espresso Vivace, Inc.
1122 E Pike St
Seattle, WA 98122-3916

Telephone: (206) 860-5869
Fax Number: (206) 860-1567
Internet Homepage: espressovivace.com
Company Email: info@espressovivace.com
Type of Business: Chain Restaurant Operator
Year Founded: 1992
Total Units: 3
Trade Names: Alley 24 (1); Brix (1); Sidewalk Bar (1)
Company-Owned Units: 3
Primary Menu: Coffee (3)
Areas of Operation: WA
Type of Foodservice: Fast Casual (3)

Key Personnel
DAVID SCHOMER - Co-Founder; Manager Quality Assurance
KASEY FRIX - General Manager; General Buyer

Ethan Stowell Restaurants
2622 NW Market St Ste A
Seattle, WA 98107-4106

Telephone: (206) 588-0030
Internet Homepage: ballardpizzacompany.com; ethanstowellrestaurants.com; goldfinchtavern.com
Company Email: info@ethanstowellrestaurants.com
Type of Business: Chain Restaurant Operator
Total Units: 15
Trade Names: Ballard Pizza Company (3); Bramling Cross (1); Cortina (1); Goldfinch Tavern (1); How to Cook a Wolf (1); Marine Hardware (1); Mkt. (1); Red Cow (1); Rione XIII (1); Staple & Fancy (1); Super Bueno (1); Tavolata (2)
Company-Owned Units: 15
Primary Menu: American (3); French/Continental (1); Italian (6); Pizza (3); Seafood (1)
Areas of Operation: WA
Type of Foodservice: Casual Dining (15)

Key Personnel
ETHAN STOWELL - Co-Founder; CEO; Partner; Executive Chef; General Buyer
SENNEN DAVID - VP Marketing; Director Food and Beverage
MICHAEL GIFFORD - Executive Chef
DAVID GLASS - Executive Chef
KYL HASELBAUER - Executive Chef
JACE JORGENSEN - Executive Chef
WILL RICHEY - Executive Chef
BRANDEN KAROW - Director Culinary Development
SANDY SMITH - Director Human Resources
MICHAEL PAGANA - Director Operations
GARY SILVER - Director Operations
ANAIS CUSTER - Manager Restaurant Operations
BRANDON GILLESPIE - Manager Division
GABRIEL HODGES - Manager Restaurant Operations
MARSHALL NALL - Manager
MEG POSEY - Manager Restaurant Operations
HEATHER PONCET - Manager Restaurant Operations
DAN RODGERS - Manager Restaurant Operations
JEFF STEINER - Manager Restaurant Operations
SAM WILSON - Manager Restaurant Operations
PAUL SOMMER - Manager

Evergreens
823 3rd Ave Ste 107
Seattle, WA 98104-1613

Telephone: (206) 973-4400
Internet Homepage: evergreens.com
Company Email: info@evergreens.com
Type of Business: Chain Restaurant Operator
Internet Order Processing: Yes
Total Units: 26
Trade Names: Evergreens (17); Garden Bar by Evergreens (9)
Company-Owned Units: 26
Primary Menu: Health Foods (26)
Projected Openings: 2
Areas of Operation: OR, WA
Type of Foodservice: Fast Casual (26)

Key Personnel
TODD FISHMAN - CEO; Partner
IAN COURTNAGE - CEO
ANA CHAUD - VP Business Development
STEPHANIE BILLS - Director Marketing

Ezell's Famous Chicken
501 23rd Ave
Seattle, WA 98122-6026

Telephone: (206) 324-4141
Internet Homepage: ezellschicken.com
Type of Business: Chain Restaurant Operator
Total Units: 13
Trade Names: Ezell's Famous Chicken (13)
Company-Owned Units: 13
Primary Menu: Chicken (13)
Areas of Operation: WA
Type of Foodservice: Fast Casual (13)

Key Personnel
LEWIS RUDD - Co-Founder; CEO; President
FAYE STEPHENS - Co-Founder
DARNELL RUDD - Co-Founder
RAJAH ANDERSON - Director Marketing

Fainting Goat Gelato
1903 N 45th St
Seattle, WA 98103-6804

Telephone: (206) 327-9459
Internet Homepage: faintinggoatseattle.com
Company Email: info@faintinggoatseattle.com
Type of Business: Chain Restaurant Operator
Year Founded: 2009
Total Units: 2
Trade Names: Fainting Goat Gelato (2)
Company-Owned Units: 2
Primary Menu: Snacks (2)
Areas of Operation: WA
Type of Foodservice: Quick Serve (2)

Key Personnel
YALCIN ATAMAN - Partner; General Buyer
SEVIM ATAMAN - Partner

Ferd'nand LLC
1531 Melrose Ave
Seattle, WA 98122-3762

Telephone: (206) 623-5882
Internet Homepage: barferdinandseattle.com; sitkaandspruce.com
Company Email: info@sitkaandspruce.com
Type of Business: Chain Restaurant Operator
Total Units: 4
Trade Names: Bar Ferdinand (1); Sitka & Spruce (1); The Corson Building (1); The London Plane (1)
Company-Owned Units: 4
Primary Menu: American (4)
Areas of Operation: WA
Type of Foodservice: Casual Dining (3); Fine Dining (1)

Key Personnel
MATT DILLON - Owner; Executive Chef
KATHY MISHIMA - Manager Operations

Fire & Vine Hospitality
2701 1st Ave Ste 300
Seattle, WA 98121

Telephone: (206) 352-1450
Fax Number: (206) 352-1539
Internet Homepage: elgaucho.com
Company Email: info@elgaucho.com
Type of Business: Chain Restaurant Operator
Year Founded: 1996
Total Sales: $64,860,000 (e)
Alcohol Sales: 40%
Number of Employees: 350
Average Check: Lunch(34); Dinner(78)
Internet Order Processing: Yes
Internet Sales: 1.00%
Total Units: 10
Trade Names: Aerlume (1); Aqua by El Gaucho (1); Crossbuck Brewing (1); El Gaucho (5); Walla Walla Steak Co. (1); Yellowhawk Resort (1)
Company-Owned Units: 10
Preferred Square Footage: 5,500; 6,000
Preferred Location Types: Freestanding; Hotel/Motel; Mobile Unit; Strip Mall
Alcohol Served: Beer, Wine, Liquor
Primary Menu: American (2); Miscellaneous (1); Seafood (1); Steak (6)
Areas of Operation: OR, WA
Type of Foodservice: Casual Dining (2); Fine Dining (8)
Primary Distributors: (Food) SYSCO Food Services of Seattle Inc., KENT, WA

Key Personnel
TERIANNE BROYLES - General Manager
TONY CAPRA - General Manager
MICHAEL JORDAN - Executive Chef
JESUS BOITES - Executive Chef
COOPER MILLS - Director Operations; General Buyer
ZACH DUNN - Manager Marketing, Social Media

Fuel Coffee
610 19th Ave E
Seattle, WA 98112-4009

Telephone: (206) 329-4700
Internet Homepage: fuelcoffeeseattle.com
Company Email: art@fuelcoffeeseattle.com
Type of Business: Chain Restaurant Operator
Total Units: 3
Trade Names: Fuel Coffee (3)
Company-Owned Units: 3
Primary Menu: Snacks (3)
Areas of Operation: WA
Type of Foodservice: Fast Casual (3)

Key Personnel
DANI CONE - Owner; General Buyer
DANIELLE HULTON - Owner
MARA WREDE - General Manager

Fuji Bakery
1030 Elliott Ave W
Seattle, WA 98119-3610

Telephone: (206) 216-3616
Internet Homepage: fujibakeryinc.com
Company Email: info@fujibakeryinc.com
Type of Business: Chain Restaurant Operator
Year Founded: 2009
Total Units: 3
Trade Names: Fuji Bakery (3)
Company-Owned Units: 3
Primary Menu: Snacks (3)
Projected Openings: 1
Areas of Operation: WA
Type of Foodservice: Quick Serve (3)
Notes: A French / France-meets-Japan bakery.

Key Personnel
SUSIEN LEE - Owner; Executive Chef; General Buyer
CHARLES CARNEY - Specialist Transportation

Great Western Pacific Inc.
1301 Alaskan Way
Seattle, WA 98101-2013

Telephone: (206) 623-8600
Fax Number: (206) 343-9173
Internet Homepage:
 thefishermansrestaurant.com;
 thecrabpotseattle.com
Type of Business: Chain Restaurant Operator
Year Founded: 1972
Total Sales: $27,380,000 (e)
Alcohol Sales: 20%
Number of Employees: 208
Average Check: Lunch(24); Dinner(60)
Internet Order Processing: Yes
Total Units: 5
Trade Names: The Crab Pot (3); The Fishermans Restaurant & Bar (2)
Company-Owned Units: 6
Preferred Location Types: Other
Alcohol Served: Beer, Wine, Liquor
Primary Menu: Seafood (5)
Areas of Operation: CA, WA
Type of Foodservice: Casual Dining (5)
Catering Services: Yes
Primary Distributors: (Full Line) SYSCO Food Services of Seattle Inc., KENT, WA

Key Personnel
HAL E. GRIFFITH - President; Executive Chef; Director Menu Development; General Buyer

Green Leaf Vietnamese Restaurant
418 8th Ave S
Seattle, WA 98104-3002

Telephone: (206) 340-1388
Internet Homepage: greenleaftaste.com
Type of Business: Chain Restaurant Operator
Year Founded: 1993
Total Units: 3
Trade Names: Green Leaf (3)
Company-Owned Units: 3
Preferred Location Types: Downtown
Primary Menu: Asian (3)
Projected Openings: 1
Areas of Operation: WA
Type of Foodservice: Casual Dining (3)

Key Personnel
PETER KUANG - Owner; Executive Chef

Heavy Restaurant Group
120 Lakeside Ave Ste 300
Seattle, WA 98122

Telephone: (206) 838-3852
Internet Homepage: barriorestaurant.com; castiron-studios.com; heavyrestaurantgroup.com; lotno3.com; meetthemooncafe.com; purplecafe.com; thecommonscafe.com
Company Email: info@heavyrg.com
Type of Business: Chain Restaurant Operator
Year Founded: 2001
Total Sales: $7,763,000 (e)
Total Units: 8
Trade Names: Barrio (1); Claret (1); Fiasco (1); Meet The Moon (1); Pablo y Pablo (1); Purple (2); The Commons (1)
Company-Owned Units: 8
Primary Menu: American (4); Italian (2); Mexican (2)
Areas of Operation: WA
Type of Foodservice: Casual Dining (8)

Key Personnel
LARRY KUROFSKY - Founder; CEO
KAREN GIBSON - CFO
WHITNEY B - General Manager
LEAH OPINIANO-BUI - Director Human Resources
BETHANY KERSEY - Director Design
TAHLIA BOLDEN - Manager Customer Service
CHRISTINA COSTANZO - Manager Customer Service
LIBBY ISENMANN - Manager Event Planning
TOBEY LAYNE - Manager Bakery
JESSICA TRUJILLO - Administrator Accounting
KATHERINE GROESBECK - Designer

Herkimer Coffee
7320 Greenwood Ave N
Seattle, WA 98103-5042

Telephone: (206) 784-0202
Internet Homepage: herkimercoffee.com
Type of Business: Chain Restaurant Operator
Year Founded: 2003
Total Units: 3
Trade Names: Herkimer Coffee (3)
Company-Owned Units: 3
Primary Menu: Snacks (3)
Areas of Operation: WA
Type of Foodservice: Fast Casual (3)

Key Personnel
MICHAEL PRINS - Owner; General Buyer

Hilltop Ale Houses
2129 Queen Anne Ave N
Seattle, WA 98109-2310

Telephone: (206) 285-3877
Internet Homepage: seattlealehouses.com
Type of Business: Chain Restaurant Operator
Year Founded: 1994
Total Sales: $4,597,000 (e)
Alcohol Sales: 20%
Number of Employees: 36
Average Check: Lunch(18); Dinner(24)
Total Units: 3
Trade Names: 74th St Ale House (1); Columbia City Ale House (1); Hilltop Ale House (1)
Company-Owned Units: 3
Preferred Square Footage: 5,500
Preferred Location Types: Freestanding
Alcohol Served: Beer, Wine, Liquor
Primary Menu: American (3)
Areas of Operation: WA
Type of Foodservice: Casual Dining (3)

Key Personnel
JEFF EAGAN - Owner
CATHY CHRISTOPHER - Executive Chef; General Buyer

Homegrown Sustainable Sandwich Shop
120 Lakeside Ave
Seattle, WA 98122

Telephone: (877) 567-9240
Internet Homepage: eathomegrown.com
Company Email: help@eathomegrown.com
Type of Business: Chain Restaurant Operator
Year Founded: 2009
Total Sales: $8,330,000 (e)
Total Units: 9
Trade Names: Homegrown Sustainable Sandwich Shop (9)
Company-Owned Units: 9
Primary Menu: Sandwiches/Deli (9)
Areas of Operation: CA, WA
Type of Foodservice: Fast Casual (9)

Key Personnel
BRAD GILLIS - Founder; CEO
CHAD COTTER - Director Catering
AINSLIE CLARK - Director Finance

Hue Ky Mi Gia Corp
1207 S Jackson St Ste 101
Seattle, WA 98144

Telephone: (206) 568-1268
Internet Homepage: huekymigia.com; saltedseaseattle.com
Company Email: info@saltedseaseattle.com
Type of Business: Chain Restaurant Operator
Year Founded: 2009
Total Units: 6
Trade Names: Hue Ky Mi Gia (2); Hue Ky Mi Gia (CenturyLink Field) (3); Salted Sea (1)
Company-Owned Units: 6
Primary Menu: Chinese (5); Seafood (1)
Areas of Operation: WA
Type of Foodservice: Casual Dining (3); Quick

Serve (3)

Key Personnel
HUY TAT - President; Executive Chef; General Buyer

Investments Property Acquisitions LLC
4720 California Ave SW
Seattle, WA 98116-4413

Telephone: (206) 932-8695
Internet Homepage: elliottbaybrewing.com
Company Email: info@brotherbarrel.com
Type of Business: Chain Restaurant Operator
Year Founded: 1994
Total Units: 4
Trade Names: Brother Barrel (1); Elliott Bay Brewhouse & Pub (3)
Company-Owned Units: 4
Primary Menu: American (4)
Areas of Operation: WA
Type of Foodservice: Casual Dining (4)

Key Personnel
TODD CARDEN - Partner
BRENT NORTON - Partner
KERRY WHITE - Executive Chef
DOUG HINDMAN - Manager Operations

Ivar's Inc.
1001 Alaskan Way Ste 109
Seattle, WA 98104-1028

Telephone: (206) 587-6500
Fax Number: (206) 624-4895
Internet Homepage: ivars.com
Company Email: webmail@keepclam.com
Type of Business: Chain Restaurant Operator
Year Founded: 1938
Total Sales: $58,860,000 (e)
Alcohol Sales: 15%
Number of Employees: 840
Average Check: Lunch(14); Dinner(14)
Internet Order Processing: Yes
Internet Sales: 2.00%
Total Units: 28
Trade Names: Ivar's Acres of Clams (1); Ivar's Mukilteo Landing (1); Ivar's Salmon House (1); Ivar's Seafood Bar (21); Ivar's Sports Venue (4)
Company-Owned Units: 28
Preferred Square Footage: 1,500; 4,000
Preferred Location Types: Airports; Freestanding; Regional Mall; Stadiums
Alcohol Served: Wine
Primary Menu: Seafood (28)
Areas of Operation: CA, WA
Type of Foodservice: Casual Dining (2); Quick Serve (26)

Primary Distributors: (Full Line) SYSCO Food Services of Seattle Inc., KENT, WA
Notes: In addition to the Ivar's restaurants and seafood bars, the company operates concession locations in various sporting venues in the Puget Sound area.

Key Personnel
BOB DONEGAN - CEO; President; CFO; VP Finance, Loss Prevention, Marketing; Treasurer
JIM SEAVER - VP Real Estate; Director Franchise Development
JUAN GARCIA - Executive Chef
PATRICK YEAROUT - Director Innovation
SABRIE EVANS - Director Human Resources
CARL TAYLOR - Director Operations; Regional Manager
SODANEY PROM - Director Procurement
CHRIS LEWARK - Director Marketing, Sales
EDGAR GARCIA - Manager Accounting, Purchasing

Jai Thai Restaurant
3423 Fremont Ave N
Seattle, WA 98103-8811

Telephone: (206) 632-7060
Fax Number: (206) 547-1593
Internet Homepage: jaithairestaurant.com
Type of Business: Chain Restaurant Operator
Year Founded: 1994
Total Sales: $4,645,000 (e)
Alcohol Sales: 3%
Number of Employees: 10
Average Check: Lunch(10); Dinner(16)
Total Units: 2
Trade Names: Jai Thai Restaurant (2)
Company-Owned Units: 2
Alcohol Served: Beer, Wine, Liquor
Primary Menu: Thai (2)
Areas of Operation: WA
Type of Foodservice: Fine Dining (2)
Primary Distributors: (Full Line) SYSCO Food Services of Seattle Inc., KENT, WA

Key Personnel
DICK NELSON - Owner; General Manager; Executive Chef

Los Locos LLC
2320 NW Market St
Seattle, WA 98107-4026

Telephone: (206) 789-0516
Internet Homepage: laislacuisine.com
Company Email: info@laislacuisine.com
Type of Business: Chain Restaurant Operator
Total Units: 2
Trade Names: La Isla Cuisine (2)
Company-Owned Units: 2

Primary Menu: Latin American/Cuban (2)
Areas of Operation: WA
Type of Foodservice: Casual Dining (2)

Key Personnel
ALFONSO GONZALEZ - Partner; General Buyer
JASON MIKOS - Partner

Macrina Bakery & Cafe
2408 1st Ave
Seattle, WA 98121-1312

Telephone: (206) 448-4032
Fax Number: (206) 374-1782
Internet Homepage: macrinabakery.com
Company Email: contactus@macrinabakery.com
Type of Business: Chain Restaurant Operator
Year Founded: 1993
Total Sales: $7,270,000 (e)
Number of Employees: 15
Average Check: Breakfast(12); Lunch(12);
Total Units: 5
Trade Names: Macrina Bakery & Cafe (5)
Company-Owned Units: 5
Alcohol Served: Beer, Wine
Primary Menu: Snacks (5)
Areas of Operation: WA
Type of Foodservice: Fast Casual (5)

Key Personnel
LESLIE MACKIE - Owner; General Buyer
CRYSTAL KITCHIN - General Manager

Maria Hines Restaurants
1411 N 45th St
Seattle, WA 98103-6706

Telephone: (206) 633-0801
Internet Homepage: agrodolcerestaurant.net; mariahinesrestaurants.com; tilthrestaurant.com
Type of Business: Chain Restaurant Operator
Year Founded: 2006
Total Units: 2
Trade Names: Agrodolce (1); Tilth (1)
Company-Owned Units: 2
Primary Menu: American (1); Italian (1)
Areas of Operation: WA
Type of Foodservice: Casual Dining (2)

Key Personnel
ALEXANDER SEVERN - General Manager
THOMAS LITRENTA - Executive Chef
KURT ARGYS - Director Catering

Marination
1660 Harbor Ave SW
Seattle, WA 98126-2028

Telephone: (206) 328-8226
Internet Homepage: marinationmobile.com; supersixseattle.com
Company Email: eat@marinationmobile.com
Type of Business: Chain Restaurant Operator
Total Units: 4
Trade Names: Marination (1); Marination Ma Kai (1); Marination Station (1); Super Six (1)
Company-Owned Units: 4
Primary Menu: American (4)
Areas of Operation: WA
Type of Foodservice: Fast Casual (4)

Key Personnel
KAMALA SAXTON - Partner; General Buyer
DAVID LAZO - Business Manager

Marles Inc.
3040 NE 45th St
Seattle, WA 98105-5002

Telephone: (206) 522-2939
Fax Number: (206) 400-1585
Internet Homepage: burgermaster.biz
Company Email: bgrmaster@aol.com
Type of Business: Chain Restaurant Operator
Year Founded: 1952
Systemwide Sales: $9,314,000 (e)
Total Sales: $7,096,000 (e)
Number of Employees: 110
Average Check: Breakfast(8); Lunch(10); Dinner(10)
Total Units: 6
Trade Names: The Burgermaster (6)
Company-Owned Units: 4
Units Franchised To: 2
Preferred Square Footage: 2,500
Preferred Location Types: Freestanding
Primary Menu: Hamburger (6)
Areas of Operation: WA
Type of Foodservice: Quick Serve (6)
Primary Distributors: (Full Line) US Foods, FIFE, WA

Key Personnel
BOB JENSEN - President; Exec VP; Treasurer; Manager Operations
MELANIE VEAZEY - CFO; Director Finance, Human Resources, Franchise Development; Manager Facility/Maintenance, Information Systems, Loss Prevention, Supply Chain, Real Estate, Design, Menu Development; General Buyer

Mezcaleria Oaxaca
2123 Queen Anne Ave N
Seattle, WA 98109-2310

Telephone: (206) 216-4446
Internet Homepage: lacartadeoaxaca.com; mezcaleriaoaxaca.com
Type of Business: Chain Restaurant Operator
Total Units: 3
Trade Names: La Carte de Oaxaca (1); Mezcaleria Oaxaca (2)
Company-Owned Units: 3
Primary Menu: Mexican (3)
Areas of Operation: WA
Type of Foodservice: Casual Dining (3)

Key Personnel
ROBERTO DOMINGUEZ - Founder; Executive Chef; General Buyer

Midwood, Inc.
1415 NW 70th St
Seattle, WA 98117-5340

Telephone: (206) 838-1960
Internet Homepage: delanceyseattle.com; essexbarseattle.com
Type of Business: Chain Restaurant Operator
Total Units: 2
Trade Names: Delancey (1); Essex (1)
Company-Owned Units: 2
Primary Menu: American (1); Pizza (1)
Areas of Operation: WA
Type of Foodservice: Casual Dining (2)

Key Personnel
BRANDON PETTIT - Partner; Executive Chef
MOLLY WIZENBERG - Partner; General Buyer

Milkwood & Co.
1510 E Olive Way
Seattle, WA 98122-2130

Telephone: (323) 577-3045
Internet Homepage: milkwoodcompany.com; neontacoseattle.com; sunsetfriedchicken.com; tortascondesa.com
Company Email: info@neontacoseattle.com
Type of Business: Chain Restaurant Operator
Total Units: 3
Trade Names: Neon Taco (1); Sunset (1); Tortas Condesa (1)
Company-Owned Units: 3
Primary Menu: Mexican (2); Sandwiches/Deli (1)
Areas of Operation: WA
Type of Foodservice: Fast Casual (3)

Key Personnel
MONICA DIMAS - Owner; Executive Chef; General Buyer

Molly Moon's Homemade Ice Cream
917 E Pine St
Seattle, WA 98122-3843

Telephone: (206) 708-7947
Internet Homepage: mollymoon.com
Company Email: info@mollymoon.com
Type of Business: Chain Restaurant Operator
Year Founded: 2008
Total Units: 7
Trade Names: Molly Moon's (7)
Company-Owned Units: 8
Primary Menu: Snacks (7)
Areas of Operation: WA
Type of Foodservice: Fast Casual (7)

Key Personnel
MOLLY M. NEITZEL - CEO; Owner; Executive Chef
DENISE BROWN - Director Finance, Human Resources
KATIE COLE - Director Marketing, Outside Sales
KEVIN NEITZEL - Manager Facility/Maintenance
ZACH DEMERS - Manager South Region

Mr. Gyros
256 NE 45th St
Seattle, WA 98105-6148

Telephone: (206) 535-8841
Internet Homepage: mrgyroseattle.com
Type of Business: Chain Restaurant Operator
Total Units: 3
Trade Names: Mr. Gyros (3)
Company-Owned Units: 3
Primary Menu: Sandwiches/Deli (3)
Areas of Operation: WA
Type of Foodservice: Fast Casual (3)

Key Personnel
SAMMY ARSHEED - Partner; General Buyer
JONI ARSHEED - Partner; Executive Chef

Neighborhood Grills
7200 E Green Lake Dr N
Seattle, WA 98115-5302

Telephone: (206) 588-4760
Fax Number: (206) 466-6862
Internet Homepage: neighborhoodgrills.com
Type of Business: Chain Restaurant Operator

Total Units: 10
Trade Names: Bremerton Bar & Grill (1); Eastlake Bar & Grill (1); Lake Forest Bar & Grill (1); Lunchbox Labratory (5); Maple Valley Bar & Grill (1); Raconteur(1)
Company-Owned Units: 10
Primary Menu: American (10)
Areas of Operation: WA
Type of Foodservice: Casual Dining (10)

Key Personnel
JOHN SCHMIDT - CEO
STACI MOLZAHN - CFO

Opper Melang Restaurant Group
5412 Ballard Ave NW
Seattle, WA 98107

Telephone: (206) 297-2673
Internet Homepage: ballardannex.com; matadorrestaurants.com; oppermelang.com; southlandwhiskeykitchen.com
Company Email: info@oppermelang.com
Type of Business: Chain Restaurant Operator
Year Founded: 2004
Total Sales: $7,417,000 (e)
Total Units: 8
Trade Names: The Matador (8)
Company-Owned Units: 8
Primary Menu: American (0); Mexican (8); Seafood (0)
Areas of Operation: CO, ID, OR, WA
Type of Foodservice: Casual Dining (8)

Key Personnel
NATHAN OPPER - Co-Founder; General Buyer
ZAK MELANG - Co-Founder; Designer
IAN BROUSSEAU - President; CFO

Pagliacci Pizza
423 E Pike St
Seattle, WA 98122-3615

Telephone: (206) 652-0877
Fax Number: (206) 652-0808
Internet Homepage: pagliacci.com
Company Email: bigcheese@pagliacci.com
Type of Business: Chain Restaurant Operator
Year Founded: 1979
Total Sales: $24,750,000 (e)
Alcohol Sales: 10%
Number of Employees: 650
Average Check: Lunch(12); Dinner(18)
Internet Order Processing: Yes
Total Units: 25
Trade Names: Pagliacci Pizza (25)
Company-Owned Units: 22
Units Franchised To: 3
Preferred Square Footage: 1,500
Preferred Location Types: Freestanding
Alcohol Served: Beer, Wine
Primary Menu: Pizza (25)
Areas of Operation: WA
Type of Foodservice: Casual Dining (25)
Catering Services: Yes
Primary Distributors: (Full Line) Food Services of America, KENT, WA

Key Personnel
MATT GALVIN - President; Partner; Director Marketing, Design, Catering; General Buyer
PAT MCDONALD - Partner; Director Facility/Maintenance, Information Systems, Real Estate, Human Resources
SCOTT FRANCE - CFO; Controller; Director Operations, Purchasing, Menu Development
JEFF WOODRUFF - VP; Director Operations
BRIDGET DOUGHERTY - General Manager
QUINN RESSLER - General Manager
LOREN SMOOT - General Manager
JULIA THOMAS - Executive Chef
JOHN CLIFFORD - Senior Director Development-Training
SHELLEY MCNULTY - Director Marketing
DON VILLEGAS - Associate Manager
SAM EISENHOOD - Coordinator Catering
PHILLIP RIVERA - Representative Customer Service

Pecado Bueno
4307 Fremont Ave N
Seattle, WA 98103-7223

Telephone: (206) 457-8837
Internet Homepage: pecadobueno.com
Company Email: info@pecadobueno.com
Type of Business: Chain Restaurant Operator
Internet Order Processing: Yes
Total Units: 4
Trade Names: Pecado Bueno (4)
Company-Owned Units: 4
Primary Menu: Mexican (4)
Areas of Operation: WA
Type of Foodservice: Casual Dining (4)

Key Personnel
JAMES SCHMIDT - Owner; General Buyer
WILLIAM H. BUENO - CFO
DANA NILSON - Director Sales, Catering

Plum Restaurants
1429 12th Ave
Seattle, WA 98122-3905

Telephone: (206) 838-5333
Internet Homepage: plumbistro.com
Type of Business: Chain Restaurant Operator
Total Units: 4
Trade Names: Plum Bistro (1); Plum Pantry (1); Quickie Too (1); Sugar Plum (1)
Company-Owned Units: 4
Primary Menu: American (2); Sandwiches/Deli (1); Snacks (1)
Areas of Operation: WA
Type of Foodservice: Casual Dining (2); Fast Casual (2)

Key Personnel
MAKINI HOWELL - Owner; Executive Chef; General Buyer

Portage Bay Foods, LLC
4130 Roosevelt Way NE
Seattle, WA 98105-6436

Telephone: (206) 547-8230
Internet Homepage: portagebaycafe.com
Company Email: office@portagebaycafe.com
Type of Business: Chain Restaurant Operator
Total Units: 4
Trade Names: Portage Bay Cafe (4)
Company-Owned Units: 4
Primary Menu: American (4)
Areas of Operation: WA
Type of Foodservice: Casual Dining (4)

Key Personnel
AMY F. GUNNAR - Partner; General Buyer
JOHN GUNNAR - Partner; General Buyer

Red Mill Restaurants, Inc.
312 N 67th St
Seattle, WA 98103-5210

Telephone: (206) 783-6362
Internet Homepage: redmillburgers.com
Type of Business: Chain Restaurant Operator
Total Units: 3
Trade Names: Red Mill Burgers (2); Red Mill Totem House (1)
Company-Owned Units: 3
Primary Menu: Hamburger (3)
Areas of Operation: WA
Type of Foodservice: Casual Dining (2); Fast Casual (1)

Key Personnel
JEANINE SHEPHERD - Partner; General Buyer
MICHAEL SHEPHERD - Partner; General Buyer

Relay Restaurant Group
3506 Stone Way N
Seattle, WA 98103-8924

Telephone: (206) 632-5685
Internet Homepage: joulerestaurant.com; revelseattle.com; troveseattle.com
Company Email: info@joulerestaurant.com
Type of Business: Chain Restaurant Operator

Internet Order Processing: Yes
Total Units: 4
Trade Names: Joule (1); Revel (1); Revelry (1); Trove (1)
Company-Owned Units: 4
Primary Menu: Asian (4)
Areas of Operation: WA
Type of Foodservice: Casual Dining (4)

Key Personnel
SEIF CHIRCHI - Partner; Executive Chef
RACHEL YANG - Partner; Executive Chef; General Buyer

Restaurants Unlimited Inc.
411 1st Ave S Ste 200
Seattle, WA 98104-3094

Telephone: (206) 634-0550
Fax Number: (206) 632-3533
Internet Homepage: kincaids.com; palomino.com; r-u-i.com; restaurantsunlimited.com
Company Email: gb@r-u-i.com
Type of Business: Chain Restaurant Operator
Year Founded: 1968
Total Sales: $90,080,000 (e)
Alcohol Sales: 30%
Number of Employees: 1,530
Average Check: Lunch(24); Dinner(48)
Internet Order Processing: Yes
Internet Sales: 2.00%
Total Units: 18
Trade Names: Clinkerdagger (1); Cutters Crabhouse (1); Henry's Tavern (2); Horatio's (1); Kincaid's (4); Maggie Bluffs (1); Manzana (1); Palisade (1); Portland City Grill (1); Scott's Bar & Grill (1); Simon & Seafort's (1); Skates on the Bay (1); Stanford's (1); Stanley & Seafort's (1)
Company-Owned Units: 18
Preferred Square Footage: 10,000
Preferred Location Types: Downtown; Freestanding; Office Complex; Regional Mall
Alcohol Served: Beer, Wine, Liquor
Primary Menu: American (6); Seafood (5); Steak/Seafood (7)
Projected Remodelings: 3
Areas of Operation: AK, AZ, CA, IN, MN, OH, OR, TX, VA, WA
Type of Foodservice: Casual Dining (18)
Catering Services: Yes
Parent Company: Landry's Restaurants Inc., HOUSTON, TX

Key Personnel
NORMAN ABDALLAH - CEO
SCOTT SMITH - COO
CHARLES BOCKES - Senior Director Facility/Maintenance, Construction
LAURA ADAMS - Director Catering
MICHAEL MEYER - Manager Food and Beverage

Sam's Tavern
1024 E Pike St
Seattle, WA 98122-3819

Telephone: (206) 397-3344
Internet Homepage: samstavernseattle.com
Type of Business: Chain Restaurant Operator
Year Founded: 2013
Total Units: 3
Company-Owned Units: 3
Primary Menu: Hamburger (3)
Areas of Operation: WA
Type of Foodservice: Casual Dining (3)

Key Personnel
JAMES SNYDER III - Owner; General Buyer

Samurai Noodle Inc
4138 University Way NE
Seattle, WA 98105-6214

Telephone: (206) 547-1774
Internet Homepage: samurainoodle.com
Type of Business: Chain Restaurant Operator
Total Units: 3
Trade Names: Samurai Noodles (3)
Company-Owned Units: 3
Primary Menu: Japanese (3)
Areas of Operation: WA
Type of Foodservice: Fast Casual (3)
Notes: Owner Phil Sancken is also a partner in the Seattle-based Caffè Appassionato chain.

Key Personnel
RYO IZAWA - Founder
PHIL SANCKEN - Owner; General Buyer

Sea Creatures Restaurants
1743 Ballard Ave NW
Seattle, WA 98107-4844

Telephone: (206) 395-9227
Internet Homepage: eatseacreatures.com
Company Email: info@eatseacreatures.com
Type of Business: Chain Restaurant Operator
Total Units: 6
Trade Names: Bar Melusine (1); Barnacle (1); Bateau (1); General Porpoise Doughnuts (1); The Walrus and the Carpenter (1); The Whale Wins (1)
Company-Owned Units: 6
Primary Menu: American (2); Seafood (3); Snacks (1)
Areas of Operation: WA
Type of Foodservice: Casual Dining (5); Fast Casual (1)

Key Personnel
RENEE ERICKSON - Partner; Executive Chef
JEREMY PRICE - Partner; General Buyer; Designer
CHAD DALE - Partner; Business Manager; Manager Real Estate Development
IRA GERLICH - Partner
YURIKO SAY - General Manager; Store Manager
JAMIE IRENE - General Manager; Store Manager
JEFF BUTLER - General Manager; Store Manager
ALEX PEMOULIE - Director Finance

Seattle Best Curry LLC
406 5th Ave S
Seattle, WA 98104-2806

Telephone: (206) 327-4838
Internet Homepage: wannyen.com
Company Email: seattlecurryman@gmail.com
Type of Business: Chain Restaurant Operator
Total Units: 1
Trade Names: Wann Yen (1)
Company-Owned Units: 1
Primary Menu: Thai (1)
Areas of Operation: WA
Type of Foodservice: Fast Casual (1)

Key Personnel
DANIEL CHEAH - Owner; General Buyer

Seattle Culinary Academy
1701 Broadway Room BE2120
Seattle, WA 98122-2413

Telephone: (206) 934-5424
Fax Number: (206) 934-4323
Internet Homepage: seattleculinary.com
Company Email: seattleculinary@seattlecolleges.edu
Type of Business: Culinary Schools
Areas of Operation: WA

Key Personnel
REGIS BERNARD - Executive Chef; General Buyer

Seattle Eats
3601 S McClellan St
Seattle, WA 98144-5615

Telephone: (206) 322-3287
Internet Homepage: seattle-eats.com
Company Email: mioposto@seattle-eats.com
Type of Business: Chain Restaurant Operator
Internet Order Processing: Yes
Total Units: 3

Trade Names: Mioposto (3)
Company-Owned Units: 3
Primary Menu: Italian (3)
Areas of Operation: WA
Type of Foodservice: Casual Dining (3)

Key Personnel
TIAH H. HARDY - Director Food and Beverage

Seattle's Little Italy
625 1st Ave
Seattle, WA 98104-2274

Telephone: (206) 622-7688
Internet Homepage: seattleslittleitaly.com
Company Email: info@seattleslittleitaly.com
Type of Business: Chain Restaurant Operator
Year Founded: 1992
Total Sales: $5,125,000 (e)
Alcohol Sales: 10%
Number of Employees: 45
Average Check: Lunch(10); Dinner(30)
Total Units: 3
Trade Names: Al Boccalino (1); Cafe Bengodi (1); Che Sara Sara (1)
Company-Owned Units: 3
Preferred Location Types: Freestanding
Alcohol Served: Beer, Wine, Liquor
Primary Menu: Italian (3)
Areas of Operation: WA
Type of Foodservice: Casual Dining (3)
Catering Services: Yes
Primary Distributors: (Food) Pacific Food Importers, KENT, WA

Key Personnel
ANGELA WILLIAMS - President; Owner

Skillet Management, LLC
1400 E Union St
Seattle, WA 98122-4150

Telephone: (206) 512-2001
Internet Homepage: skilletfood.com
Company Email: info@skilletcapitolhill.com
Type of Business: Chain Restaurant Operator
Total Units: 4
Trade Names: Skillet Diner (3); The Skillet Counter (1)
Company-Owned Units: 4
Primary Menu: American (4)
Areas of Operation: WA
Type of Foodservice: Casual Dining (3); Fast Casual (1)

Key Personnel
ANN DOWNS - President
GREG PETRILLO - CFO
NICK NOVELLO - Executive Chef
DAVID VAN GELDER - Executive Chef

CRELLIN PAULING - Director Operations
BOB BOSCH - Manager Finance

Slate Coffee Roasters
5413 6th Ave NW
Seattle, WA 98107-3520

Telephone: (206) 235-6564
Internet Homepage: slatecoffee.com
Company Email: coffeebar@slatecoffee.com
Type of Business: Chain Restaurant Operator
Internet Order Processing: Yes
Total Units: 4
Trade Names: Slate Coffee Roasters (4)
Company-Owned Units: 4
Primary Menu: Snacks (4)
Areas of Operation: WA
Type of Foodservice: Fast Casual (4)

Key Personnel
KEENAN WALKER - Partner; Director Operations
TOMMY PANIGOT - Director

Soprano's Pizza & Pasta LLC
7729 24th Ave NW
Seattle, WA 98117-4412

Telephone: (206) 789-4444
Internet Homepage: sopranos-pizza.com
Type of Business: Chain Restaurant Operator
Internet Order Processing: Yes
Total Units: 4
Trade Names: Soprano's Pizza & Pasta (4)
Company-Owned Units: 4
Primary Menu: Italian (4)
Areas of Operation: WA
Type of Foodservice: Casual Dining (4)

Key Personnel
ERDINC DOGAN - Owner; General Buyer
MIMI DOGAN - Owner

Spain Street LLC
1700 7th Ave
Seattle, WA 98101-1397

Telephone: (206) 659-0737
Internet Homepage: blueacreseafood.com; orfeorestaurant.com; steelheaddiner.com
Type of Business: Chain Restaurant Operator
Total Units: 4
Trade Names: Blueacre Seafood (1); Orfeo (1); Steelhead Diner (1); Tempesta (1)
Company-Owned Units: 4
Primary Menu: American (1); Coffee (1); Italian (1); Seafood (1)
Areas of Operation: WA
Type of Foodservice: Casual Dining (2); Fine Dining (1); Quick Serve (1)

Key Personnel
TERRESA DAVIS - Partner; CFO; General Buyer
KEVIN DAVIS - Partner; Executive Chef

Starbucks Corporation
2401 Utah Ave S Ste 800
Seattle, WA 98134-1435

Mailing Address: PO Box 34067, SEATTLE, WA, 98124-1067
Telephone: (206) 447-1575
Fax Number: (206) 447-0828
Internet Homepage: seattlesbest.com; starbucks.com; teavana.com
Company Email: info@starbucks.com
Type of Business: Chain Restaurant Operator
Year Founded: 1971
Systemwide Sales: $41,886,931,000 (e)
Publicly Held: Yes
Total Sales: $37,905,331,000 (e)
Number of Employees: 191,000
Average Check: Breakfast(8); Lunch(8); Dinner(8)
Foodservice Sales: $33,925,271,000 (e)
Internet Order Processing: Yes
Internet Sales: 2.00%
Total Units: 38,058
Trade Names: 15th Avenue Coffee and Tea; Princi; Roy Street Coffee & Tea; Seattle's Best Coffee; Starbucks Coffee; Starbucks Evenings; Starbucks Hear Music Coffeehouse; Starbucks Reserve Roastery and Tasting Room
Company-Owned Units: 19,592
Units Franchised To: 18,466
Preferred Square Footage: 523; 538; 1,000; 1,500
Preferred Location Types: Airports; Community Mall; Convenience Store/Gas Station; Downtown; Freestanding; Grocery Stores; Hotel/Motel; Institution(college/hospital); Kiosk; Lifestyle Center; Mobile Unit; Office Complex; Other; Outlet Mall; Regional Mall; Stadiums; Strip Mall; Travel Plazas
Alcohol Served: Beer, Wine
Primary Menu: Coffee (30,000); Pizza (3)
Projected Openings: 2,000
Areas of Operation: AK, AL, AR, AZ, CA, CO, CT, DC, DE, FL, GA, HI, IA, ID, IL, IN, KS, KY, LA, MA, MD, ME, MI, MN, MO, MS, MT, NC, ND, NE, NH, NJ, NM, NV, NY, OH, OK, OR, PA, PR, RI, SC, SD, TN, TX, UT, VA, VT, WA, WI, WV, WY, AB, BC, MB, NL, NS, ON, QC, SK
Foreign Countries: ARGENTINA; ARUBA; AUSTRALIA; AUSTRIA; BAHAMAS; BAHRAIN; BRAZIL; BRUNEI; BULGARIA; CANADA; CHILE; CHINA; COLOMBIA; COSTA RICA; CURACAO; CYPRUS; CZECH

REPUBLIC; DENMARK; EGYPT; EL SALVADOR; ENGLAND; FRANCE; GERMANY; GREECE; GUATEMALA; HONG KONG; INDONESIA; IRELAND; JAPAN; JORDAN; KUWAIT; LEBANON; MALAYSIA; MEXICO; MONACO; MOROCCO; NEW ZEALAND; NORTHERN IRELAND; OMAN; PANAMA; PERU; POLAND; PORTUGAL; QATAR; ROMANIA; RUSSIA; SAUDI ARABIA; SCOTLAND; SINGAPORE; SOUTH KOREA; SPAIN; SWEDEN; SWITZERLAND; TAIWAN; THAILAND; THE NETHERLANDS; THE PHILIPPINES; TURKEY; UNITED ARAB EMIRATES; VIETNAM; WALES

Type of Foodservice: Quick Serve
Foodservice Management Venues: Business & Industry; College & University; Health Care; Lodging; Transportation
Distribution Centers: MENDEN, NV; YORK, PA; GASTON, SC; AUBURN, WA
Divisional Offices: Starbucks Coffee Canada Inc., NORTH YORK, ON CANADA; Starbucks Western/Pacific Zone, FOUNTAIN VALLEY, CA
Regional Offices: Starbucks Vancouver Regional Office, VANCOUVER, BC CANADA
Notes: Total store counts exclude Teavana retail tea outlets. Foodservice revenue includes sales at company-operated stores, licensing fees & revenue from retail operations. The company also derives approximately 12% of its revenue from foodservice operations & sales of wholesale bean coffee through its specialty sales group, direct response, supermarkets, and Web site. Approximately 6% of retail sales are from coffee-making equipment and whole beans.

Key Personnel

BELINDA WONG - Chairman Division; CEO Division
TAKAFUMI MINAGUCHI - CEO Group, International Division
BRIAN NICCOL - CEO
MOLLY LIU - CEO International
CLIFF BURROWS - President Group, International Division, Division
SARA TRILLING - President Retail Operations, Division
MARK RING - President Latin America, United States
DUNCAN MOIR - President Global Development
TOM TICE - Partner Supply Chain; Director Engineering, Global, Manufacturing
CATHY SMITH - CFO
JILL WALKER - Chief Accounting Officer; Senior VP Finance
BRADY BREWER - Chief Marketing Officer
DENNIS BROCKMAN - Chief Diversity Officer Global; Chief Inclusion Officer Global; Senior VP
TRESSIE LIEBERMAN - Chief Brand Officer
KELLY BENGSTON - Chief Procurement Officer; Senior VP
LIZ MULLER - Chief Design Officer; Senior VP Design
MICHELLE BURNS - Exec VP Global-Coffee/Tea
RACHEL GONZALEZ - Exec VP; Corporate Secretary; General Counsel
ARTHUR VALDEZ - Exec VP Supply Chain, Customer Service
ANDY ADAMS - Senior VP Store Development
TONY GALE - Senior VP Design
JANET LANDERS - Senior VP Information Technology
SANDRA STARK - Senior VP Innovation, Beverages
JENNIFER FRISCH - Senior VP Human Resources
GEORGE DOWDIE - Senior VP Quality Assurance, Food Safety
TOM FERGUSON - Senior VP International Division
SCOTT KELLER - Senior VP Store Development, Design
JULIE EISEN - VP Global Marketing
COLLEEN CHAPMAN - VP Public Relations
MARC MUNSON - VP Finance
SHANA KRUSE - VP Product Strategy, Supply Chain, Store Development
MATT FITCH - VP Digital
VICKY MCMILLAN - VP Manufacturing
VIRGINIA BERGIN - VP Global Development
JULIE BROXSON - VP Human Resources
MELANIE CANTO - VP Transformation
MASSNORI MURAKAMI - VP Tax
TODD TREWHELLA - VP Store Development
ANGEL YU - VP Human Resources
KIM WILLIAMS - VP Store Development
BRAD JONES - VP Technology, Information Technology, Development
DAWN LARSEN - VP Operations, Technology
JAIME RILEY - VP Communications
ERIN SILVOY - VP
GREG SMITH - VP Financial Planning
RAYMOND SILVERSTEIN - VP Operations, Store Development, Global
NANCY BENNETT - Regional VP Southwest Region
ANNA KAKOS - General Counsel; Director Marketing
TOM JONES - General Manager
JESSICA MILLS - Senior Director Business Development
KRISTY CAMERON - Creative Director
MICHAEL LORD - Director Operations, Division
MARY CLARE BARTH - Director Division
STEVE LEGG - Director Risk Management
JOHN CADDEN - Director Store Development
HOLLY HARRIS - Director Operations
SARAH ROGERS - Director Training
STEPHEN BARDIN - Director Strategy, Innovation
GARY SOULE - Director Systems Engineering, Business Development
COLLEEN MANDELL - Director Digital Solutions
MELISSA BUSH - Director Marketing
RUBY AMEGAH - Director Product Development
JEREMY LENZ - Director Finance, Category Management, Innovation
DEBRA DERICKSON - Director Vendor Relations
RUSSELL LOFTIS - Director Facility/Maintenance
AMY POWELL - Director Operations, Integration
ADAM DIAMOND - Director Strategy, Marketing, Division
DAVID ARGENT - Director Operations
LISA BECKMAN - Director Research & Development
MEGAN CAMPBELL - Director Manufacturing
EDDIE CHOW - Director Strategic Planning
JOHN ESTILL - Director Operations
COLLEEN FARLEY DAVIS - Director
SANJA GOULD - Director Public Relations, Business Development
KRISTINE HUTCHINSON - Director Operations, Supply Chain
VIDA KILLIAN - Director Branding, Social Media
ERIN KRISTEK - Director Distribution, Direct Store Delivery
KEVIN LEE - Director Accounting
THAD LUSE - Director Engineering
MEG NYLAND - Director Development, Infrastructure, Systems
LAURA SCHMIDT - Director Compensation
ROB STERN - Director Public Affairs, Human Resources
SUZANNE LYNCH - Director Strategic Planning
MELISSA TUTOR - Director Human Resources
DANIEL WOOD - Director Engineering, Construction, Division
ROB DELLINGER - Director POS/Scanning, Development
JULIE WIETING - Director Accounting, Tax
CASEY O. CASTELLO - Director Customer Service
CAMBRIDGE LIU - Director Consumer Insights
DAN TRACEY - Director Product Development
KRISTI CRAWFORD - Director Store Development
SHANNON DANIEL - Director Technology, Human Resources
STEVE VU - Director Engineering
JEFF DOLAN - Director Store Development
KAREN CASTRO - Director Human Resources
NICK BOWLES - Director Corporate Development
SHAVONDELIA BROWN - Director Corporate Affairs, Real Estate
DAVID CHIANG - Director Category Management, Marketing
BRIAN J DANZIG - Director
PETER FILIPOVIC - Director
ERIC GAAL - Director Business Development
GREG GENTILINI - Director Financial Planning
TRAEGON HON - Director Infrastructure, Security, Corporate Affairs, Global
KATIE JONES - Director Accounting
KIMBERLY KELLERMANN - Director
SCOTT KING - Director Technology, Digital
DEAN KLEIN - Director Global Development

TRACY LAWSON - Director Finance
SANDRA LENNON - Director Human Resources
MEGAN MATHES - Director Digital
NATHAN MAYES - Director Real Estate
RYAN POST - Director
SUSAN REVIE - Director Finance
MICHAEL SHARP - Director Information Technology
SHAWN SMITH - Director Finance, Digital
NICOLE TOPEL - Director Finance
JUAN V?ZQUEZ - Director Human Resources
SHAWN HARRIS - Director Strategy, Architecture, Security
NATALIE ROMIG - Director Marketing
PHILIPPE DE MILDE - Director Technology
SUZANNE TEDROW - Director Sustainability, Store Development, Global
TIMOTHY KLEIN - Regional Director Operations
GREG SENDE - Regional Director Midwest Region
KATE MCSHANE - Regional Director
MARCEL BERGERON - Regional Director Operations
REBECCA CHAMBERLIN - Regional Director
TINA SERRANO - Regional Director
ANDREA STREEDAIN - Regional Director Operations
MITCH EVANS - Regional Director Operations
PAULA EMERICK - Senior Manager Sourcing
AMY LEVINE - Senior Manager Facility/Maintenance, Northeast Region
CHRIS ARNESON - Senior Manager Data Production
TONY ARONSON - Senior Manager Category Management
JAMES BOGERT - Senior Manager Facility/Maintenance
CATHERINE CHU - Senior Manager Tax
JIM DELEHOY - Senior Manager Store Development
ALANA EAGLEY - Senior Manager Store Development
EMMY HEIMANN - Senior Manager Human Resources
VICKI JONES - Senior Manager Recruitment, Talent Acquisitions
LORETTA LEFLER - Senior Manager Compliance
DESTINY LINAYAO - Senior Manager Branding, Merchandising
JANINE NEILS - Senior Manager Compliance
STEVEN WOOD - Senior Manager Compliance
KRIS WORTHINGTON - Senior Manager Risk Management, E-Commerce
LARA BEHNERT - Senior Manager Design
DAVID GRIFFINS - Senior Manager Facility/Maintenance
GABRIELA GONZALEZ - Senior Manager Product Development
ERIC RADVANY - Senior Manager Supply Chain
HEATHER CHANCE - Senior Manager Employee Development
ROBYN VANENGEN - Senior Manager Logistics
KATE CHRISTLIEB - Senior Manager Finance, Logistics
ROBERT GRANT - Senior Manager Finance, Inventory, Global
LISA MEDINA - Senior Manager Business Development
EMILY SMITH - Senior Manager Finance
BRETT BUCHANAN - Regional Manager Operations
BLANCA CABRALES - Regional Manager Midwest Region
BRYAN BLACK - Area Manager
STEVE PATTERSON - District Manager
CHRIS SACKLYN - District Manager
PAUL GRZEGORCZYK - District Manager
MARI KLADDER - District Manager
CHARLEY ORRISON - District Manager
STEPHEN ORSINI - District Manager
ANDREW SUGAR - District Manager Store Operations
BRENDA RONEY - Manager Training
BRAD BARNDT - Manager Design, International Division
KAREN WIGGINS - Manager Applications
JENNIFER LIU - Manager Design
DONNA BUYCE - Manager Systems
MICHELE SULSKI - Manager Talent Acquisitions
JOEY MCNINCH - Manager District
RICK BOLETO - Manager District
NAHEED NIZAM - Manager Compliance
CHAR DUBOSE - Manager Information Systems
JASON CONNELL - Manager Infrastructure
SHANI HERRMANN - Manager International
KELLIE DAVENPORT - Manager Innovation
JOE BRANNON - Manager Information Technology
NANCY BEALL - Manager District
DAVID WACHER - Manager Business Development
JOANNA BAYRON - Manager Risk Management
ALISTAIR BATES - Manager Digital Marketing, Group
ANN DEERING - Manager Marketing, Sales
JANET DERKSEN - Manager Retail Operations
LINDSEY MORAN-STUCKEY - Manager Facility/Maintenance
WADE RASMUSSON - Manager Facility/Maintenance, Information Systems
BERNADETTE N. APOSTOL - Manager Product Development
ANURAG DOSHI - Manager Engineering
ANNA M. TALLARITI - Manager Marketing, Media
BRIAN SZYDTOWSKI - Manager Accounting, Business Development
ROBIN HOWARD - Manager Compliance, Alcoholic Beverages
ERIC POKORNY - Manager Content Development
JASON WALES - Manager Information/Data Security
MICHAEL RYAN - Manager Data Quality, Information/Data Security
ALICE LEUNG - Manager Digital Solutions
TAYLOR FERNANDES - Manager Product Development-Food
ELAINE WATSON - Manager Sales
KEVIN KEENE - Manager Sourcing
IMRAN ALI - Manager Information Technology, Infrastructure
JUNE ASHLEY - Manager Communications
CHRIS BOYLE - Manager Information Technology, Network, Engineering, Global
HILLARY BUI - Manager
JON CANTRELL - Manager Technology
SARAH COCKRELL - Manager Business Development
ANNE CRAMER - Manager Product Development
ANTHONY CRUZ - Manager Finance
JONATHAN DAVIDSON - Manager Operations
CHRIS DAVIS - Manager
VERENA ERTL - Manager
JONATHAN FADDEN - Manager Information Technology
JESSICA FLEMING - Manager
JONATHAN FORD - Manager
RANDALL FRINK - Manager Business Development
HEIDI FULLER - Manager Business Development, Foodservice
KATIE GALLEGLY - Manager Consumer Insights
NEIL GIBSON - Manager Information Technology, Systems, EMEA
BENTON GRAY - Manager Marketing, Group
GREG GREEN - Manager Information Technology, Infrastructure
EMILY GUNDSTROM - Manager Finance
ANA M GUTIERREZ - Manager Business Development
TARA HEWITT - Manager Business Development
RANDY HORN - Manager Business Development
MICHAEL ISTVANKO - Manager Business Development
NANCY KAUFMAN - Manager Human Resources
RYAN KELLER - Manager Finance
ABDUL KHAN - Manager Technology, Engineering
NIU LAWRENCE - Manager Information Technology, Infrastructure
STEVE LEE - Manager Information Technology
TARA MAKELA - Manager Business Development
MATT MCCOY - Manager Business Development
GARRETT MCGUIRE - Manager Business Development
RYAN MILLER - Manager Business Development
BILL MURRAY - Manager Business Development
MELISSA NAKANISHI - Manager Technology
CINDY NHAM - Manager Finance
MIKE PAINO - Manager Manufacturing
NORA PARDO - Manager Information

Technology, Systems
MATT PHILIPPS - Manager Technology
PITI PRASERTSUKSEAN - Manager Information Technology
MIA REN - Manager Business Development
SHEREE RICHARDS - Manager Business Development
CHRIS SHARPS - Manager Safety, Global-Food
DAMIANA SMITH - Manager Procurement
TRACY STRIEBICH - Manager Marketing
ELIZABETH TAN - Manager
JOYCE VARINO - Manager
SUZY WOLFORD - Manager Business Development
KOSOL WONGWICHAKORN - Manager Information Technology
ANGEL YANG - Manager Product Development
JASON ZHAO - Manager Information Technology
KIM MITTELSTADT - Account Executive Loyalty Program
STACY CROWNER - Brand Manager Product Strategy
ANGELA STAEHLE - Brand Manager Innovation
LIZ WILLIS - Brand Manager Retail Operations
EMILY MACKINNON - Brand Manager Strategy, Innovation
ANSHU GUPTA - Brand Manager
KERSTAN LINDSAY - Brand Manager Marketing, Beverages
ERIN RUMSEY - Brand Manager Strategy
GARY PETERSON - Senior Program Manager Information Technology, Division
BRENDA WANG - Senior Program Manager Information Technology
HEIDI PEIPER - Program Manager Communications
STEPHANIE HEARD - Program Manager Communications
AMY TSZE - Program Manager Operations
ALISON EDWARDS - Program Manager
AMY GOODMAN - Program Manager Development
TIM WATERS - Program Manager Division
WEE L. KOWK - Program Manager Retail Information Systems
MONICA PETERSEN - Program Manager Information Technology
SHARON LIKAJA - Program Manager Supply Chain
JESSICA CONRADSON - Program Manager Communications
DARIN BLANK - Program Manager Global
STEVE DENSFORD - Program Manager Information Technology
CAROLINE NELSON - Program Manager Technology
MARGAUX PLUMER - Supervisor Human Resources
MARLA AGINIAN - Product Manager
ROBERT COCA - Product Manager Digital
KAREN SEMANS - Product Manager Digital, Global, Region
KURT WILHELMSEN - Senior Project Manager Technology
KRISTI GLOVER - Senior Project Manager
MARGARET STONESTREET - Senior Project Manager Strategic Planning
CHRIS KLERSY - Senior Project Manager Construction
PENNI PEOTTER - Senior Project Manager Information Technology
SUZY QUINLAN - Senior Project Manager Store Design
RYAN SATHER - Senior Project Manager Data Security
SHANI PARROTT - Senior Project Manager Information Technology
AMRITA SHAH - Senior Project Manager Information Technology
JIM SCOTT - Project Manager Construction
KATHY TRAVIS - Project Manager Construction
CHRIS POLASKI - Project Manager Information Technology
TIM RICKS - Project Manager Information Technology
JENNIFER SCHUH - Project Manager Internal Audit, Information Technology
CATHERINE VARCA - Category Manager
ALYSSA BROCK - Senior Buyer
RAFAEL ARAYA - Senior Analyst
KEVIN HALL - Senior Analyst
DEANNA WILDAY - Analyst Real Estate
MIKE KONOPINSKI - Developer Applications
JONATHAN BAKER - Engineer Information/Data Security
KATHLEEN COOK - Administrative Assistant

Steven Han Projects
2230 1st Ave
Seattle, WA 98121-1615

Telephone: (206) 374-8717
Internet Homepage: girinseattle.com; momijiseattle.com; stevenhanprojects.com; umisakehouse.com
Type of Business: Chain Restaurant Operator
Total Units: 3
Trade Names: Girin (1); Momiji (1); Umi Sake House (1)
Company-Owned Units: 3
Primary Menu: Asian (1); Japanese (2)
Areas of Operation: WA
Type of Foodservice: Casual Dining (3)

Key Personnel
STEVEN HAN - President
JUNE SONGTANTARUK - Director Marketing

Sugar Mountain
1725 Westlake Ave N Ste 200
Seattle, WA 98109

Telephone: (206) 322-1644
Fax Number: (206) 322-1701
Internet Homepage: pastaco.com; sugarmtn.net
Company Email: thestaff@sugarmtn.net
Type of Business: Chain Restaurant Operator
Total Units: 5
Trade Names: Bennett's Bistro (1); Liam's (1); Pasta & Co (2); The Butcher's Table (1)
Company-Owned Units: 5
Primary Menu: American (2); Sandwiches/Deli (2); Steak (1)
Areas of Operation: WA
Type of Foodservice: Casual Dining (2); Fast Casual (2); Fine Dining (1)

Key Personnel
KURT B. DAMMEIER - Owner; Executive Chef; General Buyer
ELLEN GERBER - CFO
TIFFANY LEE - VP Finance, Accounting
NATHANIEL W. POLKY - VP Information Technology
BERGEN BODENSTEINER - General Manager
JULIE (GARDINER) RIENDL - Director Marketing
DAN LANDAU-TAYLOR - Manager Operations
ALISON LEBER - Manager Recruitment
BEN LIBBY - Specialist Accounting

Sutliff Candy and Promotions Co Inc
7708 Aurora Ave N
Seattle, WA 98103-4752

Telephone: (206) 784-5212
Fax Number: (206) 525-4574
Internet Homepage: chocolati.com
Company Email: info@chocolati.com
Type of Business: Chain Restaurant Operator
Year Founded: 2000
Total Units: 5
Trade Names: Chocolati Cafe (5)
Company-Owned Units: 5
Primary Menu: Snacks (5)
Areas of Operation: WA
Type of Foodservice: Fast Casual (5)

Key Personnel
CHRISTIAN WONG - Owner; Executive Chef; General Buyer

Thandang Restaurant LLC
7800 Aurora Ave N
Seattle, WA 98103-4754

Mailing Address: PO Box 27529, Seattle, WA, 98165
Telephone: (206) 527-5973
Internet Homepage: thanbrothers.com
Company Email: info@thanbrothers.com
Type of Business: Chain Restaurant Operator
Total Units: 12

Trade Names: Than Brothers Pho (12)
Company-Owned Units: 12
Primary Menu: Chinese (12)
Areas of Operation: WA
Type of Foodservice: Casual Dining (12)

Key Personnel
LE-UYEN THAN - Partner
CHI DANG - Partner; General Buyer

The Derschang Group
1525 10th Ave
Seattle, WA 98122

Telephone: (206) 325-0807
Internet Homepage: thederschanggroup.com
Company Email: info@thederschanggroup.com
Type of Business: Chain Restaurant Operator
Number of Employees: 214
Total Units: 6
Trade Names: King's Hardware (1); Linda's Tavern (1); Little Oddfellows (1); Oddfellows (1); Queen City (1); Smith (1)
Company-Owned Units: 6
Primary Menu: American (5); Sandwiches/Deli (1)
Areas of Operation: WA
Type of Foodservice: Casual Dining (5); Fast Casual (1)

Key Personnel
LINDA DERSCHANG - CEO

The Lodge Sports Grille
8501 Greenwood Ave N
Seattle, WA 98103-3613

Telephone: (206) 402-3046
Internet Homepage: thelodgesportsgrille.com
Company Email: greenwood@thelodgesportsgrille.com
Type of Business: Chain Restaurant Operator
Year Founded: 2010
Total Units: 7
Trade Names: Lodge Sports Grille (7)
Company-Owned Units: 7
Primary Menu: American (7)
Areas of Operation: WA
Type of Foodservice: Fast Casual (7)

Key Personnel
ERIC HAAS - President
OSCAR GARCIA - Executive Chef
BEN RHODES - Director Operations

The Other Coast Cafe
5315 Ballard Ave NW
Seattle, WA 98107-4061

Telephone: (206) 789-0936
Internet Homepage: othercoastcafe.com
Company Email: Emily@othercoastcafe.com
Type of Business: Chain Restaurant Operator
Total Units: 3
Trade Names: The Other Coast Cafe (3)
Company-Owned Units: 3
Primary Menu: Sandwiches/Deli (3)
Areas of Operation: WA
Type of Foodservice: Casual Dining (3)

Key Personnel
EMILY MABUS - Partner; Executive Chef; General Buyer
DEAN FRAZIER - Partner

The Tommy Bahama Group
400 Fairview Ave N Ste 488
Seattle, WA 98109-5371

Telephone: (206) 622-8688
Fax Number: (206) 622-4483
Internet Homepage: tommybahama.com
Company Email: tommy@tommybahama.com
Type of Business: Chain Restaurant Operator
Year Founded: 1995
Publicly Held: Yes
Total Sales: $548,645,000 (e)
Alcohol Sales: 15%
Number of Employees: 1,145
Average Check: Lunch(18); Dinner(42)
Foodservice Sales: $54,864,000 (e)
Internet Order Processing: Yes
Internet Sales: 1.00%
Total Units: 20
Trade Names: Tommy Bahama Tropical Cafe & Emporium (20)
Company-Owned Units: 20
Preferred Square Footage: 7,800
Preferred Location Types: Community Mall; Freestanding; Lifestyle Center; Other; Outlet Mall; Regional Mall; Strip Mall
Alcohol Served: Beer, Wine, Liquor
Primary Menu: Caribbean (20)
Areas of Operation: AZ, CA, FL, HI, NV, NY, TX
Foreign Countries: JAPAN
Type of Foodservice: In-Store Feeder (20)
Catering Services: Yes
Primary Distributors: (Food) SYSCO Food Services of Albany, HALFMOON, NY
Parent Company: Oxford Industries, Inc., ATLANTA, GA

Key Personnel
DOUG WOOD - COO
JOEL GARDNER - Exec VP Retail Operations
ROB GOLDBERG - Exec VP Restaurant Operations
JOAN WRIGHT - Senior VP Operations, Human Resources
DON DONLEY - Director Culinary Operations, Culinary Development

Tom Douglas Restaurants
2030 5th Ave
Seattle, WA 98121-2505

Telephone: (206) 448-2001
Fax Number: (206) 448-1979
Internet Homepage: tomdouglas.com
Company Email: office@tomdouglas.com
Type of Business: Chain Restaurant Operator
Year Founded: 1995
Total Sales: $52,710,000 (e)
Alcohol Sales: 1%
Number of Employees: 510
Average Check: Lunch(16); Dinner(26)
Internet Order Processing: Yes
Internet Sales: 1.00%
Total Units: 17
Trade Names: Assembly Hall (1); Brave HorseTavern (1); Carlile (1); Catina Lena (1); Cuoco (1); Dahlia Lounge (1); Dalia Bakery (1); Etta's (1); Home Remedy (1); Lola (1); Palace Kitchen (1); Rub With Love Shack (1); Seatown Snack Bar (1); Serious Biscuit (1); Serious Pie (2); Tanka San (1)
Company-Owned Units: 17
Preferred Location Types: Freestanding
Alcohol Served: Beer, Wine, Liquor
Primary Menu: American (6); French/Continental (2); Greek/Mediterranean (2); Italian (1); Mexican (1); Pizza (2); Seafood (1); Snacks (1); Steak/Seafood (1)
Areas of Operation: WA
Type of Foodservice: Casual Dining (13); Fine Dining (2); Quick Serve (2)
Catering Services: Yes
Primary Distributors: (Equipment) Smith & Greene Co., KENT, WA; (Supplies) Bargreen-Ellingson Inc., SEATTLE, WA

Key Personnel
JACKIE CROSS - Partner
GRETCHEN GEISNESS - General Manager
BRAD CHASE - General Manager
MOLLY MELKONIAN - General Manager Bakery
ERIC TANAKA - General Manager; Executive Chef
CHRIS SCHWARZ - Executive Chef
NATHAN CRAVE - Executive Chef
JAMES PEEKEN - Manager Catering
JANELLE PFEIFER - Manager Event Planning
MIMI KHIN - Manager Restaurant Operations
JESSICA LUCAS - Manager Catering
CARL SON - Manager Event Planning

Top Pot Doughnuts
2124 5th Ave
Seattle, WA 98121-2511

Telephone: (206) 728-1966
Internet Homepage: toppotdoughnuts.com
Company Email:
feedback@toppotdoughnuts.com
Type of Business: Chain Restaurant Operator
Total Units: 23
Trade Names: Top Pot Doughnuts (23)
Company-Owned Units: 23
Primary Menu: Snacks (23)
Areas of Operation: TX, WA
Type of Foodservice: Quick Serve (23)

Key Personnel
MARK KLEBECK - President
CHRISTINE HART - Director Finance
JENNIFER SURBAUGH - District Manager
KRISTY JENKINS - Manager Human Resources

Trophy Cupcakes
1815 N 45th St Ste 209
Seattle, WA 98103-6856

Telephone: (206) 632-7020
Internet Homepage: trophycupcakes.com
Company Email: info@trophycupcakes.com
Type of Business: Chain Restaurant Operator
Year Founded: 2007
Internet Order Processing: Yes
Total Units: 5
Trade Names: Trophy Cupcakes (5)
Company-Owned Units: 5
Primary Menu: Snacks (5)
Areas of Operation: WA
Type of Foodservice: Fast Casual (5)

Key Personnel
JENNIFER SHEA - Co-Founder; CEO
MIKE WILLIAMSON - Co-Founder

Tutta Bella Neapolitan Pizzeria
4914 Rainier Ave S Ste B
Seattle, WA 98118-1744

Telephone: (206) 722-6400
Fax Number: (206) 722-6401
Internet Homepage: tuttabella.com
Type of Business: Chain Restaurant Operator
Year Founded: 2004
Total Sales: $14,780,000 (e)
Alcohol Sales: 20%
Number of Employees: 125
Average Check: Breakfast(6); Lunch(18); Dinner(18)
Total Units: 6
Trade Names: Tutta Bella Neapolitan Pizzeria (6)
Company-Owned Units: 6
Preferred Location Types: Downtown; Freestanding
Alcohol Served: Beer, Wine, Liquor
Primary Menu: Pizza (6)
Areas of Operation: WA
Type of Foodservice: Family Restaurant (6)
Primary Distributors: (Full Line) SYSCO Food Services of Seattle Inc., KENT, WA

Key Personnel
MATT KELLOGG - Partner
JOE FUGERE - Partner
ELIZABETH JONES - General Manager
JOYCE MORINAKA - Director Special Projects
KIMBERLY NOCCO - Director
CHAD WILSON - Director Operations
BRIAN FLICKINGER - Manager Administration, Human Resources

U:Don LLC
4515 University Way NE
Seattle, WA 98105-4510

Telephone: (206) 453-3788
Internet Homepage: freshudon.com
Company Email: info@freshudon.com
Type of Business: Chain Restaurant Operator
Total Units: 2
Trade Names: UDon Fresh Japanese Noodle Station (2)
Company-Owned Units: 2
Primary Menu: Japanese (2)
Areas of Operation: WA
Type of Foodservice: Fast Casual (2)

Key Personnel
TAK KURACHI - Owner; Executive Chef; General Buyer

Uptown Espresso Inc
525 Queen Anne Ave N
Seattle, WA 98109-4521

Telephone: (206) 441-1084
Internet Homepage: velvetfoam.com
Company Email: thevalet@velvetfoam.com
Type of Business: Chain Restaurant Operator
Total Units: 7
Trade Names: Uptown Espresso (7)
Company-Owned Units: 7
Primary Menu: Snacks (7)
Areas of Operation: WA
Type of Foodservice: Fast Casual (7)

Key Personnel
DOW LUCURELL - CEO; President; General Buyer

Via Tribunali LLC
1005 E Pike St
Seattle, WA 98122-3818

Telephone: (206) 322-9234
Internet Homepage: viatribunali.com
Type of Business: Chain Restaurant Operator
Year Founded: 2004
Total Units: 3
Trade Names: Via Tribunali (3)
Company-Owned Units: 3
Primary Menu: Pizza (3)
Areas of Operation: WA
Type of Foodservice: Casual Dining (3)
Notes: Majority owner and founder Michael McConnell is also founder and owner of the Caffe Vita chain.

Key Personnel
MICHAEL MCCONNELL - President
BRANDON BARNATO - General Manager
PETE PAULING - General Manager

Westmark Hotels Inc.
800 5th Ave Ste 2600
Seattle, WA 98104-1600

Telephone: (206) 336-6000
Fax Number: (206) 336-6100
Internet Homepage: westmarkhotels.com
Company Email:
westmark@westmarkhotels.com
Type of Business: Foodservice Operations - Hotel/Motels
Year Founded: 1961
Total Sales: $93,180,000 (e)
Alcohol Sales: 25%
Number of Employees: 300
Total Units: 8
Restaurants in Hotels: 12
Trade Names: McKinley Chalet Resort (1); Westmark Anchorage (1); Westmark Baranof (1); Westmark Fairbanks Hotel & Conference Center (1); Westmark Inn Dawson (1); Westmark Inn Skagway (1); Westmark Sitka Hotel (1); Westmark Whitehorse Hotel & Conference Center (1)
Company-Owned Units: 12
Alcohol Served: Beer, Wine, Liquor
Areas of Operation: AK, WA, YT
Foreign Countries: CANADA
Type of Foodservice: Casual Dining (12)
Primary Distributors: (Food) SYSCO Food Services of Seattle Inc., KENT, WA
Parent Company: Holland-America Line Westours, SEATTLE, WA
Notes: The company derives approximately 80% of its revenue from hotel operations.

Key Personnel
KEVIN BATTERS - General Manager
MEGHAN POPELY - General Manager

Wild Ginger of Seattle
1401 3rd Ave
Seattle, WA 98101-2105

Telephone: (206) 623-4450
Internet Homepage: thetripledoor.net; wildginger.net
Type of Business: Chain Restaurant Operator
Year Founded: 1989
Total Units: 4
Trade Names: The Triple Door (1); Wild Ginger (3)
Company-Owned Units: 4
Primary Menu: Asian (4)
Areas of Operation: WA
Type of Foodservice: Casual Dining (1); Fine Dining (3)

Key Personnel
RICK YODER - Partner; General Buyer
ANN YODER - Partner; General Buyer
KEVIN CHIANG - Executive Chef
NATHAN UY - Director Culinary Operations
MIKE KLAY - Specialist Marketing; Designer

Zeeks Pizza Inc.
419 Denny Way
Seattle, WA 98109-4489

Telephone: (206) 374-0775
Fax Number: (206) 374-0818
Internet Homepage: zeekspizza.com
Type of Business: Chain Restaurant Operator
Year Founded: 1993
Total Sales: $23,930,000 (e)
Number of Employees: 340
Internet Order Processing: Yes
Internet Sales: 1.00%
Total Units: 17
Trade Names: Zeeks Pizza (17)
Company-Owned Units: 7
Units Franchised To: 6
Alcohol Served: Beer, Wine, Liquor
Primary Menu: Pizza (17)
Areas of Operation: WA
Type of Foodservice: Casual Dining (17)

Key Personnel
DAN BLACK - President
DOUG MCCLURE - Partner
GREG MCCLURE - Exec VP Franchise Development

Zippy's Giant Burgers
9614 14th Ave SW
Seattle, WA 98106-2813

Telephone: (206) 763-1347
Internet Homepage: zippysgiantburgers.com
Company Email: zippy@w-link.net
Type of Business: Chain Restaurant Operator
Year Founded: 2008
Total Units: 1
Trade Names: Zippy's Giant Burgers (1)
Company-Owned Units: 1
Primary Menu: Hamburger (1)
Areas of Operation: WA
Type of Foodservice: Fast Casual (1)

Key Personnel
BLAINE COOK - Owner; General Buyer

Zoka Coffee Roasters & Tea Company
1220 W Nickerson St
Seattle, WA 98119-1325

Telephone: (866) 965-2669
Internet Homepage: zokacoffee.com
Company Email: customerservice@zokacoffee.com
Type of Business: Chain Restaurant Operator
Internet Order Processing: Yes
Total Units: 4
Trade Names: Zoka (4)
Company-Owned Units: 4
Primary Menu: Snacks (4)
Areas of Operation: WA
Type of Foodservice: Fast Casual (4)

Key Personnel
JEFF BABCOCK - Owner

Taylor Shellfish Company, Inc
130 SE Lynch Rd
Shelton, WA 98584-8615

Telephone: (360) 426-6178
Internet Homepage: tayloroysterbars.com; taylorshellfishfarms.com
Type of Business: Chain Restaurant Operator
Total Units: 6
Trade Names: Taylor Oyster Bar (6)
Company-Owned Units: 6
Primary Menu: Seafood (6)
Areas of Operation: WA
Type of Foodservice: Casual Dining (6)

Key Personnel
BILL TAYLOR - Partner; VP; General Buyer
PAUL TAYLOR - Partner; General Buyer
JEFF PEARSON - Partner; CFO; General Buyer
BILL DEWEY - Director Public Affairs
MARCELLE GONZALEZ - Manager Marketing

King Beast Pizza Inc.
PO Box 2690
Silverdale, WA 98383-2690

Telephone: (360) 830-0354
Type of Business: Chain Restaurant Operator
Total Sales: $73,125,000 (e)
Number of Employees: 750
Total Units: 36
Trade Names: Domino's (36)
Units Franchised From: 36
Preferred Square Footage: 1,000
Preferred Location Types: Freestanding; Strip Mall
Primary Menu: Pizza (36)
Areas of Operation: WA
Type of Foodservice: Quick Serve (36)
Franchise Affiliation: Domino's Pizza Inc, ANN ARBOR, MI

Key Personnel
GREGORY KELLER - CEO; President
KENRA KELLER - CFO
CRYSTAL COLLINS - Manager Human Resources

Orchard Foods Corp.
4550 NW Newberry Hill Rd Ste 201
Silverdale, WA 98383-8201

Telephone: (360) 698-8600
Fax Number: (360) 698-8672
Internet Homepage: orchard-foods.com
Company Email: comments@orchard-foods.com
Type of Business: Chain Restaurant Operator
Year Founded: 1989
Total Sales: $23,530,000 (e)
Number of Employees: 320
Average Check: Lunch(16); Dinner(16)
Total Units: 13
Trade Names: KFC (3); KFC/Taco Bell (1); Taco Bell (8); Taco Bell/Pizza Hut (1)
Units Franchised From: 13
Preferred Square Footage: 2,500; 3,200
Preferred Location Types: Freestanding; Strip Mall
Primary Menu: Chicken (4); Pizza (1); Taco (10)
Areas of Operation: WA
Type of Foodservice: Quick Serve (13)
Franchise Affiliation: KFC Corporation, LOUISVILLE, KY; Pizza Hut Inc., PLANO, TX; Taco Bell Corp., IRVINE, CA
Primary Distributors: (Full Line) The SYGMA

Network Inc. - Portland, CLACKAMAS, OR

Key Personnel
PETER BRAUN - President; General Manager; Director Operations, Purchasing, Facility/Maintenance, Supply Chain, Store Fixtures
ALENA LEASURE - Controller
MARTY BRAUN - Controller
THOMAS SHORT - Director Operations
BRIAN HANN - Director Operations
CAROLYN S - Manager
CAROLYN SANDERS - Manager Human Resources
DEBBIE WARREN - Specialist Accounting, Compensation

Arby's of Spokane
201 W North River Dr Ste 360
Spokane, WA 99201-2282

Telephone: (509) 325-6833
Fax Number: (509) 325-6853
Internet Homepage: arbys.com
Type of Business: Chain Restaurant Operator
Year Founded: 1968
Total Sales: $7,975,000 (e)
Number of Employees: 160
Average Check: Lunch(8); Dinner(12)
Total Units: 4
Trade Names: Arby's (4)
Units Franchised From: 4
Preferred Square Footage: 3,000
Preferred Location Types: Freestanding; Regional Mall
Primary Menu: Sandwiches/Deli (4)
Areas of Operation: WA
Type of Foodservice: Quick Serve (4)
Franchise Affiliation: Arby's Restaurant Group, ATLANTA, GA
Primary Distributors: (Full Line) Systems Services of America, SCOTTSDALE, AZ

Key Personnel
DAVE MCGANN - President; Director Facility/Maintenance, Design, Human Resources, Manager Real Estate
CYRUS VAUGHN - VP Purchasing, Sales, Real Estate
CINDY TOBIAS - Controller
JERRY PEDERSON - Director Operations

Bruchi's CheesSteaks & Subs
707 W Main Ave
Spokane, WA 99201

Telephone: (509) 474-0014
Internet Homepage: bruchis.com
Type of Business: Chain Restaurant Operator
Year Founded: 1990
Total Units: 18
Trade Names: Bruchi's CheesSteaks & Subs (18)
Company-Owned Units: 18
Primary Menu: Sandwiches/Deli (18)
Areas of Operation: CA, ID, WA
Type of Foodservice: Fast Casual (18)

Key Personnel
JASON SYDNOR - General Manager

Domino's Franchisee
2108 E Wellesley Ave
Spokane, WA 99207-4270

Telephone: (509) 487-2100
Type of Business: Chain Restaurant Operator
Total Sales: $4,092,000 (e)
Total Units: 2
Trade Names: Domino's (2)
Units Franchised From: 2
Primary Menu: Pizza (2)
Areas of Operation: WA
Type of Foodservice: Quick Serve (2)
Franchise Affiliation: Domino's Pizza Inc, ANN ARBOR, MI

Key Personnel
KELLY W. PRYOR - Owner; General Buyer

Inland Northwest Culinary Academy
1810 N Greene St
Spokane, WA 99217-5320

Telephone: (509) 533-7000
Internet Homepage: scc.spokane.edu
Company Email: SCCInfo@scc.spokane.edu
Type of Business: Culinary Schools
Areas of Operation: WA

Key Personnel
BOB LOMBARDI - Executive Chef
JEFF BROWN - Director Culinary Development; General Buyer

Longhorn Barbecue Inc.
7611 W US 2 Hwy
Spokane, WA 99224-9457

Telephone: (509) 838-8372
Fax Number: (509) 838-9142
Internet Homepage: thelonghornbbq.com
Company Email: west@longhornbarbecue.com
Type of Business: Chain Restaurant Operator
Year Founded: 1956
Total Sales: $10,284,000 (e)
Alcohol Sales: 10%
Number of Employees: 150
Average Check: Lunch(12); Dinner(14)
Total Units: 3
Trade Names: Longhorn Barbecue (3)
Company-Owned Units: 3
Preferred Location Types: Freestanding
Alcohol Served: Beer, Wine, Liquor
Primary Menu: Bar-B-Q (3)
Areas of Operation: WA
Type of Foodservice: Casual Dining (3)
Catering Services: Yes
On-site Distribution Center: Yes
Primary Distributors: (Full Line) US Foods, SPOKANE, WA
Notes: The company derives approximately 25% of its revenue from wholesale of smoked meats.

Key Personnel
RANDY INGRAM - President; Partner; Executive Chef; Director Catering
BILL MILLER - Partner; Treasurer; Manager Operations; General Buyer

Modern Food Services, Inc.
12 E Rowan Ave Ste L1
Spokane, WA 99207-1281

Telephone: (509) 484-8357
Type of Business: Chain Restaurant Operator
Total Sales: $1,484,000 (e)
Total Units: 4
Trade Names: Cinnabon
Units Franchised From: 4
Areas of Operation: WA
Type of Foodservice: Quick Serve
Franchise Affiliation: Cinnabon Inc., ATLANTA, GA

Key Personnel
GREG KOMEN - Owner; General Buyer

Spokane Foodservice Inc.
1821 W 5th Ave Ste 106
Spokane, WA 99201-5625

Telephone: (509) 489-5531
Fax Number: (509) 489-5534
Type of Business: Chain Restaurant Operator
Year Founded: 2000
Total Sales: $125,680,000 (e)
Number of Employees: 950
Average Check: Breakfast(5); Lunch(5); Dinner(5)
Total Units: 27
Trade Names: McDonald's (27)
Units Franchised From: 27
Preferred Square Footage: 2,500
Preferred Location Types: Convenience Store/Gas Station; Freestanding

Primary Menu: Hamburger (27)
Areas of Operation: ID, WA
Type of Foodservice: Quick Serve (27)
Franchise Affiliation: McDonald's Corporation, CHICAGO, IL
Primary Distributors: (Full Line) The Martin-Brower Co., SUMNER, WA

Key Personnel
MARK RAY - President; Director Purchasing, Information Systems, Real Estate
CHRIS WEBER - CFO; Director Finance
TOM KORTH - Director Operations
LES MERRIMAN - Manager Human Resources
GEORGE WUEST - Manager Facility/Maintenance

The Onion
302 W Riverside Ave
Spokane, WA 99201-0210

Telephone: (509) 747-3852
Fax Number: (509) 624-9965
Internet Homepage: theonion.biz
Company Email: NoraLLC@aol.com
Type of Business: Chain Restaurant Operator
Year Founded: 1977
Total Sales: $3,748,000 (e)
Alcohol Sales: 15%
Number of Employees: 120
Average Check: Lunch(10); Dinner(10)
Total Units: 2
Trade Names: The Onion (2)
Company-Owned Units: 2
Preferred Location Types: Freestanding
Alcohol Served: Beer, Wine, Liquor
Primary Menu: American (2)
Areas of Operation: WA
Type of Foodservice: Casual Dining (2)
Catering Services: Yes
Primary Distributors: (Full Line) US Foods, FIFE, WA

Key Personnel
KEN BELISLE - President; General Manager
DANIEL BUTLER - Executive Chef; General Buyer
CLAIRE FAVRET - Project Manager Art

The Pizza Pipeline Inc.
3633 E Sanson Ave
Spokane, WA 99217-6674

Telephone: (509) 326-1977
Fax Number: (509) 326-3017
Internet Homepage: pizzapipeline.com
Company Email: customerfeedback@pizzapipeline.com
Type of Business: Chain Restaurant Operator
Year Founded: 1988
Systemwide Sales: $18,106,000 (e)
Total Sales: $6,295,000 (e)
Number of Employees: 88
Average Check: Lunch(14); Dinner(22)
Internet Order Processing: Yes
Internet Sales: 1.00%
Total Units: 8
Trade Names: The Pizza Pipeline (8)
Units Franchised To: 8
Preferred Square Footage: 1,600; 1,900
Preferred Location Types: Freestanding; Strip Mall
Primary Menu: Pizza (8)
Areas of Operation: OR, WA
Type of Foodservice: Quick Serve (8)
On-site Distribution Center: Yes
Primary Distributors: (Equipment) Springtree Food Service, SPOKANE, WA; (Food) BakeMark USA, PICO RIVERA, CA; (Supplies) Springtree Food Service, SPOKANE, WA

Key Personnel
MICHAEL KIGHT - CEO; President; Manager Operations, Purchasing, Real Estate, Design
GENE BOIK - VP; Manager Loss Prevention, Risk Management, Quality Assurance, Supply Chain, Marketing, Human Resources, Franchising, Menu Development
GERI PAUL - Controller; Director Finance, Facility/Maintenance, Information Systems

Unlimited Possibilities, Inc.
9502 N Newport Hwy Ste 7
Spokane, WA 99218-1147

Telephone: (509) 466-1699
Type of Business: Chain Restaurant Operator
Total Sales: $1,825,000 (e)
Total Units: 3
Trade Names: Cold Stone Creamery (3)
Units Franchised From: 3
Primary Menu: Snacks (3)
Areas of Operation: WA
Type of Foodservice: Quick Serve (3)
Franchise Affiliation: Kahala Brands, SCOTTSDALE, AZ

Key Personnel
JAMES HANSEN - Partner; General Buyer
MARY HANSEN - Partner; General Buyer

Wentana, LLC
503 E 2nd Ave Ste B
Spokane, WA 99202-1405

Telephone: (509) 326-6333
Fax Number: (509) 325-1215
Internet Homepage: wendys.com
Type of Business: Chain Restaurant Operator
Year Founded: 2012
Total Sales: $130,690,000 (e)
Total Units: 48
Trade Names: Wendy's Old Fashioned Hamburgers (48)
Units Franchised From: 48
Primary Menu: Hamburger (48)
Areas of Operation: CA, ID, MT, ND, OR, WA, WY
Type of Foodservice: Quick Serve (48)
Franchise Affiliation: The Wendy's Company, DUBLIN, OH

Key Personnel
PETER B. NISBET - President
JENNIFER ROBSON - VP Real Estate
LEAH JOHNSON - Director Operations
KIMBERLY DISQUE - Director Human Resources
JONNA JONES - Director Marketing

Auntie Anne's Franchise
14700 E Indiana Ave
Spokane Valley, WA 99216-1839

Telephone: (509) 891-7077
Internet Homepage: auntieannes.com
Type of Business: Chain Restaurant Operator
Total Sales: $1,577,000 (e)
Total Units: 2
Trade Names: Auntie Anne's Hand-Rolled Soft Pretzels (2)
Units Franchised From: 2
Primary Menu: Snacks (2)
Areas of Operation: WA
Type of Foodservice: Quick Serve (2)
Franchise Affiliation: Auntie Anne's Inc., LANCASTER, PA

Key Personnel
JEFFREY MILLER - Owner; General Buyer

Conversion Concepts, Inc
608 N Argonne Rd
Spokane Valley, WA 99212-2732

Telephone: (509) 922-7242
Internet Homepage: conversionconcepts.net
Listing Type: Subsidiary
Type of Business: Chain Restaurant Operator
Total Units: 39
Trade Names: Clover (1); Papa Murphy (4); Subway (34)
Company-Owned Units: 1
Units Franchised To: 38
Primary Menu: Greek/Mediterranean (1); Pizza (4); Sandwiches/Deli (34)
Areas of Operation: WA
Type of Foodservice: Fine Dining (1); Quick Serve (38)
Franchise Affiliation: Doctor's Associates Inc., MILFORD, CT

Key Personnel
SCOTT MCCANDLESS - President; General Buyer
TRAVIS UMINSKI - Regional Manager

The Broadway Group Inc.
6409 E Sharp Ave
Spokane Valley, WA 99212-1255

Mailing Address: WA,
Telephone: (509) 534-1502
Fax Number: (509) 535-0470
Internet Homepage: broadwaygroup.com
Type of Business: Chain Restaurant Operator
Year Founded: 1962
Total Sales: $8,291,000 (e)
Alcohol Sales: 5%
Number of Employees: 217
Average Check: Lunch(10); Dinner(12)
Total Units: 7
Trade Names: Broadway Diner (7)
Company-Owned Units: 4
Units Franchised From: 3
Preferred Square Footage: 800; 3,500
Preferred Location Types: Convenience Store/Gas Station; Freestanding
Alcohol Served: Beer, Wine, Liquor
Primary Menu: American (7)
Areas of Operation: MT, NV, WA
Type of Foodservice: Casual Dining (7)
Catering Services: Yes
Primary Distributors: (Full Line) SYSCO Food Services of Seattle Inc., KENT, WA

Key Personnel
DANIEL ALSAKER - CEO; President; General Buyer
BILL FRISCH - CFO; Director Finance
ALLEN FREEMAN - CTO
TOM HEMINGWAY - VP; Director Advertising
STUART ELLISON - VP Operations, Purchasing, Loss Prevention, Human Resources, Menu Development, Food Safety; Executive Chef; Manager Information Systems, Supply Chain, Franchising, Division

Zip's Drive-In
5901 E Trent Ave
Spokane Valley, WA 99212

Internet Homepage: zipsdrivein.com
Type of Business: Chain Restaurant Operator
Total Sales: $16,610,000 (e)
Total Units: 38
Trade Names: Zip's Drive-In (38)
Company-Owned Units: 38
Primary Menu: American (38)
Type of Foodservice: Quick Serve (38)

Key Personnel
TONY ABEL - Owner

Olson Franchise Group LLC
9612 270th St NW
Stanwood, WA 98292-1906

Telephone: (425) 353-4533
Fax Number: (425) 353-4003
Internet Homepage: alfyspizza.com
Type of Business: Chain Restaurant Operator
Year Founded: 1973
Systemwide Sales: $13,856,000 (e)
Total Sales: $8,777,000 (e)
Alcohol Sales: 10%
Number of Employees: 350
Average Check: Lunch(8); Dinner(18)
Internet Order Processing: Yes
Total Units: 7
Trade Names: Alfy's Pizza (7)
Company-Owned Units: 2
Units Franchised To: 5
Preferred Square Footage: 4,500
Preferred Location Types: Freestanding; Strip Mall
Alcohol Served: Beer, Wine
Primary Menu: Pizza (7)
Projected Openings: 1
Areas of Operation: WA
Type of Foodservice: Casual Dining (7)
Primary Distributors: (Food) SYSCO Food Services of Seattle Inc., KENT, WA

Key Personnel
BRIAN OLSON - President; Partner; Manager Menu Development
BLAKE OLSON - VP Operations
BRANDON OLSON - VP Operations

The Rock Wood Fired Kitchen
14209 29th St E Ste 102
Sumner, WA 98390-9689

Telephone: (253) 987-5479
Fax Number: (253) 987-7047
Internet Homepage: therockwfp.com
Type of Business: Chain Restaurant Operator
Year Founded: 1995
Total Sales: $51,720,000 (e)
Number of Employees: 247
Average Check: Dinner(26)
Total Units: 18
Trade Names: The Rock Wood Fired Kitchen (18)
Company-Owned Units: 15
Units Franchised To: 6
Preferred Square Footage: 5,500; 6,000
Preferred Location Types: Strip Mall
Alcohol Served: Beer, Wine, Liquor
Primary Menu: Pizza (2,100)

Areas of Operation: CO, OR, TX, WA
Foreign Countries: CANADA
Type of Foodservice: Casual Dining (18)

Key Personnel
DON BELLIS - CEO; Partner

Domino's Franchisee
5402 S Washington St
Tacoma, WA 98409-2708

Telephone: (253) 473-5450
Type of Business: Chain Restaurant Operator
Total Sales: $24,014,000 (e)
Total Units: 12
Trade Names: Domino's (12)
Units Franchised From: 12
Primary Menu: Pizza (12)
Areas of Operation: WA
Type of Foodservice: Quick Serve (12)
Franchise Affiliation: Domino's Pizza Inc, ANN ARBOR, MI

Key Personnel
MICHAEL W. BROWN - Owner; General Buyer

El Toro Mexican Restaurants
5716 N 26th St
Tacoma, WA 98407-2409

Telephone: (253) 759-7889
Internet Homepage: eltorofamily.com
Company Email: info@eltorofamily.com
Type of Business: Chain Restaurant Operator
Year Founded: 1959
Total Sales: $7,065,000 (e)
Alcohol Sales: 20%
Number of Employees: 105
Average Check: Lunch(14); Dinner(18)
Total Units: 5
Trade Names: El Toro (5)
Company-Owned Units: 5
Preferred Square Footage: 5,000; 6,000
Preferred Location Types: Freestanding; Strip Mall
Alcohol Served: Beer, Wine, Liquor
Primary Menu: Mexican (5)
Areas of Operation: WA
Type of Foodservice: Casual Dining (5)
Primary Distributors: (Full Line) Food Services of America, SCOTTSDALE, AZ

Key Personnel
RUBEN ARIAS - President; Executive Chef; Director Finance, Real Estate, Design
JOHN MAYES - VP Operations
ENRIQUE ARIAS - VP; Director Operations, Facility/Maintenance; General Buyer

Forza LLC
2209 N Pearl St Ste 104
Tacoma, WA 98406-2529

Telephone: (206) 575-0888
Internet Homepage: forzacoffeecompany.com
Company Email:
 info@forzacoffeecompany.com
Type of Business: Chain Restaurant Operator
Total Sales: $2,661,000 (e)
Internet Order Processing: Yes
Total Units: 8
Trade Names: FORZA (8)
Company-Owned Units: 8
Primary Menu: Coffee (8)
Areas of Operation: WA
Type of Foodservice: Quick Serve (8)

Key Personnel
PHIL BEATTIE - Director Coffee/Tea

Harmon Brewing Co., L.L.C.
1938 Pacific Ave
Tacoma, WA 98402-3110

Telephone: (253) 383-2739
Internet Homepage: harmonbrewingco.com
Type of Business: Chain Restaurant Operator
Year Founded: 1997
Total Units: 5
Trade Names: Harmon Restaurant (1); Harmon Tap Room (1); The Hub (3)
Company-Owned Units: 5
Primary Menu: American (5)
Areas of Operation: WA
Type of Foodservice: Casual Dining (5)

Key Personnel
CAROLE FORD - Founder; Partner

Shoebox Northwest, Llc
1708 Pacific Ave
Tacoma, WA 98402-3215

Telephone: (253) 572-9800
Type of Business: Chain Restaurant Operator
Total Sales: $6,081,000 (e)
Total Units: 5
Trade Names: Jimmy John's Gourmet Sandwich Shop (5)
Units Franchised From: 5
Areas of Operation: WA
Franchise Affiliation: Jimmy John's Franchise LLC, CHAMPAIGN, IL

Key Personnel
HOWARD MANGUM - Partner
GEORGE NEEDHAM - Partner

South Sound Restaurant Group
2707 N Proctor St
Tacoma, WA 98407-5227

Telephone: (253) 922-6489
Fax Number: (253) 922-0343
Internet Homepage: hobnobtacoma.com; knappsrestaurant.com; poodledogrestaurant.com; powerhousebrewpub.com
Company Email:
 powerhousebrewery@gmail.com
Type of Business: Chain Restaurant Operator
Year Founded: 1932
Total Sales: $5,305,000 (e)
Alcohol Sales: 8%
Number of Employees: 184
Average Check: Breakfast(10); Lunch(12); Dinner(14)
Total Units: 6
Trade Names: Burs (1); Harvester (1); Hob Nob (1); Knapp's Restaurant (1); Poodle Dog (1); Powerhouse Restaurant & Brewery (1)
Company-Owned Units: 6
Preferred Location Types: Freestanding
Alcohol Served: Beer, Wine, Liquor
Primary Menu: American (6)
Areas of Operation: WA
Type of Foodservice: Casual Dining (6)
Primary Distributors: (Full Line) Food Services of America, KENT, WA

Key Personnel
TIM PATTY - President; Executive Chef; General Buyer

X Group
2811 6th Ave
Tacoma, WA 98406-6707

Telephone: (253) 254-0560
Internet Homepage: xgrouprestaurants.com
Company Email:
 INFO@XGROUPRESTAURANTS.COM
Type of Business: Chain Restaurant Operator
Year Founded: 2005
Total Units: 6
Trade Names: Asado (1); Choripan by Asado (1); Eg Brewing Co (1); Engine House No. 9 (1); The Pine Room (1); The Valley (1)
Company-Owned Units: 6
Primary Menu: American (4); Latin American/Cuban (2)
Areas of Operation: WA
Type of Foodservice: Casual Dining (6)
Catering Services: Yes

Key Personnel
JOHN XITCO - Founder; Partner; General Buyer

Saled Food Services
1919 70th Ave W Ste C
University Place, WA 98466-5541

Telephone: (253) 566-8693
Fax Number: (253) 566-7139
Type of Business: Chain Restaurant Operator
Total Sales: $32,830,000 (e)
Number of Employees: 310
Total Units: 7
Trade Names: McDonald's (7)
Units Franchised From: 7
Preferred Square Footage: 2,500
Preferred Location Types: Freestanding
Primary Menu: Hamburger (7)
Areas of Operation: WA
Type of Foodservice: Quick Serve (7)
Franchise Affiliation: McDonald's Corporation, CHICAGO, IL

Key Personnel
EDWARD MAHER - President; General Buyer

Burgerville
109 W 17th St
Vancouver, WA 98660-2932

Telephone: (360) 694-1521
Fax Number: (360) 694-9114
Internet Homepage: burgerville.com
Company Email: servicedesk@burgerville.com
Type of Business: Chain Restaurant Operator
Year Founded: 1926
Total Sales: $57,450,000 (e)
Alcohol Sales: 3%
Number of Employees: 1,525
Average Check: Lunch(8); Dinner(12)
Internet Order Processing: Yes
Total Units: 40
Trade Names: Burgerville U.S.A. (40)
Company-Owned Units: 40
Preferred Square Footage: 2,500; 3,000; 7,000
Preferred Location Types: Community Mall; Downtown; Freestanding; Strip Mall
Alcohol Served: Beer, Wine
Primary Menu: Hamburger (42)
Areas of Operation: OR, WA
Type of Foodservice: Quick Serve (42)
Catering Services: Yes
Primary Distributors: (Full Line) SYSCO Food Services of Portland Inc., WILSONVILLE, OR

Key Personnel
JEFFREY P. HARVEY - CEO; President
JOE OBRIEN - CFO
JANICE WILLIAMS - Chief Services Officer
BETH BREWER - Senior VP Operations

STACEY CHAPMAN - Senior VP Digital
CIARA LAMIA - VP Product Development
JAMES GILBERT - Director Facility/Maintenance
SONJA RAUCHENSTEIN - Director Operations

Duce Restaurants
10507 NE Fourth Plain Blvd
Vancouver, WA 98662-5753

Telephone: (360) 256-7302
Type of Business: Chain Restaurant Operator
Total Sales: $8,290,000 (e)
Total Units: 6
Trade Names: Dairy Queen (4); DQ Grill & Chill (2)
Units Franchised From: 6
Primary Menu: American (6)
Areas of Operation: WA
Type of Foodservice: Quick Serve (6)
Franchise Affiliation: International Dairy Queen Inc., BLOOMINGTON, MN

Key Personnel
DARA DEJBAKHSH - Owner; General Buyer
LAURA JACOBSON - General Manager
CRIS SPARKS - District Manager

Muchas Gracias Mexican Food
116 NE 117th Ave
Vancouver, WA 98684-5020

Telephone: (360) 254-8530
Internet Homepage: muchasgraciasfranchise.com; muchasgraciasmexicanfood.com
Company Email: info@muchasgraciasfranchise.com
Type of Business: Chain Restaurant Operator
Total Units: 17
Trade Names: Muchas Gracias Mexican Food (17)
Company-Owned Units: 17
Primary Menu: Mexican (17)
Areas of Operation: OR, WA
Type of Foodservice: Casual Dining (17)

Key Personnel
RODOLFO S. DE LA TORRE - Founder; CEO
LUCERO GARCIA - Owner
MIGUEL ESPERICUETA - VP Operations

North Star Restaurants, Inc
5900 NE 112th Ave
Vancouver, WA 98662-5761

Telephone: (360) 891-6005
Type of Business: Chain Restaurant Operator
Total Sales: $80,570,000 (e)
Total Units: 17
Trade Names: McDonald's (17)
Units Franchised From: 17
Primary Menu: Hamburger (17)
Areas of Operation: WA
Type of Foodservice: Quick Serve (17)
Franchise Affiliation: McDonald's Corporation, CHICAGO, IL

Key Personnel
MATTHEW J. HADWIN - President; General Buyer
VAL HADWIN - Owner

Northwest Premier Investments, Inc.
16701 SE McGillivray Blvd
Vancouver, WA 98683

Telephone: (360) 882-4608
Fax Number: (360) 882-4628
Type of Business: Chain Restaurant Operator
Total Sales: $73,530,000 (e)
Total Units: 83
Trade Names: Papa Murphy's Take 'N' Bake Pizza (83)
Units Franchised From: 83
Primary Menu: Pizza (83)
Areas of Operation: AZ, FL, IA, MI, TX, WA
Type of Foodservice: Quick Serve (83)
Franchise Affiliation: Papa Murphy's International Inc., VANCOUVER, WA

Key Personnel
JIM LOVELACE - Partner
ROBERT VRANAS - General Manager Area; Coach

Pacific Bells Inc.
111 W 39th St Ste A
Vancouver, WA 98660-1974

Telephone: (360) 694-7855
Fax Number: (360) 694-7873
Internet Homepage: pacificbells.com
Company Email: info@pacificbells.com
Type of Business: Chain Restaurant Operator
Year Founded: 1989
Total Sales: $1,032,000,000 (e)
Number of Employees: 2,645
Average Check: Lunch(6); Dinner(10)
Total Units: 305
Trade Names: Buffalo Wild Wings (63); Taco Bell (242)
Units Franchised From: 305
Preferred Square Footage: 2,500; 3,000
Preferred Location Types: Community Mall; Freestanding
Primary Menu: Chicken (63); Taco (242)
Areas of Operation: AL, CA, IN, MS, OH, OR, TN, WA, WI
Type of Foodservice: Casual Dining (63); Quick Serve (242)
Franchise Affiliation: Buffalo Wild Wings Inc., ATLANTA, GA; Pizza Hut Inc., PLANO, TX; Taco Bell Corp., IRVINE, CA
Primary Distributors: (Food) McLane/Hebron, HEBRON, KY

Key Personnel
TOM COOK - CEO
RICK NADER - President
GENO ORRICO - CFO
SCOTT SHEPHERD - COO
DAVID HAWTHORNE - Chief People Officer
CHRISTIAN POTTER - Chief Development Officer; General Counsel
ERIC SIMKO - Chief Strategy Officer; Chief Business Development Officer
DENNIS JANUARY - Exec VP Business Development
MATT COOK - VP Construction
DAVID BOTTOMS - VP
MELISSA TONEY - VP Human Resources
MARK TANIS - Regional VP
PAT MCKEWON - Regional VP West Region, Southeast Region
GUSTAVO ROMERO - Regional VP
JUSTIN SCHENKER - Director Operations
IVAN MORENO - Director Finance
VIRGINIA THOMAS - Director Operations
MICHAEL SINGHOSE - Director Operations
MENG SYNN - Director Customer Analytics
BRYAN HALL - Director Real Estate
LINDA CASTANEDA - Director Operations
ALEJANDRO AYALA - Director Operations
LAUREN BAIN - Director Information Technology
LESLEY CONARD - Director Operations
DONNA LADNER - Director Operations
THERESA LANZI - Director Operations
RICH LONGABERGER - Director Operations
KATIE MATTHEWS - Director Human Resources
GEORGE GLASS - Director Operations
AIMEE GIBBONS - Senior Manager Information Technology
SARAH CHAENEY - Manager Payroll
MEGAN HORROCKS - Manager Risk Management
MEGAN SINCLAIR - Manager
BECKY GRIMES - Senior Project Manager

Papa Murphy's International Inc.
8000 NE Parkway Dr Ste 350
Vancouver, WA 98662-6733

Telephone: (360) 260-7272
Fax Number: (360) 260-0500
Internet Homepage: papamurphys.com
Type of Business: Chain Restaurant Operator

Year Founded: 1995
Systemwide Sales: $1,449,984,000 (e)
Publicly Held: Yes
Total Sales: $351,972,000 (e)
Number of Employees: 1,288
Average Check: Dinner(22)
Total Units: 1,162
Trade Names: Papa Murphy's Take 'N' Bake Pizza (1,162)
Company-Owned Units: 103
Units Franchised To: 1,059
Preferred Square Footage: 1,200
Preferred Location Types: Freestanding; Strip Mall
Primary Menu: Pizza (1,162)
Areas of Operation: AK, AL, AR, AZ, CA, CO, FL, GA, HI, IA, ID, IL, IN, KS, KY, LA, MD, MI, MN, MO, MS, MT, NC, ND, NE, NM, NV, OH, OK, OR, SC, SD, TN, TX, UT, VA, WA, WI, WY, AB, BC, MB, NB, NS, NT, ON, PE, QC, SK, YT
Foreign Countries: CANADA; UNITED ARAB EMIRATES
Type of Foodservice: Quick Serve (1,162)
Primary Distributors: (Full Line) The SYGMA Network Inc. - Portland, CLACKAMAS, OR
Parent Company: MTY Food Group Inc., SAINT-LAURENT, QC CANADA

Key Personnel
MARK HUTCHENS - COO; Exec VP
CARRON HARRIS - VP Southwest Division; Senior Director Operations
TRACEY AYRES - VP Innovation
GREG GERRITZ - Senior Director Construction
SHAUNA WALKER - Senior Director Marketing
BRAD GEORGE - Senior Director Tax
LESLIE SIRIANNI THOMPSON - Senior Director Brand Marketing
SHEMAR PUCEL - Senior Director Franchise Development
AUGINNE CONBOY - Director Accounting
CATHY BERRY - Director Legal
EREZ GORDIN - Director Architecture
KATIE KIMBRELL - Director Acquisitions
ALEXIS DILTZ - Director Communications
DANA MISNER - Director Field Marketing
ANDREA BENEKE - Director Marketing
JAIME WILSON - Senior Manager Operations
GENE WOODRUFF - Senior Manager Design, Store Planning
LEEANN MCDONALD - Senior Manager Marketing
RHONDA MCGREW - Manager Franchise Development
KIRA OLSON - Manager Supply Chain
LISA ROSEBERRY - Manager Supply Chain
LISA MCNAIRY - Manager Communications

White Management
1015 N Mission St
Wenatchee, WA 98801-1516

Telephone: (509) 662-2171
Type of Business: Chain Restaurant Operator
Year Founded: 1972
Total Sales: $6,684,000 (e)
Number of Employees: 50
Average Check: Lunch(8); Dinner(8)
Total Units: 3
Trade Names: KFC/A&W (2); KFC/Taco Bell (1)
Units Franchised From: 3
Preferred Square Footage: 3,000
Preferred Location Types: Freestanding
Primary Menu: American (2); Chicken (3); Taco (1)
Areas of Operation: WA
Type of Foodservice: Quick Serve (3)
Franchise Affiliation: A&W Restaurants Inc., LEXINGTON, KY; KFC Corporation, LOUISVILLE, KY; Taco Bell Corp., IRVINE, CA
Primary Distributors: (Full Line) SYSCO Food Services of Seattle Inc., KENT, WA

Key Personnel
CALVIN WHITE - President; Director Purchasing, Real Estate
DENNIS WEBB - Manager Finance

Domino's Franchisee
4001 Kennedy Rd Ste 10
West Richland, WA 99353-7353

Telephone: (509) 627-2000
Type of Business: Chain Restaurant Operator
Total Sales: $5,979,000 (e)
Total Units: 3
Trade Names: Domino's (3)
Units Franchised From: 3
Primary Menu: Pizza (3)
Areas of Operation: WA
Type of Foodservice: Quick Serve (3)
Franchise Affiliation: Domino's Pizza Inc, ANN ARBOR, MI

Key Personnel
JERRY L. COVINGTON - Owner; General Buyer

Northwest Restaurants Inc.
18815 139th Ave NE Ste C
Woodinville, WA 98072-3565

Telephone: (425) 486-6336
Fax Number: (425) 486-6676
Type of Business: Chain Restaurant Operator
Year Founded: 1984
Total Sales: $323,850,000 (e)
Average Check: Dinner(10)
Total Units: 203
Trade Names: A&W All American Food (12); KFC (54); Taco Bell (137)
Units Franchised From: 203
Preferred Square Footage: 3,200
Preferred Location Types: Community Mall; Freestanding
Primary Menu: American (12); Chicken (54); Mexican (137); Seafood (0); Taco (53)
Areas of Operation: OR
Type of Foodservice: Quick Serve (203)
Franchise Affiliation: A&W Restaurants Inc., LEXINGTON, KY; KFC Corporation, LOUISVILLE, KY; Long John Silver's Inc., LOUISVILLE, KY; Taco Bell Corp., IRVINE, CA

Key Personnel
SAM SIBERT - CEO; Partner
BRETT SIBERT - President; Partner; General Buyer
BRANDON ROBERTSON - President
CHRIS BASINGER - VP
ADAM SIBERT - VP
CARRIE FINDLON - Executive Director
CARRIE FINLON - Executive Director
DENISE WILLIAMS - Controller
RANDOLPH WELCH - Director Construction
VALERIE PYLE - Director Human Resources
FRANK RATLIFF - Director Operations
FLETCHER BOLL - Director Development, Construction
DEREK SHAW - Director Information Technology
ROCHELLE EVANS - Area Manager
RANDY WELCH - Manager Construction
DAWN EDWARDS - Executive Assistant

Domino's Franchisee
420 S 72nd Ave Ste 140
Yakima, WA 98908-1688

Telephone: (509) 965-1500
Type of Business: Chain Restaurant Operator
Total Sales: $12,262,000 (e)
Total Units: 6
Trade Names: Domino's (6)
Units Franchised From: 6
Primary Menu: Pizza (6)
Areas of Operation: WA
Type of Foodservice: Quick Serve (6)
Franchise Affiliation: Domino's Pizza Inc, ANN ARBOR, MI

Key Personnel
JEFFREY W. SMITH - Owner; General Buyer

McDonald's of Yakima
110 S 4th Ave
Yakima, WA 98902-3428

Telephone: (509) 248-2176

Fax Number: (509) 575-3702
Internet Homepage: mcdonalds.com
Company Email: admin@mcdyak.com
Type of Business: Chain Restaurant Operator
Year Founded: 1985
Total Sales: $61,730,000 (e)
Number of Employees: 400
Average Check: Breakfast(6); Lunch(6); Dinner(6)
Total Units: 13
Trade Names: McDonald's (13)
Units Franchised From: 13
Preferred Square Footage: 2,500
Preferred Location Types: Discount Dept. Stores; Freestanding
Primary Menu: Hamburger (13)
Areas of Operation: WA
Type of Foodservice: In-Store Feeder (1); Quick Serve (12)
Franchise Affiliation: McDonald's Corporation, CHICAGO, IL
Primary Distributors: (Food) The Martin-Brower Co., SUMNER, WA

Key Personnel
GREG LURING - President; General Buyer
SHELLY HILLIER - Director Operations

Pieyak Inc
64 W Nob Hill Blvd
Yakima, WA 98902-4659

Telephone: (509) 248-2922
Fax Number: (509) 248-2922
Type of Business: Chain Restaurant Operator
Total Sales: $9,089,000 (e)
Total Units: 10
Trade Names: Papa Murphy's Take 'N' Bake Pizza (10)
Units Franchised From: 10
Primary Menu: Pizza (10)
Areas of Operation: OR, WA
Type of Foodservice: Quick Serve (10)
Franchise Affiliation: Papa Murphy's International Inc., VANCOUVER, WA

Key Personnel
DON COPP - President; General Buyer

Veronte, Inc.
2113 S 1st St
Yakima, WA 98903-2233

Telephone: (509) 452-3602
Type of Business: Chain Restaurant Operator
Total Sales: $9,578,000 (e)
Total Units: 4
Trade Names: Burger King (4)
Units Franchised From: 4
Primary Menu: Hamburger (4)
Areas of Operation: WA

Type of Foodservice: Quick Serve (4)
Franchise Affiliation: Burger King Worldwide Inc., MIAMI, FL

Key Personnel
BOB VERONTE - President; General Buyer

WISCONSIN

Mor Subs Inc
833 W Wisconsin Ave
Appleton, WI 54914-3510

Telephone: (920) 954-1123
Type of Business: Chain Restaurant Operator
Total Sales: $1,527,000 (e)
Total Units: 2
Trade Names: Subway (2)
Units Franchised From: 2
Primary Menu: Sandwiches/Deli (2)
Areas of Operation: WI
Type of Foodservice: Quick Serve (2)
Franchise Affiliation: Doctor's Associates Inc., MILFORD, CT

Key Personnel
MIKE MORTIER - Owner; General Buyer

Tom's Drive-Ins
501 N Westhill Blvd
Appleton, WI 54914-5780

Telephone: (920) 882-1500
Fax Number: (920) 731-9041
Internet Homepage: tomsdriveins.com
Company Email: feedback@tomsdriveins.com
Type of Business: Chain Restaurant Operator
Year Founded: 1960
Total Sales: $9,235,000 (e)
Number of Employees: 175
Average Check: Breakfast(8); Lunch(8); Dinner(8)
Internet Order Processing: Yes
Total Units: 8
Trade Names: Tom's Drive-In (8)
Company-Owned Units: 8
Preferred Square Footage: 1,300; 3,700
Preferred Location Types: Freestanding
Primary Menu: American (8)
Areas of Operation: WI
Type of Foodservice: Quick Serve (8)
Primary Distributors: (Full Line) Reinhart FoodService LLC, CHICAGO, IL

Key Personnel
TOM GRISHABER - Partner; Controller; Executive Chef; General Buyer
SCOT GRISHABER - Partner; Director Operations, Facility/Maintenance, Real Estate, Design, Menu Development
ANGIE GRISHABER - Manager Information Systems, Marketing, Human Resources
ELLEN JURGENSON - Manager Accounting

Domino's Franchisee
844 8th Ave
Baraboo, WI 53913

Telephone: (608) 355-5080
Type of Business: Chain Restaurant Operator
Total Sales: $3,963,000 (e)
Total Units: 2
Trade Names: Domino's (2)
Units Franchised From: 2
Primary Menu: Pizza (2)
Areas of Operation: WI
Type of Foodservice: Quick Serve (2)
Franchise Affiliation: Domino's Pizza Inc, ANN ARBOR, MI

Key Personnel
HAROLD J. NELSON - Owner; General Buyer

Cinnajims, LLC
95 N Moorland Rd
Brookfield, WI 53005-6020

Telephone: (262) 860-1284
Type of Business: Chain Restaurant Operator
Total Sales: $1,149,000 (e)
Total Units: 3
Trade Names: Cinnabon (3)
Units Franchised From: 3
Primary Menu: Snacks (3)
Areas of Operation: WI
Type of Foodservice: Quick Serve (3)
Franchise Affiliation: Cinnabon Inc., ATLANTA, GA

Key Personnel
JIM MENERALLA - Owner; General Buyer

DPNK
300 N Moorland Rd
Brookfield, WI 53005

Telephone: (262) 782-2280
Type of Business: Chain Restaurant Operator
Total Sales: $60,400,000 (e)
Total Units: 13
Trade Names: McDonald's (13)
Units Franchised From: 13
Preferred Square Footage: 2,500
Primary Menu: Hamburger (13)
Areas of Operation: WI
Type of Foodservice: Quick Serve (13)
Franchise Affiliation: McDonald's Corporation, CHICAGO, IL

Key Personnel
CHARLES DION CONN - President; General Buyer

J & D Shop Systems Inc
1300 S Calhoun Rd
Brookfield, WI 53005-6810

Telephone: (262) 789-1930
Company Email:
  Cousinssubsoffice@gmail.com
Type of Business: Chain Restaurant Operator
Total Sales: $6,306,000 (e)
Average Check: Dinner(12)
Total Units: 6
Trade Names: Cousins Subs (6)
Units Franchised From: 6
Primary Menu: Sandwiches/Deli (6)
Areas of Operation: WI
Type of Foodservice: Quick Serve (6)
Franchise Affiliation: Cousins Sub Systems Inc., MENOMONEE FALLS, WI

Key Personnel
JAMES VALENTINE - President; General Buyer

Prime Quarter Inc.
110 Commercial Dr Ste 3
Columbus, WI 53925-1160

Telephone: (920) 350-0332
Internet Homepage: primequarter.com
Type of Business: Chain Restaurant Operator
Year Founded: 1986
Total Sales: $17,132,000 (e)
Alcohol Sales: 25%
Number of Employees: 165
Average Check: Dinner(42)
Total Units: 3
Trade Names: Prime Quarter Steakhouse (3)
Company-Owned Units: 3
Preferred Square Footage: 7,500; 12,000
Preferred Location Types: Freestanding
Alcohol Served: Beer, Wine, Liquor
Primary Menu: Steak (3)
Areas of Operation: IL, WI
Type of Foodservice: Casual Dining (3)
Primary Distributors: (Full Line) SYSCO Food Services of Eastern Wisconsin, JACKSON, WI

Key Personnel
ALBERT SANGER - CEO; President; Director Operations, Purchasing, Facility/Maintenance, Supply Chain, Real Estate, Design, Menu Development

Steren Management Co.
3451 E Ramsey Ave
Cudahy, WI 53110-3008

Telephone: (414) 744-2800
Fax Number: (414) 744-4664
Type of Business: Chain Restaurant Operator
Year Founded: 1961
Total Sales: $60,770,000 (e)
Number of Employees: 590
Average Check: Breakfast(8); Lunch(10); Dinner(10)
Total Units: 13
Trade Names: McDonald's (13)
Units Franchised From: 13
Preferred Square Footage: 2,500; 3,000
Preferred Location Types: Freestanding
Primary Menu: Hamburger (13)
Areas of Operation: WI
Type of Foodservice: Quick Serve (13)
Franchise Affiliation: McDonald's Corporation, CHICAGO, IL
Primary Distributors: (Full Line) Golden State Foods Corporation, IRVINE, CA

Key Personnel
JEFF STEREN - President; General Manager; General Buyer
MARY MELSHEIMER - Manager Payroll
STAN SKIELSKI - Manager Operations, Information Systems, Real Estate, Human Resources

DORO Incorporated
3112 Golf Rd
Eau Claire, WI 54701-8013

Telephone: (715) 836-6800
Fax Number: (715) 836-6815
Type of Business: Chain Restaurant Operator
Year Founded: 1968
Total Sales: $157,180,000 (e)
Number of Employees: 4,000
Average Check: Breakfast(6); Lunch(10); Dinner(12)
Total Units: 88
Trade Names: Hardee's (83); Taco John's (5)
Units Franchised From: 88
Preferred Square Footage: 3,000
Preferred Location Types: Convenience Store/Gas Station; Downtown; Freestanding; Regional Mall; Strip Mall
Primary Menu: Hamburger (83); Taco (5)
Areas of Operation: IA, IL, MI, MN, ND, SD, WI
Type of Foodservice: Quick Serve (88)
Franchise Affiliation: Hardee's Food Systems Inc., FRANKLIN, TN; Taco John's International Inc., CHEYENNE, WY
Primary Distributors: (Equipment) HED Foodservice Equipment, ROCKY MOUNT, NC; (Food) McLane/Elkhorn, ELKHORN, WI; (Supplies) HED Foodservice Equipment, ROCKY MOUNT, NC

Key Personnel
JON MUNGER - President; Director Finance, Purchasing, Facility/Maintenance, Real Estate
DAN SHUDA - Controller; Director Accounting
PATTY CLARK-HARRINGTON - Director Human Resources
STEVE FISHER - Director Information Systems; General Buyer
MARVIN JOHNSON - Director Accounting

E & G Franchise Systems Inc.
5828 Arndt Rd
Eau Claire, WI 54701-9641

Telephone: (715) 833-1375
Fax Number: (715) 833-8523
Internet Homepage: erbertandgerberts.com
Company Email: info@erbertandgerberts.com
Type of Business: Chain Restaurant Operator
Year Founded: 1987
Systemwide Sales: $95,824,000 (e)
Total Sales: $11,000,000 (e)
Number of Employees: 20
Average Check: Lunch(10); Dinner(10)
Internet Order Processing: Yes
Total Units: 76
Trade Names: Erbert & Gerbert's Subs & Clubs (93)
Company-Owned Units: 1
Units Franchised To: 92
Preferred Square Footage: 1,200; 1,800
Preferred Location Types: Downtown; Strip Mall
Primary Menu: Sandwiches/Deli (93)
Areas of Operation: AZ, CO, IA, MI, MN, MT, NC, ND, NE, NY, OH, SD, TX, WI
Type of Foodservice: Quick Serve (93)
Catering Services: Yes

Key Personnel
ERIC WOLFE - Chairman; CEO; President
JEAN KLEVEN - CFO
SHANNON BRADY - Director Training
JEREMY BURKE - Director Marketing, Brand Marketing

Eau-D Inc.
2127 Necessity St
Eau Claire, WI 54703-4928

Telephone: (715) 836-6780
Fax Number: (715) 836-6786
Type of Business: Chain Restaurant Operator
Year Founded: 1983
Total Sales: $26,930,000 (e)

Number of Employees: 370
Average Check: Breakfast(8); Lunch(10); Dinner(10)
Total Units: 12
Trade Names: Burger King (12)
Units Franchised From: 12
Preferred Square Footage: 2,500; 4,000
Preferred Location Types: Convenience Store/Gas Station; Downtown; Freestanding
Primary Menu: Hamburger (12)
Projected Remodelings: 4
Areas of Operation: WI
Type of Foodservice: Quick Serve (12)
Franchise Affiliation: Burger King Worldwide Inc., MIAMI, FL
Primary Distributors: (Full Line) Reinhart FoodService, MARSHALL, MN

Key Personnel
MIKE DEROSA - President; Director Real Estate, Design; General Buyer
GENE HATFIELD - Director Finance, Facility/Maintenance
MARY LINN - Director Information Systems; Manager Human Resources

Lanier, Inc.
1719 N Clairemont Ave
Eau Claire, WI 54703-4966

Telephone: (715) 833-3930
Type of Business: Chain Restaurant Operator
Total Sales: $8,168,000 (e)
Total Units: 4
Trade Names: Domino's (4)
Units Franchised From: 4
Primary Menu: Pizza (4)
Areas of Operation: WI
Type of Foodservice: Quick Serve (4)
Franchise Affiliation: Domino's Pizza Inc, ANN ARBOR, MI

Key Personnel
MICHAEL LANIER - President; General Buyer

Pizza Hut of Eau Claire Inc
2602 E Clairemont Ave
Eau Claire, WI 54701-6729

Telephone: (715) 834-5346
Type of Business: Chain Restaurant Operator
Total Sales: $3,968,000 (e)
Total Units: 3
Trade Names: Pizza Hut (3)
Units Franchised From: 3
Primary Menu: Pizza (3)
Areas of Operation: WI
Type of Foodservice: Quick Serve (3)
Franchise Affiliation: Pizza Hut Inc., PLANO, TX

Key Personnel
THOMAS BROWN - President; General Buyer

C & C Administration
15285 Watertown Plank Rd
Elm Grove, WI 53122-2339

Telephone: (262) 780-0111
Fax Number: (262) 780-0112
Internet Homepage: wongswok.com
Type of Business: Chain Restaurant Operator
Year Founded: 1979
Total Sales: $3,026,000 (e)
Number of Employees: 110
Average Check: Lunch(8); Dinner(14)
Total Units: 2
Trade Names: Wong's Wok (2)
Company-Owned Units: 2
Preferred Square Footage: 3,000; 5,000
Preferred Location Types: Strip Mall
Primary Menu: Chinese (2)
Areas of Operation: WI
Type of Foodservice: Quick Serve (2)
Primary Distributors: (Food) Reinhart FoodService, OAK CREEK, WI

Key Personnel
JENNY NORVIK - Owner; General Manager; Executive Chef; General Buyer

Sheckler Subway Inc
13390 Spring Valley Rd
Fennimore, WI 53809-9513

Telephone: (608) 822-6244
Company Email: rrsheckler@hotmail.com
Type of Business: Chain Restaurant Operator
Total Sales: $5,386,000 (e)
Total Units: 6
Trade Names: Papa Murphy's Take 'N' Bake Pizza (2); Subway (4)
Units Franchised From: 6
Primary Menu: Sandwiches/Deli (6)
Areas of Operation: WI
Type of Foodservice: Quick Serve (6)
Franchise Affiliation: Doctor's Associates Inc., MILFORD, CT; Papa Murphy's International Inc., VANCOUVER, WA

Key Personnel
RANDY SHECKLER - President; General Buyer

IWI Ventures
5352 King James Way
Fitchburg, WI 53719-1700

Telephone: (608) 467-0590
Fax Number: (608) 268-6979
Type of Business: Chain Restaurant Operator
Year Founded: 2004
Total Sales: $11,130,000 (e)
Alcohol Sales: 2%
Number of Employees: 90
Total Units: 8
Trade Names: Noodles & Company (8)
Units Franchised From: 8
Preferred Square Footage: 2,500
Preferred Location Types: Freestanding; Strip Mall
Alcohol Served: Wine
Primary Menu: Miscellaneous (8)
Areas of Operation: IA, IL, WI
Type of Foodservice: Fast Casual (8)
Franchise Affiliation: Noodles & Company, BROOMFIELD, CO
Primary Distributors: (Full Line) Reinhart FoodService LLC, CHICAGO, IL

Key Personnel
BRITTON WIEDEMANN - President; General Buyer

Milio's Sandwiches
5936 Seminole Centre Ct Ste 100
Fitchburg, WI 53711

Telephone: (608) 284-7638
Fax Number: (608) 284-9088
Internet Homepage: milios.com
Company Email: info@milios.com
Type of Business: Chain Restaurant Operator
Year Founded: 1989
Systemwide Sales: $41,901,000 (e)
Total Sales: $27,050,000 (e)
Number of Employees: 628
Average Check: Lunch(12); Dinner(14)
Internet Order Processing: Yes
Total Units: 53
Trade Names: Milio's Sandwiches (53)
Company-Owned Units: 28
Units Franchised To: 25
Preferred Square Footage: 2,500
Preferred Location Types: Convenience Store/Gas Station; Freestanding; Regional Mall; Strip Mall
Primary Menu: Sandwiches/Deli (53)
Areas of Operation: IA, MN, WI
Type of Foodservice: Quick Serve (53)
Catering Services: Yes
Primary Distributors: (Food) SYSCO Food Services of Eastern Wisconsin, JACKSON, WI

Key Personnel
MIKE LIAUTAUD - President; General Manager; Director Catering; General Buyer
ROBERT JACOBS - Owner
PATTI JOYCE - Owner
JOSH WESTBY - General Manager
GERARD HELMINSKI - Director Franchise Operations

BRIAN BABINEAU - Supervisor

RAD, Inc.
288 E Johnson St
Fond Du Lac, WI 54935-3632

Telephone: (920) 923-1100
Fax Number: (920) 923-2666
Type of Business: Chain Restaurant Operator
Total Sales: $11,708,000 (e)
Total Units: 4
Trade Names: Taco Bell (4)
Units Franchised From: 4
Primary Menu: Taco (4)
Areas of Operation: WI
Type of Foodservice: Quick Serve (4)
Franchise Affiliation: Taco Bell Corp., IRVINE, CA

Key Personnel
RANDY ABITZ - President
MARK ABITZ - CFO
BRIDGET GRUELL - Director Operations; General Buyer

Buckley Enterprises LLC
2251 Hutson Rd Ste A
Green Bay, WI 54303-4712

Telephone: (920) 965-6501
Fax Number: (920) 965-6145
Company Email: general@subrock.us
Type of Business: Chain Restaurant Operator
Total Sales: $33,090,000 (e)
Total Units: 52
Trade Names: Subway (52)
Units Franchised From: 52
Primary Menu: Sandwiches/Deli (52)
Areas of Operation: WI
Type of Foodservice: Quick Serve (52)
Franchise Affiliation: Doctor's Associates Inc., MILFORD, CT

Key Personnel
PATRICK BUCKLEY - Owner; General Buyer
DEAN BUCKLEY - Owner

Schanock Investment Co.
1728 Industrial Dr
Green Bay, WI 54302-2106

Telephone: (920) 465-8440
Type of Business: Chain Restaurant Operator
Total Sales: $64,460,000 (e)
Number of Employees: 600
Total Units: 14
Trade Names: McDonald's (14)
Units Franchised From: 14
Preferred Square Footage: 2,500

Primary Menu: Hamburger (8)
Areas of Operation: WI
Type of Foodservice: Quick Serve (8)
Franchise Affiliation: McDonald's Corporation, CHICAGO, IL

Key Personnel
DAVID SCHANOCK - President; General Buyer

Tonns Inc.
1897 Velp Ave
Green Bay, WI 54303-6447

Telephone: (920) 498-8019
Fax Number: (920) 498-8019
Company Email: rs018737@tacabell.com
Type of Business: Chain Restaurant Operator
Year Founded: 1999
Total Sales: $16,400,000 (e)
Number of Employees: 180
Average Check: Lunch(8); Dinner(10)
Total Units: 6
Trade Names: Taco Bell (6)
Units Franchised From: 6
Preferred Square Footage: 2,500; 3,200
Preferred Location Types: Freestanding
Primary Menu: Taco (6)
Areas of Operation: WI
Type of Foodservice: Quick Serve (6)
Franchise Affiliation: Taco Bell Corp., IRVINE, CA
Primary Distributors: (Food) McLane/Sturtevant, STURTEVANT, WI

Key Personnel
GREG TONN - Partner; Supervisor Information Systems; General Buyer
PERRY TONN - Partner; Director Real Estate, Personnel
HEATHER VANG - General Manager

Auntie Anne's Franchise
2500 Milton Ave
Janesville, WI 53545-0452

Telephone: (608) 572-6088
Type of Business: Chain Restaurant Operator
Total Sales: $5,035,000 (e)
Total Units: 7
Trade Names: Auntie Anne's Hand-Rolled Soft Pretzels (7)
Units Franchised From: 7
Primary Menu: Snacks (7)
Areas of Operation: WI
Type of Foodservice: Quick Serve (7)
Franchise Affiliation: Auntie Anne's Inc., LANCASTER, PA

Key Personnel
NARENDRA PATEL - Owner; General Buyer

Saalsaa Bros Inc
1929 Center Ave
Janesville, WI 53546-2816

Telephone: (608) 754-4242
Type of Business: Chain Restaurant Operator
Total Sales: $24,600,000 (e)
Total Units: 40
Trade Names: Subway (40)
Units Franchised From: 40
Primary Menu: Sandwiches/Deli (40)
Areas of Operation: WI
Type of Foodservice: Quick Serve (40)
Franchise Affiliation: Doctor's Associates Inc., MILFORD, CT

Key Personnel
BRETT SAALSAA - Owner; General Buyer
SHARON MAGEE - Controller

First Kenosha Kentucky Fried Chicken, Inc
8207 22nd Ave
Kenosha, WI 53143

Telephone: (262) 697-9106
Type of Business: Chain Restaurant Operator
Total Sales: $15,960,000 (e)
Total Units: 9
Trade Names: KFC (9)
Units Franchised From: 9
Primary Menu: Chicken (9)
Areas of Operation: WI
Type of Foodservice: Quick Serve (8)
Franchise Affiliation: KFC Corporation, LOUISVILLE, KY

Key Personnel
PETER WASIELIVICH - President; General Buyer

Wasilevich Enterprises
8207 22nd Ave Ste 160
Kenosha, WI 53143-6211

Telephone: (262) 697-9106
Fax Number: (262) 697-9107
Type of Business: Chain Restaurant Operator
Year Founded: 1960
Total Sales: $12,550,000 (e)
Number of Employees: 300
Average Check: Lunch(10); Dinner(12)
Total Units: 7
Trade Names: KFC (7)
Units Franchised From: 7

Preferred Square Footage: 3,000
Preferred Location Types: Freestanding
Primary Menu: Chicken (7)
Areas of Operation: IL, WI
Type of Foodservice: Quick Serve (7)
Franchise Affiliation: KFC Corporation, LOUISVILLE, KY

Key Personnel
PETE WASILEVICH - President; Partner; Director Operations; Manager Purchasing, Loss Prevention, Real Estate; General Buyer
LINDA WASILEVICH - Partner; Controller; Manager Finance, Information Systems, Human Resources

Destination Kohler
444 Highland Dr
Kohler, WI 53044-1514

Telephone: (920) 457-8888
Fax Number: (920) 457-9441
Internet Homepage: americanclubresort.com
Company Email: info@americanclub.com
Type of Business: Foodservice Operations - Hotel/Motels
Year Founded: 1873
Total Sales: $42,713,000 (e)
Alcohol Sales: 15%
Number of Employees: 650
Average Check: Dinner(66)
Total Units: 3
Restaurants in Hotels: 5
Trade Names: Inn On Woodlake (1); Sandhill (1); The American Club (1)
Company-Owned Units: 5
Alcohol Served: Beer, Wine, Liquor
Areas of Operation: WI
Type of Foodservice: Casual Dining (5)
Primary Distributors: (Food) SYSCO Food Services of Eastern Wisconsin, JACKSON, WI
Parent Company: Kohler Co., KOHLER, WI
Notes: The company derives approximately 70% of its revenue from hotel operations.

Key Personnel
TIMOTHY VAN STELLE - Coordinator Facility/Maintenance

Brothers Franchising & Development, LLC
308 3rd St S
La Crosse, WI 54601-4007

Mailing Address: PO Box 1621, La Crosse, WI, 54602
Telephone: (608) 784-1225
Fax Number: (608) 784-0520
Internet Homepage: brothersbar.com
Type of Business: Chain Restaurant Operator
Year Founded: 1990
Total Sales: $42,980,000 (e)
Total Units: 19
Trade Names: Brothers Bar & Grill (19)
Units Franchised To: 19
Preferred Square Footage: 5,000; 7,500
Primary Menu: American (19)
Areas of Operation: CO, IA, IL, IN, KS, KY, MN, NE, OH, WI
Type of Foodservice: Casual Dining (19)

Key Personnel
ERIC M. FORTNEY - Co-Founder; VP; Corporate Secretary
CAROL J. FORTNEY - CFO; Treasurer
TONY DE SALVO - COO; VP Operations
ANTHONY CORTESE - Chief Marketing Officer
PATRICIA FORTNEY - Manager Accounting

Rottinghaus Company Inc.
510 Gillette St
La Crosse, WI 54603-3600

Telephone: (608) 784-2774
Fax Number: (608) 784-2740
Type of Business: Chain Restaurant Operator
Total Sales: $197,350,000 (e)
Number of Employees: 7,200
Average Check: Dinner(8)
Total Units: 351
Trade Names: Subway (351)
Units Franchised From: 351
Preferred Square Footage: 300; 2,000
Primary Menu: Sandwiches/Deli (351)
Projected Openings: 20
Areas of Operation: KS, MN, MO, OK, TX, WI
Type of Foodservice: Quick Serve (351)
Franchise Affiliation: Doctor's Associates Inc., MILFORD, CT

Key Personnel
ERIC NISSEN - CEO
DENNIS ROTTINGHAUS - CEO; President; Partner; General Buyer
DON ROTTINGHAUS - Partner; CFO; VP
ANTHONY HEILMAN - COO
CORY SKINNER - Chief Real Estate Officer
THOMAS SCHINDLER - VP Development
PETE HANSEN - Controller
JEFF HAMM - Director Operations
MISSINA SHARP - Director Asset Protection
JAMES MIDDENDORP - Director Facility/Maintenance
CHRISTY HINTON - Manager Payroll
JENNIE SASS - Manager Human Resources

XBN Corp
117 Lake Ave W
Ladysmith, WI 54848-1300

Mailing Address: PO Box 148, CHETEK, WI, 54728-0148
Telephone: (715) 924-3885
Type of Business: Chain Restaurant Operator
Total Sales: $5,688,000 (e)
Total Units: 10
Trade Names: Subway (10)
Units Franchised From: 10
Primary Menu: Sandwiches/Deli (10)
Areas of Operation: WI
Type of Foodservice: Quick Serve (10)
Franchise Affiliation: Doctor's Associates Inc., MILFORD, CT

Key Personnel
MARK SCHOONOVER - President; Owner; General Buyer

Great Wolf Resorts Inc.
525 Junction Rd Ste 6000
Madison, WI 53717-2153

Telephone: (608) 662-4700
Fax Number: (608) 662-4701
Internet Homepage: greatwolf.com
Company Email: info@greatwolf.com
Type of Business: Foodservice Operations - Hotel/Motels
Total Sales: $418,950,000 (e)
Alcohol Sales: 10%
Number of Employees: 150
Total Units: 72
Restaurants in Hotels: 72
Trade Names: Antler Shanty Grub (1); Bear Claw Cafe (1); Bear Paw Sweets & Eats (12); Buckets Incredible Craveables (1); Camp Critter Bar & Grille (9); Canoe Coffee (1); Dunkin Donuts (5); Gitchigoomie Grill (1); Grizzly Robs Bar (4); Hungry as a Wolf (1); Klondike Cafe (1); Lodge Wood Fired Grill (1); Loose Moose Bar & Grill (5); Lumber Jack's Cook Shanty (1); Northwoods Pizza (1); Oasis Bar & Grill (1); Pizza Hut Express (6); Spirit Island Snack Shop (12); Starbucks Coffee (4); The Loose Moose Cottage (3); Wolfs Den (1)
Company-Owned Units: 57
Units Franchised From: 15
Alcohol Served: Beer, Wine, Liquor
Areas of Operation: KS, MA, MI, NC, OH, PA, TX, VA, WA, WI, ON
Foreign Countries: CANADA
Type of Foodservice: Casual Dining (1)
Franchise Affiliation: DD IP Holder, CANTON, MA; Pizza Hut Inc., PLANO, TX
Primary Distributors: (Food) SYSCO Food Services of Baraboo, BARABOO, WI
Parent Company: Centerbridge Partners LP, NEW YORK, NY
Notes: The company derives approximately 84% of its revenue from resort and management operations.

Key Personnel
GREGORY KRYDER - CFO

ERIN WALLACE - COO
BRYAN ROBINSON - Chief People Officer; Senior VP
GREG MILLER - Chief Development Officer; Exec VP
RODNEY JONES - VP Construction, Menu Development
RHONDA KAHBIR - Director Sales

Ian's Pizza
319 N Frances St
Madison, WI 53703-1970

Telephone: (608) 257-9248
Internet Homepage: ianspizza.com
Company Email: 319nfrances@ianspizza.com
Type of Business: Chain Restaurant Operator
Total Units: 7
Trade Names: Ian's Pizza (7)
Company-Owned Units: 7
Primary Menu: Pizza (7)
Areas of Operation: CO, WA, WI
Type of Foodservice: Quick Serve (7)

Key Personnel
BRANDON STOTTLER - Partner; Executive Chef; General Buyer
RYAN FLOHR - Partner

Pizza Hut of Southern Wisconsin Inc.
434 S Yellowstone Dr Ste 101
Madison, WI 53719-1086

Telephone: (608) 833-2113
Fax Number: (608) 833-2977
Internet Homepage: pizzahut.com
Type of Business: Chain Restaurant Operator
Year Founded: 1968
Total Sales: $38,690,000 (e)
Alcohol Sales: 2%
Number of Employees: 1,530
Average Check: Lunch(22); Dinner(30)
Total Units: 32
Trade Names: Pizza Hut (32)
Units Franchised From: 32
Preferred Square Footage: 2,500
Preferred Location Types: Community Mall; Downtown; Freestanding; Regional Mall; Strip Mall
Alcohol Served: Beer, Wine
Primary Menu: Pizza (32)
Projected Openings: 30
Areas of Operation: IL, WI
Type of Foodservice: Quick Serve (32)
Foodservice Management Venues: Business & Industry; Health Care; Lodging; Schools
Catering Services: Yes
Franchise Affiliation: Pizza Hut Inc., PLANO, TX
Primary Distributors: (Full Line) McLane/Sturtevant, STURTEVANT, WI

Key Personnel
RICHARD DIVELBISS - President; Director Purchasing, Real Estate
JIM WILLIAMS - COO; Director Human Resources; General Buyer

Pizzeria Uno of Madison Inc
612 W Main St Ste 301
Madison, WI 53703-4700

Telephone: (608) 255-0605
Fax Number: (608) 255-7756
Type of Business: Chain Restaurant Operator
Total Units: 3
Trade Names: Uno Chicago Grill (3)
Company-Owned Units: 3
Primary Menu: Pizza (3)
Areas of Operation: WI
Type of Foodservice: Casual Dining (3)
Franchise Affiliation: Uno Restaurants, LLC, NORWOOD, MA

Key Personnel
TOM BEACH - President; General Buyer

Quality Pizza Inc
330 S Whitney Way Ste 100
Madison, WI 53705-4638

Telephone: (608) 236-9322
Fax Number: (608) 236-9331
Internet Homepage: rockysmadison.com
Company Email: marketing@rococoemail.com
Type of Business: Chain Restaurant Operator
Total Sales: $7,399,000 (e)
Total Units: 7
Trade Names: Rocky Rococo Panstyle Pizza (7)
Units Franchised From: 7
Primary Menu: Pizza (7)
Areas of Operation: WI
Type of Foodservice: Family Restaurant (7)
Franchise Affiliation: Rocky Rococo Restaurants, OCONOMOWOC, WI

Key Personnel
ROGER BROWN - Owner
JASON GARRIS - Manager Marketing

Von Rutenberg Ventures
5360 Westport Rd
Madison, WI 53704-1155

Telephone: (608) 850-4774
Fax Number: (608) 246-3135
Internet Homepage: capbills.com; marinersmadison.com; nautigal.com; vrv-madison.com
Company Email: vonr@gdinet.com
Type of Business: Chain Restaurant Operator
Year Founded: 1981
Total Sales: $5,745,000 (e)
Alcohol Sales: 30%
Number of Employees: 120
Average Check: Dinner(36)
Internet Order Processing: Yes
Internet Sales: 0.50%
Total Units: 3
Trade Names: Captain Bill's (1); The Mariner's Inn (1); The Nau-Ti-Gal (1)
Company-Owned Units: 3
Preferred Location Types: Freestanding; Hotel/Motel
Alcohol Served: Beer, Wine, Liquor
Primary Menu: Steak/Seafood (3)
Areas of Operation: WI
Type of Foodservice: Casual Dining (3)
Primary Distributors: (Equipment) Edward Don & Co., WOODRIDGE, IL; (Food) Reinhart FoodService LLC, CHICAGO, IL; (Supplies) Edward Don & Co., WOODRIDGE, IL

Key Personnel
BILL VON RUTENBERG - President; Partner; Executive Chef; General Buyer
JACK VON RUTENBERG - Partner; VP; General Manager
ROBERT VON RUTENBERG - Partner

P.I.P. Corp.
2760 Roosevelt Rd
Marinette, WI 54143-3832

Mailing Address: PO Box 500, MARINETTE, WI, 54143-0500
Telephone: (715) 735-8973
Fax Number: (715) 735-8975
Type of Business: Chain Restaurant Operator
Total Sales: $9,816,000 (e)
Total Units: 4
Trade Names: Burger King (4)
Units Franchised From: 4
Preferred Location Types: Freestanding
Primary Menu: Hamburger (4)
Areas of Operation: WI
Type of Foodservice: Quick Serve (4)
Franchise Affiliation: Burger King Worldwide Inc., MIAMI, FL

Key Personnel
GLEN SEYFERT - President; General Buyer

Cougar Enterprises Inc
909 Casement Ct
Medford, WI 54451-1204

Telephone: (715) 748-6542
Type of Business: Chain Restaurant Operator

Total Sales: $5,660,000 (e)
Total Units: 3
Trade Names: Hardee's (3)
Units Franchised From: 3
Primary Menu: Hamburger (3)
Areas of Operation: WI
Type of Foodservice: Quick Serve (3)
Franchise Affiliation: Hardee's Food Systems Inc., FRANKLIN, TN

Key Personnel
AL WILLIAMS - President; General Buyer
DAVE DROSTE - Owner

Michelle Sperl
342 S 8th St
Medford, WI 54451-1903

Telephone: (715) 748-6400
Type of Business: Chain Restaurant Operator
Total Sales: $1,485,000 (e)
Total Units: 2
Trade Names: Subway (2)
Units Franchised From: 2
Primary Menu: Sandwiches/Deli (2)
Areas of Operation: WI
Type of Foodservice: Quick Serve (2)
Franchise Affiliation: Doctor's Associates Inc., MILFORD, CT

Key Personnel
MICHELLE SPERL - Owner; General Buyer

Cousins Sub Systems Inc.
N83W13400 Leon Rd
Menomonee Falls, WI 53051-3306

Telephone: (262) 253-7700
Fax Number: (262) 253 7710
Internet Homepage: cousinssubs.com
Company Email: info@cousinssubs.com
Type of Business: Chain Restaurant Operator
Year Founded: 1972
Systemwide Sales: $74,490,000 (e)
Total Sales: $3,785,000 (e)
Number of Employees: 658
Average Check: Lunch(8); Dinner(8)
Internet Order Processing: Yes
Total Units: 88
Trade Names: Cousins Subs (88)
Company-Owned Units: 18
Units Franchised To: 70
Preferred Square Footage: 750; 1,300; 1,600; 1,800; 2,200
Preferred Location Types: Convenience Store/Gas Station; Downtown; Freestanding; Institution (college/hospital); Mobile Unit; Regional Mall; Strip Mall; Travel Plazas
Primary Menu: Sandwiches/Deli (88)
Projected Openings: 3
Areas of Operation: AZ, IL, WI

Type of Foodservice: Quick Serve (88)
Catering Services: Yes
Primary Distributors: (Equipment) The Boelter Companies Inc., WAUKESHA, WI; (Food) US Foods, MENOMONEE FALLS, WI; (Supplies) The Boelter Companies Inc., WAUKESHA, WI

Key Personnel
CHRISTINE SPECHT-PALMERT - CEO; Partner
JASON WESTHOFF - President
JUSTIN MCCOY - VP Marketing
JOSEPH FERGUSON - VP Real Estate, Business Development
MIKE AREND - VP Finance
KIM LESCH - Director Real Estate
HILARY KREKLING - Director Human Resources
JOHN KRAHN - Manager Training
JOHN PALMERT - Manager Franchise Sales
COURTNEY HENDRICKS - Manager Human Resources
MICHAEL BAUTCH - Manager Information Technology
NATALIE FORD - Specialist Digital Marketing

McDonald's Franchise
1492 W Mequon Rd
Mequen, WI 53092-3268

Telephone: (262) 241-6926
Fax Number: (262) 241-6927
Type of Business: Chain Restaurant Operator
Total Sales: $43,380,000 (e)
Total Units: 9
Trade Names: McDonald's (9)
Units Franchised From: 9
Primary Menu: Hamburger (9)
Areas of Operation: WI
Type of Foodservice: Quick Serve (9)
Franchise Affiliation: McDonald's Corporation, CHICAGO, IL

Key Personnel
RAFAEL LUCIANO - Owner; General Buyer

Bennett Barndt Enterprises Inc
8308 Greenway Blvd
Middleton, WI 53562-3505

Telephone: (608) 829-2582
Fax Number: (608) 829-2568
Type of Business: Chain Restaurant Operator
Total Sales: $28,540,000 (e)
Number of Employees: 300
Total Units: 6
Trade Names: McDonald's (6)
Units Franchised From: 6
Preferred Square Footage: 2,500
Preferred Location Types: Community Mall; Freestanding
Primary Menu: Hamburger (6)
Areas of Operation: WI
Type of Foodservice: Quick Serve (6)
Franchise Affiliation: McDonald's Corporation, CHICAGO, IL

Key Personnel
CARRIE BENNETT-BARNDT - President; Owner; General Buyer

Legacy Franchise Group
6405 Century Ave Ste 1
Middleton, WI 53562-2200

Telephone: (888) 359-3235
Fax Number: (608) 833-8071
Internet Homepage: countrykitchenrestaurants.com
Company Email: info@countrykitchen.net
Type of Business: Chain Restaurant Operator
Year Founded: 1939
Systemwide Sales: $37,597,000 (e)
Total Sales: $1,638,000 (e)
Alcohol Sales: 2%
Number of Employees: 670
Average Check: Breakfast(6); Lunch(10); Dinner(16)
Total Units: 31
Trade Names: Country Kitchen (31)
Units Franchised To: 31
Preferred Square Footage: 4,000; 5,000
Preferred Location Types: Freestanding; Hotel/Motel; Other
Alcohol Served: Beer, Wine, Liquor
Primary Menu: American (31)
Areas of Operation: AZ, CA, CO, FL, IA, ID, KS, MI, MN, MO, ND, NE, NJ, NY, OH, OR, SD, WI, WY, MB
Foreign Countries: CANADA
Type of Foodservice: Casual Dining (31)
Catering Services: Yes
Primary Distributors: (Full Line) SYSCO Food Services of Baraboo, BARABOO, WI

Key Personnel
CHUCK MOCCO CEO
DAVID SEMRAD - Controller
WAYNE O'QUINN - Director Purchasing

Mr Brews Taphouse
1800 Parmenter St Ste 202
Middleton, WI 53562-3185

Telephone: (608) 556-1775
Internet Homepage: mrbrewstaphouse.com
Type of Business: Chain Restaurant Operator
Total Sales: $15,500,000 (e)
Total Units: 16
Trade Names: Mr Brews Taphouse (16)
Company-Owned Units: 16

Primary Menu: American (16)
Areas of Operation: WI
Type of Foodservice: Casual Dining (16)

Key Personnel
STEVE DAY - CEO
KEN LEETCH - Senior VP Operations

Brew City Pizza Inc
6327 W Capitol Dr
Milwaukee, WI 53216-2123

Telephone: (414) 462-8999
Type of Business: Chain Restaurant Operator
Total Sales: $47,729,000 (e)
Total Units: 24
Trade Names: Domino's (24)
Units Franchised From: 24
Primary Menu: Pizza (24)
Areas of Operation: WI
Type of Foodservice: Quick Serve (24)
Franchise Affiliation: Domino's Pizza Inc, ANN ARBOR, MI

Key Personnel
DOUG BARETZ - President; General Buyer
KELLY NOLES - Manager Administration

Colectivo Coffee Roasters Inc.
2999 N Humboldt Blvd
Milwaukee, WI 53212

Telephone: (414) 273-3747
Internet Homepage: colectivocoffee.com
Company Email: info@colectivocoffee.com
Type of Business: Chain Restaurant Operator
Year Founded: 1993
Total Units: 21
Trade Names: Colectivo (21)
Company-Owned Units: 21
Primary Menu: Coffee (21)
Areas of Operation: IL, WI
Type of Foodservice: Quick Serve (21)

Key Personnel
PAUL MILLER - Partner
LINCOLN FOWLER - Partner
WARD FOWLER - Partner

Domino's Franchisee
1338 W Forest Home Ave
Milwaukee, WI 53204-3227

Telephone: (414) 645-3303
Type of Business: Chain Restaurant Operator
Total Sales: $16,511,000 (e)
Total Units: 8

Trade Names: Domino's (8)
Units Franchised From: 8
Primary Menu: Pizza (8)
Areas of Operation: WI
Type of Foodservice: Quick Serve (8)
Franchise Affiliation: Domino's Pizza Inc, ANN ARBOR, MI

Key Personnel
STEVEN R. CHIODO - Owner; General Buyer

Family Entertainment Centers
1122 N Edison St
Milwaukee, WI 53202-3135

Telephone: (414) 223-1122
Internet Homepage: louiseswisconsin.com; vagabondmke.com; waterstreetbrewery.com
Company Email: wsbmktg@aol.com
Type of Business: Chain Restaurant Operator
Year Founded: 1981
Total Sales: $22,600,000 (e)
Alcohol Sales: 3%
Number of Employees: 330
Total Units: 7
Trade Names: Louise's (1); Vagabond (1); Waterstreet Brewery (4); Waterstreet Brewery Lake Country (1)
Company-Owned Units: 7
Preferred Square Footage: 12,000
Preferred Location Types: Freestanding
Alcohol Served: Beer, Wine, Liquor
Primary Menu: American (5); Italian (1); Mexican (1)
Areas of Operation: WI
Type of Foodservice: Casual Dining (7)
Catering Services: Yes
Primary Distributors: (Full Line) US Foods, MENOMONEE FALLS, WI

Key Personnel
ROBERT C. SCHMIDT JR - President; Controller; Executive Chef; Director Operations, Facility/Maintenance, Real Estate, Design; General Buyer

Kopp's Frozen Custard
833 N Jefferson St
Milwaukee, WI 53202-3709

Telephone: (414) 765-0615
Internet Homepage: az88.com; elsas.com; hannys.net; kopps.com
Type of Business: Chain Restaurant Operator
Year Founded: 1950
Total Sales: $20,680,000 (e)
Alcohol Sales: 1%
Number of Employees: 225
Average Check: Lunch(10); Dinner(10)
Internet Order Processing: Yes
Internet Sales: 1.00%
Total Units: 6
Trade Names: AZ88 (1); Elsa's on the Park (1); Hannys (1); Kopp's Frozen Custard (3)
Company-Owned Units: 6
Preferred Location Types: Freestanding
Alcohol Served: Beer, Wine, Liquor
Primary Menu: American (2); Italian (1); Snacks (3)
Areas of Operation: AZ, WI
Type of Foodservice: Casual Dining (3); Quick Serve (3)
Primary Distributors: (Full Line) US Foods, MENOMONEE FALLS, WI

Key Personnel
KARL R. KOPP - President; Manager Menu Development; General Buyer
SUSAN LITTLEFIELD - CFO; Controller; Manager Human Resources
ALBERT D. REINHART - Exec VP
MARY MCQUIRE - VP

Marco's Pizza Inc
6234 S 27th St
Milwaukee, WI 53221-4839

Telephone: (414) 761-1100
Type of Business: Chain Restaurant Operator
Total Sales: $16,080,000 (e)
Total Units: 14
Trade Names: Marco's Pizza (14)
Units Franchised From: 14
Primary Menu: Pizza (14)
Areas of Operation: WI
Type of Foodservice: Quick Serve (14)
Franchise Affiliation: Marco's Franchising LLC, TOLEDO, OH

Key Personnel
CHRIS REHROST - President; General Buyer

Marcus Hotels & Resorts
100 E Wisconsin Ave Ste 1900
Milwaukee, WI 53202-4132

Telephone: (414) 905-1000
Fax Number: (414) 905-2250
Internet Homepage: marcushotels.com
Company Email: info@marcushotels.com
Type of Business: Foodservice Operations - Hotel/Motels
Year Founded: 1935
Publicly Held: Yes
Total Sales: $392,270,000 (e)
Alcohol Sales: 8%
Number of Employees: 8,000
Total Units: 23
Restaurants in Hotels: 15
Trade Names: AC Hotel Chicago (1); Beverly

Garland (1); Crowne Plaza Northstar Hotel (1); Heidel House Resort (1); Hilton Bloomington Hotel (1); Hilton Garden Inn (4); Hilton Madison at Monona Terrace (1); Hilton Milwaukee City Center (1); InterContinental Milwaukee (1); Marriot Cornhusker (1); Platinum Hotel & Spa (1); Sheraton Four Points (1); Sheraton Madison (1); Skirvin Hilton (1); The Arts Hotel (1); The Grand Geneva Resort & Spa (1); The Hotel Zamora (1); The Pfister Hotel (1); Timber Ridge Lodge (1); Westin Atlanta North (1)
Company-Owned Units: 15
Alcohol Served: Beer, Wine, Liquor
Areas of Operation: CA, FL, GA, IL, MN, MO, NE, NV, OK, TX, WI
Type of Foodservice: Casual Dining; Fine Dining
Parent Company: Marcus Corporation, MILWAUKEE, WI

Key Personnel
STEPHEN H. MARCUS - Chairman
ERIN LEVZOW - Vice Chairman Marketing
GREGORY S. MARCUS - CEO; President
JOSEPH KHAIRALLAH - President; COO
KIM LUECK - CIO
PETER ENGEL - CIO
RAJIV CASTELLINO - CTO
TIM KAYSER - Area Director Finance
THOMAS F. KISSINGER - Senior Exec VP; Corporate Secretary; General Counsel
STEVE MARTIN - VP Human Resources
JEFF PETERSON - VP Finance
SUSAN TERRY - VP Food and Beverage
JIM WALDVOGEL - Area VP Division; General Manager Division
DAN HOPPE - General Manager
SUSAN MADSEN - General Manager
CHRISTINE WILLIAMS - Senior Director Marketing, E-Commerce
MARK WEBER - Director Culinary Development
STEVE MAGNUSON - Director Operations
WILL GEISSEL - Director Procurement
JIM GWINN - Director Procurement
MICKEY SKREDE - Manager Event Planning, Catering

Marcus Theatres Corporation
100 E Wisconsin Ave Ste 1900
Milwaukee, WI 53202-4132

Telephone: (414) 905-1000
Fax Number: (414) 905-2250
Internet Homepage: marcuscorp.com; marcustheatres.com
Type of Business: Foodservice Operations - Movie Theatre
Year Founded: 1935
Publicly Held: Yes
Total Sales: $404,094,000 (e)
Number of Employees: 3,200
Average Check: Lunch(6); Dinner(6)
Foodservice Sales: $149,514,000 (e)
Internet Order Processing: Yes
Total Units: 79
Trade Names: Marcus Theatre (63); Movie Tavern (16)
Company-Owned Units: 79
Preferred Square Footage: 2,500
Preferred Location Types: Freestanding; Regional Mall
Primary Menu: American (16); Snacks (63)
Areas of Operation: IA, IL, MN, ND, NE, OH, WI
Type of Foodservice: In-Store Feeder (79)
Parent Company: Marcus Corporation, MILWAUKEE, WI
Notes: The company derives approximately 63% of its revenue from on-screen advertising & theater admissions.

Key Personnel
GREGORY S. MARCUS - CEO; President
ROLANDO B. RODRIGUEZ - CEO; President
KIM LUECK - CIO; VP Information Technology
MIKE DUKES - CIO
THOMAS F. KISSINGER - Senior Exec VP; Corporate Secretary; General Counsel
MARK GRAMZ - Exec VP Operations, Information Technology, Construction, Human Resources, Foodservice
JEFF TOMACHEK - Exec VP Finance, Accounting, Marketing, Sales, Strategic Planning, Food and Beverage
KEN THEWES - Senior VP Marketing
KIM BARENGO - Senior VP Marketing
CLINT WISIALOWSKI - VP Sales
CHARMAINE SCHAFF - VP Finance
DOUG PELLOCK - VP Purchasing, Construction
MARI RANDA - Director Marketing
GARRETT RAWSON - Director District
PAM STEEVES - Director Purchasing, Supply Chain
TIM WARD - Director District
BRIAN CORNELL - Director Human Resources
SH'LON ANDERSON - Director Food
KAREN GAMROTH - Director Accounting
JIMMY HAMILTON - Director Accounting
BRET HOFFMANN - Director Marketing
ALEX NEFFENGER - Director Development, Human Resources, Talent
EMILY IVIE - Manager Operations
TACHARRA EDWARDS - Manager Operations
TYLER DORN - Manager Financial Planning
CATHELLEN BLANKENBURG - Manager Sales, National

Roaring Fork Restaurant Group
241 N Broadway Ste 501
Milwaukee, WI 53202-5819

Telephone: (414) 962-4200
Fax Number: (414) 962-4500
Internet Homepage: qdobawisconsin.com
Type of Business: Chain Restaurant Operator
Total Sales: $57,210,000 (e)
Total Units: 52
Trade Names: Qdoba Mexican Grill (52)
Units Franchised From: 52
Alcohol Served: Beer, Wine, Liquor
Primary Menu: Mexican (52)
Areas of Operation: IA, IL, WI
Type of Foodservice: Fast Casual (52)
Franchise Affiliation: Qdoba Mexican Eats, SAN DIEGO, CA

Key Personnel
MICHAEL PRANKE - CEO; Owner; General Buyer
RON STOKES - President; COO
JAMES ANDERSON - CFO
RANDY BEAVER - VP Operations
HANNA ANDERSON - Director Catering
SARAH LAUNDRY - Director Human Resources
SAM FRIEDMAN - Administrator Information Technology

The Bartolotta Restaurant Group
520 W McKinley Ave
Milwaukee, WI 53212-4011

Telephone: (414) 258-7885
Fax Number: (414) 258-8313
Internet Homepage: bartolottas.com
Company Email: info@bartolottas.com
Type of Business: Chain Restaurant Operator
Year Founded: 1993
Total Sales: $17,370,000 (e)
Alcohol Sales: 30%
Number of Employees: 218
Average Check: Lunch(28); Dinner(64)
Internet Order Processing: Yes
Internet Sales: 0.50%
Total Units: 10
Trade Names: Bacchus (1); Downtown Kitchen (1); Harbor House (1); Joey Gerard's (1); Lake Park Bistro (1); Mr. B's (2); Pizzeria Piccola (1); Ristorante Bartolotta (1); Rumpus Room (1)
Company-Owned Units: 10
Preferred Location Types: Freestanding
Alcohol Served: Beer, Wine, Liquor
Primary Menu: American (2); Italian (3); Pizza (1); Seafood (1); Steak (2); Steak/Seafood (1)
Projected Openings: 1
Areas of Operation: WI
Type of Foodservice: Casual Dining (4); Fine Dining (6)
Catering Services: Yes
Primary Distributors: (Food) Reinhart FoodService, SHAWANO, WI

Key Personnel
JOSEPH BARTOLOTTA - President; Partner;

General Buyer
PAUL BARTOLOTTA - Partner; Executive Chef
LISA BAUMANN - Director Human Resources

The Chocolate Factory Subs and Icecream
5800 N Bayshore Dr Ste B102
Milwaukee, WI 53217-4555

Telephone: (414) 915-5650
Fax Number: (414) 962-0378
Internet Homepage: thechocolatefactorywi.com
Type of Business: Chain Restaurant Operator
Year Founded: 1972
Systemwide Sales: $9,337,000 (e)
Total Sales: $5,765,000 (e)
Number of Employees: 160
Average Check: Breakfast(5); Lunch(8); Dinner(8)
Total Units: 8
Trade Names: Chocolate Factory Subs and Ice Cream (8)
Company-Owned Units: 8
Preferred Location Types: Community Mall; Freestanding; Strip Mall
Primary Menu: Snacks (8)
Areas of Operation: WI
Type of Foodservice: Fast Casual (8)
Catering Services: Yes
Primary Distributors: (Full Line) SYSCO Food Services of Eastern Wisconsin, JACKSON, WI

Key Personnel
MICHAEL H. TOFFLER - VP; Manager Operations, Purchasing, Facility/Maintenance, Human Resources, Menu Development

V & J Holding Companies Inc.
6933 W Brown Deer Rd
Milwaukee, WI 53223-2103

Telephone: (414) 365-9003
Fax Number: (414) 365-9467
Internet Homepage: vjfoods.com
Company Email: customer@vjfoods.com
Type of Business: Chain Restaurant Operator
Year Founded: 1982
Total Sales: $126,960,000 (e)
Number of Employees: 3,185
Average Check: Breakfast(8); Lunch(10); Dinner(10)
Total Units: 77
Trade Names: Auntie Anne's Hand-Rolled Soft Pretzels (10); Burger King (10); Haagen-Dazs (6); MyYOMy Frozen Yogurt (1); Nino's Southern Sides (1); Pizza Hut (43); The Coffee Beanery (6)
Company-Owned Units: 3
Units Franchised From: 74
Preferred Square Footage: 2,500; 3,000
Preferred Location Types: Downtown; Freestanding; Mobile Unit; Regional Mall; Stadiums; Strip Mall
Primary Menu: Coffee (6); Hamburger (10); Pizza (43); Snacks (17); Southern (1)
Areas of Operation: MA, MI, MN, NY, OH, WI
Type of Foodservice: Quick Serve (77)
Catering Services: Yes
Franchise Affiliation: GC Pizza Hut, LLC, MT KISCO, NY
Primary Distributors: (Food) McLane/Arlington, ARLINGTON, TX

Key Personnel
VALERIE DANIELS-CARTER - CEO; Director Purchasing, Supply Chain
CALVIN L. SCOTT - VP Human Resources
TONY WEISS - Controller
TODD WITTENBERG - Director Information Systems
JEFFREY CARTER - Director Operations
JASON SPENCER - Manager Finance, Benefits

SB Acquisitions LLC
6306 Monona Dr
Monona, WI 53716-3937

Telephone: (608) 221-6777
Fax Number: (608) 819-6625
Internet Homepage: pizzapit.biz
Type of Business: Chain Restaurant Operator
Year Founded: 1969
Systemwide Sales: $14,428,000 (e)
Total Sales: $8,123,000 (e)
Alcohol Sales: 3%
Number of Employees: 108
Average Check: Lunch(6); Dinner(16)
Internet Order Processing: Yes
Internet Sales: 1.00%
Total Units: 12
Trade Names: Pizza Pit (12)
Units Franchised To: 12
Preferred Square Footage: 1,200
Preferred Location Types: Community Mall; Downtown; Freestanding; Regional Mall; Strip Mall
Alcohol Served: Beer
Primary Menu: Pizza (12)
Projected Openings: 1
Areas of Operation: IA, WI
Type of Foodservice: Casual Dining (12)
Foodservice Management Venues: Schools
Catering Services: Yes
Primary Distributors: (Full Line) SYSCO Food Services of Eastern Wisconsin, JACKSON, WI
Notes: Formerly known as Pizza Pit Ltd.

Key Personnel
JASON BELL - Partner

Oudinot, Inc.
W4215 Juniper Dr
Monroe, WI 53566-8543

Telephone: (608) 325-3408
Type of Business: Chain Restaurant Operator
Total Sales: $23,760,000 (e)
Total Units: 5
Trade Names: McDonald's (5)
Units Franchised From: 5
Preferred Square Footage: 2,500
Primary Menu: Hamburger (5)
Areas of Operation: IL, WI
Type of Foodservice: Quick Serve (5)
Franchise Affiliation: McDonald's Corporation, CHICAGO, IL

Key Personnel
SCOTT OUDINOT - President; General Buyer

AMNJ Enterprises Inc
3725 Meachem Rd
Mount Pleasant, WI 53405

Telephone: (262) 898-1754
Type of Business: Chain Restaurant Operator
Total Sales: $20,323,000 (e)
Total Units: 10
Trade Names: Domino's (10)
Units Franchised From: 10
Primary Menu: Pizza (10)
Areas of Operation: WI
Type of Foodservice: Quick Serve (10)
Franchise Affiliation: Domino's Pizza Inc, ANN ARBOR, MI

Key Personnel
NATHANIEL P. BURTON - Owner; General Buyer
NATHAN BURTON - Owner

Valley Management Inc.
18 Jewelers Park Dr Ste 100
Neenah, WI 54956-5902

Telephone: (920) 725-8969
Fax Number: (920) 725-1294
Internet Homepage: valleymanagement.com
Type of Business: Chain Restaurant Operator
Year Founded: 1990
Total Sales: $69,140,000 (e)
Number of Employees: 730
Average Check: Breakfast(8); Lunch(8); Dinner(10)
Total Units: 15
Trade Names: McDonald's (15)
Units Franchised From: 15
Preferred Square Footage: 3,000
Preferred Location Types: Convenience

Store/Gas Station; Freestanding; Regional Mall
Primary Menu: Hamburger (15)
Areas of Operation: WI
Type of Foodservice: Quick Serve (15)
Franchise Affiliation: McDonald's Corporation, CHICAGO, IL

Key Personnel
CHUCK KUEN - President; Director Operations, Facility/Maintenance, Supply Chain, Real Estate; General Buyer
DAVID A. RAUSE - Owner; Director Finance, Information Systems, Design; General Buyer
DAN KUEN - VP People
JESSICA EVANS - Manager Accounting, Administration, Human Resources

SURG Restaurant Group
9667 S 20th St
Oak Creek, WI 53154-4931

Telephone: (414) 281-1100
Internet Homepage: su-rg.com
Company Email: info@surgrestaurantgroup.com
Type of Business: Chain Restaurant Operator
Total Sales: $5,411,000 (e)
Alcohol Sales: 10%
Number of Employees: 285
Total Units: 4
Trade Names: Bugsy's Back Alley Speakeasy (1); Carnevor (1); Distil (1); Gouda's Italian Deli (1)
Company-Owned Units: 4
Preferred Location Types: Community Mall; Downtown; Freestanding
Alcohol Served: Beer, Wine, Liquor
Primary Menu: American (2); Sandwiches/Deli (1); Steak (1)
Projected Openings: 1
Areas of Operation: WI
Type of Foodservice: Casual Dining (2); Fast Casual (1); Fine Dining (1)

Key Personnel
MIKE POLASKI - Partner; General Buyer
OMAR SHAIKH - Partner; General Buyer
ANDREA BUBOLTZ - Director

Domino's Franchisee
750 E Wisconsin Ave
Oconomowoc, WI 53066-3045

Telephone: (262) 569-6999
Type of Business: Chain Restaurant Operator
Total Sales: $6,055,000 (e)
Total Units: 3
Trade Names: Domino's (3)
Units Franchised From: 3
Primary Menu: Pizza (3)
Areas of Operation: WI
Type of Foodservice: Quick Serve (3)
Franchise Affiliation: Domino's Pizza Inc, ANN ARBOR, MI

Key Personnel
JASON D. SCHEEL - Owner; General Buyer

Rocky Rococo Restaurants
105 E Wisconsin Ave Ste 101
Oconomowoc, WI 53066-3058

Mailing Address: PO Box 207, OCONOMOWOC, WI, 53066-0207
Telephone: (262) 569-5580
Fax Number: (262) 569-5591
Internet Homepage: rockyrococo.com
Company Email: president@rockyrococo.com
Type of Business: Chain Restaurant Operator
Year Founded: 1974
Systemwide Sales: $52,056,000 (e)
Total Sales: $21,760,000 (e)
Alcohol Sales: 2%
Number of Employees: 336
Average Check: Lunch(12); Dinner(12)
Internet Order Processing: Yes
Total Units: 42
Trade Names: Rocky Rococo (42)
Company-Owned Units: 19
Units Franchised To: 23
Preferred Square Footage: 1,000; 3,500
Preferred Location Types: Downtown; Freestanding; Regional Mall; Strip Mall
Alcohol Served: Beer, Wine
Primary Menu: Pizza (42); Sandwiches/Deli (1)
Areas of Operation: IL, KY, MN, WA, WI
Type of Foodservice: Quick Serve (42)
Foodservice Management Venues: Business & Industry; Schools
Catering Services: Yes
Primary Distributors: (Equipment) Fein Bros. Inc., MILWAUKEE, WI; (Food) SYSCO Food Services of Baraboo, BARABOO, WI; (Supplies) Fein Bros. Inc., MILWAUKEE, WI

Key Personnel
TOM HESTER - CEO; Director Purchasing, Real Estate, Franchising, Menu Development, Catering
TREY HESTER - President; CFO; COO; Director Information Technology; General Buyer
KURT KIMBALL - Controller; Director Finance
SEAN SCHEIHING - General Manager
DEB REHM - Director Marketing
FABIOLA MARCHENA - Director Operations

Weissgerber Group
W349N5293 Lacys Ln
Okauchee, WI 53069-9726

Mailing Address: PO Box 41, OKAUCHEE, WI, 53069-0041
Telephone: (262) 567-7047
Fax Number: (262) 567-2343
Internet Homepage: weissgerbers.com
Company Email: goldenmast@weissgerbergroup.com
Type of Business: Chain Restaurant Operator
Year Founded: 1968
Total Sales: $6,493,000 (e)
Alcohol Sales: 25%
Number of Employees: 420
Average Check: Dinner(54)
Total Units: 2
Trade Names: Golden Mast (1); Seven Seas (1)
Company-Owned Units: 2
Preferred Square Footage: 2,200
Preferred Location Types: Downtown; Freestanding
Alcohol Served: Beer, Wine, Liquor
Primary Menu: American (1); Seafood (1)
Areas of Operation: WI
Type of Foodservice: Fine Dining (2)
Primary Distributors: (Full Line) SYSCO Food Services of Baraboo, BARABOO, WI

Key Personnel
HANS WEISSGERBER JR - President; Executive Chef; Director Finance, Real Estate, Menu Development; General Buyer
LINDA WEISSGERBER - President; General Buyer
RAMONA WEISSGERBER - General Manager
GEORGE SIMOS - General Manager
LISA MARKS - General Manager; General Buyer
JOHN MOOSREINER - Executive Chef; General Buyer

Courtesy Corporation
2700 National Dr Ste 100
Onalaska, WI 54650-6709

Telephone: (608) 781-8080
Fax Number: (608) 781-8555
Internet Homepage: mccourtesy.com
Type of Business: Chain Restaurant Operator
Year Founded: 1962
Total Sales: $288,040,000 (e)
Number of Employees: 3,511
Average Check: Breakfast(8); Lunch(8); Dinner(8)
Total Units: 62
Trade Names: McDonald's (62)
Units Franchised From: 62
Preferred Square Footage: 2,500; 3,000

Preferred Location Types: Convenience Store/Gas Station; Discount Dept. Stores; Freestanding
Primary Menu: Hamburger (62)
Areas of Operation: IA, MN, WI
Type of Foodservice: Quick Serve (62)
Franchise Affiliation: McDonald's Corporation, CHICAGO, IL
Primary Distributors: (Full Line) The Martin-Brower Co., FRIDLEY, MN

Key Personnel
DICK LOMMEN - CEO; Partner; Director Information Systems, Real Estate
RICK LOMMEN - President; Partner; Director Supply Chain; General Buyer
KAYLA MULLEN - Director Marketing

Domino's Franchisee
224 Sand Lake Rd
Onalaska, WI 54650-2775

Telephone: (608) 779-3030
Type of Business: Chain Restaurant Operator
Total Sales: $4,099,000 (e)
Total Units: 2
Trade Names: Domino's (2)
Units Franchised From: 2
Primary Menu: Pizza (3)
Areas of Operation: WI
Type of Foodservice: Quick Serve (2)
Franchise Affiliation: Domino's Pizza Inc, ANN ARBOR, MI

Key Personnel
ERIK J. BURTON - Owner; General Buyer

Oshkosh Restaurants LLC.
2100 S Koeller St
Oshkosh, WI 54902-9202

Telephone: (920) 231-7511
Fax Number: (920) 231-7521
Internet Homepage: hardees.com
Type of Business: Chain Restaurant Operator
Year Founded: 1966
Total Sales: $3,870,000 (e)
Number of Employees: 225
Average Check: Breakfast(8); Lunch(8); Dinner(8)
Total Units: 2
Trade Names: Hardee's (2)
Units Franchised From: 2
Preferred Square Footage: 3,000; 3,500
Preferred Location Types: Freestanding
Primary Menu: Hamburger (2)
Areas of Operation: WI
Type of Foodservice: Quick Serve (2)
Franchise Affiliation: Hardee's Food Systems Inc., FRANKLIN, TN
Primary Distributors: (Full Line) McLane/Elkhorn, ELKHORN, WI

Key Personnel
CRAIG KINDERMAN - Owner; General Manager; General Buyer

Supple Restaurant Group
1621 Congress Ave
Oshkosh, WI 54901-2705

Telephone: (920) 232-2334
Fax Number: (920) 232-9671
Internet Homepage: supplerestaurantgroup.com
Type of Business: Chain Restaurant Operator
Year Founded: 1969
Total Sales: $18,430,000 (e)
Alcohol Sales: 100%
Number of Employees: 500
Average Check: Breakfast(8); Lunch(16); Dinner(26)
Total Units: 5
Trade Names: Fox River Brewing Co. (2); Fratello's Waterfront Brewery (1); Golden Corral Buffet & Grill (1); The Melting Pot (1)
Company-Owned Units: 3
Units Franchised From: 2
Preferred Square Footage: 9,000
Preferred Location Types: Freestanding; Regional Mall
Alcohol Served: Beer, Wine, Liquor
Primary Menu: American (5)
Areas of Operation: WI
Type of Foodservice: Casual Dining (5)
Catering Services: Yes
Franchise Affiliation: Golden Corral Corp., RALEIGH, NC; The Melting Pot Restaurants Inc., TAMPA, FL
Primary Distributors: (Full Line) SYSCO Food Services of Eastern Wisconsin, JACKSON, WI

Key Personnel
JAY SUPPLE - CEO
JOHN SUPPLE III - President; CFO; Director Advertising, Menu Development; General Buyer
HEIDI SUPPLE - Controller; General Counsel; Director Human Resources
SCOTT ROEKLE - Director Operations; General Buyer
STEVEN GABELBAUER - Manager Alcoholic Beverages

DPNK Inc.
N3250 County Road J
Poynette, WI 53955-9296

Telephone: (608) 635-3550
Fax Number: (608) 635-3560
Company Email: rzak@dpkinc.net
Type of Business: Chain Restaurant Operator
Total Sales: $170,800,000 (e)
Number of Employees: 2,085
Average Check: Breakfast(8); Lunch(10); Dinner(10)
Total Units: 37
Trade Names: McDonald's (37)
Units Franchised From: 37
Preferred Square Footage: 2,500; 3,000
Preferred Location Types: Freestanding; Regional Mall
Primary Menu: Hamburger (37)
Areas of Operation: WI
Type of Foodservice: Quick Serve (37)
Franchise Affiliation: McDonald's Corporation, CHICAGO, IL
Primary Distributors: (Full Line) SYSCO Food Services of Eastern Wisconsin, JACKSON, WI

Key Personnel
DION CONN - President; General Buyer

Culver Franchising System Inc.
1240 Water St
Prairie Du Sac, WI 53578-1091

Telephone: (608) 643-7980
Fax Number: (608) 643-7982
Internet Homepage: culvers.com
Type of Business: Chain Restaurant Operator
Year Founded: 1984
Systemwide Sales: $3,515,684,000 (e)
Total Sales: $260,120,000 (e)
Number of Employees: 137
Average Check: Lunch(8); Dinner(8)
Internet Order Processing: Yes
Internet Sales: 15.00%
Total Units: 987
Trade Names: Culver's Frozen Custard (987)
Company-Owned Units: 10
Units Franchised To: 977
Preferred Square Footage: 3,200
Preferred Location Types: Airports; Community Mall; Downtown; Freestanding; Other; Regional Mall; Strip Mall
Primary Menu: Snacks (987)
Projected Openings: 16
Areas of Operation: AZ, CO, FL, IA, ID, IL, IN, KS, KY, MI, MN, MO, ND, NE, OH, SC, SD, TN, TX, UT, WI, WY
Type of Foodservice: Quick Serve (987)
Primary Distributors: (Full Line) SYSCO Food Services of Baraboo, BARABOO, WI

Key Personnel
CRAIG C. CULVER - Chairman
ENRIQUE SILVA - CEO
JIM ESPOSITO - COO
STEVEN E. ANDERSON - VP; General Counsel
JULIE FUSSNER - VP Marketing
MATT KLUG - VP Human Resources
KELLY HANSON - VP Information Technology

RICH MODJESKI - VP
STEVE KARLS - Director Operations
TRACY BREUNIG - Director Human Resources
TAMI BENISH - Director Customer Analytics
STEVE DATKA - Director Construction, Design
TRACY NIESEN BREUNIG - Director Human Resources
JENNIFER SULLIVAN - Director Marketing
DANIEL CARDAMONE - Director Digital Marketing
KEVIN FOSTER - Director Operations
MICHAEL WIELAND - Director Operations, West Region
CHRIS CARR - Director Supply Chain
NANCY BENNETT - Director Franchising
BRIAN CURRY - Associate Director Transportation
DANIEL ORTH - Associate Director Information Technology
WENDY DODGE - Senior Manager Purchasing
NICOLE FISHER - Senior Manager
GREG RIESTERER - Manager Information Systems
MARY SCHLUTER - Manager Marketing
SHELLY HEMESATH - Assistant Manager Design
DEANE FISCHER - Consultant

Domino's Franchisee
623 Lincoln St
Rhinelander, WI 54501-3539

Telephone: (715) 362-2525
Type of Business: Chain Restaurant Operator
Total Sales: $6,127,000 (e)
Total Units: 3
Trade Names: Domino's (3)
Units Franchised From: 3
Primary Menu: Pizza (3)
Areas of Operation: WI
Type of Foodservice: Quick Serve (3)
Franchise Affiliation: Domino's Pizza Inc, ANN ARBOR, MI

Key Personnel
DANNY L. CAHEE - Owner; General Buyer

Domino's Franchisee
602 S Main St
Rice Lake, WI 54868-2578

Telephone: (715) 719-0630
Type of Business: Chain Restaurant Operator
Total Sales: $6,108,000 (e)
Total Units: 3
Trade Names: Domino's (3)
Units Franchised From: 3
Primary Menu: Pizza (3)
Areas of Operation: WI
Type of Foodservice: Quick Serve (3)
Franchise Affiliation: Domino's Pizza Inc, ANN ARBOR, MI

Key Personnel
MARK W. FORDER - Owner; General Buyer

Coleman Enterprises Inc
1180 W Fond Du Lac St
Ripon, WI 54971-9210

Telephone: (920) 745-3003
Type of Business: Chain Restaurant Operator
Total Sales: $10,950,000 (e)
Total Units: 7
Trade Names: KFC (6); KFC/Taco Bell (1)
Units Franchised From: 7
Primary Menu: Chicken (6); Taco (1)
Areas of Operation: WI
Type of Foodservice: Quick Serve (7)
Franchise Affiliation: KFC Corporation, LOUISVILLE, KY

Key Personnel
MICHAEL COLEMAN - President; General Buyer
WILLIAM COLEMAN - President

Ripon 23
535 Russell Dr
Ripon, WI 54971-1065

Telephone: (920) 748-9299
Type of Business: Chain Restaurant Operator
Total Sales: $33,430,000 (e)
Total Units: 7
Trade Names: McDonald's (7)
Units Franchised From: 7
Preferred Location Types: Freestanding
Primary Menu: Hamburger (7)
Areas of Operation: WI
Type of Foodservice: Quick Serve (7)
Franchise Affiliation: McDonald's Corporation, CHICAGO, IL

Key Personnel
JACK KING - President; General Buyer

J&J Ostrowski Enterprises
1531 County Road XX
Rothschild, WI 54474-9042

Telephone: (715) 298-2173
Fax Number: (715) 298-2178
Internet Homepage: arbysostrowski.com
Type of Business: Chain Restaurant Operator
Year Founded: 1990
Total Sales: $18,630,000 (e)
Number of Employees: 108
Average Check: Lunch(8); Dinner(8)
Total Units: 10
Trade Names: Arby's (10)
Units Franchised From: 10
Preferred Square Footage: 2,500; 3,000
Preferred Location Types: Freestanding; Strip Mall
Primary Menu: Sandwiches/Deli (10)
Areas of Operation: WI
Type of Foodservice: Quick Serve (10)
Catering Services: Yes
Franchise Affiliation: Arby's Restaurant Group, ATLANTA, GA
Primary Distributors: (Full Line) McLane/Mason City, MASON CITY, IA

Key Personnel
JENNIFER OSTROWSKI - Partner; General Manager; Director Operations

Domino's Franchisee
3910 Schofield Ave
Schofield, WI 54476-6803

Telephone: (715) 359-3030
Type of Business: Chain Restaurant Operator
Total Sales: $8,213,000 (e)
Total Units: 4
Trade Names: Domino's (4)
Units Franchised From: 4
Primary Menu: Pizza (4)
Areas of Operation: WI
Type of Foodservice: Quick Serve (4)
Franchise Affiliation: Domino's Pizza Inc, ANN ARBOR, MI

Key Personnel
KEITH E. KUHTZ - Owner; General Buyer

Domino's Franchisee
3033 Church St
Stevens Point, WI 54481-5304

Telephone: (715) 345-0901
Type of Business: Chain Restaurant Operator
Total Sales: $8,021,000 (e)
Total Units: 4
Trade Names: Domino's (4)
Units Franchised From: 4
Primary Menu: Pizza (4)
Areas of Operation: WI
Type of Foodservice: Quick Serve (4)
Franchise Affiliation: Domino's Pizza Inc, ANN ARBOR, MI

Key Personnel
KEITH KUHTZ - Owner

Domino's Franchisee
1204 Belknap St
Superior, WI 54880-2845

Telephone: (715) 394-7777
Type of Business: Chain Restaurant Operator
Total Sales: $5,977,000 (e)
Total Units: 3
Trade Names: Domino's (3)
Units Franchised From: 3
Primary Menu: Pizza (3)
Areas of Operation: WI
Type of Foodservice: Quick Serve (3)
Franchise Affiliation: Domino's Pizza Inc, ANN ARBOR, MI

Key Personnel
TROY A. GREEN - Owner; General Buyer

George Webb Corp.
W229N1687 Westwood Dr Ste A
Waukesha, WI 53186-1174

Telephone: (262) 970-0084
Fax Number: (262) 970-0093
Internet Homepage: georgewebb.com
Company Email: info@georgewebb.com
Type of Business: Chain Restaurant Operator
Year Founded: 1948
Systemwide Sales: $17,334,000 (e)
Total Sales: $6,323,000 (e)
Number of Employees: 242
Average Check: Breakfast(5); Lunch(10); Dinner(14)
Internet Order Processing: Yes
Total Units: 28
Trade Names: George Webb Restaurant (28)
Company-Owned Units: 10
Units Franchised To: 18
Preferred Square Footage: 2,200
Preferred Location Types: Freestanding; Strip Mall
Primary Menu: American (28)
Areas of Operation: WI
Type of Foodservice: Family Restaurant (28)
On-site Distribution Center: Yes
Primary Distributors: (Equipment) The Boelter Companies Inc., WAUKESHA, WI; (Food) SYSCO Food Services of Eastern Wisconsin, JACKSON, WI;(Supplies) The Boelter Companies Inc., WAUKESHA, WI

Key Personnel
PHILIP ANDERSON - President; CFO; Director Operations, Security, Inventory, Real Estate, Franchising, Food Safety
EILEEN RICHARDS - Owner
RYAN STAMM - VP Information Systems, Menu Development; Director Purchasing, Marketing; General Buyer

Wisconsin Hospitality Group LLC
2120 Pewaukee Rd Ste 200
Waukesha, WI 53188-2491

Telephone: (414) 266-5100
Fax Number: (262) 531-9530
Internet Homepage: whgonline.com
Company Email: Ashley.Dressnandt@whgroup.com
Type of Business: Chain Restaurant Operator
Year Founded: 1998
Total Sales: $33,690,000 (e)
Alcohol Sales: 20%
Number of Employees: 2,709
Average Check: Lunch(14); Dinner(22)
Total Units: 28
Trade Names: Pizza Hut (28)
Units Franchised From: 28
Preferred Square Footage: 2,500; 3,200; 3,600; 5,000
Preferred Location Types: Community Mall; Freestanding; Strip Mall
Alcohol Served: Beer, Wine, Liquor
Primary Menu: Pizza (28)
Areas of Operation: NY, WI
Type of Foodservice: Quick Serve (28)
Franchise Affiliation: Pizza Hut Inc., PLANO, TX

Key Personnel
MARK L. DILLON - CEO; President; Director Purchasing, Real Estate
TIM RANDALL - Chief Development Officer; General Counsel
CHARLES BURDITT - General Manager
JOHN HOFMANN - Director Training

Hardee's of Waupaca Inc
640 W Fulton St
Waupaca, WI 54981-1428

Telephone: (715) 258-0220
Type of Business: Chain Restaurant Operator
Total Sales: $5,915,000 (e)
Total Units: 3
Trade Names: Hardee's (3)
Units Franchised From: 3
Primary Menu: Hamburger (3)
Areas of Operation: WI
Type of Foodservice: Quick Serve (3)
Franchise Affiliation: Hardee's Food Systems Inc., FRANKLIN, TN

Key Personnel
NED LYERLY - CEO
ROBERT PRESLEY - President; Owner; General Buyer

LC of Wausau, LLC
626 S 4th Ave
Wausau, WI 54401-5356

Telephone: (715) 551-3934
Type of Business: Chain Restaurant Operator
Total Sales: $1,601,000 (e)
Total Units: 2
Trade Names: Little Caesars Pizza (2)
Units Franchised From: 2
Primary Menu: Pizza (2)
Areas of Operation: WI
Type of Foodservice: Quick Serve (2)
Franchise Affiliation: Little Caesar Enterprises Inc., DETROIT, MI

Key Personnel
DEBRA MORELAND - President; Owner; General Buyer

Allen & Murphy LLP
2500 N Mayfair Rd
Wauwatosa, WI 53226-1409

Telephone: (414) 778-2066
Type of Business: Chain Restaurant Operator
Total Sales: $3,075,000 (e)
Total Units: 4
Trade Names: Auntie Anne's Hand-Rolled Soft Pretzels (4)
Units Franchised From: 4
Primary Menu: Snacks (4)
Areas of Operation: WI
Type of Foodservice: Quick Serve (4)
Franchise Affiliation: Auntie Anne's Inc., LANCASTER, PA

Key Personnel
JOHN ALLEN - Owner; General Buyer

DeRosa Corp.
7613 W State St
Wauwatosa, WI 53213-2638

Telephone: (414) 771-3100
Fax Number: (414) 771-4024
Internet Homepage: derosacorp.com; josesbluesombrero.com; parkside23.com; thechancery.com
Type of Business: Chain Restaurant Operator
Year Founded: 1972
Total Sales: $30,820,000 (e)
Alcohol Sales: 20%
Number of Employees: 462
Average Check: Breakfast(14); Lunch(24); Dinner(30)
Internet Order Processing: Yes
Internet Sales: 1.00%
Total Units: 7

Trade Names: Chancery Pub & Restaurant (3); Jose's Blue Sombrero (3); Parkside 23 (1)
Company-Owned Units: 7
Preferred Square Footage: 3,000
Preferred Location Types: Freestanding; Hotel/Motel; Outlet Mall
Alcohol Served: Beer, Wine, Liquor
Primary Menu: American (4); Mexican (3)
Areas of Operation: WI
Type of Foodservice: Casual Dining (7)
Catering Services: Yes
Franchise Affiliation: The Original Pancake House Franchising Inc., PORTLAND, OR

Key Personnel
JOSEPH DEROSA - President; Executive Chef; Director Purchasing, Facility/Maintenance, Real Estate, Design, Store Fixtures, Menu Development; General Buyer
RHONDA MCCREEDY - CFO; Exec VP; Controller
GEORGE FLEES - VP; Director Operations
JEFF MARTIN - Director Information Systems, Information Technology

Domino's Franchisee
906 S Main St
West Bend, WI 53095-4602

Telephone: (262) 334-5577
Type of Business: Chain Restaurant Operator
Total Sales: $9,970,000 (e)
Total Units: 5
Trade Names: Domino's (5)
Units Franchised From: 5
Primary Menu: Pizza (5)
Areas of Operation: WI
Type of Foodservice: Quick Serve (5)
Franchise Affiliation: Domino's Pizza Inc, ANN ARBOR, MI

Key Personnel
ROBERT A. LORD - Owner; General Buyer

Kilian Management Services
1722 Clarence Ct
West Bend, WI 53095-8543

Telephone: (262) 338-6111
Fax Number: (262) 338-6310
Type of Business: Chain Restaurant Operator
Year Founded: 1981
Total Sales: $195,600,000 (e)
Number of Employees: 2,000
Average Check: Breakfast(8); Lunch(8); Dinner(10)
Total Units: 49
Trade Names: McDonald's (49)
Units Franchised From: 49
Preferred Square Footage: 2,500; 3,000
Preferred Location Types: Convenience Store/Gas Station; Freestanding
Primary Menu: Hamburger (49)
Areas of Operation: MI, WI
Type of Foodservice: Quick Serve (49)
Franchise Affiliation: McDonald's Corporation, CHICAGO, IL
Primary Distributors: (Food) The Martin-Brower Co. LLC, ROSEMONT, IL

Key Personnel
STEVEN KILIAN SR - President; Director Finance, Real Estate, Design; General Buyer
STEVE ROZEK - Controller
MIKE WENDORF - Director Human Resources
KAREN EDINGTON - Director Training
STEVE KILIAN JR - Director Operations, Facility/Maintenance
SCOTT FAEHNEL - Manager Operations, Information Systems, Supply Chain
STEVE GALEWSKI - Supervisor Facility/Maintenance

Breadsmith Franchising Inc.
409 E Silver Spring Dr
Whitefish Bay, WI 53217-5226

Telephone: (414) 962-1965
Internet Homepage: breadsmith.com
Company Email: contact@breadsmith.com
Type of Business: Chain Restaurant Operator
Year Founded: 1993
Systemwide Sales: $46,865,000 (e)
Total Sales: $4,930,000 (e)
Number of Employees: 36
Average Check: Breakfast(12); Lunch(12); Dinner(12)
Internet Order Processing: Yes
Internet Sales: 1.00%
Total Units: 36
Trade Names: Breadsmith (36)
Company-Owned Units: 4
Units Franchised To: 32
Preferred Square Footage: 2,000
Preferred Location Types: Downtown; Freestanding; Strip Mall
Primary Menu: Miscellaneous (36)
Projected Openings: 1
Areas of Operation: AZ, IL, IN, MD, MI, MN, MO, MS, ND, NY, OH, SC, SD, TX, WI
Type of Foodservice: Fast Casual (36)
Foodservice Management Venues: Business & Industry; College & University
Primary Distributors: (Food) Dawn Food Products Inc., CROWN POINT, IN

Key Personnel
TIM MALOUF - CEO; President
KEVIN SCHUK - VP Operations; Director Franchise Development
MILT KETCHUM - Manager Research & Development

Topper's Pizza Inc.
333 W Center St
Whitewater, WI 53190-1913

Telephone: (262) 473-6666
Fax Number: (262) 473-6697
Internet Homepage: toppers.com
Type of Business: Chain Restaurant Operator
Year Founded: 1991
Systemwide Sales: $45,047,000 (e)
Total Sales: $20,210,000 (e)
Number of Employees: 435
Average Check: Lunch(16); Dinner(34)
Internet Order Processing: Yes
Internet Sales: 10.00%
Total Units: 65
Trade Names: Topper's Pizza (54)
Company-Owned Units: 24
Units Franchised To: 34
Preferred Square Footage: 800; 1,500
Preferred Location Types: Freestanding; Strip Mall
Primary Menu: Pizza (54)
Projected Openings: 5
Areas of Operation: AR, IL, IN, KY, MN, NC, NE, OH, TX, WI
Type of Foodservice: Quick Serve (54)
Catering Services: Yes

Key Personnel
SCOTT GITTRICH - Founder; President
ADAM OLDENBURG - CEO
KENDALL RICHMOND - CFO
MAC MALCHOW - VP Development
MATT MARTIN - VP Operations
TONY ELLIS - VP Information Technology
ROBIN GITTRICH - VP Human Resources; Manager Information Systems
GREG WOLD - VP Marketing
TRACEY HAYES - Controller
JIM FERDENZI - Director Operations
BETH LARSON - Coordinator Franchise Sales
NEIL SCHURRER - Engineer Software

Monkburger Franchise Group LLC
216 1/2 Broadway
Wisconsin Dells, WI 53965

Mailing Address: PO Box 660, Wisconsin Dells, WI, 53965
Telephone: (608) 254-8386
Internet Homepage: monksbarandgrill.com
Company Email: info@monksbarandgrill.com
Type of Business: Chain Restaurant Operator
Year Founded: 1947
Systemwide Sales: $20,099,000 (e)
Total Sales: $17,030,000 (e)
Alcohol Sales: 12%
Internet Order Processing: Yes
Total Units: 6

Trade Names: Monk's Bar and Grill (6)
Company-Owned Units: 3
Units Franchised To: 3
Alcohol Served: Beer, Wine, Liquor
Primary Menu: American (6)
Areas of Operation: WI
Type of Foodservice: Casual Dining (6)

Key Personnel
THOMAS E. HELLER - President
JANE HELLER - VP
CHRISTINE J. KOBYLSKI - Controller
DAMIAN PULCHNY - Corporate Chef
ALLISON MARIE ELDER - Manager Marketing, Communications, Franchising

WEST VIRGINIA

Domino's Franchisee
23 Nell Jean Sq
Beckley, WV 25801-2200

Telephone: (304) 256-3003
Company Email: dominosbob@gmail.com
Type of Business: Chain Restaurant Operator
Total Sales: $4,060,000 (e)
Total Units: 2
Trade Names: Domino's (2)
Units Franchised From: 2
Primary Menu: Pizza (2)
Areas of Operation: WV
Type of Foodservice: Quick Serve (2)
Franchise Affiliation: Domino's Pizza Inc, ANN ARBOR, MI

Key Personnel
JOHN HORN - Owner; General Buyer

JHA Foods
2302 S Kanawha St
Beckley, WV 25801-6722

Telephone: (304) 252-0965
Type of Business: Chain Restaurant Operator
Total Sales: $20,505,000 (e)
Number of Employees: 110
Total Units: 4
Trade Names: McDonald's (4)
Units Franchised From: 4
Preferred Square Footage: 2,500
Primary Menu: Hamburger (4)
Areas of Operation: WV
Type of Foodservice: Quick Serve (4)
Franchise Affiliation: McDonald's Corporation, CHICAGO, IL

Key Personnel
JACK ALLISON - Partner; General Buyer
TIMOTHY ALLISON - Partner; General Buyer

Marquee Cinemas Inc.
552 Ragland Rd
Beckley, WV 25801-9727

Telephone: (304) 255-4036
Fax Number: (304) 252-0526
Internet Homepage: marqueecinemas.com
Type of Business: Foodservice Operations - Movie Theatre
Year Founded: 1979
Total Sales: $55,100,000 (e)
Number of Employees: 330
Average Check: Lunch(5); Dinner(5)
Total Units: 17
Trade Names: Marquee Cinemas (17)
Company-Owned Units: 17
Preferred Square Footage: 32,000
Preferred Location Types: Community Mall; Downtown; Freestanding; Regional Mall; Strip Mall
Primary Menu: Snacks (17)
Areas of Operation: CT, FL, KY, NC, TN, VA, WV
Type of Foodservice: In-Store Feeder (17)

Key Personnel
TONI Y. MCCALL - Chairman; CEO; President; General Buyer
CINDY RAMSDEN - CFO
JAMES M. COX - COO; Director Design, Business Development, Menu Development; General Buyer
ROBIN P. SHUMATE - Director Marketing, Advertising

Bluefield Dairy Queen
3136 E Cumberland Rd
Bluefield, WV 24701-4957

Telephone: (304) 325-6652
Type of Business: Chain Restaurant Operator
Total Sales: $5,834,000 (e)
Total Units: 4
Trade Names: Dairy Queen (4)
Units Franchised From: 4
Primary Menu: American (4)
Areas of Operation: WV
Type of Foodservice: Quick Serve (4)
Franchise Affiliation: International Dairy Queen Inc., BLOOMINGTON, MN

Key Personnel
BYRON SATTERFIELD - President; General Buyer

J.W. Ebert Corp.
917 W Main St Ste 201
Bridgeport, WV 26330-1886

Telephone: (304) 848-2123
Fax Number: (304) 848-2124
Internet Homepage: ebertmcdonalds.com
Type of Business: Chain Restaurant Operator
Year Founded: 1990
Total Sales: $186,390,000 (e)
Number of Employees: 2,312
Average Check: Breakfast(8); Lunch(8); Dinner(10)
Total Units: 39
Trade Names: McDonald's (39)
Units Franchised From: 39
Preferred Square Footage: 2,500; 3,000
Preferred Location Types: Freestanding
Primary Menu: Hamburger (39)
Areas of Operation: WV
Type of Foodservice: Quick Serve (39)
Franchise Affiliation: McDonald's Corporation, CHICAGO, IL

Key Personnel
JOHN EBERT - President; Director Real Estate, Design
MIKE MCLEAN - Manager Facility/Maintenance, Store Fixtures
BILL PITTMAN - Manager Finance, Human Resources

Greater Huntington Theatre Corporation
600 Washington St E
Charleston, WV 25301

Telephone: (304) 345-6541
Internet Homepage: ghtctheatres.com; ourshowtimes.com
Type of Business: Foodservice Operations - Movie Theatre
Year Founded: 1925
Total Sales: $10,264,000 (e)
Number of Employees: 75
Average Check: Lunch(6); Dinner(6)
Internet Order Processing: Yes
Internet Sales: 5.00%
Total Units: 4
Trade Names: Fountain Place Cinema 8 (1); Lewisburg Cinema 8 (1); Park Place Stadium Cinemas (1); Pierce Point Cinemas 10 (1)
Company-Owned Units: 4
Preferred Square Footage: 20,000
Preferred Location Types: Community Mall; Downtown; Freestanding
Primary Menu: Snacks (4)
Areas of Operation: WV
Type of Foodservice: In-Store Feeder (4)
Primary Distributors: (Food) US Foods, MANASSAS, VA

Notes: The company derives approximately 60% of its revenue from Admission and Commodities.

Key Personnel
DEREK HYMAN - President; General Buyer
GREG PAULEY - VP; Director Marketing

Mardi Gras Casino and Resort
1 Greyhound Dr
Cross Lanes, WV 25313-1474

Telephone: (304) 776-1000
Fax Number: (304) 776-1239
Internet Homepage: mardigrascasinowv.com
Company Email: info@mardigrascasinowv.com
Type of Business: Foodservice Operations - Casinos
Year Founded: 1985
Total Sales: $3,795,000 (e)
Number of Employees: 50
Average Check: Dinner(16)
Total Units: 4
Trade Names: Cafe Orleans (1); Crescent City (1); The French Quarter Restaurant & Bar (1); The Grill at First Turn (1)
Company-Owned Units: 4
Preferred Location Types: Freestanding; Strip Mall
Alcohol Served: Beer, Wine, Liquor
Primary Menu: American (2); French/Continental (2)
Areas of Operation: WV
Type of Foodservice: Casual Dining (2); Quick Serve (2)
Primary Distributors: (Full Line) Gordon Food Service, SHEPHERDSVILLE, KY
Parent Company: Hartman & Tyner, SOUTHFIELD, MI
Notes: Located in the Tri-State Greyhound Park.

Key Personnel
MICHAEL ALLEN - Director Security
CATHY BRACKBILL - Director Marketing
JEFF GERENCIR - Director Information Systems
LACEY MCDANIEL - Director Accounting
PHILIP PINSON - Director Operations

Holland Enterprises LLC
104 S Randolph Ave
Elkins, WV 26241-3715

Telephone: (304) 636-5510
Fax Number: (304) 636-5321
Internet Homepage: senecarealtyco.com
Type of Business: Chain Restaurant Operator
Total Sales: $3,453,000 (e)
Total Units: 6
Trade Names: Subway (6)
Units Franchised From: 6
Primary Menu: Sandwiches/Deli (6)
Areas of Operation: WV
Type of Foodservice: Quick Serve (6)
Franchise Affiliation: Doctor's Associates Inc., MILFORD, CT

Key Personnel
RICHARD HOLLAND - Owner; General Buyer

Pies & Pints
219 W Maple Ave
Fayetteville, WV 25840

Telephone: (304) 574-2200
Internet Homepage: piesandpints.net
Type of Business: Chain Restaurant Operator
Total Sales: $12,460,000 (e)
Total Units: 14
Trade Names: Pies & Pints (14)
Company-Owned Units: 14
Primary Menu: Pizza (14)
Type of Foodservice: Casual Dining (14)

Key Personnel
ROB LINDEMAN - President; Owner
CHRIS WARNER - Director Operations
JESS GODBEY - Manager Marketing

Allied Food Industries Inc.
3210 Washington Blvd
Huntington, WV 25705-1637

Mailing Address: PO Box 2407, HUNTINGTON, WV, 25725-2407
Telephone: (304) 529-3636
Fax Number: (304) 529-0055
Type of Business: Chain Restaurant Operator
Year Founded: 1984
Total Sales: $94,420,000 (e)
Number of Employees: 1,100
Average Check: Breakfast(6); Lunch(8); Dinner(0)
Total Units: 43
Trade Names: Arby's (18); Burger King (25)
Units Franchised From: 43
Preferred Square Footage: 2,500
Preferred Location Types: Freestanding
Primary Menu: Hamburger (25); Sandwiches/Deli (18)
Projected Openings: 10
Areas of Operation: AR, CO, KS, KY, OH, WV
Type of Foodservice: Quick Serve (43)
Franchise Affiliation: Arby's Restaurant Group, ATLANTA, GA; Burger King Worldwide Inc., MIAMI, FL
Primary Distributors: (Full Line) McLane/Frankfort, FRANKFORT, KY

Key Personnel
JACOB KESTENBAUM - President
TIM HECK - CFO; Controller; Director Supply Chain
CARL WADDLE - CIO
CHUCK LONDON - Manager
SANDY HALL - Administrative Assistant
TAMMY WARD - Administrative Assistant

Gino's Pizza
930 9th Ave
Huntington, WV 25701-2814

Telephone: (304) 525-2943
Fax Number: (304) 522-3085
Internet Homepage: ginospizza.com
Company Email: ginos@comcast.com
Type of Business: Chain Restaurant Operator
Year Founded: 1961
Total Sales: $16,800,000 (e)
Alcohol Sales: 3%
Number of Employees: 210
Average Check: Lunch(14); Dinner(14)
Total Units: 10
Trade Names: Gino's Pizza (10)
Company-Owned Units: 10
Preferred Square Footage: 500; 1,200
Preferred Location Types: Freestanding; Regional Mall; Strip Mall
Alcohol Served: Beer, Wine
Primary Menu: Pizza (10)
Areas of Operation: OH, WV
Type of Foodservice: Fast Casual (10)
Catering Services: Yes
Primary Distributors: (Food) US Foods, HURRICANE, WV

Key Personnel
DIANA STURM - VP Operations; Manager Risk Management, Design
NANCY SMITH - Manager Marketing, Human Resources

VDM Management
5250 US Route 60
Huntington, WV 25705-2023

Telephone: (304) 736-6658
Fax Number: (304) 736-3092
Type of Business: Chain Restaurant Operator
Total Sales: $30,310,000 (e)
Number of Employees: 99
Average Check: Lunch(8); Dinner(14)
Total Units: 26
Trade Names: Little Caesars Pizza (26)
Units Franchised From: 26
Preferred Square Footage: 1,200; 1,600
Preferred Location Types: Freestanding
Primary Menu: Pizza (26)
Projected Openings: 1
Projected Remodelings: 2

Areas of Operation: KY, OH, WV
Type of Foodservice: Quick Serve (26)
Franchise Affiliation: Little Caesar Enterprises Inc., DETROIT, MI
Primary Distributors: (Full Line) Blue Line Food Service, GROVEPORT, OH

Key Personnel
VICKI DUNN-MARSHALL - President; General Buyer
SABRINA DONAHUE-MOORE - Director Marketing
JOAN STOGSDILL - Manager Real Estate

Baltic Capital/ Mac Attack Management
1837 Sunset Vw
Milton, WV 25541-1118

Telephone: (304) 757-7779
Type of Business: Chain Restaurant Operator
Total Sales: $38,120,000 (e)
Total Units: 8
Trade Names: McDonald's (8)
Units Franchised From: 8
Preferred Square Footage: 2,500
Primary Menu: Hamburger (8)
Areas of Operation: WV
Type of Foodservice: Quick Serve (8)
Franchise Affiliation: McDonald's Corporation, CHICAGO, IL

Key Personnel
ANDERSON HAUGHEY - Owner; General Buyer

Auntie Anne's Franchise
9323 Mall Rd
Morgantown, WV 26501-8536

Telephone: (304) 983-6175
Type of Business: Chain Restaurant Operator
Total Sales: $1,590,000 (e)
Total Units: 2
Trade Names: Auntie Anne's Hand-Rolled Soft Pretzels (2)
Units Franchised From: 2
Primary Menu: Snacks (2)
Areas of Operation: WV
Type of Foodservice: Quick Serve (2)
Franchise Affiliation: Auntie Anne's Inc., LANCASTER, PA

Key Personnel
JOHN SECRETO - Owner; General Buyer

Boston Beanery Restaurant Inc
383 Patteson Dr
Morgantown, WV 26505

Telephone: (304) 599-1870
Internet Homepage: bostonbeanery.com
Type of Business: Chain Restaurant Operator
Total Units: 5
Trade Names: Apple Annie's (1); Beanery American Grill (3); Boston Beanery Restaurant & Tavern (1)
Company-Owned Units: 5
Alcohol Served: Beer, Wine, Liquor
Primary Menu: American (5)
Areas of Operation: PA, VA, WV
Type of Foodservice: Casual Dining (5)

Key Personnel
KEN COLE - President; General Buyer

Boston Hospitality Group Inc.
383 Patteson Dr
Morgantown, WV 26508-6815

Telephone: (304) 599-1870
Fax Number: (304) 594-0081
Internet Homepage: bostonbeanery.com
Type of Business: Chain Restaurant Operator
Year Founded: 1984
Systemwide Sales: $6,923,000 (e)
Total Sales: $6,266,000 (e)
Alcohol Sales: 20%
Number of Employees: 400
Average Check: Lunch(18); Dinner(42)
Total Units: 3
Trade Names: Beanery American Grill (1); Boston Beanery Restaurant & Tavern (2)
Company-Owned Units: 3
Preferred Square Footage: 4,500; 5,000
Preferred Location Types: Downtown; Freestanding; Regional Mall; Strip Mall
Alcohol Served: Beer, Wine, Liquor
Primary Menu: American (3)
Areas of Operation: PA, WV
Type of Foodservice: Casual Dining (3)
Catering Services: Yes
Primary Distributors: (Full Line) Reinhart FoodService, MOUNT PLEASANT, PA

Key Personnel
DANIEL WATTS - President; General Buyer

Nelson Hachem
1104 4th St
New Martinsville, WV 26155-2110

Telephone: (304) 455-5925
Fax Number: (304) 455-6170
Type of Business: Chain Restaurant Operator
Total Sales: $10,169,000 (e)
Total Units: 2
Trade Names: McDonald's (2)
Units Franchised From: 2
Preferred Location Types: Freestanding
Primary Menu: Hamburger (2)
Areas of Operation: WV
Type of Foodservice: Quick Serve (2)
Franchise Affiliation: McDonald's Corporation, CHICAGO, IL

Key Personnel
NELSON HACHEM - President; General Buyer

Tudor's Biscuit World Inc.
209 1st Ave S
Nitro, WV 25143-2237

Telephone: (304) 722-3511
Fax Number: (304) 727-1400
Internet Homepage: tudorsbiscuitworld.com
Type of Business: Chain Restaurant Operator
Year Founded: 1960
Systemwide Sales: $34,838,000 (e)
Total Sales: $32,910,000 (e)
Number of Employees: 1,716
Average Check: Lunch(12); Dinner(22)
Total Units: 80
Trade Names: Tudor's Biscuit World (80)
Units Franchised To: 80
Preferred Square Footage: 3,000
Preferred Location Types: Freestanding
Primary Menu: American (72)
Areas of Operation: KY, OH, VA, WV
Type of Foodservice: Quick Serve (80)
Primary Distributors: (Full Line) US Foods, HURRICANE, WV

Key Personnel
OSHEL CRAIGO - CEO; President
JEFF MACE - CIO; Controller; Manager Finance, Purchasing, Facility/Maintenance, Loss Prevention, Real Estate, Design

Epeck, Inc.
223 Lochgelly Rd
Oak Hill, WV 25901-9476

Mailing Address: P.O. Box 1634, Oak Hill,, WV, 25901
Telephone: (304) 469-2932
Fax Number: (304) 469-2640

Type of Business: Chain Restaurant Operator
Total Sales: $28,950,000 (e)
Number of Employees: 75
Total Units: 6
Trade Names: McDonald's (6)
Units Franchised From: 6
Preferred Square Footage: 2,500
Primary Menu: Hamburger (6)
Areas of Operation: WV
Type of Foodservice: Quick Serve (6)
Franchise Affiliation: McDonald's Corporation, CHICAGO, IL

Key Personnel
EDWARD KILIANY - President; General Buyer

Charton Management Inc.
373 Timberline Pkwy
Parkersburg, WV 26105-8082

Telephone: (304) 865-2222
Fax Number: (304) 865-2231
Internet Homepage: charton.biz
Company Email: info@charton.biz,
Type of Business: Chain Restaurant Operator
Year Founded: 1986
Total Sales: $17,750,000 (e)
Number of Employees: 412
Average Check: Breakfast(8); Lunch(8); Dinner(8)
Total Units: 8
Trade Names: Burger King (8)
Units Franchised From: 8
Preferred Square Footage: 1,900; 4,300
Preferred Location Types: Freestanding; Strip Mall
Primary Menu: Hamburger (8)
Projected Openings: 10
Areas of Operation: OH, WV
Type of Foodservice: Quick Serve (8)
Franchise Affiliation: Burger King Worldwide Inc., MIAMI, FL; Qdoba Mexican Eats, SAN DIEGO, CA
Primary Distributors: (Full Line) Maines Paper & Food Services Ohio, OAKWOOD VILLAGE, OH

Key Personnel
MATTHEW HERRIDGE - Partner; General Buyer
GENE WHARTON - Partner; General Buyer
GRANT WHARTON - Partner; Manager Operations; General Buyer
JEFF HARPER - CFO; Manager Finance
KYM MCAULEY - Manager Human Resources

Wal-Bon of Ohio Inc.
925 Market St
Parkersburg, WV 26101-4736

Mailing Address: PO Box 508, BELPRE, OH, 45714-0508
Telephone: (740) 423-6351
Fax Number: (740) 423-6700
Internet Homepage: mchappys.com; napolis.com
Type of Business: Chain Restaurant Operator
Year Founded: 1966
Total Sales: $9,037,000 (e)
Alcohol Sales: 5%
Number of Employees: 205
Average Check: Lunch(14); Dinner(22)
Total Units: 13
Trade Names: McHappy's Bake Shoppe (4); Napoli's Pizza (9)
Company-Owned Units: 13
Preferred Square Footage: 2,500; 3,000
Preferred Location Types: Freestanding
Alcohol Served: Beer, Wine
Primary Menu: Pizza (9); Snacks (4)
Areas of Operation: OH, WV
Type of Foodservice: Quick Serve (13)
Primary Distributors: (Full Line) SYSCO Food Services of Cleveland Inc., CLEVELAND, OH

Key Personnel
WAYNE D. WALDECK - CEO; VP Finance, Purchasing, Facility/Maintenance, Loss Prevention, Supply Chain, Marketing, Advertising, Design, Human Resources; Controller; General Buyer
WILLIAM WALDECK - President; Executive Chef; Manager Operations, Information Systems, Real Estate, Human Resources, Product Development, Food Safety
PATTY POSEY - Manager Purchasing; General Buyer

C M Subs
2515 Jackson Ave
Point Pleasant, WV 25550-2035

Telephone: (304) 675-5390
Fax Number: (304) 675-8813
Type of Business: Chain Restaurant Operator
Total Sales: $4,118,000 (e)
Total Units: 7
Trade Names: Subway (7)
Units Franchised From: 7
Primary Menu: Sandwiches/Deli (7)
Areas of Operation: OH, WV
Type of Foodservice: Quick Serve (7)
Franchise Affiliation: Doctor's Associates Inc., MILFORD, CT

Key Personnel
JOHN RAIRDIN - Owner; General Buyer

Terry Nemesek
101 New Stone Ridge Rd
Ripley, WV 25271-9799

Telephone: (304) 372-9611
Fax Number: (304) 372-1004
Type of Business: Chain Restaurant Operator
Total Sales: $28,400,000 (e)
Total Units: 6
Trade Names: McDonald's (6)
Units Franchised From: 6
Primary Menu: Hamburger (6)
Areas of Operation: WV
Type of Foodservice: Quick Serve (6)
Franchise Affiliation: McDonald's Corporation, CHICAGO, IL

Key Personnel
TERRY NEMESEK - President; Owner; General Buyer

Mesa Management Group
120 Mesa Dr
Saint Albans, WV 25177-1573

Telephone: (304) 759-2505
Fax Number: (304) 759-2507
Type of Business: Chain Restaurant Operator
Total Sales: $4,933,000 (e)
Total Units: 8
Trade Names: Subway (8)
Units Franchised From: 8
Primary Menu: Sandwiches/Deli (8)
Areas of Operation: WV
Type of Foodservice: Quick Serve (8)
Franchise Affiliation: Doctor's Associates Inc., MILFORD, CT

Key Personnel
CHELSIE KELLY - Partner; General Buyer; Agent Development
TARA CANFIELD - Partner; VP

Mac-Sto Management
93 Main St
Wheeling, WV 26003-2421

Telephone: (304) 233-1833
Fax Number: (304) 233-1835
Type of Business: Chain Restaurant Operator
Total Sales: $46,810,000 (e)
Number of Employees: 700
Total Units: 10
Trade Names: McDonald's (10)
Units Franchised From: 10
Preferred Square Footage: 2,500
Primary Menu: Hamburger (10)
Areas of Operation: OH, WV
Type of Foodservice: Quick Serve (10)

Franchise Affiliation: McDonald's Corporation, CHICAGO, IL

Key Personnel
ROSS STOLTZ - President; General Buyer

Wheeling Island Gaming Inc.
1 S Stone St
Wheeling, WV 26003-2062

Telephone: (304) 232-5050
Fax Number: (304) 231-1881
Internet Homepage: wheelingisland.com
Company Email: wi-info@delawarenorth.com
Type of Business: Foodservice Operations - Casinos
Year Founded: 1960
Total Sales: $228,610,000 (e)
Alcohol Sales: 20%
Number of Employees: 800
Average Check: Breakfast(10); Lunch(16); Dinner(32)
Total Units: 4
Trade Names: Crescent Room Coffee Bar (1); Food Court (1); The Buffet (1); The Pointe (1)
Company-Owned Units: 4
Preferred Square Footage: 2,500; 5,500; 6,000
Preferred Location Types: Freestanding; Strip Mall
Alcohol Served: Beer, Wine, Liquor
Primary Menu: American (1); Coffee (1); Miscellaneous (1); Steak/Seafood (1)
Areas of Operation: WV
Type of Foodservice: Casual Dining (2); Fine Dining (1); Quick Serve (1)
Primary Distributors: (Full Line) SYSCO Food Services of Central Pennsylvania LLC, HARRISBURG, PA
Parent Company: Delaware North Companies Inc., BUFFALO, NY
Notes: The company derives approximately 94% of its revenue from gaming, lodging and pari-mutuel operations.

Key Personnel
KIM FLORENCE - President; General Manager
MIKE MAESTLE - VP Operations
TERRY C. BURTON - Corporate Secretary
CHRIS MATA - Executive Chef; Director Purchasing, Food and Beverage
ANITRA SALKOVIC - Senior Director Human Resources
CHRIS O'MALLEY - Director Information Technology

The Greenbrier
101 Main St W
White Sulphur Springs, WV 24986

Telephone: (304) 536-1110
Fax Number: (304) 536-7854
Internet Homepage: greenbrier.com
Type of Business: Foodservice Operations - Hotel/Motels
Year Founded: 1913
Total Sales: $52,693,000 (e)
Alcohol Sales: 25%
Number of Employees: 1,000
Total Units: 1
Restaurants in Hotels: 16
Trade Names: The Greenbrier (1)
Company-Owned Units: 16
Alcohol Served: Beer, Wine, Liquor
Areas of Operation: WV
Primary Distributors: (Food) SYSCO Food Services of Virginia LLC, HARRISONBURG, VA
Parent Company: Justice Family Group, BECKLEY, WV
Notes: The company derives approximately 65% of its revenue from hotel operations. Several of the restaurants are seasonal or have limited hours of service.

Key Personnel
JIM JUSTICE - Chairman; CEO; Owner
JILLIAN JUSTICE - President
ELMER COPPOOLSE - COO
GREG FURLONG - VP Event Planning, Sales
BURT BAINE - General Manager
BRYAN SKELDING - Executive Chef; General Buyer
BETH SANTIAGO - Director Gaming/Entertainment
TAMMY REED - Manager Purchasing, Logistics
JENNIFER ANDREWS - Manager Event Planning
MICHAEL NEMEYER - Manager Floral
ALLYSON EPPLING - Supervisor Administration
MICHELE HANNA - Administrator Gaming/Entertainment

WYOMING

Johnson Restaurant Group
229 E 2nd St Ste 200
Casper, WY 82601-3199

Mailing Address: PO Box 50630, CASPER, WY, 82605-0630
Telephone: (307) 265-3029
Fax Number: (307) 473-2909
Internet Homepage: firerocksteakhouse.com; jrgrestaurants.com; wyomingaleworks.com
Company Email: accounting@jrgrestaurants.com
Type of Business: Chain Restaurant Operator
Year Founded: 1978
Total Sales: $14,070,000 (e)
Alcohol Sales: 5%
Number of Employees: 165
Average Check: Breakfast(10); Lunch(14); Dinner(20)
Total Units: 10
Trade Names: Fire Rock Steakhouse (2); J's Pub & Grill (1); Johnny J's (1); Old Chicago (5); Wyoming Ale Works (1)
Company-Owned Units: 10
Preferred Location Types: Freestanding
Alcohol Served: Beer, Wine, Liquor
Primary Menu: American (7); Hamburger (1); Steak/Seafood (2)
Areas of Operation: WY
Type of Foodservice: Casual Dining (7); Family Restaurant (1); Fine Dining (2)
Catering Services: Yes
Primary Distributors: (Full Line) US Foods, BILLINGS, MT

Key Personnel
JOHN D. JOHNSON - President; Treasurer; General Manager; Executive Chef; General Buyer
MIKE MALMBERG - VP
JIM HINTON - Controller; Director Human Resources
MARIA PARKINSON - General Manager
NOAH SIEBENALLER - Executive Chef

Movie Palaces Inc
100 E 2nd St
Casper, WY 82601-2502

Mailing Address: PO Box 2180, CASPER, WY, 82602-2180
Telephone: (307) 266-3647
Fax Number: (307) 462-0545
Internet Homepage: wyomovies.com
Company Email: mpoffice@wyomovies.com
Type of Business: Foodservice Operations - Movie Theatre
Total Sales: $13,540,000 (e)
Number of Employees: 100
Average Check: Dinner(14)
Internet Order Processing: Yes
Total Units: 10
Trade Names: Movie Palace (10)
Company-Owned Units: 10
Primary Menu: Snacks (10)
Areas of Operation: WY
Type of Foodservice: In-Store Feeder (10)

Key Personnel
RANDY PRIDE - President; Partner; Director Human Resources
CRAIG HOSEY - Partner; Manager Marketing
MIKE ITO - Partner; VP Finance

Wyoming Pizza, Inc
105 S Lincoln St
Casper, WY 82601-2638

Telephone: (307) 235-2100

Type of Business: Chain Restaurant Operator
Total Sales: $6,018,000 (e)
Total Units: 3
Trade Names: Domino's (3)
Units Franchised From: 3
Primary Menu: Pizza (3)
Areas of Operation: WY
Type of Foodservice: Quick Serve (3)
Franchise Affiliation: Domino's Pizza Inc, ANN ARBOR, MI

Key Personnel
FRANK MORAN - President

Preiss Corporation
7300 Yellowstone Rd
Cheyenne, WY 82009-2086

Telephone: (307) 635-6410
Fax Number: (307) 637-7228
Type of Business: Chain Restaurant Operator
Total Sales: $23,520,000 (e)
Number of Employees: 170
Average Check: Breakfast(8); Lunch(8); Dinner(8)
Total Units: 5
Trade Names: McDonald's (5)
Units Franchised From: 5
Preferred Square Footage: 3,500
Preferred Location Types: Discount Dept. Stores; Freestanding
Primary Menu: Hamburger (5)
Areas of Operation: WY
Type of Foodservice: Quick Serve (5)
Franchise Affiliation: McDonald's Corporation, CHICAGO, IL
Primary Distributors: (Food) The Martin-Brower Co. LLC, ROSEMONT, IL

Key Personnel
JOHN PREISS - President; Director Finance, Operations, Purchasing, Facility/Maintenance, Information Systems, Real Estate, Design, Human Resources; General Buyer

Taco John's International Inc.
808 W 20th St
Cheyenne, WY 82001-3404

Mailing Address: PO Box 1589, CHEYENNE, WY, 82003-1589
Telephone: (307) 635-0101
Fax Number: (307) 638-0603
Internet Homepage: tacojohns.com
Company Email: email@tacojohns.com
Type of Business: Chain Restaurant Operator
Year Founded: 1969
Systemwide Sales: $424,887,000 (e)
Total Sales: $36,540,000 (e)
Number of Employees: 316
Average Check: Breakfast(8); Lunch(10); Dinner(10)
Total Units: 377
Trade Names: Taco John's (377)
Company-Owned Units: 10
Units Franchised To: 367
Preferred Square Footage: 1,800; 2,000; 3,500
Preferred Location Types: Community Mall; Convenience Store/Gas Station; Downtown; Freestanding; Institution (college/hospital); Regional Mall; Strip Mall
Primary Menu: Mexican (377)
Projected Openings: 20
Areas of Operation: AR, AZ, CO, IA, ID, IL, IN, KS, KY, MI, MO, MT, ND, NE, NV, NY, OH, SD, TN, TX, VA, WA, WI, WY
Type of Foodservice: Quick Serve (377)
Catering Services: Yes
Franchise Affiliation: Good Times Restaurants Inc., LAKEWOOD, CO
Primary Distributors: (Food) VISTAR Specialty, ENGLEWOOD, CO

Key Personnel
HEATHER NEARY - CEO
RICHARD BUNDY - CFO
GREG MILLER - COO
MARK KOCER - COO
KEVIN FLAHERTY - Chief Marketing Officer
DANNY B. JAMES - Chief Development Officer
STEPHANIE GOODEN - VP Human Resources
MICHAEL D'AMICO - VP Supply Chain
RENEE MIDDLETON - VP Marketing
BOB KARISNY - VP Strategy, Innovation
PATRICIA L. HAYS - Corporate Secretary; General Counsel
BRAD BERGAUS - Executive Chef
JIM NICHOLS - Director Construction, Design
STEVE SMYTH - Manager Information Technology
CECILIA KRAMER - Manager Operations
BRANDO TIJERINA - Manager Quality Assurance
NATE WEBER - Manager Information Technology
ANNIE HANN - Manager Field Marketing

Postel Management Inc
1090 W Yellowstone Hwy
Douglas, WY 82633-2366

Telephone: (307) 358-9700
Type of Business: Chain Restaurant Operator
Total Sales: $38,140,000 (e)
Total Units: 8
Trade Names: McDonald's (8)
Units Franchised From: 8
Preferred Location Types: Freestanding; Strip Mall
Primary Menu: Hamburger (8)
Areas of Operation: WY
Type of Foodservice: Quick Serve (8)
Franchise Affiliation: McDonald's Corporation, CHICAGO, IL

Key Personnel
TIM POSTEL - President; General Buyer
TOM STINSON - General Manager

Don Pedro's Family Mexican Restaurant
203-205 Bear River Drive
Evanston, WY 82930

Telephone: (307) 789-3322
Internet Homepage: donpedrosfamilymexicanrestaurant.com
Company Email: donpedros.corp@aim.com
Type of Business: Chain Restaurant Operator
Year Founded: 1995
Total Sales: $8,162,000 (e)
Total Units: 5
Trade Names: Don Pedro's Family Mexican Restaurant (5)
Company-Owned Units: 5
Primary Menu: Mexican (5)
Areas of Operation: ND, UT, WY
Type of Foodservice: Casual Dining (5)

Key Personnel
RUBEN SEPULVEDA SR - Owner
HECTOR E. TREJO - VP; Director

Humphery's
406 W Juniper Ln
Gillette, WY 82718-5341

Mailing Address: PO Box L, SHERIDAN, WY, 82801-0630
Telephone: (307) 686-0374
Fax Number: (307) 674-1725
Type of Business: Chain Restaurant Operator
Year Founded: 1992
Total Sales: $5,688,000 (e)
Alcohol Sales: 20%
Number of Employees: 300
Average Check: Lunch(14); Dinner(22)
Total Units: 2
Trade Names: Humphrey's (1); Uncle Freddies (1)
Company-Owned Units: 2
Preferred Square Footage: 5,500; 6,000
Preferred Location Types: Freestanding
Alcohol Served: Beer, Wine, Liquor
Primary Menu: American (2)
Areas of Operation: WY
Type of Foodservice: Casual Dining (2)
Primary Distributors: (Full Line) US Foods, BILLINGS, MT

Key Personnel
JODI WILSON - Manager Human Resources

Domino's Franchisee
520 S Hwy 89
Jackson, WY 83001-8507

Telephone: (307) 733-0330
Type of Business: Chain Restaurant Operator
Total Sales: $4,055,000 (e)
Total Units: 2
Trade Names: Domino's (2)
Units Franchised From: 2
Primary Menu: Pizza (2)
Areas of Operation: WY
Type of Foodservice: Quick Serve (2)
Franchise Affiliation: Domino's Pizza Inc, ANN ARBOR, MI

Key Personnel
DAVID L. TURNER - Owner; General Buyer

Postel Management
235 McFarlane Dr
Lander, WY 82520-2949

Telephone: (307) 332-3955
Type of Business: Chain Restaurant Operator
Total Sales: $20,350,000 (e)
Total Units: 4
Trade Names: McDonald's (4)
Units Franchised From: 4
Preferred Location Types: Freestanding
Primary Menu: Hamburger (4)
Areas of Operation: WY
Type of Foodservice: Quick Serve (4)
Franchise Affiliation: McDonald's Corporation, CHICAGO, IL

Key Personnel
KEN POSTEL - Owner; General Buyer
CRAIG POSTEL - General Manager

First Street Station
101 E Grand Ave
Laramie, WY 82070-3637

Telephone: (307) 745-0141
Fax Number: (307) 745-5362
Internet Homepage: altitudechophouse.com; elmerlovejoys.com
Type of Business: Chain Restaurant Operator
Year Founded: 1986
Total Sales: $7,248,000 (e)
Alcohol Sales: 50%
Number of Employees: 65
Average Check: Lunch(18); Dinner(30)
Internet Order Processing: Yes
Total Units: 2
Trade Names: Altitude Chophouse & Brewery (1); Lovejoys Bar & Grill (1)
Company-Owned Units: 2
Preferred Location Types: Downtown
Alcohol Served: Beer, Wine, Liquor
Primary Menu: American (2)
Areas of Operation: WY
Type of Foodservice: Casual Dining (2)
Catering Services: Yes
Primary Distributors: (Full Line) SYSCO Food Services of Denver, DENVER, CO

Key Personnel
GREG SMITH - Partner
KAREN SMITH - Partner
BENJAMIN NUTT - General Manager
DENISE MARQUISS - Director Catering; General Buyer

Barry Cinemas Inc.
312 E Main St
Riverton, WY 82501-4338

Telephone: (307) 856-1303
Internet Homepage: barrycinemas.com
Type of Business: Foodservice Operations - Movie Theatre
Total Sales: $2,279,000 (e)
Average Check: Dinner(6)
Total Units: 3
Trade Names: Acme Theatre (1); Gem Theatre (1); Grand Theatre (1)
Company-Owned Units: 3
Primary Menu: Snacks (3)
Areas of Operation: WY
Type of Foodservice: In-Store Feeder (3)

Key Personnel
ADAM BARRY - Owner; General Manager; Manager Operations; General Buyer

E & B Industries Inc
1639 Elk St
Rock Springs, WY 82901-4020

Telephone: (307) 382-3501
Internet Homepage: tacotimewy.com
Company Email: elkst@tacotimewy.com
Type of Business: Chain Restaurant Operator
Total Sales: $3,815,000 (e)
Total Units: 5
Trade Names: Taco Time (5)
Units Franchised From: 5
Preferred Location Types: Freestanding
Primary Menu: Taco (5)
Areas of Operation: WY
Type of Foodservice: Quick Serve (5)
Franchise Affiliation: Kahala Brands, SCOTTSDALE, AZ

Key Personnel
DENISE STALEY - Owner; General Buyer

WY 40 Inc.
1695 Sunset Dr Ste 102
Rock Springs, WY 82901-7053

Telephone: (307) 362-9475
Fax Number: (307) 362-9476
Company Email: mcdonalds3@hotmail.com
Type of Business: Chain Restaurant Operator
Total Sales: $15,022,000 (e)
Number of Employees: 100
Average Check: Breakfast(5); Lunch(8); Dinner(8)
Total Units: 3
Trade Names: McDonald's (3)
Units Franchised From: 3
Preferred Square Footage: 2,500; 3,000
Preferred Location Types: Freestanding
Primary Menu: Hamburger (3)
Areas of Operation: WY
Type of Foodservice: Quick Serve (3)
Franchise Affiliation: McDonald's Corporation, CHICAGO, IL
Primary Distributors: (Food) Mile Hi Foods, DENVER, CO

Key Personnel
GREGORY BAILEY - President; Partner; General Manager; General Buyer
CINDY BAILEY - Partner

Domino's Franchisee
2741 W C St
Torrington, WY 82240-1835

Telephone: (307) 532-0330
Type of Business: Chain Restaurant Operator
Total Sales: $8,022,000 (e)
Total Units: 4
Trade Names: Domino's (4)
Units Franchised From: 4
Primary Menu: Pizza (4)
Areas of Operation: WY
Type of Foodservice: Quick Serve (4)
Franchise Affiliation: Domino's Pizza Inc, ANN ARBOR, MI

Key Personnel
MICHAEL D. HACKETT - Owner; General Buyer

ALBERTA

Cinnaroll Bakeries Ltd.
2140 Pegasus Rd NE
Calgary, AB T2E 8G8

Telephone: (403) 255-4556
Fax Number: (403) 259-5124
Internet Homepage: cinnaroll.com; cinnzeo.com
Company Email: info@cinnzeo.com
Type of Business: Chain Restaurant Operator
Year Founded: 1986
Systemwide Sales: $25,520,000 (e)
Total Sales: $6,735,000 (e)
Number of Employees: 1,125
Average Check: Lunch(8); Dinner(8)
Total Units: 47
Trade Names: Cinnzeo Bakery Cafe (47)
Company-Owned Units: 5
Units Franchised To: 42
Preferred Square Footage: 300; 500
Preferred Location Types: Freestanding; Regional Mall; Strip Mall
Primary Menu: Snacks (47)
Areas of Operation: AZ, FC, AB, BC, MB
Foreign Countries: CHILE; EGYPT; ENGLAND; KUWAIT; LEBANON; MEXICO; QATAR; SAUDI ARABIA; SYRIA; UNITED STATES OF AMERICA
Type of Foodservice: Quick Serve (47)
On-site Distribution Center: Yes
Primary Distributors: (Full Line) BakeMark Ingredients Canada Ltd., CALGARY, AB

Key Personnel
BRAD TURNER - CEO; General Buyer
CRAIG PARSONS - COO
ANGELA TREMAINE - Controller
ANDREA HAASE - Director Operations, Wholesale

Donald McGregor Investment Ltd.
532 53 Ave SW
Calgary, AB T2V 0C7

Telephone: (403) 252-6023
Fax Number: (403) 252-4044
Company Email: dmiltd@shaw.ca
Type of Business: Chain Restaurant Operator
Year Founded: 1971
Total Sales: $9,010,000 (e)
Number of Employees: 60
Average Check: Breakfast(5); Lunch(8); Dinner(8)
Total Units: 6
Trade Names: Dairy Queen (1); Orange Julius (5)
Units Franchised From: 6
Preferred Square Footage: 2,000
Preferred Location Types: Freestanding; Regional Mall
Primary Menu: Snacks (6)
Areas of Operation: AB
Type of Foodservice: Quick Serve (6)
Franchise Affiliation: International Dairy Queen Inc., BLOOMINGTON, MN
Primary Distributors: (Food) SYSCO Food Services of Calgary, CALGARY, AB

Key Personnel
DON MCGREGOR - President; CFO; General Manager; Director Finance, Operations, Purchasing, Store Fixtures; General Buyer
ROB MCGREGOR - VP; Director Facility/Maintenance, Information Systems, Supply Chain, Ethnic Marketing, Real Estate, Store Fixtures

Edo Japan Inc.
4838 32 St SE
Calgary, AB T2B 2S6

Telephone: (403) 215-8800
Fax Number: (403) 215-8801
Internet Homepage: edojapan.com
Company Email: ContactUs@edojapan.com
Type of Business: Chain Restaurant Operator
Year Founded: 1979
Systemwide Sales: $83,025,000 (e)
Total Sales: $11,530,000 (e)
Number of Employees: 30
Average Check: Lunch(16); Dinner(16)
Internet Order Processing: Yes
Total Units: 145
Trade Names: Edo Japan (145)
Company-Owned Units: 4
Units Franchised To: 141
Preferred Square Footage: 450; 700; 1,200
Preferred Location Types: Downtown; Regional Mall; Strip Mall
Primary Menu: Japanese (145)
Projected Openings: 3
Areas of Operation: AB, BC, ON, QC, SK
Foreign Countries: UNITED STATES OF AMERICA
Type of Foodservice: Quick Serve (145)
Primary Distributors: (Food) SYSCO Food Services of Houston Inc., HOUSTON, TX

Key Personnel
DAVE MINNETT - CEO
TERRY FOSTER - VP Operations
MARK PANNEKOEK - VP Foodservice Equip/Supplies

FranWorks Franchise Corp.
7403 MacLeod Trail SW
Calgary, AB T2H 0L8

Telephone: (403) 263-4323
Fax Number: (403) 263-0849
Internet Homepage: franworks.com
Company Email: info@franworks.com
Type of Business: Chain Restaurant Operator
Year Founded: 1998
Systemwide Sales: $295,151,000 (e)
Total Sales: $24,060,000 (e)
Alcohol Sales: 40%
Number of Employees: 15
Average Check: Lunch(24); Dinner(24)
Total Units: 99
Trade Names: Elephabt & Castle (11); Original Joe's Restaurant & Bar (62); State & Main (26)
Company-Owned Units: 45
Units Franchised To: 54
Preferred Square Footage: 3,000
Preferred Location Types: Downtown; Freestanding; Outlet Mall; Regional Mall; Strip Mall
Alcohol Served: Beer, Wine, Liquor
Primary Menu: American (99)
Projected Openings: 14
Areas of Operation: DC, IL, MA, WA, AB, BC, MB, ON, SK
Foreign Countries: UNITED STATES OF AMERICA
Type of Foodservice: Casual Dining (99)
Catering Services: Yes
Subsidiaries: The Elephant & Castle Group Inc., CALGARY, AB CANADA
Primary Distributors: (Food) SYSCO Food Services of Calgary, CALGARY, AB

Key Personnel
DEREK DOKE - President; General Buyer
JEREMY DOKE - VP Finance
JOHN REMOUNDOS - VP Franchise Development

Ginger Beef Choice Ltd.
5521 3 St SE
Calgary, AB T2H 1K1

Telephone: (403) 272-8088
Fax Number: (403) 235-0688
Internet Homepage: gingerbeef.com; gingerbeefchoice.com
Company Email: info@gingerbeef.com
Type of Business: Nontraditional Foodservice Operator
Year Founded: 1986
Systemwide Sales: $14,110,000 (e)
Total Sales: $8,234,000 (e)
Alcohol Sales: 10%
Number of Employees: 225
Average Check: Lunch(26); Dinner(26)
Total Units: 9
Trade Names: Bistro House (2); Ginger Beef Express (6); Ginger Beef Peking House (1)
Units Franchised To: 9
Preferred Square Footage: 5,000; 8,000
Preferred Location Types: Strip Mall
Alcohol Served: Beer, Wine, Liquor
Primary Menu: Asian (9)
Areas of Operation: AB

Type of Foodservice: Casual Dining (3); Quick Serve (6)
Catering Services: Yes
On-site Distribution Center: Yes
Primary Distributors: (Food) Topmade Enterprises Ltd., CALGARY, AB
Notes: The company derives approximately 99% of its revenue from wholesale operations.

Key Personnel
STANLEY LEUNG - Chairman; CEO; President
JAMES LEUNG - CFO; VP Operations, Purchasing, Store Fixtures; Corporate Secretary

Good Earth Cafes Ltd.
4020 7 St SE
Calgary, AB T2G 2Y8

Telephone: (403) 294-9330
Fax Number: (403) 294-9329
Internet Homepage: goodearthcoffeehouse.com
Company Email: info@goodearthcoffeehouse.com
Type of Business: Chain Restaurant Operator
Year Founded: 1991
Total Sales: $25,500,000 (e)
Total Units: 49
Trade Names: Good Earth Coffeehouse and Bakery (49)
Company-Owned Units: 49
Primary Menu: Sandwiches/Deli (49)
Areas of Operation: AB, BC, SK
Type of Foodservice: Fast Casual (49)

Key Personnel
NAN ESKENAZI - Co-Founder
MICHAEL GOING - Co-Founder; CEO
GERRY DOCHERTY - President; COO
CHRISTY LAING - Director Operations

Joey's Only Franchising Ltd.
3048 9 St SE
Calgary, AB T2G 3B9

Telephone: (403) 243-4584
Fax Number: (403) 243-8989
Internet Homepage: joeys.ca; joeysfranchisegroup.ca
Type of Business: Chain Restaurant Operator
Year Founded: 1985
Systemwide Sales: $29,160,000 (e)
Total Sales: $6,553,000 (e)
Alcohol Sales: 4%
Number of Employees: 66
Average Check: Lunch(22); Dinner(32)
Total Units: 33
Trade Names: Joey's Seafood Restaurant (33)
Company-Owned Units: 4
Units Franchised To: 29

Preferred Square Footage: 2,400
Preferred Location Types: Community Mall; Freestanding; Hotel/Motel; Mobile Unit; Regional Mall; Strip Mall
Alcohol Served: Beer, Wine
Primary Menu: Seafood (33)
Areas of Operation: AB, BC, ON, SK
Type of Foodservice: Casual Dining (33)
Catering Services: Yes
Primary Distributors: (Full Line) SYSCO Food Services of Edmonton, ACHESON, AB

Key Personnel
ANDY TAYLOR - President
JOE KLASSEN - Partner; Exec VP Operations
DAVID MOSSEY - Partner
THERESA KLASSEN - Exec VP Operations
TOM GRANDE - VP Purchasing, Supply Chain; General Buyer

Juniors Foods Services Ltd.
6455 MacLeod Trail SW
Calgary, AB T2H 0K3

Telephone: (403) 255-2744
Type of Business: Chain Restaurant Operator
Year Founded: 1971
Total Sales: $11,180,000 (e)
Number of Employees: 150
Average Check: Lunch(10); Dinner(12)
Total Units: 12
Trade Names: New York Fries (7); South St. Burger Co. (5)
Units Franchised From: 12
Preferred Square Footage: 300
Preferred Location Types: Community Mall; Kiosk
Primary Menu: American (12)
Areas of Operation: AB
Type of Foodservice: Quick Serve (12)
On-site Distribution Center: Yes
Franchise Affiliation: South St. Burger, TORONTO, ON

Key Personnel
BRIAN DEHAAN - President; Partner; General Buyer
NICK DEHAAN - Partner; Corporate Secretary; Director Facility/Maintenance, Information Systems, Real Estate; General Buyer
DOMINICK GEURIN - General Manager; General Buyer
ROSELLA HERRERA - Manager Branch

Landmark Cinemas of Canada
14505 Bannister Rd SE Ste 100
Calgary, AB T2X 3J3

Telephone: (403) 262-4255

Fax Number: (403) 266-1529
Internet Homepage: landmarkcinemas.com
Company Email: landmark@telusplanet.net
Type of Business: Foodservice Operations - Movie Theatre
Total Sales: $40,350,000 (e)
Total Units: 45
Trade Names: Landmark Cinema (45)
Company-Owned Units: 45
Preferred Location Types: Lifestyle Center; Regional Mall
Primary Menu: Snacks (45)
Areas of Operation: AB, BC, MB, ON, SK, YT
Type of Foodservice: In-Store Feeder (45)
Parent Company: TriWest Capital Partners, CALGARY, AB CANADA

Key Personnel
BRIAN MCINTOSH - Executive Chairman
PAUL WIGGINTON - CFO
GEOFF MULLBACK - VP Human Resources
LUIZA TILIHOIU - VP Finance
JACK GARDNER - Director Marketing, Communications

Phil's Restaurant Ltd.
5000 64 Ave SE Bay 50
Calgary, AB T2C 4V3

Telephone: (403) 720-6996
Fax Number: (403) 720-6992
Internet Homepage: phils.ca
Type of Business: Chain Restaurant Operator
Year Founded: 1956
Total Sales: $6,509,000 (e)
Alcohol Sales: 10%
Number of Employees: 125
Average Check: Breakfast(10); Lunch(12); Dinner(12)
Total Units: 5
Trade Names: Phil's Restaurant (5)
Company-Owned Units: 5
Preferred Square Footage: 5,500; 6,000
Preferred Location Types: Freestanding
Alcohol Served: Beer, Wine
Primary Menu: American (5)
Areas of Operation: AB
Type of Foodservice: Casual Dining (5)
On-site Distribution Center: Yes
Primary Distributors: (Full Line) SYSCO Food Services of Edmonton, ACHESON, AB

Key Personnel
CHRIS TETRAULT - President; Partner; Controller; Director Operations, Purchasing, Menu Development; Manager Real Estate
MELANIE TETRAULT - Partner; VP; Director Finance, Information Systems

The Elephant & Castle Group Inc.
7403 MacLeod Trail
Calgary, AB T2H 0L8

Telephone: (857) 233-2284
Fax Number: (857) 277-0824
Internet Homepage: elephantcastle.com
Company Email: info@elephantcastle.com
Listing Type: Subsidiary
Type of Business: Chain Restaurant Operator
Year Founded: 1977
Systemwide Sales: $53,701,000 (e)
Total Sales: $34,046,000 (e)
Alcohol Sales: 30%
Number of Employees: 480
Average Check: Breakfast(14); Lunch(14); Dinner(18)
Internet Order Processing: Yes
Total Units: 11
Trade Names: Elephant & Castle Pub (11)
Company-Owned Units: 10
Units Franchised To: 1
Preferred Square Footage: 3,500; 5,000
Preferred Location Types: Airports; Community Mall; Downtown; Freestanding; Regional Mall; Strip Mall
Alcohol Served: Beer, Wine, Liquor
Primary Menu: American (11)
Areas of Operation: DC, IL, MA, WA, ON
Foreign Countries: CANADA; UNITED STATES OF AMERICA
Type of Foodservice: Casual Dining (11)
Primary Distributors: (Full Line) SYSCO Canada, TORONTO, ON
Parent Company: Recipe Unlimited Corporation, VAUGHAN, ON CANADA
Headquarters: FranWorks Franchise Corp., CALGARY, AB CANADA

Key Personnel
HANS KLACKKEN - Director Foodservice

The Vintage Group
5905 11 St SE Ste 1A
Calgary, AB T2H 2A6

Telephone: (403) 261-7745
Fax Number: (403) 261-7759
Internet Homepage: vintagegroup.ca
Company Email: info@vintagegroup.ca
Type of Business: Chain Restaurant Operator
Total Sales: $13,298,000 (e)
Alcohol Sales: 12%
Total Units: 4
Trade Names: Bookers BBQ Grill & Crab Shack (1); Butcher and the Baker (1); Township Bar & Grill (1); Vintage Chophouse Tavern (1)
Company-Owned Units: 4
Alcohol Served: Beer, Wine, Liquor
Primary Menu: American (1); Sandwiches/Deli (1); Southern (1); Steak/Seafood (1)
Areas of Operation: AB, PE
Type of Foodservice: Casual Dining (2); Fine Dining (1); Quick Serve (1)

Key Personnel
LANCE HURTUBISE - CEO; President; CFO
JILL CLOW - Controller

Tim Hortons Inc.
7460 51 St SE
Calgary, AB T2C 4B4

Telephone: (403) 203-7400
Fax Number: (403) 203-7430
Listing Type: Regional Office
Type of Business: Chain Restaurant Operator
Total Units: 542
Areas of Operation: AB, BC, MB, NT, SK, YT
On-site Distribution Center: Yes
Parent Company: Restaurant Brands International, TORONTO, ON CANADA
Headquarters: Tim Hortons Inc., OAKVILLE, ON CANADA

Key Personnel
DOUG ANTHONY - VP

Tom's House of Pizza Ltd.
7730 MacLeod Trail SE
Calgary, AB T2H 0L9

Telephone: (403) 252-0111
Fax Number: (403) 255-3209
Internet Homepage: tomshouseofpizza.com
Company Email: tomshouseofpizza@gmail.com
Type of Business: Chain Restaurant Operator
Year Founded: 1963
Systemwide Sales: $5,988,000 (e)
Total Sales: $4,158,000 (e)
Alcohol Sales: 40%
Number of Employees: 40
Average Check: Lunch(12); Dinner(18)
Total Units: 4
Trade Names: Tom's House of Pizza (4)
Company-Owned Units: 4
Preferred Location Types: Freestanding; Strip Mall
Alcohol Served: Beer, Wine, Liquor
Primary Menu: Pizza (4)
Areas of Operation: AB
Type of Foodservice: Casual Dining (4)

Key Personnel
JOHN WINDLE - President; COO; Controller; General Manager; Executive Chef; General Buyer
SEBASTIEN WINDLE - General Manager; Manager Purchasing

Albert's Franchise Inc.
10550 115 St NW
Edmonton, AB T5H 3K6

Telephone: (780) 429-1259
Fax Number: (780) 426-7391
Internet Homepage: albertsfamilyrestaurants.com; tonyromas.com
Company Email: info@albertsfamilyrestaurants.com
Type of Business: Chain Restaurant Operator
Year Founded: 1959
Systemwide Sales: $25,423,000 (e)
Total Sales: $9,967,000 (e)
Alcohol Sales: 25%
Number of Employees: 522
Average Check: Breakfast(12); Lunch(20); Dinner(26)
Total Units: 18
Trade Names: Albert's Family Restaurant (9); Jungle Jim (1); Tony Roma's (8)
Company-Owned Units: 11
Units Franchised To: 6
Units Franchised From: 8
Preferred Square Footage: 4,500
Preferred Location Types: Downtown; Regional Mall; Strip Mall
Alcohol Served: Beer, Wine, Liquor
Primary Menu: American (18)
Areas of Operation: MN, AB, BC, SK
Foreign Countries: UNITED STATES OF AMERICA
Type of Foodservice: Casual Dining (18)
Franchise Affiliation: Romacorp Inc., ORLANDO, FL
Primary Distributors: (Specialty Foods) Centennial Foods, EDMONTON, AB
Notes: Systemwide sales are for Albert's Family Restaurants only and exclude all other concepts.

Key Personnel
MOISEY FELBER - President; Owner; Director Real Estate
REMIE CASTRO - Controller

Booster Juice
8915 51 Ave NW App 205
Edmonton, AB T6E 5J3

Telephone: (780) 440-6770
Fax Number: (780) 461-7161
Internet Homepage: boosterjuice.com
Company Email: franchise@boosterjuice.com
Type of Business: Chain Restaurant Operator
Year Founded: 1999
Systemwide Sales: $128,638,000 (e)
Total Sales: $10,970,000 (e)
Number of Employees: 150

Average Check: Breakfast(8); Lunch(8); Dinner(8)
Total Units: 400
Trade Names: Booster Juice (400)
Company-Owned Units: 10
Units Franchised To: 390
Preferred Square Footage: 150; 400; 800; 1,200
Preferred Location Types: Institution (college/hospital); Outlet Mall; Regional Mall; Strip Mall
Primary Menu: Snacks (400)
Projected Openings: 50
Areas of Operation: AZ, OR, UT, AB, BC, MB, NB, NL, NS, ON, QC, SK
Foreign Countries: BRAZIL; INDIA; MEXICO; UNITED STATES OF AMERICA
Type of Foodservice: Quick Serve (400)

Key Personnel
DALE S. WISHEWAN - CEO; President; Director Menu Development
LI YU - CFO
KELSEY ROTZIEN - General Manager
CURTIS SCHWABE - General Manager
LAURA STAFFORD - General Manager
LAURA LEVESQUE - General Manager
PEGGY LO - Director Marketing
RICK BOTELHO - Director Real Estate, Store Development
GLENN TUCKER - Director Franchise Development
ROSS SHAFER - Manager Training; Consultant Franchise Operations
ANDY ANDY - Manager Warehouse
ANDREW GREKUL - Manager Warehouse
DAVID KERR - Manager Information Technology
SABRINA NGUYEN - Supervisor
MARIE FE BELOY - Supervisor Foodservice
CARMEN BROWN - Project Manager Store Development

Cakemaker Canada Inc.
10654 82 Ave NW
Edmonton, AB T6E 2A7

Telephone: (780) 406-1700
Internet Homepage: cheesecakecafe.ca
Company Email: osc@cheesecakecafe.ca
Type of Business: Chain Restaurant Operator
Year Founded: 1988
Systemwide Sales: $13,980,000 (e)
Total Sales: $1,048,000 (e)
Alcohol Sales: 18%
Number of Employees: 400
Average Check: Breakfast(14); Lunch(14); Dinner(20)
Internet Order Processing: Yes
Internet Sales: 1.00%
Total Units: 4
Trade Names: Cakemaker Canada Inc. (4)
Units Franchised To: 3
Preferred Square Footage: 6,700
Preferred Location Types: Freestanding
Alcohol Served: Beer, Wine, Liquor
Primary Menu: American (4)
Projected Openings: 2
Areas of Operation: AB
Type of Foodservice: Casual Dining (4)
Primary Distributors: (Food) SYSCO Food Services of Edmonton, ACHESON, AB

Key Personnel
ROBERT BEESON - President; Director Real Estate; General Buyer
BOBBI BEESON - Director Marketing
JANICE KRILL - Manager Finance, Operations

Chiro Foods Ltd.
5041 Gateway Blvd NW
Edmonton, AB T6H 4R7

Telephone: (780) 438-8848
Fax Number: (780) 438-8070
Internet Homepage: chirofoods.com/about.html
Type of Business: Chain Restaurant Operator
Year Founded: 1984
Total Sales: $58,220,000 (e)
Alcohol Sales: 5%
Number of Employees: 610
Average Check: Breakfast(8); Lunch(10); Dinner(40)
Total Units: 33
Trade Names: A&W Restaurant (28); Famoso (5)
Units Franchised From: 33
Preferred Square Footage: 328; 6,200
Preferred Location Types: Freestanding; Institution (college/hospital); Regional Mall
Alcohol Served: Beer, Wine, Liquor
Primary Menu: American (28); Italian (5)
Areas of Operation: AB
Type of Foodservice: Casual Dining (5); Quick Serve (28)
Catering Services: Yes
Franchise Affiliation: A&W Food Services of Canada Inc., NORTH VANCOUVER, BC; Outback Steakhouse Restaurants, TAMPA, FL
Primary Distributors: (Full Line) SYSCO Food Services of Edmonton, ACHESON, AB
Notes: The company derives approximately 1% of its revenue from retail operations.

Key Personnel
BRIAN GOHEEN - President; Director Operations, Purchasing, Facility/Maintenance, Information Systems, Supply Chain, Real Estate, Design; General Buyer
JESSICA PERIN - Director Accounting; Manager Finance, Human Resources
TRAVIS DE GROOT - Director Operations
TINA GIBSON - Manager Marketing
LEAH COLEMAN - Manager Accounting

G R & M Foods, Inc.
6521 28 Ave NW
Edmonton, AB T6L 7B5

Telephone: (780) 463-2322
Type of Business: Chain Restaurant Operator
Total Sales: $7,086,000 (e)
Total Units: 3
Trade Names: Burger King (3)
Units Franchised From: 3
Preferred Location Types: Freestanding; Other
Primary Menu: Hamburger (3)
Areas of Operation: AB
Type of Foodservice: Quick Serve (3)
Franchise Affiliation: Burger King Worldwide Inc., MIAMI, FL

Key Personnel
GEORGE ESPINOSA - President; General Buyer

Royal Pizza
10433 80 Ave NW
Edmonton, AB T6E 1V1

Telephone: (780) 437-0123
Internet Homepage: royalpizza.ca
Company Email: info@royalpizza.ca
Type of Business: Chain Restaurant Operator
Year Founded: 1969
Total Units: 15
Trade Names: Royal Pizza (15)
Company-Owned Units: 4
Units Franchised To: 11
Primary Menu: Pizza (15)
Areas of Operation: AB
Type of Foodservice: Casual Dining (15)

Key Personnel
MIKE HANLEY - Owner; General Buyer

Sawmill Restaurant Group Ltd.
4810 Calgary Trail NW
Edmonton, AB T6H 5H5

Telephone: (780) 463-4499
Internet Homepage: sawmillrestaurant.com; themoosefactory.ca
Type of Business: Chain Restaurant Operator
Year Founded: 1976
Total Units: 10
Trade Names: Sawmill Prime Rib & Steak House (9); Tom Goodchild's Moose Factory (1)
Company-Owned Units: 10
Primary Menu: Steak (10)
Areas of Operation: AB, SK
Type of Foodservice: Casual Dining (10)

Catering Services: Yes

Key Personnel
TASKER GOODCHILD - President; Partner
LEN MCCULLOUGH - Partner; Director Operations

BRITISH COLUMBIA

Panago Pizza Inc.
33149 Mill Lake Rd
Abbotsford, BC V2S 2A4

Telephone: (604) 859-6621
Fax Number: (604) 850-1244
Internet Homepage: panago.com
Company Email: customercare@panago.com
Type of Business: Chain Restaurant Operator
Year Founded: 1986
Systemwide Sales: $167,962,000 (e)
Total Sales: $12,450,000 (e)
Number of Employees: 100
Average Check: Lunch(8); Dinner(8)
Internet Order Processing: Yes
Total Units: 184
Trade Names: Panago Pizza (184)
Company-Owned Units: 4
Units Franchised To: 180
Preferred Square Footage: 1,000
Preferred Location Types: Freestanding; Strip Mall
Primary Menu: Pizza (184)
Areas of Operation: AB, BC, MB, ON, SK
Type of Foodservice: Quick Serve (184)
Foodservice Management Venues: Schools
Primary Distributors: (Food) GFS Ontario, MILTON, ON

Key Personnel
SEAN DEGREGORIO - CEO
KEN ROOKE - Partner; VP
PAX ROBERTSON - COO
CHRISTY COUGHLAN - VP Marketing
JOHN GEOFROY - VP Operations, Development
TOM STACHURA - VP Technology
LAURIE CARSTENSEN - Controller; Manager Finance
SAPHIA MERKUS - Director Sourcing
MELISSA COLEMAN - Senior Manager Marketing
BRENT PERRY - Senior Manager Software Development
SALEN GOUNDER - Manager Information Technology
CARLA NAVARRETE - Manager Payroll, Employee Benefits
CHRIS WISHART - Manager Information Technology, Infrastructure
DESIREE STEPANIUK - Manager Training
LYNDA THOMAS - Manager Restaurant Operations
MARLENE VOLD - Project Manager Construction
JASMINA PARHAR - Representative Customer Service

Shefield Group
2265 W Railway St
Abbotsford, BC V2S 2E3

Mailing Address: PO Box 490, ABBOTSFORD, BC, V2T 6Z7
Telephone: (604) 852-8771
Fax Number: (604) 859-1711
Internet Homepage: shefield.com
Company Email: info@shefield.com
Type of Business: Chain Restaurant Operator
Year Founded: 1976
Systemwide Sales: $50,368,000 (e)
Total Sales: $15,513,000 (e)
Number of Employees: 300
Average Check: Breakfast(10); Lunch(10);
Total Units: 5
Trade Names: Cinnamon City (1); Gourmet Cup Beverage Station (4)
Company-Owned Units: 5
Preferred Square Footage: 500
Preferred Location Types: Hotel/Motel; Office Complex; Regional Mall
Primary Menu: Coffee (5)
Areas of Operation: AB, BC, MB, NT, ON
Type of Foodservice: Quick Serve (5)

Key Personnel
WOLFGANG LEHMANN - Co-President; Director Facility/Maintenance, Design

Cafe Fresh Franchising Corp.
8697 10th Ave
Burnaby, BC V3N 2S9

Mailing Address: PO Box 51071, BURNABY, BC, V3N 2S9
Telephone: (604) 553-1404
Fax Number: (778) 397-1404
Internet Homepage: freshrestaurants.com
Company Email: franchising@freshrestaurants.com
Type of Business: Chain Restaurant Operator
Total Sales: $12,310,000 (e)
Internet Order Processing: Yes
Total Units: 28
Trade Names: Fresh Healthy Cafe (28)
Units Franchised To: 27
Primary Menu: Sandwiches/Deli (28)
Areas of Operation: CO, FL, GA, MD, NY, OH, TX, AB, BC, ON, QC
Foreign Countries: UNITED STATES OF AMERICA
Type of Foodservice: Quick Serve (28)

Key Personnel
JEFF PARKER - President; General Buyer
BEATRICE PARKER - Director Operations

FDF Restaurant Brandz
1901 Rosser Ave Ste 401
Burnaby, BC V5C 6S3

Telephone: (604) 637-7272
Fax Number: (604) 637-8874
Internet Homepage: abccountry.ca; fatburgercanada.com; rickysfranchise.com
Company Email: marketing@rickysr.com
Type of Business: Chain Restaurant Operator
Year Founded: 1979
Systemwide Sales: $113,140,000 (e)
Total Sales: $15,640,000 (e)
Alcohol Sales: 5%
Number of Employees: 7,105
Average Check: Breakfast(14); Lunch(18); Dinner(26)
Total Units: 145
Trade Names: ABC Country Restaurant (4); Fatburger (55); Ricky's All Day Grill (85); Ricky's Cafe (1)
Company-Owned Units: 1
Units Franchised To: 90
Units Franchised From: 54
Preferred Square Footage: 3,200; 4,000; 4,500; 5,000
Preferred Location Types: Freestanding; Strip Mall
Alcohol Served: Beer, Wine, Liquor
Primary Menu: American (90); Hamburger (55)
Areas of Operation: AB, BC, MB, ON, SK, YT
Type of Foodservice: Casual Dining (89); Fast Casual (55)
Catering Services: Yes
Franchise Affiliation: Fat Brands, Inc., BEVERLY HILLS, CA
Primary Distributors: (Full Line) GFS Delta, DELTA, BC; (Full Line) Gordon Food Service, SPRINGFIELD, OH

Key Personnel
FRANK DIBENEDETTO - CEO; President; Director Real Estate, Design
JERRY INKSTER - CFO
STACEY HANSSON - Senior VP Operations, Marketing, Franchising
JASON HILDEBRAND - Director Construction

Gateway Casinos & Entertainment Inc.
4331 Dominion St
Burnaby, BC V5G 1C7

Telephone: (604) 412-0166
Fax Number: (604) 412-0117
Internet Homepage: gatewaycasinos.com
Company Email: info@gatewaycasinos.com

Type of Business: Foodservice Operations - Casinos
Year Founded: 2002
Total Sales: $220,550,000 (e)
Number of Employees: 5,600
Average Check: Breakfast(12); Lunch(16); Dinner(20)
Total Units: 28
Trade Names: Cascades Casino (3); Casino Rama Resort (1); Chances Casino (7); Gateway Casino (10); Grand Villa Casino (1); Lake City Vernon Casino(2); Playtime Casino (1); Starllight Casino (3)
Company-Owned Units: 28
Preferred Square Footage: 2,500; 3,000; 5,500; 6,000
Preferred Location Types: Other
Alcohol Served: Beer, Wine, Liquor
Primary Menu: American (8); Caribbean (2); Sandwiches/Deli (2); Snacks (3); Steak (3); Steak/Seafood (2)
Areas of Operation: AB, BC, ON
Foreign Countries: CANADA
Type of Foodservice: Casual Dining (18); Fast Casual (2); Quick Serve (8)
Primary Distributors: (Full Line) GFS Delta, DELTA, BC
Notes: Gateway Casinos & Entertainment Limited ("Gateway") announced that it has completed the acquisition of Boardwalk Gaming & Entertainment Inc.'s BC assets, which include Community Gaming Centers located in Mission, Squamish and Surrey, BC; and additional operational rights related to the former operations of Burnaby Bingo Country.

Key Personnel
TONY SANTO - CEO; General Buyer
BRAD HUTCHINGS - CFO
GRAHAM JOHNSTON - VP Security
IRFAN KHAN - Director Security

Mr. Mikes Restaurants
3700 N Fraser Way Ste 100
Burnaby, BC V5J 5H4

Telephone: (604) 536-4111
Internet Homepage: mrmikes.ca; rammp.net
Company Email: info@mrmikes.ca
Type of Business: Chain Restaurant Operator
Year Founded: 1960
Systemwide Sales: $51,921,000 (e)
Total Sales: $55,780,000 (e)
Alcohol Sales: 20%
Number of Employees: 365
Average Check: Lunch(18); Dinner(28)
Total Units: 39
Trade Names: Mr. Mike's Steakhouse & Bar (39)
Company-Owned Units: 4
Units Franchised To: 35
Preferred Square Footage: 9,000
Preferred Location Types: Freestanding; Strip Mall
Alcohol Served: Beer, Wine, Liquor
Primary Menu: Steak (39)
Areas of Operation: AB, BC
Type of Foodservice: Casual Dining (39)
Primary Distributors: (Food) GFS Delta, DELTA, BC; (Full Line) GFS Ontario, MILTON, ON

Key Personnel
AL CAVE - Vice Chairman; Partner
MIKE CORDOBA - CEO; Partner
LYN METIVIER - Owner; General Manager
TONY ZIDAR - Senior VP Operations
DON GOWAN - Senior VP Marketing, Branding
WARREN GOSS - VP Operations
SHERYL PRINGLE - VP Finance
ROB SCALI - Director Purchasing

RAMPP Hospitality Brands
3700 N Fraser Way Ste 100
Burnaby, BC v5j 5H4

Telephone: (604) 536-4111
Internet Homepage: mrmikes.ca; rammp.net
Company Email: info@mrmikes.ca
Type of Business: Chain Restaurant Operator
Year Founded: 1975
Systemwide Sales: $45,010,000 (e)
Total Sales: $14,390,000 (e)
Alcohol Sales: 5%
Number of Employees: 168
Average Check: Dinner(12)
Total Units: 42
Trade Names: Mr. Mike's (42)
Units Franchised From: 42
Preferred Square Footage: 3,200; 5,000
Preferred Location Types: Freestanding; Strip Mall
Alcohol Served: Beer, Wine, Liquor
Primary Menu: Steak/Seafood (42)
Projected Openings: 1
Areas of Operation: AB, BC, MB, ON, SK
Type of Foodservice: Casual Dining (42)
Catering Services: Yes

Key Personnel
MIKE CORDOBA - CEO; Partner
AL CAVE - Partner; Director Operations; General Buyer
ROBIN CHAKRABARTI - Partner
RICK VILLALPANDO - VP Business Development

Sammy J. Peppers Inc.
1075 Lougheed Hwy
Coquitlam, BC V3K 6N5

Telephone: (604) 525-0759
Fax Number: (604) 525-0745
Internet Homepage: sammyjs.ca
Company Email: info@sammyjs.ca
Type of Business: Chain Restaurant Operator
Year Founded: 1996
Total Sales: $19,499,000 (e)
Alcohol Sales: 20%
Number of Employees: 98
Average Check: Lunch(14); Dinner(22)
Total Units: 4
Trade Names: Sammy J's Grill & Bar (4)
Company-Owned Units: 4
Preferred Square Footage: 2,000
Alcohol Served: Beer, Wine, Liquor
Primary Menu: American (4)
Areas of Operation: BC
Type of Foodservice: Casual Dining (4)

Key Personnel
MIKE GARDNER - President; General Buyer
STEPHANIE STARNAUDO - Manager Finance, Human Resources

Murchie's Tea & Coffee (2007) Ltd.
8028 River Way
Delta, BC V4G 1K9

Telephone: (604) 946-7501
Fax Number: (604) 940-4444
Internet Homepage: murchies.com
Company Email: info@murchies.com
Type of Business: Chain Restaurant Operator
Year Founded: 1894
Total Sales: $8,614,000 (e)
Number of Employees: 90
Average Check: Lunch(8);
Internet Order Processing: Yes
Internet Sales: 1.00%
Total Units: 9
Trade Names: Murchie's Tea & Coffee (9)
Company-Owned Units: 9
Preferred Square Footage: 400
Preferred Location Types: Downtown; Freestanding; Office Complex; Regional Mall; Strip Mall
Primary Menu: Coffee (9)
Areas of Operation: BC
Type of Foodservice: In-Store Feeder (9)
Catering Services: Yes
On-site Distribution Center: Yes
Primary Distributors: (Full Line) SYSCO Food Services of Vancouver Inc., PORT COQUITLAM, BC

Key Personnel
GRANT KUEBLER - President; Partner; CFO; Manager Operations, Facility/Maintenance, Information Systems, Real Estate, Design, Human Resources, Menu Development; General Buyer
KELLY ROBINSON - Partner
KRISTA HOLTHE - Manager Operations

Serious Coffee
1A-4970 Polkey Rd
Duncan, BC V9L 6W3

Telephone: (250) 746-6511
Fax Number: (250) 746-6552
Internet Homepage: seriouscoffee.com
Company Email: admin@seriouscoffee.com
Type of Business: Chain Restaurant Operator
Year Founded: 1994
Total Units: 20
Trade Names: Serious Coffee (20)
Company-Owned Units: 4
Units Franchised To: 16
Primary Menu: Coffee (20)
Areas of Operation: BC
Type of Foodservice: Quick Serve (20)

Key Personnel
STEVE BROWN - Founder; CEO; President; Partner
BILL GRANT - Partner
DAVE GOUDY - Partner
SUSAN JIMMO - Partner

Fresh and Healthy Brands
8661 201 St Ste 200
Langley, BC V2Y 0G9

Telephone: (604) 546-7507
Fax Number: (604) 546-7401
Internet Homepage: famousfamiglia.com; freshandhealthybrands.com; juicezone.com
Company Email: franchising@juicezone.com
Type of Business: Chain Restaurant Operator
Total Sales: $2,842,000 (e)
Alcohol Sales: 5%
Total Units: 18
Trade Names: Go Grill (5); Juice Zone Fresh & Healthy Cafe (7); Pure Health Cafe (4); Yo Good (2)
Company-Owned Units: 3
Units Franchised To: 15
Preferred Location Types: Lifestyle Center
Primary Menu: Asian (5); Health Foods (10); Snacks (2)
Areas of Operation: TX, VA, BC, ON
Foreign Countries: CHINA; ENGLAND; MEXICO; PAKISTAN; SOUTH AFRICA; UNITED STATES OF AMERICA
Type of Foodservice: Casual Dining (5); Quick Serve (13)

Key Personnel
CHAD C. PARKER - CEO; President
COLE PARKER - Director Real Estate, Franchising

British Columbia Ferry Corp.
4300 Wellington Rd Ste 309
Nanaimo, BC V9T 2H3

Telephone: (250) 751-7588
Fax Number: (250) 751-2137
Listing Type: Distribution Center
Type of Business: Foodservice Operations - Theme Parks
Areas of Operation: BC
Parent Company: British Columbia Ferry Services Inc., VICTORIA, BC CANADA

Key Personnel
CLAUDE LACHANCE - Manager Distribution

A&W Food Services of Canada Inc.
300-171 Esplanade W Ste 300
North Vancouver, BC V7M 3K9

Telephone: (604) 988-2141
Fax Number: (604) 988-5531
Internet Homepage: aw.ca
Company Email: awfranchise@aw.ca
Type of Business: Chain Restaurant Operator
Year Founded: 1956
Systemwide Sales: $633,329,000 (e)
Total Sales: $167,830,000 (e)
Number of Employees: 336
Average Check: Breakfast(10); Lunch(10); Dinner(10)
Total Units: 955
Trade Names: A&W Restaurant (955)
Company-Owned Units: 9
Units Franchised To: 946
Preferred Square Footage: 400; 1,760
Preferred Location Types: Airports; Community Mall; Convenience Store/Gas Station; Downtown; Freestanding; Institution (college/hospital); Kiosk; Office Complex; Regional Mall; Strip Mall
Primary Menu: Hamburger (955)
Projected Openings: 3
Areas of Operation: AB, BC, MB, NB, NL, NS, NT, ON, PE, QC, SK, YT
Type of Foodservice: Quick Serve (955)
Distribution Centers: SCARBOROUGH, ON
Primary Distributors: (Full Line) Flanagan Foodservice Inc., KITCHENER, ON; (Full Line) SYSCO Food Services of Vancouver Inc., PORT COQUITLAM, BC; (Full Line) GFS Delta, DELTA, BC

Key Personnel
JEFFERSON J. MOONEY - Chairman Emeritus
PAUL F. B. HOLLANDS - Chairman; CEO; President
SUSAN D. SENECAL - President; COO
KELLY BLANKSTEIN - CFO
PATRICIA M. SAHLSTROM - Chief Commercial Officer; Senior VP
PATTI PARENTE - VP Real Estate
MIKE ATKINSON - VP Operations, Region
ANGELA GRIFFITHS - VP Safety-Food; Environment
AXEL FLORIAN REHKATSCH - Corporate Secretary
TOM NEWITT - Senior Director Marketing, Communications
YANICK MORIN - Senior Director Operations
NASIEM PATEL - Senior Director Technology
ANGIE TSANG - Director
LISE-ANN LABERGE - Director Store Operations, Real Estate, Franchising
KYLE MATTHEE - Director Business Development
LIZ METZAK - Director Design
LISA MARZOCCO - Director Finance
JULIA CUTT - Director Communications, Digital Marketing
THOMAS HUGHES - Director Business Development
PIERRE CLEMENT - Director Development
BRIAN PETERSON - Director
AMANDA WANG - Director Loyalty Program, Promotions
DAVID MACKINNON - Director Development
JASON MCLEAN - Director Technology, Infrastructure, Security
JORDAN KENNEDY - Regional Director Operations, Canada

Boston Pizza International Inc.
10760 Shellbridge Way Unit 100
Richmond, BC V6X 3H1

Telephone: (604) 270-1108
Fax Number: (604) 270-4168
Internet Homepage: bostonpizza.com
Company Email: contactus@bostonpizza.com
Type of Business: Chain Restaurant Operator
Year Founded: 1964
Systemwide Sales: $1,393,295,000 (e)
Publicly Held: Yes
Total Sales: $57,117,000 (e)
Alcohol Sales: 20%
Number of Employees: 2,155
Average Check: Lunch(22); Dinner(30)
Internet Order Processing: Yes
Total Units: 383
Trade Names: Boston Pizza (383)
Company-Owned Units: 3
Units Franchised To: 380
Preferred Square Footage: 3,000; 3,500; 4,100; 4,300; 5,300; 5,900
Preferred Location Types: Freestanding; Regional Mall; Stadiums; Strip Mall
Alcohol Served: Beer, Wine, Liquor
Primary Menu: Pizza (383)
Areas of Operation: AB, BC, MB, NB, NL, NS, NT, ON, PE, QC, SK, YT
Type of Foodservice: Casual Dining (383)

Primary Distributors: (Full Line) SYSCO Food Services of Vancouver Inc., PORT COQUITLAM, BC
Headquarter Offices: Boston's Restaurant & Sports Bar, DALLAS, TX
Regional Offices: Boston Pizza International Inc. (Eastern Canada), MISSISSAUGA, ON CANADA
Notes: Sales & store count reflect Canadian operations only.

Key Personnel
JIM TRELIVING - Chairman; Owner
JEFF MELNICK - President
JORDAN HOLM - President
MICHAEL HARBINSON - CFO
STEVEN SILVERSTONE - Exec VP Marketing
JONATHAN M. JESKE - Senior VP; General Counsel
PETER BLACKWELL - Senior VP Marketing, Communications
FELIX DECATA - VP Development
TIFFANY LUI - VP Finance
IAN THOMAS - VP Finance
LYNNETTE WHIPPLE - Director Compliance
CAILIN WHITE - Director Development
MARIAN RATY - Director Communications
GURMAIL JASWAL - Director Information Technology
KARLEY DAVID - Director Communications
JAMIE EMMS - Senior Manager Operations
ERIK LANDERT - Senior Manager Training
CORRIE WHITE - Senior Manager Operations
MARK SCORGIE - Regional Manager
CAREY SMITH - Regional Manager
ALLISON MCLAREN - Regional Manager
ROD GROENING - Regional Manager
ROKHSAN E. - Regional Manager Marketing
MICHAEL DAY - Manager Operations
JENNA BULL - Manager Marketing
SHANNON HYNDES - Manager Training
MARY SHIM - Manager Marketing
ODIR RODRIGUEZ - Manager Human Resources
SCOTT ZULYNIAK - Manager Operations
BRENDA SMITH - Associate Manager Marketing
SONYA WHITE - Project Manager Development, Construction
ALYSSA STANISZ - Coordinator Marketing, Community Relations
JOLANTA HANDLER - Coordinator Community Relations
TIMOTHY WONG - Senior Analyst Finance
AMY LAPOINTE - Generalist Human Resources

Famoso Neapolitan Pizzeria Inc.
3600 Lysander Lane Ste 370
Richmond, BC V7B 1C3

Telephone: (877) 210-5838
Fax Number: (604) 259-2510
Internet Homepage: famoso.ca
Company Email: info@famoso.ca
Type of Business: Chain Restaurant Operator
Year Founded: 2007
Total Sales: $13,820,000 (e)
Total Units: 29
Trade Names: Famoso Neapolitan Pizzeria (29)
Units Franchised To: 29
Primary Menu: Pizza (29)
Projected Openings: 3
Areas of Operation: AB, BC, ON, SK
Foreign Countries: CANADA
Type of Foodservice: Fast Casual (29)

Key Personnel
CHRIS BULLOCK - Partner; Chief Development Officer; General Buyer

Famous Wok Inc.
2560 Shell Rd Unit 1003
Richmond, BC V6X 0B8

Telephone: (604) 207-8871
Fax Number: (604) 207-9893
Company Email: famouswok.amanda@gmail.com
Type of Business: Chain Restaurant Operator
Year Founded: 1986
Systemwide Sales: $109,733,000 (e)
Total Sales: $2,269,000 (e)
Number of Employees: 100
Average Check: Lunch(18); Dinner(36)
Total Units: 182
Trade Names: Famous Cajun Grill (18); Famous Wok (25); Flaming Wok (66); Sizzling Wok (40); Umi of Japan (6); Umi Sushi Express (27)
Company-Owned Units: 5
Units Franchised To: 177
Preferred Square Footage: 1,000
Preferred Location Types: Regional Mall
Primary Menu: Cajun/Creole (18); Chinese (131); Japanese (33)
Areas of Operation: AK, AZ, CO, CT, IL, MA, MI, MO, NC, NM, NV, NY, OH, OK, PA, SC, TX, UT, VA, WA, WI, BC, MB, ON, SK
Foreign Countries: UNITED STATES OF AMERICA
Type of Foodservice: Family Restaurant (182)
Primary Distributors: (Full Line) SYSCO Food Services of Vancouver Inc., PORT COQUITLAM, BC

Key Personnel
G. JEFF MACK - Chairman; CEO; President; Manager Operations, Human Resources
JAMES MACK - VP; Manager Operations, Human Resources, Menu Development; General Buyer

Keg Restaurants Ltd.
10100 Shellbridge Way
Richmond, BC V6X 2W7

Telephone: (604) 276-0242
Fax Number: (604) 276-0138
Internet Homepage: kegincomefund.com; kegsteakhouse.com
Company Email: thekeg@kegrestaurants.com
Listing Type: Subsidiary
Type of Business: Chain Restaurant Operator
Year Founded: 1971
Systemwide Sales: $800,726,000 (e)
Total Sales: $882,830,000 (e)
Alcohol Sales: 28%
Number of Employees: 7,700
Average Check: Lunch(18); Dinner(42)
Internet Order Processing: Yes
Internet Sales: 1.00%
Total Units: 108
Trade Names: The Keg Steakhouse & Bar (108)
Company-Owned Units: 50
Units Franchised To: 58
Preferred Square Footage: 8,600; 8,800
Preferred Location Types: Community Mall; Downtown; Freestanding; Hotel/Motel; Lifestyle Center; Office Complex; Regional Mall; Strip Mall
Alcohol Served: Beer, Wine, Liquor
Primary Menu: Steak (108)
Areas of Operation: AZ, CO, TX, WA, AB, BC, MB, NB, NL, NS, ON, QC, SK
Foreign Countries: UNITED STATES OF AMERICA
Type of Foodservice: Casual Dining (108)
Primary Distributors: (Full Line) SYSCO Food Services of Portland Inc., WILSONVILLE, OR
Parent Company: Fairfax Financial Holdings Ltd., TORONTO, ON CANADA
Notes: The company derives approximately 3% of its revenue from retail sales.

Key Personnel
DAVID AISENSTAT - Chairman; CEO; President
NICK DEAN - President
ANDREA JANZEN - VP Real Estate
OTIS EDWARDS - VP Franchising
KRISTA KRZIYZEK - Director Human Resources
BOBBY PRICE - Director Operations

Asian Concepts Franchising Corp.
19074 22 Ave Unit 102
Surrey, BC V3S 3S6

Telephone: (778) 545-0233
Fax Number: (778) 545-0288
Internet Homepage: wokbox.ca
Company Email: info@wokbox.ca

Type of Business: Chain Restaurant Operator
Year Founded: 2004
Systemwide Sales: $32,054,000 (e)
Total Sales: $3,577,000 (e)
Total Units: 54
Trade Names: Wok Box Fresh Asian Kitchen (54)
Company-Owned Units: 1
Units Franchised To: 53
Preferred Square Footage: 1,200; 1,500; 2,000
Preferred Location Types: Airports; Lifestyle Center; Regional Mall; Strip Mall
Primary Menu: Asian (54)
Areas of Operation: AZ, FL, TX, AB, BC, MB, NL, NS, ON, SK
Foreign Countries: QATAR; UNITED STATES OF AMERICA
Type of Foodservice: Fast Casual (54)
Primary Distributors: (Food) Gordon Food Service Inc., WYOMING, MI

Key Personnel
BLAIR STEVENS - Founder Division; President Division; General Buyer

De Dutch Pannekoek House Restaurants Inc.
8484 162 St Unit 108
Surrey, BC V4N 1B4

Telephone: (604) 543-3101
Fax Number: (604) 543-3107
Internet Homepage: dedutch.com
Company Email: dedutch@dedutch.com
Type of Business: Chain Restaurant Operator
Year Founded: 1975
Systemwide Sales: $21,930,000 (e)
Total Sales: $8,691,000 (e)
Alcohol Sales: 1%
Number of Employees: 54
Average Check: Lunch(12); Dinner(22)
Total Units: 18
Trade Names: De Dutch Pannekoek House Restaurant (18)
Company-Owned Units: 8
Units Franchised To: 10
Preferred Square Footage: 1,800; 4,000
Preferred Location Types: Community Mall; Downtown; Freestanding; Strip Mall
Alcohol Served: Beer, Wine, Liquor
Primary Menu: French/Continental (18)
Areas of Operation: AB, BC
Type of Foodservice: Casual Dining (18)
Primary Distributors: (Food) GFS Delta, DELTA, BC

Key Personnel
BILL WARING - President; Controller; Manager Facility/Maintenance, Loss Prevention, Supply Chain, Real Estate, Design, Human Resources, Franchising
VICKY BIAMONTE - Director Operations, Purchasing, Information Systems, Risk Management, Menu Development
PAMELA WARING - Director Marketing
LORRAINE WARING - Manager Finance

Blenz The Canadian Coffee Company Ltd.
2285 Clark Dr Ste 250
Vancouver, BC V5N 3G9

Telephone: (604) 682-2995
Fax Number: (604) 684-2542
Internet Homepage: blenz.com
Company Email: info@blenz.com
Type of Business: Chain Restaurant Operator
Year Founded: 1991
Systemwide Sales: $30,099,000 (e)
Total Sales: $4,089,000 (e)
Number of Employees: 16
Average Check: Breakfast(6); Lunch(8); Dinner(8)
Total Units: 66
Trade Names: Blenz Coffee (66)
Company-Owned Units: 1
Units Franchised To: 65
Preferred Square Footage: 1,000
Preferred Location Types: Downtown; Freestanding; Strip Mall
Primary Menu: Coffee (66)
Areas of Operation: BC
Foreign Countries: THE PHILIPPINES
Type of Foodservice: Quick Serve (66)
Catering Services: Yes
Primary Distributors: (Food) GFS Delta, DELTA, BC

Key Personnel
AMY DEOL - Partner
GEOFFREY HAIR - Partner; Director Design, Human Resources, Store Fixtures
TINA NAZARI - Partner
BRIAN NOBLE - Partner; CFO; CTO
LARRY W. KINASH - VP Development
SARAH MOEN - VP Purchasing, Menu Development; General Buyer
NELLIE YANG - Controller
MITZI LACSAMANA - Creative Director
LORELAIN MENDOZA - Director Training
MATT SMITH - Director Marketing
MICHAEL CHAPMAN - Director Franchise Development
TAK ARAMAKI - Project Manager Construction

Cactus Restaurants Ltd.
201-550 Broadway W Ste 201
Vancouver, BC V5Z 1E9

Telephone: (604) 714-2025
Fax Number: (604) 730-6746
Internet Homepage: cactusclubcafe.com
Type of Business: Chain Restaurant Operator
Year Founded: 1988
Systemwide Sales: $76,373,000 (e)
Total Sales: $78,110,000 (e)
Alcohol Sales: 30%
Number of Employees: 3,150
Average Check: Lunch(24); Dinner(24)
Internet Order Processing: Yes
Total Units: 30
Trade Names: Cactus Club Cafe (30)
Company-Owned Units: 30
Preferred Square Footage: 4,500
Preferred Location Types: Freestanding; Strip Mall
Alcohol Served: Beer, Wine, Liquor
Primary Menu: Miscellaneous (30)
Areas of Operation: AB, BC, SK
Type of Foodservice: Casual Dining (30)
Primary Distributors: (Full Line) GFS Delta, DELTA, BC

Key Personnel
STEPHANIE LEROSE - President Human Resources
ANTONIO BELLANO - President Development, Real Estate
JEFFREY GRANUM - VP Finance
ROB FEENIE - Executive Chef; Manager Menu Development
DIVYA T. MOHAN - Senior Director Communications
LISA CRAVEIRO - Senior Director Marketing
RYAN RODDY - Senior Director Branding
CARL DEAN - Director Purchasing, Business Development
ANDREW LATCHFORD - Director Operations
ANNA GROLLE - Director Human Resources
JASON STREEFKERK - Director Culinary Operations
NICKI LICAS - Director Brand Marketing
CELINE KHAKH - Regional Director Human Resources
DARCY KUBE - Senior Manager Development, Design
MARK ROMA - Regional Manager Operations
KRISTIN HO - Regional Manager Human Resources
KEVIN HOGG - Manager Purchasing
JESSICA CAMPBELL - Manager Customer Service
KEVIN BROWNLEE - Manager Operations
GLENN BANANIA - Manager Security
ERICA WONG - Manager Accounting
CATHLEEN CUA - Senior Project Manager Human Resources

Coast Hotels & Resorts
1090 Georgia St W Ste 900
Vancouver, BC V6E 3V7

Telephone: (604) 682-7982
Fax Number: (604) 682-8942
Internet Homepage: coasthotels.com

Company Email: info@coasthotels.com
Type of Business: Foodservice Operations - Hotel/Motels
Year Founded: 1972
Total Sales: $218,110,000 (e)
Alcohol Sales: 20%
Number of Employees: 2,000
Total Units: 35
Restaurants in Hotels: 35
Trade Names: Coast Hotels (35)
Company-Owned Units: 35
Alcohol Served: Beer, Wine, Liquor
Projected Openings: 2
Areas of Operation: AK, CA, HI, ID, OR, WA, AB, BC, NT
Foreign Countries: UNITED STATES OF AMERICA
Type of Foodservice: Casual Dining (35)
Franchise Affiliation: Starbucks Corporation, SEATTLE, WA
Primary Distributors: (Food) SYSCO Food Services of Seattle Inc., KENT, WA
Notes: The company derives approximately 70% of its revenue from hotel operations.

Key Personnel
MARK HOPE - Executive Director Business Development
MANNY ILAO - Director Finance, Administration
DANNY DANG - Manager Information Technology

Dencan Restaurants Inc.
1755 Broadway W Ste 310
Vancouver, BC V6J 4S5

Telephone: (604) 730-6620
Fax Number: (604) 730-4645
Internet Homepage: dennys.ca
Company Email: feedback@dennys.ca
Type of Business: Chain Restaurant Operator
Year Founded: 1992
Total Sales: $135,580,000 (e)
Alcohol Sales: 4.50%
Number of Employees: 2,525
Average Check: Breakfast(6); Lunch(10); Dinner(10)
Total Units: 47
Trade Names: Denny's (47)
Units Franchised From: 47
Preferred Square Footage: 3,000; 5,000
Preferred Location Types: Freestanding; Hotel/Motel
Alcohol Served: Beer, Wine, Liquor
Primary Menu: American (47)
Areas of Operation: AB, BC, MB, SK
Type of Foodservice: Casual Dining (47)
Franchise Affiliation: Denny's Corporation, SPARTANBURG, SC
Primary Distributors: (Full Line) GFS Delta, DELTA, BC
Parent Company: Northland Properties Corporation, VANCOUVER, BC CANADA

Key Personnel
DEBORAH GAGNON - President; COO
RAJEEV NANDA - VP Operations
MARK GURLEVITCH - Director Operations
DONNA BRUNET - Area Manager
MEGAN GARDINER - Manager Marketing

Glowbal Restaurant Group Inc.
302 Water St
Vancouver, BC V6B 1B6

Telephone: (604) 685-4569
Fax Number: (604) 566-9292
Internet Homepage: glowbalgroup.com
Company Email: marketing@glowbalgroup.com
Type of Business: Chain Restaurant Operator
Year Founded: 2002
Total Sales: $15,630,000 (e)
Alcohol Sales: 12%
Number of Employees: 141
Average Check: Lunch(26); Dinner(40)
Total Units: 9
Trade Names: Black + Blue (1); COAST Restaurant (1); Glowbal Grill & Satay Bar (1); Italian Kitchen (1); Nosh (1); Roof (1); Trattoria (3)
Company-Owned Units: 9
Preferred Location Types: Downtown; Freestanding; Strip Mall
Alcohol Served: Beer, Wine, Liquor
Primary Menu: Italian (4); Sandwiches/Deli (1); Seafood (1); Steak (1); Steak/Seafood (2)
Projected Openings: 1
Areas of Operation: BC
Type of Foodservice: Casual Dining (6); Fine Dining (2); Quick Serve (1)
Catering Services: Yes

Key Personnel
EMAD YACOUB - CEO; President
JACK LAMONT - Director Operations
JANE FROHLICK - Senior Manager Human Resources

Hy's of Canada Ltd.
128 Pender St W Ste 303
Vancouver, BC V6B 1R8

Telephone: (604) 684-3311
Fax Number: (604) 684-3535
Internet Homepage: gothamsteakhouse.com; hyssteakhouse.com
Type of Business: Chain Restaurant Operator
Year Founded: 1956
Total Sales: $24,990,000 (e)
Alcohol Sales: 30%
Number of Employees: 290
Average Check: Lunch(48); Dinner(84)
Total Units: 5
Trade Names: Gotham (1); Hy's Steakhouse (4)
Company-Owned Units: 5
Preferred Square Footage: 6,000
Preferred Location Types: Downtown; Freestanding
Alcohol Served: Beer, Wine, Liquor
Primary Menu: Steak (5)
Areas of Operation: AB, BC, MB, ON
Type of Foodservice: Fine Dining (5)
Primary Distributors: (Food) GFS Delta, DELTA, BC

Key Personnel
NEIL AISENSTAT - CEO; President; Partner
ROB MACDONALD - Partner
SIMON RUSSELL - CFO; VP; Director Real Estate, Human Resources
MEGAN BUCKLEY - COO; VP Operations, Menu Development
JACKIE HILDEBRAND - Executive Chef

Joey Restaurant Group
820 Burrard St Ste 950
Vancouver, BC V6Z 1X9

Telephone: (604) 699-5639
Fax Number: (604) 699-5630
Internet Homepage: localpubliceatery.com; joeyrestaurants.com
Company Email: feedback@joeyrestaurants.com
Type of Business: Chain Restaurant Operator
Year Founded: 1991
Total Sales: $90,870,000 (e)
Alcohol Sales: 30%
Number of Employees: 2,020
Average Check: Lunch(24); Dinner(32)
Total Units: 39
Trade Names: Joey's Restaurant (28); Local Public Eatery (11)
Company-Owned Units: 39
Preferred Square Footage: 6,000
Preferred Location Types: Community Mall; Freestanding
Alcohol Served: Beer, Wine, Liquor
Primary Menu: Italian (28); Miscellaneous (11)
Areas of Operation: CA, WA, AB, BC, MB, ON
Foreign Countries: UNITED STATES OF AMERICA
Type of Foodservice: Casual Dining (39)

Key Personnel
JEFF FULLER - CEO
AL JESSA - President; COO
ALISON WEBB - Partner
KATHERINE ANGUS - CFO
CASEY MILES - VP Culinary Operations
CHRIS MILLS - VP; Executive Chef
BRITT INNES - VP Marketing
JONATHAN PEDLOW - VP Real Estate

LARISSA LEBLOND - General Manager
DOMINIQUE DEABREU - General Manager
JOSHUA CARLSEN - Senior Director Design; Director Facility/Maintenance, Real Estate, Construction, Design, Business Development
BRENT KOEHN - Director Operations
ANDREW MARTIN - Director Risk Management, Human Resources
JORDAN NIELSEN - Director Construction
JESSE SAHLIN - Director Food and Beverage
ANDREW NASR - Regional Manager
TYLOR KONINGS - Manager Special Projects, Construction
ERIN KOKAYKO - Coordinator Culinary Operations
SHEONA DOCKSTEADER - Coordinator Leasing
MARC STEWART - Coordinator Design
KATE WALKER RID - Designer
STEPHANIE GEE - Designer Production
JANELLE LAZESKI - Designer
ELYSIA DOUILLARD - Systems Analyst

Rest-Con Management Systems Ltd.
535 Thurlow St App 600
Vancouver, BC V6E 3L2

Telephone: (604) 220-4566
Fax Number: (604) 463-2955
Internet Homepage: sandwichtree.ca
Company Email: tonyc@sandwichtree.ca
Type of Business: Chain Restaurant Operator
Year Founded: 1978
Systemwide Sales: $60,300,000 (e)
Total Sales: $6,531,000 (e)
Alcohol Sales: 5%
Number of Employees: 15
Average Check: Breakfast(6); Lunch(6); Dinner(8)
Total Units: 30
Trade Names: The Sandwich Tree (30)
Units Franchised To: 30
Preferred Square Footage: 1,200
Preferred Location Types: Freestanding; Strip Mall
Primary Menu: Sandwiches/Deli (30)
Areas of Operation: BC, MB, NB, NS, ON
Type of Foodservice: Fast Casual (30)
Catering Services: Yes

Key Personnel
GEORGE MOEN - President

Rothesay Holdings Ltd.
1756 Pandora St
Vancouver, BC V5L 1M1

Telephone: (604) 251-6331
Fax Number: (604) 251-6156
Internet Homepage: churcheschickenbc.ca
Company Email: churcheschicken@shawbiz.ca
Type of Business: Chain Restaurant Operator
Year Founded: 1986
Total Sales: $20,200,000 (e)
Number of Employees: 229
Average Check: Lunch(8); Dinner(10)
Total Units: 16
Trade Names: Church's Chicken (16)
Units Franchised From: 16
Preferred Square Footage: 1,600
Preferred Location Types: Freestanding; Strip Mall
Primary Menu: Chicken (16)
Areas of Operation: BC
Type of Foodservice: Quick Serve (16)
Franchise Affiliation: Church's Chicken, ATLANTA, GA
Primary Distributors: (Food) Yen Bros. Food Service (2011) Ltd., VANCOUVER, BC

Key Personnel
MURDIE C. POLLON - President; Director Finance, Accounting, Information Systems, Real Estate, Human Resources; General Buyer
KEN THICKE - Director Operations

Sandman Hotels Inns & Suites
1755 Broadway W Ste 310
Vancouver, BC V6J 4S5

Telephone: (604) 730-6600
Fax Number: (604) 730-4645
Internet Homepage: sandmanhotels.ca
Company Email: info@sandman.ca
Type of Business: Foodservice Operations - Hotel/Motels
Year Founded: 1963
Total Sales: $305,220,000 (e)
Alcohol Sales: 10%
Number of Employees: 5,200
Total Units: 107
Restaurants in Hotels: 107
Trade Names: Chop (3); Denny's (29); Moxie's (67); Shark Club (8)
Company-Owned Units: 3
Units Franchised From: 104
Alcohol Served: Beer, Wine, Liquor
Areas of Operation: AB, BC, MB, QC, SK
Type of Foodservice: Casual Dining (107)
Franchise Affiliation: Denny's Corporation, SPARTANBURG, SC; Moxie's Restaurants LP, CALGARY, AB
Primary Distributors: (Food) GFS Delta, DELTA, BC
Parent Company: Northland Properties Corporation, VANCOUVER, BC CANADA
Notes: The company derives approximately 75% of its revenue from hotel operations.

Key Personnel
R. THOMAS GAGLARDI - Chairman
ROBERT PRATT - CEO; President
TAJ KASSAM - President; COO
SHAMLIN PILLAY - VP Finance, Administration
SALIM KASSAM - VP Marketing, Business Development
GRAHAM RENNIE - VP Human Resources
BRUCE WOODROW - Director Purchasing, Menu Development, Food and Beverage; General Buyer

Starbucks Vancouver Regional Office
2930 Virtual Way Ste 110
Vancouver, BC V5M 0A5

Telephone: (604) 708-9233
Fax Number: (604) 708-2216
Listing Type: Regional Office
Type of Business: Chain Restaurant Operator
Number of Employees: 65
Total Units: 306
Areas of Operation: BC, YT
Parent Company: Starbucks Corporation, SEATTLE, WA
Headquarters: Starbucks Coffee Canada Inc., NORTH YORK, ON CANADA

Key Personnel
LISA ESSINGER - VP Region
COLIN BALL - Director Region

Thai House Group
8828 Heather St Ste 101
Vancouver, BC V6P 3S8

Telephone: (604) 737-7223
Fax Number: (604) 737-2828
Internet Homepage: thaihouse.com
Company Email: thaihousegroup@gmail.com
Type of Business: Chain Restaurant Operator
Year Founded: 1988
Total Sales: $5,484,000 (e)
Alcohol Sales: 10%
Number of Employees: 75
Average Check: Lunch(14); Dinner(24)
Total Units: 3
Trade Names: Pink Elephant Thai (2); Thai House (1)
Company-Owned Units: 3
Preferred Square Footage: 3,000
Preferred Location Types: Downtown; Freestanding
Alcohol Served: Beer, Wine, Liquor
Primary Menu: Thai (3)
Areas of Operation: BC
Type of Foodservice: Casual Dining (3)
Primary Distributors: (Food) SYSCO Food Services of Vancouver Inc., PORT

COQUITLAM, BC

Key Personnel
DESMOND CHEN - President; Owner; Executive Chef; General Buyer
ERICA WONG - Coordinator Marketing

The Art Institute of Vancouver
2665 Renfrew St
Vancouver, BC V5M 0A7

Telephone: (604) 683-9200
Internet Homepage: artinstitutes.edu/vancouver
Type of Business: Culinary Schools
Areas of Operation: BC

Key Personnel
CAROLE BIRD - Executive Chef
TIMOTHY BUDD - Executive Chef

The Old Spaghetti Factory Canada Ltd.
55 Water St Ste 210
Vancouver, BC V6B 1A1

Telephone: (604) 684-1287
Fax Number: (604) 684-8035
Internet Homepage: oldspaghettifactory.ca
Company Email: admin@osf.ca
Type of Business: Chain Restaurant Operator
Year Founded: 1970
Systemwide Sales: $59,326,000 (e)
Total Sales: $45,899,000 (e)
Alcohol Sales: 20%
Number of Employees: 994
Average Check: Lunch(16); Dinner(16)
Total Units: 14
Trade Names: The Old Spaghetti Factory (14)
Company-Owned Units: 12
Units Franchised To: 2
Preferred Square Footage: 7,000
Preferred Location Types: Downtown; Freestanding
Alcohol Served: Beer, Wine, Liquor
Primary Menu: Italian (14)
Projected Openings: 1
Areas of Operation: AB, BC, MB, ON
Type of Foodservice: Casual Dining (14)
Primary Distributors: (Food) SYSCO Food Services of Toronto, MISSISSAUGA, ON

Key Personnel
PETER BUCKLEY - CEO; President
KEN LOBSON - COO
CHRIS KANUKA - Senior VP
HUNTER WYLIE - VP Operations
BILL PUCHERT - General Manager

MATTHEW CALLAN - Executive Chef

Toptable Group
1154 Robson St
Vancouver, BC V6E 1B2

Telephone: (604) 786-0540
Fax Number: (604) 688-7339
Internet Homepage: baroso.ca; araxi.com; bluewatercafe.net; cincin.net; thierrychocolates.com; toptable.ca; westrestaurant.com
Company Email: info@toptable.ca
Type of Business: Chain Restaurant Operator
Year Founded: 1981
Total Sales: $31,930,000 (e)
Alcohol Sales: 40%
Number of Employees: 360
Average Check: Dinner(96)
Internet Order Processing: Yes
Total Units: 8
Trade Names: Araxi (1); Bar Oso (1); Blue Water Cafe and Raw Bar (1); Cincin Restaurante (1); Elisa (1); IL Caminetto (1); Thierry Chocolate (1); West (1)
Company-Owned Units: 8
Preferred Location Types: Freestanding
Alcohol Served: Beer, Wine, Liquor
Primary Menu: American (2); Italian (2); Seafood (1); Snacks (1); Spanish (1); Steak (1)
Areas of Operation: BC
Type of Foodservice: Casual Dining (1); Fast Casual (1); Fine Dining (6)
Primary Distributors: (Food) SYSCO Food Services of Vancouver Inc., PORT COQUITLAM, BC

Key Personnel
MICHAEL DOYLE - President
DAVID HONG - Controller
BOBBY MILHERON - Executive Chef
JORGE MUNOZ SANTOS - Executive Chef
FRANK PABST - Executive Chef
THIERRY BUSSET - Executive Chef
ANDREW RICHARDSON - Executive Chef
STEPHAN CACHARD - Director Operations
RICARDO FERREIRA - Director Restaurant Operations
SAREENA PEDNEAULT - Director Operations

Vera's Burger Shack
42 8th Ave W Ste 3
Vancouver, BC V5Y 1M7

Telephone: (604) 683-8372
Fax Number: (604) 683-8374
Internet Homepage: verasburgershack.com
Company Email: info@verasburgershack.com
Type of Business: Chain Restaurant Operator
Year Founded: 1977

Total Sales: $8,058,000 (e)
Total Units: 13
Trade Names: Vera's Burger Shack (13)
Company-Owned Units: 1
Units Franchised To: 12
Alcohol Served: Beer, Liquor
Primary Menu: Hamburger (13)
Areas of Operation: AB, BC, ON
Type of Foodservice: Fast Casual (13)

Key Personnel
GERALD TRITT - Partner; Director Real Estate
NOAH CANTOR - Partner; General Buyer

White Spot Hospitality
1126 Marine Dr SE
Vancouver, BC V5X 2V7

Telephone: (604) 321-6631
Fax Number: (604) 325-1499
Internet Homepage: whitespot.ca; tripleos.com
Company Email: feedback@whitespot.ca
Type of Business: Chain Restaurant Operator
Year Founded: 1928
Systemwide Sales: $110,905,000 (e)
Total Sales: $86,407,000 (e)
Alcohol Sales: 10%
Number of Employees: 1,028
Average Check: Breakfast(10); Lunch(14); Dinner(16)
Internet Order Processing: Yes
Internet Sales: 1.00%
Total Units: 91
Trade Names: Triple O's (50); White Spot Restaurant (41)
Company-Owned Units: 35
Units Franchised To: 56
Preferred Square Footage: 4,500
Preferred Location Types: Freestanding; Institution (college/hospital); Strip Mall
Alcohol Served: Beer, Wine, Liquor
Primary Menu: American (91)
Areas of Operation: AB, BC
Foreign Countries: HONG KONG; THAILAND
Type of Foodservice: Casual Dining (41); Family Restaurant (50)
Primary Distributors: (Food) SYSCO Food Services of Vancouver Inc., PORT COQUITLAM, BC
Parent Company: Shato Holdings, VANCOUVER, BC CANADA

Key Personnel
DENISE BUCHANAN - VP Human Resources
CATHY TOSTENSON - VP Marketing, Menu Development
PAUL VOLK - Director Operations
KAREN DOSEN - Director Franchise Development
JENNIFER MARTIN - Director Purchasing, Supply Chain, Distribution
DINA MOFFETT - Director Operations
BILL SENGHERA - Manager Risk Management

CARINA HIRNER - Manager Human Resources

British Columbia Ferry Services Inc.
500-1321 Blanshard St Ste 500
Victoria, BC V8W 0B7

Telephone: (250) 381-1401
Fax Number: (250) 381-5452
Internet Homepage: bcferries.com
Company Email: customerservice@bcferries.com
Type of Business: Nontraditional Foodservice Operator
Year Founded: 1960
Total Sales: $1,304,151,000 (e)
Alcohol Sales: 0.50%
Number of Employees: 4,700
Average Check: Breakfast(10); Lunch(10); Dinner(14)
Internet Order Processing: Yes
Total Units: 34
Trade Names: British Columbia Ferry Corp. (34)
Company-Owned Units: 34
Preferred Square Footage: 4,500
Preferred Location Types: Other
Alcohol Served: Beer, Wine
Primary Menu: American (34)
Areas of Operation: BC
Type of Foodservice: Cafeteria (34)
Distribution Centers: NANAIMO, BC; SIDNEY, BC
Franchise Affiliation: White Spot Hospitality, VANCOUVER, BC
Primary Distributors: (Full Line) SYSCO Food Services of Vancouver Inc., PORT COQUITLAM, BC
Notes: Foodservice sales includes some on-board retail operations. The company derives approximately 91% of its revenue from tolls, operating contracts, retail, and other operations.

Key Personnel
DONALD P. HAYES - Chairman
MARK COLLINS - CEO; President
JILL SHARLAND - CFO; VP
CORRINE STOREY - COO; VP
ERWIN MARTINEZ - CIO; VP
JASON BARABASH - Exec VP; General Counsel
CYNTHIA LUKAITIS - VP; Corporate Secretary
BLAINE ELLIS - VP Human Resources
JANET CARSON - VP Marketing, Customer Service
DARREN JOHNSTON - Executive Director Operations, Fleet
JOANNE CARPENDALE - Treasurer
JEFF DAVIDSON - Director Retail Operations
MIKE CHANIN - Director
CHETAN SONDAGAR - Director Technology
KEITH KING - Manager Information Technology
ANDREA LOVEDAY - Manager Asset Management
ADRIENNE BENNER - Manager Payroll
GREGORY BIRD - Manager Technology
NICHOLAS MANSLEY - Manager Operations, Security
NADER SAGHARLOU - Engineer
VASYL SEROGIN - Engineer

Discovery Coffee
664 Discovery St
Victoria, BC V8T 4L1

Telephone: (250) 477-2323
Internet Homepage: discoverycoffee.com
Company Email: info@discoverycoffee.com
Type of Business: Chain Restaurant Operator
Total Units: 6
Trade Names: Discovery Coffee (6)
Company-Owned Units: 6
Primary Menu: Coffee (6)
Areas of Operation: BC
Type of Foodservice: Quick Serve (6)

Key Personnel
LOGAN GRAY - Owner; General Buyer

Romeo's Place Ltd.
1703 Blanshard St
Victoria, BC V8T 2W7

Telephone: (250) 383-2121
Fax Number: (250) 383-9100
Internet Homepage: romeos.ca
Company Email: romeos@shaw.ca
Type of Business: Chain Restaurant Operator
Year Founded: 1974
Systemwide Sales: $18,266,000 (e)
Total Sales: $4,944,000 (e)
Alcohol Sales: 20%
Number of Employees: 50
Average Check: Lunch(20); Dinner(30)
Total Units: 5
Trade Names: Romeo's Place (5)
Company-Owned Units: 1
Units Franchised To: 4
Preferred Square Footage: 5,000; 6,000
Preferred Location Types: Freestanding; Regional Mall; Strip Mall
Alcohol Served: Beer, Wine, Liquor
Primary Menu: Italian (5)
Areas of Operation: BC
Type of Foodservice: Casual Dining (5)
Catering Services: Yes
Primary Distributors: (Food) SYSCO Food Services of Vancouver Inc., PORT COQUITLAM, BC

Key Personnel
DIMITRI MAVRIKOS - President; Controller; General Manager; Executive Chef; Director Facility/Maintenance, Information Systems, Real Estate, Design, Human Resources, Franchising; General Buyer
BERYL METCALF - Manager Accounting

Vina Restaurants Ltd.
2508 Marine Dr
West Vancouver, BC V7V 1L4

Telephone: (604) 926-6001
Fax Number: (604) 925-8368
Internet Homepage: vinarestaurant.com
Company Email: sales@vinarestaurant.com
Type of Business: Chain Restaurant Operator
Year Founded: 1980
Total Sales: $7,799,000 (e)
Alcohol Sales: 25%
Number of Employees: 270
Average Check: Lunch(12); Dinner(22)
Total Units: 9
Trade Names: Vina Vietnamese Cuisine (9)
Company-Owned Units: 9
Preferred Square Footage: 2,500
Preferred Location Types: Freestanding; Regional Mall
Alcohol Served: Beer, Wine, Liquor
Primary Menu: Asian (9)
Projected Openings: 2
Areas of Operation: BC
Type of Foodservice: Casual Dining (9)
Catering Services: Yes

Key Personnel
FRANCIS HUI - President; Partner
BERT SANDY - Director Finance, Real Estate; Manager Purchasing, Facility/Maintenance, Supply Chain, Design, Human Resources; Buyer Beverages

MANITOBA

JW Ventures
1570 18th St Ste 58
Brandon, MB R7A 5C5

Telephone: (204) 571-3160
Fax Number: (204) 571-3164
Internet Homepage: smittysbrandon.com
Company Email: smittys@mymts.net
Type of Business: Chain Restaurant Operator
Year Founded: 1977
Total Sales: $6,288,000 (e)
Alcohol Sales: 5%
Average Check: Lunch(10); Dinner(16)
Total Units: 3
Trade Names: A&W Restaurant (1); Smitty's Restaurant & Sports Line Lounge (2)
Units Franchised From: 3
Preferred Location Types: Convenience Store/Gas Station; Freestanding; Regional

Mall
Alcohol Served: Beer, Wine, Liquor
Primary Menu: American (2); Hamburger (1)
Projected Remodelings: 1
Areas of Operation: MB
Type of Foodservice: Casual Dining (2); Quick Serve (1)
Franchise Affiliation: A&W Food Services of Canada Inc., NORTH VANCOUVER, BC; Smitty's Canada Ltd., CALGARY, AB
Primary Distributors: (Full Line) SYSCO Food Services of Winnipeg, WINNIPEG, MB

Key Personnel
JEFF CROOKS - President; Director Marketing, Advertising; General Buyer
JOANNE MCGREGOR - Controller; Director Information Systems

BHK Ltd
558 Portage Ave
Winnipeg, MB R3C 0G3

Telephone: (204) 774-6370
Internet Homepage: juniorswinnipeg.com
Type of Business: Chain Restaurant Operator
Year Founded: 1970
Total Sales: $1,489,000 (e)
Number of Employees: 12
Average Check: Breakfast(8); Lunch(10); Dinner(12)
Total Units: 3
Trade Names: Juniors Drive-In (3)
Units Franchised To: 3
Preferred Square Footage: 2,500
Preferred Location Types: Freestanding
Primary Menu: Hamburger (3)
Areas of Operation: MB
Type of Foodservice: Quick Serve (3)

Key Personnel
SAYDA ZEID - Partner; Controller; Executive Chef; Director Finance, Operations, Purchasing, Facility/Maintenance, Information Systems, Real Estate, Human Resources; General Buyer
HASSAN ZEID - Partner
AZIA ZEID - Partner

Chicken Chef Canada Ltd.
97 Plymouth St
Winnipeg, MB R2X 2V5

Telephone: (204) 694-1984
Fax Number: (204) 694-1964
Internet Homepage: chickenchef.ca
Company Email: chickenchef@mymts.net
Type of Business: Chain Restaurant Operator
Year Founded: 1978
Systemwide Sales: $31,676,000 (e)
Total Sales: $2,690,000 (e)
Number of Employees: 6
Average Check: Dinner(14)
Total Units: 36
Trade Names: Chicken Chef (36)
Units Franchised To: 36
Preferred Square Footage: 2,400
Preferred Location Types: Freestanding; Strip Mall
Primary Menu: Chicken (36)
Areas of Operation: MB, ON, SK
Type of Foodservice: Family Restaurant (36)
Catering Services: Yes
Primary Distributors: (Full Line) SYSCO Food Services of Winnipeg, WINNIPEG, MB

Key Personnel
JEFF EPP - President
RYAN THORGILSSON - VP Purchasing, Security, Inventory, Loss Prevention, Risk Management, Quality Assurance, Food Safety; Director Finance, Operations, Facility/Maintenance, Information Systems, Real Estate, Design, Human Resources, Menu Development

Chicken Delight of Canada Ltd.
395 Berry St
Winnipeg, MB R3J 1N6

Telephone: (204) 885-7570
Fax Number: (204) 831-6176
Internet Homepage: chickendelight.com
Company Email: mail@chickendelight.com
Type of Business: Chain Restaurant Operator
Year Founded: 1952
Systemwide Sales: $56,275,000 (e)
Total Sales: $28,620,000 (e)
Alcohol Sales: 1%
Number of Employees: 500
Average Check: Breakfast(8); Lunch(8); Dinner(12)
Internet Order Processing: Yes
Internet Sales: 1.00%
Total Units: 20
Trade Names: Chicken Delight (20)
Company-Owned Units: 1
Units Franchised To: 19
Preferred Square Footage: 1,800
Preferred Location Types: Community Mall; Downtown; Freestanding; Outlet Mall; Regional Mall
Alcohol Served: Beer, Wine, Liquor
Primary Menu: Chicken (20)
Areas of Operation: MB, SK
Foreign Countries: TRINIDAD & TOBAGO; UNITED STATES OF AMERICA
Type of Foodservice: Quick Serve (20)
Catering Services: Yes
On-site Distribution Center: Yes
Primary Distributors: (Full Line) SYSCO Food Services of Winnipeg, WINNIPEG, MB
Parent Company: Harz Holding Ltd., WINNIPEG, MB CANADA

Key Personnel
NADINE CARTMAN - CEO; Partner
JIM CARTMAN - President; Partner
E. SMYTHE - Director Construction
JOE DASILVA - Director Operations

Domino's Distribution Center
1635 Burrows Ave Unit 14
Winnipeg, MB R2X 3B5

Telephone: (204) 586-0632
Fax Number: (204) 586-0642
Internet Homepage: dominos.com
Listing Type: Distribution Center
Type of Business: Chain Restaurant Operator
Year Founded: 1960
Number of Employees: 11
Internet Order Processing: Yes
Areas of Operation: MB, ON
Parent Company: Domino's Pizza Inc, ANN ARBOR, MI

Key Personnel
MIKE SHUST - General Manager

Gondola Pizza Incomparable Canada 1981 Ltd.
45 Durand Rd
Winnipeg, MB R2J 3T1

Telephone: (204) 661-2851
Internet Homepage: gondola-pizza.com
Company Email: contact@gondola-pizza.com
Type of Business: Chain Restaurant Operator
Year Founded: 1962
Systemwide Sales: $13,935,000 (e)
Total Sales: $11,100,000 (e)
Alcohol Sales: 15%
Number of Employees: 320
Average Check: Lunch(14); Dinner(30)
Total Units: 15
Trade Names: Gondola Pizza Incomparable (15)
Company-Owned Units: 10
Units Franchised To: 5
Preferred Square Footage: 2,000; 3,500
Preferred Location Types: Freestanding; Strip Mall
Alcohol Served: Beer, Wine, Liquor
Primary Menu: Pizza (15)
Areas of Operation: MB
Type of Foodservice: Casual Dining (15)
On-site Distribution Center: Yes
Primary Distributors: (Food) SYSCO Food Services of Winnipeg, WINNIPEG, MB

Key Personnel
DEREK LOEWEN - President; Manager

Operations, Facility/Maintenance, Information Systems, Loss Prevention, Design, Human Resources, Menu Development
VIKTOR LOEWEN - CFO; Controller; Manager Real Estate; General Buyer
EDWIN KANNAMKARA - Supervisor

Guberman Groupe Ltd.
1445 Portage Ave
Winnipeg, MB R3G 3P4

Telephone: (204) 943-6544
Fax Number: (204) 943-0490
Internet Homepage: originalpancakehouse.ca
Company Email: guberman@mts.net
Type of Business: Chain Restaurant Operator
Year Founded: 1962
Total Sales: $15,116,000 (e)
Alcohol Sales: 1%
Number of Employees: 200
Average Check: Breakfast(8); Lunch(8); Dinner(12)
Total Units: 4
Trade Names: The Original Pancake House (4)
Company-Owned Units: 4
Preferred Square Footage: 2,500
Preferred Location Types: Freestanding
Alcohol Served: Beer, Wine
Primary Menu: American (4)
Areas of Operation: MB
Type of Foodservice: Casual Dining (4)
Franchise Affiliation: The Original Pancake House Franchising Inc., PORTLAND, OR
Primary Distributors: (Full Line) SYSCO Food Services of Winnipeg, WINNIPEG, MB

Key Personnel
HAZEL KUSHNER - President; Executive Chef; Director Operations, Purchasing, Supply Chain, Real Estate; General Buyer
ROBERT WALKER - General Manager
TERRY FRIESEN - Manager Operations

Marigold Restaurants
1245 Inkster Blvd
Winnipeg, MB R2X 1P4

Telephone: (204) 697-1245
Internet Homepage: inkstermarigold.com
Company Email: customerservice@inkstermarigold.com
Type of Business: Chain Restaurant Operator
Year Founded: 1968
Total Sales: $5,123,000 (e)
Alcohol Sales: 9%
Number of Employees: 152
Average Check: Lunch(12); Dinner(14)
Total Units: 3
Trade Names: Marigold Restaurant (3)
Company-Owned Units: 3
Preferred Square Footage: 6,000
Preferred Location Types: Freestanding
Alcohol Served: Beer, Wine, Liquor
Primary Menu: Chinese (3)
Areas of Operation: MB
Type of Foodservice: Casual Dining (3)
Catering Services: Yes
Primary Distributors: (Food) Loblaw Companies Limited,, CALGARY, AB
Parent Company: Woo Brothers Ltd., WINNIPEG, MB CANADA

Key Personnel
DAVID WOO - President
ROGER WOO - VP
PETER WOO - Director Purchasing, Facility/Maintenance, Supply Chain, Menu Development, Catering; General Buyer
ROBERT WOO - Manager Marketing

Salisbury House of Canada Commissary
1 Bannister Rd
Winnipeg, MB R2R 0P2

Telephone: (204) 633-7955
Fax Number: (204) 632-1200
Internet Homepage: salisburyhouse.ca
Listing Type: Distribution Center
Type of Business: Chain Restaurant Operator
Number of Employees: 25
Areas of Operation: MB
Parent Company: Salisbury House of Canada Ltd., WINNIPEG, MB CANADA

Key Personnel
DIEGO MONCADO - Manager Distribution, Warehouse, Transportation

Salisbury House of Canada Ltd.
787 Leila Ave
Winnipeg, MB R2V 3J7

Telephone: (204) 784-7461
Fax Number: (204) 786-2181
Internet Homepage: salisburyhouse.ca
Company Email: info@salisburyhouse.ca
Type of Business: Chain Restaurant Operator
Year Founded: 1931
Total Sales: $17,967,000 (e)
Number of Employees: 370
Average Check: Breakfast(8); Lunch(8); Dinner(12)
Total Units: 13
Trade Names: Salisbury House Restaurant (9); Sals Xpress (4)
Company-Owned Units: 13
Preferred Square Footage: 3,500
Preferred Location Types: Freestanding; Regional Mall; Strip Mall
Alcohol Served: Beer, Wine, Liquor
Primary Menu: Hamburger (13)
Areas of Operation: MB
Type of Foodservice: Family Restaurant (9); Quick Serve (4)
Catering Services: Yes
Distribution Centers: WINNIPEG, MB
On-site Distribution Center: Yes

Key Personnel
BRAD KRAMBLE - CEO; President; General Buyer
PATRICK PANCHUK - General Manager; Director Operations, Loss Prevention; General Buyer
JANIS KLASSEN - Manager Operations

Santa Lucia Pizza Winnipeg Ltd.
4 Saint Mary's Rd
Winnipeg, MB R2H 1H1

Telephone: (204) 237-4134
Internet Homepage: santaluciapizza.com
Type of Business: Chain Restaurant Operator
Year Founded: 1971
Systemwide Sales: $14,739,000 (e)
Total Sales: $5,997,000 (e)
Alcohol Sales: 10%
Number of Employees: 30
Average Check: Lunch(12); Dinner(14)
Total Units: 11
Trade Names: Santa Lucia Pizza (11)
Company-Owned Units: 4
Units Franchised To: 7
Preferred Square Footage: 2,000; 6,000
Preferred Location Types: Freestanding; Strip Mall
Alcohol Served: Beer, Wine, Liquor
Primary Menu: Pizza (11)
Areas of Operation: MB
Type of Foodservice: Casual Dining (11)
Catering Services: Yes
Primary Distributors: (Food) SYSCO Food Services of Winnipeg, WINNIPEG, MB

Key Personnel
GREG SIMEONIDIS - VP
NATASA ROBINSON - Manager Purchasing, Information Systems, Human Resources

WOW! Hospitality Concepts
529 Wellington Cres 3rd Floor
Winnipeg, MB R3M 0A1

Telephone: (204) 942-1090
Fax Number: (204) 957-5803
Internet Homepage: aussierules.ca; foodevolution-wpg.ca; celebrations.ca; jubilations.ca; muddywaters.ca;

wowhospitality.com
Company Email:
wowadmin@wowhospitality.com
Type of Business: Chain Restaurant Operator
Year Founded: 1995
Total Sales: $23,370,000 (e)
Alcohol Sales: 30%
Number of Employees: 364
Average Check: Lunch(20); Dinner(28)
Internet Order Processing: Yes
Internet Sales: 1.00%
Total Units: 8
Trade Names: 529 Wellington (1); Aussie Rules (1); Carne Italian Chophouse (1); Celebrations Dinner Theatre (1); Jubilations Dinner Theatre (2); Peasant Cookery (1); Prairie's Edge (1)
Company-Owned Units: 8
Preferred Square Footage: 10,000
Preferred Location Types: Freestanding; Strip Mall
Alcohol Served: Beer, Wine, Liquor
Primary Menu: American (1); French/Continental (2); Miscellaneous (3); Steak (1); Steak/Seafood (1)
Areas of Operation: AB, MB
Type of Foodservice: Casual Dining (7); Fine Dining (1)
Catering Services: Yes
Primary Distributors: (Food) SYSCO Food Services of Winnipeg, WINNIPEG, MB
Notes: The company derives approximately 25% of its revenue from theatre operations.

Key Personnel
DOUG STEPHEN - President; Director Purchasing, Information Systems, Menu Development
JANET CUNNINGHAM - VP Finance
MICHELLE FIELD - VP Operations
JOHN BRENAN - Controller

NEW BRUNSWICK

Pizza Shack Holdings Inc.
73 Vautour St
Cap-Pele, NB E4N 2C3

Telephone: (506) 874-4236
Internet Homepage: pizzashack.ca
Company Email: info@pizzashack.ca
Type of Business: Chain Restaurant Operator
Year Founded: 1984
Systemwide Sales: $13,403,000 (e)
Total Sales: $2,223,000 (e)
Alcohol Sales: 1%
Number of Employees: 4
Average Check: Lunch(22); Dinner(24)
Total Units: 27
Trade Names: Pizza Shack (27)
Units Franchised To: 27
Preferred Square Footage: 1,500
Preferred Location Types: Freestanding; Strip Mall
Alcohol Served: Beer, Wine, Liquor
Primary Menu: Pizza (27)
Areas of Operation: NB, NS, PE
Type of Foodservice: Casual Dining (27)
Foodservice Management Venues: Health Care; Schools
Primary Distributors: (Full Line) Saputo Dairy Products Canada, DIEPPE, NB

Key Personnel
RAY BOURQUE - CEO
ALLAIN BOURQUE - President; Director Purchasing, Franchise Development

Deluxe French Fries Limited
19 Industrial St
Dieppe, NB E1A 2B9

Telephone: (506) 857-0055
Fax Number: (506) 857-0493
Internet Homepage: deluxefrenchfries.net
Company Email: ltent@nb.aibn.com
Type of Business: Chain Restaurant Operator
Year Founded: 1949
Total Sales: $13,230,000 (e)
Number of Employees: 285
Average Check: Lunch(12); Dinner(14)
Total Units: 13
Trade Names: Deluxe French Fries, Fish & Chips (13)
Company-Owned Units: 13
Preferred Square Footage: 8,000
Preferred Location Types: Freestanding; Regional Mall
Primary Menu: Seafood (13)
Areas of Operation: NB, NS
Type of Foodservice: Family Restaurant (13)
Primary Distributors: (Food) SYSCO Food Services of Calgary, CALGARY, AB

Key Personnel
ROBERT THERIAULT - President; Director Operations, Facility/Maintenance, Real Estate, Design, Store Fixtures, Store Planning
NORM DESROCHES - Controller; Director Finance, Accounting

J. Miralco Inc.
190 Hebert Blvd
Edmundston, NB E3V 2S7

Telephone: (506) 735-6232
Fax Number: (506) 739-7018
Type of Business: Chain Restaurant Operator
Year Founded: 1985
Total Sales: $10,079,000 (e)
Number of Employees: 175
Average Check: Breakfast(8); Lunch(8); Dinner(8)
Total Units: 2
Trade Names: McDonald's (2)
Units Franchised From: 2
Preferred Square Footage: 2,500; 3,000
Preferred Location Types: Discount Dept. Stores; Freestanding
Primary Menu: Hamburger (2)
Areas of Operation: NB
Foreign Countries: UNITED STATES OF AMERICA
Type of Foodservice: Quick Serve (2)
Franchise Affiliation: McDonald's Corporation, CHICAGO, IL
Primary Distributors: (Food) The Martin-Brower of Canada Co. Ltd., DIEPPE, NB

Key Personnel
JEAN-MARC ALBERT - President; General Manager; General Buyer
DENIS ALBERT - Manager Operations

NEWFOUNDLAND AND LABRADOR

Ches's Snacks Ltd.
9 Freshwater Rd
St. John's, NL A1C 2N1

Telephone: (709) 726-2581
Fax Number: (709) 726-6886
Internet Homepage: chessfishandchips.ca
Company Email: ches.snacks@nfld.net
Type of Business: Chain Restaurant Operator
Year Founded: 1951
Total Sales: $4,706,000 (e)
Alcohol Sales: 5%
Number of Employees: 99
Average Check: Lunch(12); Dinner(16)
Total Units: 6
Trade Names: Ches's Famous Fish & Chips (6)
Company-Owned Units: 6
Preferred Location Types: Freestanding; Strip Mall
Alcohol Served: Beer, Wine, Liquor
Primary Menu: Seafood (6)
Areas of Operation: NL
Type of Foodservice: Quick Serve (6)
Catering Services: Yes
Primary Distributors: (Full Line) Atlantic Grocery Distributors Ltd., BAY ROBERTS, NL

Key Personnel
ROBERT BARBOUR - Partner; General Manager; General Buyer
ALICE BARBOUR - Partner; General Manager

NOVA SCOTIA

Pacrim Hospitality Services
30 Damascus Rd Ste 201
Bedford, NS B4A 0C1

Telephone: (902) 404-7474
Fax Number: (902) 457-3277
Internet Homepage: pacrimhospitality.com
Company Email: res@pacrimhospitality.com
Type of Business: Foodservice Operations - Hotel/Motels
Year Founded: 1974
Total Sales: $53,330,000 (e)
Alcohol Sales: 20%
Number of Employees: 1,300
Total Units: 17
Restaurants in Hotels: 10
Trade Names: Best Western (1); Candlewood Suites (1); Crowne Plaza (3); Embassy Suites (1); Four Points (1); Gander River Lodge (1); Highliner Plaza Hotel (1); Holiday Inn (1); Holiday Inn Express Hotel & Suites (1); Hotel Faubourg (1); Super 8 (3); The Atrium Inn (1); Wild Goose Lodge (1)
Company-Owned Units: 10
Alcohol Served: Beer, Wine, Liquor
Areas of Operation: NY, BC, NB, NL, NS, PE, QC
Foreign Countries: UNITED STATES OF AMERICA
Type of Foodservice: Casual Dining (10)
Primary Distributors: (Food) SYSCO Food Services of Northern New England Inc., WESTBROOK, ME
Notes: The company derives approximately 65% of its revenue from hotel operations.

Key Personnel
GLENN SQUIRES - CEO; President
JOHN SQUIRES - VP Operations, Purchasing
KEITH MACARTHUR - Controller
RUSSEL FUDGE - Manager Purchasing

Holloway Lodging Corporation
6009 Quinpool Road 10th Floor
Halifax, NS B3K 5J7

Telephone: (902) 404-3499
Fax Number: (902) 423-4001
Internet Homepage: hlcorp.ca; royalhost.com
Company Email: investorinfo@royalhost.com
Type of Business: Foodservice Operations - Hotel/Motels
Total Sales: $158,380,000 (e)
Alcohol Sales: 15%
Number of Employees: 476
Total Units: 17
Restaurants in Hotels: 17
Trade Names: Best Westerm (1); Days Inn (2); DoubleTree by Hilton (1); Holiday Inn (1); Quality Inn (2); Super 8 (8); Travelodge (1); Westmark Whitehorse HOtel (1)
Company-Owned Units: 17
Alcohol Served: Beer, Wine, Liquor
Areas of Operation: SC, AB, BC, NB, NL, NS, NT, ON, SK, YT
Foreign Countries: UNITED STATES OF AMERICA
Type of Foodservice: Casual Dining; Fine Dining
Notes: The company derives approximately 89% of its revenue from hotel management & leasing operations.

Key Personnel
JANE RAFUSE - CFO
ROB SHERMAN - Director Human Resources
LAURA DOLE - Director Sales

SAS Restaurants
1887 Upper Water St
Halifax, NS B3J 1S9

Telephone: (902) 425-1501
Internet Homepage: lowerdeck.ca
Type of Business: Chain Restaurant Operator
Year Founded: 1995
Total Sales: $4,575,000 (e)
Alcohol Sales: 30%
Number of Employees: 65
Average Check: Lunch(14); Dinner(30)
Total Units: 3
Trade Names: Lower Deck (1); Lower Deck Bar & Grill (1); Red Stag Tavern (1)
Company-Owned Units: 3
Preferred Square Footage: 5,000
Preferred Location Types: Freestanding
Alcohol Served: Beer, Wine, Liquor
Primary Menu: American (3)
Areas of Operation: NS
Foreign Countries: UNITED STATES OF AMERICA
Type of Foodservice: Casual Dining (3)
Catering Services: Yes
Primary Distributors: (Full Line) SYSCO Food Services - Atlantic Inc., LAKESIDE, NS

Key Personnel
MIKE CONDY - Owner; General Manager; General Buyer
KIM CONDY - Manager Accounting, Administration

Grinner's Food Systems Ltd.
105 Walker St
Truro, NS B2N 4B1

Mailing Address: PO Box 1040, TRURO, NS, B2N 5G9
Telephone: (902) 893-4141
Fax Number: (902) 895-7635
Internet Homepage: captsub.com/atlantic; greco.ca
Company Email: grinners@greco.ca
Type of Business: Chain Restaurant Operator
Year Founded: 1981
Systemwide Sales: $86,144,000 (e)
Total Sales: $7,375,000 (e)
Alcohol Sales: 1%
Number of Employees: 178
Average Check: Lunch(8); Dinner(12)
Total Units: 157
Trade Names: Captain Submarine (44); FROZU! (11); Greco Pizza (102)
Company-Owned Units: 10
Units Franchised To: 147
Preferred Square Footage: 1,400
Preferred Location Types: Freestanding; Grocery Stores; Kiosk; Regional Mall
Alcohol Served: Beer, Wine, Liquor
Primary Menu: Pizza (102); Sandwiches/Deli (44); Snacks (11)
Areas of Operation: NL, NS, ON, PE
Type of Foodservice: Quick Serve (157)
Foodservice Management Venues: Schools
Catering Services: Yes
Primary Distributors: (Food) GFS Ontario, MILTON, ON

Key Personnel
MICHAEL WHITTAKER - President
LISA BYERS - Controller
DON MARSHALL - Director Procurement
SHARON MITCHELL - Manager Marketing

ONTARIO

Smoke's Poutinerie Inc.
85 Kingston Rd E Unit 5
Ajax, ON L1S 7J4

Telephone: (905) 427-4444
Fax Number: (905) 427-9944
Internet Homepage: smokespoutinerie.com
Company Email: smoke@smokespoutlnerle.com
Type of Business: Chain Restaurant Operator
Year Founded: 2008
Average Check: Lunch(8); Dinner(10)
Total Units: 151
Trade Names: Smoke's Poutinerie (151)
Company-Owned Units: 43
Units Franchised To: 108
Preferred Location Types: Downtown; Institution (college/hospital); Stadiums; Strip Mall
Primary Menu: Snacks (151)
Areas of Operation: AZ, CA, FL, PA, AB, MB, NB, NL, NS, ON, QC, SK
Foreign Countries: CANADA; UNITED STATES OF AMERICA
Type of Foodservice: Fast Casual (151)
Catering Services: Yes

Key Personnel
MARK CUNNINGHAM - COO; Chief Business Development Officer
MIKE GRAHAM - VP Franchise Development

Mandarin Restaurant Franchise Corp.
8 Clipper Crt
Brampton, ON L6W 4T9

Telephone: (905) 451-4100
Fax Number: (905) 456-3411
Internet Homepage: mandarinrestaurant.com
Company Email: info@mandarinrestaurant.com
Type of Business: Chain Restaurant Operator
Year Founded: 1979
Systemwide Sales: $101,130,000 (e)
Total Sales: $23,910,000 (e)
Alcohol Sales: 10%
Number of Employees: 64
Average Check: Lunch(22); Dinner(34)
Total Units: 29
Trade Names: Mandarin (29)
Company-Owned Units: 1
Units Franchised To: 29
Preferred Square Footage: 13,000
Preferred Location Types: Strip Mall
Alcohol Served: Beer, Wine, Liquor
Primary Menu: Chinese (29)
Areas of Operation: ON
Type of Foodservice: Fine Dining (29)
Catering Services: Yes
Primary Distributors: (Food) GFS Ontario, MILTON, ON

Key Personnel
DIANA CHIU - Co-Founder
JAMES CHIU - President; CFO; Director Risk Management, Design, Human Resources, Franchising; General Buyer
TINA CHIU - COO; Manager Information Systems, Marketing
GEORGE CHIU - VP Real Estate
SUNNY LEUNG - Director Site Selection

Jetmo Inc.
129 Wellington St Unit 102
Brantford, ON N3T 5Z9

Telephone: (519) 758-0111
Fax Number: (519) 758-1393
Internet Homepage: fasteddies.ca
Company Email: customerservice@fasteddies.ca
Type of Business: Chain Restaurant Operator
Year Founded: 1987
Systemwide Sales: $6,475,000 (e)
Total Sales: $4,450,000 (e)
Number of Employees: 78
Average Check: Lunch(8); Dinner(8)
Total Units: 8
Trade Names: Fast Eddie's (8)
Company-Owned Units: 6
Units Franchised To: 2
Preferred Square Footage: 900
Preferred Location Types: Freestanding
Primary Menu: Hamburger (8)
Areas of Operation: ON
Type of Foodservice: Quick Serve (8)
Foodservice Management Venues: Prison Feeding; Schools
Primary Distributors: (Food) Stewart Foodservice Inc., BARRIE, ON

Key Personnel
MIKE GORSKI - President; CFO; Director Purchasing, Facility/Maintenance, Information Systems, Risk Management, Marketing, Real Estate, Design, Research & Development, Store Planning, Menu Development; General Buyer
MONIKA LINDSAY - Controller; Director Finance, Human Resources
JANIA GORSKI - General Manager; Director Operations, Store Fixtures

Dairy Queen Canada Inc.
1111 International Blvd
Burlington, ON L7R 3Y3

Mailing Address: PO Box 430, BURLINGTON, ON, L7R 3Y3
Telephone: (905) 639-1492
Fax Number: (905) 681-3623
Internet Homepage: dairyqueen.com
Listing Type: Subsidiary
Type of Business: Chain Restaurant Operator
Year Founded: 1940
Total Sales: $76,890,000 (e)
Number of Employees: 63
Average Check: Lunch(10); Dinner(10)
Total Units: 676
Trade Names: Brazier (188); Dairy Queen Self-Serve Only (53); Dairy Queen/Orange Julius (124); Grill & Chill (233); Limited Brazier (46); Orange Julius (32)
Units Franchised To: 676
Preferred Square Footage: 2,000; 3,000
Preferred Location Types: Airports; Community Mall; Downtown; Freestanding; Institution (college/hospital); Kiosk; Office Complex; Outlet Mall; Parks; Regional Mall; Stadiums; Strip Mall
Primary Menu: American (644); Snacks (32)
Projected Openings: 22
Areas of Operation: AB, BC, MB, NB, NL, NS, ON, PE, QC, SK
Type of Foodservice: Quick Serve (676)
Parent Company: Berkshire Hathaway Inc., OMAHA, NE
Headquarters: International Dairy Queen Inc., BLOOMINGTON, MN
Notes: The company derives approximately 75% of its revenue from the sale of equipment to stores & of product & supplies to wholesale warehouses.

Key Personnel
TROY BADER - CEO; President
JEAN CHAMPAGNE - COO Group
DAN KROPP - COO
CANDIDA NESS - Senior Director Marketing
LORI REID - Administrator Operations

SIR Corp.
5360 S Service Rd Ste 200
Burlington, ON L7L 5L1

Telephone: (905) 681-2997
Fax Number: (905) 681-0394
Internet Homepage: jackastors.com; sircorp.com
Company Email: info@sircorp.com
Type of Business: Chain Restaurant Operator
Year Founded: 1992
Publicly Held: Yes
Total Sales: $306,920,000 (e)
Alcohol Sales: 30%
Number of Employees: 5,000
Average Check: Lunch(20); Dinner(32)
Internet Order Processing: Yes
Internet Sales: 2.00%
Total Units: 58
Trade Names: Abbey's Bakehouse (1); Canyon Creek Chop House (2); Duke's Refresher (2); Jack Astor's Bar & Grill (39); Loose Moose Tap & Grill (1); Reds Midtown Tavern (1); Reds Square One (1); Reds Wine Tavern (1); Scaddabush (10)
Company-Owned Units: 58
Preferred Square Footage: 6,500
Preferred Location Types: Community Mall; Downtown; Freestanding; Office Complex; Regional Mall
Alcohol Served: Beer, Wine, Liquor
Primary Menu: American (45); Italian (10); Snacks (1); Steak (2)
Projected Openings: 2
Areas of Operation: AB, NS, ON, QC
Type of Foodservice: Casual Dining (56); Fine Dining (1); Quick Serve (1)
Catering Services: Yes
Primary Distributors: (Full Line) SYSCO Canada, TORONTO, ON

Key Personnel
GREY SISSON - Chairman
PETER FOWLER - CEO
PAUL J. BOGNAR - President; COO; Exec VP
JEFF GOOD - CFO
KIM VAN NIEUWKOOP - Senior VP Human Resources; General Counsel
MARGARET DOWELL - VP Purchasing
STEPHEN SEYMOUR - VP Information Technology
ANESIS JOHNSON-SMITH - VP Marketing

MIKE CAPPIELLO - VP Operations
KRISTA DIETRICH - VP Development, Real Estate
ANESIE JOHNSON - VP Marketing
BRUCE ELLIOT - VP Strategic Planning
GORDON MACKIE - Executive Chef; Director Culinary Development
ADRIAN WHITFIELD - Director Culinary Operations
ANDREW MOORE - Director Digital
GREG HALL - Director Procurement
MATT GOLBA - Director Retail Operations
ALVIN EVIDENTE - Manager Information Technology
GREG RUST - Manager

Tortoise Restaurant Group Inc.
3370 S Service Rd Ste 201
Burlington, ON L7N 3M6

Telephone: (905) 332-6833
Fax Number: (905) 332-0456
Internet Homepage: tortoise.ca; turtlejacks.com
Company Email: info@turtoise.ca
Type of Business: Chain Restaurant Operator
Year Founded: 1992
Systemwide Sales: $58,521,000 (e)
Total Sales: $59,810,000 (e)
Alcohol Sales: 40%
Average Check: Dinner(18)
Internet Order Processing: Yes
Total Units: 22
Trade Names: Coop Wicked Chicken (2); Cucina (1); Turtle Jack's Muskoka Grill (19)
Company-Owned Units: 6
Units Franchised To: 15
Alcohol Served: Beer, Wine, Liquor
Primary Menu: American (19); Chicken (2); Italian (1)
Areas of Operation: ON
Type of Foodservice: Casual Dining (20); Fast Casual (2)

Key Personnel
JIM LISHMAN - President; Director Menu Development; General Buyer
STUART BEESTON - Senior VP
ANTHONY LEECH - Director Food and Beverage

V Food Group
650 Jamieson Pky Unit 5
Cambridge, ON N3C 0A5

Telephone: (416) 235-0088
Fax Number: (416) 241-0001
Internet Homepage: doubledouble.ca
Company Email: pizza@doubledouble.ca
Type of Business: Chain Restaurant Operator
Year Founded: 1990
Systemwide Sales: $37,518,000 (e)
Total Sales: $24,120,000 (e)
Alcohol Sales: 1%
Number of Employees: 56
Average Check: Lunch(24); Dinner(24)
Internet Order Processing: Yes
Internet Sales: 2.00%
Total Units: 28
Trade Names: Double Double Pizza & Chicken (28)
Units Franchised To: 28
Preferred Square Footage: 1,200
Preferred Location Types: Regional Mall; Strip Mall
Primary Menu: Pizza (28)
Areas of Operation: ON
Type of Foodservice: Fast Casual (28)
Distribution Centers: CAMBRIDGE, ON
Primary Distributors: (Full Line) Reliable Food Supplies Inc., MISSISSAUGA, ON

Key Personnel
BALJIT GANGER - President; General Buyer
JIM FICKER - Director Operations

Crepe Delicious
147 Citation Dr Unit 30
Concord, ON L4K 2P8

Telephone: (905) 326-2969
Fax Number: (905) 326-9305
Type of Business: Chain Restaurant Operator
Year Founded: 2004
Total Units: 50
Trade Names: Crepe Delicious (50)
Company-Owned Units: 50
Primary Menu: French/Continental (50)
Areas of Operation: AB, BC, ON, SK
Foreign Countries: BAHRAIN; KUWAIT; QATAR
Type of Foodservice: Quick Serve (50)

Key Personnel
ODED YEFET - Founder; CEO; President
ELIK FARIN - VP Operations
LEE LEESAN - Manager Operations
MARCELLE LICHTMAN - Manager Business Development
KENAI GRIFFIN - Manager

The Great Canadian Bagel Ltd.
3300 Highway 7 Ste 101
Concord, ON L4K 4M3

Telephone: (905) 566-1903
Fax Number: (905) 566-1402
Internet Homepage: greatcanadianbagel.com
Company Email: info@greatcanadianbagel.com
Type of Business: Chain Restaurant Operator
Year Founded: 1993
Systemwide Sales: $27,020,000 (e)
Total Sales: $3,428,000 (e)
Number of Employees: 6
Average Check: Breakfast(8); Lunch(8); Dinner(8)
Total Units: 20
Trade Names: The Great Canadian Bagel (20)
Company-Owned Units: 1
Units Franchised To: 19
Preferred Square Footage: 500
Preferred Location Types: Airports; Community Mall; Downtown; Freestanding; Grocery Stores; Institution (college/hospital); Office Complex; Regional Mall; Strip Mall
Primary Menu: Bagels (20)
Projected Openings: 3
Areas of Operation: AB, BC, NB, NS, ON, SK
Type of Foodservice: Quick Serve (20)
Catering Services: Yes
Franchise Affiliation: Aegis Brands Inc, TORONTO, ON; Pizzaville Inc., WOODBRIDGE, ON
Primary Distributors: (Food) GFS Ontario, MILTON, ON
Notes: Some Great Canadian Bagel locations are co-branded with Second Cup and Pizzaville

Key Personnel
ED KWIATKOWSKI - President; Director Purchasing, Real Estate, Design, Franchise Development, Catering; Manager Menu Development
WILLIAM MANZARA - Controller; Manager Information Systems, E-Commerce
SANDY NETTLETON - Manager Purchasing

Pizza Pizza Distribution Center
500 Kipling Ave.
Etobicoke, ON M8Z 5E5

Telephone: (416) 967-1010
Fax Number: (416) 237-1423
Listing Type: Distribution Center
Type of Business: Foodservice Operations - Bowling Alley
Areas of Operation: ON, QC
Parent Company: Pizza Pizza Limited, TORONTO, ON CANADA

Key Personnel
SYED HASHMI - General Manager

The Neighborhood Group of Companies
176 Woolwich St
Guelph, ON N1H 3V5

Telephone: (519) 836-3948
Fax Number: (519) 836-6749
Internet Homepage: neighbourhoodgroup.com
Company Email: office@neighbourhoodgroup.com
Type of Business: Chain Restaurant Operator
Year Founded: 1990
Total Sales: $12,124,000 (e)
Alcohol Sales: 50%
Number of Employees: 70
Average Check: Lunch(14); Dinner(30)
Total Units: 4
Trade Names: Miijidaa Cafe + Bistro (1); The Borealis Grill & Bar (2); The Wooly Pub (1)
Company-Owned Units: 2
Units Franchised To: 2
Preferred Location Types: Downtown; Freestanding; Strip Mall
Alcohol Served: Beer, Wine, Liquor
Primary Menu: American (4)
Areas of Operation: ON
Type of Foodservice: Casual Dining (4)
Catering Services: Yes

Key Personnel
COURT DESAUTELS - President; Director Operations; General Buyer
LOUISE MCMULLEN - Director Information Systems, Logistics

Panzerotto Pizza Ltd.
25 Brownridge Rd
Halton Hills, ON L7G 0C6

Telephone: (416) 235-0000
Fax Number: (905) 864-1587
Internet Homepage: panzerottopizza.com; wingmachine.com
Company Email: info@panzerottopizza.com
Type of Business: Chain Restaurant Operator
Year Founded: 1976
Systemwide Sales: $34,207,000 (e)
Total Sales: $20,721,000 (e)
Alcohol Sales: 5%
Number of Employees: 330
Average Check: Lunch(8); Dinner(16)
Internet Order Processing: Yes
Internet Sales: 15.00%
Total Units: 120
Trade Names: Panzerotto Pizza (90); Wing Machine (30)
Units Franchised To: 120
Preferred Square Footage: 1,200
Preferred Location Types: Community Mall; Freestanding; Strip Mall
Alcohol Served: Beer
Primary Menu: Chicken (30); Pizza (90)
Areas of Operation: ON
Type of Foodservice: Quick Serve (90)
Catering Services: Yes
On-site Distribution Center: Yes
Primary Distributors: (Full Line) SYSCO Food Services of Central Ontario Inc., CAVAN MONAGHAN, ON

Key Personnel
VITO GANGAR - President
JIM FICKER - Director Operations; General Buyer

Wing Machine Inc.
25 Brownridge Rd
Halton Hills, ON L7G 0C6

Telephone: (416) 235-0000
Fax Number: (905) 864-1587
Internet Homepage: wingmachine.com
Company Email: support@wingmachine.com
Type of Business: Chain Restaurant Operator
Year Founded: 1985
Systemwide Sales: $11,526,000 (e)
Total Sales: $4,535,000 (e)
Alcohol Sales: 2%
Number of Employees: 100
Average Check: Lunch(6); Dinner(8)
Internet Order Processing: Yes
Internet Sales: 8.00%
Total Units: 24
Trade Names: Wing Machine (24)
Company-Owned Units: 2
Units Franchised To: 20
Preferred Square Footage: 1,000
Preferred Location Types: Freestanding; Strip Mall
Alcohol Served: Beer, Wine, Liquor
Primary Menu: Chicken (24)
Projected Openings: 3
Projected Remodelings: 4
Areas of Operation: ON
Type of Foodservice: Quick Serve (24)
Foodservice Management Venues: Business & Industry; Schools
Catering Services: Yes
On-site Distribution Center: Yes
Primary Distributors: (Full Line) SYSCO Food Services of Central Ontario Inc., CAVAN MONAGHAN, ON

Key Personnel
VITO GANGER - Owner; General Buyer

Wild Wing Hospitality
1700 King Rd Unit 20
King City, ON L7B 0N1

Telephone: (289) 319-2734
Internet Homepage: wildwingrestaurants.com
Company Email: inquiries@wildwingrestaurants.com
Type of Business: Chain Restaurant Operator
Total Units: 95
Trade Names: Wild Wing (95)
Company-Owned Units: 95
Areas of Operation: AB, BC, MB, ON

Key Personnel
CLARK MCKEOWN - CEO; President
TODD MATTHEWS - VP Operations

Pita Pit Ltd.
11 Princess St Ste 305
Kingston, ON K7L 1A1

Telephone: (613) 546-4494
Fax Number: (613) 546-1436
Internet Homepage: pitapit.ca
Company Email: info@pitapit.com
Type of Business: Chain Restaurant Operator
Year Founded: 1995
Systemwide Sales: $520,526,000 (e)
Total Sales: $74,960,000 (e)
Number of Employees: 30
Average Check: Breakfast(10); Lunch(10); Dinner(12)
Total Units: 655
Trade Names: Pita Pit (655)
Company-Owned Units: 23
Units Franchised To: 632
Preferred Square Footage: 600; 1,000; 1,500
Preferred Location Types: Freestanding; Strip Mall
Primary Menu: Greek/Mediterranean (655)
Areas of Operation: AL, AZ, CA, CO, DC, FL, GA, IA, ID, IL, IN, KS, KY, LA, MA, MI, MN, MO, MT, NC, ND, NM, NV, NY, OH, OK, OR, PA, SC, TN, TX, UT, VA, WA, WV, AB, BC, MB, NB, NL, NS, ON, QC, SK
Foreign Countries: AUSTRALIA; BRAZIL; CANADA; FRANCE; GREAT BRITAIN; INDIA; NEW ZEALAND; PANAMA; SOUTH KOREA; TRINIDAD & TOBAGO; UNITED STATES OF AMERICA
Type of Foodservice: Quick Serve (655)
Catering Services: Yes
Primary Distributors: (Full Line) SYSCO Kingston, KINGSTON, ON

Key Personnel
LEE STRAIT - VP Legal
BRENT SABEAN - General Counsel
PAUL BEADLE - Senior Director Finance
MATT JOHNSTON - Director Menu Development

Tim Hortons Inc.
1119 Innovation Dr
Kingston, ON K7K 7E6

Telephone: (613) 634-7055
Fax Number: (613) 634-2114
Internet Homepage: timhortons.com
Company Email: info@timhortons.com
Listing Type: Distribution Center
Type of Business: Chain Restaurant Operator
Number of Employees: 60
Total Units: 800
Projected Openings: 2
Areas of Operation: ON
Foreign Countries: UNITED STATES OF AMERICA
Distribution Centers: CALGARY, AB; LANGLEY, BC; DEBERT, NS; GUELPH, ON; KINGSTON, ON
On-site Distribution Center: Yes
Parent Company: Restaurant Brands International, TORONTO, ON CANADA
Headquarters: Tim Hortons Inc., OAKVILLE, ON CANADA

Key Personnel
PAUL LORBETSKI - Manager Purchasing

Bingemans
425 Bingeman Center Dr
Kitchener, ON N2B 3X7

Telephone: (519) 744-1555
Fax Number: (519) 744-3547
Internet Homepage: bingemans.com
Company Email: sales@bingemans.com
Type of Business: Foodservice Management Operator
Year Founded: 1940
Total Sales: $39,207,000 (e)
Number of Employees: 450
Number of Locations Served: 200
Total Foodservice Mgmt Accounts: 200
Internet Order Processing: Yes
Areas of Operation: ON
Type of Foodservice: Cafeteria (50); Full-service sit-down dining (50); Vending machines (200)
Foodservice Management Venues: Business & Industry; College & University; Health Care

Key Personnel
MARK BINGEMAN - CEO; President; General Manager; General Buyer
STEPHANIE MESSIER - Controller
MICHELLE PLAYFAIR - General Manager
SPIRO DRACOPOULOS - Director Sales
LAURIE SCHELL - Manager Sales
AMANDA O'NEILL - Manager Sales
SARAH LIVINGSTON - Supervisor
LISA BUCKING - Planner Sales
VIVIAN MURRAY - Planner Sales

Nutritional Management Services
2361 Main St
London, ON N6P 1A7

Telephone: (519) 652-2800
Fax Number: (519) 652-0867
Internet Homepage: nms.on.ca
Company Email: admin@nms.on.ca
Type of Business: Foodservice Management Operator
Year Founded: 1980
Total Sales: $26,903,000 (e)
Number of Employees: 100
Number of Locations Served: 20
Total Foodservice Mgmt Accounts: 20
Areas of Operation: ON
Type of Foodservice: Cafeteria (20)
Foodservice Management Venues: Business & Industry; College & University; Health Care; Schools
Primary Distributors: (Full Line) SYSCO Canada, TORONTO, ON

Key Personnel
MIKE THOMPSON - President
STEPHANIE MALO - VP Marketing, Sales

Sebastians
220 Adelaide St S
London, ON N5Z 3L1

Telephone: (519) 686-7201
Fax Number: (519) 686-1001
Internet Homepage: sebastians.ca
Company Email: info@sebastians.ca
Type of Business: Foodservice Operations - Hotel/Motels
Year Founded: 1981
Total Sales: $3,824,000 (e)
Average Check: Lunch(12); Dinner(12)
Total Units: 2
Trade Names: Sebastians (2)
Company-Owned Units: 2
Preferred Location Types: Freestanding; Mixed-use Center
Primary Menu: Sandwiches/Deli (2)
Areas of Operation: ON
Type of Foodservice: Cafeteria (2)
Catering Services: Yes
Distribution Centers: LONDON, ON
Primary Distributors: (Food) SYSCO Corporation, WOODSTOCK, ON

Key Personnel
ED HEALY - Owner; General Manager; General Buyer
YOIE GNOV - Executive Chef

The Larry Keen Group
17171 Cornwall Centre Rd Unit 5
Long Sault, ON K0C 1P0

Telephone: (613) 938-1333
Fax Number: (613) 936-0441
Company Email: larry@keengroup.ca
Type of Business: Chain Restaurant Operator
Total Sales: $8,432,000 (e)
Total Units: 4
Trade Names: Burger King (2); Tim Hortons (2)
Units Franchised From: 4
Preferred Location Types: Freestanding
Primary Menu: Coffee (2); Hamburger (2)
Areas of Operation: ON
Type of Foodservice: Fast Casual (2); Quick Serve (2)
Franchise Affiliation: Burger King Worldwide Inc., MIAMI, FL; Tim Hortons Inc., OAKVILLE, ON

Key Personnel
LARRY KEEN - President; General Buyer

Bento Sushi/Yo! Sushi
25 Centurian Dr Ste 208
Markham, ON L3R 5N8

Telephone: (905) 513-0028
Fax Number: (905) 513-9855
Internet Homepage: bentosushi.com
Company Email: feedback@bentosushi.com
Type of Business: Chain Restaurant Operator
Year Founded: 1996
Total Sales: $123,200,000 (e)
Total Units: 271
Trade Names: Bento Sushi (202); Yo! Sushi (69)
Company-Owned Units: 251
Units Franchised To: 20
Primary Menu: Japanese (271)
Areas of Operation: DC, FL, NY, AB, BC, MB, NB, NL, ON, PE, QC, SK
Foreign Countries: UNITED STATES OF AMERICA
Type of Foodservice: Fast Casual (271)
Notes: Bento Sushi operates in various formats, including quick-service restaurants and kiosks in supermarkets. It also supplies sushi to an additional 1,700 sites, including supermarkets and non-commercial operations.

Key Personnel
ROBIN ROWLAND - CEO
KEITH JACKSON - CFO
ERICA GALE - VP Marketing
MICHELLE NUR-CHOWDHURY - Director Operations
MARTIN XU - Director Operations

CHRIS REDDEN - Director Operations
DANIEL LAJOIE - Director Operations
KITTY K. PAT - Director Quality Assurance
MELODY KING - Manager Human Resources
KENNETH HUANG - Manager Information Technology

Freshly Squeezed Franchise Corporation
3235 14th Ave
Markham, ON L3R 0H3

Telephone: (905) 695-2614
Fax Number: (888) 886-5856
Internet Homepage: freshlysqueezed.ca
Company Email: ts@freshlysqueezed.ca
Type of Business: Chain Restaurant Operator
Year Founded: 1976
Total Sales: $38,020,000 (e)
Number of Employees: 10
Average Check: Breakfast(8); Lunch(8); Dinner(8)
Internet Order Processing: Yes
Total Units: 58
Trade Names: Freshly Squeezed (58); maccafe (2)
Company-Owned Units: 5
Units Franchised To: 53
Preferred Square Footage: 200
Preferred Location Types: Regional Mall
Primary Menu: Miscellaneous (58)
Areas of Operation: AB, NB, ON, QC
Foreign Countries: UNITED STATES OF AMERICA
Type of Foodservice: Quick Serve (58)
Primary Distributors: (Food) Ontario Food Terminal Board, TORONTO, ON

Key Personnel
TALAL SAMADI - CEO; President; COO; Controller; Executive Chef; Director Purchasing, Facility/Maintenance, Information Systems, Supply Chain, Real Estate, Design, Human Resources, Store Fixtures; General Buyer

International Franchise Corp.
210 Shields Crt
Markham, ON L3R 8V2

Telephone: (905) 479-8762
Fax Number: (905) 479-5235
Internet Homepage: yogenfruz.com
Company Email: franchising@yogenfruz.com
Type of Business: Chain Restaurant Operator
Year Founded: 1986
Total Sales: $740,040,000 (e)
Number of Employees: 1,400
Average Check: Breakfast(8); Lunch(8); Dinner(8)
Total Units: 1,450
Trade Names: Bresler's Ice Cream & Yogurt; I Can't Believe It's Yogurt; Swensen's Ice Cream; Yogen Fruz
Units Franchised To: 1,450
Preferred Square Footage: 200; 800; 1,200
Preferred Location Types: Airports; Community Mall; Convenience Store/Gas Station; Downtown; Freestanding; Grocery Stores; Institution (college/hospital); Kiosk; Mobile Unit; Office Complex; Parks; Regional Mall; Stadiums; Strip Mall
Primary Menu: Snacks (1,450)
Projected Openings: 20
Areas of Operation: AK, AL, AR, AZ, CA, CO, CT, DC, DE, FL, GA, HI, IA, ID, IL, IN, KS, KY, LA, MA, MD, ME, MI, MN, MO, MS, MT, NC, ND, NE, NH, NJ, NM, NV, NY, OH, OK, OR, PA, RI, SC, SD, TN, TX, UT, VA, VT, WA, WI, WV, WY, ON
Foreign Countries: SOUTH KOREA; SPAIN; UNITED STATES OF AMERICA
Type of Foodservice: Quick Serve (1,450)
Foodservice Management Venues: Business & Industry; College & University; Health Care; Lodging; Schools; Transportation
Catering Services: Yes
On-site Distribution Center: Yes
Primary Distributors: (Full Line) SYSCO Canada, TORONTO, ON
Notes: The company formerly known as Yogen Fruz World-Wide Inc. derives approximately 93% of its revenue from retail & wholesale sale of its products.

Key Personnel
SIMON SERRUYA - Treasurer; Corporate Secretary
JACK SERRUYA - Manager Operations, Business Development

Mary Brown's Inc.
100 Renfrew Dr Ste 130
Markham, ON L3R 9R6

Telephone: (905) 513-0044
Fax Number: (905) 513-0050
Internet Homepage: marybrowns.com
Company Email: corporate@marybrowns.com
Type of Business: Chain Restaurant Operator
Year Founded: 1969
Systemwide Sales: $82,874,000 (e)
Total Sales: $8,314,000 (e)
Number of Employees: 30
Average Check: Lunch(8); Dinner(12)
Total Units: 155
Trade Names: Mary Brown's Famous Chicken & Taters (155)
Company-Owned Units: 7
Units Franchised To: 148
Preferred Square Footage: 1,800
Preferred Location Types: Freestanding; Regional Mall; Strip Mall
Primary Menu: Chicken (155)
Projected Openings: 10
Areas of Operation: FL, AB, BC, MB, NB, NL, NS, NT, ON, SK
Foreign Countries: UNITED STATES OF AMERICA
Type of Foodservice: Family Restaurant (155)
Catering Services: Yes
Primary Distributors: (Full Line) SYSCO Food Services of Toronto, MISSISSAUGA, ON

Key Personnel
GREGORY F. ROBERTS - CEO
JEFF BARLOW - VP Marketing
FERGUS BYRNE - Senior Director Procurement

Sarku Japan
7650 Birchmount Rd
Markham, ON L3R 6B9

Telephone: (905) 474-0710
Fax Number: (905) 474-1939
Internet Homepage: sarkujapan.com
Company Email: info@sarkujapan.com
Type of Business: Chain Restaurant Operator
Year Founded: 1987
Total Sales: $192,460,000 (e)
Number of Employees: 1,856
Average Check: Lunch(8); Dinner(8)
Total Units: 216
Trade Names: Kato's Cajun (3); Ming Tree (3); Sakkio Japan (1); Sarku Japan (238)
Company-Owned Units: 239
Units Franchised To: 6
Preferred Square Footage: 500; 1,000
Preferred Location Types: Airports; Kiosk; Regional Mall
Primary Menu: Asian (1); Cajun/Creole (3); Japanese (238)
Areas of Operation: AL, AZ, CA, CO, CT, DE, FL, GA, IA, IL, IN, KS, KY, LA, MA, MD, ME, MI, MN, MO, NC, NE, NH, NJ, NY, OH, OK, OR, PA, PR, SC, TN, TX, UT, VA, WA, WI, WV
Foreign Countries: UNITED STATES OF AMERICA
Type of Foodservice: Quick Serve (245)
Primary Distributors: (Full Line) SYSCO Food Services of Seattle Inc., KENT, WA; (Full Line) US Foods, FIFE, WA
Notes: Franchising is administered by SMK Franchising, Inc., 44 Wall Street, 12th Floor, New York, NY 10005

Key Personnel
DANIEL CHIM - Vice Chairman; VP
ALEX PANG - Vice Chairman; VP
RICHARD KO - Vice Chairman; VP Operations, Facility/Maintenance, Supply Chain; Executive Chef; General Buyer
TONY CHIU - CFO; VP Information Systems, Communications, Human Resources, E-Commerce, Internet Development
TONY BURGESS - VP Development
TIM PETTIFER - Director Construction

STANLEY POON - Director Administration, Human Resources
ANDREW LING - Director Accounting
ALAN LUK - Director Development, Legal, Leasing
TOM CHAN - Senior Manager Information Technology
BRYAN CHEUNG - Manager Information Technology
MAGGIE WONG - Manager Administration
MICHAEL IP - Administrator Database

The Firkin Group of Pubs
20 Steelcase Rd W Unit 1C
Markham, ON L3R 1B2

Telephone: (905) 305-9792
Fax Number: (905) 305-9719
Internet Homepage: firkinpubs.com
Type of Business: Chain Restaurant Operator
Year Founded: 1987
Systemwide Sales: $48,134,000 (e)
Total Sales: $32,620,000 (e)
Alcohol Sales: 75%
Number of Employees: 416
Average Check: Lunch(16); Dinner(22)
Internet Order Processing: Yes
Internet Sales: 0.50%
Total Units: 26
Trade Names: Drake & Firkin (1); Falcon & Firkin (1); Fiddle & Firkin (1); Firkin & Bull (1); Firkin & Fox (2); Firkin & Friar (1); Firkin & Frigate (1); Firkin on King(1); Firkin on Yonge (1); Frog & Firkin (1); Goose & Firkin (1); Gull & Firkin (1); Harbour (1); Lion & Firkin (1); Moose & Firkin (1); Owl & Firkin (1); Pheasant & Firkin (1); Quail & Firkin (2); Swan & Firkin (1); The Churchmouse & Firkin (1); The Firkin at the Tannery (1); The Flatiron a Firkin Pub (1); The Flyer and Firkin(1); The Squire a Firkin (1)
Company-Owned Units: 10
Units Franchised To: 16
Preferred Square Footage: 3,500; 5,000
Preferred Location Types: Airports; Community Mall; Downtown; Freestanding; Lifestyle Center; Strip Mall
Alcohol Served: Beer, Wine, Liquor
Primary Menu: American (23); Eastern European (1); French/Continental (1); Indian (1)
Areas of Operation: CA, FL, IL, MD, MI, NV, TX, VA, ON
Foreign Countries: UNITED STATES OF AMERICA
Type of Foodservice: Casual Dining (26)
Primary Distributors: (Full Line) SYSCO Canada, TORONTO, ON; (Full Line) GFS Ontario, MILTON, ON
Notes: In addition to the Firkin Pub concept, the company is introducing a new concept called Alehouse & Burger Bar.

Key Personnel
ADELSON STANLEY - President Operations
SHEELAH STOVER - CFO
DAVID GODFREY - Corporate Chef; Director Culinary Development
LARRY ISAACS - Director Supply Chain, Marketing, Ethnic Marketing
DAVID MYERS - Director Operations, Purchasing
PAUL SARAIVA - Director Business Development, Store Fixtures; General Buyer
MARION CURTIS - Director Training
IAN FISHER - Director Franchise Development

Wimpy's Diner Inc.
160 Konrad Cres Unit 1
Markham, ON L3R 9T9

Telephone: (416) 269-4679
Fax Number: (416) 269-8484
Internet Homepage: wimpysdiner.ca
Company Email: info@wimpysdiner.ca
Type of Business: Chain Restaurant Operator
Year Founded: 1998
Systemwide Sales: $41,454,000 (e)
Total Sales: $5,700,000 (e)
Alcohol Sales: 5%
Number of Employees: 10
Average Check: Breakfast(10); Lunch(12); Dinner(16)
Total Units: 60
Trade Names: Wimpy's Diner (60)
Units Franchised To: 60
Preferred Square Footage: 5,500; 6,000
Preferred Location Types: Community Mall; Strip Mall
Primary Menu: American (60)
Projected Openings: 2
Areas of Operation: ON
Type of Foodservice: Casual Dining (60)

Key Personnel
JIM DAIKOS - General Manager; Director Operations, Information Systems, Design
CINDY HICKS - Manager Administration
CONSTANTINE CHLEROS - Manager Operations
JOHN RISTICH - Supervisor Operations, Menu Development

la prep
4500 Dixie Rd Unit B
Mississaua, ON L4W 1V7

Telephone: (514) 510-5001
Fax Number: (877) 516-0074
Internet Homepage: laprep.com
Company Email: info@laprep.com
Type of Business: Chain Restaurant Operator
Year Founded: 1980
Systemwide Sales: $43,551,000 (e)
Total Sales: $5,197,000 (e)
Number of Employees: 18
Average Check: Breakfast(8); Lunch(12); Dinner(12)
Total Units: 57
Trade Names: la prep (57)
Units Franchised To: 57
Preferred Square Footage: 1,500
Preferred Location Types: Airports; Community Mall; Downtown; Freestanding; Institution (college/hospital); Kiosk; Office Complex; Outlet Mall; Regional Mall; Strip Mall
Primary Menu: American (57)
Areas of Operation: FL, AB, BC, ON, QC, SK
Foreign Countries: UNITED STATES OF AMERICA
Type of Foodservice: Quick Serve (57)
Catering Services: Yes
Primary Distributors: (Food) Dubord Rainville Inc., SAINT-LAURENT, QC

Key Personnel
LAVEEN SETH - CEO; President
JOHN BEAUPARLANT - Consultant

Baker's Dozen Donuts Corporation
230 Paisley Blvd W Unit 9
Mississauga, ON L5B OC5

Telephone: (905) 272-1825
Type of Business: Chain Restaurant Operator
Year Founded: 1978
Systemwide Sales: $9,232,000 (e)
Total Sales: $1,107,000 (e)
Number of Employees: 7
Average Check: Breakfast(6); Lunch(6); Dinner(6)
Total Units: 3
Trade Names: Baker's Dozen Donuts (3)
Units Franchised To: 3
Preferred Square Footage: 2,000
Preferred Location Types: Freestanding; Regional Mall; Strip Mall
Primary Menu: Snacks (3)
Areas of Operation: ON
Foreign Countries: GREECE; ISRAEL
Type of Foodservice: Quick Serve (3)
On-site Distribution Center: Yes
Primary Distributors: (Full Line) SYSCO Food Services of Toronto, MISSISSAUGA, ON

Key Personnel
PETER PARASKAKIS - President; CFO; General Counsel; Director Real Estate, Design; General Buyer

Boston Pizza International Inc. (Eastern Canada)
1 City Centre Dr Ste 708
Mississauga, ON L5B 1M2

Telephone: (905) 848-2700
Fax Number: (905) 848-1440
Listing Type: Regional Office
Type of Business: Chain Restaurant Operator
Number of Employees: 65
Total Units: 378
Projected Openings: 15
Areas of Operation: NB, NL, NS, ON, PE, QC
Parent Company: Boston Pizza International Inc., RICHMOND, BC CANADA

Key Personnel
FELIX DECATA - VP Development
MARK BARKEY - Senior Director Operations

Compass Group Canada Ltd.
1 Prologis Blvd Ste 400
Mississauga, ON L5W 0G2

Telephone: (905) 568-4636
Fax Number: (905) 568-9392
Internet Homepage: compass-canada.com
Listing Type: Subsidiary
Type of Business: Foodservice Management Operator
Year Founded: 1960
Total Sales: $2,529,397,000 (e)
Number of Employees: 25,000
Number of Locations Served: 2,200
Total Foodservice Mgmt Accounts: 1,480
Areas of Operation: ON
Type of Foodservice: Cafeteria; Full-service sit-down dining; Quick Serve; Vending machines
Foodservice Management Venues: Business & Industry; College & University; Health Care; Other; Schools; Transportation
Primary Distributors: (Full Line) Summit Food Service , A Div of Colabor LP, LONDON, ON
Parent Company: Compass Group PLC, LONDON, ENG
Headquarters: Compass Group The Americas, CHARLOTTE, NC
Regional Offices: Groupe Compass (Quebec) Ltee, LASALLE, QC CANADA

Key Personnel
SAAJID KHAN - CEO
PAUL FINN - Senior VP Sales
IAN BASKERVILLE - Senior VP; General Counsel
IAN BULLOCK - VP Purchasing

Hilton Canada
5830 Campus Rd Ste 200
Mississauga, ON L4V 1G2

Telephone: (905) 677-9934
Fax Number: (905) 672-6422
Internet Homepage: hilton.com
Listing Type: Subsidiary
Type of Business: Foodservice Operations - Hotel/Motels
Year Founded: 1958
Total Sales: $436,200,000 (e)
Alcohol Sales: 20%
Number of Employees: 6,500
Total Units: 85
Restaurants in Hotels: 85
Trade Names: DoubleTree by Hilton; Embassy Suites; Hampton; Hilton; Hilton Garden Inn; Homewood Suites
Company-Owned Units: 85
Alcohol Served: Beer, Wine, Liquor
Projected Remodelings: 20
Areas of Operation: AB, BC, MB, NB, NS, ON, QC, SK
Type of Foodservice: Fine Dining (85)
Primary Distributors: (Food) SYSCO Food Services of Toronto, MISSISSAUGA, ON
Parent Company: Hilton Worldwide Holdings Inc., MCLEAN, VA
Notes: The company derives approximately 70% of its revenue from hotel operations.

Key Personnel
MATTHEW J. HART - Senior VP Operations, Risk Management, Quality Assurance, Human Resources, Recruitment, Food Safety; Director Food and Beverage
KEVIN PENDERGAST - Executive Chef
SHEILA JERMAN - Director Finance, Information Systems

Little Caesar's of Canada Inc.
2301 Royal Windsor Dr
Mississauga, ON L5J 1K5

Telephone: (905) 822-7899
Fax Number: (905) 822-9808
Listing Type: Regional Office
Type of Business: Chain Restaurant Operator
Total Units: 150
Areas of Operation: AB, BC, MB, NS, ON, QC, SK
On-site Distribution Center: Yes
Parent Company: Little Caesar Enterprises Inc., DETROIT, MI

Key Personnel
DIANE CLARK - Director Operations
RETA CASWELL - Manager Branch; General Buyer
CALEB CHAN - Zone Manager Safety

Nando's Canada
5865 Kennedy Rd
Mississauga, ON L4Z 2G3

Telephone: (905) 564-1118
Fax Number: (905) 502-0428
Internet Homepage: nandos.ca
Company Email: ask_us@nandoscanada.com
Type of Business: Chain Restaurant Operator
Year Founded: 1994
Total Sales: $18,189,000 (e)
Total Units: 50
Trade Names: Nando's (29)
Company-Owned Units: 50
Primary Menu: Chicken (29); Miscellaneous (0)
Areas of Operation: AB, BC, ON
Type of Foodservice: Fast Casual (29)

Key Personnel
GUY OWEN - VP Supply Chain

Niagara Parks Commission
7400 Portage Rd
Niagara Falls, ON L2G 0E5

Mailing Address: PO Box 150, NIAGARA FALLS, ON, L2E 6T2
Telephone: (905) 356-2241
Fax Number: (905) 354-6041
Internet Homepage: niagaraparks.com
Company Email: npinfo@niagaraparks.com
Type of Business: Nontraditional Foodservice Operator
Year Founded: 1885
Total Sales: $44,040,000 (e)
Alcohol Sales: 25%
Number of Employees: 1,700
Average Check: Lunch(18); Dinner(30)
Internet Order Processing: Yes
Internet Sales: 4.00%
Total Units: 5
Trade Names: Elements On The Falls (1); Legends On The Niagra (1); Queen Victoria Place (1); Queenston Heights Restaurant (1); Whirpool Restaurant (1)
Company-Owned Units: 5
Preferred Square Footage: 2,500; 5,500; 6,000
Preferred Location Types: Freestanding
Alcohol Served: Beer, Wine, Liquor
Primary Menu: American (5)
Areas of Operation: ON
Type of Foodservice: Casual Dining (2); Fine Dining (3)
Primary Distributors: (Food) SYSCO Food Services of Toronto, MISSISSAUGA, ON
Notes: The company derives approximately 75% of its revenue from park activities.

Key Personnel
DAVID ADAMES - CEO
JENNIFER WU - Chief Compliance Officer
STEVE BARNHART - Senior Director
MARCELO GRUOSSO - Senior Director Engineering, Transportation
MARGARET NEUBAUER - Senior Director Corporate Affairs
LAURA PINGUE - Senior Manager Finance
OMER YAZAROGLU - Senior Manager Operations-Food
LISA SERADA - Senior Manager Sales
ANGELA RINES - Senior Manager Transportation
MADDIE GREGORY - Manager Food and Beverage
TINA COLLUCCI - Manager Retail Operations
JACKIE LYNCH - Manager Culinary Operations
KATY WASSENAAR - Manager Communications
HENRY PAULINO - Manager Procurement, Strategic Sourcing
JENNI LAFFIN - Supervisor
SANDRA THROWER - Project Manager Information Technology
WARNER LEN - Project Manager
KAREN BROOKER - Project Manager
TAMMY ROBINSON - Administrator Accounting
ROSE YOUNG - Administrator Accounting
PAUL FORCIER - Administrator
JOE SHILLINGTON - Corporate Director Information Technology
KATY MOSLEY - Coordinator Communications

Niagra Casinos
6380 Fallsview Blvd
Niagra Falls, ON L2G 7X5

Telephone: (888) 325-5788
Internet Homepage: casinoniagara.com; fallsviewcasinoresort.com
Type of Business: Foodservice Operations - Casinos
Total Sales: $955,740,000 (e)
Alcohol Sales: 10%
Number of Employees: 27,000
Total Units: 27
Trade Names: 21 Club (1); BarBurrito (1); Breeze (1); Burger King (1); Canyon Creek Chophouse (1); Falls Deli (1); Golden Lotus (1); Grand Buffet (1); Ichiban Sushi Express (1); Il Gelato di Carlotta (1); Johnny Rockets (1); Market Buffet (1); Noodle Bar (1); Paramount Fine Foods (1); Perks Cafe (1); Ponte Vecchio (1);R5 (1); Shoeless Joe's (1); Splash (1); Starbucks Coffee (1); Subway (2); Sushi & Oyster bar (1); Sweet Point (1); The Famous (1); Tim Hortons (1); Vittorio's Italian Eatery (1)
Company-Owned Units: 20
Units Franchised From: 7
Preferred Square Footage: 2,500; 5,500; 6,000
Preferred Location Types: Other
Alcohol Served: Beer, Wine, Liquor
Primary Menu: American (8); Asian (1); Chinese (2); Coffee (2); Hamburger (2); Italian (2); Japanese (1); Sandwiches/Deli (3); Snacks (2); Steak (1); Steak/Seafood (1); Taco (1)
Areas of Operation: ON
Type of Foodservice: Casual Dining (18); Fast Casual (1); Fine Dining (1); Quick Serve (7)
Franchise Affiliation: Doctor's Associates Inc., MILFORD, CT; Starbucks Corporation, SEATTLE, WA; The Firkin Group of Pubs, MARKHAM, ON; The Johnny Rockets Group Inc., LAKE FOREST, CA; Tim Hortons Inc., OAKVILLE, ON
Primary Distributors: (Full Line) SYSCO Canada, TORONTO, ON
Parent Company: Mohegan Tribal Gaming Authority, UNCASVILLE, CT
Notes: Falls Management operates as Niagara Fallsview Casino Resort and Casino Niagara. The company derives approximately 80% of its revenues from casino/resort/retail operations.

Key Personnel
RICHARD TAYLOR - President
KEVIN WILSON - CFO
STEVE WEEL - VP Operations
CATHY PRICE - VP Marketing
COLLEEN FALCO - VP Human Resources
JIM DUNCAN - Executive Chef
SHANNON DUTTON - Director Operations-Games
JENNIFER FERGUSON - Director Marketing
BILL FRENCH - Director Operations
KEVIN GENNINGS - Director Internal Audit
RICHARD PARIS - Director Security
MIKE STANCIU - Director Security
STEVE STONE - Director Facility/Maintenance
JUSTIN YAN - Director Customer Care
GREG YOTT - Director
MARK DOYLE - Manager Operations, Sales
CAREY UYEDA - Manager Benefits, Compensation
JOHN VENDITTI - Manager Restaurant Operations
KAREN PENG - Manager Marketing, International
VICTORIA LATOCHA - Manager Financial Planning
JAMIE LEAVENS - Manager Operations, Information Technology
KAILASH MANOHAR - Manager Information Technology, Database, Security
JULIE ENNS - Manager Communications, Media Relations
ALEXANDER ACOB - Manager
DAVE BROWN - Manager Engineering
DANA COLOTELO - Manager Advertising
RAJESH DAKUA - Supervisor Beverages, Food
PAOLO ANGRILLI - Supervisor Beverages
KRYSTLE SAMSON - Specialist Recruitment
SAMANTHA FILIPPELLI - Coordinator Special Projects
LINDSIE POTTHAST - Coordinator Human Resources
MADELINE KRIEGER - Coordinator Advertising
TRACEY BREEDON - Consultant Human Resources
KATE MCINNIS - Analyst Compensation
AMANDA OAKLEY - Advisor Human Resources

Great Canadian Gaming Corporation
39 Wynford Dr
North York, ON M3C 3K5

Telephone: (604) 303-1000
Fax Number: (604) 279-8605
Internet Homepage: greatcanadiancasinos.com
Company Email: aribeiro@gcgaming.com
Type of Business: Foodservice Operations - Casinos
Publicly Held: Yes
Total Sales: $720,790,000 (e)
Number of Employees: 2,340
Average Check: Lunch(16); Dinner(28)
Total Units: 26
Trade Names: Bingo Esquimalt (1); Casino Ajax (1); Casino New Brunswick (1); Casino New/Nouveau (1); Casino Nova Scotia Halifax (1); Casino Nova Scotia Sydney (1); Casino Woodbine (1); Chances Chilliwack (1); Chances Dawson Creek (1); Chances Maple Ridge (1); Elements Casino (5); Flamboro Downs (1); Georgian Downs (1); Great Blue Heron Casino (1); Hard Rock Casino Vancouver (1); Hastings Racecourse (1); Nanaimo Casino (1); River Rock (1); ShorelinesCasino (4)
Company-Owned Units: 26
Preferred Square Footage: 2,500; 5,500; 6,000
Alcohol Served: Beer, Wine, Liquor
Primary Menu: American (11); Asian (1); Bagels (1); Cajun/Creole (1); Californian (1); Caribbean (1); Chicken (1); Chinese (1); Eastern European (1); French/Continental (1); Hot Dogs (1); Indian (1); Italian (1); Italian (1); Japanese (1); Latin American/Cuban (1)
Areas of Operation: WA, AB, BC, NS, ON
Foreign Countries: UNITED STATES OF AMERICA
Type of Foodservice: Cafeteria (1); Casual Dining (19); Family Restaurant (1); Fast Casual (1); Fine Dining (1); In-Store Feeder (1); Quick Serve (2)
Primary Distributors: (Full Line) SYSCO Food Services of Seattle Inc., KENT, WA
Notes: The company derives approximately 86% of its revenue from gaming operations.

Key Personnel
TERRANCE DOYLE - President Strategic Planning; Chief Compliance Officer Strategic Planning

MATTHEW ANFINSON - COO
SUKVINDER SINGH - Chief Compliance Officer
RON URQUHART - VP Operations
MATT NEWSOME - VP Finance
CHUCK KEELING - VP Membership Development, Member Services
RADEK KIELAR - VP Finance; Controller
DARREN GWOZD - VP Finance, Operations
GALA YEUNG CA - Executive Director Finance
JENNY POON - Director; Assistant Controller
ERIC WONG - Director
JOHN LEGGETT - Director Technology
TINA HINEMAN - Director Human Resources
GABE BAIS - Director Marketing
DAVID ZHOU - Director Gaming/Entertainment
JONATHAN SARINO - Regional Director Operations
MICHAEL MEAD - Manager
MARLO CAPALUNGAN - Manager Information Technology
MARK FODEY - Manager Operations
MATTHEW JIANG - Manager
MATT JOHNSTONE - Manager Compliance

Starbucks Coffee Canada Inc.
5140 Yonge St Ste 1205
North York, ON M2N 6L7

Telephone: (416) 228-7300
Fax Number: (416) 228-7442
Listing Type: Divisional Office
Type of Business: Chain Restaurant Operator
Total Units: 2,000
Areas of Operation: NB, NL, NS, ON, PE, QC
Parent Company: Starbucks Corporation, SEATTLE, WA
Regional Offices: Starbucks Vancouver Regional Office, VANCOUVER, BC CANADA

Key Personnel
MICHAEL CONWAY - President
SHANTEL SAWCHUCK - VP Operations

The McEwan Group
38 Karl Fraser Rd
North York, ON M3C 0H7

Telephone: (141) 644-46262
Internet Homepage: mcewangroup.ca
Company Email: eric@mcewangroup.ca
Type of Business: Chain Restaurant Operator
Total Sales: $82,493,000 (e)
Trade Names: Bymark (1); Diwan (1); Fabbrica (3); ONE Restaurant (1)
Company-Owned Units: 6
Primary Menu: Italian (3); Miscellaneous (2); Seafood (1)
Type of Foodservice: Fine Dining (6)

Key Personnel
MARK MCEWAN - CEO; Executive Chef
ERIC MCEWAN - COO

Crave It Restaurant Group
2829 Sherwood Heights Dr Suite 101
Oakville, ON L6J 7R7

Telephone: (416) 449-2211
Internet Homepage: craveitrestaurants.com; stoneysbreadcompany.com; viacibo.com
Company Email: info@craveitrestaurants.com
Type of Business: Chain Restaurant Operator
Year Founded: 2013
Total Units: 25
Trade Names: Bangkok Buri (1); The Burger's Priest (17); Via Cibo (7)
Company-Owned Units: 23
Units Franchised To: 2
Primary Menu: Hamburger (17); Thai (2)
Areas of Operation: AB, ON
Type of Foodservice: Fast Casual (25)
Headquarter Offices: The Burger's Priest, TORONTO, ON CANADA

Key Personnel
ALEX RECHICHI - Co-Founder; CEO; President
MARK RECHICHI - Co-Founder; CFO; COO
SEAN BLACK - Co-Founder; Chief Development Officer
CYNTHIA YANG - General Counsel

Innovative Food Brands
700 Kerr St Ste 100
Oakville, ON L6K 3W5

Telephone: (905) 337-7777
Fax Number: (905) 337-0331
Internet Homepage: choppedleaf.ca; teriyakiexperience.com
Company Email: info@teriyakiexperience.com
Type of Business: Chain Restaurant Operator
Year Founded: 1986
Systemwide Sales: $163,555,000 (e)
Total Sales: $57,010,000 (e)
Number of Employees: 33
Average Check: Lunch(12); Dinner(12)
Internet Order Processing: Yes
Total Units: 137
Trade Names: Chopped Leaf (69); Teriyaki Experience (68)
Units Franchised To: 137
Preferred Square Footage: 400
Preferred Location Types: Airports; Community Mall; Downtown; Freestanding; Institution (college/hospital); Office Complex; Regional Mall; Strip Mall
Primary Menu: Japanese (68); Miscellaneous (69)
Projected Openings: 22
Areas of Operation: CA, FL, GA, AB, BC, MB, NB, NS, ON, QC
Foreign Countries: BAHRAIN; COSTA RICA; EGYPT; ITALY; KUWAIT; QATAR; SOUTH AFRICA; THE NETHERLANDS; UNITED ARAB EMIRATES; UNITED STATES OF AMERICA
Type of Foodservice: Quick Serve (137)
Catering Services: Yes
Primary Distributors: (Food) SYSCO Food Services of Toronto, MISSISSAUGA, ON

Key Personnel
LOU DONATO - Founder; CEO
NICK VELOCE - President; COO
NICK JURKOVIC - VP Business Development
ANTHONY RAVELO - General Manager
RENATE FOX - Director Marketing

Lone Star Group of Companies
472 Morden Rd Ste 101
Oakville, ON L6K 3W4

Telephone: (905) 845-5852
Fax Number: (905) 338-0466
Internet Homepage: lonestartexasgrill.com
Company Email: info@lonestartexasgrill.com
Type of Business: Chain Restaurant Operator
Year Founded: 1986
Total Sales: $75,930,000 (e)
Alcohol Sales: 30%
Number of Employees: 1,095
Average Check: Lunch(12); Dinner(22)
Total Units: 23
Trade Names: Lone Star Cafe (23)
Company-Owned Units: 23
Preferred Square Footage: 7,000
Preferred Location Types: Freestanding; Strip Mall
Alcohol Served: Beer, Wine, Liquor
Primary Menu: Southwest/Tex-Mex (23)
Projected Openings: 2
Areas of Operation: ON
Type of Foodservice: Casual Dining (23)
Catering Services: Yes

Key Personnel
MARK FINDLAY - CEO; General Buyer
MARK CONNELLY - General Manager
MIKE CHARTRAND - Director Catering
BOB MACEY - Director Information Technology
CALEY FRENCH - Director Marketing
ROB MARTIN - Director Operations
TRUDY CONNOLLY - Regional Director
JONATHAN BALDWIN - Regional Director

Sanelli Foods
147 Westside Dr
Oakville, ON L6K IP2

Telephone: (289) 291-0232
Fax Number: (289) 291-6617
Internet Homepage: sanellifoods.com
Type of Business: Foodservice Management Operator
Year Founded: 1983
Total Sales: $4,259,000 (e)
Number of Employees: 5
Number of Locations Served: 150
Total Foodservice Mgmt Accounts: 150
Areas of Operation: ON
Type of Foodservice: Cafeteria (25); Quick Serve (50); Vending machines (75)
Foodservice Management Venues: Business & Industry; College & University; Health Care; Other; Parks & Recreation; Schools
Primary Distributors: (Full Line) SYSCO Food Services of Toronto, MISSISSAUGA, ON

Key Personnel
STEVEN SANELLI - President; Executive Chef; Director Finance, Operations, Information Systems, Loss Prevention, Quality Assurance, Real Estate, Human Resources; General Buyer

Tim Hortons Inc.
874 Sinclair Rd
Oakville, ON L6K 2Y1

Telephone: (905) 845-6511
Fax Number: (905) 845-0265
Internet Homepage: timhortons.com
Company Email: customer_service@timhortons.com
Type of Business: Chain Restaurant Operator
Year Founded: 1964
Systemwide Sales: $8,117,455,000 (e)
Publicly Held: Yes
Total Sales: $4,109,947,000 (e)
Number of Employees: 800
Average Check: Breakfast(5); Lunch(5); Dinner(5)
Foodservice Sales: $1,274,083,000 (e)
Internet Order Processing: Yes
Total Units: 5,833
Trade Names: Tim Hortons (5,833)
Company-Owned Units: 22
Units Franchised To: 5,811
Preferred Square Footage: 550; 1,000; 1,400; 3,090
Preferred Location Types: Airports; Community Mall; Convenience Store/Gas Station; Discount Dept. Stores; Downtown; Freestanding; Grocery Stores; Institution (college/hospital); Kiosk; Mobile Unit; Office Complex; Regional Mall; Stadiums; Strip Mall; Travel Plazas
Primary Menu: Snacks (5,833)
Projected Openings: 90
Areas of Operation: IN, KY, MD, ME, MI, NY, OH, PA, VA, WV, AB, BC, MB, NB, NL, NS, NT, NU, ON, PE, QC, SK, YT
Foreign Countries: KUWAIT; OMAN; UNITED ARAB EMIRATES; UNITED STATES OF AMERICA
Type of Foodservice: Quick Serve (5,833)
Distribution Centers: CALGARY, AB; DEBERT, NS; GUELPH, ON; KINGSTON, ON; LACHINE, QC
On-site Distribution Center: Yes
Primary Distributors: (Full Line) SYSCO Canada, TORONTO, ON
Parent Company: Restaurant Brands International, TORONTO, ON CANADA
Regional Offices: Tim Hortons Inc., CALGARY, AB CANADA; Tim Hortons Inc., LACHINE, QC CANADA
Notes: Total locations excludes self-serve licensed locations in the Republic of Ireland and the United Kingdom. The company derives approximately 69% of its revenue from distribution sales to franchisees and sales from variable interest entities.

Key Personnel
DANIEL SCHWARTZ - Executive Chairman; Co-Chairman
ALEXANDRE MACEDO - President Global
AXEL SCHWAN - President United States, Canada
MAEGAN EAST - Chief People Officer
HARDEEP GILL - General Manager Canada
STEPHEN NELSON - Director Finance, Accounting
MIKE SHERIDAN - Director Operations
JAMES GREGOIRE - Director Operations, Region
CHRIS WAKEFIELD - Director Marketing, West Division
JACQUELINE BENEDETTI - Director Operations
JENNIFER LOPEZ-GOTTARDI - Director Investor Relations
JOHN BARBER - Director Real Estate
QASIM ISLAM - Director Operations
TRICIA FRANTSI BHUPSINGH - Director Human Resources
CODY BLAISDELL - Director Operations
SARAH JOHNSTON - Director Operations
AMY BENNETT - Director Operations
TOM BABIC - Senior Manager Field Marketing
CARRIE KNOFLACH - Senior Manager Operations-Training
SIMONE CLARKE - Regional Manager Marketing
ANDREA JOHN - Manager Finance
LAURIE CHAVES - Manager Operations
BHUMIKA KAPADIA - Manager Operations
FRED KUPER - Manager
MARK MOSTACCI - Manager Compliance, Fleet, National
PHILLIPPE NADEAU - Manager Real Estate
JAY PATHIRANA - Manager
GLENN SPARKS - Manager
VOYTEK LAPCZYNSKI - Manager Development
TINA SOULLIERE CHRP - Manager Human Resources
ARVIND PODICHETTI - Manager Marketing

Waymar Food Service Ltd.
700 Oxford St
Oshawa, ON L1J 3V9

Telephone: (905) 434-4445
Fax Number: (905) 433-1111
Internet Homepage: squareboypizza.ca
Company Email: squareboypizza@rogers.com
Type of Business: Chain Restaurant Operator
Year Founded: 1979
Systemwide Sales: $23,164,000 (e)
Total Sales: $2,785,000 (e)
Number of Employees: 3
Average Check: Lunch(14); Dinner(20)
Internet Order Processing: Yes
Total Units: 15
Trade Names: Square Boy Pizza, Subs & Wings (15)
Units Franchised To: 15
Preferred Square Footage: 3,000
Preferred Location Types: Freestanding; Strip Mall
Primary Menu: Pizza (15)
Areas of Operation: ON
Type of Foodservice: Family Restaurant (15)
On-site Distribution Center: Yes

Key Personnel
WAYNE MCGIBNEY - President; Director Finance, Information Systems; General Buyer
TERRIE LATTIMER - Director Accounting, Administration, Customer Service, Human Resources

Don Cherry's Grapevine Restaurants Inc.
72 James St
Parry Sound, ON P2A 1T5

Mailing Address: P O Box 335, PARRY SOUND, On, P2A 2X4
Telephone: (905) 775-9600
Fax Number: (705) 746-1270
Internet Homepage: doncherryssportsgrill.com
Company Email: eat@doncherryssportsgrill.com
Type of Business: Chain Restaurant Operator
Year Founded: 1985
Systemwide Sales: $36,102,000 (e)
Total Sales: $6,148,000 (e)
Alcohol Sales: 30%
Number of Employees: 7
Average Check: Lunch(16); Dinner(26)

Total Units: 19
Trade Names: Don Cherry's Sports Grill (19)
Units Franchised To: 19
Preferred Square Footage: 6,000
Preferred Location Types: Freestanding; Hotel/Motel; Regional Mall; Stadiums; Strip Mall
Alcohol Served: Beer, Wine, Liquor
Primary Menu: American (19)
Areas of Operation: AB, BC, NB, NL, ON
Type of Foodservice: Casual Dining (19)

Key Personnel
DARRELL CHERRY - Partner; VP
CARLO MORI - Executive Chef; General Buyer

Wyntergreen Co.
7330 Yonge St
Thornhill, ON L4J 7Y7

Telephone: (416) 471-6031
Company Email: info@thesandwichboard.ca
Type of Business: Chain Restaurant Operator
Year Founded: 1981
Systemwide Sales: $4,019,000 (e)
Total Sales: $869,000 (e)
Number of Employees: 3
Average Check: Breakfast(6); Lunch(8);
Total Units: 8
Trade Names: The Sandwich Board (5); TSB 2000 (3)
Units Franchised To: 8
Preferred Square Footage: 600; 800
Preferred Location Types: Office Complex
Primary Menu: Sandwiches/Deli (8)
Areas of Operation: ON
Type of Foodservice: Quick Serve (8)
Catering Services: Yes
Primary Distributors: (Food) Empire Foods Ltd., MARKHAM, ON

Key Personnel
ALBERT MIRZA-KHANIAN - President; VP; Controller; General Manager; Executive Chef; Director Finance, Operations, Purchasing, Facility/Maintenance, Information Systems, Supply Chain, Marketing, Ethnic Marketing, Real Estate, Design, Human Resources, Store Fixtures, Catering; General Buyer

Aegis Brands Inc
3400-333 Bay St Ste 3400
Toronto, ON M5H 2S7

Telephone: (905) 362-1818
Fax Number: (905) 362-1121
Internet Homepage: secondcup.com
Company Email: secondcupcustomercare@secondcup.com
Type of Business: Chain Restaurant Operator
Year Founded: 1976
Systemwide Sales: $197,292,000 (e)
Publicly Held: Yes
Total Sales: $26,692,000 (e)
Number of Employees: 55
Average Check: Breakfast(6); Lunch(6); Dinner(6)
Internet Order Processing: Yes
Total Units: 82
Trade Names: St. Louis Bar and Grill (82)
Company-Owned Units: 4
Units Franchised To: 78
Preferred Square Footage: 2,000
Preferred Location Types: Airports; Community Mall; Institution (college/hospital); Office Complex; Regional Mall; Strip Mall
Primary Menu: Bar-B-Q (82); Coffee (0)
Projected Openings: 3
Areas of Operation: AB, BC, MB, NB, NL, NS, ON, QC, SK
Foreign Countries: BAHRAIN; EGYPT; JORDAN; KUWAIT; OMAN; QATAR; SAUDI ARABIA; SYRIA; TURKEY; UNITED ARAB EMIRATES
Type of Foodservice: Fast Casual (82); Quick Serve (0)
Catering Services: Yes
Primary Distributors: (Full Line) Unisource Canada, Inc., MISSISSAUGA, ON
Notes: Total stores and sales reflect only Canadian operations.

Key Personnel
MICHAEL BREGMAN - Chairman

ARAMARK Canada
811 Islington Ave
Toronto, ON M8Z 5W8

Telephone: (416) 255-1331
Fax Number: (416) 255-4706
Listing Type: Divisional Office
Type of Business: Foodservice Management Operator
Year Founded: 1942
Number of Employees: 15,577
Number of Locations Served: 1,000
Total Foodservice Mgmt Accounts: 1,000
Areas of Operation: ON
Type of Foodservice: Cafeteria (500); Quick Serve (500)
Foodservice Management Venues: Business & Industry; College & University; Health Care; Prison Feeding; Schools; Transportation
Primary Distributors: (Food) SYSCO Food Services - Atlantic Inc., LAKESIDE, NS
Parent Company: Aramark, PHILADELPHIA, PA

Key Personnel
JADE MURRAY - General Manager
MARY TOMASO - General Manager
KAMINI SURI - Executive Chef; Manager
JANET RUMBLE - Director Information Technology
MAUREEN LEWIS - Director Finance
SHIVANG PURI - Director Business Development
TARAH MARKHAM - Director Business Development
ROSA LOURO - Director Foodservice
ANDY YU MING - Director Finance
EVA TENTERE - Director Loyalty Program
MASA MASA - Director Foodservice
STEPHANIE SCHUMACH - Manager Human Resources
CINDY CARUSO - Manager Procurement
BARBRA ALEXANDER - Manager Purchasing

Burger King Restaurants of Canada Inc.
401 The West Mall Ste 700
Toronto, ON M9C 5J4

Telephone: (416) 626-6464
Fax Number: (416) 626-6676
Internet Homepage: burgerking.ca
Type of Business: Chain Restaurant Operator
Year Founded: 1972
Total Sales: $680,860,000 (e)
Number of Employees: 2,500
Average Check: Breakfast(10); Lunch(10); Dinner(10)
Total Units: 466
Trade Names: Burger King (466)
Units Franchised From: 466
Preferred Square Footage: 3,900
Preferred Location Types: Airports; Community Mall; Convenience Store/Gas Station; Downtown; Freestanding; Institution (college/hospital); Other; Regional Mall; Strip Mall
Primary Menu: Hamburger (466)
Areas of Operation: AB, BC, MB, NB, NL, NS, ON, PE, QC, SK
Type of Foodservice: Quick Serve (466)
Parent Company: Redberry Investments Corp., GREENFIELD PARK, QC CANADA

Key Personnel
ANIL KUMAR - General Manager
LORRAINE GREEN - Senior Director Supply Chain
KYLE PAGEL - Director Franchise Development
SHERRY MCFARLANE - Senior Manager Marketing
PRATIK MEHTA - Senior Manager Marketing
NICHOLAS HANSEN - Manager Digital
ATUL BAGAYATKAR - Manager

Chairman's Brand Corp.
77 Progress Ave
Toronto, ON M1P 2Y7

Telephone: (416) 288-8515

Fax Number: (416) 288-8895
Internet Homepage: neworleanspizza.ca; 241pizza.com; chairmansbrands.com; coffeetime.ca; eggsmart.ca; friendlygreek.com; robinsdonuts.com
Company Email: info@chairmansbrands.com
Type of Business: Chain Restaurant Operator
Year Founded: 1982
Systemwide Sales: $107,010,000 (e)
Total Sales: $16,390,000 (e)
Alcohol Sales: 1%
Number of Employees: 250
Average Check: Breakfast(5); Lunch(10); Dinner(10)
Total Units: 440
Trade Names: 241 Pizza (72); Coffee Time Cafe (63); Eggsmart (46); Friendly Greek (69); Mia Fresco (4); New Orleans Pizza (38); Robin's Donuts (148)
Units Franchised To: 440
Preferred Square Footage: 1,800
Preferred Location Types: Community Mall; Discount Dept. Stores; Downtown; Freestanding; Institution (college/hospital); Office Complex; Regional Mall; Strip Mall; Travel Plazas
Primary Menu: American (50); Greek/Mediterranean (69); Pizza (110); Sandwiches/Deli (63); Snacks (148)
Projected Openings: 20
Areas of Operation: AB, BC, MB, NB, ON, QC
Foreign Countries: CHINA; GREECE; POLAND
Type of Foodservice: Family Restaurant (115); Fine Dining (4); Quick Serve (321)

Key Personnel
STEVE MICHALOPOULOS - President; COO
DAN LEPIDAS - Exec VP Operations
WAYNE THOMAS - Controller
MARY ANN HALCROW - Director Information Systems
JEFF COLLINS - Director Procurement
JOE DI SAVINO - Director Operations
KEITH HAMMERSCHLAG - Director Finance
TARIQ EL-NOQRASHY - Director Development, Real Estate, Franchising
DAGMAR SCHOISWOHL - Manager Marketing, Advertising
ZORKA ODANOVIC - Manager Payroll, Human Resources
ALLEN HOEKSTRA - Manager Operations, Area
PAMELA TSIMPLIDIS - Manager Business Development

Cineplex Inc.
1303 Yonge St Main
Toronto, ON M4T 2Y9

Telephone: (416) 323-6600
Fax Number: (416) 323-6623
Internet Homepage: cineplex.com
Company Email: guestservices@cineplex.com
Type of Business: Foodservice Operations - Movie Theatre
Year Founded: 2003
Publicly Held: Yes
Total Sales: $675,330,000 (e)
Number of Employees: 10,300
Average Check: Lunch(5); Dinner(6)
Foodservice Sales: $195,846,000 (e)
Internet Order Processing: Yes
Total Units: 160
Trade Names: Cinema City; Cineplex Odeon Cinema; Coliseum; Colossus; Empire Theatre; Famous Players Theatre; Galaxy Cinema; Odeon Boucherville Drive-in; Scotiabank; SilverCity; Starcite
Company-Owned Units: 160
Preferred Square Footage: 2,500
Preferred Location Types: Freestanding; Regional Mall
Primary Menu: Snacks (162)
Areas of Operation: AB, BC, MB, NB, NL, NS, ON, PE, QC, SK
Type of Foodservice: In-Store Feeder (162)
Primary Distributors: (Food) SYSCO Food Services of Toronto, MISSISSAUGA, ON
Notes: The company derives approximately 71% of its revenue from ticket sales and other activities.

Key Personnel
ELLIS JACOB - CEO; President
WIM STOCKS - CEO
GORD NELSON - CFO
DAN MCGRATH - COO
MICHAEL KENNEDY - Exec VP Gaming/Entertainment
FAB STANGHIERI - Exec VP; General Manager
HEATHER BRIANT - Senior VP Human Resources
CHRIS DOULOS - Senior VP Real Estate, Construction, Design
KEVIN WATTS - Senior VP Event Planning
ROMMEL VELARDE - VP Customer Loyalty
RAGHU VISWANATHAN - VP Purchasing, Supply Chain
THOMAS SANTRAM - VP Corporate Affairs; General Counsel
DECIO SILVA - VP Information Systems
SEAN MCKENNA - VP Finance
ELAINE OEI - VP Digital
SCOTT HUGHES - VP Information Technology, POS/Scanning, Infrastructure
NASIR KHAN - VP Technology
BIAGIO DI CARLO - VP Operations
RICHARD WOOD - VP Real Estate, Leasing
NICK M - Executive Director Information Technology
PAUL KENNEDY - Executive Director Technology, Architecture, Digital Designs
BOBBO GOMM - Executive Director Leasing
ROBERT GOSEK - Executive Director
ADAM NOBLE - Executive Director Operations
VANESSA PORTER - Executive Director Marketing
JAMES PRPA - Director Technology
MAHSA REJALI - Director Technology, Digital
LINDA HSU - Director Operations
LAUREN AITCHISON - Director Marketing
RANA BHARANIA - Director
OLIVIA PIERRATOS - Senior Manager Digital Marketing
DAVID MORROW - Manager Operations, Infrastructure
DANIELLE WILSON - Manager Operations
KEVIN BOUCHER - Manager
JOSE HALUPA - Manager Training; Developer
ANTONIO CAIVANO - Manager Internal Audit
MARIE-LOURDES CHUNG-HIN - Manager Accounting
TANIA CINQUINO - Manager Marketing
SHAWN CRAWFORD - Manager Integration
THERESA PETT - Project Manager; Analyst

† Domco Food Services Ltd.
1090 Don Mills Rd Ste 602
Toronto, ON M3C 3R6

Telephone: (416) 449-7333
Fax Number: (416) 449-8840
Internet Homepage: domcofoodservices.com
Company Email: loic.ollivier@domcofoodservices.com
Type of Business: Foodservice Management Operator
Year Founded: 1945
Total Sales: $22,390,000 (e)
Number of Employees: 100
Number of Locations Served: 19
Total Foodservice Mgmt Accounts: 39
Areas of Operation: ON
Type of Foodservice: Full-service sit-down dining (19)
Foodservice Management Venues: Business & Industry; Schools
Primary Distributors: (Food) SYSCO Food Services of Calgary, CALGARY, AB
Parent Company: Zuppinger Holdings Ltd., TORONTO, ON CANADA

Key Personnel
WALT U. ZUPPINGER - Chairman; CEO
QUINCY SMOLIAK - Executive Director Operations
ROSE RUBINO - Controller
STEVE JOSEPHSON - Senior Director Business Development
MICHEL FOURNIER - Director Purchasing

‡ Fairmont Hotels & Resorts Inc.
3300-155 Wellington St W Ste 3300
Toronto, ON M5V 0C3

Telephone: (416) 874-2600
Fax Number: (416) 874-2601
Internet Homepage: fairmont.com

Company Email: info@fairmont.com
Type of Business: Foodservice Operations - Hotel/Motels
Year Founded: 1886
Total Sales: $1,064,300,000 (e)
Alcohol Sales: 15%
Number of Employees: 24,000
Total Units: 75
Restaurants in Hotels: 75
Trade Names: Fairmont Hotel & Resort (75)
Company-Owned Units: 75
Alcohol Served: Beer, Wine, Liquor
Projected Remodelings: 3
Areas of Operation: AZ, CA, CO, DC, HI, IL, MA, NM, NY, PA, TX, WA, AB, BC, MB, ON
Foreign Countries: BARBADOS; BERMUDA; CHINA; EGYPT; ENGLAND; GERMANY; KENYA; MEXICO; MONACO; SCOTLAND; SINGAPORE; SOUTH AFRICA; SWITZERLAND; UKRAINE; UNITED ARAB EMIRATES; UNITED STATES OF AMERICA
Type of Foodservice: Casual Dining; Fine Dining
Primary Distributors: (Food) SYSCO Food Services of Grand Rapids LLC, GRAND RAPIDS, MI
Parent Company: Fairmont Raffles Hotels International, TORONTO, ON CANADA
Notes: Total sales reflect properties under management as well as owned properties. The company derives approximately 71% of its revenue from hotel operation & management.

Key Personnel
MAX ARAMBULO - Director Operations; Manager Information Systems
ELLEN RYAN - Director Marketing, Sales, Northeast Region

Feta & Olives Inc.
1 Palace Pier Crt Ste 809
Toronto, ON M8V 3W9

Telephone: (416) 251-3353
Fax Number: (416) 251-3354
Internet Homepage: fetaolivesgrill.com
Company Email: franchising@fetaolivesgrill.com
Type of Business: Chain Restaurant Operator
Year Founded: 2007
Total Sales: $8,367,000 (e)
Total Units: 13
Trade Names: Feta & Olives Mediterranean Grill (13)
Units Franchised To: 13
Primary Menu: Greek/Mediterranean (13)
Projected Openings: 3
Areas of Operation: AB, ON
Type of Foodservice: Quick Serve (13)

Key Personnel
VICKI VASILIOU - President; General Buyer

Four Seasons Hotels and Resorts
1165 Leslie St
Toronto, ON M3C 2K8

Telephone: (416) 449-1750
Fax Number: (416) 441-4374
Internet Homepage: fourseasons.com
Company Email: info@fourseasons.com
Type of Business: Foodservice Operations - Hotel/Motels
Year Founded: 1961
Total Sales: $367,410,000 (e)
Alcohol Sales: 20%
Number of Employees: 42,927
Internet Order Processing: Yes
Total Units: 123
Restaurants in Hotels: 123
Trade Names: Four Seasons (123)
Company-Owned Units: 123
Alcohol Served: Beer, Wine, Liquor
Projected Openings: 3
Projected Remodelings: 2
Areas of Operation: AZ, CA, DC, FL, GA, HI, IL, MA, NV, NY, PA, TX, WA, WY, BC, ON
Foreign Countries: ARGENTINA; AUSTRALIA; CANADA; CHINA; COSTA RICA; CZECH REPUBLIC; EGYPT; ENGLAND; FRANCE; HUNGARY; INDIA; INDONESIA; IRELAND; ITALY; JAPAN; JORDAN; LEBANON; MALAYSIA; MAURITIUS; MEXICO; PORTUGAL; QATAR; SAUDI ARABIA; SEYCHELLES;SINGAPORE; SWITZERLAND; SYRIA; TAIWAN; THAILAND; TURKEY; UNITED STATES OF AMERICA; URUGUAY
Type of Foodservice: Casual Dining; Fast Casual; Fine Dining; Quick Serve
Primary Distributors: (Food) SYSCO Food Services of Toronto, MISSISSAUGA, ON
Notes: The company derives approximately 55% of its revenue from hotel operations & management.

Key Personnel
ISADORE SHARP - Chairman
SARAH COHEN - Exec VP; Corporate Secretary; General Counsel
ROBERT DUNIGAN - Senior VP
SCOTT TABER - Senior VP
JOHN MILLER - Senior VP Construction, Design
JOEL MONSON - Senior VP; General Counsel
CHRIS LI - VP Loyalty Program; Senior Director Benefits, Employee Compensation
ROBERT SKYVINGTON - VP Procurement
JONATHAN SELMAN - VP Information Technology
BAHRAM SEPAHI - VP Operations, Region
NATALIE GLUIC - VP Development
DANA KALCZAK - VP Construction, Design
CORY WEECH - VP Information Technology
MATTHEW WILKINS - VP Customer Service
SAM ZARLENGA - VP Design
THOMAS KROOSWIJK - General Manager
ISABELLE LAROCQUE - Director Procurement
SUDHIR DUTTA - Director Food and Beverage
DAVID CROFT - Director Integration
NICOLAS DE NIESE - Director Finance
ALEX DRAGAN - Director Procurement
LINUS CAI - Director Finance
NITIN CHANDARANA - Director Purchasing
KAREN CHIUN - Director Finance
BILLY CHOI - Director Information Technology, Infrastructure
SEBASTIAN LIGHTLY - Director Finance
CHARLES LITMAN - Director Finance
DAVID OSPALAK - Director Design
LISA PASTERNACK - Director Design
ROBERT WHALEN - Director Sales
JOANNE HALL - Senior Manager Sales
AINSLEY HARPUR CHRP - Manager Human Resources
BRENNAN HOLDER - Manager Public Relations
CAROLYN GLEN-MAR - Manager Marketing
ISABELLE LAROCQUE-MUKERJEE - Manager Procurement
EMAD HUSSAIN CPA, CA - Manager Finance
ADRIENNE JEVNISEK CPA - Manager Finance
TRICIA CHUNG - Manager Distribution
WILLIAM CHAN - Manager Information Technology
MARY CORRIGAN - Manager Finance
JODI BELL - Manager Procurement
CHRIS BEUMER - Manager Sales
SOPHIA BIKAS - Manager Sales
NEIL BREUKELMAN - Manager Technology
STEPHANIE BRIDGE - Manager Social Media
BRITTANY C. - Manager Communications
SARAH PAYNE - Manager Marketing
TONY NAVARRO - Manager Design
LUKE MOLLISON - Manager Human Resources
SANCHIA LUNG - Manager Information Systems
GUY MARTINELLO - Manager Applications
LISAJANE MCBAIN - Manager Training
PAOLA MERINO CPA - Manager Accounting
TJIEN LIE - Manager Systems Engineering
MARGARET RUSSELL - Manager Procurement
JENNY TRUONG - Manager Benefits
SARAH TUITE - Manager Public Relations
NAMITA WALSH - Manager Catering
JULIA WENDE - Manager Quality Assurance
SALLY YU - Manager Division
JENNY RIVKIND - Assistant Manager Food and Beverage
HARRY HOLLYWOOD - Supervisor Customer Service
YVONNE TANG - Project Manager
TRACEY JONES - Project Manager
BRIDGET WIGHT - Project Manager Marketing
GREG HOLLINSHEAD - Administrator Information Systems
ROBERT BRADLEY-COMBS - Administrator

Information Systems
ALAM SADIQ - Administrator Database
GANG QIU - Administrator Information Technology
NABILA RASHID - Specialist Information Systems
SAMANTHA NEALE - Specialist Sales
STACEY SULTANTI - Specialist Distribution
GASTON LAU - Specialist Information Systems
JEFF LAU - Specialist Sales
TERENCE LAU - Specialist Information Systems
VIVIAN XIAN - Specialist Information Systems
BURCU AKYILDIZ - Coordinator Accounting
DAVE GOMES - Agent Security
SCOTT SIEMMS - Consultant Information Technology
ANDREW SAMORAJ - Analyst Finance
CHRISTINE SHIN - Analyst Information Technology
ADA LING - Analyst Finance
DIANE BALASA - Analyst Risk Management
KEVIN BELL - Analyst Operations
MELISSA ROSE - Developer Applications
RICHARD XUE - Developer

Freshii Inc.
1055 Yonge St Unit 101
Toronto, ON M4W 2L2

Telephone: (647) 350-2001
Internet Homepage: freshii.com
Company Email: info@freshii.com
Type of Business: Chain Restaurant Operator
Year Founded: 2005
Systemwide Sales: $156,926,000 (e)
Publicly Held: Yes
Total Sales: $22,140,000 (e)
Total Units: 343
Trade Names: Freshii (343)
Company-Owned Units: 3
Units Franchised To: 340
Preferred Square Footage: 1,200
Primary Menu: Health Foods (343)
Projected Openings: 65
Areas of Operation: AR, AZ, CA, CT, DC, FL, ID, IL, IN, KY, MA, MD, MI, MN, MS, NC, NE, NY, OH, OR, PA, SC, TX, VA, WA, WI, AB, BC, MB, NB, NL, NS, ON, PE, QC, SK
Foreign Countries: ARUBA; AUSTRIA; CANADA; COLOMBIA; ECUADOR; PANAMA; SWEDEN; SWITZERLAND; UNITED ARAB EMIRATES; UNITED STATES OF AMERICA
Type of Foodservice: Quick Serve (343)

Key Personnel
MATTHEW CORRIN - Executive Chairman; Founder
DANIEL HAROUN - CEO
VICTOR DIAB - CFO
PAUL HUGHES - Chief Business Development Officer; General Counsel
ESTEFANIA BAFUNNO - Director Marketing

Hero Certified Burgers
78 Signet Dr Ste 201
Toronto, ON M9L 1T2

Telephone: (416) 740-2304
Fax Number: (416) 740-5398
Internet Homepage: heroburgers.com
Company Email: info@heroburgers.com
Type of Business: Chain Restaurant Operator
Total Sales: $30,650,000 (e)
Total Units: 53
Trade Names: Hero Ceritfied Burgers (53)
Company-Owned Units: 1
Units Franchised To: 54
Primary Menu: Hamburger (53)
Areas of Operation: ON
Type of Foodservice: Quick Serve (53)

Key Personnel
JOHN F. LETTIERI - CEO; President
MUKIT HASAN - Partner; VP Franchise Development
AYDIN MOHAMMADI - Partner
SILVANA GALATI - Chief Administrative Officer; Director Human Resources
JOSEPHINE PASUT - Coordinator Marketing

Il Fornello Restaurants Ltd.
576 Danforth Ave
Toronto, ON M4K 1R1

Telephone: (416) 920-9410
Fax Number: (416) 920-0474
Internet Homepage: ilfornello.com
Company Email: info@ilfornello.com
Type of Business: Chain Restaurant Operator
Year Founded: 1984
Systemwide Sales: $21,106,000 (e)
Total Sales: $9,853,000 (e)
Alcohol Sales: 20%
Number of Employees: 170
Average Check: Lunch(24); Dinner(54)
Internet Order Processing: Yes
Total Units: 6
Trade Names: Il Fornello Restaurant (6)
Company-Owned Units: 4
Units Franchised To: 2
Preferred Square Footage: 3,500
Preferred Location Types: Community Mall; Downtown
Alcohol Served: Beer, Wine, Liquor
Primary Menu: Italian (6)
Areas of Operation: ON
Type of Foodservice: Casual Dining (6)
Catering Services: Yes
Primary Distributors: (Full Line) SYSCO Food Services of Toronto, MISSISSAUGA, ON

Key Personnel
IAN SORBIE - Chairman; President; Manager Facility/Maintenance, Real Estate, Design, Franchising
STACEY PATTERSON - Manager Operations, Human Resources, Menu Development
SEAN FLEMING - Manager Supply Chain, Distribution, Research & Development

Imago Restaurants Inc.
400 University Ave Ste 1802
Toronto, ON M5G 1S5

Telephone: (416) 593-4477
Fax Number: (416) 593-4588
Internet Homepage: thedukepubs.ca
Company Email: esnider@imagorestaurants.ca
Type of Business: Chain Restaurant Operator
Year Founded: 1985
Total Sales: $34,402,000 (e)
Alcohol Sales: 40%
Number of Employees: 380
Average Check: Breakfast(8); Lunch(14); Dinner(20)
Total Units: 7
Trade Names: Duke of Cornwall (1); Duke of Devon (1); Duke of Kent (1); Duke of Richmond (1); Duke of Sommerset (1); Duke of Westminster (1); Duke of York (1)
Company-Owned Units: 7
Preferred Square Footage: 6,000
Preferred Location Types: Community Mall; Freestanding; Office Complex
Alcohol Served: Beer, Wine, Liquor
Primary Menu: Miscellaneous (7)
Projected Openings: 1
Areas of Operation: ON
Type of Foodservice: Casual Dining (7)
Primary Distributors: (Full Line) Gordon Food Service, SPRINGFIELD, OH

Key Personnel
JAMES VOSBURGH - President; General Buyer
CINDY SIMPSON - Exec VP Operations, Information Systems, Marketing, Human Resources, Menu Development

Jimmy The Greek Food Corp.
100 King St W
Toronto, ON M5X 2A1

Mailing Address: P.O. Box 334, TORONTO, ON, M5X 1E1
Telephone: (416) 214-9237
Fax Number: (416) 362-0827
Internet Homepage: jimmythegreek.com; penelopercrestaurant.com; santorini.ca
Company Email: info@jimmythegreek.com
Type of Business: Chain Restaurant Operator
Year Founded: 1985
Systemwide Sales: $36,102,000 (e)
Total Sales: $13,700,000 (e)

Alcohol Sales: 10%
Number of Employees: 200
Average Check: Breakfast(8); Lunch(14); Dinner(18)
Total Units: 57
Trade Names: Jimmy the Greek (55); Penelope Restaurant (1); Santorini Cafe (1)
Company-Owned Units: 8
Units Franchised To: 49
Preferred Square Footage: 300; 400
Preferred Location Types: Downtown; Regional Mall
Alcohol Served: Beer, Wine, Liquor
Primary Menu: Greek/Mediterranean (55)
Projected Openings: 2
Projected Remodelings: 6
Areas of Operation: AB, BC, MB, ON
Foreign Countries: UNITED ARAB EMIRATES
Type of Foodservice: Fine Dining (2); Quick Serve (55)
Catering Services: Yes
Primary Distributors: (Food) GFS Ontario, MILTON, ON

Key Personnel
JIM ANTONOPOULOS - President; Executive Chef; Manager Finance, Purchasing, Facility/Maintenance, Real Estate, Design, Menu Development
TOULA ANTONOPOULOS - Exec VP
TINA ANTONOPOULOS - VP; General Manager; Director Operations, Information Systems
JOHN GRAZALOS - Manager Human Resources

Kernels Popcorn Limited
40 Eglinton Ave E Ste 250
Toronto, ON M4P 3A2

Telephone: (416) 487-4194
Fax Number: (416) 487-3920
Internet Homepage: kernelspopcorn.com
Company Email: info@kernelspopcorn.com
Type of Business: Chain Restaurant Operator
Year Founded: 1983
Systemwide Sales: $25,338,000 (e)
Total Sales: $4,925,000 (e)
Number of Employees: 166
Average Check: Lunch(6); Dinner(6)
Internet Order Processing: Yes
Internet Sales: 1.00%
Total Units: 83
Trade Names: Kernels Popcorn (83)
Company-Owned Units: 23
Units Franchised To: 60
Preferred Square Footage: 100
Preferred Location Types: Regional Mall
Primary Menu: Snacks (83)
Areas of Operation: CA, AB, BC, MB, NS, ON, QC, SK
Foreign Countries: SOUTH KOREA; UNITED STATES OF AMERICA

Type of Foodservice: Quick Serve (83)

Key Personnel
SCOTT STAIMAN - CEO; Director Real Estate; General Buyer
ELI STAIMAN - President; COO
PENNY DANIELS - CFO; Manager Finance, POS/Scanning
LORETA MISKINIS - VP Information Systems, Internet Development; General Manager
BERNICE SINOPOLI - Director Franchising
CAROLYN MACGREGOR - Director Marketing
PAULA HURLEY - Director Operations

King Street Food Company
469B King St W
Toronto, ON M5V 1K4

Telephone: (416) 506-8800
Fax Number: (416) 506-8805
Internet Homepage: jacobssteakhouse.com; buca.ca/king; kingstreetfood.com; thesainttavern.com
Company Email: info@kingstreetfood.com
Type of Business: Chain Restaurant Operator
Year Founded: 2006
Total Units: 9
Trade Names: Bar Buca (2); Buca Osteria & Enoteca (1); Buca Yorkville (1); CXBO (1); Jacobs & Co. Steakhouse (1); Jamie's Italian (2); La Banane (1)
Company-Owned Units: 9
Alcohol Served: Beer, Wine, Liquor
Primary Menu: French/Continental (1); Italian (6); Snacks (1); Steak/Seafood (1)
Areas of Operation: ON
Type of Foodservice: Casual Dining (6); Fine Dining (2); Quick Serve (1)

Key Personnel
PETER TSEBELIS - Partner
KONSTANTINOS GIAZITZIDIS - Director Operations

McDonald's Restaurants of Canada Ltd.
100-1 McDonalds Pl Ste 100
Toronto, ON M3C 3L4

Telephone: (416) 443-1000
Fax Number: (416) 446-3443
Internet Homepage: mcdonalds.ca
Listing Type: Subsidiary
Type of Business: Chain Restaurant Operator
Year Founded: 1967
Total Sales: $5,363,100,000 (e)
Number of Employees: 40,000
Average Check: Breakfast(5); Lunch(8); Dinner(8)
Total Units: 1,472

Trade Names: McDonald's (1,472)
Company-Owned Units: 100
Units Franchised To: 1,372
Preferred Square Footage: 2,500
Preferred Location Types: Community Mall; Downtown; Freestanding; Regional Mall; Strip Mall
Primary Menu: Hamburger (1,472)
Projected Openings: 60
Projected Remodelings: 10
Areas of Operation: AB, BC, MB, NB, NL, NS, NT, ON, PE, QC, SK, YT
Type of Foodservice: Quick Serve (1,472)
Primary Distributors: (Full Line) The Martin-Brower of Canada Co. Ltd., MISSISSAUGA, ON
Parent Company: McDonald's Corporation, CHICAGO, IL

Key Personnel
GEORGE A. COHON - Chairman; Founder
JOHN E. BETTS - CEO; President
DAVID FORD - CEO Communications
ANDREW BROUGH - President Information Technology
ANDREW SECORD - CIO
LARA SKRIPITSKY - CTO; VP
JEFF KROLL - Senior VP Restaurant Operations, Supply Chain
SHELLY HANSEN - Senior VP Operations
NATALIE SAULNIER - Senior VP East Region, Region
LEN JILLARD - Senior VP People
JOEL LEVESQUE - VP; General Counsel
GEOFF NAKAMURA - VP Development, Construction
JEFF ROBINSON - VP
MICHELE BOUDRIA - Regional VP West Region
SALMAN ALI - Senior Director Information Technology
JONATHAN PARLOW - Senior Director Franchising
SCOTT SCHWINDT - Senior Director Operations, National
FRANCESCA CARDARELLI - Senior Director Strategy, Marketing, Digital Marketing
KERRY BOARDER - Director Finance
LEANNE CHAMBERLAIN - Director
ADAM COOPER - Director Digital
AMELIE DUCLOS - Director Human Resources
BILL INDZEVSKI - Director
DAN LOGAN - Director National
MARK MURPHY - Director
CARYN NARVEY - Director Legal
ANNE PARKS - Director
RENNA ROCCO - Director
DREW SADLER - Director Operations, National
MORENA SALTZMAN - Director Finance
IAN SEETON - Director National
SYLVIA SHARP - Director Communications
JERRY TOPP - Director Operations, National
MAXUS URWASS - Director
LETITIA YEUNG - Director; Global Operations
NICOLE ZENI - Senior Manager Quality

Assurance, Supply Chain
SCOTT GIBSON - Senior Manager Supply Chain
SABRINA GRECO - Senior Manager Communications
MARIJANA ZUVELA - Senior Manager Security
ERICA JUBA - Senior Manager Marketing, Media
CHRISTINE ATKINSON - Manager Operations
SEEMA ANAM - Manager
JAMIE BONE - Manager Marketing, National
ADITI BURMAN - Manager Marketing
MINA CHUNG - Manager People
BELLA CLUM - Manager Financial Planning
JOHN COLEMAN - Manager Security
DAWN CRAWFORD - Manager People
GEORGE CURRY - Manager Operations, National
JOHN DARYL ARVESU - Manager
GUYLAINE HUDON - Manager Advertising, National
NADINE MCHAYLE - Manager Customer Service
MICHELLE MCILMOYLE - Manager Marketing, National
ALEXIA MISSIN - Manager Strategic Sourcing
KELLY OLIVE-SCHAD - Manager Real Estate, Area
CATHY PERCIASEPE - Manager Supply Chain
ANDREA SALOMON - Manager Marketing, National
GABRIELLE SAMUEL - Manager
MYREN SIVA - Manager Accounting
REBECCA SMART - Manager Marketing, National
ALI TAYEBI - Manager Operations, Human Resources
CATHY WILSON - Manager Global; Analyst International
ARYANA HEIT - Manager Marketing
ALBERT RANCHOO - Store Manager
SHELLEY MOHAMED - Program Manager International
BRENDA MORRIS - Analyst Information Technology

Mr. Greek Restaurants Inc.
44 Upjohn Rd
Toronto, ON M3B 2W1

Telephone: (416) 444-3266
Fax Number: (416) 444-3484
Internet Homepage: mrgreek.com
Company Email: feedback@mrgreek.com
Type of Business: Chain Restaurant Operator
Year Founded: 1988
Systemwide Sales: $43,614,000 (e)
Total Sales: $5,649,000 (e)
Alcohol Sales: 10%
Number of Employees: 210
Average Check: Lunch(10); Dinner(16)
Internet Order Processing: Yes
Total Units: 21
Trade Names: Mr. Greek Express (17); Mr. Greek Mediterranean Grill (4)
Company-Owned Units: 4
Units Franchised To: 17
Preferred Square Footage: 2,200; 4,500
Preferred Location Types: Freestanding; Regional Mall; Strip Mall
Alcohol Served: Beer, Wine, Liquor
Primary Menu: Greek/Mediterranean (21)
Projected Openings: 20
Projected Remodelings: 6
Areas of Operation: FC, ON
Foreign Countries: KUWAIT; UNITED ARAB EMIRATES
Type of Foodservice: Casual Dining (4); Quick Serve (17)
Catering Services: Yes
Primary Distributors: (Food) Kariba Foods Ltd., SCARBOROUGH, ON

Key Personnel
GEORGE RAIOS - CEO; President; CFO; Director Purchasing, Risk Management, Human Resources, Menu Development
FRED BUTSON - VP Business Development
MARCO PETROZZI - General Manager
LAMBRINI SINOPOLI - Manager Operations

Pegasus Group
44 Upjohn Rd
Toronto, ON M3B 2W1

Telephone: (416) 385-7705
Fax Number: (416) 385-1718
Internet Homepage: lacarnita.com; foxandfiddle.com; ogradystap.ca; pegasusgroup.ca; themiller.ca
Company Email: info@pegasusgroup.ca
Type of Business: Chain Restaurant Operator
Year Founded: 1987
Systemwide Sales: $63,207,000 (e)
Total Sales: $31,360,000 (e)
Alcohol Sales: 50%
Number of Employees: 277
Average Check: Lunch(24); Dinner(24)
Total Units: 27
Trade Names: Carnita (7); Figo (1); Fox & Fiddle Pubs (13); Miller Tavern (2); O'Grady's (2); The Exchange (1); Wheat Sheaf Tavern (1)
Company-Owned Units: 9
Units Franchised To: 18
Preferred Square Footage: 3,500
Preferred Location Types: Freestanding; Strip Mall
Alcohol Served: Beer, Wine, Liquor
Primary Menu: American (17); Italian (1); Mexican (7); Steak/Seafood (2)
Projected Openings: 10
Areas of Operation: BC, MB, ON
Type of Foodservice: Casual Dining (24); Fine Dining (3)
Primary Distributors: (Food) Stewart Foodservice Inc., BARRIE, ON

Key Personnel
TERRY TSIANOS - CEO; President; Executive Chef
NICK SKENTZOS - VP Real Estate, Construction, Design
MARY STATHOUKOS - VP Finance, Information Systems, Human Resources, Franchising
MARK TENEYCKE - Director Operations, Purchasing, Supply Chain

Pinnacle Hospitality Group
500A Bloor St W 3rd Floor
Toronto, ON M5S 1Y3

Telephone: (416) 531-7638
Fax Number: (416) 531-1404
Internet Homepage: harbour60.com
Company Email: info@harboursixty.com
Type of Business: Chain Restaurant Operator
Total Sales: $30,677,000 (e)
Alcohol Sales: 25%
Average Check: Breakfast(8); Lunch(12); Dinner(18)
Total Units: 2
Trade Names: Cafe on the Square (1); Harbour 60 Steakhouse (1)
Company-Owned Units: 2
Preferred Location Types: Other
Alcohol Served: Beer, Wine, Liquor
Primary Menu: American (1); Steak (1)
Areas of Operation: ON
Type of Foodservice: Casual Dining (1); Fine Dining (1)
Catering Services: Yes
Primary Distributors: (Full Line) SYSCO Canada, TORONTO, ON

Key Personnel
TED NIKOLAOU - President; Director Real Estate, Design
BETTY BUERGER - General Manager
TONY PALERMO - Director Operations
CHRISTINE VAUGHAN - Manager Accounting, Human Resources
KIRSTIN WRIGHT - Manager Marketing, E-Commerce
GUS NIKOLAOU - General Buyer

Pizza Nova Restaurants Ltd.
2247 Midland Ave
Toronto, ON M1P 4R1

Telephone: (416) 439-0051
Fax Number: (416) 299-3558
Internet Homepage: pizzanova.com
Company Email: info@pizzanova.com
Type of Business: Chain Restaurant Operator
Year Founded: 1963
Systemwide Sales: $124,012,000 (e)

Total Sales: $10,304,000 (e)
Alcohol Sales: 4%
Number of Employees: 205
Average Check: Lunch(5); Dinner(5)
Internet Order Processing: Yes
Internet Sales: 1.00%
Total Units: 138
Trade Names: Pizza Nova (138)
Company-Owned Units: 1
Units Franchised To: 137
Preferred Square Footage: 1,300
Preferred Location Types: Freestanding; Regional Mall; Strip Mall
Primary Menu: Pizza (138)
Projected Openings: 3
Areas of Operation: NJ, NY, ON
Foreign Countries: UNITED STATES OF AMERICA
Type of Foodservice: Quick Serve (138)
Foodservice Management Venues: Schools
On-site Distribution Center: Yes

Key Personnel
DOMENIC PRIMUCCI - President; General Buyer

Pizza Pizza Limited
500 Kipling Ave
Toronto, ON M8Z 5E5

Telephone: (416) 967-1010
Fax Number: (416) 967-0891
Internet Homepage: pizzapizza.ca
Company Email: feedback@pizzapizza.ca
Type of Business: Chain Restaurant Operator
Year Founded: 1967
Systemwide Sales: $675,592,000 (e)
Publicly Held: Yes
Total Sales: $226,392,000 (e)
Alcohol Sales: 3%
Number of Employees: 4,050
Average Check: Lunch(8); Dinner(14)
Internet Order Processing: Yes
Internet Sales: 2.00%
Total Units: 743
Trade Names: Pizza 73 (99); Pizza Pizza (644)
Company-Owned Units: 7
Units Franchised To: 736
Preferred Square Footage: 900
Preferred Location Types: Community Mall; Downtown; Freestanding; Institution (college/hospital); Regional Mall; Strip Mall
Alcohol Served: Beer, Wine
Primary Menu: Pizza (743)
Projected Openings: 15
Areas of Operation: AB, BC, NS, ON, QC, SK
Type of Foodservice: Casual Dining (743); Quick Serve (462)
Catering Services: Yes
Distribution Centers: ETOBICOKE, ON
Primary Distributors: (Full Line) SYSCO Food Services of Central Ontario Inc., CAVAN MONAGHAN, ON
Parent Company: Tesari, TORONTO, ON CANADA
Notes: The company derives approximately 78% of its revenue from food sales to its franchisees & other operations. Systemwide sales includes results from both Pizza Pizza & Pizza 73.

Key Personnel
PAUL GODDARD - CEO; President
DALJINDER SINGH - Owner
CURTIS FELTNER - CFO; Senior VP
CHRISTINE D'SYLVA - CFO
PHILIP GOUDREAU - COO
CHUCK FARRELL - VP Human Resources
AMAR NARAIN - VP Information Technology
ADRIAN FUOCO - VP Marketing
CRAIG SHANNON - Regional VP Operations
ANKIT SANGHVI - General Manager
MARCELO MELO - Director Purchasing, Quality Assurance, Product Development
GALEEB MEHDI - Director Operations
RAYMOND LUK - Director Marketing, Digital Media
SYED HASHMI - Director Culinary Development
MICHELLE SAVOY - Director
BEN CAMPOLI - Director Sales
HARIS RIZWAN - Director Operations
TANYA REYNOLDS - Manager Franchising
AMBER FANCY - Manager Marketing, Canada, West Region
KHALED HASAN - Manager Sales
PARTHRAJSINH MAHIDA - Manager
MARCIO MACHADO - Supervisor Warehouse
NEIL LESTER - Corporate Director
MEAGHAN ARISS - Coordinator Franchise Development
THERESE SOUSA - Coordinator Human Resources

Restaurant Brands International
130 King St W Ste 300
Toronto, ON M5X 1E1

Telephone: (905) 845-6511
Fax Number: (905) 845-0265
Internet Homepage: rbi.com
Listing Type: Corporate Office
Type of Business: Chain Restaurant Operator
Year Founded: 2014
Systemwide Sales: $45,129,361,000 (e)
Publicly Held: Yes
Total Sales: $7,389,320,000 (e)
Number of Employees: 6,300
Average Check: Breakfast(6); Lunch(6); Dinner(6)
Total Units: 31,070
Trade Names: Burger King (19,383); Firehouse Subs (1,282); Popeyes Louisiana Kitchen (4,571); Tim Hortons (5,833); WHOPPER Bar (1)
Company-Owned Units: 115
Units Franchised To: 30,955
Preferred Square Footage: 550; 1,000; 1,400; 1,900; 3,090; 4,300
Preferred Location Types: Airports; Community Mall; Convenience Store/Gas Station; Discount Dept. Stores; Downtown; Freestanding; Grocery Stores; Institution (college/hospital); Kiosk; Mobile Unit; Office Complex; Other; Outlet Mall; Parks; Strip Mall; Travel Plazas
Primary Menu: Chicken (4,571); Hamburger (19,384); Sandwiches/Deli (1,282); Snacks (5,833)
Projected Openings: 300
Areas of Operation: AK, AL, AR, AZ, CA, CO, CT, DC, DE, FL, GA, GU, HI, IA, ID, IL, IN, KS, KY, LA, MA, MD, ME, MI, MN, MO, MS, MT, NC, ND, NE, NH, NJ, NM, NV, NY, OH, OK, OR, PA, PR, RI, SC, SD, TN, TX, UT, VA, VT, WA, WI, WV, WY, AB, BC, MB, NB, NL, NS, NT, NU, ON, PE, QC, SK, YT
Foreign Countries: ANDORRA; ANTIGUA; ARGENTINA; ARUBA; AUSTRALIA; AUSTRIA; BAHAMAS; BAHRAIN; BOLIVIA; BRAZIL; BRUNEI; CAMBODIA; CANADA; CAYMAN ISLANDS; CHILE; CHINA; COLOMBIA; COSTA RICA; CURACAO; CYPRUS; CZECH REPUBLIC; DENMARK; DOMINICAN REPUBLIC; EL SALVADOR; ENGLAND; FRANCE; GERMANY; GUATEMALA; HONDURAS; HONG KONG; HUNGARY; ICELAND; INDIA; INDONESIA; ISRAEL; ITALY;JAMAICA; JAPAN; JORDAN; KUWAIT; LEBANON; MALAYSIA; MALTA; MEXICO; NEW ZEALAND; NICARAGUA; NORTHERN IRELAND; NORWAY; OMAN;PAKISTAN; PANAMA; PARAGUAY; PERU; PORTUGAL; QATAR; RUSSIA; SAINT MAARTEN; SAUDI ARABIA; SINGAPORE; SOUTH KOREA; SPAIN; SRILANKA; ST. LUCIA; SURINAME; SWEDEN; SWITZERLAND; TAIWAN; THAILAND; THE NETHERLANDS; THE PHILIPPINES; TRINIDAD & TOBAGO; TURKEY; UNITED ARAB EMIRATES; UNITED STATES OF AMERICA; URUGUAY; VENEZUELA
Type of Foodservice: Casual Dining (1,282); Quick Serve (29,788)
Foodservice Management Venues: College & University; Military Feeding
Franchise Affiliation: TOMS King LLC, PALATINE, IL
Primary Distributors: (Food) SYSCO Canada, TORONTO, ON; (Food) Restaurant Services Inc., MIAMI, FL
Parent Company: 3G Capital, NEW YORK CITY, NY
Headquarter Offices: Burger King Worldwide Inc., MIAMI, FL; Firehouse Restaurant Group Inc., JACKSONVILLE, FL; Popeyes Louisiana Kitchen Inc., ATLANTA, GA; Tim Hortons Inc., OAKVILLE, ON CANADA
Regional Offices: Tim Hortons Inc., CALGARY, AB CANADA; Tim Hortons Inc., LACHINE, QC

2025 Chain Restaurant Operators

CANADA

Key Personnel
PATRICK DOYLE - Executive Chairman
JOSH KOBZA - CEO
TOM CURTIS - President United States, Canada
THIAGO SANTELMO - President International
MIKE HANCOCK - COO Division
JEFF HOUSMAN - Chief Human Resources Officer; Chief People Officer
FRANK LIBERIO - CIO Global
DUNCAN FULTON - Chief Communications Officer
JILL GRANAT - Exec VP; Corporate Secretary; General Counsel
MARK SCHICHTEL - Senior VP Tax
CHAKRI SOMISETTI - VP Information Technology
CAROLINA BERTI - VP Marketing, Innovation
LUIS MAIA - VP Branding
SETH ISRAEL - Executive Director Information/Data Security; Manager Information/Data Security
ALBERT GOMEZ - Executive Director Accounting
ABHIMANYU LAMBA - General Manager Manufacturing
VICTOR SIQUEIRA - Director Supply Chain
AMBAR ADHAV - Director Systems
COURTNEY CONNOLLY - Director Accounting, People
DAVID PABON - Director Systems
ASHER PERLMUTTER - Director Engineering
MATHEW EDWARDS - Director Finance, Operations
ANA CECILIA DIAZ - Director Benefits
JAY MCNEIL - Senior Manager Finance
ANDY XIONG - Senior Manager Strategic Services, Strategic Planning
ANDREA MURRAY - Senior Manager Talent
JORDAN GINTHER - Senior Manager Human Resources
LAUREN BARCLAY - Senior Manager Talent Acquisitions
DEVINDER LAMSAR - Senior Manager Communications
GINA HARDY - Senior Manager Real Estate
AHLAM SAEED - Business Manager
LINDSAY O'BRIEN - Manager Franchise Operations
BLERINA AGO - Manager Innovation
SIERRA MILLS - Manager People
STEPHEN BUCKLEY - Manager Franchise Operations
ADAM STOKES - Manager Real Estate
ANTHONY JOHNSON - Coordinator Purchasing
MARIA ALVA - Analyst Supply Chain

Shopsy's Hospitality Inc
96 Richmond St W
Toronto, ON M5H 2A3

Telephone: (416) 365-3333
Fax Number: (416) 365-7264
Internet Homepage: irishembassypub.com; pjobrien.com; quinnssteakhouse.com; shopsys.ca
Company Email: info@shopsys.ca
Type of Business: Chain Restaurant Operator
Total Sales: $8,622,000 (e)
Alcohol Sales: 7%
Number of Employees: 67
Average Check: Breakfast(18); Lunch(18); Dinner(18)
Internet Order Processing: Yes
Total Units: 5
Trade Names: Irish Embassy Pub & Grill (1); P.J. O'Brien Irish Pub & Restaurant (1); Quinn's Steakhouse & Irish Bar. (1); Shopsy's (2)
Company-Owned Units: 5
Preferred Square Footage: 5,000
Preferred Location Types: Freestanding; Strip Mall
Alcohol Served: Beer, Wine, Liquor
Primary Menu: American (2); Sandwiches/Deli (2); Steak (1)
Areas of Operation: ON
Type of Foodservice: Casual Dining (5)
Catering Services: Yes
Primary Distributors: (Food) SYSCO Food Services of Toronto, MISSISSAUGA, ON

Key Personnel
GAVIN QUINN - President
CHAO TAM - Director Operations, Purchasing; General Buyer
FRANCIS FERNANDEZ - Manager Catering

South St. Burger
2 Bishop St Ste 200
Toronto, ON M5R 1N2

Telephone: (416) 963-5005
Fax Number: (416) 963-4920
Internet Homepage: southstburger.com
Company Email: info@southstburger.com
Type of Business: Chain Restaurant Operator
Year Founded: 1984
Systemwide Sales: $37,524,000 (e)
Total Sales: $2,183,000 (e)
Number of Employees: 369
Average Check: Lunch(8); Dinner(8)
Total Units: 40
Trade Names: South Street Burger (40)
Company-Owned Units: 14
Units Franchised To: 26
Preferred Square Footage: 350
Preferred Location Types: Community Mall; Freestanding; Parks; Regional Mall
Alcohol Served: Beer, Wine
Primary Menu: Hamburger (40)
Areas of Operation: AB, BC, MB, NB, NL, NS, ON, QC, SK
Foreign Countries: SOUTH KOREA; UNITED ARAB EMIRATES
Type of Foodservice: Fast Casual (40)
Primary Distributors: (Full Line) SYSCO Food Services of Toronto, MISSISSAUGA, ON

Key Personnel
JAY GOULD - President
MICHAEL PERRIN - Director Human Resources
DONNA CHURCHILL - Manager Marketing

SPoT Coffee Canada Ltd.
141 Adelaide St W Ste 110
Toronto, ON M5H 3L5

Telephone: (416) 368-2220
Fax Number: (416) 368-4469
Internet Homepage: spotcoffee.com
Company Email: talk2us@spotcoffee.com
Type of Business: Chain Restaurant Operator
Systemwide Sales: $10,371,000 (e)
Total Sales: $17,690,000 (e)
Number of Employees: 132
Average Check: Breakfast(6); Lunch(6); Dinner(6)
Total Units: 15
Trade Names: SPoT Coffee (15)
Company-Owned Units: 11
Preferred Square Footage: 2,000; 4,000
Preferred Location Types: Freestanding
Primary Menu: Coffee (15)
Areas of Operation: NY, ON
Foreign Countries: UNITED STATES OF AMERICA
Type of Foodservice: Quick Serve (15)
Primary Distributors: (Full Line) SYSCO Food Services of Syracuse, WARNERS, NY
Notes: The company also maintains a US HQ office at 225 Delaware Ave, Ste 2, Buffalo, NY 14202

Key Personnel
JOHN LORENZO - Chairman
ANTON AYOUB - CEO; President
MIKE LORENZO - President; Director
PAUL PRICE - VP Franchise Operations
JOHN CORRENTE - VP Operations, Training
JACOB CASELLA - Manager Operations

St. Louis Franchise Ltd
2040 Yonge St Ste 200-B
Toronto, ON M4S 1Z9

Telephone: (416) 485-1094
Fax Number: (416) 485-1512
Internet Homepage: stlouiswings.com

Company Email: feedback@stlouiswings.com
Type of Business: Chain Restaurant Operator
Year Founded: 1992
Total Sales: $100,120,000 (e)
Alcohol Sales: 5%
Average Check: Dinner(36)
Total Units: 61
Trade Names: St. Louis Bar & Grill (61)
Company-Owned Units: 3
Units Franchised To: 58
Preferred Square Footage: 2,500
Preferred Location Types: Freestanding
Alcohol Served: Beer, Wine, Liquor
Primary Menu: Chicken (61)
Projected Openings: 1
Areas of Operation: NB, ON
Type of Foodservice: Fast Casual (61)

Key Personnel
BRENT POULTON - CEO; General Buyer
STEVE DREXLER - President
BRUCE STEPHENS - VP Procurement
CLAUDIA STEWART - VP Operations
TIM CROWE - Director Operations

The Bagel Stop
1450 Whitehorse Rd
Toronto, ON M3J 3A7

Telephone: (416) 398-5538
Fax Number: (416) 398-2792
Internet Homepage: thebagelstop.com
Company Email: eat@thebagelstop.com
Type of Business: Chain Restaurant Operator
Year Founded: 1987
Systemwide Sales: $12,108,000 (e)
Total Sales: $313,000 (e)
Number of Employees: 20
Average Check: Breakfast(6); Lunch(6);
Total Units: 18
Trade Names: The Bagel Stop (18)
Company-Owned Units: 1
Units Franchised To: 17
Preferred Square Footage: 300; 1,500
Preferred Location Types: Community Mall; Freestanding; Office Complex; Regional Mall
Primary Menu: Bagels (18)
Areas of Operation: BC, ON
Type of Foodservice: Fast Casual (18)
Catering Services: Yes
On-site Distribution Center: Yes

Key Personnel
ALEX ZILBERBERG - CEO; President

The Burger's Priest
1636 Queen St E
Toronto, ON M4L 1G3

Telephone: (647) 346-0617
Internet Homepage: theburgerspriest.com
Type of Business: Chain Restaurant Operator
Year Founded: 2010
Total Sales: $18,700,000 (e)
Total Units: 19
Trade Names: The Burger's Priest (19)
Company-Owned Units: 19
Preferred Location Types: Other
Primary Menu: Hamburger (19)
Projected Openings: 1
Areas of Operation: AB, ON
Type of Foodservice: Fast Casual (19)
Parent Company: Crave It Restaurant Group, OAKVILLE, ON CANADA

Key Personnel
ALEX RECHICHI - President Group
LAURA HARVEY - General Manager
MATEO LOPEZ - General Manager
STEVEN BARKER - Director Operations

East Side Mario's Restaurants Inc.
199 Four Valley Dr
Vaughan, ON L4K 0B8

Telephone: (905) 760-2244
Fax Number: (905) 568-0080
Internet Homepage: eastsidemarios.com
Listing Type: Subsidiary
Type of Business: Chain Restaurant Operator
Year Founded: 1979
Systemwide Sales: $202,670,000 (e)
Total Sales: $39,660,000 (e)
Alcohol Sales: 15%
Number of Employees: 1,159
Average Check: Lunch(12); Dinner(10)
Total Units: 78
Trade Names: East Side Mario's (78)
Company-Owned Units: 2
Units Franchised To: 76
Preferred Square Footage: 4,827; 4,980; 5,023; 5,054; 5,252
Preferred Location Types: Community Mall; Downtown; Freestanding; Regional Mall; Stadiums; Strip Mall
Alcohol Served: Beer, Wine, Liquor
Primary Menu: Italian (78)
Areas of Operation: AB, BC, NB, NL, NS, ON, PE, QC, SK
Type of Foodservice: Casual Dining (78)
Primary Distributors: (Full Line) GFS Ontario, MILTON, ON
Parent Company: Recipe Unlimited Corporation, VAUGHAN, ON CANADA
Notes: Does not operate as a separate entity as Recipe Unlimited

Key Personnel
NICHOLAS M. PERPICK - President; COO
CHRIS KAULINA - Director Operations

Pumpernickel's
30 Pennsylvania Ave Unit 4
Vaughan, ON L4K 4A5

Telephone: (905) 669-9176
Fax Number: (905) 669-9183
Internet Homepage: pumpernickels.ca
Company Email: admin@pumpernickels.ca
Type of Business: Chain Restaurant Operator
Year Founded: 1986
Total Sales: $22,740,000 (e)
Number of Employees: 40
Average Check: Breakfast(12); Lunch(14); Dinner(16)
Total Units: 16
Trade Names: Pumpernickel's (16)
Units Franchised To: 16
Preferred Square Footage: 500; 800
Preferred Location Types: Office Complex
Primary Menu: Sandwiches/Deli (14)
Areas of Operation: ON
Type of Foodservice: Quick Serve (16)
Catering Services: Yes
Primary Distributors: (Food) Reliable Food Supplies Inc., MISSISSAUGA, ON

Key Personnel
SOLY ZIV - President; Partner; Controller; General Manager Finance, Operations, Purchasing; Executive Chef; General Buyer
ZVIA ZIV - Partner; VP
OLGA SANDOR - Manager Human Resources

Recipe Unlimited Corporation
199 Four Valley Dr
Vaughan, ON L4K 0B8

Telephone: (905) 760-2244
Fax Number: (905) 405-6915
Internet Homepage: cara.com; caseysbarandgrill.com; harveys.ca; kelseys.ca; milestonesrestaurants.com; montanas.ca; primerestaurants.com; swisschalet.com; thebiermarkt.com
Company Email: kelseyscustomercare@cara.com
Listing Type: Corporate Office
Type of Business: Chain Restaurant Operator
Year Founded: 1978
Systemwide Sales: $4,326,010,000 (e)
Total Sales: $1,702,900,000 (e)
Alcohol Sales: 28%
Number of Employees: 10,000
Average Check: Lunch(8); Dinner(14)
Total Units: 266
Trade Names: 1909 Taverne Moderne (2); Anejo (1); Bier Markt (6); Blanco Cantina (1); Burger's Priest (19); Casey's Bar & Grill (1); East Side Mario's (75); Elephant & Castle (10); Harvey's (297); Kelsey's Neighborhood Bar &

Grill (68); Landing (9); Milestones Grill + Bar (44); Montana's Cookhouse Saloon (106);New York Fries (157); Original Joe's Restaurant & Bar (60); Prime Pubs (41); St-Hubert's (124); State & Main (26); Swiss Chalet Rotisserie and Grill (208); TheKeg Steakhouse & Bar (106); The Pickle Barrel (14)
Company-Owned Units: 262
Units Franchised To: 1,113
Preferred Square Footage: 5,000; 6,200
Preferred Location Types: Airports; Freestanding; Regional Mall; Strip Mall
Alcohol Served: Beer, Wine, Liquor
Primary Menu: American (799); Bar-B-Q (122); Chicken (210); Hamburger (19); Italian (76); Mexican (2); Miscellaneous (51); Steak (105)
Areas of Operation: AB, BC, MB, NB, NL, NS, ON, SK
Foreign Countries: BAHRAIN; CANADA; CHINA; MACAO; OMAN; PANAMA; QATAR; SAUDI ARABIA; UNITED ARAB EMIRATES
Type of Foodservice: Casual Dining (921); Quick Serve (454)
Catering Services: Yes
Subsidiaries: East Side Mario's Restaurants Inc., VAUGHAN, ON CANADA; The Elephant & Castle Group Inc., CALGARY, AB CANADA
Primary Distributors: (Food) Summit Foodservice/A division of Colabor, MISSISSAUGA, ON; (Supplies) Summit Food Service, A Div of Colabor LP, LONDON, ON
Headquarter Offices: Groupe St-Hubert, LAVAL, QC CANADA; Swiss Chalet Inc., VAUGHAN, ON CANADA

Key Personnel
FRANK HENNESSEY - CEO
PETER VALE - President Strategic Sourcing
KEN GRONDIN - CFO
FRANCO TASCIONE - COO
JULIE DENTON - Chief People Officer
PAULO FERREIRA - Senior Director Construction, Design
PAYMAN JANAMIAN - Senior Director Operations
CHRISTINE MULCAHY - Senior Director Safety, Quality Assurance
PAOLO DIMANNO - Director Strategic Sourcing
PAUL AMATO - Director Real Estate
JONATHAN YOUNG - Senior Manager
MARY KOLDENHOF - Manager Event Planning
CHRIS LOVELACE - Manager Operations
TORE ORIENTE - Manager Media, Production
TINA CAPPIELLO - Manager Legal, Real Estate
JOE TINOCO - Manager Systems
JACKLYN BALAGULA - Manager
CHRISTINE LUCENTI - Manager Loss Prevention
CAROLINE R. YOUNG - Specialist Food Safety
ASHLEY BATES - Senior Designer

Yum! Restaurants International (Canada) Co.
191 Creditview Rd
Vaughan, ON L4L 9T1

Telephone: (416) 664-5200
Fax Number: (905) 265-1062
Internet Homepage: kfc.ca; pizzahut.ca; tacobell.ca
Company Email: comments@yum.ca
Type of Business: Chain Restaurant Operator
Year Founded: 1997
Publicly Held: Yes
Total Sales: $2,077,800,000 (e)
Number of Employees: 75
Internet Order Processing: Yes
Total Units: 1,189
Trade Names: KFC (566); Pizza Hut (453); Taco Bell (170)
Company-Owned Units: 50
Units Franchised To: 1,139
Preferred Square Footage: 2,500; 3,000
Preferred Location Types: Community Mall; Convenience Store/Gas Station; Downtown; Freestanding; Hotel/Motel; Institution (college/hospital); Regional Mall; Strip Mall
Primary Menu: Chicken (566); Pizza (453); Taco (170)
Projected Openings: 50
Areas of Operation: AB, BC, MB, NB, NL, NS, NT, ON, PE, QC, SK
Type of Foodservice: Quick Serve (1,189)
Catering Services: Yes
Primary Distributors: (Full Line) SYSCO Food Services of Vancouver Inc., PORT COQUITLAM, BC
Parent Company: YUM! Brands Inc., LOUISVILLE, KY

Key Personnel
SEAN TAYLOR - Director
JENNIFER LIGOTTI - Senior Manager Digital Marketing, E-Commerce
ROSHAN SINGH - Manager Tax
SUNAYANA GOPAL - Manager Marketing
LUQMAN RABBANI - Manager Research & Development

▲

Pizzaville Inc.
741 Rowntree Dairy Rd Unit 1
Woodbridge, ON L4L 5T9

Telephone: (905) 850-0070
Fax Number: (905) 850-0339
Internet Homepage: pizzaville.ca
Company Email: info@pizzaville.ca
Type of Business: Chain Restaurant Operator
Year Founded: 1963
Systemwide Sales: $41,787,000 (e)
Total Sales: $954,000 (e)
Number of Employees: 67
Average Check: Lunch(8); Dinner(8)
Internet Order Processing: Yes
Internet Sales: 3.00%
Total Units: 80
Trade Names: Pizzaville Pizza & Panzerotto (80)
Company-Owned Units: 7
Units Franchised To: 73
Preferred Square Footage: 600; 800; 1,000
Preferred Location Types: Freestanding; Strip Mall
Primary Menu: Pizza (80)
Projected Openings: 3
Areas of Operation: ON
Type of Foodservice: Quick Serve (80)
On-site Distribution Center: Yes
Primary Distributors: (Full Line) SYSCO Canada, TORONTO, ON

Key Personnel
ANGELO CONTARDI - CEO; President; Director Finance, Design; Manager Risk Management
NELLA CONTARDI - CTO; Manager Purchasing, Menu Development
CESARE SCARFELLA - Manager Warehouse
AMRITA VIRK - Supervisor Human Resources

QUEBEC

Sportscene Group Inc.
1180 Nobel Place Ste 102
Boucherville, QC J4B 5L2

Telephone: (450) 641-3011
Fax Number: (450) 641-9742
Internet Homepage: cage.ca
Company Email: info@cage.ca
Type of Business: Chain Restaurant Operator
Year Founded: 1984
Systemwide Sales: $135,598,000 (e)
Publicly Held: Yes
Total Sales: $93,430,000 (e)
Alcohol Sales: 25%
Number of Employees: 1,862
Average Check: Breakfast(10); Lunch(10); Dinner(18)
Foodservice Sales: $79,416,000 (e)
Total Units: 38
Trade Names: La Cage aux Sports (38)
Company-Owned Units: 30
Units Franchised To: 14
Preferred Square Footage: 4,500; 6,000
Preferred Location Types: Community Mall; Downtown; Freestanding; Office Complex
Alcohol Served: Beer, Wine, Liquor
Primary Menu: American (38)
Projected Openings: 3
Areas of Operation: QC
Type of Foodservice: Casual Dining (38)
Primary Distributors: (Food) Dubord Rainville Inc., SAINT-LAURENT, QC
Notes: The company derives approximately

15% of its revenue from construction & renovation of La Cage au Sports restaurants. Company operated locations include some joint venture operations.

Key Personnel
JOSEE PEPIN - VP Finance
JEAN FRANCOIS DUBE - VP Operations
FRANCOIS-XAVIER PILON - VP Finance
MICHEL BEDARD - Director Construction
CAROLINE PEDNEAULT - Director Legal
SOPHIE LAUZON - Director Development, Sales, Business Development
ADRIAN SAAD - Regional Director

Restaurant Pizzapro Inc.
1157 Boul Saint-Paul
Chicoutimi, QC G7J 3Y2

Telephone: (418) 549-6276
Fax Number: (418) 549-3374
Internet Homepage: restaurants-eating-places.can.info
Type of Business: Chain Restaurant Operator
Year Founded: 1968
Total Sales: $5,259,000 (e)
Alcohol Sales: 4%
Number of Employees: 75
Average Check: Lunch(14); Dinner(14)
Total Units: 2
Trade Names: Pizzapro (2)
Company-Owned Units: 2
Preferred Square Footage: 1,250
Preferred Location Types: Freestanding
Alcohol Served: Beer, Wine
Primary Menu: Pizza (2)
Areas of Operation: QC
Type of Foodservice: Casual Dining (2)
On-site Distribution Center: Yes
Primary Distributors: (Full Line) SYSCO Canada, TORONTO, ON

Key Personnel
RICHARD TREMBLAY - President; General Manager; Executive Chef; Director Finance, Operations, Facility/Maintenance, Information Systems, Real Estate, Design, Human Resources; General Buyer

Copper Branch
1405 Rte Transcanadienne Ste 410
Dorval, QC H9P 2V9

Telephone: (514) 924-3272
Internet Homepage: copperbranch.ca
Company Email: cb@copperbranch.ca
Type of Business: Chain Restaurant Operator
Year Founded: 2014
Total Units: 56
Trade Names: Copper Branch (56)
Company-Owned Units: 56

Primary Menu: Health Foods (56)
Projected Openings: 9
Areas of Operation: FL, AB, ON, QC
Foreign Countries: UNITED STATES OF AMERICA
Type of Foodservice: Quick Serve (56)

Key Personnel
TRISH PATERSON - CEO
RICHARD HEBERT - Director Operations; Manager Operations
MARK SEGALL - Director Business Development, Franchising

Kojax Souflaki Inc.
2915 Boul St. Charles Ste 101
Kirkland, QC H9H 3B5

Telephone: (514) 693-8889
Fax Number: (514) 693-5112
Internet Homepage: kojaxsouflaki.com
Company Email: info@kojaxsouflaki.com
Type of Business: Chain Restaurant Operator
Year Founded: 1977
Systemwide Sales: $18,577,000 (e)
Total Sales: $2,143,000 (e)
Alcohol Sales: 1%
Number of Employees: 28
Average Check: Lunch(10); Dinner(14)
Total Units: 12
Trade Names: Kojax (12)
Units Franchised To: 12
Preferred Square Footage: 400; 2,000
Preferred Location Types: Community Mall; Strip Mall
Alcohol Served: Beer, Wine
Primary Menu: Greek/Mediterranean (12)
Areas of Operation: ON, QC
Type of Foodservice: Fast Casual (12)
Primary Distributors: (Full Line) Dubord Rainville Inc., SAINT-LAURENT, QC

Key Personnel
JOSEPH IACINO - CEO; Partner; Manager Operations, Information Systems, Supply Chain, Design, Store Fixtures, Menu Development; General Buyer
LOUIS IACINO - President; Partner; CFO; COO; Treasurer; Manager Real Estate; General Buyer
ANDREA BARBUSCI - Coordinator Accounting, Human Resources

Restaurant Pacini
170 Boul Taschereau App 300
La Prairie, QC J5R 5H6

Telephone: (450) 444-4749
Fax Number: (450) 444-4773
Internet Homepage: pacini.ca
Company Email: info@pacini.ca

Type of Business: Chain Restaurant Operator
Year Founded: 1980
Systemwide Sales: $38,002,000 (e)
Total Sales: $9,728,000 (e)
Alcohol Sales: 15%
Number of Employees: 867
Average Check: Breakfast(6); Dinner(30)
Total Units: 30
Trade Names: Pacini (30)
Company-Owned Units: 28
Units Franchised To: 2
Preferred Square Footage: 2,000
Preferred Location Types: Freestanding
Alcohol Served: Beer, Wine, Liquor
Primary Menu: Italian (30)
Areas of Operation: QC
Type of Foodservice: Casual Dining (30)
Catering Services: Yes

Key Personnel
MARC-ANDRE RIVARD - VP Marketing
JULIE TREMBLAY - Director Supply Chain
JOSEE DAIGNAULT - Director Government Affairs, Human Resources

Au Vieux Duluth Restaurant Inc.
815 Boul Saint-Martin W
Laval, QC H7S 1M4

Telephone: (450) 663-1165
Fax Number: (450) 663-3769
Internet Homepage: auvieuxduluth.com
Company Email: info@auvieuxduluth.com
Type of Business: Chain Restaurant Operator
Year Founded: 1982
Systemwide Sales: $41,633,000 (e)
Total Sales: $23,970,000 (e)
Number of Employees: 1,215
Average Check: Dinner(24)
Total Units: 32
Trade Names: Au Vieux Duluth (32)
Units Franchised To: 32
Preferred Square Footage: 5,000; 6,000
Preferred Location Types: Community Mall; Strip Mall
Alcohol Served: Beer, Wine, Liquor
Primary Menu: Steak/Seafood (32)
Areas of Operation: ON, QC
Type of Foodservice: Casual Dining (32)
On-site Distribution Center: Yes

Key Personnel
ANDY KRAGARIS - President; Manager Facility/Maintenance, Real Estate, Human Resources
VICKY BOURDAKOS - Controller; Director Finance
ALEX ZALDIVAR - District Manager
JOHN LEMBESSIS - General Buyer

Groupe St-Hubert
2500 Daniel Johnson Blvd Ste 700
Laval, QC H7T 2P6

Telephone: (450) 688-6500
Fax Number: (450) 688-3900
Internet Homepage: st-hubert.com
Company Email: info@st-hubert.qc.ca
Type of Business: Chain Restaurant Operator
Year Founded: 1951
Systemwide Sales: $431,443,000 (e)
Total Sales: $60,530,000 (e)
Alcohol Sales: 10%
Number of Employees: 9,597
Average Check: Lunch(18); Dinner(24)
Internet Order Processing: Yes
Internet Sales: 1.00%
Total Units: 122
Trade Names: St-Hubert's (122)
Company-Owned Units: 12
Units Franchised To: 110
Preferred Square Footage: 2,600; 6,500; 10,000
Preferred Location Types: Community Mall; Downtown; Freestanding; Regional Mall; Strip Mall
Alcohol Served: Beer, Wine, Liquor
Primary Menu: Bar-B-Q (122)
Projected Openings: 1
Areas of Operation: NB, ON, QC
Type of Foodservice: Casual Dining (122)
Distribution Centers: ANJOU, QC
Primary Distributors: (Full Line) SYSCO Food Services of Quebec, MONTREAL, QC
Parent Company: Recipe Unlimited Corporation, VAUGHAN, ON CANADA

Key Personnel
ANNIK LABROSSE - VP Marketing
NATHALIE DANIEL - VP Human Resources
KATHERINE HARTON - VP Operations

Au Coq (Les Rotisseries Limitee)
3060 Rue Hochelaga Fl 2
Montreal, QC H1W 1G2

Telephone: (514) 527-8833
Fax Number: (514) 527-0220
Internet Homepage: aucoq.ca
Company Email: rh@aucoq.ca
Type of Business: Chain Restaurant Operator
Year Founded: 1965
Total Sales: $13,584,000 (e)
Average Check: Lunch(14); Dinner(22)
Total Units: 4
Trade Names: Au Coq (4)
Company-Owned Units: 4
Preferred Location Types: Freestanding
Primary Menu: Chicken (4)
Areas of Operation: QC
Type of Foodservice: Quick Serve (4)
Primary Distributors: (Full Line) US Foods Holding Corp., ROSEMONT, IL

Key Personnel
PETER MAMMAS - President

BeaverTails Canada Inc.
3700 St Patrick Ste 106
Montreal, QC H4E 1A2

Telephone: (514) 392-2222
Fax Number: (514) 392-2223
Internet Homepage: beavertails.com
Company Email: development@beavertails.com
Type of Business: Chain Restaurant Operator
Year Founded: 1978
Systemwide Sales: $18,987,000 (e)
Total Sales: $8,334,000 (e)
Number of Employees: 12
Average Check: Breakfast(8); Lunch(8); Dinner(8)
Total Units: 111
Trade Names: BeaverTails Pastry (111)
Units Franchised To: 111
Preferred Square Footage: 300
Preferred Location Types: Kiosk; Mobile Unit
Primary Menu: Snacks (111)
Areas of Operation: AR, NJ, TN, UT, AB, BC, MB, NB, NL, NS, ON, PE, QC
Foreign Countries: JAPAN; SAUDI ARABIA; UNITED STATES OF AMERICA
Type of Foodservice: Quick Serve (111)
Catering Services: Yes
Primary Distributors: (Food) BakeMark Ingredients Canada Ltd., LAVAL, QC

Key Personnel
PINO DI IOIA - Chairman; President; Director Real Estate, Franchise Development; Manager Business Development; General Buyer
ANTHONY DI IOIA - CFO; Controller
TINA SERRAO - Creative Director
SCOTT REID - Director Development

Brioche Doree
3075 de Rouen St
Montreal, QC H1W 3Z2

Telephone: (514) 528-8877
Internet Homepage: briochedoree.us
Type of Business: Chain Restaurant Operator
Year Founded: 1976
Total Units: 33
Trade Names: Brioche Dorée (33)
Company-Owned Units: 33
Preferred Location Types: Airports; Downtown; Institution (college/hospital)
Primary Menu: French/Continental (33)
Areas of Operation: CA, DE, FL, GA, IL, IN, MI, MO, NC, NE, NY, OH, PA, TX, VA, AB, BC, ON, QC, SK
Foreign Countries: CANADA; UNITED STATES OF AMERICA
Type of Foodservice: Quick Serve (33)
Catering Services: Yes
Parent Company: Le Duff America Inc., DALLAS, TX
Notes: Total stores count is US and Canadian locations only.

Key Personnel
LOUIS LE DUFF - Founder
SOPHIE KOWALSKI - Coordinator Marketing, Digital Media

Dilallo Burger
2851 Rue Allard
Montreal, QC H4E 2M1

Telephone: (514) 767-9921
Fax Number: (514) 694-3220
Internet Homepage: dilalloburger.com
Company Email: info@dilalloburger.ca
Type of Business: Chain Restaurant Operator
Year Founded: 1929
Systemwide Sales: $3,417,000 (e)
Total Sales: $1,171,000 (e)
Alcohol Sales: 5%
Number of Employees: 40
Average Check: Lunch(10); Dinner(10)
Total Units: 4
Trade Names: Dilallo Burger (4)
Company-Owned Units: 1
Units Franchised To: 3
Preferred Square Footage: 2,500
Preferred Location Types: Freestanding; Strip Mall
Alcohol Served: Beer
Primary Menu: Hamburger (4)
Areas of Operation: QC
Type of Foodservice: Casual Dining (4)
Catering Services: Yes

Key Personnel
GIUSEPPE MASELLI - President; General Buyer
LOU DI LALLO JR - VP; General Buyer

Gouverneur Inc.
2300-1000 Sherbrooke Rue O Ste 2300
Montreal, QC H3A 3R3

Telephone: (514) 875-8822
Fax Number: (514) 875-8074
Internet Homepage: gouverneur.com
Company Email: contact@gouverneur.com
Type of Business: Foodservice Operations - Hotel/Motels
Year Founded: 1963

Total Sales: $42,710,000 (e)
Alcohol Sales: 20%
Number of Employees: 1,100
Total Units: 8
Trade Names: Gouverneur Hotel Rimouski (1); Gouverneur Hotel Sept-Iles (1); Gouverneur Hotel Shawinigan (1); Gouverneur Hotel St-Jean-sur-Richelieu (1); Gouverneur Hotel Trois-Rivieres (1); Hotel Le Chantecler (1); Hotel Montreal Place Dupuis (1); OTL GOUVERNEUR SHERBROOKE (1)
Company-Owned Units: 8
Alcohol Served: Beer, Wine, Liquor
Areas of Operation: QC
Primary Distributors: (Food) SYSCO Food Services of Grand Rapids LLC, GRAND RAPIDS, MI
Notes: The company derives approximately 70% of its revenue from hotel operations.

Key Personnel
JACQUES GOUPIL - CEO; President; Executive Chef; Director Operations, Risk Management, Quality Assurance, Recruitment, Menu Development, Food Safety, Food and Beverage
PATRICE DUMONT - VP Finance; Controller
CLAUDE ROULEAU - Director Purchasing

Au Petit Coin Breton Ltee.
2600 Boul Laurier
Quebec, QC G1V 4T3

Telephone: (418) 653-6051
Internet Homepage: aupetitcoinbreton.ca
Type of Business: Chain Restaurant Operator
Year Founded: 1963
Total Sales: $4,278,000 (e)
Alcohol Sales: 12%
Average Check: Breakfast(12); Lunch(16); Dinner(24)
Total Units: 2
Trade Names: Au Petit Coin Breton (2)
Company-Owned Units: 2
Preferred Location Types: Freestanding; Strip Mall
Alcohol Served: Beer, Wine, Liquor
Primary Menu: French/Continental (2)
Areas of Operation: QC
Type of Foodservice: Casual Dining (2)
Primary Distributors: (Full Line) SYSCO Food Services of Quebec, MONTREAL, QC

Key Personnel
DIDIER ROLIN - Partner; General Manager; Executive Chef; General Buyer
PATRICIA ROLIN - Partner; General Manager

Les Franchises Salvatore G.A. Inc.
980 Bouvier St Fl 2
Quebec, QC G2J 1A3

Telephone: (418) 624-8888
Fax Number: (418) 624-8626
Internet Homepage: pizzasalvatore.com
Company Email: marketing@pizzasalvatore.com
Type of Business: Chain Restaurant Operator
Year Founded: 1964
Systemwide Sales: $23,515,000 (e)
Total Sales: $18,970,000 (e)
Number of Employees: 300
Average Check: Lunch(14); Dinner(26)
Total Units: 13
Trade Names: Pizza Salvatore (13)
Units Franchised To: 13
Preferred Square Footage: 5,500; 6,000
Preferred Location Types: Freestanding; Regional Mall; Strip Mall
Primary Menu: Pizza (13)
Areas of Operation: QC
Type of Foodservice: Quick Serve (13)

Key Personnel
GUILLAUME ABBATIELLO - CEO; President; General Manager; General Buyer
ELISABETH ABBATIELLO - Controller; Director Finance

Restaurant Normandin
2335 Boul Bastien
Quebec, QC G2B 1B3

Telephone: (418) 842-9160
Fax Number: (418) 842-8916
Internet Homepage: restaurantnormandin.com
Company Email: info@normandi.biz
Type of Business: Chain Restaurant Operator
Year Founded: 1969
Total Sales: $113,080,000 (e)
Alcohol Sales: 100%
Number of Employees: 1,835
Average Check: Dinner(6)
Total Units: 41
Trade Names: Restaurant Normandin (41)
Company-Owned Units: 41
Preferred Square Footage: 1,200; 4,000
Preferred Location Types: Freestanding
Alcohol Served: Beer, Wine, Liquor
Primary Menu: American (41)
Areas of Operation: QC
Type of Foodservice: Casual Dining (41)
On-site Distribution Center: Yes
Primary Distributors: (Full Line) SYSCO Food Services of Quebec, MONTREAL, QC

Key Personnel
NORMAND BRIE - Chairman
NORBERT GAGNON - CEO; President
DENIS PIGEON - CEO; President
GERVAIS BRIE - Owner
PATRICK VIEN - VP Marketing
LOUISE CLOUTIER - VP Information Systems
JEAN JULIEN - VP Marketing; Director Design
REGINALD PERRON - VP Finance
SIMON PICARD - VP Construction; Director Facility/Maintenance
ANNE-CLAIRE NOBILI - Manager Restaurant Operations
JACQUES DION - Manager Restaurant Operations
DENIS GUERIN - Manager Research & Development

Restaurants Ashton Casse Croute Inc.
1100 Av Galibois App 250
Quebec, QC G1M 3M7

Telephone: (418) 682-2288
Fax Number: (418) 682-2613
Internet Homepage: chezashton.ca
Company Email: info@chezashton.ca
Type of Business: Chain Restaurant Operator
Year Founded: 1969
Systemwide Sales: $21,891,000 (e)
Total Sales: $6,339,000 (e)
Alcohol Sales: 5%
Number of Employees: 650
Average Check: Lunch(12); Dinner(12)
Total Units: 24
Trade Names: Chez Ashton (24)
Company-Owned Units: 5
Units Franchised To: 19
Preferred Square Footage: 2,500
Preferred Location Types: Freestanding; Regional Mall; Strip Mall
Primary Menu: Hamburger (24)
Projected Openings: 3
Areas of Operation: QC
Type of Foodservice: Quick Serve (24)

Key Personnel
ASHTON LEBLOND - President; General Manager; Director Franchise Development, Menu Development
DENIS GAGNE - Controller; Director Finance, Supply Chain, Real Estate, Design
CLAUDE GIGUERE - Director Information Systems, Design, E-Commerce

†
ARAMARK Quebec
100-4900 Rue Fisher
Saint-Laurent, QC H4T 1J6

Telephone: (514) 341-7770
Fax Number: (514) 341-0468
Listing Type: Branch Office
Type of Business: Foodservice Management

Operator
Year Founded: 1961
Number of Employees: 60
Number of Locations Served: 200
Total Foodservice Mgmt Accounts: 200
Areas of Operation: QC
Type of Foodservice: Cafeteria (200); Vending machines (100)
Foodservice Management Venues: Business & Industry; Schools
Primary Distributors: (Food) SYSCO Food Services of Quebec, MONTREAL, QC
Parent Company: Aramark, PHILADELPHIA, PA
Headquarters: ARAMARK Canada, TORONTO, ON CANADA

Key Personnel
NICOLAS SEGUIER - VP Human Resources; Regional VP

Foodtastic
2365 Rue Guenette
Saint-Laurent, QC H4R 2E9

Telephone: (514) 856-5555
Fax Number: (514) 856-6050
Internet Homepage: foodtastic.ca; nickelsrestaurants.com; restaurantmonza.com; restopro.net; belleetboeuf.com; bigrigbrew.com; souvlakibar.ca; vinniegambini.com; aucoq.ca; gattomatto.ca
Company Email: info@foodtastic.ca
Type of Business: Chain Restaurant Operator
Year Founded: 1990
Systemwide Sales: $57,616,000 (e)
Total Sales: $8,157,000 (e)
Alcohol Sales: 10%
Number of Employees: 9
Average Check: Breakfast(10); Lunch(14); Dinner(26)
Total Units: 60
Trade Names: Au Coq (4); Bacaro Pizzeria (10); Big Rig (2); Carlos & Pepe's (3); Gatto Matto (1); La Belle & La Bouf (10); Le Blossom (1); Monza (4); Nickels Restaurant (11); Souvlaki Bar (13); Vinnie Gambini (1)
Company-Owned Units: 60
Preferred Square Footage: 5,000
Preferred Location Types: Community Mall; Downtown; Freestanding; Hotel/Motel; Outlet Mall; Regional Mall; Strip Mall
Alcohol Served: Beer, Wine, Liquor
Primary Menu: American (2); Chicken (4); Greek/Mediterranean (13); Italian (17); Mexican (3); Miscellaneous (10); Sandwiches/Deli (11)
Areas of Operation: ON, QC
Type of Foodservice: Casual Dining (60)

Key Personnel
LAWRENCE MAMMAS - Chief Development Officer; VP Quality Assurance, Construction, Franchising
PETER MAMMAS - VP Finance; Director Information Systems, Real Estate, Design
BRUNO BERGERON - VP Business Development
VLAD CIOBANU - Director Marketing
PATRICE MONTMARQUETTE - Director Purchasing
JAMES NICOLOPOULOS - Director Finance

MTY Food Group Inc.
8210 Transcanadienne Rte
Saint-Laurent, QC H4S 1M5

Telephone: (514) 336-8885
Fax Number: (514) 336-9222
Internet Homepage: extremepita.com; mtygroup.com; muchoburrito.com
Company Email: info@mtygroup.com
Listing Type: Corporate Office
Type of Business: Chain Restaurant Operator
Year Founded: 1979
Systemwide Sales: $5,916,546,000 (e)
Publicly Held: Yes
Total Sales: $1,226,409,000 (e)
Number of Employees: 7,500
Total Units: 7,116
Trade Names: Allo mon Coco (44); America's Taco Shop (2); Baja Fresh Express (8); Baja Fresh Mexican Grill (72); Bakers Square (9); Barrio Queen (7); Baton Rouge (28); Ben & Florentine (64); Big Smoke Burger (12); BLIMPIE (111); Built Custom Burgers (5); Cafe Depot (50); Cakes N Shakes (5); Casa Grecque (27); Champps (3); Cold Stone Creamery (1,365); Country Style Donuts (223); Craft Republic (2); Cultures (26); Dagwoods Sandwiches & Salads (15); Extreme Pita (24); Famous Dave's (118); Fox & Hound (1); Frullati Cafe and Bakery (10); Giorgio Ristorante (3); Grabbagreen (4); Granite City (16); Great Steak (33); Johnnie's New York Pizzeria (2); Jugo Juice (87); Kahala Coffee Traders (5); Kim Chi Korean Delight (8); Koryo Korean BBQ (9); Koya Japan (9); Kuto (29); Küto Comptoir à Tartares (29); La Cremiere (19); La Diperie (77); La Salsa Fresh Mexican Grill (6); Madisons New York Grill & Bar (8); Manchu Wok(84); Maui Wowi (268); Mikes (66); Mr Souvlaki (19); MR. SUB (220); Ms. Vanellis (13); Mucho Burrito (146); Muffin Plus (15); NRgize Lifestyle Cafe (57);O'burger (1); Papa Murphy's (1,162); Pinkberry (93); Pizza Delight (71); Planet Smoothie (163); Ranch One (2); Real Urban BBQ (1); Rocky Mountain Chocolate Factory (101); Samurai Sam's Teriyaki Grill (13); Sauce Pizza and Wine (13); Scores (30); SensAsian (1); South St. Burger (30); Spice Bros (1); Steak Frites (3); Sukiyaki (4); Surf City Squeeze (66); Sushi Go (2); Sushi Shop (170); Sushiman (12); sweetFrog (226); Taco Time (222); Tahoe Joe's (3); Tasti D-Lite (2); TCBY (17); Thai Express/Pad Thai (306); Thai Zone (33); The Coop Wicked Chicken (8); the Counter Custom Burger (17); The Works GourmetBurger Bistro (28); Tiki-Ming (13); Timothy's World Coffee and Mmmuffins (8); Tosto Quickfire Pizza (1); Turtle Jack's (20); Tutti Frutti (20); Twisted (3);Valentine (81); Van Houtte (32); Vie & Nam (3); Villa Madina (24); Village Inn (115); Wasabi Grill and Noodle (1); Wetzel's Pretzels
Company-Owned Units: 219
Units Franchised To: 6,897
Preferred Square Footage: 400
Preferred Location Types: Convenience Store/Gas Station; Freestanding; Institution (college/hospital); Office Complex; Regional Mall; Strip Mall
Primary Menu: American (159); Asian (457); Bar-B-Q (149); Chicken (10); Chinese (13); Coffee (90); French/Continental (166); Greek/Mediterranean (70); Hamburger (174); Health Foods (430); Indian (1); Italian (3); Japanese (26); Mexican (239); Pizza (1,262); Sandwiches/Deli (436); Snacks (2,813); Steak (84); Taco (224); Thai (339)
Areas of Operation: AK, AL, AR, AZ, CA, CO, CT, DC, DE, FL, GA, GU, HI, IA, ID, IL, IN, KS, KY, LA, MA, MD, ME, MI, MN, MO, MS, MT, NC, ND, NE, NH, NJ, NM, NV, NY, OH, OK, OR, PA, PR, RI, SC, SD, TN, TX, UT, VA, VI, VT, WA, WI, WV, WY, FC, AB, BC, MB, NB, NL, NS, NT, NU, ON, PE, QC, SK, YT
Foreign Countries: CHINA; UNITED ARAB EMIRATES; UNITED STATES OF AMERICA
Type of Foodservice: Casual Dining (442); Fast Casual (800); Fine Dining (84); Quick Serve (5,819)
Foodservice Management Venues: College & University
Catering Services: Yes
Subsidiaries: Tasti D-Lite LLC, SCOTTSDALE, AZ
Franchise Affiliation: International Franchise Corp., MARKHAM, ON; Kahala Brands, SCOTTSDALE, AZ
Primary Distributors: (Food) SYSCO Food Services of Quebec, MONTREAL, QC
Headquarter Offices: Kahala Brands, SCOTTSDALE, AZ; Papa Murphy's International Inc., VANCOUVER, WA

Key Personnel
STANLEY MA - Chairman
ERIC LEFEBVRE - CEO
RENEE ST-ONGE - CFO
JEFF SMIT - COO United States
MARC BENZACAR - COO Division
NIK RUPP - COO Division
JENNY MOODY - Chief Legal Officer
VINCENT DUGAS - Senior VP Retail Operations, Manufacturing
JASON BRADING - VP Branding
SYLVAIN BOISSY - VP Business Development
DAN HEIN - VP Information Technology
ELIZABETH LUND - VP Finance
JANICE BURGESS - Director Operations

NANCY COGGER - Director Marketing
CYNTHIA SHATILLA - Director Human Resources
FREDERICK BRAYTON - Director Leasing
GERRY KAKAROUBAS - Director Operations
EMILIE MERCIER-BEAULIEU - Director Marketing
JAY DORANT - Director Operations
AMMAR GEORGES - Director Franchise Development
RICHARD KWOK - Director Construction, Design
MIKE ZYLBERSTEIN - Director Information Technology
JEFF ROOP - Director Operations
KEVIN PALANDJIAN - District Manager
ZISSIS BLIGOURAS - Manager Business Development
STEPHANIE REA - Manager Real Estate
CATHERINE CHEN - Manager Marketing
BRIAN LILLIE - Manager Franchise Development
GABRIELLE GERVAIS - Manager Real Estate
GENEVIEVE DESROCHERS - Specialist Marketing
TANIA PIETRANGELO - Analyst Operations
JOANNE BARRETTE - Analyst Purchasing

Breakfast People of America International
16 Rue Sicard Loc 50
Sainte-Therese, QC J7E 3W7

Telephone: (450) 435-2426
Fax Number: (450) 435-2428
Internet Homepage: chezcora.com; coras.net
Company Email: info@chezcora.com
Type of Business: Chain Restaurant Operator
Year Founded: 1987
Systemwide Sales: $136,800,000 (e)
Total Sales: $32,570,000 (e)
Alcohol Sales: 3%
Number of Employees: 100
Average Check: Breakfast(10); Lunch(12); Dinner(12)
Total Units: 130
Trade Names: Cora's Breakfast & Lunch (130)
Company-Owned Units: 3
Units Franchised To: 127
Preferred Square Footage: 3,400; 5,500; 6,000
Preferred Location Types: Community Mall; Downtown; Freestanding; Hotel/Motel; Outlet Mall; Strip Mall
Primary Menu: American (130)
Areas of Operation: BC, MB, NB, NL, NS, ON, PE, QC, SK
Type of Foodservice: Casual Dining (130)
On-site Distribution Center: Yes
Primary Distributors: (Full Line) SYSCO Food Services of Toronto, MISSISSAUGA, ON
Notes: The company derives approximately 20% of its revenue from retail operations.

Key Personnel
CORA MUSSELY TSOUFLIDOU - Founder; CEO; Partner; Director Finance, Real Estate, Design
NICHOLAS TSOUFLIDIS - President; Partner; General Manager; Director Operations, Purchasing, Security, Loss Prevention, Risk Management, Quality Assurance, Food Safety
LUCY NORMANDIN - Controller; Director Human Resources
ROBERTO AGOSTINELLI - General Manager Division; Director Facility/Maintenance
JENEVIEVE DUQUETTE - Director Marketing

Cinemas Guzzo
1055 Ch du Coteau
Terrebonne, QC J6W 5Y8

Telephone: (450) 961-2945
Fax Number: (450) 961-9349
Internet Homepage: cinemasguzzo.com
Company Email: vguzzo@cinemasguzzo.com
Type of Business: Foodservice Operations - Movie Theatre
Year Founded: 1974
Systemwide Sales: $46,896,000 (e)
Total Sales: $8,066,000 (e)
Number of Employees: 2,000
Total Units: 10
Trade Names: Cinemas Guzzo (10)
Company-Owned Units: 10
Preferred Location Types: Freestanding
Primary Menu: Snacks (10)
Areas of Operation: QC
Type of Foodservice: In-Store Feeder (10)
Primary Distributors: (Supplies) Metro Inc., MONTREAL, QC
Notes: The company derives approximately 85% of its revenue from theatre operations.

Key Personnel
ANGELO GUZZO - CEO; President
VINCENZO GUZZO - CEO; President
ILARIO MAIOLO - Senior VP
ÜLRICH MERCKEL - VP Information Technology
NATALIE GAGNON - VP Business Development; General Counsel
JOSE BRUZESSE - VP Finance
VITO FRANCO - Director
MARIO QUATTROCIOCCHE - Director Operations, Menu Development; General Buyer
ERIC MAGINI - Manager District

Liquid Nutrition Group Inc.
60 Belvedere Ch
Westmount, QC H3Y 1P8

Telephone: (514) 945-8000
Internet Homepage: liquidnutrition.com
Company Email: info@liquidnutrition.com
Type of Business: Chain Restaurant Operator
Total Sales: $1,499,000 (e)
Total Units: 6
Trade Names: Liquid Nutrition (6)
Units Franchised To: 6
Preferred Location Types: Downtown; Institution (college/hospital)
Primary Menu: Health Foods (6)
Areas of Operation: CA, QC
Foreign Countries: BAHAMAS; UNITED STATES OF AMERICA
Type of Foodservice: Fast Casual (6)

Key Personnel
H. GREGORY CHAMANDY - Chairman; CFO
CHANTAL CHAMANDY - CEO; President; Chief Marketing Officer
MY LINH LAM - Corporate Secretary; Controller

SASKATCHEWAN

Dee Jay's Chicken Village
2015 Mayfair Bay
Estevan, SK S4A 1X7

Telephone: (306) 634-5669
Fax Number: (306) 634-8894
Company Email: deejays@deejayscorp.com
Type of Business: Chain Restaurant Operator
Total Sales: $14,630,000 (e)
Total Units: 17
Trade Names: A&W All American Food/Long John Silver (11); Long John Silver's (6)
Units Franchised From: 17
Preferred Square Footage: 2,500; 3,200
Primary Menu: American (11); Seafood (6)
Areas of Operation: KS, ND, NE, SK
Foreign Countries: UNITED STATES OF AMERICA
Type of Foodservice: Quick Serve (17)
Franchise Affiliation: A&W Restaurants Inc., LEXINGTON, KY; KFC Corporation, LOUISVILLE, KY; Taco Bell Corp., IRVINE, CA

Key Personnel
BRIAN JOHNSON - President; General Buyer

Houston Pizza Franchise Ltd
3422 Hill Ave
Regina, SK S4S 0W9

Telephone: (306) 757-8288
Fax Number: (306) 790-1838
Internet Homepage: houstonpizza.ca
Company Email:
  houston.franchise@sasktel.net
Type of Business: Chain Restaurant Operator
Year Founded: 1970
Systemwide Sales: $19,382,000 (e)
Total Sales: $1,864,000 (e)
Alcohol Sales: 15%
Number of Employees: 10
Average Check: Lunch(14); Dinner(20)
Total Units: 10
Trade Names: Houston Pizza (10)
Units Franchised To: 10
Preferred Square Footage: 5,000; 6,000
Preferred Location Types: Freestanding; Regional Mall
Alcohol Served: Beer, Wine, Liquor
Primary Menu: Pizza (10)
Areas of Operation: AB, SK
Type of Foodservice: Casual Dining (10)
Catering Services: Yes
Primary Distributors: (Full Line) SYSCO Canada, TORONTO, ON

Key Personnel
JIM KOLITSAS - President; Partner; Director Finance, Operations, Purchasing, Facility/Maintenance, Information Systems, Loss Prevention, Marketing, Real Estate, Human Resources
MARIA KOLITSAS - Partner

Trifon's Pizza & Spaghetti House Ltd.
2046 Broad St
Regina, SK S4P 1Y3

Telephone: (306) 757-2900
Fax Number: (306) 347-9966
Internet Homepage: trifons.com
Type of Business: Chain Restaurant Operator
Year Founded: 1979
Systemwide Sales: $8,422,000 (e)
Total Sales: $3,029,000 (e)
Alcohol Sales: 100%
Number of Employees: 137
Average Check: Breakfast(5); Lunch(14); Dinner(18)
Total Units: 22
Trade Names: Trifon's Pizza & Spaghetti House (22)
Company-Owned Units: 3
Units Franchised To: 14
Preferred Square Footage: 1,500
Preferred Location Types: Community Mall; Freestanding
Alcohol Served: Beer, Wine, Liquor
Primary Menu: Italian (21)
Areas of Operation: AB, BC, MB, ON, SK
Type of Foodservice: Casual Dining (22)
Catering Services: Yes

Key Personnel
VON AGIORITIS - President; VP Operations, Supply Chain, Marketing, Real Estate, Store Planning; Controller; General Buyer
MERV MADDIE - Manager Accounting, Facility/Maintenance
TAMSIN ONEILL - Manager

Western Pizza (1979) Ltd.
335 Hoffer Dr Suite 116
Regina, SK S4N 6E2

Telephone: (306) 924-8391
Internet Homepage: western-pizza.com
Company Email: wpizza2@sasktel.net
Type of Business: Chain Restaurant Operator
Year Founded: 1976
Systemwide Sales: $13,485,000 (e)
Total Sales: $5,435,000 (e)
Alcohol Sales: 4%
Number of Employees: 125
Total Units: 25
Trade Names: Western Pizza (25)
Company-Owned Units: 4
Units Franchised To: 21
Preferred Square Footage: 2,500
Preferred Location Types: Freestanding; Regional Mall
Alcohol Served: Beer, Wine, Liquor
Primary Menu: Pizza (25)
Projected Openings: 2
Areas of Operation: AB, SK
Type of Foodservice: Quick Serve (25)
Catering Services: Yes
Primary Distributors: (Full Line) Saputo Dairy Products Canada, DIEPPE, NB

Key Personnel
SPIRO BONIS - VP; General Manager; Director Operations, Information Systems, Real Estate, Human Resources, Franchise Development

YUKON

Blackstrap Hospitality Corporation
29 Wann Rd
Whitehorse, YT Y1A 4A2

Telephone: (867) 456-4742
Type of Business: Chain Restaurant Operator
Year Founded: 1989
Total Sales: $5,685,000 (e)
Alcohol Sales: 10%
Number of Employees: 38
Average Check: Lunch(12); Dinner(12)
Total Units: 3
Trade Names: Bo'diddly's Pub & Grill (2); Whiskey Jack's Neighbourhood Pub (1)
Company-Owned Units: 3
Preferred Square Footage: 5,500; 6,000
Preferred Location Types: Freestanding
Alcohol Served: Beer, Wine, Liquor
Primary Menu: American (3)
Areas of Operation: AB, SK
Type of Foodservice: Casual Dining (3)
Parent Company: 6385842 Canada Ltd., SASKATOON, SK CANADA

Key Personnel
DEREK NEIS - CEO; President; COO; Director Purchasing, Menu Development
INGRID HASLBECK - Manager Marketing, Human Resources
RENEE NEIS - Bookkeeper

Company	Page
&pizza	232
100 MONTADITOS	275
101 Concepts	329
110 Grill	538
13 Coins LLC	1118
1502 J F K Inc	685
1859 Historic Hotels Ltd	1014
23 Restaurant Services	309
2B Hospitality	303
2JR Pizza Enterprises LLC	484
3 Carter's Subway Inc	305
3 Square Restaurant Group LLC	247
321 Coffee	672
325 Roseway	863
3Bm Enterprises Inc	249
3C Blessing, Inc.	746
3DC Enterprises	354
3M & N, Inc.	660
3Natives Acai and Juicery	319
4 Alarm, LLC	1086
4 Star Restaurant Group	399
410 Bank Street Restaurant	698
4R Restaurant Group LLC	323
4Top Hospitality	959
5 & Diner North America	526
5 Napkin Burger	764
50 Eggs, Inc.	275
5877 Corporation	702
5Buck Pizza	1072
7 Brew Drive-Thru Coffee	19
755 Restaurant Corporation	329
8.0 Management Inc.	984
80/20 Hopsitality	985
800 Degrees Woodfired Kitchen	100
801 Restaurant Group	465
85C Bakery Cafe	56
99 Subway Inc	746
A & B Pizza Inc.	681
A & D Management Co. Inc.	385
A & J Produce	707
A & N River City Inc.	385
A & R Hospitality	576
A S C Corporation	964
A S Enterprises Inc.	590
A&M Pizza	631
A&R Pars, Inc.	329
A&T Food Development, Llc	760
A&W Food Services of Canada Inc.	1169
A&W Restaurants Inc.	480
A.C. Fox Inc.	435
A.C.G. Texas	1053
A.E.S. Management Corp.	812
A.H. Management Group	438
A.P.G. Enterprise Inc.	396
A.V. Ice Creamery, Inc.	124
AB Management	77
Abalar Fast Foods, INC	846
Abbott & Avard LLC	1066
Abbott's Frozen Custard Inc.	793
Abbott's Lobsters in the Rough	222
Abby's Inc.	861
ABC Pizza House Inc.	309
Abnar Corp	500
Abrams Family Restaurants	677
Absinthe Group	149
Absolutely Italian Management Group	114
Abundant Brands	1069
Acapulco Restaurante Mexicano	596
ACES, LLC	1097
ACG Pizza Partners LLC	358
ACL Ice Cream Inc.	611
Acme Oyster House	502
Acosta Inc.	1056
Action Business Corp.	243
ACW Corp.	241
Adam's Taphouse and Grille	549
Adams Tri-Cities Enterprises Inc.	1112
Adcock QSR Group, LLC	1018
Adcorp Inc	28
ADF Companies	701
ADJ Management	916
Adornetto's Selected Italian Foods	846
ADT Pizza	231
Adventist Health	137
Adventure Holdings LLC	266
AED Enterprises LLC	808
Aegis Brands Inc	1190
AFK Ventures, Inc.	119
After Tax Dough Inc	589
Afters Ice Cream	84
Ag of Raleigh, Inc.	672
Agave & Rye	477
Agricole Hospitality	1018
Ahi Mahi Enterprise LLC	71
AJP Enterprises, LLC	1111
AJS Inc.	461
AJW Holdings, LLC	19
Al Biernat's	985
Al Dar Inc.	875
Ala Carte Entertainment Inc.	438
Aladdin's Eatery Systems Inc	829
Alamo Cafe	1056
Alamo Drafthouse	970
Alamos LS LLC	716
Albert & Carol Mueller Inc.	878
Albert DiPrizito, Jr	709
Albert Restaurant Group	1033
Albert's Franchise Inc.	1165
Alcan Investments	1115
Alex Mercuri	222
Alex's Restaurants Inc.	925
Alfalfa	757
Alicart Restaurant Group	764
Alice J Schliecher, Inc.	461
Alioto's Fish Co.	149
All American Specialty Restaurants Inc	864
All Star Management	397
All Stores Management	253
Allan's Coffee & Tea	859
Allen & Murphy LLP	1154
Allen Properties Inc.	1104
Allen Theatres Inc.	720
Allgauer's Grill	430
Alliance Management Dunkin' Donuts	703
Allied Food Industries Inc.	1157
Aloha Hospitality International	11
Aloha Poke LLC	400
Aloha Restaurants Inc.	116
Alpha Subway	24
Alta Strada LLC	537
Altamarea Group	764
Alvarado Concepts/Palo Alto Inc.	196
Amante Pizza Corp.	651
Amato Enterprises Inc.	562
Amato Sandwich Shops Inc.	563
Amazing Joe's Grill	459
Ambassador Food Services Corporation	762
Amber India	100
AMC Entertainment Holdings Inc.	465
AMC Ventures, Inc.	652
AMD Pizza LLC	26
Ameci Pizza & Pasta	58
Amelia Holdings, Inc.	122
Amergent Hospitality Group, Inc.	652
American Casino & Entertainment Properties LLC	724
American Deli International	330
American Family Foods, LLC	958
American Food & Vending	761
American Food Systems	518
American Golf Corp.	101
American Gonzo Food Corp	181
American Restaurant Holdings, Inc.	65
American Roast Beef, Inc.	935
American Social	256
American Steakhouse	225
American West Restaurant Group	122
America's Dog & Burger	400
America's Incredible Pizza Company	631
AmHeath, Inc.	645
Amici East Coast Pizzeria	162
Amici's	162
Amin Taha	923
AMNJ Enterprises Inc	1150
Ampex Brands	985
Amphora Group	1087
Ampler Restaurant Group	400
Amsher Enterprises Inc.	890
AMSU Financial, Inc.	114
AMUR, LLC	75
Amway Grand Plaza Hotel	576
Amy's Ice Creams	970
Anacapri	275
Anand, Inc.	118
Anco Inc	1108
Andersen Bakery Inc.	83
Anderson Larosa's	808
Anderson Restaurant Group	621
Anderson's Management Associates Inc.	800
Andiamo Restaurant Group	594
Andies Restaurant	400
Andrade Management Group	694
Andre Bollier Ltd.	621
Andreams Corp	303
Andrew Limited Partnerships	113
Andy's Frozen Custard	631
Andy's Pizza Inc.	581
Andy's Restaurants Inc.	17
Angilo's Pizza	808
Angona Pizza, Inc.	570
Angry Chickz	171

Angry Crab Shack 31
Anjusam, LLC 667
Annapurna's World Vegetarian Cafe 716
Anna's House 577
Anna's Taqueria 528
Annieyi Inc 1018
Another Broken Egg of America Inc 285
Ansara Restaurant Group 574
Anthony Palagano Enterprises, Inc. 713
Anthony's Inc. 1104
Anthony's Pier 4 Inc. 535
Anthony's Pizza & Pasta International 197
Antioch Pizza Shop 394
Antler Management 423
Antonio's 273
Antonio's Inc. 805
APB Management, Inc. 1087
Apollo Burger 1074
Apple Arkansas, Inc 1066
Apple Core Enterprises, Inc 684
Apple Corps, LP 471
Apple Investors Group (Anand Enterprises Inc.) 320
Apple Spice Junction 1074
Applebee's Services Inc. 622
Apple-Metro Inc. 756
Aquitaine Group 512
AR Fresh Mex, Inc. 24
Aramark 894
ARAMARK 424
ARAMARK Business Services 896
ARAMARK Campus Services(HIGHER EDUCATION) 536
ARAMARK Canada 1190
ARAMARK Conference Centers Management 897
ARAMARK Education 983
ARAMARK Healthcare Support Services . 897
ARAMARK Higher Education 897, 985
ARAMARK International Services 897
ARAMARK Quebec 1202
ARAMARK School Support Services 897
ARAMARK Sports & Entertainment Group897
Arandas Franchise 1018
Arbico East LLC 937
Arby's of Spokane 1135
Arby's Restaurant Group 330, 450
ARC Group Inc. 284
Arcadia Farms 38
Arches of Gold 119
Arches Up North Inc 568
Archways 478
Arctic Circle Restaurants Inc. 1079
Areas USA, Inc. 276
ARGO Hospitality Services, Inc. 73
Argo Management 276
Argo Tea Inc. 400
Arizona Ice Cream Company, Inc 45
Ark Restaurants Corp. 764
Arkansas Culinary School Pulaski Technical College 22
Arlekan, Inc. 796
Armstrong Subway Inc. 602
Army & Air Force Exchange Service (AAFES) 985

Arnaud's 505
Arnie's Inc. 577
Arnies Restaurants Northwest Inc. 1115
Arni's Inc. 456
Aroma Joe's Franchising, LLC 563
Arooga's Grille House & Sports Bar 885
Arriba Fresh Baja Grills Inc. 65
Arrington Enterprises Inc. 1097
Arthur's Garden Delicatessen Inc. 437
Artichoke Basille's Pizza 765
Artistry Restaurants 324
Aryzta LLC 160
Asbury Knight Investments 51
Ascott 702
Asfour Family Corporation 128
ASHA Corporation 887
Ashby Hospitality Group 238
Asheville Investment Partners 648
Ashish Subway Inc. 187
Ashley Christenson Restaurants 672
Ashley Mac's 6
Ashley's Ice Cream Cafe Inc. 222
Ashria LLC 176
Ashworth By The Sea Hotel & Restaurant 694
Asian Box 125
Asian Concepts Franchising Corp. 1170
Asian Concepts Inc. 814
Asian Mint Restaurant Group 986
Askar Brands 570
Aspen Food Service, Inc 215
Associated Hotels LLC 400
Atherton Restaurant Systems 857
Atlanta Bread Company 371
Atlantic Development Corporation of Pennsylvania 471
Atlantic Food Group, LLC 1083
Atlas Foods Inc. 682
Atlas Hotels Inc. 141
Atlas Restaurant Group 540
Atomic Burger 503
ATX Brands LLC 970
Au Coq (Les Rotisseries Limitee) 1201
Au Petit Coin Breton Ltee. 1202
Au Vieux Duluth Restaurant Inc. 1200
Auberge Resorts Collection 112
Aubree's 596
Aubrey's Inc. 947
Audubon Inc 947
Auguste Escoffier School of Culinary Arts .970
Auntie Anne's Franchise ... 7, 63, 83, 113, 115, 121, 129, 236, 249, 307, 331, 387, 426, 450, 476, 528, 529, 541, 550, 557, 558, 575, 635, 658, 661, 678, 704, 706, 708, 711, 716, 721, 724, 745, 748, 761, 763, 797, 801, 808, 812, 836, 841, 876, 884, 885, 898, 905, 910, 953, 1008, 1014, 1017, 1019, 1038, 1057, 1078, 1081, 1082, 1083, 1084, 1104, 1110, 1136, 1144, 1158
Auntie Anne's Inc. 888
Aureflam Corporation 138
Aurelio's Pizza Inc. 428
Aurify Brands LLC 765
Austin Sonic Inc. 970
Austin's American Grill 208

Authentic Mexican Restaurants Group 240
Avanti's Italian Restaurant Inc. 436
Avants Management Group 328
Ava's Cupcakes, LLC 658
Avenir Restaurant Group 141
Aver's Pizza Inc. 443
Avli442
AW Malik, Inc. 75
Axion Corporation 401
AYG Food Services 1019
Azar's Inc. 447
Azteca Management Inc. 369
Azteca Restaurant Enterprises Inc. 1109
Azuma Restaurant Group 1019
Azzip Pizza 445
B & B Hospitality Group 765
B & B Theatres 624
B & D Restaurants 26
B & J Food Enterprises, Inc. 697
B & R Food Service 621
B E Donuts, Inc. 526
B K & R Inc 113
B Squared Enterprises, LLC 947
B T N D, LLC 685
B Ventures USA LLC 101
B&B Theatres 620
B&G Food Enterprises LLC 504
B&G Milkyway 935
B.F. Saul Co. 543
b.good LLC 512
B.P. Newman Investments 1039
BAB Inc. 423
Baby Acapulco Restaurant 971
Bacci Pizza Group 401
Back of the House, Inc. 149
Back Yard Burgers Inc. 959
Backyard Breeze, Inc. 189
Bacon Enterprises 1084
Bacon Social House 197
Bad Ass Coffee Company of Hawaii 1074
Bad Bob's Barbeque Restaurant 942
Bad Daddy's International 666
Badawi Pizza Company 383
Baden Foods, Inc. 875
Bagel 13 274
Baggin's, Inc. 45
Bahama Breeze 285
Bahama Buck's Franchise Corporation .. 1041
Bahia Bowls 255
Bailey's Sports Grille 1049
Baim Enterprises 698
Baja Cantina 60
Bajco Group 806
Baker's Burgers 140
Baker's Dozen Donuts Corporation 1185
Baldinos Giant Jersey Subs & Salads 661
Balke Trucking, Inc. 22
Ballard Brands LLC 502
Balrod Enterprises Inc. 276
Balthazar 765
Baltic Capital/ Mac Attack Management ..1158
BAM Enterprises, Inc. 863
Bam-B Enterprises of Central Florida Inc. 272
Bamboo Asia 149
Bambu Desserts & Drinks, Inc. 174

Bandanas MO LLC	618	
Bandido's Inc.	447	
Banduccie Enterprises	628	
Banyan Cafe & Catering, Inc.	306	
Bao'd Up	971	
Bar Harbor Lobster Co.	285	
Barbara Lynch Gruppo	512	
Bar-B-Cutie Franchise Systems Inc.	936	
Barbeque Integrated Inc.	242	
Barberitos Inc.	328	
Bar-B-Q Heaven Inc.	450	
Bardha Enterprises	595	
Bareburger Group LLC	744	
Barfly	577	
Barleycorn's Inc.	477	
Barnacle Billy's Etc.	562	
Barnes & Noble Inc.	765	
Barnes & Noble The Kitchen	766	
Barnett Management	26	
Barney Enterprises	445	
Barney's Gourmet Hamburgers	53, 120	
Barnsider Management Corporation	521	
Barrel House	431	
Barreras Entities	1057	
Barrett Restaurants Inc.	511	
Barrio Culinary Concepts, LLC	38	
Barry Bagels	841	
Barry Cinemas Inc.	1162	
Bartaco	1080	
Bartley Management Co.	1105	
Bartmann Group	604	
Barton Group	1045	
Barton Restaurant Group, LLC	480	
Bart-Rich Enterprises	797	
BARZZA LLC	27	
Basic Food Group Inc.	207	
Basich Inc.	285	
Basil's Franchising	246	
Baskin-Robbins Franchise	112	
Bass Pro Shops	632	
Bassam Odeh, Inc.	1015	
Bates Enterprises	469	
Batista Companies	224	
Battleground Restaurants Inc.	662	
Bauer Inc	456	
Baxter Enterprises	557	
Bay Area Restaurant Management	164	
Bayou's Best Burgers,LLC	499	
Bayshore Development	356	
BayStar Restaurant Group	262	
Bazbeaux	450	
BB 2008 Inc.	83	
BB Cinnamon	401	
BB Franchising Inc.	986	
BB Riverboats	492	
bb.q Chicken	701	
BBG Specialty Foods Inc.	7	
B-Bop's Inc.	388	
BBQ Management, Inc.	509	
BC Pizza Inc.	569	
BC Restaurants, Ltd.	1055	
BCC Direct LLC	834	
BCT&G, Inc.	467	
BD's Mongolian Grill	1034	
Be Fish	1079	
Be Rich Buns, Inc.	667	
Beach Chalet Brewery & Restaurant	150	
Beach Hut LLC	138	
Beachside Hospitality Group	307	
Beans & Brews Coffee House	1074	
Bear Management Company	806	
Bearclaw Coffee Co.	587	
Bearco Management Co. Inc.	440	
Beard Papa's	320	
Bearno's Inc.	484	
Beaton Inc.	381	
Beaver Run Resort	192	
BeaverTails Canada Inc.	1201	
Becks Prime	1019	
Beef-A-Roo Inc.	430	
Bega Inc.	559	
Bell Brand Ranches, Inc	193	
Bella Luna	242	
Bella Restaurants Group	1019	
Bellacinos, Inc	587	
Bellagreen Holdings LLC	1019	
Bell-Co Enterprises	872	
Belle Epicurean	1118	
Belleria Franchise Corporation	846	
Bellevue Restaurants Inc.	825	
Bell's Chicken Villa Inc.	589	
Bellville Arch, Inc.	831	
Belote Foods LLC	12	
Ben & Jerry's Franchising Inc.	1105	
Benares	766	
Benchmarc Restaurants	766	
Bender/Agostini Organization	110	
Benevedes, Inc.	83	
Benihana Inc.	242	
Benito's Pizza	568	
Bennett Barndt Enterprises Inc.	1147	
Bennett Enterprises Inc.	837	
Bennett Management Corp	833	
Ben's Soft Pretzels	448	
Bent Tree Country Club Inc.	986	
Bentley-Miller Inc	692	
Bento Sushi/Yo! Sushi	1183	
Bentz Subway	431	
Bern's Steak House	309	
Berry Blendz Juice Enterprises Inc.	208	
Berry Investment Group, Ltd.	1117	
Berryhill Baja Grill	1019	
Bertucci's Corporation	530	
Best American Hospitality Inc.	959	
Best Bunz, Inc.	1042	
Best Burgers LLC	25	
Best Quality Pizza Group Inc.	804	
Better Buzz Coffee Company	183	
Between Rounds Franchise Corp	228	
Beyond Franchise Group, LLC	86	
BF Fort Myers Inc	302	
Bhatti, Inc.	32	
BHK Ltd	1176	
BHT Inc.	675	
Biaggi's	396	
Bickford's Grille	538	
Big Boy Restaurants International LLC	594	
Big Bran Corporation	653	
Big Burrito Restaurant Group	902	
Big Cedar Lodge	627	
Big Chicken	724	
Big City Diner	379	
Big Fish Restaurant Group	239, 715	
Big Fun Foods	98	
Big Game Brands, Inc.	331	
Big John Steak & Onion Inc.	575	
Big Mario's New York Style Pizza	1118	
Big Night Entertainment Group	512	
Big Plan Investments, LLC	892	
Big Red F Restaurant Group	189	
Big Steaks Management LLC	556	
Big Time Restaurant Group	320	
Big Whiskeys Concepts LLC	632	
Bigalora	590	
BigFoot Investment Group LLC	1116	
Biggar Enterprises Inc.	1086	
Biglari Holdings Inc.	1057	
Biju's Little Curry Shop	197	
Bill Bateman's	554	
Bill Gray's Inc.	799	
Bill Mason Enterprises	924	
Bill Miller Bar-B-Q Enterprise LTD	1057	
Bill's Sandwich Shops	892	
Billy Goat Tavern	401	
Billy Sims BBQ Restaurants	857	
Bingemans	1183	
Bionic Burger	471	
Birdcall	197	
Biscuits Cafe, Inc.	864	
Biscuitville Inc.	663	
Bjf Financial Limited Partnership	45	
BJ's Kountry Kitchen Inc.	78	
BJ's Restaurants Inc.	84	
Black Angus Steakhouse LLC	56	
Black Bear Diners Inc.	133	
Black Forest Ventures	1067	
Black Restaurant Group LLC	543	
Black Rock Coffee Bar	38	
Black Rock Restaurants	579	
Black Shamrock Partners	197	
Black Tap Craft Burgers & Beer	766	
BlackFinn Ameripub	653	
Blackjack Pizza Franchising, Inc.	217	
Blackshirt Investments, Inc.	689	
Blackstrap Hospitality Corporation	1205	
Blake's Lotaburger LLC	716	
Bland Management	1085	
Blaze Pizza LLC	125	
Blazing Buns, L.L.C.	326	
Blazing Onion Burger Company	1115	
BLD Brands	116	
Blenz The Canadian Coffee Company Ltd.	1171	
BLH Acquisition Co, LLC.	967	
Blockheads Burritos	766	
Bloomin' Brands Inc.	309	
BLT Restaurant Group	767	
Blue Bottle Coffee	120	
Blue Coast Burrito Inc.	937	
Blue Lemon	1070	
Blue Moon Burgers, Inc.	1118	
Blue Moon Mexican Cafe	715	
Blue Plate Restaurant Company	605	
Blue Ribbon Diner	651	
Blue Ribbon Restaurants	767	

Entry	Page
Blue Ridge Mountain Investments Inc	351
Blue Ridge Restaurant Group LLC	548
Blue Sky Restaurant Group	694
Blueberry Hill	428
Bluefield Dairy Queen	1156
Bluegrass Hospitality Group	481
Bluegrass Specialty Foods Inc	476
Bluegrass Subs, LLC	939
Bluestone Lane Coffee	767
Bluewater Grill	117
BMB Franchising	1020
BMJ Foods P.R. Inc.	911
BMT of Kentucky	479
BMW Management	176
BNC Food Group LLC	971
Bo Ling's	622
Board & Brew	71
Boat N Net Inc.	983
Bob & Edith's Diner	1097
Bob Childress	1095
Bob Evans Farms Inc.	835
Boba Guys	150
Bobby Byrne's Management Corp.	533
Bobby Cox Companies Inc.	1010
Bobby Salazar's Mexican Foods Inc.	77
Bobby Van's	746
Bobcar Partnership	160
Bob's Steak & Chop House	986
Boca Grande	519
Boca Restaurant Group	808
Bodan Inc./Group W Partners LLC	218
Boddie-Noell Enterprises Inc.	675
Bohlsen Restaurant Group	759
Boi Na Braza Churrascaria	1016
Boiling Point Group, Inc.	93
Boise Pizza Inc.	388
BOJ of WNC LLC	648
Bojangles Restaurants Inc.	653
Bok Bok Chicken	724
Boka Restaurant Group	401
Bolay Restaurant Partners	321
Bold Food	767
Boldt Enterprises Inc	456
Bombolotti, Inc. / FFC, Inc.	513
Bon Appetit Management Co.	125
Bonafide QSR, LTD.	1043
Bonanno Concepts	197
Bonchon Franchise LLC	987
Bonci USA	402
Bondough Inc	1096
Bone Daddy's	967
Bonefish Grill	310
Bono's Pit Bar-B-Q	262
Booeymonger Inc.	232
BoomBozz Craft Pizza & Taphouse	484
Booster Juice	1165
Boqueria Restaurants	790
Border Foods Inc.	610
Borgata Hotel, Casino & Spa	696
Boselli Brothers	213
Boselli Investments	218
Boss Tenders, Dogs & Custard	1008
Boston Beanery Restaurant Inc	1158
Boston Harbor Hotel	513
Boston Hospitality Group Inc.	1158
Boston Market Corporation	213
Boston Pie Inc.	522
Boston Pizza International Inc.	1169
Boston Pizza International Inc. (Eastern Canada)	1186
Boston Restaurant Associates	538
Boston's on the Beach	254
Boston's Restaurant & Sports Bar	987
Bottleneck Management	402
Boudin Bakery	150
Bouley International	754
Bow Tie Cinemas LLC	227
Bowen Enterprises, Inc.	983
Bower Management	888
Bowl America Inc.	1079
Bowl of Heaven Franchise Group LLC	132
Bowling Management Associates	257
Bowlmor AMF	1091
Boyd Gaming Corporation	725
Boykin Lodging Company	666
BOZ Hot Dogs	423
BPB Foods Inc.	63
BPH Burger	281
BR IP Holder LLC	520
Bradford & Lee Inc.	678
Bradford Cafe	1118
Bradley Investments Inc.	422
Bradley Investments Ltd	570
Brady's Dairy Queen Inc.	1042
Braga Management Team LLC	523
BraKat Enterprises Inc.	365
Brand Equity Development	73
Branded Restaurants	767
Brandicorp	475
Brann's Inc.	577
Braum Distribution Center	859
Bravo Restaurants Inc.	402
Brdancat Enterprises	548
Bre Mid America	441
Bread & Chocolate	1079
Bread Alone Bakery and Cafe	761
Bread Winners Cafe & Bakery	987
Bread Zeppelin Salads Elevated	987
Breadsmith Franchising Inc.	1155
Break Bread Hospitality Group	605
Breakfast People of America International	1204
Breckenridge-Wynkoop LLC	198
Breezy Point Resort	599
Brent's Delicatessen	119
Brentwood Associates	101
Brentwood Subs Inc.	958
Brew City Pizza Inc	1148
Brew Culture LLC	19
BreWingZ Sports Bar & Grill	1065
BRG Hospitality	505
Brian W. Emry	76
Bri'chae, LLC	299
Brick & Spoon	14
Brick Oven Restaurant	1073
Bricktown Brewery	851
Bridge Pizza	645
Briley Sonics	469
Brilliant Blondes	447
Brinda-Heilicher Inc.	605
Brinker International Inc.	987
Brioche Doree	1201
British Beer Company	532
British Columbia Ferry Corp.	1169
British Columbia Ferry Services Inc.	1175
Broadcast Coffee Roasters	1118
Broadway Palm Dinner Theatre Inc.	258
Broadway Station Restaurants Inc.	615
Brock & Co. Inc.	890
Brock's Eatery	310
Brock's Foodservice Management	310
Broders' Cucina Italiana	605
Bromley Food	49
Bronco Billy's Pizza Palace	179
Bronco's Holding Company	689
Brooklyn Water Enterprises Inc.	254
Brooklyn's	198
Brooks Restaurants Inc.	505
Bros. Management Inc.	947
Brothers Franchising & Development, LLC	1145
Brown & Patterson	888
Brown Bag Seafood Co.	402
Brown Derby Roadhouse Inc.	828
Brown Family Restaurants, LLC	212
Brozinni Pizzeria	450
Bruce Carey Restaurants	864
Bruchi's CheesSteaks & Subs	1135
Bruegger's Enterprises Inc.	988
Brumit Restaurant Group	649
Bruno Enterprises Inc.	456
Bru's Room Sports Grill	251
Bruster's Real Ice Cream	875
Bruxie	122
Bryant Restaurants Inc.	672
BRYN and DANE's	887
BTA Group, Inc.	534
Bubba Burger Hawaii Inc.	378
Bubbakoo's Burritos	713
Bubba's & Babe's Restaurants	1041
Bubby's Pie Co.	768
Bubs Franchise Company LLC	444
BUCA Inc.	285
Buckeye Valley/White River Valley Pizza Hut	840
Buckhead Life Restaurant Group	331
Buckhead Management Inc.	484
Buckley Enterprises LLC	1144
Buck's Pizza Franchising Inc.	881
Buddy's bar-b-q	948
Buddy's Pizza	574
Bud's Broiler Inc.	501
Bud's Chicken & Seafood	245
Buena Vista Hospitality Group	286
Buffalo Wild Wings Inc.	331
Buffalo Wing Factory	1081
Bull on the Beach	555
Bullard Restaurant Group	668
Bulldog Ale House	438
Bullets Hamburgers LLC	1093
Bullshark Inc.	193
Bullwinkle's Pizza Parlor	3
Bully's Sports Bar & Grill Inc.	741
Bumbly, LLC	268
Bunk Sandwiches Ltd	865

Name	Page
Burbowl	276
Burgatory	902
Burger 21 Inc.	311
Burger Baron Inc.	847
Burger Boss LLC	64
Burger Brothers Restaurant Group, Inc	792
Burger House Franchising, L.P.	988
Burger King Restaurants of Canada Inc.	1190
Burger King Worldwide Inc.	276
Burger Lounge	141
Burger Republic	959
BurgerBusters Inc.	1099
BurgerFi International, Inc.	283
Burgerhaus	462
Burgerim	74
BurgerMonger LLC	311
Burgers of Beaumont	979
Burgerville	1138
Burgerworx	649
Burge's Hickory Smoked Turkeys	22
Burguesa Burger Franchise LLC	988
Burke Hospitality Group	653
Burning Rice	1014
Burrell Management	478
Burrito Builders	386
Burrito Partners, LLC	802
Burtons Grill LLC	511
Busalacchi Restaurants	142
Busch Gardens Tampa Bay & Adventure Island	311
Bush and Associates Investments, Inc.	328
Bush Investments Inc	17
Bush Management	951
Butcher Block	196
Butterfield's Pancake House & Restaurant	435
Buzz Inn Steakhouse Restaurants	1115
Buzzard Billy's Armadillo Bar & Grill-o	383
By Chloe	768
Byron's Hot Dogs	403
C & B Restaurant Corporation	797
C & C Administration	1143
C & C Food Co, Inc	1067
C & C Food Systems	643
C & M Smith Restaurants Inc.	459
C & W LLC	619
C K C Inc.	194
C L Inc.	844
C M Subs	1159
C&P Restaurant Group, Inc.	290
C.C.H. Restaurant Management Inc.	362
C.G.P. Management Inc.	71
C.H.E.W., Inc.	575
C.J. Poag Enterprises	356
C4 Pizza	1040
Cabazon Indian Enterprises	85
Cabin Coffee Company	382
Cactus Restaurants	1119
Cactus Restaurants Ltd.	1171
Cadete Enterprises Inc.	531
Caesars Entertainment Corporation	725, 741
Caesars of DFW, LLC	967
Cafe Brazil LLC	989
Cafe Fresh Franchising Corp.	1167
Cafe Grumpy	748
Cafe Javasti	1119
Cafe Pesto	375
Cafe Rio Inc.	1075
Cafe Sol Azteca	528
Cafe Spice	763
Cafe Today LLC	872
Cafe Venture Company	1042
Cafe Yumm	861
Cafe Zupas LLC	1077
Cafes Inc.	1108
Caffe Appassionato	1119
Caffe Ladro	1119
Caffe Trieste	150
Caffe Vita, Inc.	1119
Cafua Management Company LLC	527
CAH Enterprises	217
Cain Group	1064
Cain Management Inc.	226
Caison Enterprises	677
Cakemaker Canada Inc.	1166
Cakes and Cones, Inc.	484
Calhoun Management Corporation	921
CaliBurger, LLC	1119
California Banquet Corp.	174
California Burgers and Fries Inc.	177
California Chicken Cafe	74
California Fish Grill	86
California Pizza Kitchen Inc.	65
California Subshine, Inc.	178
California Sunrise, Incorporated	51
California Tortilla Group Inc.	556
Calimira LLC	815
CALJAX, INC.	73
Cal'z Pizza Subs & Chicken Wings	1100
Calzona Foods, Inc.	44
CAM/RB, Inc	843
Camacho's, Inc.	102
CAM-BAS, INC.	157
Cambridge School of Culinary Arts	519
Cameron Mitchell Restaurants LLC	815
Camida Inc.	178
Campero USA	989
Campisi's Restaurants	989
Campiza Foods	1042
Canady Enterprises, Inc.	403
Cane Rosso	989
Cannon Restaurant Management, LLC	959
Canteen Vending Services	23, 38, 46, 114, 158, 198, 241, 259, 388, 396, 425, 481, 625, 654, 660, 661, 678, 689, 925, 953, 989, 1057, 1092
Canterbury Park Holding Corporation	613
Cantinetta	1119
Canyon Fast Foods, Inc.	44
Canyon Properties Inc	760
CAO Bakery & Cafe	256
Cape Atlantic Food Service, LLC	712
Capital Fast Foods, Ltd	931
Capital Restaurant Concepts Ltd	232
Capital Restaurant Group	1082
Capital Tacos	247
Capitol Foods Inc	815
Capitol Subs Group, LLC	971
Caplan Industries	884
Capriotti's Sandwich Shop Inc.	729
Capstone Restaurant Group	190
Capt. George's Seafood Restaurant	1100
Captain D's LLC	960
Captain D's of Pensacola Inc	300
Captain Johnny's	929
Cara Irish Pubs	605
Carbone's Pizza Inc.	612
Cardinal Management Co Inc	672
Carey Hilliard's Restaurants Inc.	369
Caribbean Cinemas	913
Caribbean Restaurants LLC	912
Caribou Coffee Co.	599
Carisch Inc.	614
Carlisle Corporation	954
Carlisle Restaurants Inc.	460
Carl's Jr.	943
Carl's Jr. Region 2	943
Carlyle	768
Carmel Kitchen & Wine Bar	250
Carnagio Enterprises	431
Carney Inc	476
Carolina Pizza Huts, Inc.	658
Carolina Restaurant Group Inc.	654
Carpe Diems Inc.	834
Carr Restaurant Group	421
Carrabba's Italian Grill Inc.	311
Carroll Family Restaurant Group	969
Carson Nugget Inc.	723
Carson's the Place For Ribs	403
Cartee Land Development Inc.	495
Cartel Restaurants, Inc.	332
Carter Enterprises	1044
Carvel Corporation	332
Casa Lupe Restaurants	82
Casa Mia Restaurants	1116
Casa Restaurant Group	447
Casa Rio Mexican Foods	1058
Casanova	379
Cascade Culinary Institute	860
Casciano Traverse City	592
Cascone's	622
Caspers Company	311
Cassano's Inc.	828
Castellucci Hospitality Group	360
Castleberry Investments Inc.	848
Castro Enterprises Inc.	1008
Catalina Restaurant Group Inc.	1018
Catalyst Six, Inc.	1106
Catawba Corporation	1091
Catch Hospitality Group	768
Catlee Inc.	1092
Cattle Baron Restaurants Inc.	722
Cattlemens Inc.	170
Cava Group, Inc.	232
Cazier Enterprises	1112
CBC Restaurant Corp.	989
CBDM Inc.	462
C-Ck's, Inc.	1057
CCreations, LLC	449
CCs Coffee House	496
CCW LLC	689
CEC Entertainment Inc.	1034
Cedar Corporation	69
Cedar Creek Food Group, Inc.	1069
Cedar Fair LLP	838
Cedar Mountain Management, Inc.	221

Entry	Page
Cedar Point	839
Celebration Restaurant Group, LLC	249
Celtic Group, Inc.	326
Centerplate Inc.	228
Centex Subway Inc.	982
CentraArchy Restaurant Management Co.	919
Central California Connection, LLC	140
Central Iowa KFC	383
Central Missouri Pizza Inc.	618
Centurion Restaurant Group	255
Century Casinos Inc.	194
Century Fast Foods Inc.	102
CG Yogurt LLC	180
CGE Management	131
Cha Cha Cha	150
Chairman's Brand Corp.	1190
Chakeres Theatres Inc.	840
Chameleon Group	971
Champagne French Bakery Cafe	142
Chanello's Pizza Inc.	1092
Chang's Mongolian Grill	859
Chanhassen Dinner Theatres	600
Chan's Places	1111
Chanticlear Franchise Systems	597
Chapel Hill Restaurant Group	652
Chappy's Deli	13
CharBar7	669
Char-Hut of America Inc.	253
Charleston Crab House	919
Charleston Foods Inc.	399
Charleston Sports Pub	919
Charlie Brown's Corporation	714
Charlie Graingers Franchising LLC	678
Charlie Palmer Group	768
Charlie's Chicken Franchise Systems	850
Charlie's Food Co. Inc.	752
Charo Chicken Systems Inc.	98
Charter Foods, Inc	957
Charter One Hotels & Resorts	271
Charton Management Inc.	1159
Chartwells Educational Dining Services	795
Chateau Elan Winery & Resort	352
Chattanooga Billiard Club Inc.	938
Cheba Hut Franchising Inc.	208
Checkerboard Restaurants, Inc.	508
Checkers Drive-In Restaurants Inc.	312
Cheddar's Restaurant Holding Corp.	286
Cheeseburger Bobby's Inc.	360
Cheeseburger Restaurants Inc.	130
Cheesetique	1080
Chefs International Inc	710
Chef's Pride Inc.	123
Chelo's Restaurant	915
Chelsea Grille	894
Cherry Berry	206
Cherry Street Coffee House	1120
Chers Restaurant Group, LLC	638
Chesapeake Bay Subs, LLC	920
Chesapeake Hospitality	552
Ches's Snacks Ltd.	1178
Chester's International LLC	13
CHI Management LLC	990
Chicago Connection LLC	388
Chicago Diversified Foods Corp.	430
Chicago Franchise Systems Inc.	431
Chicago Scoops LLC	518
Chicagoland Commissary	403
Chi-Chi's Pizza Inc.	61
Chick Inc.	871
Chick-A-Dilly	509
Chicken Chef Canada Ltd.	1176
Chicken Delight of Canada Ltd.	1176
Chicken Dijon Franchise Corp	110
Chicken Express	1046
Chicken Guy!	268
Chicken Kitchen USA LLC	277
Chicken Salad Chick	3
Chicken Scratch Holdings Inc.	4
Chicken Shacks	497
Chick-fil-A Franchise	1089
Chick-fil-A Franchisee	654
Chick-fil-A Inc.	332
Chickie's and Pete's	875
Chick-N-Bap	745
Chico's Tacos	1009
CHI'LANTRO	971
Chili's Grill & Bar	990
Chill-N Nitrogen Ice Cream	252
Chima Brazilian Steakhouse	256
Chin Management	513
China Grill Management Inc.	769
Chipati Inc.	403
Chipotle Mexican Grill Inc.	117
Chiro Foods Ltd.	1166
Chi's Fine Chinese cuisine	23
Chisholm Enterprises Inc.	471
Choctaw Resort Development Enterprise	641
Chompie's	27
Chop Chop Rice Co.	968
Chop Stop, Inc.	91
Chopt Creative Salad Company	769
Chow Foods Management	1120
Chow Fun Food Group	917
Christian Foods Foods LLC	631
Christos Greek Restaurant	606
Chronic Tacos Enterprises	48
Chuck-A-Rama Buffet Inc.	1075
Chugach Creamery, Inc.	3
Churchill Downs Inc.	485
Church's Chicken	333
Churchs Chicken of Norwalk	119
Chuy's Holdings Inc.	971
Ciccio Restaurant Group	312
Cichos Organization	392
CiCi Enterprises L.P.	983
Cici's Pizza Franchise	938
Cidas, LLC	694
CIELEC-IRONTON, INC.	828
Cilantro Taco Grill	441
Cima Group Inc.	1079
Cimmarusti Holdings	102
CinCin Inc.	898
Cincinnati Subs, LLC	492
Cinco Mexican Cantina	367
Cinema Entertainment Corp	614
Cinema West Theatres	128
Cinemark Holdings Inc.	1049
Cinemas Guzzo	1204
Cineplex Inc.	1191
Cinnabon Franchisee	32, 355, 978
Cinnabon Inc.	334
Cinnaholic Franchising LLC	334
Cinnajims, LLC	1141
Cinnamon's Deli Inc.	471
Cinnaroll Bakeries Ltd.	1163
Cinzetti's Italian Market Restaurants	216
Cipriani International	769
Circle C Corporation	890
Circle N Investment Corp.	21
Ciro's	312
Ciscel Corporation	85
City Barbeque Inc.	822
City Bites Inc.	847
City Brew Coffee	643
City Different Enterprises Inc.	722
City Winery	769
City Wok	124
CJ Foods	102
Cjdq Inc	398
CK Restaurant Group	226
CKE Restaurants Inc.	943
CKMS McDonald's Inc	1011
Clairday Foodservice Enterprises	22
Clancy's Inc.	459
Clara Corporation	218
Clark Cooper Concepts	1020
Classic Cinemas	424
Classic Restaurant Concepts LLC	513
Classic Restaurant Group	708
Classic Restaurants LLC	509
Classico Foods/Pizza Joe's	892
CLB Restaurants	822
CLC Restaurants, Inc.	645
Clean Eatz	678
Clean Juice	654
Clean Plate Restaurants Inc.	1014
Clementine's Restaurants Inc.	590
Clements Management	497
Cliett Inc.	676
CLK Inc.	177
CLK Management Company	604
Clover Food Lab	513
Clover Foods Inc	932
Clover Restaurant Group	543
CLP Corp.	9
Club Cal-Neva Hotel Casino	742
Cluck-U-Corporate	548
Clutch Coffee Bar	669
Clyde's Restaurant Group	233
C-Mac	398
CMK Enterprises	1075
CMR Partners, LLP/CMR Associates, LLC	446
CMX Cinemas	4
Coakley & Williams Hotel Management Co.	552
Coal Fire	550
Coal Vines	990
Coast Hotels & Resorts	1171
Coastal Deli Inc.	983
Coastal Plains Restaurants LLC	665
Coastal QSR	302
Coastal Southern Inc.	273
COBCO Enterprises	804
Cockrum & Cockrum Inc	966
Cocula	421

Company	Page
Coffee & Bagel Brands	213
Coffee & Tea Bar Holdings, LLC	403
Cohn Restaurant Group	142
ColCal Inc.	210
Cold Stone Creamery Inc.	38
Coldwater Investments, Inc.	428
Colectivo Coffee Roasters Inc.	1148
Coleman Enterprises Inc.	1153
Collier Restaurant Group	965
Colomex Inc.	194
Colon Gerena Group	913
Colonial Cafe and Ice Cream Inc.	438
Colonial Williamsburg Foundation	1102
Colorado Bagel Co LLC	198
Colter's Bar-B-Q	990
Colton's Restaurant Group Inc.	23
Columbia Restaurant Group	312
Columbia Sussex Corporation	477
Comida Corporation	31
Coming Attractions Theatres	859
Commac Foods	844
Commonwealth Pizza Inc	1098
Company Kitchen	450
Compass Group Canada Ltd.	1186
Compass Group The Americas	654
Conans Pizza Inc.	972
Concentrics Restaurants	334
Concept Acquisitions II, LLC	260
Concept Entertainment Group	865
Concept Restaurants	194
Concessions International	335
Concord Hospitality Enterprises Co.	672
Concord Hospitality Inc.	687
Concordville Inn	884
Condesa del Mar	394
Conglomerated Host Ltd.	326
Conifer Industries Inc.	562
Connecticut Wings Limited Partnership	231
Connie's Pizza Inc.	403
Connollys Pub & Restaurant	769
Connor Concepts	948
Conrad's Grill	573
Consolidated Management Company	384
Consolidated Restaurant Operations, Inc.	990
Consolidated Restaurants	122
Consolidated Restaurants Inc.	1120
Constant Rock	745
ConSul Hospitality Group	313
Consumer Food Services, L.L.C.	791
Continental Superior Management Group	1020
Conversion Concepts, Inc.	1136
Cook Out Restaurant	677
Cookie Plug	135
Cookies by Design, Inc	1050
CookNSolo, Inc.	898
Cook's Restaurant Group	709
Cooler South Enterprises, LLC	649
Coolgreens	855
Cooper Companies	954
Cooperage	716
Cooper's Hawk Holding Inc.	424
Copeland Investments	479
Copeland's of New Orleans Inc.	503
Copper Branch	1200
Copper Cellar Corporation	948
Coppola's Italian Restaurant	770
COR Enterprises Inc.	250
Cordes Creamery, Inc.	383
Cordua Restaurants LP	1020
CoreLife Eatery, LLC	798
Coriale Enterprises	792
Corky's Old Fashioned Bar-B-Q	954
Cornelius, Vaughn	600
Corner Table Restaurants, LLC	770
Cornerstone Restaurant Group	404
Cornhusker Pj LLC	687
Coromandel	221
Corporate Chefs	524
Cosi Inc.	514
Cosimo's Restaurant Group	763
Costa Vida Management	1070
Costa's Famous BBQ	5
Costley Enterprises, Inc.	857
Cottage Inn Pizza Inc.	565
Cotti Foods	132
Cotton Patch Cafe Inc.	1016
Cougar Enterprises Inc	1146
Coughlin Inc.	1105
Country Cookin' Inc.	1096
Country's Barbecue Inc.	355
Courtesy Corporation	1151
Coury Hospitality	1034
Cousins Sub Systems Inc.	1147
Couto Management Group, LLC	535
Covelli Enterprises	843
Cow Licks, Inc.	824
Cowabunga Inc.	326
Cowboy Chicken Inc.	981
Cowgirl Inc.	770
Coyote Corporation	70
Cozco Management	698
Crab Du Jour	673
Crabby Dick's	236
Cracker Barrel Distribution Center	951
Cracker Barrel Old Country Store Inc.	952
Craft Hospitality	770
Cravco III, LLC	932
Crave America	602
Crave Hot Dogs & Barbecue	678
Crave It Restaurant Group	1188
Craveable Hospitality Group	770
Craveworthy Brands	440
Crazy Crab Associates	927
CRC Brier Creek, LLC	673
Creamery at the Crossing, LLC	651
Creamistry, Inc.	188
Creative Dining Services Inc.	596
Creative Foods Corporation	755
Creighton Enterprises Inc.	185
Creole Cuisine Restaurant Concepts	505
Crepe Delicious	1181
CrepeMaker, Inc.	277
Crescent Group	693
Crescent Vending Company	894
Crest Foods Inc.	1054
Crestline Hotels & Resorts	1084
CRI Longhill	697
Criselda & Edwin Diaz	69
Crisp & Green	614
Crispers Restaurants LLC	270
Cristina's Fine Mexican Restaurant	1040
Cristy's Pizza	829
Crofton Drive Thru, Inc.	547
Crumbl Cookies	1072
Crumbley Enterprises, Inc.	359
Crushed Red	619
CS CHUNG,INC	707
CSC Inc.	576
CT Heros	220
CTK Pizza, LLC	924
Cuisine Management	282
Culinaire International Co.	991
CulinArt Inc.	792
Culinary Institute LeNotre	1020
Culinary Institute of America	758
Culinary Institute of Charleston	931
Culinary Institute of Platt College - Moore	849
Culinary Institute of Platt College - Tulsa	857
Culinary Institute of Savannah	369
Culinary Institute of the Carolinas At Greenville	925
Culinary Studies Institute Oakland	574
Culpepper's	627
Culver Franchising System Inc.	1152
Culver's Frozen Custard Franchisee	212
Cunningham Restaurant Group	451
Cupbop	29
Cupcake Royale	1120
Cura Hospitality	877
Curmac Inc	1058
Curry Up Now	150
Cutchall Management Co.	689
Cutters Point Incorporated	1111
Cutting Edge Pizza LLC	298
Cuzino's Pizza	549
Cypress Inn	15
D & B Pizza Inc	1066
D & B Properties	942
D & D Berg, LLC	685
D & D Enterprises	717
D & D Pizza Inc.	621
D & D Ventures, Inc.	979
D & G Management	931
D & J Holdings LLC	46
D & P Associates	535
D & P Restaurants LLC	1114
D E B Foods Inc	679
D G W Investment, Inc	493
D L G Management Inc	442
D of Alaska Inc	1
D Q Richeson Group	1015
D R Scholz Inc	1064
D W Reed Enterprises Inc	1044
D&M Holdings	92
D&P Ice Cream, L.L.C.	1017
D. Boyd Enterprises Inc.	78
D.C. Ben & Jerry's Ice Cream	1080
D.D. & H. Usry, Inc.	308
D.E. Foods Inc.	524
D.G. Smith Enterprises	138
D.L. Rogers Corporation	1017
D.L. Sells Inc.	942
D.O.C. Restaurant Group LLC, 7 Hills Restaurant L	151

Company	Page
D.R.M. Inc.	690
Da Edoardo Restaurants	579
Da Marco	1020
da Vinci Group	404
Dabney's Incorporated	354
Dacla Foods Inc	681
Daddy Jack's Inc.	451
Dairy Queen	384
Dairy Queen Canada Inc.	1180
Dairy Queen of Lancaster Inc	829
Dairy Queen of Nokomis	433
Dairy Queen of Somerset	495
Dairy Queen of Tyler Inc.	1067
Dairy Queens of Laredo Inc	1040
Dakota Enterprises Inc.	351
Dakota Farms Family Restaurant	685
Dakota Pizza, LLC	684
Daland Corporation	472
D'Alelio Management Company	527
Dallas Jersey Mike's, LP	1035
Dallhaus Ltd	381
Dalton Howell Inc	1040
Daly-Kenney Group	528
Dame Bros Corporation	792
D'Amico & Partners Inc.	606
Damon Morgan Corp.	831
DanBarb Inc.	61
Dancel, L.L.C.	717
Danicia Enterprises	1115
Daniel Blumenstock, Inc. dba McDonald's	627
Danny's	791
Dantanna's	335
Dante's Restaurant Inc.	907
Darden Restaurants Inc.	286
Darmco Corp.	690
Darmody Enterprises	389
Darrel Pereida	302
Dartcor Enterprises Inc.	715
Dat Dog	506
Data Group/Boes Management	822
Dattani Management Corp	287
Datz Restaurant Group	313
Davanni's Pizza & Hot Hoagies	606
Davden, Inc.	690
Dave & Buster's Inc.	991
Dave Magrogan Group	910
Davenport's Restaurant Corp.	916
Dave's Hot Chicken	126
Dave's Mac Inc	133
David A & Kathryn Hunt Inc	662
David and Sun Kim	33
David Briggs Enterprises Inc.	503
David Costa Enterprises	254
David L. Flohr & Steven J. Flohr, PTRS	83
David Moss Management	1021
David Turner Co Inc.	1048
David Vorchheimer LLC	222
Davids Fast Food Inc	357
Davidson Hotels & Resorts	335
Davio's Restaurants Inc.	514
Davis Pizza Enterprises, Inc	641
Daylight Donut Flour Company LLC	857
Dazbog Franchising, LLC	198
DBR Inc	14
DC PIE CO.	198
DCC Lee Enterprises	263
Dcfljji, Llc	256
DCW Investments	851
DD IP Holder	520
DDS Partnership	681
De Dutch Pannekoek House Restaurants Inc.	1171
De La Riva Enterprises	720
De Max Inc.	493
Dean Foods - a Baskin Robbins Distribution Center	113
Dean W. Colley Organization	752
Deanie's Seafood Restaurant	503
Death & Co.	102
DeBest Pizza, Inc.	299
Debo's Diners, Inc.	939
DeClerck Enterprises	188
Dee Jay's Chicken Village	1204
Deek's Pizza	684
Deem Sum International Inc.	151
Deep River Partners	663
Deep Roots FGO, Inc.	682
Deer Valley Ski Resort	1072
Degen Properties	686
Dejas Enterprises	651
Del Frisco's Restaurant Group Inc.	1064
Del Fuego	745
Del Sur Restaurant Group	991
Del Taco Restaurants Inc.	95
Delamor Enterprises, Inc	878
Delaware North	749
Delaware North Parks & Resorts At Yosemite	188
Delectabell Management Inc.	713
Delectable Capital	759
Deli Delicious Franchising Inc.	78
Deli Management Inc.	979
Deli Partners of Oklahoma Lp	1011
Delicious Concepts Restaurant Group	1021
Delights of Carolina Inc.	669
Delmac Management Corp	893
Delman, Inc.	933
Delmarby Inc.	558
Del's Lemonade & Refreshments	914
Deluxe French Fries Limited	1178
DelVecchio's Pizzeria	323
Demeris Barbecue	1021
Demos' Steak and Spaghetti House	958
Denali Foods Inc.	1
Dencan Restaurants Inc.	1172
Denco Family, Inc	186
Denihan Hospitality Group LLC	771
Denny's Astrodome Restaurant Inc	1021
Denny's Corporation	932
Dennys Franchise	55
Den-Tex Central Inc.	1058
Denton's Family Foods	948
DEROCHE GRILLS OF HOUMA, L.L.C.	500
DeRosa Corp.	1154
Desert Dough Company, Inc.	217
Desert Island Restaurants	39
Desert Subway Inc.	27
Desert Venture LLC	729
Desperados Mexican Restaurant	992
Destination Dogs	707
Destination Hotels & Resorts Inc.	207
Destination Kohler	1145
Detail Systems Inc.	747
Devera Management	467
Devika Restaurants Inc.	78
DeVille Foods Inc.	927
DFIT Subs, LLC	177
Dhillon Foods, Inc.	61
Diamond Hospitality	19
Diamondback Pizza, Inc	1068
DiamondRock Hospitality Company	543
DiBella's Old Fashioned Submarines Inc.	793
DiCicco's	79
DiCicco's Italian Restaurants	79
Dickendesher Inc	590
Dickey's Barbecue Restaurants Inc.	992
Dickie Brennan & Co.	506
Dick's Drive In Restaurants	1120
Dig Inn	771
Dig Seasonal Market	771
DiGiovanni Inc.	96
Dilallo Burger	1201
Dill & Parsley Natural Mediterranean	771
Dillas Quesadillas, LLC	1050
Dine Brands Global, Inc.	126
Dining Associates	795
Dining Entertainment Group	771
Dining Group South	920
Dink Inc.	1100
Dino's Pizza USA Inc.	661
Dino's The Greek Place	612
Dinosaur Bar-B-Que	797
DiPasqua Enterprises Inc.	324
Dippin' Dots Franchising Co	493
Dipson Theatres Inc.	800
Dirty Dough	44
Discovery Coffee	1175
Dish Dash, LLC	176
Dish Society	1021
Disneyland Resort	49
Disney's Hollywood Studios	268
Disruptive Restaurant Group	102
District Taco	1085
Diva Espresso	1120
Diverse Concepts	949
Diversified Restaurant Group, LLC	173
Diversified Restaurant Holdings Inc.	591
Dividend Restaurant Group	198
Divine Dining Group	929
Dixie Chili Inc.	492
Dixon Foods Group	679
DJ Clark	1038
DJ Management	1070
DJB Bott LLC	835
DJB Hospitality LLC	1092
DJTC Corp.	215
DK Restaurants	375
DLite Healthy On The Go	39
D'Lites Enterprises Inc.	252
DLR Restaurants LLC	960
DM Burritos, LLC	219
DMG Group	910
Dmor Inc	263
DMT Inc	1091
Doane Family Enterprises	843

Name	Page
Dob-Sab Inc	61
Dobski & Associates Inc.	464
Doc B's Restaurant + Bar	404
Doc Popcorn Franchising Inc.	493
Doctor's Associates Inc.	225
Dodici	793
Dodson Enterprises Inc.	646
Doe's Inc	637
Dog & Duck Family Pubs	928
Dog Haus International LLC	127
Dogfish Head Brewing & Eats	239
Doherty Enterprises Inc.	695
Dolly's Pizza Franchising Inc.	582
Domco Food Services Ltd.	1191
Dome Pizza Inc	681
Dominate Food Services L.P	713
Dominic's Restaurant	628
Domino Pizza Franchise	15
Domino's Distribution Center	83, 121, 199, 221, 260, 374, 555, 586, 601, 631, 662, 1112, 1176
Dominos Franchisee	842
Domino's Franchisee	1, 4, 6, 7, 8, 14, 15, 17, 22, 28, 52, 56, 70, 71, 82, 83, 86, 93, 98, 103, 111, 115, 116, 121, 128, 133, 135, 160, 167, 171, 178, 180, 195, 196, 209, 213, 216, 218, 219, 220, 223, 226, 229, 230, 238, 243, 248, 253, 255, 256, 258, 260, 267, 270, 272, 273, 274, 277, 282, 283, 287, 297, 300, 301, 302, 304, 306, 308, 313, 319, 351, 354, 355, 356, 357, 361, 362, 367, 373, 380, 381, 382, 385, 390, 392, 393, 398, 399, 427, 462, 464, 478, 481, 492, 494, 499, 508, 511, 519, 521, 522, 523, 526, 530, 531, 532, 534, 537, 549, 550, 559, 561, 564, 568, 573, 580, 595, 596, 598, 603, 610, 611, 613, 616, 621, 626, 627, 628, 634, 635, 636, 637, 643, 647, 651, 659, 662, 665, 668, 673, 675, 676, 677, 679, 696, 697, 699, 701, 703, 708, 712, 713, 717, 743, 745, 746, 752, 753, 755, 758, 761, 762, 763, 772, 791, 792, 795, 798, 801, 802, 808, 821, 824, 825, 830, 832, 835, 837, 843, 844, 847, 848, 851, 852, 858, 860, 861, 862, 863, 864, 870, 871, 873, 876, 877, 878, 881, 882, 885, 886, 888, 889, 890, 892, 906, 909, 911, 916, 917, 918, 924, 920, 932, 930, 939, 941, 952, 965, 966, 972, 978, 982, 992, 1007, 1008, 1009, 1017, 1021, 1037, 1038, 1039, 1040, 1044, 1047, 1050, 1055, 1068, 1073, 1082, 1084, 1090, 1092, 1097, 1098, 1103, 1105, 1109, 1110, 1111, 1117, 1135, 1137, 1140, 1141, 1148, 1151, 1152, 1153, 1154, 1155, 1156, 1162
Domino's Inc.	553
Domino's Pizza Chicago	442
Domino's Pizza Inc	565
Domino's Pizza New Bedford	528
Don Cherry's Grapevine Restaurants Inc.	1189
Don Juan Mex Grill	882
Don Mc Entire	893
Don Pan International Bakery	278
Don Pedro's Family Mexican Restaurant	1161
Don Tortaco	729
Dona Maria Tamales	730
Donald Alan Worst Inc	579
Donald McGregor Investment Ltd	1163
Donald Trager	436
Donaldson Enterprises Inc.	369
Donatos Pizzeria LLC	815
Don's Crabs Inc.	555
Don's Seafood	503
Doolittles Restaurants	606
Dorney Park & Wildwater Kingdom	873
DORO Incorporated	1142
Dorsey Culinary Academy	588
Dos Toros	772
Double A Foods Inc.	270
Double G Partners	183
Double O Inc. / Exceptional Brands LLC	966
Double P Corporation	404
Double S Foods L.L.C.	872
Double T Diner	541
DoubleDave's Pizzaworks Systems Inc.	972
Dough Boy's California Pizza	1100
Dough Management Inc.	614
Dough Nation Headquarters LLC	1058
Dough Pac, Inc.	686
Doughnuttery	772
Dover Downs Gaming & Entertainment Inc.	237
Dow Sherwood Corporation	313
Downtown Dining	114
DP Inc	237
DPNK	1141
DPNK Inc.	1152
DPQ Ventures Inc	85
Dq Treat Franchisee	216
Dr Smood Group Inc	278
Dr. Sweet Tooth	97
Drago Enterprises Corp.	53
Dragon House, LLC	246
Drain Enterprises Inc.	14
Draper Development LLC	743
DREAM ROLLS, LLC	1013
Dream Team Pizza, LLC	625
Dreamland Holding LLC	5
DRG Concepts	992
Drifter's Hamburgers	195
D's of Kentucky, Inc.	829
D's of Ohio	830
DSC	463
DST Enterprises	1071
DTCT, Inc.	404
DTH Enterprises	1042
Dtox Juice	336
DTR Subs, Inc.	58
Duale Industries Inc	379
Dublin Foods Inc.	357
Duce Restaurants	1139
Duck Donuts Franchising Company	891
DuClaw Brew Co.	541
Dufficy Enterprises, Inc	523
Duff's Buffet	246
Duffy's Management Inc.	270
Dukart Management	240
Duke Unlimited Inc.	504
Duke's Restaurants	1121
Dumser's Restaurants	555
Dunafon Enterprises Inc.	619
Dunkin' Donuts Franchise	219, 220, 221, 229, 525, 538, 560, 697, 701, 709, 761, 916
Dunkin' Donuts of Wethersfield	231
Dunn Bros. Coffee Franchising Inc.	606
Dunn-Bowling LLC	803
Dunston's Prime Steak House	992
Du-par's Restaurants	103
Durango Restaurants, LLC	1064
Durhan Sub Shop	677
Dutch Bros. Coffee	862
Dutchman Hospitality	833
Dwd Pizza Company Inc	984
DWG Enterprises, LLC	31
E & B Industries Inc.	1162
E & G Franchise Systems Inc.	1142
E&I Holdings Inc.	199
E.A.P. Management Corp.	261
E.L.F. Development	808
Eagle Eye Pizza	861
Earl of Sandwich LLC	287
Earle Enterprises LP	706
Earth Burger	1058
East Coast Tavern Group	514
East Coast Wings Corp.	679
East Hampton Sandwich Co.	993
East of Chicago Pizza Company	830
East Side Mario's Restaurants Inc.	1198
Eastbay Equities Inc.	129
Eat Here Brands	639
EAT Pizza LLC	582
Eat Well Inc.	525
Eat With Us Group	636
Eat'n Park Hospitality Group Inc.	887
EatRamen Holdings LLC	221
Eatzi's Market & Bakery	993
Eau-D Inc.	1142
Ebb Tide Beach Club	522
Eckceed Eckspectations, LLC	451
ECS Partnership	595
Ed Razban	964
Ed Reese	805
Eddie Cheng Corporation	80
Eddie's Restaurant	389
Eden Resort & Suites	889
Edgewood Resort & Conference Center	744
Edley's Bar-B-Que	960
EDN Inc.	325
Edo Japan Inc.	1163
eegee's Inc.	46
Effin Egg	262
Egg Works	730
Eggheadz LLC	485
Eggs Up Grill	931
El Borracho	1121
El Charro Enterprises	46
El Encanto Restaurants	26
El Gallo Giro	168
El Guero Canelo	47
El Mariachi	557
El Mercado	972
El Meson de Felipe Inc.	913
El Paso Mexican Grill	510
El Pollo Loco Holdings, Inc.	993

El Pollo Loco Inc. 66
El Porton Mexican Restaurant Inc. 368
El Taco Tote Franchise Systems Ltd. 1009
El Tiempo Cantina................................ 1021
El Toreo 124
El Toro Mexican Restaurants 1137
El Vaquero 816
Eldorado Diner Corp. 754
Elemental Pizza LLC.............................. 1121
Elephant & Castle Inc.............................. 772
Elephants Delicatessen............................ 865
Eli Zabar Inc. 772
Elite Restaurant Concepts 169
Elite Restaurant Group............................... 91
Elite Team LP 1046
Elizabeth's Pizza 663
Ellianos Coffee 269
Elly's Brunch & Cafe 404
ELM Restaurant Group 972
Elmer's Restaurants Inc. 865
El-T Mexican Restaurants Inc. 978
Eltana Wood-Fired Bagel Cafe 1121
Elway's 199
EM Pizza Inc 127
Emagine Entertainment LLC................... 586
Emerald Cascade Restaurant Systems, Inc.
.... 742
Emerald City Foods, Inc......................... 1116
Emerald City Pizza................................. 1116
Emerald Foods Inc 980
Emerging Brands Inc................................ 852
Emilio's Tapas Restaurant........................ 427
Emjo, Inc. 128
Enchiladas Restaurant & Catering Corp. .. 993
Encore Foods Inc 359
Encore Restaurants 993
Encore Restaurants Inc........................... 1017
Engel Management Services 973
Engen Enterprises..................................... 185
England Foods 945
Enigma Investments Inc........................... 912
Entertainment Cruises.............................. 405
Entertainment Properties Group, Inc 993
Envision Foods, LLC............................... 182
Epeck, Inc. 1158
Epic Burger, Inc. 405
Epic Wings 142
Epoch Five Enterprises LLC 812
Epoch Hospitality Group 586
EPSI Inc. 1008
Erbe Pizza I, Inc. 635
Eric Drake 902
Erik's DeliCafe Inc. 158
Erwen Management Corp 655
Esbenshade, Inc 925
Escalante's Mexican Restaurant 1022
Escape Enterprises Ltd. 816
ESCH Inc 25
Escoffier School of Culinary Arts Boulder . 190
ES-O-EN Corp. 391
Espresso Vivace, Inc.............................. 1121
Essen Foods 531
Essig Management Co. Inc. 626
Estel Foods Inc 427
Estiatorio Milos 772

Estimated Profit, LLC.............................. 922
Ethan Stowell Restaurants 1121
Eugene Forbes Enterprises 1098
Eureka Fortune, Inc. 111
Eureka System Corp. 19
Eureka! Restaurant Group 83
Eurest Dining Services 433, 804, 878, 884
Everbowl 183
EverFresh Endeavors, LLC 288
Evergreen Burgers 1111
Evergreens 1122
Everytable 103
Evolution Hospitality LLC 141
EVOS Holdings, LLC 313
Ewing-Dunn, Inc 655
Excel Investments 617
Exceptional Restaurant Co. 365
Exline Inc. 954
Experiential Brands 336
Ezell's Famous Chicken 1122
F & D Huebner LLC 662
F B Enterprises Inc. 533
F F & A 925
F W L & Sons Inc 1094
F&J Ventures 773
F. McLintocks Inc. 171
F.J.D. Fast Food Corp. 714
Fado Pubs Inc. 336
FAF Incorporated 682
Fainting Goat Gelato 1122
Fairfield Creamery, LLC......................... 222
Fairground Foods LLC.......................... 1033
Fairmont Hotels & Resorts Inc. 1191
Fajita Pete's 1022
Fala Bar 103
Falcon Holdings Management LLC 1068
Falcons Restaurant Group, LLC/ Chunara
    Food Group.. 372
Famiglia - DeBartolo, LLC 799
Family Entertainment Centers 1148
Family Restaurants Inc. 199
Famoso Neapolitan Pizzeria Inc............ 1170
Famous Amos Restaurants Inc. 263
Famous Anthony's 1096
Famous Brands International 192
Famous Five Dining Inc.......................... 944
Famous Foods of Muskegon Inc 585
Famous Foods of Richmond Inc............. 460
Famous Recipe Fried Chicken of Lima Inc 830
Famous Toastery 659
Famous Wok Inc. 1170
Fantabulous Cakes and Cones 695
Fantastic Foods Inc 539
Far West Restaurant Group LLC............ 166
Faris Properties LLC.............................. 940
Farm Burger LLC 356
Farmer Boys Food Inc. 135
Farmers Restaurant Group...................... 553
Farnsworth Enterprises 562
Farooqi Restaurant Management, Inc...... 142
Farsei Inc 1107
Fast Food Enterprises 320
Fast Food Management, Inc................... 913
Fat Boy's Pizza 504
Fat Brands, Inc. 53

Fat City Inc. 138
Fat Mo's 936
Faz Restaurants Management 129
Fazoli's Restaurant LLC 481
FazWest Group, Inc. 632
FB Society 994
FDF Restaurant Brandz 1167
Fearrington House 671
Feast BBQ... 485
FEAST Foods, LLC 116
FEC Management 547
Feel Good Brands, LLC 723
Feist Family Enterprises LLC 94
Fellini's Pizza Inc. 336
Ferber & Sons Inc. 299
Ferd'nand LLC 1122
Ferrari's Italian Villa 967
Feta & Olives Inc. 1192
Fez Fine Moroccan Cuisine 898
FIC Restaurants 538
Fiesta Ole Inc. 390
Fifth Group Restaurants 336
Fifty Seven Corporation 617
Fig & Olive Holding LLC 773
Figaro's Italian Pizza Inc. 871
Figlio Wood-Fired Pizza 816
Fiiz 1074
Filimex L.L.C. 33
Filippi's Pizza Grottos 142
Finagle A Bagel 529
Finally Fondue 831
Finally, Inc. 644
Fincher's Barbecue & Catering 362
Fins Tropicali Cuisine 697
Fiorella's Jack Stack Barbecue 622
Fire & Vine Hospitality 1122
Fire Brigade Restaurant Group, Inc. 928
Fire Marshall's, LLC 509
Fire Wings 138
Firebird Restaurant Group 994
Firebirds International 655
Firebox, LLC 297
Fired Pie, Inc. 33
Firehook Bakery & Coffeehouse 1082
Firehouse Restaurant Group Inc.............. 263
Fireman Hospitality Group 773
Firenza Pizza Franchise LLC 1080
Fireside Restaurant Company 930
Firestat, LLC 241
First Kenosha Kentucky Fried Chicken, Inc
.... 1144
First Star Partners LLC 240
First Street Station 1162
First Sun Management............................ 932
First Watch Restaurants Inc.................... 246
Fitness Food Holdings Inc. 973
Five Guys Holdings Inc. 1089
Five Olsons LLC..................................... 527
Five on Black 645
Five Star Foodservice Inc. 939
Five Star Pizza 259
Fixe Restaurant 973
Fiyi Development, Inc........................... 1013
FJ Catalano Company 524
FJH Investment Co 568

2025 Chain Restaurant Operators — Alpha Index

Flagship Restaurant Group 690
Flanigan's Enterprises Inc. 256
Flatbread, Inc. 694
Flatstick Pub 1112
Flea Street Cafe 111
Flippers Pizzeria Franchising LLC 288
Flippin' Pizza International LLC 172
Florida Pizza Management 271
Florida Success Management Group LLC 648
Flying Buffalo Inc. 325
Flying Food Group Inc. 405
Flying Pie 865
Flying Star Cafe 717
Flynn Restaurant Group LLC 151
Flynn/Meyer Co. 755
Flyrite Chicken Inc. 973
Focaccia Market & Bakery 151
Focused Management Experts Inc. 832
Fogle Enterprises 617
Fogo de Chao Inc. 1050
Foley Food & Vending Company Inc. 530
Folks Restaurant Management Group 353
FOMO Investments LLC 152
Food Concepts International LLP 1042
Food Express Inc. 663
Food Folks and Fun of Virginia, LLC 1100
Food Franchise Corporation of America, LLC 1014
Food Masters, Inc. 673
Food Service Property Corporation 700
Food Systems Unlimited Inc. 272
FoodFirst Global Restaurants Inc. 288
Foods Management Group LLC 973
Foodtastic 1203
Foosackly's 12
Foothill Pizza Inc 149
FOR Northwest LLC 1114
Forbes Mill Steakhouse 109
Ford Restaurant Group 1039
Fordham Foods (USA), Inc. 801
Fords Colony Country Club 1103
Foreman Wolf Restaurant Group 541
Fork & Salad Maui 378
Fort Smith 3 Inc. 21
Fortel's Pizza Den 615
Fortner Foods 958
Forty Niner Shops Inc. 98
Forza LLC 1138
Foster's Freeze LLC 130
Foster's Grille Inc. 1087
Founders Table Restaurant Group 773
Four Corners Taco Inc. 720
Four Cousins Burgers & Fries of NH. LLC 757
Four M Capital LLC 800
Four Queens Inc. 730
Four Seasons Hotels and Resorts 1192
Four Star Pizza Inc 909
Fourjay L.L.C. 24
Fourteen Foods 607
Fox & Hound Restaurant Group 994
Fox Restaurant Concepts 33
FPS Inc. 534
Francesca Restaurants LLC 423
Franchise Finders Inc. 663
Franchise Foods Systems, Inc. 612

Franchise Management Systems Inc. 398
Franchise Operations Inc. 837
Franco's Pizza 797
Frank Butler 647
Frank DePasquale Ventures 514
Frank Entertainment 266
Frank Pepe's Development Company LLC 224
Frankie's Franchise Systems 230
Franklin Services 826
Frant Corporation Inc. 751
FranWorks Franchise Corp. 1163
FRC Enterprises 845
Freddy's LLC 472
Frederick & Palmer, Inc 753
Fred's Fish Fry Inc. 1058
Freebirds World Burrito 973
Freedom Square Diner 880
Freeman Enterprises 115
Freeman Pizza Companies, Inc. 97
FreeRange Concepts 994
Freeway Lanes Bowling Group 845
Fresco by Scotto 773
Fresh Ale Pubs 1
Fresh and Healthy Brands 1169
Fresh Brothers 103
Fresh City 528
Fresh Concepts, LLC 604
Fresh Dining Concepts 254
Fresh Hospitality LLC 960
Fresh Ideas Food Service Management LLC 619
Fresh On The Grill Inc 158
Fresh Subs & Salads Inc 940
Freshens Quality Brands 337
Freshii Inc. 1193
Freshly Squeezed Franchise Corporation 1184
Fresquez Inc. 717
Frfc Springfield, Inc. 835
Fricker's USA 833
Friendly Franchisees Corp 93
Frisbie Management Inc. 128
Frisch's Restaurants Inc. 809
Froio Management 521
Frontier Enterprises 1059
Frost Management 273
Frugals 1117
Frutta Bowls Franchising LLC 701
FSC Franchise Co., LLC 313
FTM Enterprises, LLC 852
Fuddruckers Restaurants LLC 1022
Fudpuckers Beachside Bar & Grill 254
Fuego Tortilla Grill 982
Fuel Coffee 1122
Fugate Enterprises 472
Fuji Bakery 1122
Fulenwider Enterprises 669
Full House Resorts Inc. 730
Full Moon BBQ 10
Funck's Family Restaurants 874
FUSIAN 816
Fuzzy's Taco Shop 1035
FWC Enterprises 499
FX4 LLC 29
G & L Simons 625
G & M Waterloo, Inc 387

G & S Restaurants 569
G F I Inc 374
G R & M Foods, Inc. 1166
G R N J R Inc 604
G&H Enterprises Inc. 360
G.A. Food Services 303
G.F. Vasey Holdings, LLC 222
G.K.A.M.A. 397
G.V.C.S. 1043
g3 Restaurant Group 902
GA Enterprises Inc. 82
Gaido's of Galveston Inc. 1015
Gala Corporation 66
Galardi Group 87
Galaxy Theatres, LLC 172
Galco Foods 134
Gallagher's Steak House 774
GALO Enterprises 249
Gandolfo's DeliBoys 361
Gar Woods Grill & Pier 60
Garces Restaurant Group Inc. LLC 898
Gardunos 717
Garibaldi's Inc. 428
Garland Restaurants 475
Garlic Jim's Franchise Corp. 1115
Garozzo's Ristorante 467
Gary 1098
Gary and Becky Vick Inc 140
Gas Investments Corporation 1037
Gaspare's Pizza House and Italian Restaurant 152
Gastronomy Inc. 1075
Gate Gourmet Division Americas 1093
Gates Bar-B-Q Inc. 623
Gateway Casinos & Entertainment Inc. 1167
Gator Domino's Pizza 259
Gators Dockside Group 270
Gaunce Management INC 479
GB Restaurants Inc./Top Line Restaurants. 27
GBB Hospitality Group, LLC 980
GBMO LLC 865
GBR Pizza Inc 677
GC Partners Inc. 680
GC Southwest Holding Company 259
GCGC Fair 547
GCP Enterprises, Inc. 132
GCW Corporation 1072
GDK Development Inc. 906
CDK CO INC. 1067
Gecko Grill Enterprises LLC 29
Gecko's Hospitality Group 304
Gehrig Enterprises 502
GEN Restaurant Group, Inc. 61
Gen3 Hospitality 730
Gencarelli's 710
Gene & Georgetti 405
General Hotels Corporation 451
Genesh, Inc. 466
George Martin Restaurant Group 794
George Webb Corp. 1154
Georgia Theatre Company 369
Georgine's Restaurant 909
Gerald M. Liss Co. Inc. 805
Ger-Del, LLC 974
Gerrie N Eddie's Restaurants Inc 452

Alpha Index

GetFried Franchise USA LLC 680
GFJ Hospitality Group, Inc. 186
Ghai Management Services,Inc. 129
Ghassan's Inc. 664
Ghirardelli Chocolate Company 161
GI Entertainment and Restaurant Group Inc.
.... 314
GIA Enterprises Inc. 1107
Giacomo's Ristorante 514
Gialil Food Services 761
Gianny Corp 405
Giardino Enterprises 278
Gibson Restaurant Group 405
Gigi's Cupcakes Inc. 91
Gilbert & Sons Inc. 632
Gilbertson Restaurants L.L.C. 626
Gilchrist Enterprises 288
Gill Guys Group LLC 443
Gilley Enterprises 510
Gilligan's Management Co. 927
Gimme! Coffee 759
Gina's Pizza Inc. 117
Ginger Beef Choice Ltd. 1163
Gino's Pizza 1157
Gionino's Pizzeria Inc. 841
Giordano's Enterprises Inc. 406
Giovanni's Pizza 474
Giovanni's Pizza Inc. 474
Glacier Restaurant Group LLC 647
Glazier Works 774
Glazing Saddles LLC 981
Glencoe Management, Inc. 731
Glenhaven Management Company 458
Glg Corp. 524
Global Concessions, Inc. 337
Global Development LLC 682
Global Italian Food LLC 281
Global Miami J.V. 278
Global Orange Development 573
Gloria's Latin Cuisine 995
Gloria's Restaurants 995
Glory Days Inc 551
Glowbal Restaurant Group Inc. 1172
GLS Foods LLC 718
GLS Investments Inc. 383
GMC Enterprises Inc. 983
Go Get Em Tiger (GGET) 182
Go Green Subs, Llc 937
Go To Steve's 307
Goa Taco 774
Godfather's Pizza, Inc. 690
Godlove Enterprises Inc 139
Goecker Enterprises Inc. 923
Gold Coast Dogs Inc. 406
Gold Coast Holdings 164
Gold Hat 539
Gold Star Chili Inc. 809
Goldberg's Bagel Co. & Deli 337
Golden Alliance, Inc. 833
Golden Buddha 353
Golden Cone Inc 391
Golden Corral Corp. 673
Golden Corral East Region 674
Golden Dream 1022
Golden Entertainment 731

Golden Franchising Corp. 1054
Golden Hawk LLC 227
Golden Ice Cream LLC 796
Golden Krust Caribbean Bakery Inc. 747
Golden Nugget Inc. 731
Golden Nugget Pancake House 406
Golden Pear Corp. 796
Golden Plate, LLC 446
Golden Rule Franchising Inc. 11
Golden Spirit, LTD 836
Golden Spoon Franchising Inc. 132
Golden Star Theaters 892
Goldsmith Development, Inc. 925
Goldwing Ventures Inc. 827
Gomez Enterprises LLC 526
Gondola Pizza Incomparable Canada 1981
Ltd. 1176
Gong Cha Tea, LLC 760
Good Earth Cafes Ltd. 1164
Good Food Guys 152
Good Stuff Restaurants 134
Good Times Restaurants Inc. 214
Goodcents Fresh Deli Subs 463
Goode Co. Restaurants 1022
Goodfellas Pizzeria 481
Goodman Vending & Food Service 906
Goodrich Quality Theatres Inc. 581
Goodwin Family Foods, LLC 807
GoodWood Barbecue Company 391
Goose Island Beer Co. 406
Gosh Enterprises Inc. 816
Gotham City Restaurant Group 774
GoTo Foods 337
Gotta Luv Pizza Inc 50
Gourmet Services Inc. 338
Gourmet To Go 628
Gouverneur Inc. 1201
Governor's Restaurant 562
GPF, Inc. 12
GPK Enterprises, Inc. 167
GPR Hospitality, LLC/FG Oaks, LLC 945
GPS Hospitality, LLC 338
GR8 Plate Hospitality 980
GR8 Subs Corporation 167
Grade Inc 512
Grady's Bar-B-Q 894
Graeter's Inc. 809
Graffiti Junktion 288
Graham Crackas Inc. 362
Graham Foods 655
Graham Management 906
Grain & Berry 298
Grand Central Baking Comany 866
Grand Central Restaurant Group 774
Grand Junction Subs 681
Grand Traverse Pie Co. 593
Grand Traverse Resort & Spa 595
Grandma's Restaurant Company 600
Graspointner Management, Inc. 61
Graviss McDonald's Restaurants 495
Graziano's Group 255
Great American Cookies 365
Great American Food Corporation 1033
Great American Holding Co. 283
Great American Hotel Group, Inc 694

Great American Restaurant Properties Inc.
.... 189
Great American Restaurants 1084
Great Bons, Inc. 747
Great Canadian Gaming Corporation 1187
Great Circle Family Foods LLC 99
Great Food Services LLC 655
Great Harvest Bread Co. 644
Great Lakes Creamery LLC 445
Great Lakes Culinary Institute 593
Great Outdoor Sub Shop Inc. 1045
Great Restaurants 634
Great Service Restaurants LLC 321
Great Texas Foods 1047
Great Western Pacific Inc. 1123
Great White Bites, LLC 850
Great Wolf Resorts Inc. 1145
Great Wraps Inc. 338
Greater Grinders Inc. 1092
Greater Huntington Theatre Corporation .1156
Greater Kentucky Corporation 475
Greek From Greece - GFG Bakery 703
Greek Islands 407
Greek's Pizzeria-Pizza Forum 446
Greektown Holdings LLC 572
Green & Tonic 220
Green Apple Ventures 323
Green Beans Coffee Company LLC 163
Green Leaf Vietnamese Restaurant 1123
Green Mill Restaurants Inc. 612
Greenberry's Coffee & Tea Company ... 1082
Greenleaf Gourmet Chopshop 103
Greentree Enterprises Inc. 873
Greggco Management Co. 587
Gregg's Restaurants Inc. 915
Gregory Enterprises, Inc 462
Greg's Volcano Pizza Inc. 445
Grelyn of Maui 378
Griff's of America Inc. 1054
Griggs Enterprises Inc. 509
Grill Concepts, Inc. 187
GrillSmith LLC 314
Grimaldi's Pizza 39
Grinders Above & Beyond 837
Gringo's Mexican Kitchen 1039
Grinner's Food Systems Ltd. 1179
GRK Greek Kitchen 407
Grotto Pizza Inc. 239
Grotto's Commisary 237, 238
Groucho's Franchise System, LLC 922
Ground Pat'i Inc. 501
Ground Zero Management 72
Grounds for Coffee 1072
Groupe St-Hubert 1201
Growth Management Corporation 688
Growth Restaurants Inc. 696
GRP Management Inc. 908
GS Beaumont Enterprise 1065
GSAHTC, Inc. 143
GSW Inc 1082
GT Pizza Inc. 827
GTM Restaurant Corp. 889
Guac & Roll, LLC 233
Guapo's Restaurants 233
Guberman Groupe Ltd. 1177

Company	Page
Guckenheimer Enterprises	162
Guerrieri Management, Inc.	248
Guest Counts Hospitality	899
Guest Services Inc.	1085
Guests Inc	598
Gul Food Management, Inc.	48
Gulf States Restaurant Management LLC	10
Gunter Enterprises, Inc.	674
Gurbachan, Grewal	180
Gus Chima	175
Gus's Franchisor, LLC	945
Gusto Farm to Street	544
Guten Foods, Inc.	866
Guthrie Franchise Corp.	4
Guy and Larry Restaurants	39
Guy Fieri Signature Restaurants	541
Gyarmathy & Associates Inc.	282
Gypsy Cab Co.	303
Gyroville	256
H and H Restaurants Inc.	425
H and R Family Foods Inc	928
H B Restaurants, Inc.	995
H H Hall Management Corp	686
H Town Restaurant Group	1023
H&H West, LLC	96
H&R Restaurants LLC	11
H&R Restaurants-Oregon, LLC	873
H. James Rippon Enterprises	901
H. Salt of Southern California Inc.	115
H.B. Boy's LLC	1075
H.D.S. of Beaver Falls Inc.	876
H.I. Development Corporation	314
H.J. Wings & Things	370
H.N. Fernandez Inc.	506
H.W. Holdings Corporation	215
Habiger Enterprises	628
Hablinski Investments Inc.	969
Hacienda Colorado	199
Hacienda Mexican Restaurants	461
Hackney's on Lake Inc.	426
Hagan & Hagan Inc.	670
Hai Hospitality	974
Hakimianpour Restaurant Group	103
Hakkasan Group	731
Hal Smith Restaurant Group	850
Halal Guys Franchisee Dallas	995
Halal or Nothing, LLC	66
Halcyon	974
Hale and Hearty Soups Inc.	775
Halekulani Corp	375
Half Shell	955
Haljohn San Antonio Inc.	1059
Hall Drive Ins Inc.	459
Hallrich Incorporated	840
Halo Country LLC	570
Hamburger Mary's International LLC	184
Hamco Inc.	429
Hammer Management, Inc.	583
Hammock Restaurants, LLC	1055
Hamner Enterprises	24
Hampshire House Corp	514
Hamra Enterprises	632
Han Dynasty	899
Handel's Homemade Ice Cream & Yogurt	806
Hankins Development Corp	918
Hannah's Bretzel	407
Hanna's Systems	237
Hanner Enterprises	1106
Hannon's Food Service	642
Hapa Group Inc	190
Happi House Restaurants, LLC	158
Happy + Hale	674
Happy Day Restaurants	391
Happy Jack's	525
Happy Joe's Pizza & Ice Cream Parlor Inc.	380
Happy Mexican	955
Happy People Pizza Inc	644
Happy's Pizza LLC	574
Harbor Santa Barbara Inc.	167
Hard Times Cafe	1098
Hardee's Food Systems Inc.	944
Hardee's of Waupaca Inc	1154
Harkins Amusement Enterprises	39
Harloe Management	542
Harman Management Corp.	100, 179, 1071, 1113
Har-Mar Foods Inc.	604
Harmon Brewing Co., L.L.C.	1138
Harold's Chicken Shacks	394
Harraseeket Inn	561
Harris County Smokehouse	1023
Harris Group Inc.	353
Harrison Foods, LLC	7
Harry's Hospitality Group	240
Harry's of America	263
Hart Hotels Inc.	750
Hart Management Inc.	686
Hart Restaurant Management, Inc.	984
Hartford Pike Donuts	533
Hartford Restaurant Group	223
Hartread, Inc.	563
Hart's Ventures, LLC	940
Hartz Franchise Restaurants Ltd	1064
Harvest Restaurants	707
Harvey Cedars Shellfish Co.	702
Harvey Management Corporation	701
Hasta la Pasta Italian Grill	1037
Hat Creek Burger Company	1068
Hattie B's Hot Chicken	961
Hawaiian Bros Island Grill	616
Hawkers Asian Street Fare	289
Hazel-Wen, Inc.	886
HC Restaurant Group Inc.	407
HDOS Enterprises	54
Healthy Acquisitions Corp	518
Heart Coffee Roasters	866
Heart of America Group	431
Heartland Beef	443
Heartland Brewery Inc.	775
Heartland Restaurant Group LLC	902
Heavenly Scent Pizza LLC	982
Heavy B, LLC	626
Heavy Restaurant Group	1123
HEI Hotels and Resorts	227
Heidi's Family Restaurants Inc.	174
Heine Brothers	485
Heirloom Hospitality Group, LLC	569
Heisner Enterprises Partnership	428
Helm Restaurants	509
Helms Foodservice	269
Hemisphere Restaurant Partners LLC	607
Henley Restaurants Ltd	158
Hennessey's Tavern Inc.	134
Heritage Restaurant Brands	161
Herkimer Coffee	1123
Hero Certified Burgers	1193
Hero Systems Inc.	866
Herrell's Developement Corporation	530
Herrick Foods, LLC	48
Hersha Hospitality Trust	885
Hershey Entertainment & Resort Co.	886
Herslip Management	684
HEW Inc.	1093
Hibachi Steakhouse	899
Hickory Falls Wood-Fired Grille & Bar LLC	966
Hielan Management LLC	1018
High Tech Burrito	70
Highland Food Express, Inc.	53
Highland House Inc.	579
Highlands Bar & Grill	5
Hill Management LLC	863
Hillcrest Foods Inc.	372
Hillsborough Donuts Inc.	702
Hillstone Restaurant Group Inc.	54
Hilltop Ale Houses	1123
Hilton Atlanta Airport	339
Hilton Canada	1186
Hilton Worldwide Holdings Inc.	1090
Himalaya Holdings LLC	429
Himco, Inc.	644
Himmel Hospitality Group	515
Hines Sudden Service	232
Hip Hop Fish & Chicken	542
Hip Stone, Inc.	238
Hishmeh Enterprises	181
HJ Dana Enterprises	968
HLC Foods of Carrollton, LLC	353
HLC Foods, LLC	367
HLR Scoopers, LLC	587
Hlw Fasttrack Inc.	805
HMR Pretzel LLC	1055
HMSHost Corporation	544
Ho Wah	802
HOA Restaurant Group LLC	339
Hobeau Inc	1040
Hobee's California Restaurants	158
Hodges Management Co.	372
Hoff Enterprises	924
Hofman Hospitality Group	172
Hog Wild Pit Bar-B-Q	472
Hogan Management Company	518
Hogsalt Hospitality	407
Hojeij Branded Foods	339
Hokulia Shave Ice	1070
Holland Enterprises LLC	1157
Holland Subs, Inc.	807
Holloway Lodging Corporation	1179
HOL-MC Inc.	966
Holowicki Enterprises Inc.	827
Holy City Hospitality	920
Holy Hog Barbecue Franklin LLC	314
Home Grown Hospitality	920
Home Management Group	920
Home on the Range	

Name	Page
Folse Tramonto Restaurant Devel	506
Home Run Inc.	949
Home Run Inn Inc.	443
Home-Grown Industries Of Georgia	339
Homegrown Restaurant Concepts	340
Homegrown Sustainable Sandwich Shop	1123
Homer's Pizza, INC.	216
Homestead Restaurant & Lounge	693
Hometown Pizza	480
Honey Bear's BBQ	34
Honey Dew Associates Inc.	532
Honeybee Foods Corporation	62
Honeygrow	899
Hook & Reel Cajun Seafood & Bar	755
Hoot Owl Corporation	500
Hooters Management Corp.	250
HOOTWinc LLC	75
Hoover Foods Inc.	373
Hopdoddy Burger Bar Inc.	974
Hopkins and Company	340
Hospitality Consultants Inc.	244
Hospitality Management Corp.	995
Hospitality Management Group Inc.	921
Hospitality Partners	544
Hospitality Restaurant Group Inc.	761
Hospitality Restaurants Inc.	824
Hospitality Syracuse	762
Hoss's Steak & Sea House Inc.	881
Host Hotels & Resorts Inc.	545
Hostmark Hospitality Group	439
Hot Harry's Fresh Burritos, Inc.	532
Hot Head Burritos	828
Hot Lips Pizza	866
Hot N Juicy Crawfish	233
Hot Sauce Williams Barbeque	813
Hot Tacos, Inc.	30
HotBox Pizza	452
Hotcakes Inc.	143
Hotel duPont	240
Hotlinez of West Georgia, Inc.	354
Hotshots Sports Bar & Grill	625
Houchens Food Group, Inc.	476
House of An	169
House of Kobe	460
Houston Pizza Franchise Ltd	1205
Houston Pizza Venture LP	1023
Houston Restaurant Group, LLC	1023
Howley Bread Group, Ltd	916
HPH	775
Hsu's at Peachtree Center	340
Hubbard & Cravens Coffee	452
Huck Finn Restaurants	408
Huddle House Distribution Center	340
Huddle House Inc.	340
Huddlestun Creamery, Inc.	439
Hudson Management Corporation	642
Hue Ky Mi Gia Corp	1123
Hueing Inc.	386
Hueneke, Inc.	871
Huey Magoo's Restaurants LLC.	297
Huey's Inc.	955
Hugo's	1023
HuHot Mongolian Grills LLC	646
Humbard Enterprises	825
Humphery's	1161
Humphrey & Reanesey Enterprises, Inc	91
Hunan Lion	817
Hundal Foods Inc.	97
Hungry Howie's Distribution	271
Hungry Howie's Pizza & Subs Inc.	584
Hunt Enterprises	756
Hurricane AMT LLC	321
Huse Culinary, Inc.	452
Hyatt Hotels Corporation	408
Hyde Park Restaurant Systems Inc.	803
Hy's of Canada Ltd.	1172
HZ LM CASUAL FOODS, LLC	1065
I C By the Sea, LLC	873
I Chief, LLC	46
I Dream of Falafel	410
I F Bledsoe	9
I Heart Mac & Cheese	244
I Love Juice Bar	961
Iacono's	838
Ian's Pizza	1146
IAP Worldwide Services	248
Ibrahim Investment Corporation	1035
IC Naples, Inc.	282
Ice Cream Fun, LLC	189
Ice Slingers Inc	873
Ice Station Zebra & Associates	208
Iceberg Drive Inn Inc.	1069
Ichor Restaurant Group LLC	836
Icicle Creek Inc	645
Idaho Pizza Co.	391
IFGB, LLC / OPFGB, LLC	473
IGT Enterprises	716
Iguana Mia	249
IHOP Restaurant System	81
IKEA North America	878
Ike's Love & Sandwiches	157
Il Fornaio Corporation	64
Il Fornaio Cucina Italiana e Panetteria	65
Il Fornello Restaurants Ltd.	1193
Il Postino	775
Il Vicino Holding Company	718
Illas Management	314
Imago Restaurants Inc.	1193
IMC Management	531
Imo's Pizza	629
Impact FHS Restaurants, LLC	315
Imperial Associates LLC	510
In His Grip JM Corp.	121
In the Ballpark Inc.	662
In The Sauce Brands Inc.	473
India House	793
Indi's Fast Food Restaurant	485
Indmex Corporation	75
Indo Cal Foods, Inc.	732
Inflated Dough Inc	210
Ink! Coffee Co. of Colorado	200
Inland Northwest Culinary Academy	1135
Inmack Foods Inc.	112
Inn America Hospitality Inc.	703
Inn At Bay Harbor	568
Inn of the Mountain Gods Resort and Casino	721
Innisbrook Golf Resort	298
In-N-Out Burger	87
In-N-Out Burgers Distribution Center	52
Innovative Dining Group	184
Innovative Food Brands	1188
InnSuites Hospitality Trust	34
Insei, Inc.	253
Insomnia Cookies	894
Inspire Brands	341
Inspired Concepts	585
Intelligentsia Coffee, Inc.	410
InterContinental Hotels Group (The Americas)	341
International Coffee & Tea LLC	104
International Dairy Queen Inc.	597
International Franchise Corp.	1184
International Restaurant Management Group	252
International Restaurant Services Inc.	912
International Restaurants	46
Interstate Hotels & Resorts Inc.	1080
Interurban Management Inc.	850
Investments Property Acquisitions LLC	1124
Investors of West Tennessee Inc	946
Iowa State University Dining	380
Ippolito's	368
Irish Eyes	237
Iron Hill Brewery, LLC	883
Irvin Enterprises Inc	874
Isaac's Deli Inc.	877
Island Pizza Inc	48
Island Subway Inc	919
Island Wing Company	254
Islands Restaurants LP	59
Ison Management	804
Ital Americas Foods Corp.	914
Italian Village Restaurants Inc.	410
Italo's Pizza Shop Inc.	806
ITEC Attractions Inc.	617
ITNA Group, Inc.	160
It's a Wonderfood Life Inc.	125
Ivar's Inc.	1124
IWI Ventures	1143
Izumi Sushi & Hibachi	682
Izzy's	809
Izzy's Franchise Systems, LLC	859
J & A Foodservices Inc.	134
J & D Restaurants Inc.	1
J & D Shop Systems Inc	1142
J & J Industry Inc.	248
J & K Subway Inc	836
J & L Services	930
J & M Partnership	387
J & P Enterprises	441
J & R Hock Enterprises	94
J & S Cafeterias	665
J & S Restaurants Inc.	123, 940
J 3L Enterprises, Inc.	955
J B Enterprises Inc	935
J H Foods Ltd	195
J J M Associates Inc.	802
J J Myers LLC	559
J M L M Restaurants Inc.	613
J R of M B Inc.	930
J R One Inc	278
J S & J Restaurants Inc.	1083
J S H Enterprises Inc	946
J&B Restaurant Partners	757

Company	Page
J&F and Sons, LLC	995
J&H Foods Inc.	848
J&J Ostrowski Enterprises	1153
J&J Sweet Tooth, LLC	434
J, T and T Irrevocable Trust	822
J. Christopher's Restaurants LLC	363
J. Herndon Inc.	47
J. Miralco Inc.	1178
J. Thomas & Co. Inc.	821
J.A. Sutherland Inc.	179
J.C. Resorts LLC	92
J.C. Wong Management	752
J.D.S. Foods, Inc.	223
J.M.J. Seekers, Inc.	138
J.R. Young Enterprises Inc.	953
J.S. Foods, Inc.	143
J.S. Ventures Inc.	473
J.W. Ebert Corp.	1156
Jacara Restaurants, Inc.	171
Jack Cawthon's Bar-B-Que Inc.	961
Jack in the Box Inc.	143
Jack Marshall Foods Inc.	15
Jack Pirtle Inc.	955
Jackiana, LLC	497
Jackie's International Inc.	635
Jackmont Hospitality	342
Jack's Donuts	459
Jack's Family Restaurants Inc.	5
Jack's Urban Eats LLC	139
Jacksonville Coffee Company	264
JACO Foods	636
Jacobs Entertainment, Inc.	210
Jade Management Inc.	894
JAE Restaurant Group	301
JAHA Chicken Inc	321
Jai Kapi, LLC	304
Jai Thai Restaurant	1124
JAK Foods Inc	939
Jak Inc	934
Jak Pizza	871
Jake's Franchising LLC	220
Jalapeno Tree Holdings LLC	1054
Jamar Donuts Inc.	693
Jamba Inc.	1014
James Hanscom, LLC	386
James Mack	661
Jamsouth Inc.	361
Janbakhsh Inc.	492
Jane King Enterprises	315
Janjer Enterprises Inc.	558
Janjomar Inc.	572
Janrus & Asbek Inc.	94
Janus Hotels and Resorts Inc.	244
Japetto, Inc.	193
JAR Inc. Ltd.	190
Jardel Enterprises Inc.	211
Jaspal Enterprises inc.	93
Jasper Holdings	1011
Jaton Management Co.	539
Java Dave's Executive Coffee Service	858
Java Detour Inc.	152
Javier Torres Inc.	165
Jax Bbq, LLC	284
Jazz	1043
JB Restaurants Inc.	924
JBC Inc.	924
JCJ Tex Mex/Wings LLC	1023
JDD - Jason's Deli Distribution Center	1015
JDD Investment Co.	428
JDK Foods Inc.	365
JDK Management Co. L.P.	877
JDKD Enterprises	712
JDV Collection	152
Jean-Georges Enterprises LLC	775
Jeff Ruby Culinary Entertainment	810
Jefferson Hotel	1094
JEM Management Corporation	79
JEM Restaurant Group	921
Jenick Professional Services, LLC	669
Jeni's Splendid Ice Cream	817
Jenkins Quality Barbecue Inc.	264
Jennell Corporation	565
Jeremiah's Italian Ice	274
Jerry & Joe's Pizza	261
Jerry's Systems Inc.	557
Jersey Mike's Franchise Systems	705
Jest Enterprises	40
Jet City Pizza Co.	1115
Jetmo Inc.	1180
Jet's America Inc.	592
Jetty's	266
JFC Development LLC	10
JHA Foods	1156
Jhn Corporation Inc	462
Jib Jab Inc.	826
Jim Barnes Enterprises Inc.	12
Jim 'N Nick's Bar-B-Q	16
Jim Wagy's Management Co.	620
Jimano's Pizzeria	427
Jimboy's North America LLC	76
Jimmy Hula's Licensing, LLC	324
Jimmy John's Franchise LLC	399
Jimmy The Greek Food Corp.	1193
Jimmy's Egg Franchise Systems	851
Jimmy's Pizza Inc.	615
Jim's Family Restaurants	1077
JINYA Holdings, Inc.	56
JIPC Management	132
Jittery Joe's Coffee Franchising, LLC	328
Jivan Foods Inc.	1047
JJD Subway Inc	200
JJNJ, Inc	209
JKB Restaurants	380
JL Deers	603
JLC Food Systems	611
JM Foods, Inc.	131
JM Group	711
JM Hospitality Group	324
JM of Howell Mill LLC	358
JM Subs North Four, L.P.	134
JM Subs North One, L.P.	70
JM Team NoVa, LLC	1085
JM West, Inc.	177
JMA Enterprises	448
JMC Holdings Inc	708
JMET, LLC	1041
JMFW, LLC	1064
JMJ LLC	29
JMMN, LLC	611
JMP Pizza	359
JMS Associates, LLC	937
JMTX, LLC	968
JNH / BBH / CNH Food LLC	27
JNK Concepts	40
Jobren Inc	1056
Jockamo Upper Crust Pizza	452
Joe & The Juice	776
Joe Asadi	636
Joe D and Ka Investments, LLC	304
Joe Kowal	571
Joella's Hot Chicken	491
Joe's Kansas City BBQ	464
Joey Restaurant Group	1172
Joey's Only Franchising Ltd.	1164
John (Eddie) Webster	12
John Howie Restaurant Group	1107
John T. McGinnis Inc.	495
Johnnie's Charcoal Broiler	852
Johnny Appleseed Inc.	1076
Johnny's Downtown	813
Johnny's Pizza Franchise Systems Inc.	360
Johnny's Pizza House Inc.	511
Johnny's Tavern	467
John's Sandwich Shop Inc.	644
Johnson & Wales University Charlotte Campus	656
Johnson & Wales University Denver Campus	200
Johnson & Wales University Providence Campus	917
Johnson and Johnson	273
Johnson Haller, Inc.	82
Johnson Restaurant Group	1160
Joint Heirs Food Corp	52
Jollibee Foods Corporation	184
Jomida Inc.	686
Jon Smith Subs	321
Jonathan's Grille	944
JOR Foods Inc.	650
Jordan Enterprises	955
Jose Pepper's Restaurant Group	468
Joseph Scripture	374
Jose's Mexican Food Inc.	135
JOTO Inc.	305
Joy Enterprises, Inc.	8
Joysach Inc.	373
JP Management Corp.	91
JP Steakhouse LLC	669
JPL Management, Inc.	478
JPOC Corp.	56
JR Acquisition Corp	914
JRAN Inc.	21
J-Ray, Inc	922
JRN Inc.	941
JRS Restaurant Group	492
JRVL Inc	264
JS2 Services LLC	667
JS2, Inc.	426
JSH Enterprises, Inc.	946
JSP Management LLC	996
JTK Management Restaurants	229
JTN Commercial Investments	817
JTS BBQ, Inc.	860
Juan Pollo Inc.	140
Jubile Holdings JM	1059

Alpha Index

Jubilee Restaurant Group LLC 11
Juice It Up! 87
Juice Press 776
JuiceLand 974
JumBurrito Inc. 1046
JUMP Asian Express 827
Jungle Concepts LLC 40
Junior Senior Inc. 1043
Juniors Foods Services Ltd. 1164
Junior's Restaurants 748
Jupiter Beach Resort & Spa 266
Just Salad LLC 776
JV Enterprises of Illinois, Inc. 394
JW Ventures 1175
K & A Subs Gainesville I, LLC 308
K & K Fast Foods, Inc. 558
K & K Management 935
K & R Corp./Kashaco Inc. 99
K & S Silvers Inc. 482
K A J Subway 1046
K and JK Enterprises 452
K F C of St Peter, Inc 683
K&N Management 974
K&W Cafeterias Inc. 680
K.I.D. of Lexington, L.L.C. 482
K-1 Enterprises, Inc. 661
K2M Inc. 626
Kabb Management 579
Kabuki Restaurants, Inc. 104
Kada Partnership 458
Kades Corporation 1048
Kafe Neo Group Inc 1110
Kahala Brands 40
Kahwa Coffee Roasting Company 307
Kalaveras Inc. 163
Kaldi's Coffee Roasting Company 629
Kale Me Crazy Franchising, Inc. 342
Kanela Breakfast Club 410
Kap Enterprises Inc. 486
Karis Management 423
Karl S. Vucich LLC 512
Karl Strauss Breweries 144
Karmichael Holdings, LLC 525
Karns Enterprises 582
Katsos Management 228
Katsu International 342
Katsu-Ya Group 180
Kauai Restaurants, Inc. 188
Kaufman Enterprises 758
Kavlick Enterprises 881
Kazi Foods 375, 886
Kazi Foods Inc. 175
KB Restaurants Inc. 861
KBJN, Inc. 559
K-Bob's USA Inc. 1024
KBP Foods LLC 468
KC Hopps Ltd. 468
KCS Management 892
Kedds Inc. 688
Keegan's Grill & Taproom 34
Keelboat Concepts, Inc. 641
Keenwawa Inc 152
Keg Restaurants Ltd. 1170
Keiser University Center Culinary Arts Melbourne 275
Keiser University Center Culinary Arts Tallahassee 308
Keith Muller Enterprises 355
Kelly Companies 144
Kelly's Hospitality Group 667
Kel's Foods Inc./King Enterprises 426
Ken Kel Management 956
Kendall House Inc. 832
Kenneth Byam 916
Kenney Trousdale Inc. 1011
Kenny Brothers, Inc. 92
Kenric Management, Inc. 718
Kent Rathbun Concepts 1050
Kentucky Bell Incorporated 493
Kentucky Fried Chicken of Colbert County Inc. 14
Kentucky Fried Chicken of Ludington Inc .. 583
Kentucky Fried Chicken of McAlester 849
Kentucky Fried Chicken of Valdosta Inc. ... 374
Kenway Foods Inc 934
Kergan Bros. 501
Kernels Popcorn Limited 1194
Keva Juice Southwest 718
Keys Cafe & Bakery 603
Keyser Enterprises, Inc. 616
Keystone Apple Inc. 891
KFC Corporation 486
KFC Franchise 73
KFC of Anoka 597
KFC of Benton 17
KGB 382
KH2 Corporation 1
Khan's Mongolian Barbeque 610
Kia Tang 176
Kiawah Island Golf Resort 928
Kilian Management Services 1155
Killer Burger, Inc. 866
Killer Concepts Management Inc. 342
Kilroy's Indy 453
Kim Son Inc. 1024
Kimbaman Corp. 528
Kimchi Box 586
Kimpton Hotel & Restaurant Group LLC ... 152
King Beast Pizza Inc. 1134
King Dining, Inc. 574
King Enterprises 211
King Kohl's Food Services Inc 9
King Street Food Company 1194
King Street Grille 929
King Taco Restaurants Inc. 63
King-A Inc 1038
Kings Contrivance 548
Kings Management 467
Kings Point Ventures, LLC 763
King's Restaurants Inc. 667
King's Seafood Co. 67
Kinney Restaurant Management 978
Kinslow and Kinslow 852
Kinslow Sonic Group 856
Kirby's Prime Steakhouse 1059
Kirkwood Community College Hospitality Arts 382
Kitchen Enterprises Inc 567
Klatch Roasting 149
K-Mac Enterprises Inc. 21
Kmg Enterprises, Inc. 470
Knightsbridge Corp. 233
Knowlwood Enterprises 77
Kobe Japanese Steak House and Sushi Bar 241
Kodiak Creamery, Inc. 534
Kogi BBQ 104
Kohr Bros. Franchise Systems Inc. ... 1082
Koi Franchise LLC 41
Koi Palace Restaurants 70
Kojax Souflaki Inc. 1200
Kokkari Estiatorio 153
Kokolas Inc. 902
Kolache Factory Inc. 1037
Kold Kreations, LLC 422
Kona Grill Inc. 41
Koning Restaurants International 281
Kopp's Frozen Custard 1148
Kory Management 437
Kosch Catering & Dining Services 588
Kosmart Enterprises Inc. 884
Kosmo Inc 460
Kotobuki 794
Kraf Inc. 34
Kramer Management Inc. 626
KRB Management Inc. 533
Kreeger Enterprises 849
Krispy Kreme Distribution Center 680
Krispy Kreme Doughnut Corporation .. 656
Krispy Krunchy Foods LLC 496
KRM Restaurant Group Inc. 623
Kroll's Diner 683
Kruse & Muer Restaurants 588
KSK Management 475
KT Napier Investments LLC 213
KTL McDonald's LLC 668
KTM Restaurant Group, LLC 200
KT's Austin 975
Kuma's Corner 410
Kung Fu Tea Franchising LLC 776
Kura Sushi USA 87
Kurani Global Restaurants U.S. 357
Kurani Inc. 1
KVS Sonic Group 19
Kyle Inc. 393
Kyoto Bowl 45
L & E Management Comapny Inc 941
L & K Hodge LLC 111
L & L Franchise Inc. 375
L & P Company 810
L & R Industries Inc. 425
L & S Enterprise # 2 Inc. 195
L K Foods 59
L.A. Italian Kitchen Management Inc. ... 182
L.C.I. Enterprises Inc. 1009
L.P.G. Enterprises 718
L3 Hospitality Group 410
La Baguette 850
La Bamba Mexican Restaurants Group .. 399
La Boulangerie de San Francisco 153
La Calle Doce 996
La Car Of N C, Inc. 674
La Cazuela Mexican Restaurants 373
La Cima Restaurants LLC 343
LA Cluckers Inc. 8

Company	Page
La Colombe Torrefaction, Inc.	899
La Cosecha Inc.	363
LA Crawfish	1024
La Familia Cortez Restaurants	1059
La Fogata	200
La Gondola Spaghetti House	432
La Jolla Beach & Tennis Club Inc.	92
La Madeleine Inc.	996
La Parma	800
La Pizza Loca Distribution Center	168
la prep	1185
La Raza Pizza Inc.	453
La Rosa Chicken & Grill	705
La Rosa Enterprises Inc.	380
La Villa Pizzeria	757
Labovitz Enterprises	601
Lad Corp.	437
LAD Foods Inc.	15
Ladeki Restaurant Group	92
Laemmle Theaters	104
Lake Culinary Institute	255
Lakeshore Partnership	596
Lal Restaurant Group	793
Lalo Enterprises Inc.	284
Lamar, Inc.	671
LaMar's Donuts	200
Lamberti Restaurant Consulting	698
Lambert's Cafe	631
Land & Sea Group	539
Land Mark Products Inc.	385
Landfall Development Corp	601
Landmark Cinemas of Canada	1164
Landmark Theatre Corp.	104
Landon Investment Co Inc	79
Landry's Distribution Center	1024
Landry's Restaurants Inc.	1024
Lane Enterprises	463
Langseth-Wofford Inc	1041
Lanier, Inc.	1143
Lanini Corp	29
Lappert's Gourmet Ice Cream	135
Larco Enterprises Inc.	849
Lardas Systems Inc.	85
Larkburger	200
LaRosa's Inc.	810
Larry Blumberg and Associates Inc.	8
Larry Wilson, LLC	746
Larry's Giant Subs Inc.	264
Las Palapas	1059
Las Palmas	442
Las Palmas Mexican Restaurant	367
Las Palmas Mexican Restaurants Inc.	961
Las Vegas Sands Corp.	732
Lascari's & Sons Inc.	187
Lasco Enterprises, LLC	1025
Late Harvest Kitchen	453
Latin Concepts LLC	1081
LaTrelle's Management Corp.	1038
Latshaw & Menditto Inc	911
Laughing Planet Cafe LLC	867
Laurel Foodsystems	903
Laurier Enterprises	1112
Laurino Enterprises	798
Lavco Food Services Inc.	475
Lavin Enterprises	721
Lawndale Meadows	429
Lawrence Enterprises	759
Lawry's Restaurants Inc.	127
Lawson's Restaurant	480
Laxmi-Bhavan Inc.	302
Lazlo Inc.	688
Lazy Dog Restaurant & Bar	67
Lazy Flamingo Inc.	304
LC 3S Inc.	130
LC Corporate LLC	629
LC of Watertown, LLC	754
LC of Wausau, LLC	1154
LCL Food Services Inc.	278
Le Bouchon	410
Le Boulanger The Baker, LLC	79
Le Macaron French Pastries	305
Le Moo	486
Le Pain Quotidien	776
Leaf Management	363
Leakas Quality Food Inc.	890
Leal's Mexican Food, Inc	968
Learco Restaurant Management, LLC	1053
Lebanese Taverna Inc.	1081
Ledo Pizza System Inc.	539
Lee Wesley Restaurants, LLC	264
Lee*s Sandwiches International Inc.	158
Leeann Chin Inc.	598
Lee's Famous Recipe of Cincinnati Inc.	810
Lee's Famous Recipes Inc.	258
Lee's Hoagie House Restaurants	907
Leesco Inc	24
Left Bank Restaurant Group	119
Lefty's Famous Cheesesteaks, Hoagies & Grill	566
Legacy Franchise Group	1147
Legacy Restaurant Group LLC	470
Legacy Restaurants	1025
Legal Sea Foods Inc.	515
Legendary Baking	434
Legendary Restaurant Brands LLC	996
Lehigh Valley Ice Cream Factory, Inc	910
Lehigh Valley Restaurant Group	874
Leigh Enterprises	34
LemonShark Franchising, LLC	54
Lenfam Management Co.	714
Lenny's Franchise Systems, LLC	956
Leon Springs Gas Ltd.	1060
Leonard Management	686
Leonard's Steak-N-Shake	633
Leona's Restaurants Inc.	411
Leonidas Cafe	411
Leon's	571
Leopoldino Inc.	378
Leo's Coney Island	569
Lepsco Inc.	843
Les Franchises Salvatore G.A. Inc.	1202
Le's Vietnamese Restaurant	519
Lessing's Inc.	756
Lester's Diner	257
Letnes Brothers	614
Lettuce Entertain You Enterprises Inc.	411
LeVecke and Company	45
Levy Restaurants	343, 412
Lewis Family McDonald's	804
Lexarb Inc	482
LG's Prime Steak House	94
Libby Hill Seafood Restaurant Inc.	664
Liberty Burger Inc.	996
Liberty House Restaurant Corp.	343
Licon Enterprises, Inc.	1047
Liedtke Enterprises	758
Liepman Restaurants Inc.	1063
Lilac Blossom	695
Lilly Enterprises, Inc	969
Lime An American Cantina	201
Linar Co. Distribution Center/Arni's	457
Linchris Hotel Corp.	524
Lindy Gertie Enterprises, Inc.	398
Lindy's Fried Chicken Inc.	308
Lionheart, Ltd.	1083
Lipscomb-Smith Enterprises, Inc.	732
Liquid Fire, LLC	370
Liquid Living	843
Liquid Nutrition Group Inc.	1204
Little Anita's Mexican Food	718
Little Bonanza Casino	742
Little Caesar Enterprises Inc.	572
Little Caesar's	1041
Little Caesars of Atlanta, LLC	373
Little Caesar's of Canada Inc.	1186
Little Dipper Hot Pot House	1085
Little Foods Inc.	636
Little Greek Franchise Development LLC	315
Little India Restaurant	201
Little King Inc.	691
Little Ricky's Rib Joint	443
Little Sesame	234
Livanos Restaurant Group	777
Live Nation	104
Lizard's Thicket Inc.	922
Lloyd's Ice Cream Inc.	445
LM Restaurants Inc.	674
LMS Group, Inc.	99
Lo Lo's Inc	34
Loafin Joe's Inc.	20
Locals 8 Restaurant Group	223
Lockwood McKinnon Taco Ventures Inc.	526
Loco Ventures	161
Locos Franchise Company, Inc.	328
Lodging Enterprises Inc.	473
Lodo Restaurant Group	201
Loeks Theatres, Inc.	577
Loews Hotel Holding Corporation	777
Logan Enterprises	830
Logan's Roadhouse Inc.	1025
Logos Pizza Inc.	11
Lolita's Restaurants	62
Lollicup USA Inc.	62
Lombardi's Family Concepts	997
Lombardo's Restaurant	629
Lone Star Apple, LLC	1009
Lone Star Group of Companies	1188
Lonesome Dove Western Bistro	1011
Long John Silver's Inc.	487
Longhi's Restaurant	379
Longhorn Barbecue Inc.	1135
Longhorn Cafe	1060
LongHorn Steakhouse	289
Lonigro Enterprises, Inc.	588
Loop Restaurant Group Inc.	265

Name	Page
Lori's Diner	153
Loroam, Inc.	297
Los Barrios Mexican Restaurant	1060
Los Cucos Mexican Cafe	1047
Los Dos Molinos	35
Los Locos LLC	1124
Los Ranchos Restaurants Inc.	279
Lottsa Cheese Inc	933
Louis Pappas Restaurants Group	319
Louise's Trattoria Inc.	172
Lou's Finer Delicatessen Inc.	591
Love's Group	434
Loving Hut USA	159
LTP Management Group	257
Luby's Inc.	1026
Luca Pizza Di Roma	449
Luciano Management	1060
Lucky Dining Inc	595
Lucky Seven Bagel Company, LLC	602
Lucky Strike Entertainment	172
Lucky Wishbone	47
Lucky's Burgers and Brew	352
Lucwork Enterprises Inc.	436
Ludlow Enterprises	565
Lufrankton LLC	706
Luihn Four Inc.	670
Lujac Inc.	395
Luke's Lobster	777
Lumberjacks Franchises, Inc.	134
Lunan Corporation	413
Lupe Tortillas Mexican Restaurants	1026
Lure Fish House	58
Lusardi's	778
Lux Restaurants	453
Lyfe Kitchen	413
Lyndal Enterprises Inc.	882
Lynn Enterprises Inc	618
Lynn Haven Investors	1101
Lynn-Ja Inc.	937
Lyon Et Al	51
Lyon Management Company Inc.	357
Lyons Group Ltd	515
M & G Pizza Enterprises	24
M & J Management Corp	903
M and M Investments Inc	642
M and S Restaurants	482
M B C Subway Inc.	384
M Crowd Restaurant Group	1035
M Hospitality	265
M Kyrro Foods, Inc.	136
M Lehmann Enterprises	93
M Street Cafe	612
M&N Foods, LLC	886
M. C. Hartshorn, Inc.	936
M. Pernecky Management	127
M.E. Theatres Inc.	801
M.E.K. Corp.	847
M.J. Roberts Inc.	1101
M.J. Salem Corp.	934
M.P. Cleary Inc.	754
Maak Alamo LLC	907
Maaks Inc.	595
Mabes Enterprises Inc.	431
MAC Pizza LLC	571
MAC Pizza Management	982
Macado's Inc.	1096
Macalibur Limited	697
Macatak Inc	720
Macayo Restaurants LLC	35
Mac-Clark Restaurants Inc.	798
MAC'D	153
MacLaff Inc	501
Macrina Bakery & Cafe	1124
Mac-Sto Management	1159
Mad Anthony's Inc.	1113
Madden's on Gull Lake	599
Maggiano's Little Italy	997
Maggio Corp.	875
Magic Wok Management	732
Magnum Enterprises, Inc.	1098
Magnum Foods Inc.	852
Mahana Fresh	247
Mahendra Patel	824
Main Event Entertainment, LP	1051
Main Street Management	487
Main Waters Enterprises	926
Mainstreet Ventures Inc.	566
Maison Kayser	778
Maiwand Kabob	548
Majestic Retail Group, Inc.	62
Major Food Group	778
MAK Management	807
Makar Foods, Inc.	96
Malament Enterprises Inc	551
Malamis Holdings, LLC	546
Malawi's Pizza	1073
Malco Theatres Inc.	956
Malinen Management, LLC	611
Malnati Organization Inc.	433
Mama Maria's Italian Restaurant & Pizza	238
Mamaka Bowls	20
Mama's Daughters' Diner	1051
Mambo Seafood Restaurants	1026
Mamie Raines Inc.	11
Mamoun's Falafel	778
Management Associates	884
Management Resources Co.	937
Managing Foods	247
Mancy's Family	841
Mandarin Holdings/Leeann Chin Inc	607
Mandarin Restaurant Franchise Corp.	1180
Manero's Restaurant	298
Mangen Group	173
Mangia Bene, Inc.	639
Mangia Brick Oven Pizza	712
Mangione Inc.	99
Mann Theatres Inc.	598
Manna Inc.	487
Mannat Food Inc.	1045
Mann's McDonalds	381
Manny's Original Chophouse	323
Manuel's	975
Manuel's Mexican Food	35
Maoz Vegetarian U.S.A. Inc.	778
Mapes Food Service, Inc.	35
Maple Street Biscuit Company	284
Mar Pizza Inc.	125
Marathon Restaurants	899
Marcello's Father & Son Restaurant	413
March Investment Inc	683
Mar-Chek, Inc.	554
Marchetti Management Services	228
Marco's Franchising LLC	841
Marco's Pizza Inc	1148
Marcus Hotels & Resorts	1148
Marcus Theatres Corporation	1149
Mardi Gras Casino and Resort	1157
Marene Inc.	821
Margaritas Management Group	695
Margaritaville Enterprises	289
Maria Empanada	201
Maria Hines Restaurants	1124
Mariane Inc./Bells & Birds	581
Mariano's Mexican Restaurants Inc.	969
Maria's Taco Shop	112
Marich Inc.	826
Marie Callender's Inc.	51
Marigold Restaurants	1177
Marination	1125
Marino's Pizza Inc.	585
Marion Restaurants Inc.	457
Mario's Restaurant & Bar	753
Mario's South Side Saloon	903
Mark of Excellence	1033
Mark Tredwell	361
Markor Enterprises	9
Mark's Feed Store Bar B Q	487
Mark's Pizzeria	754
Marles Inc.	1125
Marlow's Tavern	326
Marmalade LLC	59
Marpor Corporation	912
Marquee Cinemas Inc.	1156
Marquis & Co	900
Marriott International Inc.	545
Marsha Brown Enterprises	892
Marshall Hotels & Resorts Inc.	558
Martin Enterprises	733
Martinez Distributors	279
Martinez Management Inc.	38
Martin's BBQ Joint	961
Martin's Restaurant Systems Inc.	362
Marx Enterprises, Inc.	1101
Mary Brown's Inc.	1184
Mary Murray	425
Mary's Market Cafe & Bakery LLC	437
Mary's Pizza Shack of California Corp.	173
MAS Restaurant Group	1026
MAS Sandwiches, LLC	1048
Mascott Corporation	702
Mason Harrison Ratliff Enterprises	852
Massey's Pizza Inc.	817
Massimo Zanetti Beverage USA	1093
Mastoran Corp.	536
Matchbox Food Group	234
Matco of Waterloo Inc	387
Matt's Chicago Dog	656
Maurice's Piggie Park BBQ	933
Max & Erma's Restaurants Inc.	647
Max Restaurant Group	223
Max's Restaurants	174
May Van Corp	570
Mayuri, Inc.	1109
Mazatlan Mexican Restaurant	1117
Mazzio's Corporation	858

Company	Page
MBA International Inc.	1093
MBR Management	627
Mc Donald's of Harrodsburg	479
Mc Donald's of Hartwell	360
Mc Donald's Restaurants Inc	32
Mca Chicago Inc	413
McAlister's Corporation	343
McCan's Sonic Group	1012
McCatur Inc.	7
Mcclanahan Management Inc	1063
McCoy Associates	521
MCD Management	685
McDermott Oil Company	381
McDonald's Central Division	441
McDonald's Corporation	413
McDonalds Enterprise of Folsom	1109
McDonalds Franchise	144, 779
McDonald's Franchise	4, 15, 18, 168, 219, 259, 279, 374, 421, 432, 435, 441, 529, 534, 567, 601, 649, 755, 849, 860, 887, 890, 980, 1048, 1055, 1147
McDonald's Management Co.	961
McDonald's of Baton Rouge	497
McDonald's of Bend OR	860
McDonalds of Bishop	55
McDonald's of Boulder	190
McDonald's of Corrales	722
McDonald's of Durango	206
McDonald's of Enid	848
McDonald's of Harrison	827
McDonald's of Livermore	97
McDonald's of London	483
McDonald's of Marietta	832
McDonald's of Mitchell	934
McDonald's of Northwest Arkansas	25
McDonald's of Scottsdale	41
McDonald's of Spencer	461
McDonald's of Vermilion County	422
McDonald's of Winchester	495
McDonald's of Yakima	1140
McDonald's Restaurants of Canada Ltd.	1194
McDonald's Restaurants of Hawaii	376
McDonald's Tri-County Management	880
McDonald's USA LLC	183, 1027
McEnaney Enterprises	494
McEssy Investment Company	429
McFadke Inc.	720
McGrath's Fish House Inc.	871
McGraw Enterprises Inc.	440
McGuire's Irish Pub	300
McIntyre Management	886
McKaren Industries Inc.	997
McKenzie Enterprise Associates LLC	494
McKibbon Hotel Management Inc.	315
MCL Corp.	494
MCL Enterprises, Inc.	47
MCL Restaurant & Bakery	453
McLeroy's Enterprises, Inc.	354
McLiff Vending & Office Coffee Services	975
McLoone's Restaurants	705
McMaflah, Inc	492
McMenamins Pubs & Breweries	867
McNib Corp.	88
McNulty's Bier Markt/Bar Cento	813
McOffice, LLC	1092
McQuire Management Group	958
McSoifer's Inc.	382
McWorth Management	964
M-D Sanders Restaurants Inc.	861
Meadowbrook Restaurant Company Inc.	353
Meadowood Napa Valley Resort	139
Meadows Original Frozen Custard	881
Meatball Management LLC	779
Mechtley Enterprises, Inc.	470
Medieval Times Management Inc.	1035
Medina County Foods Inc.	838
MEGHA INVESTMENTS, LLC	733
Meijer Inc.	578
Mel K Management	807
Mel Oshiro	1114
Mel-Lin Enterprises	889
Mellon & Son Inc.	30
Mel's Drive-In	153
Melt Bar & Grilled	829
MEL-Z ENTERPRISE, INC.	59
Memphis Championship Barbecue	733
Menchie's Group Inc.	74
Mendez Enterprises	415
Mendocino Farms	175
Meoli Company	239
Mercado Juarez Cafe Inc.	969
Mercedes Restaurants, Inc.	436
Merchants Hospitality	779
Merchants Row Restaurant	521
Meridian Restaurant Unlimited LLC	1078
Meritage Hospitality Group Inc.	578
Meruelo Group	169
Mesa Management Group	1159
Mesa Rosa Inc.	975
Mesa SW Restaurants	997
MESK Investments	1116
Messick Properties LLC	1044
Metro Bd LLC	799
Metro Corral Partners Inc.	324
Metro Franchising	755
Metro H&N, Inc.	580
Metropolitan Restaurant Management Company	1085
Metropolitan Theatres Corporation	105
Metrotainment Cafes	344
Metz Culinary Management	880
Mexicali Restaurant Inc.	52
Mexican Villa Resaurants, LLC	633
Mexican Village Restaurant	573
Mexicue	779
Meyer Enterprises	1015
Mezcaleria Oaxaca	1125
Mezeh Mediterranean Grill	540
MFP Franchise Systems Inc.	368
MGC Enterprises	1083
MGM Resorts International	733
MHC Inc.	537
Mi Casa Too	723
Mi Pueblo, Inc.	305
Miami Subs Grill Corp.	244
Mian Group	380
Micah Camden Restaurant Group	867
Micale Management	698
Michael Del Pietro Restaurant Group	620
Michael McCorsley	354
Michael Silverman, LLC	249
Michael Symon Restaurants	813
Michael's Restaurant	170, 534
Michelle Sperl	1147
Michigan Multi-King Corporation	593
Michigan Pizza Hut Inc.	590
Mici Handcrafted Italian	201
Midamerica Hotels Corporation	618
Midan Organization	415
Middle Tennessee Pizza Inc.	958
Midnight Moon Co. Inc.	2
Mid-South Food Service Inc.	647
Midtown Cafe	962
Midwest R Corporation	823
Midwood, Inc.	1125
Mighty Quinn's Barbecue	779
Mighty Taco Inc.	753
Miguel's Jr	64
Mik-Di Enterprises	625
Mike Anderson's Seafood Restaurants	497
Mike Terry Enterprises	998
Mikuni Restaurant Group, Inc.	111
Milabon, LLC	548
Milano Restaurants International	79
Miles Management Corp	181
Milio's Sandwiches	1143
Milkshake Concepts	998
Milkwood & Co.	1125
Mille Fleurs	131
Millennium Management Group	268
Millennium Restaurant Group	581
Miller Apple L.P.	576
Miller Group	396
Miller Managment LLC	817
Miller's Ale House Inc.	289
Milligan Enterprises Inc	464
Milos Hamburgers	9
Milt Guggia Enterprises Inc.	169
Milton's Pizza & Pasta	674
Mimi Cheng's	779
Mimi's Hummus	748
Mina Group	154
Minc	97
Minking Inc.	684
Minsky's	623
Minuteman Pizza	838
Mio Sushi International	867
Mio's Development LLC	830
Miracle Restaurant Group, LLC	602
Mission BBQ	552
Mitra QSR KNE, LLC	1051
Miza Foods Inc	940
MJG Corporation	722
MJM 5G LLC	1076
MJPT II & Associates, LTD	818
MK Restaurant Concepts, LLC	251
MKG Enterprises, LLC	1096
MMJ	392
Moana Restaurant Group	164
Mobro Enterprises Inc	187
Moby Dick House of Kabob	553
Moby Dick Seafood Restaurant Inc.	488
MOD Pizza LLC	1107
Modern Food Services, Inc.	1135
Modern Restaurant Concepts	191

Company	Page
Modrak Group	457
Moe's Original Franchise System	217
Moe's Southwest Grill Largo	248
Moe's Southwest Grill LLC	344
Moffett Foodservice	505
Mohegan Tribal Gaming Authority	229
Mohr & Mohr Inc	867
Molina's Enterprises Inc.	1027
Molly Malone's Irish Pub and Restaurant	488
Molly Moon's Homemade Ice Cream	1125
Molly Pitcher Inn	711
Momex Foods Inc	269
Momofuku Restaurants	780
Monarch Casino & Resort Inc.	742
Monell's Dining & Catering	962
Mongolian Concepts LLC	1035
Monical Pizza Corporation	397
Monjunis	510
Monkburger Franchise Group LLC	1155
Montage Hotels & Resorts	94
Montana Pizza Inc	646
Monte Cello's Italian Restaurants Inc.	903
MONTE Restaurant Development Group	540
Montes Enterprises Inc	252
Montgomery Catering	13
Montgomery Inn Inc.	811
Moore & Moore Investments Inc.	364
Moore Hospitality, Inc.	559
Moose Inc.	376
MOOYAH Franchise LLC	1051
Mor Subs Inc	1141
Morgan Enterprises	615
Morgan's Foods Inc.	813
Moriarty Creamery, LLC	1012
Morris Food Service	849
Morrison Healthcare	369
Mortellaro's Mcdonalds	836
Mo's Seafood Factory	542
Moseley Partners, LLC	1098
Mosher Management	821
Motel Associates Inc.	924
MotorCity Casino	573
Mount Fuji Japanese Steak House	757
Mountain Mike's Pizza	120
Mountain Range Restaurants LLC	45
Mountain Valley Corporation	1102
Mountain West Wendy's	1070
Mountainside Pizza Inc.	218
Movie Palaces Inc	1160
Movie Tavern LLC	506
Moxie Java International LLC	390
Mozzi's Pizza Inc.	449
MP2 Enterprises	1079
Mr Brews Taphouse	1147
Mr Submarine	424
Mr. Chow Inc.	55
Mr. Fries Man	80
Mr. Gatti's Inc.	1012
Mr. Greek Restaurants Inc.	1195
Mr. Gyros	1125
Mr. Jim's Pizza Inc.	1010
Mr. Mikes Restaurants	1168
Mr. Pickle's Inc.	100
Mr. Stax Inc.	180
Mr. Subb Inc.	752
Mr. Submarine, Inc.	395
Mr.Empanada Franchise Corp.	315
MRB Holdings	742
MRD INC	2
Mrs. Winner's Franchising Group, LLC	356
MSK Enterprises Inc.	1055
MSK Management	699
MSWG Chapel Hill, LLC	660
MSWG of Rochester, Inc.	793
MTB Management Inc.	646
MTY Food Group Inc.	1203
Muchas Gracias Mexican Food	1139
Muginoho USA Inc.	780
Mulligan's Beach House	307
Multisystem Restaurants Inc.	914
Munch A Licious, LLC	121
Mundo Management LLC	106
Murchie's Tea & Coffee (2007) Ltd.	1168
Murphy Adams Restaurant Group	975
Murphy's Deli Franchising Inc.	1027
Muscle Maker Inc.	88
Mustards Grill	188
MVP Restaurant Partners LLC	315
MVP Sonic Group	642
My Burger	607
Myles Restaurant Group	281
Myriad Restaurant Group	780
Myrtle Beach Friends LLC	930
MZK Enterprise, LLC	1027
MZM Foods, Inc.	144
N & R Dining, Inc.	1103
N S & T Inc.	842
N.G.P Management LLC	529
Naf Naf	415
Nakato Japanese Restaurant	344
Naked Tchopstix	453
Nando Corporation	398
Nando's Canada	1186
Nando's USA	234
Napier Enterprises Inc.	216
Napoli Management	532
Nashville JM, LLC	952
NATC Donuts Inc.	704
Nath Companies Inc.	598
Nathan's Famous Inc.	760
National Amusements Inc.	530
National Casting Company Inc	136
National Coney Island Inc.	588
Nation's Foodservice Inc.	72
Native Foods Cafe LLC	634
Natron Corp.	575
Natures Table Franchise Co.	290
Nature's Way Cafe Franchising LLC	267
Navco Corp.	837
Nayana	427
NBR Tomatina LLC	164
NCB, Inc.	306
Ne Ro Inc	446
Neal Brown Hospitality	454
Nee Mee Corp	1065
Neek Inc.	48
Nehmeh Enterprises, Inc	583
Neighborhood Grills	1125
Neighborhood Hospitality, Inc.	479
Neighborhood Restaurant Group	479
Neighborhood Restaurant Partners	345
Neighborhood Ventures Inc.	967
Nekter Franchise Inc.	166
Nellis Management Company	387
Nelson Hachem	1158
Neltac Inc.	1110
Nerangis Enterprises	1104
Nevaeh	570
New Adventure Inc	576
New Bohemia	608
New Britain Donuts	226
New Castle Hotels & Resorts	227
New England Culinary Institute	1105
New Haven Donuts Inc	226
New London Corp.	601
New River Valley Pizza	1096
New South Pizza Inc.	656
New South Restaurant Group	638
New Start, LC	1074
New York Pizza Development, LLC	290
Newcomb Farms Family Restaurant	527
Newk's Franchise Company	639
Newland Management	1101
Newmad Corporation	708
Newport Ave Donuts Inc.	917
Newport Harbor Corp	918
Newport Hospitality Group	1103
Newton Associates Inc	1060
Newton Investments Inc.	856
Next Level Burger Company, Inc.	860
Ney Nagler Weyman Corp.	345
NHG Enterprises LLC	1111
Niagara Parks Commission	1186
Niagra Casinos	1187
Nice Ventures, Inc.	154
Niche Food Group	619
Nichols Management Inc.	621
Nick & Toni's Cafe	753
Nick The Greek	159
Nick's Pizza & Pub	422
Nielsen's Frozen Custard	1069
NIK.	1110
Nisbet Enterprises	268
Nixon Deli Franchises, LLC	949
NL Group	998
Noble Crust	307
Noble Food Group	567
Noble House Hotels and Resorts	1113
Noble Investment Group LLC	345
Noble Roman's Inc.	454
Noble's Restaurants	657
Nobu Restaurants	780
NOHSC Restaurant Group	504
Noodles & Company	192
Nookies	415
NorJam, LLC	710
Nor-Mar Management Services Inc.	191
Norm's Restaurant Inc.	53
Nornet Management	429
Norsan Food Group	358
Norsco Management Inc	299
North Central Virginia Restaurants, Inc	1104
North Country Management Group	560
North East Georgia Inc.	359
North Pacific Management Inc.	868

Name	Page
North Shore Poke Co. Inc.	85
North Star Restaurants, Inc	1139
Northcott Hospitality International LLC	600
Northeast Donut Shop Management Inc.	900
Northern Arizona Fast Foods, Inc.	28
Northhays, Inc	464
Northstar Cafe	818
North-Wend Foods Inc.	2
Northwest Burgers and Fries Inc.	863
Northwest Food Management Group Inc.	1112
Northwest Group, Inc.	873
Northwest Pizza Company, Inc.	645
Northwest Premier Investments, Inc.	1139
Northwest Restaurants Inc.	1140
Not Your Average Joe's Inc.	527
Nova Restaurant Group	602
Novo Operations, Inc.	567
Nowak Enterprises, Inc	300
NRD Capital Management II LLC	352
NRJM Inc.	438
NTG Enterprises	370
Num Pang	780
Number 5	746
Nuop Corp	704
Nutrition Management Services Co.	888
Nutritional Management Services	1183
Nu-Ventures Inc.	587
Nu-Way Weiners Inc.	362
NuYo Frozen Yogurt, Inc.	144
NYC Bagel & Sandwich Shop	702
O and O Enterprises Inc	440
O K Enterprises, Inc.	684
O M, Inc.	159
O&M Restaurant Group	853
Oak Hotels Inc	757
Oasis Pizza Inc	48
Obresky Enterprises Inc	608
O'Bryan's Nine Irish Brothers, LLC	462
OC Food Express, Inc.	63
Ocean Reef Club	267
Ocean Restaurant Corp	868
Ocean View Foods, Inc.	57
Oceanside Management Group	234
O'Charley's Restaurants	962
Ochlocknee Ventures, LLC	931
O'Connor Management Group	300
Odeh Premier - B Operational Enterprises, L.P.	1015
Odessa Enterprises, Inc.	1000
Oerther Foods Inc.	290
Offerdahl's Cafe Grille Inc.	283
Oggi's Pizza & Brewing Co.	141
Ohana Poké Co.	106
OK Sub of OKC Inc	853
Old Town Tortilla Factory	41
Olde Towne Partners LLC	818
Ole International Foods	392
Olga's Kitchen Inc.	583
Olive Garden	290
OLS Hotels and Resorts	74
Olson Franchise Group LLC	1137
Olympia Hotel Management	563
OM Management, Inc.	189
Omelet House	739
Omni Hotels & Resorts	998
On The Border LLC	1036
One Off Hospitality Group	415
One Olive Group, LLC	159
One World Cuisine	519
One World Enterprises	444
Onieal's Restaurant & Bar	703
Ono Hawaiian BBQ	71
Onset Donuts Inc.	537
OOC Inc.	154
Opaa Food Management Inc.	618
Opi Enterprises Inc	578
Opper Melang Restaurant Group	1126
Orange Contemporary Brunch	415
Orchard Foods Corp.	1134
Oregano Inc.	41
O'Reilly Group	1051
Original ChopShop	42
Original Pancake House	211
OSAAT Enterprises LLC	657
Osborne Ventures LLC	32
OSF International, Inc.	868
Oshkosh Restaurants LLC.	1152
Osteria al Doge	780
OTAC Inc.	540
Ott & Ballard Enterprises, LLC	500
Otte Restaurants Inc	687
Oudinot, Inc.	1150
Our Family Franchise, Inc.	284
Out West Restaurant Group, Inc.	144
Outback Steakhouse Restaurants	316
Outlaw Enterprises, Inc.	919
Outlaws' Bar & Grill	685
Outrigger Enterprises	376
Owen O'Leary's	518
Oxford Common's Submarines Inc	660
Oxford Foods Inc.	639
P & D Hamburgers	699
P & G	903
P & S of Kansas Inc.	466
P R H Foods Inc	31
P. Hendel Products Partnership	762
P. Terry's	976
P.F. Chang's China Bistro Restaurants	42
P.I.P. Corp.	1146
P.J.J. Inc.	643
P.J.W. Restaurant Group	714
Pacific Bells Inc.	1139
Pacific Catch	65
Pacific Concessions Inc.	174
Pacific Dining Car Inc.	106
Pacific Hotel Management LLC	162
Pacific Meritage	164
Pacific Sliders, LLC	1114
Pacific Theatres Exhibition Corp.	106
Pacifica Del Mar	71
Pacifica Hotel Company	88
Paciugo Franchising L.P.	998
PacPizza LLC	165
Pacrim Hospitality Services	1179
Padow's Hams and Deli Inc.	1086
Padrino's	300
Paesano Di San Antonio Inc.	1060
Paesan's Pizza & Restaurant	743
Pagliacci Pizza	1126
Paisans Pizza	395
Pak Foods LLC	1027
Pala Casino, Resort, Spa	124
Palace Entertainment Holdings LLC	118
Palace Vending Inc.	946
Paladar Restaurant Group	813
Palas Hospitality	921
Palenque Group	1040
Palio's Pizza Cafe	968
Pallino	1107
Palm Beach Kennel Club	321
Palm Springs Chicken Take-Out Inc	261
Palmaccio Management	367
Pal's Sudden Service	946
Pal's Sudden Service Inc.	946
Pam Miller, Inc.	496
Pama's Subs & Salads Inc	905
Pan Pacific Hotel & Resorts	154
Panago Pizza Inc.	1167
Panchero's Franchise Corporation	383
Pancho's Mexican Foods Inc.	956
Panda Inc.	691
Panda Restaurant Group Inc.	136
Panera Bread Company	629
Panera Bread of Iowa	382
Panini Kabob Grill	67
Panini Pete's	8
Panini's Franchise Group	845
Panther Coffee	279
Panzerotto Pizza Ltd.	1182
PAP, LLC	638
Papa Gino's Holdings Corp.	522
Papa John's Distribution Center	29, 189, 291, 662, 868, 884
Papa Johns International Inc.	488
Papa Kelsey's Inc.	390
Papa Murphy's International Inc.	1139
Papa Murphy's Take 'N' Bake Pizza Franchise	934
Papa Restaurant Management	868
Papa's Pizza Inc.	861
Papaya King Operations Inc.	781
Pappa Genos' Steak & Cheese	1027
Pappas Restaurants, Inc.	1028
Parade Enterprises	708
Paradigm Investment Group, LLC	145
Paradise Companies LLC	640
Paradise Pizza Inc	320
Paradiso Mexican Restaurant	683
Paragon Hospitality Enterprises	115
Parasole Restaurant Holdings Inc.	603
Parco Ltd.	384
Parikh Network	796
Paris and Potter Management Corporation	661
Paris Baguette USA Inc.	63
Park Burger	201
Parker's Barbeque	665
Parkhurst Dining Services	887
Parochetti Enterprises Inc.	432
Parrish Foods	998
PARS Group LLC	1113
Parsons QSR, LLC	759
Paschen Management Corp. Inc.	58
Passion Food Hospitality LLC	234
Pasta Jay's	191

Name	Page
Pasta Mama Inc.	106
Pasta Pasta/Cafe Joelle	795
Pasto Itiliano Restaurant & Bar	463
Pat & J, Inc.	247
Pat Kuleto's Restaurant Development & Management	155
Pat O'Brien's Bar Inc.	506
Patachou Inc.	454
Patann, Inc	44
Patch Management Inc.	1043
Patina Restaurant Group LLC	781
Patrick Anderson	836
Patrick Marianne Corp	796
Patronies, Inc.	648
Pat's Management LLC	710
Patterson-Erie Corp.	883
Paul Martin's American Grill	88
Paul Messer's McDonald's	374
Paul Revere's Pizza International, Ltd.	382
Paul Ross	797
Paul Snyder	446
Paws Inc.	826
Paymon's Mediterranean Cafe and Hookah Lounge	739
PB Restaurants LLC	416
PB&J Restaurants Inc.	468
Pbjd Enterprises Inc	193
PCH Venture Group, Inc.	98
PDM Foods Company LLC.	907
Peabody Peabody Inc.	466
Peachwave Frozen Yogurt	580
Peak Enterprises, Inc. Galeau, LLC	345
Peak Interest LLC	691
Peak Resorts Inc.	635
Peak Restaurant Group, LLC	1077
Pearl Restaurant Group	794
Pearl's Restaurant Group	853
Pebblebrook Hotel Trust	546
Pecado Bueno	1126
Pechanga Resort & Casino	177
Pecos Valley Pizza Incorporated dba Dominos Pizza	722
Pedro's Tacos	141
Peet's Coffee & Tea Inc.	73
Peg/Lion, LLC	121
Pegasus Group	1195
Peg's Glorified Ham n Eggs	743
Pei Wei Asian Diner	1036
Peking Duck House	781
Peking Pavilion	1094
Pellegrino & Sons LLC	930
Peninsula Firehouse, Inc.	1091
Penn Brothers Enterprises	482
Penn National Gaming Inc.	910
Penn Station Inc.	834
Penn's Fish House Inc.	640
Peno Mediterranean Grill	679
Pentax Restaurant Group	934
Peoria Ice Cream Company	422
Pepe's Inc.	416
Pepi Corporation	1028
Pepitos Restaurant	608
Peppercorn's Grill	223
Pepperoni's Inc	1065
Peppino's Pizzeria	565
Peppi's Inc.	903
Pereira Holdings, LLC	320
Perfect Delivery Inc.	925
Perfect Pizza Pie Inc	298
Performance Foods Corporation	832
Pergom Inc.	915
Perimeter Foods Inc	637
Perimeter Foods, Inc.	357
Perkins Restaurant & Bakery	956
Perna Group	747
Perry & Brady Enterprises Inc.	352
Perry's	155
Perry's Restaurant Corp.	1028
Personal Touch Food Service Inc.	750
Pertoria, Inc.	831
Peru 1 LLC	436
PET Investments, LLC	602
PetePeg, LLC	448
Peter DeFries Corporation	719
Peter DeFries Distribution Center	719
Peter Luger Inc.	748
Peterson-Burge Enterprises/Desert De Oro Foods	30
Pete's Fish & Chips Inc.	32
Pete's Garage	585
Pete's Restaurants	201
Petrus Brands Inc.	372
Pfau Properties	571
PFC Classic Dining Restaurant Group	394
PFS Management Co. Inc.	162
PhaseNext Hospitality	1052
Phelan Holdings, Inc.	245
Phelan Management Services, Inc	721
Phil Mook Enterprises	248
Phil Stefani Signature Restaurants	416
Phillip Stocker Co.	633
Phillips Foods Inc.	542
Philly Foods Inc.	88
Philly Franchising Co.	345
Phil's Restaurant Ltd.	1164
Philz Coffee	155
Phoenix Taco, LLC	657
Phoenix Theatres LLC	949
PhoNatic Real Vietamese Cuisine	976
Pi Pizzeria	630
Piazza Family Restaurants Inc.	97
Picazzos Pizza	44
Piccadilly Restaurants LLC	497
Piccolo Restaurant	758
Pick Up Stix Inc.	95
Pickapple Franchise LLC	180
Pickard Enterprises	811
Picnik	976
Pieology Pizzeria	133
Pierre's	262
Pies & Pints	1157
Pieyak Inc	1141
Piezoni	522
Piezzetta	559
Pile High Subs, Inc.	1098
Pilot Flying J	949
PinChasers	316
Pincho Factory	252
Pinecrest Subway Inc	675
Pinehurst Resort LLC	671
Pinkbox Doughnuts	739
Pinnacle Hospitality Group	1195
Pinnacle Restaurant Corp.	642
Pinstripes Inc.	433
Pio Pio	753
Pioneer College Caterers Inc.	467
Pioneer Food Service Inc.	1108
Piperade	155
PITA Mediterranean Street Food	367
Pita Pit Inc.	389
Pita Pit Ltd.	1182
Pita's Republic	316
Pizano's Pizza & Pasta LLC	416
Pizza 9 Franchise Corporation	719
Pizza Enterprises, Inc.	72
Pizza Eureka	159
Pizza Factory Inc.	119
Pizza Fusion Holdings	891
Pizza Guys Franchises Inc.	130
Pizza Hut Inc.	1052
Pizza Hut of Arizona Inc.	47
Pizza Hut of Eau Claire Inc	1143
Pizza Hut of Fort Wayne Inc.	448
Pizza Hut of Maryland Inc.	548
Pizza Hut of Southern Wisconsin Inc.	1146
Pizza Hut of the Rockies	212
Pizza King Wise	1104
Pizza Loves Emily Group	749
Pizza Luce Management	608
Pizza My Heart, Inc.	110
Pizza Nova Restaurants Ltd.	1195
Pizza Papalis	593
Pizza Partners, Inc.	1045
Pizza Patron Inc.	999
Pizza Pizza Distribution Center	1181
Pizza Pizza Limited	1196
Pizza Plus Inc.	936
Pizza Pro Inc.	18
Pizza Properties, Inc	1009
Pizza Resources Corporation	442
Pizza Roma Corp.	904
Pizza Shack Holdings Inc.	1178
Pizza Shoppe Franchising Inc.	623
Pizza Shuttle	851
Pizza Studio Holding Company	57
Pizza the Pie LLC	374
Pizza Twist	139
Pizza Works Inc.	620
Pizza World USA Franchise Corp.	427
PizzaRev	186
Pizzarose, LLC	35
Pizzaville Inc.	1199
Pizzeria Bianco	35
Pizzeria Cinque, Inc.	879
Pizzeria Uno of Madison Inc	1146
Pizzerias LLC	279
Pizzicato Gourmet Pizza	868
PJ Hawaii LLC	376
PJ Operations LLC	482
PJ United Inc.	5
PJ's Coffee of New Orleans LLC	499
PKD Raj & Associates, Inc.	145
PL Squared Inc.	984
Plamondon Companies Inc.	550
Planet Hollywood International Inc.	291

Name	Page
Planet Sub	623
Planet Wings Enterprises	763
Plank's Bier Garden	818
Platinum Corral LLC	666
Platinum Pizza Holdings	602
Playa Bowls	697
Plaza 23 Diner	711
Plaza Azteca Mexican Restaurant	893
Pluckers Wing Factory & Grill	976
Plum Restaurants	1126
PlumpJack Group	155
PMG 56, LLC, MN Series	597
PMTD Restaurants LLC	364
Poke Bar	185
Poke Go	145
Poke Poke	976
Pokeatery	163
Pok-e-Jo's Smokehouse Inc.	976
Poke-Ria	166
Poll Restaurants	794
Pollard's Enterprises Inc.	1101
Pollman's Bake Shop Inc.	12
Pollo Tropical Operations Inc.	279
Polly's Inc.	49
PONKO Chicken	346
Ponte Vedra Beach Resorts	301
Pool's Restaurant Group	361
Popco Inc	590
Popeyes Louisiana Kitchen Inc.	346
Poppos Taqueria	242
Pop's Inc	376
Poquito Mas	176
Port City Java Inc.	679
Port of Subs Inc.	743
Portage Bay Foods, LLC	1126
Portland Foods Inc.	869
Portofino	483
Porto's Bakery & Cafe	81
Posados Cafe Inc.	980
Posh Tomato	749
Postel Management	1162
Postel Management Inc	1161
Potato Corner USA	106
Potbelly Corporation	416
Potomac Family Dining Group	1088
PPV Inc	665
PR Management Corp.	523
Prairie Pizza	657
Praise IAG Franchisor LLC	189
PRB Management LLC	76
Preferred Hospitality Inc.	136
Preferred Meal Systems	395
Preiss Corporation	1161
Premier Food Concepts, LLC	145
Premier Hospitality Inc.	510
Premier Restaurant Group	417
Press Waffle Company	1052
Pressed Juicery Inc.	107
Prestige Worldwide S&A, LLC	324
Pret A Manger (USA) Ltd	782
Pretzel King, LLC	81
Pretzel Twister Inc.	671
Pretzelmaker Inc.	366
Pretzels Plus Inc.	885
Pride Restaurant Group	36
Primanti Bros.	904
Primary Aim LLC	847
Prime Quarter Inc.	1142
Prime Steak Concepts	42
Primo Inc.	833
PrimoHoagies Franchising, Inc.	715
Prince Food Systems Inc.	1028
Prince Resorts Hawaii	376
Princeton Food Services Inc.	711
Privett Management Group	251
Pro Mac Inc.	825
Proper House Group	316
Prosperity Systems Inc.	556
Protein House	29
Protos Pizza	202
Provence Breads & Cafe	962
Prunella Holdings LLC	238
PS Cleveland	841
PS Management Inc	811
PSI Pizza Inc.	889
Psl Enterprises Ltd	802
Pub Inc.	1076
Puccini's Smiling Teeth	454
Pudge Brothers Pizza	196
Puesto Mexican Restaurants	145
Pulido Associates Inc.	1012
Pulp Franchising Inc.	828
Pumpernickel's	1198
Punch Bowl Social	202
Punch Burger	454
Punch Pizza	612
Purcell Foods Inc	671
Purdum Restaurants	818
Pure Green Juice & Smoothies	307
Purple Submarine	297
Puttshack	417
Pyramid Enterprises, LLC	547
Pyramid Hotel Group LLC	516
Pyro's Fire Fresh Pizza	941
Q Mar, Inc.	1049
Q S C Inc	834
Q-BBQ	429
Qdoba Mexican Eats	146
QS America	326
QSC Enterprises	700
QSC Ventures Inc.	130
QSR Management Inc	700
Qsr's of Texas Inc	1013
Quaintance-Weaver	664
Quaker Steak & Lube	844
Quality Branded	782
Quality Dining Inc.	458
Quality Pizza Inc	1146
Quality Restaurant Concepts	16
Quality Restaurants Inc	597
Quarterdeck Seafood Bar & Neighborhood Grill	257
Queen City Pizza	910
Queen Enterprises Inc	826
Quest Food Management Services Inc.	430
Quick Quality Restaurants	700
Quorum Hotels & Resorts	999
Qwench/DRNK	107
R & B 421, Inc.	397
R & B Pizza Inc.	72
R & C Creamery, Inc.	912
R & D Foods Inc	1055
R & E Pizza People, Inc.	580
R & K Management	237
R & L LOZANO OPERATING LTD	1049
R & R Ventures Inc.	540
R & S Dairy Queens Inc.	1048
R Brothers Enterprises, LLC	175
R&K Spero McDonald's	224
R&L Subs, Inc.	675
R&R BBQ	1076
R. J. Management	825
R.A.C.M., Inc.	1069
R.E. Weichbrodt Inc.	790
R.J. Bowen Inc.	1038
R.M. Gibson, Inc.	668
R.W. Forsum Enterprises	129
R/C Theatres Management Corp.	556
Raccoon Valley Partners	387
Rachel's Kitchen	739
Rackson Corporation	709
RAD, Inc.	1144
Radcliff Co.	489
Radiant Group of Companies	941
Raffel Brothers	563
Rafferty's Inc.	476
Rafiq Enterprises Inc	1065
Ragin Cajun	1029
RAHE Inc.	1102
Rainbow Cone LLC	417
Rainbow Pizza, LLC	1067
Raising Cane's LLC	498
Raize Dough Enterprises	68
Raja Enterprises Inc	59
Rallco Inc.	483
Ralph Stephens	360
RAM International LLC	1114
Rammy's International Inc.	442
Ramona's Restaurant Group LLC	80
Ramp Industries, Inc.	303
RAMPP Hospitality Brands	1168
RamRock LLC	1029
Ram's Horn Restaurants Inc.	591
Rancho Grande Cantina	626
Rand Knotts Enterprises Inc.	1047
Randy's Donuts	86
Raper Organizaton	473
Rapid Fired Pizza LLC	828
Rappahannock Oyster Co.	1000
Rashid CSC Inc.	553
RAVE Restaurant Group Inc.	1066
Raven and the Peach	700
Raving Fans Restaurant Group	271
Raw Juce	244
Rawza, Inc.	872
Ray Lackey Enterprises	677
Rayner Enterprises	793
Raysway Inc	323
Razors Edge Pizza Inc	23
Razzoo's Inc.	967
RB Properties Inc.	235
RBS Subs, Inc.	660
R-C Investments	968
RDR Foods	187
RDSL Enterprises, LLC	981

Name	Page
Reaal Inc.	756
Reading International Inc.	782
Real Food Eatery	900
Reata	1012
Recipe Unlimited Corporation	1198
Red Bar & Restaurant	758
Red Boy Pizza Franchising	120
Red Hot Stuff, LLC	354
Red Letter J, Inc.	473
Red Lion Hotels Corporation	202
Red Lobster Seafood Co.	291
Red Mango FC LLC	999
Red Mill Restaurants, Inc.	1126
Red Pepper	684
Red Restaurant Group	803
Red Robin Gourmet Burgers Inc.	207
Redarhcs Inc.	175
RedBrick Pizza Worldwide, Inc.	999
RedKing Foods LLC	604
Redstone American Grill	602
Redwood Restaurants	76
Regal Entertainment Group	950
Regency Hotel Management, LLC	935
REGO Restaurant Group	202
Reinerth Enterprises Inc.	194
Reins International USA	80
Rel Maples Institute of Culinary Arts	965
Relay Restaurant Group	1126
Rem Inc.	999
Remington Hotel Corp.	1000
Remington Hotels	1000
Renaissance Entertainment Corporation	213
Renaissance Restaurant Group, LLC	648
Reno Ltd.	1017
Renzios Inc.	211
Resorts Beef Ltd	593
Restaurant Associates Managed Services	783
Restaurant Brands International	1196
Restaurant Bricco	231
Restaurant BT	317
Restaurant Business Inc.	118
Restaurant Concepts Inc.	687, 848
Restaurant Developers Corporation	814
Restaurant Development Group Ltd	703
Restaurant Growth Services, LLC	962
Restaurant Holdings	904
Restaurant Holdings Inc.	246
Restaurant Management Co.	32
Restaurant Management Company	473
Restaurant Management Corp.	907
Restaurant Management Group	366
Restaurant Management Inc.	811
Restaurant Normandin	1202
Restaurant Pacini	1200
Restaurant Partners Inc.	292
Restaurant Pizzapro Inc.	1200
Restaurant Zone, Inc.	556
Restaurants Ashton Casse Croute Inc.	1202
Restaurants of America Inc.	203
Restaurants Unlimited Inc.	1127
Restaurants-America	426
Rest-Con Management Systems Ltd.	1173
Restwend LLC	559
Retzer Resources	637
Revelator Coffee Company	6
Revere Restaurant Group	909
Reyes International Enterprises, Inc.	62
Rey's Pizza	280
RFD Inc.	185
RGMS, Inc.	273
RGT Management, Inc.	957
RHF Enterprises	807
Rhode Rockets Inc./ROCACONN Inc.	917
Rhombus Guys	683
Rib City Inc.	258
RibCrib Corporation	858
Rice Enterprises	904
Rice Garden Inc.	129
Rice Mediterranean Kitchen	280
Rich Products Corp.	750
Richard Landon Hoffman, Inc.	115
Richard Sandoval Restaurants	203
Richards Restaurants Inc.	444
Richmond Restaurant Group, Inc.	1095
Richworth Properties	1044
Rick Bayless Restaurants	417
Riese Restaurants	783
Right Way Restaurants Inc	10
Rightway Brands, Inc.	203
Rimel's Zenbu Cardiff LLC	98
RingSide Steakhouse - Uptown	869
Rio Grande Mexican Restaurants	209
Rio Vista Management Group Inc.	257
Ripon 23	1153
Rip's Country Inn	547
RiRa Group of Companies	346
Rise & Dine Restaurants, Inc.	818
Rise & Shine Restaurant Group	123
Rise Pies Handcrafted Pizza	805
Rise Southern Biscuits & Righteous Chicken	660
Rishtaa Inc.	76
Rising Roll Gourmet Co.	346
Rising Sun Corp.	951
Ristorante Il Cantinori	783
Rita's Franchise Co.	909
Ritual Coffee Roasters	156
RIV Corporation	501
River City Food Company	578
River City Grill Inc.	302
River Rock Entertainment Authority	81
River Street Riverboat Co.	370
River Sub Ltd	1061
Rivera Dairy Queen	1061
Rivercity Dairy Queen	383
RJ Nelson Enterprises	393
RJD Management	680
RJK & Company	519
RJMG Incorporated	80
Rjss Corporation	1078
Rkj Enterprise Inc	355
RLJ Lodging Trust	546
RLMK Inc.	182
RM Hospitality Group	783
RMC Inc.	214
RMG LC, LLC	946
RMH Franchise	346
RMR Colorado LLC	211
RNB Sanchez Inc.	184
Ro Jo Foods LLC	616
Roaring Fork Restaurant Group	1149
Roast Kitchen	784
Roasters Inc.	327
Robeks Corp.	107
Robert Dreesch	939
Rob-Kraft Inc.	215
Robroy Restaurants Inc.	305
ROBWAT Management Inc.	798
ROC N Burgers, LLC	800
Rock & Brews Franchising LLC	110
Rock N Roll Sushi	12
Rockfire Grill	113
Rockfish Seafood Grill Inc.	1054
Rockham 5G DE/NJ/PA LLC	883
Rockin' Baja Inc.	146
Rockit Ranch Productions	417
Rocky Mountain Business Ventures	218
Rocky Rococo Restaurants	1151
Rocky's of Northville	586
Rod Fraser Enterprises	122
Rodebrad of Taylorville	441
Rodney Scott's Whole Hog Barbecue	921
Rod-N-Reel	547
Roger Clark	1045
Rogers Family Investments Inc.	648
Rogman Corporation	476
Rogue Ales Brewery	864
Roly Poly Franchise Systems	265
Romacorp Inc.	292
Romad Company	564
Roman's Road Pizza Inc.	621
Romeo's Inc.	691
Romeo's Pizza Inc	833
Romeo's Place Ltd.	1175
Romulus Inc.	36
Ron of Japan	418
Ronald & Patty Hendrickson	604
Ronda Foods LLC	1076
Ron-Rick Inc.	457
Ronzio Management Inc.	916
Rooster's Inc.	822
Rosati's Franchise and Development LLC	441
Rosati's Franchising Inc.	425
Rosberg Management	689
Roscoe's House of Chicken N Waffles	84
Rosebud Restaurants	418
Rosen Plaza Hotel	292
Rosewood Hotels & Resorts Inc.	1000
Rotelli Pizza & Pasta Inc.	245
Rothesay Holdings Ltd.	1173
Roti Mediterranean Grill	418
Rotolo's Pizzeria	498
Rotthaus Company Inc.	1145
Roughrider Pizza Hut Inc	682
Round Table Franchise Corp.	64
Round the Clock Family Restaurants	449
Round The Table Hospitality	418
Roy Rogers Restaurants	550
Royal Family Businesses	243
Royal Pin Leisure Centers Corporate Offices	454
Royal Pizza	1166
Royal Waffle King	364
Roy's	1001
RoysBoys Pizza LLC	362

Name	Page
RPH Management, Inc	9
RPM Management Co.	928
RPM Pizza Inc.	638
RPW Georgia Inc.	365
RREMC Restaurants LLC	322
RSI	470
RSVT Holding, LLC	796
RtK, Inc.	847
RTPJ Inc	1013
R-U Hungry	182
Rubber City LLC	801
Rubio's Restaurants Inc.	60
Ruby Corp.	67
Ruby Tuesday Inc.	953
Rucker Restaurant Holdings, LLC	32
Rudino's Pizza & Grinders	675
Rudoni Management Inc.	585
Rudy's Hot Dog Inc.	842
Rumbi Holdings LLC	1076
Runza Restaurants Inc.	688
Ruoff Management Group	705
Rush Bowls	191
Rush's Food Systems Inc.	933
Russ' Restaurants Inc.	580
Russell Enterprises	1086
Russo's Inc.	270
Russo's Restaurants	1029
Russ's Commissary	580
Rust Enterprise	669
Rusty Pelican Cafe	1110
Rusty's Pizza Parlors Inc.	167
Ruth's Hospitality Group Inc.	325
RWT LLC	465
Ryan Restaurant Corporation	643
Rye Ridge Deli & Restaurant	795
S & G Foods Inc	77
S & J Allday Foods, Inc.	7
S & K Management	436
S & M Desert Pizza, Inc.	27
S & S Cafeterias	363
S & S Food Administrators	363
S & S Related Companies	1029
S & Z Enterprises	230
S B K Inc	589
S Group	839
S&D Spicy Kitchens	500
S&M Durlak	1095
S&S Franchise Development, Inc	457
S. Buckner, Inc.	1009
S.E.P. Administration LLC	386
S.H. Myers Inc.	390
S.M.A.K. Creamery, LLC	317
S.P. Food Services, Inc.	16
SA Restaurants Group, Inc.	930
Saalsaa Bros Inc	1144
SACO Management	28
Saco, Inc.	593
Sadaza Management	890
Sage Dining Services Inc.	554
Sage Hospitality Resources LLC	203
Sage Management	462
Sage Restaurant Group	203
Sagebrook Restaurant Management	799
Sagemark Ltd.	437
Sahm's	447
Saigon Restaurant Group	358
SAJJ Mediterranean	112
Sala Thai	235
Salad and Go	29
Salad Collective	210
Saladworks Inc.	879
Salata Inc.	1029
Saled Food Services	1138
Salem Management Company, Inc	807
Salema Management	526
Salem's Gyros & Subs	317
Salisbury House of Canada Commissary	1177
Salisbury House of Canada Ltd.	1177
Sal's Group	525
Salsa Fiesta Grill	243
Salsa Fresca Mexican Grill	221
Salsarita's Holdings LLC	657
Salt & Straw	869
Salt Creek Grille Restaurant LLC	68
Salt Lake Brewing Co.	1077
Salt Lick BBQ	1008
Salty Iguana	470
Salty's Seafood Grill	869
Salvaggio's Italian Deli	191
Salvatore Scallopini Inc.	584
Sam Patel	480
Samba Brands Management	784
Sammy J. Peppers Inc.	1168
Sammy's Pizza Inc.	601
Sam's Italian Foods	561
Sam's No. 3	204
Sam's Restaurant Systems	747
Sam's Tavern	1127
Samurai Noodle Inc	1127
San Diego Restaurant Management Co.	146
San Pedro Fish Market Grille	163
Sandman Hotels Inns & Suites	1173
Sandwich Specialists, Inc.	537
Sandy's Associates Inc.	446
Sanelli Foods	1189
Sangha Enterprises	97
Sanibel Majik Inc.	304
SanLar Enterprises	679
Santa Cruz Seaside Co. Inc.	168
Santa Fe Cattle Co.	498
Santa Fe Dining	723
Santa Fe Mexican Grill	271
Santa Lucia Pizza Winnipeg Ltd.	1177
Sanweco Inc.	560
Saputo Inc.	589
SAQ Enterprise Inc.	354
Sarah L. Teck, Inc.	535
Saren Restaurants Inc.	437
Sarku Japan	1184
Sarpino's USA Inc.	430
SAS Restaurants	1179
Sasaki Sogyo USA Inc.	926
Sasnak, LLC	1010
Satgur Enterprises, Inc.	98
Sather Management Corp	450
Sauce Holdings LLC	42
Saulat Enterprises	356
Savannah Restaurants Corp.	370
SAVOR	879
Sawmill Restaurant Group Ltd	1166
SAW's BBQ, LLC	10
Saxbys Coffee, LLC	900
SB Acquisitions LLC	1150
SB Food Express, Inc.	58
Sbarro Holdings LLC	819
SBB Enterprises, Inc.	284
Sbm Food Corporation	139
Sboro's Family Restaurants	799
Scalini Fedeli	784
Scanlan Management LLC	377
Schaffer Enterprises	425
Schanock Investment Co.	1144
Schlotzsky's Franchisee	10
Schlotzsky's Ltd.	347
SCHMIDT FAMILY RESTAURANT GROUP	838
Schmitt Management Corporation	394
Schnippers	784
Schoop's Hamburgers Inc.	449
Schuckers Inc.	275
Schuster Enterprises Inc.	355
Schutz Organization	167
Schwartz Brothers Restaurants	1108
Scoop This!, LLC	52
Scooter's Coffee LLC	692
Scott Hiatt Sport, Inc.	666
Scott M & A Corporation	838
Scottish Food Systems Inc.	668
Scotto Bros. LLC	800
Scott's Apple, Inc.	883
Scott's Seafood	120
Scotty's	584
Scoville Hot Chicken	357
SDS Restaurant Group, LLC	665
Sea Creatures Restaurants	1127
Sea Island Shrimp House	1061
Seabra Group	708
Seabreeze Pizza, LLC	245
Seagle Pizza Inc	477
Seaman Restaurant Corp	872
Seasons of Japan	352
Seasons Pizza	238
Seattle Best Curry LLC	1127
Seattle Culinary Academy	1127
Seattle Eats	1127
Seattle's Little Italy	1128
SeaWorld Entertainment Inc.	293
SeaWorld of California	146
SeaWorld of Florida	203
Sebastians	1183
Sebis Inc	664
Second Alarm Restaurant Group, Inc.	931
Sefmo, Inc.	554
Sekisui	957
Select Restaurants Inc.	814
Sellia Corporation	534
Selrico Services Inc.	1061
Sema Inc.	926
Seminole Hard Rock Entertainment Inc.	293
Seminole Lanes and Sunrise Lanes	305
Seneca Gaming Corporation	791
Senior Pizza Inc	976
Senor Frijoles Inc.	267
Sensor Enterprises, Inc.	922
Seoul Taco	634

Company	Page
Sepco Inc	695
Serafina Restaurant Group	784
SERG Restaurant Group	927
Sergio's Restaurants	280
Serious Coffee	1169
Sertex of Longview, Inc	1041
SERVUS!	456
Sesame Inn	904
Sesame Place	889
Seven Crown Resorts Inc.	89
Seven Hills Restaurant Group Inc	891
Seven Mile Cafe	1007
Seven Out, LLC	347
Seven Restaurants	8
SF Group, Inc.	20
SFS 39 Inc	156
SGK Idaho, Inc.	391
SGS Creamery, Inc.	662
Shah Ventures LLC	905
Shahir Bros., Inc.	1029
Shahmun Corporation	128
Shake Enterprises	115
Shake Shack Inc.	784
Shakers Restaurant Corporation	1089
Shakes Frozen Custard Inc.	20
Shakespeare's Pizza	619
Shakey's USA	48
Shalhoub Enterprises, Inc.	124
Shamrock Company	427
Shamrock LLC	947
Shaner Hotel Group Ltd.	908
Shapiro's Delicatessen	455
Sharing The Bread, Inc.	590
Sharky's Franchise Group LLC	186
Sharmac Corp.	116
Sharp Holding Inc.	1086
Shawkins, Inc.	423
Sheckler Subway Inc.	1143
Sheehan Brothers	840
Sheena Management	593
Shefield Group	1167
Shell Shack, Inc.	981
Shell Square Subway	507
Shellmark Corp	495
Shelton Restaurant Group LLC	496
Sheridan Technical Center	261
Sheridan's Franchise Systems	470
Sherman Foods, LLC	638
Sherman's Delicatessen & Bakery	124
Shibley Management Inc.	807
Shield's Franchise Restaurants LLC	594
Shilo Management Co.	869
Shipley Do-Nuts	1030
Shiro of Japan	751
Shivstone Inc.	260
Shoebox Northwest, Llc	1138
Shogun Teppan Steak & Sushi	127
Shoney's North America Corp.	963
Shoney's of Knoxville Inc.	950
Shoney's of Richmond Inc.	1095
Shopsy's Hospitality Inc	1197
Shore Thing Restaurants, LLC	696
Shorty Smalls Restaurant Group Inc.	853
Shorty's Inc.	280
Show Me Bread Inc.	617
Show Palace Dinner Theatre	261
Showmars of America Inc.	657
SHRI Modheswari Corp., Inc	499
Shrimp Basket	300
Shuckin' Shack Franchising, LLC	651
Shugrue's Restaurant & Lounge	30
Shula's Restaurant Group	259
Shun Lee Palace	785
Shyam Creamery, LLC	1086
SI Restaurants, LLC	374
Sickies Garage	683
Side Pockets Inc.	466
Sidmar Management Corp.	699
Siena	228
Sierra Monterey Restaurant Systems, Inc.	195
Sign of The Beefcarver Inc.	589
Silver Diner Development Inc.	557
Silver Mine Subs Inc.	209
Silver State Restaurants Inc	739
Simco Group	156
Simms Restaurant Group	110
Simply Tacos Inc.	133
Simsim Outstanding Shawarma	146
Singleton Food Services inc.	359
Sinkula Investments Ltd. Co.	478
SIOUX CITY DQ INC	386
SIR Corp.	1180
Sir Pizza of Kentucky Inc.	483
Six Flags Entertainment Corp. (Food Service)	1016
Sizzle Pie	869
Sizzler USA Inc.	113
Sizzling Platter LLC	1071
Sizzling Steak Concepts, Inc.	507
SJAC Food Groups LLC	371
Skal Restaurant Group	222
SKBH Bobs	52
Skillet Management, LLC	1128
Skip Salome Enterprises Inc	836
Skipolini's Pizza	183
SKS, LLC	1083
Skyline Chili Inc.	824
Skyline Chili of Oakley	811
Skyport Companies Inc./First Meridian Services	211
Slammed Pizza Inc.	93
SlapFish Restaurant Group	85
Slate Coffee Roasters	1128
SLI Enterprises	1045
Slice Factory	395
Sliderz, MG Inc.	283
Slim Chickens	20
Slip Management	669
Sloan's Franchise LLC	322
SLS Hotel Beverly Hills	107
SM Restaurants Inc.	325
Smallcakes A Cupcakery	469
Smalls Sliders Franchising LLC	347
SMART MANAGEMENT & CO., INC.	73
Smashburger Master LLC	204
SME Inc.	449
SmitCo Eateries Inc.	20
Smith & Wollensky Restaurant Group	516
Smith Bros. Restaurant Corp.	127
Smith Dairy Queens Ltd.	980
Smith Family Restaurants	940
Smith Foods of Corydon Inc	444
Smithfield's Chicken 'N Bar-B-Q	651
Smoke's Poutinerie Inc.	1179
Smokin Subs, Inc. Bigger Better Subs, Inc.	443
Smoking Pig BBQ Company	159
Smolar Management Company	713
Smoothie King Franchises Inc.	1001
SMS Enterprises Inc	713
Smugglers Enterprises, Inc.	303
SNAP Cutom Pizza & Salads	900
Snappy Tomato Pizza Co.	477
Snarf's Sandwiches	204
S-N-C, Inc.	685
Snooze Import Export LLC	204
Snowball Pizza Inc	251
Snowbird Ski & Summer Resort	1070
Snowdays	785
Snowed Inn LLC	724
So Hospitality Group	633
Sobeck Enterprises	568
Sobik's Corporation	272
SoBol Inc.	792
Sodak Tacos Inc	465
Sodalicious	1073
SoDel Concepts	236
Sodexo	536, 874
Sodexo (Campus Services Division)	242
Sodexo Dining Service	874
Sodexo Inc.	551
SoFresh	317
Soft Pretzel Franchise Systems, Inc.	876
Soho Leisure Group	317
Solon Management Inc.	118
Sombrero Mexican Food	93
Some Guys Pizza Pasta Grill	455
Someburros, Inc.	27
Somers Pubs Inc.	516
Sonesta International Hotels Corp.	529
Sonic Corp.	853
Sonic Drive-In	942
Sonic Drive-In Franchise	209
Sonic Drive-In of Denton	1007
Sonic Drive-In of Kansas Inc.	463
Sonic Drive-In of Stuttgart	25
Sonic Drive-in Restaurant	52
Sonic Drive-Ins of North Georgia	361
Sonic Irons Group	922
Sonic of Nowata	851
Sonnenalp Resort	217
Sonny Bryan's Smoke House	1001
Sonny's Franchise Company	274
Sonoma Restaurant Group	658
Sonshine Creamery, LLC	547
Sophie's Cuban Cuisine Franchising Inc.	785
Soprano's Pizza & Pasta LLC	1128
Sotherly Hotels Inc.	1103
Sotto Sotto	347
Soul Provider, Inc.	309
Soulman's Bar-B-Que	1056
Sound City Foods Inc.	1109
Souper Salad Inc.	1001
South American Restaurants Corp.	913

Company	Page
South GA Burgers, LLC	365
South Sound Restaurant Group	1138
South St. Burger	1197
South Texas Dairy Queen Inc.	1053
South Texas Pizza Inc.	1069
Southeast Corporation	1049
Southeast Jack, Inc.	926
Southeast Michigan Management Corp.	582
Southeast QSR LLC	364
Southeast Restaurant Group	507
Southeast Restaurants Corp.	930
Southern Baked Pie Company	359
Southern Foodservice Management Inc.	13
Southern Hospitality Restaurant & Bar	785
Southern Legacy Waffles, LLC	327
Southern Multifoods Inc.	1037
Southern Ohio Pizza Inc	840
Southern Oregon Elmer's, L.L.C.	862
Southern Partners LLC	637
Southern Pizza Co.	638
Southern Proper Hospitality Group	347
Southern Restaurant Group Inc.	254
Southern Rock Restaurants LLC	944
Southernmost Restaurant Group	268
Southpaw	232
Southport Brewing Company	227
South-Wen Inc.	1040
SouthWest Florida Restaurant Investments Inc.	258
Southwest Grill of New York, LLC	751
Southwest KFC	858
Souvla	156
Spaghetti Warehouse Restaurants Inc.	1002
Spain Street LLC	1128
Spangles Inc.	474
Sparetime Recreation	561
SPB Hospitality	1030
Specialty Restaurants Corp.	50
Spell Restaurant Group	299
Sperry's Restaurant Inc.	963
SPFS Inc.	953
Spice Wing	373
Spicy Pie	683
Spiegel Investment CC	282
Spikes Fish House	95
Spike's Junkyard Dogs, USA LLC	511
SPIN! Concepts Inc.	624
Spire Hospitality	433
Spires Restaurants Inc.	123
Spitz	107
Spokane Foodservice Inc.	1135
Sportscene Group Inc.	1199
SPoT Coffee Canada Ltd.	1197
Springfield Investments, Inc.	371
Springfield Restaurant Group	891
Sprinkles Cupcakes CA Inc.	185
Square King Foods, Inc.	92
Square One Concepts	43
Squealers Barbeque	458
SRA Venture Corp.	72
SRC Subs, LLC	116
SRG Concepts	555
SRS Management Inc.	582
SSCP Management	1002
SSP America	1088
St Andrews Country Club	245
ST Management Group	786
St. Clair Restaurant Management Inc.	273
St. Juste Management Corp.	1061
St. Louis Franchise Ltd	1197
St. Mar Enterprises Inc.	75
St. Martin's Wine Bistro	1002
STA Management, LLC	591
Staab Management Co. Inc.	687
Stacked - Food Well Built	85
Stafford's Hospitality Inc.	587
Stage & Company	594
Stageline Pizza Co.	644
Stagg Restaurant Partnership	1061
Stan Clark Companies	856
Stan Rivera Inc	217
Stanek Inc.	387
Stanley Neal	552
Stanton & Associates Inc.	581
Staples Restaurants LLC	1117
Star Acquisitions Inc	136
Star Buffet Inc.	43
Star Concessions	1002
Star Provisions	348
Starbucks Coffee Canada Inc.	1188
Starbucks Corporation	1128
Starbucks Distribution Center	911
Starbucks Vancouver Regional Office	1173
Starbucks Western/Pacific Zone	77
Starlite Cruises	306
Starr Restaurant Group	900
StarrChex LLC	940
Stata, LLC	84
State College Subs, LLC	908
Station Casinos Inc.	739
Stauf's Coffee	819
Stauros Enterprises, Inc.	1110
STC Inc.	592
Steak -N- Egger	421
Steak-Out Franchising Inc.	368
Steelhead Brewing Co.	862
Steen Enterprises	603
Stellar Restaurant Group	516
Stephan Pyles Concepts	1002
Steren Management Co.	1142
Sterling Foods	91
Sterling Restaurants, LLC	348
Steve Erhard	614
Steven Han Projects	1131
Stewart Systems Inc	586
Sticky Fingers	929
Stine Enterprises, Inc	30
Stingley Management	26
Stock In Trade Restaurant Group	1003
Stockade Companies LLC	1056
Stokely Hospitality Enterprises	966
Sto-Mac	754
StoneFire Grill Management	186
Stoner's Pizza Joint	367
Stonewood Holdings LLC	253
Straits Restaurant LLC	163
Strang Corporation	814
Strategic Hotels & Resorts Inc.	418
Stratford University	1080
Straw Hat Pizza	81
Straw Hat Restaurants Inc.	165
Streets of New York Inc.	36
Strings Restaurant Group	82
Strizzi's Restaurants	72
Stroud's Restaurant & Bar	463
Studio Movie Grill	1003
Stumptown Coffee Roasters	869
Su Casa	1071
Sub Central	425
Sub Station II Inc.	922
Sub Zero Ice Cream	1073
Subco East, Inc	938
Subco Enterprises Inc	560
Subco Inc	1087
Submarina Inc.	1030
Submarine House	821
Subs Enterprises, Inc.	171
Subs Inc.	645
Subslingers Inc.	610
Substantial Investments	560
Subway	177, 872
Subway 1	366
Subway 21139, Inc.	763
Subway Carriage House Inc	946
Subway Development	687
Subway Development Agent Advisory Corporation	429
Subway Development of San Diego	147
Subway Franchise	80, 96, 135, 163, 170, 217, 389, 478, 489, 494, 496, 582, 610, 878, 882, 942, 953, 979, 1003
Subway Franchisee	6, 111, 460, 665, 845, 923
Subway Management Corporation	317
Subway of Alaska Inc	2
Subway of Clewiston Inc	251
Subway of Martinsville	1090
Subway of New Braunfels	1048
Subway of Portland Inc	965
Subway Operation of Ohio	835
Subway Sandwiches & Salads	175, 666
Subway Sandwiches & Salads of Kern County	52
Subway Subs of Connecticut Incorporated	226
Subway Systems Inc.	448
Subway, Ltd.	385
Subzero Nitrogen Ice Cream	1073
SUDH Management	706
Sugar Creek Pizza, LLC	824
Sugar Fork Foods Inc.	351
Sugar Mountain	1131
Sugarfina, LLC	86
Sugarfire Smokehouse	634
Sullivan's Fine Food at Rocky Hill	951
Sumida & Associates Inc.	379
Summerwood Corporation	879
Summit Restaurant Group, LLC	616
Summitt Ventures Inc	470
Sun Holdings LLC	1003
Sun Valley Company	393
Sundance Partners Ltd.	1078
Sunlife Organics	110
Sunnyside Restaurant Group	235
Sunset Entertainment Group	107
Sunset Equities	466
Sunset Equities, Inc.	467

Company	Page
Sunshine Restaurant Partners	307
Sunstate Restaurant Management Inc.	250
Sunstone Hotel Investors Inc.	89
Sunway Restaurant Corporation	303
Suparossa Restaurant Group	419
Super Chix, Inc.	1077
Super Subby's Inc.	821
Superior Bar & Grill	510
Superior Concepts Inc.	600
Superior Fast Foods, LLC	26
SuperMex Restaurants Inc.	99
Supple Restaurant Group	1152
Surf Shack Coastal Kitchen LLC	317
Surf Taco	711
Surfside Coffee LLC	280
SURG Restaurant Group	1151
Sushi Sake	281
Sushi Zushi Inc.	1062
SushiBoy Inc.	80
Sushirrito	156
Sushma Gupta	171
Sustainable Restaurant Group	870
Sutliff Candy and Promotions Co Inc	1131
Suzanne of Richmond, Inc.	588
Svoboda and Henk Inc.	692
Swadley's Barbeque Restaurants & Catering Co.	854
Sweeney Enterprises	796
Sweet CeCe's Franchising, LLC	945
Sweet Chick	749
Sweet Dreams, LLC	230
Sweet P Enterprises Inc.	25
Sweetberry Bowls	702
Sweetfin Poke	170
Sweetgreen, Inc.	68
Sweetleaf Coffee Roasters	749
Sweetwater Franchise Group	642
Sweetwaters Group LLC	567
Swensons Drive In	801
SWH Mimi's Cafe Holding Company Inc.	1003
Swig	1073
Swissotel Hotels Inc.	419
SWS Operations	247
Syberg's Family Restaurants	630
SYDLEY International, LLC	1090
Sylvan Food Systems Inc.	933
T & B Concepts LLC	658
T & C Foods Inc	838
T & C Foods Inc.	6
T & J Inc.	584
T & K LP	111
T & W Subway	521
T Bones Great American Eatery	693
T Q M Inc	439
T S Restaurants	379
T W Management	564
T.B. & G. Inc.	469
T.G.G. Inc.	51
T.G.I. Friday's Inc.	1004
T.J. Rockwell's American Grill & Tavern	882
T.L. Cannon Management Corp.	301
T.R. Foods Inc.	445
T.R.M. Enterprises	22
Tabellco Inc.	159
Table 301	926
Tableseide Restaurant Group	305
Tacala LLC	16
Tacky Jacks Seafood Restaurant and Tavern	14
Taco Bamba Taqueria	1086
Taco Bell Corp.	89
Taco Bill Inc.	51
Taco Bill of Baltimore, Inc.	552
Taco Bueno Restaurants LP	1010
Taco Burrito King	419
Taco Bus	318
Taco Cabana Inc.	1062
Taco Casa	1013
Taco Casa Franchise	642
Taco Inn	688
Taco John's International Inc.	1161
Taco John's of St Joseph Inc	628
Taco King	2
Taco Mac Restaurant Group	327
Taco Mayo Franchise Systems Inc.	854
Taco Shack	977
Taco Shop	683
Taco Surf	171
Taco Time Northwest	1118
Taco Treat of Great Falls	645
Taco Via	624
Tacodeli Holdings	977
Tacombi	786
Tacos 4 Life Grill	19
Tacos and Company Holdings LLC	90
Tacotarian	740
TAG Restaurant Group	205
Taher Inc. - Restaurant Division	609
Tai Wah, Inc	140
TailGate Brewery	963
Tailgaters Sports Grill & Il Primo	30
Taim Holdings LLC	786
Taira's Inc.	720
Tajima Restaurant Group	147
Takeg Enterprises, Inc.	170
Takorean	235
Talbot's On The Water, Inc.	575
Talk of the Town Restaurant Group	294
TaMolly's of America Ltd.	1066
Tampico Restaurant Inc.	504
Tanaka of Tokyo Restaurants Ltd.	377
Tandem Corp.	660
Tands Inc.	667
Tandy Pizza LLC	1016
Tanner Management Company L.L.C.	475
Tao Group	786
Tap House Management Group	435
Tap Ventures LLC	455
Tapioca Express Inc.	173
Taqueria Del Sol	348
Taqueria El Riincosito	1111
Taqueria Jalisco	984
Tar Heel Capital Corp.	650
Tarantini Panzarotti Inc.	699
Target Corporation	608
Tarka Indian Kitchen	977
Tarrant Millican of Texas, Inc.	1044
Taste America Restaurant Group	419
Taste Buds Inc.	507
Taste Inc.	121
Taste of India	275
Tasti D-Lite LLC	43
Tasty Burger Corp.	532
Tasty Restaurant Group	108
Tasty Tacos Inc.	384
Tasty's Fresh Burgers and Fries	208
Tavern Restaurant Group Inc.	811
Taverna Opa	261
Tavistock Restaurants LLC	294
Tay Ho Food Corp.	166
Taylor Enterprises, Inc.	871
Taylor Restaurants, Inc.	592
Taylor Shellfish Company, Inc	1134
Taylor's Steakhouse	108
Taziki's Cafe	17
TBG Food Acquisition Corp.	798
TBL Investments	664
Tc4 & Co.	1063
TCB Management Co	1091
TCBY Systems LLC	193
TCBY The Country's Best Yogurt	23
TCR Enterprises	1089
TD Food Group Inc.	377
TDS Services, Inc.	432
Team Goliath Inc	479
Team Lyders	569
Team Maryland Inc.	554
Team Schostak Family Restaurants	583
Team St. Pete Inc.	250
Team Washington Inc.	1099
Teddy's Bigger Burgers	377
Ted's Cafe Escondido	854
Ted's Fish Fry Inc.	799
Ted's Jumbo Red Hots Inc.	751
Ted's Montana Grill LLC	348
Tee Jaye's Country Place Inc.	819
Tempo Restaurant	419
Ten D Enterprises	641
Ten Star Enterprises Inc.	842
Tenda Chick	4
Tennyson Enterprises	386
Tennyson Foods Inc	303
Terhune's Inc.	459
Teriyaki Madness LLC	205
Terra Momo Restaurant Group	704
Terry & Karen White Enterprises	15
Terry Nemesek	1159
Texas Chicken & Burgers	349
Texas de Brazil	1004
Texas Restaurant Group Inc.	977
Texas Roadhouse Inc.	489
Texas Subs Inc.	1013, 1063
Texas Turkeys Inc. DBA	100
Texcellent	1068
TGC Foods Inc.	555
Thai Basil	139
Thai Ginger Restaurants Inc.	1117
Thai House Group	1173
Thandang Restaurant LLC	1131
The Alaska Culinary Academy	3
The Anchor Group, LLC	919
The Art Institute of San Antonio	1062
The Art Institute of Vancouver	1174
The Art Institute of Virginia Beach	1101
The Bacin Group	420

Name	Page
The Bagel Restaurant & Deli	420
The Bagel Stop	1198
The Baked Bear	147
The Bali Hai Restaurant	147
The Barn Restaurant	839
The Bartolotta Restaurant Group	1149
The Bento Group	260
The Big Pit	240
The Biltmore Co.	649
The Biscuit Bar	1053
The Black Dog Tavern Co. Inc.	536
The Bloomin Apple, LLC	928
The Boathouse at Lakeville	224
The Boiling Crab	77
The Breakers	297
The Briad Group	704
The Briar Group	518
The Brigantine Restaurant Corp.	147
The Broadmoor	195
The Broadway Group Inc.	1137
The Broken Yolk Cafe	147
The Buffalo Spot	36
The Buona Companies	395
The Burger's Priest	1198
The Burrito Shop Inc.	61
The Butcher's Daughter	749
The Butcher-The Baker Management Co. Inc.	923
The C & C Organization	131
The Capital Grille	294
The Carson Valley Inn and Casino	741
The Chateau of Waltham	537
The Cheese Course, Inc.	323
The Cheesecake Factory Incorporated	57
The Chen Group	283
The Chestnut Land Co	805
The Chiles Group	242
The Chocolate Factory Subs and Icecream	1150
The Cinnamon Bums Inc.	870
The Cliff House	156
The Cock 'n Bull Inc.	893
The Coffee Beanery Ltd.	576
The Coffee Village	880
The Commander's Palace Family Of Restaurants	507
The Common Man Family of Restaurants	692
The Como Restaurant	791
The County Line Inc.	977
The Coyote Cafe	723
The Crab Cooker	178
The Crack Shack	148
The Creamery Shop Corporation	913
The Crossing	630
The Culinary Institute of Michigan Baker College	585
The Dapper Doughnut	724
The Delectable Egg Restaurants	205
The Derschang Group	1132
The Desmond Hotel	744
The Dinex Group LLC	786
The Dolly Llama	108
The Dollywood Company	965
The Donut Stop	968
The Drafting Room Inc.	883
The Edward Thomas Collection	55
The Elephant & Castle Group Inc.	1165
The Enterprise Fish Company	170
The Epicurean Group	573
The Equinox Resort & Spa	1105
The Fifty/50 Restaurant Group	420
The Firkin Group of Pubs	1185
The First & Last Tavern	224
The Flame Broiler Inc.	68
The Franklin Restaurant Group	517
The Gilmore Collection	579
The Glynn Hospitality Group	517
The Goddess Restaurant Group	420
The Golden M Company	552
The Good Food Group	945
The Graduate Restaurants Inc.	161
The Grapevine Inc.	308
The Great American Bagel	442
The Great Canadian Bagel Ltd.	1181
The Great Greek Mediterranean Grill	322
The Great TN Pizza Company Inc.	951
The Greenbrier	1160
The Greene Turtle Franchising Corporation	549
The Grill Room	260
The Grove, Inc.	740
The Gyro Shack	389
The Haagen-Dazs Shoppe Company Inc.	609
The Habit Restaurants Inc	90
The Halal Guys Inc.	744
The Halal Shack	744
The Halal Way CT LLC	226
The Happ Inn	434
The Hastings Company	650
The Henry Ford Museum	571
The Herndon Group, Inc.	963
The Hickory House	825
The Human Bean	864
The Hummus & Pita Co.	787
The Hummus Republic	184
The International Culinary Center New York	787
The International Culinary School Atlanta	349
The International Culinary School Dallas	1004
The Irish Pub	901
The Iron Cactus	979
The Ivy	108
The Jan Companies	915
The Jeffrey Corp.	550
The Johnny Rockets Group Inc.	96
The Kati Roll Company Franchising Corporation	787
The Kewpee Inc.	830
The Kickin' Crab	166
The King Group	284
The Kitchen	191
The Knowles Restaurants	714
The Krystal Co.	358
The Larry Keen Group	1183
The Little Mint Inc.	670
The Lodge Sports Grille	1132
The Lost Cajun	209
The Lost Pizza Co Inc.	639
The Lucques Group	185
The Madera Group	108
The Magic Kingdom	269
The Marwaha Group	50
The McEwan Group	1188
The Melt	157
The Melting Pot Franchise	358, 439
The Melting Pot Restaurants Inc.	318
The Merritt Group	721
The Metro Wine Bar & Bistro	854
The Mixx	624
The Moore Sonic Group	855
The Munirs Company	73
The Naples Group	210
The Napoli Group	692
The Neighborhood Dining Group Inc.	364
The Neighborhood Group of Companies	1182
The Old Oyster Factory	927
The Old Spaghetti Factory Canada Ltd.	1174
The Omni Homestead Resort	1088
The ONE Group LLC	787
The Onion	1136
The Organic Coup	157
The Original Crabby Bill's Seafood Inc.	262
The Original Hot Dog Factory	371
The Original Pancake House Franchising Inc.	870
The Other Coast Cafe	1132
The Other Place	381
The Palm Restaurant Group	235
The Palms Casino Resort	740
The Pasta House Company	630
The Patio Restaurants Inc.	397
The Peddler Steakhouse	945
The Peninsula Hotels	55
The Pepper Tree Restaurant	196
The Petroleum Club	855
The Phoenix Restaurant Group	1078
The Piada Group, LLC	820
The Pie Hole	108
The Pier House Resort & Caribbean Spa	268
The Pike Corporation	274
The Pines Restaurant Inc.	461
The PIPA Group	905
The Pizza King Inc.	457
The Pizza Pipeline Inc.	1136
The Pizza Press	50
The Pizza Ranch Inc.	385
The Portillo Food Service Distribution Center	393
The Portillo Restaurant Group	434
The Prime Rib	542
The Queen Mary	99
The Quiznos Master LLC	205
The Ralph Brennan Restaurant Group	508
The Range Cafe	719
The Red Lion Inn	535
The Restaurant Company	1095
The Restaurant Group	787
The Restaurant School	901
The Richards Advantage	652
The River Palm Terrace	699
The Rock Wood Fired Kitchen	1137
The Rose Group	893
The Rosenthal Group Inc.	420
The Ruby Slipper Cafe	508
The Sagamore	746

Name	Page
The Salad Station	500
The Sand Piper Cafe	3
The Sandwich Factory	846
The Saxton Group	1005
The Scottsdale Plaza Resort	43
The Sheik Restaurant	265
The Shipyard Brewing Company	564
The Simple Greek	877
The Skinny Dip Frozen Yogurt Bar	1101
The Smoothie Factory Inc.	1005
The Starboard Group	252
The Steak n Shake Operations Inc.	455
The Stinking Rose	157
The Taco House	205
The Taco Maker Inc.	914
The Temple Group, Inc.	392
The Tides Wharf	55
The Toasted Frog	684
The Toasted Yolk Cafe	1030
The Tommy Bahama Group	1132
The Twins Group Inc.	834
The Upper Crust Pizzeria	511
The Varsity Inc.	349
The Vintage Group	1165
The Vintage Press Restaurante	183
The Waldwin Group Inc	532
The Wells Co.	490
The Wendy's Company	189, 318, 822
The Wendy's Company-Atlanta Division	327
The Western Sizzlin Corp.	1097
The Westin Peachtree Plaza	349
The White Barn Inn	561
The Whole Donut Group	224
The Wolak Group	560
The Xaviars Restaurant Group	752
The Zenith Company	483
Theo's Restaurant	806
Thermal Vision Investments, Inc	958
ThinkFood Group	236
This is It! Southern BBQ	359
Thomas 5 Ltd.	823
Thomas Cuisine Management	392
Thomas Distributing, Inc.	1046
Thomas E. Strauss Inc.	906
Thomas Keller Restaurant Group	188
Thomel Enterprises, Inc.	883
Thompson Hospitality	1094
Thornton Park Restaurant Group	295
Threadgill's	977
Three Brothers III Inc dba Zito's Pizza	123
Three Brothers Pizza	546
Three Guys Restaurant	788
Three Powers Foods, Inc.	119
Thrive Restaurant Group	474
Thumb Big Boy Restaurants, Inc.	567
Thumbs Up Diner	349
ThunderCloud Inc.	978
Thunderdome Restaurant Group	827
Tico Boston	517
Tiffany's Restaurant Inc.	707
Tiffin Indian Cuisine	901
Tiger Pride LLC	620
Tijuana Flats Burrito Company	274
Tilford Restaurant Group	634
Tim Hortons Inc.	1165, 1183, 1189
Timberline Cool Treats, LLC	1108
Timoney & Borrelli Enterprises Inc	876
Timothy L. Behm Inc.	82
Tin Drum Asiacafe LLC	349
Tin Lizzy's Cantina	349
TJLM Food Services, Inc.	136
TJM Foods, Inc.	436
TKS Restaurants, LLC	148
TLG Restaurants, LLC	1031
TMD Management LLC	353
TME Enterprises	371
TMJ Group	501
TNT Pizza Partners Inc.	466
Toarmina's Pizza Inc.	572
Toast	421
Toastique	236
Tobacco Road Restaurant Group Inc	652
Todd English Enterprises	517
Toftrees Resort	908
Togo's Eateries LLC	160
Tokyo Express Inc.	36
Tokyo Joe's	208
Toli Management	762
Tom and Chee Worldwide LLC	812
Tom Douglas Restaurants	1132
Tom McKennie Group	743
Tomato Express, Inc.	483
Tomdan Enterprises Inc.	114
TomKats Inc	963
Tommy's Pizza Inc.	820
Tom's BBQ Systems, Inc.	28
Tom's Drive-Ins	1141
Tom's House of Pizza Ltd.	1165
TOMS King LLC	435
Tomsec Inc.	613
Tomtreyco, Inc.	843
To-Ne of Iowa, Inc.	384
Tonns Inc.	1144
Tony Packo's Inc.	842
Tony's Restaurant, Inc	1031
TooJay's Management Corporation	322
Top Dining Inc.	938
Top Pot Doughnuts	1133
Top Shelf	36
TopGolf International, Inc.	1005
Topper's Craft Creamery	323
Topper's Pizza Inc.	1155
Tops Bar-B-Q Inc.	957
Topsy's International Inc.	624
Toptable Group	1174
Torero's Restaurant Inc.	1108
Tortoise Restaurant Group Inc	1181
Toscana Kitchen & Bar	241
Tossed Franchise Corporation	245
Total Quality Inc.	826
Toucan, Inc	455
Tour de France	788
Townsend Foods, Inc.	959
TR Worldwide Phillyfood LLC	712
TRAA Corporation	710
TRACK Investments, LLC	664
Tracs Food Inc	1033
Trader Vic's Restaurants Inc.	64
Tradewinds Island Resorts On Saint Pete Beach	306
Trangen Inc.	206
Transwest Corral	72
Trapani & Trapani	982
TravelCenters of America Inc.	845
Travinia Italian Kitchen	650
Treebeards	1031
Trefz Corporation	219
Trefz Distribution Center	229
Trejo's Tacos	109
Tremont 647	520
Tri City Foods, Inc	424
Tri City Management	598
Tri N Subway, Inc	624
Tri P's Management Corporation	109
Tri Taco Inc.	216
Tria Co.	591
Triad Hotspots, Inc.	681
Triangle Restaurant Management	554
Tri-Arc Food Systems Inc.	675
Tri-Arch	814
TriBox, LLC	1015
Tricor Inc.	658
Trident Holdings LLC	938
Trifon's Pizza & Spaghetti House Ltd.	1205
Trigo Hospitality	592
Trinity Corporation	484
Triple	215
Triple C Pizza LLC	1081
Triple M Industries	1062
Triple T Enterprises Inc.	389
Tri-Star Pizza Enterprises	646
Tri-Star Restaurant Group LLC	378
Triumph Brewing Company	704
Trophy Cupcakes	1133
Tropical Smoothie Franchise Development Corp.	350
Troubleshooters Inc.	364
True Food Kitchen	37
TRUFOODS, LLC	788
Truluck's Restaurant Group	1031
Trump National Golf Club	131
Tucker's Place	625
Tucson Golden Corral	47
Tudor's Biscuit World Inc.	1158
Tug Valley Arch	494
Tully's	745
Tumbleweed Inc.	490
Tupelo Honey Cafe	650
Turk Enterprises Inc	628
Turner Food & Spirits Co.	370
Tutta Bella Neapolitan Pizzeria	1133
Tutti A Tavola LLC	788
Twin Arches Mc Donald's	216
Twin Cities TJs	611
Twin Coast Enterprises, Inc.	695
Twin Restaurant Holding LLC	1005
Twin Scoop, L.L.C.	863
Twin Subs, Inc.	650
Twisted Taco Franchise Inc.	350
Two Boots	789
Two Domer Management, LLC	982
Two Guys Pizza	908
Two Lads, Inc.	923
Two Mile Landing Restaurant & Marina	715
Two Stones Pub	239

Company	Page
Twoshoes, Inc.	1048
TYP Restaurant Group Inc.	69
U Don LLC	1133
Ultimate Scoop, LLC	392
Ultra Mac Corporation	215
UltraStar Cinemas	162
Una Mas Restaurants Inc.	160
Uncle Dan's Rib House	1068
Uncle Jack's Steakhouse	745
Uncle Julio's Corp	1036
Uncle Louie G	796
Uncle Maddio's Pizza Joint	350
Uncle Tony's USA Inc.	918
Union Joints LLC	570
Union Square Hospitality Group	789
United Franchise Group	322
United Investment Solutions, Inc.	116
United Restaurant Group LP	1086
United Vending & Food Services	934
Universal Orlando Resort	295
Universal Studios Hollywood	179
Unlimited Possibilities, Inc.	1136
Uno Restaurants, LLC.	531
UP Inc.	490
Upchurch Management	301
Upland Brewing Company	444
Uptown Espresso Inc	1133
Upward Projects	37
Urban Coffee Lounge	1113
Urban Farmhouse	1095
Urban Kitchen Group	148
Urban Plates LLC	59
Urban Wok	614
Urbane Cafe	181
Urth Caffe Inc.	109
US Foods Companies	221
US Merit Inc.	1067
US Pizza Co. Inc.	23
US Restaurants Inc.	877
U-Swirl, Inc.	206
V & J Holding Companies Inc.	1150
V & K Food Corporation	174
V and K Retail, Inc.	876
V Food Group	1181
V&V Foods LLC	368
Vail Resorts Inc.	193
Valenti Management Inc.	318
Valentino's of America Inc.	689
Valle Luna	37
Valley Dairy	889
Valley Management Associates	135
Valley Management Inc.	1150
Valley Pizza Inc.	10
Valley Services Inc.	637
Valley Subs of Arizona, L.L.C.	28
Valleyfair	613
Van Leeuwen Ice Cream	789
Van Master Management Inc.	591
Vance H Houston	932
Vandalay Pizza Industries, Inc	271
Vandelay Hospitality Group	1005
Vanmar Inc.	947
Van's Pig Stand	856
Variety Management	844
Vasco Properties	641
Vaughn Brothers Inc.	641
VDM Management	1157
VeganBurg Inc.	157
Velvet Taco	1006
Venice Ristorante	212
Vera's Burger Shack	1174
Veronte, Inc.	1141
Vetri Family	901
Via 313 Pizzeria	978
Via Tribunali LLC	1133
Vibe Restaurants	1031
Vicious Biscuit	929
Vida and Estilo Corporation	281
Vie de France Yamazaki Inc.	1099
Vigilucci's	60
Vilarino's Inc.	261
Villa Restaurant Group	707
Villa Roma Resort Hotel Inc.	751
Village Inn	609
Village Inn Pancake House of Springfield Inc.	633
Village Tavern Inc.	681
Villarreal Pizza Inc	7
Vina Restaurants Ltd.	1175
Vincent Mandola Family Restaurants	1031
Vince's Enterprises Inc.	1106
Vinckier Foods	596
Vineyard Industries Inc.	355
Vinny Vannucchi's	426
Virginia Wings Inc.	1087
Virginia Wings of Norfolk Lc	812
Vision F.S., Inc.	98
Vision Foods, Inc.	372
Vitality Bowls	165
VitaNova Brands	1062
Vittles Company	299
Viva Burrito Development Corp.	47
Viva Chicken	671
VJ's Foodservice	613
VKC Group	1065
Vocelli Pizza	905
VOLO Restaurant	421
Volterra	1113
Von Ebert Brewing LLC	870
Von Rutenberg Ventures	1146
VooDoo BBQ Franchising	508
Voodoo Doughnut LLC	870
VPS Inc.	860
VTP Enterprises	76
VZS Concessions	980
W & M Restaurants, Inc.	634
W.G. Grinders Inc.	829
W.H. Braum Inc.	855
W.W. Pizza Inc.	460
WaBa Grill Franchise Corp	62
Wack Company Restaurant	860
Wade Cary Enterprise Inc.	676
Wade Enterprises	535
Wadleigh Food Services, Inc.	564
Waffle House Inc.	366
Wagamama US	517
Wagner & Son LLC	848
Wahlburgers	525
Wahoo's Fish Taco LLC	166
Wake Pizza LLC	666
Wal-Bon of Ohio Inc.	1159
Walcorp, Inc.	1087
Wali Enterprises, LLC	440
Walin Enterprises Inc	78
Walker Franchises Inc	586
Walker Holding LLC	660
Walker Subway Development Corp	855
Walk-On's Enterprises	498
Walmart Stores Inc.	17
Walsh Management, Inc.	909
Walt Disney World Co.	269
Ward's Food Systems Inc.	639
Warner Food Mangement, Inc.	75
Washington Park Grille	206
Wasilevich Enterprises	1144
Water Club Restaurants	789
Water Street Ltd	984
Waterford Hotel Group Inc.	231
Waterfront Enterprises	118
Waterfront Seafood Market Restaurant	388
Waterloo Restaurant Group	978
Watermark Donut Co.	533
Waters of Hickory, Inc	659
Waugh Enterprises	1006
Waymar Food Service Ltd.	1189
Wayne's Fast Food Corporation	13
WBF Management Inc.	740
WBIsland, Inc.	927
WBNippers, Inc.	964
WDI International Inc.	178
Weachter & Associates, LLC	1010
Weathervane Seafood Restaurants	561
Webb Family Enterprises	121
Webber Restaurant Group	523
Webe Subs Inc	319
Weber Enterprises	862
Weber Grill Restaurant	438
Weck's Inc.	719
Weissgerber Group	1151
Welcome To Moe's, Inc	265
Welsh Family Holdings, LLC	692
Wen Den Inc	1008
Wenco Wooster Inc.	802
Wenconn Inc.	219
Wend Colorado LLP	214
Wendium of Florida, LLC	281
Wendy's FourCrown Inc.	610
Wendy's of Bloomington Inc	444
Wendy's of Bowling Green	477
Wendy's of the Pacific Inc.	114
Wendy's of Western Virginia	1097
Wenesco Restaurants Inc.	700
Wen-Lake Corporation	271
Wen-Star, Inc	373
Wentana, LLC	1136
Wenwest Inc	165
Wequassett Inn Resort and Golf Club	524
We're Cooking Inc.	350
We're Rolling Pretzel Company	801
Wess Clerc	603
West Cassell Enterprises	1048
West End Restaurants LLC	964
West Foods Inc.	24
West Quality Food Service	640

Company	Page
Westaar V, Inc.	825
Westaco Inc.	43
WestConn Ltd	220
Western Bagel Baking Corp.	181
Western Management	855
Western Maryland Fast Foods	553
Western Pizza (1979) Ltd.	1205
Western States Foods	1077
Westgate Resorts	251
Westin Moana Surfrider Hotel	377
Westmark Hotels Inc.	1133
Westmont Hospitality Group	1032
Westside Pizza	389
Wexler's Deli	109
What A Combo Inc.	640
What-A-Burger Drive-Ins Inc.	659
Whataburger Inc.	1037
Whataburger of East Texas	1041
Whataburger of Mesquite Inc.	1046
Whataburger Restaurants LLC	1062
Wheat Montana Farms & Bakery	646
Wheeling Island Gaming Inc.	1160
WHG Restaurant Group, Inc.	122
Which Wich Inc.	1006
White Castle Management Co.	820
White Castle System Inc.	490, 631, 812, 820
White Family Enterprises, Inc.	76
White House Chicken Systems Inc.	802
White Lodging Services Corp.	457
White Management	1140
White Restaurant Group	1072
White Rhino Coffee	981
White Spot Hospitality	1174
Whitey's Ice Cream Inc.	432
Whitsons Culinary Group	758
Whitt's B-B-Q.	964
Whole Hog Cafe LLC	23
Wholesome International LLC	905
Wick's P&P LLC	490
Widdicombe Enterprises	50
Wienerschnitzel 358	85
Wife Saver Inc.	931
Wigwam Golf Resort and Spa	31
Wilburn Enterprises	496
Wild Ginger of Seattle	1134
Wild Willy's Burgers	564
Wild Wing Cafe	670
Wild Wing Hospitality	1182
Wildberry Pancakes & Cafe, Inc.	439
WildFin American Grill	1112
Wildflower Bread Company	44
Wiles Restaurants Inc	95
Wil-Ken Enterprises Inc.	474
Willadsen Enterprises	863
William G. Hall & Co.	1013
William Penn Inn Inc.	874
Williams Fried Chicken Inc.	1006
Williams Investment Co.	325
Willie's Restaurants	1032
Willis & Willis Investments, Inc.	37
Willis Investments Corporation	719
Williston Holding Company	1032
Willy's Mexicana Grill	350
Wimpy's Diner Inc.	1185
Wind & Sea Restaurants	70
Windmill Franchise Corp.	705
Windram Enterprises, Inc.	751
Windward Management	582
Winegardner & Hammons Inc.	804
Wing It On Franchising, LLC	230
Wing Machine Inc.	1182
Wing Zone Franchise Corp.	351
Winghouse, Inc.	272
Wings and Rings	831
Wings Etc. Inc.	448
Wings To Go Inc.	553
Wingstop Restaurants Inc.	1006
Winking Lizard Inc.	803
Wintco Inc.	856
Wisconsin Hospitality Group LLC	1154
Wit-Rey Inc.	2
WKAB Investments, LLC	446
WKRP Management LLC	469
WKS Restaurant Corp	68
WMCR Corporation	565
Wocester Restaurant Group	539
Wolfe Enterprises	941
Wolfgang Puck Inc.	740
Wolfnights	790
Wonton Group	109
Wood Ranch BBQ & Grill Inc.	186
Wooden Angel	876
Woods Coffee	1114
Woodside Hotels & Resorts	112
Woodstock Inn	1106
Woody's Bar-B-Q Inc.	266
World of Beer Franchising Inc.	319
World of Good Tastes	139
Worlds of Fun & Oceans of Fun	624
Worthington Enterprises	832
WOW! Hospitality Concepts	1177
WR Restaurants Management LLC	935
Wright Investment Properties Inc.	942
WTC Ventures	964
WY 40 Inc.	1162
Wyandot Barbeque	464
Wymer Management	1032
Wyndham Hotel Group	709
Wyntergreen Co.	1190
Wyoming Pizza, Inc	1160
Wyvern Restaurants, Inc	170
X Group	1138
X2L Inc.	951
Xanterra Parks & Resorts	212
XBN Corp.	1145
Xi'an Famous Foods	790
Xperience Restaurant Group	69
Y&S Food Partnership	435
Y.H.D. Foods, Inc.	609
Yadarr, Inc.	1015
Yadav Enterprises, Inc.	78
Yamato Steak House of Japan	923
Yampa Sandwich Company	206
Yang Chow Restaurants	109
Yano Management	620
Yarbrough Companies Inc.	6
Yard House USA Inc.	90
Yats Cajun Creole	456
Yellow Cab Holdings Pennsylvania LLC	755
Yen Brevard, LLC	275
Yes Sir/E Bob, Inc	584
Yin McDonald's	180
Ynot Italian	1101
Yo Fresh Inc. LLC	790
Yobe Acquisition, LLC	502
Yocco's Hot Dog King	882
Yogurt Creations, Inc.	161
Yogurt Mountain LLC	6
Yogurtland Franchisee	26, 28, 50, 56, 58, 59, 82, 110, 113, 123, 131, 136, 140, 148, 160, 167, 187, 194, 367, 499, 741, 981, 1033, 1069
Yogurtland Franchising Inc.	1010
Yogurtology Franchising, LLC	319
Yolanda's Inc.	181
Yolk.	421
Yolo Food Systems, LLC	937
Yonutz! Fantastical Donuts and Ice Cream	308
York Enterprises of Millington Tennessee LLC	952
Yoshinoya America Inc.	178
Yotes Two, Inc	936
Young's Jersey Dairy	846
Your Pie Corporate	327
Your Pizza Shop Corp.	832
YPYKA Inc.	618
YSS, Inc.	302
Yum Yum Donut Shops Inc.	63
YUM! Brands Inc.	491
Yum! Restaurants International (Canada) Co.	1199
Yumilicious Franchise LLC	1007
Z & H Foods, Inc.	1065
Z Hospitality Group	794
ZaLat Pizza	1053
Zan Inc.	3
Zankou Chicken Inc.	182
Zantigo Franchising Corporation	615
Zarda Bar-B-Q & Catering Co.	616
Zaro's Bake Shop Inc.	747
Zaxby's Franchising Inc.	328
Zaxby's Houston LLC	329
Zeeks Pizza Inc.	1134
Zeigler Direct, LLC	1053
Zeppes Franchise Co.	803
Zero's Mr. Submarine Inc.	1102
Zesto Snack Shops Inc.	351
Ziggi's Coffee	216
Zingerman's Community of Business	567
Zipps Sports Grill	44
Zippy's Giant Burgers	1134
Zippy's Inc.	378
Zip's Drive-In	1137
Zoey & Yummy Inc	422
Zoka Coffee Roasters & Tea Company	1134
Zolman Systems, Inc.	551
Zoological Society of San Diego	148
Zorbaz	600
Zoup! Fresh Soup Company LLC	575
zpizza International	94
Zuma	790